PREFACE

One of our principal goals in writing and developing BIOLOGY, third edition has been to share with beginning biology students our sense of excitement about modern biological science. We want to give students an understanding and appreciation of the vast diversity of living organisms, their remarkable adaptations to their environments, and their evolutionary and ecological relationships. Special emphasis is placed on the basic unity of life and the fundamental similarities of the challenges that have been faced and solved by all living organisms. We are very aware of our responsibility to impress upon our readers that we share planet Earth with many varieties of living organisms and that we are interdependent with other life forms.

SPECIAL FEATURES OF THE THIRD EDITION

The evolution of BIOLOGY through its editions reflects the advances in the biological sciences and in biological education. Every effort has been made to update its content and pedagogy so that this book accurately presents modern biology.

Three Themes

In this new edition we emphasize three basic themes of biology: transmission of information, evolution of life, and flow of energy through living systems. As we introduce the concepts of modern biology, we explain how these three processes are connected and how life depends upon them.

The Author Team

Rapid advances in the biological sciences require a team of authors who specialize in particular areas of biology. The author team of the third edition includes Dr. Eldra Solomon, zoologist and physiologist; Dr. Linda Berg, botanist; Dr. Diana Martin, cell biologist/geneticist; and Dr. Claude A. Villee, Professor Emeritus, Harvard University. All of the authors are experienced college biology teachers.

Learning Aids

Learning the principles of biology is a challenging endeavor. A variety of learning aids are included within the textbook to help the student achieve mastery of the concepts presented.

1. A **Chapter Outline** at the beginning of each chapter provides the student with an overview of the major topics covered in the chapter.
2. **Learning Objectives** at the beginning of each chapter indicate exactly what the student must be able to do in order to demonstrate mastery of the material in the chapter.
3. **Concept-statement heads** introduce each section, by previewing and summarizing the key idea that will be discussed in that section.
4. **Making the Connection boxes** and **Focus boxes** help students connect concepts and spark interest.

   Making the Connection boxes facilitate integration of concepts presented in various chapters of the book. For example, in Chapter 44, Making the Connection: Cellular and Organismic Respiration relates the cellular concepts presented in Chapter 7 with the discussion of gas exchange in Chapter 44. **Focus boxes** spark student interest, present applications of concepts discussed, and familiarize students with the directions and methods of research in modern biology. For example, in Chapter 19, Focus on the Kaibab Squirrel: Evolution in Action presents a topic of interest to students and also describes a current example of speciation in progress.
5. **Career Visions** present a variety of professional possibilities in the biological sciences for students to explore. An interview with a former biology major is presented in each part of the book. Those interviewed talk about how they decided on and pre-

pared for a career after majoring in biology and describe what they do professionally. Careers include a science writer, a teacher, and an electron microscopist, among others.

6. Numerous **tables,** many of them illustrated, summarize and organize material presented in the text.

7. Carefully rendered **illustrations,** many of them new in this edition, support concepts covered in the text. Sequential art is included that incorporates the use of close-ups "exploded" to reveal greater detail. Composite pieces of line art and photographs help students interpret electron micrographs. **Scale bars** accompany micrographs to provide a guide that clarifies size.

8. **Boldface terms** facilitate easy identification of key terms and their definitions and provide emphasis.

9. A **Chapter Summary** in outline form at the end of each chapter provides a review of the material presented.

10. A **Post-Test** provides the opportunity to evaluate mastery of the material within the chapter; answers are provided.

11. **Review Questions** focus on thinking critically about important concepts and applications.

12. A list of **Recommended Readings** at the end of each chapter provides references for further learning.

13. A separate **Glossary** is provided to facilitate rapid location of definitions of terms.

14. **Appendices** provide help in understanding biological terms, measurement, career information, and biological classification.

The Organization of BIOLOGY, Third Edition

Educators present the major topics of an introductory biology course in a variety of orders. Such lack of consensus is understandable, for reasonable arguments can be advanced for each of the many possible combinations and permutations. All the aspects of biology are intimately related, and each could be grasped much more readily if all the others had been mastered previously. Because this feat cannot be accomplished, each instructor must select the topic sequence that seems optimal. For this reason, we have carefully designed each of the eight parts so that they do not depend heavily on preceding chapters and parts. The eight parts and their chapters can be presented in any number of sequences with pedagogic success.

Part I: The Organization of Life

Chapter 1, A View of Life: Basic Concepts of Biology,

introduces several major concepts of biology, including the fundamental similarities of all living things; the organization of life on individual and ecological levels; the transfer of information; the evolution of life on our planet; the diversity of life and how biologists classify living things; energy transfer between living organisms; and how science works. Chapters 2 and 3 focus on the molecular level of organization and lay the foundations in chemistry needed for an understanding of biological processes. Chapters 4 and 5 focus on the cellular level of organization, with emphasis on recent advances in cellular biology.

Part II: The Energy of Life

Part II focuses on the energy transactions involved in life processes. Chapter 6 introduces energy in living systems. Chapters 7 and 8 then discuss the grand metabolic adaptations by which living systems obtain and utilize energy by cellular respiration and photosynthesis. New art has been developed to help clarify these complex processes.

Part III: The Continuity of Life: Genetics

This unit begins with a discussion of mitosis and meiosis. Chapter 10 describes patterns of inheritance. Chapter 11 discusses the coding of information in molecules of DNA, and Chapter 12 presents RNA and protein synthesis. Chapter 13 discusses gene regulation. In Chapter 14, we focus on genetic engineering, such as recombinant DNA and its applications. Chapter 15 focuses on human genetics. In Chapter 16 we introduce the role of genes in development, including the latest findings in this exciting area of biology.

Part IV: Evolution

The unit on evolution has been expanded for this edition. Chapter 17 introduces Darwinian evolution and presents evidence for evolution. In Chapter 18, we examine evolution at the population level. Chapter 19 describes the evolution of new species and macroevolution. Chapter 20 summarizes the evolutionary history of life on Earth. In Chapter 21 we recount the evolution of the primates, including human evolution.

Part V: Diversity of Life

An evolutionary framework is used in our survey of the kingdoms of organisms. In Chapter 22 we discuss how and why organisms are classified. Chapter 23 is devoted to the viruses and to kingdom Prokaryotae. Chapter 24 focuses on the protists and Chapter 25 describes the fungi. Chapters 26 and 27 present the members of the plant kingdom, whereas Chapters 28 through 30 focus on the diversity of animals. The discussion of each group of organisms focuses on their evolutionary relationships and on their structural and functional adaptations.

Part VI: Plant Structure and Life Processes

This Part integrates plant structure and function, beginning in Chapter 31 with a discussion of plant growth and development. The coverage of genetic and environmental controls of differentiation is an important addition. Chapters 32 through 34 discuss the structure and physiology of leaves, stems, and roots. Chapter 35 describes reproduction in flowering plants, including asexual reproduction, flowers, fruits, and seeds. Chapter 36 focuses on plant hormones and responses.

Part VII: Animal Structure and Life Processes

This part emphasizes the structural, functional, and behavioral adaptations that animals have evolved to meet environmental challenges. As each system of the animal body is discussed, a comparative approach is used to examine how various animal groups have solved similar and diverse problems. Chapter 37 is devoted to the architecture of the animal body, emphasizing the various tissues and organ systems. Then Chapters 38 through 49 present animal life processes. Each chapter begins by comparing how different animal groups carry on digestion, gas exchange, internal transport, etc. Then the human adaptations for carrying on the processes are considered. The unit ends with a discussion of behavioral adaptations in Chapter 50.

Part VIII: Ecology

The ecology unit has been reorganized and rewritten in this edition. Chapters 51 through 54 provide the foundations of ecology, with the final chapter (55) focusing on environmental problems caused by humans.

Supplements

To further facilitate learning and teaching, a supplement package has been carefully designed for the student and instructor. It includes a *Study Guide, Instruc-*tor's Resource Manual, Lecture Outline on Disc, Test Bank, Computerized Test Bank* (available for the IBM PC and Apple Macintosh series), and *BIOXL* (available in both IBM and Macintosh formats). A set of 250 full-color **Overhead Transparencies** based on diagrams in the book; a set of 150 **Electron Micrograph Overhead Transparencies; BioArt,** which is composed of 100 black-and-white unlabeled line drawings from the text; and 25 **Sequence Overhead Transparencies,** which contain topics displayed in a series of stages, or layers, are also included in BIOLOGY's supplement package. A set of 250 **35mm Slides,** all in full color, is also available.

A *Laboratory Manual* written by Russell V. Skavaril, Mary M. Finnen, and Steven M. Lawton, all of Ohio State University, and an accompanying *Laboratory Instructor's Manual* are available. The *Saunders General Biology Videodisc* has been prepared to enhance lecture or laboratory presentation of material that is difficult to visualize. The 60-minute videodisc contains more than 1500 still images and a collection of video clips from *Encyclopaedia Britannica* and other sources, in addition to animated figures from the text. The videodisc will be accompanied by the *Saunders General Biology Videodisc Directory,* which contains complete descriptions, barcode labels, reference numbers, and instructions for using the videodisc, and by a software interface that will enable instructors to customize the videodisc for lectures as well as enable students to use the videodisc for self-directed study.

ACKNOWLEDGMENTS

The development and production of this new edition of BIOLOGY required extensive interaction and cooperation among the authors and the many individuals in our home and professional environments. We appreciate the valuable input and support from editors, colleagues, students, family, and friends.

We are grateful to the editorial and production staffs at Saunders College Publishing for their help and support throughout this project. We thank our Publisher Elizabeth Widdicombe and our Acquisitions Editor Julie Levin Alexander for their support, enthusiasm, and ideas. Our Developmental Editor Richard Koreto efficiently guided us through the revision process, providing us with many thoughtful reviews and useful suggestions. When Richard left Saunders, his work on the project was ably assumed by Developmental Editor Christine Connelly.

Our Art Editor Ray Tschoepe worked along with us from the very beginning, using his artistic talents and scientific knowledge to reconceptualize much of the art. We thank Photo Editor Robin Bonner for helping us find the outstanding photographs that enhance the text. We also appreciate the fine work of Dennis Drenner, who was commissioned to prepare specific photographs for our book, and Don Lovett, Trenton State College, who was commissioned to prepare scale bars for micrographs throughout the book. Alison Munoz, Supplements Developmental Editor, ably coordinated the supplements package.

We greatly appreciate our Project Editor Martha Brown, who shared her expertise, efficiently guiding the project through the intricacies of production. When Martha left to take on the challenges of motherhood, her position was ably assumed by Project Editor Becca Gruliow. We thank Art Director Carol Bleistine for coordinating the art program and the design. All of these dedicated professionals and many others at Saunders provided the skill and attention needed to produce BIOLOGY, third edition. We thank them for their help and support throughout this project.

We also appreciate the boxes contributed by Dr. Hector Quintero of Interamerican University of Puerto Rico–San German Campus, Dr. Alex Middleton of the University of Guelph, Dr. Armando Rodriguez of Interamerican University of Puerto Rico–Bayamon Campus, and Dr. Vernon Thomas of the University of Guelph. Their specialized knowledge is a valuable contribution.

We are grateful to the professionals who contributed their time and insight to the Career Visions: Jennie Dusheck, Rosa Buxeda, Linda Lopez, Patricia Lough, Todd Buck, Ted Wesemann, Timothy R. Henderson, and Robert M. Pinto.

We thank our families and friends for their understanding, support, and encouragement as we struggled through many revisions and deadlines. We especially thank Mical Solomon, Amy Solomon, Belicia Efros, Kathleen M. Heide, Alan and Jennifer Berg, and Charles and Margaret Martin for their input and support.

Our colleagues and students who have used our book have provided valuable input by sharing their responses to the second edition of BIOLOGY with us. We thank them and ask again for their comments and suggestions as they use this new edition. We can be reached through our editors at Saunders College Publishing.

Reviewers

We express our thanks to the many biologists who have read the manuscript during various stages of its preparation and provided us with valuable suggestions for improvement. Their input has contributed greatly to our final product. Third edition reviewers include

Sylvester Allred, *Northern Arizona University*
J.T. Beatty, *University of British Columbia*
Dorothy Berner, *Temple University*
Nicole Bournias, *California State University at San Bernardino*
Barry Bowman, *University of California at Santa Cruz*
David Carr, *University of Maryland at College Park*
Joyce Corban, *Wright State University*
Wiliam Cordes, *Loyola University*
David Cotter, *Georgia College*
Kenneth Curry, *University of South Mississippi*
Thomas Davis, *University of New Hampshire*
Lee Drickamer, *Southern Illinois University at Carbondale*
Peter Ducey, *State University of New York, Cortland*
John Evans, *Memorial University of Newfoundland*
Bernard Frye, *University of Texas at Arlington*
Michael Gaines, *University of Kansas*
Elizabeth Godrick, *Boston University*
Paul Goldstein, *University of Texas at El Paso*
Nels Granholm, *South Dakota State University*
Edward J. Greding, Jr., *Del Mar College*
Mark Gromko, *Bowling Green University*
Jean Heitz, *University of Wisconsin at Madison*
Jean Helgeson, *Collin County Community College*
Carl Hoagstrom, *Ohio Northern University*
Pat Humphrey, *Ohio University*
Alice Jacklet, *SUNY at Albany*
Paul Lago, *University of Mississippi*
Charles Mallery, *University of Miami*
James Mauseth, *University of Texas at Austin*
Joesph Michalewicz, *Holy Family College*
Roger Milkman, *University of Iowa*
John Moner, *University of Massachusetts at Amherst*
Russell Monson, *University of Colorado at Boulder*
Debbie Mueler, *Cardinal Stritch College*
John Murray, *University of Pennsylvania*
William H. Nelson, *Morgan State University*
Carolyn Ogren, *Parkland College*
Beulah Parker, *North Carolina State University*
David Polcyn, *California State at San Bernardino*
Mimi Sayed, *Michigan State University*
Jane Shoup, *Purdue University at Calumet*
J. Kenneth Shull, Jr., *Appalachian State University*
Paul Small, *Eureka College*
Ian Tizard, *Texas A&M University*
Elizabeth Waldorf, *Mississippi Gulf Community College*
Clarence Wolfe, *North Virginia Community College*

TO THE STUDENT

Biology is one of the most varied subjects one can study It is therefore not surprising that biologists are a diverse group, with different interests, talents, and personalities. Almost anyone who has a desire to understand living things can find a suitable niche in the field of biology.

The thousands of students we have taught have differed in their life goals and learning styles. Some have had excellent backgrounds in science, others poor ones. Regardless of their backgrounds, it is common for students taking their first college biology course to find they must work much harder than they expected. You can make the task easier by using approaches to learning that are usually successful for a broad range of students.

Many students "study" passively. An active learner always has questions in mind and is constantly making connections. For example, in biology there are many processes that must be understood. Do not try to blindly memorize these; instead think about causes and effects, so that every process becomes a story. Eventually you will see that many processes are connected by common elements.

Active learning is facilitated if you do some of your studying in a small group. In a study group the roles of teacher and learner should become interchangeable, for the best way to make sure you understand is to teach. A study group allows you to be challenged in a nonthreatening environment and can provide some emotional support.

One stumbling block for many students is the necessity to learn a great deal of terminology. In fact, it would be much more difficult to learn and communicate if we did not have this terminology, for words are really "tools for thinking." Learning terminology generally becomes easier because most biological terms are modular. They are composed of mostly Latin and Greek roots, and once you learn many of these you will find you may have a good idea of the meaning of a new word even before it is defined. For this reason we have included Appendix A, Understanding Biological Terms. Of course, to make sure you understand the precise definition, you will want to use the Index and Glossary. The more you use biological terms, in both speech and writing, the more comfortable you will be.

Although biology is a demanding subject, the time and effort you spend studying will be well spent, because this is a very exciting time to be a biologist. Today we have the tools to study living things in ways that were only a dream in the not too distant past. As we gain new information, our concepts are constantly evolving. We find this to be one of the most exhilarating aspects of biology, and we hope you will too!

The skillful integration of three themes throughout distinguishes **Biology, third edition** as a text that unifies the significant processes in biology. Transmission of information, evolution, and transfer of energy through living systems combine to provide an excellent framework that contributes to the building of students' intuitive understanding.

These three themes are highlighted not only in textual discussion, but often in the "Making the Connection" boxes throughout the text. Novel in their approach, these boxes show how material from various chapters is connected, thus establishing the relevance of ccverage for students.

High-interest "Focus" boxes draw attention to interesting biological phenomena and current research.

Practical and usable "Career Visions" boxes inform students of possible career paths or opportunities that are available to biology majors. The net result of this kind of box is that students receive persuasive information about the merits of continuing their biology education.

Energy-Releasing Pathways and Biosynthesis 181

MAKING THE CONNECTION

Relating Respiration to Energy, Information, and Evolution

Three of the most important themes of biology (and of this text) are (1) energy transfer, (2) transmission of information, and (3) evolution (see Chapter 1). All three themes are tied to the concepts presented in this chapter.

It is quite obvious that *energy* is involved in respiration because cellular respiration is the process of making the energy of food available to the cell. Food molecules are broken down to release the energy locked in their chemical bonds—an example of catabolism. The energy released by catabolic processes can be used by the cell for anabolism: to biosynthesize complex molecules needed by the cell.

Information is critical to the overall operation of the elaborate transformations of metabolism. Imagine what would happen if cells did not possess feedback controls to regulate metabolic pathways. Clearly the communication among

molecules implied by the word *information* is necessary for a balanced metabolism within each cell. For example, information helps control the thousands of cellular respiratory reactions that occur every second, pouring forth streams of ATP, water, and carbon dioxide in each one of the billions of cells of the human body.

It is instructive to consider respiration in the context of *evolution*. Glycolysis, for example, must have evolved early in the evolutionary history of cells because it occurs in *all* eukaryotic cells as well as in many prokaryotic cells. The enzymes of glycolysis are found universally in cells of many bacteria, all protists, all fungi, all animals, and all plants. *Information* is also tied to *evolution* in this example because all these organisms have similar genetic information that instructs their cells to make the enzymes of glycolysis.

Figure 7–16 The generalizations about cellular metabolism also apply to the metabolism of a multicellular organism. In an adult organism the rates of synthesis and degradation are essentially equal, whereas in a growing organism the rate of synthesis must be faster than the rate of catabolism. However, even in an adult organism there is a continuous turnover of molecules. (M. P. Kahl/ VIREO, Academy of Natural Sciences)

---

number of insecticides and drugs are irreversible enzyme inhibitors (see Focus on Enzyme Inhibition and Antibacterial Drugs).

Enzymes themselves can act as poisons if they get into the wrong compartment of the body. As little as 1 mg of crystalline trypsin injected intravenously can kill a rat. The proteolytic enzymes of the pancreas, trypsin and chymotrypsin, are synthesized in the form of **precursors,** molecules that can be converted to the active enzyme. These precursors, which are somewhat

larger than the active enzyme, are packaged in granules and secreted into the duct of the pancreas. Because the precursors are inactive, the pancreas is not digested by the enzymes it synthesizes. The inactive enzymes are made active by other enzymes that cleave off a portion of the precursor molecule to yield the active enzyme. Acute pancreatitis, a serious, even fatal disease, occurs when the proteolytic enzymes become active while still within the pancreas and digest cells and blood vessels.

FOCUS ON

Enzyme Inhibition and Antibacterial Drugs

Many bacterial infections are treated with drugs that directly or indirectly inhibit bacterial enzyme activity. For example, sulfa drugs have a chemical structure similar to that of the nutrient para-aminobenzoic acid (PABA). When PABA is available, microorganisms can synthesize the vitamin folic acid. Humans do not synthesize folic acid from PABA, and that is why sulfa drugs selectively affect bacteria. When a sulfa drug is present, competitive inhibition occurs within the bacterium—the drug competes with PABA for the active site of the bacterial enzyme. When the bacteria use the sulfa drug instead of PABA, they synthesize a compound that has a

structure somewhat similar to that of folic acid. However, this imposter folic acid does not work as a coenzyme. Instead, it competitively inhibits the enzyme's action so that the bacteria are unable to make needed amino acids and nucleotides.

Penicillin and related antibiotics irreversibly inhibit a bacterial enzyme, transpeptidase. This enzyme is responsible for establishing some of the chemical linkages in the bacterial cell wall (see Chapter 23). Unable to produce properly constructed cell walls, cytoplasm spills out and susceptible bacteria are prevented from multiplying effectively (see figure). Human cells do not have cell walls

and do not employ this enzyme. Thus, except for individuals allergic to penicilin, this drug is harmless to humans.

Penicillin is an irreversible enzyme inhibitor. (a) Normal bacteria. Insert shows the new cell wall laid down between daughter cells of a dividing bacterium. (b) Penicillin has damaged these bacterial cell walls. The insets are magnified approximately ×54,000. (Courtesy of Drs. Victor Lorian and Barbara Atkinson, with permission of *The American Journal of Clinical Pathology*)

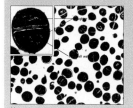
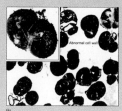

Abnormal cell wall

(a)   (b)

158

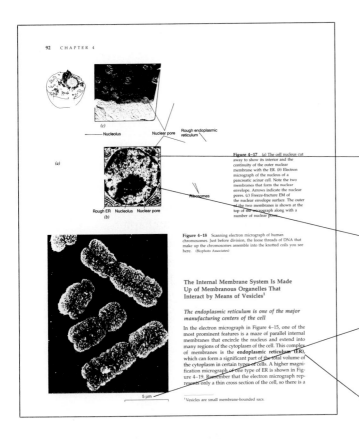

Figure 4–17 (a) The cell nucleus cut away to show its interior and the continuity of the outer nuclear membrane with the ER. (b) Electron micrograph of the nucleus of a pancreatic acinar cell. Note the two membranes that form the nuclear envelope. Arrows indicate the nuclear pores. (c) Freeze-fracture EM of the nuclear envelope surface. The outer of the two membranes is shown at the top of the micrograph along with a number of nuclear pores.

Figure 4–18 Scanning electron micrograph of human chromosomes. Just before division, the loose threads of DNA that make up the chromosomes assemble into the knotted coils you see here. (Biophoto Associates)

The Internal Membrane System Is Made Up of Membranous Organelles That Interact by Means of Vesicles[1]

The endoplasmic reticulum is one of the major manufacturing centers of the cell

In the electron micrograph in Figure 4–15, one of the most prominent features is a maze of parallel internal membranes that encircle the nucleus and extend into many regions of the cytoplasm of the cell. This complex of membranes is the **endoplasmic reticulum (ER)**, which can form a significant part of the total volume of the cytoplasm in certain types of cells. A higher magnification micrograph of one type of ER is shown in Figure 4–19. Remember that the electron micrograph represents only a thin cross section of the cell, so there is a

5 µm

[1] Vesicles are small membrane-bounded sacs.

The evolution of **BIOLOGY, third edition** is particularly apparent in the incorporation of superb artwork—most of it revised or new. Students and instructors will respond enthusiastically to this visual enhancement that includes

• Sequential art that incorporates the use of close-ups "exploded" to reveal greater detail

• Composite pieces of line art and photographs to help students interpret electron micrographs

• Scale bars accompanying the electron micrographs, providing a guide that clarifies size

Boldface terms facilitate easy identification of key terms and their definitions and provide emphasis.

Numerous **tables,** many of them illustrated, summarize and organize material presented in the text.

Table 8-1 SUMMARY OF PHOTOSYNTHESIS

Reaction Series	Summary of Process	Needed Materials	End Products
A. Light-dependent reactions (take place in thylakoid membranes)	Energy from sunlight used to split water, manufacture ATP, and reduce NADP⁺		
1. Photochemical reactions	Chlorophyll energized; reaction center gives up energized electron to electron acceptor	Light energy; pigments (chlorophyll)	Electrons
2. Electron transport	Electrons are transported along chain of electron acceptors in thylakoid membranes; electrons reduce NADP⁺; splitting of water provides some of H⁺ that accumulates inside thylakoid space	Electrons, NADP⁺, H₂O, electron acceptors	NADPH, O₂
3. Chemiosmosis	H⁺ are permitted to move across the thylakoid membrane down a proton gradient; they cross the membrane through special channels; energy released is used to produce ATP	Proton gradient, ADP + Pᵢ	ATP
B. Light-independent reactions (take place in stroma)	Carbon fixation: carbon dioxide is used to make sugar	Ribulose bisphosphate, CO₂, ATP, NADPH, necessary enzymes	Carbohydrates, ADP + Pᵢ, NADP⁺

Photosynthesis, like cellular respiration, is a reduction-oxidation (redox) process (see Chapter 7). Recall that during cell respiration, organic compounds are oxidized. Hydrogens (or their electrons) are split off from the fuel molecule and transferred along a series of acceptor molecules to molecular oxygen, forming water. Electrons lose energy as they are passed through the chain of acceptor molecules, and that energy is used by the mitochondrion to make ATP. In photosynthesis, the direction of electron flow is reversed from that of respiration. Water is split, and the electrons of hydrogen are transferred to chlorophyll and then through a series of electron acceptors. During this transfer, light energy raises the energy level of the electrons. Ultimately, some of the energy is used to reduce carbon dioxide, forming glucose.

The summary equation for photosynthesis describes what happens but not how it happens. The "how" is much more complex and involves many steps. The reactions of photosynthesis are divided into two parts, the light-dependent and the light-independent reactions (Table 8–1).

In Light-Dependent Reactions, Light Energy Is Used To Make the High-Energy Compounds, ATP and NADPH

The light-dependent reactions occur only in the presence of light. During this phase of photosynthesis, several important events take place. Chlorophyll absorbs light energy, which is immediately converted to electrical energy as electrons flow from the chlorophyll molecule. Some of this energy is used to make ATP by chemiosmosis; during this process, electrical energy is transformed to chemical energy. Some of the light energy trapped by the chlorophyll is used to split water, a process known as **photolysis.** Oxygen (O₂) from the water is released (Figure 8–4), and the hydrogen from the water combines with the hydrogen acceptor NADP⁺, forming NADPH.[1] Here again, electrical energy is converted to chemical energy.

Carbohydrates Are Produced during the Light-Independent Reactions

Although the light-independent reactions do not require light directly, they do depend on the products of the light-dependent reactions (Figure 8–5). In the light-independent reactions, the energy of the NADPH and ATP produced during the light-dependent phase of photosynthesis is used to manufacture carbohydrate molecules. The raw materials from which carbohydrates are made are carbon dioxide from the air and

[1] Although the correct way to write the reduced form of NADP⁺ is NADPH + H⁺, for simplicity's sake, we present the reduced form as NADPH.

Concept statement heads serve as a preview and summary of conceptual discussion to follow, providing a fresh approach to the organization of material.

CHAPTER 1

A View of Life

OUTLINE

Characteristics of living things
Transmission of information
Evolution: A unifying concept
Energy flow through living systems
The scientific method

We stand on the brink of the 21st century—an exciting time to begin the study of **biology**, the science of life. During the past few decades research in the basic science of biology has yielded amazing knowledge about ourselves—the human species—and about the millions of other diverse life forms with which we share our planet. Applications of this basic research have provided us with the technology to transplant hearts, manipulate genes, conquer many diseases, and increase world food supply. Recent research in molecular biology and genetics has led to new insights into disease processes, leading to the first human gene-therapy tests. As we prepare to enter the 21st century, we can appreciate what a powerful force biology has been in providing us with the quality of life most of us enjoy.

As biologists continue to study interrelationships of the living things that inhabit our planet, they enhance our awareness of our own impact on other living things and on the environment (Figure 1-1). This book is a starting point for your exploration of biology. It will provide you with the tools that will enable you to become a part of this fascinating science. Perhaps you will decide to become a research biologist and help unravel the complexities of the human brain, breed disease-resistant strains of wheat or rice, identify new species of animals or bacteria, or discover a cure for cancer. Or perhaps you will choose to enter an applied field of biology such as dentistry, medicine, or veterinary medicine. Even if you are not planning a career in one of the biological sciences, learning about this exciting science will enable you to better understand yourself, your environment, and the organisms with which you share your planet. As you become biologically literate you will increase your understanding of the impact biology continues to have on your life and on society.

In this first chapter we will introduce three basic themes of biology—transmission of information, evolution of life, and flow of energy through living systems. First, we need to develop a more precise understanding of what life is.

The green tree frog and the fiddlehead fern on which it is perched are complex living systems.   (M. L. Dembinsky, Jr./ Dembinsky Photo Associates)

2

A **Chapter Outline** at the beginning of each chapter provides the student with an overview of the major topics covered in the chapter.

LEARNING OBJECTIVES

After you have studied this chapter you should be able to

1. Define biology and discuss its applications to human life and society.
2. Distinguish between living and nonliving things by describing the features that characterize living things.
3. Summarize the importance of information transfer to living systems, giving specific examples.
4. Give a brief overview of the theory of evolution and explain why it is the principal unifying concept in biology.
5. Apply the theory of natural selection to any given adaptation, suggesting a logical explanation of how the adaptation may have evolved.
6. Construct a hierarchy of biological organization including individual and ecological levels.

7. Demonstrate the binomial system of nomenclature using several specific examples.
8. Classify an organism, such as a human, according to kingdom, phylum or division, class, order, family, genus, and species.
9. Contrast the five kingdoms of living organisms and cite examples of each group.
10. Relate metabolism and homeostasis and give specific examples of these life processes.
11. Contrast the roles of producers, consumers, and decomposers, and cite examples of their interdependence.
12. Design an experiment to test a given hypothesis using the procedure and terminology of the scientific method.

LIFE CAN BE DEFINED IN TERMS OF THE CHARACTERISTICS OF LIVING THINGS

It is relatively easy to determine that a human being, an oak tree, and a butterfly are living whereas rocks are not. Despite their diversity, the living things that inhabit our planet share a common set of characteristics that distinguish them from nonliving things. These features include a precise kind of organization, a variety of chemical reactions we term metabolism, the ability to maintain an appropriate internal environment even when the external environment changes (a process referred to as homeostasis), movement, responsiveness, growth, reproduction, and adaptation to environmental change. We consider each of these characteristics in the following sections.

Living Things Are Composed of Cells

The cell theory, one of the fundamental unifying concepts of biology, states that all living things are composed of basic units called cells and of substances pro-

(a)   (b)   (c)

Figure 1–1   Modern biology examines the world of life in all its details and interactions. (a) An American elk browsing on lodgepole pine (*Pinus contorta*) in a coniferous forest. Biologists are concerned with the physical characteristics of the elk and the pine, how each organism functions, their behavior, and their interaction with each other and with other living things in the environment. (b) Genetic researchers study chromosomes, which are made up of the chemical compound DNA, the hereditary material of living things. (c) Biologists also study the effects of human activities on the environment. Because humans have cut an estimated 90% of the U.S. Northwest's forests and continue to cut down about 70,000 acres of trees each year, this ecosystem is seriously threatened. The biologist shown here is working to protect the spotted owl, a forest inhabitant that lives in the Douglas firs (*Pseudotsuga menziesii*). Only about 2000 spotted owl pairs remain. (a, Ed Reschke; b, University of Michigan, by Larime Photo/Dembinsky Photo Associates; c, R. M. Collins III)

Learning Objectives at the beginning of each chapter indicate exactly what the student must be able to do in order to demonstrate mastery of the material in the chapter.

A **Chapter Summary** in outline form at the end of each chapter provides a review of the material presented.

A **Post-Test** provides the opportunity to evaluate mastery of the material within the chapter; answers are provided.

Review Questions focus on thinking critically about important concepts and applications.

A list of **Recommended Readings** at the end of each chapter provides references for further learning.

---

182 CHAPTER 7

SUMMARY

I. Cells use three different types of catabolic pathways to extract free energy from nutrients: aerobic respiration, anaerobic glycolysis, and fermentation.
II. During aerobic respiration, a fuel molecule such as glucose is oxidized, forming carbon dioxide and water with the release of energy (up to 36 to 38 ATPs per molecule of glucose).
III. Aerobic respiration is a redox process in which hydrogen is transferred from glucose (which becomes oxidized) to oxygen (which becomes reduced).
IV. The chemical reactions of aerobic respiration occur in four stages: glycolysis, formation of acetyl CoA, the citric acid cycle, and the electron transport system/chemiosmosis.
   A. During glycolysis a molecule of glucose is degraded, forming two molecules of pyruvate.
      1. Two ATP molecules (net) are produced during glycolysis.
      2. Four hydrogen atoms are removed from the fuel molecule (as two NADH).
   B. The two pyruvate molecules each lose a molecule of carbon dioxide, and the remaining acetyl groups combine with coenzyme A, producing acetyl CoA. One NADH is formed as each pyruvate is converted to acetyl CoA.
   C. Each acetyl CoA enters the citric acid cycle by combining with a four-carbon compound, oxaloacetate, to form citrate, a six-carbon compound.
      1. With two turns of the citric acid cycle, the two acetyl CoAs representing the original glucose molecule are completely degraded.
      2. Two carbon dioxides are released and hydrogens are transferred to three NAD+ and one FAD with each turn of the cycle; only one ATP is produced directly by substrate-level phosphorylation per turn.
   D. Hydrogen atoms (or their electrons) removed from fuel molecules are transferred from one electron acceptor to another down a chain of acceptor molecules that make up the electron transport system.
      1. The final acceptor in the chain is molecular oxygen, which combines with the hydrogen to form water.
      2. According to the chemiosmotic theory, energy liberated in the electron transport chain is used to establish a proton gradient across the inner mitochondrial membrane.
      3. The flow of protons back through the membrane from the intermembrane space to the mitochondrial matrix (by way of the enzyme ATP synthetase) releases energy, which is used to synthesize ATP.
V. Organic nutrients other than glucose are converted into appropriate compounds and fed into the glycolytic or citric acid pathways.
   A. Amino acids are deaminated and the carbon skeleton converted to a metabolic intermediate such as pyruvate.

B. Both the glycerol and fatty acid components of lipids are oxidized as fuel. Fatty acids are converted to acetyl coenzyme A molecules by the process of β-oxidation.
VI. In anaerobic respiration, fuel molecules are broken down in the absence of oxygen; the final hydrogen acceptor is nitrate or sulfate.
VII. Fermentation is an anaerobic process in which the final acceptor of electrons from NADH is an organic compound derived from the initial nutrient. There is a net gain of only two ATPs per glucose molecule, compared with about 36 to 38 ATPs produced per glucose molecule by aerobic respiration.
   A. Yeast cells carry on alcohol fermentation, in which ethyl alcohol and carbon dioxide are the final products.
   B. Certain fungi, certain bacteria, and certain animal cells (in the absence of sufficient oxygen) carry on lactate fermentation, in which hydrogen atoms are added to pyruvate, forming lactate.
VIII. The cells of living things exist in a dynamic state and are continuously building up and breaking down the many different cell constituents.
   A. Each cell usually synthesizes its own complex macromolecules, and each step in the process is catalyzed by a separate enzyme.
   B. Biosynthetic reactions are strongly endergonic and require ATP to drive them.

Summary Reactions for Aerobic Respiration

Summary reaction for the complete oxidation of glucose:

$C_6H_{12}O_6 + 6 O_2 \longrightarrow 6 CO_2 + 12 H_2O + Energy$

Summary reaction for glycolysis:

$C_6H_{12}O_6 + 2 ATP + 2 ADP + 2 P_i + 2 NAD^+ \longrightarrow$
$2 \text{ pyruvate} + 4 ATP + 2 NADH + 2 H_2O$

Summary reaction for the conversion of pyruvate to acetyl CoA:

$2 \text{ pyruvate} + 2 \text{ coenzyme A} + 2 NAD^+ \longrightarrow$
$2 \text{ acetyl CoA} + 2 CO_2 + 2 NADH$

Summary reaction for the citric acid cycle:

$2 \text{ acetyl CoA} + 6 NAD^+ + 2 FAD + 2 ADP + 2 P_i + 2 H_2O$
$\longrightarrow 4 CO_2 + 6 NADH + 2 FADH_2 + 2 ATP + 2 CoA$

Summary reactions for the processing of the hydrogens of NADH and FADH₂ in the electron transport system:

$NADH + H^+ + 3 ADP + 3 P_i + 1/2 O_2 \longrightarrow$
$NAD^+ + 3 ATP + H_2O$

$FADH_2 + 2 ADP + 2 P_i + 1/2 O_2 \longrightarrow$
$FAD + 2 ATP + H_2O$

Energy-Releasing Pathways and Biosynthesis **183**

POST-TEST

1. The process of splitting larger molecules into smaller ones is an aspect of metabolism called _____.
2. The synthetic aspect of metabolism is referred to as _____.
3. A chemical process during which a substance gains electrons is called _____.
4. The pathway through which glucose is degraded to pyruvate is referred to as _____.
5. The reactions of glycolysis take place within the _____.
6. Before pyruvate enters the citric acid cycle, it is decarboxylated, oxidized, and combined with coenzyme A, forming carbon dioxide and _____.
7. In the first step of the citric acid cycle, acetyl CoA reacts with oxaloacetate to form _____.
8. During the citric acid cycle, the acetyl of acetyl CoA is oxidized, resulting in the production of two molecules of _____.
9. The citric acid cycle must turn _____ times to process the acetyl CoAs formed from one molecule of glucose.
10. Dehydrogenase enzymes remove hydrogens from fuel molecules and transfer them to primary acceptors such as _____ and _____.
11. The final hydrogen acceptor in the electron transport chain is _____.

12. The _____ model proposes that electron transport and ATP synthesis are coupled by a proton gradient across the inner mitochondrial membrane.
13. When protons move across a membrane and down an energy gradient in chemiosmosis, energy is released and used to synthesize _____.
14. One important part of the feedback inhibition of aerobic respiration is the inhibitory effect of ATP on phosphofructokinase, an enzyme required in _____.
15. A net profit of only _____ ATPs can be produced anaerobically from the fermentation of one molecule of glucose, compared with a maximum of _____ ATPs produced in aerobic respiration.
16. Yeasts and bacteria that can shift to anaerobic respiration or fermentation when oxygen is in short supply are called _____.
17. The anaerobic process by which alcohol or lactate is produced as a product of glycolysis is referred to as _____.
18. When deprived of oxygen, yeast cells obtain energy by fermentation, producing carbon dioxide and _____.
19. During strenuous muscle activity, the pyruvate in muscle cells may accept hydrogen to become _____.
20. Anaerobic catabolism is inefficient because the fuel molecule is only partially _____.

REVIEW QUESTIONS

1. What is the specific role of oxygen in the cell? What happens when cells that can only respire aerobically are deprived of oxygen?
2. Mitochondria are often referred to as the "power plants" of the cell. Justify this with a specific explanation.
3. What is the evolutionary significance of glycolysis?
4. Refer to Figure 7–8, the diagram of the steps in the citric acid cycle. Look at each reaction and, without reading the description, determine what type of reaction it is (dehydrogenation, decarboxylation, or make-ready).
5. Draw a mitochondrion and indicate the locations of the following:
   a. enzymes of the citric acid cycle
   b. the electron transport system
   c. the proton gradient that drives ATP production
6. How does the chemiosmotic model relate to aerobic respiration? How does a proton gradient contribute to ATP synthesis?

7. Explain the roles of the following in aerobic respiration:
   a. NAD+
   b. cytochromes
8. Calculate how much energy (as ATPs) is made available to the cell from a single glucose molecule by the operation of glycolysis, the formation of acetyl CoA, the citric acid cycle, and the electron transport system.
9. Trace the fate of hydrogens removed from glucose during glycolysis when oxygen is present in muscle cells. Trace the fate of hydrogens removed from glucose when the amount of oxygen available is insufficient to support aerobic respiration.
10. Why is it advantageous that synthetic reactions are generally not the reverse of reactions in which molecules are catabolized?

RECOMMENDED READINGS

Alberts, B., D. Bray, J. Lewis, M. Raff, K. Roberts, and J. D. Watson. *Molecular Biology of the Cell*, 2nd ed. Garland Publishing, New York, 1989. An in-depth treatment of energy conversion in cells.

Stryer, L. *Biochemistry*, 3rd ed. W. H. Freeman, San Francisco, 1988. A well-illustrated, readable text that covers the concepts of cellular energetics from the ground up.

CONTENTS OVERVIEW

CONTENTS

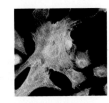

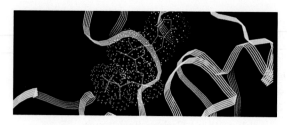

PART III

THE CONTINUITY OF LIFE: GENETICS 208

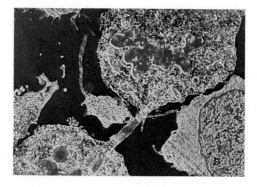

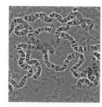

PART V
THE DIVERSITY OF LIFE 488

PART VII

STRUCTURES AND LIFE PROCESSES IN ANIMALS 776

37 The Animal Body: Tissues, Organs, and Organ Systems 778

38 Protection, Support, and Movement: Skin, Skeleton, and Muscle 795

39 Neural Control: Neurons 814

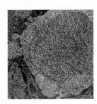

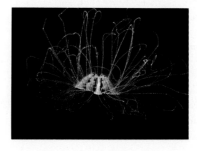

The Organization of Life

Life is highly organized. Biologists study and seek to understand the exquisite organization that characterizes both individual life forms and the world of life. In Part I we study two basic levels of organization—the chemical and cellular levels. We also introduce three basic themes of biology that help us understand the organization of life—evolution, transmission of information, and flow of energy through the world of life.

How evolution contributes to the organization of life is a major theme of this book. Scientists have accumulated a wealth of evidence showing that the life forms on our planet are related—that complex organisms have evolved through time from simpler life forms.

Organization also depends on the precise, orderly transmission of information. Instructions for organizing each living thing and each new generation are encoded in the DNA molecules that make up the genes.

Energy is required to maintain the precise order that characterizes living things. Maintaining the chemical transactions and cellular organization essential to life requires a continuous input of energy.

The ringtail lemur is a native of
Madagascar. Many species of lemurs have
become rare because humans have
destroyed the forests in which they live.

(Fran Lanting/Minden Pictures)

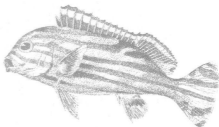

A View of Life

We stand on the brink of the 21st century—an exciting time to begin the study of **biology,** the science of life. During the past few decades research in the basic science of biology has yielded amazing knowledge about ourselves—the human species—and about the millions of other diverse life forms with which we share our planet. Applications of this basic research have provided us with the technology to transplant hearts, manipulate genes, conquer many diseases, and increase world food supply. Recent research in molecular biology and genetics has led to new insights into disease processes, leading to the first human gene-therapy tests. As we prepare to enter the 21st century, we can appreciate what a powerful force biology has been in providing us with the quality of life most of us enjoy.

As biologists continue to study interrelationships of the living things that inhabit our planet, they enhance our awareness of our own impact on other living things and on the environment (Figure 1–1). This book is a starting point for your exploration of biology. It will

The green tree frog and the fiddlehead fern on which it is perched are complex living systems. (M. L. Dembinsky, Jr./ Dembinsky Photo Associates)

provide you with the tools that will enable you to become a part of this fascinating science. Perhaps you will decide to become a research biologist and help unravel the complexities of the human brain, breed disease-resistant strains of wheat or rice, identify new species of animals or bacteria, or discover a cure for cancer. Or perhaps you will choose to enter an applied field of biology such as dentistry, medicine, or veterinary medicine. Even if you are not planning a career in one of the biological sciences, learning about this exciting science will enable you to better understand yourself, your environment, and the organisms with which you share your planet. As you become biologically literate you will increase your understanding of the impact biology continues to have on your life and on society.

In this first chapter we will introduce three basic themes of biology—transmission of information, evolution of life, and flow of energy through living systems. First, we need to develop a more precise understanding of what life is.

After you have studied this chapter you should be able to

1. Define biology and discuss its applications to human life and society.
2. Distinguish between living and nonliving things by describing the features that characterize living things.
3. Summarize the importance of information transfer to living systems, giving specific examples.
4. Give a brief overview of the theory of evolution and explain why it is the principal unifying concept in biology.
5. Apply the theory of natural selection to any given adaptation, suggesting a logical explanation of how the adaptation may have evolved.
6. Construct a hierarchy of biological organization including individual and ecological levels.
7. Demonstrate the binomial system of nomenclature using several specific examples.
8. Classify an organism, such as a human, according to kingdom, phylum or division, class, order, family, genus, and species.
9. Contrast the five kingdoms of living organisms and cite examples of each group.
10. Relate metabolism and homeostasis and give specific examples of these life processes.
11. Contrast the roles of producers, consumers, and decomposers, and cite examples of their interdependence.
12. Design an experiment to test a given hypothesis using the procedure and terminology of the scientific method.

LIFE CAN BE DEFINED IN TERMS OF THE CHARACTERISTICS OF LIVING THINGS

It is relatively easy to determine that a human being, an oak tree, and a butterfly are living whereas rocks are not. Despite their diversity, the living things that inhabit our planet share a common set of characteristics that distinguish them from nonliving things. These features include a precise kind of organization, a variety of chemical reactions we term metabolism, the ability to maintain an appropriate internal environment even when the external environment changes (a process referred to as homeostasis), movement, responsiveness, growth, reproduction, and adaptation to environmental change. We consider each of these characteristics in the following sections.

Living Things Are Composed of Cells

The cell theory, one of the fundamental unifying concepts of biology, states that all living things are composed of basic units called cells and of substances pro-

(a)

(b)

(c)

Figure 1–1 Modern biology examines the world of life in all its details and interactions. (*a*) An American elk browsing on lodgepole pine (*Pinus contorta*) in a coniferous forest. Biologists are concerned with the physical characteristics of the elk and the pine, how each organism functions, their behavior, and their interaction with each other and with other living things in the environment. (*b*) Genetic researchers study chromosomes, which are made up of the chemical compound DNA, the hereditary material of living things. (*c*) Biologists also study the effects of human activities on the environment. Because humans have cut an estimated 90% of the U.S. Northwest's forests and continue to cut down about 70,000 acres of trees each year, this ecosystem is seriously threatened. The biologist shown here is working to protect the spotted owl, a forest inhabitant that lives in the Douglas firs (*Pseudotsuga menziesii*). Only about 2000 spotted owl pairs remain. (*a*, Ed Reschke; *b*, University of Michigan, by Larime Photo/Dembinsky Photo Associates; *c*, R. M. Collins III)

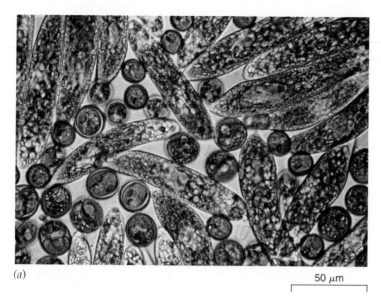

(a)

50 μm

(b)

Figure 1–2   Single-celled and multicellular life forms. (a) Single-celled life forms are generally smaller and less specialized than multicellular organisms. The euglenoids (photosynthetic one-celled organisms) shown here each consist of one intricate cell that performs all of the functions essential to life. (The elongated forms are *Euglena* sp.; the others are Trachelomonas.) (b) Both the round-leaf sundew (*Drosera rotundifolia*) and the insect it has trapped are complex multicellular organisms. Each consists of thousands of specialized cells that carry on specific tasks. (a, Visuals Unlimited/T. E. Adams; b, Skip Moody/Dembinsky Photo Associates)

duced by cells. Although living things vary greatly in size and appearance, all (except the viruses[1]) are composed of these small building blocks. Some of the simplest life forms, such as bacteria, are unicellular—they consist of a single cell. In contrast, the body of a human or an oak tree is made of billions of cells. In such complex multicellular organisms, life processes depend on the coordinated functions of the component cells (Figure 1–2).

Living Things Grow and Develop

Some nonliving things appear to grow. Crystals may form in a supersaturated solution of a salt; as more of the salt comes out of solution, the crystals may enlarge. However, this is not growth in the biological sense. Biologists restrict the term *growth* to those processes that increase the amount of living substance in the organism. **Growth,** therefore, is an increase in mass brought about by an increase in the *size* of the individual cells, by an increase in the *number* of cells, or by both (Figure 1–3). Growth may be uniform in the several parts of an organism, or it may be greater in some parts than in others so that the body proportions change as growth occurs.

Some organisms—most trees, for example—continue to grow indefinitely. Many animals have a defined growth period that terminates when a characteristic size is reached in adulthood. One of the remarkable aspects of the growth process is that each part of the organism continues to function as it grows.

Figure 1–3   Biological growth involves the refashioning of raw materials to construct the organism as determined by its genetic material. The young yellow baboon shown here with its parents will eat and grow until it reaches adult size. This family was photographed in Kenya, East Africa. (Stan Osolinski/Dembinsky Photo Associates)

---

[1] As we will see in Chapter 23, viruses can carry on life activities and reproduce only by using the metabolic machinery of *the cells they parasitize,* and so are said to be on the borderline between living and nonliving things.

Living things develop as well as grow. **Development** includes all the changes that take place during the life of an organism. Humans and many other organisms begin life as a fertilized egg, which then grows and develops specialized structures and body form.

Metabolism Includes the Chemical Processes Essential to Growth, Repair, and Reproduction

In all living organisms chemical reactions and energy transformations take place that are essential to nutrition, growth and repair of cells, and conversion of energy into usable forms. The sum of all the chemical activities of the organism is called **metabolism.** Metabolic reactions occur continuously in every living organism, and they must be carefully regulated to maintain a balanced internal state. The tendency of organisms to maintain a relatively constant internal environment is termed **homeostasis,** and the mechanisms that accomplish the task are known as **homeostatic mechanisms.** Metabolism and homeostasis are discussed further in a later section of this chapter and in other sections of this book.

Movement Is a Basic Property of Cells

Movement, although not necessarily locomotion (moving from one place to another), is another characteristic of living things. Most animals move very obviously—they wiggle, crawl, swim, run, or fly. The movements of plants are usually much slower and less obvious but occur nonetheless. For example, plants orient their leaves to the sun. The living material within cells is itself in continuous motion.

Locomotion may result from the beating of tiny hairlike extensions of the cell called **cilia** or longer structures known as **flagella** (Figure 1–4), from the contraction of muscles, or from the slow oozing of the cell, a process called amoeboid motion. A few animals, such as sponges, corals, and oysters, have free-swimming larval stages but do not move from place to place as adults. Even though these adults (described as sessile) remain firmly attached to some surface, they may have cilia or flagella. These structures beat rhythmically, moving the surrounding water that brings food and other necessities to the organism.

Living Things Respond to Stimuli

Living things respond to **stimuli,** physical or chemical changes in their internal or external environment. Stimuli that evoke a response in most organisms are changes in the color, intensity, or direction of light; changes in

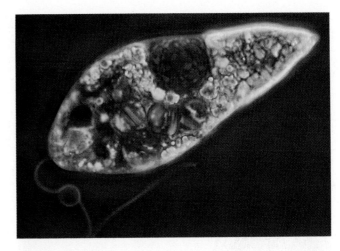

Figure 1–4 Movement is characteristic of all living things. The euglenoid flagellates, such as the *Strombomonas conspersa* shown here, move about by beating their long whiplike flagella. (Biophoto Associates)

temperature, pressure, or sound; and changes in the chemical composition of the surrounding soil, air, or water. In complex animals such as humans, certain cells of the body are highly specialized to respond to certain types of stimuli; for example, cells in the retina of the eye respond to light. In simpler organisms, such specialized cells may be absent, but the whole organism may respond to stimuli. Certain single-celled organisms, for example, respond to bright light by retreating.

The responses of plants may not be as obvious as those of animals, but plants do respond to light, gravity, water, touch, and other stimuli principally by the differential growth of parts of their bodies. The streaming motion of the cytoplasm in plant cells may be speeded up or stopped by changes in the amount of light. A few plants, such as the Venus flytrap of the Carolina swamps (Figure 1–5), are remarkably sensitive to touch and can catch insects. Their leaves are hinged along the midrib and possess a scent that attracts insects. The presence of an insect on the leaf, detected by trigger hairs on the leaf surface, stimulates the leaf to fold. When the edges come together, the hairs interlock to prevent escape of the prey. The leaf then secretes enzymes that kill and digest the insect. These plants are usually found in soil that is deficient in nitrogen. Capturing insects enables these plants to obtain part of the nitrogen they require for growth from the prey they "eat."

Living Things Reproduce

Although at one time worms were thought to arise from horsehairs in a water trough, maggots from decaying meat, and frogs from the mud of the Nile, we now

Figure 1–5 A few plants, such as the Venus flytrap, can respond to the touch of an insect by trapping it. Here a leaf of the Venus flytrap is shown attracting and capturing a lacewing. The leaves of this plant have a scent that attracts insects. When trigger hairs on the leaf surface detect the presence of an insect, the leaf, hinged along its midrib, folds. The edges come together and hairs interlock, preventing the escape of the prey. The leaf then secretes enzymes that kill and digest the insect. (Grant Heilman)

know that each can come only from previously existing organisms. One of the fundamental principles of biology is that ''all life comes only from living things.'' If any one characteristic can be said to be the very essence of life, it is the ability of an organism to reproduce its kind.

In simple organisms such as the amoeba, reproduction may be **asexual**—that is, without sex (Figure 1–6). When an amoeba has grown to a certain size it reproduces by splitting into two to form two new amoebas. Before it divides, an amoeba makes a duplicate copy of its hereditary material (genes) and distributes one complete set to each new cell. Except for size, each new amoeba is identical to the parent cell.

In most plants and animals, **sexual reproduction** is carried out by the production of specialized egg and sperm cells that unite to form the fertilized egg, from which the new organism develops. With sexual reproduction, each offspring is generally not a duplicate of a single parent but is the product of the interaction of various genes contributed by both the mother and the father. Genetic variation is the raw material for the vital processes of evolution and adaptation.

Populations Evolve and Become Adapted to the Environment

The ability of a population to evolve (change) and adapt to its environment is the characteristic that enables it to survive in a changing world. **Adaptations** are traits that enhance an organism's ability to survive in a particular environment. They may be structural, physiological, behavioral, or a combination of all of these. The long, flexible tongue of the frog is an adaptation for catching insects, and the thick fur coat of the polar bear is an adaptation for surviving frigid temperatures. Every biologically successful organism is a complex collection of coordinated adaptations produced through evolutionary processes.

INFORMATION MUST BE TRANSMITTED WITHIN INDIVIDUALS, BETWEEN INDIVIDUALS, AND FROM ONE GENERATION TO THE NEXT

In order for a living thing to grow, develop, carry on self-regulated metabolism, move, respond, and reproduce, it must have precise instructions. The information a living thing needs to carry on all of these processes is coded and delivered in the form of chemical substances and electrical impulses.

DNA Transmits Information from One Generation to the Next

Humans give birth only to human babies, not to giraffes or rose bushes. In organisms that reproduce sexually, each offspring is a combination of the traits of its parents. In 1953, James Watson and Francis Crick worked out the structure of **DNA,** the chemical substance that

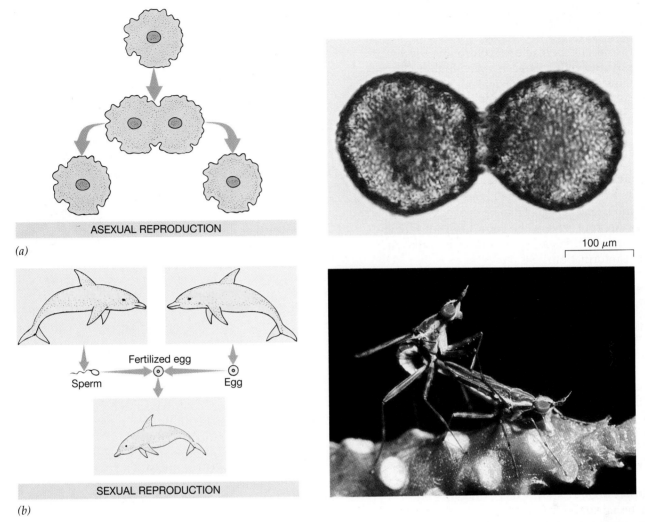

ASEXUAL REPRODUCTION

(a)

SEXUAL REPRODUCTION

(b)

100 µm

Figure 1–6 Approaches to reproduction. (*a*) Asexual reproduction. In asexual reproduction, one individual gives rise to two or more offspring—all identical to the parent. Asexual reproduction in *Difflugia*, a one-celled organism (*top right*). (*b*) In sexual reproduction, two parents each contribute a sex cell; these join to give rise to the offspring, which is a combination of the traits of both parents. A pair of tropical flies mating (*bottom right*).   (*a*, Visuals Unlimited/Cabisco; *b*, L. E. Gilbert, University of Texas at Austin/Biological Photo Service)

makes up the **genes,** the units of hereditary material. Their work led to the understanding of the genetic code that transmits information from generation to generation. The genetic code is the same for every living organism—a dramatic example of the unity of life (Figure 1–7).

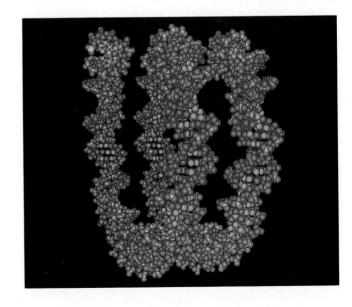

Figure 1–7 An organism's ability to transmit information from one generation to the next is essential to the continuity of life. DNA, the hereditary material of life, is shown in a computer-drawn simulation of the colored plastic space-filling molecular models used by biologists. The colored balls represent the different atoms that make up DNA: *dark blue,* carbon; *red,* oxygen; *white,* hydrogen; *blue,* nitrogen; *yellow,* phosphorus. (Computer Graphics Group, Lawrence Livermore Laboratory/Biological Photo Service)

Information Is Transmitted by Many Types of Molecules and by Nervous Systems

The genes are also responsible for controlling the development and functioning of each individual organism. DNA contains the "recipes" for making all of the **proteins** needed by the organism. Proteins are very large molecules that are slightly different in each type of organism and in each individual. For example, blood cells are different from muscle cells, in large part because they have different types of proteins.

Hormones are chemical messengers that transmit information from one part of an organism to another. A hormone can signal cells to produce or secrete a certain substance. As you proceed in your study of biology, you will learn about many types of molecules that code or transmit information.

Most animals have nervous systems that transmit information by way of both electrical impulses and molecules called neurotransmitters. Information conveyed by the nervous system keeps the individual informed of changes both in the outside world and within the body.

Information is also transmitted from one organism to another. Mechanisms for this type of communication include release of chemicals, visual displays, and sound.

EVOLUTION IS THE PRIMARY UNIFYING CONCEPT OF BIOLOGY

Every organism is the product of complex interactions between the genes of its ancestors and environmental conditions. If every organism of a species[1] were exactly like every other, any change in the environment might be disastrous to all, and the species would become extinct. Adaptation to changes in the environment involves changes in populations rather than in individual organisms. Most adaptations occur over long periods of time and involve many generations. Adaptations are the result of evolutionary processes.

How populations of organisms have changed, or **evolved,** over time has been a basic focus of investigation and debate. The theory of evolution has become the greatest unifying concept of biology. Although evolution is discussed in depth in Chapters 17 through 21, we present a brief overview here to give you the tools necessary to understand other aspects of biology. Although evolution is itself a subdiscipline of biology, some element of an evolutionary perspective is present in al-most every specialized field within biology. Biologists in almost every subdiscipline try to understand the features and functions of organisms and their constituent cells and parts by considering them in light of the long, continuing process of evolution. Additionally, biologists are constantly searching for evolutionary relationships among different organisms.

Natural Selection Is an Important Mechanism by Which Evolution Proceeds

Although the concept of evolution had been discussed by philosophers and naturalists through the ages, Charles Darwin and Alfred Wallace first brought the theory of evolution to general attention and suggested a plausible mechanism to explain it. In his book *On the Origin of Species by Means of Natural Selection,* published in 1859, Darwin synthesized many new findings in geology and biology and delineated a comprehensive theory of evolution that has helped shape the nature of biological science to the present day. Darwin presented a wealth of evidence that the present forms of life on Earth descended with modifications from previously existing forms—his **theory of organic evolution.** His book raised a storm of controversy in both religion and science, some of which still lingers. It also generated a great wave of scientific research and observation that has provided much additional evidence that evolution is responsible for the great diversity of organisms present on our planet.

Darwin based his theory of natural selection on the following four observations: (1) Individual members of a species show some variation from one another. (2) Many more organisms are produced than can possibly find food and survive into adulthood (Figure 1–8).

Figure 1–8   Strings of eggs of the American toad (*Bufo americanus*). Many more eggs are produced than can possibly develop into adult toads. Random events might be largely responsible for determining which of these developing organisms will hatch, reach adulthood, and reproduce. However, certain traits that each organism might have also contribute to its probability of success in its environment. Although not all organisms are as prolific as the toad, the generalization that more organisms are born than survive is true throughout the living world.   (Visuals Unlimited/W. Banaszewski)

---

[1] A species can be thought of as a group of organisms with similar structure and function; in nature they play a similar role, breed only with each other, and share a common ancestry.

Evolution in Action: The Case of the Peppered Moth

An interesting case of evolution in action has been documented in England since 1850. The tree trunks in a certain region of England were once white because of a type of fungus, a lichen, that grew on them. The common peppered moth was beautifully adapted for landing upon these white tree trunks because its light color blended with the trunks and protected it from predacious birds (see figure). At that time black moths were rare.

Then human beings changed the environment. They built industries that polluted the air with soot, killing the lichens and coloring the tree trunks black. The light-colored moths became easy prey to the birds. Now the black moths blended with the dark trunks and escaped the sharp eyes of predators. In these new surroundings, the dark moths were better adapted and were selected for survival. Eventually, more than 90% of the peppered moths in the industrial areas of England were dark. Interestingly, with recent efforts to control air pollution, there has been an increase in the population of the light-colored moths.

Adaptation of the peppered moth was studied in the 1950s by H. B. D. Kettlewell of Oxford, who marked hundreds of male moths with a spot of paint under their wings and then released them in both rural and industrial areas. Observers reported that birds preyed on the moths that were more visible. After a period of time, surviving moths were recaptured by attracting them with light or females. Based on observation and on the percentage of each type of moth recaptured, these studies confirmed that significantly more dark moths survived in industrial areas and more light moths survived in rural areas.

Dark and light peppered moths.　(John D. Cunningham/Visuals Unlimited)

(3) A struggle for survival takes place among the many individuals produced. Individuals who possess characteristics that give them some advantage in the struggle for existence are more likely to survive than those who lack these characteristics. (4) The survivors pass these advantageous characteristics on to their offspring and to future generations. Although Darwin did not know about DNA or understand the mechanisms of inheritance, we now understand that the variations among organisms are a result of different varieties of genes that code for each characteristic. The sources of these variations are random **mutations,** chemical changes in DNA that persist and can be inherited. Mutations modify the genetic code and provide the raw material for evolution.

Populations Evolve as a Result of Selective Pressures from Changes in the Environment

Natural selection favors organisms with traits that best enable them to cope with pressures exerted by the environment. These organisms are most likely to survive and produce offspring. As these successful organisms pass on their genetic recipe for survival, their traits become more widely distributed in the population. Over long periods of time, as organisms continue to change (and as the environment itself changes, bringing different selective pressures), the members of the population become increasingly unlike their ancestors (see Focus on Evolution in Action).

A successful organism is adapted to its environment. Adaptations, and thus well-adapted organisms, are the products of evolution. The long neck of the giraffe, for example, is an adaptation for reaching leaves on trees (Figure 1–9). The antelope-like ancestors of modern-day giraffes did not have elongated necks. As with other traits, there was a bell-shaped distribution of neck heights. Most of the ancestors of modern giraffes had necks that were about the same length, but a few had relatively short necks and others had relatively long necks. The ancestral giraffes with the shortest necks could not compete effectively for the leaves on the trees of the African veldt. They were less likely to survive and reproduce. Those with longer than average

(a)   *(b)*

Figure 1–9   A successful organism is adapted to its environment. *(a)* The long neck of the giraffe is an adaptation for reaching leaves high on trees. The giraffe shown here is browsing high on *Acacia.* *(b)* The scorpion fish blends with its background so well that it looks like a rock on the ocean floor. It is well adapted to make dinner of any small organism that unwarily swims by. *(a*, Visuals Unlimited/Walt Anderson; *b*, Robert Shupak)

necks were best able to reach the leaves on trees. These giraffes survived and reproduced, passing on their genes for long necks. Through thousands of generations, the giraffe neck became longer and longer.

Biological Organization Reflects the Course of Evolution

Evolution has generally proceeded from the simple to the complex. Whether we study an individual organism or the world of life as a whole, we can identify a pattern of increasing complexity (Figure 1–10).

Living things have several levels of organization

The **chemical level** is the simplest level of organization. It includes the basic particles of all matter, atoms, and combinations of atoms called molecules. An **atom** is the smallest unit of a chemical element (fundamental substance) that retains the characteristic properties of that element. For example, an atom of iron is the smallest possible amount of iron. Atoms combine chemically to form **molecules.** For example, two atoms of hydrogen combine with one atom of oxygen to form one molecule of water.

Life evolved from atoms and molecules. At the **cellular level** we find that many diverse molecules may associate with one another to form complex and highly specialized structures within cells called **organelles.**

The organelles are suspended within (or surround) the jelly-like cytoplasm of the cell. The **cell** itself is the basic structural and functional unit of life, the simplest part of living matter that can carry on all of the activities necessary for life. The **plasma membrane** that surrounds the cell and the **nucleus** that contains the hereditary material are examples of organelles.

In most multicellular organisms, cells associate to form **tissues,** such as muscle tissue in animals or epidermis (a tissue that forms a protective covering) in plants. Tissues, in turn, are arranged into functional structures called **organs,** such as the heart or stomach in animals or roots and leaves in plants. Each major group of biological functions is performed by a coordinated group of tissues and organs, called an **organ system.** The circulatory and digestive systems are examples of organ systems. Functioning together with great precision, the organ systems make up the complex multicellular **organism.**

There are several levels of ecological organization

Organisms interact to form still more complex levels of biological organization. All of the members of one species that live in the same area make up a **population.** The populations of organisms that inhabit a particular area and interact with one another form a **community.** Thus, a community can be composed of hundreds of different types of life forms. All communities of living

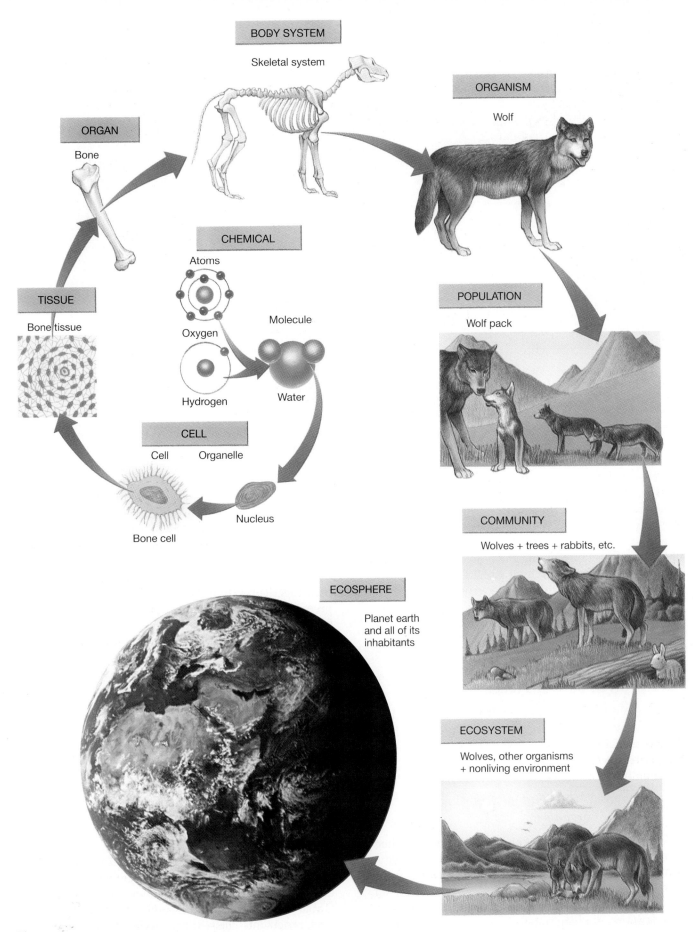

BODY SYSTEM

Skeletal system

ORGAN

Bone

ORGANISM

Wolf

CHEMICAL

Atoms

Oxygen

Molecule

Hydrogen

Water

TISSUE

Bone tissue

CELL

Cell   Organelle

Nucleus

Bone cell

POPULATION

Wolf pack

COMMUNITY

Wolves + trees + rabbits, etc.

ECOSPHERE

Planet earth and all of its inhabitants

ECOSYSTEM

Wolves, other organisms + nonliving environment

Figure 1–10 Levels of biological organization.

Table 1–1   CLASSIFICATION OF DOMESTIC CAT, HUMAN BEING, AND WHITE OAK

Category	Classification of Cat	Classification of Human	Classification of White Oak
Kingdom	Animalia	Animalia	Plantae
Phylum (or division)	Chordata	Chordata	Magnoliophyta
Subphylum (or subdivision)	Vertebrata	Vertebrata	None
Class	Mammalia	Mammalia	Magnoliopsida
Order	Carnivora	Primates	Fagales
Family	Felidae	Hominidae	Fagaceae
Genus and species	*Felis catus*	*Homo sapiens*	*Quercus alba*

things on Earth are collectively referred to as the **biosphere.**

A community together with its nonliving environment is referred to as an **ecosystem.** An ecosystem can be as small as a pond (or even a puddle) or as vast as the Great Plains of North America or the Arctic tundra. The largest ecosystem is the planet Earth with all its inhabitants—the **ecosphere.** The ecosphere represents all of the interactions among the biosphere, the Earth's atmosphere, the Earth's hydrosphere (water in any form), and the Earth's lithosphere (crust). The study of how organisms of a community relate to one another and to their physical environment is called **ecology.**

Millions of Kinds of Organisms Have Evolved on Our Planet

The variety of living organisms that have evolved on our planet staggers the imagination. In order to study life, we need a system for organizing, naming, and classifying its myriad forms.

Biologists use a binomial system for classifying organisms

To facilitate effective communication with one another, biologists have developed a formal system of classifying and naming organisms. The science of classifying and naming organisms is known as **taxonomy** (or biosystematics), and the biologists who specialize in classification are **taxonomists.**

In the 18th century Carolus Linnaeus, a Swedish botanist, developed a system of classification that, with

some modification, is still used today. The basic unit of classification is the **species.** Closely related species may be grouped together in the next higher unit of classification, the **genus** (plural, genera).

The Linnaean system is referred to as the **binomial system of nomenclature** because each species is assigned a two-part name. The first part of the name designates the genus, and the second part, the **specific epithet.** This is often a descriptive word expressing some quality of the organism. The specific epithet is always used together with the full or abbreviated generic name preceding it. For example, the dog, *Canis familiaris* (sometimes abbreviated *C. familiaris*), and the timber wolf, *Canis lupus* (*C. lupus*), belong to the same genus. The cat, *Felis domestica,* belongs to a different genus. The scientific name of the American white oak is *Quercus alba,* whereas the name of the European white oak is *Quercus robur.* Another tree, the white willow, *Salix alba,* belongs to a different genus. Our own scientific name is *Homo sapiens.*

Note that each kind of organism has its own scientific name; the first part of the name indicates the genus and is capitalized, and the second part of the name indicates the specific epithet and is not capitalized. Both names are italicized.

Taxonomic classification is hierarchical

Just as species may be grouped together in a common genus, a number of related genera constitute a **family** (Table 1–1). In turn, families may be grouped into **orders,** orders into **classes,** and classes into **phyla** (for animals) or **divisions** (for plants or fungi). The family Canidae includes all doglike carnivores (animals that

(a)

(b)

(c)

(d)

(e)

Figure 1–11 A survey of the kingdoms of life. (*a*) A member of kingdom Prokaryotae. The bacterium *Micrococcus* has been magnified several hundred times in this false-colored scanning electron micrograph. (*b*) A member of kingdom Protista. Living radiolaria. These one-celled organisms (amoeboid protozoa) secrete elaborate and beautiful skeletons made of silica. These skeletons become part of the mud on the ocean floor and eventually are compressed and converted into siliceous rock. (*c*) Mushrooms belong to kingdom Fungi. (*d*) The plant kingdom claims many beautiful and diverse forms. Shown here is the red passionflower (*Passiflora* sp.). (*e*) African lions, *Panthera leo*, among the fiercest of animals, are also among the most sociable; they live peaceably in prides (groups) of as many as 35. (*a*, Visuals Unlimited/ David M. Phillips; *b*, Manfred Kage/Peter Arnold, Inc.; *c* and *d*, Richard H. Gross; *e*, Courtesy of Busch Gardens, Tampa)

eat mainly meat). This family includes 12 genera and about 34 living species. Family Canidae, along with family Ursidae (bears), family Felidae (catlike animals), and several other families that eat mainly meat, is placed in order Carnivora. Order Carnivora, order Primates (the order to which humans belong), and several other orders belong to class Mammalia (mammals). Class Mammalia, class Aves (birds), class Reptilia (reptiles), and four other classes are grouped together as subphylum Vertebrata. The vertebrates belong to phylum Chordata, which is part of kingdom Animalia.

Most biologists recognize five kingdoms

Since the time of Aristotle, biologists have divided the living world into two kingdoms, Plantae and Animalia. After microscopes were developed it became increasingly obvious that many organisms could not easily be assigned to either the plant or animal kingdom.

According to the system of classification used in this book, organisms are assigned to one of five kingdoms: Prokaryotae (formerly called Monera), Protista, Fungi, Plantae, or Animalia (Figure 1–11). The members of kingdom Plantae, the plants, and of kingdom Animalia, the animals, are the organisms most familiar to us.

The single-celled bacteria belong to kingdom **Prokaryotae.** They differ from all other organisms in that they lack a discrete nucleus and also lack other cellular organelles. Kingdom **Protista** consists of protozoa, algae, water molds, and slime molds. These organisms are single-celled or simple multicellular organisms.

Kingdom **Fungi** is composed of the molds and yeasts. These organisms do not carry on photosynthesis. They obtain their nutrients by secreting digestive enzymes into food and then absorbing the predigested food. Fungi make an important contribution to the living world as decomposers, breaking down dead organisms and organic wastes into simple inorganic materials that can be reused by living things.

Plants are complex multicellular organisms adapted to carry out photosynthesis, the process in which light energy is converted to the chemical energy of food molecules. Plants possess a number of characteristic features, including a **cuticle** (a waxy covering over aerial parts that reduces water loss); **stomata** (tiny openings in stems and leaves for gas exchange); and multicellular **gametangia** (organs that protect developing reproductive cells). The kingdom Plantae includes both nonvascular plants (mosses) and vascular plants (ferns, conifers, and flowering plants).

Animals are multicellular organisms that must eat other organisms for nourishment. Complex animals have a high degree of tissue specialization and body organization, which have evolved along with motility, complex sense organs, nervous systems, and muscular systems.

A more detailed presentation of the kingdoms can be found in Chapters 22 through 30, and classification of living things is summarized in Appendix A. We refer to these groups repeatedly throughout this book as we consider the many kinds of problems faced by living things and the various adaptations that have evolved in response to these problems.

LIFE DEPENDS ON A CONTINUOUS INPUT OF ENERGY

Life on Earth depends on a continuous input of energy from the sun. Every activity of a living cell or organism requires energy, and whenever energy is used to perform biological work, some energy is converted to heat and dispersed into the environment.

Energy Flows through Individual Cells and Organisms

Recall that all of the energy and chemical processes that occur within cells and organisms are referred to as metabolism. To grow and maintain itself, an organism must have energy. Thus, each cell of an organism constantly takes in nutrients. Some nutrients are used as

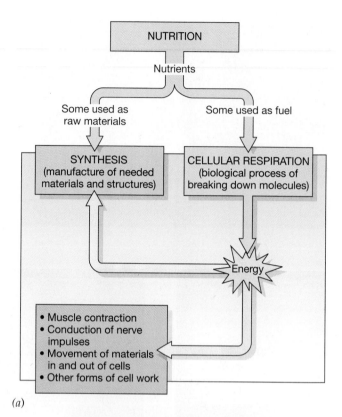

(a)

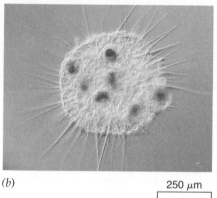

(b)   250 μm

Figure 1–12 Metabolic reactions occur continuously in every living organism. (a) Relationships of some metabolic activities. Some of the nutrients provided by proper nutrition are used to synthesize needed materials and cell parts; other nutrients are used as fuel for cellular respiration, a process that captures energy stored in food. This energy is needed for synthesis and for other forms of cellular work. Cellular respiration also requires oxygen, which is provided by the process of gas exchange. Wastes from the cells such as carbon dioxide and water must be excreted from the body. (b) Like most organisms, this one-celled amoeba must take in nutrients and oxygen in order to stay alive. The dark spots within the cell are food.   (b, Phil A. Harrington/Peter Arnold, Inc.)

"fuel" for **cellular respiration,** a process during which some of the energy (stored in their molecules) is released for use by the cells (Figure 1–12). This energy can be used for cellular work or for synthesis of needed materials such as new cellular components.

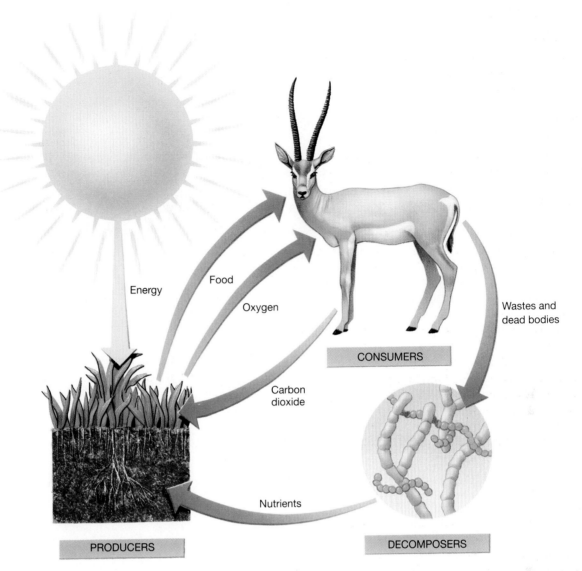

Energy

Food

Oxygen

Carbon dioxide

Nutrients

Wastes and dead bodies

CONSUMERS

DECOMPOSERS

PRODUCERS

Figure 1–13 Interdependence of producers, consumers, and decomposers. The sun provides energy for photosynthesis. Using that energy, producers manufacture their own food. Producers provide oxygen and food containing energy and nutrients for the consumers. In turn, the consumers provide the carbon dioxide needed for photosynthesis by the producers. The decomposers break down wastes and dead bodies so that minerals are recycled.

In all organisms, metabolic processes must be carefully and constantly regulated to maintain a balanced internal state. When enough of some cellular product has been made, its manufacture must be decreased or turned off. When the supply of energy declines, appropriate processes for obtaining more energy must be turned on. These self-regulating control systems are remarkably sensitive and efficient. Recall that this tendency to maintain a relatively constant internal environment is termed homeostasis, and the mechanisms that accomplish the task are homeostatic mechanisms.

Most cells require a constant supply of glucose (a simple sugar), which they break down to obtain energy. In humans and many other animals, the circulatory system delivers glucose and other nutrients to all of the cells. Elaborate homeostatic mechanisms maintain a relatively constant blood-sugar (glucose) level. When the blood-sugar level begins to fall, these mechanisms let us know that it is time to eat and also convert stored food to glucose so that the glucose concentration in the blood returns to normal levels.

Energy Flows through Ecosystems

Like individual organisms, ecosystems depend on a continuous input of energy. A self-sufficient ecosystem contains three types of organisms—producers, consumers, and decomposers—and has a physical environment appropriate for their survival. These organisms depend on each other and on the ecosystem for nutrients, energy, oxygen, and carbon dioxide (Figure 1–13). However, there is a one-way flow of energy through ecosystems because organisms cannot recycle energy. During every energy transaction, some of it is dispersed to the environment as heat (Figure 1–14).

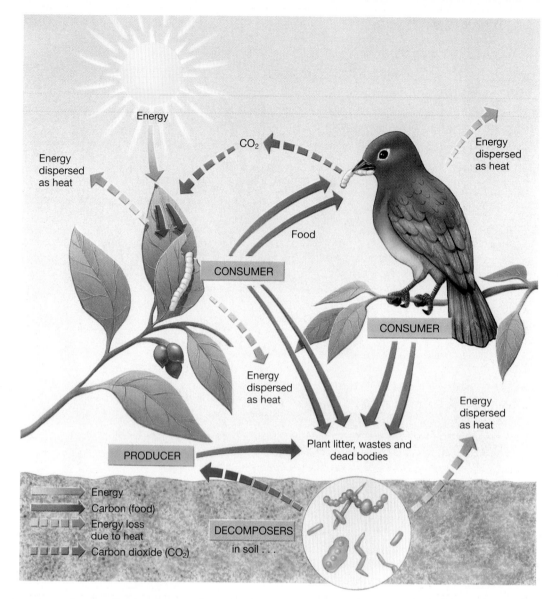

Figure 1–14 Flow of energy and carbon through the ecosphere. Carbon and many other chemical elements are continuously recycled. Carbon is converted from carbon dioxide gas to food by producers. Consumers obtain carbon by eating producers. Carbon leaves the consumers and producers in the form of wastes and dead material, which are broken down by decomposers.

Consumers break down carbon-containing compounds during cellular respiration, converting them in part back to carbon dioxide, and the cycle begins anew. Energy, on the other hand, cannot be recycled. Some of it is dispersed as heat during every energy transaction. For this reason a constant energy input from the sun is required to keep the ecosphere in operation.

Producers manufacture their own food

Producers, or **autotrophs,** are plants, algae, and certain bacteria that can produce their own food from simple raw materials. Most of these organisms use sunlight as an energy source and carry out photosynthesis.

During photosynthesis the energy from sunlight is used to synthesize complex molecules from carbon dioxide and water. The light energy is transformed into chemical energy, which is stored within the chemical bonds of the food molecules produced. Oxygen, which is required not only by plant cells but also by the cells of most other organisms, is produced as a byproduct of photosynthesis.

Carbon dioxide + Water + Energy $\longrightarrow$ Food + Oxygen

Consumers obtain energy by eating producers

Animals, including human beings, are **consumers.** The consumers are **heterotrophs,** organisms that depend on producers for food, energy, and oxygen. They obtain energy by breaking down food molecules originally produced during photosynthesis. Recall that the biological process of breaking down "fuel" molecules is known as cellular respiration. When chemical bonds are broken during cellular respiration, their stored energy is made available for life processes (see Figure 1–12).

Food + Oxygen $\longrightarrow$ Carbon dioxide + Water + Energy

Gas exchange between producers and consumers by way of the nonliving environment helps maintain the life-sustaining mixture of gases in the atmosphere. Thus, consumers also contribute to the balance of the ecosystem.

Decomposers obtain energy from wastes and dead organisms

Decomposers—the bacteria and fungi—are heterotrophs that make their living by breaking down the wastes and the bodies of dead organisms. In their process of obtaining energy, these organisms make the components of wastes and dead organisms available for reuse. If decomposers did not exist, nutrients would remain locked up in the dead bodies of organisms, and the supply of elements required by living systems would soon be exhausted.

BIOLOGY IS STUDIED USING THE SCIENTIFIC METHOD

This book is about the systematic study of living things— the science of biology. What distinguishes science is its insistence on rigorous methods to examine a problem and its attempts to devise experiments to validate its findings. The essence of the scientific method is asking questions and then searching for answers to those questions. But the questions must arise from observations and experiments, and the answers must be potentially testable by further observation and experiment.

Science is systematic because of the attention it gives to organizing knowledge, making it readily accessible to all who wish to build on its foundation. In this way science is both a personal and a social endeavor. Science is not mysterious. Anyone who understands its rules and procedures can take on its challenges. Science seeks to give us precise knowledge about those aspects of the world that are accessible to its methods of inquiry. It is not a replacement for philosophy, religion, or art. Being a scientist does not prevent one from participating in these other fields of human endeavor, nor does being an artist prevent one from practicing science.

Science Is Based on Systematic Thought Processes

The systematic thought processes on which science is based generally fall into two categories: deduction and induction. With **deductive reasoning,** we begin with supplied information, called *premises,* and draw conclusions on the basis of that information. Deduction proceeds from general principles to specific conclusions.

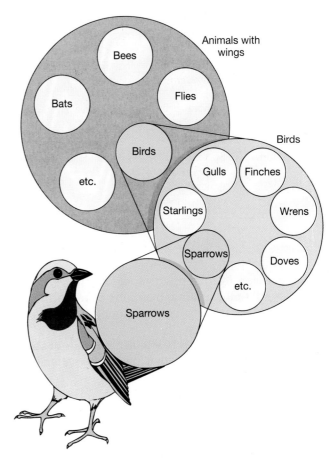

Figure 1–15 A diagrammatic example of a syllogism, the classic form of deductive reasoning. If all birds have wings and sparrows are birds, then sparrows must have wings.

For example, if we accept the premise that all birds have wings, and the second premise that sparrows are birds, we can conclude deductively that sparrows have wings (Figure 1–15).

Induction is almost the opposite of deduction (Table 1–2). With **inductive reasoning,** we begin with specific observations from which we seek to draw a conclusion or discover a unifying rule or general principle. The inductive method can be used to organize raw data into manageable categories by answering the question, "What do all these facts have in common?" A weakness of this method of reasoning is that conclusions contain *more* information than the reported facts on which they are based. We go from many observed examples to all possible examples when we formulate the general principle. This is known as the **inductive leap.** Without it, we could not arrive at generalizations. However, we must be sensitive to the possibility that the conclusion is not valid.

The extra information that inductive conclusions contain can come only from the creative insight of a human mind, and creativity, however admirable, is not infallible. Here is an example of inductive reasoning:

Table 1–2 METHODS OF THOUGHT

Method	Progression	Conclusion (information content)	Validity of Conclusion	Major Uses
Deduction	General principle to specific conclusion	Decreased	Valid if premises are valid	Discovering explicit relationships among facts
Induction	Specific observations to generalized conclusions	Increased	Valid or invalid, even if observations are accurate	Synthesis of data; discovering new general principles

When released from support, apples, oranges, rocks, and trees fall to the ground; therefore, a force acting on these objects attracts them to the ground (i.e., the force of gravity).

Even if a conclusion is based on thousands of observations, it is still possible that new observations can challenge the conclusion. However, the greater the number of cases that are tested, the more likely we are to draw accurate scientific conclusions (Figure 1–16). The scientist seeks to state with confidence that any specific conclusion has a certain statistical probability of being correct.

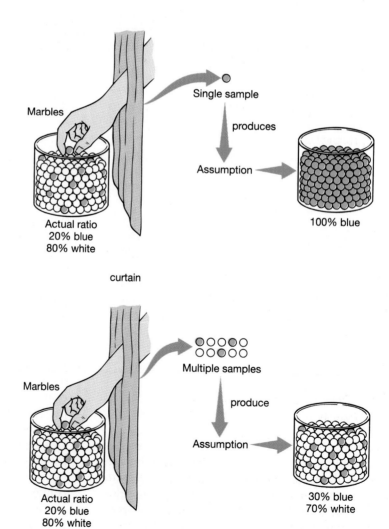

Figure 1–16 The greater the number of samples taken, the more likely we can make valid assumptions.

Predictions Are Tested by Observation and Experiment

The ultimate sources of all the facts of science are careful observations and experiments, made free of bias and with suitable controls and carried out in as quantitative a fashion as possible. The data collected may then be analyzed so that some sort of order may be made of the observations. The data can be synthesized or reassembled so that whatever relationships may exist can be discovered. On the basis of these initial observations, the scientist makes a generalization or constructs a **hypothesis.** A hypothesis is an educated guess about the nature of the collected data, about connections in a chain of events, or even about cause-and-effect relationships between events. Predictions made on the basis of a hypothesis can be further tested by controlled experiments.

Let us examine two examples of science in action. Early biologists observed that the nucleus was the most prominent part of the cell, and they hypothesized that it might be essential for the well-being of the cell. Experiments were performed in which the nucleus of a single-celled amoeba was removed surgically with a microneedle. After this surgery, the amoeba continued to live and move, but it did not grow and after a few days it died. These results suggested that the nucleus is necessary for the metabolic processes that provide for growth and cell reproduction (Figure 1–17).

But, the investigators asked, what if the operation itself and not the loss of the nucleus caused the amoeba to die? They performed a *controlled experiment* in which two groups of amoebae were subjected to the same operative trauma. However, in the **experimental group** the nucleus was removed, whereas in the **control group** it was not. In the control group, a microneedle was inserted into the amoebae and pushed around inside the cell to simulate the operation of removing the nucleus; then the needle was withdrawn, leaving the nucleus inside. Amoebae treated with such a sham operation recover and subsequently grow and divide, but the amoebae without nuclei die. This confirmed the hypothesis that it is the removal of the nucleus and not simply the operation that causes the death of the amoebae.

Let us consider another example of the scientific method. Suppose a pharmaceutical company wants to test a new drug to determine whether it will improve memory in elderly patients with memory problems. To test the drug, the company solicits the cooperation of physicians who work with such patients. The physicians administer a memory test and then prescribe the drug to 500 patients for a period of 2 months. They then administer another memory test and find that the patients demonstrate a 20% increase in their ability to remember things. Can the drug company legitimately

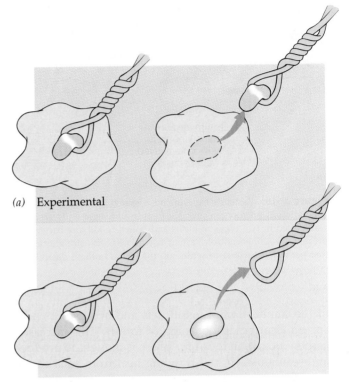

(a) Experimental

(b) Control

Figure 1–17 A controlled experiment demonstrating that the nucleus is essential for the well-being of the cell. (*a*) When its nucleus is surgically removed with a microneedle, the amoeba dies. (*b*) A control amoeba subjected to similar surgical procedures (including insertion of a microneedle), but without actual removal of the nucleus, does not die.

conclude that its hypothesis is correct, that the drug does indeed improve memory in elderly patients? Alternative explanations might be possible. The attention paid to the patients might in itself have stimulated them to be more attentive, for instance.

To avoid such objections, the experiment must have a control. A second similar group of patients must be given a **placebo,** a harmless starch pill similar in size, shape, color, and taste to the pill being tested. Neither group of patients should be told which pill—the drug or the placebo—has been given. In fact, to prevent bias, most medical experiments today are carried out in "double-blind" fashion: Neither the patient nor the physician knows who is getting the experimental compound and who is getting the placebo. The pills or treatments are coded in some way unknown to physician or patient. Only after the experiment is over and the results are in is the code broken to identify the control and experimental patients. Another example of a controlled experiment is shown in Figure 1–18.

Not all experiments can be so neatly designed; for one thing, it is often difficult to establish appropriate controls. For example, we know that the carbon dioxide content of the Earth's atmosphere is increasing because

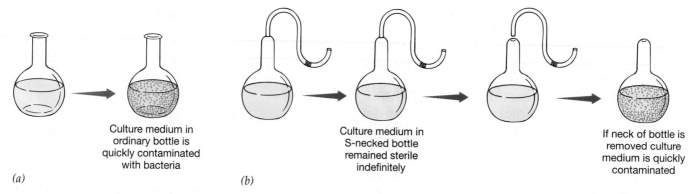

Culture medium in
ordinary bottle is
quickly contaminated
with bacteria

(a)

(b)

Culture medium in
S-necked bottle
remained sterile
indefinitely

If neck of bottle is
removed culture
medium is quickly
contaminated

Figure 1–18   Pasteur's experiments disproving the spontaneous generation of microorganisms. Nutrient broth (sugar and yeast) was placed in two types of flasks and boiled to kill any bacteria present. (*a*) As his control, Pasteur used flasks with straight necks that permitted bacteria to settle into the broth. In these flasks, the broth was soon teeming with bacteria. Pasteur's experimental flasks, shown in (*b*), had long, S-shaped necks that did not permit bacteria to enter, even though the flasks were open to the air. Bacteria did not grow in such flasks unless the necks were removed.

of the combustion of fossil fuels and because of widespread clearing and burning of forests. This increased carbon dioxide in the atmosphere is thought to produce a "greenhouse effect," trapping heat from solar radiation. Some scientists have warned that this thermal blanket around the globe may increase the average temperature of the Earth and ultimately alter its climate. Yet in the recent past scientists have also argued that the accumulation of particulates in the atmosphere (soot) would moderate or cancel the effect of the carbon dioxide increase. Even if the temperature of the Earth does increase, however, given other variables in the Earth's atmosphere, how can we be certain that the temperature change has resulted from human activities?

This raises an important practical question. Obviously we do not have a second, unindustrialized Earth whose climate could be compared with our own. Without such a control, scientists have had to base their predictions of the future climate on mathematical modeling techniques that fall short of perfection. Should we postpone action pending the development of a perfectly predictive model? Clearly, that would involve a long wait, and by then it might be impossible to act effectively.

A Well-Supported Hypothesis May Become a Theory

Nonscientists often use the word *theory* incorrectly when they mean to refer to a hypothesis. A hypothesis becomes a **theory** only when it is supported by a large body of observations and experiments. A good theory relates facts that previously appeared to be unrelated. A good theory grows; it relates additional facts as they become known; it may even suggest practical applications. It predicts new facts and suggests new relationships among phenomena.

A good theory, by showing the relationships among classes of facts, simplifies and clarifies our understanding of natural phenomena. Einstein wrote, "In the whole history of science from Greek philosophy to modern physics, there have been constant attempts to reduce the apparent complexity of natural phenomena to simple, fundamental ideas and relations." A theory that, over a long period of time, has yielded true predictions with unvarying uniformity, and is thus almost universally accepted, may be referred to as a scientific **principle** or **law.**

SUMMARY

I. A living organism is able to grow and develop, carry on metabolism, maintain homeostasis, move, respond to stimuli, and reproduce; in addition, species evolve and adapt to the environment.
   A. All living things are composed of cells.
   B. Living things grow by increasing the size and number of their cells.

C. Metabolism refers to all the chemical activities that take place in the organism, which include the chemical reactions essential to nutrition, growth and repair, and conversion of energy to usable forms.
D. Homeostasis is the tendency of organisms to maintain a constant internal environment.
E. Movement, although not necessarily locomotion, is

characteristic of living things.

F. Living things respond to physical and chemical changes in their external or internal environment.

G. Reproduction may be asexual, in which the offspring are usually identical to the parent, or sexual, in which the offspring generally reflect the characteristics of two parents.

II. Information encoded in DNA is transmitted from one generation to the next. DNA, proteins, hormones, and nervous systems transmit information within individuals.

III. Populations of organisms evolve over time in response to changes in the environment.

A. Natural selection favors organisms with traits that enable them to cope with environmental changes; these organisms are most likely to survive and produce offspring.

B. As successful organisms pass on their genes for survival, their traits become more widely distributed in the population.

C. Well-adapted organisms are the products of evolution.

D. Biological organization reflects the course of evolution.

1. A complex organism is organized at the chemical, cellular, tissue, organ, and organ system levels.

2. The basic unit of ecological organization is the population. Various populations form communities; a community and its physical environment are referred to as an ecosystem. The planet Earth and all of its inhabitants may be regarded as a giant ecosystem, the ecosphere.

E. Millions of kinds of organisms have evolved on our planet.

1. Biologists use a binomial system of nomenclature in which the name of each kind of organism includes a genus and a specific epithet.

2. Taxonomic classification is hierarchical; it includes species, genus, family, order, class, phylum or division, and kingdom.

3. Living organisms can be classified into five kingdoms—Prokaryotae (bacteria), Protista (protozoa, algae, water molds, and slime molds), Fungi (molds and yeasts), Plantae, and Animalia.

IV. Life depends on a continuous energy input; activities of living cells require energy.

A. During cellular respiration, cells capture the energy stored in nutrients. Some of that energy is then used to synthesize needed materials or to carry on other cell activities.

B. A self-sufficient ecosystem includes producers that make their own food, consumers that depend on producers for energy, and decomposers that obtain energy by breaking down wastes and dead organisms.

V. Scientific method is a system of observation, hypothesis, experiment, more observation, and revised hypothesis.

A. Deductive reasoning and inductive reasoning are two categories of systematic thought processes used in the scientific method.

B. A hypothesis is a trial idea about the nature of an observation or relationship.

C. A properly designed scientific experiment has a control and must be as free as possible from bias.

POST-TEST

1. The sum of all the chemical activities of the organism is its _____ .

2. The tendency of organisms to maintain a constant internal environment is termed _____ .

3. A _____ is a physical or chemical change in the internal or external environment that evokes a response in an organism.

4. Cilia and flagella are used by some organisms for _____ .

5. The splitting of an amoeba into two is an example of _____ _____ .

6. A population must be able to _____ to changes in its environment in order to survive.

Match the following terms in Column A with their descriptions in Column B.

Column A
7. Atom
8. Cell
9. Molecule
10. Organ
11. Organ system
12. Organism
13. Organelle
14. Tissue

Column B
a. Group of tissues arranged into a functional structure
b. Combination of two or more atoms
c. Smallest particle of an element that retains the characteristic properties of that element
d. Specialized structure within cell
e. Association of similar cells to carry out a specific function
f. Structural and functional unit of life
g. Groups of organs that function together to carry out one or more of the major life functions
h. Group of coordinated organ systems

15. In an ecosystem we can distinguish producers, consumers, and decomposers. Plants are _____; fungi and most bacteria are _____; animals are _____.
16. Information is transmitted from one generation to the next encoded in the molecule _____.
17. In cellular respiration, _____ stored in nutrients is released for use by cells.
18. In the binomial system of nomenclature, the first part of an organism's name designates the _____.

19. The yeasts and molds are assigned to kingdom _____.
20. Bacteria are assigned to kingdom _____.
21. A trial idea about the nature of connections within a chain of events is termed a _____.
22. A _____ is a scientifically accepted, well-tested hypothesis or group of related hypotheses offered to explain phenomena.

REVIEW QUESTIONS

1. Contrast a living organism with a nonliving object.
2. In what ways might the metabolisms of an oak tree and a tiger be similar? Relate these similarities to the biological themes of transmission of information, energy, and evolution.
3. What would be the consequences if an organism's homeostatic mechanisms failed? Explain your answer.
4. What components do you think might be present in a balanced forest ecosystem? In what ways are consumers dependent on producers? On decomposers? Include energy considerations in your answer.
5. Why do you suppose that the binomial system of nomenclature has survived for more than 200 years and is still used by biologists?

6. How might you explain the sharp claws and teeth of tigers in terms of natural selection?
7. Contrast a hypothesis and a law.
8. How would you describe the mode of operation of the scientific method?
9. What is meant by a "controlled" experiment?
10. Devise a suitably controlled experiment to test each of the following hypotheses:
    a. A strain of mold found in your garden produces an effective antibiotic (a chemical that inhibits the growth of bacteria).
    b. The rate of growth of a bean seedling is affected by temperature.
    c. Beri-beri is caused by a deficiency of the vitamin thiamine.

❑

Atoms and Molecules:
The Chemical Basis of Life

Everything on our planet is made of atoms and molecules. In living things, these basic components are *organized* in very specific ways. Much of modern biology is concerned with **molecular biology**—that is, the chemistry and physics of the molecules that constitute living things. The three unifying concepts of biology—transmission of information, evolution, and energy—that we introduced in Chapter 1 all depend upon the interaction and activity of atoms and molecules. For example, atoms and molecules interact with one another very precisely to maintain the energy flow essential to life.

In order to understand life processes, we must know the basic principles of chemistry. For this reason, we begin our study of life by learning about its simplest components, atoms and molecules.

A polarized light micrograph of crystalline cytosine, which is a component of DNA and RNA (×40). (Alfred Pasieka/ Science Photo Library, Photo Researchers, Inc.)

As molecular biologists have learned more about biologically important molecules, metabolic reactions, and the genetic code, our understanding of living organisms has increased dramatically. Two important generalizations have emerged:

1. Even though living things are strikingly diverse, their chemical composition and metabolic processes are remarkably similar (Figure 2–1). This explains why much of what biologists learn from studying bacteria or rats in laboratories can be applied to other organisms, including humans.

2. The physical and chemical principles governing living systems are the same as those governing nonliving systems. No unique laws of physics or chemistry govern living systems.

After you have studied this chapter you should be able to

1. Recognize the chemical elements important in living things.
2. Describe the properties and roles of electrons, protons, and neutrons in determining atomic structure.
3. Distinguish among the terms *atomic number*, *mass number*, *atomic mass*, and *molecular mass*.
4. Define the term *electron orbital*, and relate orbitals to energy levels; relate the number of valence electrons to the chemical properties of the elements.
5. Distinguish between the types of chemical bonds; give the characteristics of each type.

6. Define and use the terms *cation* and *anion*.
7. Distinguish between and apply the terms *oxidation* and *reduction*.
8. Distinguish between inorganic and organic compounds.
9. Discuss the properties of water molecules and their importance in living things.
10. Contrast acids and bases, and discuss their properties.
11. Use the pH scale in describing the hydrogen ion concentration in living systems, and describe how buffers help minimize changes in pH.
12. Describe the composition of a salt, and explain why salts are important in living organisms.

MATTER IS COMPOSED OF CHEMICAL ELEMENTS

Elements are substances that cannot be broken down into simpler substances by ordinary chemical reactions. The matter of the universe is composed of 92 naturally occurring elements, ranging from hydrogen, the lightest, to uranium, the heaviest. About 98% of an organism's mass[1] is composed of just six elements: oxygen,

carbon, hydrogen, nitrogen, calcium, and phosphorus. Approximately 14 other elements are consistently present in living things, but in smaller quantities. Some of these, such as iodine and copper, are known as **trace elements** because they are present in such minute amounts. The chemical elements found in living organisms cycle between them and the nonliving environment.

Scientists have assigned each element a **chemical symbol**—usually the first letter or first and second letters of the English or Latin name of the element. For example, O is the symbol for oxygen, C for carbon, H for hydrogen, N for nitrogen, and Na for sodium (the Latin name is *natrium*). Table 2–1 lists the elements that make up a living organism and briefly explains why each is important.

---

[1] For convenience we consider mass and weight to be equal, even though this is not always true. Mass does not depend upon the force of gravity; weight does. Thus, you would have the same mass on the moon as you do on Earth, but your weight would be less on the moon because of its lower gravity.

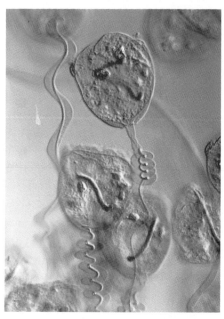

(a)

50 μm

(b)

Figure 2–1 The chemical composition and metabolic processes of all living things are remarkably similar. (*a*) The metabolic reactions that take place within the cells of these one-celled protozoa, *Vorticella* sp., are similar to those carried on within the cells of the more complex roseate spoonbill, *Ajaia ajaja* (*b*). This wading bird uses its spoonlike beak to gather shellfish and aquatic insects from tidal areas. (*a*, Visuals Unlimited/A. M. Siegelman; *b*, James Carmichael)

Table 2–1 ELEMENTS THAT MAKE UP THE HUMAN BODY

Name	Chemical Symbol	Approximate Composition of Human Body by Mass (%)	Importance or Function
Oxygen	O	65	Required for cellular respiration; present in most organic compounds; component of water
Carbon	C	18	Forms backbone of organic molecules; can form four bonds with other atoms
Hydrogen	H	10	Present in most organic compounds; component of water
Nitrogen	N	3	Component of all proteins and nucleic acids
Calcium	Ca	1.5	Structural component of bones and teeth; important in muscle contraction, conduction of nerve impulses, and blood clotting; also in cell walls (structural component) of plants
Phosphorus	P	1	Component of nucleic acids; structural component of bone; important in energy transfer
Potassium	K	0.4	Principal positive ion (cation) within cells; important in nerve function; affects muscle contraction
Sulfur	S	0.3	A component of most proteins
Sodium	Na	0.2	Principal positive ion in interstitial (tissue) fluid; important in fluid balance; essential for conduction of nerve impulses
Magnesium	Mg	0.1	Needed in blood and body tissues; a component of many important enzyme systems; component of chlorophyll in plants
Chlorine	Cl	0.1	Principal negative ion (anion) of interstitial fluid; important in fluid balance
Iron	Fe	Trace amount	Component of hemoglobin, myoglobin, and certain enzymes
Iodine	I	Trace amount	Component of thyroid hormones

Other elements, found in very small amounts in the body (the trace elements), include manganese (Mn), copper (Cu), zinc (Zn), cobalt (Co), fluorine (F), molybdenum (Mo), selenium (Se), and a few others.

ATOMS ARE THE BASIC PARTICLES OF ELEMENTS

Whatever physical state matter may assume—gas, liquid, or solid—it is composed of units called atoms. An **atom** is the smallest portion of an element that retains its chemical properties. Atoms are much smaller than the tiniest particle visible under a light microscope. By special scanning electron microscopy (see Chapter 4), with magnification as much as 5 million times, researchers have been able to photograph some of the larger atoms such as uranium and thorium.

ATOMS CONSIST OF SUBATOMIC PARTICLES

Physicists have discovered a considerable number of subatomic particles, but for our purposes we need con-

sider only three: protons, neutrons, and electrons. Each **proton** has one unit of a positive electrical charge; **neutrons** are uncharged particles with about the same mass as protons. Protons and neutrons make up almost all of the mass of an atom and are concentrated in the **atomic nucleus.** Each **electron** has one unit of a negative electrical charge and an extremely small mass (only about 1/1800 of the mass of a proton). The electrons, as we will see, behave as though they were spinning about in the empty space surrounding the atomic nucleus (Figure 2–2).

Protons and Neutrons Make Up the Atomic Nucleus

Each kind of element has a fixed number of protons in the atomic nucleus. This number, called the **atomic number,** is written as a subscript to the left of the chem-

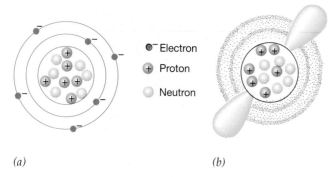

(a)   (b)

● Electron
⊕ Proton
○ Neutron

Figure 2–2 Two ways of representing an atom. (a) The Bohr model of a carbon atom. Although the Bohr model is not an accurate way to depict electron configuration, it is commonly used because of its simplicity and convenience. (b) An electron cloud. Dots represent the probability that the electron is in that particular location at any given moment.

ical symbol. Thus $_1H$ indicates that the hydrogen nucleus contains one proton, and $_8O$ that the oxygen nucleus contains eight protons. It is the atomic number, the number of protons in its nucleus, that determines an atom's identity.

The total number of protons plus neutrons in the nucleus is the **atomic mass.** The atomic mass of an element is a number that indicates how heavy an atom of that element is compared with an atom of another element. The mass of any single atom or molecule is exceedingly small, much too small to be conveniently expressed in terms of grams or even micrograms. Such masses are expressed in terms of the **atomic mass unit** (amu), also called the **dalton,** equal to the *approximate* mass of a proton or neutron. The atomic mass is indicated by a superscript to the left of the chemical symbol. The common form of oxygen atom, with eight protons and eight neutrons in its nucleus, has an atomic number of 8 and a mass number of 16. It is indicated by the symbol $^{16}_8O$.

Isotopes Differ in Number of Neutrons

Most elements consist of atoms with different numbers of neutrons and thus different masses. Such atoms are called **isotopes.** Isotopes of the same element have the same number of protons and electrons; only the number of neutrons varies. The three isotopes of hydrogen, ^1_1H, ^2_1H, and ^3_1H, contain zero, one, and two neutrons, respectively. Carbon-12 and carbon-14, two isotopes of carbon, are illustrated in Figure 2–3.

The standard for comparing elements is based on assignment of an atomic mass of exactly 12 to $^{12}_6C$, the most common isotope of carbon. The atomic mass for an element reflects the masses of the mixtures of isotopes that occur in nature. For example, although more than 99% of the hydrogen atoms in a naturally occur-

ring sample have an atomic mass of 1 amu (to be precise, on the carbon-12 scale it is 1.0000078 amu), the atomic mass of hydrogen is 1.0079 amu. This reflects the fact that a small amount of deuterium, ^2_1H (mass number 2) and an even smaller amount of tritium, ^3_1H (mass number 3), occur along with the common form of hydrogen, ^1_1H.

All of the isotopes of a given element have essentially the same chemical characteristics. However, some isotopes with an excess of neutrons are unstable and tend to break down, or decay, to a more stable isotope (usually becoming a different element). Such isotopes are termed **radionuclides** (or **radioisotopes**) because they emit high-energy radiation when they decay.

Radionuclides such as ^3H (tritium), ^{14}C, and ^{32}P have been extremely valuable research tools in biology and, along with radionuclides of other elements, are useful in medicine for both diagnosis and treatment (Figure 2–4). Despite the difference in the number of neutrons, the body treats all isotopes of a given element in a similar way. The reactions of a sugar, hormone, or drug can be followed in the body by labeling the substance with a radionuclide such as carbon-14 or tritium. For example, the active component in marijuana (tetrahydrocannabinol) can be labeled and administered intravenously. Then the amount of radioactivity in the blood and urine can be measured at successive intervals. Results of such measurements have determined that this compound appears in the blood, and products of its metabolism can be detected in the urine for several weeks.

Because radiation can interfere with cell division, radioactive isotopes have been used in the treatment of cancer (a disease characterized by rapidly dividing cells). Radionuclides are also used to test thyroid gland

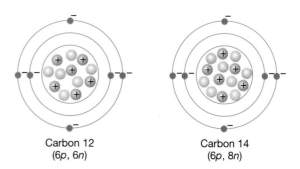

Carbon 12   Carbon 14
(6p, 6n)   (6p, 8n)

Figure 2–3 Isotopes of carbon. Carbon-12 is the more common isotope of carbon. Its nucleus contains six protons and six neutrons, so its atomic mass is 12. Carbon-14 is a rare radioactive isotope of carbon. Because it contains eight neutrons in its nucleus rather than six, its atomic mass is 14. Both types of carbon have six protons, so both have atomic number six. Carbon-14 is often used in research to trace the fate of carbon atoms in metabolic processes.

Figure 2–4 Anthropologists use radioisotope content to date and study fossils. This skeleton of an 11th-century inhabitant of a South African Iron Age village posed an anthropological puzzle. Physically, the man's skeleton was different from those of the other villagers, suggesting that he was not a native of the area. However, when the skeleton was analyzed for isotopes, the ratio of carbon isotopes was found to be similar to that of other skeletons from the same village. Because different kinds of plants incorporate different proportions of isotopes into the food produced from them, this similarity of isotope content indicates that these individuals all ate the same foods. Thus, anthropologists concluded that this man had probably spent most of his life in the village after migrating there from a distant region. (From Nicholas J. van der Merive, *American Scientist* 70(1982), 596–606)

function, to measure the rate of red blood cell production, and to study many other aspects of body function and chemistry.

Electrons Are Located in Energy Levels Outside the Nucleus

The space outside the atomic nucleus contains the electrons. Although the mass of electrons makes only a negligible contribution to the mass of an atom, electrons carry an electrical charge that profoundly affects the chemical properties of the atom. Each electron bears a charge of -1, exactly equal but opposite to the charge on a proton. The electrons are attracted by the positive charge of the protons.

The atoms of each type of element have a characteristic number of electrons around the nucleus. The number and relative positions of the electrons may change during chemical reactions. In a neutral atom the number of protons in the nucleus equals the number of electrons around it. The atom as a whole has no net charge; that is, it is in a state of electrical neutrality. The positive charges of the protons equal the negative charges of the electrons.

Electrons occur in characteristic regions of space termed **orbitals.** The lowest energy orbital, the $1s$ orbital, is nearest the nucleus and is spherical in shape (Figure 2–5a). Other electron orbitals farther from the nucleus, the p, d, and f orbitals, are either spherical or dumbbell-shaped or are represented by more complex three-dimensional coordinates. Orbitals represent the places where electrons are most probably found. Electrons whirl around the nucleus, now close to it, now farther away, so that an electron cloud surrounds the nucleus. One way of illustrating an atom is to show its electron orbitals as clouds, as in Figure 2–2b. The density of the shaded areas is proportional to the probability that an electron is present there at any given moment.

Several electrons may have similar energies; these make up an **electron shell** and are said to be in the same **energy level.** The number of electrons in the outer energy level determines the chemical properties of atoms. The energy levels or shells of electrons in an atom can be represented by a series of concentric circles around the nucleus, as in Figure 2–2a. It is important to remember, however, that electrons do *not* circle the nucleus in fixed concentric pathways. Although each orbital may contain no more than two electrons, there may be several orbitals within a given energy level.

The way that electrons are arranged around an atom is referred to as the **electron configuration** of that atom. Electrons always fill the orbitals nearest to the nucleus before occupying those farther away. The maximum number of electrons in the innermost shell (which is a single spherical orbital) is two; the second shell has four orbitals (one spherical and three dumbbell-shaped) and thus can contain a maximum of eight electrons (Figure 2–5). The third shell has a maximum of 18 elec-

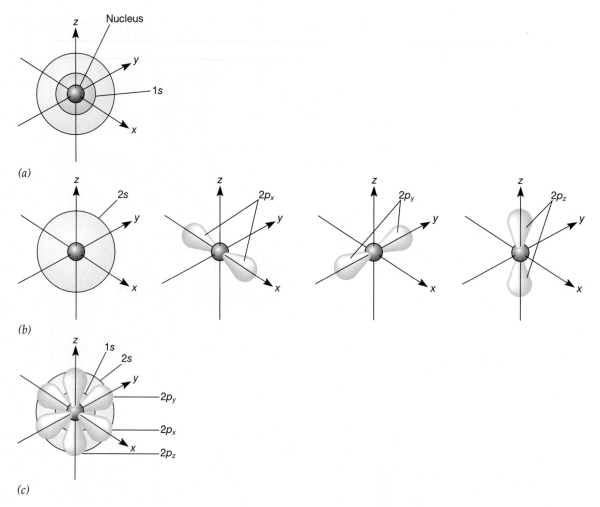

(a)

(b)

(c)

Figure 2–5   Representation of atomic orbitals. (a) The first energy level is a single spherical orbital (designated 1s) that can hold a maximum of two electrons. The electrons depicted in the diagram could be present anywhere within the deep blue area. (b) The second energy level has four orbitals, one spherical (2s) and three dumbbell-shaped (2p). (c) Orbitals of the first and second energy levels superimposed on one another.

trons arranged in nine orbitals, and the fourth has 32 electrons in 16 orbitals. Although the third and outer shells can each contain more than eight electrons, they are stable when only eight are present. We may consider the first shell to be complete when it contains two electrons and the other shells to be complete when they each contain eight electrons. The atomic structures of some elements important in biological systems—carbon, hydrogen, oxygen, nitrogen, sodium, and chlorine—are shown in Figure 2–6.

Remember that each atom is largely empty space. The distance from an electron to the protons and neutrons in the central nucleus may be 1000 times greater than the diameter of the nucleus itself. The tendency of the negatively charged electrons to fly off into space is countered by their attraction to the atomic nucleus by the positive charge of the protons in the nucleus.

The more distant the energy level is from the nucleus, the greater is the energy of the electrons in that level. An electron can be moved to an orbital farther from the nucleus by providing it with more energy, or an electron can give up energy and sink back to a lower energy level in an orbital nearer the central nucleus. Energy is required to move a negatively charged electron farther away from the positively charged nucleus.

When energy is added to the system, an electron can jump from one level to the next, *but it cannot stop in the space in between.* To move an electron from one level to the next, the atom must absorb a discrete packet of energy known as a **quantum,** which contains just the right amount of energy for the transition—no more and no less. The term *quantum leap* is used in everyday language to indicate a sudden discontinuous move from one level to another.

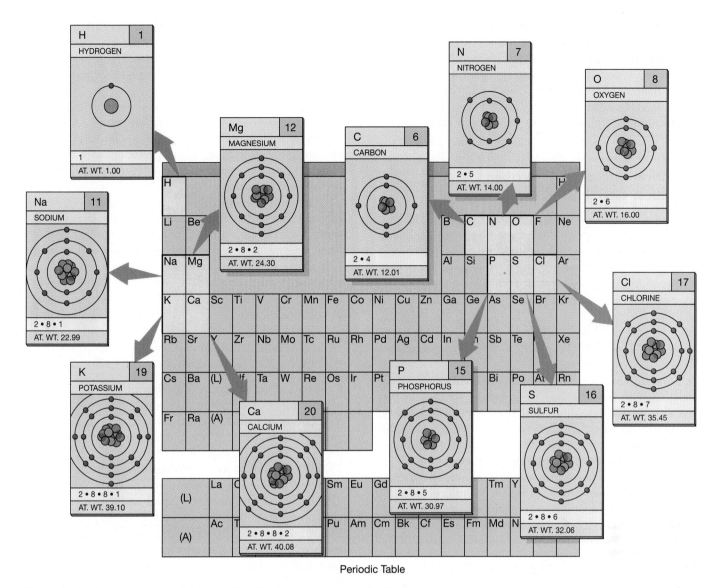

Figure 2–6 A representation of the periodic table showing Bohr models of some biologically important atoms.

ATOMS FORM MOLECULES AND COMPOUNDS

Two or more atoms may combine chemically to form a **molecule.** When two atoms of oxygen combine chemically, a molecule of oxygen is formed. Atoms of different elements can combine to form chemical compounds. A **chemical compound** consists of two or more different elements combined in a fixed ratio. For example, water is a chemical compound consisting of two atoms of hydrogen combined with one atom of oxygen. The properties of a chemical compound can be quite different from those of its component elements: At room temperature, water is usually a liquid; hydrogen and oxygen are gases.

Chemical Formulas Describe Chemical Compounds

A **chemical formula** is a shorthand method for describing the chemical composition of a compound. Chemical symbols are used to indicate the types of atoms in the molecule, and subscript numbers are used to indicate the number of each type of atom present. The chemical formula for molecular oxygen, O_2, tells us that this molecule consists of two atoms of oxygen. The chemical formula for water, H_2O, indicates that each molecule consists of two atoms of hydrogen and one atom of oxygen. (Note that when a single atom of one type is present, it is not necessary to write 1; we do *not* write H_2O_1.)

Another type of formula is the **structural formula,** which shows not only the types and numbers of atoms in a compound but also their arrangement. In each specific chemical compound the atoms are always arranged in the same way. From the chemical formula for water, H_2O, you could only guess whether the atoms were arranged H—H—O or H—O—H. The structural formula settles the matter, indicating that the two hydrogen atoms are attached to the oxygen atom.

Chemical Equations Describe Chemical Reactions

During any moment in the life of an organism, be it a mushroom or a butterfly, many complex chemical reactions are taking place. The chemical reactions that occur between atoms and compounds—for example, between methane (natural gas) and oxygen—can be described by means of chemical equations:

$$CH_4 \ + \ 2\,O_2 \ \longrightarrow \ CO_2 \ + 2\,H_2O + Energy$$

Methane   Oxygen   Carbon   Water
                      dioxide

In a *chemical equation*, the **reactants** (the substances that participate in the reaction) are generally written on the left side of the equation, and the **products** (the substances formed by the reaction) are written on the right side. The arrow means *"yields"* and indicates the direction in which the reaction tends to proceed.

The number preceding a chemical symbol or formula indicates the number of atoms or molecules reacting. Thus, $2\,O_2$ means two molecules of oxygen, and $2\,H_2O$ means two molecules of water. The absence of a number indicates that only one atom or molecule is present.

Reactions may proceed in the reverse direction (to the left) as well as forward (to the right); at **equilibrium** the rates of the forward and reverse reactions are equal. Reversible reactions are indicated by double arrows:

$$N_2 \ + \ 3\,H_2 \ \rightleftharpoons \ 2\,NH_3$$

Nitrogen   Hydrogen   Ammonia

In this example, the arrows are drawn different lengths to indicate that when the reaction is at equilibrium there is more product than reactant.

CHEMICAL BONDS HOLD ATOMS TOGETHER

The chemical behavior of an atom is determined primarily by the number and arrangement of electrons in the *outermost* energy level (electron shell). In a few elements, called the "noble gases," the outermost shell is filled. These elements are chemically inert, meaning that they do not readily combine with other elements. Two such elements are helium, with two electrons (a complete shell), and neon, with ten electrons (a complete inner shell of two and a complete second shell of eight).

The electrons in the outermost energy level of an atom are referred to as **valence electrons.** When the outer energy level of an atom contains fewer than eight electrons, the atom tends to lose, gain, or share electrons to achieve an outer energy level of eight (zero or two in the lightest elements).

The atoms of a molecule are held together by forces of attraction called **chemical bonds.** Each bond represents a certain amount of potential chemical energy. Bond energy is the energy necessary to break a bond. The atoms of each element form a specific number of bonds with the atoms of other elements—a number dictated by the valence electrons. The two principal types of chemical bonds are covalent bonds and ionic bonds.

Electrons Are Shared in Covalent Bonds

Covalent bonds involve the sharing of electrons between atoms. A compound consisting mainly of covalent bonds is called a **covalent compound.** A simple example of a covalent bond is the one joining two hydrogen atoms in a molecule of hydrogen gas, H_2 (Figure 2–7). Each atom of hydrogen has one electron, but two electrons are required to complete the first energy level. The hydrogen atoms have equal capacities to attract electrons, so neither donates an electron to the other. Instead, the two hydrogen atoms share their single electrons so that each of the two electrons is attracted simultaneously to the two protons in the two hydrogen nuclei. The two electrons thus whirl around *both* atomic nuclei and join the two atoms together.

A simple way of representing the electrons in the outer shell of an atom is to use dots placed around the chemical symbol of the element to represent the electrons. In a water molecule two hydrogen atoms are covalently bonded to an oxygen atom:

$$H\cdot + H\cdot + \cdot \overset{\cdot\cdot}{O}\cdot \ \longrightarrow \ H\!:\!\overset{\cdot\cdot}{O}\!:\!H$$

Oxygen has six valence electrons; by sharing electrons with two hydrogen atoms, it completes its outer level of eight. Each hydrogen atom obtains a complete outer level of two. (Note that in the structural formula H—O—H, each pair of shared electrons is represented by a single line. Unshared electrons are usually omitted in a structural formula.)

The carbon atom has four electrons in its outer energy level. These four electrons are available for covalent bonding:

$$\cdot \overset{\cdot}{C} \cdot$$

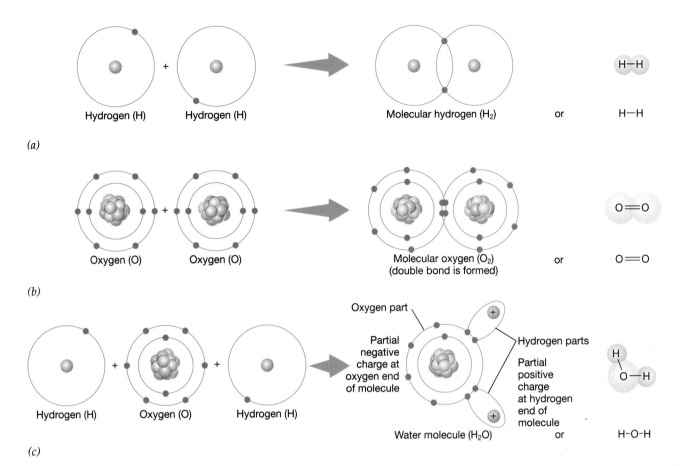

Figure 2–7 Formation of covalent compounds. (*a*) Two hydrogen atoms achieve stability by sharing electrons, thereby forming a molecule of hydrogen. The structural formula shown on the right is a simpler way of representing molecular hydrogen. The straight line between the hydrogen atoms represents a single covalent bond. (*b*) Two oxygen atoms share two pairs of electrons to form molecular oxygen. Note the double bond. (*c*) When two hydrogen atoms share electrons with an oxygen atom, the result is a molecule of water. Note that the electrons tend to stay closer to the nucleus of the oxygen atom than to the hydrogen nuclei. This results in a partial negative charge on the oxygen portion of the molecule and a partial positive charge at the hydrogen end. Although the water molecule as a whole is electrically neutral, it is a polar covalent compound.

When one carbon and four hydrogen atoms share electrons, a molecule of methane, CH_4, is formed:

$$\begin{matrix} & H & & & H \\ & \cdot\cdot & & & | \\ H & \colon C \colon H & \text{or} & H- & C & -H \\ & \cdot\cdot & & & | \\ & H & & & H \end{matrix}$$

Each atom shares its outer-level electrons with the other, thereby completing the first energy level of each hydrogen atom and the second energy level of the carbon atom.

The nitrogen atom has five electrons in its outer shell:

$$\cdot \ddot{N} \cdot$$

When a nitrogen atom shares electrons with three hydrogen atoms, a molecule of ammonia, NH_3, is formed:

$$\begin{matrix} & \cdot\cdot & & & \\ H & \colon N \colon H & \text{or} & H-N-H \\ & \ddot{H} & & | \\ & & & H \end{matrix}$$

When an electron pair is shared between two atoms, the covalent bond is referred to as a **single bond.** Two oxygen atoms may achieve stability by forming covalent bonds with one another. Each oxygen atom has six electrons in its outer shell. To become stable, the two atoms share two pairs of electrons, forming molecular oxygen (Figure 2–7*b*). When two pairs of electrons are shared in this way, the covalent bond is referred to as a **double bond.** When three pairs of electrons are shared, the covalent bond is called a triple bond.

A Molecule Has a Characteristic Size and Shape

Each kind of molecule has a characteristic size and shape. The functions of molecules in the living cell are largely dictated by their geometric shapes. A molecule that consists of two atoms, for example, has a linear shape. Molecules composed of more than two atoms

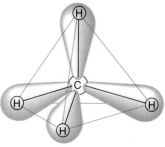

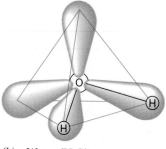

(a)   Methane (CH$_4$)   (b)   Water (H$_2$O)

Figure 2–8   The molecular shapes of methane and water. (a) The four hydrogens of methane are located at the corners of a tetrahedron. (b) The water molecule assumes a ''V'' shape.

may have more complicated shapes. The geometric shape of a molecule provides the optimal distance between the atoms to counteract the repulsion of electron pairs.

When an atom forms covalent bonds with other atoms, the orbitals in the outer shell may become rearranged, or **hybridized.** Atoms that have valence electrons in both the *s* and *p* orbitals undergo a rearrangement such that the *s* and *p* orbitals hybridize to form four new molecular orbitals, which extend outward from the nucleus. When the ends of the orbitals are connected, the result is a three-dimensional pyramid called a **tetrahedron.** When four hydrogen atoms combine with a carbon atom to form a molecule of methane, one hydrogen atom is present at each of the four corners of the tetrahedron, and they share a pair of electrons in the hybrid orbital with the carbon atom. The water molecule, H$_2$O, also has a tetrahedron-shaped oxygen atom made of four hybridized *s* and *p* orbitals, but only two of the four corners interact with hydrogen atoms (Figure 2–8).

Covalent Bonds Can Be Nonpolar or Polar

The atoms of each element have a characteristic affinity for electrons. **Electronegativity** is a measure of an atom's attraction for electrons in chemical bonds. When the atoms in a molecule have similar electronegativity, the electrons are shared equally and the covalent bond is described as **nonpolar.** The covalent bond of the hydrogen molecule is nonpolar; so are the covalent bonds of oxygen and methane.

In a covalent bond between two different elements, such as oxygen and hydrogen, the electronegativity of the atoms may be different. If so, electrons are pulled closer to the atomic nucleus of the element with the greater electron affinity (in this case, oxygen). A covalent bond between atoms of different electronegativity is called a **polar covalent bond.** In a water molecule the electrons tend to be closer to the nucleus of the oxygen atom than to the nuclei of the hydrogen atoms. The water molecule as a whole is electrically neutral, but it

is polar because each hydrogen atom has a partial positive charge and the oxygen atom has a partial negative charge (see Figure 2–7c).

The polarity of compounds is important in understanding the structure and properties of biological membranes. Covalent bonds may have all degrees of polarity, from those in which the electrons are exactly shared (as in the hydrogen molecule) to those in which the electrons are much closer to one atom than to the other (as in water).

Atoms Gain or Lose Electrons to Form Ionic Bonds

An **ionic bond** is an extreme case of polarity in which the electrons are pulled completely from one atom and transferred to the other. When an atom gains or loses electrons, it becomes a charged particle called an **ion.** An atom with one, two, or three electrons in its outer shell tends to lose electrons to other atoms. When such an atom loses electrons, it becomes positively charged as a result of the excess of protons in its nucleus. Positively charged ions are termed **cations.** Atoms with five, six, or seven valence electrons tend to gain electrons from other atoms and become negatively charged **anions.** Cations and anions play essential roles in the transmission of nerve impulses, muscle contraction, and many other life processes (Figure 2–9). An **ionic compound** is a substance consisting of anions and cations bonded together by their opposite charges.

A good example of how ionic bonds are formed is the attraction between sodium and chlorine. A sodium atom, with atomic number 11, has two electrons in its inner shell, eight in the second, and one in the third. A sodium atom cannot fill its third shell by obtaining seven electrons from other atoms, for it would then have a very large unbalanced negative charge. Instead, it gives up the single electron in its third shell to some electron acceptor, leaving the second shell as the complete outer shell (Figure 2–10). A chlorine atom, with atomic number 17, has 17 protons in its nucleus, two electrons in its inner shell, eight in the second shell, and

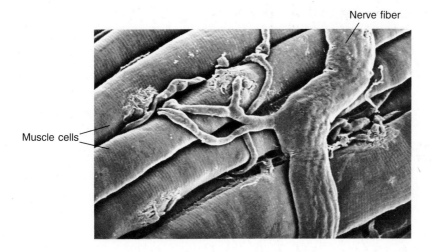

Nerve fiber

Muscle cells

Figure 2–9   Ions play important roles in biological processes. Sodium, potassium, and chloride ions are among the ions that are essential in the conduction of nerve impulses. This scanning electron micrograph shows a nerve fiber communicating with several muscle cells. The nerve fiber transmits impulses to the muscle cells, stimulating them to contract. The muscle cells are rich in calcium ions, which are essential for muscle contraction.   (From Desaki, J., *Biomedical Research Supplement*, 1981, 139–143)

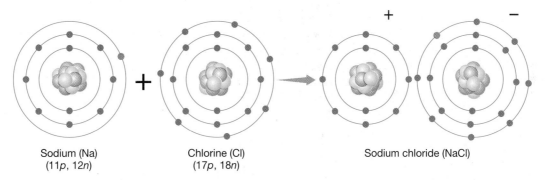

Sodium (Na)
(11*p*, 12*n*)

Chlorine (Cl)
(17*p*, 18*n*)

Sodium chloride (NaCl)

Figure 2–10   Formation of an ionic compound. Sodium donates its single valence electron to chlorine, which has seven electrons in its outer energy level. With this additional electron, chlorine completes its outer energy level. The two atoms are now electrically charged ions. They are attracted to one another by their unlike electrical charges, forming the ionic compound sodium chloride. The force of attraction holding these ions together is called an *ionic bond.*

seven in the third shell. The chlorine atom achieves a complete outer shell not by losing the seven electrons in its third shell, for it would then have a vast positive charge, but by accepting an electron from an electron donor such as sodium to complete its outer third shell.

When sodium reacts with chlorine, its outermost electron is transferred completely to chlorine. The sodium ion now has 11 protons in its nucleus and 10 electrons circling the nucleus. Its net charge is 1^+. The chloride ion has 17 protons in its nucleus, 18 electrons circling the nucleus, and a net charge of 1^-. These ions attract each other as a result of their opposite charges. They are held together by this electrical attraction in ionic bonds to form sodium chloride,[1] common table salt.

Compounds joined by ionic bonds, such as sodium chloride, have a tendency to **dissociate** (separate) into their individual ions when placed in water. In the solid form of an ionic compound, the constituent ions require considerable energy to be pulled apart. Water, however, is an excellent **solvent;** as a liquid it is capable of dissolving many substances. This is because of the polarity of water molecules. The localized partial positive charges (on the hydrogen atom) and partial negative charges (on the oxygen atom) on each water molecule attract the anions and cations on the surface of an ionic solid. As a result, the solid dissolves. In solution, each cation and anion of the ionic compound is surrounded by oppositely charged ends of the water molecules (Figure 2–11). This process is known as **hydration.**

[1] In both covalent and ionic binary compounds (*binary* denotes compounds consisting of two elements), the element having the greater attraction for the shared electrons is named second, and an *-ide* ending is added to the stem name—e.g., sodium chloride, hydrogen fluoride. The *-ide* ending is also used to indicate an anion, as in chloride (Cl^-) and hydroxide (OH^-).

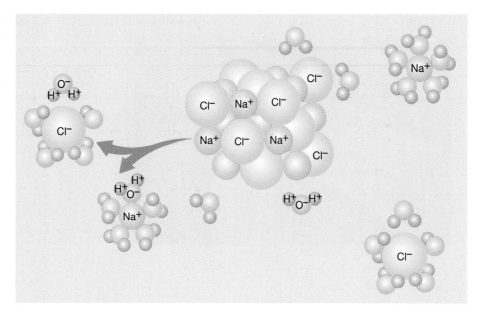

Figure 2–11   Hydration of an ionic compound. The crystal of NaCl consists of regularly spaced ionic bonds between the Na^+ and Cl^-. When NaCl is added to water, the partial negative ends of the water molecules are attracted to the positive sodium ions and tend to pull them away from the chlorine ions. At the same time, the partial positive ends of the water molecules are attracted to the negative chloride ions, separating them from the sodium ions. When the NaCl is dissolved, each of the sodium and chlorine ions is surrounded by water molecules electrically attracted to it.

$$NaCl \xrightarrow{\text{in } H_2O} Na^+ + Cl^-$$

Sodium   Sodium   Chloride
chloride   ion   ion

$$CaCl_2 \xrightarrow{\text{in } H_2O} Ca^{2+} + 2\,Cl^-$$

Calcium   Calcium   Chloride
chloride   ion   ions

$$Na_2SO_4 \xrightarrow{\text{in } H_2O} 2\,Na^+ + SO_4^{2-}$$

Sodium   Sodium   Sulfate
sulfate   ions   ion

The term *molecule* does not adequately explain the properties of ionic compounds such as NaCl. Hydrated sodium and chlorine ions do not interact with each other to the extent that "molecules" of sodium chloride can be said to exist. Likewise, when NaCl is in its solid crystal state, each ion is actually surrounded by six ions of opposite charge. The molecular formula NaCl indicates that sodium and chlorine ions are present in a one-to-one ratio, but in the actual crystal, no discrete molecules composed of one Na^+ ion and one Cl^- ion are present.

Hydrogen Bonds Are Weak Attractions Involving Partially Charged Hydrogen Atoms

Another type of bond that is important in biological systems is the **hydrogen bond.** When hydrogen is combined with oxygen (or with another relatively electronegative atom), it has a partial positive charge because its electron is positioned closer to the oxygen atom. Hydrogen bonds tend to form between an electronegative atom and a hydrogen atom that is covalently bonded to oxygen or nitrogen (Figure 2–12). The atoms involved may be in two parts of the same molecule or in two different molecules. Hydrogen bonds are very important in determining the properties of water.

Hydrogen bonds are weak and are readily formed and broken. They have a specific length and orientation; this feature is very important in their role in helping determine the three-dimensional structure of large molecules such as DNA and proteins. Although they

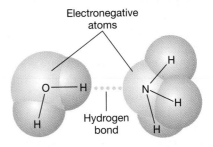

Figure 2–12   A hydrogen bond. The nitrogen atom of an ammonia molecule (NH_3) is joined to a hydrogen atom of a water molecule (H_2O) by a hydrogen bond. In a hydrogen bond, a hydrogen atom connected to an electronegative atom by a polar covalent bond is shared with another electronegative atom by a weak electrical attraction.

are relatively weak individually, the large number of bonds present compensates for the weakness of the individual bonds.

van der Waals Forces and Hydrophobic Attractions Are Other Interactions between Atoms

The attractive forces between molecules, called **van der Waals forces,** occur when the molecules are very close together and are due to the interaction of regions of slight opposite charge. Van der Waals forces are weaker and less specific than the other types of interactions we have considered. They are most important when they occur in large numbers and when the shapes of the molecules involved permit close contact between the atoms. As with hydrogen bonds, the bonding force of a single interaction is very weak. In molecules and structures that have a large number of these interactions working together, however, the binding force can be very large.

Hydrophobic (water-hating) **interactions** occur between groups of nonpolar molecules. Such groups tend to cluster together and are insoluble in water. This clustering is a result of the hydrogen bonds that hold the water molecules together and in a sense drive the nonpolar molecules together. Hydrophobic interactions explain why oil tends to form globules when it is added to water.

COMPOUNDS HAVE MOLECULAR MASS

The **molecular mass** of a compound is the sum of the atomic masses of its component atoms; thus, the molecular mass of water, H_2O, is $(2 \times 1 \text{ amu}) + (16 \text{ amu})$, or 18 amu. (Owing to the presence of isotopes, atomic mass units are not whole numbers. However, for our purposes each atomic mass value has been rounded off to a whole number.) The molecular mass of the simple sugar glucose, $C_6H_{12}O_6$, which is a key compound in cellular metabolism, is $(6 \times 12 \text{ amu}) + (12 \times 1 \text{ amu}) + (6 \times 16 \text{ amu})$, or 180 amu.

The amount of a compound whose mass in grams is equivalent to its molecular mass is termed 1 **mole.** Thus 1 mole of glucose has a mass of 180 grams. A 1-molar solution, represented by $1\,M$, contains 1 mole of the substance (e.g., 180 grams of glucose) in 1 liter of solution. Chemical compounds react with each other in quantitatively precise ways. For example, when glucose is burned in a fire or metabolized in a cell, 1 mole of glucose reacts with 6 moles of oxygen to form 6 moles of carbon dioxide (CO_2) and 6 moles of water.

$$C_6H_{12}O_6 + 6\,O_2 \longrightarrow 6\,CO_2 + 6\,H_2O + \text{Energy}$$

| Glucose | Oxygen | Carbon dioxide | Water |

The mole is a very useful unit because we cannot do experiments with individual atoms or molecules. The very large number of units in a mole, 6.02×10^{23}, is known as *Avogadro's number,* named for the Italian physicist Amadeo Avogadro, who first calculated it. Molecular biologists usually deal with smaller amounts of chemical compounds—millimoles (mmoles, one thousandth of a mole) or micromoles (μmoles, one millionth of a mole).

OXIDATION INVOLVES THE LOSS OF ELECTRONS; REDUCTION INVOLVES THE GAIN OF ELECTRONS

Rusting—the combination of iron with oxygen—is a familiar example of oxidation and reduction:

$$4\,Fe + 3\,O_2 \longrightarrow 2\,Fe_2O_3$$

Oxidation is a chemical process in which an atom, ion, or molecule loses electrons. In rusting, iron is changed from its metallic state to its iron(III) (Fe^{3+}) state; it is being oxidized.

$$4\,Fe \longrightarrow Fe^{3+} + 12\,e^-$$

The e^- is a symbol for an electron; the + sign represents an electron deficit. (When an atom loses an electron, it acquires a positive charge from the excess of one proton. Loss of two electrons produces an atom with a double positive charge, and so on.) At the same time iron is being oxidized, oxygen is changed from its molecular state to its charged state:

$$3\,O_2 + 12\,e^- \longrightarrow 6\,O^{2-}$$

When oxygen accepts the electrons removed from the iron, it is reduced. **Reduction** is a chemical process in which an atom, ion, or molecule gains electrons. Oxidation and reduction reactions occur simultaneously because one substance must accept the electrons that are removed from the other. Oxidation-reduction reactions are sometimes referred to as **redox reactions.**

Electrons are not easily removed from covalent compounds unless an entire atom is removed. In living cells, oxidation almost always involves the removal of a hydrogen atom from a compound; reduction often involves the addition of hydrogen (see Chapter 6).

INORGANIC COMPOUNDS ARE RELATIVELY SIMPLE COMPOUNDS WITHOUT CARBON BACKBONES

Chemical compounds can be divided into two broad groups—inorganic and organic. **Organic compounds** are generally large and complex and always contain

Figure 2–13 Planet Earth is sometimes referred to as the *water planet* because most of its surface is covered with water. Here, Earth is seen from Apollo II, about 98,000 nautical miles away.

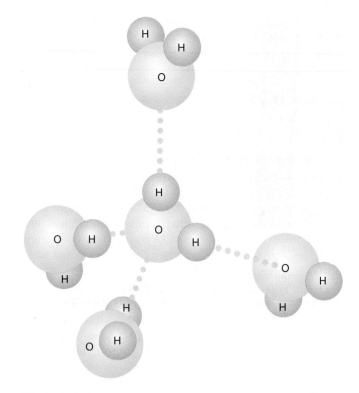

Figure 2–14 Hydrogen bonding of water molecules. Each water molecule tends to form hydrogen bonds with four neighboring water molecules. The hydrogen bonds are indicated by dotted lines.

carbon. They are discussed in Chapter 3. **Inorganic compounds** are relatively small, simple substances. A few very simple compounds, including carbon dioxide and compounds containing carbonate (CO_3^{2-}), are classified as inorganic compounds even though they contain carbon. Among the biologically important groups of inorganic compounds are water, simple acids and bases, and simple salts.

WATER IS ESSENTIAL TO LIFE

A large part of the mass of most organisms is water. In human tissues the percentage of water ranges from 20% in bones to 85% in brain cells. The water content is greater in embryonic and young cells and decreases as aging occurs. About 70% of our total body weight is water; as much as 95% of a jellyfish or certain plants is water. Water is the source, through plant metabolism, of the oxygen in the air we breathe, and its hydrogen atoms are incorporated into the many organic compounds in the bodies of living things. Water is also the solvent for most biological reactions and a reactant or product in many chemical reactions.

Water not only is important inside organisms but is also one of the principal environmental factors affecting them. Many organisms live within the sea or in freshwater rivers, lakes, or puddles. Water's unique combination of physical and chemical properties has permitted living things to appear, to survive, and to evolve on planet Earth (Figure 2–13).

Water Molecules Are Polar

Water molecules are polar—that is, they bear a partial positive and a partial negative charge. The water molecules in liquid water and in ice are held together in part by hydrogen bonds. The hydrogen atom of one water molecule, with its partial positive charge, is attracted to the oxygen atom of a neighboring water molecule, with its partial negative charge, forming a hydrogen bond. Each water molecule can form hydrogen bonds with a maximum of four neighboring water molecules (Figure 2–14).

Water Is an Excellent Solvent

Because its molecules are polar, water is an excellent solvent, a liquid capable of dissolving many different kinds of substances, especially polar compounds. Earlier in this chapter, we discussed how polar water molecules pull the ions of ionic compounds apart so that they dissociate. Because of its solvent properties and the tendency of the atoms in certain compounds to form ions when in solution, water plays an important role in facilitating chemical reactions.

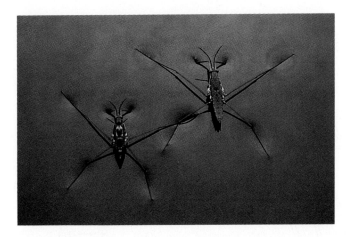

Figure 2–15 Water has a very high surface tension because of the strength of all of its hydrogen bonds. These water striders, although more dense than water, can walk on the surface of a pond. Fine hairs at the ends of the legs spread the weight over a large area, allowing the body to be supported by the surface tension of the water.   (Dennis Drenner)

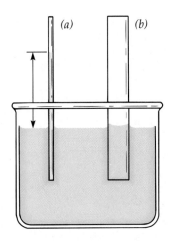

Figure 2–16 The cohesive and adhesive forces of water account for capillary action. (*a*) In the smaller tube, adhesive forces attract water molecules to charged groups on the surfaces of the tube. Other water molecules inside the tube are then "pulled along" by cohesive forces, which are actually caused by hydrogen bonds between the water molecules. (*b*) In the large-diameter tube, a smaller percentage of the water molecules line the glass. Because of this, the adhesive forces are not strong enough to overcome the cohesive forces of the water beneath the surface level of the container, and water in the tube rises only slightly.

Water Exhibits Both Cohesive and Adhesive Forces

Water molecules are mutually attracted to themselves and to some other substances by cohesive and adhesive forces. Water molecules have a very strong tendency to stick to each other; that is, they are **cohesive.** This is due to the hydrogen bonds among the molecules. Water molecules also stick to many other kinds of substances (i.e., those substances that have charged groups of atoms or molecules on their surfaces). These **adhesive forces** explain how water makes things wet. Water has a high degree of **surface tension** because of the cohesiveness of its molecules; its molecules have a much greater attraction for each other than for molecules in the air. Thus, water molecules at the surface crowd together, producing a strong layer as they are pulled downward by the attraction of other water molecules beneath them (Figure 2–15).

Adhesive and cohesive forces account for the tendency, termed **capillary action,** of water to rise in narrow tubes (Figure 2–16). Water also moves through the microscopic spaces between soil particles to the roots of plants by capillary action.

Water Helps Maintain a Stable Temperature

Water has a high **specific heat;** that is, the amount of energy required to raise the temperature of water by 1 degree Celsius is quite large. The high specific heat of water results from the hydrogen bonding of its molecules. Raising the temperature of a substance involves adding heat energy to make its molecules move faster—

to increase the kinetic energy of the molecules. Some of the hydrogen bonds holding the water molecules together must first be broken to permit the molecules to move more freely. Much of the energy added to the system is used up in breaking the hydrogen bonds, and only a portion of the heat energy is available to speed the movement of the water molecules (increase the temperature of the water). When liquid water changes to ice, a great deal of heat is liberated into the environment.

Because so much heat loss or heat input is required to lower or raise the temperature of water, the oceans and other large bodies of water have relatively constant temperatures. Thus, many organisms living in the oceans are provided with a relatively constant environmental temperature. The properties of water are crucial in stabilizing temperatures on Earth. The quantity of water on the Earth's surface is enormous; this large mass resists both the warming effect of heat and the cooling effect of low temperatures. Also, the high water content of organisms helps them maintain a relatively constant internal temperature. Such minimizing of temperature fluctuations is important because biological reactions can take place only within a relatively narrow temperature range.

Because its molecules are held together by hydrogen bonds, water has a high **heat of vaporization.** To change 1 gram of liquid water into 1 gram of water vapor, 540 calories of heat are required. A **calorie** is a unit of heat energy (defined as 4.184 joules) that equals

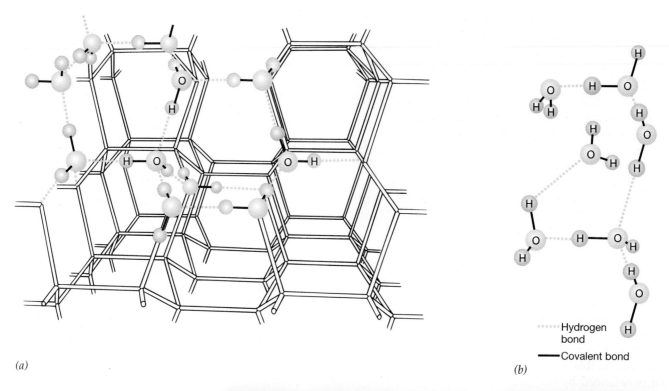

(a)

(b)

········· Hydrogen
bond

────Covalent bond

Figure 2–17 The hydrogen bonding
in ice compared with that in liquid
water. (*a*) Note the regular, evenly
distanced hydrogen bonds in the
superstructure of ice. (*b*) When ice
melts, the hydrogen bonds occur less
consistently and are of unequal length,
and the crystal structure collapses. (*c*)
Icebergs, Portage Glacier, Alaska.
Because water expands as it freezes,
ice is one of the very few substances
that is lighter in its solid than in its
liquid form. Thus ice will float on
water instead of accumulating on the
bottom. (*c*, Barbara O'Donnell/Biological
Photo Service)

(c)

the amount of heat required to raise the temperature of
1 gram of water 1 degree Celsius. Because water absorbs heat as it changes from a liquid to a gas, the
human body can dissipate excess heat as sweat evaporates from the skin, and a leaf can keep cool in the
bright sunlight as water evaporates from its surface.

Density of Water Is Maximum at 4°C

Hydrogen bonds contribute another important property of water. Whereas most substances become more
dense as the temperature decreases, water is most
dense at 4°C and then begins to expand again (becoming less dense) as the temperature decreases further.
Liquid water expands as it freezes. This expansion occurs because the hydrogen bonds joining the water molecules in the crystalline lattice keep the molecules far
enough apart to give ice a density about 10% less than
the density of liquid water at 4°C. As a result, ice floats
on the more dense cold water (Figure 2–17).

When ice has been heated enough to increase its
temperature above 0°C, the hydrogen bonds between

the water molecules are broken. The water molecules are then free to slip closer together. The density of water is greatest at 4°C, above which water begins to expand again as the speed of its molecules increases.

This unusual property of water has been important in enabling life to appear, survive, and evolve in the way it has on the Earth. If ice had a greater density than water, it would sink, and eventually all ponds, lakes, and even oceans would freeze solid from the bottom to the surface, making life impossible. When a body of deep water cools, it becomes covered with floating ice. The ice insulates the liquid water below it, preventing the water from freezing and permitting a variety of animals and plants to survive below the icy surface.

Water Molecules Dissociate Slightly

A further characteristic of water molecules is their slight tendency to **ionize**—that is, to dissociate into hydrogen ions (H^+) and hydroxide ions (OH^-).[1] In pure water, a very small number of water molecules form ions in this way. The tendency of water to dissociate is balanced by the tendency of hydrogen ions and hydroxide ions to reunite to form water:

$$HOH \rightleftharpoons H^+ + OH^-$$

Because water splits into one hydrogen ion and one hydroxide ion, the concentrations of hydrogen and hydroxide ions in pure water are exactly equal. Such a solution is said to be **neutral,** neither acidic nor basic (alkaline). The slight tendency of water molecules to form ions results in a concentration of hydrogen ions and of hydroxide ions of 0.0000001 (10^{-7}) moles per liter for each ion.

ACIDS YIELD HYDROGEN IONS; BASES ARE PROTON ACCEPTORS

An **acid** is a substance that dissociates in solution to yield hydrogen ions (H^+) and an anion.

$$Acid \longrightarrow H^+ + Anion$$

An acid is a proton *donor*. (Recall that a hydrogen ion, or H^+, is nothing more than a proton.) Acids turn blue litmus paper red and have a sour taste. Hydrochloric acid (HCl) and sulfuric acid (H_2SO_4) are examples of inorganic acids. Lactic acid ($CH_3CHOHCOOH$) from sour milk and acetic acid (CH_3COOH) from vinegar are two common organic acids.

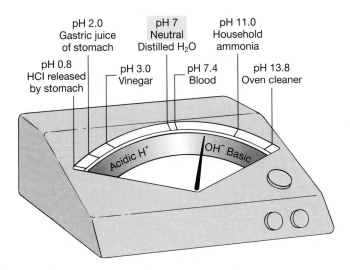

Figure 2–18 The pH scale. The pH meter is a device used to measure pH. A solution with a pH of 7 is neutral because the concentrations of H^+ and OH^- are equal. The lower the pH below 7, the more H^+ ions are present, and the more acidic the solution is. As the pH increases above 7, the concentration of H^+ ions decreases and the concentration of OH^- increases, making the solution more alkaline (basic).

A **base** is defined as a proton *acceptor*. Most bases are substances that dissociate to yield a hydroxide ion (OH^-) and a cation when dissolved in water. Bases turn red litmus paper blue and feel slippery to the touch. Sodium hydroxide (NaOH) and ammonium hydroxide (NH_4OH) are common inorganic bases. In later chapters we encounter a number of organic bases such as the purine and pyrimidine bases that are components of nucleic acids.

Acids and bases dissociate when dissolved in water, releasing H^+ ions and OH^- ions, respectively. When the concentration of hydrogen ions in a solution is greater than 0.0000001 M ($10^{-7} M$), the solution is acidic. When the concentration of hydrogen ions is less than $10^{-7} M$ (and the concentration of hydroxide ions is greater than $10^{-7} M$), the solution is basic, or alkaline.

Because the concentration of hydrogen ions in biological fluids is usually low, it is convenient to express the degree of acidity or alkalinity in terms of **pH,** defined as the logarithm of the reciprocal of the hydrogen ion concentration. The pH scale is thus a logarithmic one, extending from 0, the pH of a 1 M acid such as HCl, to 14, the pH of a 1 M base such as NaOH (Figure 2–18). The hydrogen ion concentration of pure water is $10^{-7} M$. The logarithm of $1/10^{-7}$ is 7.0; hence, the pH of water is 7.0 (Table 2–2). At pH 7.0 the concentrations of H^+ ions and OH^- ions are exactly equal, $10^{-7} M$.

Because the scale is logarithmic, a solution with a pH of 6 has a hydrogen ion concentration 10 times greater than a solution with a pH of 7. A pH of 5 represents another tenfold increase in the concentration of hydrogen ions, so a solution with a pH of 5 is 10 × 10 or

---

[1] The H^+ immediately combines with an electronegative region of a water molecule, forming a hydronium ion (H_3O^+). However, by convention H^+, rather than the more accurate H_3O^+, is used.

Table 2–2   THE RELATION OF pH TO HYDROGEN ION CONCENTRATION

Substance	$[H^+]$	$1/[H^+]$	$\log 1/[H^+]$	pH
Pure water, neutral solution	$0.0000001, 10^{-7}$	10^7	7	7
Gastric juice	$0.01, 10^{-2}$	10^2	2	2
Household ammonia	$0.00000000001, 10^{-11}$	10^{11}	11	11

100 times more acidic than a solution with a pH of 7. Solutions with a pH of less than 7 are acidic and contain more H^+ ions than OH^- ions. Solutions with a pH greater than 7 are alkaline, or basic, and contain more OH^- ions than H^+ ions. The contents of most animal and plant cells are neither strongly acidic nor alkaline but are an essentially neutral mixture of acidic and basic substances. Any considerable change in the pH of the cell is incompatible with life (Figure 2–19). The pH of living cells ordinarily ranges around the value of 7.2 to 7.4. Human blood has a normal pH of 7.4.

Figure 2–19 The trees shown here (photographed in Great Smoky Mountain National Park) may be casualties of acid rain. Sulfur oxides, emitted from fossil fuel plants and industry, and nitrogen oxides, mainly from automobile exhaust, are converted in the moist atmosphere into acids of, respectively, sulfur and nitrogen, such as sulfurous and nitrous acid. These acids are dispersed over wide areas by airflow patterns in the atmosphere. Whereas the pH of unpolluted rain averages 5.6, in some parts of the United States and Canada the pH of rain has been measured at 4.2 and even lower. Most fish species die at a pH of 4.5 to 5.0. (M. L. Dembinsky, Jr./Dembinsky Photo Assoc.)

Salts Form from Acids and Bases

When an acid and a base are mixed together, the H^+ of the acid unites with the OH^- of the base to form a molecule of water. The remainder of the acid (an anion) combines with the remainder of the base (a cation) to form a salt. For example, hydrochloric acid reacts with sodium hydroxide to form water and sodium chloride:

$$HCl + NaOH \longrightarrow H_2O + NaCl$$

A **salt** is a compound in which the hydrogen atom of an acid is replaced by some other cation. A salt contains a cation other than H^+ and an anion other than OH^-. Sodium chloride, NaCl, is a compound in which the hydrogen ion of HCl has been replaced by the cation Na^+.

When a salt, an acid, or a base is dissolved in water, its dissociated charged particles can conduct an electrical current; these substances are called **electrolytes.** Sugars, alcohols, and many other substances do not form ions when dissolved in water; they do not conduct an electrical current and are referred to as **nonelectrolytes.**

Cells and extracellular fluids (such as blood) of animals and plants contain a variety of dissolved salts. These salts are the source of many important mineral ions. Such ions are essential for fluid balance, acid-base balance, and, in animals, nerve and muscle function, blood clotting, bone formation, and many other aspects of body function. Sodium, potassium, calcium, and magnesium are the chief cations present, and chloride, bicarbonate, phosphate, and sulfate are important anions (Table 2–3).

The body fluids of terrestrial animals differ considerably from sea water in their total salt content. However, they resemble sea water in the kinds of salts present and in their relative abundance. The total concentration of salts in the body fluids of most invertebrate marine animals is equivalent to that in sea water, about 3.4%. Vertebrates, whether terrestrial, freshwater, or marine, have less than 1% salt in their body fluids.

Most biologists think that living systems arose in the sea. The cells of early organisms became adapted to function optimally in the salt water. As larger animals evolved, body fluids evolved containing a similar pattern of salts. Later, when organisms migrated into fresh

Table 2–3 SOME BIOLOGICALLY IMPORTANT IONS

Name	Formula	Charge
Sodium	Na^+	1 +
Potassium	K^+	1 +
Hydrogen	H^+	1 +
Magnesium	Mg^{2+}	2 +
Calcium	Ca^{2+}	2 +
Iron	Fe^{2+} or Fe^{3+}	2 + [iron(II)] or 3+ [iron(III)]
Ammonium	NH_4^+	1 +
Chloride	Cl^-	1 −
Iodide	I^-	1 −
Carbonate	CO_3^{2-}	2 −
Bicarbonate	HCO_3^-	1 −
Phosphate	PO_4^{3-}	3 −
Acetate	CH_3COO^-	1 −
Sulfate	SO_4^{2-}	2 −
Hydroxide	OH^-	1 −
Nitrate	NO_3^-	1 −
Nitrite	NO_2^-	1 −

One of the most common buffering systems, and one that is important in human blood, is carbonic acid and the bicarbonate ion. Bicarbonate ions are formed in the body as follows:

$$CO_2 + H_2O \rightleftharpoons H_2CO_3 \rightleftharpoons H^+ + HCO_3^-$$

Carbon dioxide   Water   Carbonic acid   Bicarbonate ion

As indicated by the arrows, the reactions are reversible.

When excess hydrogen ions are present in blood or other body fluids, bicarbonate ions combine with them to form carbonic acid, a weak acid.

$$H^+ + HCO_3^- \rightleftharpoons H_2CO_3$$

Carbonic acid

The carbonic acid is unstable and quickly breaks down into carbon dioxide and water.

Buffers also maintain a relatively constant pH when hydroxide ions are added. A buffer may release hydrogen ions, which combine with the hydroxide ions to form water.

$$OH^- + H_2CO_3 \longrightarrow HCO_3^- + H_2O$$

water or onto land, that pattern of salts was retained in their body fluids. Some animals have evolved kidneys and other organs, such as salt glands, that selectively retain or secrete certain ions, resulting in body fluids with somewhat different relative concentrations of salts. The concentration of each ion is determined by the relative rates of its uptake and excretion by the organism.

Although the concentration of salts in cells and body fluids of plants and animals is small, the amounts and concentrations of the respective cations and anions are kept remarkably constant. Any marked change results in impaired cellular functions and may lead to death.

Buffers Minimize pH Change

Many homeostatic mechanisms operate to maintain appropriate pH values. For example, the pH of human blood is about 7.4 and must be maintained within very narrow limits. Should the blood become too acidic (for example, as a result of respiratory disease), coma and death may result. Excessive alkalinity can result in overexcitability of the nervous system and even convulsions.

A **buffer** is a substance or combination of substances that resists changes in pH when an acid or base is added. The buffer accepts or donates hydrogen ions. A buffer consists of a weak acid and a salt of that acid, or a weak base and a salt of that base (Figure 2–20).

Figure 2–20 Buffering is used clinically as a remedy for excess stomach acid. The bubbles are CO_2 from the reaction between an acid (citric acid) and the bicarbonate ion (HCO_3) from sodium bicarbonate. (Charles D. Winters)

SUMMARY

I. The chemical composition and metabolic processes of all living things are very similar; the physical and chemical principles that govern nonliving things also govern living systems.

II. An element is a substance that cannot be decomposed into simpler substances by chemical reactions.
   A. The matter of the universe is composed of 92 elements, ranging from hydrogen, the lightest, to uranium, the heaviest.
   B. Six elements—carbon, hydrogen, oxygen, nitrogen, phosphorus, and calcium—make up about 98% of an organism's content by weight.

III. Atoms are composed of a nucleus containing protons and neutrons and a cloud of electrons around the nucleus in characteristic energy levels and orbitals.
   A. Atoms of the same element that contain different numbers of neutrons, and therefore have different mass numbers, are called *isotopes*.
   B. In a neutral atom, the number of protons equals the number of electrons, so the atom has no net electrical charge.

IV. Atoms are joined by chemical bonds to form larger, more complex structures called *compounds*.
   A. Covalent bonds are strong, stable bonds formed when atoms share electrons, forming molecules.
      1. Covalent bonds are nonpolar if the electrons are shared equally between the two atoms.
      2. Covalent bonds are polar if one atom has a greater affinity for electrons than the other.
   B. An ionic bond is formed when one atom donates electrons to another. An ionic compound is made up of positively charged ions (cations) and negatively charged ions (anions).
   C. Hydrogen bonds are relatively weak bonds formed when a hydrogen atom in one molecule is attracted to a highly electronegative element such as oxygen or nitrogen in another molecule or in another part of the same molecule.

V. The molecular mass of a compound is the sum of the atomic masses of its component atoms.

VI. Oxidation is a chemical process in which a substance loses electrons; reduction is a chemical process in which a substance gains electrons.

VII. Organic compounds are large and complex and contain carbon; inorganic compounds are relatively small and simple.

VIII. Water accounts for a large part of the mass of most organisms, is important in many chemical reactions that occur within living things, and has unique properties that also affect the environment.
   A. Because its molecules are polar, water is an excellent solvent.
   B. Water molecules are cohesive because of the hydrogen bonding between the molecules; water molecules also adhere to many other kinds of substances. Water has a high degree of surface tension because of the cohesiveness of its molecules.
   C. Water has a high specific heat, which helps organisms maintain a relatively constant internal temperature; this property also helps keep the oceans and other large bodies of water at a constant temperature.
   D. Other important properties of water include its high heat of vaporization, its unusual density (ice is less dense than liquid water), its slight tendency to form ions, and its ability to dissolve many different kinds of compounds.

IX. An acid is a substance that dissociates in solution to yield hydrogen ions and an anion; a base generally dissociates in solution to yield hydroxide ions. Acids are proton donors; bases are proton acceptors.
   A. The pH scale extends from 0 to 14, with 7 indicating neutrality. As the pH decreases below 7, the solution is more acidic. As a solution becomes more basic (alkaline), its pH increases from 7 toward 14.
   B. A buffer consists of a weak acid and a salt of that acid, or a weak base and a salt of that base. Buffers resist changes in the pH of a solution when acids or bases are added.
   C. A salt is a compound in which the hydrogen atom of an acid is replaced by some other cation. Salts provide the many mineral ions essential for fluid balance, nerve and muscle function, and many other body functions.

POST-TEST

1. The six elements that make up some 98% of the mass of most organisms are _____, _____, _____, _____, _____, and _____.

2. The chemical symbol for carbon is _____; for hydrogen, _____; and for oxygen, _____.

3. Elements such as cobalt, present in minute amounts in living things, are referred to as _____ _____.

4. The three major types of subatomic particles are _____, _____, and _____.

5. Particles with a negative electric charge and an extremely small mass are _____.

6. The number of protons in the nucleus, called the _____ _____, is written as a subscript to the left of the chemical symbol.

7. The sum of the protons and the neutrons in the nucleus of the atom, termed the _____ _____, is indicated by a superscript to the left of the chemical symbol.

8. Atoms of the same element containing the same number of protons but different numbers of neutrons are _____.

9. Electrons move about the central nucleus of the atom in characteristic regions termed _____.

10. Each orbital may contain at most _____ electrons.

11. The tendency of the negatively charged electrons to fly off into space is countered by their attraction to the atomic nucleus due to the _____ charge of the protons in the nucleus.
12. The atoms of a few elements, such as helium, have a complete outermost shell of electrons; these are called _____ _____.
13. The attraction holding two atoms together is called a _____ _____.
14. Electrically charged atoms are called _____.
15. Positively charged atoms are termed _____, and negatively charged atoms are termed _____.

Match the terms in Column A with their definitions in Column B.

Column A
16. Covalent bond
17. Hydrogen bond
18. Ionic bond
19. Molecule
20. Products
21. Reactants
22. Valence electrons

Column B
a. Electrons in the outer orbit that determine how many electrons an atom can donate, receive, or share
b. The combination of two or more atoms joined by covalent chemical bonds
c. Substances participating in a reaction
d. Substances produced in a chemical reaction
e. Transfer of an electron from an electron donor to an acceptor and the binding together of two particles of opposite charge
f. Atoms joined by sharing electrons
g. Weak bond that holds water molecules together

23. The amount of energy required to change 1 gram of liquid water to 1 gram of water vapor is termed the _____ _____ of water.
24. An acid is a proton _____; a base is a proton _____.
25. A _____ is a substance that resists change in pH when an acid or base is added.

REVIEW QUESTIONS

1. What is the relationship between (a) atoms and molecules, (b) molecules and compounds, (c) atoms and ions?
2. What is a radioisotope? How are radioisotopes used in biological research?
3. How is the bonding capacity of an atom related to the configuration of its electrons? Give an example.
4. Compare ionic and covalent bonds, and give specific examples of each.
5. Write a chemical equation depicting the hydration of: (a) sodium chloride; (b) calcium chloride.
6. What properties of water make it an essential component of living systems?
7. How would a solution with a pH of 5 differ from one with a pH of 9? From one with a pH of 7?
8. Why are buffers important in living organisms? Give a specific example of how a buffer system works.
9. Differentiate clearly among acids, bases, and salts. What are the functions of salts in living organisms?
10. Why must oxidation and reduction occur simultaneously?
11. Describe a reversible reaction that is at equilibrium.
12. What are hydrogen bonds? What is their significance in living systems?

RECOMMENDED READINGS

Baum, S. J., and C. W. Scaife. *Chemistry: A Life Science Approach*, 3rd ed. Macmillan, New York, 1987. A chemistry text emphasizing subjects of special interest to biology students.

Bettelheim, F. A., and J. March. *Introduction to General, Organic and Biochemistry*, 3rd ed. Saunders College Publishing, Philadelphia, 1991. A very readable reference text for those who would like to know more about the chemistry basic to life.

Mohner, V. A. The challenge of acid rain. *Scientific American*, August, 1988, Vol. 259, No. 2. A discussion of an important environmental problem.

CHAPTER 3

The Chemistry of Life: Organic Compounds

OUTLINE

The carbon atom

Isomers

Functional groups

Polymers

Carbohydrates

Lipids

Proteins

Nucleic acids

Most of the chemical compounds present in living organisms contain backbones of covalently bonded carbon. These biological molecules are known as **organic compounds,** because at one time they were thought to be produced only by living (organic) organisms. In 1928 the German chemist Friedrich Wöhler synthesized urea, a metabolic waste product. Since that time, scientists have learned that any organic compound found in living organisms can be synthesized and that many organic compounds exist that are not found in organisms.

Perhaps because it can form a greater variety of molecules than any other element, carbon has emerged as the central component of organic compounds. More than five million organic compounds have been identified. The carbon atom can form bonds with a greater number of different elements than any other type of atom. Hydrogen, oxygen, and nitrogen are atoms frequently bonded

to carbon. Organic compounds that consist of only carbon and hydrogen are known as **hydrocarbons.** Living organisms use hydrocarbon skeletons to build diverse organic compounds. Fossil fuels are hydrocarbons formed from organic compounds originating in organisms that lived and died millions of years ago.

Organic compounds are the main structural components of cells and tissues (Figure 3–1). They participate in and regulate metabolic reactions, transmit information, and provide energy for life processes. In this chapter, we focus on some of the major groups of organic compounds that are important in living organisms, including carbohydrates, lipids, proteins, and nucleic acids (DNA and RNA). Most of these compounds are constructed in the cell from simpler molecular components. For example, protein molecules are built from smaller compounds called amino acids.

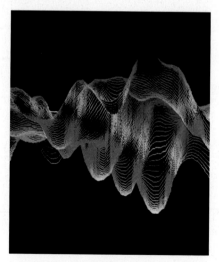

False-color scanning tunneling micrograph (STM) of DNA. An image is formed by scanning a fine point just above the specimen surface and electronically recording the height of the point as it moves. This image shows a section of a double-stranded DNA molecule with the coils of the helix at center (row of orange/yellow peaks). (Lawrence Berkeley Laboratory/Science Photo Library/Photo Researchers, Inc.)

After you have studied this chapter you should be able to

1. Describe the properties of carbon that make it the central component of organic compounds.
2. Distinguish among three principal types of isomers.
3. Identify the major functional groups present in organic compounds.
4. Compare the major groups of organic compounds—carbohydrates, fats, proteins, and nucleic acids—with respect to their chemical composition and function.
5. Distinguish among monosaccharides, disaccharides, and polysaccharides, and discuss those of major importance in living things.
6. Distinguish among neutral fats, phospholipids, and steroids, and describe the composition, characteristics, and biological functions of each group.
7. Describe the functions and chemical structure of proteins.
8. Outline the levels of organization of protein molecules.
9. Describe the chemical structure of nucleotides and nucleic acids, and discuss the importance of these compounds in living organisms.

THE CHEMISTRY OF LIVING THINGS IS ORGANIZED AROUND THE CARBON ATOM

Carbon's unusual properties permit formation of the large, complex molecules essential to life. A carbon atom has a total of six electrons—two in its first energy level and four in its second energy level. Two carbon atoms can share two electron pairs with each other, forming double bonds (—C=C—). In some compounds, triple carbon-to-carbon bonds (—C≡C—) are formed. Carbon chains can be unbranched or branched, and carbon atoms can also be joined into rings (Figure 3–2). In some compounds, rings and chains are joined.

The shape of a molecule is important in determining its biological properties and function. Carbon-containing molecules have a three-dimensional structure due to the tetrahedral nature of their bond angles. When a carbon atom forms four covalent single bonds with other atoms, the electron orbitals in its outer energy level become elongated and project from the carbon atom toward the corners of a tetrahedron (Figure 3–3). The angle between any two of these bonds is about 109.5 degrees. This bond angle is similar in diverse organic compounds.

(a)

(b)

Figure 3–1 Carbon is the basis of organic compounds, of which all living things are made. (a) Elemental forms of carbon. Artificial diamonds, a pure form of carbon, are seen at the bottom. Graphite, another form of carbon, is seen at the top. Graphite is a component of pencil lead. (b) Carbon accounts for more than half the dry weight of an organism. The chemistry of this ruby-throated hummingbird (*Archilochus calobris*) (and that of the plant on which it is feeding) is organized around the carbon atom.
(a, General Electric; b, Dwight R. Kuhn)

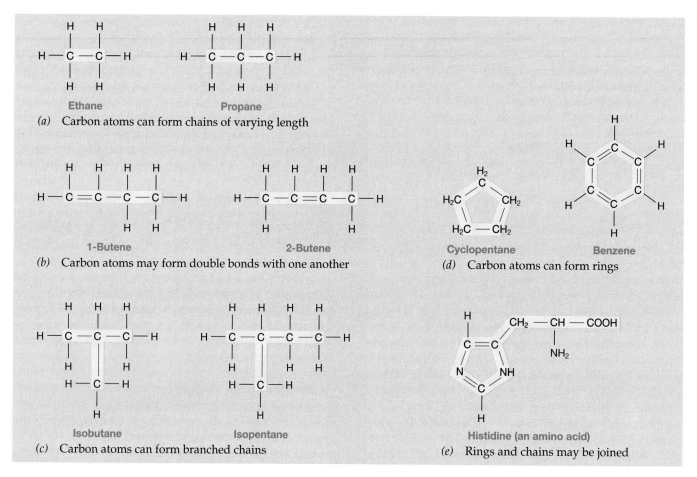

Figure 3–2   Some simple organic compounds. These structural formulas illustrate common variations in the architecture of organic molecules. Note that each carbon atom has four covalent bonds.

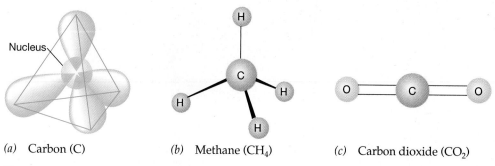

(a)   Carbon (C)   (b)   Methane (CH₄)   (c)   Carbon dioxide (CO₂)

Figure 3–3   Carbon bonds. A carbon atom can form four covalent bonds. (a) The bonds of a carbon atom point to the four corners of a tetrahedron. This arrangement maximizes the distance between the atoms bonded to the carbon atom. (b) Methane consists of a single carbon atom bonded to four hydrogen atoms.

The hydrogens are bonded symmetrically around the carbon at the points of a tetrahedron. (c) In carbon dioxide, each oxygen atom is connected to the carbon atom by a double bond. The bonds are parallel, and the molecule assumes a linear configuration.

Generally, there is freedom of rotation around each carbon-to-carbon single bond. This property permits organic molecules to be flexible and to assume a variety of shapes, depending on the extent to which each single bond is rotated. Double and triple bonds do not permit rotation, so regions of a molecule with such bonds tend not to be flexible.

ISOMERS HAVE THE SAME MOLECULAR FORMULA

Compounds that have the same molecular formula but different structures and thus different properties are called **isomers.** Isomers do not have identical physical or chemical properties and may have different common names. Cells can distinguish between isomers: Usually, one is biologically active and the other is not. Three types of isomers are structural isomers, geometric isomers, and enantiomers.

Structural isomers are compounds that differ in the covalent arrangements of their atoms (Figure 3–4). For example, there are two structural isomers of the four-carbon hydrocarbon butane, one with a straight chain and the other with a branched chain (isobutane). The larger the compound is, the more structural isomers are possible. There are only two structural isomers of butane, but there may be up to 366,319 isomers of $C_{20}H_{42}$.

Geometric isomers are compounds that are identical with regard to the arrangement of their covalent bonds but differ in the order in which groups are arranged in space. Geometric isomers, also called *cis-trans* isomers, are present in some compounds with carbon-to-carbon double bonds. Because double bonds are not flexible like single bonds, atoms joined to the carbons of a double bond cannot rotate freely about the axis of the bonds. The *cis-trans* isomers may be drawn as shown in Figure 3–4*b*. The designation *cis* indicates that the two larger components are on the same side of the double bond. If the two larger components are on opposite sides of the double bond, the compound is designated a *trans* isomer.

Ethanol (C_2H_6O)   Dimethyl ether (C_2H_6O)

(a)   Structural isomers

trans-2-butene   *Cis*-2-butene

(b)   Geometric isomers

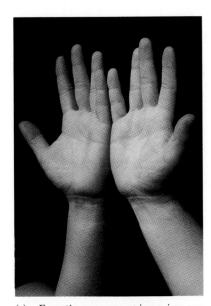

(c)   Enantiomers are mirror images   Enantiomers of lactic acid

Figure 3–4   Isomers. Different compounds can have the same molecular formula, but with the atoms arranged differently. (*a*) Structural isomers differ in the covalent arrangement of their atoms. (*b*) Geometric, or *cis-trans*, isomers have identical covalent bonds but differ in the order in which groups of atoms are arranged in space. (*c*) Enantiomers are molecules that are mirror images of one another.   (*c*, Dennis Drenner)

Enantiomers are molecules that are mirror images of one another. Recall that the four groups bonded to a single carbon atom are arranged at the vertices of a tetrahedron. If the four bonded groups are all different, the central carbon is described as asymmetric. Figure 3–4c illustrates that the four groups can be arranged about the asymmetric carbon in two different ways that are mirror images of each other. The two molecules are enantiomers if they cannot be superimposed on one another no matter how they are rotated in space.

Enantiomers are currently designated D- or L- based on the absolute configuration of the groups bonded to the tetrahedral carbon atom. The three-carbon compound glyceraldehyde is used as the standard for the description of all enantiomers. The D-isomer of any compound is the one that has the last asymmetric carbon in the same orientation as D-glyceraldehyde. Compounds related to L-glyceraldehyde are referred to as L-isomers.

When chemists synthesize organic compounds in their laboratories, a mixture containing equal amounts of D- and L-isomers is produced. In cells, only one of the two enantiomers of a compound is produced. For example, most sugars important for cells are D-sugars. Although enantiomers have similar chemical properties and identical physical properties (except for the direction in which they rotate plane-polarized light), cells distinguish between the two isomers, and only one form is biologically active.

FUNCTIONAL GROUPS FORM BONDS WITH OTHER MOLECULES

The hydrocarbon backbone of an organic compound does not interact readily with other compounds. However, one or more of the hydrogen atoms bonded to the carbon skeleton of a hydrocarbon can be replaced by other groups of atoms. These groups of atoms, referred to as **functional groups,** readily form associations such as ionic and hydrogen bonds with other molecules. In this way functional groups help determine the types of chemical reactions in which the compound participates.

Each class of organic compounds is characterized by the presence of one or more specific functional groups. For example, as illustrated in Table 3–1, alcohols contain functional groups known as hydroxyl groups. Note that the symbol R is used to represent the remainder of the molecule of which the functional group is a part.

An important property of the functional groups found in biological molecules is their solubility in water. Positively and negatively charged functional groups are water-soluble because they associate strongly with the polar water molecule.

Bonds between carbon and hydrogen are nonpolar, so a functional group containing only a carbon-hydrogen bond such as a methyl group ($-CH_3$) is also nonpolar. Oxygen-hydrogen and nitrogen-hydrogen bonds are polar; they have a partial positive electrical charge at the hydrogen end of the bond and a partial negative electrical charge at the oxygen or nitrogen end. Thus, hydroxyl and amino groups are polar. Double bonds formed between carbon and oxygen ($C=O$) are also polar; there is a partial positive charge at the carbon end and a partial negative charge at the oxygen end. Consequently, carboxyl and aldehyde groups are polar. Carboxyl groups have acidic properties; the hydrogen ion tends to dissociate as an H^+ ion. Functional groups that are polar interact with charged ions or with other polar groups. Compounds containing polar functional groups tend to dissolve in water because the polar groups attract water molecules.

Most compounds present in cells contain two or more different functional groups. For example, every amino acid (amino acids are molecular subunits of proteins) contains at least two functional groups—an amino group and a carboxyl group. The chemical properties of these functional groups determine the general properties of amino acids. However, many amino acids contain additional functional groups that determine the specific properties of each type of amino acid. When we know what kinds of functional groups are present in an organic compound, we can predict its chemical behavior.

MANY BIOLOGICAL MOLECULES ARE POLYMERS

Many biological molecules such as proteins and nucleic acids are very large, consisting of thousands of atoms. Such giant molecules are known as **macromolecules.** Many macromolecules are **polymers,** produced by linking together small organic compounds called **monomers** (Figure 3–5). Just as all the words in this book have been written by arranging the 26 letters of the alphabet in various combinations, monomers can be

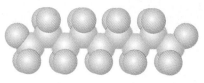

Figure 3–5 Monomers may be linked together to form polymers. A small polyethylene polymer is shown here. The two-carbon compound ethylene (C_2H_4) is the monomer linked together to form this polymer.

Table 3–1 SOME BIOLOGICALLY IMPORTANT FUNCTIONAL GROUPS

Functional Group	Structural Formula	Class of Compounds Characterized by Group	Example	Description
Hydroxyl	R—OH	Alcohols	Ethanol (the alcohol contained in beverage)	Polar because electronegative oxygen attracts covalent electrons
Amino	R—NH₂	Amines	Amino acid	Ionic; amino group acts as base
Carboxyl	R—C—OH (with =O)	Carboxylic acids (organic acids)	Amino acid	Ionic; the H can dissociate as an H⁺ ion
Ester	R—C—O—R (with =O)	Esters	Methyl acetate	Related to carboxyl group, but has hydrocarbon group in place of the OH hydrogen; polar
Carbonyl	R—C—H (with =O)	Aldehydes	Formaldehyde	Carbonyl carbon bonded to at least one H atom; polar
	R—C—R (with =O)	Ketones	Acetone	Carbonyl group bonded to two other carbons; polar
Methyl	R—CH₃	Component of many organic compounds	Methane	Nonpolar
Phosphate	R—O—P—OH (with =O and OH)	Organic phosphates	Phosphate ester (as found in ATP)	Dissociated form of phosphoric acid; the phosphate ion is covalently bonded by one of its oxygen atoms to one of the carbons; ionic
Sulfhydryl	R—SH	Thiols	Cysteine	Help stabilize internal structure of proteins

Table 3–2 SOME OF THE GROUPS OF BIOLOGICALLY IMPORTANT ORGANIC COMPOUNDS

Class of Compounds	Component Elements	Description	How to Recognize	Principal Function in Living Systems
Carbohydrates	C, H, O	Contain approximately 1 C:2 H:1 O (but make allowance for loss of oxygen and hydrogen when sugar units are linked)	Count the carbons, hydrogens, and oxygens.	Cellular fuel; energy storage; structural component of plant cell walls; component of other compounds such as nucleic acids and glycoproteins
		1. Monosaccharides (simple sugars)—mainly five-carbon (pentose) molecules such as ribose or six-carbon (hexose) molecules such as glucose and fructose	Look for the ring shapes: hexose or pentose	Cellular fuel; components of other compounds
		2. Disaccharides—two sugar units linked by a glycosidic bond, e.g., maltose, sucrose	Count sugar units.	Components of other compounds
		3. Polysaccharides—many sugar units linked by glycosidic bonds, e.g., glycogen, cellulose	Count sugar units.	Energy storage; structural components of plant cell walls
Lipids	C, H, O	Contain less oxygen relative to carbon and hydrogen than do carbohydrates		Energy storage; cellular fuel, structural components of cells; thermal insulation
		1. Neutral fats. Combination of glycerol with one to three fatty acids. Monacylglycerol contains one fatty acid; diacylglycerol contains two fatty acids; triacylglycerol contains three fatty acids. If fatty acids contain double carbon-to-carbon linkages (C=C), they are unsaturated; otherwise they are saturated.	Look for glycerol at one end of molecule: $H-\overset{\mid}{\underset{\mid}{C}}-O-$ $H-\overset{\mid}{\underset{\mid}{C}}-O-$ $H-\overset{\mid}{\underset{\mid}{C}}-O-$	Cellular fuel; energy storage

grouped together to form an almost infinite variety of larger molecules. And just as we use different words to convey information, cells use different molecules to convey information. The thousands of different complex organic compounds present in living things are constructed from about 40 small, simple monomers. For example, the 20 common types of amino acid monomers can be linked together end to end in countless ways to form the polymers we know as proteins.

Each organism is unique owing to differences in monomer sequence within its DNA, the polymer that constitutes the genes. Cells and tissues within the same organism are also different owing to variations in their component polymers. Muscle tissue is different from brain tissue in large part because of differences in the types and sequences of amino acids in their proteins. Ultimately this protein structure is dictated by the sequence of monomers within the DNA of the organism.

The synthetic process by which monomers are covalently linked is called **condensation**. Because the *equivalent* of a molecule of water is removed during the reactions that combine monomers, the term *dehydration synthesis* is sometimes used to describe the process. However, in biological systems, synthesis of a polymer is not simply the reverse of breakdown (which involves adding water). Synthetic processes require energy and

Table 3–2 SOME OF THE GROUPS OF BIOLOGICALLY IMPORTANT ORGANIC COMPOUNDS (*continued*)

Class of Compound	Component Elements	Description	How to Recognize	Principal Function in Living Systems
		2. Phospholipids. Composed of glycerol attached to one or two fatty acids and to an organic base containing phosphorus	Look for glycerol and side chain containing phosphorus and nitrogen.	Components of cell membranes
		3. Steroids. Complex molecules containing carbon atoms arranged in four interlocking rings (three rings contain six carbon atoms each and the fourth ring contains five)	Look for four interlocking rings:	Some are hormones; others include cholesterol, bile salts, vitamin D.
		4. Carotenoids. Red and yellow pigments; consist of isoprene units	Look for isoprene units.	Retinal (important in photoreception) and vitamin A are formed from carotenoids.
Proteins	C, H, O, N, usually S	One or more polypeptides (chains of amino acids) coiled or folded in characteristic shapes	Look for amino acid units joined by C—N bonds.	Serve as enzymes; structural components; muscle proteins; hemoglobin
Nucleic acids	C, H, O, N, P	Backbone composed of alternating pentose and phosphate groups, from which nitrogenous bases project. DNA contains the sugar deoxyribose and the bases guanine, cytosine, adenine, and thymine. RNA contains the sugar ribose and the bases guanine, cytosine, adenine, and uracil. Each molecular subunit, called a *nucleotide*, consists of a pentose, a phosphate, and a nitrogenous base.	Look for a pentose-phosphate backbone. DNA forms a double helix.	Storage, transmission, and expression of genetic information

are regulated by different enzymes (proteins that regulate chemical reactions).

Polymers can be degraded to their component monomers by **hydrolysis** (which means "to break with water"). Bonds between monomers are broken by the addition of water. A hydrogen from the water molecule attaches to one monomer, and the hydroxyl from the water attaches to the adjacent monomer. Specific examples of dehydration and hydrolysis reactions are presented as we discuss the groups of organic compounds in more detail. The principal groups of biologically important organic compounds are summarized in Table 3–2.

CARBOHYDRATES INCLUDE SUGARS, STARCHES, AND CELLULOSE

Sugars, starches, and cellulose are **carbohydrates.** Sugars and **starches** serve as energy sources for cells; **cellulose** is the main structural component of the walls that surround plant cells. Carbohydrates contain carbon, hydrogen, and oxygen atoms in a ratio of approximately one carbon to two hydrogens to one oxygen $(CH_2O)_n$. The term *carbohydrate*, meaning "hydrate (water) of carbon," reflects the 2:1 ratio of hydrogen to oxygen, the same ratio found in water (H_2O). Carbohydrates contain one sugar (monosaccharides), two

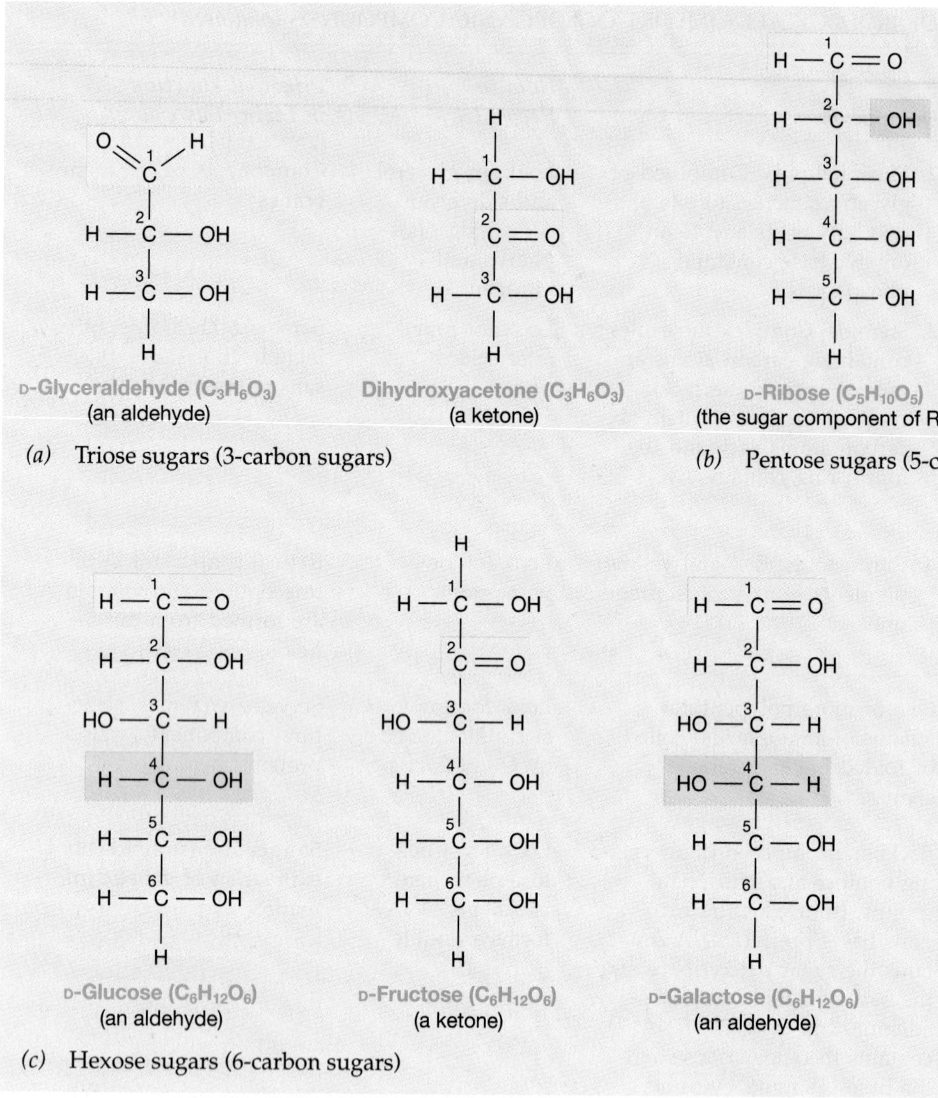

Figure 3-6 Structural formulas of some important monosaccharides (simple sugars). The monosaccharides are represented here as straight chains, called *stick formulas*. Although it is convenient to show monosaccharides in this form, they are more accurately depicted as ring structures (see Figure 3-7). Note that glucose, fructose, and galactose are structural isomers—they have the same chemical formula, $C_6H_{12}O_6$, but their atoms are arranged differently.

(a) Triose sugars (3-carbon sugars)

(b) Pentose sugars (5-carbon sugars)

(c) Hexose sugars (6-carbon sugars)

D-Glyceraldehyde ($C_3H_6O_3$) (an aldehyde)

Dihydroxyacetone ($C_3H_6O_3$) (a ketone)

D-Ribose ($C_5H_{10}O_5$) (the sugar component of RNA)

Deoxyribose ($C_5H_{10}O_4$) (the sugar component of DNA)

D-Glucose ($C_6H_{12}O_6$) (an aldehyde)

D-Fructose ($C_6H_{12}O_6$) (a ketone)

D-Galactose ($C_6H_{12}O_6$) (an aldehyde)

sugar units (disaccharides), or many sugar units (polysaccharides).

Monosaccharides Are Simple Sugars

Monosaccharides are simple sugars that typically contain from three to seven carbon atoms. The simplest carbohydrates are the two three-carbon sugars (trioses), glyceraldehyde and dihydroxyacetone (Figure 3-6). Ribose and deoxyribose are common pentoses, sugars that contain five carbons; they are components of nucleic acids (DNA, RNA, and related compounds). Glucose, fructose, galactose, and other sugars that consist of six carbons are called **hexoses.**

Glucose ($C_6H_{12}O_6$), the most abundant monosaccharide, is extremely important in life processes. During photosynthesis, algae and plants produce glucose from carbon dioxide and water using sunlight as an energy source. Then, during cellular respiration, cells break the bonds of the glucose molecule, releasing the stored en-

ergy so that it can be used for cellular work. Glucose is also used as a component in the synthesis of other types of compounds such as amino acids and fatty acids. So central is glucose in metabolism that its concentration is carefully kept at a homeostatic (relatively constant) level in the blood of humans and other complex animals.

In the glucose molecule a hydroxyl group is bonded to each carbon except one; that carbon is double-bonded to an oxygen atom, forming a carbonyl group. In glucose the carbonyl group is at the end of the chain, so glucose is an aldehyde; if the carbonyl group is at any other position, the monosaccharide is a ketone. (By convention, the carbon skeleton of a sugar is numbered beginning with the carbon at or nearest to the carbonyl end of the open chain.)

Glucose and fructose are structural isomers—they have identical molecular formulas, but their atoms are arranged differently. In fructose, a ketone, the double-bonded oxygen is linked to a carbon within the chain

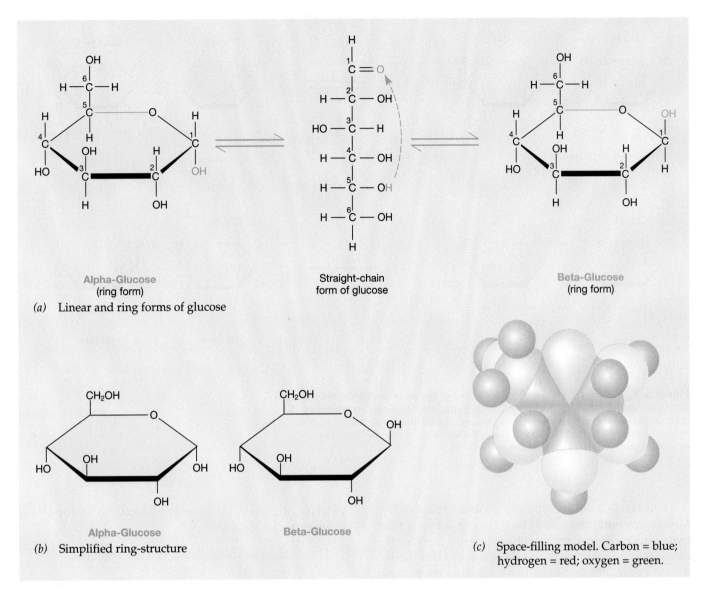

Alpha-Glucose
(ring form)

Straight-chain
form of glucose

Beta-Glucose
(ring form)

(a) Linear and ring forms of glucose

Alpha-Glucose

Beta-Glucose

(b) Simplified ring-structure

(c) Space-filling model. Carbon = blue;
hydrogen = red; oxygen = green.

Figure 3–7 Ring forms of glucose. (*a*) When the straight-chain form of glucose (center) dissolves in water, the molecule bends so that the —OH group on carbon 5 comes close to the ═O on carbon 1. The hydrogen moves from one oxygen to the other. This permits carbon 1 to bond with the oxygen on carbon 5, producing a ring structure. Two isomeric forms are possible that differ in the orientation of the —OH group. In α-glucose, the —OH of carbon 1 is below the ring; in β-glucose, above the ring. The thick, tapered bonds in the lower portion of each ring indicate that the molecule is a three-dimensional structure. The thickest bonds represent the part of the molecule that would project out of the page toward you. (*b*) Simplified drawing of the ring structure of glucose. A carbon atom is assumed by convention to be present at each angle in the ring unless another atom is shown. Most hydrogen atoms have been omitted. (*c*) A space-filling model of a glucose molecule.

rather than to a terminal carbon as in glucose (which is an aldehyde). Because their atoms are arranged differently, the two sugars have different chemical properties. For example, fructose tastes sweeter than glucose.

Glucose and galactose differ from one another in another way. Both are hexoses and both are aldehydes. However, they differ in the arrangement of their atoms around carbon atom 4. They are mirror images, or enantiomers.

The "stick" formulas in Figure 3–6 give a clear but somewhat unrealistic picture of the structures of some common monosaccharides. As has been discussed, mol-

ecules are not the simple two-dimensional structures depicted on a printed page. In fact, the properties of each compound depend in part on its three-dimensional structure. Thus, three-dimensional formulas are helpful in understanding the relationship between molecular structure and biological function. Molecules of glucose and other monosaccharides in solution are not extended straight carbon chains as shown in Figure 3–6, but rather boat-shaped or chair-shaped rings. They assume these configurations when a covalent bond connects carbon 1 to the oxygen attached to carbon 5 or carbon 4 (Figure 3–7).

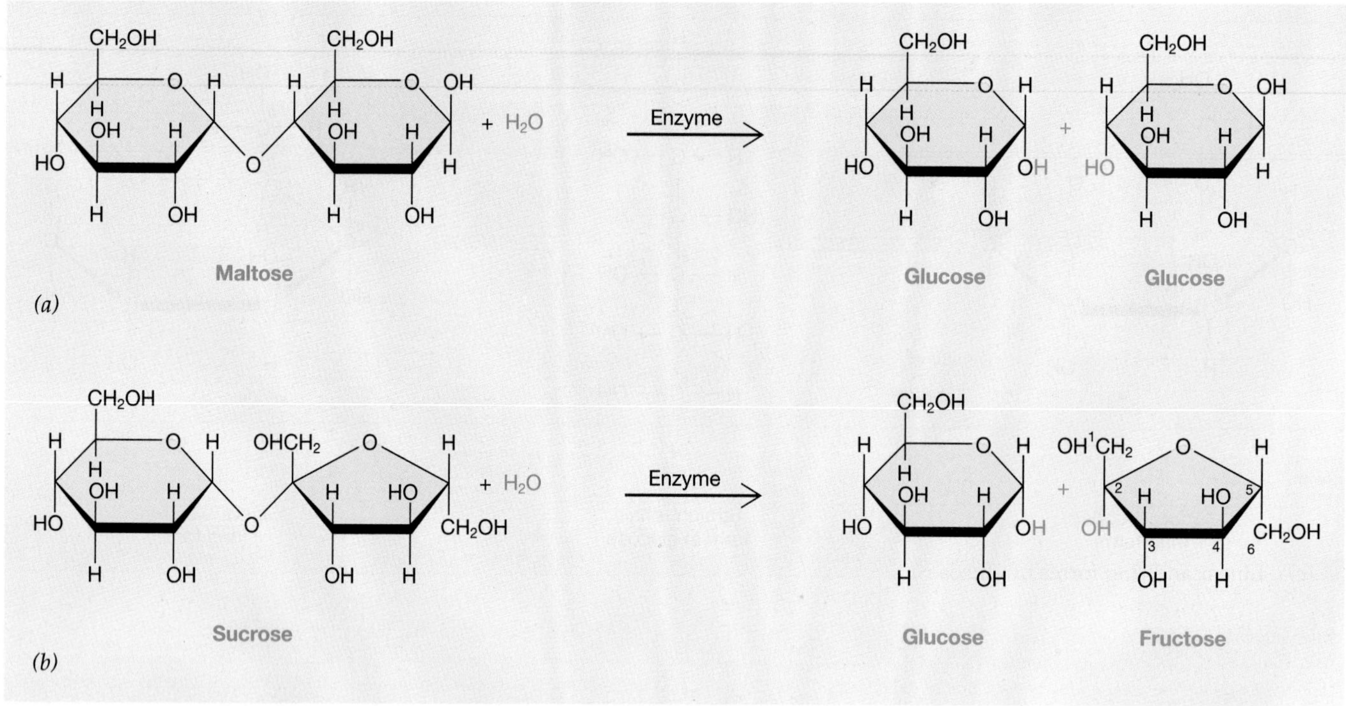

Figure 3–8 A disaccharide can be cleaved to yield two monosaccharide units. (*a*) Maltose may be broken down (as it is during digestion) to form two molecules of glucose. This is a hydrolysis reaction that requires the addition of water. (*b*) Sucrose can be hydrolyzed to yield a molecule of glucose and a molecule of fructose. Note that an enzyme, a protein catalyst, is needed to promote these reactions.

Glucose in solution typically exists as a ring of five carbons and one oxygen. When glucose forms a ring, two isomeric forms are possible, differing only in the orientation of a hydroxyl (—OH) group. When the hydroxyl group attached to carbon 1 is below the plane of the ring, the glucose is designated *α-glucose*. When this same hydroxyl group is above the plane of the ring, the compound is designated *β-glucose.*

Disaccharides Consist of Two Monosaccharide Units

A **disaccharide** (two sugars) consists of two monosaccharides covalently bonded to one another. The two monosaccharide units are joined by a **glycosidic linkage,** which generally forms between carbon 1 of one molecule and carbon 4 of the other molecule. The disaccharide maltose (malt sugar) consists of two covalently liked *α-glucose* units. Sucrose, the sugar we use to sweeten our foods, consists of a glucose unit combined with a fructose unit. Lactose (the sugar present in milk) is composed of one molecule of glucose and one of galactose.

A disaccharide can be hydrolyzed, that is, split by the addition of water, into two monosaccharide units.

During digestion, maltose is hydrolyzed to form two molecules of glucose:

$$\text{Maltose} + \text{Water} \longrightarrow \text{Glucose} + \text{Glucose}$$

Similarly, sucrose is hydrolyzed to form glucose and fructose:

$$\text{Sucrose} + \text{Water} \longrightarrow \text{Glucose} + \text{Fructose}$$

Structural formulas for the compounds in these reactions are shown in Figure 3–8.

Polysaccharides Are Large Polymers

The most abundant carbohydrates are the **polysaccharides,** a group that includes starches, glycogen, and celluloses. A polysaccharide is a macromolecule consisting of repeating units of simple sugars, usually glucose. Although the precise number of sugar units present varies, typically thousands of units are present in a single molecule. The polysaccharide may be a single long chain or a branched chain. Because they are composed of different isomers of glucose or because the glucose units are arranged differently, polysaccharides have very different properties.

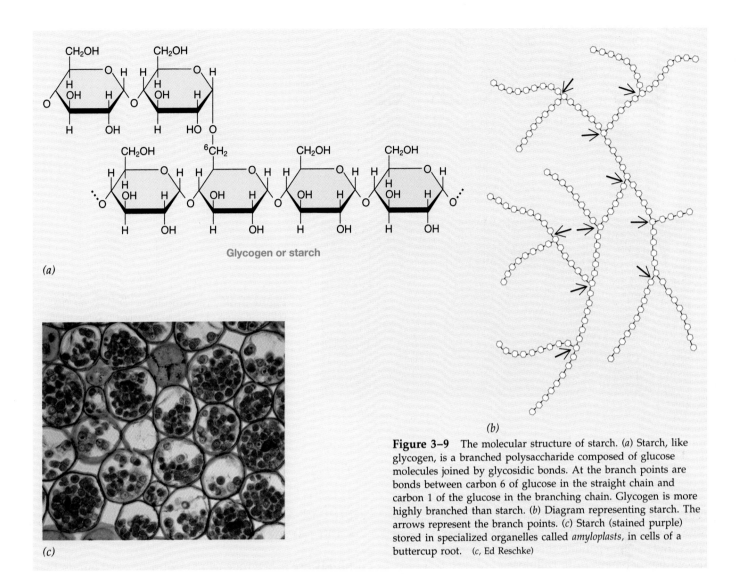

Figure 3–9 The molecular structure of starch. (*a*) Starch, like glycogen, is a branched polysaccharide composed of glucose molecules joined by glycosidic bonds. At the branch points are bonds between carbon 6 of glucose in the straight chain and carbon 1 of the glucose in the branching chain. Glycogen is more highly branched than starch. (*b*) Diagram representing starch. The arrows represent the branch points. (*c*) Starch (stained purple) stored in specialized organelles called *amyloplasts*, in cells of a buttercup root. (*c*, Ed Reschke)

Starch, the typical storage form of carbohydrate in plants, is a polymer consisting of α-glucose subunits. The monomers are joined by alpha 1—4 linkages (Figure 3–9). Starch occurs in two forms, amylose and amylopectin. Amylose, the simpler form, is unbranched. Amylopectin, the more common form, usually consists of about 1000 units in a branched chain. Branching takes place at about every 20 to 25 units and involves a C-1 to C-6 glycosidic linkage.

Plants store starch as granules within specialized organelles called **plastids.** When energy is needed for cellular work, the plant can hydrolyze the starch, releasing the glucose subunits. Humans and other animals that eat plant foods have enzymes that hydrolyze starch.

Glycogen (sometimes referred to as *animal starch*) is the form in which glucose is stored in animal tissues. This polysaccharide is highly branched and more water-soluble than plant starch. Glycogen is stored mainly in liver and muscle cells.

Carbohydrates are the most abundant group of organic compounds on Earth, and cellulose is the most abundant carbohydrate, accounting for 50% or more of all the carbon in plants (Figure 3–10). Wood is about half cellulose, and cotton is at least 90% cellulose. Plant cells are surrounded by strong supporting cell walls consisting mainly of cellulose. Cellulose is an insoluble polysaccharide composed of many glucose molecules joined together. The bonds joining these sugar units are different from those in starch.

Recall that in starch the subunits are α-glucose and the glycosidic bonds are alpha 1—4 linkages. In cellulose β-glucose is the monomer and the linkages are beta 1—4 bonds. These bonds are not split by the enzymes that hydrolyze the alpha linkages in starch. Humans, like most organisms, do not have enzymes that can digest cellulose and cannot use cellulose as a nutrient. However, as discussed in Chapter 40, cellulose is an important component of dietary fiber and helps keep the digestive tract functioning properly. Some micro-

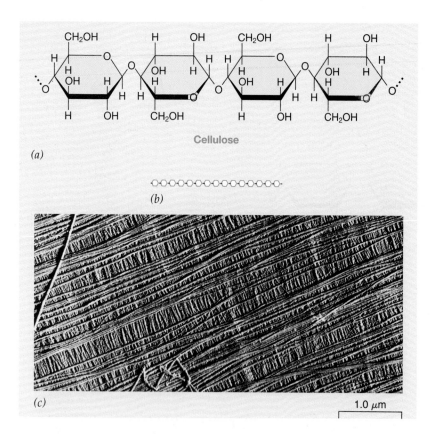

Cellulose

(a)

(b)

(c)

1.0 μm

Figure 3–10   The structure of cellulose. (a) The cellulose molecule is an unbranched polysaccharide composed of approximately 10,000 glucose units joined by glycosidic bonds. (b) A more diagrammatic representation of cellulose structure. Each hexagon represents a glucose molecule bonded by a glycosidic bond to the adjacent glucose molecule. (c) An electron micrograph of cellulose fibers from the cell wall of a marine alga.   (c, Omikron/Photo Researchers, Inc.)

organisms can digest cellulose to glucose. In fact, cellulose-digesting bacteria live in the digestive systems of cows and sheep, enabling these grass-eating animals to obtain nourishment from cellulose.

Some Modified and Complex Carbohydrates Are Important Biological Molecules

Many derivatives of monosaccharides are important biological molecules. The amino sugars glucosamine and galactosamine are compounds in which a hydroxyl group (—OH) is replaced by an amino group (—NH$_2$). Galactosamine is present in cartilage. Glucosamine is the molecular unit present in **chitin,** the main component of the external skeletons of insects, crayfish, and other arthropods (Figure 3–11). A tough modified polysaccharide, chitin is also found in the cell walls of fungi.

Carbohydrates may also be combined with proteins to form **glycoproteins,** compounds present on the outer surface of many eukaryotic cells. Most proteins secreted by cells are glycoproteins. Carbohydrates can combine with lipids to form **glycolipids,** compounds present on the surfaces of animal cells that are important in interactions among cells.

LIPIDS ARE FATS OR FATLIKE SUBSTANCES

Lipids are a heterogeneous group of compounds that have a greasy or oily consistency and are relatively insoluble in water. Like carbohydrates, lipids are composed of carbon, hydrogen, and oxygen atoms. However, they have relatively less oxygen in proportion to carbon and hydrogen than do carbohydrates. Oxygen atoms are characteristic of hydrophilic (water-loving) functional groups, so lipids, with little oxygen, are much less soluble in water than most carbohydrates; in fact, lipids tend to be hydrophobic (water-hating). Among the groups of lipids important biologically are the neutral fats, phospholipids, steroids, carotenoids (red and yellow plant pigments), and waxes. Lipids are important biological fuels, serve as structural components of cell membranes, and some are important hormones.

Neutral Fats Are Composed of Glycerol and Fatty Acids

The most abundant lipids in living things are the **neutral fats.** These compounds are an economical form of

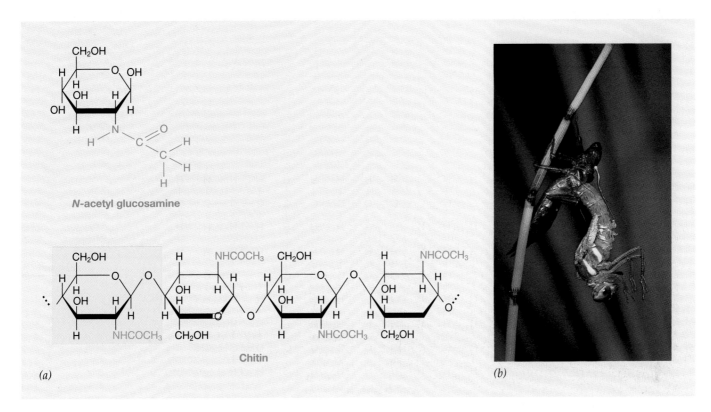

N-acetyl glucosamine

Chitin

(a)

(b)

Figure 3–11 Chitin is a polysaccharide that rivals cellulose as the most common organic compound in the ecosphere. (*a*) The amino sugar *N*-acetyl glucosamine (NAG) is the monomer found in chitin. The polymer chitin consists of NAG subunits joined by glycosidic bonds. (*b*) Chitin is an important component of the armor-like exoskeleton (outer covering) of arthropods such as this dragonfly. In the process of molting, shown here, the dragonfly sheds its exoskeleton so that it can grow. A new, larger exoskeleton develops. (*b*, Dwight R. Kuhn)

fuel reserves storage because they yield more than twice as much energy per gram as do carbohydrates. Carbohydrates and proteins can be transformed by enzymes into fats and stored within the cells of adipose (fat) tissue.

A neutral fat consists of glycerol joined to one, two, or three fatty acids. **Glycerol** is a three-carbon alcohol that contains three —OH groups (Figure 3–12). A **fatty acid** is a long, straight chain of carbon atoms with a carboxyl group (—COOH) at one end. About 30 different fatty acids are commonly found in lipids, and they typically have an even number of carbon atoms. For example, butyric acid, present in rancid butter, has four carbon atoms, and oleic acid, the most widely distributed fatty acid in nature, has 18 carbon atoms.

Saturated fatty acids contain the maximum possible number of hydrogen atoms, whereas **unsaturated fatty acids** contain some carbon atoms that are double-bonded with one another and are not fully saturated with hydrogen. Fatty acids with more than one double bond are called **polyunsaturated fatty acids.** Fats containing unsaturated fatty acids are oils, and most of them are liquid at room temperature. Saturated fats tend to be solid at room temperature; butter and animal fat are examples. At least two fatty acids (linoleic and arachidonic) are essential nutrients that must be included in the diet because the human body cannot synthesize them.

When a glycerol molecule combines chemically with one fatty acid, a **monoacylglycerol** (sometimes called *monoglyceride*) is formed. When two fatty acids combine with a glycerol, a **diacylglycerol** (or *diglyceride*) is formed, and when three fatty acids combine with one glycerol molecule, a **triacylglycerol** (or *triglyceride*) is formed. In combining with glycerol, the carboxyl end of the fatty acid attaches to the oxygen of one of glycerol's —OH groups, forming a covalent linkage known as an **ester bond.** In the overall reaction that produces a fat, a molecule of water is removed from the glycerol and fatty acid. During digestion the neutral fats are hydrolyzed to produce fatty acids and glycerol.

Phospholipids Are Components of Cell Membranes

Phospholipids represent an important class of lipids called **amphipathic lipids,** which form cell membranes. In amphipathic molecules, one end is **hydrophilic** and the other end is **hydrophobic.** A phospholipid consists of a glycerol molecule attached to two fatty acids and to

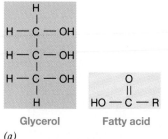

Glycerol   Fatty acid

(a)

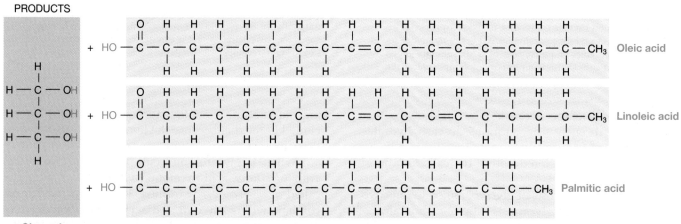

A triacylglycerol

(b)

(c)

Figure 3–12 Neutral fats. (*a*) Structures of glycerol and of a fatty acid. The carboxyl (—COOH) group is present in all fatty acids. The R represents the remainder of the molecule, which varies with each type of fatty acid. (*b*) Hydrolysis of a triacylglycerol yields glycerol plus three fatty acids. Note that the triacylglycerol is an unsaturated fat— two of its fatty acid components contain double bonds between carbon atoms. (*c*) Honeybees on a brood comb. The comb is composed of wax secreted by special abdominal glands of the bees. It is a compound consisting of fatty acids and alcohols, and although it is classified as a lipid, it can be digested by very few animals. (*c*, Charles D. Winters)

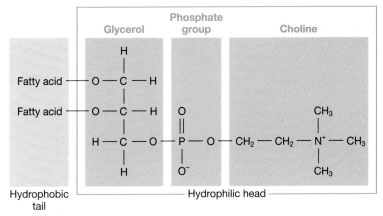

(a) Phosphatidic acid

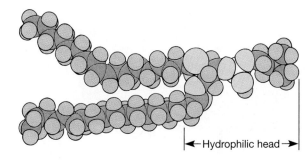

(b) Lecithin

Figure 3–13 Phospholipids. (*a*) Many phospholipids are derivatives of phosphatidic acid, a compound consisting of glycerol chemically combined with two fatty acids and a phosphate group. (*b*) Lecithin (or phosphatidylcholine) is a phospholipid found in cell membranes. It forms when phosphatidic acid combines with the compound choline. The structural formula for lecithin is shown here along with a space-filling model.

a phosphate group and linked to an organic compound such as choline. The organic compound usually contains nitrogen (Figure 3–13). (Note that phosphorus and nitrogen are absent in the neutral fats.)

The two ends of the phospholipid molecule differ physically as well as chemically. The fatty acid portion of the molecule is hydrophobic and not soluble in water. However, the portion composed of glycerol and the organic base is ionized and readily water-soluble. This end of the molecule is said to be *hydrophilic*. The amphipathic properties of these lipid molecules cause them to assume a certain configuration in the presence of water, with their hydrophilic water-soluble heads facing outward toward the surrounding water and their hydrophobic tails facing in the opposite direction. The cell membrane is formed from a lipid bilayer (i.e., two layers of phospholipid molecules). Their hydrophobic tails meet in the middle and their hydrophilic heads are oriented toward the outside of the cell membrane (Figure 3–14).

Carotenoids Are Plant Pigments

The red and yellow plant pigments called **carotenoids** are classified with the lipids because they are insoluble in water and have an oily consistency. These pigments, found in the cells of all plants, play a role in photosynthesis. The carotenoid molecule consists of five carbon monomers known as *isoprene units* (Figure 3–15*a*).

Splitting in half a molecule of the yellow plant pigment carotene yields a molecule of vitamin A, or retinol (Figure 3–15*b*). Retinal, the light-sensitive chemical present in the retina of the eye, is a derivative of vitamin A. Interestingly, eyes have evolved independently in three different lines of animals—mollusks, insects, and vertebrates. These animals have no common evolutionary ancestor equipped with eyes, yet the eyes of each of them have the same compound, retinal, involved in the process of light reception. That retinal is present in each of these types of eyes is the result of some unique fitness of this kind of molecule for the process of light reception.

Steroids Contain Four Rings of Carbon Atoms

A **steroid** consists of carbon atoms arranged in four interlocking rings; three of the rings contain six carbon atoms, and the fourth contains five (Figure 3–16). The length and structure of the side chains that extend from these rings distinguish one steroid from another. Steroids are synthesized from isoprene units.

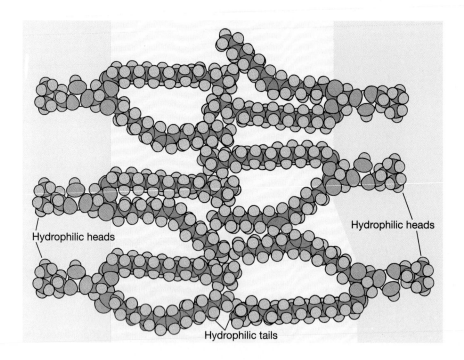

Hydrophilic heads

Hydrophilic heads

Hydrophilic tails

(a)

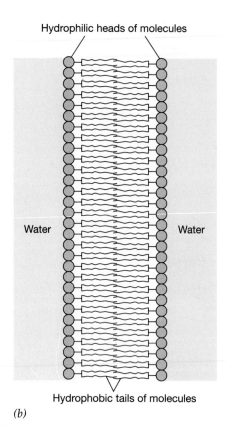

Hydrophilic heads of molecules

Water

Water

Hydrophobic tails of molecules

(b)

Figure 3–14   In the presence of water, lipid molecules are oriented with their hydrophilic water-soluble heads facing outward toward the surrounding water. The hydrophobic tails face in the opposite direction. (*a*) Space-filling model of complex lipids in a bilayer. Two layers of phospholipid molecules are present with their hydrophobic tails meeting in the middle. (*b*) A lipid bilayer, such as is found in cell membranes.

Among the steroids of biological importance are cholesterol, bile salts, reproductive hormones, and hormones secreted by the adrenal cortex. Cholesterol is a structural component of animal cell membranes; plant cell membranes contain molecules similar to cholesterol. Bile salts emulsify fats in the intestine so that they can be enzymatically hydrolyzed. Steroid hormones regulate certain aspects of metabolism in a variety of animals, including vertebrates, insects, and crabs.

PROTEINS ARE MACROMOLECULES FORMED FROM AMINO ACIDS

Proteins are of central importance in the chemistry of life. These macromolecules serve as structural components of cells and tissues, so growth and repair, as well as maintenance of the organism, depend on an adequate supply of these compounds. Many proteins serve as **enzymes,** molecules that regulate the thousands of different chemical reactions that take place in a living system.

The protein constituents of a cell are the clue to its lifestyle. Each cell type has characteristic types, distri-

butions, and amounts of protein that determine what the cell looks like and how it functions. A muscle cell is different from other cell types by virtue of its large content of the contractile proteins myosin and actin, which are largely responsible for its appearance as well as for its ability to contract. The protein hemoglobin, found in red blood cells, is responsible for the specialized function of oxygen transport.

Although carbohydrates and lipids have the same structure among different species, most proteins are species-specific—that is, their structure varies from species to species. The specific proteins present (determined by the instructions in the genes) are largely responsible for differences among species. Thus, the proteins in the cells of a dog vary somewhat from those in the cells of a fox or a giraffe. The degree of difference in the proteins of two species is thought to depend on evolutionary relationships. Organisms distantly related by evolution have proteins that differ more markedly than those of closely related forms.

Some proteins differ slightly even among individuals of the same species, so that each individual is biochemically unique. Only genetically identical organisms—identical twins or members of closely inbred strains of organisms—have identical proteins.

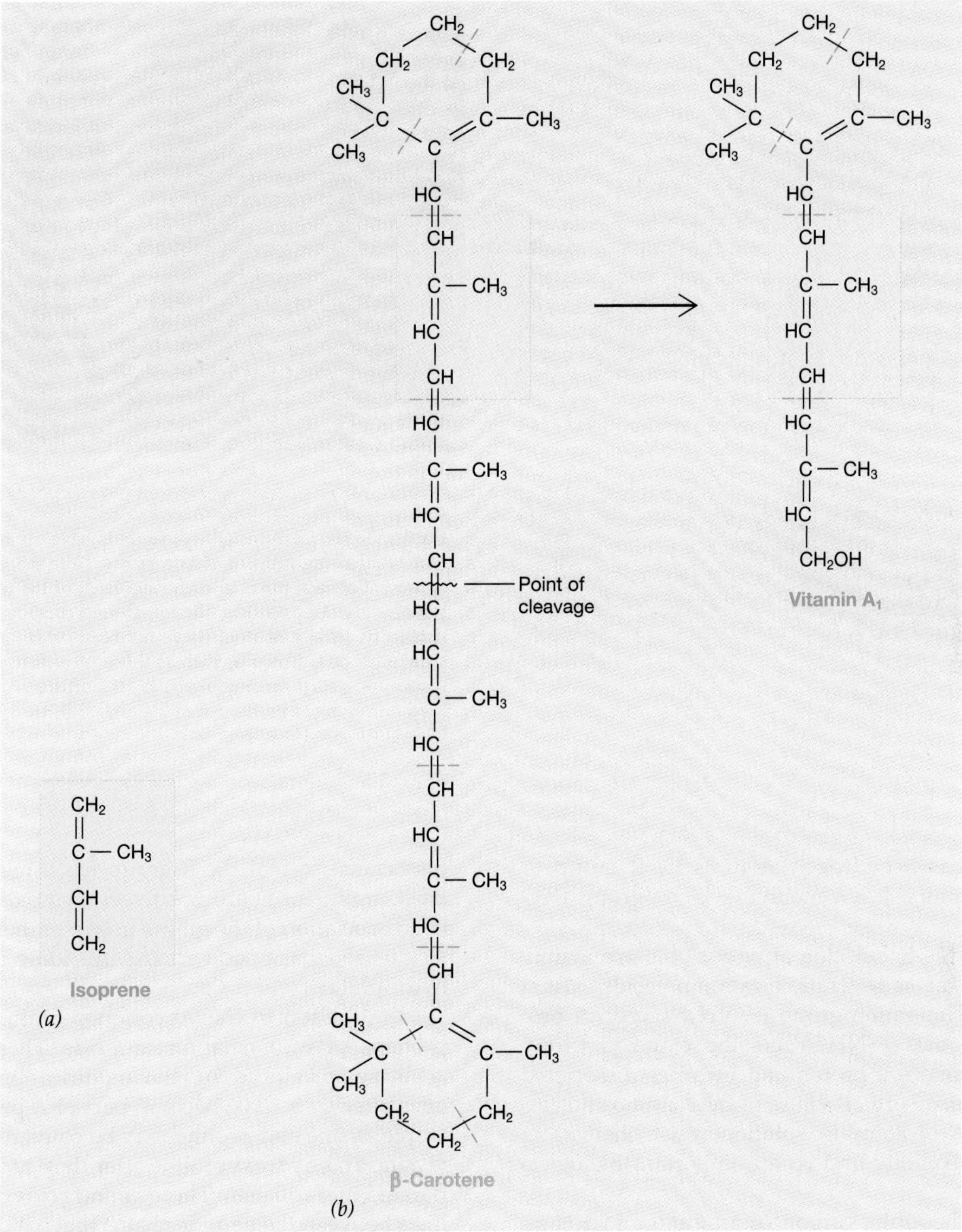

Figure 3–15 Carotenoids. (*a*) Isoprene is the monomer present in carotenoids. (*b*) Beta-carotene, the yellow pigment present in some plants. This carotenoid gives carrots, sweet potatoes, and other orange vegetables their color. Most animals can convert carotenoids to vitamin A. The dashed lines indicate the boundaries of the individual isoprene units within β-carotene.

Amino Acids Contain a Carboxyl and an Amino Group

A basic knowledge of protein chemistry is essential for understanding nutrition as well as other aspects of metabolism. Proteins are composed of carbon, hydrogen, oxygen, nitrogen, and usually sulfur. Atoms of these elements are arranged into molecular subunits called **amino acids.** About 20 kinds of amino acids are commonly found in proteins. Most amino acids have an amino group ($-NH_2$) and a carboxyl group ($-COOH$) bonded to the same asymmetric carbon atom, the **alpha carbon.** Amino acids differ in the R group or side chain bonded to the alpha carbon. **Glycine,** the simplest

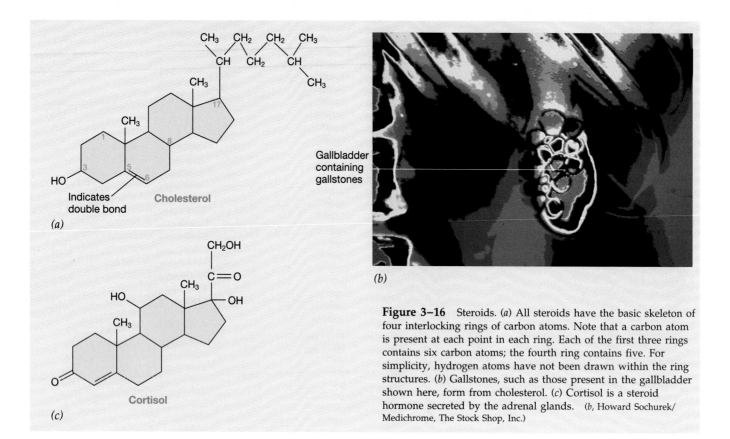

(a)

(b)

(c)

Gallbladder
containing
gallstones

Cholesterol

Indicates
double bond

Cortisol

Figure 3–16   Steroids. (a) All steroids have the basic skeleton of four interlocking rings of carbon atoms. Note that a carbon atom is present at each point in each ring. Each of the first three rings contains six carbon atoms; the fourth ring contains five. For simplicity, hydrogen atoms have not been drawn within the ring structures. (b) Gallstones, such as those present in the gallbladder shown here, form from cholesterol. (c) Cortisol is a steroid hormone secreted by the adrenal glands.   (b, Howard Sochurek/ Medichrome, The Stock Shop, Inc.)

amino acid, has a hydrogen atom as its R group or side chain; alanine has a methyl (—CH$_3$) group (Figure 3–17).

Amino acids in solution at neutral pH are mainly dipolar ions. This is generally how amino acids exist at cellular pH. The amino group (—NH$_2$) accepts a proton and becomes —NH$_3^+$, and the carboxyl group (—COOH) donates a proton and becomes dissociated —COO$^-$ (Figure 3–18). Because of their amino and carboxyl groups, proteins in solution resist changes in acidity and alkalinity and so are important biological buffers.

Because the alpha carbon of an amino acid is an asymmetric carbon, each amino acid can exist as two enantiomers (Figure 3–19). The two mirror images are called the L-isomer and the D-isomer. When amino acids are synthesized in the laboratory, a mixture of L- and D-amino acids is produced. However, the amino acids present in living systems are almost exclusively L-isomers. Exceptions are a few D-amino acids present in the antibiotics produced by fungi.

The amino acids are grouped in Figure 3–17 by the properties of their side chains. Amino acids with nonpolar side chains are classified as hydrophobic, whereas those with polar side chains are classified as hydrophilic. Acidic amino acids have side chains that contain a carboxyl group. At cellular pH the carboxyl group is dissociated so that the R group has a negative charge. Basic amino acids are positively charged as a result of the dissociation of the amino group in their side chains. Acidic and basic side chains are ionic and therefore hydrophilic.

In addition to the 20 common amino acids, some proteins have unusual amino acids. These rare amino acids are produced by the modification of common ones after they have become part of a protein. For example, lysine and proline may be converted to hydroxylysine and hydroxyproline after they have been incorporated into collagen. These amino acids can form cross links between the peptide chains that make up collagen. Such cross links are responsible for the firmness and great strength of the collagen molecule, which is a major component of cartilage, bone, and other connective tissues.

With some exceptions, bacteria and plants can synthesize all of their needed amino acids from simpler substances. If the proper raw materials are available, the cells of humans and animals can manufacture some, but not all, of the biologically significant amino acids. Those that animals cannot synthesize and so must obtain in the diet are known as **essential amino acids.** Animals differ in their biosynthetic capacities; what is an essential amino acid for one species may not be for another.

NONPOLAR

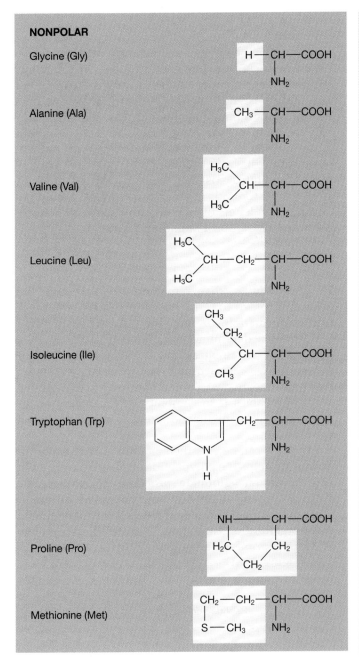

POLAR

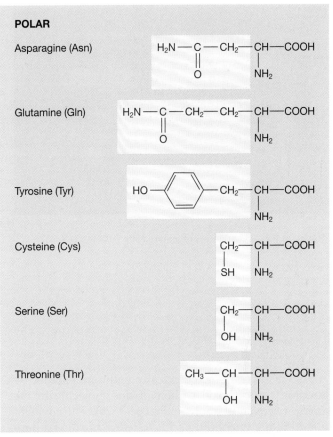

ELECTRICALLY CHARGED

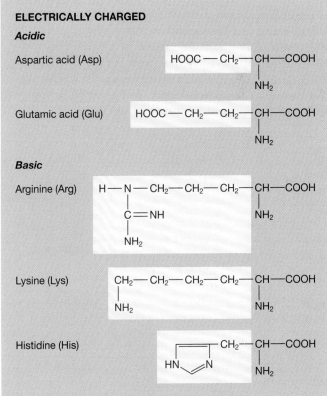

Figure 3–17 The amino acids commonly found in proteins. The amino acids are grouped here according to the properties of their side chains (R groups). The three-letter symbols are the conventional abbreviations for the amino acids.

Figure 3–18 The ionic form of amino acids. At the pH of living cells, amino acids exist mainly as dipolar ions.

Figure 3–19   Enantiomers of amino acids.   (Dennis Drenner)

A polypeptide may contain hundreds of amino acids joined in a specific linear order. The backbone of the chain consists of the repeating sequence —N—C—C—N—C—C— and includes all of the atoms except those in the side chains. The side chains of the amino acids extend from this backbone. A protein consists of one or more polypeptide chains. An almost infinite variety of protein molecules is possible. It should be clear that the various proteins differ from one another with respect to the number, types, and arrangement of amino acids they contain. The 20 types of amino acids found in biological proteins may be thought of as letters of a protein alphabet; each protein is a word made up of amino acid letters.

Proteins Have Four Levels of Organization

The polypeptide chains making up a protein are twisted or folded to form a macromolecule with a specific **conformation,** or three-dimensional shape. This conformation determines the function of the protein. For example, the unique shape of an enzyme permits it to "recognize" and act on its substrate (the substance the enzyme regulates). Similarly, the shape of a protein hormone enables it to combine with receptors on its target cell (the cell the hormone is designed to act upon).

Proteins can be classified as fibrous or globular. In **fibrous proteins** the polypeptide chains are arranged in long sheets; in **globular proteins** the polypeptide chains are tightly folded into a compact spherical shape. Most enzymes are globular proteins. Four different levels of organization can be distinguished in the protein molecule—primary, secondary, tertiary, and quaternary (Figure 3–21).

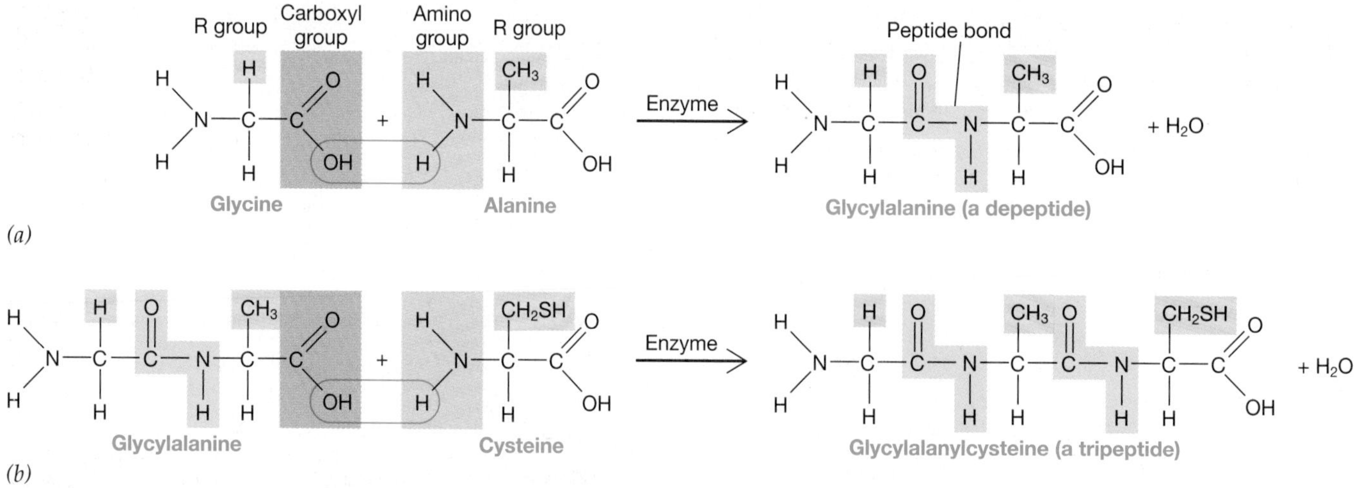

Polypeptide Chains Are Built from Amino Acids

Amino acids combine chemically with one another by bonding the carboxyl carbon of one molecule to the amino nitrogen of another (Figure 3–20). The covalent bond linking two amino acids together is called a **peptide bond.** When two amino acids combine, a **dipeptide** is formed; a longer chain of amino acids is a **polypeptide.** One end of the chain has a free amino group. At the opposite end is a free carboxyl group. The other amino and carboxyl groups of the amino acid monomers (except those in side chains) are part of the peptide bonds. The complex process by which polypeptides are synthesized is discussed in Chapter 13.

Figure 3–20   Formation of polypeptide chains. (*a*) Formation of a dipeptide. Two amino acids combine chemically to form a dipeptide. Water is produced as a byproduct during this reaction. (*b*) A third amino acid is added to the dipeptide to form a chain of three amino acids (a tripeptide, or small polypeptide). The bond between two amino acids is a peptide bond. Additional amino acids can be added to form long polypeptide chains.

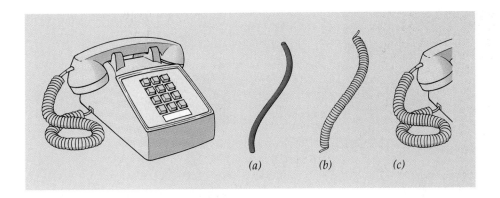

Figure 3–21 Protein structure. The telephone cord provides a familiar example for demonstrating (*a*) primary, (*b*) secondary, and (*c*) tertiary structure.

Primary structure is determined by the amino acid sequence

The sequence of amino acids in a polypeptide chain is its **primary structure.** This sequence, discussed in Chapter 12, is specified by the instructions in a gene. Using analytical methods developed in the early 1950s, investigators can determine the exact sequence of amino acids in a protein molecule. Insulin, a hormone secreted by the pancreas and used in the treatment of diabetes, was the first protein for which the exact sequence of amino acids in the polypeptide chains was identified. Insulin consists of 51 amino acid units in two linked chains (Figure 3–22).

Secondary structure results from hydrogen bonding

Peptide chains ordinarily do not lie out flat or coil randomly, but rather undergo conformational changes to yield a specific three-dimensional structure. This **secondary structure** of protein molecules involves the coiling of the peptide chain into a helix or some other regular conformation. The regularity is due to hydrogen bonds between the atoms of the uniform backbone of the polypeptide chain.

A common secondary structure in protein molecules is known as the **alpha helix.** This involves the formation of spiral coils of the polypeptide chain (Figure 3–23*a*). The alpha helix is a very uniform geometric structure with 3.6 amino acids occupying each turn of the helix. The helical structure is determined and maintained by the formation of hydrogen bonds between amino acids in successive turns of the spiral coil. Hydrogen bonds form between the amino group of one amino acid and the oxygen of the third amino acid down the polypeptide chain.

The alpha helix is the basic structural unit of fibrous proteins such as wool, hair, skin, and nails. The fiber is elastic because the hydrogen bonds can be broken and then reformed. This is why human hairs can be stretched to some extent and then snap back to their original length.

A second type of secondary structure is the **beta-pleated sheet** (Figure 3–23*b*). Here the hydrogen bonding takes place between different polypeptide chains. Each zigzag chain is fully extended, and the hydrogen bonding between them results in a sheetlike structure. Pleated sheets can also form between different regions of the same polypeptide chain (see Figure 3–23). This structure is flexible rather than elastic. Fibroin, the protein of silk, is characterized by a beta-pleated-sheet structure, and the cores of many globular proteins consist of beta sheets.

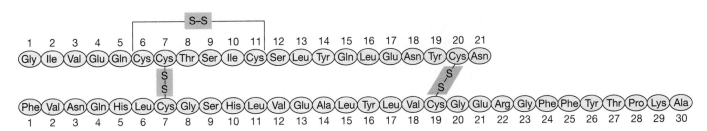

Figure 3–22 Primary structure of the two polypeptide chains that make up the protein insulin. The primary structure is the linear sequence of amino acids. Each oval in the diagram represents an amino acid. The letters inside the ovals are symbols for the names of the amino acids. Insulin is a very small protein.

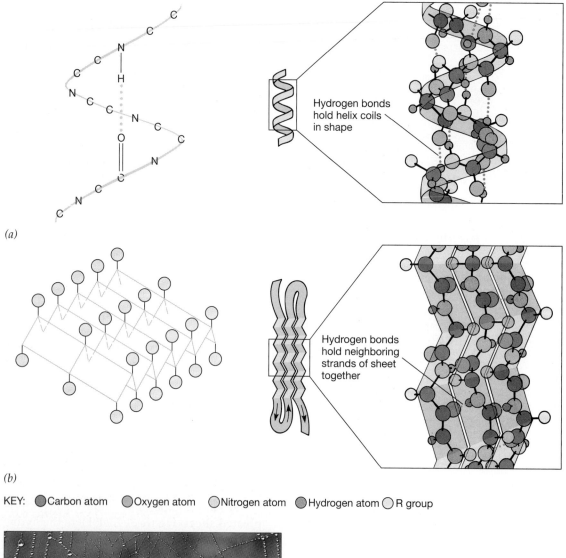

(a)

(b)

KEY: ● Carbon atom ● Oxygen atom ○ Nitrogen atom ● Hydrogen atom ○ R group

Hydrogen bonds hold helix coils in shape

Hydrogen bonds hold neighboring strands of sheet together

(c)

Figure 3–23 The secondary structure of proteins. (*a*) One type of secondary structure is the alpha helix. The folds in the helix are held together mainly by hydrogen bonds between oxygen and hydrogen atoms. (The R groups have been omitted in the diagram at left.) (*b*) A second type of secondary structure is the beta-pleated sheet. In this structure the backbone of the polypeptide chain is stretched out into a zigzag shape. (*c*) The silk used by this spider to wrap its prey is an extremely strong and flexible protein, fibroin, which exhibits a beta-pleated-sheet structure. The silk fibers harden as they are spun from the glands in the spider's abdomen. (*c*, Skip Moody/Dembinsky Photo Associates)

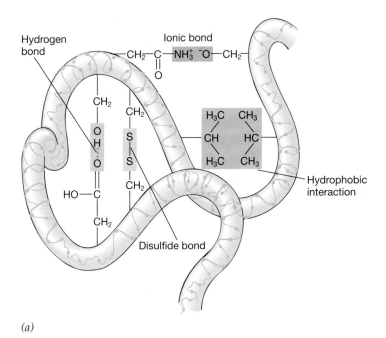

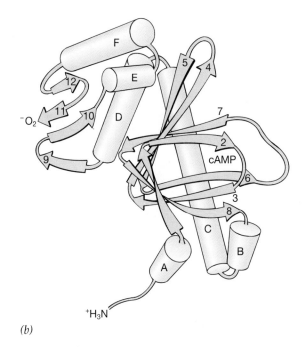

(a)

(b)

Figure 3–24 The tertiary structure of a protein. (*a*) The tertiary structure results from the coiling and folding of the alpha helix (or other secondary structure) into an overall globular or other shape. Hydrogen bonds, bonds between sulfur atoms, ionic attractions between R groups, and hydrophobic interactions are among the forces that hold the parts of the molecule in the designated shape. (*b*) Schematic drawing of the tertiary structure of a polypeptide that has both alpha-helical and beta-sheet secondary structure. The polypeptide is a subunit of a DNA-binding protein (CAP) from the bacterium *Escherichia coli*. The regions of the polypeptide that are in alpha-helical conformation are represented as blue tubes lettered A through F. Regions in beta conformation are represented as gray arrows numbered 1 to 12. Green lines represent connecting regions.

Tertiary structure depends on interactions between R groups

The **tertiary structure** of a protein molecule is the overall shape assumed by each polypeptide chain (Figure 3–24). This three-dimensional structure is determined by four main factors that involve interactions among R groups (side chains).

1. Hydrogen bonds between R groups of amino acid subunits in adjacent loops of the same polypeptide chain.
2. Ionic attraction between R groups with positive charges and those with negative charges.
3. Hydrophobic interactions resulting from the tendency of nonpolar R groups to associate in the interior of the globular structure away from the surrounding water.
4. Covalent bonds known as disulfide bonds (—S—S—) that link the sulfur atoms of two cysteine subunits. Disulfide bonds may link two parts of the same polypeptide chain or join two different chains.

Quaternary structure depends on the arrangement of two or more polypeptide chains

Proteins composed of two or more polypeptide chains have a **quaternary structure,** the arrangement assumed by the polypeptide chains, each with its own primary, secondary, and tertiary structures, to form the biologically active protein molecule. Hemoglobin, the protein in red blood cells that is responsible for oxygen transport, is an example of a globular protein with quaternary structure (Figure 3–25). Hemoglobin consists of 574 amino acids arranged in four polypeptide chains—two identical alpha and two identical beta chains. Its chemical formula is $C_{3032}H_{4816}O_{872}N_{789}S_8Fe_4$.

Protein Structure Determines Function

The structure of a protein helps determine its biological activity. A single protein may have varying structure and more than one function. Many proteins are modular, consisting of two or more globular sections, called **domains,** connected by less compact regions of the polypeptide chain. Each domain may have a different function.

Conformation is partially determined by the primary structure of the polypeptide. Predicting the structure of a protein from its primary sequence of amino acids, however, is quite difficult owing to the many possible combinations of folding patterns. Computer programs are being developed to predict the three-dimensional shape of a protein from its amino acid sequence (Figure 3–26).

Alpha chains
(α-globins)

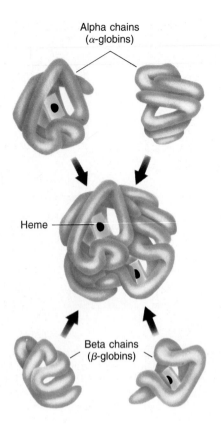

Heme

Beta chains
(β-globins)

Figure 3–25 When a protein consists of two or more polypeptide strands, as hemoglobin does, it is said to have a quaternary structure. Each of the four polypeptides in hemoglobin is joined to an iron-containing molecule, the heme, but only two of the hemes can be seen in this view of the molecule.

The biological activity of a protein can be disrupted by changes in the amino acid sequence or in the conformation of a protein. For example, the disorder known as *sickle cell anemia* results when a particular mutation occurs that changes the amino acid sequence of hemoglobin. This mutation results in the substitution of the amino acid valine for glutamic acid at position 6, that is, the sixth amino acid from the terminal end in the beta chain. The substitution of valine with an uncharged side chain for glutamic acid with a charged side chain makes the hemoglobin less soluble and more likely to form crystal-like structures that change the shape of the red blood cell.

Changes in the three-dimensional structure of a protein also disrupt its biological activity. When a protein is heated or treated with any of a number of chemicals, its tertiary structure becomes disordered and the

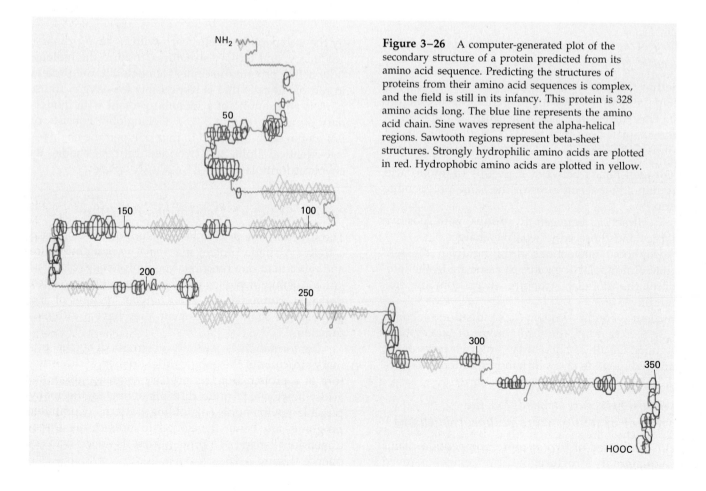

Figure 3–26 A computer-generated plot of the secondary structure of a protein predicted from its amino acid sequence. Predicting the structures of proteins from their amino acid sequences is complex, and the field is still in its infancy. This protein is 328 amino acids long. The blue line represents the amino acid chain. Sine waves represent the alpha-helical regions. Sawtooth regions represent beta-sheet structures. Strongly hydrophilic amino acids are plotted in red. Hydrophobic amino acids are plotted in yellow.

coiled peptide chains unfold to give a more random conformation. This unfolding is accompanied by a loss of the biological activity of the protein—for example, its ability to act as an enzyme. Such change in shape and loss of biological activity are termed **denaturation** of the protein. Denaturation generally cannot be reversed. However, under certain conditions, some proteins that have been denatured return to their original shape and biological activity when normal environmental conditions are restored.

DNA AND RNA ARE NUCLEIC ACIDS

Nucleic acids transmit hereditary information and determine what proteins a cell manufactures. There are two classes of nucleic acids found in cells: **ribonucleic acids (RNA)** and **deoxyribonucleic acids (DNA)**. DNA comprises the genes, the hereditary material of the cell, and contains instructions for making all the proteins needed by the organism (Figure 3–27). RNA functions in the process of protein synthesis. Like proteins, nucleic acids are large, complex molecules. They were first isolated by Miescher in 1870 from the nuclei of pus cells; their name—nucleic acid—reflects that they are acidic and were first identified in nuclei.

Nucleic Acids Consist of Nucleotide Subunits

Nucleic acids are polymers of **nucleotides,** molecular units that consist of (1) a five-carbon sugar, either ribose or deoxyribose, (2) a phosphate group, and (3) a nitrogenous base, a ring compound containing nitrogen. The nitrogenous base may be either a double-ringed purine or a single-ringed pyrimidine (Figure 3–28). DNA commonly contains the purines adenine (A) and guanine (G) and the pyrimidines cytosine (C) and thymine (T) together with the sugar deoxyribose and phosphate. RNA contains the purines adenine and guanine and the pyrimidines cytosine and uracil (U), together with the sugar ribose and phosphate. The removal of the phosphate group from a nucleotide yields a compound, termed a *nucleoside,* composed of the base and sugar.

The molecules of nucleic acids are made of linear chains of nucleotides. The nucleotides are joined by **phosphodiester linkages,** each consisting of a phosphate group and the covalent bonds that attach it to the sugars of adjacent nucleotides (Figure 3–29). The specific information of the nucleic acid is coded in the unique sequence of the four kinds of nucleotides present in the chain (see Chapter 12). DNA is composed of two nucleotide chains entwined around each other in a double helix.

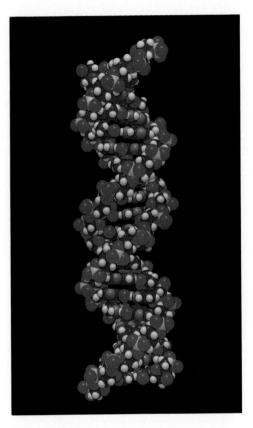

Figure 3–27 Computer-generated simulation of the colored plastic space-filling molecular models of DNA used by chemists. *Red,* oxygen; *blue,* nitrogen; *dark blue,* carbon; *yellow,* phosphorus; *white,* hydrogen. This photograph shows 20 base pairs of DNA in the crystalline B form first studied by Watson and Crick. (N. L. Max, University of California/Biological Photo Service)

Some Single and Double Nucleotides Are Central to Cell Function

Besides their importance as subunits of nucleic acids, nucleotides serve other vital functions in living cells. **Adenosine triphosphate (ATP),** composed of adenine, ribose, and three phosphates (Figure 3–30), is of major importance as the energy currency of all cells. The two terminal phosphate groups are joined to the nucleotide by unstable bonds, indicated by the ~P symbol. The biologically useful energy of these bonds can be transferred to other molecules. Most of the chemical energy of the cell is stored in the phosphate bonds of ATP, ready to be transferred to other molecules.

A nucleotide may be converted by enzymes called **cyclases** to a cyclic form. ATP, for example, is converted to cyclic adenosine monophosphate (cyclic AMP) by the enzyme adenylate cyclase (Figure 3–31). Cyclic nucleotides mediate the effects of some hormones and regulate certain aspects of cellular function (Chapter 47).

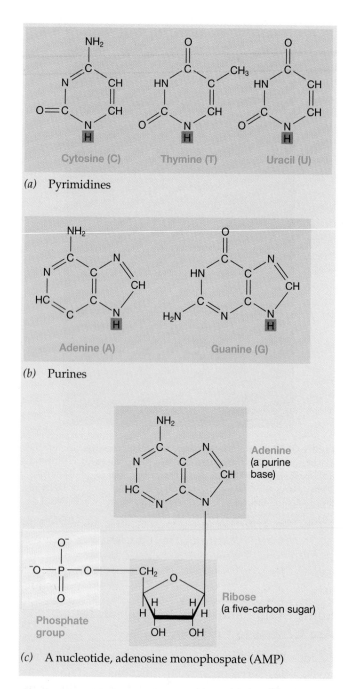

(a) Pyrimidines

(b) Purines

(c) A nucleotide, adenosine monophospate (AMP)

Figure 3–28 A nucleic acid consists of subunits called *nucleotides*. Each nucleotide consists of (1) a nitrogenous base, which may be either a purine or a pyrimidine, (2) a five-carbon sugar, either ribose (in RNA) or deoxyribose (in DNA), and (3) a phosphate group. (a) The three major pyrimidine bases found in nucleotides. (b) The two major purine bases found in nucleotides. (c) A nucleotide, adenosine monophosphate (AMP).

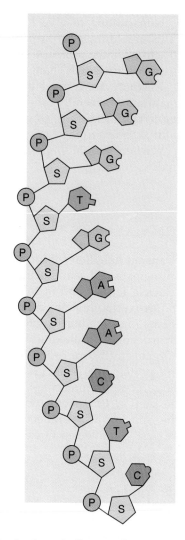

Figure 3–29 A schematic diagram of a nucleic acid molecule (DNA or RNA). The four bases of each nucleic acid are arranged in various specific sequences. P, phosphate; S, sugar; G, guanine; C, cytosine; A, adenine; T, thymine.

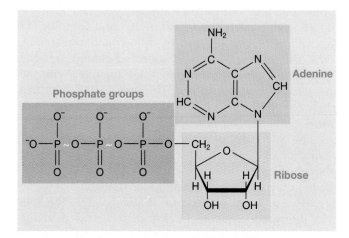

Figure 3–30 The structure of ATP, a nucleotide that has unstable bonds joining the two terminal phosphate groups to the nucleotide.

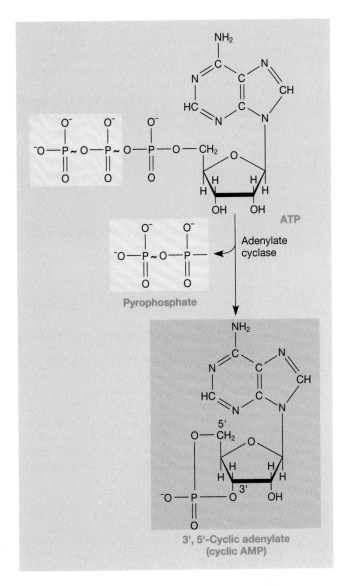

Figure 3–31 The formation of cyclic AMP from ATP.

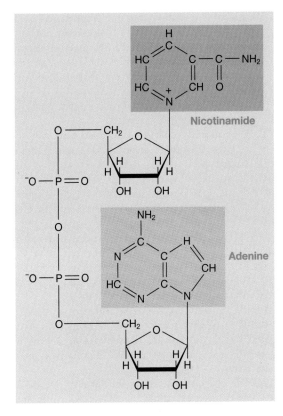

Figure 3–32 The structure of NAD$^+$, an important hydrogen and electron acceptor and donor. The nicotinamide portion of the molecule accepts hydrogen and is reduced in the process.

Cells contain several dinucleotides, which are of great importance in metabolic processes. For example, as discussed in Chapter 7, **nicotinamide adenine dinucleotide (NAD$^+$)** is a primary electron and hydrogen acceptor and donor in biological oxidations and reductions within cells (Figure 3–32).

SUMMARY

I. The major groups of biologically important organic compounds are carbohydrates, lipids, proteins, and nucleic acids.

II. Chains of carbon atoms form the backbone of a large variety of organic compounds essential to life.

   A. The carbon atom can form stable single covalent bonds with four other atoms, or it can form double or triple bonds with other atoms.

   B. Carbon bonds with a greater number of different elements than any other type of atom. Carbon atoms can form straight or branched chains or can be joined into rings.

III. Isomers are compounds that have the same molecular formula but different structures.

   A. Structural isomers differ in the covalent arrangements of their atoms.

   B. Geometric isomers, or *cis-trans* isomers, differ in the spatial arrangements of their atoms.

   C. Enantiomers are isomers that are mirror images of each other. Enantiomers may be designated D or L, depending on their configuration. Cells can distinguish between these configurations.

IV. Organic compounds are made up of specific functional groups with characteristic properties.

   A. Partial charges on atoms at opposite ends of a bond are responsible for the polar property of a functional group.

   B. Polar functional groups interact with other polar groups or with charged ions. Polar functional groups dissolve in water.

   C. Acidic and basic functional groups also dissolve in water.

V. Long chains of similar organic compounds linked together are called *polymers*. Proteins and nucleic acids are large polymers referred to as macromolecules.

VI. Carbohydrates contain carbon, hydrogen, and oxygen in a ratio of approximately one carbon to two hydrogens to one oxygen.
   A. Monosaccharides are simple sugars such as glucose, fructose, and ribose.
   B. Two monosaccharides can bond with a glycosidic linkage, forming a disaccharide such as maltose or sucrose.
   C. Most carbohydrates are polysaccharides, long chains of repeating units of a simple sugar.
      1. Carbohydrates are typically stored in plants as starch and in animals as glycogen.
      2. The cell walls of plant cells are composed mainly of the polysaccharide cellulose.
   D. Derivatives of monosaccharides and complex carbohydrates (e.g., glycoproteins and glycolipids) are important biological compounds.

VII. Lipids are composed of carbon, hydrogen, and oxygen but have relatively less oxygen in proportion to carbon and hydrogen than do carbohydrates. Lipids have a greasy or oily consistency and are relatively insoluble in water.
   A. The body stores fuel in the form of neutral fats. A fat consists of a molecule of glycerol combined with one to three fatty acids.
      1. Three types of neutral fats are monoacylglycerols, diacylglycerols, and triacylglycerols.
      2. Fatty acids, and therefore fats, can be saturated or unsaturated.
   B. Phospholipids are structural components of cell membranes. The amphipathic property of the phospholipid molecule is responsible for the configuration phospholipids assume in water.
   C. Steroid molecules contain carbon atoms arranged in four interlocking rings. Cholesterol, bile salts, and certain hormones are important steroids.

VIII. Proteins are large, complex molecules made of simpler subunits, called *amino acids,* that are joined by peptide bonds. They are composed of carbon, hydrogen, oxygen, nitrogen, and sulfur.
   A. Proteins are important structural components of cells and tissues. Many serve as enzymes. Most proteins are species-specific.
   B. Proteins are composed of various arrangements of 20 different amino acids. Two amino acids combine to form a dipeptide. A longer chain of amino acids is a polypeptide.
      1. All amino acids contain an amino group and carboxyl group but vary in their side chains. The side chains of amino acids dictate their chemical properties.
      2. Amino acids generally exist as dipolar ions in the body and serve as important biological buffers.
      3. Essential amino acids are amino acids that animals cannot synthesize and must obtain in their diets.
   C. Four levels of organization can be distinguished in protein molecules.
      1. Primary structure is the sequence of amino acids in the peptide chain.
      2. Secondary structure is the coiling of the peptide chains into a helix or some other regular conformation due to hydrogen bonding.
      3. Tertiary structure is the overall shape of the polypeptide chains as dictated by chemical properties and interactions of specific amino acids.
      4. Quaternary structure is the spatial relationship of the combination of two or more polypeptide chains.

IX. The nucleic acids DNA and RNA store information that governs the structure and function of the organism.
   A. Nucleic acids are composed of long chains of nucleotide subunits, each composed of a nitrogenous base, a purine or a pyrimidine; a five-carbon sugar (ribose or deoxyribose); and a phosphate group.
   B. ATP is a nucleotide of special significance in energy metabolism. NAD^+ is an electron and hydrogen acceptor in biological oxidations.

POST-TEST

Select the most appropriate term from Column B for each entry in Column A.

Column A
1. Monosaccharide
2. Steroid
3. Nucleic acid
4. Fatty acid
5. Important constituent of cell membranes
6. Subunits of proteins
7. Energy currency of cell
8. Compounds with the same molecular formula but different structures
9. Component of fat
10. Organic compounds consisting only of carbon and hydrogen

Column B
a. Cellulose
b. DNA
c. Glucose
d. Cholesterol
e. Oleic acid
f. ATP
g. Glycerol
h. Hydrocarbons
i. Amino acids
j. Phospholipids
k. Isomers

11. Peptide bonds link _____ _____.
12. The primary structure of a protein refers to the sequences of _____ _____.
13. When sucrose is hydrolyzed, _____ and _____ are formed.
14. _____ is an important component of the cell walls of plant cells.
15. The fatty acid portion of the phospholipid is _____ and does not dissolve in water.
16. The three functional groups that make up the amino acid are the _____, the _____, and the R group.
17. Animals store glucose in the form of _____.
18. The three components of a nucleotide are _____, _____, and _____.

REVIEW QUESTIONS

1. Of all the elements, why do you suppose carbon is the central element of organic compounds?
2. Contrast a monosaccharide such as glucose with a polysaccharide such as starch in terms of structure and function.
3. Why is each of the following compounds biologically important?
    (a) Steroids
    (b) Phospholipids
    (c) Polysaccharides
    (d) Nucleic acids
    (e) Amino acids
4. Draw a structural formula of a simple amino acid and identify the carboxyl group, amino group, and R group.
5. There are thousands of different types of proteins. How does one protein differ from another?
6. Compare proteins with nucleic acids.
7. Why are neutral fats important? What are the molecular components of a neutral fat?
8. Contrast the three different types of isomers.
9. Discuss the ways in which the biological activity of a protein may be disrupted.

RECOMMENDED READINGS

Baum, S. J., and C. W. Scaife. *Chemistry: A Life Science Approach,* 3rd ed. Macmillan, New York, 1987. A chemistry text that is designed for students of biology and presents chemical subjects of special interest to biologists.

Bettelheim, F. A., and J. March. *Introduction to General, Organic and Biochemistry,* 3rd ed. Saunders College Publishing, Philadelphia, 1991. A very readable reference text for those who would like to know more about the chemistry basic to life.

Campbell, M. K. *Biochemistry.* Saunders College Publishing, Philadelphia, 1991. An introduction to biological molecules and processes; well written and well illustrated.

Darnell, J., H. Lodish, and D. Baltimore. *Molecular Cell Biology.* Scientific American Books, New York, 1990. A presentation of many of the molecular aspects involved in cell structure and function.

Richards, F. M. The protein folding problem. *Scientific American,* January 1991, Vol. 264, No. 1, pp. 54–63. A discussion of the mechanisms involved when a protein folds into its biologically active shape.

Stryer, L. *Biochemistry,* 3rd ed. W. H. Freeman, San Francisco, 1988. An advanced, well-written, and beautifully illustrated reference book on the subjects discussed in this chapter.

CHAPTER 4

❏

Cellular Organization

OUTLINE

The cell theory
Characteristics of cells
Limits on cell size
How cells are studied
Eukaryotic and prokaryotic cells
Parts of a eukaryotic cell

Every cell is a virtual microcosm of life, for the cell is the smallest unit that can carry out all life activities. Although some are more complex than others, every cell has all of the physical and chemical components needed for its own maintenance, growth, and division. Cells convert energy from one form to another and use that energy to do various kinds of work, ranging from mechanical work to chemical synthesis. Cells store genetic information in DNA molecules, which are faithfully replicated and passed to the progeny during cell division. Cells use the information in the DNA to control their metabolism and specify their structures. Of course a cell is an open system that requires exchange of materials and energy with the environment, but when provided with essential nutrients and an appropriate environment, some cells can be kept alive and growing in the laboratory for many years. By contrast, no isolated cell part is capable of sustained survival.

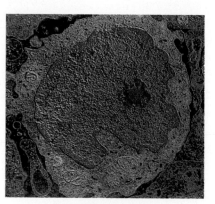

False-color transmission electron micrograph (TEM) of a lymphocyte, a type of white blood cell. (CNRI/Science Photo Library/Photo Researchers, Inc.)

Cells are the building blocks of even the most complex multicellular organisms. They are extraordinarily versatile modules that can be modified in a variety of ways to carry out specialized functions.

Cells provide dramatic testimony for the underlying unity of all living things. When we examine a wide range of seemingly very diverse organisms, ranging from simple bacteria to the most complex plants and animals, we find striking similarities at the cellular level. Careful studies of shared cellular features help us trace the evolutionary history of various groups and furnish powerful evidence that all organisms alive today had a common origin.

LEARNING OBJECTIVES

After you have studied this chapter you should be able to

1. Justify why the cell should be considered the basic unit of life and explain some of the ramifications of the cell theory.
2. Point out the basic needs of all living things and explain how a cell is able to meet its needs.
3. Explain why resolving power is an important feature of a good microscope, and discuss the differences between light and electron microscopes.
4. Discuss the general characteristics of prokaryotic and eukaryotic cells.
5. Evaluate size relationships among different cells and cell structures.
6. Explain why the relationship between surface area and volume of a cell is important in determining cell size limits.
7. Describe the structures and functions of principal organelles in plant and animal cells. Be able to locate and label them on a diagram or photomicrograph.

8. Describe the structure of the nucleus and relate this information to its function in eukaryotic cells.
9. Distinguish between smooth and rough endoplasmic reticulum in terms of both structure and function, and discuss the relationship between the endoplasmic reticulum and other internal membranes in the cell.
10. Follow the fate of certain proteins synthesized on the endoplasmic reticulum as they are subsequently processed, modified, and sorted by the Golgi complex.
11. Describe the functions of lysosomes, and explain what happens when they leak.
12. Distinguish between the functions of chloroplasts and mitochondria, and explain why both organelles synthesize ATP.
13. Describe the structures of the major types of fibers that make up the cytoskeleton. Explain the importance of the cytoskeleton to the cell.
14. Relate the structural features of cilia and flagella to the way in which these organelles are able to move.

THE CELL IS THE SMALLEST UNIT OF LIFE

The unifying concept that cells are the fundamental units of all living things is a part of the **cell theory.** Two German scientists, botanist Matthias Schleiden in 1838 and zoologist Theodor Schwann in 1839, were the first to point out that plants and animals are composed of groups of cells and that the cell is the basic unit of living organisms.

The cell theory was extended in 1855 by Rudolph Virchow, who stated that new cells are formed only by the division of previously existing cells. In other words, cells do not arise by spontaneous generation from nonliving matter (an idea that was rooted in the writings of Aristotle and had persisted over many centuries). About 1880, another famous biologist, August Weismann, pointed out an important corollary to Virchow's statement, that all the cells living today can trace their ancestry back to ancient times. Evidence that all cells living today have a common origin is provided by the basic similarities of their structures and the molecules of which they are made.

BECAUSE OF THEIR COMMON ORIGINS AND COMMON NEEDS, CELLS SHARE MANY FUNDAMENTAL FEATURES

First and foremost, a cell must be able to keep its contents together and separated from the environment. For this reason all cells, from bacteria to human cells, are enclosed in a surface membrane, commonly known as the **plasma membrane.**[1] Cells must also be able to accumulate materials and energy stores and to exchange materials with the environment, usually in a highly regulated fashion. Therefore, the plasma membrane must serve as an extremely selective barrier, making the interior of the cell an enclosed compartment with a chemical composition quite different from the outside.

All living cells need one or more sources of energy, but a cell rarely obtains energy in a form that is immediately usable. All cells must therefore have the ability to convert energy to a convenient form, usually ATP (see Chapter 3). Although the specifics vary, the basic strategies cells use for energy conversion are very similar. The chemical reactions that convert energy from one form to another are essentially the same in all cells, from bacteria to those of complex plants and animals.

Every cell also needs to be able to control its activities and specify its structure. Information needed to do this is stored in the form of **deoxyribonucleic acid (DNA)** (see Chapter 3). Recall from Chapter 3 that the DNA molecule contains a linear sequence of components called nucleotides. This sequence of nucleotides serves as a code in all cells which specifies the sequence of amino acids (primary structure) in proteins. Proteins are the molecules that carry out most cell functions.

---

[1] The term *membrane* is widely used in biology to refer to any structure that is like a thin sheet. However, the cellular membranes discussed in this chapter have a unique structure consisting of a lipid bilayer and other molecular components (see Chapters 3 and 5).

Many proteins are **enzymes,** special molecules that catalyze virtually every chemical reaction that takes place in living things. By acting as catalysts, enzymes dramatically speed up specific metabolic reactions so that they take place at rates compatible with life. Thus, by specifying the structure of proteins and enzymes, which in turn direct both the synthesis and the breakdown of all biological molecules (including lipids, carbohydrates, and nucleic acids), the DNA molecule directs the metabolism of the cell.

DNA uses a second nucleic acid, **ribonucleic acid (RNA),** as an intermediary. The sequence of bases in DNA that encodes a protein is copied as a sequence of bases in RNA through a process known as **transcription.** The particular kind of RNA called **messenger RNA** is responsible for carrying the information needed for synthesis of proteins (a process known as **translation**). The translation process itself is complex, requiring complicated machinery (see Chapter 12).

Finally, a cell must be able to reproduce itself. This means that the information stored in DNA must be reproduced and passed intact to the two daughter cells. DNA has the unique ability to make an exact duplicate of itself through a process called **replication** (see Chapter 11).

The pathway for the flow of genetic information in the cell is summarized in Figure 4–1.

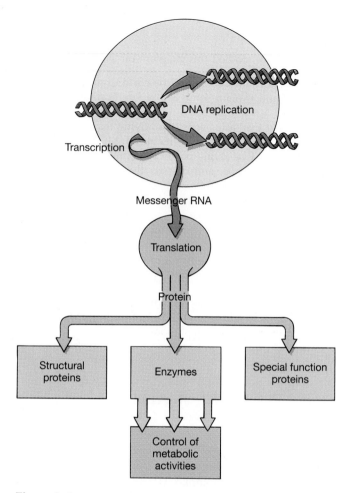

Figure 4–1 The flow of genetic information in cells.

LIMITATIONS ON TRANSPORT ACROSS THE PLASMA MEMBRANE IMPOSE LIMITS ON CELL SIZE

Although their sizes vary over a wide range (Figure 4–2), most cells are microscopically small. We therefore require very small units in order to measure cells and their internal structures. The basic unit of linear measurement in the metric system is the meter, which is just a little longer than a yard (back endsheets). The millimeter (mm) is 1/1000 of a meter and is about as long as the bar enclosed in parentheses (-). The unit that is most convenient for measuring cells is the micrometer (μm). A bar 1 μm long is far too short to be seen with the unaided eye, for it is 1/1,000,000 (one millionth) of a meter or 1/1000 of a millimeter long. Most of us have difficulty thinking about units that are too small to see, but it is very helpful to remember that a micrometer has the same relationship to a millimeter that a millimeter has to a meter. As small as it is, the micrometer is actually too large to measure most subcellular structures. For these purposes we use the nanometer (nm), which is 1/1,000,000,000 (one billionth) of a meter or 1/1000 of a micrometer. To mentally move down to the world of the nanometer, we make a now familiar transition. The nanometer is one thousandth of a micrometer, which in turn is one thousandth of a millimeter, which is one thousandth of a meter.

A good light microscope allows us to see most types of bacterial cells, and some specialized animal cells are large enough to be seen with the naked eye. The human egg cell, for example, is about 130 μm in diameter, or approximately the size of the period at the end of this sentence. The largest cells are birds' eggs, but they are atypical because almost the entire mass of the egg is food reserves in the form of yolk, which is not a functioning part of the cell.

The sizes and shapes of cells are related to the functions they perform (Figure 4–3). Some cells, such as the amoeba and the white blood cell, can change their shape as they move about. Sperm cells have long, whiplike tails, called flagella, for locomotion. Nerve cells possess long, thin extensions that permit them to transmit messages over great distances. The extensions on some nerve cells in the human body may be as long as 1 meter. Other cells, such as epithelial cells, may be almost rectangular in shape and are stacked much like building blocks to form sheetlike structures.

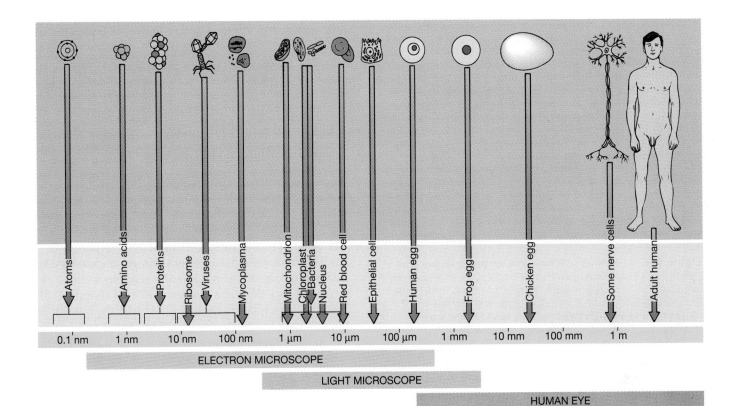

| 0.1 nm | 1 nm | 10 nm | 100 nm | 1 μm | 10 μm | 100 μm | 1 mm | 10 mm | 100 mm | 1 m |

ELECTRON MICROSCOPE

LIGHT MICROSCOPE

HUMAN EYE

Figure 4–2 Relative sizes of some well-known cells, their organelles, and other components. Because the size range is very wide, a logarithmic scale (in which there is a tenfold difference between successive units) is used to make the figure more compact. If a linear scale had been used, the figure would be more than 10,000 kilometers wide! Prokaryotic cells vary in size from 1 to 10 μm long; eukaryotic cells (cells of plants and animals) generally fall within the range of 10 to 100 μm long. The nuclei of animal and plant cells range from about 3 to 10 μm in diameter. Mitochondria are about the size of bacteria, whereas chloroplasts are usually larger, about 5 μm long.

(a) Ovum (egg) and sperm cells

(b) Amoeba

(c) Bacterial cells

(d) Nerve cell

(e) Epithelial cells

(f) Plant cell (parenchyma)

Figure 4–3 The size and shape of cells are related to the cells' functions. (a) An ovum (egg cell) and sperm cells. Ova are among the largest cells; sperm cells are comparatively tiny. Note the long tail (flagellum) used by the sperm cell in locomotion. By whipping its flagellum, the sperm can move toward the egg. (b) The amoeba changes its shape as it moves from place to place. (c) Bacterial cells are small, which enables them to grow and divide rapidly. (d) Nerve cells are specialized to transmit messages from one part of the body to another. (e) Epithelial cells join to form tissues that cover body surfaces and line body cavities. (f) The bulk of the organs of most young plants consist of parenchyma cells.

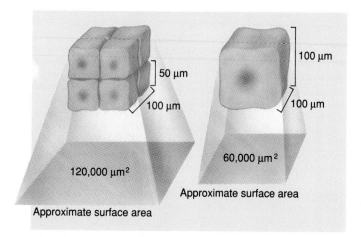

50 µm

100 µm

100 µm

100 µm

120,000 µm²

60,000 µm²

Approximate surface area

Approximate surface area

Figure 4–4 Eight small cells have a much greater surface area (plasma membrane) in relation to their total volume than does one large cell. This concept is easier to grasp if you imagine that each of these cells is a potato. The amount of mashed potatoes you could prepare from eight small potatoes would be the same as from one large one, but which would you rather peel?

Why are most cells so small? If you consider what a cell must do to grow and survive, it may be easier to understand the reasons for its small size. A cell must take in food and other materials through its plasma membrane. Once inside, molecules of these substances must move to their correct locations, where they are converted into other forms. Also, waste byproducts generated by various metabolic reactions must rapidly move out of the cell before they accumulate to toxic concentrations. Because cells are small, the distances molecules have to travel within them are relatively short, which speeds up many cellular activities. In addition, because essential molecules and waste products must all pass through the plasma membrane, the more surface area the cell has, the faster a given quantity of molecules can pass through it. This means that a critical factor in determining cell size is the ratio of its surface area to its volume. If you think of a cell shaped like a cube, you see that as the length of one side is increased, the increase in the *surface area* of the cube is proportional to the *square* of the side, but the increase in *volume* is proportional to the *cube* of that number (Figure 4–4).

The fact that as a cell becomes larger its volume increases more rapidly than its surface area places an upper limit on the size of cells. Above that size, the number of molecules required by the cell could not be transported into the cell fast enough to sustain its needs. Of course, not all cells are spherical or cuboidal in shape. Some very large cells may have more favorable ratios of surface to volume because of their shapes. Much of the variation in cell shape represents different ways of increasing the ratio of surface to volume. For example, some cells such as the particular epithelial

cells pictured in Figure 4.3*e* have finger-like projections of the plasma membrane, called microvilli, which significantly increase the surface area used to absorb nutrients.

CELLS ARE STUDIED BY A COMBINATION OF METHODS

Because cells are so small, scientists have had to be extremely clever in developing methods for studying them. Traditionally, one of the most important tools used to study cell structure has been the microscope. In fact cells were not described until 1665, when Robert Hooke examined a piece of cork using a microscope he had made. Hooke did not actually see cells in the cork; rather, he saw the walls of dead cork cells (Figure 4–5). Not until much later was it realized that the interior of the cell is the important part of the structure.

Refined versions of the *light microscope* (Figure 4–6*a*), along with the development of certain organic chemicals that specifically stain different cellular structures, enabled biologists to discover by the early 20th century that cells contain a number of different internal structures called **organelles** (literally, "little organs").

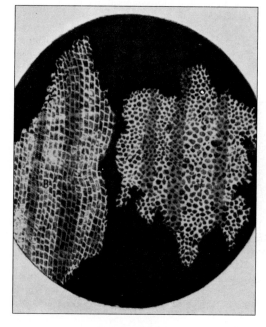

Figure 4–5 A drawing by Robert Hooke of the microscopic structure of a thin slice of cork. Hooke was the first to describe cells, basing his observations on the cell walls of these dead cork cells. Hooke used the term *cell* because the tissue reminded him of the small rooms that monks lived in during that period. (From the book *Micrographica*, published in 1665, in which Hooke described many of the objects that he had viewed using the compound microscope he had constructed)

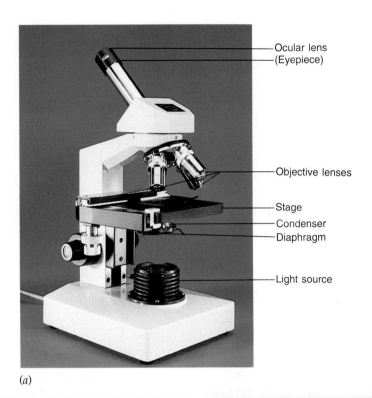

Ocular lens
(Eyepiece)

Objective lenses

Stage
Condenser
Diaphragm

Light source

(*a*)

Figure 4–6 (*a*) A student light microscope. (*b*) through (*e*) Epithelial cells using (*b*) bright field (transmitted light), (*c*) dark field, (*d*) phase contrast, and (*e*) Nomarski differential interference microscopy. The phase contrast and differential interference microscopes enhance detail by increasing the differences in optical density in different regions of the cells. (*a*, Carolina Biological Supply Company; *b–e*, Biological Photo Research)

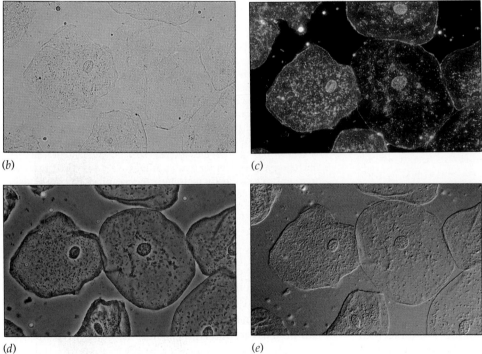

(*b*)

(*c*)

(*d*)

(*e*)

We now know that each type of organelle performs specific functions required for the cell's existence. The development of biological stains was essential for those discoveries because the interior of most cells is transparent in the light microscope. Most of the methods used to prepare and stain cells for observation, however, also killed the cells in the process. More recently, sophisticated types of light microscopes have been developed that use interfering waves of light to enhance the internal structures of cells. With *phase contrast* and *Nomarski differential interference microscopes*, some internal structures can be seen in unstained living cells (Figure 4–6*d* and *e*). One of the most striking things that can be observed with these microscopes is that living cells

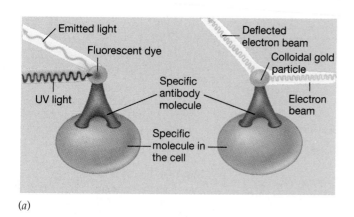

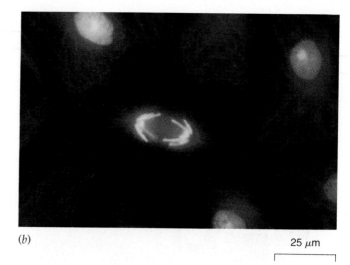

(a)

(b)

25 μm

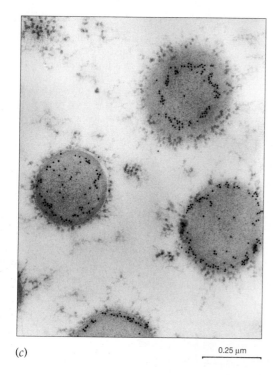

(c)   0.25 μm

Figure 4–7   The use of a specific antibody to determine the cellular location of a specific molecule. (*a*) The antibody molecule on the left has been linked to a fluorescent dye, which emits visible light when illuminated with ultraviolet light. The antibody molecule on the right has been linked to a gold particle, which can be detected because it deflects the electron beam. (*b*) Confocal fluorescence micrograph (see text) of cultured animal cells. The cell in the center is dividing. The DNA of the nuclei and chromosomes is yellow; the microtubules are red. (*c*) Transmission electron micrograph of part of a rat adrenal medullary cell. Gold particles were linked to antibody molecules; the resulting complex binds specifically to the membranes of vesicles within the cell. (*b*, courtesy of Dr. John M. Murray, Department of Anatomy, University of Pennsylvania; *c*, courtesy of Carl Zeiss, Inc.)

contain numerous internal structures that are constantly moving and changing in shape and location. **Fluorescence microscopes** are used to detect the locations of specific molecules in cells. Fluorescent stains (like paints that glow under black light) are molecules that absorb light energy of one wavelength and then release some of that energy as light of a longer wavelength. One such stain binds specifically to DNA molecules and emits green light after absorbing ultraviolet light. Cells can be stained and the location of the DNA can be determined by observing the position of the green fluorescent light within the cell. Some fluorescent stains can be chemically bonded to **antibodies,** special protein molecules that can bind to a highly specific region of a cellular molecule (Figure 4–7*a*) (see Chapter 43). A single type of antibody molecule can

bind to only one type of structure, such as a part of a specific protein or some of the sugars in a specific polysaccharide. Purified fluorescent antibodies that are known to bind to a specific protein isolated from a cell can be used to determine where that protein is located. Recently, powerful new computer imaging methods have allowed the development of the **confocal fluorescence microscope,** which greatly improves the resolution of structures labeled by fluorescent dyes (Figure 4–7*b*).

Cells and their components are so small that ordinary light microscopes can distinguish only the gross details of many cell parts. In most cases all that can be seen clearly is the outline of a structure and its ability to be stained by some dyes and not by others. Not until the development of the **electron microscope (EM),**

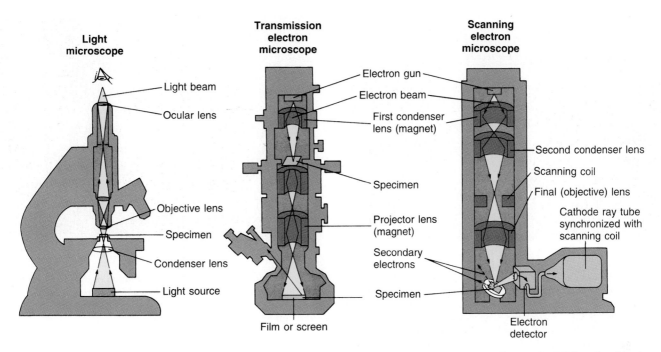

Figure 4–8 Comparison of a light microscope (*left*) with transmission (TEM) (*center*) and scanning (SEM) electron microscopes (*right*). All three microscopes are focused by similar principles. A beam of light or an electron beam is directed by the condenser lens onto the specimen and is magnified by the objective lens and the projector lens in the TEM or the objective lens and the eyepiece in the light microscope. The TEM image is focused onto a fluorescent screen, and the SEM image is viewed on a type of "television" screen. Lenses in the electron microscopes are actually magnets that bend the beam of electrons.

which came into wide use in the 1950s, were researchers able to study the fine details, or **ultrastructure,** of cells.

Two features of a microscope determine how clearly you can view a small object. The **magnification** of the instrument is the ratio of the size of the image seen with the microscope to the actual size of the object. The best light microscopes usually magnify an object no more than 1000 times, whereas the electron microscope can magnify it 250,000 times or more. The other, even more important, feature of a microscope is its **resolving power.** Resolving power is the ability to see fine detail. It is defined as the minimum distance between two points at which they can both be distinguished separately rather than being seen as a single blurred point. Resolving power depends on the quality of the lenses and the *wavelength* of the illuminating light; the shorter the wavelength, the greater the resolution. The visible light used by light microscopes has wavelengths ranging from 400 to 700 nm; this limits the resolution (resolving power) of the light microscope to details no smaller than the diameter of a small bacterial cell.

Whereas the best light microscopes have about 500 times more resolving power than the human eye, the electron microscope increases our resolving power more than 10,000 times (Figures 4–8 and 4–9). This is because electrons have very short wavelengths, on the order of about 0.1 to 0.2 nm. Although this implies that the limit of resolution in the electron microscope comes close to the diameter of a water molecule, such resolution is difficult to achieve with biological material. It can be approached, however, when isolated molecules such as proteins or DNA are examined.

The image formed by the electron microscope cannot be seen directly. The electron beam itself consists of energized electrons, which, because of their negative charge, can be focused by electromagnets just as images are focused by glass lenses in a light microscope (see Figure 4–8). For **transmission electron microscopy (TEM)** one prepares an extraordinarily *thin section* of the cells or tissue embedded in plastic by cutting the specimen with a glass or diamond knife. The preparation is then placed on a small metal grid. The electron beam passes through the specimen and then falls on a photographic plate or a fluorescent screen that works much like a television screen. When you look at electron microscope photographs in this chapter (and elsewhere), keep in mind that they represent only a thin cross section of a cell.

In order to reconstruct how something inside the cell looks in three dimensions, it is necessary to study many consecutive cross-sectional views (called serial sections) through the object. To understand the enormity of such a task, try thinking what it would be like to reconstruct the contents of your home from a set of thousands of consecutive 1-cm sections. Special meth-

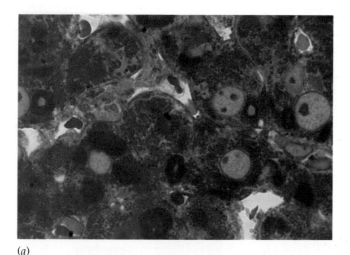

(a)

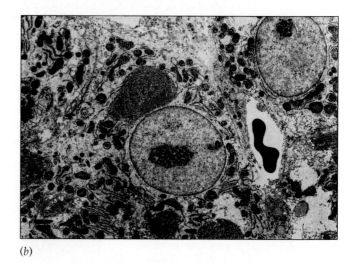

(b)

Figure 4–9   Comparison of a photograph taken with a modern light microscope and one taken with an electron microscope. (*a*) Rat liver cells magnified a total of 1800 times, as seen through a Nomarski interference microscope. (The magnification is greater than the theoretical limits of about 1000 times because the image has been photographed and then enlarged. Photographic enlargements do not increase the resolution of the image, so the additional magnification is sometimes referred to as *empty magnification*.) (*b*) The same cells, at the same magnification, seen through an electron microscope. The clearer detail is a result of the greater resolving power of the electron microscope.   (Courtesy of Dr. F. George Zaki; Squibb Institute for Medical Research)

ods also allow the detection of specific molecules in electron microscope images using antibody molecules that have colloidal gold particles bound to them. The dense gold particles block the electron beam and identify the location of the proteins recognized by the antibodies as precise black spots on the electron micrograph (see Figure 4–7c).

In another type of electron microscope, the **scanning electron microscope (SEM)**, the electron beam does not pass through the specimen. Instead, the specimen is coated with a thin gold film. When the electron beam strikes various points on the surface of the specimen, secondary electrons are emitted whose intensity varies with the contour of the surface. The recorded emission patterns of the secondary electrons give a three-dimensional picture of the surface of the specimen (Figure 4–10). This special kind of micrograph provides information about the shape and external features of the specimen that cannot be obtained with the transmission electron microscope.

The electron microscope is a powerful tool for studying cell structure, but often it provides only clues about the *functions* of organelles and other cell components. To determine what organelles actually do, researchers had to be able to purify different parts of cells so that they could be studied by physical and chemical methods. **Cell fractionation** procedures are methods for purifying organelles. Generally, cells are broken apart as gently as possible and the mixture is subjected to centrifugal force by spinning in a device called a **centrifuge.** The greater the number of rpm's (revolutions per minute), the greater the centrifugal force. This per-

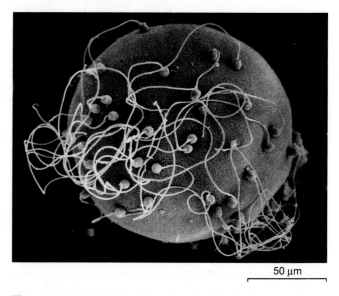

50 μm

Figure 4–10   Scanning electron micrograph of many sperm on the surface of the egg of the surf clam, *Spisula*.   (Visuals Unlimited/ David M. Phillips)

mits various cell components to be separated on the basis of their different densities (Figure 4–11). The purified organelles can then be examined to determine what kinds of proteins and other molecules they might contain, as well as the nature of the chemical reactions that take place within them. Today, cell biologists often use a combination of experimental approaches to understand the functions of cellular structures.

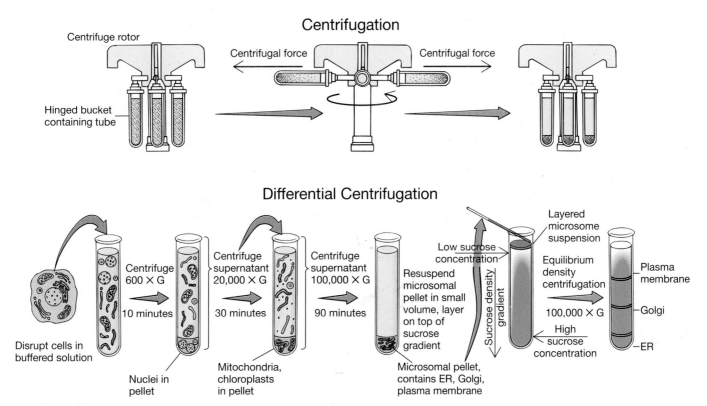

Figure 4–11 Cell fractionation. Cell membranes and organelles are usually separated by centrifuges, machines that can spin test tubes. Spinning the tubes exerts a centrifugal force on the contents, which sediments particles suspended in solution (such as membranes and organelles from disrupted cells), forming a pellet at the bottom of the tube. Different cell parts have different densities, which allows us to separate them into cell fractions by centrifuging the suspension at increasing speeds (**differential centrifugation**). Membranes and the organelles from the resuspended pellets can then be further purified by **equilibrium centrifugation,** which involves layering that solution on top of a **density gradient,** usually made up of sucrose. When the density gradient is centrifuged, organelles and membranes migrate and form bands in the region of the gradient equal to their density. The purified cell fractions are then collected by puncturing the tube bottom and collecting samples of the solution.

EUKARYOTIC CELLS ARE COMPLEX AND CONTAIN MEMBRANOUS ORGANELLES; PROKARYOTIC CELLS ARE SIMPLER

Organisms can be placed into two groups with fundamentally different cell plans, according to the structure and complexity of their cells. **Eukaryotes** are organisms whose cells contain membrane-bounded organelles. The most prominent of these is the *nucleus,* which serves to localize the hereditary material, DNA. In fact, the name eukaryote means "true nucleus."

There are a number of advantages to dividing the cell into membrane-bounded internal compartments. When molecules that participate in a particular chemical reaction are concentrated in only a small part of the total cell volume, the reactants can "find each other" more easily, and the rate of the reaction can be radically increased. Membrane-bounded compartments also keep certain reactive compounds away from other parts of the cell that might be adversely affected by them.

Membranes also allow the storage of energy. The membrane provides a barrier that is analogous to a dam on a river. Energy can be stored when there is a difference in the concentration of some substance on the two sides of the membrane. That energy can then be converted to chemical energy in the form of ATP as the molecules move across the membrane from the side of high concentration to the side of low concentration. This process of energy conversion (discussed in Chapters 7 and 8) is a basic mechanism cells use to capture and convert energy to sustain life.

Membranes in cells also serve as important work surfaces. For example, a number of chemical reactions in cells are carried out by enzymes that are bound to membranes. By organizing the enzymes that carry out successive steps of a series of reactions close together on a membrane surface, certain biological molecules that the cell requires can be made much more rapidly.

Table 4–1 summarizes the types of organelles typically found in eukaryotic cells. Some organelles may be

Table 4–1 EUKARYOTIC CELL STRUCTURES AND THEIR FUNCTIONS

Structure	Description	Function
The Cell Nucleus		
Nucleus	Large structure surrounded by double membrane; contains nucleolus and chromosomes	Control center of cell
Nucleolus	Granular body within nucleus; consists of RNA and protein	Site of ribosomal RNA synthesis; ribosome assembly
Chromosomes	Composed of a complex of DNA and protein known as chromatin; visible as rodlike structures when the cell divides	Contain genes (units of hereditary information that govern structure and activity of cell)
The Membrane System of the Cell (Endomembrane System)		
Plasma membrane	Membrane boundary of living cell	Encloses cellular contents; regulates movement of materials in and out of cell; helps maintain cell shape; communicates with other cells
Endoplasmic reticulum (ER)	Network of internal membranes extending through cytoplasm	Synthetic site of membrane lipids and many membrane proteins; origin of intracellular transport vesicles carrying proteins to be secreted
Smooth	Lacks ribosomes on outer surface	Lipid biosynthesis; drug detoxification
Rough	Ribosomes stud outer surface	Manufacture of many proteins destined for secretion or for incorporation into membranes
Ribosomes	Granules composed of RNA and protein; some attached to ER, some free in cytoplasm	Synthesize polypeptides
Golgi complex	Stacks of flattened membrane sacs	Modifies proteins, packages secreted proteins, sorts other proteins to vacuoles and other organelles
Lysosomes	Membranous sacs (in animals)	Contain enzymes to break down ingested materials, secretions, wastes
Vacuoles	Membranous sacs (mostly in plants, fungi, algae)	Transport and store materials, wastes, water
Microbodies (e.g., peroxisomes)	Membranous sacs containing a variety of enzymes	Sites of many diverse metabolic reactions
Energy-Transducing Organelles		
Mitochondria	Sacs consisting of two membranes; inner membrane is folded to form cristae	Site of most reactions of cellular respiration; transformation of energy originating from glucose or lipids into ATP energy
Plastids (e.g., chloroplasts)	Double membrane structure enclosing internal thylakoid membranes; chloroplasts contain chlorophyll in thylakoid membranes	Chlorophyll captures light energy; ATP and other energy-rich compounds are formed and then used to convert CO_2 to glucose
The Cytoskeleton		
Microtubules	Hollow tubes made of subunits of tubulin protein	Provide structural support; have role in cell and organelle movement and cell division; components of cilia, flagella, centrioles
Microfilaments	Solid, rodlike structures consisting of actin protein	Provide structural support; play role in cell and organelle movement and cell division
Centrioles	Pair of hollow cylinders located near center of cell; each centriole consists of nine microtubule triplets (9×3 structure)	Mitotic spindle forms between centrioles during animal cell division; may anchor and organize microtubule formation in animal cells; absent in higher plants
Cilia	Relatively short projections extending from surface of cell covered by plasma membrane; made of two central and nine peripheral microtubules ($9 + 2$ structure)	Movement of some single-celled organisms; used to move materials on surface of some tissues
Flagella	Long projections made of two central and nine peripheral microtubules ($9 + 2$ structure); extend from surface of cell; covered by plasma membrane	Cellular locomotion by sperm cells and some single-celled organisms

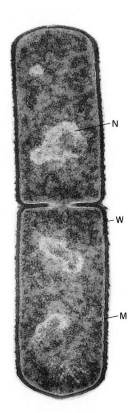

Figure 4–12 The structure of a prokaryotic cell that is about to complete cell division. An electron micrograph of the bacterium, *Bacillus subtilis*. This cell has a prominent cell wall (W) surrounding the plasma membrane (M). The nucleoid regions (N) are clearly visible. (Courtesy of A. Ryter)

found only in specific cells. For example, chloroplasts, structures that trap sunlight for energy conversion, are found only in cells that carry on photosynthesis, such as certain plant cells. The many specialized organelles of eukaryotic cells allow them to overcome some of the problems associated with large size, so eukaryotic cells can be considerably larger than prokaryotic cells.

The cells of **prokaryotes** (meaning "before the nucleus") lack a nucleus and are generally much smaller than eukaryotic cells. Prokaryotes are single-celled organisms that belong to the kingdom Prokaryotae, which includes the bacteria and the cyanobacteria (see Chapter 23). The DNA in prokaryotic cells is usually confined to one or more nuclear regions, sometimes called **nucleoids** (Figure 4–12). Nucleoids are not enclosed by a separate membrane.

Like eukaryotic cells, prokaryotic cells have a **plasma membrane,** which confines the contents of the cell to an internal compartment, but they do not have distinct internal membrane systems in the form of organelles. In some prokaryotic cells the plasma membrane may be folded inward to form a complex of membranes along which the energy-transforming reactions of the cell are thought to take place. Some prokaryotic cells may also have **cell walls** or **outer membranes,**

which are structures that enclose the entire cell, including the plasma membrane. Prokaryotic cells are discussed in more detail in Chapter 23.

THE MANY PARTS OF A EUKARYOTIC CELL INTERACT IN AN INTEGRATED FASHION

Early biologists believed that the cell consisted of a homogeneous jelly, which they called *protoplasm*. With the electron microscope and other modern research tools, perception of the world within the cell has been greatly expanded. We now know that the cell is highly organized and complex (Figures 4–13 to 4–16). It has its own control center, internal transportation system, power plants, factories for making needed materials, packaging plants, and even a "self-destruct" system. Today the word *protoplasm*, if used at all, is used in a very general way. Specifically, the portion of the protoplasm outside the nucleus is called the **cytoplasm,** and the corresponding material within the nucleus is termed the **nucleoplasm.** Various organelles are suspended within the fluid component of the cytoplasm, which is generally referred to as the **cytosol.** Therefore, the term *cytoplasm* includes both the cytosol and all of the organelles other than the nucleus.

The Cell Nucleus Is the Primary Command Center of the Cell

The most prominent organelle is usually the **nucleus.** In most cases the nucleus is spherical or oval and averages 5 μm in diameter. Owing to its size and the fact that it often occupies a relatively fixed position near the center of the cell, some early investigators guessed long before experimental evidence was available that the nucleus served as the control center of the cell (see Focus on *Acetabularia*, pages 88–89). Most cells have one nucleus, although there are a few exceptions.

The nuclear envelope is made up of two membranes and controls passage of materials between the nucleus and the cytoplasm

The nuclear envelope consists of two concentric membranes that separate the nuclear contents from the surrounding cytoplasm (Figure 4–17). These membranes are fused at intervals, forming **nuclear pores.** Nuclear pores appear to allow the passage of materials to the cytoplasm from the interior of the nucleus and vice versa, but the process is highly selective, permitting only specific molecules to pass through these openings.

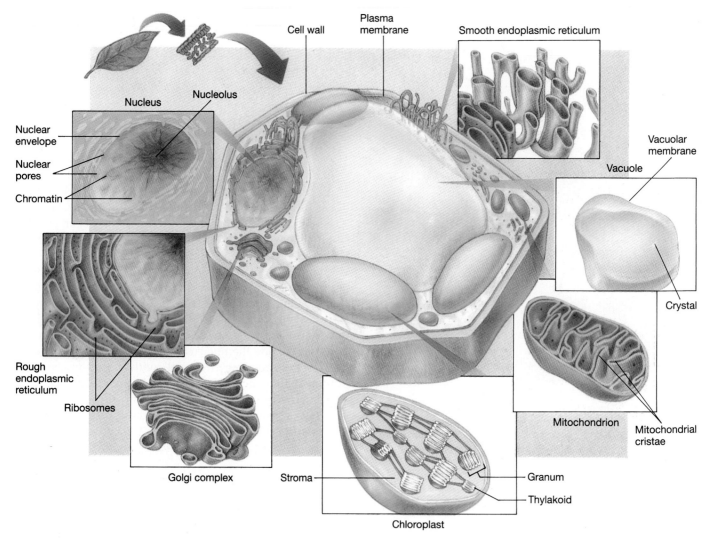

Nucleus
Nucleolus
Nuclear envelope
Nuclear pores
Chromatin
Cell wall
Plasma membrane
Smooth endoplasmic reticulum
Vacuolar membrane
Vacuole
Crystal
Rough endoplasmic reticulum
Ribosomes
Golgi complex
Stroma
Granum
Thylakoid
Chloroplast
Mitochondrion
Mitochondrial cristae

Figure 4–13 Diagram of a generalized plant cell. Some plant cells do not have all the organelles shown in this diagram. Cells from photosynthetic tissues contain chloroplasts, for example, whereas root cells do not. Chloroplasts or other plastids, a cell wall, and prominent vacuoles are characteristic of plant cells. Many of the other components are also found in animal cells.

Attached to the inside of the nuclear envelope is a layer of specific proteins called **lamins** that apparently serve as a skeletal framework for the nucleus and may play an important role in the breakdown and reassembly of the nuclear envelope during cell division (see Chapter 9).

Chromosomes are made up of a DNA/protein complex called chromatin

Almost all the DNA in a cell is located in the interior of the nucleus. The DNA molecules make up the **genes,** which contain the chemically coded instructions for producing virtually all the proteins needed by the cell. The nucleus controls protein synthesis (which takes place in the cytoplasm) by sending messenger RNA molecules, which are copies of the parts of genes that code for proteins (see Chapter 12), through the nuclear membrane to the cytoplasm. The messenger RNA must become attached to small beadlike structures called **ribosomes** in order for its message to be interpreted so that a specific protein can be synthesized.

The DNA is associated with proteins to form a complex known as **chromatin,** which appears to be an irregular network of granules and strands in cells that are not dividing. Although chromatin appears disorganized, it is not. Because DNA molecules are extremely long and thin, they must be packed inside the nucleus in a very regular fashion. The chromatin is organized by arrangement into structures called **chromosomes.** As a cell divides, the chromosomes must be duplicated within the nucleus, and the two copies must be sepa-

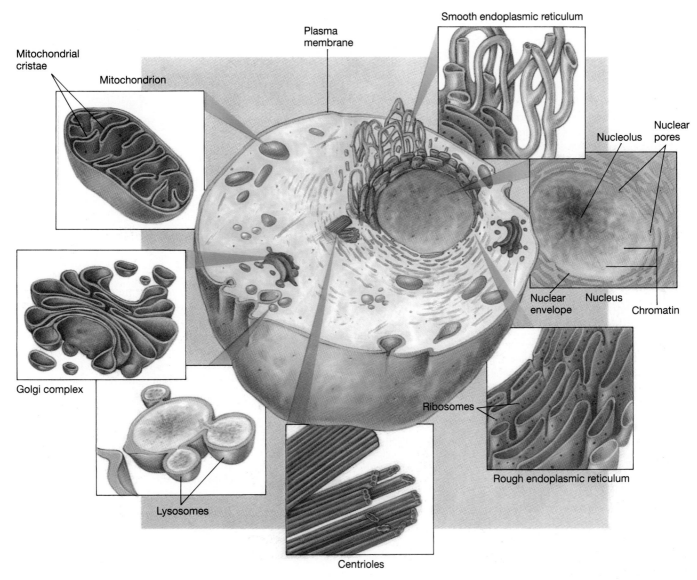

Mitochondrial cristae

Mitochondrion

Plasma membrane

Smooth endoplasmic reticulum

Nucleolus

Nuclear pores

Nuclear envelope

Nucleus

Chromatin

Golgi complex

Ribosomes

Rough endoplasmic reticulum

Lysosomes

Centrioles

Figure 4–14 A generalized animal cell. Depending on the cell type, certain organelles may be more or less prominent features.

rated in such a way that no portion of either is lost or ends up in the wrong place. As the cell prepares to divide, the DNA and proteins that form each chromosome become even more tightly coiled than usual, so that the chromosomes get shorter and thicker and ultimately become visible in the microscope (Figure 4–18).

The nucleolus is the site of ribosomal RNA synthesis and ribosome assembly

In many cells the most visible structure within the nucleus is the **nucleolus** (plural, *nucleoli*), which usually stains differently from the surrounding chromatin. The nucleolus, a compact body that is *not* membrane-bounded, is the site of **ribosome** assembly. The ribosomes are small, but complex, beadlike structures composed of ribosomal RNA and ribosomal proteins. Ribosomal RNA is synthesized in the nucleolus. The ribosomal proteins are synthesized in the cytoplasm and imported into the nucleolus. After these components are properly assembled, the ribosomes leave the nucleus through the nuclear pores and enter the cytoplasm, where they serve as an essential part of the protein synthesis machinery.

Acetabularia: The Mermaid's Wineglass and the Control of Cellular Activities

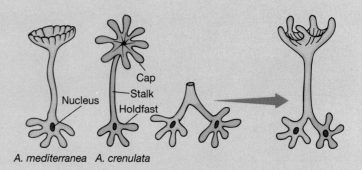

A. mediterranea   A. crenulata

As discussed in Chapter 1, we can learn something about the role of the nucleus by removing it from a cell and examining the consequences. When the nucleus of a single-celled amoeba is removed with a micro-needle, the amoeba continues to live and move, but it does not grow and dies after a few days. A control amoeba, subjected to similar trauma but without removal of the nucleus, does not die. We conclude that the nucleus is necessary for the metabolic processes that provide for growth and cell reproduction.

Acetabularia Is Easy to Manipulate Because It Is a Single Giant Cell

To the romantically inclined, the little seaweed *Acetabularia* resembles a mermaid's wineglass, although the literal translation of its name, "vine-gar cup," is somewhat less elegant.

In the 19th century biologists discovered that this marine eukaryotic alga consists of a single giant cell. At about 5 cm in length, *Acetabularia* is small for a seaweed but gigantic for a cell. It consists of (1) a rootlike **holdfast,** (2) a long cylindrical **stalk,** and (3) a cuplike **cap.** The nucleus is found in the holdfast, about as far away from the cap as it can be.

Regeneration Experiments Demonstrated That the Cap Shape Is under the Control of Something in the Stalk or the Holdfast

If the cap of Acetabularia is removed experimentally, another one grows

after a few weeks. Such behavior, common among lower organisms, is called **regeneration.** This fact attracted the attention of investigators, especially J. Hämmerling and J. Brachet, who became interested in whether a relationship exists between the nucleus and the physical characteristics of the alga. Because of its great size, *Acetabularia* could be subjected to surgery that would be impossible with smaller cells. These researchers performed a brilliant series of experiments that in many ways laid the foundation for much of our modern knowledge of the nucleus. In most experiments they used two species, *A. mediterranea,* which has a smooth cap, and *A. crenulata,* which has a cap broken up into a series of finger-like projections.

The kind of cap that is regenerated depends on the species of *Acetabularia* used in the experiment. As you might expect, *A. crenulata* regenerates a "cren" cap, and *A. mediter-*

ranea regenerates a "med" cap. But it is possible to graft together two capless algae of different species. Through this union, they regenerate a common cap that has characteristics intermediate between those of the two species involved. Thus, it is clear that something about the lower part of the cell controls cap shape.

Stalk Exchange Experiments Indicated That Short-Term Control Can Be Exerted by the Stalk, but Long-Term Control Is in the Holdfast

It is possible to attach a section of *Acetabularia* to a holdfast that is not its own by telescoping the cell walls of the two into one another. In this way the stalks and holdfasts of different species may be intermixed.

First, we take *A. mediterranea* and *A. crenulata* and remove their caps. Then we sever the stalks from the holdfasts. Finally, we exchange the parts.

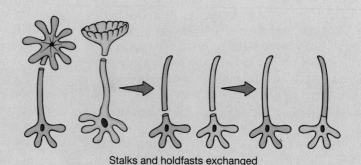

Stalks and holdfasts exchanged

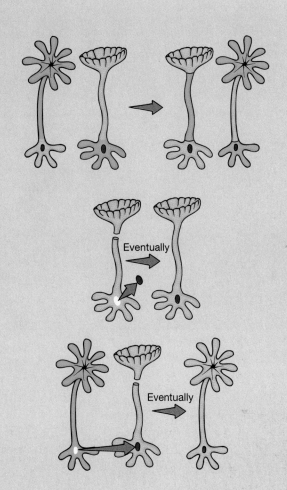

What happens? Not, perhaps, what you would expect! The caps that regenerate are characteristic not of the species donating the holdfasts but of those donating the stalks!

However, if the caps are removed once again, this time the caps that regenerate are characteristic of the species that donated the holdfasts. This continues to be the case no matter how many more times the regenerated caps are removed.

From all these results Hämmerling and Brachet deduced that the ultimate control of the *Acetabularia* cell is associated with the holdfast. Because there is a time lag before the holdfast appears to take over, they hypothesized that it produces some cytoplasmic temporary messenger substance whereby it exerts its control, and that initially the grafted stems still contain enough of that substance from their former holdfasts to regenerate a cap of the former shape. But this still leaves us with the question of what it is about the holdfast that accounts for its apparent power. An obvious suspect is the nucleus.

Nuclear Exchange Experiments Demonstrated That the Nucleus Is the Ultimate Source of Information for the Control of Cellular Activities

If the nucleus is removed and the cap cut off, a new cap regenerates. *Acetabularia,* however, can usually regenerate only once without a nucleus. If the nucleus of an alien species is now inserted, and the cap is cut off once again, a new cap is regenerated that is characteristic of the species of the nucleus! If more than one kind of nucleus is inserted, the regenerated cap is intermediate in shape between those of the species that donated the nuclei.

As a result of these and other experiments, biologists began to accept certain basic ideas. The control of the cell exerted by the holdfast is attributable to the nucleus that is located there. Further, the nucleus is the apparent source of some "messenger substance" that can temporarily exert

control but is limited in quantity and cannot be produced without the nucleus. This information helped provide a starting point for research on the role of the nucleic acids in the control of all cells.

Today we see these ideas extended in our modern view of information flow and control in the cell (see Figure 4–1). We now know that the nucleus of eukaryotes controls the cell's activities because it contains DNA (deoxyribonucleic acid), the ultimate source of biological information. DNA can pass on its information to successive generations because it is able to precisely duplicate or replicate itself. The information in the DNA is used to specify the sequence of amino acids in all of the proteins

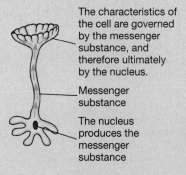

The characteristics of the cell are governed by the messenger substance, and therefore ultimately by the nucleus.

Messenger substance

The nucleus produces the messenger substance

of the cell. In order for DNA to carry out its mission, it uses ribonucleic acid (RNA) as the cytoplasmic messenger substance.

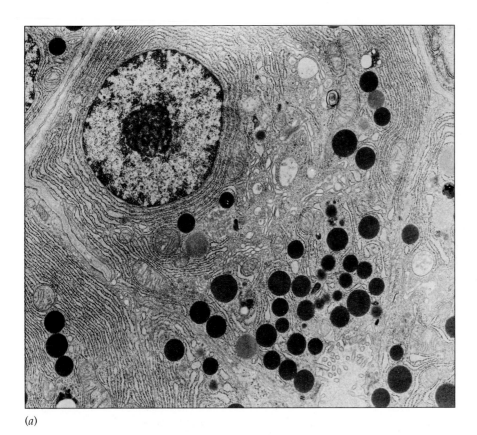

(a)

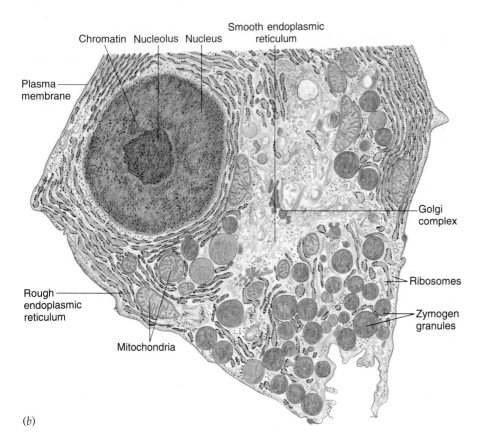

Chromatin Nucleolus Nucleus Smooth endoplasmic reticulum

Plasma membrane

Rough endoplasmic reticulum

Mitochondria

Golgi complex

Ribosomes

Zymogen granules

(b)

Figure 4–15 The structure of an animal cell. (*a*) Electron micrograph of a human pancreas cell, whose specialized function is to secrete large amounts of a protein. Most of the structures of a typical animal cell are present. However, like most animal cells, it has certain features associated with its specialized functions. Most of the membranes in the cell are rough endoplasmic reticulum, because that is the site where the secreted protein is synthesized. The large, circular dark bodies are zymogen granules containing inactive enzymes. When released from the cell they catalyze chemical reactions such as the breaking down of peptide bonds of ingested proteins in the intestine. (*b*) A drawing based on the electron micrograph, illustrating the structures shown in this cross section. Another cell type may have many of the same membrane fractions, but other organelles may occupy most of the cytoplasm. Heart muscle cells, for example, are packed with mitochondria and would have very little endoplasmic reticulum. (*a*, Dr. Susumu Ito, Harvard Medical School)

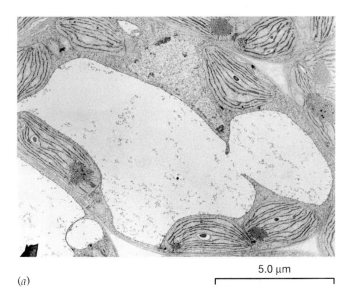

(a)

5.0 μm

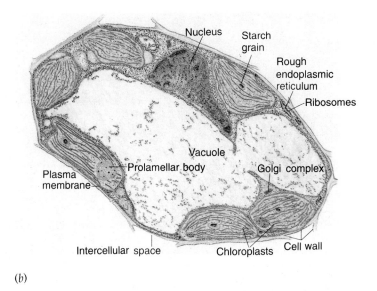

Nucleus
Starch grain
Rough endoplasmic reticulum
Ribosomes
Vacuole
Prolamellar body
Golgi complex
Plasma membrane
Intercellular space
Chloroplasts
Cell wall

(b)

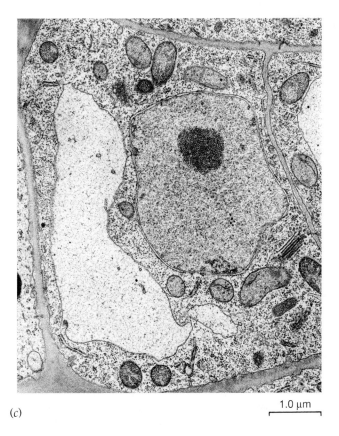

(c)

1.0 μm

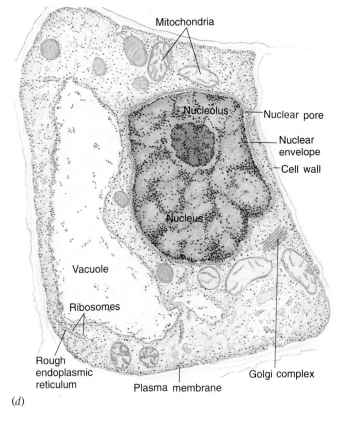

Mitochondria
Nucleolus
Nuclear pore
Nuclear envelope
Cell wall
Nucleus
Vacuole
Ribosomes
Rough endoplasmic reticulum
Plasma membrane
Golgi complex

(d)

Figure 4–16 The structure of a plant cell. (*a*) and (*b*) Electron micrograph and drawing illustrating a cell from the leaf of a young bean plant, *Phaseolus vulgaris*. The vacuole dominates most of the cross section of the cell. Prolamellar bodies are membranous regions typically seen in developing chloroplasts. (*c*) and (*d*) A root cell from *Arabidopsis thailiana*. In the root cell there are no chloroplasts, and more mitochondria are evident in the cross section. (*a*, courtesy of Dr. Kenneth Miller, Brown University; *c*, Biophoto Associates)

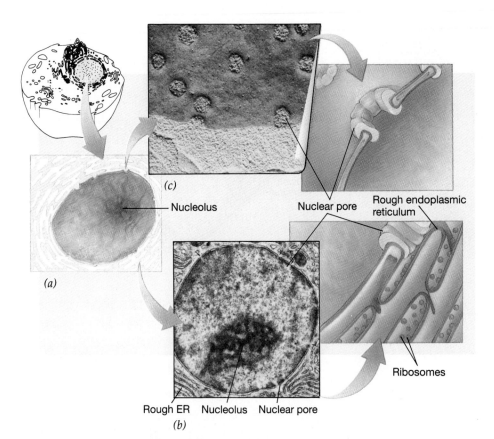

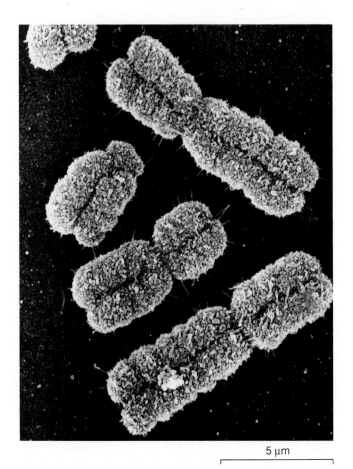

(a)

(c)

Nucleolus

Nuclear pore

Rough endoplasmic reticulum

Ribosomes

Rough ER   Nucleolus   Nuclear pore
(b)

Figure 4–17 (*a*) The cell nucleus cut away to show its interior and the continuity of the outer nuclear membrane with the ER. (*b*) Electron micrograph of the nucleus of a pancreatic acinar cell. Note the two membranes that form the nuclear envelope. Arrows indicate the nuclear pores. (*c*) Freeze-fracture EM of the nuclear envelope surface. The outer of the two membranes is shown at the top of the micrograph along with a number of nuclear pores.

Figure 4–18 Scanning electron micrograph of human chromosomes. Just before division, the loose threads of DNA that make up the chromosomes assemble into the knotted coils you see here. (Biophoto Associates)

The Internal Membrane System Is Made Up of Membranous Organelles That Interact by Means of Vesicles[1]

The endoplasmic reticulum is one of the major manufacturing centers of the cell

In the electron micrograph in Figure 4–15, one of the most prominent features is a maze of parallel internal membranes that encircle the nucleus and extend into many regions of the cytoplasm of the cell. This complex of membranes is the **endoplasmic reticulum (ER),** which can form a significant part of the total volume of the cytoplasm in certain types of cells. A higher magnification micrograph of one type of ER is shown in Figure 4–19. Remember that the electron micrograph represents only a thin cross section of the cell, so there is a

5 μm

---

[1] Vesicles are small membrane-bounded sacs.

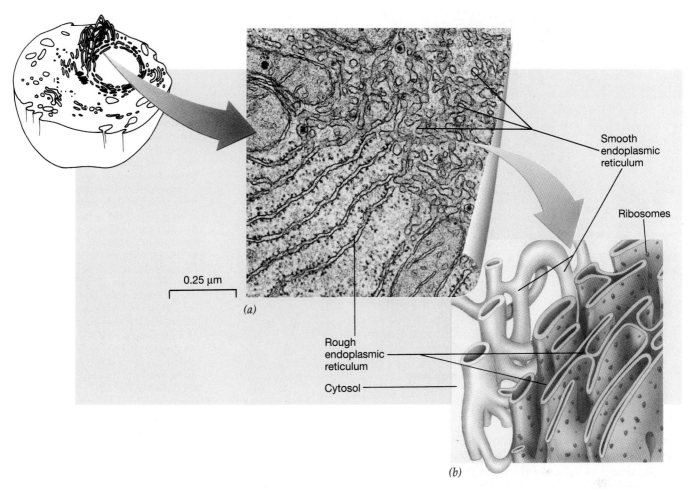

Figure 4–19 Endoplasmic reticulum (ER). (*a*) Transmission electron micrograph showing both rough and smooth ER in a liver cell. The rough ER consists of parallel arrays of broad, flat sacs. The outer surface (cytosolic side) of the rough ER membrane is studded with ribosomes; the surface facing the inner compartment (ER lumen side) is smooth. The smooth ER is more tubular in form and does not have attached ribosomes. (*b*) Diagram comparing the rough and smooth ER. (*a*, Visuals Unlimited/R. Bolender–D. Fawcett)

tendency to interpret the photographs as depicting a series of tubes. In fact, these membranes usually consist of a series of tightly packed and flattened saclike structures (Figure 4–19*a*) that form interconnected compartments within the cytoplasm. The internal space formed by the membrane sheets is called the ER **lumen.** In most cells the ER lumen forms a single internal compartment. Evidence also suggests that the ER membrane is continuous with the outer membrane of the cell nucleus (see Figure 4–17) so that the compartment formed between the two nuclear membranes is connected to the ER lumen. The membranes of other organelles are not directly connected to the ER and appear to form distinct and separate compartments within the cytoplasm.

The ER membranes and the lumen contain a large variety of enzymes that catalyze many different types of chemical reactions. In some cases the membranes serve as a framework for systems of enzymes that carry out sequential biochemical reactions. Other ER enzymes are located within the ER lumen. The two surfaces of the membrane contain different sets of enzymes and represent regions of the cell with different synthetic capabilities, just as different regions of a factory are used to make different parts of a particular product.

Notice that in both Figures 4–15 and 4–19, one membrane face (the cytosolic side) is studded with dark particles, the **ribosomes,** whereas the other membrane face (the lumen side) appears to be bare. Ribosomes are a major component of the protein-synthesizing machinery of the cell, and many of the ribosomes found in the cell at any one time can be found bound to the ER surface. Not all proteins are synthesized on the surface of the ER membranes; in fact, some are synthesized on ribosomes found free within the cytoplasm. All cells, both prokaryotic and eukaryotic, contain ribosomes.

The ER plays a central role in the synthesis and assembly of proteins. Many proteins that are exported from the cell (such as digestive enzymes) or are destined for other organelles are formed on ribosomes attached to the ER membrane. These proteins are trans-

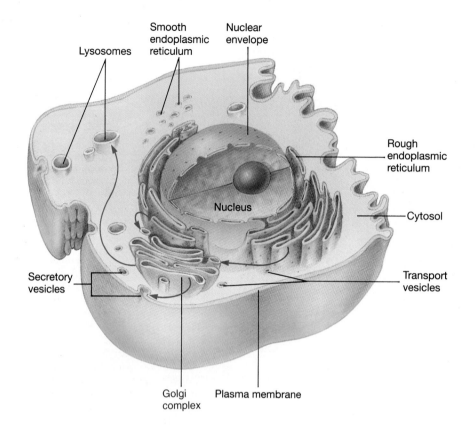

Lysosomes

Smooth
endoplasmic
reticulum

Nuclear
envelope

Rough
endoplasmic
reticulum

Nucleus

Cytosol

Secretory
vesicles

Transport
vesicles

Golgi
complex

Plasma membrane

Figure 4–20 The internal membrane, or endomembrane, system consists of functionally different membranes that communicate with each other. Some membranes are physically connected, and others communicate through vesicles that bud from one membrane and fuse with another membrane in the system. Many of the membrane components originate in the ER and then progress to the cell surface or to other organelles by way of the Golgi complex. A molecule in the lumen of the ER might move via vesicles through several other compartments in the system and then pass through the plasma membrane to the outside by way of a secretory vesicle. The internal compartments enclosed by the internal membranes can thus be considered equivalent to the exterior of the cell.

ported across the membrane into the ER lumen, where they may be modified by enzymes that add complex carbohydrates or lipids to them. Other enzymes in the ER lumen may be involved in assisting proteins in folding to assume their proper conformation. The proteins are then transferred to other membranes by small **transport vesicles,** which bud off the ER membrane and then insert into the target membrane. The ER and the membranes that communicate with it in this manner are sometimes collectively referred to as the **internal membrane system** or the **endomembrane system** (Figure 4–20). These include the ER, the nuclear and plasma membranes, and the Golgi complex and lysosome membranes (discussed later).

Two distinct regions of the ER can be seen in electron micrographs. Although these regions have different functions, their membranes are connected and their internal spaces are continuous. **Rough ER** has ribosomes attached to it and consequently appears rough in electron micrographs. **Smooth ER** is more tubular in nature and does not have ribosomes bound to it, so its outer membrane surfaces have a smooth appearance. The smooth ER is the primary site of phospholipid, steroid, and fatty acid metabolism. Smooth ER also serves an important function by localizing detoxifying enzymes that break down chemicals such as carcinogens (cancer-causing molecules) and convert them to water-soluble products that can be excreted from the body. Certain types of cells, such as liver cells, which synthe-

size and process much of the cholesterol and other bodily lipids and serve as the major detoxification site of the body, contain extensive amounts of smooth ER. The smooth ER may be a minor membrane component in other cells of the body.

The Golgi complex is a factory for processing and packaging proteins

The **Golgi complex** (also known as the Golgi body or Golgi apparatus) was first described in 1898 by the Italian microscopist Camillo Golgi, who found a way to specifically stain that organelle. In many cells the Golgi complex consists of stacks of flattened membranous sacs, which may be distended in certain regions because they are filled with cellular products (Figure 4–21). Each of the flattened sacs has an internal space, or **lumen.** However, unlike the endoplasmic reticulum, these internal spaces of the Golgi complex and the membranes that form them are not continuous. In a cross-section view like Figure 4–21e, many of the ends of the sheetlike layers of Golgi membranes are distended. The arrangement of the membranes in that figure is characteristic of well-developed Golgi complexes in many types of cells. In some animal cells the Golgi complex is often located at one side of the nucleus; in other animal and plant cells there are many Golgi bodies, usually consisting of separate stacks of membranes dispersed throughout the cell.

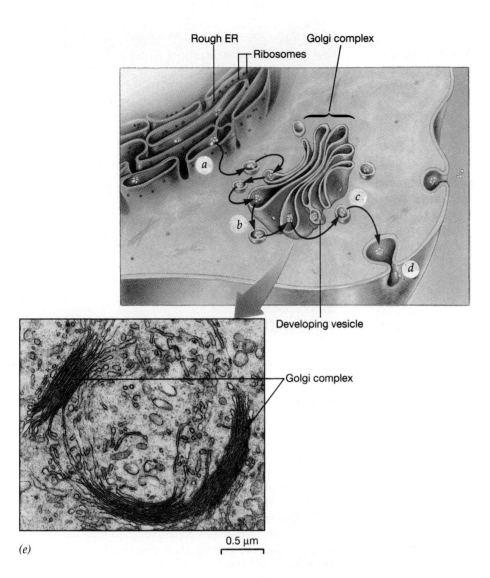

Rough ER   Golgi complex

Ribosomes

a

b

c

d

Developing vesicle

Golgi complex

0.5 μm

(e)

Figure 4–21 The Golgi complex. Labels (*a*) through (*d*) (in top illustration) show the passage of proteins through the Golgi complex during the secretory cycle of a mucus-secreting goblet cell that lines the intestine. By labeling newly synthesized proteins briefly with radioactive amino acids, it is possible to follow their movement in the cell at different times after their synthesis. (*a*) Immediately after synthesis, the proteins are found in the ER, where they were formed on membrane-bound ribosomes. (*b*) Minutes later, some of the labeled proteins have migrated to the inner layers of the Golgi complex. (*c*) A short time later, the labeled proteins can be seen at the outer face of the Golgi apparatus. Many are inside vesicles, which develop at the outer surface of the organelle. (*d*) In the final stages of secretion, labeled proteins can be seen in membrane vesicles between the Golgi complex and the plasma membrane. Some of the membrane vesicles have fused with the plasma membrane and have released their contents outside the cell. (*e*) Electron micrograph of a section through Golgi complexes in a sperm cell of a ram.

The Golgi complex functions principally as an apparatus for processing, sorting, and modifying proteins. Most proteins that are secreted from the cell, are a part of the plasma membrane, or are routed to other organelles of the internal membrane system, pass through the Golgi complex. After those proteins have been synthesized on ribosomes attached to the rough ER, they are transported to the Golgi complex enclosed in small transport vesicles formed from the ER membrane. These vesicles then fuse with the membranes of the complex that are closest to the nucleus (Figure 4–21*a* and *b*; see also Chapter 5). The proteins then pass through the separate layers of the organelle (moving by way of membrane transport vesicles).

While moving through the Golgi complex, the proteins are modified in different ways, resulting in the formation of complex biological molecules (Figure 4–21*c*). Often, carbohydrates are added to the protein or previously added carbohydrates are further modified. Some sugars are actually added to the protein in the rough ER, but these may be further modified in the

Golgi complex. The resulting **glycoproteins** are proteins with complex branched-chain polysaccharides attached to a number of different amino acids. Each type of protein is modified in a different way. In some cases the carbohydrates and other molecules that are added to the protein are used as "sorting signals," allowing the Golgi complex to route the protein to different parts of the cell. The Golgi complex of plant cells also produces some extracellular polysaccharides used as components of the cell wall.

Lysosomes are compartments for digestion

Small sacs of digestive enzymes called **lysosomes** are dispersed in the cytoplasm of animal cells (Figure 4–22). The enzymes in these organelles break down complex molecules, including lipids, proteins, carbohydrates, and nucleic acids, originating both inside and outside the cell. About 40 different enzymes have been identified in lysosomes; most are active near pH 5.

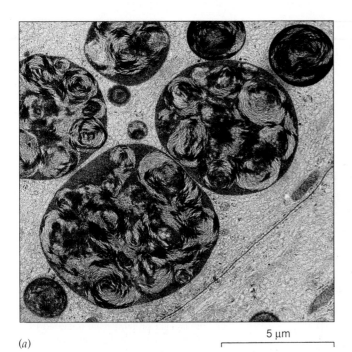

(a)

5 μm

(b)

Figure 4–22   (a) Electron micrograph showing different stages of lysosome formation. Primary lysosomes bud off from the Golgi complex. After a lysosome encounters material to be digested, it is known as a *secondary lysosome*. The secondary lysosomes shown here contain various materials being digested. (b) Distribution of lysosomes in cells. These cells are stained with a dye that emits a yellow-orange fluorescent light in an acid environment.   (a, Don Fawcett, Photo Researchers, Inc.; b, courtesy of Dr. Paul Gallup)

These enzymes originate in the Golgi complex, where they are identified and sorted to the lysosomes by unique carbohydrate signals that have been attached to the proteins.

In a cell that is short of fuel, lysosomes may break down organelles so that their components may be used as an energy source. Lysosomes are also used to degrade foreign molecules that have been ingested by cells. When a white blood cell or a scavenger cell ingests a bacterium or debris from dead cells, the foreign matter is enclosed in a vesicle formed from part of the plasma membrane. One or more lysosomes then fuse with the vesicle that contains foreign matter to form a larger vesicle called a *secondary lysosome*. The powerful digestive enzymes in the lysosome come in contact with the foreign molecules and degrade them into their components.

When a cell dies, the lysosome membranes break down, releasing the digestive enzymes into the cytoplasm, where they break down the cell itself. This "self-destruct" system accounts for the rapid deterioration of many cells following death.

Lysosomes are involved in many normal processes, such as the resorption of the tail of a tadpole undergoing metamorphosis. However, some forms of tissue damage, as well as part of the aging process, may be related to "leaky" lysosomes. Rheumatoid arthritis is thought to result in part from damage done to cartilage cells in the joints by enzymes released from lysosomes.

Vacuoles are large, fluid-filled sacs

Although lysosomes have been identified in almost all kinds of animal cells, their occurrence in plant and fungal cells is open to debate. Many of the functions carried out by lysosomes in animal cells are performed in plant and fungal cells by a large, single membrane-bounded sac referred to as the **vacuole** (see Figure 4–16). Although the terms *vacuole* and *vesicle* are sometimes used interchangeably, vacuoles are usually larger structures, sometimes produced by the merging of many vesicles.

As much as 90% of the volume of a plant cell may be occupied by a large central vacuole containing water, stored food, salts, pigments, and wastes. Plants lack systems for disposing of metabolic waste products that are toxic to the cells; such waste products often aggregate and form small crystals inside the vacuole, making the vacuole look almost "empty" in the EM. The vacuole may also serve as a storage compartment for inorganic compounds in plant cells and for storage molecules such as proteins in seeds. Compounds that are noxious to predators may also be stored in some plant vacuoles as a means of defense.

Vacuoles can have numerous other functions and are actually present in many types of animal cells and most commonly in single-celled protists. Most protozoa have food or digestion vacuoles, which fuse with lysosomes so that the food they contain can be digested (Figure 4–23), and many have contractile vacuoles, which remove excess water from the cell.

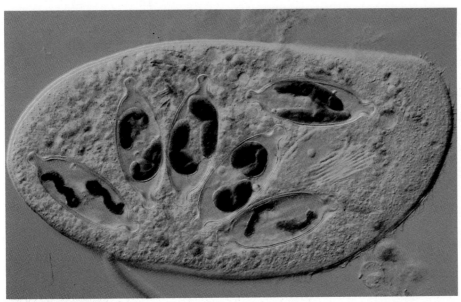

50 μm

Figure 4–23 The protozoon *Chilodonella*. Inside its body are vacuoles containing ingested diatoms (diatoms are small, photosynthetic protists). From the number of diatoms scattered about its insides, one might judge that *Chilodonella* has a rather voracious appetite. (M. I. Walker/Photo Researchers, Inc.)

Microbodies are compartments that carry out specialized chemical reactions

Microbodies are membrane-bounded organelles containing a variety of enzymes that catalyze an assortment of metabolic reactions. During the breakdown of lipids, hydrogen peroxide (H_2O_2), a substance toxic to the cell, is produced. **Peroxisomes** (Figure 4–24), the type of microbody in which these reactions occur, contain enzymes that split hydrogen peroxide, rendering it harmless. Peroxisomes in liver and kidney cells may be important in detoxifying certain compounds such as ethanol, the alcohol in alcoholic beverages.

Plant cells contain two main types of microbodies. A type of peroxisome that is found in leaves plays a part in photosynthesis (see Chapter 8). Another type of microbody, the **glyoxysome,** contains enzymes used to convert stored fats in plant seeds to sugars. The sugars are used by the young plant as an energy source and as a component needed to synthesize other compounds. Animal cells lack glyoxysomes and cannot convert fatty acids into sugars.

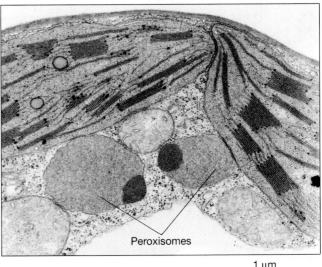

Peroxisomes

1 μm

Figure 4–24 Two peroxisomes in a leaf cell of tobacco. Three mitochondria and portions of two chloroplasts are seen adjacent to the peroxisomes. (E. H. Newcomb and S. E. Frederick, University of Wisconsin/Biological Photo Service)

Mitochondria and Chloroplasts Are Energy-Converting Organelles

When a cell obtains energy from its environment, it is usually in the form of chemical energy in food molecules (such as glucose) or in the form of light energy. These types of energy must be converted to forms that can be used more conveniently by cells. Some of these energy conversions go on in the cytosol, but others take place in mitochondria and chloroplasts, structures sometimes referred to as energy-transducing organelles because they are specialized to facilitate conversion of energy from one form to another. Most commonly energy is converted to ATP. You will recall from Chapter 3 that the chemical energy of ATP can be used to drive a variety of chemical reactions in the cell. Figure 4–25 summarizes the main activities that take place in mitochondria, which are found in almost all eukaryotic cells, and chloroplasts, which are found only in algae and certain plant cells.

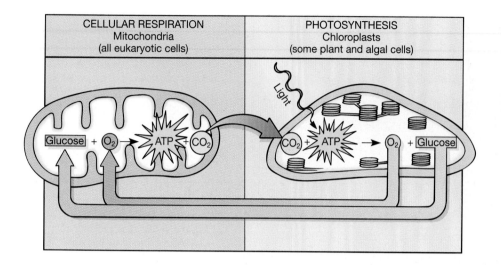

| CELLULAR RESPIRATION Mitochondria (all eukaryotic cells) | PHOTOSYNTHESIS Chloroplasts (some plant and algal cells) |

Figure 4–25 A simplified view of the relationship between cellular respiration, which takes place in mitochondria in all eukaryotic cells, and photosynthesis, which is carried out in chloroplasts in some plant and algal cells.

Mitochondria make ATP through the process of cellular respiration

Virtually all eukaryotic cells (plant, animal, fungal, and protist) contain complex organelles called **mitochondria** (singular, *mitochondrion*). These organelles are the site of **cellular respiration** (see Chapter 7), a process that includes most of the reactions that convert the chemical energy present in certain foods to ATP. Cellular respiration requires oxygen and results in the release of carbon atoms from food molecules as carbon dioxide. Mitochondria are most numerous in cells that are very active and therefore have high energy requirements. More than 1000 have been counted in a single liver cell, but the number varies among cell types. Mitochondria vary in size, ranging from 2 to 8 μm in length, and they are capable of changing size and shape rapidly. Mitochondria usually give rise to other mitochondria by growth and division.

Each mitochondrion is bounded by a double membrane, which forms two different compartments within the organelle (Figure 4–26; see also Chapter 7 for more detailed descriptions of structure). The **intermembrane space** is the compartment formed between the outer and inner membranes; the **matrix** is the compartment enclosed by the inner membrane. The outer membrane of the mitochondrion is smooth and somewhat like a sieve in that it allows many small molecules to pass through it. By contrast, the inner membrane is a selectively permeable membrane and strictly regulates the types of molecules that can move across it; this membrane is folded repeatedly into projections, called **cristae,** that serve to increase its surface area. The matrix compartment contains enzymes that are used to break down food molecules and release their energy. The inner membrane contains a complex series of enzymes

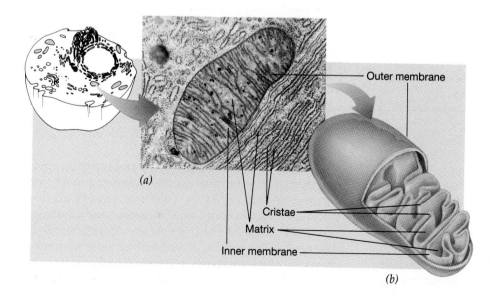

(a)

Outer membrane

Cristae

Matrix

Inner membrane

(b)

Figure 4–26 The mitochondrion. (*a*) Electron micrograph of a typical mitochondrion from the pancreas of a bat, showing the cristae and matrix. (*b*) Diagram of a mitochondrion cut open to show the cristae.   (*a*, Keith Porter)

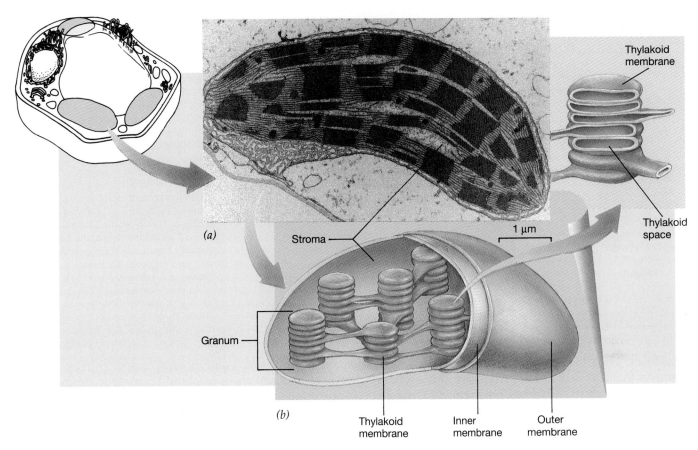

(a)

(b)

Figure 4–27 The chloroplast. (*a*) Electron micrograph of a chloroplast, showing its fine structure. The thylakoids, an interconnected set of flat, disclike sacs, are arranged in stacks called *grana*. (*b*) An inside view of a chloroplast showing the arrangement of the thylakoids. The membranous interconnections between thylakoids can only be suggested in this diagram.   (*a*, L. K. Shumway/Photo Researchers, Inc.)

and other proteins that are involved in transforming the chemical energy in food molecules into chemical energy stored in ATP.

Chloroplasts convert light energy to chemical energy through the process of photosynthesis

Certain plants and algal cells carry out a complex set of energy conversion reactions known as photosynthesis (see Chapter 8). Organelles known as **chloroplasts** contain the green pigments **chlorophyll *a*** and ***b***, which trap light energy for photosynthesis. Chloroplasts also contain a variety of yellow and orange light-absorbing pigments known as **carotenoids** (see Chapter 3). A unicellular alga may have only a single large chloroplast, whereas a plant leaf cell may have as many as 20 to 100.

Chloroplasts are typically disc-shaped complex structures bounded by an inner and an outer membrane (Figure 4–27; see also Chapter 8 for more detailed descriptions of structure). The space enclosed by the inner membrane, called the **stroma,** contains enzymes responsible for producing glucose from carbon dioxide and water using energy trapped from sunlight. The

inner chloroplast membrane also encloses a third system of membranes, consisting of an interconnected set of flat, disclike sacs called **thylakoids.** The thylakoids are arranged in stacks called **grana** (singular, *granum*).

The thylakoid membranes form a third compartment (innermost) within the chloroplasts called the **thylakoid space.** These chlorophyll-rich membranes are similar to the inner membranes of the mitochondria in that they are involved in the formation of ATP. Energy trapped from sunlight by the chlorophyll molecules is used to excite electrons; the energy in these excited electrons is then used to form molecules of ATP and other energy-rich compounds. The energy contained in those molecules is then used to form glucose from carbon dioxide and water in the stroma.

Chloroplasts are only one of several types of organelles known as **plastids,** which produce and store food materials in cells of plants and algae. All plastids develop from **proplastids,** which are precursor organelles found in unspecialized plant cells, particularly in growing, undeveloped tissues. Depending on the special functions that these cells will eventually have, the proplastids can mature into chloroplasts when stimu-

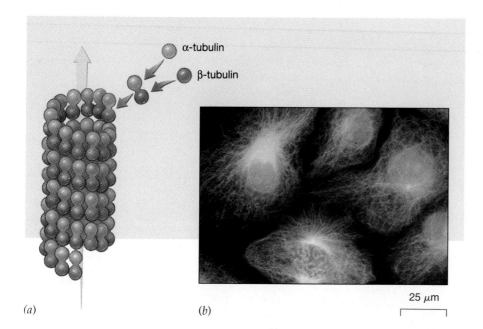

α-tubulin

β-tubulin

(a)   *(b)*

25 μm

Figure 4–28   Microtubules. *(a)* Structure and assembly of microtubules. Microtubules are constructed by adding dimers of α-tubulin and β-tubulin to an end of the hollow cylinder. Each turn of the spiral takes 13 dimers. Disassembly occurs by removal of subunits from the ends of the filaments. *(b)* Confocal fluorescence micrograph showing the extensive distribution of microtubules. These cells were stained with fluorescent antibodies, which bind to the tubulin, permitting the microtubules to be viewed (green). Different fluorescent antibodies were used to stain the DNA (orange).   *(b,* courtesy of Dr. John M. Murray, Department of Anatomy, University of Pennsylvania)

lated by exposure to light; **chromoplasts,** which contain pigments that give fruits and flowers their characteristic colors; or **leucoplasts,** which are not pigmented and are found primarily in roots and tubers, where they are used to store starch.

Mitochondria and chloroplasts have many prokaryote-like features

Although most of the DNA in eukaryotic cells resides in the nucleus, both mitochondria and chloroplasts have DNA molecules in their inner compartments. These DNA molecules specify a small number of the proteins found in these organelles. The majority of the mitochondrial and chloroplast proteins, however, are made on free ribosomes outside the organelles and then transported to their appropriate locations within. The existence of a separate set of DNA molecules in mitochondria and chloroplasts, along with other characteristics that are prokaryote-like, have suggested to some biologists that these organelles may have actually evolved from prokaryotic organisms that originally lived inside larger cells and gradually evolved so that they were no longer autonomous organisms. This idea has become a major part of one theory concerning how eukaryotic organisms came into existence (see Chapter 20).

The Cytoskeleton Is a Dynamic Network of Protein Fibers

If you look closely at cells from different animal tissues, you find striking and characteristic differences in cell shape. If you watch these cells while they are growing in the laboratory, it also becomes apparent that the cells can change shape and in many cases can move about. The shapes of these cells and their ability to move are determined in large part by a complex network of protein fibers found within all eukaryotic cells called the **cytoskeleton.** The term is somewhat misleading because it implies a static structure, whereas the cytoskeleton as a whole is highly dynamic and constantly changing.

The protein filaments that make up the cytoskeletal framework were originally classified on the basis of their relative sizes. The two major types of filaments that make up the cytoskeleton in all eukaryotic cells are **microfilaments** (also known as **actin filaments**), which are 7 nm in diameter, and **microtubules,** which are 25 nm in diameter. Both microfilaments and microtubules are fibers formed from beadlike *globular* protein subunits, which can be rapidly assembled and disassembled. Although both types of fibers are major components of the cytoskeleton, they also play a role in forming other structures involved in cellular movement and organization.

In many animal cells there is also a third class of filaments, **intermediate filaments,** which have a diameter of 8 to 10 nm, intermediate between those of the other two. Intermediate filaments are made from *fibrous* protein subunits and are more stable than microtubules and microfilaments.

Microtubules are readily assembled hollow rods

Microtubules are hollow, rod-shaped structures (Figure 4–28). In addition to playing a role in the formation of the cytoskeletal structure, they are involved in the movement of chromosomes during cell division and are the major structural components of cilia and flagella,

Centrioles

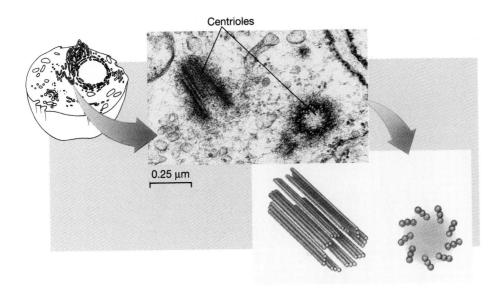

0.25 µm

Figure 4–29 Transmission electron micrograph and interpretive drawing of a pair of centrioles. Note that one centriole has been cut longitudinally and one transversely. (Photo, B. F. King, School of Medicine, University of California, Davis/Biological Photo Service)

special structures used in locomotion. For microtubules to act as a structural framework or participate in cell movement, they must be anchored to other parts of the cell. In nondividing cells, the microtubules appear to extend from a region called the **cell center** or **microtubule-organizing center**. In the cell center of almost all animal cells are two structures arranged at right angles to each other called **centrioles** (Figure 4–29). These structures are made of nine sets of three microtubules arranged to form a hollow rod. The centrioles replicate before cell division and appear to play a role in microtubule assembly, although their specific function is unknown. Although they have the equivalent of a microtubule-organizing center, cells of higher plants do not have centrioles, which suggests either that centrioles are not essential to the microtubule assembly process or that alternative assembly mechanisms are possible.

Microtubules Are Assembled from Beadlike Tubulin Subunits

Microtubules are formed from dimers[1] of protein subunits called **tubulins** (see Figure 4–28*a*). Each dimer is made up of two very similar subunits, α and β. Microtubules grow by the addition of dimers preferentially to one end of the tubules and can be readily disassembled by the removal of subunits, which can then be recycled to form microtubules in other parts of the cell (see Figure 4–28). In addition to having structural properties, microtubules appear to serve as tracks along which or-

ganelles can be moved to different locations. Mitochondria, secretory vesicles, and other organelles apparently are attached to the microtubules and then transported to various parts of the cell along the microtubule network by ATP-requiring proteins, which act as "motors" for the movement. One such motor protein, named *kinesin*, has been isolated and can be shown to direct the movement of isolated organelles along purified microtubules (Figure 4–30).

The ability of microtubules to be assembled and disassembled rapidly can be seen during cell division (see Chapter 9), when much of the cytoskeletal apparatus in cells appears to break down. Many of the tubulin subunits are then reassembled into a structure called

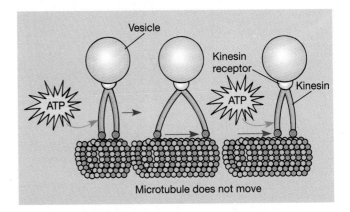

Figure 4–30 Model of a kinesin motor. Kinesin molecules are attached to specific receptors on the vesicle. ATP energy allows the kinesin molecules to "walk" along the microtubule, carrying the vesicle along.

---

[1] A dimer is a structure formed by the association of two monomers (similar, simpler units).

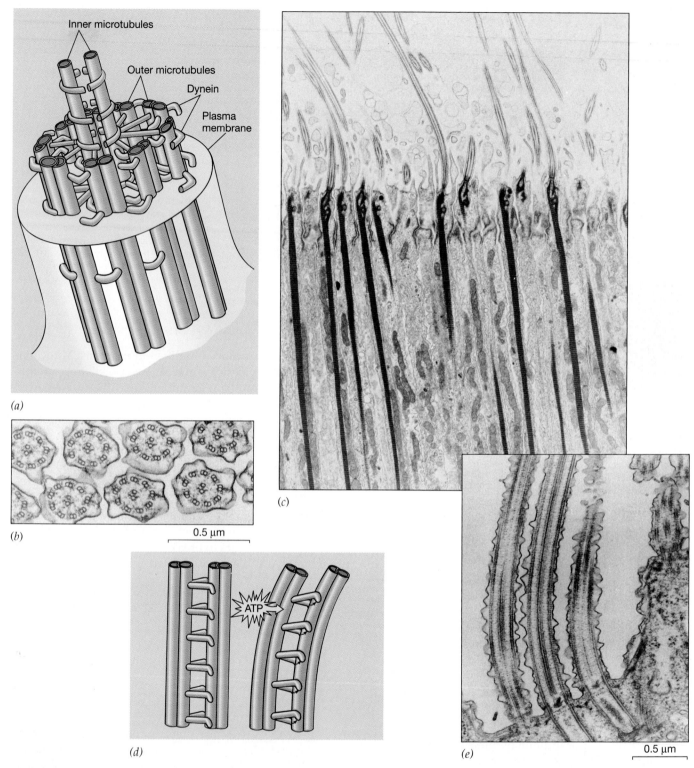

(a)

Inner microtubules

Outer microtubules

Dynein

Plasma membrane

(b)

0.5 μm

(c)

ATP

(d)

(e)

0.5 μm

Figure 4–31 Cilia. (*a*) Structure of a cilium. Each cilium contains microtubules in a 9 + 2 arrangement. Nine attached pairs (doublets) are arranged in a circle, with two unattached microtubules in the center. The arms shown in the figure are force-generating proteins that use energy from ATP to bend the cilia by "walking" up and down the neighboring pair of microtubules. (*b*) Electron micrograph of cross sections through cilia showing the 9 + 2 arrangement of microtubules. (*c*) Electron micrograph of the bases of the cilia that cover the gills of the primitive chordate *Branchiostoma*. (*d*) The dynein arms move the microtubules by forming and breaking cross bridges on the adjacent microtubules so that one tubule "walks" along its neighbor. (*e*) Electron micrograph of a longitudinal section of the cilia of the protist *Tetrahymena*, an organism often used in genetic research. Some of the interior microtubules may be clearly seen. In the original photograph, some of the connections between the microtubules also are evident. (*b, e,* W. L. Dentler, University of Kansas/Biological Photo Service; *c*, Dr. M. C. Holley)

(a)

(b)

(c)

(d)

Figure 4–32 How cilia grow. (*a*) A carpet of cilia lining the trachea of a rat. (*b*) One of the millions of cells bearing those cilia, at an early stage of their life. The new cilia project like spines from the cell surface. In (*c*) they are much longer, and in (*d*) they form a pattern like a crown or flower on the top of the cell. In the center of the radiating cilia are a group of finger-like microvilli. (*a–c*, courtesy of Dr. Ulf Nordin, *Acta Otolaryngol*, 94, 1982; *d*, courtesy of Drs. James A. Papp and Joseph T. Martin, *American Journal of Anatomy*, 169, 1984)

the **spindle,** which serves as a framework for the orderly distribution of chromosomes when the cell divides.

Cilia and Flagella Are Microtubule-Containing Structures That Are Used in Cell Movements

Many cells have movable whiplike structures projecting from their surfaces that exhibit a beating motion. If a cell has one, or only a few, of these appendages and they are relatively long in proportion to the size of the cell, they are called **flagella** (singular, *flagellum*). If the cell has many short appendages, they are called **cilia** (singular, *cilium*). Both cilia and flagella are used by cells to move through a watery environment or to move liquids and particles across the surface of the cell. These structures are commonly found on one-celled and small multicellular organisms. In animals flagella serve as the tails of sperm cells, and cilia commonly occur on the surfaces of cells that line internal ducts of the body (e.g., respiratory passageways).

Regardless of the kind of cell, all cilia and flagella are structurally alike. Each consists of a slender, cylindrical stalk covered by an extension of the plasma membrane. The core of the stalk contains a group of microtubules arranged so that there are nine pairs of tubules around the circumference and two microtubules in the center (Figure 4–31). This **9 + 2 arrangement** is characteristic of all eukaryotic cilia and flagella. The microtubules move by sliding in pairs past each other. The sliding force is generated by *dynein* proteins, which are attached to the microtubules like small arms. These proteins use the energy stored in ATP in such a way that the arms on one pair of tubules are able to "walk" along the adjacent pair of tubules, causing the entire structure to bend back and forth. Thus, the microtubules on one side of a cilium or a flagellum extend farther toward the tip than those on the other side, resulting in a beating motion (Figure 4–31*d*).

At the base of each cilium and flagellum is a **basal body,** which has nine sets of three microtubules in a cylindrical array (see Figure 4–29). Both basal bodies and centrioles are referred to as **9 × 3** structures due to the similarities in the arrangement of their microtubules. The basal body appears to be the organizing structure for the cilium or flagellum when it first begins to form. However, experiments have shown that as growth proceeds, the tubulin subunits are added to the tips of the microtubules rather than the base of the structure (Figure 4–32).

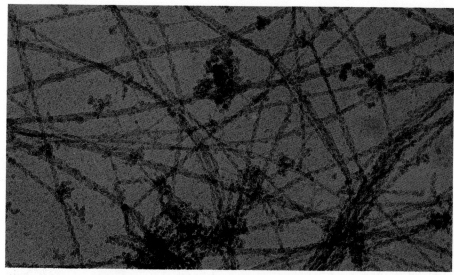

0.1 μm

Figure 4–33 Actin filaments. An electron micrograph of isolated actin filaments, spread on a plastic film. (Visuals Unlimited/M. Schliwa)

Microfilaments are readily assembled, intertwined strings of globular proteins

Microfilaments are solid fibers composed of the protein *actin* and actin-associated proteins (Figure 4–33). In muscle cells actin is associated with another protein, myosin, to form fibers that generate the forces involved in muscle contraction (see Chapter 38). Actin microfilaments perform two different types of functions in nonmuscle cells. When actin is associated with myosin, it can form contractile structures that are involved in various cell movements. Actin can also be cross-linked with other proteins to form bundles of fibers that provide mechanical support for various cell structures.

Stress fibers are actin bundles that lie close to the plasma membrane of fibroblast (connective tissue) cells and appear to provide the stress or tension that causes these cells to assume a flattened shape. Actin fibers themselves cannot contract, but they can generate movement by rapidly assembling and disassembling.

Many types of cells have finger-like *microvilli* projecting from their surfaces. These structures can extend and retract as a result of the polymerization and depolymerization of actin fibers within the microvilli. Actin microfilaments associated with myosin are involved in transient functions such as cell division in animals, in which contraction of a ring of actin complexed with myosin causes the constriction of the cell to form two daughter cells. This occurs after microtubules act to separate duplicated chromosomes (see Chapter 9).

Intermediate filaments help to stabilize cell shape

Intermediate filaments are very stable, tough fibers made of polypeptides that can range widely in size among different cell types and different species of animals. These fibers are thought to help strengthen the cytoskeleton and are abundant in parts of a cell that may be subject to mechanical stress. The assembly of these filaments is probably irreversible; unpolymerized subunits are not abundant in cells. Cells may be able to regulate the length of intermediate filaments, however, by use of enzymes that break down their polypeptides into smaller fragments. It is not clear whether they are involved in cellular functions aside from their structural role. Figure 4–34 depicts the possible relationships among various cytoskeletal elements, including intermediate filaments, microtubules, and microfilaments.

Most Cells Are Surrounded by an Extracellular Matrix

Although the contents of the cell are effectively contained by the plasma membrane, most cells are also surrounded by some type of secreted coating that extends beyond the cell surface. Plant cells are surrounded by thick **cell walls** that contain multiple layers of the polysaccharide *cellulose*. These molecules are formed into bundles of fibers that make up the bulk of the cell wall (Figure 4–35). Other polysaccharides are used in the cell wall to form cross links between the cellulose fibers. Each layer of cellulose fibers in a plant cell wall runs in a different direction from the adjacent layer, giving the structure great mechanical strength. A growing plant cell secretes a thin *primary cell wall*, which can stretch and expand as the cell increases its size. After the cell stops growing, either new wall material is secreted that thickens and solidifies the primary wall or multiple layers of a *secondary cell wall* with a different composition are formed between the primary wall and the plasma membrane.

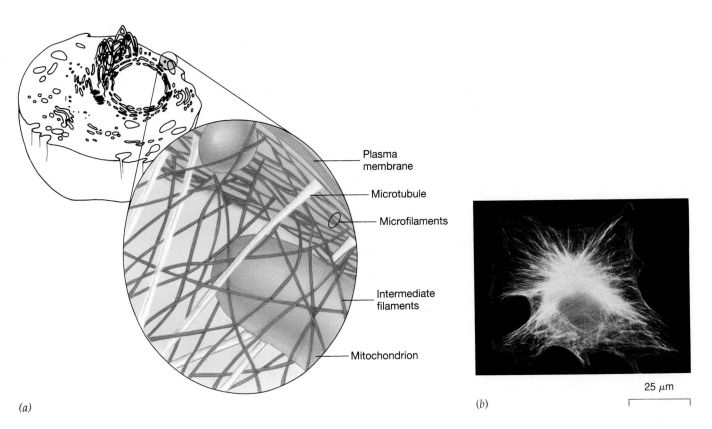

(a)   *(b)*

Figure 4–34 Elements of the cytoskeleton. (*a*) The cytoskeleton consists of networks of several types of fibers, including microtubules, microfilaments, and intermediate filaments. The cytoskeleton contributes to the shape of the cell, anchors organelles, and sometimes rapidly changes shape during cellular locomotion. (*b*) Micrograph showing a fibroblast cell. Microfilaments are stained in red, microtubules in green. (*b*, Visuals Unlimited/M. Schliwa)

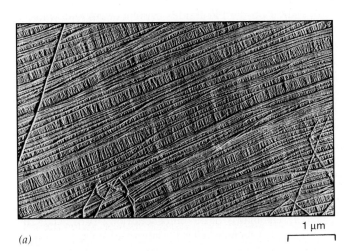

(a)

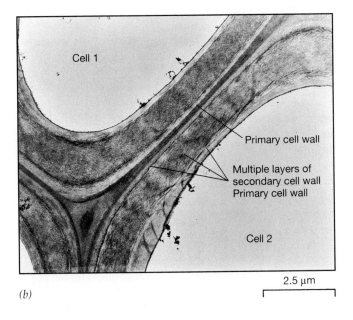

(b)

Figure 4–35 The structure of the plant cell wall. (*a*) A plant cell wall consists of multiple layers of cellulose fibers secreted from the cell. (*b*) Between two adjacent plant cells is a region containing gluelike polysaccharides, called pectins, which cement the cells together. A growing plant cell first secretes a thin primary wall that is flexible and can stretch as the cell grows. The thicker layers of the secondary wall are secreted after the cell stops growing. (*a*, Omikron, Photo Researchers, Inc.; *b*, Biophoto Associates)

Animal cells do not have rigid cell walls, although many secrete proteins and polysaccharides that are bound to their outer surfaces and fill spaces between cells in tissues. The **glycocalyx** is a coat formed by polysaccharide side chains of lipids and proteins that are a part of the plasma membrane. Many of these molecules contain negatively charged regions, which give a negative charge to the surfaces of most cells. In many cases these coatings play a role in cellular contact and recognition, in addition to increasing the mechanical strength of multicellular tissues.

SUMMARY

I. The cell is considered the basic unit of life because it is the smallest self-sufficient unit of living material.

II. Modern cell theory states that organisms are composed of cells and products of cells. All cells arise by division of preexisting cells.

III. Biologists have learned much about cellular structure by studying cells with light and electron microscopes. The electron microscope has superior resolving power, enabling investigators to see details of cell structures not observable with conventional microscopes. Information about the function of cellular structures requires the use of cell fractionation and biochemical methods in addition to microscopic observations.

IV. Every cell is surrounded by a plasma membrane that forms a cytoplasmic compartment, which contains the contents of the cell.

   A. Membrane-bounded compartments allow cells to conduct specialized activities within small areas of the cytoplasm, are used to concentrate molecules, serve as a system of energy storage, and are used to organize metabolic reactions within the cell.

   B. Cells are small so that the ratio of surface area to cell volume is favorable for rapid transport of molecules into or out of the cell.

   C. Prokaryotic cells are bounded by a plasma membrane but lack a nucleus and have little or no internal membrane organization.

   D. Eukaryotic cells have a nucleus and cytoplasm, which is organized into membrane-bounded compartments called *organelles*. Plant cells differ from animal cells in that they possess rigid cell walls, plastids, and large vacuoles; complex plant cells lack centrioles.

V. The organelles of eukaryotic cells assume many diverse functions.

   A. The nucleus, the control center of the cell, contains genetic information in the form of genes on the chromosomes.

      1. The nucleus is bounded by a double-membrane system with pores that communicate with the cytoplasm.

      2. Genetic information in the nucleus is carried by the DNA, which is complexed with protein to form a material known as *chromatin*. Chromatin complexes are organized into chromosomes, which become visible when the cell divides.

      3. The nucleolus is a region in the nucleus that is the site of ribosomal RNA synthesis and ribosome assembly.

   B. The endoplasmic reticulum (ER) is a series of folded internal membranes that has many functions.

      1. Rough ER is studded along its outer walls with ribosomes, which manufacture proteins.

      2. Smooth ER is the site of lipid biosynthesis and detoxifying enzymes.

      3. Proteins synthesized on rough ER can be transferred to other membranes or secreted from the cells by transport vesicles, which are formed by membrane budding and are then targeted to different cellular membrane locations.

   C. The Golgi complex is a series of flattened membrane sacs that process, sort, and modify proteins synthesized on the ER. It adds carbohydrates and lipids to proteins and can route proteins (by way of transport vesicles) to the plasma membrane, to the outside of the cell, and to the lysosomes and possibly other membrane systems.

   D. Lysosomes function in intracellular digestion; they contain degradative enzymes that break down substances taken into cells, as well as worn-out cell structures.

   E. Microbodies are membrane-bounded sacs that can contain enzymes with diverse functions. Peroxisomes are microbodies that break down hydrogen peroxide.

   F. Mitochondria are double-membrane organelles in which the inner membrane is folded to form cristae.

      1. The matrix of the mitochondrion (space inside the inner membrane) is the site where energy-rich molecules derived from glucose or fatty acids are broken down, releasing chemical energy.

2. Proteins in the inner mitochondrial membrane are involved in transforming energy released by the breakdown of glucose or fatty acids into chemical energy stored in ATP.

G. Cells of algae and plants contain plastids; chloroplasts are double membrane structures enclosing internal thylakoid membranes, which are organized as stacks of flat, disclike structures called grana.
   1. Thylakoid membranes contain chlorophyll, which traps energy in sunlight and plays a role in its conversion to chemical energy in the form of ATP.
   2. The stroma is the space between the inner membrane and the thylakoid membrane. The stroma is the site of carbohydrate synthesis from carbon dioxide and water, using energy from the ATP synthesized in the thylakoids.

H. The cytoskeleton is an internal framework made of at least three types of fiber. Much of the cytoskeleton can be rapidly disassembled and reassembled in a different form, altering the shape of the cell.
   1. Microtubules are hollow cylinders formed from subunits of the protein tubulin.
   2. Microfilaments, filaments with a smaller diameter than microtubules, are formed from subunits of the protein actin.
   3. Intermediate filaments are formed from several different types of protein.
   4. Microfilaments and microtubules can be rapidly assembled and disassembled; intermediate filaments are stable structures.

I. Cilia and flagella are structures that project from the cell surface and are used for cell movement. They are formed from microtubules (9 + 2 structure) and covered by the plasma membrane.

J. Microtubules are used to form centrioles and basal bodies (9 × 3 structure), which appear to be organizing centers for microtubule formation in animal cells.

K. Actin microfilaments can generate movement by rapid polymerization and depolymerization. Actin microfilaments associated with other proteins such as myosin can slide past one another, generating force and movement.

L. Plant cells secrete cellulose and other polysaccharides to form rigid cell walls.

M. Some animal cells are covered by a glycocalyx, a coating formed from carbohydrate regions of glycoproteins and glycolipids on the surface of the cell.

POST-TEST

1. The ability of a microscope to reveal fine detail is known as _____.

2. Proteins that are to be secreted from the cell are synthesized by ribosomes bound to the _____.

3. The hereditary material _____ is found in the _____ of prokaryotic cells. In eukaryotic cells it is complexed with proteins to form _____, which becomes tightly coiled structures called _____ in dividing cells.

4. Powerful hydrolytic enzymes contained in the _____ are released when the cell dies and digest the cellular remains.

5. Membrane-bounded organelles that break down H_2O_2 are termed _____.

6. The shelflike folds of the inner mitochondrial membrane called _____ are the site of _____ synthesis.

7. The _____ are organelles involved in the synthesis and storage of carbohydrates.

8. Chlorophyll, which is located in the _____ membranes of chloroplasts, is used to trap energy from _____ for use in _____ synthesis.

9. The cylindrical, hollow cytoplasmic filaments called _____ play a role in controlling the shape and movement of cells.

10. The flexible framework in the cytoplasm of the cell called the *cytoskeleton* is mainly composed of _____, _____, and _____ filaments.

11. _____ and _____ are movable, whiplike structures projecting from the cell surface. These are used to move the cell through surrounding liquid or to move liquid across the surface of the cell. The core of each is composed of a 9 + 2 arrangement of _____ with _____ in the center and _____ pairs around the circumference.

12. In addition to having a plasma membrane, plant cells are surrounded by a _____ _____, formed primarily from fibers of the polysaccharide _____, which is secreted from the cell.

13. _____ are the membrane compartments in plant cells that are used for the storage of water and waste products. They may also have functions similar to _____ of animal cells.

14. Ribosomes are assembled in the _____ region of the _____ in eukaryotic cells.

15. The Golgi complex modifies proteins by adding complex carbohydrates to certain amino acids in the polypeptide chains to form _____.

Match the subcellular organelles in Column A with their functions in Column B.

Column A
16. Glyoxysomes
17. Centrioles
18. Chromosomes
19. Cilia
20. Flagella
21. Golgi complex
22. Lysosomes
23. Microfilaments
24. Microtubules
25. Mitochondria
26. Nucleolus
27. Nucleus
28. Plastids
29. Ribosomes
30. Rough endoplasmic reticulum
31. Smooth endoplasmic reticulum
32. Vacuole

Column B
a. Organelles containing enzymes that convert stored fats into sugars
b. Site of lipid biosynthesis
c. System of internal membranes, site of protein synthesis for plasma membrane and secreted proteins
d. Particles composed of RNA and proteins and involved in protein synthesis
e. Packages and processes secretory products of the cell
f. Packets of hydrolytic (digestive) enzymes
g. Move materials along the cell surface
h. Long projections from the cell surface that move the cell along

i. Contains DNA and chromosomes
j. Ribosome assembly site
k. Contain the genes
l. Membrane compartment that regulates water and waste
m. Site of most reactions of cellular respiration
n. Thin fibers that provide structural support inside the cell
o. Component of cilia, flagella, and centrioles
p. Pairs of cylindrical structures containing microtubules in a 9×3 arrangement
q. Membranous structures containing pigments

REVIEW QUESTIONS

1. Trace the development of the cell theory. Why is this theory important to an understanding of how living things work?
2. What are the main differences between prokaryotic and eukaryotic cells?
3. Draw diagrams of a prokaryotic cell, a plant cell, and an animal cell. Label the organelles. Which organelles might be found in a plant cell but not an animal cell (and vice versa)?
4. Sketch the membranes of chloroplasts and mitochondria. Label the membranes and their compartments. Describe the activities that take place on the different membranes and in the different compartments of these organelles.
5. What are the functions of each of the following?
   a. ribosomes
   b. endoplasmic reticulum
   c. Golgi complex
   d. lysosomes
6. Trace the path of a protein from its site of synthesis to its final destination for the following:
   a. a secreted protein
   b. a protein found inside the lysosome
   c. a protein associated with the plasma membrane
7. Describe the differences between microfilaments and microtubules. Compare their structure and the different roles they play in cell structure and function.
8. Why are lysosomes sometimes referred to as the "self-destruct system" of the cell?
9. Describe plant cell walls. How are they formed?

RECOMMENDED READINGS

Alberts, B., D. Bray, J. Lewis, M. Raff, K. Roberts, and J. D. Watson. *Molecular Biology of the Cell*. Garland, New York, 1989, Chapters 4, 7, 8, 9, 11, and 20. A comprehensive text on cell biology, well written and well illustrated.

Darnell, J., H. Lodish, and D. Baltimore. *Molecular Cell Biology*. Scientific American Books, New York, 1990, Chapters 1, 5, 6, 14, 18, 19, and 20. Another text that is comparable to Alberts et al.

de Duve, C. *A Guided Tour of the Living Cell*. Scientific American Library, New York, 1984. An engrossing, beautifully illustrated tour of the cell in the form of journeys through different membrane and organelle systems.

Loewy, A., P. Siekovitz, J. Menninger, and J. Gallant. *Cell Structure and Function: An Integrated Approach*. Saunders College Publishing, Philadelphia, 1991. An up-to-date introductory cell biology text.

CHAPTER 5

❏

Biological Membranes

To carry out the many chemical reactions necessary to sustain life, a cell must maintain an appropriate internal environment. This is possible because all cells are physically separated from the outside world by a limiting plasma membrane, which defines the cell as a distinct entity. Many biologists, in fact, view the origin of biological membranes as an essential step in the origin of life. One can argue that membranes made the evolution of complex cells possible, because the extensive internal membranes of eukaryotes form additional compartments with unique environments for highly specialized activities.

Cellular membranes are not inanimate walls; they are complex and dynamic structures made from lipid and protein molecules that are in constant motion. The unusual properties of membranes allow them to perform many functions. These include serving as work surfaces for many chemical reactions, regulating movement of materials in and out of the cell, transmitting signals and information between the environment and the interior of the cell, and acting as an essential part of an energy transfer and storage system (see Chapters 6, 7, and 8).

To understand how membranes do these things, we must first consider what is known about the structure and composition of membranes. This chapter then examines how materials ranging from simple to complex molecules and particles are able to move across membranes. It also considers specialized structures that permit complex interactions between membranes of different cells. Although most of our discussion centers on the structure and functions of plasma membranes, many of the concepts are also applicable to internal membrane systems.

Breast cells grown in culture and stained with fluorescent antibodies.
(Nancy Kedersha, ImmunoGen, Inc.)

LEARNING OBJECTIVES

After you have studied this chapter you should be able to

1. Evaluate the importance of membranes to the cell, emphasizing their various functions.
2. Make a detailed sketch of the fluid mosaic model of cell membrane structure.
3. Explain how the properties of the lipid bilayer are responsible for many of the physical properties of a cell membrane.
4. Explain how the various classes of membrane proteins associate with the lipid bilayer; discuss the different roles that membrane proteins assume.
5. Contrast the physical processes of diffusion and osmosis with the carrier-mediated physiological processes by which materials are transported across cell membranes.

6. Solve simple problems involving osmosis; for example, predict whether cells will swell or shrink under various osmotic conditions.
7. Summarize the main ways that small hydrophilic molecules can move across membranes.
8. Differentiate between the processes of facilitated diffusion and active transport; discuss the ways in which energy is supplied to active transport systems.
9. Compare endocytotic and exocytotic transport mechanisms.
10. Describe the structures and compare the functions of desmosomes, tight junctions, gap junctions, and plasmodesmata.

BIOLOGICAL MEMBRANES ARE LIPID BILAYERS WITH ASSOCIATED PROTEINS

When you examine an electron micrograph and compare the sizes of different structures in the cell, one of the most striking things is how exceedingly uniform and thin membranes seem to be (Figure 5–1). Cell membranes are no more than 10 nm thick.

Long before the development of the electron microscope, it was known that membranes are composed of both lipids and proteins. Work by researchers in the 1920s and 1930s had provided clues that the core of the

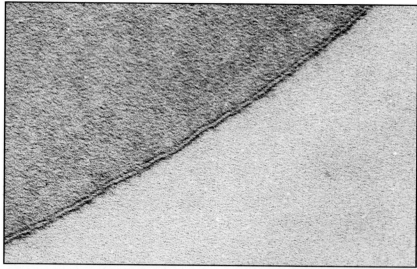

(a)

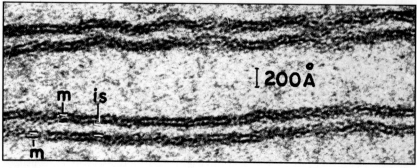

(b)

Figure 5–1 (a) The plasma membrane is the interface between the cell and its environment. (b) Transmission electron micrograph of four plasma membranes. The black line is a size marker indicating 200 Ångstrom units, or 20 nm. The dark lines represent the hydrophilic heads of the lipids, while the light zone represents the hydrophobic tails. "m," membrane; "is," intracellular space. (a, Omikron, Photo Researchers, Inc.)

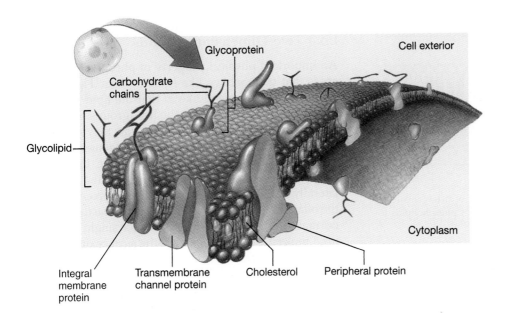

Figure 5–2 The fluid mosaic model of membrane structure. A representation of the plasma membrane from a eukaryotic cell, illustrating the various structures of some of the plasma membrane proteins.

cell membrane is composed of lipids, mostly phospholipids (see Chapter 3). Furthermore, by examining the membrane of the mammalian red blood cell (which has only a plasma membrane) and comparing the surface area of the membrane with the total number of lipid molecules per cell, investigators were able to calculate that the phospholipids are probably arranged so that the membrane is no more than two phospholipid molecules thick! Because many proteins have a diameter greater than 10 nm, a major problem in understanding the basic structure of membranes was to determine how the molecules that make up cell membranes can be arranged to fit in such a small space. In 1972, S. J. Singer and G. L. Nicolson proposed a model of membrane structure that represents a synthesis of the known properties of biological membranes. According to their *fluid mosaic* model, membranes consist of a fluid bilayer of lipid molecules (a double layer of lipid) in which the proteins are embedded, much like the tiles in a mosaic picture. Figure 5–2 depicts the plasma membrane of a eukaryotic cell; prokaryotic plasma membranes are discussed in Chapter 23.

We now know that lipids are primarily responsible for the physical properties of biological membranes. This is because they have unique features that allow them to form bilayered structures as well as other attributes. How is it possible for membrane lipids to behave in this way?

Phospholipids Associate as Bilayers in Water Because Each Molecule Is Roughly Cylindrical and Has Hydrophobic and Hydrophilic Regions

Recall from Chapter 3 that phospholipids contain two fatty acid chains linked to two of the three carbons of a

glycerol molecule. The fatty acid chains are nonpolar hydrophobic (water-hating) molecules. Bonded to the third carbon of the glycerol is a negatively charged (hydrophilic, or water-loving) phosphate group, which in turn is linked to a polar (hydrophilic) organic molecule). Molecules of this type, which have distinct hydrophobic and hydrophilic regions, are called **amphipathic molecules.** All lipids that make up the core of biological membranes have amphipathic characteristics.

Because one end of each phospholipid associates freely with water and the opposite end does not, the most favorable orientation for them to assume in water results in the formation of a bilayer structure (Figure 5–3). This arrangement allows the hydrophilic headgroups of the phospholipids to associate freely with the

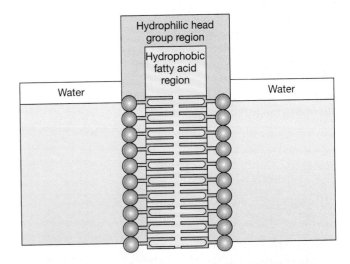

Figure 5–3 A phospholipid bilayer. Phospholipids form bilayers in water so that the hydrophobic fatty acid chains are not exposed to the water. The headgroups of the phospholipids on each surface of the bilayer are hydrophilic and are in contact with the aqueous medium.

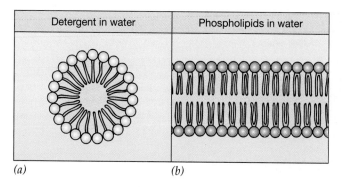

Detergent in water	Phospholipids in water

(a)   *(b)*

Figure 5–4 A comparison of (a) the tendency of detergents to form spherical structures with (b) the tendency of phospholipids to form bilayers.

aqueous medium while the hydrophobic fatty acid chains are buried in the interior of the structure away from the water molecules.

Not all lipids can form bilayers. Triacylglycerols, for example, are so predominantly hydrophobic that they form oil droplets within the cell. Steroids, such as cholesterol, are also so hydrophobic that they are only slightly soluble in water.

Many common detergents are amphipathic molecules, containing a single hydrocarbon chain (like a fatty acid) at one end and a hydrophilic region at the other. These molecules are roughly cone shaped, with the hydrophilic end forming the broad base and the hydrocarbon tail leading to the point. Because of their shapes, these molecules tend to form spherical structures in water (Figure 5–4a). Detergents are able to "solubilize" oil because the oil molecules are able to associate with the hydrophobic interiors of the spheres.

Phospholipids tend to have uniform widths. This allows them to be arranged in a bilayer like two layers of cylindrical objects such as oil drums (Figure 5–4b). Thus the important features of membrane-forming lipids are that the molecules have (1) two distinct regions, one strongly hydrophobic and the other strongly hydrophilic (making them strongly amphipathic), and (2) shapes that allow them to associate with water most favorably as a bilayer structure.

Biological Membranes Behave Like Two-Dimensional Fluids

An important physical property of phospholipid bilayers is that they behave like *liquid crystals* (Figure 5–5). The bilayers are crystal-like in that the lipid molecules form an ordered array with the headgroups on the outside and fatty acid chains on the inside; they are liquid-like in that, despite the orderly arrangement of their molecules, their hydrocarbon chains are in constant motion. Thus molecules are free to rotate and can move laterally within their single layer. Such movement gives the bilayer the property of a *two-dimensional fluid*. Under normal conditions this means that a single phospholipid molecule can travel across the surface of a eukaryotic cell in seconds.

The fluid-like qualities of lipid bilayers also allow molecules embedded in them to move along the plane of the membrane (as long as they are not anchored in some way). This was elegantly demonstrated by David Frye and Michael Ediden with experiments in which they followed the movement of membrane proteins on the surface of two cells that had been joined together (Figure 5–6). When the plasma membranes of a mouse cell and a human cell are fused, within minutes membrane proteins from each cell migrate and become randomly distributed over the single continuous plasma membrane that surrounds the joined cells.

Certain properties of membrane lipids have significant effects on the fluidity of the bilayer. Remember from Chapters 2 and 3 that molecules are free to rotate around single covalent bonds. Because most of the bonds in hydrocarbon chains are single bonds, the chains themselves can undergo very rapid, twisting motions that increase as the temperature increases. Although most biological membranes are in the liquid-crystalline state in living cells, the motion of the fatty acid chains is slowed at low temperatures. Van der Waals interactions (see Chapter 3) can take place between hydrocarbon chains lined up close to each other, thus converting a phospholipid bilayer to a solid gel state. You may be familiar with a similar situation with cooking fats. Some fats are solid at room temperature, whereas others are liquid. One of the major differences

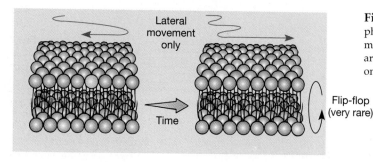

Lateral movement only

Time

Flip-flop (very rare)

Figure 5–5 Fluid properties of a phospholipid bilayer. Most phospholipid bilayers in cells are in a liquid-crystalline state. This means that the hydrocarbon chains of the phospholipid molecules are in constant motion, allowing each molecule to move laterally on the same side of the bilayer.

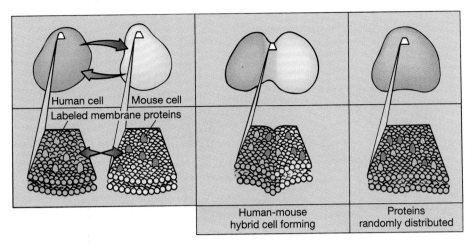

Figure 5–6   In an elegant series of experiments, membrane proteins of mouse cells and human cells were labeled with fluorescent dye markers in two different colors. When the plasma membranes of a mouse cell and a human cell were then fused, mouse proteins were observed migrating to the human side and human proteins to the mouse side. After a short time the proteins from both mouse and human were randomly distributed on the cell surface. This demonstration was convincing evidence that proteins in membranes are not part of a static structure like bricks in a wall, but instead are highly mobile entities in a two-dimensional fluid.

between these two types of fat is the number of double bonds in the hydrocarbon chains of their fatty acids. If a fatty acid is saturated it has no double bonds; if it is unsaturated it has one (monounsaturated) or two or more (polyunsaturated). Double bonds produce "kinks" in the molecules which prevent the hydrocarbon chains from coming close enough together to form van der Waals contacts, thus effectively lowering the temperature at which the oil or the lipids of the membrane crystallize.

Many organisms regulate the unsaturated fatty acid content of their membrane lipids to compensate for temperature changes so as to provide an optimal fluid state for their membranes. In addition, some molecules, such as the sterol cholesterol, fit between phospholipid molecules and act as "fluidity buffers." At low temperatures cholesterol molecules prevent hydrocarbon chains from becoming close enough to form van der Waals attractions, which would promote crystallization. At high temperatures cholesterol molecules appear to restrict the excessive motion of fatty acid chains, which might result in the membrane becoming weakened or unstable.

Biological Membranes Tend To Form Closed Vesicles and To Fuse with Other Membranes

Lipid bilayers, particularly those in the liquid-crystalline state, also have other important physical properties. Bilayers by themselves tend to resist forming free ends; as a result, they tend to be self-sealing and under most conditions spontaneously round up to form closed vesicles. Fluid bilayers also are flexible, allowing cell membranes to change shape without breaking. Finally, under appropriate conditions lipid bilayers have the ability to fuse with other bilayers. Membrane fusion is an important cellular phenomenon (Figure 5–7). When a vesicle fuses with another membrane, both membrane bilayers and their compartments become continuous. This allows materials to be transferred from one compartment to another or to move from a secretory vesicle to the outside of a cell by a process known as *exocytosis*. In a similar but reverse process, *endocytosis*, large molecules are brought into the cell from the outside by forming vesicles from a section of membrane. Both endocytosis and exocytosis are discussed later in this chapter.

Integral Proteins Are Partially or Fully Embedded in the Lipid Bilayer; Peripheral Proteins Are Bound to the Membrane Surface

It was not always clear how proteins might be associated with membranes. Early investigators, in fact, found it difficult to accept the idea that proteins could associate with any part of membranes other than their surfaces. It was widely assumed that membrane proteins must be very uniform and must have shapes that allow them to lie like thin sheets on the membrane surface. However, several lines of evidence eventually argued against these ideas. One was that membranes purified by cell fractionation contain many different proteins that vary widely in size, composition, and

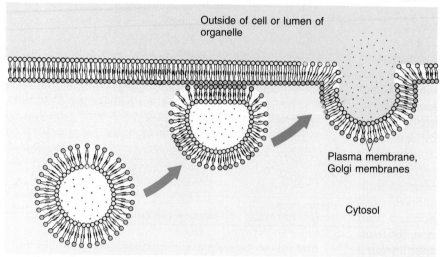

Outside of cell or lumen of organelle

Plasma membrane, Golgi membranes

Cytosol

(a) Exocytosis, endomembrane transport

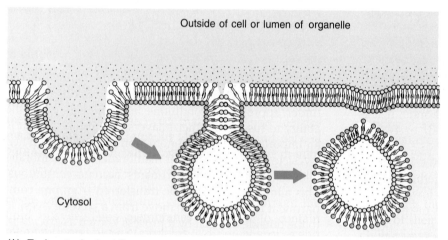

Outside of cell or lumen of organelle

Cytosol

(b) Endocytosis, budding

Figure 5–7 Membrane fusion in endocytosis and exocytosis. Both processes involve the fusion of lipid bilayers. (a) Exocytosis and movement of molecules between organelles involve the contact and fusion of a vesicle with a membrane, releasing the vesicle's contents into another compartment or to the outside of the cell. (b) Endocytosis and the formation of intracellular transport vesicles originate from an invagination or a "bud" from the membrane, followed by the fusion of two regions of the membrane that come in contact with each other. Notice that in exocytosis the two cytoplasmic sides of the membrane make contact with each other to initiate membrane fusion, while in endocytosis the two noncytoplasmic layers make the first contacts. This means that endocytosis and exocytosis are not exactly the same processes in reverse but somewhat different types of cellular events.

structure. Another came from physical chemical studies that showed that many membrane proteins are **globular,** with diameters so large that the membrane would have to be very thick if they were located only on the surface. Finally, studies of a number of individual membrane proteins showed that one region (or domain) of the molecule could always be found on one side of the bilayer, while another part of the protein might be located on the opposite side. It appeared that, rather than forming a thin surface layer, many membrane proteins extend into or completely through the lipid bilayer. Thus membranes appeared to contain many different types of proteins of different shapes and sizes that are associated with the bilayer in a mosaic pattern. However, this pattern is far from static, for the fluidity of the lipids allows many of the proteins to move around in the plane of the bilayer to produce an ever-changing configuration.

Membrane proteins are grouped into two major classes defined by how tightly they are associated with the lipid bilayer (see Figure 5–2).

Peripheral proteins are membrane proteins that can be easily removed from the membrane without disrupting the structure of the bilayer. They usually bind to exposed regions of integral proteins and are held there by noncovalent interactions.

Integral membrane proteins are firmly bound to the membrane; usually they can be released only by disrupting the bilayer with detergents. Many have regions of their polypeptide chains (consisting of hydrophobic amino acids) that pass through the hydrophobic interior of the lipid bilayer. Some of these proteins may pass all the way through the membrane once so that large hydrophilic regions are on either side; other integral proteins may be almost completely buried within the lipid bilayer with polypeptide chains that pass back

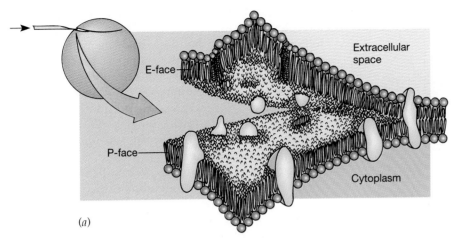

(a)

(b)

Extracellular space

E-face

P-face

Cytoplasm

0.25 μm

Figure 5–8 Freeze-fracture electron microscopy. (*a*) In the freeze-fracture method, the path of membrane cleavage is along the hydrophobic interior of the lipid bilayer, resulting in two complementary fracture faces: (1) an inner half-membrane presenting the P-face, from which project the majority of the membrane proteins and (2) a relatively smooth, outer half-membrane presenting the E-face, which shows occasional protein particles. In good fractures particles are visible on both of the inside faces of the fractured membrane, as shown in the figure. These particles are integral membrane proteins inserted in the lipid bilayer. Freeze-fractured bilayers of lipids alone do not have particles on the fracture planes. (*b*) A freeze fracture made of a membrane from a cell of the eye of a monkey. Notice the greater number of proteins on the P-face of the membrane. (*b*, Don Fawcett/ Photo Researchers, Inc.)

and forth across the membrane as many as 24 times. Both of these types of integral proteins are also called *transmembrane proteins.* Another group of integral proteins is located mostly on one side of the membrane (in the cytosol or protruding from the cell surface), with only a small hydrophobic "anchoring" region of the polypeptide chain extending into the bilayer. Recently, other integral proteins have been described that are anchored to the membrane by covalently bound lipids attached to certain amino acids in the polypeptide chain.

Integral membrane proteins are able to insert into the lipid bilayer because the regions of the molecules that are within the membrane have hydrophobic surfaces, compatible with the interior of the bilayer. If a membrane protein has a region with a hydrophilic surface, it is usually found protruding from the membrane, in contact with the aqueous medium. (*Note:* The difference between soluble and membrane-bound proteins is not that one has hydrophobic amino acids and the other does not; rather, in soluble proteins the hydrophobic amino acids are buried in the interior of the molecule away from the water, whereas in integral membrane proteins the hydrophobic stretches of amino acids are in contact with the fatty acid chains of the bilayer.)

Membranes Are Asymmetric; Each Side of the Bilayer Has Its Own Set of Proteins

One of the most remarkable demonstrations that proteins are actually embedded in the lipid bilayer comes from freeze-fracture electron microscopy (Figure 5–8), which enables investigators to literally see the membrane from "inside out." When the two sides of a membrane are compared by this method (as in Figure 5–8), large numbers of particles are found on one side and very few on the other. These particles are proteins embedded in the bilayer. This does not necessarily mean that there are more proteins on one side of the membrane than on the other, but rather that most are more firmly attached to a given side. Thus, the protein molecules that make up biological membranes are *asymmetrically distributed.* Each side of a membrane has different characteristics because each type of protein is oriented in the bilayer in only one way. Proteins are not randomly placed into membranes; asymmetry is produced by the highly specific way in which each protein is inserted in the bilayer.

As an example, look again at Figure 5–2 and notice the different ways that protein molecules are oriented in the plasma membrane. Notice, for example, that carbohydrates are attached to the parts of the proteins exposed on the surface of the cell, but not to the parts exposed to the cytosol.

As you recall from Chapter 4, plasma membrane proteins are initially formed by ribosomes on the rough endoplasmic reticulum (ER) and are inserted through the ER membrane as they are synthesized. Only a part of those proteins passes through the membrane, so each completed protein has some regions that are located in the ER lumen and other regions that remain in the cytosol. Enzymes that attach the sugars to certain amino acids on the protein are located only in the lumen of the

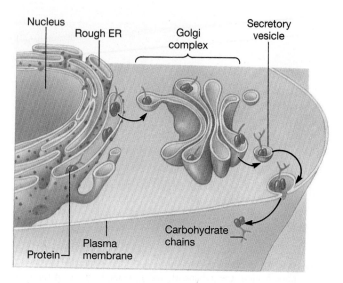

Figure 5–9 The transport pathway of proteins destined for the plasma membrane. Notice that the regions of a protein found on the extracellular surface of the plasma membrane originated in the lumen of the rough ER and then passed through the compartments of the Golgi complex and secretory vesicles. Carbohydrates were added to these protein regions in the ER lumen and then modified in the Golgi complex. For simplicity, only the parts of the protein within each compartment are shown.

ER. Thus, carbohydrates can be added only to the parts of proteins that are located in that compartment. If you follow the vesicle budding and membrane fusion events that are part of the transport process (Figure 5–9), you can see that the same part of the protein that protruded into the ER lumen is also transferred to the lumen of the Golgi complex, where additional enzymes are located that can further modify the carbohydrate groups. That region of the protein also remains inside a membrane compartment of a secretory vesicle as it buds from the Golgi complex. When the secretory vesicle fuses with the plasma membrane, the carbohydrate-containing part of the protein that was formerly located on the inside of the vesicle becomes the part of the membrane protein that is exposed on the cell surface.

Functions of Membrane Proteins Include Reception of Signals, Binding of Specific Molecules, Transport across the Membrane, and Catalyzing Certain Reactions

Why should a membrane such as the plasma membrane illustrated in Figure 5–2 require so many different proteins? This diversity is a reflection of the number of activities that take place in or on the membrane. Generally, plasma membrane proteins fall into several broad functional groups (Figure 5–10). A number of them are

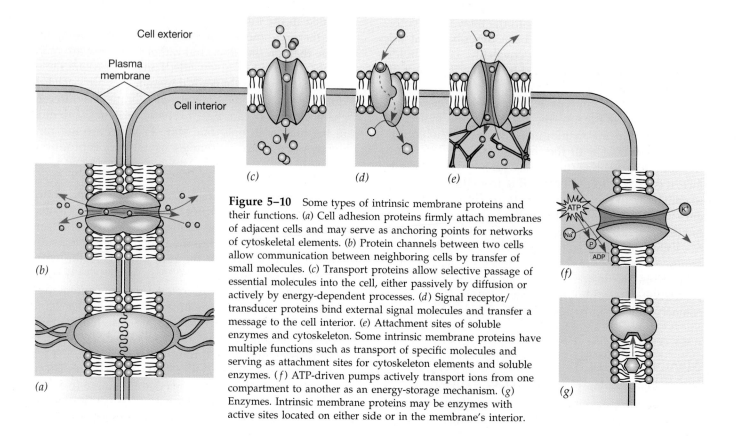

Figure 5–10 Some types of intrinsic membrane proteins and their functions. (*a*) Cell adhesion proteins firmly attach membranes of adjacent cells and may serve as anchoring points for networks of cytoskeletal elements. (*b*) Protein channels between two cells allow communication between neighboring cells by transfer of small molecules. (*c*) Transport proteins allow selective passage of essential molecules into the cell, either passively by diffusion or actively by energy-dependent processes. (*d*) Signal receptor/transducer proteins bind external signal molecules and transfer a message to the cell interior. (*e*) Attachment sites of soluble enzymes and cytoskeleton. Some intrinsic membrane proteins have multiple functions such as transport of specific molecules and serving as attachment sites for cytoskeleton elements and soluble enzymes. (*f*) ATP-driven pumps actively transport ions from one compartment to another as an energy-storage mechanism. (*g*) Enzymes. Intrinsic membrane proteins may be enzymes with active sites located on either side or in the membrane's interior.

Table 5–1 PERMEABILITY OF THE LIPID BILAYER TO DIFFERENT SUBSTANCES

Type of Molecule	Example	Permeability
Hydrophobic	N_2, O_2, hydrocarbons	Freely permeable
Small polar	H_2O, CO_2, glycerol, urea	Freely permeable
Large polar	Glucose, other uncharged monosaccharides, disaccharides	Not permeable
Ions/charged molecules	Amino acids, H^+, HCO_3^-, Na^+, K^+, Ca^{2+}, Cl^-, Mg^{2+}	Not permeable

involved in the *membrane transport* of small molecules. Others are membrane-bound *receptor proteins* that can bind to signal molecules such as hormones (see Chapters 36 and 47) and respond by transmitting a signal across the membrane, which in turn triggers a change in some cellular activity. This is one of the many ways that the cell receives information from its environment. *Enzymes* that modify molecules needed near the cell surface can also be found associated with both sides of the plasma membrane, while other integral or peripheral proteins may be parts of specialized structures that link cells together or transmit signals between neighboring cells. The remainder of this chapter examines this functional diversity of membrane proteins.

LIPID BILAYERS ALLOW ONLY CERTAIN MOLECULES TO CROSS FREELY; ALL OTHERS REQUIRE SPECIAL TRANSPORT SYSTEMS

Whether a membrane permits a substance to pass through it depends on the size and charge of its molecules and on the composition of the membrane. A membrane is said to be *permeable* to a given substance if it permits it to pass through and *impermeable* if it does not. A *selectively permeable* membrane allows some but not other substances to pass through it.

Certain types of molecules can move easily through the lipid bilayers of biological membranes. Water molecules, for example, can rapidly cross a fluid lipid bilayer by passing through gaps that occur as a fatty acid chain momentarily moves out of the way. Gases such as oxygen, carbon dioxide, and nitrogen; small polar molecules like glycerol; plus larger nonpolar (hydrophobic) substances such as hydrocarbons can also freely traverse a lipid bilayer. Slightly larger polar molecules, such as glucose, and charged ions of any size do not pass freely through the bilayer either because of their size or because they are repulsed by a layer of electrical charges on the surface of the membrane (Table 5–1).

Although the bilayer is relatively impermeable to ions, cells must be able to move ions and large and small polar molecules such as proteins and sugars across membranes. The permeability of membranes to those substances is due primarily to the activities of specialized membrane proteins. All of the biological membranes surrounding cells, nuclei, vacuoles, mitochondria, chloroplasts, and the other subcellular organelles are selectively permeable to different types of molecules.

In response to varying environmental conditions or cellular needs, a plasma membrane may be a barrier to a particular substance at one time and actively promote its passage at another. By regulating chemical traffic in this way, a cell can exert some control over its own internal ionic and molecular composition, which can be very different from that on the outside. In the nonliving world, materials move passively by physical processes such as diffusion; in living organisms some particles can diffuse across the bilayer, but other materials can be moved very rapidly by physiological processes, such as active transport, exocytosis, and endocytosis. These processes (discussed later in this chapter) require the expenditure of metabolic energy by the cell.

Diffusion, through Random Motion, Results in a Net Movement of Particles from a Region of High Concentration to a Region of Low Concentration

Some substances pass into or out of cells and move about within cells by simple diffusion, a physical process based on random motion. At temperatures above absolute zero (0 Kelvin or −273° Celsius—the point where all motion stops), all atoms and molecules possess kinetic energy, or energy of motion. The three states of matter—solid, liquid, and gas—differ with respect to the freedom of movement of their constituent molecules. The molecules of a solid are closely packed, and the forces of attraction between them allow them to vibrate but not to move around. In a liquid the mole-

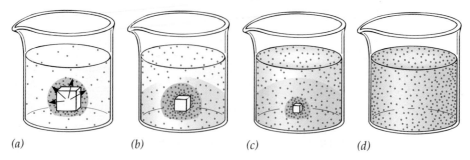

(a) *(b)* *(c)* *(d)*

Figure 5–11 The process of diffusion. When a small lump of sugar is dropped into a beaker of water, its molecules dissolve, as shown in (*a*). The sugar molecules begin to diffuse throughout the water in the container, as seen in (*b*) and (*c*). The arrows in (*a*) indicate net movement of sugar molecules; individual molecules move randomly in all directions. Eventually, diffusion results in an even distribution of sugar molecules throughout the water in the beaker, as shown in (*d*).

cules are farther apart; the attractions are weaker, and the molecules move about with considerable freedom. In a gas the molecules are so far apart that intermolecular forces are negligible; molecular movement is restricted only by the walls of the container that encloses the gas. This means that atoms and molecules in liquids and gases can move apart from each other in a kind of "random walk."

The kinetic energy associated with random motion is responsible for **diffusion,** the *net* movement of particles (atoms, ions, and molecules) from a region of higher concentration to one of lower concentration such that eventually the particles are evenly distributed (Figure 5–11). We can therefore say that *diffusion involves a* **net** *movement of particles down a* **concentration gradient** (a change in the concentration of a substance from one point to another). This does not mean that particles are prohibited from moving in the opposite direction (against the gradient). However, because there are initially more particles in the region of high concentration, it logically follows that more particles move randomly from that region into the low-concentration region than from the region of low concentration into the region of high concentration.

The rate of diffusion is determined by the movement of the molecules, which in turn is a function of their size and shape, their electrical charges, and the temperature. As the temperature rises, the molecules move faster and the rate of diffusion increases. The molecules of any number of different substances in a mixture diffuse independently of each other; ultimately a state of equilibrium (condition of no net change in the system) is reached in which they are uniformly distributed. More commonly in biological systems, equilibrium is never attained. For example, carbon dioxide is continually formed within the cell when sugars and other molecules are metabolized during the process of cellular respiration. Carbon dioxide readily diffuses across the plasma membrane but then is rapidly removed by the bloodstream. This limits the opportunity for the molecules to reenter the cell, so a sharp concentration gradient of carbon dioxide molecules always exists across the membrane.

Dialysis is the diffusion of a solute across a selectively permeable membrane

To demonstrate **dialysis,** one can fill a cellophane bag[1] with a sugar solution and immerse it in a beaker of pure water (Figure 5–12). If the cellophane membrane is permeable to sugar as well as to water, the sugar molecules pass through it, and the concentrations of sugar molecules in the water on the two sides of the membrane eventually become equal. Subsequently, both solute and water molecules continue to pass through the membrane, but a state of equilibrium is attained and there is no net change in their concentrations. Kidney dialysis is a practical application of this process; waste products are small molecules that diffuse readily across the artificial membrane used in the dialysis apparatus. They can therefore be removed from the bloodstream, but blood cells, blood proteins, and other large molecules are unable to diffuse and thus are retained.

Osmosis is the diffusion of water (solvent) across a selectively permeable membrane

The selective permeability of cell membranes results in a special kind of diffusion called **osmosis,** which involves the movement of *solvent* (in this case, water) molecules through a selectively permeable membrane.

---

[1]Cellophane is often used as an "artificial membrane." It is made from cellulose and can be formed into a thin sheet that allows the passage of water molecules through it. Such membranes can be constructed with varying permeability to different solutes and can be very different from biological membranes in their permeability. (When cellophane is used to package foods, it must be coated so that it is impermeable to air and water.)

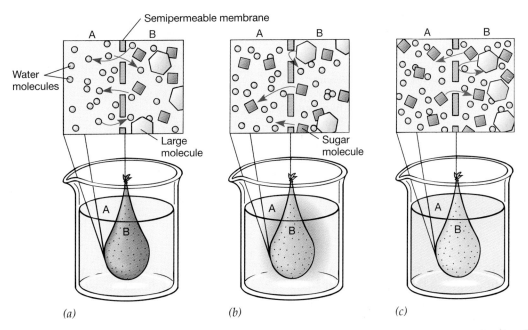

Figure 5–12 Dialysis. (a) A cellophane bag filled with a sugar solution is immersed in a beaker of water. The cellophane acts as a selectively permeable membrane, permitting passage of the sugar and water molecules, but preventing passage of larger molecules (hexagons). (b) The arrows indicate the net movement of sugar molecules through the membrane into the water of the beaker. (c) Eventually the sugar becomes distributed equally between the two compartments. Although sugar molecules continue to diffuse back and forth, the net movement is zero. The same is true for the water molecules. Dots represent water molecules; squares represent sugar molecules.

The water molecules pass freely in both directions, but, as in all types of diffusion, *net* movement is from the region where the water molecules are more concentrated to the region where they are less concentrated. Most solute molecules cannot diffuse freely through the selectively permeable cell membrane (see Table 5–1).

The principles involved in osmosis can be illustrated by use of an apparatus called a U-tube (Figure 5–13). The U-tube is divided into two sections by a selectively permeable membrane that allows solvent (water) molecules to pass freely but excludes solute molecules (e.g., sugar, salt). A water/solute solution is placed on one side, and pure water is placed on the other. The side containing the solute dissolved in the water has a lower effective concentration of water than the pure water side. In order to dissolve in water the solute must be able to interact with the partial electrical charges on the polar water molecules; therefore the solute must itself be charged (ionic) or polar. When the

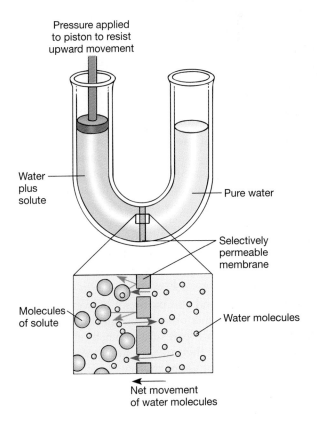

Figure 5–13 Demonstration of osmosis. The U-tube contains pure water on the right and water plus a solute on the left, separated by a selectively permeable membrane that allows water molecules, but not solute molecules, to diffuse across the membrane. The arrows indicate the direction of movement of water molecules. The fluid level rises on the left and falls on the right because *net* movement of water is to the left. The force that must be exerted by the piston in order to prevent the rise in fluid level is equal to the osmotic pressure of the solution.

Table 5–2 OSMOTIC TERMINOLOGY

Solute Concentration in Solution A	Solute Concentration in Solution B	Tonicity	Direction of Net Movement of Water
Greater	Less	A hypertonic to B B hypotonic to A	B to A
Less	Greater	B hypertonic to A A hypotonic to B	A to B
Equal	Equal	Isotonic	No net movement

solute and the water interact, many of the water molecules become "bound up," so they are no longer free to diffuse across the membrane. Therefore, there is a net movement of water molecules from the pure water side (with a high effective concentration of water) to the water/solute side (with a lower effective concentration of water). As a result, the fluid level drops on the pure water side and rises on the water/solute side. Because the solute molecules do not move across the membrane, equilibrium is not attained. Net movement of water continues, and the fluid level continues to rise on the side containing the solute. Under weightless conditions this process could go on indefinitely, but on Earth the weight of the rising column of fluid eventually exerts enough pressure to stop further changes in fluid levels, although water molecules continue to pass through the selectively permeable membrane in both directions.

We define the **osmotic pressure** of a solution as the tendency of water to move into that solution by osmosis. In our U-tube example, we could measure the osmotic pressure by inserting a piston on the water/solute side of the tube and measuring how much pressure must be exerted by the piston to prevent the rise of fluid on that side of the tube. A solution with a high solute concentration has a low water concentration and a high osmotic pressure (Table 5–2); conversely, a solution with a low solute concentration has a high concentration of water and a low osmotic pressure.

A Solution with a Higher Relative Osmotic Pressure Is Hypertonic, While One with a Lower Relative Osmotic Pressure Is Hypotonic; Isotonic Solutions Have the Same Osmotic Pressure

Dissolved in the fluid compartment of every living cell are salts, sugars, and other substances that give that fluid a certain osmotic pressure. When a cell is placed in a fluid with exactly the same osmotic pressure, there is no net movement of water molecules either into or out of the cell; the cell neither swells nor shrinks. Such a fluid is said to be **isotonic or isoosmotic** (i.e., of equal osmotic pressure) to the fluid within the cell. Normally,

our blood plasma (the fluid component of blood) and all of our body fluids are isotonic to our cells; they contain a concentration of water equal to that in the cells. A solution of 0.9% sodium chloride (sometimes called *physiologic saline*) is isotonic to the cells of humans and other mammals. Human red blood cells placed in 0.9% sodium chloride neither shrink nor swell (Figure 5–14a).

If the surrounding fluid has a concentration of dissolved substances greater than the concentration within the cell, it has a higher osmotic pressure than the cell and is said to be **hypertonic (hyperosmotic)** to the cell; a cell in a hypertonic solution loses water and shrinks. Human red blood cells placed in a solution of 1.3% sodium chloride shrink (see Figure 5–14b). If a cell that has a cell wall is placed in a hypertonic medium, it loses water to its surroundings, and its contents shrink away from the wall; this process is called **plasmolysis.** Plasmolysis occurs in plants when large amounts of salts or fertilizers are contained in the soil or water around them.

If the surrounding fluid contains a lower concentration of dissolved materials than the cell, it has a lower osmotic pressure and is said to be **hypotonic (hypoosmotic)** to the cell; water then enters the cell and causes it to swell. Red blood cells placed in a solution of 0.6% sodium chloride gain water, swell, and burst (Figure 5–14c). Many cells that normally live in hypotonic environments have adaptations to prevent excessive water accumulation. For example, certain protozoa have a contractile vacuole that they use to expel excess water (see Chapter 24).

Turgor Pressure Is the Internal Hydrostatic Pressure Usually Present in Cells Possessing Cell Walls

The rigid cell walls of plant cells, algae, bacteria, and fungi enable these cells to withstand, without bursting, an external medium that is very dilute, containing only a very low concentration of solutes. Because of the substances dissolved in the cytoplasm, the cells are hypertonic to the outside medium (conversely, the outside

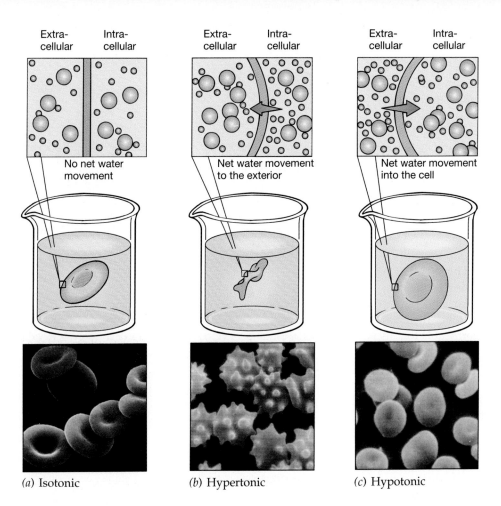

No net water movement

Net water movement to the exterior

Net water movement into the cell

(a) Isotonic

(b) Hypertonic

(c) Hypotonic

Figure 5–14 Osmosis and the living cell. (*a*) A cell is placed in an isotonic solution. Because the concentration of solutes (and thus of water molecules) is the same in the solution as in the cell, water can pass in and out of the cell, but the net movement is zero. (*b*) A cell is placed in a hypertonic solution. This solution has a greater solute concentration (and thus a lower water concentration) than does the cell. This results in a net movement of water out of the cell (*arrow*), and the cell becomes dehydrated, shrinks, and may die. (*c*) A cell is placed in a hypotonic solution. The solution has a lower solute (and thus a greater water) concentration than does the cell. The cell contents therefore have higher osmotic pressure than the solution. There is a net movement of water molecules into the cell (*arrow*), causing the cell to swell. The cell may even burst. (Micrographs of human red blood cells courtesy of Dr. R. F. Baker, University of Southern California Medical School)

Figure 5–15 (*a*) Turgor pressure in a plant cell. In hypotonic surroundings, the contents of the cell fill the space within the wall. (*b*), (*c*) If the cell is placed in a hypertonic medium, it loses water and its contents shrink. The cell is said to be plasmolyzed. (*d*) Section through a dividing *Escherichia coli*, a bacterium that has plasmolyzed due to a hypertonic environment. (*d*, M. E. Bayer, Institute for Cancer Research, Philadelphia/Biological Photo Service)

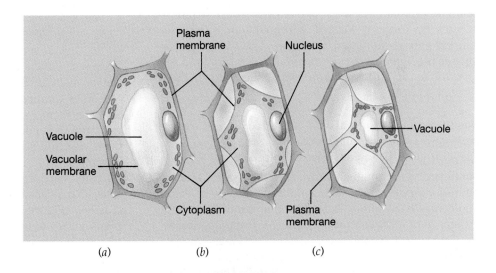

Plasma membrane

Nucleus

Vacuole

Vacuolar membrane

Vacuole

Cytoplasm

Plasma membrane

(*a*)   (*b*)   (*c*)

medium is hypotonic to the cytoplasm). Water moves into the cells by osmosis, filling their central vacuoles and distending the cells. The cells swell, building up a pressure, termed **turgor pressure,** against the rigid cellulose cell walls (Figure 5–15). The cell walls can be stretched only very slightly, and a steady state is reached when the resistance to stretching of the cell walls prevents any further increase in cell size and there is no net movement of water molecules into the cells

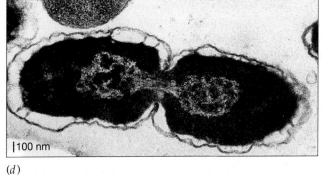

100 nm

(*d*)

121

(although, of course, molecules continue to move back and forth across the plasma membrane). Turgor pressure in the cells is an important factor in providing support for the body of nonwoody plants. Thus, lettuce becomes limp in a salty salad dressing and a flower wilts as a result of a lack of water.

Carrier-mediated transport requires special integral membrane proteins to move small molecules and ions

A lipid bilayer is relatively impermeable to most of the larger polar molecules (see Table 5–1). This is advantageous to cells for a number of reasons. Most of the compounds required in metabolism are polar, and the impermeability of the cell membrane prevents their loss by diffusion. A lipid bilayer is also impermeable to ions, which play important roles in many physiological processes. Some ions, such as calcium ions, are used as intracellular signals, and changes in their cytoplasmic concentration trigger changes in a number of cellular processes (such as muscle contraction, discussed in Chapter 38). As a cell controls the influx and efflux of ions, it is able to directly or indirectly control many metabolic activities. Cells also must continually acquire essential polar nutrient molecules such as glucose and amino acids. To transport ions and nutrients through membranes, systems of carrier proteins apparently evolved very early in the origin of cells. This transfer of solutes by proteins located within the membrane is termed **carrier-mediated transport.** The two forms of carrier-mediated transport, facilitated diffusion and active transport, differ in their capabilities and in their energy sources.

Facilitated Diffusion Carriers Can Effectively Move Substances Only in the Direction of a Concentration Gradient (from High to Low)

In all processes in which substances move across membranes by passive diffusion, the net transfer of those molecules from one side to the other results from the existence of a concentration gradient. If the membrane is permeable to a substance, then it moves from the side of the membrane where it is more highly concentrated to the side where it is less concentrated. This gradient across the membrane is actually a form of stored energy. A concentration gradient can be established as a result of certain processes taking place in the cell. The stored energy of the concentration gradient is released when molecules move from a region of high concentration to one of low concentration, and therefore the movement is spontaneous. (These types of energy and spontaneous processes are discussed in greater detail in Chapter 6.)

In the type of transport known as **facilitated diffusion,** the membrane may be made permeable to a sub-

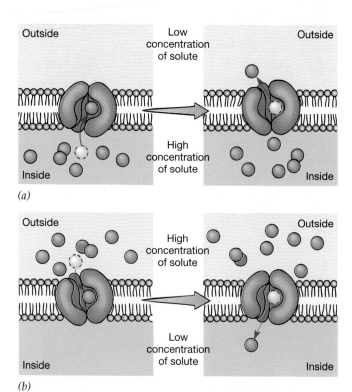

(a)

(b)

Figure 5–16 A model for the facilitated diffusion of glucose. The transport protein is capable of binding glucose on one side of the plasma membrane and then changing its shape so that a channel is opened to the other side. Glucose molecules can be transported from the inside of the cell to the outside (a) or from the outside to the inside (b), but net movement is always from a region of high glucose concentration to a region of low glucose concentration.

stance, such as an ion, by a specific *carrier protein* that combines temporarily with the solute particle and accelerates its movement through the membrane. The carrier protein is not changed by this action; after it transports a solute particle, it is free to bind with another (Figure 5–16). An important example of a facilitated diffusion carrier is the glucose transporter in red blood cells. These cells keep the internal concentration of glucose low (Figure 5–16b) by immediately adding a phosphate group to entering glucose molecules, converting them to highly charged glucose phosphates that cannot pass back through the membrane. Thus a steep concentration gradient for glucose is continually maintained and glucose rapidly enters the cell only to be immediately changed to the phosphorylated form.

The mechanism of glucose transport is not entirely clear. It appears that the carrier protein does not form a "hole" in the membrane for glucose to pass through; if that were the case, related molecules or molecules smaller than glucose could also pass through the pore. It is more likely that glucose binds specifically to a region of the protein that is exposed to the outside of the cell; this binding changes the shape of the protein, allowing the glucose molecule to be released on the inside. According to this model, when the glucose is released into the cytoplasm, the protein reverts to its original structure and is available to bind the next glucose molecule on the outside of the cell.

A Carrier-Mediated Active Transport System Can "Pump" a Substance against a Concentration Gradient

Although adequate amounts of some substances can be transported across cellular membranes by diffusion, a cell often needs to move solutes against a concentration gradient. Many substances are required by the cell in concentrations higher than those outside the cell. These molecules are moved across cellular membranes by **active transport** mechanisms. Because active transport requires that particles be "pumped" from a region of low concentration to a region of high concentration (i.e., *against a concentration gradient*), the energy inherent in the gradient is unavailable and hence a different energy source (often ATP) is required.

One of the most striking examples of an active transport mechanism is the **sodium-potassium pump,** which is found in all animal cells (Figure 5–17). The

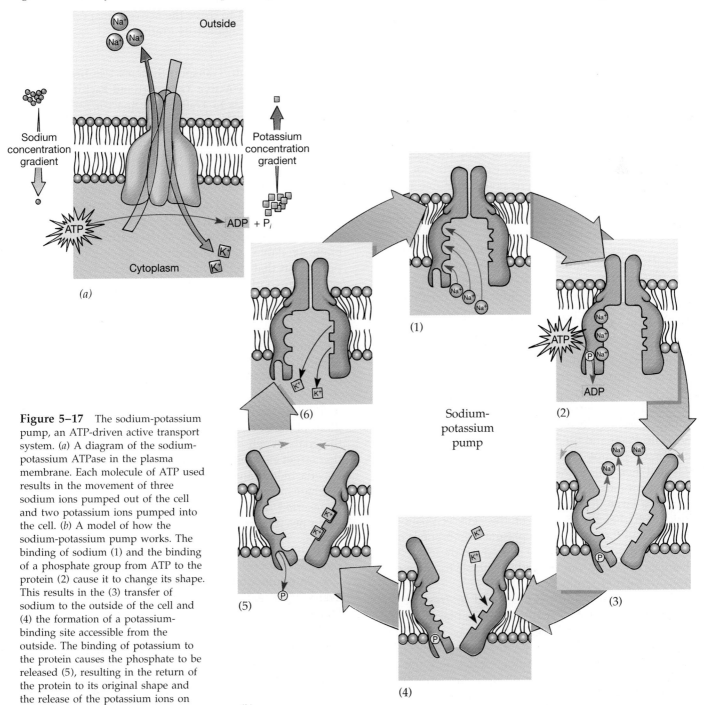

Figure 5–17 The sodium-potassium pump, an ATP-driven active transport system. (*a*) A diagram of the sodium-potassium ATPase in the plasma membrane. Each molecule of ATP used results in the movement of three sodium ions pumped out of the cell and two potassium ions pumped into the cell. (*b*) A model of how the sodium-potassium pump works. The binding of sodium (1) and the binding of a phosphate group from ATP to the protein (2) cause it to change its shape. This results in the (3) transfer of sodium to the outside of the cell and (4) the formation of a potassium-binding site accessible from the outside. The binding of potassium to the protein causes the phosphate to be released (5), resulting in the return of the protein to its original shape and the release of the potassium ions on the inside of the cell (6).

pump is a group of specific proteins in the plasma membrane that uses energy in the form of ATP to exchange sodium ions on the inside of the cell for potassium ions on the outside of the cell. The exchange is unequal, so that usually only two potassium ions are imported inside for every three sodium ions exported. Because these particular concentration gradients involve ions, an electrical potential (separation of electrical charges) is generated across the membrane, and we say that the membrane is polarized.

Both sodium and potassium ions are positively charged, but because there are fewer potassium ions inside, relative to the sodium ions outside, the inside of the cell is negatively charged relative to the outside. We refer to such a gradient as an electrochemical gradient because it involves not only a concentration difference on the two sides of the membrane, but also a charge difference. These gradients are also a form of energy storage (like water stored behind a dam), which can be used to drive other transport systems. So important is the electrochemical gradient produced by these pumps that some cells (e.g., nerve cells) expend 70% of their total energy metabolism just to power this one transport system.

Sodium-potassium pumps (as well as all other ATP-driven pumps) are transmembrane proteins that extend entirely through the membrane. By undergoing a series of conformational changes, the pumps are able to exchange sodium for potassium across the plasma membrane. Unlike facilitated diffusion, at least one of the conformational changes in the pump cycle requires energy, which is released from ATP. The energy appears to be transferred to the pump proteins from ATP by the covalent bonding of one of the ATP phosphate groups to the protein, followed by removal of the phosphate later in the pump cycle.

The use of electrochemical potentials for energy storage is not confined to the plasma membrane of animal cells. Plant and fungal cells use ATP-driven plasma membrane pumps to transfer protons from the cytoplasm of their cells to the outside. Removal of positively charged protons from the cytoplasm of these cells results in a large difference in the concentration of protons, such that the outside of the cells is positively charged and the inside of the plasma membrane is negatively charged. The energy stored in these electrochemical gradients can be made available to do certain kinds of cellular work.

Other proton pumps can be used in "reverse" to synthesize ATP. As we shall see in Chapters 7 and 8, bacteria, mitochondria, and chloroplasts use energy from food or from light to establish proton concentration gradients. When the protons move through the proton carriers from a region of high concentration of protons to a region of low concentration, ATP is synthesized. These electrochemical gradients form the basis for the major energy-conversion system in all cells.

Linked Cotransport Systems Indirectly Provide Energy for Active Transport

The electrochemical concentration gradients generated by the sodium-potassium pump also provide sufficient energy to power the active transport of a number of other essential substances. In these systems a transport protein can **cotransport** the required molecule *against* its concentration gradient, along with a sodium or a potassium ion *down* its gradient. Energy from ATP is used indirectly in this process, for it is used to produce the sodium/potassium gradient; the energy of this gradient is then used to drive the active transport of a required substance against its gradient.

Integrated Multiple Transport Systems Use Indirect Linkages between Active Transport and Facilitated Diffusion Processes to Transport a Specific Substance

In some cells, more than one system may work to transport a given substance. For example, the transport of glucose from the intestine to the blood occurs through a thin sheet of epithelial cells that line the intestine (Figure 5–18) and have highly specialized regions on their plasma membranes. The surface that is exposed to the intestine has many **microvilli,** finger-like protrusions that effectively increase the surface area of the membrane available for absorption. The glucose transporter protein on that region of the cell surface is part of an active transport system for glucose that is "driven" by the cotransport of sodium. The sodium concentration inside the cell is kept low by an ATP-requiring sodium-potassium pump that transports sodium out of the cell and into the blood. Because of its high concentration inside the cell, glucose can be transported to the blood by facilitated diffusion.

Understanding the mechanisms behind the placement of different transport proteins in two separate regions of the same plasma membrane represents some of the goals of cell biologists today. What are the signals that target each protein to its appropriate region on the plasma membrane? If the cell did not have a specific mechanism for handling this problem, proteins might be inserted randomly on both sides of the cell, leading to no net transport of glucose.

Energy for Facilitated Diffusion Is Provided by a Concentration Gradient for the Substance Being Transported; Active Transport Requires Some Other Type of Energy Expenditure

It is a common misconception that diffusion, whether simple or facilitated, is somehow "free of cost" and that only active transport mechanisms require energy. Remember that diffusion always involves net movement of a substance down its concentration gradient and that energy is required to do the work of establishing and maintaining the gradient. Think back to the example of

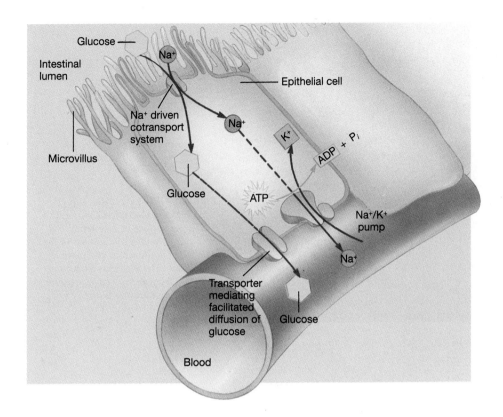

Figure 5–18 Coupled glucose transport systems in intestinal epithelia allow glucose to be transported through the cell from the intestine to the blood. Glucose is actively transported into the cell by a sodium-driven cotransport system located only on the part of the plasma membrane in contact with the intestinal lumen. The sodium gradient across the plasma membrane is maintained by a sodium-potassium pump, which actively transports sodium from the cytoplasm into the blood, keeping the intracellular concentration low. Active transport of glucose into the cell keeps its intracellular concentration high, so that it is transported into the blood by a different, facilitated diffusion transporter located only on the regions of the plasma membrane in contact with the blood.

facilitated diffusion of glucose. The cell maintains a steep gradient (high outside, low inside) by phosphorylating the glucose molecules once they enter the cell. However, an ATP is "spent" for every glucose molecule phosphorylated (not to mention such additional costs as the energy required to make the enzymes that carry out the reaction).

So how, exactly, *does* active transport differ from facilitated diffusion? Active transport systems can work *against* a concentration gradient (pumping materials from a region of low concentration to a region of high concentration). The energy stored in the concentration gradient is not only unavailable to the system, but it actually works against it. For this reason, another energy source, often ATP, is required. We have seen in the case of cotransport systems how energy can even be provided by a concentration gradient for some other substance (e.g., sodium or potassium ions). Of course, ATP energy is indirectly involved because it is used to power the pump that produces the sodium/potassium gradient. As we shall see in Chapters 6, 7, and 8, energy can come from other sources as well.

Exocytosis and endocytosis are ways of transporting large particles by means of vesicles or vacuoles

In both simple and facilitated diffusion and in carrier-mediated active transport, individual molecules and ions pass through the plasma membrane. Larger quantities of material, such as particles of food or even whole cells, must also be moved into or out of cells. Such cellular work requires that cells expend energy directly (and thus is a form of active transport) and involves membrane fusion. In **exocytosis,** a cell ejects waste products or specific secretion products such as hormones by the fusion of a vesicle with the plasma membrane of the cell (Figure 5–19). Exocytosis results in the incorporation of the membrane of the secretory vesicle into the plasma membrane. This is also the primary mechanism by which plasma membranes grow larger.

In **endocytosis,** materials are taken into the cell. Several types of endocytotic mechanisms operate in biological systems. In **phagocytosis** (literally, "cell eating"), the cell ingests large solid particles such as bacteria or food (Figure 5–20). Phagocytosis is a mechanism used by protozoa and by several classes of white blood cells to ingest particles, some of which are as large as an entire bacterium. During ingestion, folds of the plasma membrane enclose the particle, which has bound to the surface of the cell, and form a vacuole around it. When the membrane has encircled the particle, it fuses at the point of contact, leaving the vacuole floating freely in the cytoplasm. The vacuole then fuses with lysosomes, and the ingested material is degraded.

In the form of endocytosis known as **pinocytosis** ("cell drinking"), the cell takes in dissolved materials. Tiny droplets of fluid are trapped by folds in the plasma

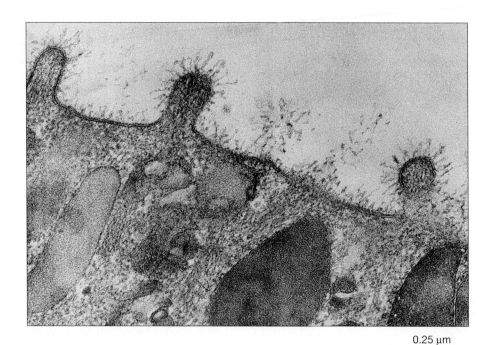

Figure 5–19 Exocytosis. A high-magnification electron micrograph of the upper surface of a secreting cell. Secretion granules can be seen in the cytoplasm approaching the plasma membrane. The filaments projecting diffusely from the cell surface are of unknown significance but may be proteins.   (J. F. Gennaro/Photo Researchers, Inc.)

0.25 µm

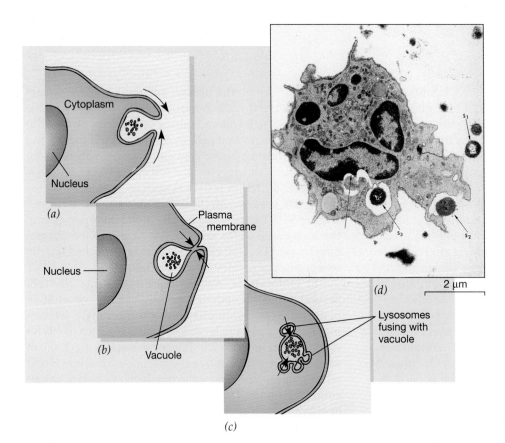

2 µm

Figure 5–20 Phagocytosis. (*a*) In phagocytosis the cell ingests large solid particles, such as bacteria. Folds of the plasma membrane surround the particle to be ingested, forming a small vacuole around it. (*b*) This vacuole then pinches off inside the cell. (*c*) Lysosomes may fuse with the vacuole and pour their potent digestive enzymes onto the ingested material. (*d*) A white blood cell in the presence of *Streptococcus pyogenes*. One bacterium (S_1) is free, one bacterium (S_2) is being phagocytized, and a third (S_3) has been phagocytized and is seen within a vacuole. Note that near the vacuole (*see arrow*) the white blood cell's own nucleus has been partly digested.   (*d*, C. L. Sanders, Battelle Pacific Northwest Labs/Biological Photo Service)

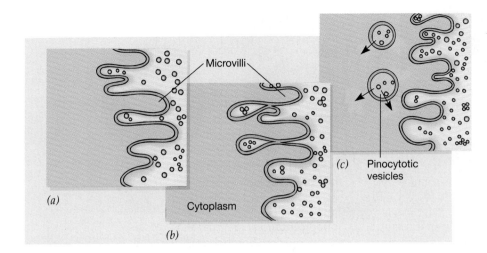

Figure 5–21 In pinocytosis tiny droplets of fluid are trapped by folds of the plasma membrane (*a*), which then pinch off (*b*) into the cytoplasm as small fluid-filled vesicles (*c*). The content of these vesicles is then slowly transferred to the cytoplasm across their membrane linings.

membrane (Figure 5–21), which pinch off into the cytoplasm as tiny vesicles. The liquid contents of these vesicles are then slowly transferred into the cytoplasm; the vesicles may themselves become progressively smaller, to the point that they appear to vanish.

In a third type of endocytosis, called **receptor-mediated endocytosis,** specific proteins or particles combine with *receptor proteins* embedded in the plasma membrane of the cell. The receptor-bound molecules then migrate into *coated pits,* which are regions on the cytoplasmic surface of the membrane coated with whisker-like structures. These coated pits form *coated vesicles* (Figure 5–22) by endocytosis. The coating on a vesicle consists of proteins, which momentarily form a basket-like structure around it. Seconds after the vesicles are released, however, the coating dissociates from them, leaving the vesicles free in the cytoplasm. The vesicles then fuse with other similar vesicles to form *endosomes,* larger vesicles in which the materials being transported are free inside and no longer attached to the membrane receptors. An endosome can divide to form two kinds of vesicles: One kind contains the receptors and can be returned to the plasma membrane; the other, which contains the ingested particles, fuses with lysosomes and is then processed by the cell.

Cholesterol in the blood is taken up by animal cells by receptor-mediated endocytosis. Much of the receptor-mediated endocytosis pathway was detailed through studies of the receptor for low-density lipoprotein (LDL—a primary cholesterol carrier in blood) by investigators M. Brown and J. Goldstein, who in 1986 were awarded the Nobel Prize for their pioneering work. These investigations also have important medical implications, for cholesterol that remains in the blood instead of entering the cells can become deposited on the artery walls and increase the risk of heart attack.

The recycling of the LDL receptor to the plasma membrane through vesicles illustrates a problem common to all cells that employ endocytotic and exocytotic mechanisms. In cells that are constantly involved in secretion, an equivalent amount of membrane must be returned to the interior of the cell for each vesicle that fuses with the plasma membrane; if it is not, the cell surface keeps expanding, even though the growth of the cell itself may be arrested. A similar situation exists for cells that use endocytosis. A macrophage, for example, ingests the equivalent of its entire surface membrane in about 30 minutes, requiring an equivalent amount of recycling or new membrane synthesis for the cell to maintain its surface area.

SPECIALIZED CONTACTS (JUNCTIONS) FORM BETWEEN SOME CELLS OF MULTICELLULAR ORGANISMS

Cells in close contact with each other may develop specialized intercellular junctions that involve their plasma membranes as well as other components. These structures allow neighboring cells to form strong connections with each other or to establish rapid communications between adjacent cells. In animals there are three common types of intercellular contacts: desmosomes, tight junctions, and gap junctions. Plant cells are connected by plasmodesmata.

Desmosomes Are Points of Attachment between Some Animal Cells

Adjacent epithelial cells, such as those found in the upper layer of the skin, are so tightly bound to each other that strong mechanical forces are required to separate them. They are held together by button-like structures, called **desmosomes,** that are present on the two

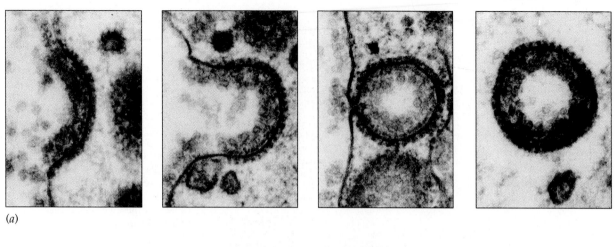

(a)

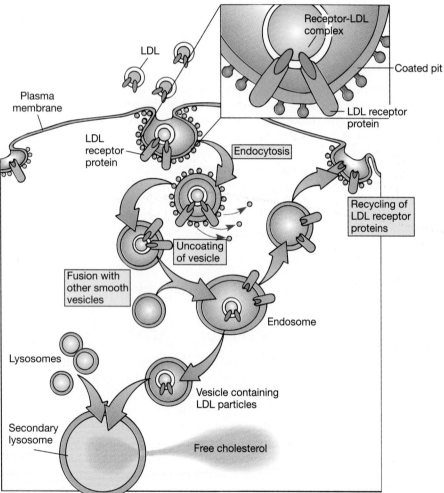

(b)

Figure 5-22 Receptor-mediated endocytosis. (*a*) Series of transmission electron micrographs showing the formation of a coated vesicle from a coated pit. (*b*) Low-density lipoprotein (LDL) particles, which transport cholesterol in the blood, attach to specific receptor proteins on the plasma membrane. The receptor-LDL complexes move along the surface of the fluid membrane and cluster in coated pit regions of the membrane surface. Endocytosis of the coated pit results in the formation of a coated vesicle in the cytoplasm. Seconds later the coat is removed, and the vesicles fuse with their counterparts to form large, smooth vesicles called endosomes. The receptors and the LDL particles dissociate in the endosomes and move to different regions of the vesicles. New vesicles form from the endosomes. Those containing the receptors move to the surface and fuse with the plasma membrane, recycling the receptors to the cell surface. Vesicles containing the LDL particles fuse with lysosomes. Hydrolytic enzymes then release the cholesterol from the particles for use by the cell. (*a*, From Perry, M. M., and A. B. Gilbert, *J. Cell. Sci.* 39:257–272, 1979)

adjacent cell surfaces (Figure 5-23). Each desmosome consists of regions of dense material associated with the cytosolic side of each plasma membrane. The two cells are held together by protein filaments that cross the 24-nm-wide intercellular space between the desmosomes.

Desmosomes are anchored on the insides of the cells to systems of intermediate filaments. Thus the intermediate filament networks of adjacent cells are connected so that mechanical stresses are distributed throughout the tissue. The function of the desmosomes

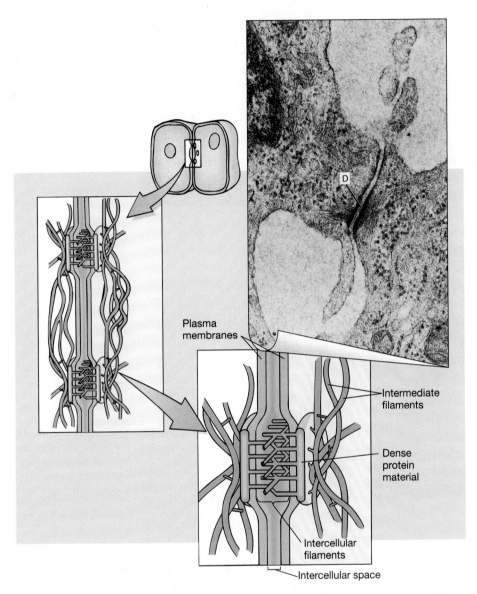

Plasma
membranes

Intermediate
filaments

Dense
protein
material

Intercellular
filaments

Intercellular space

Figure 5–23 The structure of a desmosome. Paired discs associated with the plasma membranes of adjacent cells are connected by intercellular protein filaments. Intracellular intermediate filaments attached to the discs are connected to other desmosomes. The transmission electron micrograph shows a desmosome between two cells of the ovarian epithelium of a rabbit. (Anderson, E., *J. Morphol.* 150:135–166, 1976)

appears to be purely mechanical; they hold cells together at one point like a rivet or a spot weld. As a result, cells can form strong sheets, but substances can still pass freely through the spaces between the plasma membranes.

Tight Junctions Seal Off Intercellular Spaces between Some Animal Cells

Tight junctions are literally areas of tight connections between the membranes of adjacent cells. These connections are so tight that the spaces around the cells have completely disappeared; certain substances can thus be prevented from passing through the layer of cells. Electron micrographs of tight junctions show that in the region of the junction the membranes of the two cells are in actual contact with each other (Figures 5–24 and 5–25) held together by proteins linking the two cells.

Cells connected by tight junctions are used to seal off body cavities. For example, tight junctions between cells lining the intestine prevent substances in the intestine from entering the body or the bloodstream by passing around the cells. The sheet of cells thus acts as a selective barrier; food substances required by the body must be transported to the blood through the cytoplasm

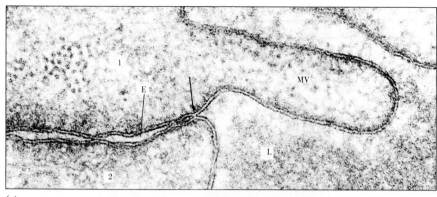

(a)

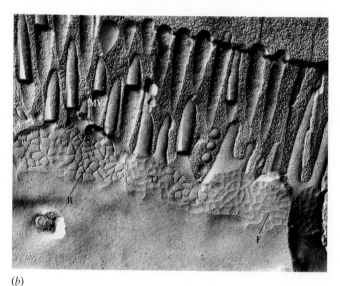

(b)

Figure 5–24   Tight junctions between adjacent cells. The tight junctions occur at the points of contact between two cells and would extend completely around the cells in a three-dimensional view. (a) Thin-section electron micrograph showing points of fusion between the plasma membranes between two cells (marked 1 and 2) lining the intestine. One junction is marked by the arrow. MV = microvillus, L = lumen (interior) of the intestine, E = extracellular space between the two cells. (b) Freeze-fracture electron micrograph through a region of tight junctions (TJ). The cylinders are parts of microvilli (MV) seen from inside the cell. R and F refer to the regions where the membranes contact to form the tight junctions.   (a, G. E. Palade; b, Friend, *J. Cell Biol.* 53:758, 1972)

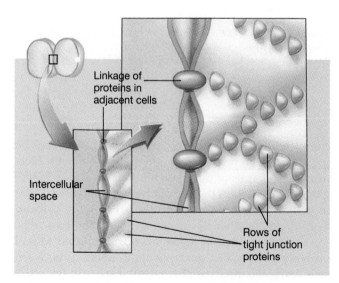

Figure 5–25   A model of the structure of a tight junction between adjacent cells, formed by linkages between rows of proteins.

of intestinal cells, as we saw in Figure 5–18, and some toxins and unwanted materials are prevented from entering the blood.

Gap Junctions Contain Pores That Permit Transfer of Small Molecules and Ions between Some Animal Cells

A third type of intercellular connection in animal cells, the **gap junction,** is like the desmosome in that it bridges the space between cells, but the space it bridges is somewhat narrower (Figure 5–26). Gap junctions also differ in that they not only connect the membranes but

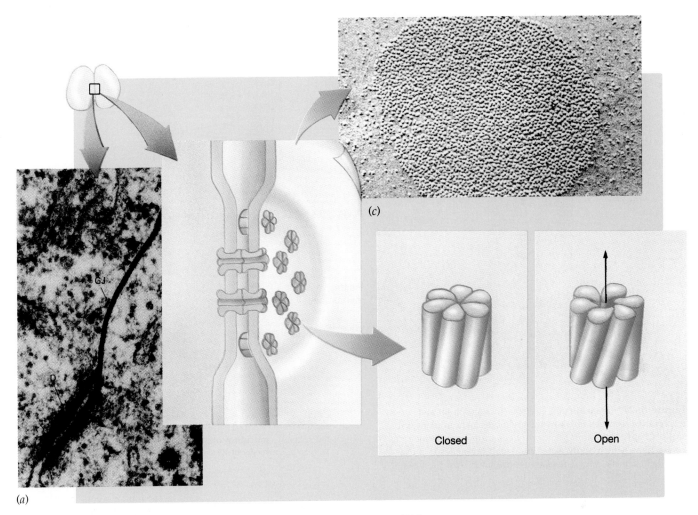

(c)

Closed   Open

(a)

Figure 5–26   Junctions. (*a*) A gap junction (GJ) and a desmosome (D) between ovarian cells of a rabbit. Note the difference in the spaces between the two plasma membranes in each structure. (*b*) Model of a gap junction based on electron-microscopic and x-ray diffraction data. The two membranes contain cylinders composed of six protein subunits arranged to form a pore. Two cylinders from opposite membranes are joined to form a pore about 1.5–2.0 nm in diameter connecting the cytoplasmic compartments of the two cells. (*c*) Freeze-fracture replica of the P-face (P) gap junction between two ovarian cells of a mouse, showing the numerous protein particles present. (*d*) Model illustrating how a gap junction pore might open and close.   (*a*, Alberfini, D. F., and Anderson, E., *J. Cell Biol.*, 63:234–250, 1974; *c*, Anderson, E., *J. Morphol.* 156:339–366, 1978)

also act as pores connecting the cytoplasm of adjacent cells. Gap junctions consist of hexagonal arrays of proteins forming clusters of pores, which are about 1 to 2 nm in diameter. Small inorganic molecules (e.g., ions) and some biological molecules (e.g., derivatives of ATP) can pass through the pores, but larger molecules are excluded. When appropriate marker substances are injected into one of a group of cells connected by gap junctions, the marker passes rapidly into the adjacent cells but does not enter the space between the cells.

Gap junctions provide for rapid chemical and electrical communications between cells. Cells in the pancreas, for example, are linked together by gap junctions in such a way that if one of a group of cells is stimulated to secrete insulin, the signal is passed through the junctions to the other cells in the cluster, ensuring a coordinated response to the initial signal. Heart muscle cells are also linked by gap junctions in order to provide electrical coupling that synchronizes the contraction of cells.

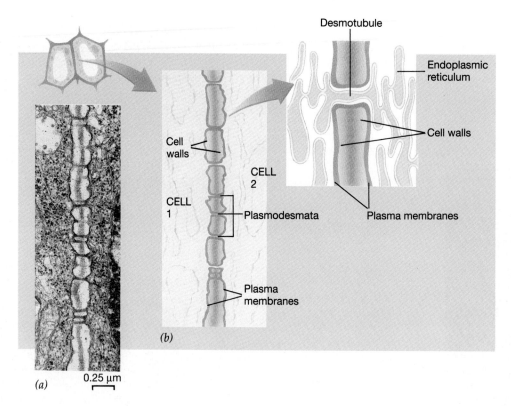

Figure 5–27 Transmission electron micrograph (*a*) and interpretive drawing (*b*) showing plasmodesmata in plant cell walls. Channels through plant cell walls form cytoplasmic connections, which allow water and small molecules to move between adjacent cells. The channels are lined with the fused plasma membranes of the two adjacent cells. In the center of most plasmodesmata are desmotubules, cylinders formed from endoplasmic reticulum membranes from both cells. (*a*, E. H. Newcomb, University of Wisconsin/Biological Photo Service)

Plasmodesmata Are Cytoplasmic Channels That Allow Movement of Molecules and Ions between Plant Cells

Plant cells are isolated from one another by rigid, thick cell walls. Hence they have no need of desmosomes for strength. These walls are usually impregnated with waterproofing material (see Chapter 31), making tight junctions unnecessary. However, they do require connections that are functionally equivalent to the gap junctions of some animal cells. **Plasmodesmata** (singular, *plasmodesma*) are 20- to 40-nm-wide channels through adjacent cell walls that are used to connect the cytoplasm of neighboring cells (Figure 5–27). The plasma membranes of neighboring cells are continuous with each other through the plasmodesmata, allowing molecules and ions, but not organelles, to pass through the openings from cell to cell. Most plasmodesmata contain a cylindrical membranous structure, called the *desmotubule*, which also runs through the opening and connects the ER of the two adjacent cells.

SUMMARY

I. Cellular membranes are complex structures that (1) physically separate the interior of the cell from the outside world and (2) form compartments inside the cells of complex organisms that allow them to perform complex functions.
   A. Membranes have many different structural and functional roles.
      1. They regulate the passage of materials.
      2. They receive information that permits the cell to sense changes in its environment and respond to them.
      3. They contain specialized structures that allow specific contacts and communications with other cells.
      4. They serve as work surfaces for various biochemical reactions.
   B. According to the fluid mosaic model of membrane structure, membranes consist of a fluid lipid bilayer in which a variety of proteins are embedded.
      1. The lipid bilayer is arranged so that the hydrophilic headgroups of the phospholipids are at the two surfaces of the bilayer and their hydrophobic fatty acid chains are in the interior.
      2. In almost all biological membranes the lipids of the bilayer are in a fluid or liquid-crystalline state, which allows the molecules to move rapidly in the plane of the membrane.
      3. Integral membrane proteins are embedded in the bilayer in such a way that their hydrophilic surfaces are exposed to the aqueous environment and their hydrophobic surfaces are in contact with the hydrophobic interior of the bilayer.
      4. Peripheral membrane proteins are associated with the surface of the bilayer and are easily removed without disrupting the structure of the membrane.
      5. Membrane proteins and lipids are asymmetrically positioned in the bilayer so that one side of the membrane has a different composition and structure from the other.
II. Biological membranes are selectively permeable; that is, they allow the passage of some substances but not others.
   A. Some molecules pass through membranes by simple diffusion.
      1. Diffusion is the net movement of a substance down its concentration gradient (from a region of high to a region of low concentration).
      2. Dialysis is the diffusion of a solute across a membrane.

   3. Osmosis is a kind of diffusion in which molecules of water pass through a selectively permeable membrane from a region where water is more concentrated to a region where water is less concentrated.
   4. The osmotic pressure of a solution is determined by the amount of dissolved substances (solutes) in solution. Cells regulate their internal osmotic pressure to prevent shrinking or bursting. Plant cells can be under high internal hydrostatic pressure because the cell walls prevent the cells from expanding and bursting.
   B. Some substances pass through membranes by facilitated diffusion, in which a carrier protein helps a molecule move through the membrane. Facilitated diffusion utilizes the energy of a concentration gradient for the substance being transported and cannot work against the gradient.
   C. In carrier-mediated active transport the cell expends metabolic energy to move ions or molecules against a concentration gradient.
   D. In endocytosis (phagocytosis, pinocytosis, and receptor-mediated endocytosis) materials such as food may be moved into the cell; a portion of the plasma membrane envelops the material, enclosing it in a vacuole, or small vesicle, which is then released inside the cell.
   E. In exocytosis, the cell ejects waste products or secretes substances such as mucus.
III. Plasma membranes of animal and plant cells contain specialized structures that allow them to have contact and communication with adjacent cells.
   A. Desmosomes, tight junctions, and gap junctions are specialized structures associated with the plasma membrane of animal cells.
      1. Desmosomes weld cells together to form strong tissues.
      2. Tight junctions seal membranes of adjacent cells together to prevent substances from passing around cells.
      3. Gap junctions are protein pores in membranes that allow communication between the cytoplasm of adjacent cells.
   B. Plasmodesmata are openings in plant cell walls that allow the plasma membranes and the cytoplasm of adjacent cells to be continuous so that molecules and ions can pass through.

POST-TEST

1. Most of the physical properties of a biological membrane are determined by the properties of its _____ _____.

2. The fatty acid interior of the lipid bilayer is _____, whereas the surface of the bilayer is _____.

3. Bilayers are formed from _____ lipids, that is, lipids that have prominent _____ and _____ regions on the molecule.

4. _____ membrane proteins have domains with _____ surfaces that are associated with the interior

of the bilayer. _____ membrane proteins are associated with the bilayer through interactions with other membrane components on the surface of the membrane.

5. Net movement of particles from a region of high concentration to a region of low concentration is called _____.

6. A solution that has an equivalent concentration of _____ and hence the same osmotic pressure as the fluid inside the cell is said to be _____ to the cell's contents.

7. When a plant cell is placed in solution A, the contents inside the cell membrane can be seen to shrink away from the cell wall. Solution A is _____ to the interior of the plant cell.

8. When red blood cells are placed in solution B, the cells are seen to expand, and many of them burst. Solution B is _____ to the interior of the red blood cells.

9. When glucose enters cells by moving down its concentration gradient with the help of a carrier protein and does not require an additional source of energy, it does so by _____ _____.

10. When the glucose concentration outside the cell is lower than its concentration inside the cell, it must be moved into the cell by _____ _____.

11. The sodium-potassium pump is an _____ _____ system that pumps _____ from the inside of the cell to the outside and pumps _____ from the outside of the cell to the inside.

12. Active transport systems that derive their energy from transport of a second molecule down its concentration gradient are called _____ systems.

13. Large molecules and large particles are transported into cells by an endocytotic mechanism called _____.

14. Molecules that bind to specific molecules on the plasma membrane and then move into the interior of the cell through small vesicles do so by the process of _____.

15. _____ are specialized regions of the plasma membrane in animal cells that "spot weld" adjacent cells together.

16. _____ _____ contain specialized protein pores in the plasma membranes of animal cells that allow small molecules to pass from the cytoplasm of one cell to the cytoplasm of its neighbor.

17. _____ _____ are specialized regions of plasma membranes in animal cells that prevent substances from passing around the outsides of cells in a tissue.

18. _____ provide for water and small molecules to be transferred to adjacent plant cells.

REVIEW QUESTIONS

1. Sketch a diagram of the plasma membrane showing the lipid bilayer, the various types of membrane proteins, and the carbohydrates on the outer surface of the membrane.

2. Illustrate how a transmembrane protein would be positioned in a lipid bilayer. How do the hydrophilic and hydrophobic regions of the protein affect its orientation?

3. Describe the pathway used by cells to place carbohydrates on plasma membrane proteins. Explain why this results in the carbohydrate groups being on only one side of the lipid bilayer.

4. What is the source of energy for diffusion? State a rule for predicting the movement of particles along a concentration gradient. Is the rule different for facilitated diffusion compared with simple diffusion?

5. Distinguish clearly between osmosis and dialysis.

6. Predict the consequences if a plant cell were to be placed in a(n) (1) isotonic, (2) hypertonic, (3) hypotonic environment. Would you have to modify any of your predictions for an animal cell?

7. What are some of the functions of the plasma membrane? Discuss the nature of the proteins that carry out those functions, and explain how their properties make them especially adapted for their functions.

8. What is the main energy source for active transport? In what ways are facilitated diffusion and carrier-mediated active transport similar? In what major way do they differ?

9. Why can't larger polar molecules and ions cross a lipid bilayer? Would it be advantageous to the cell if they could?

10. Draw a diagram illustrating how membrane lipid bilayers fuse during the processes of exocytosis and endocytosis. Is one the exact reverse of the other? Why?

11. Discriminate between the processes of phagocytosis and pinocytosis.

12. How are desmosomes and tight junctions functionally similar? How do they differ? Do they share any structural similarities?

13. What is the justification for considering gap junctions and plasmodesmata to be functionally similar?

RECOMMENDED READINGS

Alberts, B., D. Bray, J. Lewis, M. Raff, K. Roberts, and J. D. Watson. *Molecular Biology of the Cell,* 2nd ed. Garland Publishing, New York, 1989, Chapter 6. A discussion of the structure and functions of the plasma membrane.

Darnell, J., H. Lodish, and D. Baltimore. *Molecular Cell Biology,* 2nd ed. Scientific American Books, New York, 1990, Chapters 13 and 14. A comprehensive treatment of the structure and functions of the plasma membrane and transport functions.

de Duve, C. *A Guided Tour of the Living Cell.* Scientific American Library, New York, 1984. An illustrated tour of the cell in the form of journeys through different membrane and organelle systems.

Science Writer

JENNIE DUSHECK

Jennie Dusheck received her undergraduate degree in zoology from the University of California, Berkeley, in 1978. She is now the editor of Science Notes, *an award-winning newsletter written and illustrated by students in the science communication program at the University of California, Santa Cruz. Dusheck is herself a graduate of this program and has worked as a science writer since 1985. She has published numerous articles and book reviews in the* San Francisco Chronicle, Santa Cruz Sentinel, Pacific Discovery, *and* Science News.

What made you decide to major in biology?

I've always had a lot of different interests. I went back and forth between biology or zoology and English. I was also thinking of majoring in astronomy or geology. I was a little daunted by all the prerequisites for biology, especially chemistry, but by the time I had to declare a major in my junior year, I'd already completed all of them. So I decided I might as well go ahead and enjoy the fun part, which was the second 2 years.

How did you decide on Berkeley?

I'm originally from San Francisco, so I applied to Berkeley and Davis. In high school, I'd had an idea that I wanted to be a veterinarian. Since Davis has a veterinary school, it was my first choice at the time. I wasn't accepted at Davis, but once I got to Berkeley, I was really glad to be there. And I

quickly realized that I didn't want to be a veterinarian, after all.

What is the Berkeley biology program like?

You can study a lot of different things at Berkeley in biology. I majored in zoology and focused on evolution and ecology, animal behavior, and whole animal science, although that wasn't a *formal* concentration.

There were certain requirements. For example, you could take either a marine biology class in which you learned all the local invertebrates or a field biology class in which you learned all the local vertebrates. I took

a two-quarter sequence in which we studied all of the reptiles, amphibians, mammals, and birds of California. We went out hiking in the field every weekend with a professor. We also had weekly labs and lectures. So, it was pretty intensive. I learned a lot and I enjoyed every minute of it. I loved the upper-division classes. All of the professors are really top-notch. They're engaged, they're willing to spend time with undergraduates, and they're excited about their own work and convey that excitement to the students.

What courses did you especially like, and which ones did you struggle with?

My favorite courses were mammalogy, ecology, and evolution, and I struggled with all of them. Cell biology was a real struggle, but I enjoyed that one, too.

Was there a particular professor who inspired you or encouraged you to choose a career in biology?

As a group my professors were inspiring. They were all wonderful. They made all of us really admire science as a discipline, and they demanded that we think rigorously and critically. They also gave us a good, basic understanding of how science works and how scientists think. All of these skills have been very valuable to me in my career.

Did you do any interesting research projects while you were in school?

Yes, I did two as an undergraduate. One focused on the singing habits of robins—when they sing, how long they sing, and how their habits are influenced by their environment. I looked at the effects of different amounts of daylight, humidity, and the number of other birds nearby. Then I did a senior project on the behavior of field mice, looking at interactions between females and comparing them to interactions between males. During the course of this project, I made an original discovery: that the dominant males mark the walls of their tunnels. It's a behavior you wouldn't normally see because it occurs underground. They swagger down their tunnels, using secretions from glands on their hips to mark the sides.

Let's talk about how your career began. What did you do after school?

After I graduated, one of my zoology professors recommended me for my first real job. I was a technician for 2 years in the wildlife department at Berkeley. We were comparing the diets of cattle and three species of deer to see whether they were competing for the same food. I also worked for the Bay Area Air Pollution Control District. Both were part-time jobs. Then I went to graduate school at Davis for 3 years. My advisor was a lepidopterist in the zoology department, so I did my research on butterflies. After I got my master's degree, I went back to Berkeley, where I worked in an embryology lab on a project funded by NASA. The idea was to see how frog embryos (tadpoles) develop at zero gravity. They were going to send frogs into space.

Was it at that time that you began doing some science writing?

Yes, I enrolled in a science writing class at Berkeley. It's an undergraduate course, but I was able to take it through the university extension program after I'd graduated. I did a lot of

reporting for that class and really enjoyed it. I discovered that I liked calling people up and asking them what they were doing and that people liked being interviewed. It was a fun way of indulging my interest in science. While I was in that class I applied to the science communication program at U.C., Santa Cruz, and my writing professor at Berkeley gave me a recommendation.

How many years is that program?

It's a 1-year program, after which they put graduates into summer internships. I went to Washington, DC, and worked for *Science News* for the summer. Then I came back, did some textbook work, and started editing newsletters at U.C., Santa Cruz.

And that's how you became the editor of *Science Notes*? Tell us about that.

I work with the students in the Santa Cruz Science Communication Program. All of them have undergraduate degrees in science and almost all have done some research work. Some also have a master's or even a Ph.D. degree. They want to become science writers. I assign them stories to do on campus about science at U.C., Santa Cruz, for publication in *Science Notes*. They write the articles and I edit them. It's a very intense kind of editing, because most of them have never written feature stories before. I may have to ask that a story be rewritten as many as five times. I also do all of the art editing for the newsletter. I give assignments to students in our science illustration program and supervise their completion. Then I do all of the layout and paste-up—all of the production for the newsletter.

Do you work out of your home?

Yes. You know, I really have what I was looking for, something that would allow me to stay involved in science *and* in publishing.

Do you come into contact with a lot of different interesting people?

Oh, yes. Scientists to some extent, and the students themselves are all interesting. This year, one is a paleontologist from Berkeley who is also an art-

ist. Another is a veterinarian from southern California. They've done all kinds of things. They tend to have a background in field biology, but not always.

What other kinds of jobs are out there for science writers?

There is textbook writing: Some people become authors and work with publishers directly. You can write for magazines or newspapers. Probably the biggest market for science writers is in public information offices at universities. They really need people who can explain science to newspaper and television reporters and other media people. There is some work in video. People who do television or even film documentaries all need writers who know about science. Another area is museum and aquarium work. And there are a lot of companies that do environmental impact reports for businesses. They need people who can not only write the reports but also do the field research for them. That's really an example of technical writing, however. Unlike science writing, which is aimed at the general public, technical writing is for more specialized audiences, such as engineers or scientists.

What's the best way to prepare for and then go about looking for a job in science writing?

One good way is to major in science and then either teach yourself how to write or go through a program like the one at Santa Cruz. You can also just launch yourself by freelancing and accumulating writing clips. It's a gradual process, but if you're good at what you do, it's easy to get a job. Some top-notch science students are also among the best writers in the country. They will go far in science writing.

PART II

Energy Transfer through Living Systems

Living things cannot exist without energy. It is used by cells when they grow and when they reproduce. It is required to synthesize and transport materials. Every activity of every living cell or organism requires energy.

The sun provides the energy that powers life. The energy produced from nuclear fusion reactions on this hot, glowing sphere radiates into space in all directions. A tiny portion of that energy is captured by Earth's plants and other photosynthetic organisms, which convert it to chemical energy in organic molecules. When plants or animals need the energy that is stored in organic molecules, they perform cell respiration, which breaks the organic molecules apart to extract the energy. Likewise, decomposers break down organic wastes and dead organisms to extract energy.

The energy that living things use to do biological work cannot be reused. This energy is not destroyed with use. It escapes from Earth and radiates into space as low-grade heat.

CHAPTER 6

□

The Energy of Life

Living cells require energy to carry on life processes. Cells have no way of producing new energy or of recycling the energy they have used. Therefore, life depends on a continuous input of energy. That energy flows in a one-way direction through every cell and organism, and through the ecosphere. Most producers trap light energy from the sun during photosynthesis and incorporate some of that energy in the chemical bonds of carbohydrates and other organic compounds. Then a portion of that chemical energy can be transferred to the consumers, which eat the producers, and to the decomposers, which feed on them all sooner or later.

An organism is considered an open system with respect to energy because of the one-way energy flow through it. Energy is captured, temporarily stored, and then used to perform biological work (Figure 6–1). During these processes energy is converted to heat and dispersed into the environment. Thus, organisms obtain the energy they need from their environment and, eventually, release some of that energy back to their surroundings in the form of heat.

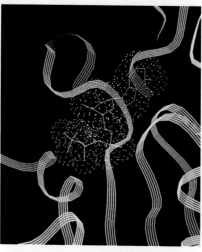

Computer graphics close-up view of an ATP molecule bound to phosphoglycerate kinase, an enzyme that catalyzes the transfer of phosphate groups from ATP to another compound. (*Red*, oxygen; *white*, carbon; *blue*, nitrogen.) (Photo Researchers, Oxford Molecular Biophysics Laboratory/Science Photo Library/Photo Researchers, Inc.)

Because energy cannot be reused, organisms must continually obtain fresh supplies. Cells have evolved complex mechanisms that provide sufficient energy for their survival. Just what are these mechanisms that permit cells to capture and store energy? What is the role of dATP? How do enzymes affect energy dynamics in cells? How is energy transferred between organisms?

This chapter focuses on some of the principles of energy capture, storage, transfer, and use. In Chapter 7 we explore some of the main metabolic pathways used by cellular respiration. Finally, in Chapter 8 we discuss the chemical and energy transformations of photosynthesis.

After you have studied this chapter you should be able to

1. Define the term *energy* and contrast potential and kinetic energy.
2. State the first and second laws of thermodynamics and discuss their applications to living organisms and to the ecosphere.
3. Contrast entropy, enthalpy, and free energy.
4. Describe the energy dynamics of a reaction in equilibrium.
5. Distinguish between endergonic and exergonic reactions and explain how they may be coupled so that the second law of thermodynamics is not violated.

6. Illustrate the chemical structure of ATP and summarize its role in cellular metabolism.
7. Explain the function of enzymes and describe how they work.
8. Describe how factors such as pH and temperature influence enzymatic activity.
9. Compare the actions and effects of the various types of enzyme inhibitors.

BIOLOGICAL WORK REQUIRES ENERGY

Energy may be defined as the capacity to do work; more comprehensively, energy is the ability to produce a change in the state or motion of matter. We can define **matter** as anything that has mass and takes up space. Here we are concerned with the ability of living systems to do biological work. It takes enough energy to light a 75-watt bulb just to keep your brain in operation as you read these words. And at this very moment you are expending considerable amounts of energy to maintain your breathing, concentrate urine in your kidneys, digest food, circulate your blood, and maintain countless other metabolic activities. These are all forms of biological work.

Energy can exist in several different forms. These include heat, as well as electrical, mechanical, chemical, sound, and radiant energy (the energy of electromagnetic waves, such as radio waves, visible light, x rays, and gamma rays).

Figure 6–1 This bobcat is expending energy in an effort to capture the snowshoe hare. If caught and eaten, the hare will provide nutrients containing energy for future activity. For its part, the hare is expending a great deal of energy in its effort to escape becoming an energy source for the bobcat. (Sharon Cummings/ Marvin L. Dembinsky, Jr., Photography Associates)

Energy Can Be Described as Potential or Kinetic

Potential energy is stored energy; it has the capacity to do work owing to its position or state. In contrast, **kinetic energy** is the energy of motion. A boulder at the top of a hill has potential energy because of its position. As the boulder rolls down the hill, the potential energy is converted to kinetic energy. It requires the input of energy to push the boulder back up the hill and restore the potential energy of its position at the top.

Another example of the conversion of potential energy to kinetic energy is the release of a drawn bow (Figure 6–2). The tension in the bow and string represents stored energy; when the string is released, this potential energy is released, so that the motion of the bow propels the arrow. It requires the input of additional energy to draw the bow once again and restore the potential energy. Most of the actions of organisms involve a complex series of energy transformations. For example, to prepare for a running event, athletes eat foods that build up their reserves of glycogen. During the event, the athletes' bodies continuously convert the energy stored in the glycogen into the kinetic energy used to run the race.

Heat Is a Form of Energy That Can Be Conveniently Measured

To study energy transformations, scientists must be able to measure energy. How is this done? Heat is a convenient form in which energy can be measured because all other forms of energy can be converted into heat. In fact, the study of energy and its transformations has been named **thermodynamics**—that is, heat dynamics.

Although several units may be used in measuring energy, the most widely used in biological systems is

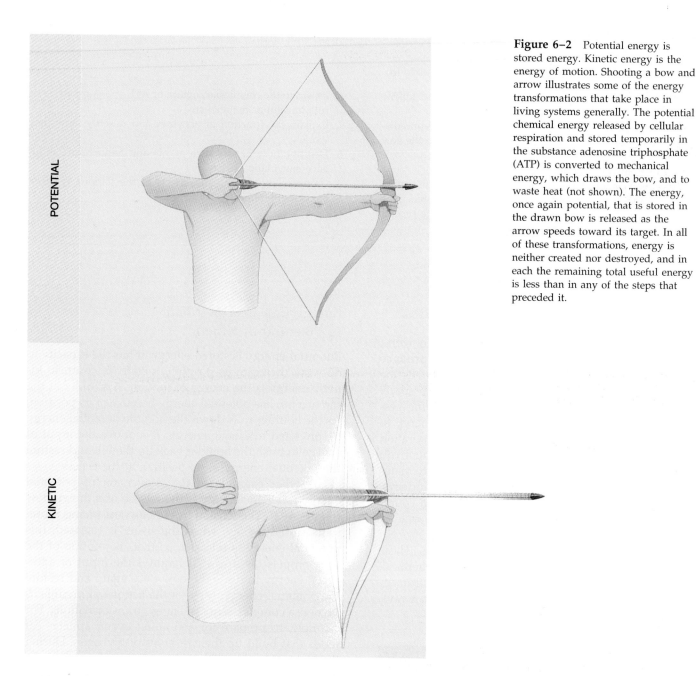

Figure 6–2 Potential energy is stored energy. Kinetic energy is the energy of motion. Shooting a bow and arrow illustrates some of the energy transformations that take place in living systems generally. The potential chemical energy released by cellular respiration and stored temporarily in the substance adenosine triphosphate (ATP) is converted to mechanical energy, which draws the bow, and to waste heat (not shown). The energy, once again potential, that is stored in the drawn bow is released as the arrow speeds toward its target. In all of these transformations, energy is neither created nor destroyed, and in each the remaining total useful energy is less than in any of the steps that preceded it.

the **kilocalorie (kcal).** A kilocalorie is the amount of heat required to raise the temperature of 1 kg of water from 14.5 to 15.5°C. Nutritionists use the kilocalorie to measure the potential energy of foods and usually refer to it as a *Calorie* (with a capital C).

TWO LAWS OF THERMODYNAMICS GOVERN ENERGY TRANSFORMATIONS

All of the activities of our universe—from the life and death of cells to the life and death of stars—are governed by the laws of thermodynamics.

The Quantity of Energy in the Universe Does Not Change

According to the **first law of thermodynamics,** known also as the *law of conservation of energy,* the energy of the universe is constant. Similarly, the total energy of any **system**—that is, of any object and its surroundings—remains constant. The term *surroundings* refers to the rest of the universe. As an object undergoes a change, it may absorb energy from its surroundings or deliver energy into its surroundings. The difference in the energy content of the object in its initial and final states must be equalled by a corresponding change in the energy content of the surroundings.

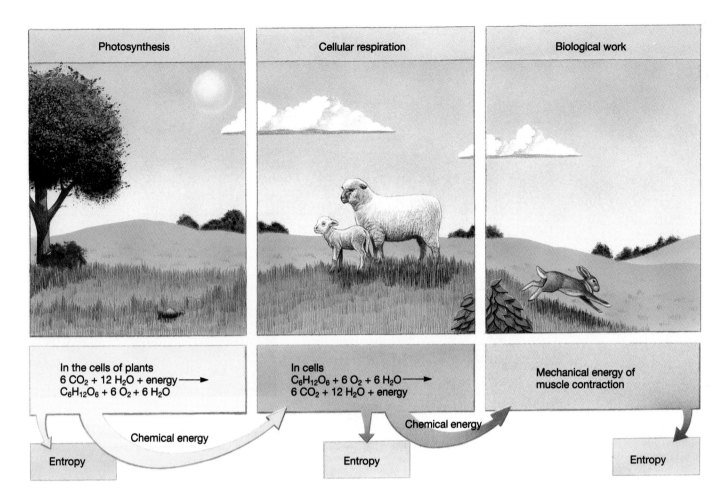

Figure 6–3 Three major types of processes that transform energy in the world of life are photosynthesis, cellular respiration, and biological work. (The chemical reactions shown are simplified. See Chapters 7 and 8 for more detail.)

The first law of thermodynamics holds that during ordinary chemical or physical processes, energy can be transferred and changed in form but can be neither created nor destroyed. The universe is a closed system when it comes to energy. As far as we know, the energy present when it formed some 20 billion years ago is all the universe can ever have; it cannot be added to or subtracted from.

Although an organism can neither make nor destroy energy, it can capture some from its environment and use it for its own needs. Organisms can also transform energy from one form to another. During photosynthesis, plant cells transform light energy to electrical energy and then to chemical energy stored in chemical bonds. Some of that chemical energy may later be transformed by some animal that eats the plant to the mechanical energy of muscle contraction or some other needed form (Figure 6–3).

As these many transformations take place, some of the energy is converted to heat energy and dissipated into the environment. Although this energy can never again be used by the organism, it is not really "lost"; it still exists in the surrounding physical environment.

The Entropy of the Universe Is Increasing

Order is an extremely unlikely state. If you were to drop a crystal vase, the fragments of glass would not spontaneously jump back into place to reconstruct the vase; in fact, it would be very difficult for you to gather all the small shards of glass and fit them together to mend the vase. Out of the multitude of possible ways in which the pieces could be assembled, only one would represent the highly ordered form that was the vase.

According to the **second law of thermodynamics,** the entropy of the universe is continuously increasing. **Entropy** may be defined as a randomized, disordered state of energy that is unavailable to do work (Figure 6–4). Entropy is a measure of randomness or disorder. The second law holds that physical and chemical processes proceed in such a way that the entropy of the system increases. In almost all energy transformations,

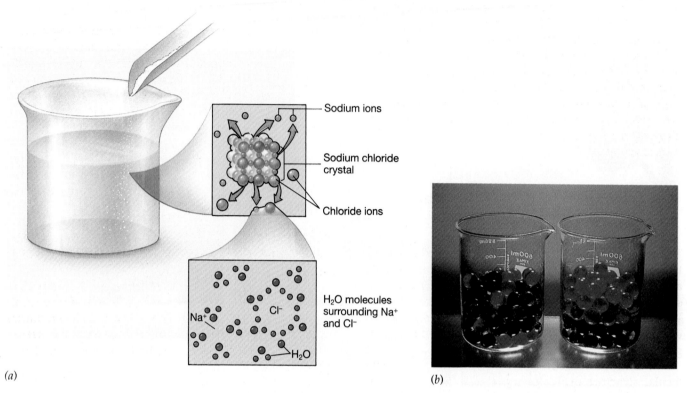

- Sodium ions

- Sodium chloride crystal

- Chloride ions

H₂O molecules surrounding Na⁺ and Cl⁻

(a)

(b)

Figure 6–4   Entropy. (*a*) As particles leave a crystal to go into a solution, they become more disordered. The entropy of this system increases during the process. (*b*) Imagine that you shake a beaker containing two colors of marbles. A disordered arrangement (*right*) is much more probable than an ordered arrangement (*left*) in which all marbles of the same color remain together.   (*b*, Charles Steele)

there is a loss of some energy in the form of heat to the surroundings (Figure 6–5). The energy thus lost is no longer available to do work.

Heat is actually the energy of the random motion of molecules and is the most disorganized form of energy. Heat can be made to do work only when a temperature difference causes it to flow from a warmer region to a cooler region. Temperature is the same throughout a living cell, so heat cannot be used to do biological work.

Although the total amount of energy in the universe remains constant, the energy available to do work is decreasing with time. This is because useful forms of energy are continuously degraded to heat, which is the least useful form of energy. Because entropy in the universe is continuously increasing, eventually, some billions of years in the future, all energy will be random and uniform in distribution. With only this useless form of energy, no work will be possible; the universe will have run down.

It is important to understand that the second law of thermodynamics is consistent with the first law. The total amount of energy in the universe is not decreasing with time, but the energy available to do work is being degraded to random molecular motion.

The force that drives all processes in living and nonliving systems is the tendency of systems to reach the condition of maximal entropy. Energy in the form of heat is either given up or absorbed by an object to allow

Figure 6–5   As a bird flies, some of its energy is lost as heat. That energy is gained by the surroundings, so the net energy change for the bird plus its surroundings is zero.   (Dennis Drenner)

the system to reach the state of maximum entropy. Because of the second law of thermodynamics, no process requiring energy is ever 100% efficient.

Because living organisms are highly organized, they are very unstable. In fact, life is a constant struggle against the second law of thermodynamics. The survival of individual organisms, as well as of ecosystems, depends on continuous energy input. Thus, producers must carry on photosynthesis, and consumers and decomposers must eat.

METABOLIC REACTIONS INVOLVE ENERGY TRANSFORMATIONS

The myriad chemical reactions of cells that enable them to carry on their activities—to grow, move, maintain and repair themselves, reproduce, and respond to stimuli—together make up an organism's metabolism. We have defined *metabolism* as all the chemical and energy transformations that occur within the living organism.

A chemical reaction is a change involving the molecular structure of one or more substances; matter is changed from one substance with characteristic properties to another with new properties. During the reaction, energy is released or absorbed. Chemical reactions involve the rearrangement of atoms. Some chemical bonds may be broken and new ones may form. Energy is required to produce chemical bonds; when a chemical bond breaks, the same amount of energy is released that was required to produce it. For example, hydrochloric acid (HCl) reacts with the base sodium hydroxide (NaOH) to yield water (H_2O) and the salt sodium chloride (NaCl). In the process, energy is released as heat:

$$HCl + NaOH \longrightarrow H_2O + NaCl + Energy \ (heat)$$

The chemical properties of the reactants, in this case, HCl and NaOH, may be very different from those of the products, in this example, H_2O and NaCl. However, the *number* of atoms of a given element in the products is equal to the *number* of atoms of that element in the reactants. Atoms are neither destroyed nor created in a chemical reaction but simply change partners, as in a complex atomic square dance.

Enthalpy Is the Total Heat Content of a System

The total heat content, or **enthalpy, *H*,** of a system is its total potential energy. In a chemical reaction, the enthalpy of reactants or products equals their total bond energies. When bonds are formed or broken, energy is absorbed or released.

Free Energy Is Energy Available To Do Work

Entropy and enthalpy are related by a third dimension of energy, termed **free energy.** We can think of free energy as that component of the total energy of a system that is available to do work under conditions of constant temperature and pressure. Free energy is thus the aspect of thermodynamics of greatest interest in biology.

Entropy, represented by the letter *S*, and free energy, represented by the letter *G*, are related inversely; as entropy increases, the amount of free energy decreases. The two are related by the following equation:

$$\Delta G = \Delta H - T\Delta S$$

in which *H* is the enthalpy of the system and *T* is the absolute temperature in degrees Kelvin.[1] The symbol Δ means "change in."

All physical and chemical processes proceed with a decline in free energy until they reach an equilibrium at which the free energy of the system is at a minimum and the entropy is at a maximum. Free energy is useful energy in biological systems; entropy is a state of degraded, useless energy.

Chemical Reactions May Be Exothermic or Endothermic

Nearly every physical or chemical event in both living and nonliving systems is accompanied by the transfer of heat to the surroundings or by the absorption of heat from the surroundings. A process in which heat is transferred to the surroundings is **exothermic** (Figure 6–6). A process in which heat is absorbed from the surroundings is **endothermic.**

Many of the machines used in industry are heat engines that release energy. A familiar example of a heat engine is an engine driven by steam produced by the burning of coal to heat water in a boiler. Although heat is a useful form of energy in engines, it is not a useful way of transferring or storing energy in living systems. Under conditions of constant pressure, heat can do work only when it can flow from a region of higher temperature to a region of lower temperature. Living organisms are basically isothermal (equal-temperature) systems. No significant temperature gradient—that is, difference in temperature—exists among the various parts of a cell or the various cells in a tissue. Cells cannot act as heat engines because they have no means of permitting heat to flow from a warmer to a cooler object. Furthermore, temperatures

[1]See endsheets.

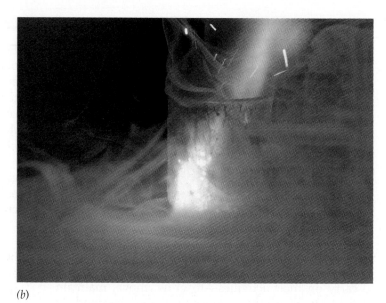

(a)   (b)

Figure 6–6 An exothermic reaction. (a) The element bromine is in the beaker, and the element aluminum is on the table. (b) When the aluminum is added to the bromine, the reaction is so vigorous that the aluminum melts and glows white hot. (Dennis Drenner)

above 50°C would denature and inactivate enzymes and other cellular components.

Cells use the energy stored in the chemical bonds of complex organic molecules. However, this energy must be properly channeled if it is to perform work. Random energy release or the sudden release of large amounts of heat would be more likely to produce metabolic chaos than the order essential to living things. Endothermic and exothermic reactions in living systems are carefully regulated and involve the transfer of very small amounts of energy.

Chemical Reactions Are Reversible

Heat cannot be stored in living cells. When heat is released in the cell, it radiates to the surrounding environment. For this reason free energy transformations that release a large amount of heat deplete the energy supply of the organism. Generally, when energy transformations take place in living systems, only a small amount of free energy is released as heat at one time.

In most biochemical reactions there is little free energy difference between reactants and products. As a result, as long as external energy inputs continue to be available, most of the reactions that occur within living cells—including the important reactions of metabolism—are theoretically reversible. In fact, reversibility is characteristic of many biochemical reactions. Reversibility of biochemical reactions allows cells to control their release of free energy in accordance with their

needs, and it permits many of their large biological molecules to be rebuilt or otherwise recycled for continued use in metabolic processes.

Reversibility is indicated by a double arrow: $\rightleftharpoons$. Whether a reaction occurs and whether it proceeds from right to left or left to right depend on factors such as the energy relations of the several chemicals involved, their relative concentrations, and their solubility.

Reversible Reactions Reach a State of Equilibrium

Suppose that over a 10-year period the population of a city remains the same. Some new folks have moved into town, but others have moved out or perhaps died; thus, the net change in the population is zero. We might say that the population in this city is in the state of *dynamic equilibrium:* Even though individuals move in or out, the rate of change in one direction is equal to the rate of change in the opposite direction, and the net change is zero.

Consider a reaction in terms of the numbers of each type of molecule involved. At the beginning of a reaction, only the reactant molecules may be present. These molecules move about and collide with one another with sufficient energy to react. As more and more product molecules are produced, fewer and fewer reactant molecules are left. As the product molecules increase in number, they collide more frequently, and some have sufficient energy to initiate the reverse reaction. The reaction thus proceeds in both directions simultaneously and eventually reaches an equilibrium in which the rate of the reverse reaction is about the same as the rate of the forward reaction.

FOCUS ON

The Law of Mass Action

The **law of mass action** states that, when all other conditions are constant, the rate of the reaction is proportional to the concentrations of the reactants and products. Consider a bottle of club soda. It is essentially a solution of carbon dioxide dissolved in water under high pressure. Yet that bottle of club soda is not really just dissolved carbon dioxide; it is a solution of carbonic acid. To make it, carbon dioxide had to react with water in this fashion:

$$H_2O + CO_2 \longrightarrow H_2CO_3$$

As everyone knows, if the cap is left off, the opposite occurs:

$$H_2CO_3 \longrightarrow H_2O + CO_2$$

Bubbles of gas fizz to the surface; if the bottle is left open long enough, eventually no CO_2 is left. This is clearly an example of a reversible reaction. Notice that its direction depends on the pressure of the carbon dioxide gas. However, this is just another way of saying that its direction depends on the concentration of carbon dioxide gas.

When the club soda is manufactured, it is treated with high-pressure carbon dioxide. This causes large amounts of carbon dioxide to dissolve in water, producing a high concentration of the dissolved gas. The only way this concentration can be reduced is for it to react with the water to become carbonic acid. Yet this in turn produces increasing concentrations of carbonic acid, which increases the likelihood that some of those carbonic acid molecules will break down. Ultimately an equilibrium is reached, whereby just as many carbonic acid molecules break down as are forming. At that point the solution contains varying concentrations of all three molecular species: carbon dioxide, water, and carbonic acid. So it will continue as long as the bottle remains unopened.

As soon as the cap is removed, carbon dioxide rushes out, and further amounts are lost by diffusion into the air, which has a very low carbon dioxide content. This reduces the concentration of carbon dioxide in the solution, rendering it less probable that molecules of carbon dioxide will collide with water molecules to make carbonic acid. In fact, the opposite occurs: The decrease in carbon dioxide means that carbonic acid already present is converted to carbon dioxide and water, with the carbon dioxide steadily leaving the system. When equilibrium is reached, the concentrations of both carbon dioxide and carbonic acid are considerably less than they were in the unopened bottle.

What this example illustrates is that when there is little free energy difference on the two sides of a chemical equation, the direction of its reaction is governed mostly by the *concentrations* attained by products and reactants, with the reaction tending to proceed so as to minimize the difference in concentration between the chemical species on the two sides of the equation. If one of them is continually removed, for instance, by gaseous diffusion, evaporation, or precipitation, then even despite minimal energy differences, the reaction nevertheless proceeds to completion. In biological pathways, both intermediate and final products are often removed and converted to other chemical compounds. Such removal drives the sequence of reactions.

For each reaction, the thermodynamic **equilibrium constant (K)** expresses the chemical equilibrium reached by the system. This is a fixed ratio of products and reactants. For the reaction

$$A + B \longrightarrow C + D$$

$$K = \frac{[C] \times [D]}{[A] \times [B]}$$

The brackets around the letters mean "the concentration of." The equilibrium constant is different for every reaction; it is determined by the tendency of the reaction components to reach maximum entropy, or minimum free energy, for the system. A reaction with a very small K (say, 10^{-7}) hardly proceeds at all. A reaction with a very large K (say, 10^7) goes almost to completion.

When a reaction is at equilibrium, the free energy difference between the products and reactants of a chemical reaction is zero. Any change, such as a change in temperature or pressure, that affects the reacting system may cause the equilibrium to shift. The reaction may then proceed in a specific direction until once again the free energy difference is zero and a new equilibrium has been established.

When there is little free energy difference between the two sides of a chemical equation, the direction of a reaction is governed mainly by the concentrations of the reactants and products. The reaction tends to proceed in the direction that minimizes the difference in concentration between the substances on the two sides of the equation. If one of them—say, the product—is continuously removed as it is formed, the reaction indeed proceeds to completion; that is, all the reactant molecules are used up (see Focus on the Law of Mass Action).

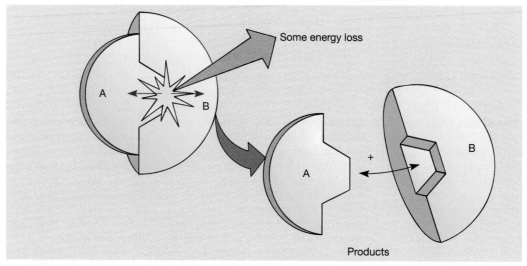

(a)   Exergonic reaction

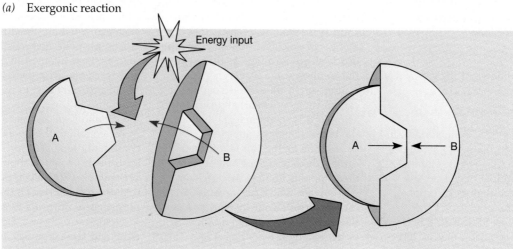

(b)   Endergonic reaction

Figure 6–7   Exergonic and endergonic reactions. (a) In an exergonic reaction there is a net loss of energy. The products have less energy than was present in the reactants. (b) In endergonic reactions there is a net gain in energy. An endergonic reaction occurs only when energy lost from some other system is fed into the reaction. The product has more energy than was present in the reactants.

Spontaneous Reactions Do Not Require Outside Energy

A reaction that produces products containing less free energy than the original reactants tends to proceed spontaneously. A **spontaneous reaction** can occur without the addition of outside energy. Spontaneous reactions are not necessarily instantaneous; in fact, they may occur over a long period of time. Spontaneous reactions, which release free energy and can therefore perform work, are also referred to as **exergonic reactions** (Figure 6–7). Because energy is released, the products contain less energy than the reactants. Exergonic reactions have a high equilibrium constant, K, and a negative free energy change, ΔG.

Reactions that are not spontaneous require an input of free energy and are said to be **endergonic.** In an endergonic reaction, free energy is absorbed from the surroundings; as a result, the products contain more energy than the reactants. Endergonic reactions have a very low equilibrium constant and a positive free energy change (Figure 6–8).

Most exothermic (heat-releasing) reactions are also exergonic, but if the disorder of the reacting system has increased, then more free energy is released than would be indicated by the amount of heat released. This increase in entropy can sometimes be sufficient to make even an endothermic (heat-absorbing) reaction or process occur spontaneously. Such is the case with the melting of ice and the dissolving of certain solids in liquids.

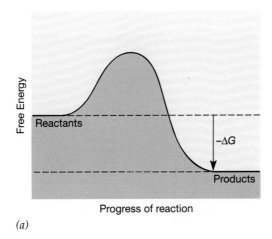

(a)

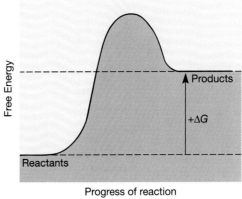

(b)

Figure 6–8 Energy changes in exergonic and endergonic reactions. (*a*) In exergonic reactions free energy is released, and the product has less energy than the reactants. (*b*) In endergonic reactions there is a net input of free energy, so the products contain more energy than the reactants. Note that even the exergonic reaction requires some input of energy to get started. This initial investment energy is termed *activation energy*.

Exergonic and Endergonic Reactions Can Be Coupled in Living Systems

Many metabolic reactions in a living organism—protein synthesis, for example—are endergonic. These reactions are driven by the energy released from exergonic reactions. Indeed, in the living cell endergonic and exergonic reactions are **coupled;** the thermodynamically favorable exergonic reaction provides the energy required to drive the thermodynamically unfavorable endergonic reaction. In such coupled systems the endergonic reaction can proceed only if the decline in the free energy of the exergonic reaction to which it is coupled is larger than the gain in free energy of the endergonic reaction.

How does a living organism, from the time it is "born" until the time it dies, employ outside energy to compensate for its continuous loss of free energy? Two factors make these energy inputs available: First, organisms are part of a large universe with a vast reserve of free energy. Second, they have within themselves special structures, enzymes, and genetic information needed to direct their negatively entropic life processes.

To see how the chemical machinery of the cell is able to supply the energy to direct an endergonic reaction, consider the free energy change, ΔG, in the following reaction:

$$(1) \; A \longrightarrow B + C \qquad \Delta G = +5 \, \text{kcal/mole}$$

Because ΔG is positive, free energy is absorbed rather than released and the reaction is not spontaneous. By way of contrast, consider the following reaction:

$$(2) \; C \longrightarrow D \qquad \Delta G = -8 \, \text{kcal/mole}$$

This reaction can proceed spontaneously because it loses free energy and therefore has a *negative* ΔG.

Note that, whereas the reaction $A \rightarrow B + C$ has a positive free energy change (+5 kcal/mole), the reaction $C \rightarrow D$ has a larger negative free energy change (−8 kcal/mole). Because the free energies of reactions are additive, cells can use exergonic reactions to drive endergonic reactions. When reactions (1) and (2) are coupled, they form a system that has an overall negative free energy change (−3 kcal/mole); that is, energy is released. This released energy can be used by cells for cellular work.

To sum it up,

(1) A $\longrightarrow$ B + C	$\Delta G = +5 \, \text{kcal/mole}$
(2) C $\longrightarrow$ D	$\Delta G = -8 \, \text{kcal/mole}$
A $\longrightarrow$ B + D	$\Delta G = -3 \, \text{kcal/mole}$

If D is the desired product, then this is a thermodynamically feasible way to produce it. The second reaction pulls the first one along.

Generally, for each endergonic reaction occurring in a living cell, there is a coupled exergonic reaction to drive it. Often, the exergonic chemical reaction involves the breakdown of adenosine triphosphate.

ADENOSINE TRIPHOSPHATE (ATP) IS THE ENERGY CURRENCY OF THE CELL

Staying alive requires a continuous expenditure of energy. Cells must grow, maintain, and repair themselves. These activities require the synthesis of proteins and other needed compounds as well as the manufacture of

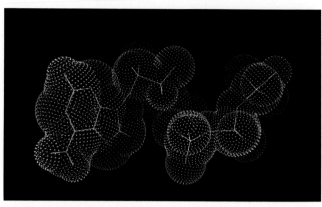

(a)

Figure 6–9 ATP, the energy currency of all living things. *(a)* ATP is composed of adenine, ribose, and three phosphate groups. The bonds linking the two terminal phosphate groups of ATP (shown in *yellow*) are unstable and easily hydrolyzed. They have a large potential for transferring the phosphate group together with some of the energy of the bond. *(b)* A computer-generated model of ATP. The red balls are oxygen atoms; the blue, nitrogen; the green, carbon; the yellow, phosphate; and the white, hydrogen. Note the hydrogen atom attached to the last oxygen in the triphosphate group. At different pH values, this and other oxygen atoms might be bonded with hydrogen or be present in ionized form. *(b, courtesy of Computer Graphics Laboratory, University of California, San Francisco)*

cellular organelles and new cells. In order to maintain homeostatic conditions, cells must continuously transport ions and other substances across cell membranes. Cells also carry on mechanical work, such as contraction or the beating of cilia. What is the immediate source of energy for cellular work?

In all living cells, energy is temporarily packaged within a remarkable chemical compound called **adenosine triphosphate (ATP),** which stores large amounts of energy for very short periods of time. We may think of ATP as the energy currency of the cell. When you work you earn money, so you might say that your energy is symbolically stored in the money you earn; in the same way, the energy of the cell is stored in ATP. When you earn extra money, you might deposit some in the bank; similarly, the cell might deposit energy as lipid (in fat cells) or as glycogen (in liver and muscle). Moreover, just as you dare not make less money than you spend, so too the cell must avoid energy bankruptcy, which would mean its death. Finally, just as you (alas) do not keep what you make very long, so too the cell continuously spends its ATP.

The ATP Molecule Has Three Main Parts

ATP is a nucleoside triphosphate consisting of three main parts (Figure 6–9): (1) a nitrogen-containing base, adenine, which also occurs in nucleic acids; (2) ribose, a five-carbon sugar; and (3) three inorganic phosphate groups identifiable as phosphorus atoms surrounded by oxygen atoms. Inorganic phosphate is usually designated P_i. Notice that the phosphate groups are attached to the end of the molecule in a series, rather like three passenger cars behind a locomotive. The couplings—that is, the chemical bonds attaching to the last two phosphates—also resemble those of a train in that they can be attached and detached.

The Bonds between the Phosphate Groups Are Unstable

The bonds linking the phosphate groups of ATP are unstable; they can be broken by hydrolysis. All three phosphate groups are negatively charged and tend to repel one another. As a result, the phosphate bonds are relatively weak and easily broken. When ATP is hydrolyzed, some of the energy released is used to form new bonds and some is lost as heat. Energy is released during the reaction as a result of the chemical change to a more stable condition.

When the third phosphate is removed, the remaining molecule is **adenosine diphosphate (ADP).** This is an exergonic reaction releasing approximately 7.3 kcal of energy per mole of ATP that is hydrolyzed:

$$ATP + H_2O \longrightarrow ADP + P_i \qquad \Delta G = -7.3 \, \text{kcal/mole}$$

When the two terminal phosphate groups (called a *pyrophosphate group*) are removed, the molecule that remains is adenosine monophosphate (AMP).

ATP Links Exergonic and Endergonic Reactions

The energy from the hydrolysis of ATP is coupled to endergonic processes within the cell with the help of specific enzymes. This process involves the transfer of a phosphate group from ATP to some other compound. The addition of a phosphate group to a molecule is referred to as **phosphorylation.** It is conventional to designate these phosphate bonds by wavy lines, which means that they and some of their energy are easily transferred (see Figure 6–9).

When a phosphate is attached to AMP, it becomes ADP, and when a phosphate is added to ADP, ATP is produced. These reactions are readily reversible.

$$AMP + P_i + Energy \longrightarrow ADP$$
$$ADP + P_i + Energy \longrightarrow ATP$$

As the equations indicate, energy is required to add a phosphate to either the AMP or the ADP molecule. Conversely, because energy can be neither created nor destroyed, the energy is released and/or transferred to another molecule when the phosphate is detached. Thus, ATP is an important link between exergonic (energy-releasing) and endergonic (energy-requiring) reactions (Figure 6–10).

ATP Cannot Be Stockpiled

ATP is formed from ADP and inorganic phosphate when nutrients are oxidized or when the radiant energy of sunlight is trapped in photosynthesis. Energy released from exergonic reactions is packaged in ATP molecules for use in endergonic reactions. This energy may be used to produce lipids or polysaccharides, molecules stockpiled for long-term energy storage.

The cell contains a pool of ADP, ATP, and phosphate. The cell maintains a high ratio of ATP to ADP (about 10:1). However, large quantities of ATP cannot be stockpiled in the cell; in fact, studies suggest that a bacterial cell has no more than a 1-second supply of ATP. Thus, ATP molecules are used almost as quickly as they are produced. A human at rest uses about 45 kg of ATP each day, but the amount present in the body at any given moment is less than 1 gram. Every second in every cell an estimated 10 million molecules of ATP are made from ADP and phosphate and an equal number are hydrolyzed, yielding their energy to whatever life processes may require them (Figure 6–11).

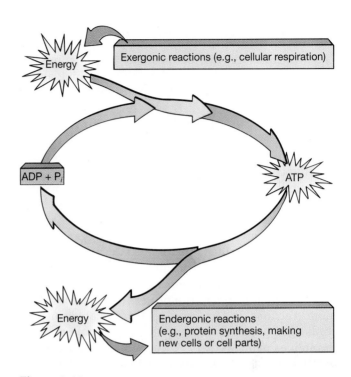

Figure 6–10 ATP is an important link between endergonic and exergonic reactions in living cells.

Figure 6–11 The chemical energy of ATP is converted to light energy in the light organs of this deep-sea angler fish, *Caulophryne jordani.* The energy transformation actually occurs within luminous bacteria that inhabit the light organs of the fish. (© Norbert Wu 1991)

ENZYMES ARE CHEMICAL REGULATORS

The principles of thermodynamics help us predict whether a reaction can occur but tell us nothing about the speed of the reaction. A glucose solution keeps indefinitely in a bottle if it is kept free of bacteria and molds and not subjected to high temperature or strong acids or bases. Living cells cannot wait for centuries for glucose to break down spontaneously, nor can they use extreme conditions to cleave glucose molecules. Cells regulate chemical reactions with **enzymes,** protein catalysts that affect the speed of a chemical reaction without being consumed by the reaction.

Cells require a steady release of energy, and they must be able to regulate that release to meet metabolic energy requirements. Accordingly, organic compounds are oxidized and energy is extracted in small amounts during cellular respiration, a process that includes 30 or more reactions. In fact, most cellular metabolism proceeds by a series of steps, so that a molecule may go through as many as 20 or 30 chemical transformations before it reaches some final state. Even then, the seemingly completed molecule may enter yet another chemical pathway and become totally transformed or consumed in the course of energy production. The changing needs of the cell require a system of flexible chemical control. The key directors of this control system are the remarkable enzymes.

Enzymes Lower the Activation Energy Necessary To Initiate a Chemical Reaction

Like all catalysts, enzymes affect the rate of a reaction by lowering the energy needed to activate the reaction. Even a strongly exergonic reaction, which releases more than enough energy as it proceeds, is prevented from beginning by an energy barrier. This is because, for new chemical bonds to form, existing ones must first be broken. The energy required to break these bonds and start the reaction going is called **activation energy.** An enzyme greatly reduces the activation energy necessary to initiate a chemical reaction (Figure 6–12).

In a population of molecules of any kind, some molecules have a relatively high energy content, others have a lower energy content. The energy content of the entire population of molecules conforms to a bell-shaped curve of normal distribution. Only molecules with a relatively high energy content are likely to react to form the product. If the activation barrier is lowered, the reaction proceeds more quickly. An enzyme lowers the activation energy of the reaction, and as a result a larger fraction of the population of molecules reacts at any one time. The enzyme is thought to accomplish this by forming an unstable intermediate complex with the **substrate,** the substance on which it operates. This com-

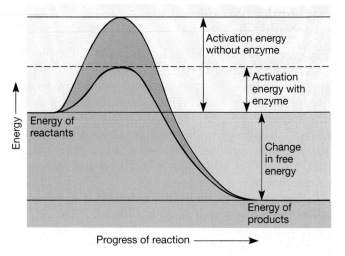

Figure 6–12 A catalyst such as an enzyme speeds up a reaction by lowering its activation energy. A catalyzed reaction (blue curve) proceeds more quickly than an uncatalyzed reaction (red curve) because it has a lower barrier of activation energy to overcome.

plex decomposes, forming the product and freeing the catalyst to react with a second molecule of reactant.

An enzyme can only promote a chemical reaction that could be made to proceed without it. No catalyst can change the operation of the second law of thermodynamics, so enzymes do not influence the direction of a chemical reaction or the final concentrations of the molecules involved. They simply speed up reaction rates.

Most Enzyme Names End in -ase

Enzymes are usually named by the addition of the suffix -ase to the name of the substance acted upon. For example, sucrose is split to glucose and fructose by the enzyme **sucrase.** There are group names for enzymes that catalyze similar reactions. Lipases cleave triacylglycerols, proteinases cleave the peptide bonds in proteins, and dehydrogenases transfer hydrogens from one compound to another.

Enzymes Are Very Efficient Catalysts

The catalytic ability of some enzymes is truly remarkable. For example, one molecule of the iron-containing enzyme **catalase** brings about the decomposition of 5 million molecules of hydrogen peroxide (H_2O_2) per minute at 0°C. Hydrogen peroxide is a poisonous substance produced as a byproduct in a number of enzyme reactions (Figure 6–13). Catalase protects cells by destroying peroxide.

Figure 6–13 A bombardier beetle uses the catalyzed decomposition of hydrogen peroxide as a defense mechanism. The oxygen gas formed in the decomposition forces out water and other chemicals with explosive force. Since the reaction is very exothermic, the water comes out as steam. (Thomas Eisner and Daniel Aneshansley/Cornell University)

Hydrogen peroxide can be split by iron atoms alone, but only at a very slow rate. It would take 300 years for an iron atom to split the same number of molecules of H_2O_2 that a molecule of catalase (containing one iron atom) splits in 1 second!

Enzymes Are Specific

Most enzymes are highly **specific,** catalyzing only a few closely related chemical reactions or, in many cases,

only one particular reaction. For example, the enzyme urease, which decomposes urea to ammonia and carbon dioxide, attacks no other substrate. The enzyme sucrase splits only sucrose; it does not act on maltose or lactose. Peroxidase decomposes several different peroxides, including hydrogen peroxide.

A few enzymes are specific only in that they require that the substrate have a certain kind of chemical bond. For example, the lipase secreted by the pancreas splits the ester bonds connecting the glycerol and fatty acids of a wide variety of fats.

Enzymes Work by Forming Enzyme-Substrate Complexes

Enzymes form temporary chemical compounds with their substrates. When the enzyme-substrate complex breaks up, the product is released and the original enzyme molecule is regenerated.

Enzyme + Substrate 1 + Substrate 2 $\longrightarrow$ Enzyme-substrate complex

Enzyme-substrate complex $\longrightarrow$ Enzyme + Product(s)

The enzyme itself is not permanently altered or consumed by the reaction and can be reused.

As shown in Figure 6–14, each enzyme contains one or more regions, called **active sites.** The active sites of some enzymes have been shown to be actual indentations in the enzyme molecule. They are formed by the side chains of certain amino acids in the enzyme. Active sites are located close to the enzyme's surface. During the course of a reaction, substrate molecules occupying these sites are brought close together and react with one another.

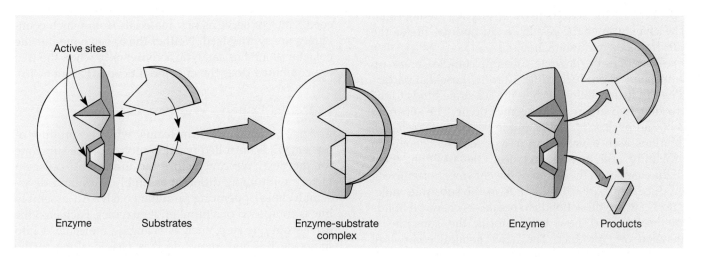

Figure 6–14 Lock-and-key mechanism of enzyme action. The substrate fits the active sites of the enzyme molecule much as a key fits a lock. However, in this model the lock acts on the key rather than the other way around. When the products separate from the enzyme, the enzyme is free to catalyze the production of additional products; the enzyme is not permanently changed by the reaction. In recent years the lock-and-key concept of enzyme action has undergone some modification, as shown in Figure 6–15.

Lock-and-key model

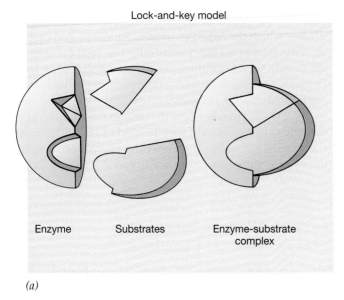

Enzyme Substrates Enzyme-substrate complex

(a)

Induced-fit model

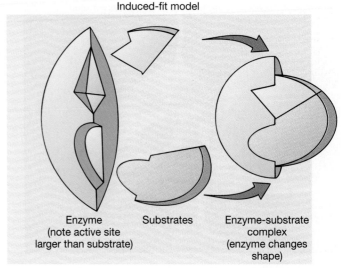

Enzyme (note active site larger than substrate) Substrates Enzyme-substrate complex (enzyme changes shape)

(b)

Figure 6–15 Comparison of models of enzyme action. (*a*) The lock-and-key model. (*b*) The induced-fit model. Chemical reactions are favored when substrate molecules get close enough to one another to react, when they are presented to each other in the right orientation, and when their existing chemical bonds are strained. Enzymes often facilitate all three of these processes. The substrate's bonds are strained, apparently because most active sites on the enzyme are a bit bigger than the substrate molecules. Accordingly, when the fit is forced on the active site, it exerts a kind of pull on the substrate, helping to pull it apart. To be sure, the fit of the enzyme and substrate must not be too poor, or they will have no affinity for one another.

Two models have been proposed to explain the process of enzyme-substrate binding. According to the **lock-and-key model,** an enzyme can be thought of as a molecular lock into which only specifically shaped molecular keys—the substrates—can fit (Figure 6–14). However, unlike a lock and key, the shape of the enzyme does not seem to be exactly complementary to that of the substrates. According to the **induced-fit model** of enzyme action, when the substrate combines with the enzyme, it may induce a change in the shape of the enzyme molecule (Figure 6–15). This change is possible because the active sites of an enzyme are not rigid. The change in shape results in an optimal fit for the substrate-enzyme interaction.

Why does the enzyme-substrate complex break up into chemical products different from those that participated in its formation? When the substrate binds to the enzyme, two important outcomes occur. The substrate is bound in close *proximity* and in the correct *orientation* to atoms with which it can now react. The changes in proximity and orientation speed the reaction. Even slight changes in the shape of the enzyme molecule can produce strain in critical bonds in the substrate molecules, causing these bonds to break. As chemical bonds are broken and new bonds form, the substrate is changed into product. The new chemical compound thus formed has little affinity for the enzyme and moves away from it. The enzyme can then catalyze the reaction of more substrate molecules to form more product.

Many Enzymes Require Cofactors

Some enzymes—for example, pepsin, secreted by the stomach—consist only of protein. Other enzymes have two components, a protein referred to as the **apoenzyme** and an additional chemical component called a **cofactor.** The cofactor of some enzymes is a metal ion. In fact, most of the trace elements—elements like iron, copper, zinc, and manganese, which are required in very small amounts—function as cofactors.

An organic, nonpolypeptide compound that serves as a cofactor is called a **coenzyme.** Most vitamins are coenzymes or serve as raw materials from which coenzymes are synthesized. Neither the apoenzyme nor the cofactor alone has catalytic activity; only when the two are combined does the enzyme function (Figure 6–16).

Enzymes Usually Work in Teams

Enzymes usually work in teams, with the product of one enzyme-controlled reaction serving as the substrate for the next. We can picture the inside of a cell as a factory with many different assembly lines (and disassembly lines) operating simultaneously. An assembly line is composed of a number of enzymes. Each enzyme carries out one step, such as changing molecule A into molecule B. Then, molecule B is passed along to the next enzyme, which converts it into molecule C, and so on.

$$A \xrightarrow{\text{Enzyme 1}} B \xrightarrow{\text{Enzyme 2}} C$$

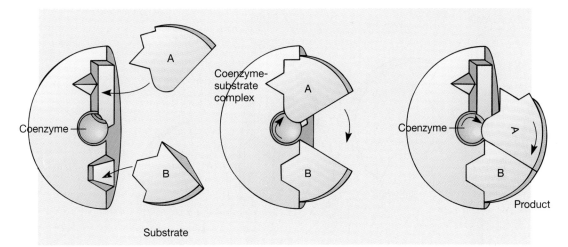

Coenzyme

Coenzyme-
substrate
complex

A

B

Coenzyme

A

B

Product

Substrate

Figure 6–16 Coenzyme action. Some enzymes are not able to attach directly to the substrates whose chemical reactions they catalyze. Such an enzyme employs accessory coenzymes to serve as adaptors, aiding the attachment of one or more substrates to the enzyme's active sites. First one substrate combines with the coenzyme to form a coenzyme-substrate complex. Then the coenzyme-substrate complex combines with the second substrate, forming a complex that yields the products and releases the coenzyme. Some familiar vitamins serve as coenzymes for vital enzymes of cellular metabolism.

An example of a short assembly line occurs in germinating barley seeds, which possess two enzymes that convert starch to glucose. The first, amylase, hydrolyzes starch to maltose; the second, maltase, splits maltose to glucose. Ten different enzymes, working consecutively, are required to convert glucose to pyruvate (Chapter 7). The same series of enzymes is found in human cells, in green leaves, and in bacteria.

The Cell Regulates Enzymatic Activity

Enzymes regulate the chemistry of the cell, but what controls the enzymes? One mechanism of enzyme control depends simply on the amount of enzyme produced. The synthesis of each type of enzyme is directed by a specific gene. The gene, in turn, may be switched on by a signal from a hormone or by some other type of cellular product (discussed in Chapters 13 and 47). When the gene is switched on, the enzyme is synthesized. The amount of enzyme present then influences the rate of the reaction.

If the pH and temperature are kept constant and if an excess of substrate is present, the rate of an enzymatic reaction is directly proportional to the concentration of enzyme present (Figure 6–17b). Similarly, if the enzyme concentration, pH, and temperature are kept

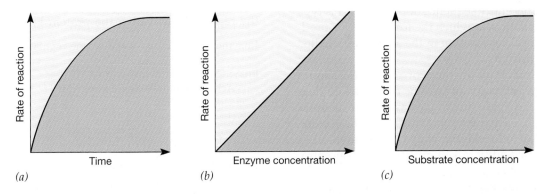

(a) Time

(b) Enzyme concentration

(c) Substrate concentration

Figure 6–17 The rate of an enzyme reaction is influenced by several factors. (a) Reaction rate as a function of time. As the substrate is consumed and the reaction approaches equilibrium, the reaction rate drops to zero. (b) Reaction rate as a function of the amount of enzyme added. Enough substrate and cofactors are added so that these do not limit the rate of the reaction. (c) Reaction rate as a function of the amount of substrate. Enough enzyme and cofactors are added so that these do not limit the rate of the reaction.

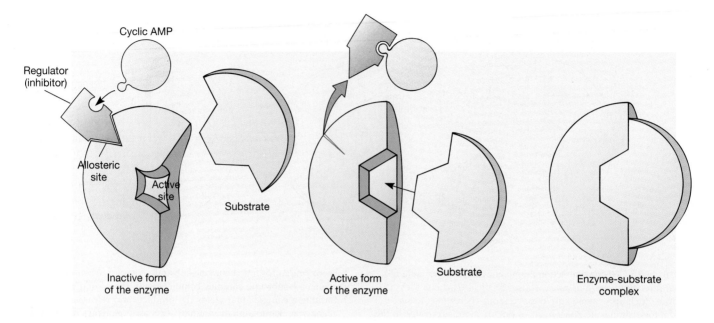

Figure 6–18 The enzyme protein kinase is inhibited by a regulator protein that binds reversibly to the allosteric site. When the enzyme is in this inactive form, the shape of the active site is modified so that substrate cannot combine with it. Cyclic AMP removes the regulator activating the enzyme. The substrate can then combine with the active site.

constant, the initial rate of an enzymatic reaction is proportional to the concentration of substrate present, up to a limiting value (Figure 6–17c).

The product of one enzymatic reaction may control the activity of another enzyme, especially in a complex sequence of enzymatic reactions. For example, in the following system,

$$A \xrightarrow{\text{Enzyme 1}} B \xrightarrow{\text{Enzyme 2}} C \xrightarrow{\text{Enzyme 3}} D \xrightarrow{\text{Enzyme 4}} E$$

each step is catalyzed by a different enzyme. The final product, E, may inhibit the activity of Enzyme 1. When the concentration of E is low, the sequence of reactions proceeds rapidly. However, an increasing concentration of E serves as a signal for Enzyme 1 to slow down and eventually to stop functioning. Inhibition of Enzyme 1 stops this entire sequence of reactions. This type of enzyme regulation, in which the formation of a product inhibits an earlier reaction in the sequence, is called **feedback inhibition.**

Another important method of enzymatic control depends on the activation of enzyme molecules. In their inactive form the active sites of the enzyme are inappropriately shaped, so that the substrates do not fit. Among the factors that influence the shape (conformation) of the enzyme are acidity, alkalinity, and the concentration of certain salts.

Some enzymes, known as **allosteric enzymes,** possess a receptor site, called an **allosteric site,** on some region of the enzyme molecule other than the active site. (The word *allosteric* means "another space.") Most allosteric enzymes contain more than one polypeptide chain, each with its own active site. The allosteric site is often located where the polypeptides are joined. Substances that affect enzyme activity by binding to allosteric sites are called **regulators.** Some regulators are *inhibitors* that keep the enzyme in its inactive shape. Others are *activators* that stabilize the active shape of the enzyme (the shape with a functional active site).

The enzyme protein kinase is an allosteric enzyme with only one polypeptide chain; both the active site and the allosteric sites are located on this single chain. Its regulator is a protein that binds reversibly to the allosteric site. This regulator is an inhibitor that inactivates the enzyme. Protein kinase is in this inactive form most of the time (Figure 6–18). When protein kinase activity is needed, the compound cyclic AMP (cAMP) contacts the enzyme-regulator complex and removes the regulator, activating the protein kinase.

Enzyme + Regulator $\longrightarrow$ Enzyme-regulator complex

Enzyme-regulator complex + cAMP $\longrightarrow$
    Active enzyme + Regulator-cAMP

Enzymes Are Most Effective at Optimal Conditions

Enzymes generally work best under certain narrowly defined conditions referred to as *optima.* These include appropriate temperature, pH, and salt concentration. Any departure from optimal conditions adversely affects enzyme activity.

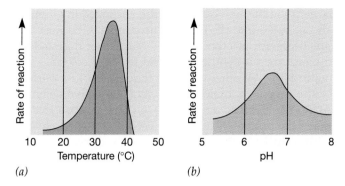

Figure 6–19 The effect of temperature (*a*) and pH (*b*) on the rate of enzyme-catalyzed reactions. Substrate and enzyme concentrations are constant.

Temperature affects enzyme activity

Most enzymes have an optimal temperature at which the rate of reaction is fastest. For human enzymes, the temperature optima are near body temperature (35 to 40°C). Enzymatic reactions occur slowly or not at all at low temperatures, but the catalytic activity reappears when the temperature is raised to normal. The rates of most enzyme-controlled reactions increase with increasing temperature, within limits (Figure 6–19). High temperatures rapidly inactivate most enzymes by denaturing the protein. Its molecular conformation is altered by the unwinding of its secondary and tertiary structure. This inactivation is usually not reversible; that is, activity is not regained when the enzyme is cooled.

Most organisms are killed by even short exposure to high temperature; their enzymes are inactivated, and they are unable to continue metabolism. There are a few remarkable exceptions to this rule: Certain species of bacteria can survive in the waters of hot springs, such as the ones in Yellowstone Park, where the temperature is almost 100°C; these organisms are responsible for the brilliant colors in the terraces of the hot springs. Still other bacteria live at temperatures much above that of boiling water in undersea hot springs, where the extreme pressure keeps water in its liquid form rather than as steam.

Each enzyme has an optimal pH

Most enzymes have an optimal pH and are active only over a narrow pH range. The optimal pH for most human enzymes is between 6 and 8 (Figure 6–19*b*). Pepsin, a protein-digesting enzyme secreted by cells lining the stomach, is remarkable in that it works only in a very acid medium—optimally at pH 2. In contrast, the optimal pH of trypsin, the protein-splitting enzyme secreted by the pancreas, is 8.5, on the alkaline side of neutrality.

The activity of an enzyme may be markedly changed by any alteration in acidity or alkalinity. Full enzyme activity requires a specific number of positive and negative charges on the enzyme. Changes in pH add or remove hydrogen ions from the protein, thereby changing its number of positive and negative charges and affecting its activity. Many of the enzymes that operate within cells become inactive when the medium is made very acid or very alkaline. Strong acids or bases irreversibly inactivate enzymes by permanently changing their molecular conformation.

Enzymes can be inhibited by certain chemical agents

Most enzymes can be **inhibited** (so that their activity is decreased) or even destroyed by certain chemical agents. Enzyme inhibition may be reversible or irreversible. Reversible inhibitors form weak chemical bonds with the enzyme.

Reversible inhibition can be competitive or noncompetitive. In **competitive inhibition,** the inhibitor competes with the normal substrate for binding to the active site of the enzyme (Figure 6–20). A competitive inhibitor usually is structurally similar to the normal substrate and so fits into the active site and combines with the enzyme. However, it is not similar enough to substitute fully for the normal substrate in the chemical reaction, and the enzyme cannot attack it to form reaction products. A competitive inhibitor occupies the active sites only temporarily and does not permanently damage the enzyme. In fact, competitive inhibition can be reversed by an increase in the substrate concentration. The substrate can then out-compete the inhibitor for a place in the active site.

In **noncompetitive inhibition,** the inhibitor binds with the enzyme at a site other than the active site. Such an inhibitor inactivates the enzyme by altering its shape so that the active site cannot bind with the substrate. Many important noncompetitive inhibitors are metabolic substances that regulate enzyme activity by combining reversibly with the enzyme.

In **irreversible inhibition,** an inhibitor combines with a functional group of an enzyme and permanently inactivates or destroys the enzyme. Most poisons are irreversible inhibitors. Nerve gases, for example, poison the enzyme acetylcholinesterase, which is important to the function of nerves and muscles. Cytochrome oxidase, one of the enzymes that transport electrons in cellular respiration, is especially sensitive to cyanide. Death results from cyanide poisoning because cytochrome oxidase is irreversibly inhibited and can no longer transfer electrons from substrate to oxygen. A number of insecticides and drugs are irreversible enzyme inhibitors (see Focus on Enzyme Inhibition and Antibacterial Drugs).

Enzymes themselves can act as poisons if they get into the wrong compartment of the body. As little as 1 mg of crystalline trypsin injected intravenously can kill a rat. The proteolytic enzymes of the pancreas, trypsin and chymotrypsin, are synthesized in the form of **precursors,** molecules that can be converted to the active enzyme. These precursors, which are somewhat larger than the active enzyme, are packaged in granules and secreted into the duct of the pancreas. Because the precursors are inactive, the pancreas is not digested by the enzymes it synthesizes. The inactive enzymes are made active by other enzymes that cleave off a portion of the precursor molecule to yield the active enzyme. Acute pancreatitis, a serious, even fatal disease, occurs when the proteolytic enzymes become active while still within the pancreas and digest cells and blood vessels.

FOCUS ON

Enzyme Inhibition and Antibacterial Drugs

Many bacterial infections are treated with drugs that directly or indirectly inhibit bacterial enzyme activity. For example, sulfa drugs have a chemical structure similar to that of the nutrient para-aminobenzoic acid (PABA). When PABA is available, microorganisms can synthesize the vitamin folic acid. Humans do not synthesize folic acid from PABA, and that is why sulfa drugs selectively affect bacteria. When a sulfa drug is present, competitive inhibition occurs within the bacterium—the drug competes with PABA for the active site of the bacterial enzyme. When the bacteria use the sulfa drug instead of PABA, they synthesize a compound that has a structure somewhat similar to that of folic acid. However, this imposter folic acid does not work as a coenzyme. Instead, it competitively inhibits the enzyme's action so that the bacteria are unable to make needed amino acids and nucleotides.

Penicillin and related antibiotics irreversibly inhibit a bacterial enzyme, transpeptidase. This enzyme is responsible for establishing some of the chemical linkages in the bacterial cell wall (see Chapter 23). Unable to produce properly constructed cell walls, cytoplasm spills out and susceptible bacteria are prevented from multiplying effectively (see figure). Human cells do not have cell walls and do not employ this enzyme. Thus, except for individuals allergic to penicillin, this drug is harmless to humans.

Penicillin is an irreversible enzyme inhibitor. (*a*) Normal bacteria. Insert shows the new cell wall laid down between daughter cells of a dividing bacterium. (*b*) Penicillin has damaged these bacterial cell walls. The insets are magnified approximately ×54,000. (Courtesy of Drs. Victor Lorian and Barbara Atkinson, with permission of *The American Journal of Clinical Pathology*)

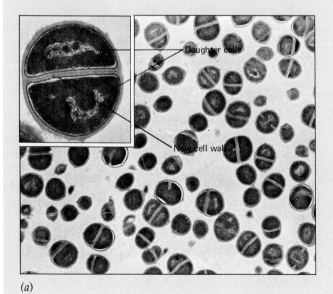

(a)

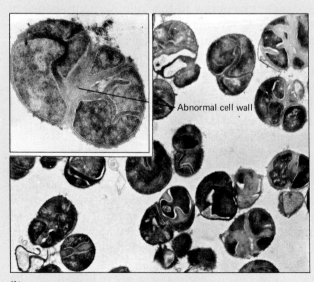

(b)

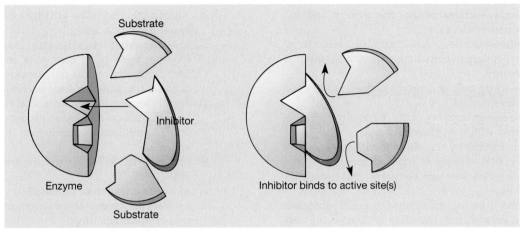

(a) Competitive inhibition

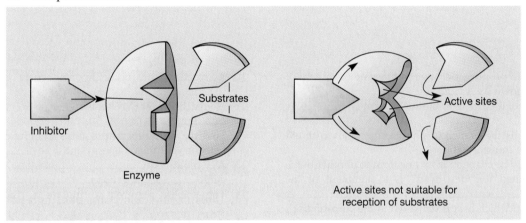

(b) Noncompetitive inhibition

Figure 6–20 Competitive and noncompetitive inhibition. (*a*) In competitive inhibition, the inhibitor competes with the normal substrate for the active site of the enzyme. A competitive inhibitor occupies the active site only temporarily. (*b*) In noncompetitive inhibition, the inhibitor binds with the enzyme at a site other than the active site, altering the shape of the enzyme and thereby inactivating it. Noncompetitive inhibition may be reversible. Allosteric action, used by cells to control enzyme action, is a somewhat similar process (see Figure 6–18).

SUMMARY

I. Life depends on a continuous input of energy. Producers capture energy during photosynthesis and incorporate some of that energy in the chemical bonds of organic compounds. Some of this energy can then be transferred to consumers and decomposers.

II. Energy can be defined as the capacity to do work.
   A. Potential energy is stored energy; kinetic energy is energy of motion.
   B. A common unit used to measure energy is the kilocalorie.

III. The first law of thermodynamics states that energy can be neither created nor destroyed but can be transferred and changed in form. The second law of thermodynamics states that disorder in the universe is continuously increasing.

   A. The first law explains why organisms cannot produce energy but must continuously capture it from somewhere else.
   B. The second law explains why no process requiring energy is ever 100% efficient; in every energy transaction, some energy is dissipated as heat. The term *entropy* refers to the measure of randomness or disorder in a system.

IV. In a chemical reaction, energy may be released or absorbed in the form of heat. An exothermic reaction releases heat. An endothermic reaction absorbs heat.

V. When a chemical reaction is in equilibrium, the rate of change in one direction is exactly the same as the rate of change in the opposite direction; the free energy difference between the reactants and products is zero.

VI. Spontaneous reactions release free energy and can therefore perform work.
   A. Reactions that release free energy are exergonic reactions; endergonic reactions require a net input of free energy.
   B. In the living cell, endergonic and exergonic reactions are coupled.
VII. ATP is the energy currency of the cell; energy is temporarily stored within its chemical bonds.
   A. ATP is formed by the phosphorylation of ADP, a process that requires an input of energy.
   B. ATP is a link between exergonic and endergonic reactions.
VIII. An enzyme is an organic catalyst; it greatly increases the speed of a chemical reaction without being consumed itself.

A. An enzyme lowers the activation energy necessary to get a reaction going.
B. Enzymes bring substrates into close contact so that they can more easily react with one another.
C. Some enzymes consist of an apoenzyme and a cofactor. An organic cofactor is called a *coenzyme.*
D. A cell can regulate enzymatic activity by controlling the amount of enzyme produced and by regulating conditions that influence the shape of the enzyme.
E. Enzymes work best at specific temperatures and pH levels.
F. Most enzymes can be inhibited by certain chemical substances. Reversible inhibition may be competitive or noncompetitive.

POST-TEST

1. The ability to produce a change in the state or motion of matter is known as _____.
2. The energy of a particle in motion is termed _____ _____.
3. _____ is the branch of physics that deals with energy and its transformations.
4. "Energy may be changed from one form to another but is neither created nor destroyed" is a statement of the _____.
5. A reaction in which heat is delivered to the surroundings is described as _____.
6. A reaction that requires an input of free energy is described as _____.
7. In thermodynamics, the term _____ is applied to a disordered state of the system.
8. "Physical and chemical processes proceed in such a way that the entropy of the system becomes maximal" is a statement of the _____.
9. The _____ energy, ΔG, of a system is that part of the total energy of the system available to do work under conditions of constant _____ and _____.

10. A reaction can occur spontaneously only if ΔG is _____.
11. A reaction that releases energy to the system is _____.
12. To drive a reaction that requires an input of energy, some reaction that yields energy must be _____ to it.
13. ATP consists of _____, _____, and three inorganic _____ groups.
14. The energy required to initiate a reaction is called _____ energy.
15. A substance that affects the rate of a chemical reaction without being consumed by the reaction is a(n) _____.
16. _____ are biological catalysts produced by cells.
17. Enzymes and their substrates combine temporarily to form a(n) _____.
18. The small portion of an enzyme molecule that combines with the substrate is the _____ _____.
19. A(n) _____ inhibitor alters the shape of the enzyme, rendering it inactive.

REVIEW QUESTIONS

1. Trace the flow of energy from producer to consumer.
2. Contrast potential and kinetic energy, and give examples of each.
3. Contrast exergonic and endergonic reactions.
4. Life is sometimes described as a constant struggle against the second law of thermodynamics. Explain why this is true. How do organisms succeed in this struggle?
5. Why are coupled reactions biologically important?
6. Explain how energy is obtained from ATP. Discuss why ATP is an important link between exergonic and endergonic reactions.

7. What is activation energy? What is the relationship of a catalyst to activation energy?
8. Give the function of each of the following: (a) active site of an enzyme; (b) coenzyme; (c) allosteric site.
9. Describe three factors that influence enzymatic activity.
10. Contrast competitive and noncompetitive inhibition.

RECOMMENDED READINGS

Alberts, B., D. Bray, J. Lewis, M. Raff, K. Roberts, and J. D. Watson. *Molecular Biology of the Cell,* 2nd ed. Garland Publishing, New York, 1989. A detailed, well-written account of the energy conversions that take place within chloroplasts and mitochondria.

Atkins, P. W. *The Second Law.* W. H. Freeman, San Francisco, 1984. A basic, understandable introduction to thermodynamics with an extensive section devoted to its biological implications.

Cloud, P. The biosphere. *Scientific American*, September 1983, pp. 176–189. A fascinating discussion of the relationship between microbial, animal, and plant life on Earth and the physical environment, as well as the energy transfer pathways that knit it all together.

Darnell, J., H. Lodish, and D. Baltimore. *Molecular Cell Biology,* 2nd ed. Scientific American Books, New York, 1989. A readable and detailed account of energy transformations within the cell.

Stryer, L. *Biochemistry*, 3rd ed. W. H. Freeman, San Francisco, 1988. A well-illustrated and very readable text of general biochemistry with excellent sections on cellular energetics.

❏

CHAPTER 7

Energy-Releasing Pathways and Biosynthesis

Cells are tiny factories that process materials on the molecular level. They work round the clock to produce useful substances that will help to maintain the life of the cell or the organism of which the cell is a part. These useful materials are needed by the cell for growth, reproduction, movement, response to stimuli, and maintenance of a constant internal environment.

Many important molecules are assembled from simpler raw materials during hundreds of different chemical reactions. The synthesis of complex molecules from simpler building blocks is an aspect of metabolism known as **anabolism,** and the individual reactions are called **anabolic reactions.** Many anabolic reactions are endergonic and require the energy of adenosine triphosphate (ATP) to drive them.

Animals eat other organisms to obtain energy. Here a river otter consumes a long-nosed sucker. (Visuals Unlimited/Michael S. Quinton)

Thus, cells must continually obtain energy from the environment and use it to make ATP. For example, cells extract free energy from organic food molecules such as glucose (Figure 7–1). These nutrients are broken down, and some of their chemical energy is transferred to ATP for later use in cellular work. The process of splitting larger molecules into smaller ones is an aspect of metabolism known as **catabolism,** and the individual reactions involved are called **catabolic reactions.** During the catabolism of glucose, cells break down glucose one piece at a time in a series of steps, thereby releasing the energy in the chemical bonds of the glucose molecule in a controlled fashion. Cells use three different catabolic pathways to extract free energy from nutrients: aerobic respiration, anaerobic respiration, and fermentation.

LEARNING OBJECTIVES

After you have studied this chapter you should be able to

1. Write a general equation illustrating hydrogen and electron transfer from a compound to a hydrogen acceptor such as NAD^+.
2. Write a summary reaction for aerobic respiration, giving the origin and fate of each substance involved.
3. List and give a brief overview of the four stages of aerobic respiration, and indicate where the reactions of each stage take place in the cell; indicate the number of ATP molecules used and produced and the transactions in which hydrogen transfer occurs.
4. Draw a diagram to illustrate chemiosmosis and explain (1) how a gradient of protons is established across the inner mitochondrial membrane and (2) the process by which the proton gradient drives ATP synthesis.
5. Summarize how the products of protein and lipid metabolism feed into the same metabolic pathway that oxidizes glucose.
6. Compare and contrast aerobic and anaerobic pathways used by cells to extract free energy from nutrients; include ATP formation, the final hydrogen acceptor, and end products.
7. Compare and contrast alcohol and lactate fermentation.
8. Compare and contrast anabolic and catabolic reactions.

CATABOLISM MAY BE AEROBIC OR ANAEROBIC

Which catabolic pathway a cell uses to break down nutrients depends on the enzymes it can produce and the type of environment it inhabits. Most cells that live where oxygen is plentiful use the very efficient **aerobic** pathway, which requires molecular oxygen. Some cells that inhabit the soil or water where oxygen is in short supply are adapted to use less efficient **anaerobic** pathways, which do not require oxygen.

During **aerobic respiration,** nutrients are catabolized to carbon dioxide and water. One of the most common pathways of aerobic respiration involves the breakdown of the nutrient glucose. The overall reaction for the aerobic respiration of glucose is summarized as follows:

$$C_6H_{12}O_6 + 6\,O_2 + 6\,H_2O \longrightarrow 6\,CO_2 + 12\,H_2O + \text{Energy (as ATP)}$$

Cells do not break down glucose to carbon dioxide and water in a single reaction. Instead, the complete catabolism of glucose occurs in a long sequence of enzymatic reactions, to be examined more closely later in this chapter.

Figure 7–1   A gecko consuming lizard prey. Energy is transferred from prey to predator.   (Dwight R. Kuhn)

Some types of bacteria engage solely in **anaerobic respiration,** a clear advantage in soil or stagnant ponds where oxygen is in short supply. In anaerobic respiration, an inorganic substance such as nitrate (NO_3^-) or sulfate (SO_4^{2-}) is used in place of oxygen. The end products in this type of anaerobic respiration are inorganic substances and, of course, energy. A representative reaction for anaerobic respiration is summarized as follows:

$$C_6H_{12}O_6 + 12\,KNO_3 \longrightarrow 6\,CO_2 + 6\,H_2O + 12\,KNO_2 \\ + \text{Energy (as ATP)}$$

Certain bacteria and fungi that are adapted to anaerobic conditions use a third pathway, called **fermentation.** The end products of fermentation are organic compounds and energy. Under conditions of insufficient oxygen, human muscle cells can temporarily use a type of fermentation. A representative reaction for fermentation is summarized as follows:

$$C_6H_{12}O_6 \longrightarrow 2\,CO_2 + 2\,C_2H_5OH + \text{Energy (as ATP)}$$

Most plants and animals can survive only in an environment that provides oxygen. These organisms rely on aerobic respiration for energy and are **strict aerobes.** Anaerobic bacteria, which do not require oxygen, are referred to as **anaerobes.** Some strict anaerobes are actually poisoned by oxygen. More versatile are yeasts and certain bacteria that carry on aerobic respiration when oxygen is available but shift to anaerobic respiration or fermentation when oxygen is in short supply; these organisms are known as **facultative anaerobes.**

OXIDATION-REDUCTION REACTIONS OCCUR IN METABOLISM

Energy is transferred in cells by the flow of electrons and protons. Generally, a sequence of oxidation-reduction reactions takes place as a hydrogen atom or its electron is transferred from one compound to another. **Oxidation** is the chemical process in which a substance loses electrons, whereas **reduction** is the chemical process in which a substance gains electrons. Because electrons released during an oxidation reaction cannot exist in the free state in living cells, every oxidation reaction must be accompanied by a reduction reaction in which the electrons are accepted by another atom or molecule. The oxidized molecule (the one that released electrons) gives up energy, and the reduced molecule (the one that accepted electrons) receives energy. Oxidation-reduction reactions, referred to as **redox reactions,** are an essential part of cellular respiration, photosynthesis, and other chemical reactions that take place in cells.

Hydrogens and Electrons Are Transferred in Redox Reactions

Electrons are not easy to remove from covalent compounds unless an entire atom is removed. In living cells oxidation almost always involves the removal of a hydrogen atom (a proton plus an electron) from a compound, whereas reduction involves a gain in hydrogen atoms.

When hydrogen atoms are removed from an organic compound, they take with them some of the energy stored in their chemical bonds. The hydrogen, along with its energy, is transferred to a hydrogen acceptor molecule, which is generally a coenzyme. One of the most frequently encountered hydrogen acceptor coenzymes is **nicotinamide adenine dinucleotide,** more conveniently referred to as **NAD⁺.** This coenzyme temporarily stores large amounts of free energy. Here is a generalized equation showing the transfer of hydrogen from a compound we call X to NAD⁺:

$$XH_2 + NAD^+ \longrightarrow X + NADH + H^+$$
Oxidized   Reduced

Note that the NAD⁺ is reduced when it combines with hydrogen. Before it is reduced, NAD⁺ is an ion with a net charge of +1. When H is added (more specifically, two electrons and one proton), the charge is neutralized. The reduced form of the compound, **NADH,**[1] is electrically neutral (Figure 7–2). Some of the energy stored in the bonds holding the hydrogens to molecule X has been transferred by this reaction to the NADH. This energy can now be used for some metabolic process, or it can be transferred through a complex series of reactions to ATP. As will be discussed, the transfer of energy in both photosynthesis and aerobic respiration involves sequences of redox reactions. The acceptor compounds that make up these sequences participate in energy flow.

Other important hydrogen or electron acceptor compounds include **flavin adenine dinucleotide (FAD)** and the **cytochromes.** FAD is a nucleotide that accepts hydrogens and their electrons, whereas the cytochromes are proteins that contain iron; the iron component accepts electrons from hydrogens and then transfers these electrons to some other compound. FAD and cytochromes, like NAD⁺, are important in aerobic respiration. Such electron acceptors provide a mechanism by which the cell efficiently captures energy from fuel molecules (Figure 7–3).

---

[1] Although the correct way to write the reduced form of NAD⁺ is NADH + H⁺, for simplicity's sake we present the reduced form as NADH throughout the remainder of this chapter.

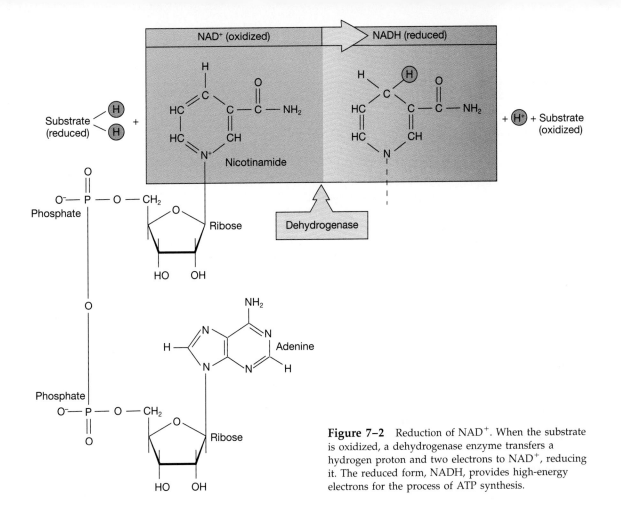

Figure 7–2 Reduction of NAD$^+$. When the substrate is oxidized, a dehydrogenase enzyme transfers a hydrogen proton and two electrons to NAD$^+$, reducing it. The reduced form, NADH, provides high-energy electrons for the process of ATP synthesis.

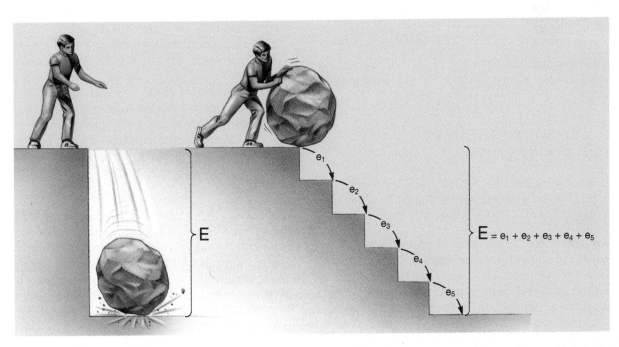

Figure 7–3 The total energy released by a falling object is the same whether the object is released all at once or in a series of steps. Similarly, in aerobic respiration the energy of an electron liberated from a glucose molecule is the same, regardless of whether it is released all at once or gradually as it passes to successive electron acceptors. As part of a complicated scheme involving the diffusion of protons across membranes, these acceptors permit the *controlled* extraction of some of the energy generated by these processes.

165

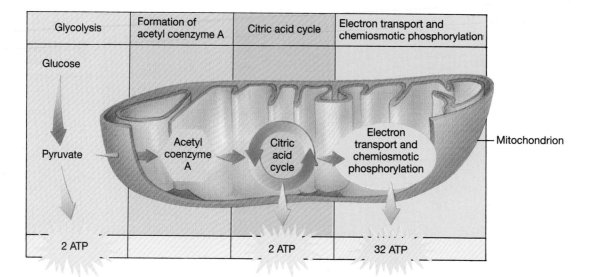

Glycolysis	Formation of acetyl coenzyme A	Citric acid cycle	Electron transport and chemiosmotic phosphorylation

Figure 7–4 Four main phases in aerobic respiration are (1) glycolysis, (2) the formation of acetyl coenzyme A from pyruvate, (3) the citric acid cycle, and (4) the electron transport system and chemiosmosis. Glycolysis occurs in the cytosol. Pyruvate, the product of glycolysis, enters a mitochondrion, where cellular respiration continues. Most ATP is synthesized during electron transport/chemiosmosis.

Aerobic Respiration Is a Redox Process

Aerobic respiration is a multistep redox process in which hydrogen is transferred from glucose to oxygen. Glucose is oxidized, and oxygen is reduced.

$$\overbrace{C_6H_{12}O_6 + 6\,O_2}^{\text{Oxidation}} + 6\,H_2O \longrightarrow \underbrace{6\,CO_2 + 12\,H_2O}_{\text{Reduction}}$$

$$+ \text{Energy (as ATP)}$$

During this process, the potential energy of the electrons (of hydrogen atoms) is used for ATP synthesis.

THERE ARE FOUR STAGES IN AEROBIC RESPIRATION

The chemical reactions of the aerobic respiration of glucose can be grouped into four stages (Figure 7–4; Table 7–1):

1. **Glycolysis.** A six-carbon glucose molecule is converted to two three-carbon molecules of pyruvate[1] with the formation of ATP and NADH.
2. **Formation of acetyl coenzyme A.** Each pyruvate is oxidized to a two-carbon molecule (acetate) that combines with coenzyme A, forming acetyl coenzyme A; carbon dioxide and NADH are released.
3. **The citric acid cycle.** The acetate of acetyl coenzyme A combines with a four-carbon molecule (oxaloacetate) to form a six-carbon molecule (citrate). Citrate eventually reforms oxaloacetate, with the release of carbon dioxide, ATP, and the reduced, high-energy compounds NADH and FADH$_2$.
4. **The electron transport system and chemiosmosis.** The hydrogens (or their electrons) removed from glucose during the preceding stages are transferred along a chain of electron acceptor compounds. As the electrons are passed from one electron acceptor to another, hydrogen ions (protons) are pumped across the inner mitochondrial membrane, forming a proton gradient (see Chapter 5). In chemiosmosis the energy of this proton gradient is used to produce ATP.

Most reactions involved in aerobic respiration are one of three types: dehydrogenations, decarboxylations, and "make-ready" reactions. **Dehydrogenations** are reactions in which two hydrogens (actually, two electrons plus two protons) are removed from the substrate and transferred to a coenzyme such as NAD$^+$ or FAD, which acts as a primary acceptor. **Decarboxylations** are reactions in which a carboxyl group (—COOH) is removed from the substrate as a molecule of CO$_2$. The carbon dioxide we exhale each day is derived from decarboxylations that occur in our body cells. In **"make-ready" reactions** molecules undergo rearrangements so that they can subsequently undergo further dehydrogenations or decarboxylations. As we

---

[1]Pyruvate and many other compounds in glycolysis and the citric acid cycle exist as ions at the pH found in the cell. They sometimes associate with H$^+$ to form acids. For example, pyruvate forms pyruvic acid. In some textbooks these compounds are presented in the acid form.

Table 7-1 SUMMARY OF AEROBIC RESPIRATION

Phase	*Summary*	*Some Starting Materials*	*Some End Products*
1. Glycolysis (in cytosol)	Series of about ten reactions in which glucose is degraded to pyruvate; net profit of 2 ATPs; hydrogens are released; can proceed anaerobically	Glucose, ATP, NAD^+	Pyruvate, ATP, NADH
2. Formation of acetyl CoA (in mitochondria)	Pyruvate is degraded and combined with coenzyme A to form acetyl CoA; hydrogens are released; CO_2 is released	Pyruvate, coenzyme A	Acetyl CoA, CO_2, NADH
3. Citric acid cycle (in mitochondria)	Series of reactions in which the acetyl portion of acetyl CoA is degraded to CO_2; hydrogens are released	Acetyl CoA, H_2O	CO_2, NADH, $FADH_2$, ATP
4. Electron transport and chemiosmosis (in mitochondria)	Chain of several electron transport molecules; H's (or their electrons) are passed along chain; energy released is used to form proton gradient; ATP is synthesized as protons move across the gradient; oxygen is final H-acceptor	NADH, $FADH_2$, oxygen	ATP, H_2O

examine the individual reactions of aerobic respiration, we will encounter many examples of these three basic types.

In Glycolysis, Glucose Is Converted to Pyruvate

Glycolysis (literally, "splitting sugar") is the sequence of reactions that converts a glucose molecule (a six-carbon compound) to two molecules of pyruvate (a three-carbon compound) with the production of NADH and ATP. Each reaction in glycolysis is catalyzed by a specific enzyme, and there is a net gain of two ATP molecules. The reactions of glycolysis take place in the cytosol. Such necessary ingredients as ADP, NAD^+, and inorganic phosphates float freely in the cytosol and are used as needed. Glycolysis does not require oxygen and can proceed under aerobic or anaerobic conditions.

The reactions of glycolysis are shown in Figure 7–5. In a highly simplified model, glycolysis is divided into two major phases. The first phase corresponds to the first four steps illustrated in Figure 7–5. During this phase, phosphate is added to the glucose molecule; the addition of phosphate to a molecule is termed **phosphorylation.** The glucose molecule is split, forming two molecules of the three-carbon compound glyceraldehyde-3-phosphate (PGAL). This part of glycolysis (the breakdown of glucose to PGAL) *requires* the input of energy and phosphate from two molecules of ATP.

We may summarize this portion of glycolysis as follows:

$$\text{Glucose} + 2\,\text{ATP} \dashrightarrow 2\,\text{PGAL} + 2\,\text{ADP}$$

Six-carbon compound   Three-carbon compound

A dashed arrow is used to indicate that the equation summarizes a sequence of several reactions.

In the second phase of glycolysis (Steps 5 through 9 in Figure 7–5), each PGAL is oxidized by the removal of two hydrogen atoms, and certain other atoms are rearranged so that each molecule of PGAL is transformed into a molecule of pyruvate. During these reactions, enough chemical energy is released from the sugar molecule to produce four ATP molecules. These ATPs are produced by enzymes without the involvement of membranes and proton gradients, in a process called **substrate-level phosphorylation.**

$$2\,\text{PGAL} + 4\,\text{ADP} + 2\,P_i \longrightarrow 2\,\text{pyruvate} + 4\,\text{H} + 4\,\text{ATP}$$

Three-carbon compound   Three-carbon compound

Note that in the first phase of glycolysis two molecules of ATP are consumed, but in the second phase four molecules of ATP are *produced.* Thus, glycolysis *yields* a net energy profit of two ATPs.

The two hydrogen atoms removed from each PGAL immediately combine with the hydrogen carrier molecule, NAD^+:

$$NAD^+ + 2\,\text{H} \longrightarrow NADH$$

Oxidized   Reduced

The fate of these hydrogen atoms is discussed in conjunction with the electron transport system.

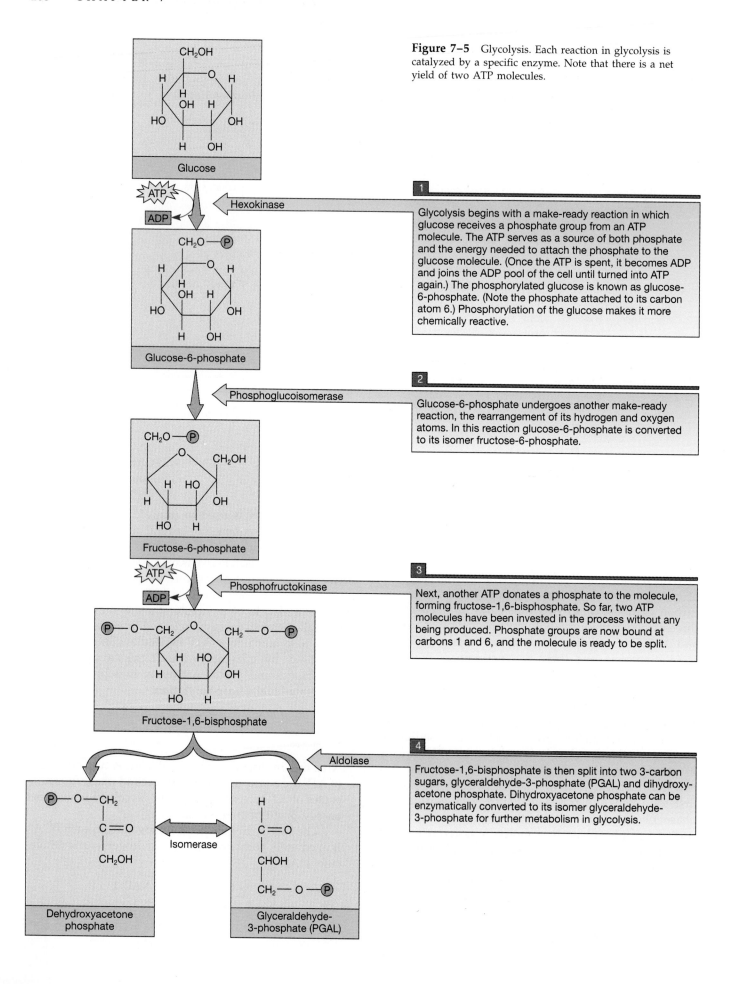

Figure 7–5 Glycolysis. Each reaction in glycolysis is catalyzed by a specific enzyme. Note that there is a net yield of two ATP molecules.

Glucose

Hexokinase

1

Glycolysis begins with a make-ready reaction in which glucose receives a phosphate group from an ATP molecule. The ATP serves as a source of both phosphate and the energy needed to attach the phosphate to the glucose molecule. (Once the ATP is spent, it becomes ADP and joins the ADP pool of the cell until turned into ATP again.) The phosphorylated glucose is known as glucose-6-phosphate. (Note the phosphate attached to its carbon atom 6.) Phosphorylation of the glucose makes it more chemically reactive.

Glucose-6-phosphate

Phosphoglucoisomerase

2

Glucose-6-phosphate undergoes another make-ready reaction, the rearrangement of its hydrogen and oxygen atoms. In this reaction glucose-6-phosphate is converted to its isomer fructose-6-phosphate.

Fructose-6-phosphate

Phosphofructokinase

3

Next, another ATP donates a phosphate to the molecule, forming fructose-1,6-bisphosphate. So far, two ATP molecules have been invested in the process without any being produced. Phosphate groups are now bound at carbons 1 and 6, and the molecule is ready to be split.

Fructose-1,6-bisphosphate

Aldolase

4

Fructose-1,6-bisphosphate is then split into two 3-carbon sugars, glyceraldehyde-3-phosphate (PGAL) and dihydroxy-acetone phosphate. Dihydroxyacetone phosphate can be enzymatically converted to its isomer glyceraldehyde-3-phosphate for further metabolism in glycolysis.

Isomerase

Dehydroxyacetone phosphate

Glyceraldehyde-3-phosphate (PGAL)

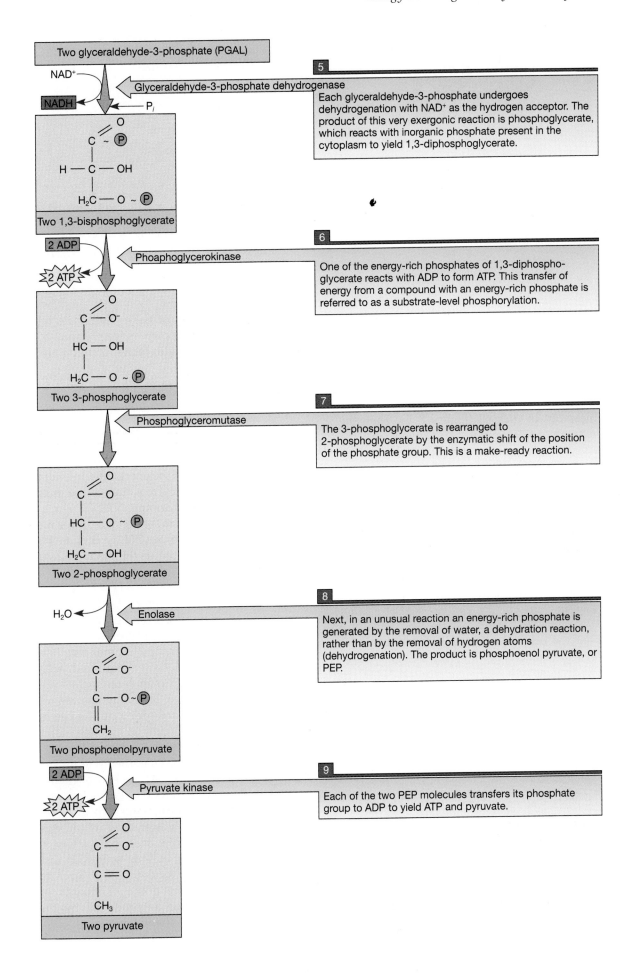

Two glyceraldehyde-3-phosphate (PGAL)

NAD⁺

NADH

Pᵢ

Glyceraldehyde-3-phosphate dehydrogenase

5

Each glyceraldehyde-3-phosphate undergoes dehydrogenation with NAD⁺ as the hydrogen acceptor. The product of this very exergonic reaction is phosphoglycerate, which reacts with inorganic phosphate present in the cytoplasm to yield 1,3-diphosphoglycerate.

Two 1,3-bisphosphoglycerate

2 ADP

2 ATP

Phoaphoglycerokinase

6

One of the energy-rich phosphates of 1,3-diphospho-glycerate reacts with ADP to form ATP. This transfer of energy from a compound with an energy-rich phosphate is referred to as a substrate-level phosphorylation.

Two 3-phosphoglycerate

Phosphoglyceromutase

7

The 3-phosphoglycerate is rearranged to 2-phosphoglycerate by the enzymatic shift of the position of the phosphate group. This is a make-ready reaction.

Two 2-phosphoglycerate

H₂O

Enolase

8

Next, in an unusual reaction an energy-rich phosphate is generated by the removal of water, a dehydration reaction, rather than by the removal of hydrogen atoms (dehydrogenation). The product is phosphoenol pyruvate, or PEP.

Two phosphoenolpyruvate

2 ADP

2 ATP

Pyruvate kinase

9

Each of the two PEP molecules transfers its phosphate group to ADP to yield ATP and pyruvate.

Two pyruvate

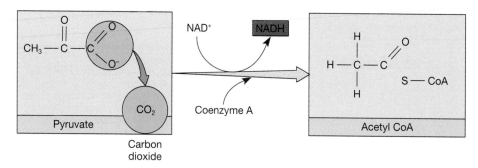

Figure 7–6 Formation of acetyl CoA. Pyruvate, the end product of glycolysis, enters a mitochondrion and undergoes oxidative decarboxylation. First, the carboxyl group is split off as carbon dioxide. Then the remaining two-carbon fragment is oxidized and its hydrogens transferred to NAD^+. Finally, the oxidized two-carbon group, an acetyl group, is attached to coenzyme A. Coenzyme A has a sulfur atom that attaches to the acetyl group by a very unstable bond, shown as a wavy line.

Each Pyruvate Is Converted to Acetyl CoA

The pyruvate molecules formed in glycolysis enter the mitochondria, where they are converted to **acetyl coenzyme A (acetyl CoA).** In this complex series of reactions, pyruvate undergoes oxidative decarboxylation. First, a carboxyl group is removed as carbon dioxide, which diffuses out of the cell (Figure 7–6). Then the two-carbon fragment remaining is oxidized, and the hydrogens that were removed during the oxidation are accepted by NAD^+. Finally, the oxidized two-carbon fragment, an acetyl group, is attached to coenzyme A, which is manufactured in the cell from one of the B vitamins, pantothenic acid. The reaction is catalyzed by a multienzyme complex that contains several copies of each of three different enzymes. The overall reaction for the formation of acetyl coenzyme A is the following:

$$2 \text{ pyruvate} + 2 \text{ NAD}^+ + 2 \text{ CoA} \longrightarrow 2 \text{ acetyl CoA} + 2 \text{ NADH} + 2 \text{ CO}_2$$

Note that the original glucose molecule has now been oxidized to two acetyl groups and two CO_2 molecules. The hydrogens removed have reduced NAD^+ to NADH. At this point in aerobic respiration, four NADH molecules have been formed from a single starting glucose molecule, two during glycolysis and two during the formation of acetyl CoA from pyruvate.

The Citric Acid Cycle Oxidizes Acetyl CoA

The **citric acid cycle** is also known as the **tricarboxylic acid (TCA) cycle** and as the **Krebs cycle** after Sir Hans Krebs, who worked out its details in the 1930s. The citric acid cycle takes place in the mitochondria and consists of eight steps, illustrated and described in Figures 7–7 and 7–8. Each reaction is catalyzed by a specific enzyme.

The first reaction of the cycle occurs when acetyl CoA transfers its two-carbon acetyl group to the four-carbon compound **oxaloacetate,** forming **citrate,** a six-carbon compound:

$$\text{Oxaloacetate} + \text{Acetyl CoA} \longrightarrow \text{Citrate} + \text{CoA}$$

| Four-carbon compound | Two-carbon compound | Six-carbon compound |

The citrate then goes through a series of chemical transformations, losing first one and then a second carboxyl group as CO_2. Most of the energy made available by the oxidative steps of the cycle is transferred as energy-rich electrons to NAD^+, forming NADH. For each acetyl group that enters the citric acid cycle, three molecules of NAD^+ are reduced to NADH. In Step 6 (Figure 7–8), electrons are transferred to the electron acceptor FAD rather than to NAD^+.

In one turn of the citric acid cycle, two molecules of CO_2 and eight hydrogen atoms (eight protons and eight electrons) are removed, forming three NADH and one $FADH_2$. The CO_2 produced accounts for the two carbon atoms of the acetyl group that entered the citric acid cycle. You may wonder why more hydrogen is generated by these reactions than entered the cycle with the acetyl CoA molecule. These hydrogens come from water molecules that are added during the reactions of the cycle.

Because two acetyl CoA molecules are produced from each glucose molecule, the cycle must turn twice to process each glucose. At the end of each turn of the cycle, the four-carbon oxaloacetate is left, and the cycle is ready for another turn. After two turns of the cycle, the original glucose has lost all of its carbons and may be regarded as having been completely consumed. Only one molecule of ATP is produced directly by a substrate-level phosphorylation with each turn of the citric acid cycle. The rest of the ATP that is formed during aerobic respiration is produced by the electron transport system and chemiosmosis.

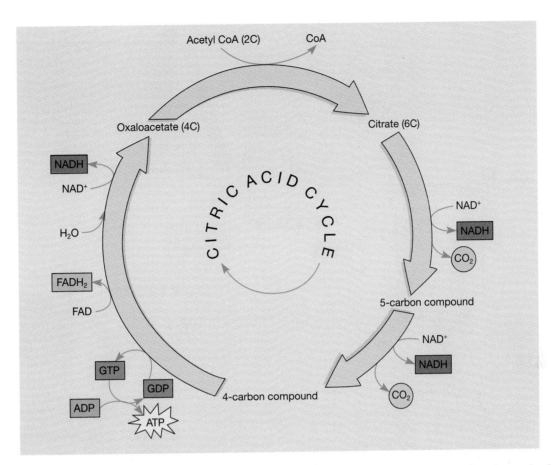

Figure 7–7 An overview of the citric acid cycle. A two-carbon acetyl group combines with the four-carbon compound oxaloacetate to form the six-carbon compound citrate. During the course of the cycle, citric acid (and its derivatives) undergoes two decarboxylations, four dehydrogenations, and several make-ready reactions. One ATP is generated at the substrate level. The four-carbon oxaloacetate is regenerated, and the cycle begins anew. Note that the CO_2 produced accounts for the two carbons that entered the cycle as part of one acetyl CoA molecule.

The Electron Transport System Is Coupled to Chemiosmosis

Let us consider the fate of all the hydrogens removed from a molecule of glucose during glycolysis, acetyl CoA formation, and the citric acid cycle. Recall that the hydrogens were transferred to primary hydrogen acceptors—NAD^+ and FAD, forming NADH and $FADH_2$. These reduced compounds now enter the **electron transport chain,** where the high-energy electrons of their hydrogens are shuttled from one acceptor to another. As the hydrogen electrons are passed along, some of their energy is used to make ATP by a process called **chemiosmosis.**

The electron transport chain accepts hydrogens or their electrons from the previous three stages

The electron transport system is a chain of electron acceptors embedded in the inner membrane of the mitochondrion. Hydrogens are passed from NADH to flavin mononucleotide (FMN), the first acceptor in the chain (Figure 7–9). As these hydrogens are transferred from one to another of the electron acceptor molecules, the hydrogen protons become separated from their electrons. When the hydrogen protons (H^+) separate from their electrons, they are released into the surrounding medium.

Hydrogens, or their electrons, pass down the electron transport chain in a series of redox reactions. The electrons entering the electron transport system have a relatively high energy content. As they pass along the chain of electron acceptors, they lose much of their energy, some of which is used to pump the protons across the inner mitochondrial membrane. This sets up an electrochemical gradient (a form of potential energy; see Chapter 5) across the inner mitochondrial membrane; the electrochemical gradient provides the energy for ATP synthesis (Figure 7–10).

The electron acceptors in the electron transport chain include FMN, ubiquinone (CoQ), and a group of closely related proteins called cytochromes. Cytochrome molecules accept only the electron from each

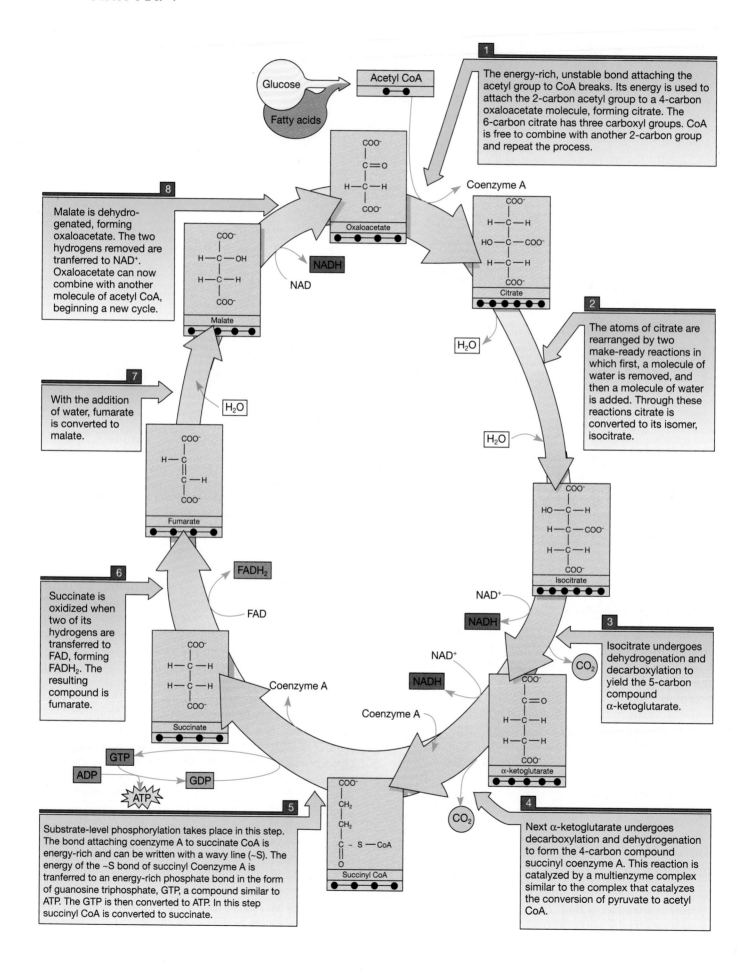

1 The energy-rich, unstable bond attaching the acetyl group to CoA breaks. Its energy is used to attach the 2-carbon acetyl group to a 4-carbon oxaloacetate molecule, forming citrate. The 6-carbon citrate has three carboxyl groups. CoA is free to combine with another 2-carbon group and repeat the process.

Glucose

Fatty acids

Acetyl CoA

Coenzyme A

COO^-
$C=O$
$H-C-H$
COO^-
Oxaloacetate

COO^-
$H-C-H$
$HO-C-COO^-$
$H-C-H$
COO^-
Citrate

NADH

NAD

8 Malate is dehydrogenated, forming oxaloacetate. The two hydrogens removed are tranferred to NAD^+. Oxaloacetate can now combine with another molecule of acetyl CoA, beginning a new cycle.

COO^-
$H-C-OH$
$H-C-H$
COO^-
Malate

H_2O

2 The atoms of citrate are rearranged by two make-ready reactions in which first, a molecule of water is removed, and then a molecule of water is added. Through these reactions citrate is converted to its isomer, isocitrate.

H_2O

H_2O

7 With the addition of water, fumarate is converted to malate.

COO^-
$H-C$
$C-H$
COO^-
Fumarate

COO^-
$HO-C-H$
$H-C-COO^-$
$H-C-H$
COO^-
Isocitrate

NAD^+

NADH

FADH$_2$

FAD

6 Succinate is oxidized when two of its hydrogens are transferred to FAD, forming FADH$_2$. The resulting compound is fumarate.

COO^-
$H-C-H$
$H-C-H$
COO^-
Succinate

Coenzyme A

NAD^+

NADH

Coenzyme A

3 Isocitrate undergoes dehydrogenation and decarboxylation to yield the 5-carbon compound α-ketoglutarate.

CO_2

COO^-
$C=O$
$H-C-H$
$H-C-H$
COO^-
α-ketoglutarate

GTP

ADP

GDP

ATP

COO^-
CH_2
CH_2
$C \sim S-CoA$
O
Succinyl CoA

CO_2

5 Substrate-level phosphorylation takes place in this step. The bond attaching coenzyme A to succinate CoA is energy-rich and can be written with a wavy line (~S). The energy of the ~S bond of succinyl Coenzyme A is tranferred to an energy-rich phosphate bond in the form of guanosine triphosphate, GTP, a compound similar to ATP. The GTP is then converted to ATP. In this step succinyl CoA is converted to succinate.

4 Next α-ketoglutarate undergoes decarboxylation and dehydrogenation to form the 4-carbon compound succinyl coenzyme A. This reaction is catalyzed by a multienzyme complex similar to the complex that catalyzes the conversion of pyruvate to acetyl CoA.

◀ **Figure 7–8** The citric acid cycle. During this series of reactions, acetyl CoA, produced from glucose and other organic compounds, is metabolized to yield carbon dioxide and hydrogen. The hydrogen is immediately combined with NAD^+ or FAD and fed into the electron transport system. With each turn of the cycle, two carbons and eight hydrogens (that is, eight protons and eight electrons) are split off from the fuel molecule.

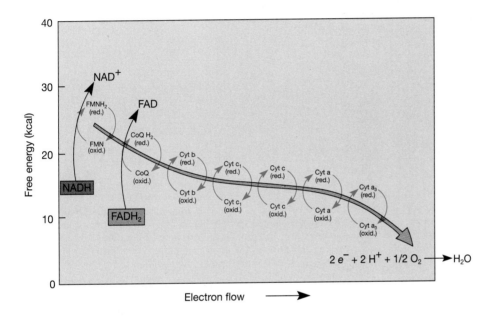

Figure 7–9 The electron transport chain. Hydrogens or their electrons are transferred from one electron acceptor molecule to another. The acceptor molecules are alternately oxidized and reduced as they transfer and accept hydrogen, the final electron (and hydrogen) acceptor being molecular oxygen. Water is produced as a product of these reactions. The energy released as electrons move to lower energy levels is used to make ATP by chemiosmosis.

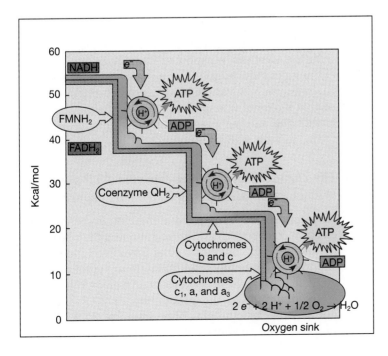

Figure 7–10 Electron transport may be compared with a stream of water (electrons) that has three waterfalls. The flow of water drives water wheels (the proton gradient). There are three sites in the electron transport system where ATP is produced. The electrons end up in the pond at the bottom of the waterfalls, where they unite with protons and oxygen to yield H_2O. Electron transfer from NADH to oxygen is very exergonic, releasing about 53 kcal/mole. If released all at once, most of this energy would be lost as heat. Instead, the energy is released slowly in a series of steps, as shown here, and used to transport protons across the inner mitochondrial membrane. The potential energy established by the proton gradient is the source of energy needed to synthesize ATP. For each pair of hydrogens that enters this pathway, a maximum of three ATP molecules is produced.

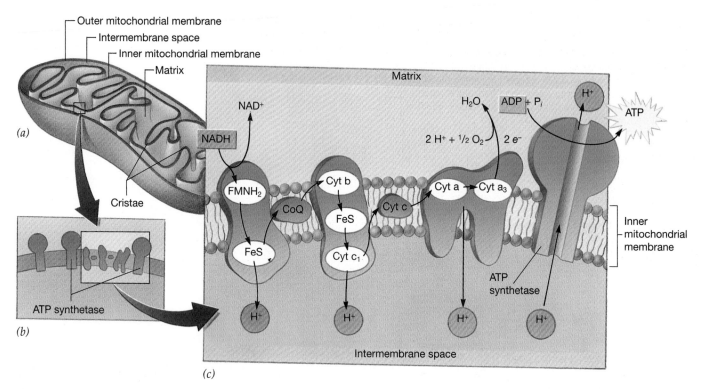

Figure 7–11   Chemiosmosis. (*a*) and (*b*) According to the chemiosmotic model, the electron transport chain in the inner mitochondrial membrane is a proton pump. (*c*) The electron acceptors in the membrane are located in three main complexes. FMN, which oxidizes NADH, is located in the first complex. The cytochrome b-c_1 complex consists of two cytochromes and some additional electron acceptors. The third complex includes cytochromes a and a_3. Coenzyme Q and cytochrome c are mobile carriers that transfer electrons between the complexes. At three sites in the chain, the energy released during electron transport is used to transport protons (H^+) from the mitochondrial matrix to the intermembrane space, where a high concentration of protons accumulates. The protons are prevented from diffusing back into the matrix through the inner membrane except through special channels in ATP synthetase in the membrane. The flow of the protons through ATP synthetase generates ATP at the expense of the free energy released as the protons pass from a region of high concentration to a region of lower concentration.

hydrogen, not the entire atom. The several types of cytochromes hold electrons at slightly different energy levels. Electrons are passed along from one cytochrome to the next in the chain, losing energy as they go. Finally, the last cytochrome in the chain, cytochrome a_3, passes two electrons to molecular oxygen. Simultaneously, the electrons reunite with protons to form hydrogen, and the chemical union of the hydrogen and oxygen produces water.

Thus, oxygen is the final hydrogen acceptor in the electron transport system, which explains why organisms that respire aerobically require oxygen. What happens when cells that are strict aerobes are deprived of oxygen? When no oxygen is available to accept the hydrogen, the last cytochrome in the chain is stuck with its electrons. When that occurs, each acceptor molecule in the chain remains stuck with electrons, and the entire system is blocked all the way back to NADH. As a result, no further ATPs are produced by way of the electron transport system. Most cells of complex organisms cannot live long without oxygen because the amount of

energy they produce in its absence is insufficient to sustain life processes.

Lack of oxygen is not the only factor that interferes with the electron transport system. Some poisons, including cyanide, inhibit the normal activity of the cytochrome system. Cyanide binds tightly to cytochrome a_3 so that it cannot transport electrons on to oxygen. This blocks the further passage of electrons through the chain, halting ATP production.

The chemiosmotic model explains ATP synthesis that is associated with electron transport

As electrons are transferred along the acceptors in the electron transport chain, sufficient energy is released at three points to convey protons across the inner mitochondrial membrane and ultimately to synthesize ATP.

The flow of electrons in electron transport is usually coupled tightly to the production of ATP and does not occur unless the phosphorylation of ADP can also proceed. This prevents a waste of energy, because high-

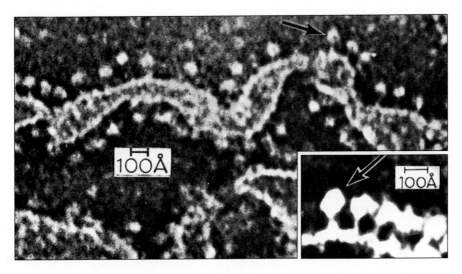

Figure 7–12   Electron micrograph of the inner mitochondrial membrane. The lollipop-like structures attached to the surface of the membrane are respiratory assemblies composed of complexes of the enzyme ATP synthetase.   (Robert Pugh)

energy electrons do not flow unless ATP can be produced. If electron flow were uncoupled from the phosphorylation of ADP, there would be no production of ATP, and the energy of the electrons would be wasted as heat. Because the phosphorylation of ADP to form ATP is coupled with the oxidation of electron transport components, this process of making ATP is referred to as **oxidative phosphorylation.**

It had long been known that oxidative phosphorylation occurs in mitochondria, and many experiments had shown that the transfer of two electrons from each NADH to oxygen results in the production of three ATP molecules. However, for a long time, just *how* ATP synthesis is related to electron transport remained a mystery. Then, in 1961 Peter Mitchell proposed the **chemiosmotic model,** which was based on experiments he did with bacteria and for which he was awarded the Nobel Prize in 1978. Mitchell proposed that electron transport and oxidative phosphorylation (ATP synthesis) are coupled by a proton gradient across the inner mitochondrial membrane. According to the chemiosmotic model, the stepwise transfer of electrons from NADH or FADH$_2$ through the electron carriers to oxygen results in the release of energy. This energy is used to pump protons across the inner mitochondrial membrane into the space between the inner and outer mitochondrial membranes (Figure 7–11).

Protons are pumped across the inner mitochondrial membrane by three electron transfer complexes, each associated with particular steps in the electron transport system. The difference in the concentration of protons (H$^+$) between the mitochondrial matrix and the intermembrane space represents potential energy (much like water that is concentrated behind a dam).

The inner mitochondrial membrane is impermeable to the passage of protons, which can flow back into the matrix of the mitochondrion only through special channels in the inner mitochondrial membrane. These channels occur in the enzyme **ATP synthetase.** ATP synthetase forms complexes called **respiratory assemblies** that project from the inner surface of the membrane and are visible by electron microscopy (Figure 7–12). As the protons move down the energy gradient (that is, through ATP synthetase to the other side of the inner mitochondrial membrane), the energy released is used by ATP synthetase to produce ATP.

THE AEROBIC RESPIRATION OF EACH GLUCOSE MOLECULE YIELDS A MAXIMUM OF 36 TO 38 ATPs

Let us now review where biologically useful energy is released in aerobic respiration and calculate the total energy yield from the complete oxidation of glucose. Table 7–2 summarizes the arithmetic involved. (1) In glycolysis glucose is activated by the addition of two ATP molecules and converted ultimately to 2 pyruvate + 2 NADH + 4 ATP, yielding a net profit of two ATPs. (2) The two pyruvates are metabolized to 2 acetyl CoA + 2 CO$_2$ + 2 NADH. (3) In the citric acid cycle the two acetyl CoA molecules are metabolized to 4 CO$_2$ + 6 NADH + 2 FADH$_2$ + 2 ATP.

Because the oxidation of NADH in the electron transport system yields three ATPs per molecule, the 10 NADH molecules can yield up to 30 ATPs. The two NADH molecules from glycolysis, however, yield ei-

FOCUS ON

Shuttles across the Mitochondrial Membrane

The inner mitochondrial membrane is not permeable to NADH, which is a large molecule. The NADH produced in the cytosol from the degradations in glycolysis cannot diffuse into the mitochondria to transfer their electrons to the electron transport system. Unlike ATP and ADP, NADH does not have a carrier protein to transport it across the membrane. Instead, several systems have evolved to transfer the *electrons* of NADH (although not the NADH molecules themselves) into the mitochondria.

In liver, kidney, and heart cells, a special shuttle system transfers the electrons from NADH through the inner mitochondrial membrane. Once inside the matrix, the electrons are passed to a different NAD^+, one already in the matrix. These electrons then enter the electron transport system in the inner mitochondrial membrane, and three molecules of ATP are produced per pair of electrons.

In skeletal muscle, brain, and some other types of cells, another type of shuttle operates. Because this shuttle requires more energy than the shuttle in liver, kidney, and heart cells, the electrons are at a lower energy level when they enter the electron transport chain. They are accepted by coenzyme Q rather than by NAD^+ and so generate only two ATP molecules per pair of electrons. This is why the number of ATPs produced by aerobic respiration of a molecule of glucose in skeletal muscle cells is 36 rather than 38.

ther two or three ATPs each (in certain types of cells, it takes some energy to shuttle the glycolytically produced NADH across the mitochondrial membrane; see Focus on Shuttles across the Mitochondrial Membrane). Thus, the total number of ATPs formed using the energy from NADH is 28 to 30. The oxidation of $FADH_2$ yields two ATPs per molecule, so the two $FADH_2$ molecules yield four ATPs. (4) Summing these ATPs (2 from glycolysis, 2 from the citric acid cycle, and 32 to 34 from electron transport), we see that the complete aerobic metabolism of one molecule of glucose yields a maximum of 36 to 38 ATPs. Note that all but two ATP molecules were generated by reactions taking place in the mitochondria, and all but two of those generated in the mitochondria (the two formed by substrate-level phosphorylation in the citric acid cycle) were produced by the electron transport system.

When a mole of glucose is burned in a calorimeter, some 686 kcal are released as heat.[1] Because the free energy stored in one phosphate bond of ATP is about 7.3 kcal per mole, when 36 to 38 ATPs are generated during the aerobic respiration of glucose, the total energy stored in ATP amounts to 7.3 kcal per mole × 36, or about 263 kcal per mole. Thus, the efficiency of aerobic respiration is 263/686, or about 38%. (By comparison, a steam power plant has an efficiency of 35% to 36% in converting its fuel energy into electricity.) The remainder of the energy in the glucose is released as heat, used by some animals to help maintain body temperature.

[1] A calorimeter is an instrument that measures heats of reaction. A sample is placed in a compartment surrounded by a chamber of water. As the sample burns, the temperature of the water rises, providing a measure of the heat released during the reaction.

Table 7–2 ENERGY YIELD FROM THE COMPLETE OXIDATION OF GLUCOSE

1. Net ATP profit from glycolysis		2 ATP* (substrate-level phosphorylation)
Also from glycolysis:	2 NADH ---→	4–6 ATP (oxidative phosphorylation)
2. 2 pyruvate to 2 acetyl CoA	2 NADH ---→	6 ATP (oxidative phosphorylation)
3. 2 acetyl CoA through citric acid cycle and electron transport system		2 ATP (substrate-level phosphorylation)
	6 NADH ---→	18 ATP (oxidative phosphorylation)
	2 $FADH_2$ ---→	4 ATP (oxidative phosphorylation)
Total ATP profit		36–38 ATP

*These are the only two ATPs that can be generated anaerobically; production of all other ATPs depends on the presence of oxygen.

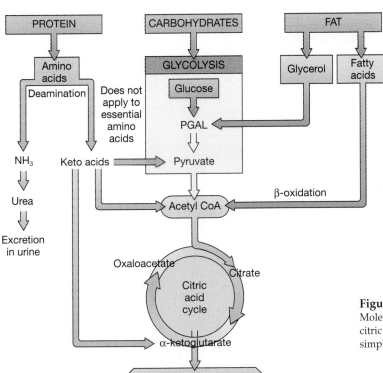

Figure 7–13 Catabolism of carbohydrates, proteins, and fats. Molecular subunits of these compounds enter glycolysis or the citric acid cycle at various points. This diagram is greatly simplified and illustrates only a few of the principal pathways.

NUTRIENTS OTHER THAN GLUCOSE ALSO PROVIDE ENERGY

Many organisms depend on nutrients other than glucose (or in addition to glucose) as a source of energy. Humans and many other animals usually obtain more of their energy by oxidizing fatty acids than by oxidizing glucose. Amino acids from protein digestion are also used as fuel molecules. Such nutrients are transformed into one of the metabolic intermediates that are fed into glycolysis or the citric acid cycle (Figure 7–13).

Amino acids are metabolized by reactions in which the amino group is first removed, a process called **deamination.** In mammals and some other animals, the amino group is converted to urea and excreted, but the carbon chain is metabolized and eventually enters the citric acid cycle. The sequence of reactions varies somewhat with different amino acids, but for each, a series of reactions modifies the carbon skeleton to produce a compound that is part of the citric acid cycle. Alanine, for example, undergoes deamination to become pyruvate, glutamate is converted to α-ketoglutarate (alpha-ketoglutarate), and aspartate yields oxaloacetate. Ultimately, the carbon chains of all the amino acids are metabolized in this way.

Each gram of lipid contains more than twice as much energy as 1 gram of glucose or amino acids. Lipids are rich in calories because they have a lot of hydrogen atoms. (Recall that the electrons of hydrogen in organic compounds have a great deal of potential energy.) When completely metabolized in aerobic respiration, a molecule of a six-carbon fatty acid generates up to 44 ATPs (compared with 36 to 38 ATPs for a molecule of glucose, which also has six carbons).

Both the glycerol and fatty acid components of a neutral fat (see Chapter 3) are used as fuel; phosphate is added to glycerol, converting it to PGAL or another compound that enters glycolysis. Fatty acids are oxidized and split enzymatically into two-carbon compounds (acetyl groups) that are bound to coenzyme A; that is, fatty acids are converted to acetyl CoA. This process, which occurs in the mitochondrial matrix, is called **β-oxidation** (beta-oxidation). Acetyl CoA molecules formed by β-oxidation enter the citric acid cycle.

CELLS REGULATE AEROBIC RESPIRATION

Aerobic respiration requires a steady input of fuel molecules and oxygen. Under normal conditions these materials are adequately provided and do not affect the rate of respiration. Instead, the rate of aerobic respiration is regulated by how much ADP and phosphate are

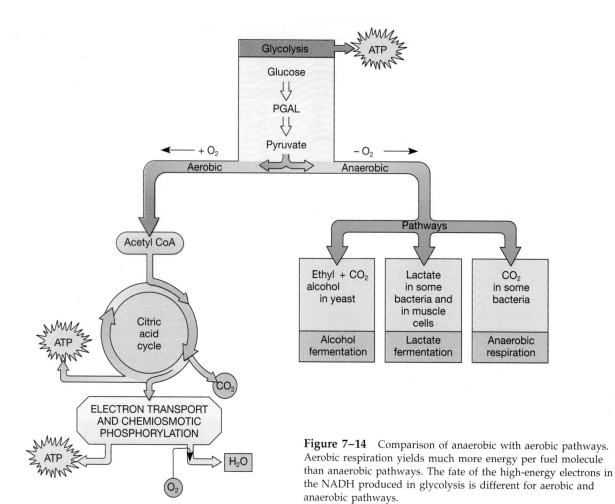

Figure 7–14   Comparison of anaerobic with aerobic pathways. Aerobic respiration yields much more energy per fuel molecule than anaerobic pathways. The fate of the high-energy electrons in the NADH produced in glycolysis is different for aerobic and anaerobic pathways.

available. In a resting muscle cell, for example, ATP synthesis continues until all the ADP has been converted to ATP. When there is no more ADP, oxidative phosphorylation stops. Because electron flow is tightly coupled to oxidative phosphorylation, the flow of electrons also stops, which in turn shuts down the citric acid cycle.

When an energy-requiring process like muscle contraction occurs, ATP is split to yield ADP and inorganic phosphate plus energy. The ADP formed can then serve as an acceptor of phosphate and energy to become ATP once again; aerobic respiration resumes until the ADP has again been converted to ATP.

The control of most metabolic pathways is exerted on an enzyme that catalyzes a reaction early in the pathway (see discussion of feedback inhibition in Chapter 6). This enzyme is usually inhibited by the presence of the end product of the pathway. One of the important control points in aerobic respiration in mammals is an enzyme that catalyzes an early reaction of glycolysis. This enzyme, phosphofructokinase, is inhibited by the presence of ATP and activated by the presence of ADP and AMP (adenosine monophosphate, a molecule

formed when two phosphates are removed from ATP). Therefore, this enzyme is inactivated when energy supply (ATP) levels are high and activated when energy supplies are low.[1]

Phosphofructokinase is an allosteric enzyme (see Chapter 6) and possesses receptor sites for both enzyme inhibitors (in this case, ATP) and enzyme activators (in this case, ADP and AMP). When respiration produces more ATP than the cell currently needs, some of the excess ATP binds to phosphofructokinase, changing its conformation (shape) so that it is no longer active. Thus, glycolysis (and aerobic respiration) slows down and less ATP is produced.

As excess ATP is used by the cell, ADP (and AMP) is produced. Now the inhibitor site of phosphofructokinase is no longer occupied by ATP. Instead, the activator sites are filled with ADP/AMP. Thus, the enzyme is activated and respiration proceeds, generating more ATP.

---

[1] Other materials, including citrate, also affect the activity of phosphofructokinase.

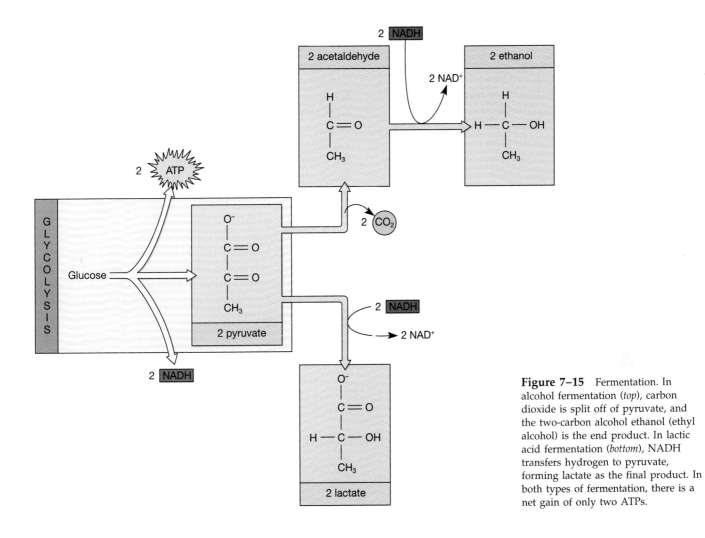

Figure 7–15 Fermentation. In alcohol fermentation (*top*), carbon dioxide is split off of pyruvate, and the two-carbon alcohol ethanol (ethyl alcohol) is the end product. In lactic acid fermentation (*bottom*), NADH transfers hydrogen to pyruvate, forming lactate as the final product. In both types of fermentation, there is a net gain of only two ATPs.

ANAEROBIC PATHWAYS ARE LESS EFFICIENT THAN AEROBIC RESPIRATION

As stated previously, cells use three types of pathways to extract free energy from nutrients: aerobic respiration, anaerobic respiration, and fermentation, which is also anaerobic (Figure 7–14). Anaerobic pathways, including fermentation, take place in the cytosol. In all three processes, glucose or other nutrients are oxidized, and their high-energy electrons are transferred to NAD^+, which becomes reduced to NADH. What happens to these electrons is different in each of the three pathways.

In aerobic respiration, we have seen that oxygen is the ultimate acceptor for the hydrogens removed from nutrient molecules during glycolysis, the formation of acetyl CoA, and the citric acid cycle. During anaerobic respiration, oxygen is not used as a hydrogen (electron) acceptor. Instead, an inorganic compound such as nitrate or sulfate serves as the final acceptor of hydrogen.

In fermentation the final acceptor of hydrogen is an organic compound (rather than an inorganic one, as in anaerobic respiration).

Two Common Types of Fermentation Are Alcohol Fermentation and Lactate Fermentation

Yeasts (see Figure 25–2) can carry on **alcohol fermentation.** First they degrade glucose to pyruvate using the process of glycolysis. When deprived of oxygen, yeast cells split carbon dioxide off from pyruvate, forming a two-carbon compound called acetaldehyde (Figure 7–15). Hydrogen from the NADH produced during glycolysis is then transferred to acetaldehyde, forming **ethyl alcohol.** Alcohol fermentation is the basis for the production of beer, wine, and other alcoholic beverages. Yeast cells are also used in baking to produce the carbon dioxide that causes dough to rise (the alcohol evaporates during baking).

Certain fungi and bacteria carry on **lactate (lactic acid) fermentation.** In this alternative pathway, hydrogens removed from glucose as NADH during glycolysis are transferred to pyruvate, forming **lactate.** Lactate is produced when bacteria sour milk or ferment cabbage to form sauerkraut. It is also produced during activity in the muscle cells of humans and other complex animals. During strenuous physical activity such as running, the amount of oxygen delivered to muscle cells may be insufficient to keep pace with the rapid rate of aerobic respiration. Not all of the hydrogen atoms accepted by NAD^+ can be processed in the usual manner through the electron transport chain because there is a shortage of oxygen. In this situation muscle cells shift temporarily from aerobic respiration to lactate fermentation. The hydrogens are transferred to pyruvate to form lactate. As lactate accumulates in muscle cells, it contributes to muscle fatigue.

Why don't cells that use fermentation to obtain energy stop the process at pyruvate? That is, why must they go on to form ethyl alcohol or lactate, both of which are more toxic to cells? The answer centers around NAD^+. Cells have a limited quantity of NAD^+, which is reduced to NADH during glycolysis. Fermenters convert pyruvate to ethyl alcohol or lactate as a means of oxidizing NADH to form NAD^+ again. If fermentation ended at pyruvate, ultimately all of the NAD^+ would be in the form of NADH, and no further glycolysis could occur. Freeing NAD^+ from NADH by producing ethyl alcohol or lactate allows cells to continue to break down glucose by glycolysis.

Both alcohol fermentation and lactate fermentation are very inefficient because the fuel is only partially oxidized. Alcohol, the end product of fermentation by yeast cells, can be burned and can even be used as automobile fuel; obviously, it contains a great deal of energy that the yeast cells are unable to extract using anaerobic methods. Lactate, a three-carbon compound, contains even more energy than the two-carbon alcohol. In contrast, during aerobic respiration all available energy is removed because the fuel molecules are completely oxidized to CO_2. A net profit of only two ATPs is produced by the fermentation of one molecule of glucose, compared with up to 36 to 38 ATPs when oxygen is available.

The inefficiency of anaerobic metabolism necessitates a large supply of fuel. For example, skeletal muscle cells, which often metabolize anaerobically for short periods, store large quantities of glucose in the form of glycogen (see Chapter 38). By rapidly degrading many fuel molecules, an anaerobically respiring cell can compensate somewhat for the small amount of energy that can be gained from each fuel molecule. To perform the same amount of work, an anaerobic cell must consume up to 20 times as much glucose or other carbohydrate as a cell using aerobic respiration.

METABOLISM ALSO INCLUDES BIOSYNTHETIC PROCESSES

Our discussion thus far has focused on processes that break down organic molecules and conserve their energy in the biologically useful form of ATP. Cells also possess a remarkable array of enzymes that catalyze a variety of biosynthetic processes. This anabolic (building up, or synthesizing, of complex molecules) aspect of metabolism is quite complex, but several basic generalizations can be made:

1. Each cell type usually synthesizes its own proteins, nucleic acids, lipids, polysaccharides, and other complex molecules and does not receive them preformed from other cells. Muscle glycogen, for example, is synthesized within the muscle cell and is not derived from liver glycogen.

2. Each step in the biosynthesis of a molecule is catalyzed by a separate enzyme.

3. Although certain steps in a biosynthetic sequence may proceed without the use of ATP, the overall synthesis of complex molecules requires chemical energy (ATP and similar compounds) at various points along the way.

4. Anabolic processes use as raw materials relatively few substances, among which are acetyl CoA, glycine, succinyl CoA, ribose, pyruvate, and glycerol. Many of these molecules are intermediates in the metabolism of glucose, lipids, and amino acids.

5. In general, anabolic processes are not simply the reverse of catabolic processes in which the molecule is degraded, but include one or more separate steps that differ from any step in catabolism. The fact that anabolic and catabolic processes are controlled by different enzymes permits separate control mechanisms to govern the synthesis and degradation of complex molecules.

6. Each cell's constituent molecules are in a dynamic state—that is, some molecules are being degraded while others are being synthesized. Both anabolism and catabolism are continually occurring.

Even a cell that is not growing or increasing in mass uses a considerable portion of its total energy for the chemical work of biosynthesis. A cell that is growing rapidly allocates a correspondingly larger fraction of its total energy to biosynthetic processes, especially to the biosynthesis of protein (Figure 7–16). For example, a rapidly growing bacterial cell may use as much as 90% of its total energy for protein synthesis.

MAKING THE CONNECTION

Relating Respiration to Energy, Information, and Evolution

Three of the most important themes of biology (and of this text) are (1) energy transfer, (2) transmission of information, and (3) evolution (see Chapter 1). All three themes are tied to the concepts presented in this chapter.

It is quite obvious that *energy* is involved in respiration because cellular respiration is the process of making the energy of food available to the cell. Food molecules are broken down to release the energy locked in their chemical bonds—an example of catabolism. The energy released by catabolic processes can be used by the cell for anabolism: to biosynthesize complex molecules needed by the cell.

Information is critical to the overall operation of the elaborate transformations of metabolism. Imagine what would happen if cells did not possess feedback controls to regulate metabolic pathways. Clearly the communication among molecules implied by the word *information* is necessary for a balanced metabolism within each cell. For example, information helps control the thousands of cellular respiratory reactions that occur every second, pouring forth streams of ATP, water, and carbon dioxide in each one of the billions of cells of the human body.

It is instructive to consider respiration in the context of *evolution*. Glycolysis, for example, must have evolved early in the evolutionary history of cells because it occurs in *all* eukaryotic cells as well as in many prokaryotic cells. The enzymes of glycolysis are found universally in cells of many bacteria, all protists, all fungi, all animals, and all plants. *Information* is also tied to *evolution* in this example because all these organisms have similar genetic information that instructs their cells to make the enzymes of glycolysis.

Figure 7–16 The generalizations about cellular metabolism also apply to the metabolism of a multicellular organism. In an adult organism the rates of synthesis and degradation are essentially equal, whereas in a growing organism the rate of synthesis must be faster than the rate of catabolism. However, even in an adult organism there is a continuous turnover of molecules.   (M. P. Kahl/ VIREO, Academy of Natural Sciences)

SUMMARY

I. Cells use three different types of catabolic pathways to extract free energy from nutrients: aerobic respiration, anaerobic respiration, and fermentation.

II. During aerobic respiration, a fuel molecule such as glucose is oxidized, forming carbon dioxide and water with the release of energy (up to 36 to 38 ATPs per molecule of glucose).

III. Aerobic respiration is a redox process in which hydrogen is transferred from glucose (which becomes oxidized) to oxygen (which becomes reduced).

IV. The chemical reactions of aerobic respiration occur in four stages: glycolysis, formation of acetyl CoA, the citric acid cycle, and the electron transport system/chemiosmosis.

  A. During glycolysis a molecule of glucose is degraded, forming two molecules of pyruvate.
    1. Two ATP molecules (net) are produced during glycolysis.
    2. Four hydrogen atoms are removed from the fuel molecule (as two NADH).

  B. The two pyruvate molecules each lose a molecule of carbon dioxide, and the remaining acetyl groups combine with coenzyme A, producing acetyl CoA. One NADH is formed as each pyruvate is converted to acetyl CoA.

  C. Each acetyl CoA enters the citric acid cycle by combining with a four-carbon compound, oxaloacetate, to form citrate, a six-carbon compound.
    1. With two turns of the citric acid cycle, the two acetyl CoAs representing the original glucose molecule are completely degraded.
    2. Two carbon dioxides are released and hydrogens are transferred to three NAD^+ and one FAD with each turn of the cycle; only one ATP is produced directly by substrate-level phosphorylation per turn.

  D. Hydrogen atoms (or their electrons) removed from fuel molecules are transferred from one electron acceptor to another down a chain of acceptor molecules that make up the electron transport system.
    1. The final acceptor in the chain is molecular oxygen, which combines with the hydrogen to form water.
    2. According to the chemiosmotic theory, energy liberated in the electron transport chain is used to establish a proton gradient across the inner mitochondrial membrane.
    3. The flow of protons back through the membrane from the intermembrane space to the mitochondrial matrix (by way of the enzyme ATP synthetase) releases energy, which is used to synthesize ATP.

V. Organic nutrients other than glucose are converted into appropriate compounds and fed into the glycolytic or citric acid pathways.

  A. Amino acids are deaminated and the carbon skeleton converted to a metabolic intermediate such as pyruvate.

  B. Both the glycerol and fatty acid components of lipids are oxidized as fuel. Fatty acids are converted to acetyl coenzyme A molecules by the process of β-oxidation.

VI. In anaerobic respiration, fuel molecules are broken down in the absence of oxygen; the final hydrogen acceptor is nitrate or sulfate.

VII. Fermentation is an anaerobic process in which the final acceptor of electrons from NADH is an organic compound derived from the initial nutrient. There is a net gain of only two ATPs per glucose molecule, compared with about 36 to 38 ATPs produced per glucose molecule by aerobic respiration.

  A. Yeast cells carry on alcohol fermentation, in which ethyl alcohol and carbon dioxide are the final products.

  B. Certain fungi, certain bacteria, and certain animal cells (in the absence of sufficient oxygen) carry on lactate fermentation, in which hydrogen atoms are added to pyruvate, forming lactate.

VIII. The cells of living things exist in a dynamic state and are continuously building up and breaking down the many different cell constituents.

  A. Each cell usually synthesizes its own complex macromolecules, and each step in the process is catalyzed by a separate enzyme.

  B. Biosynthetic reactions are strongly endergonic and require ATP to drive them.

Summary Reactions for Aerobic Respiration

Summary reaction for the complete oxidation of glucose:

$$C_6H_{12}O_6 + 6\ O_2 + 6\ H_2O \longrightarrow 6\ CO_2 + 12\ H_2O + Energy$$

Summary reaction for glycolysis:

$$C_6H_{12}O_6 + 2\ ATP + 2\ ADP + 2\ P_i + 2\ NAD^+ \longrightarrow$$
$$2\ pyruvate + 4\ ATP + 2\ NADH + 2\ H_2O$$

Summary reaction for the conversion of pyruvate to acetyl CoA:

$$2\ pyruvate + 2\ coenzyme\ A + 2\ NAD^+ \longrightarrow$$
$$2\ acetyl\ CoA + 2\ CO_2 + 2\ NADH$$

Summary reaction for the citric acid cycle:

$$2\ acetyl\ CoA + 6\ NAD^+ + 2\ FAD + 2\ ADP + 2\ P_i + 2\ H_2O$$
$$\longrightarrow 4\ CO_2 + 6\ NADH + 2\ FADH_2 + 2\ ATP + 2\ CoA$$

Summary reactions for the processing of the hydrogens of NADH and $FADH_2$ in the electron transport system:

$$NADH + H^+ + 3\ ADP + 3\ P_i + 1/2\ O_2 \longrightarrow$$
$$NAD^+ + 3\ ATP + H_2O$$

$$FADH_2 + 2\ ADP + 2\ P_i + 1/2\ O_2 \longrightarrow$$
$$FAD + 2\ ATP + H_2O$$

POST-TEST

1. The process of splitting larger molecules into smaller ones is an aspect of metabolism called _____.
2. The synthetic aspect of metabolism is referred to as _____.
3. A chemical process during which a substance gains electrons is called _____.
4. The pathway through which glucose is degraded to pyruvate is referred to as _____.
5. The reactions of glycolysis take place within the _____.
6. Before pyruvate enters the citric acid cycle, it is decarboxylated, oxidized, and combined with coenzyme A, forming carbon dioxide and _____ _____.
7. In the first step of the citric acid cycle, acetyl CoA reacts with oxaloacetate to form _____.
8. During the citric acid cycle, the acetyl of acetyl CoA is oxidized, resulting in the production of two molecules of _____ _____.
9. The citric acid cycle must turn _____ times to process the acetyl CoAs formed from one molecule of glucose.
10. Dehydrogenase enzymes remove hydrogens from fuel molecules and transfer them to primary acceptors such as _____ and _____.
11. The final hydrogen acceptor in the electron transport chain is _____.
12. The _____ model proposes that electron transport and ATP synthesis are coupled by a proton gradient across the inner mitochondrial membrane.
13. When protons move across a membrane and down an energy gradient in chemiosmosis, energy is released and used to synthesize _____.
14. One important part of the feedback inhibition of aerobic respiration is the inhibitory effect of ATP on phosphofructokinase, an enzyme required in _____.
15. A net profit of only _____ ATPs can be produced anaerobically from the fermentation of one molecule of glucose, compared with a maximum of _____ ATPs produced in aerobic respiration.
16. Yeasts and bacteria that can shift to anaerobic respiration or fermentation when oxygen is in short supply are called _____ _____.
17. The anaerobic process by which alcohol or lactate is produced as a product of glycolysis is referred to as _____.
18. When deprived of oxygen, yeast cells obtain energy by fermentation, producing carbon dioxide and _____ _____.
19. During strenuous muscle activity, the pyruvate in muscle cells may accept hydrogen to become _____.
20. Anaerobic catabolism is inefficient because the fuel molecule is only partially _____.

REVIEW QUESTIONS

1. What is the specific role of oxygen in the cell? What happens when cells that can only respire aerobically are deprived of oxygen?
2. Mitochondria are often referred to as the "power plants" of the cell. Justify this with a specific explanation.
3. What is the evolutionary significance of glycolysis?
4. Refer to Figure 7–8, the diagram of the steps in the citric acid cycle. Look at each reaction and, without reading the description, determine what type of reaction it is (dehydrogenation, decarboxylation, or make-ready).
5. Draw a mitochondrion and indicate the locations of the following:
   a. enzymes of the citric acid cycle
   b. the electron transport system
   c. the proton gradient that drives ATP production
6. How does the chemiosmotic model relate to aerobic respiration? How does a proton gradient contribute to ATP synthesis?
7. Explain the roles of the following in aerobic respiration:
   a. NAD^+
   b. cytochromes
8. Calculate how much energy (as ATPs) is made available to the cell from a single glucose molecule by the operation of glycolysis, the formation of acetyl CoA, the citric acid cycle, and the electron transport system.
9. Trace the fate of hydrogens removed from glucose during glycolysis when oxygen is present in muscle cells. Trace the fate of hydrogens removed from glucose when the amount of oxygen available is insufficient to support aerobic respiration.
10. Why is it advantageous that synthetic reactions are generally not the reverse of reactions in which molecules are catabolized?

RECOMMENDED READINGS

Alberts, B., D. Bray, J. Lewis, M. Raff, K. Roberts, and J. D. Watson. *Molecular Biology of the Cell*, 2nd ed. Garland Publishing, New York, 1989. An in-depth treatment of energy conversion in cells.

Stryer, L. *Biochemistry*, 3rd ed. W. H. Freeman, San Francisco, 1988. A well-illustrated, readable text that covers the concepts of cellular energetics from the ground up.

Photosynthesis: Capturing Energy

O U T L I N E

Chloroplasts
Converting light energy into chemical energy
Light-dependent reactions
Light-independent reactions

Almost all life in the biosphere has for billions of years run on solar energy. Plants, algae, and certain bacteria are producers that are uniquely capable of absorbing and converting solar energy into stored chemical energy by the process of **photosynthesis** (Figure 8–1). The chemicals produced by photosynthesis are carbohydrates formed from the simple raw materials, water and carbon dioxide; oxygen is given off in the process. Each year these remarkable organisms produce more than 200 billion tons of food. The chemical energy that is stored in this food fuels the metabolic reactions that sustain life.

Producers are **autotrophs** (from the Greek *auto,* "self," and *trophos,* "nourishing"), organisms that can make their food from inorganic raw materials and so are not dependent on other organisms for nourishment. A few bacteria are **chemosynthetic autotrophs,** producers that make

Branches of trees grow high to expose
leaves to the sun's energy.
(J. P. Nacivet/Photo Researchers, Inc.)

their organic compounds by oxidizing simple inorganic substances such as sulfur or ammonia. Chemosynthetic autotrophs do not require light as an energy source for these reactions. The vast majority of producers, however, are **photosynthetic autotrophs,** organisms that use light as their energy source for manufacturing organic compounds.

Consumers and decomposers are **heterotrophs** (from the Greek *heter,* "other," and *trophos,* "nourishing"), organisms that cannot make their own food and so must depend on other organisms for their nourishment. These organisms obtain their energy by consuming producers or organisms that have eaten producers; thus, heterotrophs are ultimately dependent on the energy-transforming abilities of photosynthetic organisms. Photosynthesis sustains not only the plants and other producers but also almost all the animals and other organisms in the biosphere.

L E A R N I N G   O B J E C T I V E S

After you have studied this chapter you should be able to

1. Diagram the internal structure of a chloroplast, and explain how this structure facilitates the process of photosynthesis.
2. Write a summary reaction for photosynthesis showing the origin and fate of each substance involved.
3. Distinguish between the light-dependent and light-independent reactions of photosynthesis, and summarize the events that occur in each phase.
4. Describe the physical properties of light, and explain how the absorption of photons can activate a pigment such as chlorophyll.

5. Contrast cyclic and noncyclic photophosphorylation.
6. Summarize the chemical reactions involved in the conversion of CO_2 to glucose in the Calvin cycle, and indicate how many molecules of ATP and NADPH are required for the process.
7. Explain how a proton gradient is established across the thylakoid membrane and how this gradient functions in ATP synthesis.
8. Discuss how the C_4 pathway increases the effectiveness of the Calvin cycle in certain types of plants.

IN EUKARYOTES, PHOTOSYNTHESIS TAKES PLACE IN CHLOROPLASTS

When a section of leaf tissue is examined under the microscope, we can see that the green pigment, **chloro-phyll,** is not uniformly distributed in the cell but is confined to small organelles called **chloroplasts.** In plants chloroplasts are located mainly in the cells of the **meso-phyll,** a tissue inside the leaf. Each mesophyll cell has 20 to 100 chloroplasts.

(a)

(b)

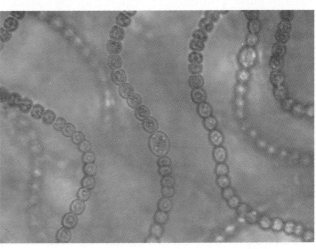

(c)   50 μm

Figure 8–1 Photosynthetic organisms include (*a*) plants (corn, *Zea mays*), (*b*) algae (the kelp *Macrocystis pyrifera*), and (*c*) cyanobacteria(*Nostoc* sp.). Plants are primarily terrestrial, whereas algae are primarily aquatic. Algae may be either microscopic or large seaweeds. Cyanobacteria are prokaryotic organisms that photosynthesize like plants and algae. In addition, some photosynthetic bacteria trap the light's energy in a different way than the organisms shown.   (*a*, Dennis Drenner; *b*, Visuals Unlimited/ D. Gotshall; *c*, Runk/Schoenberger from Grant Heilman)

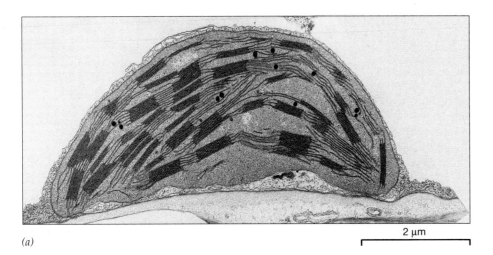

(a)

2 μm

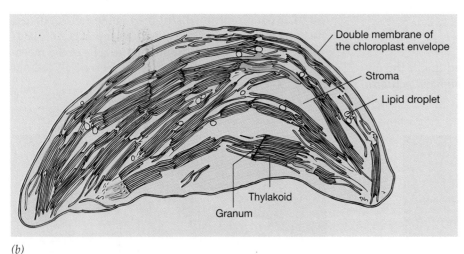

(b)

Double membrane of
the chloroplast envelope

Stroma

Lipid droplet

Thylakoid

Granum

Figure 8–2 Structure of the
chloroplast. (*a*) Electron micrograph of
a chloroplast from a leaf cell of corn
(*Zea mays*). Note the grana, which are
stacks of thylakoids. The pigments
necessary for the light-capturing
reactions of photosynthesis are
associated with thylakoid membranes,
whereas the enzymes necessary for the
manufacture of carbohydrate are found
in the stroma. (*b*) Artist's rendition of
electron micrograph. (*a*, E. H. Newcomb
and W. P. Wergin, University of Wisconsin/
Biological Photo Service)

Electron microscopy reveals that the chloroplast, like the mitochondrion, is bounded by an outer and an inner membrane (Figure 8–2). The inner membrane encloses a fluid-filled region called the **stroma,** which contains most of the enzymes required for the reactions of photosynthesis. The inner chloroplast membrane also encloses a third system of membranes, which forms an interconnected set of flat, disclike sacs called **thylakoids.** In some regions, thylakoid sacs are arranged in stacks referred to as **grana.** Each granum looks something like a stack of coins, with each "coin" being a thylakoid (Figure 8–3). Some thylakoid membranes extend from one granum to another. Chlorophyll and other photosynthetic pigments are associated with the thylakoid membranes. These membranes, like the inner mitochondrial membrane (see Chapter 7), are involved in ATP synthesis.

Photosynthetic prokaryotes have no chloroplasts, but thylakoids often occur as extensions of the plasma membrane and are arranged around the periphery of the prokaryotic cell.

IN PHOTOSYNTHESIS, PLANTS CONVERT LIGHT ENERGY INTO THE CHEMICAL ENERGY OF SUGAR MOLECULES

During photosynthesis, chlorophyll traps energy from sunlight and uses it to make the high-energy compounds, ATP and NADPH. The energy contained in ATP and NADPH is then used in the reactions that form energy-rich carbohydrates. The principal raw materials for photosynthesis are water and carbon dioxide. Using the energy that chlorophyll molecules trap from sunlight, water is split, its oxygen liberated, and its hydrogen combined with carbon dioxide to produce carbohydrate molecules. The reactions of photosynthesis are summarized as follows:

$$6\,CO_2 + 12\,H_2O \xrightarrow[\text{chlorophyll}]{\text{Light,}} C_6H_{12}O_6 + 6\,O_2 + 6\,H_2O$$

Carbon   Water   Glucose   Oxygen   Water
dioxide

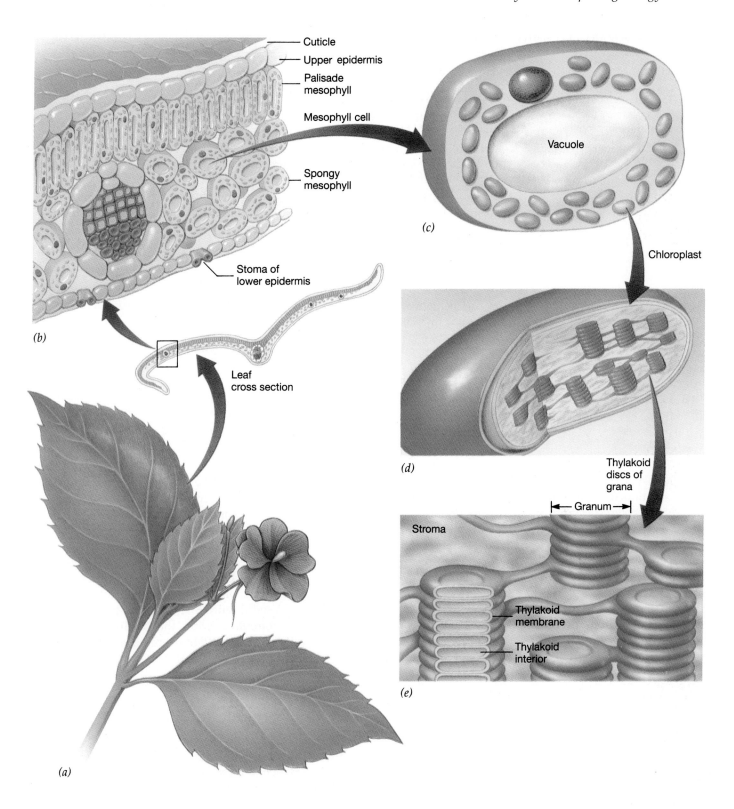

Cuticle
Upper epidermis
Palisade mesophyll
Mesophyll cell
Spongy mesophyll
Stoma of lower epidermis
Vacuole
(c)
(b)
Leaf cross section
Chloroplast
(d)
Thylakoid discs of grana
Granum
Stroma
Thylakoid membrane
Thylakoid interior
(e)
(a)

Figure 8–3 Photosynthesis from different perspectives. (*a*) Photosynthesis occurs in the green tissues of the plant. (*b*) A cross section of a leaf reveals a structure marvelously adapted for photosynthesis. The middle portion of the leaf, the mesophyll, is the photosynthetic tissue. Carbon dioxide enters the leaf through tiny pores called stomata, and water is carried to the mesophyll in veins. (*c*) A typical mesophyll cell contains numerous chloroplasts.

(*d*) Each chloroplast is surrounded by a double membrane. Within the chloroplast, membranous thylakoids are stacked to form grana. The fluid-filled matrix surrounding the grana is the stroma. (*e*) A close-up of the interior of the chloroplast. Chlorophyll is located in the thylakoid membranes. The thylakoids are involved in the light-dependent reactions of photosynthesis, whereas the light-independent reactions of photosynthesis take place in the stroma.

Table 8-1   SUMMARY OF PHOTOSYNTHESIS

Reaction Series	Summary of Process	Needed Materials	End Products
A. Light-dependent reactions (take place in thylakoid membranes)	Energy from sunlight used to split water, manufacture ATP, and reduce $NADP^+$		
1. Photochemical reactions	Chlorophyll energized; reaction center gives up energized electron to electron acceptor	Light energy; pigments (chlorophyll)	Electrons
2. Electron transport	Electrons are transported along chain of electron acceptors in thylakoid membranes; electrons reduce $NADP^+$; splitting of water provides some of H^+ that accumulates inside thylakoid space	Electrons, $NADP^+$, H_2O, electron acceptors	NADPH, O_2
3. Chemiosmosis	H^+ are permitted to move across the thylakoid membrane down a proton gradient; they cross the membrane through special channels; energy released is used to produce ATP	Proton gradient, $ADP + P_i$	ATP
B. Light-independent reactions (take place in stroma)	Carbon fixation: carbon dioxide is used to make sugar	Ribulose bisphosphate, CO_2, ATP, NADPH, necessary enzymes	Carbohydrates, $ADP + P_i$, $NADP^+$

Photosynthesis, like cellular respiration, is a reduction-oxidation (redox) process (see Chapter 7). Recall that during cell respiration, organic compounds are oxidized. Hydrogens (or their electrons) are split off from the fuel molecule and transferred along a series of acceptor molecules to molecular oxygen, forming water. Electrons lose energy as they are passed through the chain of acceptor molecules, and that energy is used by the mitochondrion to make ATP. In photosynthesis, the direction of electron flow is reversed from that of respiration. Water is split, and the electrons of hydrogen are transferred to chlorophyll and then through a series of electron acceptors. During this transfer, light energy raises the energy level of the electrons. Ultimately, some of the energy is used to reduce carbon dioxide, forming glucose.

The summary equation for photosynthesis describes what happens but not how it happens. The "how" is much more complex and involves many steps. The reactions of photosynthesis are divided into two parts, the light-dependent and the light-independent reactions (Table 8–1).

In Light-Dependent Reactions, Light Energy Is Used To Make the High-Energy Compounds, ATP and NADPH

The light-dependent reactions occur only in the presence of light. During this phase of photosynthesis, sev-eral important events take place. Chlorophyll absorbs light energy, which is immediately converted to electrical energy as electrons flow from the chlorophyll molecule. Some of this energy is used to make ATP by chemiosmosis; during this process, electrical energy is transformed to chemical energy. Some of the light energy trapped by the chlorophyll is used to split water, a process known as **photolysis.** Oxygen (O_2) from the water is released (Figure 8–4), and the hydrogen from the water combines with the hydrogen acceptor $NADP^+$, forming NADPH.[1] Here again, electrical energy is converted to chemical energy.

Carbohydrates Are Produced during the Light-Independent Reactions

Although the light-independent reactions do not require light directly, they do depend on the products of the light-dependent reactions (Figure 8–5). In the light-independent reactions, the energy of the NADPH and ATP produced during the light-dependent phase of photosynthesis is used to manufacture carbohydrate molecules. The raw materials from which carbohydrates are made are carbon dioxide from the air and

---

[1] Although the correct way to write the reduced form of $NADP^+$ is NADPH + H^+, for simplicity's sake, we present the reduced form as NADPH.

Figure 8–4 On sunny days the oxygen released by aquatic plants may sometimes be visible as bubbles in the water. This plant (*Elodea*) is actively carrying on photosynthesis, as evidenced by the oxygen bubbles. (E. R. Degginger)

hydrogen from NADPH (originally split off from water).

During the light-independent reactions, chemical energy from the ATP and NADPH produced during the light-dependent phase is transferred to the chemical bonds of carbohydrate molecules. This form of energy packaging is more suitable for long-term storage than molecules like ATP and NADPH. Some of the carbohydrate molecules produced during the light-independent phase are used later as fuel molecules. Others are used as starting materials in the manufacture of various types of organic compounds needed by plant cells; for example, with the addition of such minerals as nitrates and sulfur from the soil, plant cells can convert carbohydrates into amino acids, the building blocks of proteins.

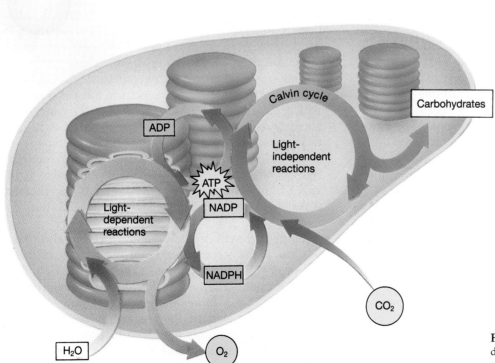

Figure 8–5 Summary of the light-dependent and light-independent reactions of photosynthesis.

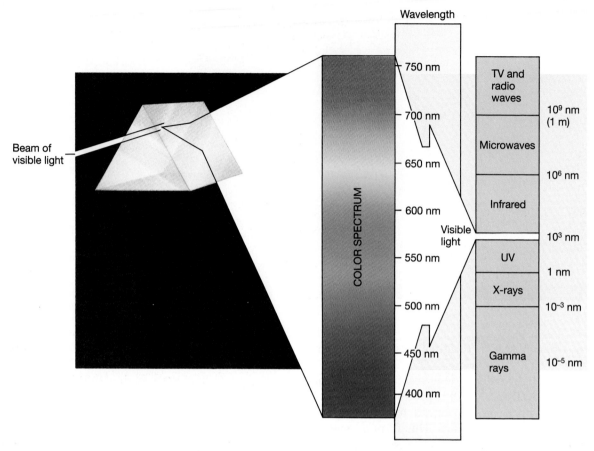

Figure 8–6 The electromagnetic spectrum. Electromagnetic waves of various lengths radiate through space. Visible light is only a portion of the electromagnetic spectrum and consists of a mixture of wavelengths (from approximately 380 to 760 nm). A prism sorts light into its component colors by bending light of different wavelengths by different degrees. During photosynthesis, energy from visible light is used to synthesize organic compounds.

THE LIGHT-DEPENDENT REACTIONS CAPTURE ENERGY

In the light-dependent reactions, the radiant energy from sunlight is used to make ATP and to reduce the electron acceptor molecule $NADP^+$, forming NADPH. The light energy captured by photosynthesis is temporarily stored within these two compounds. The light-dependent reactions are summarized as follows:

$$12\,H_2O + 12\,NADP^+ + 18\,ADP + 18\,P_i \xrightarrow{\text{Light,} \atop \text{chlorophyll}} 6\,O_2 + 12\,NADPH + 18\,ATP$$

Light Exhibits Properties of Both Waves and Particles

Because life on our planet depends on light, it is important to understand the nature of light and how it permits photosynthesis to occur. Light is a very small portion of a vast, continuous spectrum of radiation called the electromagnetic spectrum (Figure 8–6). All radiations in this spectrum travel in waves. A **wavelength** is the distance from one wave peak to the next. At one end of the spectrum are gamma rays, which have very short wavelengths (measured in nanometers). At the other end of the electromagnetic spectrum are radio waves, which have wavelengths so long that they are measured in kilometers. The different colors of light correspond to different regions of the visible spectrum and are identified by their wavelengths, which run from 380 to 760 nm. Within the spectrum of visible light, violet light (approximately 400 nm) has the shortest wavelength and red light (approximately 750 nm) the longest.

Light behaves not only like a wave but also like a particle. Light is composed of small particles, or packets, of energy called **photons.** The energy in photons varies for light of different wavelengths: the shorter the wavelength, the more energy per photon, and the longer the wavelength, the less energy per photon. In other words, the energy per photon is inversely proportional to the wavelength of light.

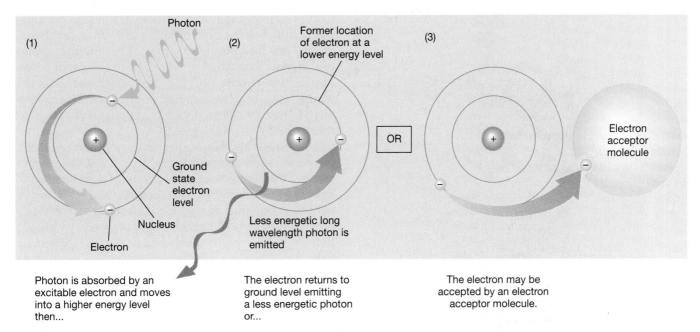

Figure 8–7 Light excites certain types of biological molecules, moving electrons into higher energy levels. When a photon of light energy strikes an atom or a molecule of which the atom is a part (1), the energy of the photon may push the electron to an orbit farther from the nucleus. If the electron "falls" back to the next lower energy level, a less energetic photon is reemitted (2). If the appropriate electron acceptors are available, the electron may leave the atom (3). In photosynthesis a primary electron acceptor captures the energetic electron and passes it along a chain of acceptors.

Why does photosynthesis depend on visible light rather than on some other wavelength of radiation? We can only speculate on the answer. One reason may be that most of the radiation reaching our planet from the sun is within this portion of the electromagnetic spectrum; thus, living organisms may have evolved the ability to use visible light because it was the most abundant form of light available. Another reason may be that only radiation within the visible light portion of the spectrum excites certain types of biological molecules, moving electrons into higher energy levels. Radiation with wavelengths longer than that of visible light does not possess enough energy to excite biological molecules. Radiation with wavelengths shorter than that of visible light is so energetic that it disrupts the bonds of many biological molecules.

Photons interact with atoms in a variety of ways, all of which depend on the electron structure of the atom. Recall that an atom consists of an atomic nucleus surrounded by electrons located in one or more energy levels. The lowest energy state an atom possesses is called the **ground state,** but energy can be added to an electron so that it attains a higher energy level. When an electron is raised to a higher energy level than its ground state, the atom is said to be *excited,* or energized.

When a molecule absorbs a photon of light energy, one of its electrons is raised to a higher energy state. One of two things may then happen, depending on the atom and its surroundings (Figure 8–7). The electron may soon return to its ground state and the energy is dissipated as heat or as light of a longer wavelength than the wavelength of the absorbed light; this emission of light is called **fluorescence.** Alternatively, the excited electron may leave the atom and be accepted by an electron acceptor molecule; this is what occurs in photosynthesis.

Chlorophyll Is a Pigment That Absorbs Light

Pigments are substances that absorb visible light; different pigments absorb light of different wavelengths. **Chlorophyll,** the main pigment of photosynthesis, absorbs light primarily in the blue and red regions of the visible spectrum. Green light is not appreciably absorbed by chlorophyll; instead, it is reflected. Plants usually appear green because their leaves reflect most of the green light that strikes them.

The chlorophyll molecule is made of atoms of carbon and nitrogen joined in a complex porphyrin ring that is strikingly similar to the heme portion of the red pigment hemoglobin in red blood cells and to cytochromes present in all cells (Figure 8–8). However, chlorophyll contains an atom of magnesium in the center of the ring instead of an atom of iron. The chlorophyll molecule has a long hydrophobic tail, which holds it in the thylakoid membrane. This tail is com-

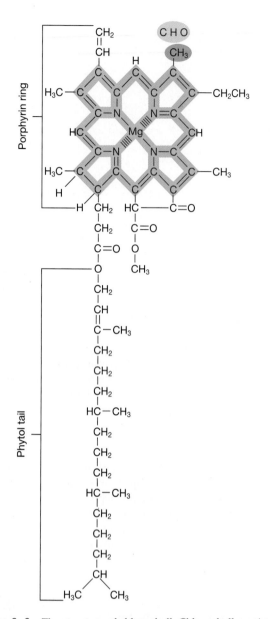

Figure 8–8   The structure of chlorophyll. Chlorophyll consists of a porphyrin ring and a phytol tail. The magnesium atom in the center of the ring is the part of the molecule that is excited by light. The hydrophobic phytol tail is embedded in the thylakoid membrane. On the top right side of the diagram, the methyl group (—CH₃) distinguishes chlorophyll *a* from chlorophyll *b*, which has an aldehyde group (—CHO) in this position.

posed of phytol, a long-chain alcohol containing 20 carbon atoms. Because of their shape, many chlorophyll molecules can be grouped together like a stack of saucers. Each thylakoid membrane is filled with precisely oriented chlorophyll molecules, an arrangement that permits the generation and utilization of the minute electrical currents that power photosynthesis.

There are several kinds of chlorophyll. The most important is **chlorophyll *a***, the pigment that initiates the light-dependent reactions. **Chlorophyll *b*** is an ac-

cessory pigment that also participates in photosynthesis. It differs from chlorophyll *a* only in a functional group on the porphyrin ring: The methyl group (—CH₃) in chlorophyll *a* is replaced in chlorophyll *b* by an aldehyde group (—CHO). This difference shifts the wavelengths of light absorbed and reflected by chlorophyll *b*, so that chlorophyll *b* is yellow-green, whereas chlorophyll *a* is bright green.

Plant cells also have other accessory photosynthetic pigments, such as **carotenoids,** which are yellow and orange. Carotenoids absorb different wavelengths of light than chlorophyll and so broaden the spectrum of light that provides energy for photosynthesis. Chlorophyll may be excited either by light or by energy passed to it from other pigments that have become excited by light. Thus, when a carotenoid molecule is excited, its energy can be transferred to chlorophyll *a*.

Absorption Spectra and Action Spectra Indicate That Chlorophyll Is the Main Light-Gathering Pigment of Photosynthesis

An instrument called a spectrophotometer is used to measure the relative abilities of different pigments to absorb different wavelengths of light. An **absorption spectrum** of a pigment is a graph of its absorption of different wavelengths of light. However, absorption spectra of photosynthetic pigments do not tell us what wavelengths are most effective in photosynthesis.

The relative effectiveness of different wavelengths of light in photosynthesis is given by an **action spectrum** of photosynthesis (Figure 8–9), determined in one of the classic experiments in biology. In 1883 the German biologist T. W. Engelmann took advantage of the shape of the chloroplast in *Spirogyra*, a green alga that occurs as slimy strings in freshwater habitats, especially slow-moving or still waters (Figure 8–10*a*). The individual cells of *Spirogyra* are exquisitely beautiful, each containing a long, spiral, emerald-green chloroplast embedded in cytoplasm. Engelmann exposed these cells to a color spectrum produced by a prism. He reasoned that photosynthesis would take place most rapidly in the areas where the chloroplast was illuminated by the colors most readily absorbed by chlorophyll—if chlorophyll were indeed responsible for photosynthesis.

Yet how could photosynthesis be measured in those technologically unsophisticated days? Engelmann knew that photosynthesis produces oxygen, and that certain motile bacteria are attracted to areas of high oxygen concentration (Figure 8–10*b*). He determined the action spectrum of photosynthesis by observing that the bacteria swam toward the portions of *Spirogyra* located in the red and blue regions of the spectrum. The fact that the bacteria did not move toward red and blue areas when *Spirogyra* was absent showed that bacteria

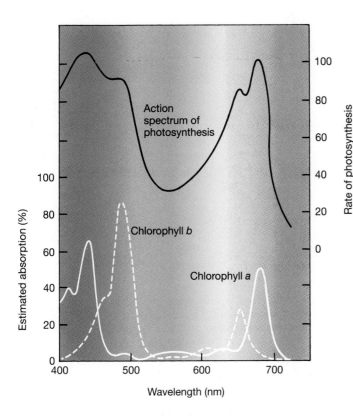

Figure 8–9   Absorption spectra for chlorophylls *a* and *b,* and action spectrum for photosynthesis. The solid white curve on the bottom illustrates the absorption spectrum for chlorophyll *a.* The dashed white curve illustrates the absorption spectrum of chlorophyll *b.* Chlorophyll absorbs light mainly in the blue and red regions of the spectrum. The black curve at the top (action spectrum of photosynthesis) illustrates the effectiveness of various wavelengths of light in powering photosynthesis. Note how closely the combined absorption spectra of chlorophylls *a* and *b* resemble the action spectrum of photosynthesis.

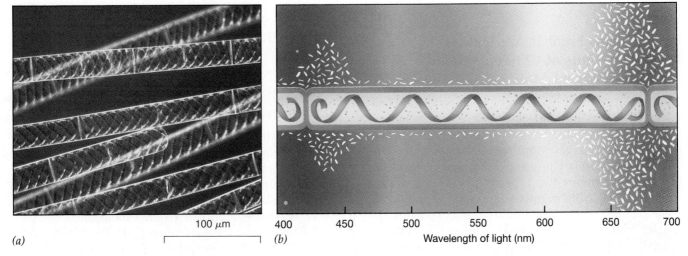

(a)   *(b)*

Figure 8–10   Engelmann's experiment to demonstrate the wavelengths of light most effective for photosynthesis. (*a*) Filaments of *Spirogyra,* the green alga that Engelmann used in his experiment. (*b*) Engelmann illuminated a filament of *Spirogyra* with light that had been passed through a prism, producing a spectrum. In this way, different parts of the filament were exposed to different wavelengths of light. He used aerobic bacteria that

moved toward the portions of the algal filament emitting the most oxygen. Watching through a microscope, Engelmann observed that the bacteria aggregated most densely along the cells in the blue and red portions of the spectrum. This indicated that blue and red light works most effectively for photosynthesis.   (*a,* Visuals Unlimited/T. E. Adams)

are not merely attracted to any region where red or blue light is being absorbed. Because the action spectrum of photosynthesis closely matched the absorption spectrum of chlorophyll, Engelmann concluded that chloro-

phyll in the chloroplasts (and not another compound in another organelle) is responsible for photosynthesis. Numerous more sophisticated studies have since confirmed Engelmann's conclusions.

The action spectrum of photosynthesis is somewhat different from the absorption spectrum of chlorophyll, particularly in such strongly colored producers as red algae. The explanation is twofold. First, red algal chloroplasts contain accessory photosynthetic pigments in such large amounts that they mask the color of the chlorophyll and absorb the green light that chlorophyll itself would reflect. Second, and more to the point, the accessory pigments transfer the energy of excitation produced by green light to chlorophyll molecules. The presence of such accessory pigments in algae lets them use light in the green area of the spectrum more efficiently than could, for example, a chrysanthemum plant. This is an important adaptation, for it permits algae to live in deep aquatic habitats, where the red light most effective in photosynthesis has been filtered out by passage through the water.

Terrestrial plants also contain accessory photosynthetic pigments. The presence of accessory photosynthetic pigments can be demonstrated by chemical analysis of almost any leaf, although it is obvious in most trees when their leaves change color in the fall. Toward the end of the growing season, chlorophyll is broken down (and its magnesium is stored in the permanent tissues of the tree), leaving accessory pigments in the leaves.

Photosystems I and II Are Light-Harvesting Units of Chlorophyll and Accessory Pigment Molecules

The light-dependent reactions of photosynthesis begin when chlorophyll *a* and accessory pigments absorb light. According to the currently accepted model, chlorophyll molecules, accessory pigments, and associated electron acceptors are organized into units called **photosystems.** There are two types of photosystems, each containing 200 to 300 pigment molecules. In addition to these pigment molecules, Photosystem I contains one special molecule of chlorophyll *a*, known as **P700** because its optimal absorption peak is at 700 nm. Photosystem II utilizes another special molecule of chlorophyll *a*, **P680**, which has its optimal absorption peak at 680 nm.

All pigment molecules of a photosystem apparently serve as antennae to gather radiant energy (Figure 8–11). When they absorb light energy, it is passed from one pigment molecule to another until it reaches the P700 or P680 pigment molecule. These chlorophyll *a* molecules are located in the **reaction center** of the photosystem. Only P700 or P680 at the reaction center is able to give up its energized electron to a primary electron acceptor, which is reduced in the process.

During light-dependent reactions, there are two pathways for electron flow: noncyclic photophosphory-

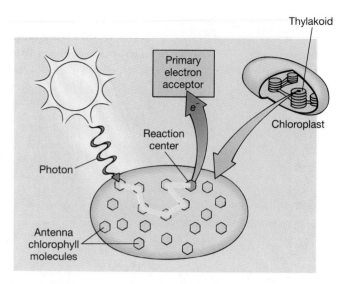

Figure 8–11 How a photosystem traps light energy. The many chlorophyll molecules in the photosystem are excited by photons and transfer their excitation energy to the specially positioned chlorophyll molecule at the reaction center.

lation and cyclic photophosphorylation. The term **photophosphorylation** is used because electrons are energized by photons of light and then contribute their energy to the phosphorylation of ADP, thereby synthesizing ATP.

Noncyclic Photophosphorylation Produces ATP and NADPH

In **noncyclic photophosphorylation,** which is the more common light-dependent reaction, both photosystems are used, and there is a one-way flow of electrons, ultimately from water to $NADP^+$. For every two electrons that enter this pathway, there is an energy yield of two ATP molecules and one NADPH molecule.

This pathway begins when P700 (Photosystem I) is energized by the absorption of light and two electrons are transferred to a primary acceptor and then to ferredoxin. Then ferredoxin transfers the electrons to the electron acceptor $NADP^+$ (Figure 8–12). When $NADP^+$ is in an oxidized condition, it is positively charged. When it accepts electrons, the electrons unite with protons to form hydrogen, so the reduced form of $NADP^+$ is NADPH. The reduction of $NADP^+$ requires two electrons.

When electrons are transferred to $NADP^+$, forming NADPH, Photosystem I becomes positively charged. It could never emit more electrons, regardless of whether it became excited, unless two electrons were somehow first restored to it; those needed electrons are donated by Photosystem II.

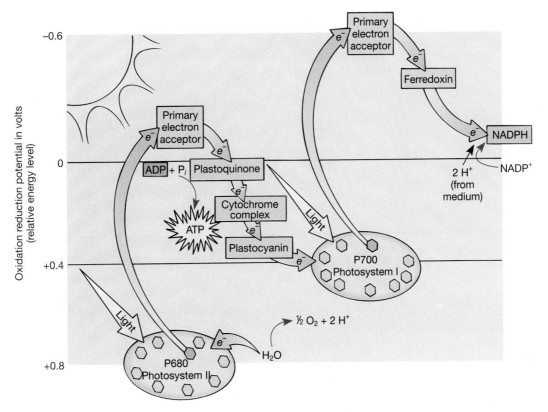

Figure 8–12 · Noncyclic photophosphorylation. When Photosystem II is activated by absorbing photons, electrons are passed along an electron acceptor chain and are eventually donated to Photosystem I and finally to NADP⁺. Photosystem II is responsible for the splitting of water and the production of atmospheric oxygen. This pathway is sometimes referred to as the *Z scheme* because of its zigzag route.

Like Photosystem I, Photosystem II is activated by a photon of light energy and gives up two electrons to a primary electron acceptor (Figure 8–12). The electrons pass from one acceptor to another through a chain of easily oxidized and reduced acceptor molecules. As electrons are transferred along this chain of electron acceptors, they become less and less energized. Some of the energy released is used to establish a proton gradient, which leads to the synthesis of ATP by chemiosmosis. Electrons emitted from Photosystem II are eventually donated to Photosystem I.

At this point, ATP has been synthesized and electrons have been transferred to NADP⁺ (forming NADPH) and returned to P700. However, P680, the chlorophyll *a* in the reaction center of Photosystem II, is now short of electrons. The missing electrons are replaced by electrons from water. When P680 absorbs light energy, it becomes positively charged and exerts a strong pull on the electrons in water molecules. Water is split by a process called **photolysis** into its components: electrons, protons (H^+), and oxygen. The electrons are then donated to P680 (and ultimately transferred to NADP⁺), the protons are ultimately transferred to NADP⁺, and the oxygen is released into the atmosphere.

Cyclic Photophosphorylation Produces ATP

Cyclic photophosphorylation is the simplest light-dependent reaction. Only Photosystem I is involved, and the pathway is cyclic because excited electrons that originate from P700 at the reaction center eventually return to P700 (Figure 8–13). Energized electrons are transferred along an electron transport chain within the thylakoid membrane. A series of redox reactions takes place, as in the mitochondrial electron transport system. As they are passed from one acceptor to another, the electrons lose energy, some of which is used to pump protons across the thylakoid membrane. An ATP synthetase enzyme in the thylakoid membrane uses the energy of the proton gradient to manufacture ATP. The cycle is completed when the spent electrons are returned to P700 (the electrons in P700 are now back in the ground state).

For every two electrons that enter cyclic photophosphorylation, one ATP molecule is synthesized by chemiosmosis. NADPH is not produced and oxygen is not generated. By itself, cyclic photophosphorylation could not serve as the basis of photosynthesis because, as we explain below, NADPH is required for CO_2 to be reduced to carbohydrate.

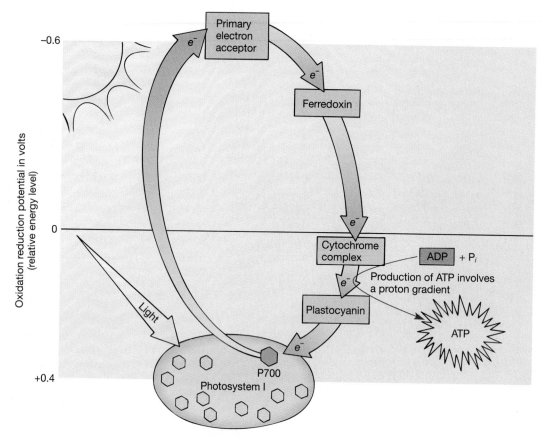

Figure 8–13 Cyclic photophosphorylation. When pigment molecules in Photosystem I absorb light, energy is transferred to P700, a special form of chlorophyll *a*. P700 gives up its energized electrons to a primary electron acceptor. Electrons are transferred through a sequence of electron acceptors back to chlorophyll *a* in the reaction center. As electrons are passed along this electron transport chain, energy is released that is used for ATP synthesis. Note that only Photosystem I is involved. Photolysis of water does not occur, so neither oxygen nor NADPH is produced.

Cyclic photophosphorylation occurs in plant cells when there is too little NADP⁺ to accept electrons from ferredoxin. Biologists think that this process was used by ancient bacteria to produce ATP from light energy (see Focus on The Evolution of Photosystems I and II). A reaction pathway analogous to cyclic photophosphorylation in plants is present in modern photosynthetic bacteria.

The Transport of Protons across Thylakoid Membranes Is Coupled with the Production of ATP

Like mitochondria, chloroplasts synthesize ATP by chemiosmosis. The photosystems and electron acceptors of the light-dependent reactions are embedded in the thylakoid membrane. Energy released from electrons traveling through the chain of acceptors is used to pump protons from the stroma across the thylakoid membrane into the thylakoid space. These protons accumulate within the thylakoids. Because protons are actually hydrogen ions, the accumulation of protons causes the pH of the thylakoid interior to fall. In fact, the pH approaches 4 in bright light. This produces a pH difference of about 3.5 pH units across the thylakoid membrane, which is more than a 1000-fold difference in hydrogen ion concentration.

In accordance with the general principles of diffusion, the highly concentrated hydrogen ions inside the thylakoid would be expected to diffuse out. However, they are prevented from doing so because the thylakoid membrane is impermeable to H^+ except at certain points bridged by an ATP synthetase enzyme called the **CF_0-CF_1 complex.** This complex extends across the thylakoid membrane, projecting from the membrane surface both inside and outside and forming channels through which protons can leak out of the thylakoid (Figure 8–14).

The concentrated proton solution inside the thylakoid represents a highly ordered (low-entropy) state. If the protons could move out of the thylakoid into the surrounding space, the resulting random and more or less even distribution of protons within the chloroplast

FOCUS ON

The Evolution of Photosystems I and II

Photosynthesis is an extremely ancient biological process that has apparently changed a great deal since it first appeared more than 3 billion years ago. The utilization of light energy to manufacture organic molecules first evolved in ancient bacteria that were similar to the green sulfur bacteria that exist today.

Initially there was only one photosystem, Photosystem I, which used a green pigment called **bacteriochlorophyll** to gather light energy. Photosystem I operated alone, generating ATP from light energy by cyclic photophosphorylation. However, cyclic photophosphorylation does not provide the reducing power of NADPH,

which is needed to manufacture carbohydrate molecules from CO_2. (Recall that in cyclic photophosphorylation, the electrons from chlorophyll are not passed to $NADP^+$ but are instead returned to chlorophyll.) Ancient photosynthetic bacteria, like some of their modern counterparts, used electron donors such as hydrogen sulfide (H_2S) rather than H_2O to generate the reducing power needed to manufacture carbohydrates in photosynthesis:

$$H_2S \longrightarrow S + 2\,H^+ + 2\,e^-$$

This process is not very efficient, however.

Some 2.8 billion years ago, a new group of bacteria called **cyanobacteria** evolved. Cyanobacteria possessed chlorophyll *a* instead of bacteriochlorophyll and were able to photosynthesize more efficiently because they possessed a more powerful series of light-harvesting reactions. These new reactions, called noncyclic photophosphorylation, involved the combination of a second photosystem, Photosystem II, with the reactions of Photosystem I. Water provided the electrons to generate NADPH, which in turn provided the reducing power to manufacture carbohydrate molecules from CO_2.

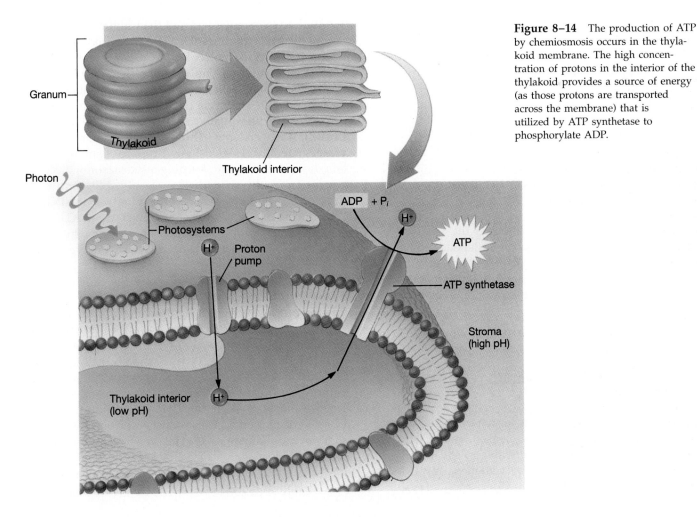

Figure 8–14 The production of ATP by chemiosmosis occurs in the thylakoid membrane. The high concentration of protons in the interior of the thylakoid provides a source of energy (as those protons are transported across the membrane) that is utilized by ATP synthetase to phosphorylate ADP.

Figure 8–15   Calvin's classic experiment that elucidated the steps in carbon fixation of photosynthesis, also known as the Calvin cycle. Calvin and his colleagues grew algae in the green "lollipop." $^{14}CO_2$ was bubbled through the algae, and they were periodically killed by dumping the "lollipop" contents into a beaker of boiling alcohol. By identifying which compounds contained the ^{14}C at different times, Calvin was able to determine the steps of carbon fixation in photosynthesis.   (Melvin Calvin, University of California, Berkeley)

would be a high-entropy state. The second law of thermodynamics identifies this situation as one in which there is a potential for useful work resulting from the change in entropy. What happens is that, as the protons pass through the CF_0-CF_1 complex, energy is released, and ATP synthetase catalyzes ATP synthesis using this energy. Details of exactly how this is done are the subject of current investigation.

THE LIGHT-INDEPENDENT REACTIONS FIX CARBON

The light-independent reactions use the ATP and NADPH manufactured by the light-dependent reactions to reduce carbon dioxide to carbohydrate, a process called **CO$_2$ fixation.** The light-independent reactions may be summarized as follows:

$$12\ NADPH + 18\ ATP + 6\ CO_2 \longrightarrow$$
$$C_6H_{12}O_6 + 12\ NADP^+ + 18\ ADP + 18\ P_i + 6\ H_2O$$

Most Plants Use the Calvin (C$_3$) Cycle To Fix Carbon

The light-independent reactions form a cycle known as the **Calvin cycle.** M. Calvin, A. Benson, and others at the University of California were able to elucidate the details of this cycle, for which Dr. Calvin was awarded a Nobel Prize in 1961 (Figure 8–15).

With each complete turn of the Calvin cycle, a portion of a carbohydrate molecule is produced. Six turns of the cycle use six molecules of CO_2 and produce one glucose molecule. As you read the following description of the Calvin cycle, follow the reactions illustrated in Figure 8–16. The cycle begins with a pentose (five-carbon) sugar phosphate called **ribulose bisphosphate (RuBP).** A key enzyme (**ribulose bisphosphate carboxylase,** generally referred to as **Rubisco**) combines carbon dioxide with RuBP, forming a six-carbon molecule.

Instantly, the six-carbon molecule splits into two three-carbon molecules called **phosphoglycerate (PGA).** With the energy and reducing power from ATP and NADPH (both produced in the light-dependent reactions), the PGA molecules are converted to **glyceraldehyde-3-phosphate,** known simply as **PGAL.**

With six turns of the Calvin cycle, the plant cell is in a position to harvest the six CO_2 molecules it has put into the process, not in their original form but as carbohydrate. Two PGAL molecules leave the system, to be used in carbohydrate synthesis. Each of these three-carbon molecules of PGAL is essentially half a hexose (six-carbon sugar) molecule. They are usually joined in pairs to produce glucose or fructose. In some plants glucose and fructose are then joined to produce sucrose (common table sugar). This we harvest from sugar cane, sugar beets, and maple sap. The plant cell also uses glucose to produce starch or cellulose.

Notice that although two PGAL molecules are removed from the cycle after six turns, ten PGAL mole-

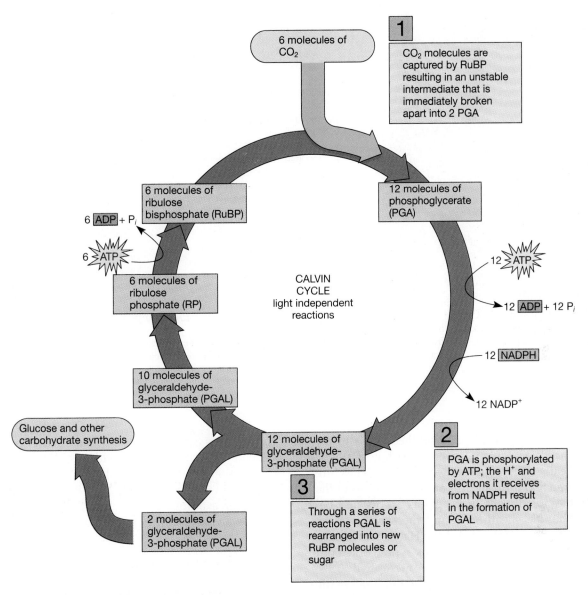

Figure 8–16 The light-independent reactions of photosynthesis, also known as the Calvin cycle. This diagram depicts six turns of the cycle. For every six turns, six molecules of CO_2 are converted into one molecule of a six-carbon sugar such as glucose. The energy (and reducing power) that drives the Calvin cycle comes from the products of the light-dependent reactions (that is, ATP and NADPH).

cules remain; this represents 30 carbon atoms in all. Through a complex series of reactions, these 30 carbons and their associated atoms are rearranged into six molecules of ribulose phosphate, which is phosphorylated to produce RuBP, the very five-carbon compound with which we started. This same ribulose bisphosphate is now in a position to begin the process of CO_2 fixation and eventual PGAL production once again.

In summary, the inputs required for the light-independent reactions are six molecules of CO_2, hydrogen from NADPH, and ATP. In the end, the six carbons from the CO_2 can be accounted for by the harvest of a hexose (six-carbon) molecule. The remaining PGAL molecules are used to synthesize the RuBP molecules with which more CO_2 molecules may combine.

Many Plants with a Tropical Origin Fix Carbon Using the C₄ Pathway

Most plants are referred to as **C₃ plants** because the first product of CO_2 fixation (using the Calvin cycle) is a three-carbon compound, PGA. Some plants, referred to as **C₄ plants**, are able to fix carbon dioxide into the four-carbon compound **oxaloacetate.** These plants eventually use the Calvin cycle to produce carbohydrate, but first they incorporate CO_2 into oxaloacetate.

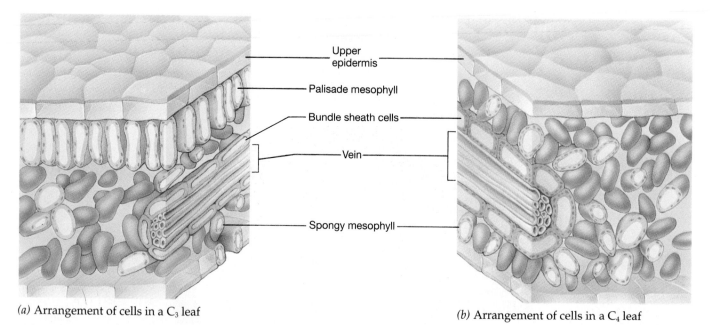

Upper epidermis

Palisade mesophyll

Bundle sheath cells

Vein

Spongy mesophyll

(a) Arrangement of cells in a C$_3$ leaf

(b) Arrangement of cells in a C$_4$ leaf

Figure 8–17   Comparison of the leaf structures of a C$_3$ plant and a C$_4$ plant. *(a)* In C$_3$ plants the Calvin cycle takes place within the mesophyll cells of the leaf. *(b)* In C$_4$ plants, reactions that fix CO$_2$ into four-carbon compounds take place in the mesophyll cells. Then the Calvin cycle occurs in the bundle sheath cells, which surround the veins of the leaf.

Leaf anatomy is distinctive in C$_4$ plants. In addition to having mesophyll cells (photosynthetic cells in the middle of the leaf), C$_4$ plant leaves have photosynthetic **bundle sheath cells** (Figure 8–17). These cells are tightly packed and form sheaths around the veins of the leaf. The mesophyll cells in C$_4$ plants are located between the bundle sheath cells and the surface of the leaf. The C$_4$ pathway (also called the **Hatch-Slack pathway,** after M. D. Hatch and C. R. Slack, who worked out many of its steps) occurs in the mesophyll cells, whereas the Calvin cycle takes place within the bundle sheath cells.

The C$_4$ pathway is present in addition to the Calvin cycle in a number of plant orders and apparently has evolved independently several times. Plants with the C$_4$ pathway evidently appeared first in geographical areas with high temperatures, high light intensities, and limited amounts of water. (See Focus on Photosynthesis in Desert Plants for a related photosynthetic pathway.) Plants with the C$_4$ pathway tolerate higher temperatures and higher light intensities, lose less water by transpiration (evaporation), and have higher rates of photosynthesis and growth than plants that use only the Calvin cycle. Among the many quick-growing and aggressive plants that use the C$_4$ pathway are sugar cane, corn, and crabgrass (Figure 8–18). The yields of C$_4$ crop plants are two to three times greater than those of C$_3$ plants. If this pathway could be incorporated into more of our crop plants by genetic manipulation, we might well be able to greatly increase food production in some parts of the world.

The essential feature of the C$_4$ pathway is that it concentrates carbon dioxide in the bundle sheath cells. Carbon dioxide enters the leaf through tiny pores, called **stomata,** that open and close in response to such factors as water content and light intensity. On hot, dry days, for example, plants close their stomata to conserve water. When the stomata of C$_3$ plants are closed,

Figure 8–18   Small crabgrass, *Digitaria ischaemum,* a C$_4$ plant. (Grant Heilman)

FOCUS ON

Photosynthesis in Desert Plants

Plants living in very dry, or **xeric,** conditions have a number of special anatomical adaptations that enable them to survive (see Focus on Comparative Plant Anatomy in Chapter 32). Many xeric plants have physiological adaptations as well. For example, their stomata may open during the cooler night and close during the hot day to reduce water loss from transpiration. This is in contrast to most plants, which have stomata that are open during the day and closed at night. But xeric plants that have their stomata closed during the day cannot exchange gases for photosynthesis. (Plants typically fix carbon dioxide during the day, when sunlight is available.)

Many xeric plants evolved a special photosynthetic pathway called **crassulacean acid metabolism,** or **CAM,** that in effect solves this dilemma. The name comes from the stonecrop plant family (the Crassulaceae) which possesses the CAM pathway, although it has been found also in more than 25 other plant families. A number of unrelated plants, including pineapple and most cacti, have it. Although the CAM pathway is most common in flowering plants, especially dicots, it also occurs in several monocots, in *Welwitschia* (a gymnosperm), and in some ferns.

CAM plants fix CO_2 during the night, when stomata are open, into malate (a four-carbon compound),

The snake plant (*Sansevieria trifasciata*), a member of the Crassulaceae, is a typical CAM plant that grows in arid habitats. (Dennis Drenner)

which is stored in the vacuole. During the day, when stomata are closed and gas exchange cannot occur between the plant and the atmosphere, the malate is decarboxylated to yield CO_2 again. Now the CO_2 is available *within the leaf tissue* to be fixed into sugar by the usual photosynthetic pathway, the C_3 pathway.

CAM photosynthesis may sound familiar to you; it is very similar to the C_4 pathway. There are important differences between CAM and C_4 photosynthesis, however. C_4 plants initially fix carbon dioxide into four-carbon organic acids in mesophyll cells. The acids are later decarboxylated to produce CO_2, which is fixed by the C_3 pathway in the bundle sheath cells. In other words, the C_4 and C_3 pathways occur in *different locations* within the leaf of a C_4 plant. In CAM plants, the initial fixation of CO_2 occurs at night. Decarboxylation of malate and subsequent production of sugar from CO_2 by the normal C_3 photosynthetic pathway occur during the day. In other words, the C_4 and C_3 pathways occur at *different times* within the same cell of a CAM plant.

The CAM pathway is a very successful adaptation to xeric conditions. CAM plants are able to have gas exchange for photosynthesis *and* to reduce water loss significantly. Plants with CAM photosynthesis survive in deserts where neither C_3 nor C_4 plants can.

---

the supply of carbon dioxide is greatly diminished and photosynthesis is significantly slowed. The C_4 reactions enhance carbon fixation by increasing the level of CO_2 in bundle sheath cells, thereby driving the Calvin cycle.

In the C_4 pathway, CO_2 is added to the three-carbon compound phosphoenol pyruvate (PEP), forming oxaloacetate (which has four carbons) (Figure 8–19). The reaction is catalyzed by PEP carboxylase, an enzyme that has a high affinity for carbon dioxide and binds it effectively even when carbon dioxide is at low

concentrations. Oxaloacetate is converted to other four-carbon compounds, usually malate. The malate then passes to the bundle sheath cells, where a different enzyme catalyzes the decarboxylation of malate to yield pyruvate (which has three carbons) and CO_2.

$$\text{Malate} + \text{NADP}^+ \longrightarrow \text{Pyruvate} + CO_2 + \text{NADPH}$$

The CO_2 released in the bundle sheath cell condenses with ribulose bisphosphate and goes through the Calvin cycle in the usual manner. The pyruvate

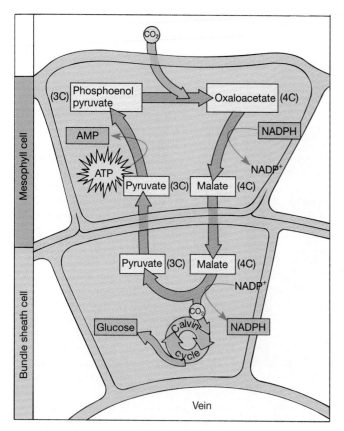

Figure 8–19   The C_4 pathway for CO_2 fixation. CO_2 combines with phosphoenol pyruvate (PEP) in mesophyll cells, forming a four-carbon compound that is converted to malate. Malate goes to the bundle sheath cell, where it is decarboxylated. The CO_2 thus released in the bundle sheath cell is used to make sugar by way of the Calvin cycle. Because the C_4 system consumes some energy, ultimately made available only by photosynthesis, this system is important to the plant only at high light intensities. Under these conditions, it can fix more carbon than the C_3 system can fix by itself.

formed in the decarboxylation reaction returns to the mesophyll cell, where it is used to regenerate phosphoenol pyruvate by reacting with ATP.

The role of the C_4 pathway is to increase the concentration of CO_2 within the bundle sheath cells so as to drive the C_3 cycle there. The operation of the C_4 pathway serves to increase the concentration of CO_2 within the bundle sheath cells some 10 to 60 times over that in the cells of plants having only the C_3 pathway.

The combined C_3-C_4 pathway involves the expenditure of 30 ATPs per hexose, rather than the 18 ATPs used in the absence of the C_4 pathway. The expenditure of the extra ATPs ensures a high concentration of CO_2 in the bundle sheath cells and permits them to carry on photosynthesis at a rapid rate.

When light is abundant, the rate of photosynthesis is limited by the concentration of CO_2, and C_4 plants,

with their higher levels of CO_2 in bundle sheath cells, have the advantage. At lower light intensities and temperatures, C_3 plants have the advantage. For example, winter rye, a C_3 plant, grows lavishly in cool weather when crabgrass cannot. The reason is that plants with C_4 metabolism require more energy to fix CO_2 than do C_3 plants.

Photorespiration Reduces Photosynthetic Efficiency

Many C_3 plants, including certain agriculturally important crops such as soybeans, wheat, and potatoes, do not yield as much carbohydrate from photosynthesis as might be expected. This reduction in yield is especially significant during very hot spells in summer. The reason is an unusual series of reactions involving ribulose bisphosphate, RuBP. Recall that RuBP carboxylase is responsible for CO_2 fixation by attaching CO_2 to RuBP in the Calvin cycle. Under certain conditions, this enzyme binds RuBP to O_2 instead of CO_2. When this occurs, some of the intermediates involved in the Calvin cycle are degraded to CO_2 and H_2O. This process is called **photorespiration** because (1) it occurs during the daylight; (2) it requires oxygen, like aerobic respiration; and (3) it produces CO_2 and H_2O, like aerobic respiration. Unlike aerobic respiration, however, energy in the form of ATP is not produced during photorespiration. Photorespiration reduces photosynthetic efficiency because it removes some of the intermediates that are used in the Calvin cycle. As a result, CO_2 fixation does not occur as rapidly. The reason plants photorespire is unknown. From our viewpoint, the process is wasteful, particularly because it reduces the yields of important crop plants.

Photorespiration occurs when the concentration of CO_2 is low and the concentration of O_2 is high in the chloroplasts. This would be expected to happen on hot, dry days because these conditions cause water stress in plants. As a result, plants close their stomata, the tiny pores in the leaf surface through which gas exchange occurs, to help conserve water. Once the stomata close, photosynthesis in the chloroplasts rapidly uses up the CO_2 remaining in the leaf and O_2 produced in photosynthesis accumulates in the chloroplasts.

Not all plants have a reduction in photosynthetic efficiency due to photorespiration. C_4 plants have evolved mechanisms to bypass photorespiration. Photorespiration is negligible in C_4 plants because the concentration of CO_2 in bundle sheath cells is always high. Some scientists are attempting to transfer genes for the C_4 pathway to C_3 crops such as soybeans and wheat. If this is accomplished, these plants will be able to produce a lot more carbohydrate during hot weather.

MAKING THE CONNECTION

A Comparison of Aerobic Respiration and Photosynthesis

Photosynthesis and aerobic respiration have a number of features in common. Both are intimately connected with the energy requirements of living things; both are essential for life. The overall equations for aerobic respiration and photosynthesis appear to be almost exactly opposite one another. In photosynthesis:

$$6\,CO_2 + 12\,H_2O \xrightarrow{\text{Light energy}} C_6H_{12}O_6 + 6\,O_2 + 6\,H_2O$$

In aerobic respiration:

$$C_6H_{12}O_6 + 6\,O_2 + 6\,H_2O \longrightarrow 6\,CO_2 + 12\,H_2O + ATP\text{ energy}$$

Let's compare other aspects of these two processes.

1. **Raw materials**: The starting materials for photosynthesis are CO_2 and H_2O; for aerobic respiration they are $C_6H_{12}O_6$ and O_2.
2. **End products**: Photosynthesis produces $C_6H_{12}O_6$ and O_2; aerobic respiration produces CO_2 and H_2O.
3. **Which cells have these processes**: Photosynthesis occurs only in cells that contain chlorophyll; aerobic respiration (or some other energy-releasing pathway) occurs in every actively metabolizing cell of every organism.
4. **Physical conditions needed**: Photosynthesis occurs only in the light (although the light-independent reactions can occur in darkness); respiration occurs in both light and darkness.

5. **Organelles involved**: The chloroplast is the site of photosynthesis; aerobic respiration occurs in the cytosol (glycolysis) and the mitochondrion.
6. **ATP production**: In photosynthesis, ATP is produced using the energy of light (photophosphorylation); in aerobic respiration, ATP is produced by substrate-level phosphorylation and by the oxidation of food molecules (oxidative phosphorylation).
7. **High-energy compound that carries hydrogen**: $NADP^+$ is reduced (forming NADPH) in photosynthesis; NAD^+ is reduced (forming NADH) in respiration.
8. **Involvement of ATP and NADPH/NADH**: In photosynthesis, both ATP and NADPH are produced during the light-dependent reactions and both are used to drive the light-independent reactions; the energy of NADH produced during the early stages of aerobic respiration is used to generate ATP, which is then used to perform useful work in the cell.
9. **Pathway of energy**: In photosynthesis, the energy of light $\longrightarrow$ chlorophyll $\longrightarrow$ NADPH/ATP $\longrightarrow$ sugar molecules; in respiration, the energy in food (sugar) molecules $\longrightarrow$ NADH/ATP $\longrightarrow$ energy for work in the cell.
10. **Pathway of hydrogens** (and their high-energy electrons): In photosynthesis, hydrogen from water $\longrightarrow$ NADPH $\longrightarrow$ sugar; in aerobic respiration, hydrogen from food (sugar) molecules $\longrightarrow$ NADH $\longrightarrow O_2$, forming water.

SUMMARY

I. Most producers are photosynthetic autotrophs and use light as an energy source for manufacturing organic compounds from carbon dioxide and water.

II. In plants, photosynthesis occurs in chloroplasts, which are located mainly within mesophyll cells inside the leaf.
- A. Chloroplasts are organelles bounded by a double membrane; the inner membrane encloses the stroma and thylakoids.
- B. Chlorophyll and other photosynthetic pigments are found within the thylakoid membranes of chloroplasts.
- C. The thylakoids are arranged in stacks called grana.

III. During photosynthesis, light energy is captured by chlorophyll and used to chemically combine the hydrogen from water with carbon dioxide to produce carbohydrates. Oxygen is released as a byproduct.
- A. During the light-dependent reactions of photosynthesis, chlorophyll absorbs light and becomes energized. Some of the energy of the energized chlorophyll is used to make ATP; some is used to split water. Hydrogen from the water is transferred to $NADP^+$, forming NADPH.
- B. The light-independent reactions of photosynthesis use the energy of ATP and NADPH to manufacture carbohydrate molecules from CO_2.

IV. Chlorophyll is a pigment that captures light energy. Its absorption spectrum is very similar to the action spectrum of photosynthesis.

V. Light behaves as both a wave and a particle. Particles of light energy, called photons, can excite pigment molecules such as chlorophyll. The resulting high-energy electrons are accepted by electron acceptor compounds.

   A. Chlorophyll molecules and accessory pigments are organized into photosystems.

   B. Only a special chlorophyll *a* in the reaction center of a photosystem actually gives up its energized electrons to a nearby electron acceptor.

VI. In noncyclic photophosphorylation, the electrons emitted by Photosystem I are passed through a chain of electron acceptors to $NADP^+$.

   A. In this process electrons from P680 in Photosystem II are donated to P700 in Photosystem I.

   B. Water is split and its electrons are donated to P680 in Photosystem II. Oxygen is released in the process.

   C. A series of redox reactions takes place as energized electrons are passed along a chain of electron acceptors. Some of the energy is used to pump protons across the thylakoid membrane, providing the energy to generate ATP.

VII. In cyclic photophosphorylation, electrons from Photosystem I are eventually returned to Photosystem I; ATP is produced, but not NADPH, and no oxygen is generated.

VIII. During the light-independent reactions, energy from ATP and NADPH is used to chemically combine carbon dioxide with hydrogen.

   A. The light-independent reactions proceed by way of the Calvin cycle.

   B. In the Calvin cycle, carbon dioxide is combined with ribulose bisphosphate (RuBP), a five-carbon sugar.

   C. Six turns of the Calvin cycle result in the synthesis of 12 PGAL. Two molecules of PGAL are used to produce one molecule of glucose; the remaining PGAL molecules are modified to regenerate six of the CO_2 acceptor molecules (RuBP).

   D. ATP and NADPH molecules are consumed in the conversion of CO_2 into carbohydrate.

IX. In the C_4 pathway, the enzyme PEP carboxylase binds CO_2 effectively, even when CO_2 is at a low concentration.

   A. The initial reactions take place within mesophyll cells. The carbon dioxide is fixed in oxaloacetate, which is then converted to malate.

   B. The malate moves into a bundle sheath cell and CO_2 is removed from it. The released CO_2 then enters the Calvin cycle.

X. In photorespiration, C_3 plants consume oxygen and generate carbon dioxide. This process, which decreases photosynthetic efficiency, occurs on bright, hot, dry days when plant cells close their stomata, preventing the passage of CO_2 into the leaf.

Summary Equations for Photosynthesis

The light-dependent reactions:

$$12\,H_2O + 12\,NADP^+ + 18\,ADP + 18\,P_i \longrightarrow 6\,O_2 + 12\,NADPH + 18\,ATP$$

The light-independent reactions:

$$12\,NADPH + 18\,ATP + 6\,CO_2 \longrightarrow C_6H_{12}O_6 + 12\,NADP^+ + 18\,ADP + 18\,P_i + 6\,H_2O$$

By canceling out the common items on opposite sides of the arrows in these two coupled equations, we obtain the simplified overall equation for photosynthesis:

$$6\,CO_2 + 12\,H_2O \longrightarrow C_6H_{12}O_6 + 6\,O_2 + 6\,H_2O$$

POST-TEST

1. Most producers are photosynthetic _____.
2. Chlorophyll is associated with organelles known as _____.
3. In photosynthesis _____ _____ and _____ are the inorganic raw materials used to produce glucose; _____ is released during the process.
4. In photolysis some of the energy captured by chlorophyll is used to split _____.
5. Light is composed of particles of energy called _____.
6. The relative effectiveness of different wavelengths of light in photosynthesis is demonstrated by an _____ _____.
7. In plants the electron donor in the light-dependent reactions is _____.
8. In addition to having chlorophyll, most plants contain accessory photosynthetic pigments such as _____.

9. Only the special chlorophyll *a* in the reaction center of a _____ gives up its electron to an electron acceptor.
10. In photophosphorylation, electrons that have been energized by light contribute their energy to add phosphate to _____, producing _____.
11. In _____ photophosphorylation there is a one-way flow of electrons to $NADP^+$, forming NADPH.
12. The oxygen released in photosynthesis is derived from _____.
13. The transfer of electrons through a sequence of electron acceptors provides energy to pump _____ across the thylakoid membrane.
14. The inputs for the light-independent reactions are _____, _____, and _____.
15. The process of _____ _____ involves the chemical combination of carbon dioxide with ribulose bisphosphate.

16. When carbon dioxide is a limiting factor, plants that have the _____ pathway have an advantage.
17. In C_4 plants the Calvin cycle takes place in _____ _____ cells; in these cells malate is decarboxylated, yielding _____ for photosynthesis.

18. In photorespiration, ribulose bisphosphate reacts with _____ instead of CO_2.

REVIEW QUESTIONS

1. What is the role of light in photosynthesis?
2. What is the role of chlorophyll in photosynthesis?
3. What does an absorption spectrum of chlorophyll demonstrate? What does an action spectrum of photosynthesis demonstrate?
4. How is oxygen produced during photosynthesis?
5. How are ATP and NADPH produced and used in the process of photosynthesis?
6. How is sugar produced from CO_2 in photosynthesis?
7. What strategies might be employed in the future to increase world food supply? Base your answer on your knowledge of photosynthesis and related processes.

RECOMMENDED READINGS

Kemp, P. R., G. L. Cunningham, and H. P. Adams. Specialization of mesophyll structure in C_4 grasses. *BioScience*, July/August 1983. Discusses the relationship between structure and function as it relates to C_4 photosynthesis.

Mauseth, J. D. *Botany: An Introduction to Plant Biology.* Saunders College Publishing, Philadelphia, 1991. A readable introduction to photosynthesis, with emphasis on environmental and internal factors that affect photosynthesis.

Nakatani, H. Y. Photosynthesis. *Carolina Biology Reader.* Carolina Biological Supply Company, Burlington, NC, 1988. A clear description of photosynthesis with emphasis on the light-dependent reactions.

Prince, R. C. Redox-driven proton gradients. *BioScience*, January 1985. Discusses how ATP is produced during electron transport.

Taiz, L., and E. Zeiger. *Plant Physiology.* Benjamin Cummings, Redwood City, CA, 1991. An in-depth examination of the photochemistry of photosynthesis.

Youvan, D. C., and B. L. Marrs. Molecular mechanisms of photosynthesis. *Scientific American,* June 1987. Explores molecular aspects of photosynthesis.

Teacher

R O S A   B U X E D A

When she entered college at the University of Puerto Rico, Mayaguez, Rosa Buxeda, like many biology majors, was a pre-med student. But a fascination with microbiology and an inspirational professor changed her career course toward teaching. She taught microbiology for several years, but was not satisfied that she was giving the most she could to her students. Buxeda has therefore embarked on a Ph.D. program at Rutgers University. When she returns to the University of Puerto Rico as a professor, she will be both repaying a debt to her teachers and manifesting her vision of educating and inspiring students in her native country.

When did your interest in studying science begin?

In high school I participated in the scientific fair and won second prize for a project using magnets to generate electricity. That was my first experimental project, and it gave me a lot of insight because most of the work we did in high school was basically theoretical.

In high school did you have a mentor, or someone who was inspirational to you?

Not at that point; I liked many fields. I was not sure what I wanted to study in college. I liked mathematics, biology, and chemistry as well, so it was difficult to make a choice. I knew I wanted to work in an area that has to do with life, but one which could at the same time be integrated with other fields, like mathematics and chemistry. I decided that my best option was to

go into a biology program at the University of Puerto Rico, Mayaguez. Basically, my idea was to get into the medical school.

So you declared yourself a pre-med student and began your studies. What happened then?

In my second year I took a course in microbiology, which really changed my perspective on my professional career.

In what ways?

First of all, discovering the existence of life beyond the human eye was quite exciting. Moreover, I was really surprised to find that those small organisms are everywhere, and that they have a tremendous impact on our lives. The laboratory section of that course was challenging, and we exam-

ined samples from food, from the soil, and from many other sources under the microscope. Another exciting feature of the course was the professor himself. He was a recent Ph.D. graduate, and as he taught, he took the time to share with us his experiences as a graduate student. He is now the chancellor of the University of Puerto Rico, Mayaguez. His name is Dr. Alejandro Ruiz. So at that point I became interested in doing graduate work, particularly in the area of microbiology.

Was there any way of specializing in undergraduate school, or did you follow a strict curriculum?

After I took Dr. Ruiz's course, I became so interested in microbiology that I started taking electives. There was a program created in my university called industrial microbiology. I switched from pre-med into that program, so I had an opportunity to take more specialized courses such as physiology of microorganisms, industrial microbiology, ecology of microorganisms, and mycology. I really started to focus in on different aspects of microbiology.

Were you able to do any research work while you were an undergraduate?

Yes, I had the opportunity to work through three summer internships in the biomedicine department at Lawrence Livermore National Laboratory. I really got a good idea of what research is all about. That experience, combined with my microbiology courses and Dr. Ruiz's example, created a turning point in my life—a desire to get into graduate school.

How did you make a decision about graduate school?

Professor Pablo Rodriguez, Dean of the Faculty of Arts and Sciences at the University of Puerto Rico, advised me that many universities offer very good research programs in microbiology, and that a lot of scholarships are available. I started writing letters for applications, and asking about the various financial aid and scholarship packages.

What school did you settle on for your master's degree?

The University of Wisconsin, Madison. I earned a master's degree in the area of bacteriology. Then, at the end of my studies, I felt there was something I was missing. I thought it was time for me to give something back. I remembered my professor at the University of Puerto Rico who encouraged students to go to graduate school, and how that person had changed my life. I thought that if I went back to Puerto Rico and taught at the university, I would be able to touch other people's lives the way he had touched my life.

So you returned to the University of Puerto Rico?

Yes, I was an instructor in the microbiology program. It was a wonderful experience, one of the most satisfying experiences I have had in my professional life. It was very rewarding to be able to transmit my knowledge to other people. I shared with my students many of my own experiences as a graduate student. Many of them right now are graduate students themselves at other universities. When I talk to them, they tell me, "You know the course on physiology of microorganisms you taught me four years ago? Well, your notebook has been a great help to me through graduate school." Rewards like that are very special.

It sounds as if you began immediately to pay back the debt to Dr. Ruiz and other professors like him.

Oh, yes. But the fact that I had only a master's degree was a drawback. After teaching for three years, I came to the conclusion that if I wanted to give the best to my students, I needed more preparation. That's when I decided to earn a Ph.D. in order to return to teaching as a qualified professor.

What made you choose Rutgers University for your Ph.D. work?

I was invited to visit the campus, where I met faculty members and toured the laboratories. I really enjoyed the faculty and the quality of work they were doing. One of the most important decisions a graduate student has to make is whom to work with and what projects that person can offer. I have been very fortunate working with Dr. George Carman. He has all the characteristics of an excellent advisor: always available for his students, excellent guidance, and friendship.

You are about to finish your Ph.D. What is your research project?

I am working on kinetic analysis and regulation of two forms of phosphatidylinositol 4-kinase from yeast, and whether the regulation of these enzymes may be related to overall phospholipid synthesis in yeast.

Since teaching is your ultimate goal, how are you going to integrate your research experience into your career?

It is possible to design courses that make use of your research experience. For example, you can give lectures about the research area you are working in, and give students the most up-to-date information in that particular area. Biology is such a diverse field that few people can keep up with all of the latest developments in every area. But teachers who specialize in a particular field can give students updated information in that field, so that when students leave with a B.S. degree, their knowledge is state-of-the-art.

What other techniques and abilities do you want to cultivate on your way to becoming a great teacher?

I want to share with my students my experiences as a graduate student. Some teachers limit themselves to bringing students the knowledge written in a book. It is not enough to stand in front of the class and repeat definitions and descriptions. That approach misses one of the most important goals of teaching—showing students how to learn, how to associate ideas, how to enjoy the experience of learning something new. To stimulate students, teachers need to dedicate time, to read about the subject, to prepare for the lecture or lab to make it a more challenging experience. And when this becomes the standard approach to teaching, we will see more and more students pursuing higher degrees. It's just a matter of motivating students at the right time in their lives. I want them to have alternatives, to know that in addition to going to medical school, in addition to being medical technologists, they can also go to graduate school and do a lot.

You plan to return to the University of Puerto Rico to teach?

Yes. I want to go back to Puerto Rico. Teaching is an excellent way to make a positive contribution to future generations. It allows you to open people's minds to the exciting world of graduate school and to help students realize that the opportunities are there; it's just a matter of reaching for them.

What kind of messages do your students send back to you that make you so inspired by teaching?

They comment on the way I am able to communicate the knowledge. I don't simply read the textbook and recite what's in it. I try to give life to what is in the book. I try to bring them experiences from life that will allow them to make sense of what is in the book, and to apply the knowledge every day. Sometimes it is very difficult, but I try my best within the limits of what I am teaching. Basically, what students have told me is they appreciate the way I transmit the knowledge. I am very fortunate to have that ability.

PART III

The Continuity of Life: Genetics

Every organism, even the simplest, contains a massive amount of information. Copies of this information are contained in every cell, organized into units called **genes,** which are made of DNA. Genes ultimately control all aspects of the life of an organism, including its metabolism, form, development, and reproduction. They are responsible for the continuity of life because they provide the essential link between generations. This transmission of genetic information from parent to offspring is called **heredity,** and the branch of biology concerned with the structure, transmission, and expression of hereditary information is called **genetics.** Since the beginning of this century, the science of genetics has undergone remarkable advances. Today the field of molecular genetics is having a profound impact on many diverse areas of biology.

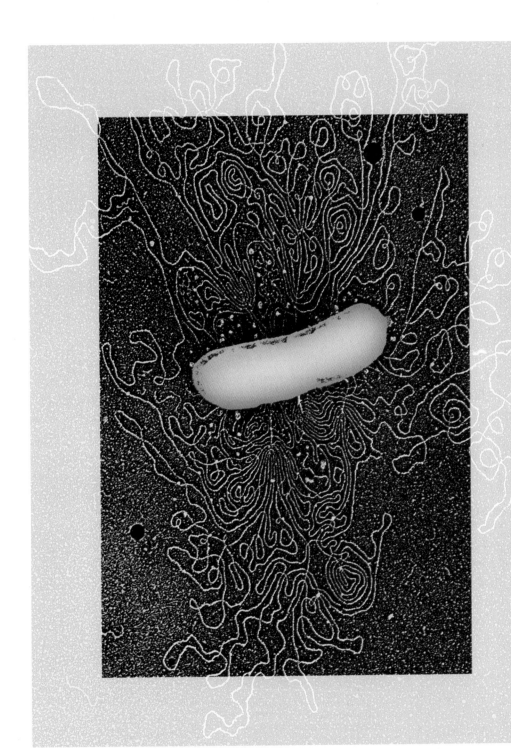

False color transmission electron
micrograph of DNA spilling out of an
Escherichia coli cell.
(Dr. Gopal Murti/Science Photo Library/
Photo Researchers, Inc.)

CHAPTER 9

Chromosomes, Mitosis, and Meiosis

OUTLINE

Eukaryotic chromosomes
The cell cycle, mitosis and cytokinesis
Cell division and reproduction
Meiosis

All cells are formed by the division of preexisting cells. When a cell divides, copies of its genetic information (DNA) must be precisely transmitted to each daughter cell through a complex series of processes. Both prokaryotic and eukaryotic cells must first faithfully copy (replicate) their DNA.

A eukaryotic nucleus contains multiple DNA molecules. These molecules are very long and thin, and to prevent tangling they must be packaged with proteins and organized into rodlike structures called **chromosomes.** Prokaryotic cells do not have such chromosomes because they have much less DNA and its packaging is much simpler.

Chromosomes must be distributed to the daughter cells in a highly organized way. Most cell divisions in the body cells of eukaryotes involve a process called **mitosis,** which ensures that each daughter cell receives one copy of every chromosome in the parent cell. The distribution of genetic material in prokaryotic cells is much simpler, but it too must be very precise if the daughter cells are to be genetically identical to the parent cell.

Sexual reproduction in eukaryotes occurs by fusion of two sex cells, or **gametes,** to form a single cell, called a **zygote.** In higher plants and animals the gametes are the eggs and sperm. To prevent zygotes from having twice as many chromosomes as the parents, each gamete must contain only half the number of parental chromosomes. This is ensured by a special type of division called **meiosis.**

False color transmission electron micrograph of a human lymphocyte undergoing mitotic division. (CNRI/Science Photo Library/Photo Researchers, Inc.)

After you have studied this chapter you should be able to

1. Illustrate the structure of a duplicated chromosome, labeling the sister chromatids, sister centromeres, and sister kinetochores.
2. Identify the stages in the eukaryotic cell cycle, describe the principal events characteristic of each, and point out some ways in which the cycle is controlled.
3. Explain the significance of mitosis, and diagram the process.
4. Discriminate between asexual and sexual reproduction.
5. Distinguish between haploid and diploid cells, and define homologous chromosomes.
6. Contrast the events of mitosis and meiosis.
7. Compare the roles of mitosis and meiosis and of haploidy and diploidy in various generalized life cycles.

EUKARYOTIC CHROMOSOMES ARE MADE UP OF DNA, PROTEIN, AND RNA

The carriers of genetic information in eukaryotes are the **chromosomes** (Figure 9–1) contained within the cell nucleus. Although the term *chromosome* means "colored body," chromosomes are virtually colorless; the name refers to their ability to be stained darkly by certain dyes.

Chromosomes are made up of a complex material called **chromatin,** which consists of fibers containing about 60% protein, 35% deoxyribonucleic acid (DNA), and 5% ribonucleic acid (RNA). When a cell is not dividing, the chromatin is in the form of long, thin threads, although it usually has a granular appearance when viewed with the light microscope. At the time of cell division, the chromatin fibers condense and become visible as distinct, rodlike chromosomes. The structure of chromatin is described in more detail in Chapter 11.

A typical bacterial chromosome is a single circle of DNA with very few associated proteins. Bacterial reproduction is discussed in more detail in Chapter 23.

DNA Is Organized into Informational Units Called Genes

Each chromosome may contain hundreds or even thousands of genes. For example, humans are thought to have 100,000 or more genes, although the actual number is not known.

Our concept of the gene has changed considerably since the beginnings of the science of genetics, but our definitions have always centered on the gene as an informational unit that ultimately affects some characteristic of the organism. For example, we speak of genes controlling eye color in humans, wing length in flies, seed color in peas, and so on.

Today a *gene* can be roughly defined as a part of a DNA molecule that can be copied in the form of an RNA molecule through a process known as *transcription* (see Chapter 12), plus adjacent regions of the DNA that are required to regulate transcription. Different kinds of

RNA molecules have different specific functions. Many are responsible for carrying the code that specifies a particular sequence of amino acids in a polypeptide chain. This means that genes control the structure of all of the proteins of the organism, including the enzymes. In their role as catalysts, enzymes in turn regulate its metabolic reactions. (We discuss some of the limitations of this definition of the gene in Chapter 13.)

Chromosomes of Different Species Differ in Number and Informational Content

Every individual of a given species has a characteristic number of chromosomes in most nuclei of its body cells. Most body cells in a human have exactly 46 chromosomes. Figure 9–1 compares the normal chromosome constitutions, or **karyotypes,** of human females and males (see Chapter 15).

Humans are not unique in having 46 chromosomes; some other species of animals and plants also have 46, whereas others have different chromosome numbers. A certain species of roundworm has only 2 chromosomes in each cell; some crabs have as many as 200 per cell, and some ferns have more than 1000. Most animal and plant species have between 10 and 50 chromosomes. Numbers above and below this are uncommon.

Humans are not humans merely because they have 46 chromosomes, and in fact some humans have abnormal karyotypes with more or fewer than 46 (see Chapter 15). The *number* of chromosomes is not what makes each species unique, but rather the *information* specified by the genes on the chromosomes.

THE EUKARYOTIC CELL CYCLE IS AN ALTERNATING SEQUENCE OF CELL GROWTH AND DIVISION

Usually when cells reach a certain size, they must either stop growing or divide. Some cells, such as nerve, skeletal muscle, and red blood cells, do not normally divide

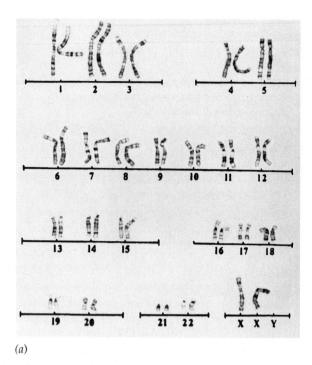

(a)

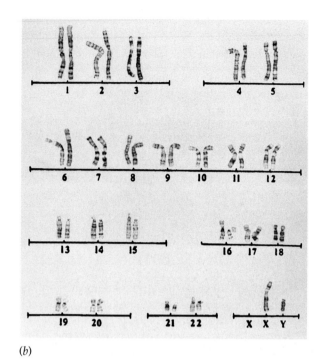

(b)

Figure 9–1   The chromosome constitutions, known as karyotypes, of a normal human female (a) and male (b). The apparent size differences between the female and male chromosomes have no significance; they merely reflect different degrees of chromosomal contraction in the particular cells photographed. The process of karyotyping is discussed in Chapter 15.   (Leonard Sciorra)

once they are mature. The activities of growing and dividing cells can be described in terms of the life cycle of the cell, or the **cell cycle.**

In cells capable of dividing, the cell cycle is the period from the beginning of one division to the beginning of the next and is represented in diagrams as a circle (Figure 9–2). The time it takes to complete one cell cycle is the **generation time, T.** The generation time can vary widely but is often about 8 to 20 hours in actively growing plant and animal cells.

Cell division involves two main processes, mitosis and cytokinesis. **Mitosis,** a complex process involving the nucleus, ensures that each new nucleus receives the same number and types of chromosomes as were present in the original nucleus. **Cytokinesis,** which generally begins before mitosis is complete, is the division of the cytoplasm of the cell to form two cells. Multinucleate cells are formed if mitosis is not followed by cytokinesis; this is a normal condition for some kinds of cells.

Interphase Is the Time between Divisions and Includes the Duplication of Chromosomes

Most of the life of the cell is spent in **interphase,** the stage between successive cell divisions. The cell is very active during this time, synthesizing needed materials and growing. Most proteins and other materials are

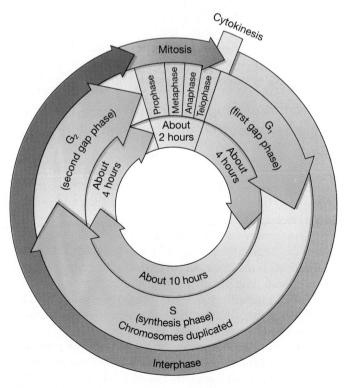

Figure 9–2   The cell cycle. Time intervals are relative; actual time varies with the cell type and species.

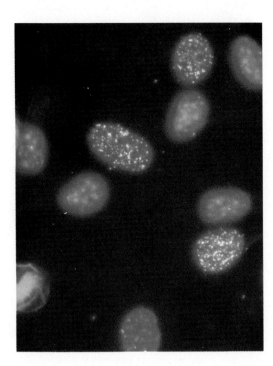

Figure 9–3 A photomicrograph of interphase mouse cells that have incorporated radioactive thymidine (a DNA precursor) into their DNA during the S phase. Nuclei containing newly synthesized DNA are at G_2 and can be recognized by the orange grains. Nuclei without grains are in G_1 of the cell cycle. (Jonathan G. Izant)

synthesized throughout interphase. The major exceptions are molecules needed for the cell to divide; synthesis of these molecules occurs at relatively restricted times and provides a way of subdividing interphase.

During the early 1950s, it was recognized that chromosomes undergo duplication during interphase and later separate and are distributed to the daughter nuclei during mitosis. The period of DNA replication during interphase serves as a major landmark, termed the *synthesis phase,* or **S phase** (Figures 9–2 and 9–3). Other chromosomal components, such as the proteins, are also synthesized at this time. The duplication of the chromosomes is a complex process, to be discussed in Chapter 11.

The time between mitosis and the beginning of the S phase is termed the **G_1 phase,** or first gap phase. The G_1 phase of an actively cycling cell is involved with growth and, toward the end of G_1, increased activity of enzymes required for DNA synthesis. These activities make it possible for the cell to enter the S phase. Nondividing cells usually remain in a stage called G_0, roughly equivalent to G_1.

After it completes the S phase, the cell enters a second gap phase, the **G_2 phase.** At this time increased protein synthesis occurs as the final steps in the cell's preparation for division take place. The completion of the G_2 phase is marked by the beginning of mitosis.

Identical Chromosomes Are Distributed into Different Nuclei during Mitosis

Each mitotic division is a continuous process, with each stage merging into the next. However, for descriptive purposes, mitosis has been divided into four stages: prophase, metaphase, anaphase, and telophase. Refer to Figures 9–4 and 9–5 as you read the description of each phase of mitosis.

Duplicated chromosomes become visible in the microscope during prophase

The first stage of mitosis, **prophase,** begins when the long chromatin threads begin to condense and appear as mitotic chromosomes. This condensation is accomplished mainly by a coiling process in which chromosomes become simultaneously shorter and thicker. The chromosomal material can thus be distributed to the daughter cells without tangling.

When stained with certain dyes and viewed through the light microscope, chromosomes are visible as dark, rod-shaped bodies during prophase. Each chromosome has been duplicated during the preceding S phase and consists of a pair of identical units, termed **sister chromatids.** Each chromatid contains a nonstaining, constricted region called the **centromere.** Sister chromatids are tightly associated in the vicinity of their centromeres (Figures 9–6 and 9–7). Although the chemical basis for this close association is not completely understood, evidence suggests that special kinds of DNA and special proteins that bind to DNA are involved. Each centromere contains a structure called the **kinetochore** to which microtubules can bind.

A dividing cell is usually described as a globe, with an equator that determines the midplane or equatorial plane and two opposite poles. This terminology is used for all cells regardless of their actual shape.

Fibers form between the poles and begin to organize into the **mitotic spindle,** a complex structure consisting mainly of microtubules. The mitotic spindle is responsible for the separation of the chromosomes during anaphase.

Plant and animal cells differ in the details of mitotic spindle formation. In animal cells, each of the two centrioles (see Chapter 4) duplicates during interphase. Microtubules radiate from the region surrounding the centriole pairs, which migrate toward opposite poles. Additional microtubules form clusters extending outward in all directions from the centrioles at the poles; these structures are called **asters** (Figure 9–8).

Centrioles may be involved in organizing the spindle in animal cells. They are also thought to be necessary for the formation of the basal bodies of cilia and flagella (see Chapter 4). The mechanism just described apparently provides for the orderly distribution of

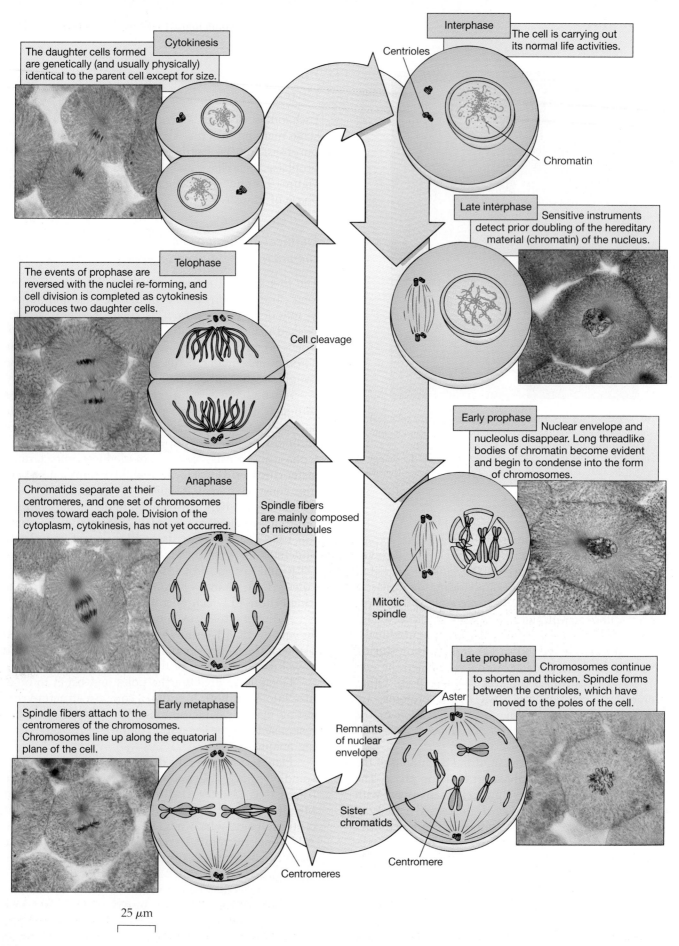

Cytokinesis

The daughter cells formed are genetically (and usually physically) identical to the parent cell except for size.

Interphase

The cell is carrying out its normal life activities.

Centrioles

Chromatin

Telophase

The events of prophase are reversed with the nuclei re-forming, and cell division is completed as cytokinesis produces two daughter cells.

Cell cleavage

Late interphase

Sensitive instruments detect prior doubling of the hereditary material (chromatin) of the nucleus.

Anaphase

Chromatids separate at their centromeres, and one set of chromosomes moves toward each pole. Division of the cytoplasm, cytokinesis, has not yet occurred.

Spindle fibers are mainly composed of microtubules

Early prophase

Nuclear envelope and nucleolus disappear. Long threadlike bodies of chromatin become evident and begin to condense into the form of chromosomes.

Mitotic spindle

Early metaphase

Spindle fibers attach to the centromeres of the chromosomes. Chromosomes line up along the equatorial plane of the cell.

Remnants of nuclear envelope

Aster

Late prophase

Chromosomes continue to shorten and thicken. Spindle forms between the centrioles, which have moved to the poles of the cell.

Sister chromatids

Centromere

Centromeres

25 μm

Figure 9–4 The cell cycle. Individual steps in the cycle are explained in labels within the figure. The drawings depict generalized animal cells with a diploid chromosome number of four. The photomicrographs show whitefish cells. The chief difference between these animal cells and plant cells is the lack of centrioles in the plant cells. (Ed Reschke)

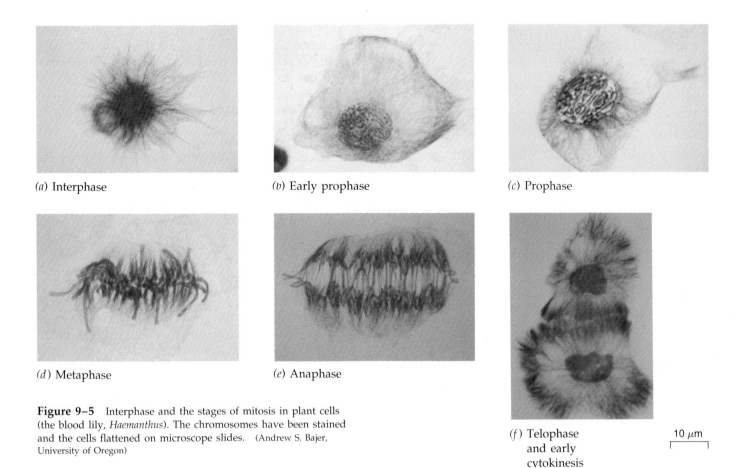

(a) Interphase

(b) Early prophase

(c) Prophase

(d) Metaphase

(e) Anaphase

(f) Telophase and early cytokinesis

10 μm

Figure 9–5 Interphase and the stages of mitosis in plant cells (the blood lily, *Haemanthus*). The chromosomes have been stained and the cells flattened on microscope slides. (Andrew S. Bajer, University of Oregon)

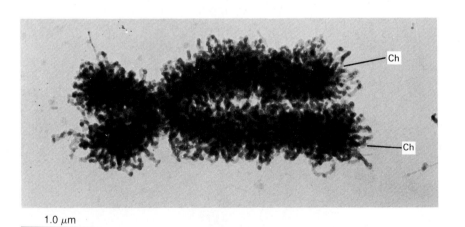

Ch

Ch

1.0 μm

Figure 9–6 A human chromosome isolated and photographed at the metaphase stage of mitosis. The chromatin fibers of the sister chromatids (*Ch*) have become slightly uncoiled. (E. J. DuPraw)

these organelles, ensuring that each daughter cell receives a pair of centrioles. Centrioles are not found in the cells of flowering plants and more advanced gymnosperms (see Chapter 27). Both of these groups lack flagellated sperm and other flagellated or ciliated cells.

During prophase, the nucleolus (see Chapter 4) diminishes in size and usually disappears. Toward the end of prophase, the nuclear envelope breaks down, and each chromatid becomes attached to some of the spindle microtubules at its kinetochore (see Figure 9–8a). The duplicated chromosomes then move from pole to pole and finally become aligned along the equatorial plane of the cell, midway between the two poles.

Duplicated chromosomes line up on the midplane of the cell during metaphase

The period during which the chromosomes are lined up along the equatorial plane of the cell (the *metaphase plate*) constitutes **metaphase.** The mitotic spindle is complete. It is composed of numerous microtubules extending from each pole to the equatorial region,

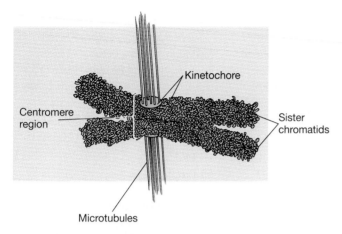

Figure 9–7   The structure of a mitotic metaphase chromosome. The paired structures indicated by the brace are the sister centromeres. Note that the sister chromatids are attached in the vicinity of their centromeres and that each centromere contains a structure known as a kinetochore, which serves as a microtubule attachment site.

where they generally overlap (**polar microtubules**) and from the kinetochores to the poles (**kinetochore microtubules**) (Figure 9–8*a*). At mitotic metaphase the individual sister kinetochores are attached by spindle microtubules to *opposite* poles of the cell.

In animal cells the spindle microtubules end near the centrioles, in a region occupied by the **pericentriolar material** (a cloud of matter around the centrioles), but do not actually touch the centrioles. In the cells of higher plants, the spindle microtubules end near a similar region, called the **microtubule-organizing center (MTOC)**.

During metaphase each chromatid is completely condensed and appears quite thick and distinct. Because chromosomes can usually be seen more clearly at metaphase than at any other time, they are usually photographed at this stage to be studied for the detection of certain chromosome abnormalities (see Figure 9–1 and Chapter 15).

Chromosomes move toward the poles during anaphase

Anaphase begins as the forces holding the sister chromatids together in the vicinity of their centromeres are released. *Each chromatid is now referred to as an independent chromosome.* The separated chromosomes slowly move to opposite poles. The kinetochores of the chromosomes are still attached to spindle microtubules and these lead the way, with the chromosome arms trailing behind. Anaphase ends when all of the chromosomes have reached the poles.

The overall mechanism of chromosome movement in anaphase is still poorly understood, although significant progress is being made in this area. Microtubules lack elastic or contractile properties. So how do the

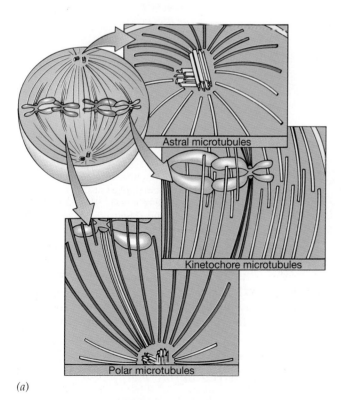

(*a*)

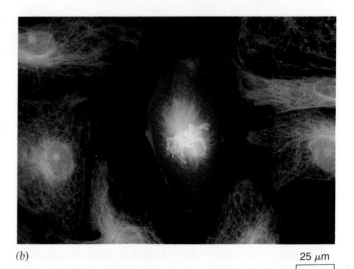

(*b*)   25 μm

Figure 9–8   (*a*) A diagram of a mitotic spindle of an animal cell, showing relationships among kinetochore microtubules, polar microtubules, and astral microtubules and chromosomes and centrioles. (*b*) Fluorescent-stained mitotic cells with well-defined spindle and asters.   (*b*, courtesy of Dr. John M. Murray, Department of Anatomy, University of Pennsylvania)

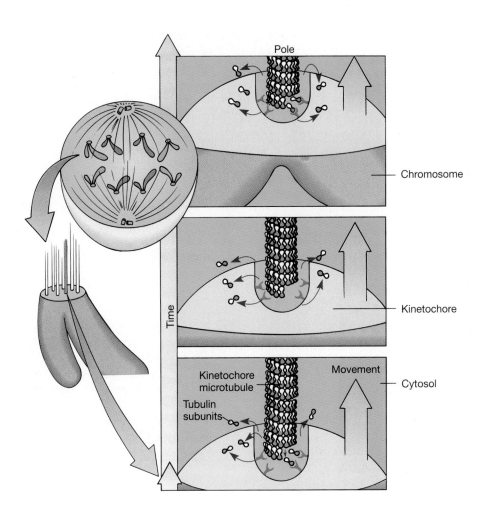

Figure 9–1 (label) Pole

Chromosome

Kinetochore

Kinetochore
microtubule

Movement

Cytosol

Tubulin
subunits

Time

Figure 9–9 A model for disassembly of microtubules at the kinetochore.

chromosomes move apart? Are they pushed or pulled, or do other forces operate?

Careful analyses of electron micrographs have yielded two main findings: (1) As anaphase continues, the kinetochore microtubules shorten. One current hypothesis suggests that chromosomes move as tubulin subunits are removed from the ends of the microtubules, particularly at the kinetochore (Figure 9–9). If the kinetochore remains firmly attached to the end of the microtubules, even as they are disassembled at their ends, the net result is chromosome movement toward the poles. (2) During anaphase the spindle as a whole elongates and may thus help to "push" the chromosomes apart. The spindle may lengthen as microtubules originating at opposite poles slide past one another in the region of overlap at the equator.

Two separate nuclei are formed during telophase

The final stage of mitosis, **telophase,** is characterized by a return to interphase-like conditions. The chromosomes decondense by uncoiling. A new nuclear envelope forms around each set of chromosomes, made at least in part from small vesicles and other components

derived from the old nuclear envelope. The spindle microtubules disappear, and nucleoli become apparent.

Two Separate Daughter Cells Are Formed by Cytokinesis

Cytokinesis, the division of the cytoplasm to yield two daughter cells, usually overlaps mitosis, generally beginning during telophase (see Figure 9–4).

Cytokinesis of an animal cell begins with a furrow that encircles the cell in the equatorial region (Figure 9–10a). The furrow, which is formed by a ring of microfilaments, gradually deepens and separates the cytoplasm into two daughter cells, each with a complete nucleus.

In plant cells, cytokinesis occurs by the formation of a **cell plate** (Figure 9–10b), a partition that is constructed in the equatorial region of the spindle and grows laterally to the cell wall. The cell plate forms from vesicles that originate in the Golgi complex (see Chapter 4). Each daughter cell forms a plasma membrane and a cellulose cell wall *outside of the plasma membrane* on its side of the cell plate.

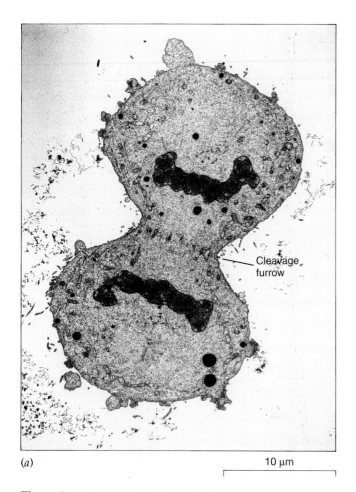

(a)

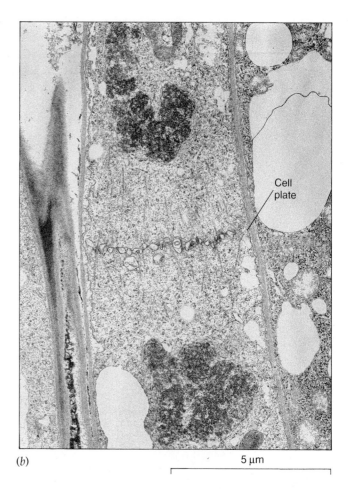

Cell plate

(b)

10 µm

5 µm

Figure 9–10   (a) A Cultured animal cell undergoing cytokinesis. (b) Telophase and cytokinesis in a maple leaf, *Acer saccharinum*. (a, T. E. Schroeder, University of Washington/Biological Photo Service;

b, E. H. Newcomb and B. A. Palevitz, University of Wisconsin/Biological Photo Service)

Mitosis Typically Produces Two Cells Genetically Identical to the Parent Cell

The remarkable regularity of the process of cell division ensures that each of the daughter nuclei receives exactly the same number and kind of chromosomes that the parent cell had. Thus, with a few exceptions, every cell of a multicellular organism has exactly the same genetic makeup. If a cell receives more or fewer than the characteristic number of chromosomes through some malfunction of the cell division process, the resulting cell may show marked abnormalities and be unable to survive.

Mitosis provides for the orderly distribution of chromosomes (and of centrioles, if present), but what about the various cytoplasmic organelles? For example, all eukaryotic cells, even plant cells, possess mitochondria. Photosynthetic plant cells cannot carry out photosynthesis without chloroplasts. These organelles con-

tain their own DNA and appear to form by the division of previously existing mitochondria or plastids or their precursors. Because many copies are present in each cell, organelles are apportioned more or less equally between the daughter cells at cytokinesis.

The Cell Cycle Is Controlled by an Internal Genetic Program Interacting with External Signals

When conditions are optimal, some prokaryotic cells (which divide nonmitotically—see Chapter 23) can divide every 20 minutes. The generation times of eukaryotic cells are generally much longer, although the frequency of cell division varies widely among different species and among different tissues of the same species. Some cells in the central nervous system usually cease dividing after the first few months of life, whereas blood-forming cells, digestive tract cells, and skin cells divide frequently throughout life. Under optimal conditions of nutrition, temperature, and pH, the eukaryotic cell cycle length is constant for any cell type. Under less favorable conditions, however, generation time may be longer.

The length of a cell cycle is the time required for the cell to carry out, through interaction with certain external signals, a precise program that has been built into it. The program has several parts, involving synthesis of the DNA and other chromosomal constituents, growth of the cell, and orderly transition between the steps of the cycle.

Recent studies indicate that certain basic mechanisms of genetic control of the cell cycle are common to all eukaryotes. A protein called **maturation promoting factor (MPF)** is required for the cell to make the transition from G_2 to mitosis. Although not all of the details are understood, MPF formation appears to be controlled in the following way: **Cyclin,** a protein whose level oscillates during the cell cycle, is thought to interact with another protein to form **pre-MPF,** an inactive form of MPF. Specific enzymes are required to convert pre-MPF to active MPF, which in turn helps initiate mitosis. This system has been highly conserved during the evolution of eukaryotes; it is found in organisms as diverse as yeast (a simple single-celled eukaryote), frogs, clams, and plants.

Certain drugs can stop the cell cycle. Some of these prevent DNA synthesis, whereas others inhibit the synthesis of proteins that control the cycle as well as structural proteins that contribute to the mitotic spindle. Because cancer cells (see Chapter 16) often divide much more rapidly than most normal body cells, they may be most affected by these drugs. Many of the side effects of certain anticancer drugs (e.g., nausea, hair loss) are attributable to the drugs' effects on rapidly dividing cells in the digestive system, hair follicles, and so forth.

Certain plant hormones are known to stimulate mitosis. Chief among these are the **cytokinins,** which act as promoters of mitosis both in normal growth and in wound healing (see Chapter 36).

The cell cycle can also be affected by cold temperatures and other agents that interfere with the normal function of the mitotic spindle. **Colchicine,** a drug used to block cell division in eukaryotic cells, binds with tubulin, the major microtubule protein. This causes the spindle to break down and prevents the chromosomes from moving to the opposite poles of the cell. As a result, a cell may end up with an extra set of chromosomes. In general, plants are relatively tolerant of extra chromosome sets (a condition known as **polyploidy**); in fact, polyploid plants tend to be larger and more vigorous than normal plants. Animals with extra chromosome sets are known but are relatively rare.

VARIOUS MODES OF REPRODUCTION REQUIRE DIFFERENT TYPES OF CELL DIVISION

Although the details of the reproductive process vary greatly among different kinds of organisms, we can distinguish two basic types of reproduction—asexual and sexual. In **asexual** reproduction a single parent usually splits, buds, or fragments to produce two or more individuals (Figure 9–11). In most forms of asexual reproduction all of the cells are produced by mitosis, so their genes and inherited traits are identical to those of the parent. Such a group of genetically identical organisms is termed a **clone.** Asexual reproduction is usually a rapid process; it permits organisms well adapted to their environment to produce new generations of similarly adapted organisms.

In contrast, **sexual** reproduction involves the union of two specialized sex cells, or **gametes,** to form a single cell called a **zygote.** Usually the gametes are contributed by two different parents, but in some cases a single parent furnishes both gametes. In the case of animals and plants, the gametes are the egg and the sperm and the fertilized egg is the zygote.

Offspring produced sexually are not genetically identical to their parents, so some may be able to survive environmental changes or other stresses better than either parent, whereas others, with a different combination of traits, may be less able to survive.

Because you now understand the roles of chromosomes in inheritance, you may recognize a problem in eukaryotic sexual reproduction: If each gamete has the same number of chromosomes as the cells of the parent that produced it, then the zygote would be expected to have twice as many chromosomes, and this doubling would occur generation after generation. How do organisms avoid producing zygotes with ever-increasing

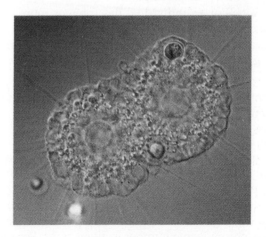

Figure 9–11   An amoeboid protozoon (*Actinoparys sol*) in binary fission, a form of asexual reproduction.   (Phillip A. Harrington/Peter Arnold, Inc.)

chromosome numbers? To answer this question, we need more information about the types of chromosomes found in cells.

Chromosomes normally exist in pairs in the somatic (body) cells of higher plants and animals. Thus, the 46 chromosomes in human cells constitute 23 different pairs. The members of a pair, called **homologous chromosomes,** are similar in size, shape, and the position of their centromeres. When stained by special techniques, chromosomes often show characteristic banding patterns for each pair. In most species, chromosomes vary enough in their morphological features that cytologists can distinguish the different homologous pairs (see Figure 9–1).

The most important feature of homologous chromosomes is that they carry information for controlling the same kinds of genetic traits, although not necessarily identical information. For example, members of a pair of homologous chromosomes might each carry a gene that specifies hemoglobin structure; however, one member might have the information for normal hemoglobin whereas the other might specify the abnormal form of hemoglobin associated with sickle cell anemia (see Chapter 15).

If a cell or nucleus contains two of each kind of chromosome (two sets of chromosomes), it is said to have a **diploid** chromosome number. If only one chromosome of each homologous pair is present, it has the **haploid** number. In humans the diploid chromosome number is 46 and the haploid number is 23. When the sperm and egg fuse at fertilization, each gamete contributes a haploid set of chromosomes; the diploid number is thereby restored in the fertilized egg (zygote). When the zygote divides by mitosis to form the first two cells of the embryo, each daughter cell receives the diploid number of chromosomes and this is repeated in subsequent mitotic divisions. Thus, most human body cells are diploid.

If a cell or an individual has three or more sets of chromosomes, we say that it is polyploid. Polyploidy is relatively rare among animals but quite common among plants. In fact, almost one half of all flowering plants and almost three fourths of all grasses are polyploid. As mentioned above, such plants are often larger and more hardy than diploid members of the same group and may be important commercially (Figure 9–12). Modern bread wheat (*Triticum aestivum*) is a hexaploid with 42 chromosomes, derived from three different diploid species with 14 chromosomes each (see Chapter 19).

The abbreviation for the chromosome number found in the gametes of a particular species is n, and the zygotic chromosome number is given as $2n$. For organisms that are not polyploid, the haploid chromosome number is equal to n and the diploid number is equal to $2n$. The designation of chromosome sets in polyploids is discussed in Chapter 19. For simplicity, in the rest of

Figure 9–12   Modern bread wheat is a hexaploid plant.   (Sharon Cummings/Dembinsky Photo Associates)

this chapter we assume that the organisms used as examples are not polyploid. We therefore use the designations diploid and $2n$, and haploid and n, interchangeably, although the terms diploid and $2n$ are not strictly synonymous.

DIPLOID CELLS GIVE RISE TO HAPLOID CELLS DURING MEIOSIS

We have examined the process of mitosis, which ensures that each daughter cell receives exactly the same number and kind of chromosomes that the parent cell had. A diploid cell that undergoes mitosis produces two diploid cells; similarly a haploid cell produces two haploid cells. A constant chromosome number in successive generations of sexually reproducing organisms is ensured by a special type of cell division called **meiosis.** The term *meiosis* means "to make smaller," referring to the fact that the process involves two successive cell divisions during which the chromosome number is reduced by one half.

Meiosis is directly involved in gamete (egg and sperm) formation in animals. In plants and some other organisms meiosis gives rise to haploid *spores.* These then divide mitotically, and some of their descendants become haploid gametes. When two haploid gametes unite, the fusion of their nuclei reconstitutes the diploid chromosome number in the zygote. The role of meiosis is discussed in the Making the Connection box on page 225.

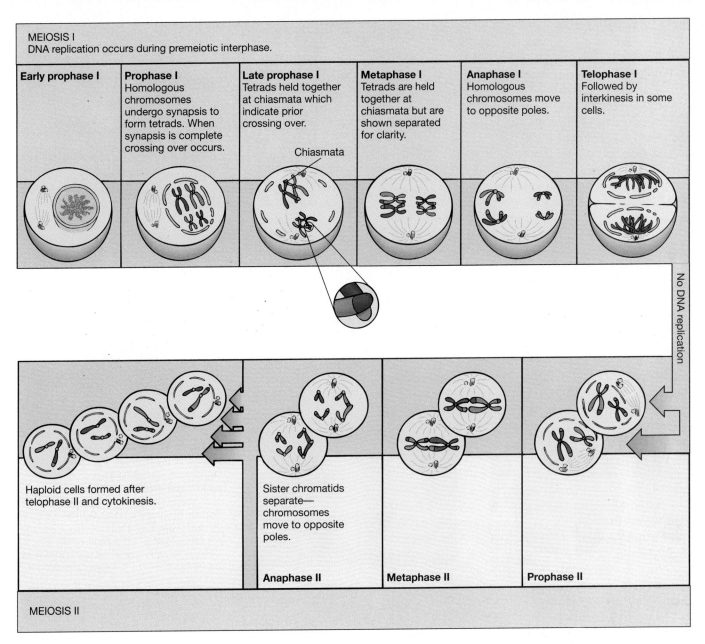

MEIOSIS I
DNA replication occurs during premeiotic interphase.

Early prophase I	Prophase I	Late prophase I	Metaphase I	Anaphase I	Telophase I
	Homologous chromosomes undergo synapsis to form tetrads. When synapsis is complete crossing over occurs.	Tetrads held together at chiasmata which indicate prior crossing over.	Tetrads are held together at chiasmata but are shown separated for clarity.	Homologous chromosomes move to opposite poles.	Followed by interkinesis in some cells.

Chiasmata

No DNA replication

Haploid cells formed after telophase II and cytokinesis.

Sister chromatids separate—chromosomes move to opposite poles.

Anaphase II   Metaphase II   Prophase II

MEIOSIS II

Figure 9–13 The stages of meiosis. The diploid number for the cell is four.

Haploid Cells Produced by Meiosis Have Unique Combinations of Genes

The events of meiosis are similar to the events of mitosis, with important differences: (1) Meiosis involves two successive nuclear and cytoplasmic divisions, with the potential to yield a total of four cells. (2) Despite two successive nuclear divisions, the DNA and other chromosomal components are duplicated only once, during the interphase preceding the first meiotic division. (3) Each of the four cells produced in meiosis contains the haploid number of chromosomes—i.e., only one representative of each homologous pair. (4) During meiosis, the genetic information from both parents is shuffled so each resulting haploid cell (which either is a gamete itself or ultimately gives rise to one or more gametes) has a virtually unique combination of genes.

Meiosis Involves Segregation of Homologous Chromosomes into Different Daughter Cells

Meiosis typically consists of two nuclear and cytoplasmic divisions, designated the *first* and *second meiotic divisions*, or simply **meiosis I** and **meiosis II**. Each includes a prophase, metaphase, anaphase, and telophase. During meiosis I, the members of each homologous pair of chromosomes separate and are distributed into separate nuclei. In meiosis II the chromatids that make up each chromosome separate and are distributed to the nuclei of the daughter cells. The following discussion describes meiosis in an animal with a diploid chromosome number of four. Refer to Figures 9–13 and 9–14 as you read.

As in mitosis, the chromosomes are duplicated during the S phase of interphase, before meiosis actually

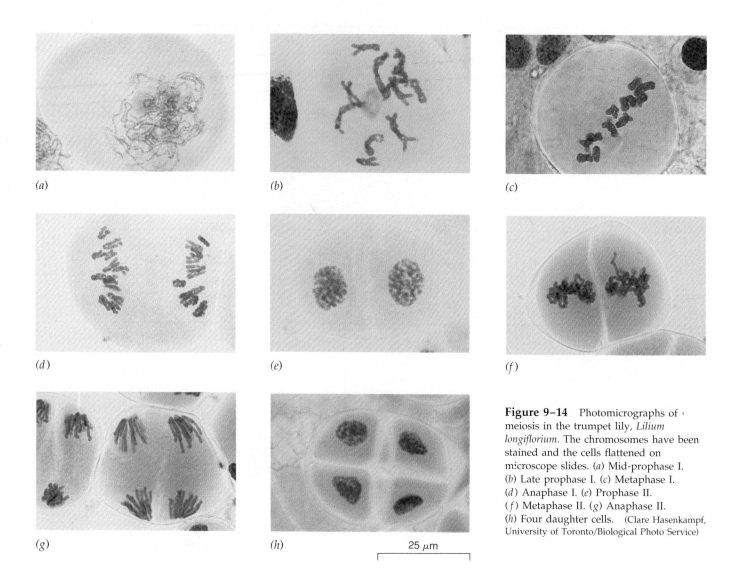

(a)

(b)

(c)

(d)

(e)

(f)

(g)

(h)

25 μm

Figure 9–14 Photomicrographs of meiosis in the trumpet lily, *Lilium longiflorium*. The chromosomes have been stained and the cells flattened on microscope slides. (*a*) Mid-prophase I. (*b*) Late prophase I. (*c*) Metaphase I. (*d*) Anaphase I. (*e*) Prophase II. (*f*) Metaphase II. (*g*) Anaphase II. (*h*) Four daughter cells.   (Clare Hasenkampf, University of Toronto/Biological Photo Service)

begins, and each duplicated chromosome consists of two chromatids joined in the vicinity of their centromeres. During *prophase I*, while the chromatids are still elongated and thin, the homologous chromosomes come to lie lengthwise side by side. This process is called **synapsis,** which means "fastening together." In our example, because the diploid number is four, there are two homologous pairs.

It is customary when discussing higher organisms to refer to one member of each homologous pair as a **maternal homologue,** because it was originally inherited from the female parent, and to the other as a **paternal homologue,** because it was contributed by the male parent during the formation of the zygote. Because each chromosome was duplicated during the premeiotic interphase and now consists of two chromatids, synapsis results in the association of *four* chromatids. The resulting complex is known as a **bivalent** or a **tetrad.** The term *bivalent*, in which the prefix *bi-* refers to the two homologous chromosomes, is commonly used by cytogeneticists. The term *tetrad* (*tetra-* = 4) is preferred by some geneticists interested in following the fates of

the four chromatids. We will use the term *tetrad* in further discussions.

The number of tetrads equals the haploid number of chromosomes. In our example there are two tetrads; in human cells there are 23 tetrads (and a total of 92 chromatids) at this stage.

During synapsis homologous chromosomes become closely associated. Electron microscopic observations reveal that a characteristic structure, known as the **synaptonemal complex,** forms between the synapsed homologues (Figure 9–15). Genetic material may be exchanged between homologous (nonsister) chromatids by **crossing over,** a process in which enzymes break, exchange parts, and rejoin the chromatids to produce new combinations of genes. The resulting **genetic recombination** greatly enhances the amount of genetic variation among the offspring of sexual partners. This process is discussed in more detail in Chapter 10.

In many species, prophase I is a lengthy phase during which the cell grows and synthesizes nutrients. This is especially true during the formation of some egg cells because materials need to be made for the benefit of the

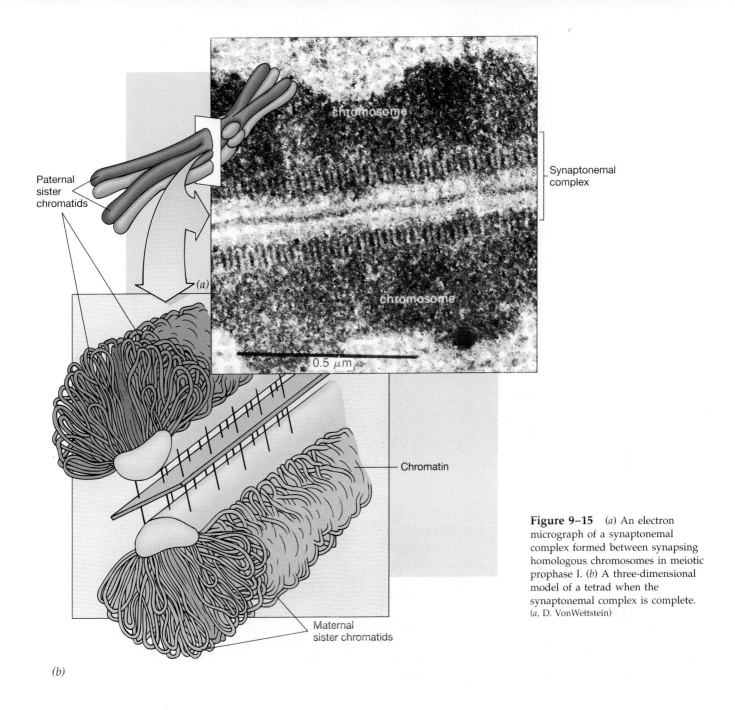

Paternal sister chromatids

(a)

Synaptonemal complex

0.5 μm

chromosome

chromosome

Chromatin

Maternal sister chromatids

(b)

Figure 9–15 (*a*) An electron micrograph of a synaptonemal complex formed between synapsing homologous chromosomes in meiotic prophase I. (*b*) A three-dimensional model of a tetrad when the synaptonemal complex is complete. (*a*, D. VonWettstein)

future embryo. In many types of meiotic cells, the chromosomes assume unusual shapes during this phase. For example, lampbrush chromosomes, found in the female meiotic cells (oocytes) of some amphibians, are composed of hundreds of pairs of loops projecting from the chromatid axis. They owe their name to their resemblance to the brushes used to clean old-fashioned oil lamps (Figure 9–16). The loops are sites of intense RNA synthesis. The RNA is used to direct the synthesis of specific proteins.

In addition to synapsis and crossing over, events similar to those seen during mitotic prophase also take place. A spindle of microtubules and other components forms, and in animal cells a pair of centrioles moves to each pole and astral rays are formed. The nuclear envelope disappears in late prophase I, and the structure of

the tetrads can sometimes then be clearly seen under the microscope (Figure 9–17). The sister chromatids continue to be closely aligned along their lengths, but the homologous chromosomes are no longer closely associated and their centromeres (and kinetochores) are separated from one another. The homologous chromosomes are then held together only at specialized regions, termed **chiasmata** (singular *chiasma*). Each chiasma is a site at which homologous chromatids previously broke, exchanged, and rejoined (crossing over), resulting in an X-shaped configuration.

Prophase I ends when the tetrads become aligned on the equatorial plane; the cell is now said to be at *metaphase I*. The sister kinetochores of one chromosome are attached by spindle fibers to only one of the two poles, and those of the homologous chromosome are

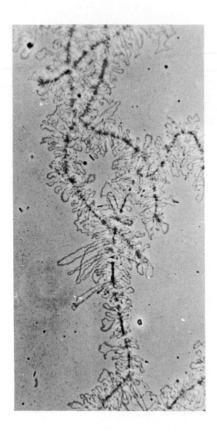

Figure 9–16 A photomicrograph of part of a tetrad from a female meiotic cell (oocyte) of the newt *Triturus viridescens,* showing the loops radiating from the central thread. The appearance of these loops inspired their name, *lampbrush chromosomes.* (Dennis Gould)

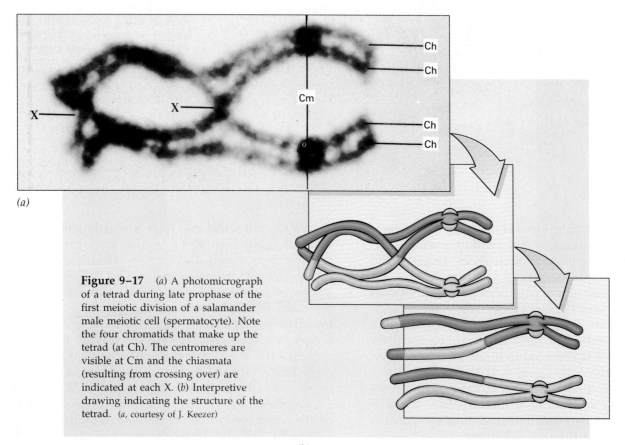

(a)

(b)

Figure 9–17 (a) A photomicrograph of a tetrad during late prophase of the first meiotic division of a salamander male meiotic cell (spermatocyte). Note the four chromatids that make up the tetrad (at Ch). The centromeres are visible at Cm and the chiasmata (resulting from crossing over) are indicated at each X. (b) Interpretive drawing indicating the structure of the tetrad. (a, courtesy of J. Keezer)

Mitosis and Meiosis Occupy Different Positions in Various Kinds of Life Cycles

Various groups of sexually reproducing eukaryotes differ with regard to the occurrence of meiosis and mitosis in their life cycles. Many simple eukaryotes (including some fungi and algae) remain haploid (dividing mitotically) throughout most of their lives, with individuals being unicellular or multicellular. Two haploid gametes (produced by mitosis) fuse to produce a diploid zygote, which undergoes meiosis to restore the haploid state (see figure *a*). Examples of these types of life cycles can be found in Chapters 24 and 25.

Most of us are familiar with the life cycle of humans and other animals (see figure *b*). The body (somatic) cells of an individual organism multiply by mitosis and are diploid; the only haploid cells produced are the gametes. These are formed when certain **germ line** cells undergo meiosis. The formation of gametes is known as **gametogenesis.** Male gametogenesis, termed **spermatogenesis,** results in the formation of four haploid sperm cells for each cell that enters meiosis.

In contrast, female gametogenesis, termed **oogenesis,** results in the formation of a single egg cell, or **ovum,** for every cell that enters meiosis. This is accomplished by a process that apportions virtually all of the cytoplasm to only one of the two nuclei at each of the meiotic divisions. At the end of the first meiotic division, one nucleus is retained and the other, called the first **polar body,** is excluded from the cell and ultimately degenerates. Similarly, at the end of the

second division, one nucleus becomes the second polar body and the other nucleus survives. In this way, one haploid nucleus becomes the recipient of most of the accumulated cytoplasm and nutrients from the original meiotic cell. (See Chapter 48 for a more detailed description.)

The most complex life cycles are displayed by plants and some algae (see figure *c*). These life cycles, characterized by an **alternation of generations,** consist of a multicellular diploid stage, termed the **sporophyte generation,** and a multicellular haploid stage, termed the **gametophyte generation.** Diploid sporophyte cells undergo meiosis to form haploid spores, each of which then divides mitotically to produce a multicellular haploid gametophyte. Gametophytes produce gametes by mitosis. The female and male gametes (eggs and sperm) then fuse to form a diploid zygote, which divides mitotically to produce a multicellular diploid sporophyte.

In higher plants, including flowering plants, the diploid sporophyte—which includes the roots, stem, and leaves of the plant body—is the dominant form. The gametophytes are small and inconspicuous. For example, a pollen grain contains a haploid male gametophyte that forms haploid sperm nuclei by mitosis. More detailed descriptions of alternation of generations can be found in Chapters 26 and 27.

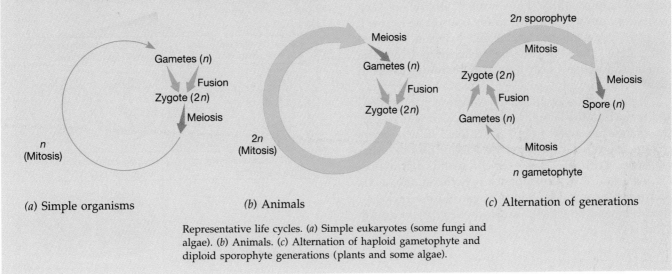

(a) Simple organisms   (b) Animals   (c) Alternation of generations

Representative life cycles. (*a*) Simple eukaryotes (some fungi and algae). (*b*) Animals. (*c*) Alternation of haploid gametophyte and diploid sporophyte generations (plants and some algae).

---

attached to the other pole. (By contrast, in mitosis the sister kinetochores are attached to opposite poles.) During *anaphase I,* the homologous chromosomes of each pair separate, or disjoin, and move toward opposite poles. Each pole receives a random mixture of maternal and paternal chromosomes, but only one member of each pair is present at each pole. The sister chromatids are still united at their centromere regions. Again, this differs from mitotic anaphase, in which the sister chromatids pass to opposite poles.

During *telophase I,* the chromatids decondense, the nuclear envelope may reorganize, and cytokinesis generally takes place. In telophase I in our example, there are two duplicated chromosomes at each pole, for a total of four chromatids; in humans there are 23 duplicated chromosomes (46 chromatids) at each pole.

During the interphase-like stage that follows, called **interkinesis,** there is no S phase because no further chromosome replication takes place. Interkinesis is very brief in most organisms and absent in some.

Because the chromosomes usually remain partially condensed between divisions, the prophase of the second meiotic division is also brief. *Prophase II* is similar to mitotic prophase in many respects. There is no pairing of homologous chromosomes (indeed, only one homologue of each pair is present in each nucleus) and no crossing over.

During *metaphase II*, the chromosomes line up on the equatorial planes of their cells. The first and second metaphases can be easily distinguished in diagrams; at metaphase I the chromatids are arranged in bundles of four (tetrads), and at metaphase II they are in groups of two (as in mitotic metaphase). This is not always so obvious in natural chromosomes.

During *anaphase II* the chromatids, attached to spindle fibers at their kinetochores, separate and move to opposite poles, just as they would at mitotic anaphase. As in mitosis, each chromatid now becomes known as a chromosome. Thus, at *telophase II* there is one homologue for each homologous pair at each pole. Each homologue is an unduplicated chromosome. Nuclear envelopes then re-form, the chromosomes gradually elongate to form chromatin threads, and cytokinesis occurs.

The two successive divisions have the potential to yield four haploid nuclei, each containing *one* of each kind of chromosome. Each resulting haploid cell has a different combination of genes. This genetic variation has two sources: (1) During meiosis the maternal and paternal chromosomes are "shuffled" and one of each pair is randomly distributed to the poles at anaphase I. (2) DNA segments are exchanged between maternal and paternal homologues during crossing over. The genetic consequences of these events are discussed in more detail in Chapter 10.

Figure 9–18 is a simplified comparison of mitosis and meiosis. Mitosis is a single division in which *sister* chromatids separate from each other. If we ignore crossing over, we can say that *homologues* disjoin (separate) during meiosis I, and *sister* chromatids disjoin during meiosis II. It is also correct to say that homologous centromeres (or kinetochores) disjoin during meiosis I and sister centromeres (or kinetochores) disjoin during meiosis II.

Figure 9–18   A simplified view of meiosis compared with mitosis. The diploid number of the cell is four. (*a*) Mitosis. Note that each daughter cell contains an identical complement of four unduplicated chromosomes (two pairs), which is the diploid number. (*b*) Meiosis. Two divisions take place, giving rise to four daughter cells. Each daughter cell contains only two unduplicated chromosomes, one of each homologous pair. The chromosomes shown in blue originally came from one parent, those in red from the other. In prophase I of meiosis, homologous chromosomes synapse to form tetrads.

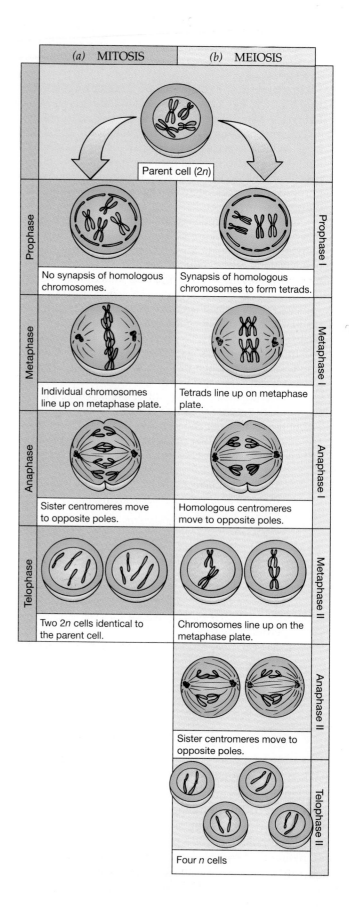

SUMMARY

I. In the production of a new generation, genetic information is transferred from parent to offspring; this process is termed *heredity*. Genetics is the study of the structure, transmission, and expression of genes.

II. Genes are made of DNA. DNA is complexed with protein and RNA to form the chromatin fibers that make up chromosomes.
   A. A gene is the portion of chromosomal DNA that codes for a specific RNA molecule, which may in turn code for a specific polypeptide.
   B. A diploid organism of a given species has a characteristic number of pairs of chromosomes per cell. The two members of each pair, called *homologous chromosomes*, are similar in length, shape, and other structural features and carry genes affecting the same kinds of traits of the organism.

III. The eukaryotic cell cycle is the period from the beginning of one division to the beginning of the next division.
   A. Interphase can be divided into the first gap phase (G_1), the chromosomal synthesis phase (S), and the second gap phase (G_2).
      1. During the G_1 phase, the cell grows and prepares for the S phase.
      2. DNA and the chromosomal proteins are synthesized during the S phase.
      3. During the G_2 phase, protein synthesis increases in preparation for cell division.
   B. During mitosis, identical chromosomes are distributed to each pole of the cell, and a nuclear envelope forms around each set.
      1. During prophase, the chromosomes become visible in the microscope, the nucleolus disappears, the nuclear envelope breaks down, and the mitotic spindle begins to form.
      2. During metaphase, the duplicated chromosomes, composed of a pair of sister chromatids, line up along the equatorial plane of the cell; the mitotic spindle is complete.
      3. During anaphase, the sister chromatids separate from one another and move to opposite poles of the cell. Each chromatid is now considered to be a chromosome.
      4. During telophase, a nuclear envelope reforms around each set of chromosomes, nucleoli become

apparent, the chromosomes uncoil, and the spindle disappears.
   C. During cytokinesis, which generally begins in telophase and therefore overlaps mitosis, the cytoplasm divides, forming two individual cells.

IV. There are two major forms of reproduction: asexual and sexual.
   A. Offspring produced by asexual reproduction usually have hereditary traits identical to those of the single parent. These offspring constitute a clone. Usually all of the cells involved are produced by mitosis.
   B. In sexual reproduction two haploid sex cells, or gametes, fuse to form a single diploid zygote.
      1. A diploid cell undergoing *meiosis* completes two successive cell divisions to give rise to four haploid cells. Meiosis must take place at some time in the life cycle of a sexually reproducing organism if gametes are to be haploid.
         a. During meiotic prophase I the members of a homologous pair of chromosomes undergo synapsis and crossing over, during which segments of DNA strands are exchanged between homologous (nonsister) chromatids.
         b. The members of each pair of homologous chromosomes separate during meiotic anaphase I and are distributed to different daughter cells.
         c. During meiosis II, the two chromatids of each homologous chromosome separate, and one is distributed to each daughter cell.
      2. When a zygote is formed, each parent contributes one member of each homologous pair.

V. Various groups of organisms differ with respect to the roles of mitosis and meiosis in their life cycles.
   A. Simple eukaryotes may be regularly haploid; the only diploid stage is the zygote, which undergoes meiosis to restore the haploid state.
   B. The somatic cells of animals are diploid; the only haploid cells are the gametes (produced by meiosis).
   C. Plants (and some algae) have alternation of generations. A diploid sporophyte forms spores by meiosis. These divide mitotically to form haploid gametophytes, which produce gametes mitotically. Two haploid gametes then fuse to form a diploid zygote, which divides mitotically to produce a new diploid sporophyte.

POST-TEST

1. The tendency of individuals to resemble their parents is termed _____.
2. Chromosomes are composed of chromatin fibers, which are made up of _____, _____, and _____.
3. The period from the beginning of one cell division to the beginning of the next is termed the _____ _____.
4. DNA for the new sets of chromosomes is synthesized during the _____ stage of the cell cycle.
5. To facilitate description of the process, mitosis has been divided into four stages: _____, _____, _____, and _____.
6. A duplicated chromosome consists of a pair of _____ _____.
7. The centromere of each chromatid contains a specialized structure, the _____, to which some of the spindle fibers attach.
8. The period during which the chromosomes are lined up on the equatorial plane of the cell constitutes _____.

9. The division of the cytoplasm to yield two daughter cells is called _____.

10. The drug _____ binds to tubulin, the major microtubule protein, thereby blocking cell division.

11. The splitting, budding, or fragmenting of a single parent to give rise to two or more offspring with hereditary traits identical to those of the parent is termed _____ reproduction.

12. A group of genetically identical individuals is called a _____.

13. The members of a pair of chromosomes are referred to as _____ chromosomes.

14. Cells that contain two complete sets of chromosomes are _____, whereas those that contain more than two complete sets are _____.

15. Gametes contain the _____ chromosome number.

16. The pairing of homologous chromosomes during prophase I is known as _____. The chromosome configuration produced by such an association of homologous chromosomes is termed a(n) _____ or a(n) _____.

17. The exchange of segments of homologous chromatids during meiotic prophase I is known as _____.

18. In a human with the diploid chromosome number of 46, each sperm or egg contributes _____ chromosomes to the zygote.

19. Alternation of haploid and diploid generations is characteristic of _____ and some algae.

REVIEW QUESTIONS

1. Which component of chromatin is considered to be the most important in carrying genetic information?

2. What is the relationship between genes and chromosomes? What are the functions of genes?

3. Two species may have the same chromosome number and yet be very different. Explain.

4. Describe the structure of a duplicated chromosome, paying special attention to the sister chromatids, the centromeres, and the kinetochores. What are the functions of centromeres and of kinetochores?

5. What are the stages of the cell cycle and mitosis?

6. Define the following terms:
   a. diploid
   b. haploid
   c. homologous chromosomes

7. How does meiosis differ from mitosis? Are there any points of similarity between mitosis and meiosis?

8. What roles do mitosis, meiosis, and gamete formation play in the three basic kinds of life cycles?

9. Assume that an animal has a diploid chromosome number of ten.
   a. How many chromosomes would it have in a typical body cell, such as a skin cell?
   b. How many chromosomes would be present in a cell at mitotic prophase? How many chromatids?
   c. How many tetrads would form in the prophase of the first meiotic division?
   d. How many chromosomes would be present in each gamete? Are these duplicated chromosomes?

RECOMMENDED READINGS

Alberts, B., D. Bray, J. Lewis, M. Raff, K. Roberts, and J. D. Watson. *Molecular Biology of the Cell*, Chapters 13 and 15. Garland, New York, 1989. An extensive, detailed, and well-written discussion of cell growth and division, covering the control of cell division, the cell cycle, and the events of mitosis and meiosis.

McIntosh, J. R., and K. L. McDonald. The mitotic spindle. *Scientific American*, October 1989. A review of current under-

standing of the mechanisms involved in mitotic chromosome separation.

Murray, A. W., and M. W. Kirschner. What controls the cell cycle. *Scientific American*, March 1991. A review of the universal regulators involved in controlling the cell cycle.

The Basic Principles of Heredity

The basic rules of inheritance in eukaryotes were discovered by Gregor Mendel (1822–1884), an abbot who bred pea plants in his monastery garden at Brünn, Austria (now Brno, Czechoslovakia). Mendel was the first scientist effectively to apply quantitative methods to the study of inheritance. He did not merely describe his observations; he planned his experiments carefully, recorded the data, and subjected the results to mathematical analysis. Although his work was unappreciated in his lifetime, it was "rediscovered" in 1900. Three of his major findings—now known as Mendel's principles of dominance, segregation, and independent assortment—became the foundation of the science of genetics.

Early geneticists initially extended Mendel's principles by corre-

Gregor Mendel (1822–1884).
(The Bettmann Archive)

lating the *transmission of genetic information* from generation to generation with the behavior of chromosomes during meiosis. They also refined his methods and, through their studies on a variety of organisms, both verified Mendel's findings and added to a growing list of so-called exceptions to Mendel's principles. These include such phenomena as linkage, sex linkage, and polygenic inheritance.

Geneticists study not only the transmission of genes, but also the *expression of genetic information*. As you will see in this and succeeding chapters, our understanding of the relationship between an organism's genes and its appearance has become increasingly sophisticated as we have learned more about the flow of information in cells.

After you have studied this chapter you should be able to

1. Define and use correctly the terms *allele, locus, genotype, phenotype, dominant, recessive, homozygous, heterozygous,* and *test cross.*
2. Apply Mendel's principles to solve problems in genetics involving monohybrid and dihybrid crosses.
3. Explain how the method of progeny testing is used by commercial breeders to establish a genetic strain that breeds true for a given trait.
4. Discriminate between independent and mutually exclusive events; apply the product law and sum law appropriately when predicting the outcomes of genetic crosses.
5. Solve problems in genetics involving incomplete dominance, epistasis, polygenes, multiple alleles, and X-linked traits.

6. Explain some of the ways in which genes may interact to affect the appearance of a single trait; discuss how it is possible for a single gene to affect many features of the organism simultaneously.
7. Analyze data from a dihybrid test cross to distinguish between independent assortment and linkage. Relate each to specific events in meiosis. Map the relative positions of linked genes on a chromosome.
8. Discuss the genetic determination of sex and the role of the Y chromosome in determining male sex in humans; contrast the mechanism of sex determination in humans and other mammals with that in various other animals and some plants; compare dosage compensation of X-linked genes in mammals and *Drosophila.*
9. Assess the effects of inbreeding versus outbreeding on a population; illustrate the genetic basis of hybrid vigor.

GREGOR MENDEL FIRST FORMULATED THE PRINCIPLES OF INHERITANCE

Gregor Mendel was not the first plant breeder; **hybrid** plants and animals (offspring of two genetically dissimilar parents) had been known for a long time. When Mendel began his breeding experiments in 1857, two main facts about inheritance were widely recognized: (1) All hybrid plants with the same two kinds of parents look alike. (2) When hybrids themselves are mated they do not breed true; their offspring show a mixture of traits. Some look like their parents, and some have features like their grandparents. Mendel's genius lay in his ability to recognize a pattern in the way the parental traits reappear in the offspring of hybrids. No one before had categorized and counted the offspring and analyzed these regular patterns over several generations.

Just as geneticists do today, Mendel chose the organism for his experiments very carefully. The garden pea, *Pisum sativum,* had a number of advantages. Pea plants are easy to grow, and many varieties of peas were available through commercial sources. It is impossible to study inheritance without such genetic **variation.** (If every person in the population had blue eyes, it would be impossible to study the inheritance of eye color.)

Another advantage of pea plants is that **controlled pollinations** are relatively easy to conduct. Pea flowers (Figure 10–1) have both male and female parts. The male **anthers** (pollen-producing parts of the flower) can be removed to prevent self-fertilization. Pollen from a different source can then be applied to the **stigma** (receptive surface of the female parts). Pea flowers are easily protected from other sources of pollen because the reproductive structures are completely enclosed by the

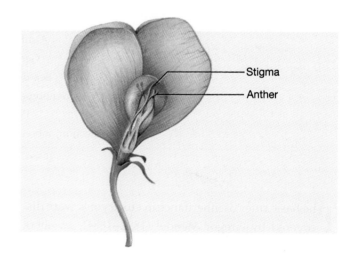

Figure 10–1   A cut-away drawing of a pea flower illustrating the pollen-producing anthers and the stigma, that portion of the female part of the flower that receives the pollen. Notice how the reproductive structures are enclosed by the petals.

petals. Covering the pollinated flowers with small bags provides additional protection from pollinating insects.

Although his original pea seeds were obtained from commercial sources, Mendel did some important preliminary work before he started his actual experiments. For several years he worked to develop genetically pure, or **true breeding,** lines for a number of inherited traits. A true breeding line for a given trait, such as tall plants, produces only tall plants, generation after generation. During this time he apparently chose those characteristics of his pea strains that could be best studied and probably discarded or ignored a number of others. He probably also made the initial observations that would later form the basis of his theories.

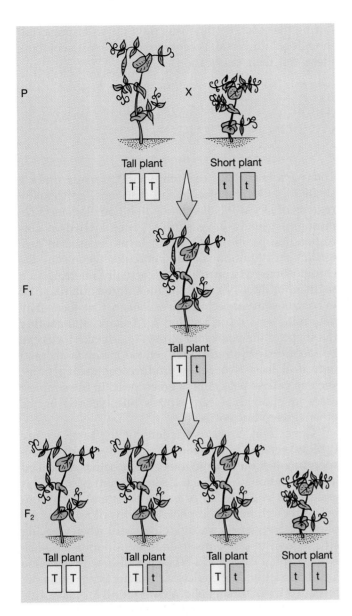

Figure 10–2 A diagram illustrating one of the crosses carried out by Gregor Mendel. Crossing a tall pea plant with a short pea plant yielded only tall offspring in the F_1 generation. However, when these offspring self-pollinated or when two individuals were crossed, the next generation included tall and short plants in a ratio of about 3:1.

one of the two parents (Figure 10–2). For example, when he crossed tall plants with short plants of the **parental,** or **P, generation,** all of the progeny were tall. These offspring are the **first filial** (Latin for "sons and daughters") **generation,** or **F_1 generation.** The second filial generation, or **F_2 generation,** is produced by a cross between two F_1 offspring or by self-pollination of a single F_1 individual. The F_2 generation included 787 tall plants and 277 short plants. Because the hereditary factor for shortness reappeared in the F_2 generation, it clearly had not been "lost" in the F_1 generation.

Mendel's experiments led to his discovery and explanation of three major principles of heredity: dominance, segregation, and independent assortment. We consider the first two now and the third later in the chapter.

The Principle of Dominance States That One Gene Can Mask the Expression of Another in a Hybrid

From such results Mendel proposed that each kind of inherited feature of an organism is controlled by two "factors" that are present in every individual. Mendel's "hereditary factors" are essentially what we call genes today, so we will use that term in our discussion.

On the basis of his findings, Mendel formulated what has become known as his **principle of dominance,** which states that in an F_1 hybrid the gene from one of the parents masks expression of the gene from the other parent. The gene expressed in the F_1 generation (tallness in our example) is said to be **dominant;** the one hidden (shortness) is said to be **recessive.** This finding was at odds with the prevailing idea of **blending inheritance,** which implied that a hybrid should be intermediate between the two parents. Although we know today that the principle of dominance does not always apply (exceptions are considered later in this chapter), the recognition that one gene can mask the expression of another was an important intellectual leap on Mendel's part.

The Principle of Segregation States That the Genes of a Pair Separate When Gametes Are Formed

Mendel further proposed that, when gametes are formed, the two genes behave like particles and become separated so that each sex cell (egg or sperm) contains only one member of each pair. The two genes remain intact during this process (one does not "contaminate" or eliminate the other); thus, recessive traits are not lost and can reappear in the F_2 generation. This idea, referred to as the **principle of segregation,** also ran counter to the notion of blending inheritance, which

Mendel eventually chose strains with seven clearly contrasting pairs of traits: yellow versus green seeds, round versus wrinkled seeds, green versus yellow pods, tall versus short plants, inflated versus constricted pods, white seed coats versus gray seed coats, and flowers borne on the ends of the stems versus flowers appearing all along the stems.

When Mendel crossed plants from two true breeding lines with contrasting traits, the members of the first generation of offspring all looked alike and resembled

envisioned hereditary determinants as fluids that became inseparably mixed once they were combined in a hybrid.

In our example, the F_1-generation tall plants had two genes, one for tallness (which we designate T) and one for shortness (which we designate t), but because the tall gene was dominant, these plants were tall. However, when these F_1 plants formed gametes, the gene for tallness separated (segregated) from the gene for shortness, so that half of the gametes contained a gene for tallness and the other half contained a gene for shortness. The random process of fertilization led to three possible combinations of factors in the F_2 offspring: one quarter with two tallness genes (TT), one quarter with two shortness genes (tt), and one half with one gene each for tallness and shortness (Tt). Because both TT and Tt plants are tall, on average one could expect approximately three quarters (787/1064) to express the dominant gene (tall) and about one quarter (277/1064) the recessive gene (short).

Today we know that segregation of genes is a direct result of the separation of homologous chromosomes during meiosis. Later, at the time of fertilization, each haploid gamete contributes one chromosome of each homologous pair and therefore one gene for each gene pair (T or t in our example). Although gametes and fertilization were known at the time Mendel carried out his research, mitosis and meiosis had not yet been discovered. It is truly remarkable that Mendel was able to formulate his ideas mainly on the basis of mathematical abstractions. Today his principles are much easier to understand because we are able to think about them in concrete terms, by relating the transmission of genes to the behavior of chromosomes.

Mendel reported these and other findings (discussed later in this chapter) at a meeting of the Brünn Society for the Study of Natural Science and published his results in the transactions of that society in 1866. At that time biology was largely a descriptive science, and biologists had little interest in applying quantitative and experimental methods such as Mendel had used. The importance of his results and his interpretations of those results was not appreciated by other biologists of the time, and his findings were neglected for nearly 35 years.

In 1900 Hugo DeVries in Holland, Karl Correns in Germany, and Erich von Tschermak in Austria rediscovered Mendel's paper and found that it provided explanations for their own research findings. They gave credit to Mendel by naming the basic laws of inheritance after him. By this time, biologists had a much greater appreciation of the value of experimental methods. The details of mitosis, meiosis, and fertilization had been described, and in 1903 W. S. Sutton pointed out the connection between Mendel's segregation of genes and the separation of homologous chromosomes

during meiosis. The time was right for widespread (although not universal) acceptance and extension of these ideas and their implications.

ALLELES OCCUPY CORRESPONDING LOCI ON HOMOLOGOUS CHROMOSOMES

Today we know that each chromatid is made up of a single long DNA molecule and that genes are actually regions of DNA. We also know that homologous chromosomes usually have similar genes located in corresponding positions. The term **locus**[1] is used to designate the location of a particular gene on the chromosome. Of course we are actually referring to a segment of the DNA that has the information required to control some aspect of the organism. One locus may determine seed color, another seed shape, still another the shape of the pods, and so on. A particular locus can be identified (by traditional genetic methods at least) only if at least two genes produce contrasting traits, such as yellow peas versus green peas. In the simplest cases an individual can express one (yellow) or the other (green) but not both.

Genes that govern variations of the same feature (yellow versus green seed color) and occupy corresponding loci on homologous chromosomes are called **alleles** (Figure 10–3). Each allele (variant) of a locus is assigned a single letter (or group of letters) as its symbol. Although more complicated forms of notation are often used by geneticists, it is customary when working simple genetic problems to indicate a dominant allele with a capital letter and a recessive allele with the same lowercase letter. The choice of the letter is generally determined by the first allelic variant found for that locus. For example, the dominant allele that governs the yellow color of the seed might be designated Y, and the recessive allele responsible for the green color would then be designated y. Because discovery of the yellow allele made identification of this locus possible, we refer to the locus as the *yellow* locus, although pea seeds are most commonly green.

Remember that the term *locus* is used to designate not only a position on a chromosome, but also a type of gene controlling a particular *kind* of characteristic; thus, Y (yellow) and y (green) represent a specific pair of alleles of a locus involved in determining seed color in peas. Although you may be uncomfortable initially with the fact that geneticists sometimes use the term *gene* to specify a locus and at other times to specify one of the alleles for that locus, the meaning is usually clear from the context.

---

[1] In mathematics a locus is a dimensionless point; a genetic locus, being a segment of DNA, is obviously not dimensionless!

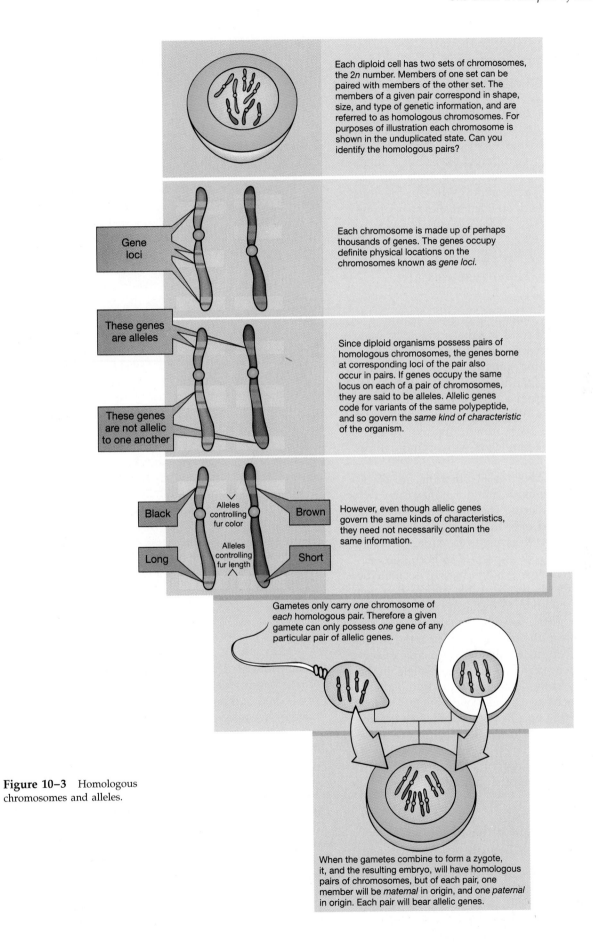

Each diploid cell has two sets of chromosomes, the *2n* number. Members of one set can be paired with members of the other set. The members of a given pair correspond in shape, size, and type of genetic information, and are referred to as homologous chromosomes. For purposes of illustration each chromosome is shown in the unduplicated state. Can you identify the homologous pairs?

Gene loci

Each chromosome is made up of perhaps thousands of genes. The genes occupy definite physical locations on the chromosomes known as *gene loci.*

These genes are alleles

These genes are not allelic to one another

Since diploid organisms possess pairs of homologous chromosomes, the genes borne at corresponding loci of the pair also occur in pairs. If genes occupy the same locus on each of a pair of chromosomes, they are said to be alleles. Allelic genes code for variants of the same polypeptide, and so govern the *same kind of characteristic* of the organism.

Black

Brown

Alleles controlling fur color

Long

Short

Alleles controlling fur length

However, even though allelic genes govern the same kinds of characteristics, they need not necessarily contain the same information.

Gametes only carry *one* chromosome of *each* homologous pair. Therefore a given gamete can only possess *one* gene of any particular pair of allelic genes.

When the gametes combine to form a zygote, it, and the resulting embryo, will have homologous pairs of chromosomes, but of each pair, one member will be *maternal* in origin, and one *paternal* in origin. Each pair will bear allelic genes.

Figure 10–3 Homologous chromosomes and alleles.

A MONOHYBRID CROSS INVOLVES INDIVIDUALS WITH DIFFERENT ALLELES FOR A GIVEN GENE LOCUS

The basic principles of genetics and the use of genetic terms are best illustrated by examples. The simplest case is a **monohybrid cross**—that is, a cross between two individuals that carry different alleles for a single locus. Our first example in this section deals with the expected ratios in the F_2 generation, as did our previous example of Mendel's work on tall and short pea plants.

Heterozygotes Carry Two Different Alleles for a Locus; Homozygotes Carry Identical Alleles

Figure 10–4 shows a monohybrid cross featuring a locus that governs coat color in guinea pigs. The male comes from a true breeding line of black guinea pigs. We say that he is **homozygous** for black because the two alleles he carries for this locus are *identical*. The brown female is also from a true breeding line and is homozygous for brown. What color would you expect the F_1 offspring to be? Dark brown? Spotted? It is impossible to make such a prediction without more information.

In this particular case, the F_1 offspring are black, but they are **heterozygous,** meaning that they carry two *different* alleles for this locus. The allele for brown coat color can be expressed only in a homozygous brown individual; it is referred to as a *recessive allele*. The allele for black coat color can be expressed in both homozygous black and heterozygous individuals; it is said to be a *dominant allele*. On the basis of this information, we can use standard notation to designate the dominant black allele as B and the recessive brown allele as b.

During meiosis in the male parent (BB), the two B alleles separate according to Mendel's principle of segregation so that each sperm has only one B allele. In the formation of eggs in the female (bb), the two b alleles separate so that each egg has only one b allele. The fertilization of each b egg by a B sperm results in a heterozygous F_1 animal with the alleles Bb—that is, one allele for brown coat and one for black coat. Because this is the only possible combination of alleles present in the eggs and sperm, all of the offspring are Bb.

The Phenotype of an Individual Does Not Always Reveal Its Genotype

The fact that some alleles may be dominant and others recessive means that we cannot always determine which alleles are carried by an organism simply by looking at it. The term used to specify the *appearance* of an individual in a given environment with respect to a

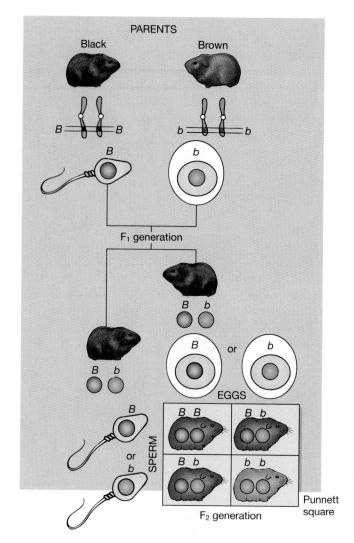

Figure 10–4 A monohybrid cross. The cross is between a homozygous brown guinea pig and a homozygous black guinea pig. The F_1 generation includes only black individuals. However, the mating of two of these offspring yields F_2-generation offspring in the expected black:brown ratio of 3:1, indicating that the F_1 individuals are heterozygous.

certain inherited trait is known as its **phenotype.** The *genetic constitution* of that organism, most often expressed in symbols, is its **genotype.** In the cross we have been considering, the genotype of the female parent is homozygous recessive, bb, and her phenotype is brown. The genotype of the male parent is homozygous dominant, BB, and his phenotype is black. The genotype of all the F_1 offspring is heterozygous, Bb, and their phenotype is black. To prevent confusion we always indicate the genotype of a heterozygous individual by writing the symbol for the dominant allele first and the recessive allele second (always Bb, never bB).

The phenomenon of dominance partly explains why an individual may resemble one parent more than the other, even if the two parents make equal contributions to their offspring's genetic constitution. Dominance is not completely predictable and can be determined only by experiment. In one species of animal, black coat may be dominant to brown; in another species, brown may be dominant to black.

A Punnett Square Predicts the Ratios of Genotypes and Phenotypes of the Offspring of a Cross

During meiosis in heterozygous (*Bb*) black guinea pigs, the chromosome containing the *B* allele becomes separated from its homologue, the chromosome containing the *b* allele, so each sperm or egg contains *B* or *b* but never both. Gametes containing *B* alleles and those containing *b* alleles are formed in equal numbers by heterozygous *Bb* individuals. Because no special attraction or repulsion occurs between an egg and a sperm containing the same allele, fertilization is a random process.

The possible combinations of eggs and sperm at fertilization may be represented in the form of a "checkerboard" devised by an early geneticist, Sir Reginald Punnett, and known as a **Punnett square** (see Figure 10–4). The types of gametes from one parent are represented across the top, and those from the other parent are indicated along the left side; the squares are then filled in with the resulting F_2 zygote combinations. Three fourths of all F_2 offspring are genotypically *BB* or *Bb* and phenotypically black; one fourth are genotypically *bb* and phenotypically brown. The genetic mechanism responsible for the approximate 3:1 F_2 ratios (called *monohybrid F_2 phenotypic ratios*) obtained by Mendel in his pea-breeding experiments is again evident. The corresponding genotypic ratio is $1 BB : 2 Bb : 1 bb$.

A Monohybrid Test Cross Is Used To Detect Heterozygosity

One third of the black guinea pigs in the F_2 generation derived from the mating of F_1 hybrids are themselves homozygous, *BB*; the other two thirds are heterozygous, *Bb*. Guinea pigs with the genotypes *BB* and *Bb* are alike phenotypically; they both have black coats. Geneticists distinguish the homozygous (*BB*) and heterozygous (*Bb*) black-coated guinea pigs by a **test cross,** in which each black guinea pig is mated with a homozygous brown (*bb*) guinea pig (Figure 10–5). In a test cross, the two types of gametes produced by the heterozygous parent are not "hidden" in the offspring by dominant alleles coming from the other parent. Therefore, through a test cross one can deduce the genotypes of all of the classes of offspring directly from their phenotypes. If all of the offspring were black, what inference would you make about the genotype of the black parent? If any of the offspring were brown, what conclusion would you draw regarding the genotype of the black parent? Would you be more certain about one of these inferences than the other?

Mendel did just these sorts of experiments, breeding heterozygous tall (*Tt*) pea plants with homozygous recessive (*tt*) short ones. He predicted that the heterozygous parent would produce equal numbers of *T* and *t* gametes, whereas the homozygous short parent would produce only *t* gametes and that this should lead to equal numbers of tall (*Tt*) and short (*tt*) individuals among the progeny. Another value of a test cross is that it allows us to test rather directly the hypothesis that

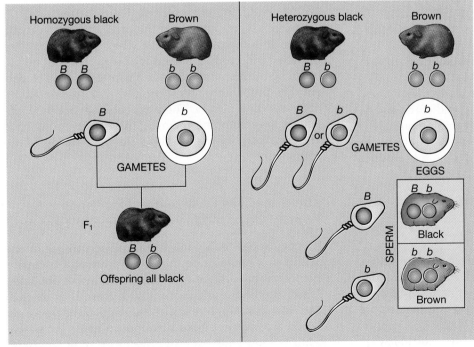

(a)   *(b)*

Figure 10–5 Test crosses to determine the genotype of a black guinea pig. (*a*) If a black guinea pig is mated with a brown guinea pig and all of the offspring are black, the black parent probably has a homozygous genotype.
(*b*) However, if any of the offspring are brown, the black guinea pig must be heterozygous for color.

there is 1:1 segregation of alleles in the heterozygous parent. Thus, Mendel's principles of dominance and segregation not only explained the known facts, such as the monohybrid F₂ 3:1 phenotypic ratio, but also enabled him to predict the results of other experiments, in this case the 1:1 **monohybrid test cross** phenotypic ratio.

This sort of testing is of great importance to the commercial breeding of animals or plants when the breeder is trying to establish a strain that will breed true for a certain trait. Two bulls, for example, may look equally healthy and vigorous, yet the daughters of one may have qualities of milk production distinctly superior to those of the daughters of the other bull. A breeder tests the genotypes of the breeding stock by making test matings and observing the offspring; if the offspring are superior with respect to the desired trait, the parents are thereafter used regularly for breeding.

THE LAWS OF PROBABILITY ARE USED TO PREDICT THE LIKELIHOOD OF GENETIC EVENTS

All genetic ratios are properly expressed in terms of probabilities. In the examples just discussed, among the offspring of two individuals heterozygous for the same gene pair, the ratio of the phenotypes of the dominant and recessive alleles is 3:1. A better way to express our expectations is that there are 3 chances in 4 (¾) that any particular individual offspring of two heterozygous individuals will express the phenotype of the dominant allele and 1 chance in 4 (¼) that it will express the phenotype of the recessive allele. Although we sometimes speak in terms of percentages, probabilities must always be calculated as fractions (e.g., ¾) or decimal fractions (e.g., 0.75)—that is, numbers between 0 and 1. If an event is certain to occur, its probability is 1; if it is certain not to occur, its probability is 0.

Often we wish to *combine* two or more probabilities. The Punnett square, which we use to predict the results of genetic crosses, also allows us to combine probabilities. When we use a Punnett square we are intuitively following two important rules, known as the **product law** and the **sum law.**

The Product Law Predicts the Combined Probabilities of Independent Events

Events are independent if the occurrence of one does not affect the probability of the other. For example, the probability of obtaining heads on the first toss of a coin is ½; the probability of obtaining heads on the second toss (an independent event) is also ½. If two or more events are *independent* of each other, the probability of their both occurring is the *product* of their individual

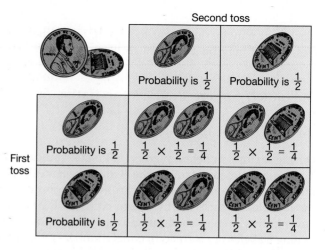

Figure 10–6 Application of the laws of probability. When one tosses a coin twice, the probability of getting heads on the first toss is ½, and the probability of getting tails on the first toss is also ½. Identical predictions apply to the second toss. The outcome of the first toss does not affect the outcome of the second toss, so these events are independent, and we combine them by multiplying the individual probabilities (according to the product law). As shown in the Punnett square, there are four different classes of combined outcomes of two successive tosses. These are mutually exclusive, and we therefore combine them by adding them (according to the sum law). For example, heads/heads and tails/tails are mutually exclusive outcomes. If we wish to calculate the probability that we will get *either* heads/heads *or* tails/tails, we add: ¼ + ¼ = ½. These same laws of probability are used to predict genetic events.

probabilities. If this seems strange to you, keep in mind that when we multiply two numbers less than 1, the product is a smaller number. The probability of obtaining heads first and also second on successive tosses of the coin is the product of their individual probabilities (½ × ½ = ¼, or 1 chance in 4) (Figure 10–6).

Similarly, we can apply the product law to genetic events. If both parents are *Bb*, what is the probability that they will produce a child who is *bb*? For the child to be *bb*, he or she must receive a *b* gamete from each parent. The probability of a *b* egg is ½ and the probability of a *b* sperm is also ½. These probabilities are independent, so we combine them by the product rule (½ × ½ = ¼). You may wish to check this result using a Punnett square.

The Sum Law Predicts the Combined Probabilities of Mutually Exclusive Events

Events are mutually exclusive if the occurrence of one *precludes* occurrence of the other. Mutually exclusive events can be thought of as different ways of obtaining some specified result. Naturally, if there is more than one way to obtain a result, the chances of its being obtained are improved; we therefore combine the probabilities of mutually exclusive events by summing (adding) their individual probabilities.

For example, if we flip a coin twice, what is the probability that it will come up heads one time and tails the other time if we do not specify the order in which these events are to occur? There are two mutually exclusive ways to obtain this outcome. We could get heads the first time (probability ½) and tails the second (probability ½); we use the product law to calculate the combined probability of these independent events, which is ¼. Alternatively, we could also get tails the first time and heads the second; the probability of this occurring is also ¼. We combine the probabilities of these mutually exclusive outcomes using the sum law: ¼ + ¼ = ½. That is, the probability of getting heads once (and only once) and tails once (and only once) on two successive tosses of the coin is ½.

We can also apply the sum law to genetic events. For example, if both parents are *Bb*, what is the probability that they will produce a child like themselves (*Bb*)? There are two mutually exclusive ways of obtaining a *Bb* child. A *B* egg can combine with a *b* sperm. The probability of this outcome is ¼ (calculated by the product rule). A *b* egg can combine with a *B* sperm; this probability is also ¼. Because these two ways of obtaining a *Bb* child are mutually exclusive, we combine their probabilities using the sum law (¼ + ¼ = ½). Again, a Punnett square serves as a useful check.

The Laws of Probability Can Be Applied to a Variety of Calculations

The laws of probability have wide applications. For example, what are the probabilities that a family with two (and only two) children will have two girls, two boys, or one girl and one boy? The probability of having a girl first is ½, and the probability of having a girl second is also ½. These are independent events, so we combine their probabilities by multiplying: ½ × ½ = ¼. In the same way, the probability of having two boys is also ¼. In families that have both a girl and a boy, the girl can be born first or the boy can be born first. The probability that a girl will be born first is ½, and the probability that a boy will be born second is also ½. We use the product law to combine the probabilities of these two independent events: ½ × ½ = ¼. Similarly, the probability that a boy will be born first and a girl second is also ¼. These two kinds of families represent mutually exclusive outcomes, i.e., two different ways of obtaining a family with one boy and one girl. Having two different ways of obtaining the desired result improves our chances, so we use the sum law to combine the probabilities: ¼ + ¼ = ½. Notice that the probabilities of the three types of families (all mutually exclusive outcomes) add up to 1. This serves as a useful check that the calculations have been done correctly. You may also wish to confirm these results by making a Punnett square.

In working with probabilities, it is important to keep in mind a point that many gamblers forget. We can say that "chance has no memory." This means that if events are truly random, past events have no influence on the probability of the occurrence of independent future events. The color of the iris of the human eye is controlled by alleles at several loci, but alleles at one locus are primarily responsible. The allele for brown eye color, *B*, is usually dominant to the allele for blue, *b*. If two heterozygous brown-eyed people marry, what is the probability that they will have a blue-eyed child? Clearly, there is 1 chance in 4 that any child of theirs will have blue eyes. Each fertilization is a separate, independent event; its result is not affected by the results of any previous fertilizations. If these two brown-eyed parents have had three brown-eyed children and are expecting their fourth child, what is the probability that the child will have blue eyes? The unwary might guess that this one *must* have blue eyes, but in fact there is still only 1 chance in 4 that the child will have blue eyes and 3 chances in 4 that the child will have brown eyes.

If we phrase the question differently, however, we obtain a very different answer. If two heterozygous people marry and expect to have four children, what is the probability that all four will have brown eyes? The probability of brown eyes for each child is ¾, so we combine these independent events by the product rule: ¾ × ¾ × ¾ × ¾ = $^{81}/_{256}$ or 0.32. Why the different answers for the two types of problems? Remember that once a brown-eyed child is born, probability (¾) is replaced by certainty (1), so the calculation becomes 1 × 1 × 1 × ¾ = ¾ = chance that the fourth child will have brown eyes (or ¼ chance of blue eyes).

When working probability problems, common sense is more important than blindly memorizing rules. Examine your results to see if they appear reasonable; if they do not you should reevaluate your assumptions.

A DIHYBRID CROSS INVOLVES INDIVIDUALS THAT HAVE DIFFERENT ALLELES AT TWO LOCI

Simple monohybrid crosses each involve a pair of alleles representing a single locus. Mendel also analyzed crosses involving alleles representing two or more loci. A mating between individuals having different alleles at two loci is called a **dihybrid cross.** When two pairs of alleles are located in nonhomologous chromosomes, each pair is inherited independently; i.e., each pair segregates during meiosis independently of the other.

An example of a dihybrid cross carried through the F₂ generation is illustrated in Figure 10–7. When a homozygous black, short-haired guinea pig (*BBSS*, because short hair is dominant to long hair and black is dominant to brown) and a homozygous brown, long-

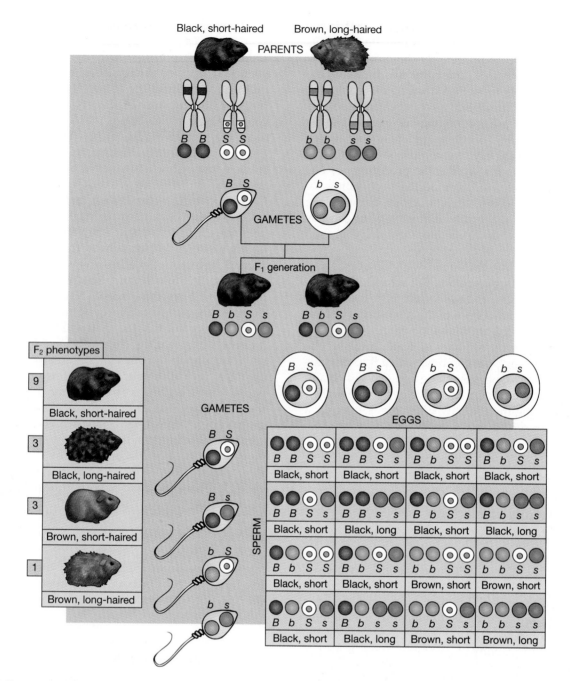

Figure 10–7 A dihybrid cross. When a black, short-haired guinea pig is crossed with a brown, long-haired one, all of the offspring are black and have short hair. However, when two members of the F_1 generation are crossed, the ratio of phenotypes is 9:3:3:1. Note that the two pairs of alleles considered here assort independently.

haired guinea pig (*bbss*) are mated, the *BBSS* animal produces gametes that are all *BS* and the *bbss* individual produces gametes that are all *bs*. Each gamete contains one and only one allele for each of the two loci. The union of the *BS* and *bs* gametes yields only individuals with the genotype *BbSs*. All these F_1 offspring are heterozygous for hair color and for hair length, and all are phenotypically black and short-haired.

The Principle of Independent Assortment States That the Members of Different Gene Pairs Segregate and Assort into Gametes Independently

Each F_1 individual produces four kinds of gametes with equal probability: *BS*, *Bs*, *bS*, and *bs*. Hence, the Punnett square has 16 squares representing the zygotes, some of

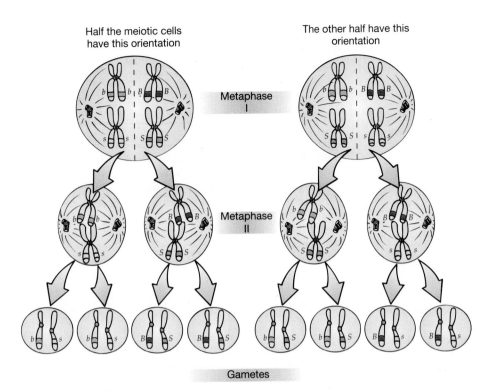

Figure 10–8 The meiotic basis of independent assortment. There are two independent ways that alleles of two unlinked loci can line up at meiotic metaphase I and subsequently disjoin at anaphase I. The first orientation produces half *BS* gametes and half *bs* gametes. The second orientation produces half *Bs* gametes and half *bS* gametes. Approximately half of the meiotic cells have the first orientation and the other half have the second, resulting in an overall 1:1:1:1 ratio for the four possible types of gametes.

which are genotypically or phenotypically alike. There are 9 chances in 16 of obtaining a black, short-haired individual; 3 chances in 16 of obtaining a black, long-haired individual; 3 chances in 16 of obtaining a brown, short-haired individual; and 1 chance in 16 of obtaining a brown, long-haired individual. This 9:3:3:1 phenotypic ratio is expected in a dihybrid F_2 if the loci are on nonhomologous chromosomes.

On the basis of similar results, Mendel formulated his third principle of inheritance, now called Mendel's **principle of independent assortment,** which states that members of one gene pair segregate from one another independently of the members of the other gene pairs. Each gamete contains one allele for each locus, but the alleles of different loci are assorted at random with respect to each other in the gametes.

See Focus on Solving Genetics Problems and Focus on Deducing Genotypes for a summary of procedures used in solving genetic problems illustrating Mendel's principles of dominance, segregation, and independent assortment.

The Mechanics of Meiosis Are the Basis for Independent Assortment

Today we recognize that independent assortment occurs because there are two different ways for two pairs

of homologous chromosomes to be distributed during meiosis. These occur randomly, with about half of the meiotic cells having one orientation and half the opposite orientation (Figure 10–8). As we shall see, independent assortment is actually a special case, and this principle does not apply if the two gene pairs are **linked,** that is, located on the same pair of homologous chromosomes.

THE LINEAR ORDER OF LINKED GENES ON A CHROMOSOME CAN BE "MAPPED" BY CALCULATING THE FREQUENCY OF CROSSING OVER

Chromosomes are inherited as units and they pair and separate during meiosis as units, so all of the alleles at different loci on a given chromosome tend to be inherited together. If the chromosomal units never changed, the genes on any one chromosome would always be inherited together. However, during meiosis, when the chromosomes pair and undergo synapsis (see Chapter 9), crossing over may occur.

During **crossing over,** homologous (nonsister) chromatids may exchange segments of chromosomal material by a process of breakage and rejoining

FOCUS ON

Solving Genetics Problems

Simple Mendelian genetics problems are like puzzles. They can be fun and easy to work if you follow certain conventions and are methodical in your approach.

1. Always use standard designations for the generations. The generation with which a particular genetic experiment is begun is called the *P*, or *parental, generation*. Offspring of this generation (the "children") are called the *F₁*, or *first filial, generation*. The offspring resulting when two F₁ individuals are bred constitute the *F₂*, or *second filial, generation* (the "grandchildren").

2. Write down a key for the symbols you are using for the allelic variants of each locus. Use uppercase to designate a dominant allele and lowercase to designate a recessive allele. Use the same letter of the alphabet to designate both alleles of a particular locus. If you are not told which is dominant and which is recessive, the phenotype of the F₁ generation is a good clue.

3. Determine the genotypes of the parents of each cross by making use of the following types of evidence:
   a. Are they from true breeding lines? If so, they should be homozygous.
   b. Can their genotypes be reliably deduced from their phenotypes? This is usually true if they express the recessive phenotype.
   c. Do the phenotypes of their offspring provide any information? See Focus on Deducing Genotypes for an example of how these determinations can be made.

4. Indicate the possible kinds of gametes formed by each of the parents. It is helpful to draw a circle around the symbols for each kind of gamete.
   a. If it is a monohybrid cross, we must apply the principle of segregation; i.e., a heterozygote *Aa* forms two kinds of gametes: *A* and *a*. Of course a homozygote, such as *aa*, forms only one kind of gamete: *a*.
   b. If it is a dihybrid cross, we must apply both the principle of segregation *and* the principle of independent assortment. For example, an individual heterozygous for two loci would have the genotype *AaBb*. *A* segregates from *a*, and *B* segregates from *b*. The assortment of *A* and *a* into gametes is independent of the assortment of *B* and *b*. Therefore *A* is equally likely to end up in a gamete with *B* or *b*. The same is true for *a*.

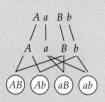

Segregation of the alleles of each locus

Independent assortment of alleles of different loci

5. Set up a Punnett square, placing the possible types of gametes from one parent down the left side and the possible types from the other parent across the top.

6. Fill in the Punnett square and read off (and sum up) the genotypic and phenotypic ratios of the offspring. Avoid confusion by consistently placing the dominant allele first and the recessive allele second in heterozygotes (*Aa*, never *aA*). If it is a dihybrid cross, it is very important always to write the two alleles of one locus first and the two alleles of the other locus second. It does not matter which locus you choose to write first, but once you have decided on the order it is critical that you maintain it consistently. This means that if the individual is heterozygous for both loci you will always use the form *AaBb*. Writing this particular genotype as *aBbA*, for example, would cause confusion.

7. If you do not need to know the frequencies of all of the expected genotypes and phenotypes, you may use the rules of probability as a shortcut. For example, if both parents are *AaBb*, what is the probability of an *AABB* offspring? To be *AA*, the offspring must receive an *A* gamete from each parent. The probability that a given gamete is *A* is ½ and each gamete represents an independent event, so we combine their probabilities by multiplying (½ × ½ = ¼). The probability of *BB* is calculated similarly and is also ¼. The probability of *AA* is independent of the probability of *BB*, so again we use the product rule to obtain their combined probabilities (¼ × ¼ = ¹⁄₁₆).

(Figure 10–9). This exchange of chromatid segments occurs at random along the length of the paired homologous chromosomes. Several exchanges may occur at different points during a single meiotic division. In general, the greater the physical distance between any two genes in the chromosome, the greater is the likelihood that the genes will be separated by crossing over.

In fruit flies a locus controlling wing shape (the dominant allele *V* for normal wings and the recessive allele *v* for vestigial wings) and a locus controlling body

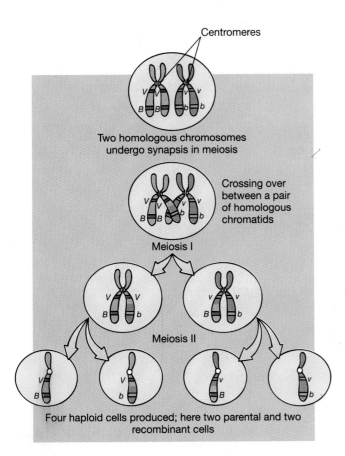

Centromeres

Two homologous chromosomes
undergo synapsis in meiosis

Crossing over
between a pair
of homologous
chromatids

Meiosis I

Meiosis II

Four haploid cells produced; here two parental and two
recombinant cells

Figure 10–9 Crossing over and genetic recombination. Crossing over, the exchange of segments between chromatids of homologous chromosomes, permits the recombination of genes (for example, *Bv* and *bV*). The farther apart genes are located on a chromosome, the greater is the probability that they will be separated by an exchange of segments.

color (the dominant allele *B* for gray and the recessive allele *b* for black) are located in the same pair of homologous chromosomes (Figure 10–10). They therefore tend to be inherited together and are said to be *linked.* If a homozygous *BBVV* fly is crossed with a homozygous *bbvv* fly, the F₁ flies all have gray bodies and normal wings, and their genotype is *BbVv*. However, if these F₁ flies are crossed with homozygous *bbvv* flies (a **dihybrid test cross**), the offspring appear in a ratio that differs from the ordinary dihybrid test cross ratio.

If the loci governing these characteristics were *not* linked, their alleles would undergo *independent assortment* during meiosis. The heterozygous parent would produce four kinds of gametes (*BV*, *Bv*, *bV*, and *bv*) in equal numbers. As a result of independent assortment, new gene combinations not present in the parental generation are produced. Any process that leads to new gene combinations is called **recombination.** In our example, *Bv* and *bV* are both recombinant gametes. Of course the homozygous recessive parent produces only one kind of gamete, *bv*. Thus, ¼ of the offspring would appear gray-bodied and normal-winged (*BbVv*), ¼ black-

bodied and normal-winged (*bbVv*), ¼ gray-bodied and vestigial-winged (*Bbvv*), and ¼ black-bodied and vestigial-winged (*bbvv*). (Notice that the dihybrid test cross, like a monohybrid test cross, allows us to determine the genotypes of the offspring directly from their phenotypes.) If the loci *were* absolutely linked (if no exchange of chromosomal segments occurred), only the **parental types**—flies with gray bodies and normal wings and flies with black bodies and vestigial wings— would appear among the offspring, and these would be present in approximately equal numbers.

However, in our example, there is an exchange between these two loci in some of the meiotic cells of the heterozygous female flies (see Figure 10–9). Because of this crossing over, some gray-bodied, vestigial-winged flies and some black-bodied, normal-winged flies are seen among the offspring. These **recombinant types** are the flies that received a **recombinant** gamete from the heterozygous F₁ parent.

Remember that a recombinant gamete is one that contains a *combination* of genes that was not present in the parental (P) generation, and that if the loci are unlinked, recombination results from independent assortment. However, if the loci are linked, a recombinant gamete must carry a chromatid that has undergone crossing over so it now contains a *new combination* of alleles for these two loci. In this instance, about 20% of the gametes are recombinant (*bV* or *Bv*). These account for the two classes of recombinant offspring: gray flies with vestigial wings, *Bbvv* (approximately 10% of the total), and black flies with normal wings, *bbVv* (also about 10% of the total). In such crosses, about 40% of the offspring are gray flies with normal wings, *BbVv*, and another 40% are black flies with vestigial wings, *bbvv*. These two make up the **parental,** or nonrecombinant, class of offspring.

The genetic distance between two loci in a chromosome is measured in **map units,** or recombination units, which are a measure of the percentage of crossing over between them. There is a rough correlation between this genetic distance and the actual physical distance along the chromosome. One can calculate the percentage of recombination by adding the number of individuals in the two recombinant classes of offspring (10+10), dividing by the *total number* of offspring (40+40+10+10), and multiplying by 100. Thus, the *V* locus and the *B* locus can be said to have 20% recombination between them. By convention, 1% recombination between two loci equals a distance of 1 map unit, so they can be said to be 20 map units apart.

The frequencies of recombination between specific linked loci have been measured in a number of species. All of the experimental results are consistent with the hypothesis that genes are present in a linear order in the chromosomes. Figure 10–11 illustrates the method for determining the order of genes in a chromosome.

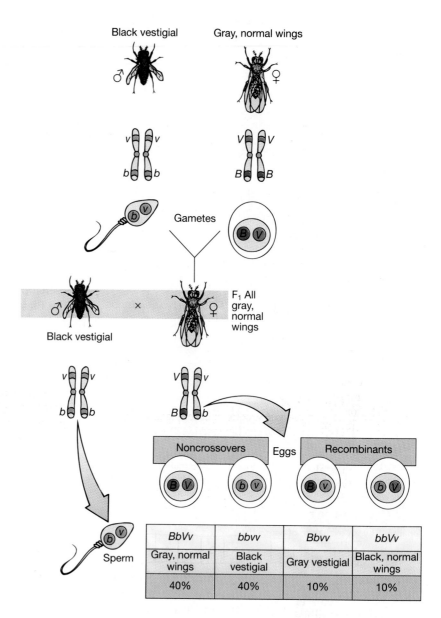

Black vestigial   Gray, normal wings

Gametes

F₁ All gray, normal wings

Black vestigial

Noncrossovers Eggs Recombinants

Sperm

BbVv	*bbvv*	*Bbvv*	*bbVv*
Gray, normal wings	Black vestigial	Gray vestigial	Black, normal wings
40%	40%	10%	10%

Figure 10–10 A cross involving linkage and crossing over. In fruit flies, the genes for vestigial versus normal wings and for black versus gray body are linked; they are located on the same chromosome pair. (Fruit flies are unusual in that crossing over occurs only in females and not in males. It is far more common for crossing over to occur in both sexes.)

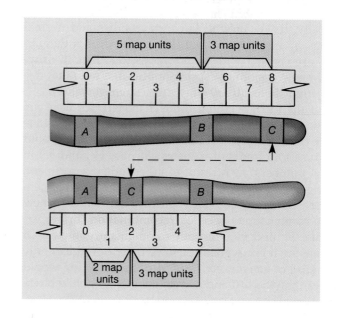

Figure 10–11 Genetic mapping. Gene order (i.e., which gene lies between the other two) is determined by the percentage of recombination between each of the possible pairs. In this hypothetical example, the percentage of recombination between *A* and *B* is 5% (corresponding to 5 map units) and that between *B* and *C* is 3% (3 map units). If the recombination between *A* and *C* is 8% (8 map units), *B* must be in the middle. However, if the recombination between *A* and *C* is 2%, then *C* must be in the middle.

Deducing Genotypes

The science of genetics resembles mathematics in that it consists of a few basic principles, which, once grasped, enable the student to solve a wide variety of problems. Very often the genotypes of the parents can be deduced from the phenotypes of their offspring. In chickens, for example, the allele for rose comb (*R*) is dominant to the allele for single comb (*r*). Suppose that a cock is mated to three different hens, as shown in the figure. The cock and hens A and C have rose combs; hen B has a single comb. Breeding the cock with hen A produces a rose-combed chick, with hen B a single-combed chick, and with hen C a single-combed chick. What types of offspring can be expected from further matings of the cock with these hens?

Because the allele for single comb, *r*, is recessive, all of the hens and chicks that are phenotypically single-combed must be *rr*. We can deduce that hen B and the offspring of hens B and C are genotypically *rr*.

All individuals that are phenotypically rose-combed must have at least one *R* allele. The fact that the offspring of the cock and hen B was single-combed proves that the cock is heterozygous *Rr*, because, although the single-combed chick received one *r* allele from its mother, it must have received the second one from its father.

The fact that the offspring of the cock and hen C had a single comb

Deducing the parental genotypes from the phenotypes of the offspring. In chickens, the allele for rose comb (*R*) is dominant to

the allele for single comb (*r*). Determine the unknown parental genotypes.

proves that hen C is heterozygous, *Rr*. It is impossible to decide from the data given whether hen A is homozygous *RR* or heterozygous *Rr*; further breeding would be necessary to determine this. (Can you suggest an appropriate mating?)

Additional matings of the cock with hen B should result in one half rose-combed and one half single-combed individuals; additional matings of the cock with hen C should produce three fourths rose-combed and one fourth single-combed chicks.

Crossing over occurs at random, and more than one crossover between two loci in a single tetrad (bivalent) can occur in a given cell undergoing meiosis. We can observe only the frequency of offspring receiving recombinant gametes from the heterozygous parent, not the actual number of crossovers. In fact, the actual frequency of crossing over is slightly more than the observed frequency of recombinant gametes. This is because the simultaneous occurrence of two crossovers involving the same two homologous chromatids recon-

stitutes the original combination of genes (Figure 10–12). When two loci are relatively close together, this effect is minimized.

All of the genes in a particular chromosome tend to be inherited together and therefore are said to constitute a **linkage group.** The number of linkage groups determined by genetic tests is equal to the number of pairs of chromosomes. By putting together the results of many crosses, scientists have developed detailed linkage maps for a number of eukaryotes, including the

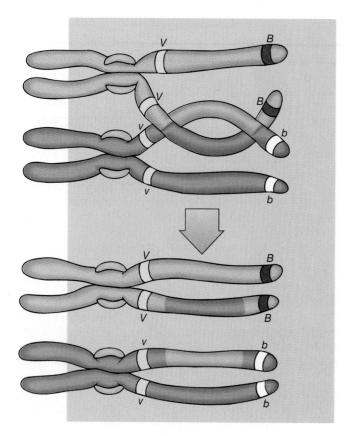

Figure 10–12 Double crossing over involving the same homologous chromatids does not result in the formation of recombinant gametes.

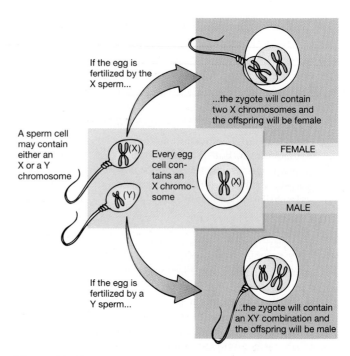

Figure 10–13 Sex is determined at the time of fertilization by the sperm. An X-bearing sperm produces a female; a Y-bearing sperm produces a male.

fruit fly (which has four pairs of chromosomes), the mouse, yeast, and *Neurospora* (a fungus). In addition, special genetic methods have made possible the development of a detailed map for *Escherichia coli*, a bacterium with a single circular chromosome, and a number of other prokaryotes and viruses. More sophisticated maps of chromosomes are currently made by means of recombinant DNA technology (see Chapter 14). These methods have been particularly useful in producing maps of human chromosomes (see Chapter 15).

SEX IS COMMONLY DETERMINED BY SPECIAL SEX CHROMOSOMES

Sex chromosomes are an exception to the general rule that the two members of a homologous pair of chromosomes are alike in size and shape. The cells of the females of many species of animals contain two identical sex chromosomes, called **X chromosomes.** In contrast, the set of two sex chromosomes in males consists of a single X chromosome and a smaller **Y chromosome** with which the X chromosome undergoes partial syn-

apsis during meiosis. Human males have 22 pairs of **autosomes,** which are chromosomes other than the sex chromosomes, plus one X chromosome and one Y chromosome; females have 22 pairs of autosomes plus two X chromosomes.

The Y Chromosome Determines Male Sex in Mammals

Do human males have a male phenotype because they have only one X chromosome or because they have a Y chromosome? Much of the evidence that bears on this question comes from studies of persons with abnormal sex chromosome constitutions (see Chapter 15). A person with an XXY constitution is a nearly normal male in external appearance but has underdeveloped gonads (Klinefelter syndrome). A person with one X but no Y chromosome has the appearance of an immature female (Turner syndrome). Hence we think that the Y is the male-determining chromosome, and progress has been made in identifying at least one gene on the Y that is involved in this process.

In humans and other species in which the normal male has one X and one Y chromosome, half of the sperm contain an X chromosome and half contain a Y chromosome. All eggs contain one X chromosome (Figure 10–13). Fertilization of an X-bearing egg by an

X-bearing sperm results in an XX female zygote; fertilization by a Y-bearing sperm results in an XY male zygote. We would expect to have equal numbers of X- and Y-bearing sperm and a 1:1 ratio of females to males. In fact, however, more males are conceived than females and more males die before birth. Even at birth the ratio is not 1:1; about 106 boys are born for every 100 girls. It is not known why this occurs, but the Y-bearing sperm is assumed to have some competitive advantage.

An XY mechanism of sex determination is thought to operate in most species of animals, although it is not universal and many of the details may vary. The fruit fly, *Drosophila*, has XX females and XY males, but the Y is not male-determining; a fruit fly with an X chromosome and no Y chromosome has a male phenotype. In birds and butterflies the mechanism is reversed, with males being the equivalent of XX and females the equivalent of XY.

In **hermaphroditic** animals, organs of both sexes are found in the same individual. These animals do not have sex chromosomes. Most flowering plants are hermaphrodites. When the sexes are in separate flowers but on the same plant, the plants are said to be **monoecious;** corn, walnuts, and oaks are examples of such plants. Far fewer flowering plants are **dioecious,** having male and female floral organs on separate plants. A few dioecious plants, such as asparagus, apparently have sex chromosomes, although they are not necessarily comparable to those of animals.

X-Linked Genes Have Unusual Inheritance Patterns

The human X chromosome contains many loci that are required in both sexes, whereas the Y chromosome contains only a few genes, principally one or more genes for maleness. Traits controlled by genes located in the X chromosome, such as color blindness and hemophilia, are sometimes called **sex-linked** traits. It is more appropriate, however, to refer to these as **X-linked** traits because they follow the pattern of transmission of the X chromosome and strictly speaking are not linked to the sex of the organism per se.

A female receives one X from her mother and one X from her father. A male receives his Y chromosome, which makes him male, from his father. From his mother he inherits a single X chromosome and therefore all of his genes for X-linked traits. In the male, every X chromosome allele present is expressed, whether that allele was dominant or recessive in the female parent. A male is always **hemizygous** for every X-linked locus. The term *hemi* means "half"; a hemizygous male is neither homozygous nor heterozygous for X-linked traits.

Various forms of notation are used for problems involving X linkage. We will use a simple system of indicating the X with alleles as superscripts. The Y chromosome is written without superscripts because it does not carry an allele of interest.

For most X-linked loci, the abnormal or uncommon allele is recessive in the female and the normal or most common allele is dominant. Therefore, two recessive X-linked alleles must be present in a female for the abnormal phenotype to be expressed, whereas in the hemizygous male a single abnormal allele is expressed. As a practical consequence, although these abnormal alleles may be carried by a female, they are usually expressed only in their male offspring.

To be expressed in a female, a recessive X-linked allele must be present on both X chromosomes; that is, the alleles must be inherited from both parents. A color-blind female, for example, must have a color-blind father and a mother who is at least heterozygous for color blindness (Figure 10–14). Such a combination is unusual. In contrast, a color-blind male need only have a mother who is heterozygous for color blindness; his father can be normal. Hence, X-linked recessive traits are generally much more common in males than in females, a fact that may partially explain why human male embryos are more likely to die.

Sex-Influenced Genes Are Autosomal, but Their Expression Is Affected by the Individual's Sex

Not all of the characteristics that differ in the two sexes are X-linked. Certain **sex-influenced** traits are inherited through autosomal genes, but the *expression* of alleles at these loci can be altered or influenced by the sex of the animal. Therefore, males and females with the same genotype with respect to these loci may have different phenotypes. Pattern baldness in humans, characterized by premature loss of hair on the front and top of the head but not on the sides, is far more common among males than among females. It has been proposed that a single pair of alleles is involved. The allele responsible for pattern baldness is dominant in males and recessive in females. Because of this unusual situation we modify our notation, designating the pattern baldness allele as B_1 and the allele for normal hair growth as B_2. Individuals with the genotype B_1B_1 show pattern baldness, regardless of sex. Persons with a B_1B_2 genotype are bald if they are male but not bald if they are female. Individuals with the genotype B_2B_2 are not bald, regardless of sex. Evidence suggests that the expression of most sex-influenced traits is strongly modified by sex hormones. For example, male hormones (see Chapter 48) are strongly implicated in the expression of pattern baldness.

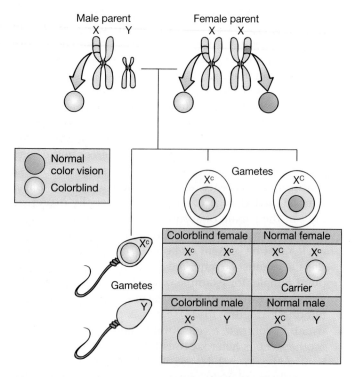

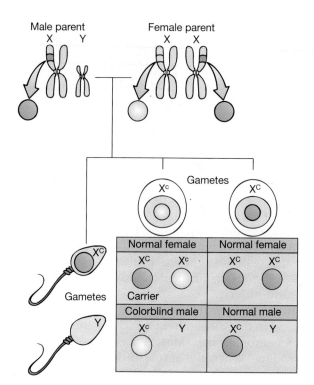

Figure 10–14 X-linkage. Two crosses involving color blindness, an X-linked recessive trait. Note that the Y chromosome does not carry a gene for color vision.

Dosage Compensation Equalizes the Expression of X-Linked Genes in Males and Females

The X chromosome contains numerous genes that are required by both sexes, yet a normal female has two copies ("doses") for each locus, whereas a normal male has only one. Generally, a mechanism of **dosage compensation** is required to make the two doses in the female and the single dose in the male equivalent. Male fruit flies accomplish this by increasing the metabolic activity of their single X chromosome. In most tissues the male X chromosome is just as active as the two X chromosomes present in the female.

Dosage compensation in mammals generally involves inactivation of one of the two X chromosomes in the female. During interphase a dark spot of chromatin, called a **Barr body,** is visible at the edge of the nucleus of each female mammalian cell (Figure 10–15). The Barr body has been found to represent one of the two X chromosomes, which has become dense and dark staining. The other X chromosome resembles the autosomes in that during interphase it is a greatly extended thread that is not evident by light microscopy. From this and other evidence, the British geneticist Mary Lyon has suggested that in any one cell of a female mammal, only

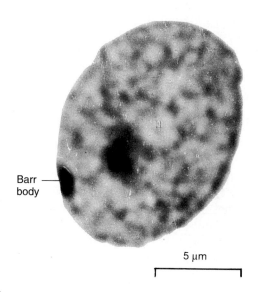

Figure 10–15 A Barr body in human fibroblasts cultured from the skin of a female. (Dr. Dorothy Warburton/Peter Arnold, Inc.)

one of the two X chromosomes is active; the other is inactive and is seen as a Barr body.

Because only one X chromosome is active in any one cell, a female mammal that is heterozygous at an X-linked locus expresses one of the alleles in about half her cells and the other allele in the other half. This is sometimes (but not always) evident in the phenotype.

Figure 10–16   A calico cat. This cat has X-linked genes for both black and yellow (or orange) pigmentation of the fur, but because of random X chromosome inactivation, black is expressed in some clones of cells and yellow (or orange) is expressed in others. Because other genes affecting fur color are also present, white patches are usually evident as well.   (Larime Photographic/Dembinsky Photo Associates)

Mice and cats have several X-linked genes for certain coat colors. Females that are heterozygous for such genes may show patches of one coat color in the midst of areas of the other coat color. This phenomenon, termed **variegation,** is evident in calico (Figure 10–16) and tortoise-shell cats. Early in development, when relatively few cells are present, X chromosome inactivation occurs randomly in each cell. When any one of these cells divides by mitosis, the cells of the resulting clone (group of genetically identical cells) all have the same active X chromosome, and therefore a patch of cells that all express the same color develops.

THE RELATIONSHIP BETWEEN GENOTYPE AND PHENOTYPE IS NOT ALWAYS STRAIGHTFORWARD

The relationship between a given locus and the characteristic it controls may be simple: A single pair of alleles at a locus may regulate the appearance of a single characteristic of the organism (e.g., tall versus short). Alternatively, the relationship may be more complex: A pair of alleles at a locus may participate in the control of several characteristics, or alleles at many loci may cooperate to regulate the appearance of a single characteristic. Not surprisingly, these more complex relationships are quite common.

As you will learn in Chapters 11 and 12, each locus is a segment of DNA in which biological information is stored as a triplet (three-base) code in the sequence of nucleotides that compose the double helix of the DNA molecule. The information is "read out," and in a great many cases a specific protein is ultimately synthesized. The presence of a specific protein, such as an enzyme, usually provides the chemical basis for the genetic trait. Because most biologically important molecules are synthesized by complex metabolic pathways involving a number of enzymes, it is not difficult to appreciate why relationships between genes and the characteristics of the organism are complex.

We may assess the phenotype on one or many levels. It may be a morphological characteristic such as shape, size, or color. It may be a physiological characteristic or even a biochemical trait, such as the presence or absence of a specific enzyme required for the metabolism of some specific molecule. The phenotypic expression of genes may be altered by changes in the environmental conditions under which the organism develops.

Dominance Is Not Always Complete

Studies of the inheritance of many traits in a wide variety of organisms have clearly shown that one member of a pair of alleles may not be completely dominant to the other. Indeed, it is improper to use the terms *dominant* and *recessive* in such instances. For example, red and white are common flower colors in Japanese four o'clocks. Each color breeds true when these plants are self-pollinated. What flower color might we expect in the offspring of a cross between a red-flowering plant and a white-flowering one? Without knowing which is dominant, we might predict that all would have red flowers or all would have white flowers. This cross was first made by the German botanist Karl Correns (one of the rediscoverers of Mendel's work), who found that all F_1 offspring have pink flowers! Does this result in any way prove that Mendel's assumptions about inheritance are wrong? Quite the contrary, for when two of these pink-flowered plants were crossed, offspring appeared red-flowered, pink-flowered, and white-flowered in a ratio of 1:2:1 (Figure 10–17).

In this instance, as in all other aspects of science, results that differ from those predicted simply prompt scientists to reexamine and modify their assumptions to account for the exceptional results. The pink-flowered plants are clearly the heterozygous individuals, and neither the red allele nor the white allele is completely dominant. When the heterozygote has a phenotype that is intermediate between those of its two parents, the genes are said to show **incomplete dominance.** In these crosses the genotypic and phenotypic ratios are identical.

Incomplete dominance is not unique to Japanese four o'clocks. Red- and white-flowered sweet pea plants also produce pink-flowered plants when crossed, and numerous additional examples are known in both plants and animals.

In both cattle and horses, reddish coat color is not completely dominant to white coat color. Heterozygous individuals have coats that are roan-colored—that is, reddish—but with spots of white hairs. If you saw a white mare nursing a roan-colored foal, what would you guess was the coat color of the foal's father? Be-

cause the reddish and white colors are expressed independently in the roan heterozygote, we sometimes refer to this as a case of **codominance.** Strictly speaking, *incomplete dominance* refers to instances in which the heterozygote is intermediate in phenotype, and *codominance* refers to instances in which two alleles are expressed independently in the heterozygote. The human ABO blood group (see Chapter 15) provides a classic example of codominant alleles.

Multiple Alleles for a Locus May Exist in a Population

The examples given so far have dealt with situations in which each locus was represented by a maximum of two allelic variants, and in most of these examples one of the alleles has been dominant and one recessive. It is true that a single diploid individual has only two alleles for a particular locus and that a haploid gamete has only one allele for each locus. However, if we survey a population, we may find more than two alleles for a particular locus. If three or more alleles for a given locus exist within the population, we say that locus has **multiple alleles.** A great many loci can be shown to have multiple alleles if the population is surveyed carefully. Usually, each identifiable allele can produce a distinct phenotype, and certain patterns of dominance and recessivity can be discerned when the alleles are combined in various ways.

In rabbits, for example, a *C* allele causes a fully colored coat. The homozygous recessive genotype, *cc*, causes albino coat color. There are two additional allelic variants of the same locus, c^h and c^{ch}. In a homozygous rabbit, the allele c^h causes the "Himalayan" pattern, in which the body is white but the tips of the ears, nose, tail, and legs are colored. An individual homozygous

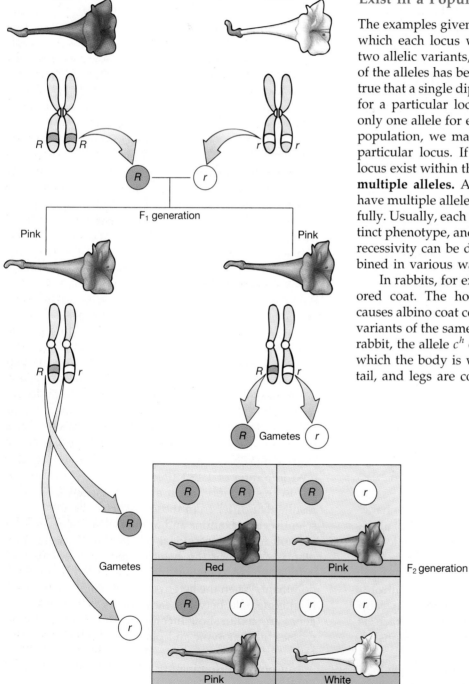

Figure 10–17 Incomplete dominance in Japanese four o'clocks. Red is incompletely dominant to white in some types of flowers. A plant with the genotype *Rr* has pink flowers.

Single comb *pprr*	Pea comb *PPrr* or *Pprr*	Walnut comb *P_R_*	Rose comb *ppRR* or *ppRr*

Figure 10–18 The different types of genetically determined combs in roosters. Two gene pairs govern the inheritance of these types of combs.

for the c^{ch} allele has the "chinchilla" pattern, in which the entire body has a light gray color. On the basis of the results of genetic crosses, these alleles can be arranged in a series—$C > c^{ch} > c^{h} > c$—in which each is dominant to those following it and recessive to those preceding it. In other series of multiple alleles, some may be codominant and others incompletely dominant so that the heterozygotes have a phenotype intermediate between those of their parents.

A Single Gene May Affect Multiple Aspects of the Phenotype; Alleles of Different Loci May Interact to Produce a Phenotype

In the examples presented so far, the relationship between a gene and its phenotype has been direct, precise, and exact, and the loci considered have controlled the appearance of single traits. However, the relationship of gene to characteristic may be quite complex.

Most genes probably have many different effects, a quality referred to as **pleiotropy.** This is dramatically evident in many genetic diseases, such as cystic fibrosis and sickle cell anemia (see Chapter 15), in which multiple symptoms can be traced to a single pair of alleles. Albino individuals have a lack of pigment in the skin, hair, and eyes, demonstrating that a single locus can simultaneously affect a number of characteristics. In addition, virtually every feature of the organism is actually controlled by a large number of loci. We are not always aware of this because not all of these loci have been identified.

Epistasis is a common type of gene interaction in which the presence of a particular allele of one gene pair determines whether certain alleles of another gene pair are expressed. Several pairs of alleles may interact to affect a single trait, or one pair may inhibit or reverse the effect of another pair. More than 12 pairs of alleles interact in various ways to produce coat color in rabbits, and more than 100 pairs are concerned with eye color and shape in fruit flies.

One of the simplest types of gene interaction is illustrated by the inheritance of combs in poultry (Figure 10–18). The allele for a rose comb, *R*, is dominant to that for a single comb, *r*. Another gene pair governs the inheritance of a pea comb, *P*, versus a single comb, *p*. A single-combed fowl must therefore have the genotype *pprr*; a pea-combed fowl is either *PPrr* or *Pprr*; and a rose-combed fowl is either *ppRR* or *ppRr*. When a homozygous pea-combed fowl is mated to a homozygous rose-combed one, the offspring have neither a pea nor a rose comb, but a completely different type, called a *walnut comb*. The walnut comb phenotype is produced whenever a fowl has one or two *R* alleles plus one or two *P* alleles. What would you predict about the types of combs among the offspring of two heterozygous walnut-combed fowl, *PpRr*? How does this form of epistasis affect the ratio of phenotypes in the F_2 generation? Is it the typical mendelian 9:3:3:1 ratio?

We have already seen that coat color in guinea pigs is determined by the *B* and *b* allelic pair, with the *B* allele for black coat dominant to the *b* allele for brown coat. The expression of either phenotype, however, depends on the presence of a dominant allele at yet another locus. This allele, *C*, codes for the enzyme tyrosinase, which converts a colorless precursor into the pigment melanin and hence is required for the production of any kind of pigment. The recessive allele (*c*) codes for an inactive form of the enzyme. Thus, an animal that is homozygous recessive for this allele essentially lacks the enzyme and produces no melanin. It is therefore a white-coated, pink-eyed albino, regardless of the combination of *B* and *b* alleles. Albinism, or lack of melanin pigment, is not restricted to guinea pigs, but is found in humans and a variety of other animals (Figure 10–19).

When an albino guinea pig with the genotype *ccBB* is mated to a brown guinea pig with the genotype *CCbb*, the F_1 generation is black coated, *CcBb*. When two such animals are mated, their offspring appear black-coated, brown-coated, and albino in a ratio of 9:3:4. (Make a Punnett square to verify this.) In this example of epistasis, pairs of genes representing two entirely different loci interact in such a way that one dominant (*C*) produces its effect regardless of whether the other is present, but the second (*B*) produces its effect only when the other is present.

Figure 10–19 Albino koala.
(Tom McHugh/Photo Researchers, Inc.)

You might wonder why heterozygous *Cc* individuals do not show at least some lightening of the coat color, since they produce only about half the normal amount of tyrosinase enzyme. It turns out that half the normal amount of enzyme is usually adequate to produce normal amounts of pigment. This is a very common phenomenon and accounts for many (although certainly not all) cases of dominance.

POLYGENES ACT ADDITIVELY TO PRODUCE A PHENOTYPE

The inherited components of many human characteristics, such as height, body form, and skin color, are not inherited through alleles at a single locus. Many commercially important characteristics in domestic plants and animals, such as milk and egg production, cannot be separated into distinct alternate classes. Alleles at several, perhaps many, different loci affect each characteristic. The term **polygenic inheritance** is applied when multiple independent pairs of genes have similar and additive effects on the same characteristic.

Polygenes are responsible for the inheritance of skin color in humans. It is now thought that alleles representing four or more different loci are involved in determining skin color, but the principle of polygenic inheritance can be illustrated with pairs of alleles at only three unlinked loci (Figure 10–20). These can be designated *A* and *a*, *B* and *b*, and *C* and *c*. The capital letters represent *incompletely dominant* alleles producing dark skin. The more capital letters, the darker the skin, because the alleles affect skin color in an *additive* fashion.

A person with the darkest skin would have the genotype *AABBCC*, and a person with the lightest skin would have the genotype *aabbcc*. The F_1 offspring of an *aabbcc* person and an *AABBCC* person are all *AaBbCc* and have an intermediate skin color. The offspring of two such triple heterozygotes would have skin colors ranging from very dark to very light.

Polygenic inheritance is therefore characterized by an F_1 generation that is intermediate between the two completely homozygous parents and by an F_2 generation that shows wide variation between the two parental types. Most of the F_2-generation individuals have one of the intermediate phenotypes; only a few show the extreme phenotypes of the grandparents (P generation). On average, only 1 of 64 is as dark as the very dark grandparent, and only 1 of 64 is as light as the very light grandparent. The alleles *A*, *B*, and *C* each produce about the same amount of darkening of the skin; hence, the genotypes *AaBbCc*, *AABbcc*, *AAbbCc*, *AaBBcc*, *aaBBCc*, *AabbCC*, and *aaBbCC* all produce similar intermediate phenotypes.

The model used here for the inheritance of skin color in humans is a rather simple example of polygenic inheritance because only three major allelic pairs are used. The inheritance of height in humans involves alleles representing ten or more loci. Because many allelic pairs are involved and because height is modified by a variety of environmental conditions, the heights of adults range from perhaps 125 to 215 cm. If we were to measure the heights of 1000 adult American men selected at random, we would find that only a few are as tall as 215 cm or as short as 125 cm. The heights of most would cluster around the mean, about 170 cm. When the number of people at each height is plotted against height (in centimeters) and the points are connected, the result is a bell-shaped curve, called a **normal distribution curve** (Figure 10–21). If you were to measure the heights of 1000 people of both sexes, what sort of curve would you expect the data to generate?

SELECTION, INBREEDING, AND OUTBREEDING ARE USED TO DEVELOP IMPROVED STRAINS

How do geneticists go about establishing a breed of cow that will give more milk, a strain of hens that will lay bigger eggs, or a variety of corn with more kernels per ear? By selecting organisms that manifest the desired phenotype and using these organisms in further matings, a true breeding strain with the commercially advantageous trait is gradually developed. Such a strain should be homozygous for all of the polygenes involved, whether they be dominant, recessive, or additive in their effects.

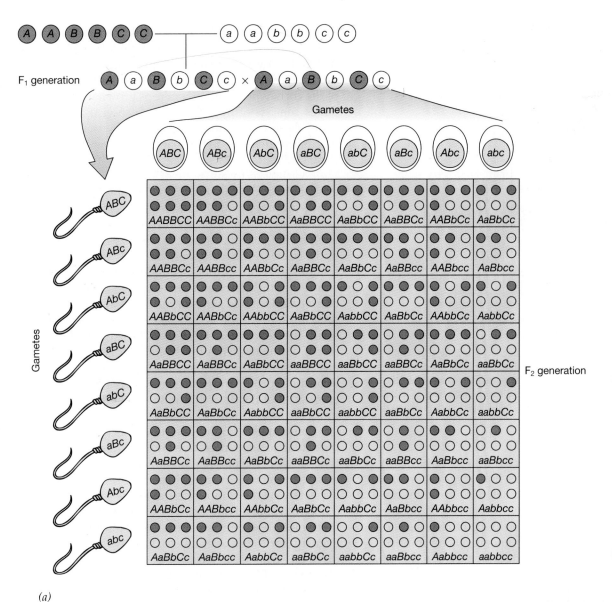

(a)

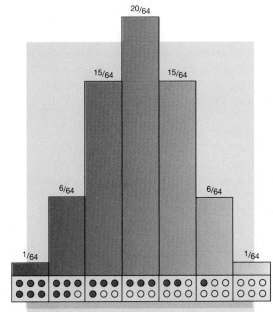

(b)

Figure 10–20   A simplified model of polygenic inheritance of skin color in humans. (*a*) Here it is assumed that skin color is governed by alleles at three loci. The alleles producing dark skin are represented by capital letters, but they are not dominant. Instead they act in an additive fashion. (*b*) The expected phenotypic ratios in the F₂ generation.

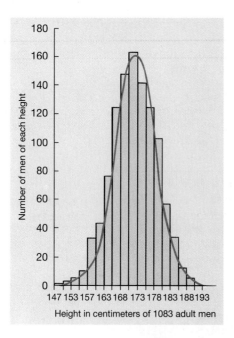

Figure 10–21 A normal distribution curve showing the distribution of height in 1083 adult white males. The blocks indicate the actual number of men whose heights were within the unit range. For example, there were 163 men whose heights were between 170 and 173 cm. The smooth, bell-shaped curve is known as a normal curve.

There is a limit to the effectiveness of breeding by selection. When a strain becomes homozygous for all of the polygenes involved, further selective breeding cannot increase the desired quality. Moreover, because of **inbreeding**—the mating of two closely related individuals—the strain may become homozygous for multiple undesirable traits as well. Certain dog breeds, for instance, are known for their susceptibility to congenital dislocation of the femur. Evidence suggests that human inbreeding increases the frequency of genetic disease in the population (see Chapter 15), although the individual risk is relatively small. For this reason marriages of close relatives (first cousins or closer) are forbidden by law in many states.

The mating of individuals of totally unrelated strains, termed **outbreeding,** frequently leads to off-spring that are much better adapted for survival than is either parent. Such improvement reflects a phenomenon called **hybrid vigor.** Mongrel dogs are often hardier than highly inbred purebreds. A large proportion of the corn, wheat, and other crops grown in the United States consists of hybrid strains. Each year the seed to grow these crops must be obtained by mating of the original strains. The hybrids are heterozygous at a great many loci and give rise, even when self-fertilized, to a wide variety of forms, none of which is as good as the original hybrid. (The seeds produced by F_1 hybrid corn plants are not normally planted, but eaten instead!)

One explanation of hybrid vigor is the following: Each of the parental strains is homozygous for certain undesirable recessive genes, but any two strains are homozygous for different undesirable genes. Each strain contains dominant genes to make up for the recessive undesirable genes of the other strain. One strain then might have the genotype *AAbbCCdd*, and another strain the genotype *aaBBccDD*. (The capital letters represent dominant genes for desirable traits and the lowercase letters recessive genes for undesirable traits.) The hybrid offspring, with the genotype *AaBbCcDd*, would express all of the desirable and none of the undesirable traits of the two parental strains.

Sometimes an individual that is heterozygous at a particular locus expresses a more extreme phenotype than either of the parental homozygotes. Geneticists call this phenomenon **overdominance.** If the phenotype of the heterozygote is more desirable, we say that there is a **heterozygote advantage.** The use of this term implies that at least sometimes there is an advantage to heterozygosity for the sake of heterozygosity. In humans, individuals who are heterozygous for the recessive allele responsible for sickle cell anemia (*s*) and the normal dominant allele (*S*) appear to have increased resistance to the parasite that causes malaria, a significant advantage in areas of the world where malaria is still uncontrolled. Homozygous normal individuals (*SS*) appear to be less resistant to malaria. Homozygous sickle cell individuals (*ss*) are at a distinct disadvantage owing to severe anemia and other serious effects of the sickle cell allele (Chapter 18).

SUMMARY

I. Mendel's inferences from his experiments with the breeding of garden peas have been tested repeatedly in all kinds of diploid organisms and found to be generally true. These principles have been extended and now can be stated in a more modern form.

   A. Today we know that the genes are in chromosomes; we use the term *locus* to refer to the site a gene occupies in the chromosome.

   B. Different forms of a particular gene are called *alleles;* they occupy corresponding loci on homologous chromosomes. Genes therefore exist as pairs of alleles in diploid individuals.

   C. An individual that carries two identical alleles for a given locus is said to be *homozygous* for that locus. If the two alleles are different, that individual is said to be *heterozygous* for that locus.

D. According to Mendel's principle of dominance, one allele (the dominant allele) may mask the expression of the other allele (the recessive allele) in a heterozygous individual. For this reason two individuals with the same appearance (phenotype) may differ from each other in genetic constitution (genotype). Dominance does not always apply, and alleles may be incompletely dominant or codominant.

E. According to Mendel's principle of segregation, during meiosis the alleles for each locus separate, or segregate, from each other as the homologous chromosomes separate. When haploid gametes are formed, each contains only one allele for each locus.

F. According to Mendel's principle of independent assortment, during meiosis each pair of alleles segregates independently of the pairs of alleles located in other pairs of homologous chromosomes. Alleles of different loci therefore assort randomly into the gametes. This can result in recombination, that is, production of new combinations of genes that were not present in the parental (P) generation.

G. Each chromosome behaves genetically as if it were composed of genes arranged in a linear order. Genes that are in the same chromosome are said to be *linked* and may not undergo independent assortment. Recombination of linked genes can occur as a result of crossing over (breaking and rejoining of homologous chromatids) in meiotic prophase. By measuring the frequency of recombination (resulting from crossing over) between various genes, it is possible to construct a genetic map of a chromosome.

H. A cross between homozygous parents (P generation) that differ from each other with respect to their alleles at one locus is called a *monohybrid cross*; if they differ at two loci, it is a *dihybrid cross*. The first generation of offspring is heterozygous and is called the *first filial*, or *F₁, generation*; the generation produced by a cross of two F₁ individuals is the *second filial*, or *F₂, generation*. If an F₁ individual is crossed with a homozygous recessive individual, the cross is called a *test cross*.

II. Genetic ratios can be expressed in terms of probabilities.

A. Any probability is expressed as a fraction or decimal fraction—that is, the number of favorable events divided by the total number of events. This can range from 0 (an impossible event) to 1 (a certain event).

B. Probabilities can be multiplied and added like any other fractions.

C. The probability of two independent events occurring together is the product of the probabilities of each occurring separately.

D. The probability that one or the other of two mutually exclusive events will occur is the sum of their separate probabilities.

III. The sex of humans and many other animals is determined by the X and Y sex chromosomes or their equivalents. Chromosomes that are not sex chromosomes are called *autosomes*.

A. Normal female mammals have two X chromosomes; normal males have one X and one Y.

B. The fertilization of an X-bearing egg by an X-bearing sperm results in a female (XX) zygote. The fertilization of an X-bearing egg by a Y-bearing sperm results in a male (XY) zygote.

C. The Y chromosome in mammals appears to be responsible for determining male sex.

D. The X chromosome contains many important genes that are unrelated to sex determination and are required by both males and females. A male receives all of his X-linked genes from his mother. A female receives X-linked genes from both parents.

E. A female mammal shows dosage compensation of X-linked genes. Only one of the two X chromosomes is expressed in each cell; the other is inactive and is seen as a dark-staining Barr body at the edge of the interphase nucleus.

IV. The term *multiple alleles* is applied to three or more alleles that can occupy a single locus on the chromosome; each allele produces a specific phenotype. A diploid individual has any two of the alleles; a haploid individual or gamete has only one.

V. The relationship between a gene and its phenotype may be quite complex.

A. Most genes have many different effects; this is known as *pleiotropy*.

B. The presence of a particular allele of one gene pair may determine whether alleles of another gene pair are expressed; this is called *epistasis*.

VI. In polygenic inheritance, multiple independent pairs of genes may have similar and additive effects on the phenotype.

A. Many human characteristics, such as height and skin color, as well as many characteristics in other animals and plants, are inherited through polygenes.

B. In polygenic inheritance, the F₁ generation is intermediate between the two parental types and shows little variation. The F₂ generation shows wide variation between the two parental types.

VII. Inbreeding, the mating of two closely related individuals, greatly increases the probability that an individual offspring will be homozygous for recessive genes. Outbreeding, the mating of totally unrelated individuals, increases the probability that the offspring will be heterozygous at many loci. These heterozygous individuals may be stronger and better able to survive than either parent (*hybrid vigor*).

POST-TEST

1. The specific site in the chromosome occupied by a given gene is termed its _____.

2. Genes governing different forms of the same character (e.g., green seeds versus yellow seeds) and occupying corresponding loci in homologous chromosomes are termed _____.

3. A cross between two organisms differing with respect to alleles of a single locus is a(n) _____ cross.

254 CHAPTER 10

4. An organism's genetic constitution, expressed in symbols, is called its _____.
5. The appearance of an individual with respect to a given inherited characteristic is known as its _____.
6. An allele that is fully expressed in the phenotype of a heterozygous individual is a(n) _____ allele.
7. A(n) _____ allele can only be expressed in the phenotype of a homozygous individual.
8. An organism with two identical alleles for a particular locus is said to be _____ for that locus; an organism with two different alleles for a particular locus is said to be _____ for that locus.
9. The offspring of the parental (P) generation are called the _____ _____ generation. This is abbreviated as the _____ generation.
10. The probability that two independent events will coincide is the _____ of their individual probabilities.
11. The probability that one or the other of two mutually exclusive events will occur is the _____ of their individual probabilities.
12. A probability of _____ expresses a certainty; a probability of _____ expresses an impossibility.
13. In crosses involving a pair of alleles that show incomplete dominance, the genotypic and phenotypic ratios are _____.
14. A mating of individuals that have different alleles at two loci is called a(n) _____ cross.
15. If a particular characteristic of the organism is governed by several pairs of genes that have similar and additive effects, we say that characteristic is under _____ control.
16. If three or more alleles for a given locus are present in the population, we say that locus has _____ alleles.
17. The genes in a given chromosome tend to be inherited together and are said to be _____.
18. The mating of two closely related individuals, such as first cousins, is termed _____.
19. The offspring of totally unrelated parents may be better adapted for survival than either parent. This phenomenon is called _____ _____.

REVIEW QUESTIONS

1. Sketch a series of diagrams showing each of the following. Be sure to end each series with haploid gametes.
   a. How does a pair of alleles for a single locus segregate in meiosis?
   b. How do the alleles of two loci located in different pairs of chromosomes assort independently in meiosis?
   c. How would the alleles of two loci located in the same pair of homologous chromosomes (linked loci) behave in meiosis? Would they assort independently?
2. In peas, yellow seed color is dominant to green. State the colors of the offspring of the following crosses:
   a. homozygous yellow × green
   b. heterozygous yellow × green
   c. heterozygous yellow × homozygous yellow
   d. heterozygous yellow × heterozygous yellow
3. If two animals heterozygous for a single pair of alleles were mated and have 200 offspring, about how many would be expected to have the phenotype of the dominant allele (i.e., to look like the parents)?
4. When two long-winged flies were mated, the offspring included 77 with long wings and 24 with short wings. Is the short-winged condition dominant or recessive? What are the genotypes of the parents?
5. A blue-eyed man, both of whose parents were brown-eyed, married a brown-eyed woman whose father was blue-eyed and whose mother was brown-eyed. If eye color is inherited simply, what are the genotypes of the individuals involved?
6. Outline a breeding procedure whereby a true-breeding strain of red cattle could be established from a roan bull and a white cow.
7. What is the probability of rolling a seven with a pair of dice? Which is a more likely outcome, rolling a six with a pair of dice or rolling an eight?
8. In rabbits, spotted coat (S) is dominant to solid color (s) and black (B) is dominant to brown (b). These loci are unlinked. A brown spotted rabbit from a pure line is mated to a solid black one, also from a pure line. What are the genotypes of the parents? What would be the genotype and phenotype of an F_1 rabbit? What would be the expected genotypes and phenotypes of the F_2 generation?
9. The long hair of Persian cats is recessive to the short hair of Siamese cats, but the black coat color of Persians is dominant to the brown-and-tan coat color of Siamese. Make up appropriate symbols for the alleles of these two unlinked loci. If a pure black, long-haired Persian is mated to a pure brown-and-tan, short-haired Siamese, what will be the appearance of the F_1 offspring? If two of these F_1 cats are mated, what is the chance that a long-haired, brown-and-tan cat will be produced in the F_2 generation? (Use the shortcut probability method to obtain your answer, then check it with a Punnett square.)
10. The expression of an allele called *frizzle* in fowl causes abnormalities of the feathers. As a consequence, the animal's body temperature is lowered, adversely affecting the functions of many internal organs. When one gene affects many characteristics of the organism in this way, we say that gene is _____.
11. A walnut-combed rooster is mated to three hens. Hen A, which is walnut-combed, has offspring in the ratio of 3 walnut : 1 rose. Hen B, which is pea-combed, has offspring in the ratio of 3 walnut : 3 pea : 1 rose : 1 single. Hen C, which is walnut-combed, has only walnut-combed offspring. What are the genotypes of the rooster and the three hens?
12. What kinds of matings result in the following phenotypic ratios?
   a. 3 : 1
   b. 1 : 1
   c. 9 : 3 : 3 : 1
   d. 1 : 1 : 1 : 1
13. The weight of the fruit in a certain variety of squash is

determined by two pairs of genes: *AABB* produces fruits weighing 4 lb each, and *aabb* produces fruits weighing 2 lb each. Each gene represented by a capital letter adds ½ lb to the weight. When a plant that produces 4-lb fruits is crossed with a plant that produces 2-lb fruits, all of the offspring produce fruits that weigh 3 lb each. What would be the weights of the fruits produced by the F₂ plants, if two of these F₁ plants were crossed?

14. The X-linked *barred* locus in chickens controls the pattern of the feathers, with the alleles *B* for barred pattern and *b* for no bars. If a barred male (X^BY) is mated to a nonbarred female (X^bX^b), what will be the appearance of the male and female progeny? Do you see any commercial usefulness for this? (*Hint:* It is notoriously difficult to determine the sexes of newly hatched chicks.)

15. Individuals of genotype *AaBb* were mated to individuals of genotype *aabb*. One thousand offspring were counted:
Aabb 474
aaBb 480
AaBb 20
aabb 26
This type of cross is known as a(n) _____ _____. Are these loci linked? What are the two parental classes and the two recombinant classes of offspring? What is the percentage of recombination between these two loci? How many map units apart are they?

16. Genes *A* and *B* are 6 map units apart, and *A* and *C* are 4 map units apart. Which gene is in the middle if *B* and *C* are 10 map units apart? Which is in the middle if *B* and *C* are 2 map units apart?

RECOMMENDED READINGS

Mendel, G. Experiments in plant hybridization. Reprinted in *Genetics: Readings from Scientific American*. W. H. Freeman and Co., San Francisco, 1990. Try reading this translation of Mendel's classic paper from the perspective of other scientists of his time (lacking knowledge of chromosomes, mitosis, and meiosis).

There are a number of well-written college level genetics texts that cover the principles of genetics in eukaryotes. The following are two representative examples:

Russell, P. *Genetics*. 3rd ed., Harper Collins, New York, 1992.
Suzuki, D. T., A. J. F. Griffiths, J. Miller, and R. C. Lewonton. *An Introduction to Genetic Analysis*. 4th ed. W. H. Freeman, New York, 1989.

CHAPTER 11

DNA: The Carrier of Genetic Information

Following the rediscovery of Mendel's laws, geneticists conducted elegant experiments to learn how genes are arranged on chromosomes and how they are transmitted from generation to generation. However, two very basic questions remained unanswered: What are genes made of? How do genes work? Although studies of inheritance patterns did not answer these questions, they contributed to an emerging set of predictions about the molecular characteristics of genes and how they might function.

Among the properties attributed to genes was their ability to store information in a stable form that can be accurately copied and passed from generation to generation. However, it was thought that the genetic material could not always be perfectly constant, because genetic changes,

Computer simulation of a piece of synthetic DNA used in biophysical studies on the different structural forms of DNA. (Dr. Kenneth Breslauer, Rutgers University)

called **mutations,** had been observed to appear suddenly and to be transmitted subsequently to future generations. Therefore it was thought that the molecule responsible for inheritance would have to be relatively stable but have the capacity to change under some circumstances.

It was also recognized that a mechanism was required to retrieve the information stored in the genetic material and to use it to direct cellular functions. Because proteins are so important to every aspect of cellular structure and metabolism, they were considered to be the prime candidates for the genetic material. Today we know that **deoxyribonucleic acid,** not protein, is the molecule that is responsible for inheritance. In this chapter we examine the unique features of DNA that allow it to carry out this role.

After you have studied this chapter you should be able to

1. Summarize the evidence that accumulated during the 1940s and early 1950s demonstrating that DNA is the fundamental genetic material.
2. Relate the chemical and physical features of DNA to the structure proposed by Watson and Crick.
3. Sketch how nucleotide subunits are linked together to form a single DNA strand.
4. Illustrate how the two strands of DNA are oriented with respect to each other.
5. Point out the base-pairing rules for DNA, and describe how complementary bases bind to each other.

6. Cite experimental evidence that allowed scientists to differentiate between semiconservative replication of DNA and alternative models (conservative and dispersive replication).
7. Summarize how DNA replicates and identify some of the unique features of the process.
8. Explain why DNA replication is discontinuous in one strand and continuous in the other and why the process is bidirectional.
9. Compare the organization of DNA in chromosomes of prokaryotic and eukaryotic cells.

MOST GENES CARRY INFORMATION FOR MAKING PROTEINS

The idea that genes and enzymes (which we now know are proteins) are related in some way was first clearly stated in 1908 by an English physician, Archibald Garrod, who theorized that certain inherited diseases in humans are caused by a block in a sequence of chemical reactions within the body.

In his book, *Inborn Errors of Metabolism*, Garrod discussed a genetic disease called **alkaptonuria**, which is inherited as a simple mendelian trait. The condition involves a block in the metabolic reactions that break down the amino acids phenylalanine and tyrosine; the urine of affected persons turns black when exposed to air (Figure 11–1). Homogentisic acid, the substance that turns black, is an intermediate in this breakdown pathway; it is normally oxidized and eventually converted to carbon dioxide and water.

Garrod theorized that persons with alkaptonuria lack the oxidation enzyme, causing homogentisic acid to accumulate in their tissues and blood and to be excreted in their urine. Before the second edition of his book had been published in 1923, it was found that affected persons do indeed lack the enzyme that oxidizes homogentisic acid. Garrod was right: A specific gene could be associated with the absence or presence of a

specific enzyme. Despite the implications of this finding, little work was done in this area, primarily because errors in metabolism appeared to occur only in patients with rare diseases, which made genetic experiments impossible.

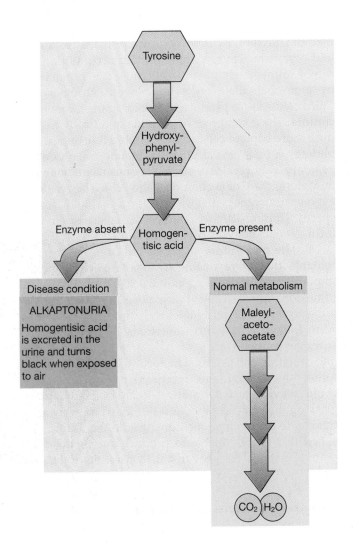

Figure 11–1   Pathway by which the amino acid tyrosine is catabolized. The mutation that causes alkaptonuria (black urine) produces a defect in the enzyme that normally converts homogentisic acid to maleylacetoacetate. Homogentisic acid thus accumulates in the blood and is excreted through the urine. When the homogentisic acid in the urine comes in contact with air, it oxidizes and turns black. Garrod proposed that the alkaptonuria gene causes the absence of a specific enzyme, or an "inborn error of metabolism."

A major advance in understanding the relationship between genes and enzymes came in the early 1940s, when George Beadle and Edward Tatum developed a new approach to the problem. Most efforts until that time had centered on studying known genes and attempting to determine what biochemical reactions they affected. Experimenters examined previously identified genes, such as those controlling eye color in *Drosophila* or pigments in plants. They found that such traits are controlled by a series of biosynthetic reactions, but it was not clear whether the genes themselves act as enzymes or determine the specificities of enzymes in more complex ways.

Beadle and Tatum decided to take the opposite approach. Rather than try to identify the enzymes affected by single genes, they decided to look for mutations interfering with known metabolic reactions that produce essential molecules such as amino acids and vitamins. They used the bread mold *Neurospora* for their studies for several reasons. First, wild-type[1] *Neurospora* can make all of its essential biological molecules when it is grown on a simple minimal medium containing sugar, salts, and the vitamin biotin. A mutant that cannot make a substance such as an amino acid can still grow if that substance is simply added to the minimal medium. Second, *Neurospora* grows primarily as a haploid organism. Thus, a mutation that occurs in a gene can be immediately identified because it is not masked by a normal allele on a homologous chromosome. Third, *Neurospora* produces haploid spores, known as **conidia.** These can grow and divide mitotically to produce more haploid cells. Two haploid cells can fuse and undergo a brief sexual phase of the life cycle (see the generalized life cycles of simple organisms in the figure in Making the Connection on page 225). The resulting zygote undergoes meiosis to form haploid sexual spores. Thus, researchers can use sexual crosses to perform genetic analyses of isolated mutants.

Beadle and Tatum searched for large numbers of mutants that were unable to synthesize biologically important molecules (e.g., amino acids, purines, pyrimidines, vitamins). They first exposed the haploid conidia to x rays or ultraviolet radiation, both of which were known to produce mutations. Following exposure, the conidia were grown on a **complete medium,** one containing all essential molecules, so that many different types of mutants produced by the irradiation could survive and reproduce. If an isolated mutant grew on the complete medium but failed to grow after transfer to the minimal medium, Beadle and Tatum reasoned that it was unable to produce one of the compounds essential for growth. Further testing of the mu-

tant on media containing different combinations of amino acids, purines, vitamins, and so on enabled the investigators to determine the exact essential compound (Figure 11–2). Each mutant strain isolated in that way was then verified by genetic crossing experiments to have a mutation in only one gene.

Their findings can be illustrated with a class of mutants that require the amino acid arginine. Two compounds, ornithine and citrulline, are known to be precursors to arginine in its biosynthetic pathway. The order of these intermediates in the pathway is shown below. Beadle and Tatum found that some of the arginine-requiring mutants could grow on ornithine, citrulline, or arginine; others could grow only on citrulline or arginine, and still others could grow only on arginine.

$$X \longrightarrow \text{ornithine} \longrightarrow \text{citrulline} \longrightarrow \text{arginine}$$

$$\begin{array}{ccc} \text{Enzyme} & \text{Enzyme} & \text{Enzyme} \\ \text{A} & \text{B} & \text{C} \end{array}$$

A mutation that inactivated the enzyme normally responsible for catalyzing reaction A would correspond to the first group of mutants, because enzymes B and C would still be able to convert ornithine or citrulline to arginine. Any mutation inactivating the enzyme that catalyzes reaction B would be placed in the second group, because in these mutants citrulline could be converted to arginine but ornithine could not. Neither ornithine nor citrulline would be able to support growth in a mutant lacking enzyme C, because both of these precursors are produced before the blocked step (Figure 11–3).

Using this approach, Beadle and Tatum analyzed large numbers of mutants affecting a number of metabolic pathways. They found that *for each individual gene identified, only one enzyme was affected.* This one-to-one correspondence between genes and enzymes was succinctly stated as the **one gene, one enzyme hypothesis.**

The idea that a gene might encode the information for a single enzyme held for almost a decade, until it was found that many genes encode proteins that are not enzymes. In addition, some studies showed that many proteins may be constructed from two or more polypeptide chains (e.g., the α and β subunits of hemoglobin, see Chapter 3), each of which may be encoded by a different gene. The definition was therefore modified to state that *one gene is responsible for one polypeptide chain.* Even this definition has proved to be only partially correct (see Chapter 13).

GENES ARE MADE OF DEOXYRIBONUCLEIC ACID (DNA)

Although we now know that genes are made of deoxyribonucleic acid, or DNA, when the molecular nature of the gene was first studied most scientists were con-

---

[1] Wild-type is a term commonly applied to nonmutant strains or individuals.

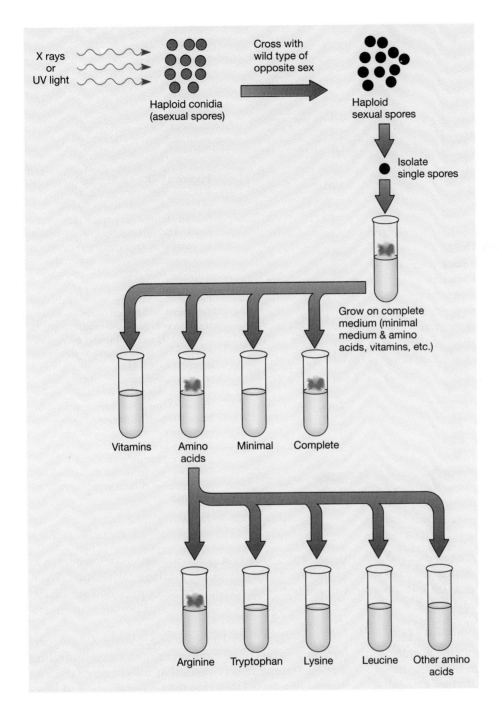

Figure 11–2 Isolation and identification of mutant strains of *Neurospora*. Beadle and Tatum determined the basic relationship between genes and enzymes by isolating and characterizing large numbers of mutants defective in a number of well-known metabolic pathways. Haploid asexual spores (conidia) of *Neurospora* were irradiated to produce random mutations and then mated with another strain to produce haploid sexual spores. Isolated spores were then allowed to grow on a complete medium containing all the amino acids and vitamins that are normally made by *Neurospora*. Each strain was also tested on a minimal medium to determine if a mutation was present. No growth on minimal medium indicated the presence of a biochemical mutation. Mutant strains were then tested for growth on minimal medium supplemented with individual vitamins or amino acids. In this case the medium containing the amino acid arginine is the one that supports growth, indicating that the mutation affects some part of the arginine biosynthetic pathway.

vinced that the genetic material had to be protein. Proteins are made up of more than 20 different kinds of amino acids in many different combinations, allowing each type of molecule to have unique properties; in contrast, nucleic acids are made of only four nucleotides in what appeared to be a regular and uninteresting arrangement. Beadle and Tatum's experiments had shown that genes control the production of enzymes, which are proteins. Given their obvious complexity and diversity compared with other molecules, proteins seemed to be the stuff of which genes are made.

EVIDENCE THAT DNA IS THE HEREDITARY MATERIAL WAS FIRST FOUND IN MICROORGANISMS

Because many researchers thought that DNA could not be the hereditary material, several early clues to its role were not widely recognized. In 1928 Frederick Griffith made a curious observation concerning two strains of pneumococcus bacteria. A smooth (S) strain, named for its formation of smooth colonies on solid growth medium, was known to be **virulent,** or lethal; when it is

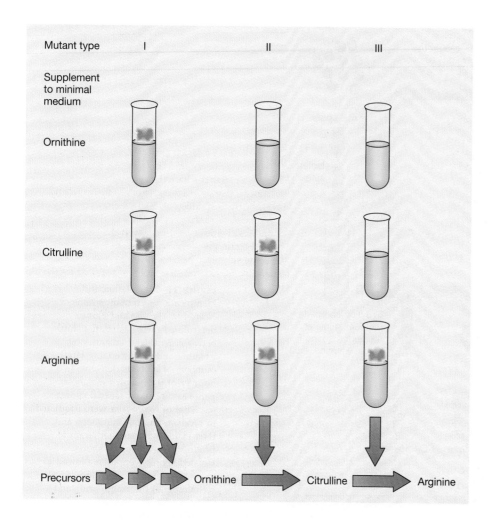

Mutant type	I	II	III

Supplement to minimal medium

Ornithine

Citrulline

Arginine

Precursors → → → Ornithine → Citrulline → Arginine

Figure 11–3 Associating *Neurospora* mutants with steps in a metabolic pathway. By analyzing different mutant strains that require the same amino acid or vitamin, it was possible to verify that each mutant gene affects only a single enzymatic step in the pathway. In this example, a number of different mutant strains that require the amino acid arginine were tested to determine which step in the pathway was blocked. Arginine-requiring strains I, II, and III were all found by genetic crossing methods to have mutations in different genes. Mutant type I grows on ornithine, citrulline, and arginine and must therefore be blocked prior to the formation of all three compounds. Mutant type II is unable to grow on ornithine but allows the conversion of citrulline to arginine. Mutant type III can grow only on arginine and must therefore be blocked at a point after the synthesis of both ornithine and citrulline.

injected into mice, the animals contract pneumonia and die. A related rough (R) strain, which forms colonies with a rough surface, was known to be **avirulent,** or nonlethal. Griffith found that when a mixture of *heat-killed* S-strain cells and live R-strain cells was injected into mice, the mice frequently died. Griffith was then able to isolate living S-strain cells from the dead mice.

Because neither the heat-killed S strain nor the living R strain could be converted to the living virulent form when injected by itself, something in the heat-killed cells appeared to convert the avirulent cells to the lethal form. This phenomenon, called **transformation,** was thought to be caused by some chemical substance (called the "transforming principle") in the dead bacteria that "transformed" a related strain to a genetically stable new form (Figure 11–4). Later, in 1944, Avery, MacLeod, and McCarty of the Rockefeller Institute chemically identified the transforming principle as DNA.

During the next few years, new evidence accumulated that the haploid nuclei of pollen grains and gametes such as sperm contain only half the amount of DNA found in diploid somatic cells of the same species.

Because the idea that genes are on chromosomes was generally accepted, these findings correlating DNA content with chromosome number provided strong circumstantial evidence of DNA's importance in inheritance.

In 1952, Alfred Hershey and Martha Chase performed a series of elegant experiments demonstrating that **bacteriophages** (viruses that infect bacteria) do so by injecting their DNA into the bacterial cells and leaving most of their protein on the outside (Figure 11–5). This finding emphasized the importance of DNA in the reproduction of the virus and was seen by many to be another important indication of the role of DNA as the hereditary material.

THE STRUCTURE OF DNA ALLOWS IT TO CARRY INFORMATION AND TO SELF-REPLICATE

DNA was not widely accepted as the genetic material until James Watson and Francis Crick proposed a model for its structure that has extraordinary explanatory

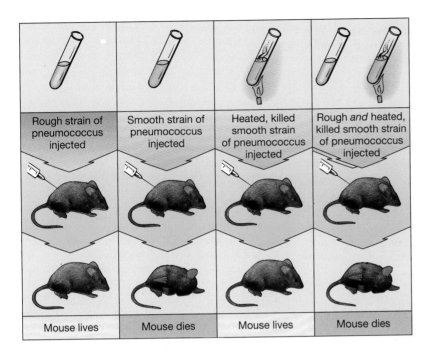

Figure 11–4 Frederick Griffith demonstrated the transfer of genetic information from dead, heat-killed pneumococcus bacteria to living pneumococci of a different strain. Although neither the rough (R) strain nor the heat-killed smooth (S) strain could kill a mouse, a combination of the two did. Autopsy of the dead mouse showed the presence of living, S-strain pneumococci. These results indicated that some substance in the heat-killed S strain was responsible for the transformation of the R strain to virulence. Later, Avery and coworkers demonstrated that purified DNA isolated from the S strain confers virulence on the R-strain bacteria, establishing that the DNA carries the genetic information necessary for the bacterial transformation.

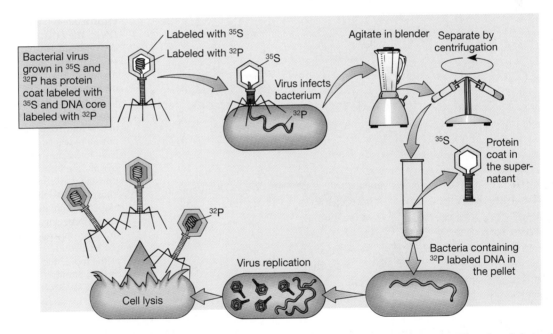

Figure 11–5 The Hershey-Chase experiment demonstrated that only the DNA of a bacterial virus is necessary for the reproduction of new viruses. The virus consists of a DNA core, which contains phosphorus but no sulfur atoms, surrounded by a protein coat, which contains sulfur but no phosphorus atoms. By growing the virus on a medium containing the radioactive isotopes ^{32}P and ^{35}S, Hershey and Chase were able to label the protein and DNA specifically with different isotopes. They found that only the ^{32}P-labeled DNA entered the bacterium and that the ^{35}S-labeled virus protein could be separated from the cells after infection without interfering with the replication of the virus. All the genetic information needed for the synthesis of new protein coats and new viral DNA was provided by the parental viral DNA.

power. The story of how the structure of DNA came to be determined is one of the most remarkable chapters in the history of modern biology.

As we shall see, a great deal was known about the physical and chemical properties of DNA when Watson and Crick became interested in the problem. Their all-important contribution was to integrate all of this information into a model that demonstrates how the molecule can both carry information and serve as its own template (pattern) for self-duplication.

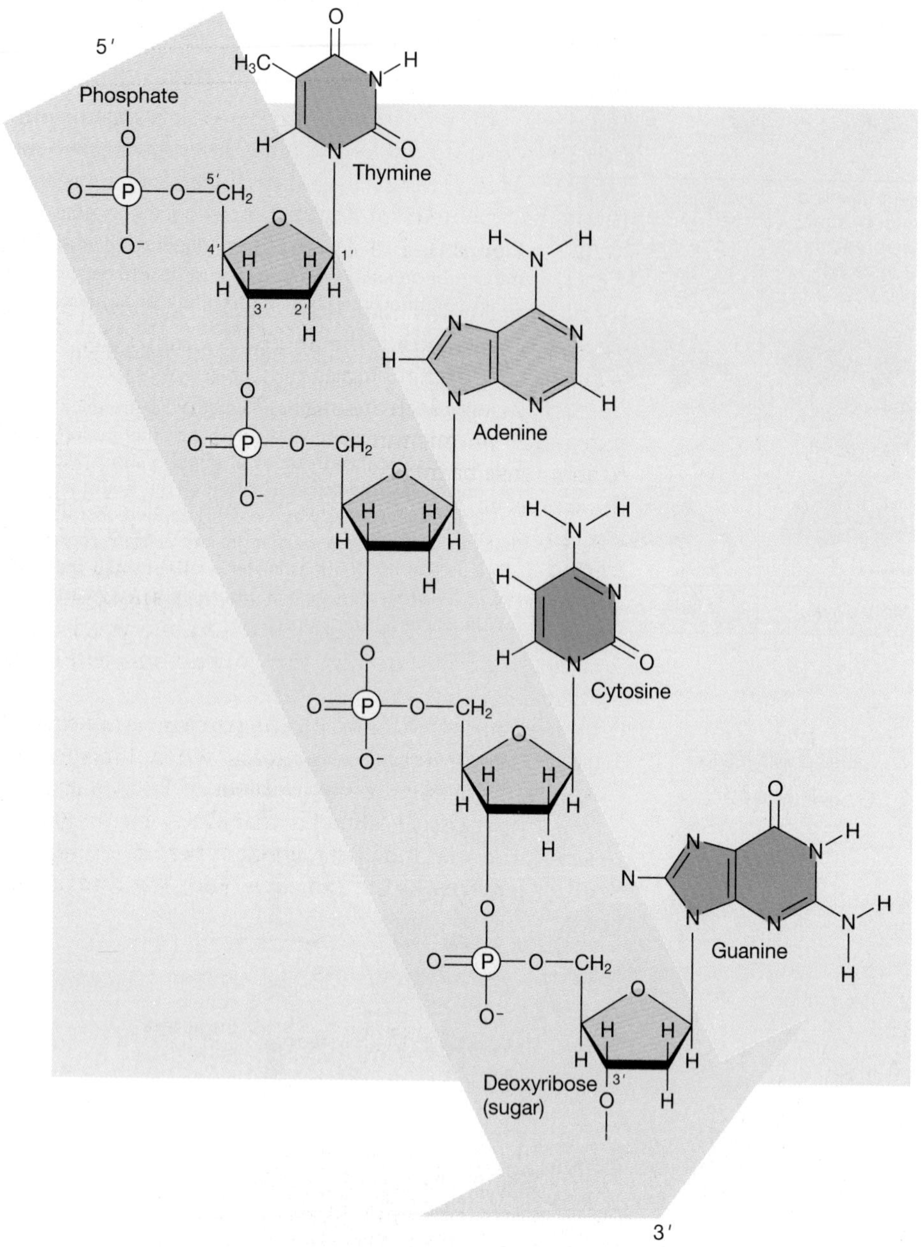

Figure 11–6 Chemical structure of DNA. The DNA molecule is made of deoxyribonucleoside monophosphate subunits. Each subunit is composed of a phosphate group linked to the sugar deoxyribose at its 5′ carbon atom. Deoxyribose sugars are shown in tan. Linked to the 1′ carbon of the sugar is one of four nitrogenous bases. The purine bases, adenine and guanine, have two-ring structures; the pyrimidine bases, thymine and cytosine, have one-ring structures. Phosphodiester linkages connect the 5′ and 3′ carbon atoms of adjacent deoxyribose sugars. The schematic drawing illustrates the polarity of the polynucleotide chain, with the 5′ end at the top of the figure and the 3′ end at the bottom.

Nucleotides Can Be Covalently Linked in Any Order To Form Long Polymers

As discussed in Chapter 3, each DNA building block is a **nucleotide** consisting of a pentose sugar (**deoxyribose**), a phosphate, and a nitrogenous base. The bases include the **purines,** adenine (A) and guanine (G), and the **pyrimidines,** thymine (T) and cytosine (C). As shown in Figure 11–6, the nucleotides are linked together by covalent bonds to form an alternating sugar-phosphate backbone.

The structure of the nucleotide subunits in DNA is identical to that of AMP (see Chapter 3), except that the sugar has a hydrogen atom instead of a hydroxyl group on the 2′ carbon atom (hence the name *deoxyribose*).[1] The nitrogenous base is attached to the 1′ carbon of the sugar, and the phosphate is attached to the 5′ carbon. As shown in Figure 11–7, the nucleotides are linked together by covalently joining the 3′ carbon of one sugar to the 5′ phosphate of the adjacent sugar to form a 3′,5′ **phosphodiester** linkage. It is thus possible to form a polymer of indefinite length. We now know that

---

[1] It is conventional to number the carbon atoms in a molecule, using a system devised by organic chemists. In nucleic acid chemistry the "prime" designations, such as 2′, designate individual carbon atoms in the sugar, to distinguish them from those in the base.

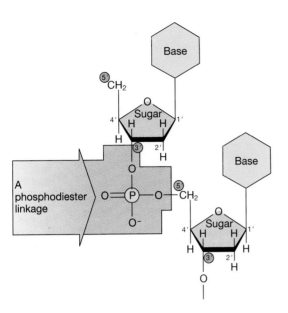

Figure 11-7   A phosphodiester linkage.

most DNA molecules found in cells are millions of bases long and that the nucleotides can be linked together in any order. Figure 11-6 illustrates that a single polynucleotide chain has a direction to it. No matter how long the chain, one end has a 5' carbon and the other a 3' carbon that is not linked to another nucleotide.

DNA Is Made of Two Polynucleotide Chains Intertwined To Form a Double Helix

Important information about the structure of DNA came from x-ray diffraction studies on crystals of purified DNA carried out by Rosalind Franklin in the laboratory of M. H. F. Wilkins. X-ray diffraction is a powerful method for determining distances between atoms of molecules arranged in a regular, repeating crystalline structure (Figure 11-8). X rays have such extremely short wavelengths that they can be scattered by the electrons surrounding the atoms in a molecule. Atoms with dense electron clouds (e.g., phosphorus, oxygen) tend to deflect electrons more strongly than do atoms with lower atomic numbers. When a crystal is exposed to an intense beam of x rays, the regular arrangement of the atoms in the crystal causes the x rays to be diffracted, or bent, in specific ways. The pattern of diffracted x rays is seen on film as dark spots. Mathematical analysis of the arrangement and distances between the spots can then be used to determine precise distances between atoms and their orientation within the molecules.

Franklin had already produced clear x-ray crystallographic films of DNA patterns when Watson and Crick began to pursue the problem of DNA structure. The pictures clearly showed that DNA has a type of helical structure and three major types of regular, repeating patterns in the molecule with the dimensions

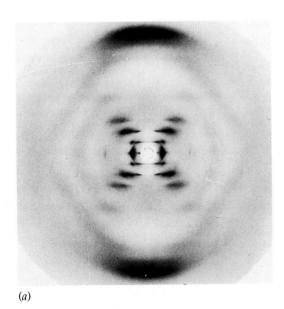

(a)

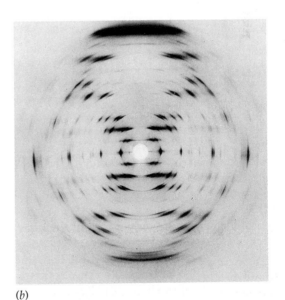

(b)

Figure 11-8   X-ray diffraction photographs of suitably hydrated fibers of DNA. (*a*) Pattern obtained using the sodium salt of DNA. (*b*) Pattern obtained using the lithium salt of DNA. This pattern permits a most thorough analysis of DNA. The diagonal pattern of spots (reflections) stretching from 11 o'clock to 5 o'clock and from 1 o'clock to 7 o'clock provides evidence for the helical structure of DNA. The elongated horizontal reflections at the tops and bottoms of the photographs provide evidence that the purine and pyrimidine bases are stacked 0.34 nm apart and are perpendicular to the axis of the DNA molecule.   (Dr. S. D. Dover, Division of Biomolecular Sciences, Kings College, London)

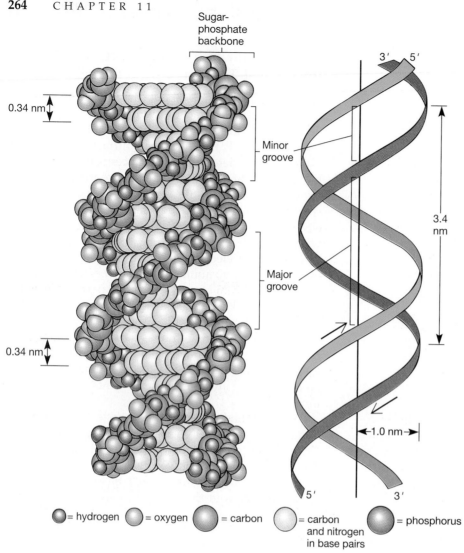

Sugar-phosphate backbone

0.34 nm

Minor groove

Major groove

0.34 nm

Minor groove

3.4 nm

1.0 nm

= hydrogen   = oxygen   = carbon   = carbon and nitrogen in base pairs   = phosphorus

Figure 11–9   Molecular models of DNA. On the left is a space-filling model of the DNA double helix. On the right is a diagrammatic model of the DNA double helix with certain of its dimensions shown in nanometers (nm). The ribbons represent the sugar-phosphate backbone of each strand; the arrows indicate that the two strands extend in opposite directions.

0.34 nm, 3.4 nm, and 2.0 nm. Franklin and Wilkins had inferred from these patterns that the nucleotide bases (which are flat molecules) are stacked like rungs of a ladder. Using this information, Watson and Crick began to build scale models of the DNA components and then fit them together to agree with the experimental data.

After a number of trials, the two worked out a model that fit the existing data (Figure 11–9). The nucleotide chains conformed to the dimensions of the x-ray data only if each DNA molecule consisted of *two* polynucleotide chains arranged in a coiled **double helix.** In their model, the sugar-phosphate backbones of the two chains form the outside of the helix. The bases belonging to the two chains associate as pairs in the center. The reasons for the 0.34-nm and 3.4-nm periodicities are readily apparent from the model: Each pair of bases is exactly 0.34 nm from the adjacent pairs above and below. Because exactly ten base pairs are present in each full turn of the helix, each turn is 3.4 nm high. To fit the data, the two chains must run in opposite direc-

tions; therefore, each end of the double helix must have an exposed 5′ phosphate on one strand and an exposed 3′ hydroxyl group on the other. Because the two strands run in opposite directions, they are said to be **antiparallel** to each other.

In Double-Stranded DNA, Hydrogen Bonds Form between Adenine and Thymine and between Guanine and Cytosine

Other features of the model required additional integration of chemical and x-ray diffraction data. By 1950, the base composition of DNA from a number of organisms and tissues had been determined by Erwin Chargaff and his coworkers at Columbia University. They found a simple relationship among the bases that turned out to be an important clue to the structure of DNA. Regardless of the source of the DNA, in Chargaff's words, the "ratios of purines to pyrimidines and also of adenine to thymine and of guanine to cytosine were not far

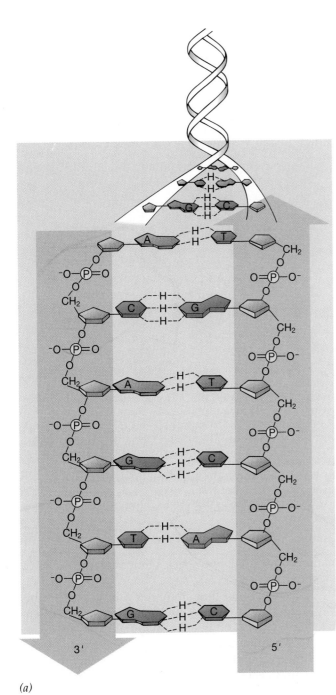

(a)

Adenine   Thymine

Guanine   Cytosine

(b)

Figure 11–10 (*a*) Physical structure of DNA. The two sugar-phosphate chains run in opposite directions. This orientation permits the complementary bases to pair. (*b*) Diagram of the hydrogen bonding between base pairs adenine (A) and thymine (T) (*top*) and guanine (G) and cytosine (C) (*bottom*). The AT pair has two hydrogen bonds; the GC pair has three.

from 1." In other words, in DNA molecules, A = T and G = C.

The x-ray diffraction studies indicated that the double helix has a precise and constant width, as shown by the 2.0-nm reflections. This finding is actually connected to Chargaff's rules. Notice in Figure 11–6 that the pyrimidines, cytosine and thymine, contain only one ring of atoms and are smaller than the purines, guanine and adenine, which contain an additional five-membered ring. Study of the models made it clear to Watson and Crick that if each cross-rung of the ladder were to contain one purine and one pyrimidine, the width of the helix at that point would be exactly 2.0 nm;

the combination of two purines (each of which is 1.2 nm wide) would be wider and that of two pyrimidines would be narrower.

Further examination of the model showed that adenine can pair with thymine (and guanine with cytosine) in such a way that hydrogen bonds form between them; the opposite combinations, cytosine with adenine and guanine with thymine, do *not* lead to favorable hydrogen bonding.

The nature of the hydrogen bonding between adenine and thymine and between guanine and cytosine is shown in Figure 11–10. Two hydrogen bonds can form between adenine and thymine and three between guanine and cytosine. This concept of *specific base-pairing* neatly explains Chargaff's rules. The amount of cytosine has to equal the amount of guanine, because every cytosine in one chain must have a paired guanine in the other chain. Similarly, every adenine in the first chain must have a thymine in the second chain. Thus, the sequences of bases in the two chains are **complementary,** but not identical, to each other; in other words, *the sequence of nucleotides in one chain dictates the complementary sequence of nucleotides in the other.* For example, if one strand has the sequence:

$$3' \quad A\,G\,C\,T\,A\,C \quad 5'$$

the other strand has the complementary sequence:

$$5' \quad T\,C\,G\,A\,T\,G \quad 3'$$

The double-helix model strongly suggested that the sequence of bases in DNA can provide for the storage of genetic information. Although there are restrictions on how the bases pair with each other, the number of possible sequences of bases in a strand is virtually unlimited. Because DNA molecules in a cell can be millions of nucleotides long, they can store enormous amounts of information.

DNA REPLICATION IS SEMICONSERVATIVE: EACH DOUBLE HELIX CONTAINS AN "OLD" STRAND AND A NEWLY SYNTHESIZED STRAND

Two immediately apparent and distinctive features of the Watson-Crick model made it seem more likely that DNA is the genetic material. We have already mentioned that DNA can carry coded information in its sequence of bases. The model also suggested a way in which information in DNA could be precisely copied—a process known as **DNA replication.** The importance of the replication mechanism was known to Watson and Crick, who noted in a classic and now famous piece of understatement at the end of their first brief paper, "It has not escaped our notice that the specific pairing we have postulated immediately suggests a possible copying mechanism for the genetic material."

The model suggested that, because the nucleotides pair with each other in a complementary fashion, each strand of the DNA molecule could serve as a template, or pattern, for the synthesis of the opposite strand (Figure 11–10). It would simply be necessary for the hydrogen bonds between the two strands to break and the two chains to separate. Each half-helix could then pair with complementary nucleotides to replace its missing partner. The result would be two DNA double helices, each identical to the original one and consisting of one original strand from the parent molecule and one newly synthesized complementary strand. This type of infor-

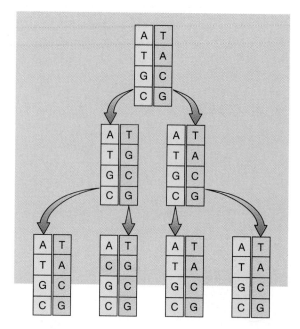

Figure 11–11 How a mutation might be stabilized by DNA replication. If genes are information coded in the sequence of bases on a DNA molecule, then a change (mutation) made in even one of the bases is copied accurately by complementary base pairing. In the example, an adenine base in one of the DNA strands has been changed to guanine (this could occur by a rare error in DNA replication or by one of several other known mechanisms). When the DNA molecule is replicated again, one of the strands gives rise to a molecule that is exactly like the parent strand; the other, mutated, strand gives rise to a molecule with a new combination of bases that will be perpetuated generation after generation.

mation copying is known as a **semiconservative** mechanism.

The recognition that DNA could be copied in this way suggested how DNA could provide a third essential characteristic of genetic material—the ability to mutate. Mutations, or genetic changes, were known to arise in genes and then to be transmitted faithfully to succeeding generations. According to the double-helix model, mutations could represent a *change in the sequence of bases in the DNA.* If DNA is copied by a mechanism involving complementary base-pairing, any change in the sequence of bases on one strand would result in a new sequence of complementary bases during the next replication cycle. The new base sequence would then be passed on to daughter molecules by the same mechanism used to copy the original genetic material, as if no change had occurred (Figure 11–11).

Although the semiconservative replication mechanism suggested by Watson and Crick was (and is) a simple and compelling model, experimental proof was needed to establish that DNA in fact duplicates in that manner. First it was necessary to rule out several other possibilities. For example, with a *conservative* replication mechanism, both parent (or old) strands would remain

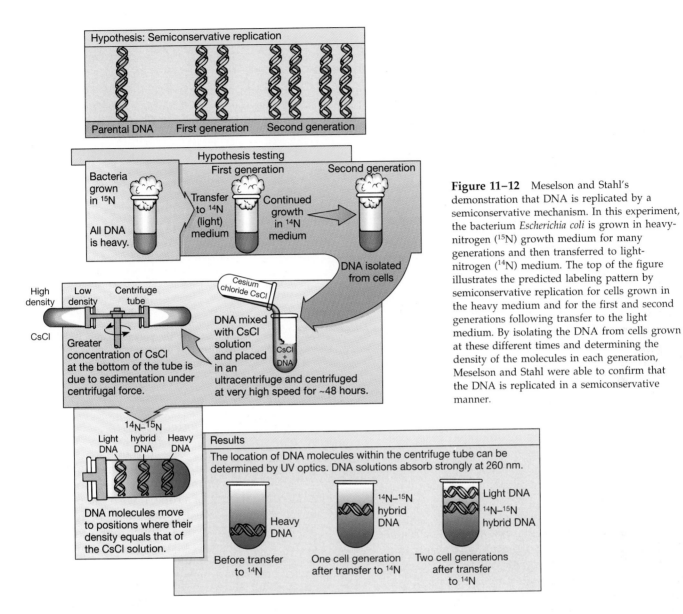

Figure 11–12 Meselson and Stahl's demonstration that DNA is replicated by a semiconservative mechanism. In this experiment, the bacterium *Escherichia coli* is grown in heavy-nitrogen (^{15}N) growth medium for many generations and then transferred to light-nitrogen (^{14}N) medium. The top of the figure illustrates the predicted labeling pattern by semiconservative replication for cells grown in the heavy medium and for the first and second generations following transfer to the light medium. By isolating the DNA from cells grown at these different times and determining the density of the molecules in each generation, Meselson and Stahl were able to confirm that the DNA is replicated in a semiconservative manner.

together, and the two newly synthesized strands would form a second double helix. With a *dispersive* mechanism, after replication the DNA would contain random regions of both parental and newly synthesized strands. To discriminate between the semiconservative replication mechanism and other possibilities, it was necessary to distinguish between old and newly synthesized strands of DNA.

One way to accomplish this is to use a heavy-nitrogen isotope ^{15}N (ordinary nitrogen is ^{14}N) to label DNA strands. Large molecules such as DNA can be separated on the basis of differences in their density, using a technique known as **density gradient centrifugation.** When DNA is mixed with a solution containing cesium chloride (CsCl) and centrifuged at high speed, the solution forms a density gradient in the centrifuge tube, ranging from a low density at the top to the highest density at

the bottom. During the centrifugation the DNA molecules migrate to the region of the gradient identical to their own density.

In 1957, Matthew Meselson and Franklin Stahl grew cells of the bacterium *Escherichia coli* on a medium that contained ^{15}N in the form of ammonium chloride (NH_4Cl). The cells used the ^{15}N to synthesize bases, which were then incorporated into DNA (Figure 11–12). The resulting heavy nitrogen–containing DNA molecules were extracted from some of the cells; when they were subjected to density gradient centrifugation they accumulated in the high-density region of the gradient. The rest of the bacteria (which also contained ^{15}N-labeled DNA) were transferred to a different growth medium in which the NH_4Cl contained the naturally abundant, lighter ^{14}N isotope; they were then allowed to undergo several more cell divisions.

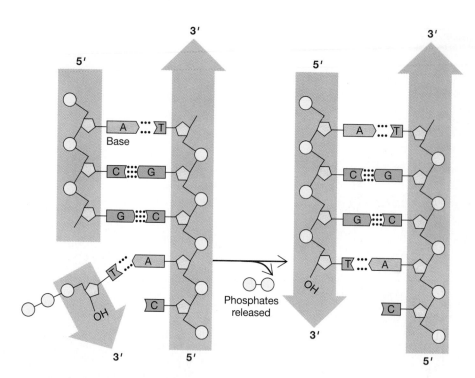

Figure 11–13 DNA synthesis. The building blocks for the DNA molecule are nucleotides with three phosphates (nucleoside triphosphates). Two of the phosphates are released when the nucleotides are linked to the 3' carbon of the sugar at the end of the growing chain. The specificity of the polymerase enzymes that catalyze the polymerization reactions requires that each growing chain always elongate in the 5' → 3' direction.

The newly synthesized DNA strands were expected to be less dense because they incorporated bases containing the lighter ^{14}N isotope. Indeed, molecules of DNA from cells isolated after one generation had a density indicating that they contained half as many ^{15}N atoms as the "parent" DNA. After another cycle of cell division, two species of DNA appeared in the density gradient at levels indicating that one consisted of "hybrid" DNA helices (labeled with equal amounts of ^{15}N and ^{14}N DNA), whereas the other contained only DNA with the naturally occurring light isotope. Each strand of the parental double-helix molecule was thus conserved in a *different* daughter molecule, exactly as predicted by the semiconservative replication model.

DNA Replication Is Complex and Has a Number of Unique Features

Although the general principles of DNA replication are simple and straightforward predictions from the Watson-Crick model, the process actually requires a complex structure containing a large number of proteins and enzymes that work together as a "replication machine." Many of the essential features of replication are universal, although some differences exist between prokaryotes and eukaryotes because their DNA is organized differently. In bacterial cells, such as *E. coli*, most or all of the DNA is in the form of a single, *circular*, double-stranded molecule. Each unreplicated eukaryotic chromosome contains a single, *linear* double-stranded molecule, associated with a great deal of protein and some RNA.

DNA strands must be unwound during replication

Watson and Crick recognized that in their double-helix model the two DNA strands are wrapped around one another, like the strands of a rope. If we try to pull apart the strands, the rope must either rotate or twist into tighter coils. We would expect similar things to happen when complementary DNA strands are separated for replication. Unwinding is accomplished by **DNA helicase enzymes,** which travel along the helix, unwinding the strands as they move. Once the strands are separated, **helix-destabilizing proteins** bind to single DNA strands, preventing re-formation of the double helix until the strands are copied. Because DNA molecules are very long and thin, the strain on the molecule must be relieved as the two strands are unwound. Special enzymes, called **topoisomerases,** produce breaks in the DNA molecules and then rejoin the strands, relieving strain by effectively untying knots that develop during replication.

DNA synthesis always proceeds in a 5' → 3' direction

The enzymes that catalyze the linking together of the nucleotide subunits are called **DNA polymerases.** They have several limitations that contribute to the complexity of the replication process. They are able to add nucleotides only to the 3' end of a polynucleotide strand that is *paired* to the strand being copied (Figure 11–13). Nucleotides known as **nucleoside triphosphates** are used as substrates for the polymerization reaction; these

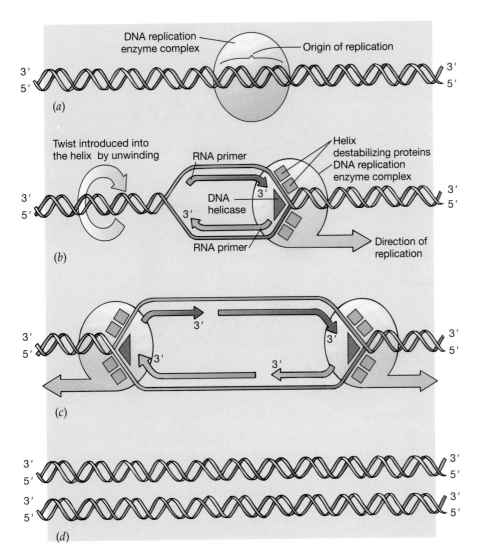

Figure 11–14 (*a*) DNA synthesis begins at a specific base sequence, termed the *origin of replication.* (*b*) Strands are separated at the origin and unwound by DNA helicase, which "walks" along the DNA molecule preceding the DNA-synthesizing enzymes. Single-stranded regions are prevented from re-forming into double strands by helix-destabilizing proteins, which bind to single-stranded DNA. The region of active DNA synthesis is associated with the "replication fork," formed at the junction of the single strands and the double-stranded region. DNA synthesis proceeds on both single strands of the fork in a 5' → 3' direction. (*c*) As the new strands continue to grow in the first direction, unwinding and replication initiate on the other side of the origin, so that replication proceeds in both directions. (*d*) Completion of replication results in the formation of two daughter molecules, each containing one newly synthesized strand.

are similar to ATP in that they contain three phosphate groups linked to the 5' carbon of the sugar group, plus a base. As the nucleotides are linked together, two of the phosphates are removed. Like the hydrolysis of ATP, these reactions are strongly exergonic (see Chapter 6) and do not require additional energy. Because the new polynucleotide chain is elongated by the linkage of the 5' phosphate group of the next nucleotide subunit to the 3' hydroxyl group of the sugar at the end of the strand, the new strand of DNA always grows from its 5' → 3' direction.

DNA synthesis requires an RNA primer

A second limitation of the DNA polymerases is that they can add nucleotides only to the 3' end of an *existing* polynucleotide strand. So how can DNA synthesis be initiated once the two strands are separated? The answer is that a short piece (usually about five nucleotides) of an **RNA primer** (Figure 11–14) is first synthesized by an aggregate of proteins called a **primosome.**

RNA, or **ribonucleic acid** (see Chapter 12), is a nucleic acid polymer consisting of nucleotide subunits that associate by complementary base-pairing with the single-stranded DNA template at the point of initiation of replication. DNA polymerase can then add subunits to the 3' end of the RNA primer. The primer is later degraded by specific enzymes and the space is filled in with DNA.

DNA replication is discontinuous in one strand and continuous in the other

A major obstacle in understanding DNA replication was the fact that the complementary DNA strands run in opposite directions. Because DNA synthesis proceeds only in the direction of 5' → 3' (which means that the strand being copied is being read in a 3' → 5' direction), it appears to be necessary to copy one of the strands starting at one end of the double helix and the other strand starting at the opposite end. We know, however, that this is not the case. DNA replication be-

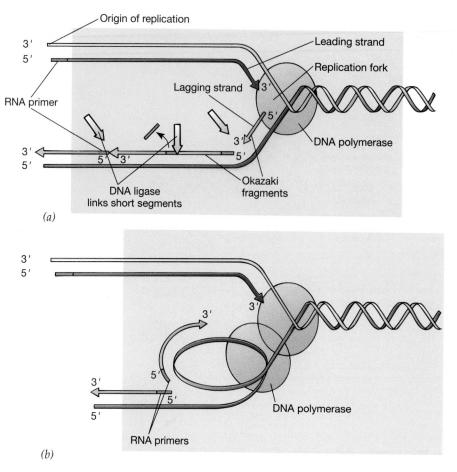

Figure 11–15 Discontinuous replication. Because elongation can proceed only in a $5' \rightarrow 3'$ direction, the two strands of the replication fork are copied in different ways. (*a*) The *leading strand* is synthesized continuously in a direction toward the replication fork, whereas the *lagging strand* is synthesized in short pieces called *Okazaki fragments*, in a direction away from the replication fork. Initiation of synthesis for both strands requires an *RNA primer* because DNA can be elongated only by addition to the 3' end of an existing strand. After elongation has begun, the RNA primer is degraded, the gaps are filled in with DNA, and the adjoining fragments are linked together by DNA ligase. (*b*) The lagging strand may form a loop, which would allow the leading and lagging strands to be synthesized simultaneously.

gins at specific sites on the DNA molecule, termed **origins of replication,** and both strands are replicated at the same time at a Y-shaped structure referred to as the **replication fork** (Figure 11–15a). The 3' end of one of the new strands is always growing *toward* the replication fork. Because this strand can be formed smoothly and continuously, it is called the **leading strand.** The 3' end of the other new strand is always growing *away* from the replication fork. Therefore this strand, termed the **lagging strand,** must be synthesized in short (100- to 1000-nucleotide) pieces, called **Okazaki fragments** after their discoverer, Reijii Okazaki. Each Okazaki fragment is initiated by a separate RNA primer and is then extended toward the 5' end of the previously synthesized fragment by DNA polymerase. More than one type of DNA polymerase is involved in this process, and each is a complex enzyme with several functions. As the growing fragment approaches the one synthe-

sized previously, one part of DNA polymerase degrades the previous RNA primer, allowing a different polymerase to fill in the gap between the two fragments. The fragments are then joined together by **DNA ligase,** an enzyme that links the 3' end of one DNA fragment to the 5' end of another.

It has been suggested (Figure 11–15b) that simultaneous synthesis of both the leading strand and the lagging strand is possible because the lagging strand forms a loop, thus allowing the DNA polymerase to remain at the fork while adding subunits to the 3' end of each strand.

Most DNA synthesis is bidirectional

When double-stranded DNA is separated, two forklike structures are formed so that the molecule is replicated in both directions from the origin of replication. Prokar-

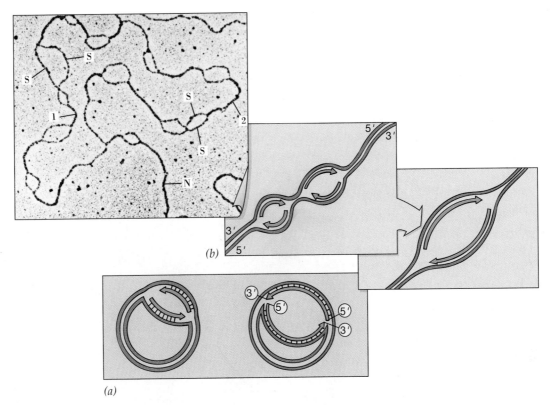

Figure 11–16 Bidirectional replication of DNA in bacterial and eukaryotic chromosomes. The leading strands and lagging strands are not represented in the illustrations. (*a*) The circular chromosome in *E. coli* has only one origin of replication. DNA synthesis proceeds from that point in both directions around the chromosome until the two replication forks meet. (*b*) Eukaryotic chromosomal DNA contains multiple origins of replication. DNA synthesis also proceeds in both directions from those origins until the replication fork from one "replication bubble" meets the replication fork from an adjacent bubble. The photograph shows a segment of a eukaryotic chromosome that has been partially replicated. The conditions used to produce this picture also resulted in the separation of some of the newly formed DNA. 1 and 2 are the daughter double helices; N is a portion of the double helix not yet replicated. The double helix is separated in the regions marked S, illustrating its double structure.   (Photo courtesy of H. J. Kriegstein and D. S. Hogness)

yotic cells usually have only one origin of replication on each circular chromosome (Figure 11–16*a*), so the two replication forks proceed around the circle and eventually meet at the other side to complete the formation of two new DNA molecules.

A eukaryotic chromosome is composed of one extremely long linear DNA molecule, so the process is speeded up by having multiple origins of replication (Figure 11–16*b*). Synthesis continues at each replication fork until it meets one coming from the opposite direction, resulting in the formation of a chromosome containing two DNA double helices.

DNA IN CHROMOSOMES IS PACKAGED IN A HIGHLY ORGANIZED WAY

Prokaryotic and eukaryotic cells differ markedly in their DNA content as well as the organization of DNA molecules. An *E. coli* cell normally contains about 4×10^6 base pairs (almost 1.35 mm) of DNA in its single circular chromosome. In fact, the total length of the DNA is about 1000 times greater than the length of the cell itself. The DNA molecule must, therefore, with the help of special proteins, be twisted and folded compactly to fit inside the bacterial cell.

A typical eukaryotic cell contains much more DNA than a bacterium, and it is organized in the nucleus as multiple chromosomes, which vary widely in size and number among different species. Although a human cell nucleus is about the size of a large bacterial cell, it contains more than 1000 times the amount of DNA found in *E. coli*. The haploid DNA content of a human cell is about 3×10^9 base pairs; if stretched end to end, it would be almost 1 m long.

In eukaryotes, DNA, which is acidic and negatively charged, is wound around basic (positively charged) **histone** proteins to form structures called **nucleosomes.** The fundamental unit of the complex consists of a beadlike structure with about 140 base pairs of DNA wrapped around a disc-shaped core of eight histone molecules (Figure 11–17), plus additional histones bound to the section of DNA that links two neighboring beads. The nucleosomes are part of the **chromatin,** the nucleoprotein complex that makes up the chromosomes (Figure 11–18). They are organized into large coiled loops held together by a set of nonhistone **scaffolding proteins.** Figure 11–19 illustrates the dense packing of DNA fibers on a histone-depleted mouse chromosome.

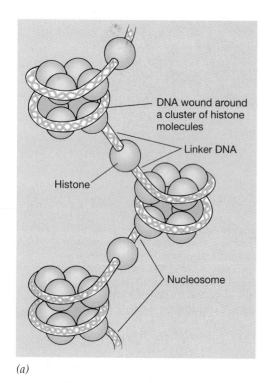

(a)

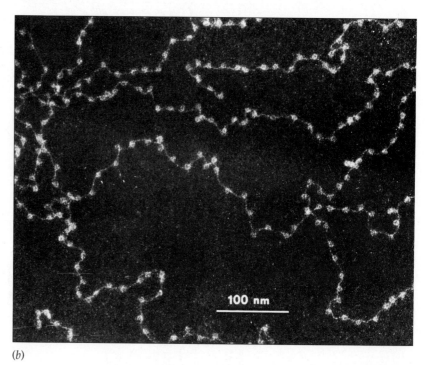

(b)

Figure 11–17 The units of histone surrounded by DNA in the chromosomes are called nucleosomes. (a) A model for the structure of a nucleosome. Each nucleosome bead contains a set of eight histone molecules, which form a protein core around which the double-stranded DNA is wound. The DNA wound around the histone consists of 146 nucleotide pairs; another segment of DNA about 60 nucleotide pairs long links nucleosome beads. A linker DNA segment plus one nucleosome bead together constitute a nucleosome. One type of histone covers the linker DNA between adjacent nucleosome beads. This histone appears to be responsible for packing nucleosomes and may help link them to one another. (b) Nucleosomes from the nucleus of a chicken red blood cell. Each spherical structure and its adjacent linker are a nucleosome. Normally nucleosomes are packed more closely together, but the preparation procedure has spread them apart, revealing the DNA linkers. (b, courtesy of D. E. Olins and A. L. Olins)

Figure 11–19 Electron micrographs of a mouse chromosome ▶ depleted of histones. (a) Note how densely packed the DNA fibrils are, even though they have been released from the proteins that organize them into tightly coiled structures. The dark structure running from left to right across the bottom of the photograph is composed of scaffolding proteins. (b) Higher magnification of the area outlined in (a). The DNA is still organized in the form of loops which protrude from the scaffolding. (Courtesy of U. Laemmli, from *Cell* 12:817, 1988. Copyright by Cell Press)

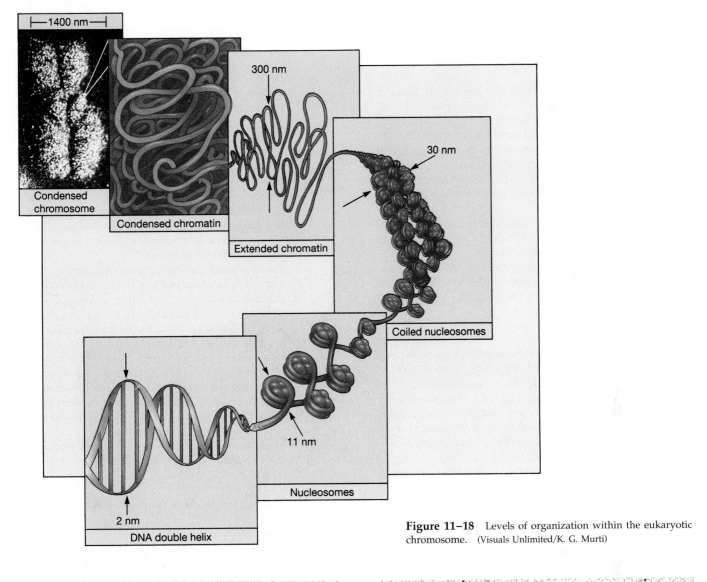

Figure 11–18 Levels of organization within the eukaryotic chromosome. (Visuals Unlimited/K. G. Murti)

1400 nm

Condensed chromosome

Condensed chromatin

300 nm

Extended chromatin

30 nm

Coiled nucleosomes

Nucleosomes

11 nm

2 nm

DNA double helix

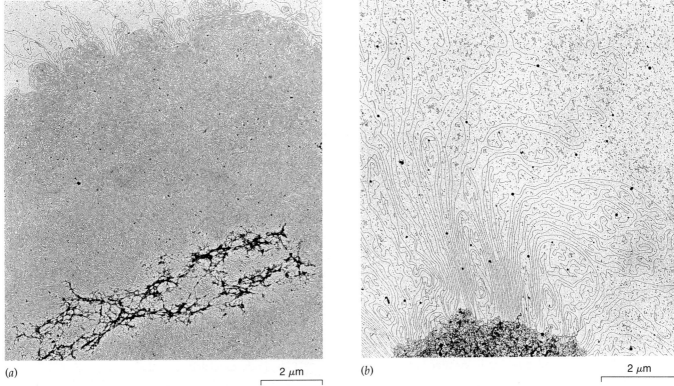

(a)

2 μm

(b)

2 μm

SUMMARY

I. Many early geneticists thought that genes were made of proteins. Proteins were known to be complex and variable, whereas nucleic acids were thought of as rather simple molecules with a limited ability to store information.
   A. Garrod's work on inborn errors of metabolism and that of Beadle and Tatum with *Neurospora* mutants suggested that each protein is specified by a single gene.
   B. Several lines of evidence supported the idea that DNA is the genetic material.
      1. In "transformation" experiments, the DNA of one strain of bacterium can endow a related bacterium with new genetic characteristics.
      2. When a bacterial cell becomes infected with a virus, only the DNA from the virus enters the cell; this DNA is sufficient for the virus to reproduce and form new virus particles.
   C. Watson and Crick's studies on the structure of DNA demonstrated how information can be stored in the structure of the molecule and how DNA molecules can serve as templates for their own duplication.
II. DNA is a very regular polymer of nucleotides.
   A. Each nucleotide subunit contains a nitrogenous base, which may be one of the purines (adenine or guanine) or one of the pyrimidines (thymine or cytosine). Each base is covalently linked to a five-carbon sugar, deoxyribose, linked to a phosphate group.
   B. The "backbone" of each single DNA chain is formed by alternating sugar and phosphate groups, linked by covalent bonds. Each phosphate group is attached to the 5' carbon of one deoxyribose and to the 3' carbon of the neighboring deoxyribose.
   C. Each DNA molecule is composed of two polynucleotide chains, which associate as a double-helix structure. The two chains are antiparallel (meaning they run in opposite directions); at each end of the DNA molecule one chain has an exposed 5' deoxyribose carbon and the other has an exposed 3' deoxyribose carbon.
   D. The deoxyribose-phosphate backbone of each chain is on the outside of the double helix; the purine and pyrimidine bases are on the inside.
   E. The two chains of the helix are held together by hydrogen bonding between specific base pairs. Adenine (A) forms two hydrogen bonds with thymine (T); guanine (G) forms three hydrogen bonds with cytosine (C).
      1. Complementary base-pairing between A and T and between G and C is the basis of Chargaff's rules, which state that A = T and G = C.

   2. Because the two strands of DNA are held together by complementary base-pairing, it is possible to predict the base sequence of one strand if one knows the base sequence of the other strand.
III. During DNA replication, the two strands of the double helix unwind. Each strand serves as a template for the formation of a new complementary strand.
   A. DNA replication is semiconservative—that is, each daughter double helix contains one strand from the parent molecule and one newly synthesized strand.
   B. DNA replication is a complex process requiring a number of different enzymes.
      1. The enzyme that adds new deoxyribonucleotides to a growing DNA strand is a DNA polymerase.
      2. Additional enzymes and other proteins are required to unwind and stabilize the separated DNA helix, to form primers, to prevent tangling and knotting, and to link together fragments of newly synthesized DNA.
   C. DNA synthesis always proceeds in a 5' → 3' direction. This requires that the synthesis of one DNA strand (the lagging strand) be discontinuous, in short pieces called *Okazaki fragments*. The opposite strand (the leading strand) is synthesized continuously.
   D. DNA replication is bidirectional, starting at one point, termed the *origin of replication*, and proceeding in both directions from that point. A eukaryotic chromosome may have multiple origins of replication and may be replicating at many points along its length at any one time.
IV. DNA is organized into chromosomes.
   A. Chromosomes of prokaryotic cells are usually circular DNA molecules.
   B. Eukaryotic chromosomes have several levels of organization.
      1. The DNA is associated with basic proteins called *histones* to form *nucleosomes*, each of which consists of a histone bead with DNA wrapped around it, plus an adjacent linker DNA with a histone attached.
      2. The nucleosomes are organized into large coiled loops held together by nonhistone scaffolding proteins.
      3. DNA molecules are much longer than the nuclei or the cells that contain them. The organization of DNA into chromosomes allows the DNA to be accurately replicated and segregated into daughter cells without tangling.

POST-TEST

1. Early evidence that DNA is the genetic material came from _____ experiments which showed that purified _____ is capable of changing a bacterial strain to a genetically stable new form.
2. Nucleotides found in DNA contain the five-carbon sugar _____. Attached to its 5' carbon is a _____ group. Attached to its 1' carbon is one of four _____ bases. The bases adenine and guanine are called

_____; the bases thymine and cytosine are referred to as _____.
3. The backbone of a DNA strand is formed from alternating _____ and _____, joined by _____ bonds.
4. Chargaff's rules were formulated by analysis of the _____ composition of DNA from different species. These findings stated that the number of _____

bases equals the number of _____ bases and the number of _____ bases equals the number of _____ bases.

5. The basic information that Watson and Crick used to construct their model of DNA came from knowledge of the chemical structure of DNA and the _____ diffraction studies of Franklin and Wilkins.

6. Each DNA molecule consists of two anti-_____ chains arranged in a double _____.

7. The two chains of DNA are held together by _____ bonds between adenine and _____ and between guanine and _____.

8. The process of DNA synthesis is called DNA _____.

9. DNA is replicated by a _____ mechanism; each double helix contains one _____ strand and one _____ strand.

10. For DNA replication to start, the two strands must be separated at a point in the molecule known as the _____ _____ _____.

11. The new strand of DNA is always synthesized starting at its _____ end; additional nucleotides are added at its growing _____ end.

12. The DNA molecules are formed from precursors, which contain _____ phosphate groups.

13. DNA replication is referred to as a *discontinuous process,* which means that one of the strands must be synthesized in short pieces, called _____ _____. The other strand of DNA is synthesized as a _____ molecule.

14. DNA is synthesized by an enzyme called _____ _____. The pieces of the lagging (discontinuous) strand are joined together by an enzyme called _____.

15. The DNA in prokaryotic cells is usually in the form of a _____ molecule; the DNA in a eukaryotic chromosome is a single, _____ molecule.

16. Prokaryotic chromosomes generally have _____ origin(s) of replication, whereas eukaryotic chromosomes have _____ origin(s) of replication.

17. Most DNA synthesis in both prokaryotic and eukaryotic cells is _____, which means that it proceeds in both directions from the origin of replication.

18. The *E. coli* bacterial cell contains about _____ _____ the amount of DNA found in a human cell. The length of DNA in an *E. coli* cell is about _____, whereas the length of DNA in a single human cell is about _____.

19. DNA in eukaryotic cells is organized into structures called _____, which are composed of about 140 base pairs of DNA wrapped around a core of histone proteins plus an adjacent region of linker DNA with an additional histone.

20. _____ fibers, which are composed of nucleosomes, are organized into coiled _____, which are held together by nonhistone _____ _____.

REVIEW QUESTIONS

1. What characteristics must a molecule have if it is to serve as genetic material?

2. How did the experiments of Avery and coworkers point to DNA as the essential genetic material? Did the Hershey-Chase experiment establish that DNA is the genetic material in all organisms? Did either of these experiments demonstrate how DNA could function as the chemical basis of genes?

3. Sketch the structure of a single strand of DNA. What types of subunits make up the chain? How are they linked?

4. Describe the structure of double-stranded DNA as determined by Watson and Crick. What important features of its structure show how it can serve as the genetic material?

5. Does a single strand of DNA obey Chargaff's rules? How do Chargaff's rules relate to the structure of DNA?

6. What are some of the mechanical problems encountered in DNA replication? How are they dealt with by the cell?

7. Why is DNA replication continuous for one strand but discontinuous for the other?

8. Compare the structures of a bacterial chromosome and a eukaryotic chromosome. What effects do these differences have on replication?

9. How do the dimensions of a bacterial cell compare with the length of the DNA contained within it? What is the relationship between the diameter of a human cell nucleus and the average length of DNA per human chromosome?

RECOMMENDED READINGS

Felsenfeld, G. DNA. *Scientific American*, October 1985, pp. 58–67. An excellent, well-illustrated article on the structure and organization of DNA.

Judson, H. F. *The Eighth Day of Creation: Makers of the Revolution in Biology.* Simon & Schuster, New York, 1979. A beautifully written and fascinating account of the history of molecular biology.

Watson, J. D. *The Double Helix.* Atheneum, New York, 1968. Watson's view of the discovery of the structure of DNA. Somewhat controversial, but entertaining and insightful reading.

Watson, J. D., and F. H. C. Crick. Molecular structure of nucleic acids: A structure for deoxyribose nucleic acid. *Nature* 171:737–738, 1953. Watson and Crick's original report—a simple, clearly written two-page paper that shook the scientific world.

Watson, J. D., N. H. Hopkins, J. W. Roberts, J. A. Steitz, and A. M. Weiner. *Molecular Biology of the Gene,* 4th ed. Benjamin Cummings, Menlo Park, CA, 1987. The most recent edition of Watson's classic text.

RNA is usually single-stranded, although internal regions of some RNAs may have complementary sequences that allow them to fold back and pair to form short double-stranded segments. As shown in Figure 12–2, in RNA the sugar is ribose (rather than deoxyribose) and the base uracil substitutes for thymine. Uracil, like thymine, is a pyrimidine and can form two hydrogen bonds with adenine. Hence, uracil and adenine are a complementary pair.

When a protein-coding gene is expressed, an RNA copy is made of the information in the DNA (Figure 12–3). This process resembles DNA replication in that the sequence of bases in the RNA strand is determined by complementary base-pairing with one of the DNA strands. Because RNA synthesis involves making a copy of information in one kind of nucleic acid (DNA) in the form of another nucleic acid (RNA), we refer to this process as **transcription.** The RNA that carries the specific information for making a protein is called **messenger RNA, or mRNA.**

In the second stage of gene expression, the transcribed information in the mRNA is converted into the amino acid sequence of a protein. This process is called **translation** because it involves transformation of the "nucleic acid language" in the mRNA molecule into the "amino acid language" of the protein.

The protein-coding information contained within mRNA is specified by **codons,** which are combinations of three consecutive bases. Each codon in the mRNA specifies one amino acid; for example, one codon that corresponds to the amino acid threonine is 5'—ACG—3' (Table 12–1). Translation requires cellular machinery that can recognize and decode the codons in the mRNA. **Transfer RNAs (tRNAs)** are critical parts of the decoding machinery; each tRNA is an "adapter" molecule that can link with a specific amino acid and recognize the appropriate mRNA codon for that particular amino acid. Codon recognition is possible because each tRNA molecule has a sequence of three bases, called the **anticodon,** which associates with the mRNA codon by complementary base-pairing. In our example, the exact anticodon for threonine is 3'—UGC—5'.

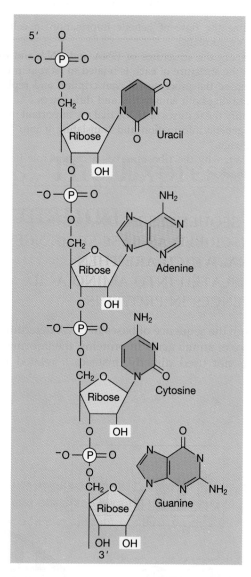

Figure 12–2   An RNA molecule. RNA is made of ribonucleotide subunits linked together by 5'–3' bonds like those found in DNA. Three of the nitrogenous bases—adenine, guanine, and cytosine—are the same as those found in DNA. Instead of having thymine, however, RNA has the base uracil, which pairs with adenine. All four nucleotides contain the five-carbon sugar ribose, which has a hydroxyl group on the 2' carbon atom.

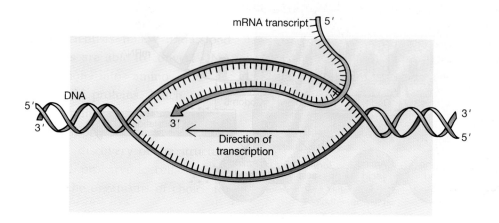

Figure 12–3   Transcription. Information in the DNA that codes for a protein is transcribed in the form of a molecule of messenger RNA (mRNA). The mRNA molecule is formed by complementary base-pairing with the transcribed strand of DNA.

Table 12–1 THE GENETIC CODE: CODONS OF mRNA THAT SPECIFY A GIVEN AMINO ACID

First Position (5' end)	Second Position	Third Position (3' end) U	C	A	G
U	U	UUU UUC Phenylalanine		UUA UUG Leucine	
	C	UCU UCC UCA UCG Serine			
	A	UAU UAC Tyrosine		UAA UAG Stop	
	G	UGU UGC Cysteine		UGA Stop	UGG Tryptophan
C	U	CUU CUC CUA CUG Leucine			
	C	CCU CCC CCA CCG Proline			
	A	CAU CAC Histidine		CAA CAG Glutamine	
	G	CGU CGC CGA CGG Arginine			
A	U	AUU AUC AUA Isoleucine			(start) AUG Methionine
	C	ACU ACC ACA ACG Threonine			
	A	AAU AAC Asparagine		AAA AAG Lysine	
	G	AGU AGC Serine		AGA AGG Arginine	
G	U	GUU GUC GUA GUG Valine			
	C	GCU GCC GCA GCG Alanine			
	A	GAU GAC Aspartic acid		GAA GAG Glutamine	
	G	GGU GGC GGA GGG Glycine			

Translation also requires the linking of amino acids in the correct order. This is accomplished by **ribosomes** (see Chapter 4), complex organelles composed of two different subunits, each containing a number of proteins and **ribosomal RNA (rRNA).** Ribosomes attach to the end of the mRNA and travel along it, allowing the tRNAs to decode the message so that the amino acids are properly positioned and joined by peptide bonds in the correct sequence to form a polypeptide.

These events could not take place without direction by the genetic code. The puzzle before the discoveries of Watson and Crick was how the four bases in DNA could be used to govern the assembly of 20 amino acids into a vast variety of cellular proteins. When scientists examined this problem in light of the new model of DNA, they found that the DNA bases could serve as a four-letter alphabet. Three-letter combinations of the four bases (4^3) made it possible to form a total of 64 "words," more than sufficient to specify all of the naturally occurring amino acids. More than 10 years later the "cracking" of the genetic code was completed, verifying the existence of the three-base **triplet code** that is common to all organisms.

TRANSCRIPTION IS THE SYNTHESIS OF RNA FROM A DNA TEMPLATE

Several kinds of RNA are transcribed from DNA. These include ribosomal RNA (rRNA) and transfer RNA (tRNA), as well as messenger RNA (mRNA). Most

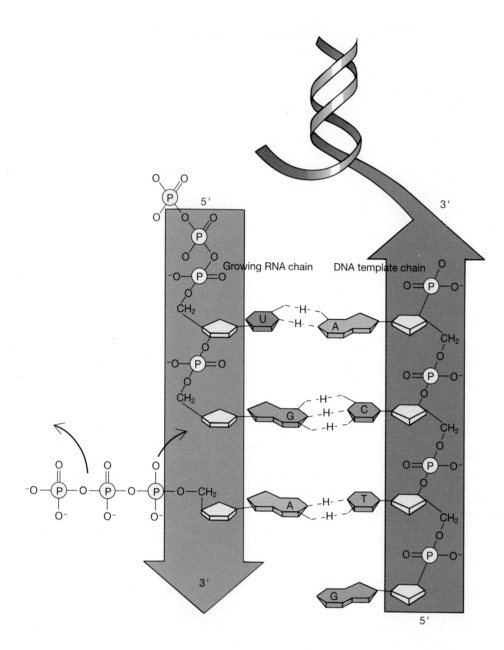

Figure 12–4   The transcription process. As the DNA helix is unwound, the exposed DNA strand on the right is copied. The bases of incoming nucleoside triphosphates pair with complementary bases on the DNA template strand. RNA polymerase cleaves two phosphates from each nucleoside triphosphate and covalently links the remaining phosphate to the 3′ end of the growing RNA chain. Thus, RNA, like DNA, is synthesized in a 5′ → 3′ direction.

RNA is synthesized by **DNA-dependent RNA polymerases,** enzymes that are present in all cells. These enzymes require DNA as a template and have many similarities to DNA polymerase. They use nucleoside triphosphates (nucleotides with three phosphate groups) as substrates, removing two of the phosphates as the subunits are covalently linked to the 3′ end of the RNA (Figure 12–4).

Messenger RNA Contains Base Sequences That Code for Protein

Usually only one of the strands in a protein-coding region of DNA is transcribed (Figure 12–5a). Consider a length of DNA that contains the DNA bases 5′—ATTGCCAGA—3′. Its complementary strand would read 3′—TAACGGTCT—5′, which specifies an entirely different amino acid sequence. Thus, only one of the DNA strands in a gene is complementary to the mRNA and that is the strand that is transcribed. The transcribed strand is also referred to as the template strand.

Whenever nucleic acid molecules associate by complementary base-pairing, the two strands are antiparallel. Just as the two paired strands of DNA are antiparallel, the transcribed strand of the DNA and the complementary RNA strand are also antiparallel to each other. Because a chromosome-sized, double-stranded DNA molecule includes thousands of genes, a particular strand may serve as the transcribed strand for some genes and the nontranscribed strand for others (Figure 12–5b).

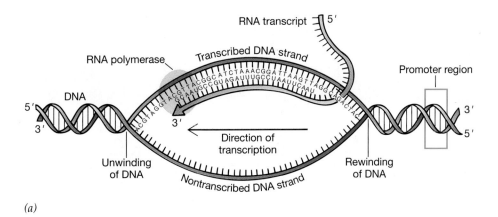

(a)

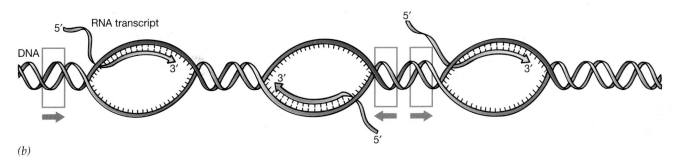

(b)

Figure 12–5 Transcription of bacterial mRNA. (*a*) The RNA is synthesized in a 5′ → 3′ direction from the transcribed or template strand of the DNA molecule. Transcription starts downstream from DNA promoter sequences, which serve as the RNA polymerase recognition site. The promoter sequences are not transcribed. Termination sequences downstream from the coding sequences in the gene signal the RNA polymerase to stop transcription and be released from the DNA. (*b*) Only one of the two strands is transcribed for a given gene, but the opposite strand may be transcribed for a neighboring gene. Each transcript is started at its own promoter.

RNA polymerase begins transcription by recognizing a specific "**promoter**" base sequence at the beginning of a gene. Unlike DNA synthesis, RNA synthesis does not require a primer. The first nucleotide at the 5′ end of a new mRNA chain retains its triphosphate group, but as each additional nucleotide is incorporated at the 3′ end of the growing molecule, two of its phosphates are removed, leaving the remaining phosphate to become part of the sugar/phosphate backbone (as in DNA). The last nucleotide to be incorporated has an exposed 3′ hydroxyl group (Figure 12–6).

Generally, we refer to a sequence of bases in a gene or the mRNA sequence transcribed from it as *upstream* or *downstream* of some reference point. **Upstream** means toward the 5′ end of the mRNA sequence or the 3′ end of the transcribed DNA strand. **Downstream** means toward the 3′ end of the RNA or the 5′ end of the transcribed DNA strand.

Upstream   Downstream

    5′—A—T—G—A—C—T—3′   (nontranscribed
                                   DNA strand)

    3′—T—A—C—T—G—A—5′   (transcribed
                                   DNA strand)

        Direction of transcription

      ⟶

Triphosphate 5′—A—U—G—A—C—U—3′ OH (RNA)

In the bacterium *Escherichia coli,* transcription of a gene is initiated when RNA polymerase (with the help of another protein) recognizes a specific promoter sequence of bases upstream from the protein-coding sequence. Different genes may have slightly different promoter sequences, so the cell can direct which genes are transcribed at any one time. Bacterial promoters are usually about 40 bases long and are positioned in the DNA just upstream of the point at which transcription will begin. Once the polymerase has recognized the correct promoter, it unwinds the helix and transcribes only the template strand of the DNA molecule.

The termination of transcription, like its initiation, is controlled by a set of specific base sequences. These sequences at the end of the gene act as "stop" signals for the RNA polymerase.

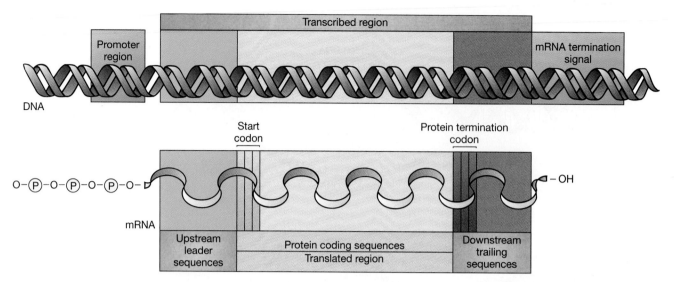

Figure 12–6 Structure of a bacterial mRNA molecule and the region of DNA from which it is transcribed. RNA polymerase recognizes promoter sequences in the DNA located five to eight bases upstream from the base where RNA synthesis is initiated. RNA synthesis stops when the polymerase encounters termination signals downstream from the protein-coding sequences. The ribose at the 5′ end of the mRNA molecule has three phosphate groups attached to its 5′ carbon. The ribose at the 3′ end of the molecule has an exposed hydroxyl group attached to its 3′ carbon. Ribosome-recognition sites are located in 5′ leader sequences of the mRNA, which are upstream from the protein-coding sequences. Protein-coding sequences begin at a start codon following the leader sequences and end at a termination codon near the 3′ end of the molecule. Noncoding trailing sequences, which can vary in length, follow the protein-coding sequences.

Messenger RNA Contains Additional Base Sequences That Do Not Directly Code for Protein

The completed bacterial RNA contains more than the nucleotide sequence that codes for the protein (see Figure 12–6). RNA polymerase starts transcription of a gene well upstream of the protein-coding sequences. As a result, the mRNA has a noncoding **leader sequence** at its 5′ end. The leader contains recognition signals for ribosome binding, which allow the ribosomes to be properly positioned to translate the message. In bacterial cells one or more proteins may be encoded by a single mRNA molecule (see Chapter 13). The leader sequence is followed by the **coding sequences,** which contain the actual messages for the proteins. At the end of the coding sequences are special termination signals that specify the end of the protein. These are followed by noncoding 3′ trailing sequences, which can vary in length.

THE NUCLEIC ACID MESSAGE IS DECODED DURING TRANSLATION

Translation, or protein synthesis, adds another level of complexity to the process of information transfer because it involves the conversion of the four-base nucleic acid code to the 20–amino acid alphabet of proteins.

Translation involves the coordinated functioning of more than 100 kinds of macromolecules, including the protein and RNA components of the ribosomes, mRNA, amino acids linked to tRNAs, and a number of other factors.

An Amino Acid Must Be Attached to Its Specific Transfer RNA Before It Can Become Incorporated into a Polypeptide

Amino acids are joined together by peptide bonds to form proteins (see Chapter 3). This joining involves linking the amino and carboxyl groups of adjacent amino acids. Peptide bond formation is only one aspect of the translation process, however, because the amino acids must be joined together in the correct sequence specified by the codons in the mRNA. The structural differences between a polynucleotide chain and a polypeptide chain are so great that no simple way exists for amino acids to interact directly with an mRNA molecule to make a protein.

Francis Crick recognized this problem and proposed that a molecule was needed to serve as an "adapter" in protein synthesis and bridge the gap between mRNA and proteins. Crick's adapters turned out to be transfer RNA (tRNA) molecules. DNA contains special tRNA genes that are transcribed to form the tRNA. Amino acids are covalently linked to their respective tRNA molecules by specific enzymes called

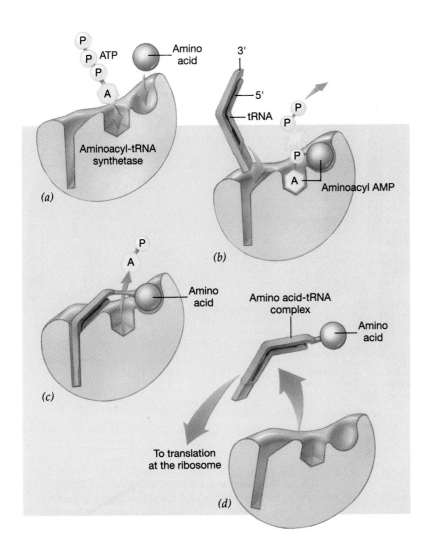

Figure 12–7 Formation of the amino acid–tRNA complex, catalyzed by aminoacyl-tRNA synthetase (*a*). Through an ATP-requiring reaction (*b*), the amino acid is coupled to the 3′ end of the tRNA through its carboxyl group (*c*) and released (*d*).

aminoacyl-tRNA synthetases, which use ATP as an energy source (Figure 12–7). The resulting complexes, called **aminoacyl tRNAs,** are able to bind to the mRNA coding sequence so as to align the amino acids in the correct order to form the peptide chain. Amino acids that have been attached to tRNAs can react to form peptide bonds spontaneously.

Transfer RNA Molecules Have Specialized Regions with Specific Functions

Although tRNA molecules are considerably smaller than mRNA or rRNA molecules, they have a complex structure. A tRNA molecule must have several specific properties:

1. It must be recognized by a specific aminoacyl-tRNA synthetase that adds the correct amino acid.
2. It must have a region that serves as the attachment site for the amino acid.
3. It must be recognized by ribosomes.
4. It must have an **anticodon,** a specific complementary binding sequence for the correct mRNA codon.

The tRNAs are polynucleotide chains about 70 nucleotides long (Figure 12–8), each with a number of unique base sequences as well as some that are common to all. Complementary base-pairing within each tRNA molecule causes it to be doubled back and folded to form three or more loops of unpaired nucleotides (Figure 12–8*b*). The amino acid–binding site is at the end of a "stem" that forms at the 3′ end of the molecule (Figure 12–8*a*). The *carboxyl* group of the amino acid is bound to the exposed 3′ hydroxyl group of the terminal adenine nucleotide, leaving the *amino group* free to participate in peptide bond formation. The three-base sequence that serves as the anticodon site is in the middle of the second loop.

Ribosomes Bring Together All the Components of the Translational Machinery

The importance of ribosomes and the role of protein synthesis in cellular metabolism are exemplified by a rapidly growing *E. coli* cell, which contains some 15,000 ribosomes, nearly one third of the total mass of the cell.

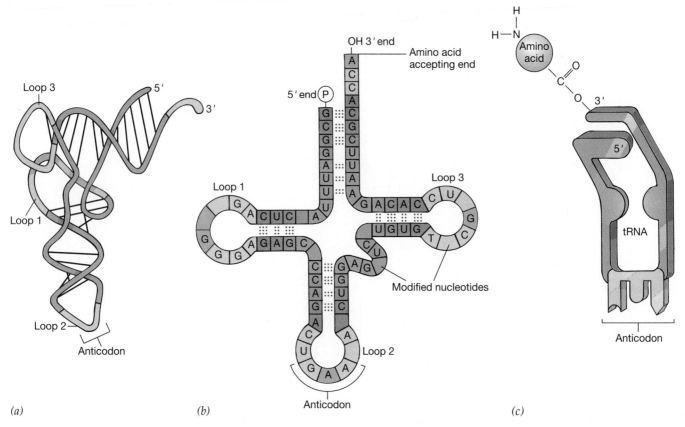

Figure 12–8 Structure of tRNA molecules, which are the compounds that "read" the genetic code. (a) Diagram of the actual shape of a tRNA molecule. Its three-dimensional shape is determined by hydrogen bonds that form between complementary bases, which are most clearly observed in the two-dimensional cloverleaf form (b). One loop contains the triplet anticodon that forms specific base pairs with the mRNA codon. The amino acid is attached to the terminal ribose at the 3' OH end, which has the nucleotide sequence CCA. Each tRNA has G at its 5' end and also contains several modified nucleotides. The pattern of folding results in a constant distance between the anticodon and amino acid in all tRNAs examined. (c) Schematic diagram of how the amino acid is attached to its tRNA by its carboxyl group, leaving its amino group exposed for peptide bond formation.

Although prokaryotic and eukaryotic ribosomes are not identical, ribosomes from all organisms are composed of two subunits. In bacteria the smaller of these subunits contains 21 proteins and one RNA molecule, and the larger contains 35 proteins and two RNA molecules. Ribosomal RNA, which has a structural rather than an informational role, is transcribed from DNA.

Each ribosomal subunit can be isolated intact in the laboratory and then separated into each of its RNA and protein constituents. Under certain conditions it is then possible to reassemble each subunit in a functional form by adding each component in its correct order. Through this approach, together with sophisticated electron microscopic studies, it has been possible to determine the three-dimensional structure of the ribosome (Figure 12–9a) as well as how it is assembled in the living cell. The large subunit contains a depression on one surface into which the small subunit fits. The mRNA fits in a groove formed between the contact surfaces of the two subunits.

Within each ribosome are two depressions, the **A** and **P** binding sites for tRNA molecules (Figure 12–9b). The A site is so named because the *a*minoacyl tRNA binds at this location. The tRNA holding the *p*eptide chain occupies the P site. Following peptide bond formation between the amino acid at the A site and the end of the growing peptide chain, the tRNA (now with the entire peptide chain attached) moves to the P site of the ribosome, leaving the A site available for the next aminoacyl-tRNA molecule.

One of the roles of the ribosome is to hold the mRNA template, the aminoacyl-tRNA precursor, and the growing peptide chain in the correct orientation so that the genetic code can be read and the peptide bond formed.

Translation Includes Initiation, Elongation, and Termination

The process of protein synthesis is generally considered to occur in three distinct stages: **initiation, elongation,** and **termination** (Figures 12–10 and 12–11). The initiation process consists of a number of steps and requires a number of proteins, called **initiation factors.** Initiation begins with the loading of a special **initiation tRNA** onto the small ribosomal subunit. In all organisms the

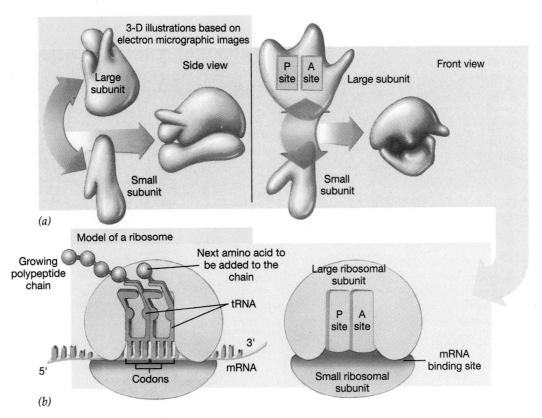

Figure 12–9 (*a*) Model of a ribosome based on three-dimensional reconstructions of electron microscopic images. Front and side views are shown. (*b*) Diagram showing ribosome-binding sites. The mRNA passes through a space in the ribosome formed between the two subunits. Located within the ribosome are two binding sites for tRNAs that recognize adjacent codons. The A site (aminoacyl-tRNA site) binds an aminoacyl tRNA that will be used to add an amino acid to the growing chain. The P site (peptidyl-tRNA site) binds the tRNA that is linked to the growing polypeptide chain.

Figure 12–10 Initiation of protein synthesis. (*a*) Ribosomal subunits are dissociated following translation of a message. (*b*) Formation of an initiation complex, which consists of protein initiation factors, formylated methionine tRNA, and the small ribosomal subunit, which binds to recognition sequences near the 5′ end of the mRNA. (*c*) The large ribosomal subunit binds to the initiation complex. Formylated methionine tRNA is bound to the P site of the completed ribosome, its anticodon paired with the initiation codon AUG. (*d*) The second aminoacyl tRNA recognizes the adjacent codon and binds to the A site.

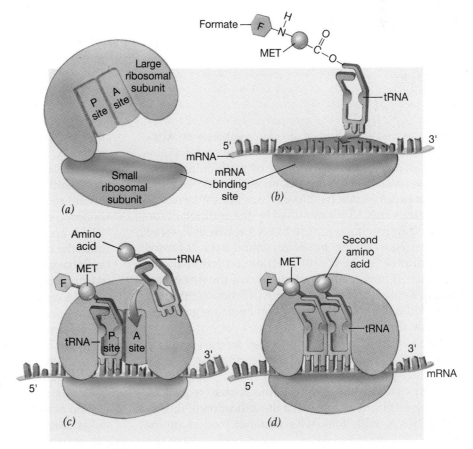

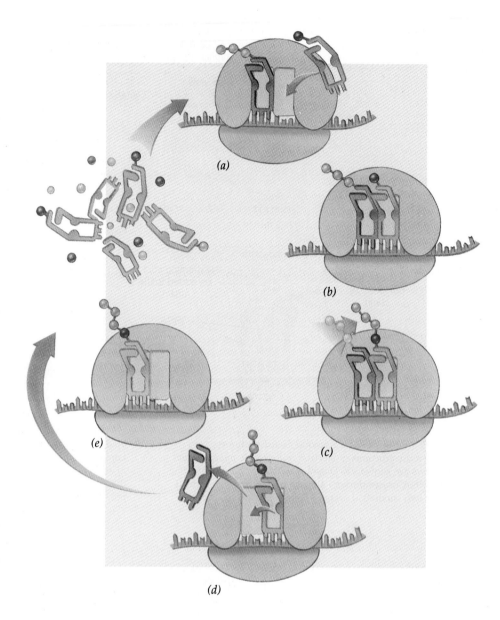

Figure 12–11 Peptide elongation mechanism. (*a*) The peptidyl tRNA occupies the P site. (*b*) A tRNA binds to the A site by base-pairing with the complementary codon at that position. (*c*) A peptide bond has formed between the amino group of the amino acid from the tRNA at the A site and the carboxyl group of the amino acid that was attached to the tRNA at the P site. The polypeptide chain is now attached at its carboxyl end to the tRNA at the A site. (*d*) The tRNA is ejected from the P site, after which the peptidyl tRNA and its complementary mRNA codon are translocated to the P site. (*e*) The A site is now ready to accept the next aminoacyl tRNA designated by the mRNA codon occupying the A site.

codon for the initiation of protein synthesis is AUG, which codes for the amino acid methionine (Table 12–1). *E. coli* contains two types of methionine tRNA that recognize the codon AUG, an initiator tRNA and a regular tRNA. After methionine has been attached to the initiator tRNA, it is modified by the addition of formic acid to its amino group. Every protein in *E. coli* is synthesized with the modified amino acid **N-formyl methionine** (Figure 12–10) at its amino terminal end. Formylated methionine is used only for the first amino acid in a polypeptide chain; if an AUG codon appears in the middle of a protein-coding sequence, a regular methionine tRNA is used.

Once the initiator tRNA is loaded on the small subunit, the initiation complex binds to the special **ribosome-recognition sequences** near the 5′ end of the mRNA; these are upstream of the coding sequences. Binding results in alignment of the anticodon of the initiator tRNA with the AUG initiation codon of the

mRNA. The large ribosomal subunit then binds to the complex, forming the completed ribosome.

The addition of other amino acids to the forming polypeptide is called **elongation.** The initiator tRNA is bound to the P site of the ribosome, leaving the A site unoccupied so that it can be filled by the aminoacyl tRNA specified by the next codon. Figure 12–11 outlines the events involved in elongation. The appropriate aminoacyl tRNA binds to the A site by specific base-pairing of its anticodon with the complementary mRNA codon. This binding step requires energy, which in this case comes from guanosine triphosphate (GTP), an energy donor similar to ATP. (You may recall from Chapter 7 that GTP is a product of one of the reactions of the citric acid cycle.)

The amino group of the amino acid at the A site is now aligned with the carboxyl group of the preceding amino acid at the P site. Peptide bond formation then takes place between the amino group of the new amino acid and the carboxyl group of the preceding amino acid. This reaction is spontaneous and does not require additional energy. In this process, the amino acid attached at the P site is released from its tRNA and becomes attached to the aminoacyl tRNA at the A site.

Recall from Chapter 3 that polypeptide chains have direction, or polarity. The amino acid on one end has a free amino group (the amino terminal end), and the amino acid at the other end has a free carboxyl group (the carboxyl terminal end). Following the sequence through reveals that amino acids are always added to the carboxyl terminal end. *Protein synthesis always proceeds from the amino terminal end to the carboxyl terminal end of the growing peptide chain.*

After the peptide bond is formed, the tRNA molecule is removed from the P site and released so that a new amino acid can be added to it. The growing peptide chain, *which is now attached to the tRNA in the A site,* is then translocated to the P site, leaving the A site open for the next tRNA–amino acid complex. This **translocation** process requires energy, which is again supplied by GTP. The ribosome and the message move in relation to each other so that the codon specifying the next amino acid in the polypeptide chain is positioned in the unoccupied A site. This process involves movement of the ribosome in the 3' direction along the mRNA molecule; thus, *translation of the mRNA always proceeds in a 5' to 3' direction.* The end of the mRNA molecule that is synthesized first during transcription is also the first to be translated into protein.

$$5'——————3' \text{ mRNA}$$

Direction of translation →

$$\underset{H}{\overset{H}{N}}——————\overset{O}{\underset{OH}{C}} \quad \text{polypeptide}$$

Formation of each peptide bond requires only about 1/20 of a second, so an average-sized protein of about 360 amino acids is completed in about 18 seconds.

The synthesis of the peptide chain is terminated by "release factors" that recognize **termination,** or **stop, codons** at the end of the coding sequence. The codons UAA, UGA, and UAG are special stop signals that do not code for any amino acid. Recognition of a termination codon by the release factors causes the ribosome to dissociate into its two subunits, which can then be used to form a new initiation complex with another mRNA molecule.

A Polyribosome Is a Complex of One mRNA and Many Ribosomes

In *E. coli* and other prokaryotes, transcription and translation are *coupled* (Figure 12–12): Ribosomes can bind to the 5' end of the growing mRNA and initiate translation long before the message is completed. As many as 15 ribosomes may be bound to a single mRNA molecule, spaced as close together as 80 nucleotides. Messenger RNA molecules bound to clusters of ribosomes are referred to as **polyribosomes,** or sometimes **polysomes.**

Although a number of polypeptide chains can be actively synthesized on a single messenger at any one time, the half-life (the time it takes for half of the molecules to be degraded) of mRNA molecules in bacterial cells is only about 2 minutes. Usually, degradation of the 5' end of the mRNA begins even before synthesis is complete, and once the ribosome recognition sequences are degraded, no more ribosomes can attach to the mRNA and initiate protein synthesis.

TRANSCRIPTION AND TRANSLATION ARE MORE COMPLEX IN EUKARYOTES THAN IN PROKARYOTES

Although the basic mechanisms of transcription and translation are quite similar in all organisms, some significant differences exist between eukaryotes and prokaryotes, particularly with regard to the characteristics of their mRNAs. Whereas bacterial mRNAs are used immediately after transcription without further processing, eukaryotic mRNA molecules undergo specific **posttranscriptional modification and processing.**

Although bacterial mRNA is translated as it is being transcribed from the DNA, eukaryotic RNA is not. Eukaryotic chromosomes are confined to the nucleus of the cell, and protein synthesis takes place in the cytoplasm. The mRNA must be transported through the nuclear envelope and into the cytoplasm before it can be translated. In addition, the original transcript must be modified in several ways (while it is still in the nucleus) before it becomes competent for transport and translation (Figure 12–13).

Modification of the eukaryotic message begins when the growing RNA transcript is about 20 to 30 nucleotides long. At that point enzymes add a **cap** to the 5' end of the mRNA chain. The cap is in the form of an unusual nucleotide, 7-methyl guanylate, which is guanosine monophosphate with a methyl group added to one of the nitrogens in the base. The capping nucleotide is also unusual in that *it is attached "backwards" to the 5' end of the mRNA!* Instead of the usual 5'—3' phosphate linkage, the 5' phosphate of the cap is linked to the 5' phosphate at the end of the molecule, forming a 5'—5' linkage. Eukaryotic ribosomes cannot bind to an uncapped message.

Capping may also protect the RNA from certain types of degradation and may be partially responsible

0.5 μm

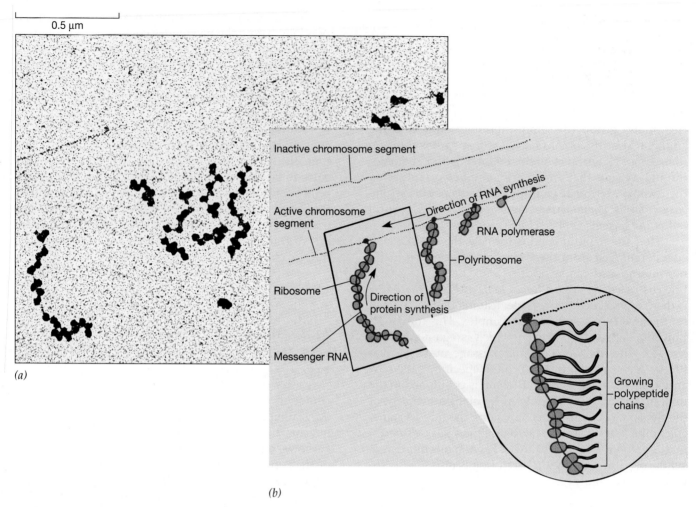

(a)

(b)

Figure 12–12 Coupled transcription and translation in *E. coli.* (*a*) Electron micrograph of two strands of DNA, one inactive and the other actively producing mRNA. Protein synthesis begins while the mRNA is being completed, as multiple ribosomes attach to the mRNA to form a polyribosome. (*b*) Diagrammatic representation of the coupled transcription and translation processes.   (O. L. Miller, Jr., et al., from *Science* 169:392, 1970)

for the fact that eukaryotic mRNAs are much more stable than prokaryotic mRNAs. Eukaryotic mRNAs have half-lives ranging from 30 minutes to as long as 24 hours; the average half-life of an mRNA molecule in a mammalian cell is about 10 hours (compared with 2 minutes in a bacterial cell).

A second modification of eukaryotic mRNA occurs at the 3′ end of the molecule. Near the 3′ end of each completed message is a sequence of bases that serves as a signal for the addition of a "tail" with many adenines, known as a **polyadenylated** (or **poly-A**) **tail.** Within about 1 minute of completion of the transcript, enzymes in the nucleus recognize this **polyadenylation signal** and cut the mRNA molecule at that site. This is followed by the addition of a string of 100 to 250 adenine nucleotides to the 3′ end. The function of polyadenylation is not clear; perhaps it also helps stabilize the mRNA against degradation.

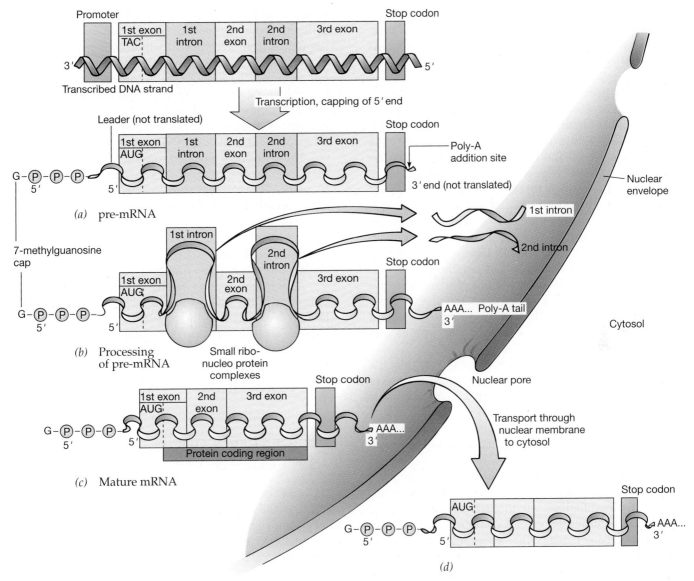

Figure 12–13 Transcription and processing pathway of RNA in the eukaryotic cell nucleus. A typical eukaryotic gene may have multiple exons (coding sequences) and introns (noncoding sequences). (*a*) A DNA sequence containing both exons and introns is transcribed by RNA polymerase to make the primary transcript or mRNA precursor. As the pre-mRNA is synthesized, the molecule is "capped" by the addition of a modified base to its 5′ end. (*b*) The 3′ end of the synthesized RNA molecule is cleaved at a sequence that designates the poly-A addition site. A poly-A tail (50 to 200 nucleotides long) is then added to the exposed 3′ OH group. (*c*) Introns are removed from the molecule and the exons are spliced together. (*d*) The mature mRNA is transported through the nuclear envelope into the cytoplasm to be used for protein synthesis.

Both Noncoding Nucleotide Sequences (Introns) and Coding Sequences (Exons) Are Transcribed from Eukaryotic Genes

The final step in mRNA modification is one of the most surprising findings in molecular biology. Many eukaryotic genes have **interrupted coding sequences,** caused by long sequences of bases within the protein-coding sequences of the gene that do not code for amino acids

in the final protein product! The noncoding regions within the gene are called **introns** (*in*tervening sequences), as opposed to **exons** (*ex*pressed sequences), which are parts of the protein-coding sequence.

The number of introns found in genes is quite variable. For example, the β-globin gene, which produces one component of hemoglobin, contains two introns; the ovalbumin gene of egg white contains seven; and the gene specifying another egg-white protein, conalbumin, contains 16. In many cases the combined lengths of the introns are much greater than those of the exon sequences. For instance, the ovalbumin gene contains about 7700 base pairs, whereas the exon sequences together are only 1859 bases long.

When a gene that contains introns is transcribed, the entire gene is copied as a large RNA transcript referred to as **precursor mRNA, or pre-mRNA.** This molecule contains both exon and intron sequences. (Note that the terms *intron* and *exon* are used to refer to corresponding nucleotide sequences in DNA and RNA.)

For the pre-mRNA to be made into a functional message, not only must it be capped and have a poly-A tail added, but the introns must be removed and the exons spliced together to form a continuous protein-coding message. The splicing reactions are mediated by special base sequences within and to either side of the introns. Splicing itself can occur by several different mechanisms. In many instances the splicing involves the association of **small nuclear ribonucleoprotein complexes (snRNPs)**, which bind to the introns and catalyze the excision and splicing reactions.

Surprisingly, in some cases the RNA within the intron has the ability to splice itself without the use of proteins. This ability may be related to the fact that some RNAs are capable of acting as enzymes. The discovery of this property led to the recognition of a new class of biological catalysts, termed **ribozymes,** which are formed from RNA molecules rather than proteins.

Although most eukaryotic mRNAs require capping, tailing, and splicing reactions, not all mRNA molecules are modified by all three mechanisms. Some messages, for example, do not contain introns and so do not require splicing. Other eukaryotic mRNAs are capped but do not contain introns or poly-A tails.

Evidence Exists That New Combinations of Exons Have Arisen during Evolution

Why do introns occur in eukaryotic genes? It seems incredible that as much as 75% of the original transcript of a gene might be useless information that has to be removed to make a working message. One hypothesis is based on the idea that, although proteins are synthesized as continuous linear amino acid sequences, they actually are *modular* in that they are made up of various functional regions, called **domains.** For example, the active site of an enzyme might compose one domain, whereas a different domain might enable that enzyme to bind to a particular cellular structure.

Walter Gilbert has proposed that introns separate nucleotide sequences that *code for different structural and functional protein domains.* He postulates that new proteins with new functions can emerge rapidly when new combinations of exons are produced by genetic recom-

bination between intron regions of genes that code for different proteins. Analysis of the DNA and amino acid sequences from a number of eukaryotic genes has provided evidence for this hypothesis of **exon shuffling.** For example, the low-density lipoprotein (LDL) receptor protein (a protein found on the surface of human cells that binds to cholesterol transport molecules) has a number of domains that are related to parts of several other proteins with totally different functions.

These findings have led some scientists to speculate that the number of basic "exon families" (and their corresponding protein domains) is actually relatively small, and that all of the diverse array of proteins found today evolved from just a few thousand domain prototypes. Not all scientists agree, however. It will require additional data and more sophisticated methods of analysis to resolve this question.

As we shall see in Chapter 13, intron excision provides one of the many ways in which eukaryotes regulate the expression of their genes. This opportunity for control, together with the fact that eukaryotic RNAs are far more stable than those of prokaryotes, may balance the energy cost of maintaining a large load of noncoding DNA.

THE GENETIC CODE IS READ AS A SERIES OF CODONS

We have seen that prokaryotes show a direct correspondence in the sequence of subunits from DNA to mRNA to protein. Thus, the three are **colinear.**

In 1961 Crick and his coworkers concluded from a mathematical analysis of the coding problem that three consecutive nucleotides (a triplet) in a strand of mRNA must provide the code for a single amino acid in a polypeptide chain. They further concluded that the triplets must not overlap. They reasoned that the code is read, one triplet at a time, from a fixed starting point, which would establish the **reading frame.** Because there are no "commas" separating the triplets, an alteration in the reading frame would result in incorporation of incorrect amino acids.

Experimental evidence allowing the assignment of specific triplets to specific amino acids was obtained by Marshall Nirenberg and Heinrich Matthaei. By constructing artificial mRNA molecules with known base sequences, they were able to determine which amino acids would be incorporated into protein in purified protein synthetic systems. When the synthetic mRNA polyuridylic acid (UUUUUUUUU...) was added to a mixture of purified ribosomes, aminoacyl tRNAs, and essential cofactors needed to synthesize protein, only phenylalanine was incorporated into the resulting polypeptide chain. The inference that UUU is the triplet that codes for phenylalanine was inescapable. Similar experiments showed that polyadenylic acid (AAAAAAAA . . .) codes for a polypeptide of lysine and polycytidylic acid (CCCCCCCC . . .) for a polypeptide of proline.

By using mixed nucleotide polymers (such as a random polymer of A and C) as artificial messengers, it became possible to assign the other nucleotide triplet codons to specific amino acids. However, three of the codons—UAA, UGA, and UAG—were not found to specify any amino acid. These codons, the stop, or termination, codons mentioned earlier, are now known to be the signals that specify the end of the coding sequence for a polypeptide chain.

Taken together, these experiments led to the coding assignments of all 64 possible codons, listed in Table 12–1. Investigators were also able to demonstrate conclusively that the code is a nonoverlapping triplet code.

Remember that *the genetic code we define and use is an mRNA code.* The tRNA anticodon sequences as well as the DNA sequence from which the message is transcribed are complementary to the sequences shown in Table 12–1. For example, the mRNA codon for the amino acid methionine is 5′—AUG—3′. It is transcribed from the DNA base sequence 3′—TAC—5′, and the corresponding tRNA anticodon is 3′—UAC—5′.

The Genetic Code Is Virtually Universal

The most remarkable feature of the genetic code became apparent as it was examined in a diverse array of organisms: *The genetic code is essentially* **universal.** The mRNA code is the same in *E. coli*, plants, and humans, strongly suggesting that it is an ancient legacy, derived by evolution of all living organisms from a common ancestor.

Recently some very minor exceptions to the universality of the genetic code have been discovered. In several single-celled protozoa, two of the stop codons, UAA and UAG, code for a single amino acid. The other exceptions are found in mitochondria, which contain their own DNA and protein-synthesis machinery for a small number of genes. These minor coding differences vary with the organism, but almost all of the coding assignments in each case are identical to the standard genetic code.

The Genetic Code Is Redundant

Some of the amino acids in the codon assignments in Table 12–1 are specified by more than one codon. This **redundancy** in the code has certain characteristic patterns. The codons CCU, CCC, CCA, and CCG are synonomous in that they all code for the amino acid proline. The only difference among the four codons in-

volves the nucleotide at the 3′ end of the triplet. Although the code may be read three nucleotides at a time, only the first two nucleotides appear to contain specific information for proline. A similar pattern can be seen for many other amino acids. Only methionine and tryptophan have single-triplet codes. All other amino acids are specified by two to six different codons.

There are 61 codons that specify amino acids; although most cells contain only about 40 different tRNA molecules, some of these tRNAs can pair with more than one codon, so all of the codons can still be used. This apparent breach of the base-pairing rules was first proposed by Francis Crick as the **wobble hypothesis.** Crick reasoned that the third nucleotide of a tRNA anticodon (which is the 5′ base of that sequence) may sometimes be capable of forming hydrogen bonds with more than one kind of third nucleotide (the 3′ base) of an mRNA codon. Investigators later established this experimentally by determining the anticodon sequences of tRNA molecules and testing their specificities in artificial systems. Some tRNA molecules can recognize as many as three separate codons specifying the same amino acid.

A GENE IS DEFINED AS A FUNCTIONAL UNIT

In Chapter 11 we traced the development of ideas regarding the nature of the gene. For a time it was useful to define a gene as a sequence of nucleotides that codes for one polypeptide chain. As we have continued to learn more about how genes work, we have revised our definition. We now know that some genes produce RNA molecules such as rRNA and tRNA, whereas others code for the RNA component of the small nuclear ribonucleoprotein complexes used to modify complex mRNA molecules. Recent studies have also shown that in eukaryotic cells a single gene may be capable of producing more than one polypeptide chain by modifications in the way the mRNA is processed (see Chapter 13).

A gene may be defined in terms of its product. One useful definition is that a gene includes a *transcribed nucleotide sequence (plus associated sequences regulating its transcription) that yields a product with a specific cellular function.*

MUTATIONS ARE CHANGES IN DNA

One of the first major discoveries about genes was that they can undergo changes, called **mutations.** We now know that mutations are caused by changes in the nucleotide sequence of the DNA. As explained in Chapter

11, once the DNA sequence is changed, DNA replication copies the altered sequence just as it would copy a normal sequence, making the mutation stable over an indefinite number of generations. In most cases the mutant gene has no greater tendency than the original gene to mutate again. Mutations provide the diversity of genetic material that makes it possible to study inheritance and the molecular nature of genes. As we shall see in later chapters, mutations also provide the variation necessary for evolution to occur within a given species.

Genes can be altered by mutation in a number of ways (Figure 12–14). The simplest type of mutation, called a **point mutation,** or **base-substitution mutation,** involves a change in only one pair of nucleotides. It is now possible to determine where a specific point mutation occurs in a gene by using recombinant DNA methods to isolate the gene and determine its sequence of bases (see Chapter 14). Often these mutations result from errors in base-pairing that occurred during the replication process, such as replacement of an AT base pair with a GC, CG, or TA pair. Such a mutation may cause the altered DNA to be transcribed as an altered mRNA, which may be translated into a peptide chain with only one amino acid different from the normal sequence.

Mutations that result in the substitution of one amino acid for another are sometimes referred to as **missense mutations.** Substitution of a different amino acid into a protein in this way can have a wide range of effects. If the amino acid substitution occurs at or near the active site of an enzyme, the activity of the altered protein may be decreased or even destroyed. If a missense mutation involves a change in an amino acid that is not part of the active site or involves the substitution of a closely related amino acid (one with very similar chemical characteristics), the mutation may be *silent* (undetectable), at least if one simply examines the effects it has on the whole organism. Because silent mutations occur relatively frequently, the true number of mutations in an organism or a species is much greater than what is actually observed.

Nonsense mutations are point mutations that can change an amino acid–specifying codon into a termination codon. A nonsense mutation in a gene usually destroys the function of the gene product; in the case of a gene specifying a protein, the part of the polypeptide chain that follows the termination codon is missing.

In **frameshift mutations,** nucleotide pairs are *inserted into* or *deleted from* the molecule. Insertion or deletion of a base in a DNA sequence causes an alteration of the *reading frame.* As a result of this shift, codons downstream of the insertion site specify an *entirely new sequence of amino acids.* Depending on where the insertion or deletion occurs in the gene, a number of different effects can be generated. In addition to producing an entirely new polypeptide sequence immediately after the change, frameshift mutations usually produce a stop or termination codon within a short distance of the mutation, thus terminating the already altered polypeptide chain. A frame shift in a gene specifying an enzyme most likely results in a loss of enzyme activity. If the enzyme is an essential one, the effect on the organism can be disastrous.

Other types of mutations may be due to a change in chromosome structure (see Chapters 13, 15, and 16). These types of changes usually have a wide range of effects because they involve large numbers of genes.

One type of mutation whose mechanism of action has only recently been understood is caused by DNA sequences that "jump" into the middle of a gene. These movable sequences of DNA, called **transposons,** not only disrupt the functions of some genes but under some conditions also activate inactive genes (see Focus on Reverse Transcription, Jumping Genes, and Pseudogenes).

All of the mutations discussed so far can occur infrequently but spontaneously, as a consequence of either mistakes in DNA replication or defects in the mitotic or meiotic segregation of chromosomes. Some regions of DNA are much more likely than others to undergo mutation. Such **hot spots** are often single nucleotides or short stretches of repeated nucleotides. They may consist of unusual bases that spontaneously change their structure or short stretches of repeated nucleotides, which can cause DNA polymerase to "slip." Mutations in certain genes can increase the overall mutation rate, probably by making DNA replication less precise.

(*Text discussion continued on p. 296*)

Figure 12–14 Effects of mutations involving one or a few base pairs. In each example the normal DNA sequence has been specifically mutated to produce the mRNA molecule shown. Base-pair substitutions can produce several different types of mutations. Silent mutations have no visible effect on the protein because although a codon has been changed it still specifies the same or a related amino acid. Missense mutations produce proteins of the same length as the normal protein. These mutant proteins range from being completely functional to having no activity, depending on the type of amino acid changed and its location in the polypeptide chain. Nonsense mutations, caused by a change of an amino acid–specifying codon to a termination codon, result in the production of a truncated protein that is usually not functional. Frameshift mutations, which result from the insertion or deletion of one or two bases, usually have more drastic effects; they cause the base sequence following the mutation to shift to a new reading frame, altering the structure and function of the protein. A frame shift may also produce a termination codon downstream from the mutation, which has the same effect as a nonsense mutation caused by base substitution.

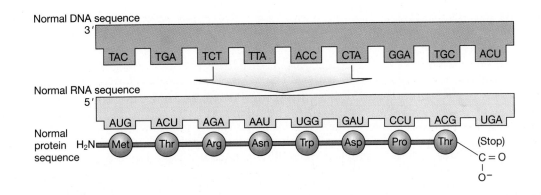

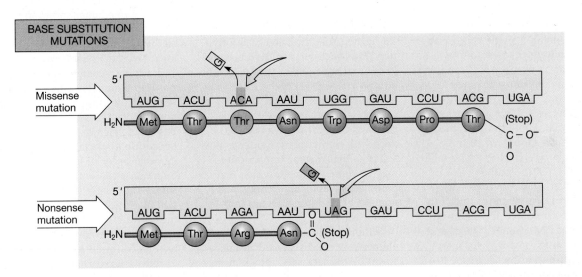

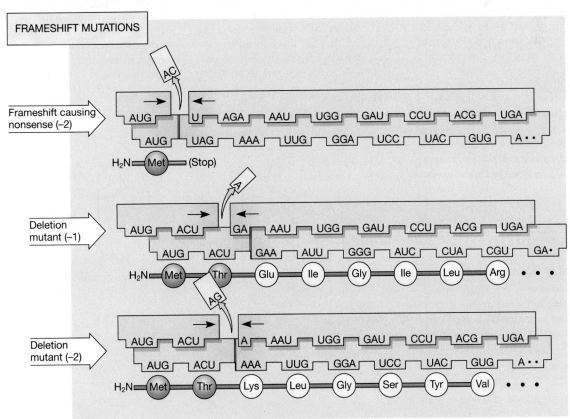

FOCUS ON

Reverse Transcription, Jumping Genes, and Pseudogenes

For several decades, one of the central ideas of molecular biology was that genetic information always flows from DNA to RNA to protein. An important exception to this rule was discovered by Howard Temin in 1964 through his studies on certain viruses. Although viruses are noncellular, they contain a single type of nucleic acid and are capable of reproducing in a host cell. Temin was studying certain unusual cancer-causing tumor viruses that have RNA, rather than DNA, as their genetic material. He found that infection of a host cell by one of these particular viruses is blocked by inhibitors both of DNA synthesis and of transcription. These findings suggested that DNA synthesis and transcription are required for the multiplication of RNA tumor viruses and that there must be a way for information to flow in the "reverse" direction (that is, from RNA to DNA).

Temin proposed that a **DNA provirus** is formed as an intermediary in the replication of RNA tumor viruses. This hypothesis required a new kind of enzyme—one that would synthesize DNA using RNA as a template. In 1970, Temin and David Baltimore discovered just such an enzyme, and in 1975 they shared the Nobel Prize for their discovery. This RNA-directed DNA polymerase, also known as **reverse transcriptase,** was found in all RNA tumor viruses. (Some non–tumor-forming RNA viruses, however, replicate themselves directly without using a DNA intermediary.)

After an RNA tumor virus enters the host cell, the viral reverse transcriptase synthesizes a DNA strand that is complementary to the viral RNA. Next, a complementary DNA strand is synthesized, thus completing the double-stranded DNA provirus, which is then integrated into the host cell's DNA. The provirus DNA is transcribed, and the resulting viral mRNA is translated to form specific viral proteins. Additional viral RNA molecules are produced and then incorporated into mature virus particles enclosed by protein coats. Because of their reversal of the usual direction of information flow, such viruses have become known as **retroviruses** (figure *a*). The AIDS virus (HIV-1) is the most widely known retrovirus.

Until recently, reverse transcription was thought to be associated only with retroviruses. Evidence now suggests that reverse transcription may be quite common, which may partially explain such curious phenomena as "jumping" genes and pseudogenes.

Jumping genes, or **mobile genetic elements,** were discovered in maize (corn) by Barbara McClintock in the 1950s. She observed that certain genes appeared to be "turned off" and "turned on" spontaneously. She deduced that the mechanism involved a gene that moved from one region of a chromosome to another, where it would either activate or inactivate genes in that vicinity. It was not until the development of recombinant DNA methods (see Chapter 14) and the discovery of jumping genes in a wide variety of organisms that this phenomenon began to be understood. In recognition of her insightful findings, McClintock was awarded the Nobel Prize in 1983.

Jumping genes, also called **transposable elements** or **transposons,** are segments of DNA that range from a few hundred to several thousand bases. The elements themselves seem to require a special **transposase** enzyme in order to be incorporated into a new location within the chromosome. The longer elements may contain other genes that "go along for the ride."

Many of the transposable elements have been found to have similarities to retroviruses. Their DNA has unusual base sequences at each end, and their genes are remarkably similar, especially those that code for the proteins required for reverse transcription and integration into the chromosome.

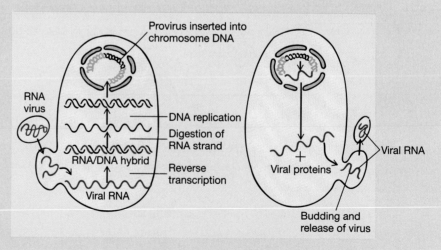

(a)

Experiments in Gerald Fink's laboratory have provided evidence that reverse transcriptase is involved in the mechanism by which some transposons move. In these cases the DNA sequence itself does not jump from one location to another; instead, the *information moves through an RNA intermediate* (figure *b*). Fink and his colleagues used recombinant DNA methods (see Chapter 14) to insert an intron into the DNA sequence of a yeast transposon as a way of identifying it. They then set up conditions that allowed them to recover and analyze the transposed sequence once it had "jumped." When the transposed sequence appeared at a new location, the intron had been removed, just as introns are removed during the processing of normal mRNA molecules.

Because the enzymes are known only to splice RNA, it appears that the transposed DNA sequence had been produced from a processed RNA copy of the original DNA rather than from the DNA itself. This would require the RNA sequence to be converted back to DNA by reverse transcriptase activity within the yeast cells.

Other evidence of nonviral reverse transcriptase activities in cells comes from analyses of **pseudogenes,** which closely resemble certain types of normal genes in mammalian cells. Pseudogenes are DNA sequences that are almost identical to those of normal genes, except that they are riddled with mutations that prevent them from functioning in normal protein synthesis. Many pseudogenes resemble DNA copies of mRNA, for where a normal gene would contain one or more introns, the pseudogenes do not. Many pseudogene DNA sequences also end with long poly-A tails. One hypothesis concerning the origin of pseudogenes is that they are derived from the processed mRNAs of normal genes, which were retro-transcribed into DNA by reverse transcriptase and the copies reinserted into the chromosome. Because they lack promoter sequences, they are not expressed and simply act as excess baggage, silently accumulating mutations. It is estimated that there may be hundreds or thousands of such sequences in normal human DNA.

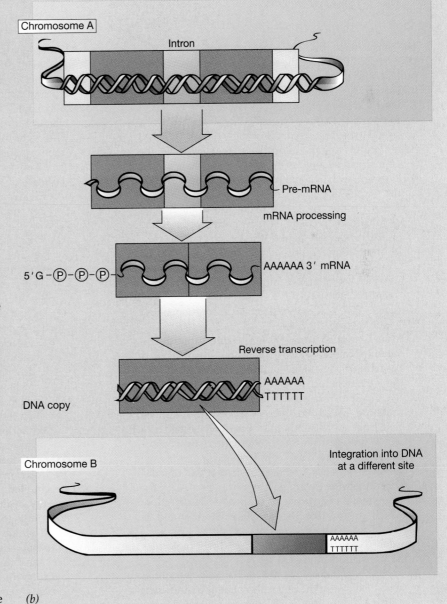

(b)

Not all mutations occur spontaneously; many of the types of mutations discussed above can also be caused by agents known as **mutagens.** Among these are various types of ionizing radiation, including x rays, gamma rays, cosmic rays, and ultraviolet rays. Some chemical mutagens react with and modify specific nucleotide bases in the DNA, leading to mistakes in complementary base-pairing when the DNA molecule is replicated. Other mutagens are inserted in the DNA molecule and change the normal reading frame during replication.

The overall observed mutation rate is much lower than the frequency of damage to DNA, because all organisms have special systems of enzymes that can repair certain kinds of alterations in the DNA. Nevertheless, some new mutations do persist. In fact, each of us is very likely to have some mutant gene that was not present in either of our parents. Although some of these mutations can produce an altered phenotype, most are not noticeable because they are recessive.

Mutations that occur in the cells of the body (somatic cells) are not passed on to the offspring. However, these mutations are of concern because there is a close relationship between somatic mutations and cancer. Many mutagens are also **carcinogens,** agents that produce cancer in higher organisms (see Chapter 16).

SUMMARY

I. The mechanism by which information encoded in DNA is used to specify the sequences of amino acids in proteins involves two processes: transcription and translation.
   A. During transcription an RNA molecule that is complementary to the transcribed or template DNA strand is synthesized. Messenger RNA (mRNA) molecules contain information that specifies the amino acid sequences of polypeptide chains.
   B. During translation a polypeptide chain specified by the mRNA is synthesized.
      1. Each triplet (three-base sequence) in the mRNA constitutes a codon, which specifies one amino acid in the polypeptide chain.
      2. Translation requires adapter molecules (tRNAs) and complex machinery, including ribosomes, which contain rRNA molecules and many different proteins.
II. Messenger RNA is synthesized by DNA-dependent RNA polymerase enzymes.
   A. RNA is formed from ribonucleoside triphosphate subunits, each of which contains the sugar ribose, a base (uracil, adenine, guanine, or cytosine), and three phosphates.
   B. RNA polymerase initially binds to a special DNA sequence, called the *promoter region.*
   C. Like DNA, RNA subunits are covalently joined by a 5'—3' linkage to form an alternating sugar/phosphate backbone. The same base-pairing rules are followed as in DNA replication, except that uracil is substituted for thymine.
   D. RNA synthesis proceeds in a $5' \rightarrow 3'$ direction, which means that the template DNA strand is "read" in a $3' \rightarrow 5'$ direction.
III. Transfer RNAs (tRNAs) are the "decoding" molecules in the translation process.
   A. Each tRNA molecule is specific for only one amino acid. One part of the molecule contains a three-base anticodon, which is complementary to a codon on the mRNA. Attached to one end of the tRNA molecule is the amino acid specified by the complementary mRNA codon.
   B. Amino acids are covalently bound to tRNA by aminoacyl-tRNA synthetase enzymes, each of which is specific for a particular combination of amino acid and tRNA.
IV. Ribosomes bring together all of the mechanical machinery necessary for translation. They couple the tRNAs to their proper codons on the mRNA, facilitate the formation of peptide bonds between amino acids, and translocate the mRNA so that the next codon can be read.
   A. Each ribosome is made of a large and a small subunit; each subunit contains rRNA and a large number of proteins.
   B. *Initiation,* the first stage of translation, includes the binding of the small ribosomal subunit protein, plus initiation factors and the initiation tRNA, to the 5' region of the mRNA, followed by binding of the large ribosomal subunit.
   C. During the *elongation cycle,* amino acids are added one by one to the growing polypeptide chain.
      1. Elongation proceeds in a $5' \rightarrow 3'$ direction along the mRNA.
      2. The polypeptide chain grows from its amino end to its carboxyl terminal end.
   D. *Termination,* the final stage of translation, occurs when the ribosome reaches one of three special termination, or stop, codons, which do not specify any amino acid. This triggers release of the completed polypeptide chain.
   E. In bacterial cells, transcription and translation are coupled. Translation of the mRNA molecule usually begins before the 3' end of the transcript is completed.
   F. A single mRNA molecule can be translated by groups of ribosomes called *polyribosomes.*
V. The basic features of transcription and translation are the same in prokaryotic and eukaryotic cells, but eukaryotic genes and their mRNA molecules are more complex than those of bacteria.
   A. After transcription, eukaryotic mRNA molecules are capped at the 5' end with a modified guanosine triphosophate. Many also have a tail of poly-A nu-

cleotides added at the 3' end. These modifications appear to protect the molecules from degradation, giving them long lifetimes compared with bacterial mRNA.

    B. In many eukaryotic genes the coding regions, called *exons*, are interrupted by noncoding regions, called *introns*. Both introns and exons are transcribed, but the introns are later removed from the mRNA precursor and the exons are spliced together to produce a continuous protein-coding sequence.

VI. The genetic code is defined at the mRNA level. There are 61 codons that code for amino acids, plus three codons that serve as stop signals.

    A. The start signal for all proteins is the codon AUG, which also specifies the amino acid methionine.

    B. The genetic code is nearly universal, strongly suggesting that all organisms are descended from a common ancestor. The only exceptions to the standard code are minor variations.

    C. Some amino acids are specified by more than one codon; thus, the code is said to be *redundant*. In many cases one tRNA molecule recognizes more than one codon for the same amino acid. This phenomenon, known as *wobble*, is caused by the ability of the third nucleotide in some anticodons to violate base-pairing rules and pair with more than one kind of base in the third position of a codon.

    D. The genetic code is read from mRNA as a series of nonoverlapping triplets that specify a single sequence of amino acids.

VII. Because genes can code for specific RNA molecules as well as for proteins, a gene can be defined as a sequence of nucleotides (plus closely associated regulatory sequences) that can be transcribed to yield a product with a specific cellular function.

VIII. Mutations can produce many effects. Types of mutations range from disruption of the structure of a chromosome to a change in only a single pair of nucleotide bases.

    A. A point mutation can destroy the function of a protein if it alters a codon so that it specifies a different amino acid (missense mutation) or becomes a termination codon (a nonsense mutation). A point mutation has minimal effects if the amino acid is not altered or if the codon is changed to specify a similar amino acid in the protein.

    B. Insertion or deletion of one or two base pairs in a gene invariably destroys the function of that protein because it results in a frameshift mutation that changes the codon sequences downstream from the mutation.

    C. Mutations can be produced by errors in DNA replication, by physical agents such as x rays or ultraviolet rays, or by chemical mutagens. Mutations can also occur through transposable genetic elements, or "jumping genes," which move from one part of a chromosome to another, disrupting the function of a part of the DNA. Some damage to DNA can be repaired by special systems of enzymes.

POST-TEST

1. The process by which information is copied from DNA to mRNA is called _____ .

2. The process by which genetic information in mRNA is decoded to specify the amino acid sequence of a protein is called _____ .

3. An amino acid is specified in the genetic code as a sequence of _____, called a(n) _____ .

4. The type of RNA molecule that "decodes" the information in a codon and translates it into an amino acid is _____ .

5. The "machine" that facilitates formation of peptide bonds between amino acids during translation is a(n) _____ .

6. Messenger RNA is synthesized by DNA-dependent _____ _____ .

7. Ribonucleotides differ from the deoxyribonucleotide subunits found in DNA in that the sugar is _____ and the base _____ is substituted for _____ .

8. The "start" signals for transcription on DNA are _____ regions, which are just before the point at which synthesis of the _____ end of the mRNA will begin.

9. The nucleotide sequence of the tRNA molecule that is complementary to the appropriate codon on the mRNA is called the _____ .

10. An amino acid is attached by its _____ group to the _____ end of its tRNA molecule.

11. The energy for forming a peptide bond is derived from the process of amino acid activation, an ATP-requiring process that results in the attachment of the amino acid to its _____ .

12. A ribosome is made of two subunits, each of which contains _____ and _____ molecules.

13. The first stage of protein synthesis is a two-step process called _____ . The first step involves the binding of the small ribosomal subunit, protein _____ factors, and aminoacyl tRNA to the _____ end of the mRNA.

14. The second stage of protein synthesis is the _____ cycle, which involves the sequential binding of the tRNA specified by each codon, _____ bond formation, and translocation of the ribosome to the next codon on the mRNA.

15. The final stage of protein synthesis, called _____, occurs when the ribosome reaches a(n) _____ codon. This causes the completed peptide chain to be released and the _____ subunits to dissociate from the mRNA.

16. A complex consisting of a group of ribosomes bound to a single mRNA molecule is a(n) _____ .

17. Many eukaryotic genes contain noncoding sequences, called _____, which interrupt protein-coding _____ sequences.

18. After it has been transcribed, the 5′ end of a eukaryotic mRNA is _____ by the addition of a modified _____.

19. Many eukaryotic mRNAs have a modified 3′ end consisting of a(n) _____ tail.

20. For precursor mRNA to become functional mRNA, it must be _____ and tailed. Its introns are removed and its _____ are spliced together to make a continuous protein-coding sequence of bases.

21. Mutations that change a single base pair in a gene, thereby converting an amino acid–specifying codon to a termination codon, are called _____ mutations. Mutations caused by the insertion or deletion of one or two bases in a gene are called _____ mutations.

REVIEW QUESTIONS

1. A transcribed DNA strand has the following nucleotide sequence:

   3′—TACTGCATAATGATT—5′

   What would be the sequence of codons in the mRNA transcribed from this strand and also the nucleotide sequence of the complementary nontranscribed DNA strand? What would be the exact anticodon for each codon? Use Table 12–1 to determine the amino acid sequence of the polypeptide. Be sure to label the 5′ and 3′ ends of the nucleic acids and the carboxyl and amino terminal ends of the polypeptide.

2. Why can't amino acids become incorporated into polypeptides without the aid of tRNA?

3. What are ribosomes made of? Do ribosomes themselves carry information to specify the amino acid sequence of proteins?

4. In what ways are DNA polymerase and RNA polymerase similar? How do they differ?

5. Outline the steps involved in protein synthesis. Describe the steps of initiation, elongation, and termination.

6. Explain how the genetic code was deciphered. What experimental procedures needed to be developed before this could be accomplished?

7. How many amino acids could be specified if the genetic code were a doublet code? Why is redundancy important to the idea of wobble? If you could "reinvent" the code, would you make any changes? Why or why not?

8. What are the main types of mutations? What effects do they have on the protein product?

9. Compare and contrast the formation of mRNA in prokaryotic and eukaryotic cells. How do the differences affect the way in which each type of mRNA is translated? Does one system have any obvious advantage in terms of energy cost? Which system offers greater opportunities for control of gene expression?

RECOMMENDED READINGS

Darnell, J. E., Jr. RNA. *Scientific American*, October 1985, pp. 68–88. An excellent discussion of the role of RNA in the translation of nucleic acid information into protein and interesting speculations on how RNA itself may have been the first genetic material.

Darnell, J., H. Lodish, and D. Baltimore. *Molecular Cell Biology.* Scientific American Books, New York, 1990. A comprehensive discussion of transcription and translation in prokaryotic and eukaryotic cells.

Watson, J. D., N. H. Hopkins, J. W. Roberts, J. A. Steitz, and A. M. Weiner. *Molecular Biology of the Gene*, 4th ed., Benjamin Cummings, Menlo Park, CA, 1987. The most recent edition of Watson's classic text.

CHAPTER 13

Gene Regulation: The Control of Gene Expression

Each type of cell in a multicellular organism has a characteristic shape, carries out very specific activities, and makes a distinct set of proteins. Yet, with few exceptions, they all contain the same genetic information. Why, then, are they not identical in structure and molecular composition? Genes are regulated, and only certain subsets of the total genetic information are expressed in any given cell.

What are the mechanisms that control the expression of a gene? Let us consider a gene that codes for a protein that is an enzyme. It is fully expressed only when it is transcribed into mRNA, the mRNA is translated into protein, and the protein actively catalyzes a specific reaction. Gene expression, then, is the result of a series of processes, each of which can be controlled in many different ways. The control mechanisms require information in the form of various sig-

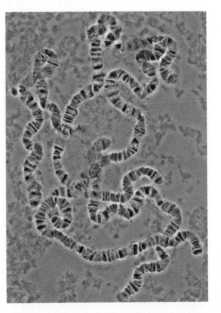

Chromosomes from the salivary gland of a *Drosophila* larva; actively transcribed genes appear as "puffed" regions. (Peter J. Bryant/Biological Photo Service)

nals (some originating within the cell and others coming from the environment) that interact with DNA, RNA, or protein.

Some of the main strategies used to regulate gene expression include controlling (1) the amount of mRNA that is available, (2) the rate of translation of the mRNA, and (3) the activity of the protein product.

In bacterial cells energy efficiency and economical use of resources are usually the primary considerations. As a result, most gene regulation in prokaryotes is at the transcriptional level. In eukaryotes there is a much greater emphasis on fine tuning the control systems, which is consistent with the greater complexity of these cells and the need to control development in multicellular organisms (see Chapter 16). As a result, eukaryotic gene regulation occurs at many levels.

After you have studied this chapter you should be able to

1. Explain why the organization of genes into operons is advantageous to bacteria.
2. Diagram the main components of an inducible operon, such as the lactose operon, and explain the functions of the operator and promoter regions.
3. Sketch the structure of an mRNA molecule produced by the lactose operon and relate that structure to the organization of the DNA in the operon.
4. Differentiate between positive and negative control; show how both types of control operate in the regulation of the lactose operon.
5. Explain why some genes, such as those of the lactose operon, are inducible and others, such as those of the tryptophan operon, are repressible.
6. Define what is meant by constitutive expression of a gene.

7. Provide an example of posttranscriptional control in a prokaryote.
8. Sketch the structure of a typical eukaryotic gene and the DNA sequences involved in the regulation of that gene.
9. Describe the different functional domains that might be found in a eukaryotic DNA-binding protein.
10. Explain why multiple copies of some genes are required in eukaryotic cells.
11. Illustrate how a change in chromosome structure might affect the activity of a gene.
12. List two ways that a gene in a multicellular organism might be able to produce different products in different types of cells.
13. Identify some of the types of regulatory controls that can be exerted in eukaryotes after mature mRNA is formed.

GENE REGULATION IN PROKARYOTES EMPHASIZES ECONOMY

An *Escherichia coli* cell has between 2000 and 4000 genes. Some encode proteins that are always needed (e.g., enzymes involved in glycolysis). These genes, which are constantly transcribed, are called **constitutive genes.** Other gene products are needed only when the bacterium is growing under special conditions.

For instance, the bacteria living in the colon of an adult cow are not normally exposed to the milk sugar lactose. If those cells were to end up in the colon of a calf, however, they would have lactose available as a source of energy. This poses a dilemma. Should a bacterial cell invest energy and materials to produce lactose-metabolizing enzymes just in case it ends up in the digestive system of a calf? Given that the average lifetime of an actively growing *E. coli* cell is about 30 minutes, such a strategy appears wasteful. Yet if *E. coli* cells do not have the capacity to produce those enzymes, they might starve in the midst of an abundant food supply. *E. coli* handles this problem by regulating the production of many of its enzymes so that it efficiently uses available organic molecules.

Cells have two basic ways of controlling their metabolic activity: They can regulate the *activity* of certain enzymes (how effectively an enzyme molecule works), and they can control the *number* of enzyme molecules present in each cell. Some enzymes may be regulated in both ways in the same cell. An *E. coli* cell growing on glucose is estimated to need about 800 different enzymes. Some of these must be present in large amounts, whereas others are required only in small quantities. In order for the cell to function properly, each enzyme must be efficiently controlled.

Operons in Prokaryotes Allow for Coordinated Control of Functionally Related Genes

The French researchers François Jacob and Jacques Monod are credited with the first demonstration, in 1961, of how some genes are regulated at the biochemical level. They studied the genes that code for the enzymes that metabolize the disaccharide lactose (see Chapter 3). For *E. coli* to use lactose as an energy source, the sugar must be cleaved into the monosaccharides glucose and galactose by the enzyme **β-galactosidase.** Galactose is then converted to glucose by another enzyme, and the resulting two glucose molecules are further broken down by the glycolysis pathway (see Chapter 7).

E. coli cells growing on glucose contain very little of the β-galactosidase enzyme, perhaps no more than one to three molecules per cell. However, cells grown on lactose have as many as 3000 β-galactosidase molecules per cell, accounting for about 3% of the total cellular protein. Levels of two other enzymes, galactose permease and galactoside transacetylase, also increase when the cells are grown on lactose. The permease is needed to transport lactose efficiently across the bacterial plasma membrane; without it, the lactose cannot enter the cell and be cleaved by β-galactosidase. The transacetylase is also involved in lactose metabolism, although its function is less clear.

Mutants have long served as powerful research tools for molecular geneticists. Jacob and Monod were able to identify mutant strains in which a single genetic defect resulted in the loss of all three enzymes. This finding, along with other information, led them to the

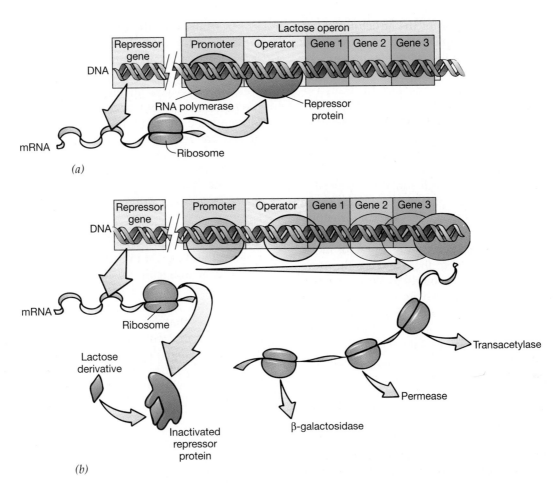

Figure 13–1 The lactose operon. The genes for three enzymes used by *E. coli* to metabolize the disaccharide lactose are organized as a single unit, called an *operon*. All three genes are transcribed as part of a single mRNA molecule. A sequence of bases called the *operator* is next to the promoter region. *(a)* In the absence of lactose, a repressor protein, encoded by a gene separate from the operon, binds to the operator region. By preventing RNA polymerase from binding to the promoter, the bound repressor protein blocks transcription of the structural genes. *(b)* When lactose is present, a metabolic derivative of the sugar binds to the repressor at an allosteric site, altering the structure of the protein so that it can no longer bind to the operator. This allows RNA polymerase to bind to the promoter and synthesize the mRNA. The lactose operon is referred to as an *inducible operon* because it is normally inactive and requires an inducer (in the form of the metabolic derivative of lactose) to turn on transcription.

conclusion that the coding DNA sequences for all three enzymes are linked together on the bacterial chromosome as a unit, the **lactose operon** (Figure 13–1), and are subject to a common control mechanism. RNA polymerase binds to a single promoter site upstream from the coding sequences and proceeds to transcribe the DNA, forming a single mRNA molecule that contains the coding information for all three proteins. This mRNA contains translation termination and initiation codons between the enzyme-coding sequences, so that it is translated as three separate protein molecules. Because all three enzymes are translated from the same mRNA molecule, their synthesis can be coordinated by turning a single molecular "switch" off or on.

The switch that controls mRNA synthesis is called the **operator;** it is a sequence of bases which overlaps part of the promoter region and is upstream from the first structural (protein-coding) gene in the lactose op-

eron. When lactose is absent, a protein called the **lactose repressor** binds tightly to the operator region. Because the repressor protein is large enough to cover part of the promoter sequence, RNA polymerase is unable to bind to the lactose promoter site, and transcription of the lactose operon is effectively blocked.

The lactose repressor protein is encoded by a regulatory gene located in a different region of the *E. coli* chromosome, several thousand bases upstream from the operator site. Unlike the lactose operon genes, the repressor gene is constitutive; that is, it is always "on," so small amounts of the repressor protein are produced continually. This protein is able to diffuse throughout the cell and bind specifically to the lactose operator sequence. When cells are grown in the absence of lactose, the operator site is nearly always occupied by a repressor molecule. Only on rare occasions, when the operator site is briefly unoccupied, can RNA polymerase bind and initiate transcription of the structural genes. Because *E. coli* mRNA is rapidly degraded (having a half-life of about 2 to 4 minutes), very few proteins are translated from that mRNA.

Lactose is able to "turn on," or *induce*, the transcription of the lactose operon because the lactose repressor protein contains a second functional region separate from its DNA binding site. This is an **allosteric binding site** (see Chapter 6) for allolactose, a metabolite of lactose. If lactose is present in the growth medium, a few molecules are able to enter the cell and are converted to allolactose. When a molecule of allolactose binds to the repressor at the allosteric site, it alters the conformation of the protein so that its DNA binding site can no longer recognize the operator. When all of the repressor molecules have allolactose bound to them and are therefore inactivated, RNA polymerase binds to the unblocked promoter, and the operon is actively transcribed.

The *E. coli* cell continues to produce β-galactosidase and the other lactose operon proteins until virtually all of the lactose is used up. When intracellular levels of lactose drop, the repressor proteins no longer have the allolactose sugar bound to them. They then assume a conformation that allows them to bind to the operator region and shut down transcription of the operon.

Mutants play an essential role in allowing researchers to dissect a regulatory system such as the lactose operon. Among other things, they allow investigators to map the positions of the genes on the DNA and to infer the normal functions of genes by studying what happens when they are missing or altered. This information is usually combined with results of direct biochemical studies.

For example, various *constitutive* lactose operon mutants were identified; these transcribed the structural genes of the lactose operon at a significant rate even in the absence of lactose. One group of constitutive mutants had abnormal genes with map positions in a region that is not close to the lactose operon itself. The genes responsible for the constitutive behavior of a second group had a map position in the region of the lactose operon but did not directly involve any of the three structural genes.

On the basis of these findings, Jacob and Monod hypothesized the existence of a regulatory gene that is separate from the genes of the lactose operon and responsible for producing a repressor protein. Although the specific defect may vary, the mutants of the first group do not produce active repressor proteins; hence no binding to the lactose operator and promoter takes place, and the lactose operon is transcribed constitutively. The members of the second group of constitutive mutants produce normal repressor molecules but have abnormal operator sequences incapable of binding the repressor.

In contrast to the constitutive mutants, other mutants failed to transcribe the lactose operon, even when lactose was present. Some of the abnormal genes had the same map position as the regulatory gene. They were found to have an altered allosteric binding site on the repressor protein, such that allolactose cannot bind, although the ability of the repressor to bind to the operator is unaffected.

An inducible gene is not transcribed unless a specific inducer inactivates its repressor

The lactose operon is called an **inducible system.** An inducible gene or operon is usually controlled by a repressor that keeps it in the "off" state. The presence of an **inducer molecule** (in this case allolactose) renders the repressor inactive and so the gene or operon is turned "on." Inducible genes or operons usually code for enzymes that are part of catabolic pathways, which break down molecules to provide both energy and components for anabolic reactions. This type of regulatory system enables the cell to save the energy costs of making enzymes when there are no substrates available for them to act on.

A repressible gene is transcribed unless a specific repressor/corepressor complex is bound to the DNA

Another type of gene regulation system in bacteria is associated mainly with anabolic pathways, in which amino acids, nucleotides, and other essential molecules are synthesized from simpler precursors. Regulation of these pathways normally involves **repressible enzymes.**

Repressible genes and operons are usually "on" and are turned "off" only under special conditions. In most cases the molecular signal used to regulate these genes is the end product of the metabolic pathway. When the supply of the end product (e.g., an amino acid) is low, all enzymes in the pathway are actively synthesized. When intracellular levels of the end product are high, enzyme synthesis is repressed. Because compounds such as amino acids are continuously needed by the growing cell, the most effective strategy is to keep the genes that control their production "on" except when a large supply of the amino acid is available. The ability to turn the genes off allows cells to avoid overproduction of amino acids and other molecules that are essential but energetically expensive to make.

The tryptophan operon is an example of a repressible system. In both *E. coli* and a related bacterium, *Salmonella*, the operon consists of five structural genes that

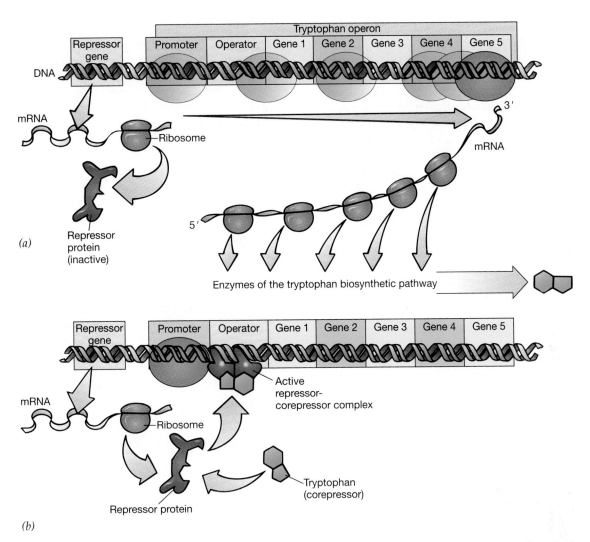

Figure 13–2 The tryptophan operon. Genes for enzymes that synthesize the amino acid tryptophan are organized in a *repressible operon* (one that is normally actively transcribed). *(a)* A regulatory gene encodes a repressor protein that is initially inactive (cannot bind to the operator). *(b)* When intracellular tryptophan levels are high, the amino acid binds to an allosteric site on the repressor protein, changing its conformation. The resulting active form of the repressor binds to the operator region, blocking transcription of the operon until tryptophan is again required by the cell.

code for the enzymes required for synthesis of the amino acid tryptophan; these are clustered together as a transcriptional unit with a single promoter and a single operator (Figure 13–2). A distant regulatory gene codes for a diffusible repressor protein, which differs from the lactose repressor in that it is synthesized in an inactive form and is unable to bind to the operator region.

The DNA-binding site of the repressor becomes effective only when tryptophan, its **corepressor,** binds to an allosteric site on the repressor. When intracellular tryptophan levels are low, the repressor protein is inactive and unable to bind to the operator region of the DNA. As the concentration of intracellular tryptophan rises, some tryptophan binds to the allosteric site of the repressor, altering its conformation so that it binds tightly to the operator DNA sequence. This has the ef-

fect of switching the operon "off" and thereby blocking transcription.

Negative regulators repress transcription; positive regulators activate transcription

The features of the lactose and tryptophan operons described so far are examples of **negative control.** Systems under negative control are those in which the DNA-binding regulatory protein is a *repressor* that turns *off* transcription of the gene. Some regulatory systems involve positive regulators, that is, *activator* proteins that bind to DNA and thereby stimulate transcription of a gene. The lactose operon contains both negative and positive controlling elements (Figure 13–3).

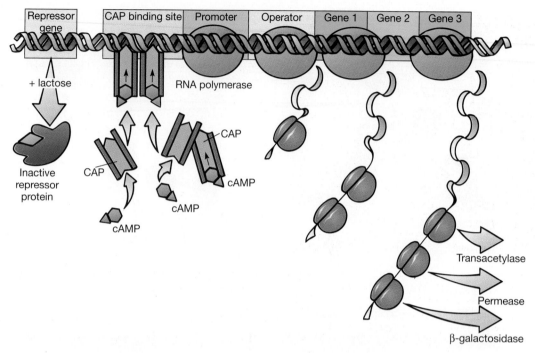

(a) Glucose low, cAMP high

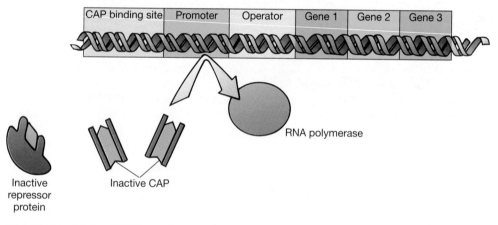

(b) Glucose high, cAMP low

Figure 13–3 Positive control of the lactose operon. The lactose promoter by itself is weak and binds RNA polymerase inefficiently even when the lactose repressor is inactive because lactose is present. The catabolite activator protein is an allosteric regulator that can bind to a sequence of bases adjacent to the promoter, allowing RNA polymerase to bind efficiently, thereby stimulating transcription of the operon. The CAP molecule contains two polypeptides. When each has cyclic AMP (cAMP) bound to its allosteric site, the protein can bind to the DNA sequence. The cell's cAMP concentration is inversely proportional to the glucose concentration. (a) When glucose levels are low, cAMP binds to CAP, which then activates transcription of the operon by binding to the DNA. (b) When glucose levels are high, cAMP is low. CAP is in an inactive form and cannot activate transcription.

Positive control of the lactose operon requires that the cell be able to sense the absence of the sugar glucose, which is the initial substrate in the glycolysis pathway (see Chapter 7). Lactose, like glucose, is a catabolite and can undergo stepwise breakdown to yield energy. However, because lactose must first be converted to glucose, it is most efficient for *E. coli* cells to use the available supply of glucose first. By using glucose as the preferred substrate, the cell is spared the considerable energy cost of making additional enzymes, such as *β*-galactosidase.

The lactose operon actually has a very inefficient promoter sequence; that is, it has a low affinity for RNA polymerase even when the repressor protein is inacti-

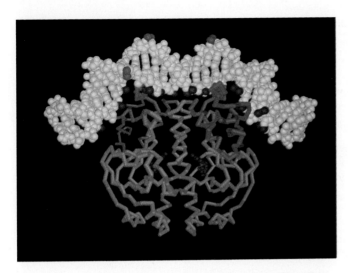

Figure 13–4 A computer-generated picture depicting the three-dimensional structure of active CAP binding to DNA. Notice that the binding of CAP causes bending of the DNA double helix. CAP is a dimer consisting of two identical polypeptide chains, each of which binds one molecule of cAMP. (Courtesy of S. C. Schultz, G. C. Shields, and T. A. Steitz, Yale University)

vated. However, a DNA sequence adjacent to the promoter site is a binding site for another protein, called the **catabolite activator protein (CAP)** (Figure 13–4).

CAP increases the affinity of the promoter region for RNA polymerase, allowing the enzyme to recognize the promoter efficiently and to bind tightly to the DNA.

In its active form CAP has **cyclic AMP, or cAMP** (Figure 3–31), an altered form of adenosine monophosphate, bound to an allosteric site. As the cells become depleted of glucose, cAMP levels increase. The cAMP molecules bind to the CAP, and the resulting complex then binds to the CAP-binding site near the lactose operon promoter and stimulates transcription of the operon. Thus, the operon is fully active only if lactose is present and intracellular glucose levels are low. The properties of negative and positive control systems are summarized in Table 13–1 (see page 306).

A regulon is a group of functionally related operons controlled by a common regulator

CAP differs from the lactose and tryptophan repressors in that it can control transcription of operons involved in the metabolism of a number of other catabolites, such as the sugars galactose, arabinose, and maltose, as well as lactose. A group of operons controlled by one regulator of this type is generally referred to as a **regulon** (Figure 13–5).

Other multigene systems in bacteria are also controlled in this manner. For example, genes involved in nitrogen and phosphate metabolism are organized into regulons that consist of multiple sets of operons controlled by one or more combinations of regulatory genes. Other complex multigene systems respond to changes in environmental conditions, such as rapid shifts in temperature, exposure to radiation, changes in osmotic pressure, and changes in oxygen levels. Spe-

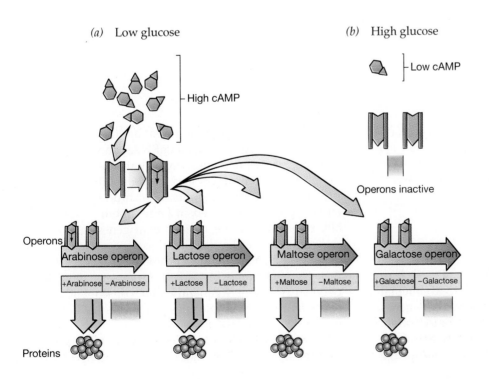

(a) Low glucose

(b) High glucose

Low cAMP

High cAMP

Operons inactive

Operons

Arabinose operon

+Arabinose −Arabinose

Lactose operon

+Lactose −Lactose

Maltose operon

+Maltose −Maltose

Galactose operon

+Galactose −Galactose

Proteins

Figure 13–5 The carbon utilization regulon in *E. coli*. Operons that convert a number of different sugars to glucose are under positive control by the CAP. *(a)* When glucose levels are low, cAMP levels increase, activating the CAPs, which bind to their recognition sites in the promoter regions of all operons. If the inducer for an operon is available, its repressor is inactivated and transcription of the message takes place at a rapid rate. *(b)* When glucose levels are high, cAMP levels are low, rendering CAP inactive. Under these conditions, none of the operons is active, even if the appropriate carbon source is available.

Table 13–1 TYPES OF TRANSCRIPTIONAL CONTROL IN PROKARYOTES*

NEGATIVE CONTROL

Inducible genes

Repressor protein alone	→	**Active repressor "turns off" regulated gene(s)**
Lactose repressor alone	→	Lactose operon not transcribed
Repressor protein + inducer	→	**Inactive repressor/inducer complex fails to "turn off" regulated gene(s)**
Lactose repressor + allolactose	→	Lactose operon transcribed

Repressible genes

Repressor protein alone	→	**Inactive repressor fails to "turn off" regulated gene(s)**
Tryptophan repressor alone	→	Tryptophan operon transcribed
Repressor protein + corepressor	→	**Active repressor/corepressor complex "turns off" regulated gene(s)**
Tryptophan repressor + tryptophan	→	Tryptophan operon not transcribed

POSITIVE CONTROL

Activator protein alone	→	**Activator alone cannot "turn on" regulated gene(s)**
CAP alone	→	Transcription of lactose operon not stimulated
Activator protein + coactivator	→	**Functional activator/coactivator complex "turns on" regulated gene(s)**
CAP + cAMP	→	Transcription of lactose operon stimulated

*A general description of each type is followed by a specific example. A negative regulator is a repressor that "turns off" transcription of the regulated gene(s). Conversely, a positive regulator is an activator that "turns on" transcription.

cific mutants often provide clues to the existence of a regulon system. A single mutation that destroys the activity of the CAP, for example, prevents the cell from metabolizing not only lactose but many other sugars also regulated by CAP.

Not all constitutive genes are transcribed at the same rate

Many of the gene products encoded by the *E. coli* chromosome are needed only under certain environmental or nutritional conditions. As we have seen, these genes are generally regulated at the level of transcription. They can be turned on and off as metabolic and environmental conditions change. By contrast, constitutive genes are continually transcribed, but they are not necessarily transcribed (or their mRNAs translated) at the same rate. Some enzymes work more effectively or are more stable than others and consequently need to be present in smaller amounts. Constitutive genes that encode proteins required in large amounts are generally transcribed more rapidly than genes for proteins required at lower levels. The transcription rate of these genes is controlled by their promoter sequences. Genes that have efficient ("strong") promoters bind RNA polymerase more frequently and consequently transcribe more mRNA molecules than those that have inefficient ("weak") promoters.

Genes that code for repressor or activator proteins that regulate metabolic enzymes are usually constitutive and produce their protein products constantly. Because each cell usually needs relatively few molecules of any specific repressor or activator protein, promoters for those genes tend to be relatively weak.

Some Posttranscriptional Regulation Occurs in Prokaryotes

Although much of the variability in protein levels in *E. coli* is determined by controlling transcription, for some genes other regulatory mechanisms operate after transcription. These **posttranscriptional** controls may work at various levels of gene expression.

Translational controls regulate the rate at which a particular mRNA molecule is translated. Because the lifetime of an mRNA molecule in a bacterial cell is very short, a molecule that is translated rapidly can produce more proteins than one that is translated slowly. Some mRNA molecules in *E. coli* are translated as much as 1000 times faster than others. Most of the differences appear to be due to the speed at which ribosomes can attach to the mRNA and begin translation.

Posttranslational controls generally act as switches that activate or inactivate one or more existing enzymes. These systems allow the cell to respond to changes in the intracellular concentrations of essential molecules, such as amino acids, by rapidly adjusting the activities of its enzymes. A common method for adjusting the rate of synthesis in a metabolic pathway is through **feedback inhibition** (see Chapter 6). The end product binds to the first enzyme in the pathway at an allosteric site, temporarily inactivating the enzyme. When the first enzyme in the pathway does not function, all of the succeeding enzymes are deprived of substrates. Notice that this differs from the end-product repression of the tryptophan operon discussed above. In that case, the end product of the pathway prevented the formation of new enzymes. Feedback inhibition acts as a fine-tuning mechanism that regulates the activity of the existing enzymes in a metabolic pathway.

GENE REGULATION IN EUKARYOTES IS MULTIFACETED

Like bacteria, eukaryotic cells must respond to changes in their environment by turning on and off appropriate sets of genes. Multicellular eukaryotes require additional modes of regulation that permit individual cells to become committed to specialized roles and groups of cells to organize into tissues and organs. In previous chapters we discussed the fact that all aspects of information transfer—including replication, transcription, and translation—are far more complicated in eukary-

otes. Not surprisingly, this complexity provides additional opportunities for control of gene expression.

Unlike many of the prokaryotic genes, most eukaryotic genes are not found in operon-like clusters. However, each eukaryotic gene has specific regulatory sequences, which are essential in the control of transcription.

Many of the "housekeeping" enzymes (those needed by all cells) appear to be encoded by constitutive genes, which are expressed in all cells at all times. Some inducible genes have also been found; these respond to environmental threats or stimuli such as heavy metal ingestion, virus infection, and heat shock.

Some genes appear to be inducible only at certain periods in the life of the organism; they are thought to be controlled by **temporal regulation** mechanisms. Finally, a number of genes are under the control of **tissue-specific regulation.** For example, a gene involved in the production of a particular enzyme may be regulated by one stimulus (e.g., a hormone) in muscle tissue, by an entirely different stimulus in pancreatic cells, and by a third stimulus in liver cells.

Eukaryotic Transcription Is Controlled at Many Sites and by Many Different Regulatory Molecules

Eukaryotic promoters vary in efficiency, depending on their upstream promoter elements

In eukaryotic as well as prokaryotic cells, the transcription of all genes requires a promoter to which RNA polymerase binds. In multicellular eukaryotes the RNA polymerase binds to a sequence of bases, known as a **TATA box,** about 30 base pairs upstream from the transcription initiation site (Figure 13–6). The promoter region also contains one or more sequences of 8 to 12 bases known as **upstream promoter elements (UPEs)** within a short distance of the RNA polymerase–binding site. The efficiency of the promoter seems to depend on the number and type of UPEs. Thus, a constitutive gene containing only one UPE would be weakly expressed, whereas one containing five or six UPEs would be actively transcribed.

Enhancers are DNA sequences that increase the rate of transcription

Regulated eukaryotic genes require not only the promoter elements but also DNA sequences called **enhancers.** Whereas the promoter elements are required for accurate and efficient initiation of mRNA synthesis, enhancers increase the *rate* of RNA synthesis after initiation.

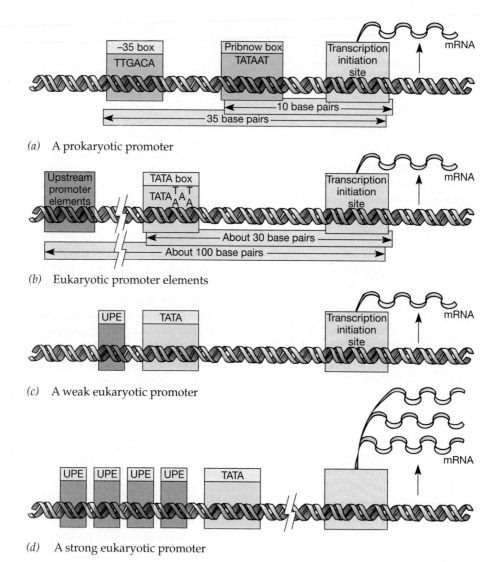

(a) A prokaryotic promoter

(b) Eukaryotic promoter elements

(c) A weak eukaryotic promoter

(d) A strong eukaryotic promoter

Figure 13–6 A comparison of prokaryotic and eukaryotic promoter elements. *(a)* Prokaryotic promoters consist of two short DNA sequences, called the Pribnow box and the −35 box, which are usually centered, respectively, 10 and 35 bases upstream from the transcription initiation site (the base in the DNA at which mRNA synthesis begins). The base sequences shown in the boxes are those most commonly found in the DNA in those regions. The two "boxes" are RNA polymerase–binding sites on the DNA. *(b)* Promoters in eukaryotes usually consist of a "TATA box," located 30 base pairs upstream from the transcription initiation site. The most commonly found sequence of bases in the TATA box is shown in the diagram (either T or A can be present at the positions where they are shown together). Eukaryotic promoters must also have one or more upstream promoter elements (UPEs). The efficiency of the promoter depends on the number of UPEs. *(c)* A weakly expressed constitutive gene contains only one UPE. *(d)* In contrast, a strongly expressed gene is likely to contain several UPEs. UPEs are thought to be binding sites for proteins that increase the rate of transcription by increasing the affinity of RNA polymerase for the promoter region.

Enhancer sequences are remarkable in many ways. Although present in all cells, a particular enhancer is functional only in particular types of cells. An enhancer can regulate a gene on the same DNA molecule from very long distances (up to thousands of bases away from the promoter) and can be either upstream or downstream of the promoters it controls (Figure 13–7). Furthermore, if an enhancer sequence is experimentally cut out of the DNA and inverted, it still regulates the gene it normally controls. Evidence suggests that at least some enhancers interact with proteins that regulate transcription.

Transcription factors are regulatory proteins that have several functional domains and may work in various combinations

A number of DNA-binding regulatory proteins have been identified in both prokaryotes and eukaryotes, and many researchers are studying how these proteins

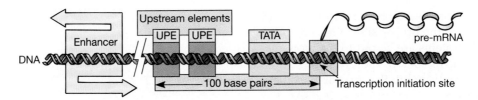

Figure 13–7 Enhancers are eukaryotic DNA sequences that can stimulate transcription of a gene by several orders of magnitude, at distances of thousands of bases from the promoter. An enhancer can work in either direction, upstream or downstream, from the promoter. The figure shows a eukaryotic gene controlled by an upstream enhancer. The promoter, consisting of the TATA box and UPEs, is within about 100 bases of the transcription initiation site; the enhancer sequence is several thousand bases from the promoter.

work. Many DNA-binding regulatory proteins appear to be modular molecules; that is, they have more than one structural region (domain) and each region has a different function.

Every prokaryotic regulator has a DNA-binding domain plus other domains that can activate RNA polymerase or bind inducers such as allolactose or corepressors such as tryptophan. The DNA-binding regions of the lactose repressor and CAP contain two α-helical segments that are inserted into the grooves of the DNA without unwinding the double helix. Recall from Chapter 3 that an α-helix of a protein is arranged such that the peptide bonds are in the interior of the helix and the functional groups of the amino acids are on the surface of the helix. This allows certain functional groups of amino acids to form hydrogen bonds with specific base pairs in the DNA. The hydrogen bonds that form between the regulatory protein and the DNA differ from those involved in complementary base-pairing (Figure 13–8).

Transcription in eukaryotes is more complicated than in prokaryotes and requires multiple regulatory proteins that are bound to different parts of the promoter. The "general transcription machinery" is a complex of proteins that binds to the "TATA" region of the promoter near the transcription initiation site. That

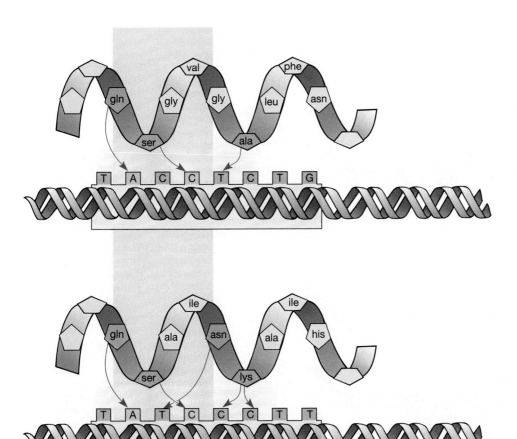

Figure 13–8 Comparison of the amino acid–base pair interactions of two related DNA-binding proteins. Only certain amino acids in the "recognition helix" regions bond with the bases of DNA. Two of the amino acids are the same in the two proteins and recognize the same bases; other amino acids differ, allowing the two proteins to recognize specific combinations of bases.

complex is required for RNA polymerase to bind and initiate transcription at the proper site. Other combinations of regulatory proteins are bound to the more distant enhancer or UPE regions of the promoter. Those proteins then make contact with the general machinery and control the activity of the RNA polymerase.

Eukaryotic regulators, like those of prokaryotes, may be either activators or repressors; we discuss only eukaryotic activators here because they seem to be more common and have been studied more intensively.

Each activator has several functional domains, including a DNA-binding region. In some cases the binding region consists of one or more recognition α-helices that can be inserted into specific regions of the DNA, in a manner similar to that described previously for some prokaryotic regulators. Some other activators have multiple "zinc fingers," which are loops of amino acids held together by zinc ions (Figure 13–9). Certain amino acid functional groups exposed in each "finger" have been shown to recognize specific DNA sequences.

Both enhancers and UPEs apparently become functional when specific regulatory proteins are bound to them. The DNA between the enhancer and promoter sequences is thought to form a loop that allows an activator bound to an enhancer to come in contact with one or more target proteins associated with the general transcriptional complex. When this occurs, transcription is stimulated (Figure 13–10).

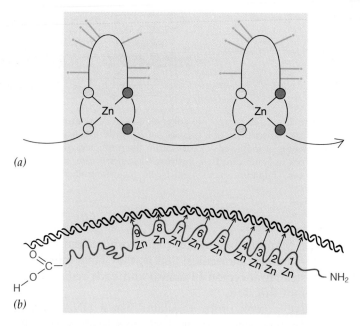

Figure 13–9 "Zinc-finger" DNA-binding proteins. (a) Zinc atoms cause regions of the polypeptides to form finger-like loops, which can insert into the grooves of the DNA and bind to specific base sequences. The colored circles represent amino acids that bind to the zinc atoms and form the loop. Each loop consists of about 13 amino acids. The lines projecting from the loop represent amino acids that are thought to recognize specific base sequences in the DNA. (b) Zinc-finger proteins that have been described have between two and nine fingers. Each finger is thought to fit into a separate groove in the DNA of a control region for a specific gene.

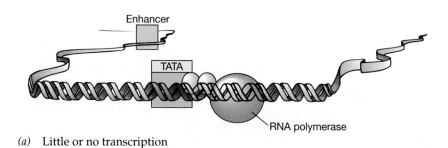

(a)   Little or no transcription

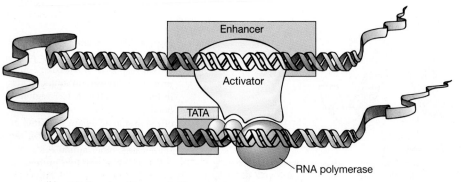

(b)   High rate of transcription

Figure 13–10 Control of transcription by an enhancer located a considerable distance from the promoter. (a) The general transcriptional machinery, including RNA polymerase, is bound to the promoter, but the gene is transcribed at a very low rate or not at all. (b) A regulatory protein that functions as a transcriptional activator has become bound to the enhancer. The intervening DNA forms a loop, allowing the activator to contact one or more target proteins in the general transcriptional machinery, thus stimulating transcription.

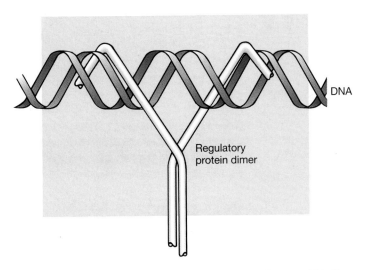

Figure 13–11 Regulatory proteins forming a dimer and binding to DNA.

other instances they are different, and the resulting *heterodimer* may have very different regulatory properties.

For a very simple example, let us assume that three regulatory proteins—A, B, and C—are involved in controlling a particular gene. These three proteins can associate as dimers in six different ways: three kinds of homodimers (AA, BB, and CC) and three kinds of heterodimers (AB, AC, and BC). The fact that some regulatory proteins can join together in different combinations that have different properties greatly increases the number of ways that transcription can be controlled.

Transcriptional units may overlap in eukaryotes

A given gene may sometimes be transcribed in more than one way, and somewhat different forms of its protein product may be produced as a result. For example, the enzyme invertase, which cleaves the disaccharide sucrose, exists in two forms in yeast: an intracellular form and a form secreted from the cell into the growth medium. Both forms are encoded by the same gene (Figure 13–12), but their mRNAs are transcribed from two different transcription initiation sites. The longer mRNA encodes the extracellular form of the enzyme, which is a longer polypeptide with extra amino acids at its amino-terminal end. Those amino acids serve as a "signal sequence" that indicates the protein is to be processed through the Golgi complex and secreted from the cell. The smaller mRNA encodes a protein that lacks the signal sequence and remains in the cytosol.

Other genes have tissue-specific overlapping transcriptional units. The primary pre-mRNA transcript of

Notice that each activator must have at least two functional domains: a DNA recognition site that usually binds to an enhancer or UPE and a "gene activation site" that contacts the target in the general transcriptional complex. In addition, many activators are functional only as pairs or *dimers*, and these have special domains that are required for dimer formation. Figure 13–11 shows how one type of transcription factor is thought to form dimers and bind to specific base sequences in the DNA.

In some cases the two polypeptides that make up the dimer may be identical and form a *homodimer*. In

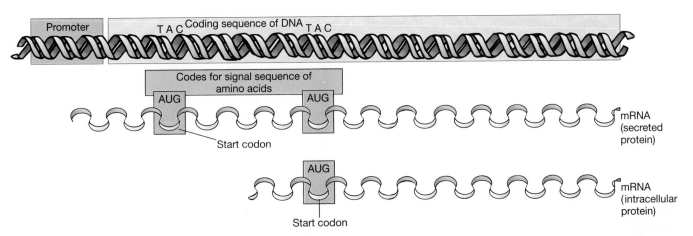

Figure 13–12 Overlapping transcription units. Two forms of the same protein can be made from a single gene by the initiation of transcription at two different sites. The yeast invertase gene encodes an mRNA with two start codons (AUG) in its coding region. If transcription is initiated between the two regions, a short mRNA is made that yields, when translated, an intracellular form

of the enzyme. If transcription starts at a point upstream from both AUG codons, a longer message is made. Translation begins at the first start codon, producing an enzyme with a "signal sequence" at the amino-terminal end of the polypeptide chain which targets the protein to the endoplasmic reticulum and then to the Golgi complex for secretion from the cell.

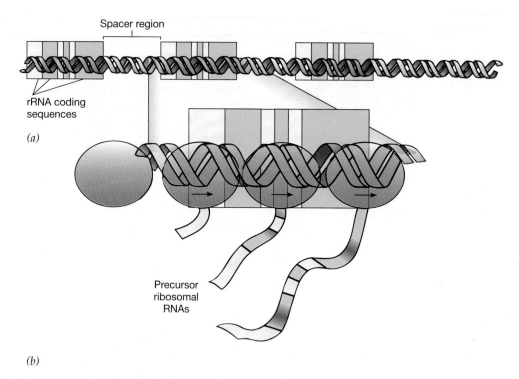

Spacer region

rRNA coding
sequences

(a)

Precursor
ribosomal
RNAs

(b)

Figure 13–13 Repeated gene sequences. Multiple copies of genes are required when large amounts of their products are needed by the cell. *(a)* Human ribosomal RNA genes are arranged as 200 to 300 tandemly repeated copies. Each transcription unit encodes a single copy of three of the ribosomal RNAs. *(b)* The requirement for rRNA is so great in actively growing cells that each of the units must be maximally loaded with RNA polymerases.

the gene for amylase (an enzyme that breaks down starch) in the mouse salivary gland is several thousand bases longer than its counterpart in the mouse liver. This is because in the salivary gland transcription starts at a site on the DNA that is farther upstream. Although the coding portions of the mRNAs in both cell types are identical after splicing and processing, transcription occurs about 100 times more frequently in the salivary gland than in the liver, resulting in the production of higher levels of the salivary amylase enzyme.

The organization of the chromosome may affect the expression of some genes

Multiple Copies of Some Genes Are Required

A single gene cannot always provide enough copies of its mRNA to meet the cell's needs. The requirement for high levels of certain products may be met if multiple copies of the genes that encode them are present in the chromosome. Genes of this type, whose products are essential for all cells, may occur as tandemly repeated gene sequences in all cells. Other genes, which may be required by only a small group of cells, may be selectively replicated in those cells in a process called **gene amplification** (see Chapter 16).

Within an array of repeated genes, each copy is almost identical to the others. Histone genes, which code for the proteins that associate with DNA to form nucleosomes (see Chapter 11), are usually found as multiple copies of 50 to 500 genes in multicellular organisms.

Genes for rRNA and tRNAs also occur in multiple copies in all cells. To ensure that the rRNA molecules are made in equal amounts, the RNA genes are arranged as multiple transcription units, each containing one copy of the three rRNA genes (Figure 13–13). Most eukaryotic species contain 150 to 450 such transcription units per cell. The demand for rRNA is so great in actively growing mammalian cells that, although hundreds of copies of the genes are present, each gene must be copied simultaneously by many RNA polymerases. A single rRNA gene in these cells is usually copied simultaneously by approximately 100 RNA polymerase enzymes.

Changes in Chromatin Structure May Inactivate Some Genes

In multicellular eukaryotes, only a subset of the genes present in a cell are active at any one time. The genes that are inactivated differ among cell types and in many cases seem to be irreversibly quiescent.

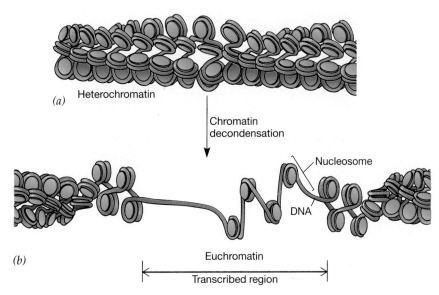

(a) Heterochromatin

Chromatin decondensation

Nucleosome

DNA

(b)

Euchromatin

Transcribed region

Figure 13–14 The structure of a chromosome affects transcription. *(a)* An inactive region of DNA such as heterochromatin is organized into tightly associated nucleosomes. *(b)* Active genes are associated with decondensed chromatin (euchromatin). Chromatin decondensation is often a response to specific inducing signals. The loosely packed chromatin increases the accessibility to RNA polymerases required for translation of the region.

Some of the inactive genes appear to be associated with highly compacted chromatin, which can be seen as densely staining regions of chromosomes during cell division. These regions of chromatin remain tightly coiled throughout the cell cycle and even during interphase are visible as darkly staining fibers, called **heterochromatin.** Evidence suggests that the DNA of heterochromatin is not transcribed. When one of the two X chromosomes is inactivated in female mammals, most of the inactive X chromosome becomes heterochromatic and is seen as the Barr body (see Chapter 10). Active genes are associated with a more loosely packed chromatin structure, called **euchromatin** (Figure 13–14).

The Long-lived, Highly Processed mRNAs of Eukaryotes Provide Many Opportunities for Posttranscriptional Control

Prokaryotic mRNA has a half-life that is usually measured in minutes; eukaryotic mRNA, even when it turns over rapidly, is far more stable. Prokaryotic mRNA is transcribed in a form that can be translated immediately. In contrast, eukaryotic mRNA molecules require further modification and processing before they can be used in protein synthesis (see Chapter 12). The message is capped, spliced, and polyadenylated and then transported from the nucleus to the cytoplasm to initiate translation. These events represent potential control points at which translation of the message and production of its encoded protein can be regulated.

Some pre-mRNAs can be processed in more than one way

Because of the complexity of eukaryotic genes and the processing of their messages, cells can use the same gene to produce more than one type of protein. Several forms of regulation involving mRNA processing have been discovered. In some instances, the same gene can be used to produce one type of protein in one tissue and a different type of protein in another tissue (Figure 13–15).

In the thyroid gland, the calcitonin gene produces a polypeptide hormone used to retain calcium in the body (see Chapter 47). In the brain and nervous tissue, the same gene produces an entirely different polypeptide that is used as a neurotransmitter (a chemical that transmits signals between nerve cells—see Chapter 39). The two forms of mRNA are controlled by **differential nuclear RNA processing,** involving two possible polyadenylation sites (Figure 13–15a). In the thyroid gland, polyadenylation of the transcribed message at the first site results in a short transcript, which is then spliced to form a message for calcitonin. Polyadenylation at a site further downstream in nervous tissue results in the formation of a longer transcript, which is spliced differently and then translated to produce the neurotransmitter. Other types of differential mRNA processing use multiple splicing patterns, which generate different mRNAs depending on the locations of the exon splicing sites (Figure 13–15b).

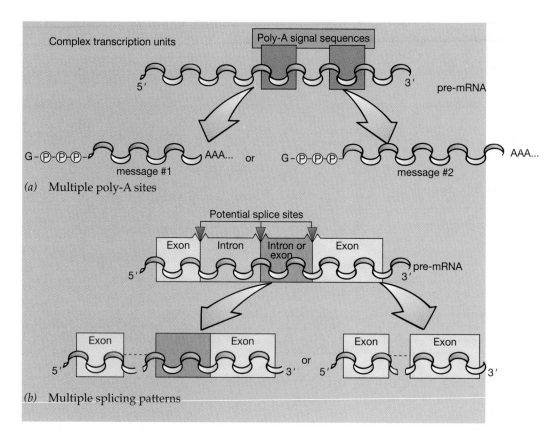

Figure 13–15 Differential mRNA processing. Complex transcription units can be processed in several ways to yield two or more mRNAs, each of which encodes a different protein. (a) Multiple polyadenylation signals can be present in the pre-mRNA transcript; mRNAs encoding different proteins are produced, depending on which site is cleaved and polyadenylated. (b) Multiple splicing patterns result in the formation of different mRNAs.

The stability of mRNA molecules can vary

Controlling the lifetime of a particular kind of mRNA molecule makes it possible to control the number of protein molecules translated from it. In some cases messenger RNA stability is under hormonal control. This is true for mRNA that codes for vitellogenin, for example, a protein made in the livers of certain female animals, such as frogs and chickens.

After it is synthesized, vitellogenin is transported to the oviduct, where it is used in the formation of yolk proteins in the egg. Vitellogenin synthesis is regulated by the hormone estradiol. When estradiol levels are high, the half-life of vitellogenin mRNA in frog liver is about 500 hours. When cells are deprived of estradiol, the half-life of the mRNA drops rapidly to less than 16 hours. This leads to a rapid decrease in cellular vitellogenin mRNA levels and decreased synthesis of the vitellogenin protein. In addition to affecting the stability of the mRNA, the hormone seems to control the rate at which the mRNA is synthesized.

The Activity of Eukaryotic Proteins May Be Altered by Posttranslational Chemical Modifications

Eukaryotic enzyme activity can also be regulated after the protein is synthesized. As in bacteria, many metabolic pathways in eukaryotes contain allosteric enzymes that are regulated through feedback inhibition. In addition, many eukaryotic proteins are extensively modified after they are synthesized.

In *proteolytic processing* the proteins are synthesized as inactive precursors, which are converted to an active form by removal of a portion of the polypeptide chain. Other proteins may be regulated in part by a process of *selective degradation*, which keeps their numbers constant within the cell. *Chemical modification*, through the addition or removal of functional groups, can reversibly alter the activity of an enzyme. One very common way of modifying the activity of an enzyme or other protein is the addition or removal of phosphate groups. These alterations allow the cell to respond rapidly to fast-changing environmental or nutritional conditions.

MAKING THE CONNECTION

A Comparison of the Regulatory Systems in Prokaryotes and Eukaryotes

Prokaryotic and eukaryotic cells have distinctly different strategies for regulating the activity of their genes. In large part these differences reflect the ways in which the organisms make their living. Because bacterial cells exist independently, each cell must be able to perform all of its own essential functions. And because they grow rapidly and have relatively short lifetimes, they carry little excess baggage.

The dominant theme of prokaryotic gene regulation is *economy*, and controlling transcription is usually the most cost-effective way to regulate gene expression. The organization of related genes into operons and regulons that can be rapidly turned on and off as units allows these cells to synthesize only the gene products needed at any particular time. This type of regulation requires rapid turnover of mRNA molecules, so that messages do not accumulate and do not continue to be translated when they are not needed.

Bacteria rarely regulate enzyme levels by degrading proteins. Once the synthesis of a protein ends, the previously synthesized protein molecules are diluted out so rapidly in subsequent cell divisions that breaking them down is usually not necessary. Only when cells are starved or deprived of essential amino acids are proteases used to break down proteins no longer needed for survival to recycle their amino acids.

Eukaryotic cells have different regulatory requirements. In multicellular organisms, groups of cells cooperate with each other in a division of labor. Because a single gene may need to be regulated in different ways in different types of cells, eukaryotic gene regulation is relatively complex, occurring not only at the level of transcription but also at other levels of gene expression. Eukaryotic cells also usually have long lifetimes, during which they may need to respond repeatedly to many different stimuli. Rather than synthesize new enzymes each time they respond to a stimulus, these cells make extensive use of preformed enzymes and other proteins that can be rapidly converted from an inactive to an active state.

Much of the emphasis of gene regulation in multicellular organisms is on *specificity* in the form and function of the cells in each tissue. Each type of cell has certain genes that are active and others that may never be used. Apparently the adaptive advantages of cellular cooperation in eukaryotes far outweigh the detrimental effects of carrying a load of inactive genes through many generations of somatic (body) cells.

SUMMARY

I. Most regulated genes in bacteria are organized into units, called *operons*, which may encode several proteins.
  A. Each operon is controlled by a single promoter region upstream from the protein-coding regions.
  B. A sequence of bases called the *operator* overlaps the promoter and serves as the regulatory switch controlling the operon.
    1. A repressor protein binds specifically to the operator sequence, preventing RNA polymerase from binding to the promoter and thus blocking transcription of the operon.
    2. When the repressor is not bound to the operator, RNA polymerase can bind to the promoter and transcription can proceed.
  C. An inducible operon such as the lactose operon is normally turned off. The repressor protein is synthesized in an active state and binds to the operator. If cells are exposed to lactose, a metabolite of that sugar binds to an allosteric site on the repressor protein, causing it to

change shape. The altered repressor cannot bind to the operator, and the operon is transcribed.
  D. A repressible operon such as the tryptophan operon is normally turned on. The repressor protein is synthesized in an inactive state and cannot bind to the operator. A metabolite (usually the end product of a metabolic pathway) acts as a corepressor. When intracellular corepressor levels are high, one of the molecules binds to an allosteric site on the repressor, changing its shape so that it can bind to the operator and thereby turn off transcription of the operon.
  E. Repressible and inducible operons are under negative control. When the repressor protein binds to the operator, transcription of the operon is turned off.
  F. Some inducible operons are also under positive control. A separate protein can bind to the DNA and activate transcription of the gene.
    1. The lactose operon is activated by the CAP (catabolite activator protein), which binds to the

promoter region, stimulating transcription by binding RNA polymerase tightly.

2. To bind to the lactose operon, CAP requires a coactivator, cAMP (cyclic adenosine monophosphate). Levels of cAMP increase as levels of glucose decrease.

G. A group of operons can be organized into a multigene system, known as a regulon, which is controlled by a single regulatory protein. CAP activates a number of operons associated with the metabolism of carbohydrates.

II. Constitutive genes are neither inducible nor repressible; they are active at all times. Regulatory proteins such as CAP and the repressor proteins are produced constitutively. The activity of these genes is controlled by how efficiently RNA polymerase binds to their promoter regions.

III. DNA-binding regulatory proteins work by recognizing and binding to specific sequences of bases in the DNA. Regions of the proteins fit into the grooves of the DNA molecules and hydrogen-bond to specific functional groups of the base pairs.

IV. The expression of some prokaryotic genes is modified after the mRNA is translated.

A. The rate of translation of a particular mRNA may be regulated.

B. The activity of key enzymes in some metabolic pathways can be controlled by feedback inhibition.

V. Eukaryotic genes are generally not organized into operons. Regulation of eukaryotic genes can occur at the levels of transcription, mRNA processing, translation, and the protein product.

A. The promoter of a regulated eukaryotic gene consists of an RNA polymerase–binding site and short DNA sequences known as *upstream promoter elements*

(UPEs). The efficiency of the promoter is determined by the number and types of UPEs within the promoter region.

B. Inducible eukaryotic genes are controlled by enhancer elements, which can operate thousands of bases away from the promoter. Proteins that bind to enhancers appear to facilitate RNA polymerase binding to the promoter. This may require that the DNA between the enhancer and the promoter form a loop so that contact can be made.

C. Transcription factors are regulatory proteins that bind to DNA and either activate or repress transcription.

D. The activity of eukaryotic genes is affected by chromosome structure.

1. Some genes whose products are required in large amounts exist as multiple copies in the chromosome. Other genes may be selectively amplified in only some cells by DNA replication.

2. Genes can be inactivated by changes in chromosome structure. Densely packed regions of chromosomes called *heterochromatin* contain inactive genes. Active genes are associated with a loosely packed chromatin structure called *euchromatin*.

E. Many eukaryotic genes are regulated after the RNA transcript is made.

1. Gene regulation can occur as a consequence of mRNA processing. In some cases a single gene can produce different forms of a protein, depending on how the pre-mRNA is polyadenylated or spliced.

2. Certain regulatory mechanisms increase the stability of mRNA, allowing more proteins to be formed per mRNA molecule prior to degradation.

3. Posttranslational control of eukaryotic genes can occur by feedback inhibition or by modification of the structure of the protein.

POST-TEST

1. Regulated prokaryotic genes are organized into clusters called _____.

2. A regulatory region that overlaps the promoter sequences and is associated with inducible and repressible operons is called the _____.

3. A repressor protein that binds to the operator region of an operon blocks transcription of the structural genes by preventing _____ _____ from binding to the promoter. If a regulator blocks transcription when it binds to the DNA, we refer to this as an example of _____ control.

4. Inducible operons are controlled by regulatory proteins that are normally in a(n) _____ state. When a metabolite binds to a(n) _____ site, it changes the _____ of the protein and renders it _____.

5. Repressible operons are controlled by regulatory proteins that are normally _____. When the _____ binds to the allosteric site of the repressor protein, it is converted to a(n) _____ repressor.

6. Positive gene control involves proteins that bind to the DNA and _____ transcription.

7. CAP is a positive regulator that requires _____ _____ to bind to the CAP site of an operon.

8. When glucose is unavailable, the cAMP levels of an *E. coli* cell are _____.

9. CAP is a controlling element of a system of multiple operons involved in carbohydrate metabolism called a(n) _____.

10. Genes not under regulatory control are termed _____ genes. They encode enzymes needed by cells at all times and are transcribed _____.

11. An example of a constitutive gene is the lactose _____ gene.

12. DNA-binding regulatory proteins work by inserting part of the polypeptide into one or more _____ in the DNA molecule so that amino acids form _____ bonds with specific bases in the regulatory sequence.

13. Some metabolic pathways are regulated by _____ _____, in which the end product blocks the activity of the first enzyme in the pathway.

14. In eukaryotic cells, the promoter region of genes consists of an RNA polymerase–binding site and adjacent

_____ _____ elements. The efficiency of the promoter in binding to RNA polymerase is determined by the _____ of these elements in front of the gene.

15. Inducible eukaryotic genes may be controlled by _____, which can be positioned thousands of bases away from the promoter.

16. Some single eukaryotic genes can make different forms of the protein they encode by differential _____ processing.

17. Eukaryotic genes whose products are required in large numbers may be present in _____ copies on the eukaryotic chromosome. Other genes that are required in large numbers in some cells but not in others may be _____ by selective replication of a small part of the chromosome.

18. Genes that are present in tightly coiled regions of chromosomes called _____ are _____.

19. Active genes are found in loosely packed chromatin called _____.

REVIEW QUESTIONS

1. Make a sketch of the lactose operon and briefly describe its function. Be sure to include the following elements:
   a. structural genes
   b. promoter
   c. operator
   d. CAP-binding site

2. What structural features does the tryptophan operon have in common with the lactose operon? What features are different?

3. Why do we define the tryptophan operon as repressible and the lactose operon as inducible?

4. The genes that code for the lactose repressor and the tryptophan repressor are not tightly linked to the operons they regulate. Would it be advantageous if they were? Explain your answer.

5. Develop a simple hypothesis that would explain the behavior of each of the following types of mutants in *E. coli*:
   a. *Mutant a:* The map position of this mutation is in the tryptophan operon. The mutant cells are constitutive; that is, they produce all of the enzymes coded for by the tryptophan operon, even if large amounts of tryptophan are present in the growth medium.
   b. *Mutant b:* The map position of this mutation is in the tryptophan operon. The mutant cells do not produce any of the enzymes coded for by the tryptophan operon under any conditions.
   c. *Mutant c:* The map position of this mutation is some distance from the tryptophan operon. The mutant cells are constitutive; that is, they produce all of the enzymes coded for by the tryptophan operon, even if the growth medium contains large amounts of tryptophan.
   d. *Mutant d:* The map position of this mutation is some distance from the tryptophan operon. The mutant cells do not produce any of the enzymes coded for by the tryptophan operon under any conditions.

6. How is glucose involved in the positive control of the lactose operon? How is the CAP similar to the lactose repressor protein? How is it different?

7. Compare the types of bacterial genes that are associated with inducible operons, those that are associated with repressible operons, and those that are constitutive. Predict the category into which each of the following would be most likely to fit:
   a. a gene that codes for RNA polymerase
   b. a gene that codes for an enzyme required to break down maltose
   c. a gene that codes for an enzyme used in the synthesis of adenine

8. Compare the structure of a prokaryotic promoter region with known eukaryotic promoter regions. How does the regulation of inducible eukaryotic genes differ from the regulation of inducible prokaryotic genes?

9. Explain why it is necessary for certain genes in eukaryotic cells to be present in multiple copies.

10. How can the activity of some eukaryotic genes be affected by the structure of the chromosome?

11. Make a sketch showing how differential mRNA processing can give rise to different forms of a eukaryotic protein.

RECOMMENDED READINGS

Darnell, J., H. Lodish, and D. Baltimore. *Molecular Cell Biology.* Scientific American Books, New York, 1990. A comprehensive discussion of transcription and translation in prokaryotic and eukaryotic cells.

McKnight, S. L. Molecular zippers in gene regulation. *Scientific American*, 264:4, April 1991.

Ptashne, M. How gene activators work. *Scientific American*, 260:1, January 1989.

❏

Genetic Engineering

Arevolution occurred in the field of biology beginning in the mid-1970s as the development of **recombinant DNA technology** led to radically new approaches to research. This technology not only has been applied to genetic studies but also has had a major impact in areas ranging from development to evolution.

Recombinant DNA techniques were initially developed as tools to allow scientists to obtain a great many copies of any specific DNA segment so that it could be studied biochemically. This can now be done in a number of ways, but most methods involve introducing foreign DNA into cells of microorganisms. Under the right conditions, this DNA is replicated and transmitted to the daughter cells when the cell divides. In this way a particular DNA sequence can be amplified, or **cloned,** to provide millions of identical copies that can be isolated in pure form. Methods for cloning DNA in vitro have also been developed.

A cotton boll that is free of insect damage because the plant has been genetically engineered to produce a natural insecticide. (Courtesy of the Monsanto Company)

Studies of cloned DNA sequences have been of immense value in allowing scientists to understand the organization of genes and the relationship between genes and their products. In fact, most of our knowledge of the complex structure and control of eukaryotic genes (discussed in Chapters 12 and 13) is derived from the application of these methods.

Recombinant DNA technology also has many practical applications. One of the rapidly advancing areas of study today is **genetic engineering**—the modification of the DNA of an organism to produce new genes with new characteristics. Genetic engineering can take many forms, ranging from the production of strains of bacteria that manufacture useful protein products to the development of higher plants and animals that express foreign genes. Unprecedented advances in fields such as pharmaceutics, medicine and human genetics, and agriculture have resulted.

After you have studied this chapter you should be able to

1. Draw a sketch that demonstrates how a typical restriction enzyme cuts DNA molecules, and give examples of the ways in which these enzymes are used in recombinant DNA technology.
2. Summarize the properties of plasmids that allow them to be used as DNA cloning vectors.
3. Differentiate between a genomic DNA library and a cDNA library.
4. Explain why one would clone the same eukaryotic gene from both a genomic library and a cDNA library.

5. Identify some of the uses of DNA hybridization probes.
6. Describe how a gene is restriction mapped and explain why restriction mapping is useful.
7. Draw a diagram that illustrates the most widely used DNA sequencing technique.
8. List some important proteins and other products that can be produced by genetic engineering techniques.
9. List some of the difficulties encountered in using *Escherichia coli* to produce proteins coded by eukaryotic genes, and explain the rationale behind using transgenic plants and animals to solve some of those problems.

RECOMBINANT DNA METHODS GREW OUT OF RESEARCH IN MICROBIAL GENETICS

Recombinant DNA technology was not developed quickly. It actually began with the first studies of the genetics of bacteria and the viruses that infect them, the **bacteriophages** (literally "bacteria eaters"—see Chapter 23). Only after decades of basic research and the accumulation of extensive knowledge did the current technology become feasible and available to the many scientists who now use these methods (Figure 14–1).

Among other things, bacteria have provided researchers with special enzymes, known as restriction enzymes, which cut DNA molecules only in specific places. In addition, recombinant DNA molecules are most often introduced into bacterial cells or bacteriophages so that they can be amplified (or cloned), and certain aspects of their genetic systems facilitate this process.

Restriction Enzymes Are "Molecular Scissors" That Cleave DNA Reproducibly

A major breakthrough in the development of recombinant DNA technology was the discovery of bacterial enzymes called **restriction enzymes,** which are able to cut DNA molecules only at specific base sequences. One restriction enzyme may recognize and cut a DNA molecule at the base sequence 5'—AAGCTT—3', whereas another cuts only the sequence 5'—GATC—3'. Bacteria

Figure 14–1 Recombinant DNA. (*a*) Researchers study proteins produced by recombinant DNA technology. (*b*) Scientists use gene-splicing to introduce bacterial genes into plants. (*a*, Will & Deni McIntyre/ Photo Researchers, Inc.; *b*, Matt Meadows/ Peter Arnold, Inc.)

(*a*)   (*b*)

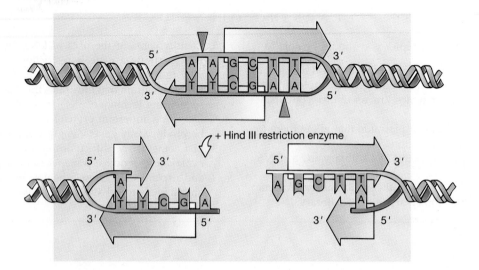

Figure 14–2 Restriction enzymes. Many restriction enzymes cut DNA at sequences of bases that are palindromic (each strand has the same base sequence, but in the opposite direction). Cutting the sequence leaves complementary sticky ends.

normally use these enzymes as a defense mechanism, to attack bacteriophage DNA that enters the cell. The bacteria protect their own DNA from attack by altering it in some way after it is synthesized. Purification of these enzymes enabled scientists to cut DNA from chromosomes into shorter fragments in a controlled way (Figure 14–2).

Many of the restriction enzymes used for recombinant DNA studies cut **palindromic** sequences, which means that the base sequence of one strand reads the same as its complement, but in the opposite direction. (Thus, the complement of our example, 5'—AAGCTT—3', reads 3'—TTCGAA—5'.) By cutting both strands of the DNA in an asymmetric manner, these enzymes leave fragments with complementary, single-stranded ends; these are called **sticky ends** because they can pair (by hydrogen bonding) with the complementary single-stranded ends of other DNA molecules that have been cut with the same enzyme. Once two molecules have been joined together in this way, they can be treated with **DNA ligase,** an enzyme that covalently links the two fragments to form a stable recombinant DNA molecule (Figure 14–3).

Restriction enzymes vary widely in the number of bases in the DNA sequences that they recognize, ranging from as few as 4 to as many as 23 bases. Based on probability alone, we expect the restriction sequence of a "four base cutter" to occur in a DNA molecule once on the average of every 4^4, or 256, bases, whereas one that recognizes six bases would cut fragments that average 4^6, or 4096, bases in size. Restriction enzymes that recognize sequences with large numbers of bases are particularly suited for studying very large DNA molecules such as those that make up entire chromosomes.

Recombinant DNA Is Formed When DNA Is Spliced into a Vector (DNA Carrier)

Most recombinant DNA molecules are isolated and amplified by introducing them into cells of the bacterium *E. coli.* To isolate a specific piece of DNA (after it has been cut by a restriction enzyme), that fragment must first be incorporated into a suitable carrier, or **vector molecule** (see Figure 14–3). The DNA of bacteriophages or special DNA molecules called **plasmids** is commonly used as a vector. A plasmid is a small circular DNA molecule that can replicate inside a bacterial cell. These plasmids can be isolated from bacterial cells in pure form and then introduced into other cells by a method called **transformation** (see Chapter 11), which involves altering the bacterial cell wall to make it permeable to the plasmid DNA molecules. Once a plasmid enters a cell, it is replicated and distributed to the daughter cells during cell division. Plasmids do not carry genes that are essential to the *E. coli* cells, but they often carry genes that are useful under some environmental conditions, such as those that confer resistance to particular antibiotics.

The plasmids now used in recombinant DNA work have been extensively "engineered" to include a number of features helpful in the isolation and analysis of cloned DNA (Figure 14–4). A limiting property of any plasmid, however, is the size of the DNA fragment that

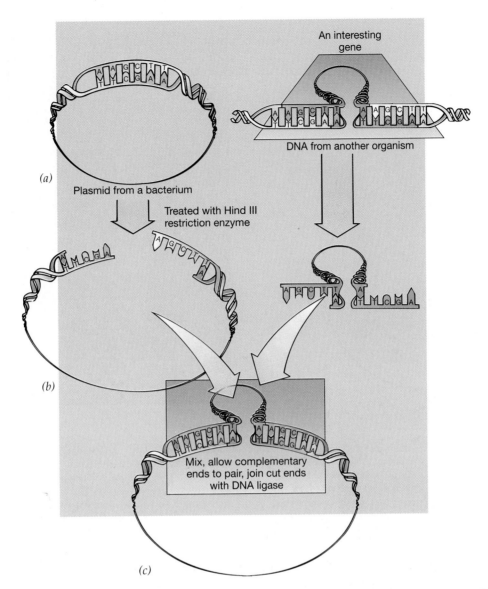

Figure 14–3 Producing a recombinant DNA molecule. DNA molecules from two different sources (*a*) are cut with the same restriction enzyme to form DNA molecules with complementary single-stranded ends (*b*). In this example one molecule is a circular plasmid from a bacterium. The recombinant DNA (*c*) is constructed by mixing the two types of molecules so that their cohesive ends pair. DNA ligase then forms covalent 5′—3′ phosphodiester bonds between the junctions of the two molecules.

it can effectively carry. The size of a DNA segment is often given in kilobases, with 1 **kilobase (kb)** being equal to 1000 bases. Fragments of less than 10 kb can usually be inserted into plasmids for use in *E. coli.* However, larger fragments require the use of bacteriophage vectors, which can handle up to 15 kb of DNA.

Recombinant DNA can also be introduced into cells of higher organisms. For example, engineered viruses are used as vectors in mammalian cells. These viruses have been disabled so that they do not kill the cells they infect; instead their DNA, and any foreign DNA they carry, becomes incorporated into the chromosomes of the cell following infection. As discussed later, other

methods have been developed that do not require a biological vector. These involve injecting the DNA directly into the cell nucleus or allowing cells to incorporate DNA that has been adsorbed onto the surface of calcium phosphate crystals.

Cloning Techniques Provide the Means for Replicating and Isolating Many Copies of a Specific Recombinant DNA Molecule

Because a single gene is only a small part of the total DNA in an organism, isolating the piece of DNA con-

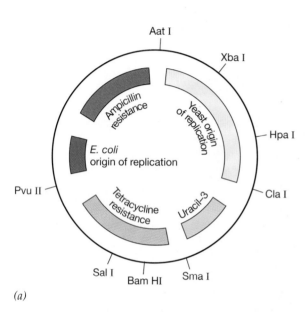

(a)

(b)

0.5 μm

Figure 14–4 Plasmids used in recombinant DNA technology. (*a*) A map of a genetically engineered plasmid vector used for both *E. coli* and the yeast *Saccharomyces cerevisiae.* This vector has been constructed from DNA fragments isolated from plasmids, *E. coli* genes, and yeast genes in order to have useful features. Letters on the outer circle designate sites for restriction enzymes that cut the plasmid only at that one position. The plasmid has two origins of replication, one for *E. coli* and one for yeast, allowing it to replicate independently in either type of cell. Resistance genes for the antibiotics ampicillin and tetracycline and the yeast URA-3 gene (for an enzyme involved in uracil biosynthesis) are also shown. The URA-3 gene is used to transform yeast cells lacking that particular enzyme; cells that take up the plasmid are able to grow on a uracil-deficient medium. (*b*) Electron micrograph of a plasmid from *E. coli.* (*b*, Dr. Stanley Cohen/Science Photo Library/Photo Researchers, Inc.)

taining that particular gene is like finding a needle in a haystack. A powerful detector is needed.

Isolating a gene from an organism such as a human first requires the construction of a **library,** or gene bank, from the human DNA (Figure 14–5). The first step is to cut the DNA with a restriction enzyme, generating a population of DNA fragments. These fragments vary in size and in the genetic information they carry, but they all have identical sticky ends. The plasmid vector DNA is treated with the same restriction enzyme, which converts the circular plasmids into linear molecules with sticky ends complementary to those of the human DNA fragments. The two kinds of DNA (human and plasmid) are mixed together under conditions that promote hydrogen bonding of complementary bases, and the paired ends of the plasmid and human DNA are then joined by DNA ligase.

The result is a mixture of recombinant plasmids, each containing a different human DNA sequence. Each plasmid then has to be amplified or cloned, so that there are millions of copies to work with, allowing identification of the one containing the sequence of interest. This process occurs inside the cells of *E. coli.* First the recombinant plasmids are inserted into antibiotic-sensitive *E. coli* cells by transformation. This is done under conditions in which there is a low ratio of plasmids to cells, so it should be rare for a cell to receive more than one plasmid molecule, and not all cells receive a plasmid. The cells are incubated on a nutrient medium that also contains antibiotics, so only cells that have incorporated a plasmid (which contains a gene for antibiotic resistance) grow.

The researcher may then spread a sample of the bacterial culture on solid growth medium. If the suspension of cells is dilute enough, the cells are widely separated. When each cell reproduces it gives rise to a **colony,** which is a clone of genetically identical cells. All of the cells of a particular colony contain the same recombinant plasmid, so during this process a specific sequence of human DNA has also been cloned. The

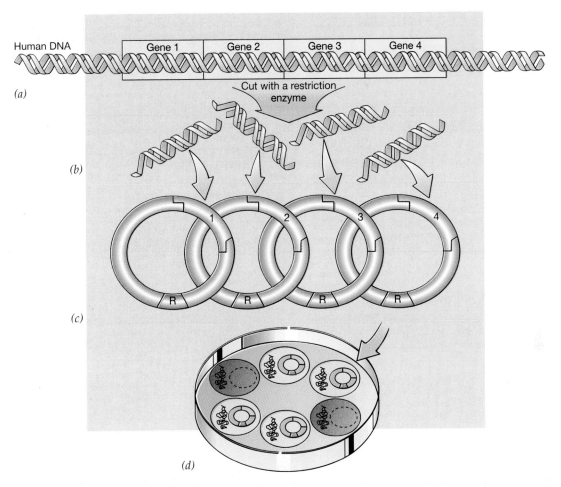

Figure 14–5 Construction of a genomic library from human DNA. DNA from human cells (*a*) is cut with a specific restriction enzyme into fragments (*b*) that are attached by DNA ligase to a complementary restriction site in a vector molecule, which also contains an antibiotic resistance gene (R) (*c*). The recombinant plasmids are used to transform an antibiotic-sensitive *E. coli* strain under conditions that ensure that each bacterial cell receives no more than one plasmid molecule (*d*). The cells are then grown on antibiotic-containing solid nutrient medium. Only those that receive the plasmid survive.

major task is to determine which colony (of thousands) contains the cloned fragment of interest. There are a number of ways in which this can be done.

A specific DNA sequence can be detected by a complementary genetic probe

A common approach to the problem of detecting the DNA of interest involves the use of a **genetic probe,** which is usually a radioactively labeled segment of RNA or single-stranded DNA that is complementary to the target gene. Suppose that a researcher wishes to identify the gene that codes for insulin. Because the amino acid sequence of insulin is known, it is possible to synthesize a radioactive single-stranded DNA molecule complementary to the DNA sequence that codes for insulin. This is not as simple as it may sound, because even if the amino acid sequence of all or part of a protein is known, those amino acids could be coded for

by a number of different base sequences (see Chapter 12). The single-stranded DNA probe **hybridizes** (becomes attached by complementary base-pairing) with the DNA sequence that codes for insulin (Figure 14–6). If the DNA from a small group of cells from a particular colony binds to the probe (Figure 14–7), that DNA becomes radioactive and can be detected by x-ray film. The rest of the cells in the colony can then be grown in quantity for further testing.

A genomic library contains fragments of all the DNA in the genome

The total DNA per cell of an organism is referred to as that organism's **genome.** If the DNA is extracted from human cells, as in our example, we refer to it as human genomic DNA. A very large population of recombinant plasmids, each containing a fragment of the genome, is referred to as a **genomic library.** A library (plasmid

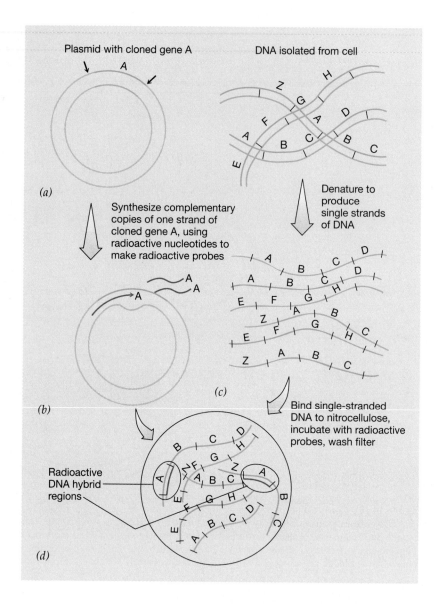

Figure 14–6 Identifying complementary DNA sequences by hybridization with radioactive DNA probes. Total cellular DNA contains a large number of different genes. A single gene (or a sequence of bases) in that DNA can be detected by using a cloned copy of the gene on a vector (*a*) to make complementary radioactive probe molecules (*b*). DNA isolated from the cell is denatured to produce single strands of DNA (*c*), which are then bound to the surface of a nylon membrane (*d*). The membrane is incubated with the radioactive DNA probe, which specifically hybridizes (pairs) with complementary regions of the bound DNA.

population) will contain redundancies in that many human DNA sequences will be cloned many times, purely by chance. However, each individual recombinant plasmid (which is analogous to a "book" in the library) contains only a single fragment of the total human genome. Each of these fragments is usually smaller than a gene; therefore several clones must usually be isolated to study the complete gene.

A cDNA library is complementary to mRNA and does not contain introns

Many eukaryotic genes contain introns, and bacterial cells cannot remove introns from RNA. To avoid cloning those parts of a gene that do not code for proteins, libraries can also be constructed from DNA copies of the eukaryotic mRNA. Those copies are made by isolating mRNA and making DNA copies of the message using **reverse transcriptase** (see Chapter 12). The complementary DNA (cDNA) copies of the message can then be inserted into the DNA of a plasmid or virus vector to form a **cDNA library** (Figure 14–8).

Cloning a gene from both a cDNA library and a genomic library has several advantages. Analysis of the genomic DNA clones gives useful information about the structure of the gene on the chromosome and the structure of the primary pre-mRNA transcript, as well as nontranscribed regulatory regions.

Analysis of cDNA clones allows investigators to determine certain characteristics of the protein encoded by the gene, including its exact amino acid sequence. The structure of the processed mRNA can also be studied. Furthermore, because the cDNA copy of the mRNA does not contain intron sequences, comparison of the cDNA and genomic DNA base sequences reveals the locations of intron and exon coding sequences on the chromosome.

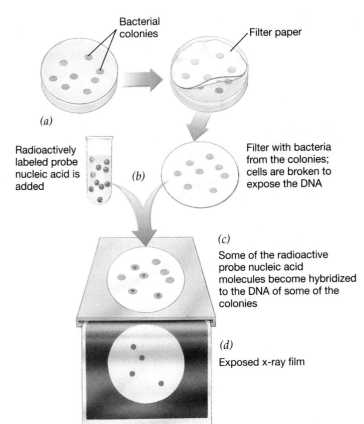

Bacterial colonies

Filter paper

(a)

Radioactively labeled probe nucleic acid is added

(b)

Filter with bacteria from the colonies; cells are broken to expose the DNA

(c)

Some of the radioactive probe nucleic acid molecules become hybridized to the DNA of some of the colonies

(d)

Exposed x-ray film

Figure 14–7 Isolating a gene by means of a genetic probe. (*a*) *E. coli* cells containing a DNA library are spread on solid nutrient medium in dishes so that only one cell is found in each location. Each cell gives rise to genetically identical descendants to form a colony on the medium. Each colony contains plasmids with only a single DNA fragment from the library. (*b*) To identify which colonies contain at least part of the required gene, a few cells from each colony are transferred to nitrocellulose filters which bind the DNA from the cells. (*c*) The filter is incubated with a radioactive DNA probe that is complementary to the desired gene. (*d*) DNA from cells that contain the sequence complementary to the probe become radioactive and can be detected by x-ray film. The pattern of spots on the film allows one to remove from the original culture plates those colonies containing the correct plasmid.

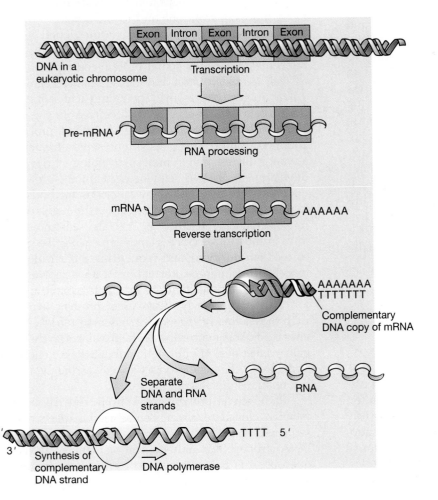

Exon Intron Exon Intron Exon

DNA in a eukaryotic chromosome

Transcription

Pre-mRNA

RNA processing

mRNA AAAAAA

Reverse transcription

AAAAAAA
TTTTTTT

Complementary DNA copy of mRNA

Separate DNA and RNA strands

RNA

5′
3′
TTTT   5′

Synthesis of complementary DNA strand

DNA polymerase

Figure 14–8 Constructing complementary DNA (cDNA) from a eukaryotic mRNA. The cDNA for constructing libraries is made by isolating mRNA from cells. Reverse transcriptase is used to make a complementary DNA copy of the RNA. Synthesis of the second DNA strand is usually done by using DNA polymerase to make a complementary DNA copy of the cDNA strand.

Cloned cDNA sequences are also useful when it is desirable to produce a eukaryotic protein in *E. coli.* Bacteria lack the enzymes to remove introns from eukaryotic mRNA transcripts. When an intron-containing human gene such as the gene for human growth hormone is introduced into *E. coli,* the bacterium is unable to remove the introns from the transcribed RNA to make a functional mRNA for the production of its protein product. If a cDNA clone of the gene is inserted into the bacterium, however, its transcript contains an uninterrupted coding region. A functional protein can be synthesized if the gene is inserted downstream of an appropriate bacterial promoter.

The Polymerase Chain Reaction Is a Technique for Amplifying DNA in Vitro

The methods to amplify a specific DNA sequence described above all involve cloning DNA in cells, usually those of bacteria. These processes are time-consuming and require an adequate DNA sample as starting material. The **polymerase chain reaction (PCR)** technique allows researchers to amplify a tiny sample of DNA millions of times in a few hours. Using DNA polymerase, a DNA target sequence can be replicated in a test tube to produce two DNA molecules. The double strands of each molecule are separated by heating and replicated again so there are four. After the next cycle of heating and replication there are eight molecules and so on, with the number of DNA molecules doubling with each cycle. After 20 such cycles this exponential process yields 2^{20}, or over 1 million, copies of the target sequence! A special heat-resistant DNA polymerase (which originated in a bacterium that lives in hot springs) is used because it remains stable through many heating cycles. Despite occasional technical problems, the PCR technique has been invaluable to researchers. It allows the amplification and analysis of tiny DNA samples from seemingly unlikely sources, ranging from fossil leaves and archeological remains to evidence from crime scenes. The potential applications seem virtually limitless.

A Cloned Gene Sequence Is Usually First Analyzed by Restriction Mapping, Followed by DNA Sequencing

A cloned piece of DNA can be used as a research tool for a wide variety of applications. Even if the purpose of cloning the gene is to obtain the encoded protein for some industrial or pharmaceutical process, a great deal of information must be obtained about the gene and how it functions before it can be "engineered" for a particular application.

One of the first things done with a gene after it has been cloned is to construct a **restriction map** of the DNA fragment. Restriction mapping of DNA involves identifying sites that are attacked by specific restriction enzymes, which serve as landmarks for further studies. That information is then used to isolate (subclone) smaller DNA fragments for a variety of purposes. The mapping procedure involves cutting the DNA fragment with various combinations of restriction enzymes and then separating the DNA fragments by **gel electrophoresis** (Figure 14–9) to determine the molecular weight of each cut fragment. After the size of each fragment is known, the positions of the restriction sites and the distances between them can be determined (Figure 14–10). Once the restriction map has been established, subcloned regions of the DNA fragment can be sequenced or used as DNA probes for analytical purposes.

DNA sequencing (Figure 14–11) is usually done by copying a strand of the cloned DNA in four different reaction mixtures, using a modified form of DNA polymerase. The copies are made so that the newly synthesized DNA chain is terminated randomly at positions corresponding to one of the four bases in each reaction mixture. The lengths of the fragments from each reaction are then determined by gel electrophoresis, allowing one to read off the sequence of bases on the cloned DNA fragment from one end to the other.

Knowing the DNA sequence in the cloned gene allows investigators to identify which parts of the DNA molecule contain the actual protein-coding sequences, as well as which parts may be regulatory regions involved in gene expression. The amino acid sequence of the protein can then be read directly from the DNA, along with other signals involved in mRNA processing and modification. This in itself represents a tremendous advance for research in molecular biology. Prior to the development of DNA sequencing methods, protein sequences were determined by laborious methods from highly purified protein samples. Although protein microsequencing technology has also advanced rapidly, in most cases cloning and sequencing the gene is easier than purifying and sequencing a particular protein. DNA sequence information is now kept in large computer databases that are available to investigators for comparing newly discovered protein sequences with those already known. By searching for DNA (and amino acid) sequences in the database, researchers can gain a great deal of information about the function and structure of the gene product as well as the evolutionary relationships among genes.

Radioactive probes made from restriction fragments of cloned genes can also be used to detect related sequences in DNA or RNA from other cells. Because the DNA probe binds only to complementary DNA sequences, it is not necessary to purify those fragments

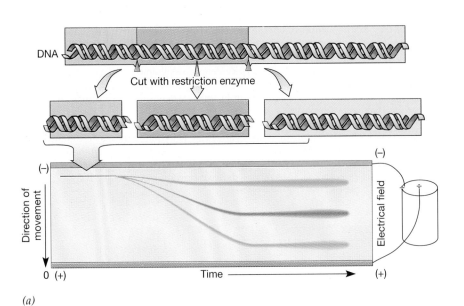

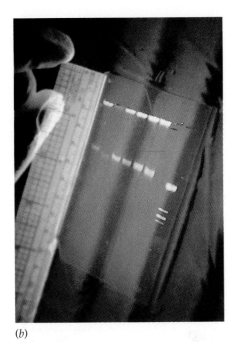

(a)

(b)

Figure 14–9 Gel electrophoresis of DNA fragments. (*a*) The size of DNA fragments can be determined by electrophoresis through agarose or polyacrylamide gel. The gel material is poured as a thin slab on a glass or Plexiglas holder, and samples containing DNA fragments of different sizes are loaded in wells formed at one end of the gel. DNA molecules are negatively charged, so the molecules migrate through the gel toward the positive pole of an electrical field. The rate at which the molecules travel through the gel is inversely proportional to their molecular weight. Therefore, the smallest DNA fragments travel the longest distance. Including DNA fragments of a known size in some of the wells allows accurate measurement of the molecular weights of the unknown fragments. (*b*) A gel containing separated DNA fragments. The gel is stained with the dye ethidium bromide, which binds to DNA and is fluorescent under UV light. (*b*, Visuals Unlimited/Michael Gabridge)

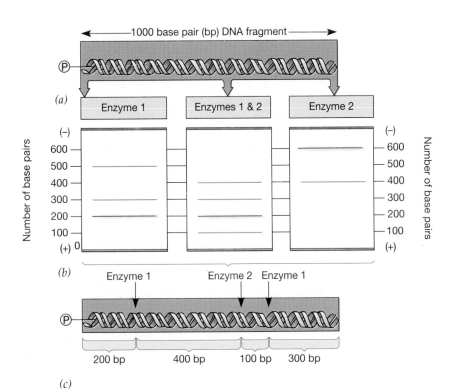

(c)

Figure 14–10 Restriction mapping of a cloned DNA fragment. Restriction maps are constructed by determining the sizes of fragments produced when purified DNA is digested by various restriction enzymes. (*a*) One end of a 1000-base-pair DNA fragment is labeled with radioactive phosphorus. Samples of the DNA are cut by either or both of two different restriction enzymes. (*b*) The sizes of DNA fragments and the location of the radioactive fragment (yellow) are determined by gel electrophoresis. (*c*) The positions of the restriction sites in the original fragment with respect to the radioactive end of the molecule are then deduced.

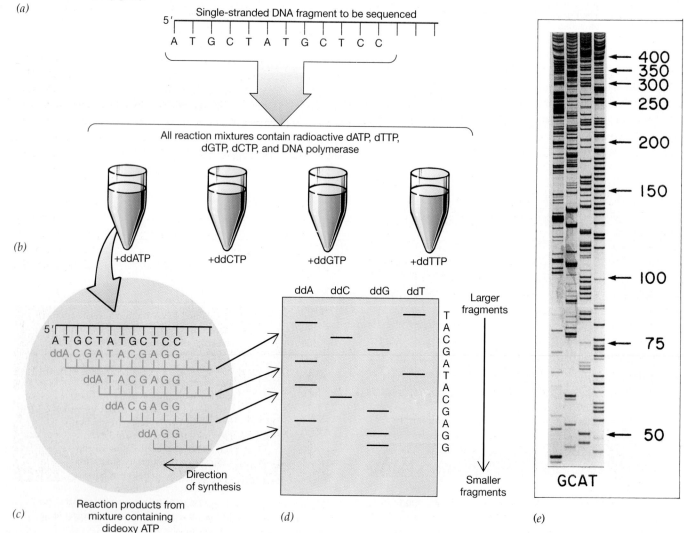

Figure 14–11 Sequencing DNA. The most commonly used method for sequencing DNA involves synthesis of complementary copies of a single DNA strand by DNA polymerase. The newly synthesized DNA strands are radioactively labeled at one end so that they can be identified. (*a*) The procedure uses the random incorporation of *dideoxy*nucleotides, modified nucleotides that lack a 3' hydroxyl group and thus block further elongation of the new DNA chain. (*b*) Four different reaction mixtures are used to sequence a DNA fragment; each contains a small amount of a single dideoxynucleotide, such as dideoxy-ATP (adenine), and larger amounts of the four normal deoxynucleotides. (*c*) The random incorporation of dideoxy-ATP into the growing chain generates a series of smaller DNA fragments ending at all the possible positions where adenine is found in the original fragment. (*d*) The radioactive products of each reaction mixture are separated by gel electrophoresis and located by exposing the gel to x-ray film. The nucleotide sequence of the newly synthesized DNA is read directly from the film. (*e*) An exposed x-ray film of a DNA sequencing gel. The four lanes represent G, C, A, and T dideoxy reaction mixes, respectively. (*e*, courtesy of B. Slatko, New England Biolabs)

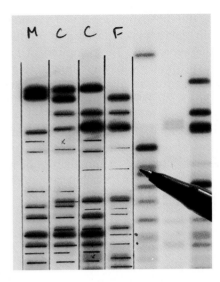

Figure 14–12 Analysis of a restriction fragment length polymorphism (RFLP). This analysis is done by using restriction enzymes to cut the DNA from two or more individuals and then separating the fragments by gel electrophoresis. The DNA on the gel is then allowed to hybridize with a genetic probe representing a sequence that is repeated and interspersed throughout the genome. The resulting patterns can then be compared. (David Parker/Science Photo Library/Photo Researchers, Inc.)

relatedness between individuals. It is also very useful in settling cases of disputed parentage. The most controversial use of this technology is in the field of forensics. If even small amounts of blood, semen, or other DNA-containing tissue are left at the scene of a crime, one or more target DNA sequences can be amplified by the PCR technique, cut with appropriate restriction enzymes, and subjected to electrophoresis. The resulting pattern of bands is commonly referred to as a "DNA fingerprint." The methodology may someday be a way of positively identifying the guilty and exonerating the innocent. Such evidence has been ruled admissible in some court cases and inadmissible in others. One difficulty arises from the fact that the DNA samples are usually small and may have been degraded. A second problem is that we have inadequate data on just how "unique" each individual pattern might be. For example, a pattern that is quite rare in the general population might be relatively common in a particular ethnic group. Resolving these concerns is a matter of ongoing research.

GENETIC ENGINEERING HAS MANY PRACTICAL APPLICATIONS

Recombinant DNA technology has provided not only a new and unique set of tools for examining fundamental questions about how living cells work but also new approaches to problems of applied technology in many other fields. In some cases the production of genetically engineered proteins and organisms has begun to have considerable impact on our lives. The most striking of these have been in the fields of pharmaceutics and medicine.

Human insulin produced by *E. coli* was one of the first genetically engineered proteins to be commercially produced (Figure 14–13). Prior to the development of the altered bacterium to produce the human hormone, insulin was derived exclusively from other animals.

from the rest of the cellular DNA or RNA. The DNA to be probed is simply cut with restriction enzymes, and the entire collection of fragments is separated by electrophoresis. The gel has a banded appearance, with each band containing fragments of a particular size. The separated fragments are then bound to nylon membranes, which pick up the DNA much as a blotter picks up ink. When the DNA on the membrane is incubated with the radioactive probe, the probe binds to any complementary fragments, thus marking their locations. This type of blot hybridization (called a "Southern blot" after its inventor, E. M. Southern) has widespread applications. It is often used to diagnose certain types of genetic disorders because the radioactive probes can sometimes be used to identify DNA sequences associated with certain genetic defects.

Restriction enzymes can also be used to examine the variability of genes within a population of organisms. Random mutations and recombination in the DNA may result in individual differences in the number and location of sites where a particular restriction enzyme acts and therefore differences in the lengths of the fragments produced. Such **restriction fragment length polymorphisms** (commonly known as **RFLPs**, or "Riflips") can be used to determine how closely related different members of the population are to each other (Figure 14–12).

RFLP analysis has been found to be an especially powerful tool in the fields of population and evolutionary biology because it can measure the degree of genetic

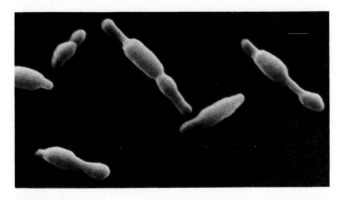

Figure 14–13 Scanning electron micrograph of *E. coli* cells "bulging" with human insulin. (Courtesy of Dr. Daniel C. Williams and the Lilly Microscope Laboratory)

Many diabetic persons become allergic to the insulin from animal sources because the amino acid sequence differs slightly from human insulin. The ability to produce the human protein by recombinant DNA methods has resulted in significant medical benefits to diabetics.

Genetically engineered human growth hormone (see Chapter 47) is required by some children to overcome growth deficiencies. Human growth hormone could previously be obtained only from cadavers. Only small amounts were available, and evidence suggested that some of the preparations were contaminated with viruses. Similarly, genetically engineered Factor VIII, the blood clotting factor lacking in persons with hemophilia A (see Chapter 15), is free of risk of contamination by the HIV-1 virus that causes AIDS. The list of products that can be produced in this way is ever growing.

Additional Engineering Is Required for a Recombinant Eukaryotic Gene To Be Expressed in Bacteria

Even if a gene has been isolated and successfully introduced into *E. coli*, the bacterium does not necessarily make the encoded protein in large quantities. Several obstacles stand in the way of producing gene products of higher organisms in bacteria. One is that the gene has to be correctly associated with an appropriate set of regulatory and promoter sequences that the bacterial RNA polymerase can recognize. Recall from Chapters 12 and 13 that the regulatory regions of prokaryotic and eukaryotic genes are quite different. A usual approach to this problem is to combine the amino acid coding portion of a eukaryotic gene with a bacterial promoter sequence that can be strongly expressed. Some eukaryotic genes, for example, are fused to the lactose operon regulatory region (see Chapter 13). In that state, the protein product of the eukaryotic gene is synthesized when the bacterium is fed lactose in the growth medium.

We have already discussed the fact that bacterial cells cannot process RNA molecules containing eukaryotic intron sequences, and that one solution to this problem is to introduce a cDNA copy of the gene. Other problems may arise in the expression of a recombinant protein in *E. coli* because of differences in the ways the proteins are expressed in prokaryotic and eukaryotic cells.

Insulin, for example, is made in human cells from a large polypeptide that is folded in a specific way by the formation of three disulfide bonds (see Chapter 3) between six sulfur-containing amino acids. After the polypeptide is folded, parts of the protein are removed by proteolytic (protein-digesting) enzymes, leaving the insulin as two separate polypeptide chains held together by the disulfide bonds. *E. coli* lacks the specific enzymes necessary to cut the larger protein and is not able to fold the molecule properly. To overcome these problems, the gene was engineered to produce the two polypeptides separately. The recombinant proteins are then purified from the cells and allowed to associate in vitro. This procedure results in a relatively low yield of the active hormone, because the insulin can fold in several ways, only one of which results in a functional hormone. It has been possible to circumvent some of these problems by introducing the gene into eukaryotic cells such as yeast or cultured mammalian cells, which contain the protein-processing machinery required to produce fully functional proteins.

Transgenic Organisms Incorporate Foreign DNA into Their Cells

Higher organisms that have incorporated foreign genes are referred to as **transgenic** organisms, a term generally limited to plants and animals. A number of approaches are being used to insert foreign genes into plant or animal cells. Viruses are often used as vectors, although other methods, such as direct injection of DNA into cells, have also been used.

Transgenic animals are useful in research and perhaps commercially

One approach to genetic engineering of animal proteins is to use live animals that have incorporated a foreign gene to make the recombinant protein. These transgenic animals usually are produced by microinjecting the DNA of a particular gene into the nucleus of a recipient fertilized egg cell (Figures 14–14 and 16–19). The eggs are then implanted into the uterus of a female and allowed to develop.

In one study of this type, the gene for growth hormone was isolated from a library of genomic rat DNA and combined with the promoter region of a mouse gene that normally produces metallothionein, a protein whose synthesis is stimulated by the presence of heavy metals such as zinc. The metallothionein regulatory sequences were used as a switch to turn the production of rat growth hormone on and off at will. After the engineered gene was injected into fertilized mouse egg cells, the eggs were implanted into the uterus of a mouse and allowed to develop into embryos. Embryos in which the gene transplant had been successful grew rapidly when exposed to small amounts of zinc. One mouse, which developed from an egg that had received two copies of the growth hormone gene, grew to more than double the normal size. As might be expected, such mice are often able to transmit their increased growth capability to their offspring.

Transgenic offspring have already been shown to have valuable research applications in a wide range of studies. These include regulation of gene expression

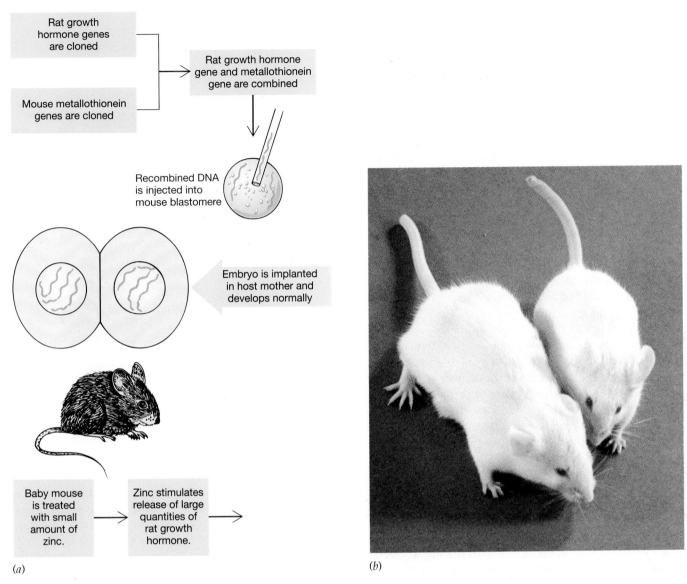

(a)

(b)

Figure 14–14   (a) How to make a giant mouse. (b) The mouse on the right is normal, while the mouse on the left is a transgenic, expressing rat growth hormone.   (photo by R. L. Brinsler).

(see Chapter 13), immune system function, genetic diseases, viral diseases, and genes responsible for the development of cancer.

Transgenic animals have been used to develop strains that secrete important proteins in milk. For example, the gene for tissue plasminogen activator (TPA), a protein that dissolves blood clots that cause heart attacks, has been introduced into transgenic mice, and the gene for human blood clotting factor has been similarly introduced into sheep. These recombinant genes have been fused to the regulatory sequences of the milk protein genes and are therefore activated only in mammary tissues involved in milk production. The advantage of producing the protein in milk is that it is produced in large quantities and can be harvested simply by milking the animal. The protein is then purified from the milk. The animals are not harmed by the introduction of the

gene and, because the progeny of the transgenic animal usually also produce the recombinant protein, transgenic strains can be established simply by breeding the animals.

Sometimes viruses are used as recombinant DNA vectors. RNA viruses called **retroviruses** make DNA copies of themselves by reverse transcription (see Focus on Reverse Transcription, Jumping Genes, and Pseudogenes in Chapter 12). Sometimes those DNA copies become integrated into the host chromosomes, where they are replicated along with host DNA. For example, genetically altered mouse leukemia viruses are retroviruses that can be used as vectors to incorporate recombinant genes into cultured cells. Under certain conditions genes carried by the engineered virus can be expressed in the animal cells to produce genetically engineered proteins.

A major disadvantage of introducing genes into cultured animal cells is that the yields of the proteins encoded by the foreign DNA carried by the viruses are generally low. However, these types of vectors show some promise as a means of **gene therapy** for human genetic disorders (see Chapter 15).

Transgenic plants are increasingly important in agriculture

Plants have been selectively bred for thousands of years. The success of such efforts depends upon the presence of desirable traits in the variety of plant being selected or in closely related wild or domesticated plants whose traits can be transferred by cross-breeding. Primitive varieties, or closely related species, of cultivated plants often have traits, such as disease resistance, that could be advantageously introduced into varieties more suited to modern needs.

If genes are introduced into plants from strains or species with which they do not ordinarily interbreed, the possibilities for improvement are greatly increased. Research funding has been made available to plant geneticists because of the economic potential of increased plant yields. Geneticists working with plants are perhaps also at greater liberty to experiment with new techniques than those working with animals because manipulation of plant genes does not usually involve the same type of ethical considerations.

Unfortunately, a suitable vector for the introduction of recombinant genes into many types of plant cells has proved very difficult to find. The most widely used vector system employs the crown gall bacterium, *Agrobacterium tumefaciens*. This bacterium normally produces plant tumors (Figure 14–15) by introducing a special plasmid, called the Ti (for *tumor-inducing*) plasmid, into the cells of its host. The plasmid induces abnormal growth by forcing the plant cells to produce elevated levels of a plant growth hormone, cytokinin (see Chapter 36). The plasmid also diverts the metabolism of the host cells to produce substances known as opines, simple derivatives of amino and keto acids that are preferred nutrients for the bacterium.

It is possible to "disarm" the Ti plasmid so that it does not induce tumor formation and to use it as a vector to insert genes into plant cells. The cells into which the altered plasmid is introduced are essentially normal except for the genes that have been inserted. Genes placed in the plant genome in this fashion may be transmitted sexually, via seeds, to the next generation, but they can also be propagated asexually if desired.

A major problem with the Ti vector is that, with a few exceptions, only dicotyledonous plants (see Chapter 27) can be infected by *A. tumefaciens*. Unfortunately, the grain plants that are the main food source for humans are monocotyledonous plants and are therefore

Figure 14–15 A crown gall tumor growing on a tree. The growth of this tumor is induced by a plasmid carried by *Agrobacterium tumefaciens*. The bacterial strain used in genetic engineering contains a plasmid that does not cause tumors. (Leonard Lessin/Peter Arnold, Inc.)

outside the host range of the bacterium. Intensive research is under way to develop vector systems for monocotyledonous plants. One approach has been the development of a genetic "shotgun." Microscopic metal fragments are coated with DNA and then shot into plant cells, penetrating the cell walls. Some of the cells retain the DNA and are transformed by it. Those cells can then be cultured and used to regenerate an entire plant (see Chapter 16).

An additional complication of plant genetic engineering is that a number of important plant genes are located on the DNA of the chloroplasts (see Chapters 4 and 8). Chloroplasts are essential in photosynthesis, which is the basis for plant productivity. Obviously, it would be useful to develop methods for changing the portion of the plant's DNA that resides within the chloroplast. Methods of chloroplast engineering are currently the focus of intense research.

Safety guidelines have been developed for recombinant DNA technology

People who have experienced the direct applications of recombinant DNA technology today would undoubtedly agree that those developments have been important and beneficial. In the 1970s, when the new technology was introduced, however, many scientists considered the potential misuses to be at least equally significant. The possibility that an organism with undesirable effects on the environment might be accidentally produced was a concern. Totally new strains of bacteria or other organisms, with which the world has no previous experience, might be difficult to control. This possibility was recognized by those who developed the recombinant DNA methods and led them to insist on stringent guidelines for making the new technology safe.

Recent history has failed to bear out these worries. Experiments over the past years in thousands of university and industrial laboratories have seen recombinant DNA manipulations carried out safely. One of the main concerns—the accidental release of laboratory bacterial strains containing dangerous genes into the environment—has turned out to be groundless. Laboratory strains of *E. coli* are poor competition for the wild strains in the outside world and quickly perish. Experiments thought to entail unusual risks are carried out in special facilities designed to contain dangerous disease-causing organisms and allow researchers to work with them safely. The fears of accidentally cloning a danger-ous gene or releasing a dangerous organism into the environment seem to be laid to rest. This does not mean, however, that *intentional* manipulations of dangerous genes are not a possibility.

Most scientists today recognize the importance of recombinant DNA technology and agree that the perceived threat to humans and the environment was overestimated. Many of the restrictive guidelines for using recombinant DNA have been relaxed as the safety of the experiments has been established. Stringent restrictions still exist, however, in certain areas of recombinant DNA research where dangers are known and questions are still unanswered about possible effects on the environment. These restrictions are most evident in research that proposes to introduce recombinant organisms into the wild, such as agricultural strains of plants whose seeds or pollen might spread in an uncontrolled manner. A great deal of research activity is now concentrated on determining the effects of introducing recombinant organisms in a natural environment; within the next few years we should know more clearly whether such dangers exist.

SUMMARY

I. Recombinant DNA technology is concerned with isolating and amplifying specific sequences of DNA by incorporating them into vector DNA molecules. The resulting recombinant DNA can then be propagated and amplified in organisms such as *E. coli*.

A. Restriction enzymes are used to cut DNA into specific fragments.

  1. Each type of restriction enzyme recognizes and cuts DNA at a highly specific base sequence.

  2. Many restriction enzymes cleave DNA sequences so as to produce single-stranded cut ends that are complementary to each other (sticky ends).

B. The most common recombinant DNA vectors are constructed from naturally occurring circular DNA molecules called plasmids or from bacterial viruses called bacteriophages; both of these are naturally occurring in some bacteria.

C. Recombinant DNA molecules are often constructed by allowing the complementary ends of a DNA fragment and a plasmid (which have both been cut with the same restriction enzyme) to associate by complementary base-pairing. The DNA strands are then covalently linked by DNA ligase to form the recombinant molecule.

D. Single genes are isolated from recombinant DNA libraries, which are mixtures of DNA fragments inserted into appropriate vectors.

  1. Genomic libraries are formed from the total DNA of an organism. Genes that are present in recombinant DNA genomic libraries from eukaryotes contain introns. Those genes can be amplified in *E. coli* along with the molecule that contains them, but the protein is not properly expressed in *E. coli*.

  2. When a cDNA library is produced, DNA copies are made of mRNA isolated from eukaryotic cells; these are then incorporated into recombinant DNA vectors. Because the introns have been removed from mRNA molecules, eukaryotic genes in cDNA libraries can sometimes be expressed in *E. coli* to make their protein products.

E. Analysis of a cloned sequence can yield useful information about the gene and its protein and can enable investigators to identify and subclone DNA fragments for use as molecular probes.

  1. The first step in analyzing a cloned DNA sequence is to construct a restriction map, thereby identifying sites that are cut by specific restriction enzymes.

  2. Determining the nucleotide sequence of a cloned DNA fragment gives information about the structure of the gene and the probable amino acid sequence of the encoded proteins.

  3. Subcloned restriction fragments of a cloned gene can be made radioactive and used as DNA probes to identify related complementary DNA and RNA sequences. The DNA or RNA to be identified is separated from other nucleic acids by gel electrophoresis and then blotted onto special paper. The radioactive DNA probe is then hybridized by complementary base-pairing to the DNA bound to the paper, and the radioactive band or bands of DNA can be identified.

    a. DNA blotting methods are used in diagnosis and in identifying carriers of some genetic diseases.

b. The degree of genetic relationship among the individuals in a population can be estimated by studying restriction fragment length polymorphisms (RFLPs).

II. Genetic engineering is a technology that uses genetic and recombinant DNA methods to devise new combinations of genes to produce improved pharmaceutical and agricultural products.

A. Genes isolated from one organism can be modified and expressed in other organisms ranging from *E. coli* to transgenic plants and animals.

1. Expression of eukaryotic proteins in bacteria, such as *E. coli*, requires that the gene be linked to regulatory elements that the bacterium can recognize. In addi-

tion, bacterial cells do not contain many of the enzymes needed for the posttranslational processing of eukaryotic proteins.

2. Expression of eukaryotic genes in eukaryotic host organisms shows great promise, because the processing and modification machinery for eukaryotic proteins is already present in these cells.

a. Production of important pharmaceutical products can be engineered in transgenic animals so that the products are secreted in milk.

b. Genetic engineering of plants and domestic animals holds the promise of increasing the availability of food.

POST-TEST

1. Specific DNA sequences can be isolated by combining a DNA fragment from one organism with a vector DNA molecule so that the resulting _____ DNA molecule can be amplified in an organism such as *E. coli.*

2. Many restriction enzymes cut DNA at base sequences that are _____, yielding DNA fragments that have single-stranded complementary, or sticky, ends.

3. Recombinant DNA vectors used in *E. coli* are usually small, circular DNA molecules called _____ or bacterial viruses called _____.

4. A recombinant DNA plasmid is usually constructed by allowing the complementary ends of a DNA fragment and a plasmid that have been cut with the same _____ _____ to associate by hydrogen bonding. The single-stranded ends are then covalently linked together by _____ _____.

5. A _____ library is composed of the total DNA of an organism. If the DNA is from a eukaryotic cell, many of the genes will contain _____ sequences.

6. A _____ library is composed of DNA fragments made from mRNA molecules that have been copied by _____ _____.

7. A first step in analyzing a DNA sequence once it has been cloned is to construct a _____ _____ of the DNA in order to locate landmarks that can be used for further studies.

8. DNA sequencing today usually involves making copies of a cloned DNA sequence under conditions that _____ the DNA chain at points where specific bases are located.

9. Short fragments of a cloned DNA sequence can be used as radioactive DNA _____, which can be used to locate complementary nucleic acid fragments by blot hybridization methods.

10. A problem with producing human proteins such as insulin in bacteria is that the bacterial cells do not contain the necessary machinery for _____ processing of the proteins.

11. Plants and animals that have been modified by the introduction of recombinant DNA are referred to as _____ strains.

REVIEW QUESTIONS

1. Diagram the process by which recombinant DNA molecules are usually constructed.

2. How is a gene library constructed? What are the relative merits of genomic libraries and cDNA libraries?

3. Sketch an example illustrating how a restriction map of a gene is made.

4. What are some of the problems that might arise if you were trying to produce a eukaryotic protein in a bacterium? How might some of these problems be solved by using transgenic plants or animals?

RECOMMENDED READINGS

Darnell, J., H. Lodish, and D. Baltimore. *Molecular Cell Biology.* W. H. Freeman, New York, 1990. Chapters 5 and 6 are well-written accounts of the tools of molecular biology and recombinant DNA, starting with the cells and organisms used in the technology and proceeding to its methods and applications.

Mullis, K. B. The unusual origin of the polymerase chain reaction. *Scientific American* 262(4):56–65, April 1990. A highly personal first-hand account of the development of the PCR

technique and an excellent illustration of the nature of scientific insight.

Neufield, P. J., and N. Colman. When science takes the witness stand. *Scientific American* 262(5):46–53, May 1990. A discussion of the use of "DNA fingerprinting" in forensics, with an emphasis on the need for appropriate standards.

Watson, J. D., M. Gilman, J. Witkowski, and M. Zoller. *Recombinant DNA,* 2nd ed. W. H. Freeman, New York, 1992. An up-to-date source of information about genetic engineering.

❑

Human Genetics

Geneticists quite naturally have great interest in the study of human genetics. Humans do not serve well as the subjects of most types of genetic research, however. For the study of the mode of inheritance in any species, geneticists should ideally (1) have standard stocks of genetically identical individuals—that is, **isogenic strains**—that are homozygous at virtually all of their loci, (2) conduct **controlled matings** between members of different isogenic strains, and (3) raise the offspring under carefully controlled conditions. Of course, the human population is very diverse and individuals are heterozygous for many genes. Human families are small, and 20 to 30 years or more elapse between generations. It is therefore virtually impossible, as well as unethical, to conduct such studies on humans.

Family portrait. (G. M. Brod/Custom Medical Stock Photo, Inc.)

Despite the inherent difficulties, study of human genetics is progressing very rapidly. The field has been revolutionized by combining genetic engineering technology (see Chapter 14) with a variety of more traditional approaches, including pedigree analysis and population studies. This work has been greatly facilitated by the medical attention given to genetic diseases in humans. The extensive medical records of diseases serve as a very useful data pool upon which hypotheses may be based and against which they may be tested. Furthermore, genetic studies of other organisms have provided invaluable insights. Indeed, many phenomena in human inheritance that were initially quite puzzling have been explained by solving analogous problems in the inheritance of bacteria, yeasts, fruit flies, and mice.

After you have studied this chapter you should be able to

1. Explain why humans have been traditionally considered poor subjects for the study of inheritance. Point out some of the ways in which these limitations have been overcome.
2. Distinguish between environmentally induced and inherited abnormalities and between chromosome abnormalities and single gene defects.
3. Make a sketch illustrating how nondisjunction can occur in meiosis. Show how nondisjunction can be responsible for specific chromosome abnormalities such as Down syndrome, Klinefelter syndrome, and Turner syndrome.
4. Describe how amniocentesis is used in the prenatal diagnosis of human genetic abnormalities; state the relative ad-

vantages and disadvantages of amniocentesis and chorionic villus sampling.
5. Discuss the scope and implications of genetic counseling.
6. Relate each ABO type to the appropriate genotype(s). Explain the genetic and physiological basis for Rh incompatibility between a mother and a fetus.
7. Explain why quantitative traits in humans are thought to be under the control of polygenes.
8. Discuss the implications of the Human Genome Initiative, including the costs and possible benefits.
9. List some of the ways genetics affects human society. Explain why the perpetuation of various myths about human genetics is also harmful to society.

ANALYSIS OF INHERITANCE PATTERNS IN HUMANS REQUIRES ALTERNATIVE METHODS

Early studies of human heredity usually dealt with readily identified pairs of contrasting traits and their distribution among members of a family, as illustrated by the **pedigree** in Figure 15–1. This method is still useful, but because human families tend to be small and

information on certain family members may be lacking, it has serious limitations.

Human geneticists therefore also use methods that allow them to make inferences about the mode of inheritance of a trait based on studies of its distribution in an entire population. By applying the laws of probability to data obtained from a relatively large sample of individuals who are representative of the population, it is often possible to determine if the mode of inheritance is simple or complex, if more than one locus is involved,

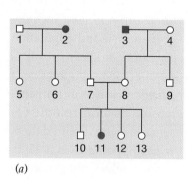

(a)

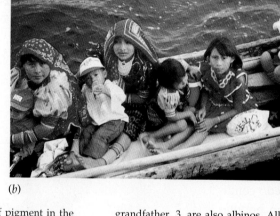

(b)

Figure 15–1 (a) A pedigree for albinism (lack of pigment in the hair, skin, and eyes), which is inherited as an autosomal recessive trait, which means it is not carried on a sex chromosome. Males are indicated by squares and females by circles. Individuals showing the trait under study are indicated by red symbols; those not showing the trait are indicated by white symbols. Relationships are indicated by connecting lines, and all members of the same generation are placed on the same row. Thus, 11 is an albino girl whose paternal grandmother, 2, and maternal

grandfather, 3, are also albinos. All of her other relatives shown are phenotypically normal. Notice that the inheritance pattern could not be autosomal dominant or X-linked dominant because neither of 11's parents is albino. If the trait were X-linked recessive, her mother would have to be a heterozygous carrier and her father would have to be an albino (which he is not).
(b) Albinism is very common among the Cuna people living on the San Blas Islands of Panama. (b, Photo Edit)

and so on. Some of the methods used by population geneticists are introduced in Chapter 18.

As we shall see later in this chapter, human inheritance can be studied most effectively through the combination of these and other approaches with the methods of molecular biology and recombinant DNA technology.

MOST HUMAN TRAITS ARE DUE TO COMPLEX GENETIC AND ENVIRONMENTAL INTERACTIONS

The development of each organ of the body is regulated by a large number of genes that interact in complex ways. The mechanisms of inheritance of many physical traits and hundreds of specific enzymes are now known. In fact, the loci of many genes have been identified, and chromosome maps, although incomplete, have been worked out for each human chromosome.

The age at which a particular gene expresses itself phenotypically may vary widely. Most characteristics develop before birth, but some, such as hair and eye color, are not fully expressed until shortly after birth. Others, such as muscular dystrophy, become evident in early childhood, and still others, such as glaucoma and Huntington's disease, develop only in adulthood.

SOME BIRTH DEFECTS ARE INHERITED

A **birth defect,** or congenital defect, is one that is present at birth; it may or may not be inherited. Some birth defects are inherited; others are produced by environmental factors that affect the developmental process. For example, if a woman contracts the viral disease rubella (commonly known as German measles) during the first 3 months of pregnancy, a substantial risk exists that her offspring will develop malformations. Environmental factors that have been linked with birth defects are discussed in Chapter 49.

Certain abnormalities are the result of mutations involving a single locus; sickle cell anemia and albinism are examples of this type of defect. Other abnormalities, such as Down syndrome, result from an abnormal number of chromosomes.

CHROMOSOMAL ABNORMALITIES ARE RESPONSIBLE FOR SOME BIRTH DEFECTS

Cytogenetics is the study of chromosomes and their role in inheritance. Many of the basic principles of genetics were discovered by experiments with simpler organisms, in which it was possible to relate genetic data with the number and structure of the chromosomes. Some of the organisms used in genetics, such as the fruit fly *Drosophila*, have very few chromosomes (only four pairs). In *Drosophila* salivary glands and certain other tissues, the chromosomes are large enough that their structural details are readily evident (see Chapter 16). Therefore, this organism has provided unique opportunities for correlating certain kinds of genetic changes with certain kinds of alterations in chromosome structure. Although the science of human cytogenetics is not nearly as refined, many useful determinations are still possible.

Karyotyping Is the Analysis of Chromosomes

Representative normal human karyotypes for males and females are shown in Figure 9–1. The term **karyotype** refers both to the chromosome composition of an individual and to a photomicrograph showing that composition. In karyotyping, cells from the bone marrow, blood, or skin are incubated with chemicals that stimulate mitosis. These chemicals are derived from certain plants and are called **lectins.** The cells are then treated with the drug colchicine (see Chapter 9), which arrests them at mitotic metaphase. They are then placed in a hypotonic solution (see Chapter 5), which causes them to swell, enabling the chromosomes to spread out so they can be readily visualized. The cells are then flattened on microscope slides and the chromosomes stained to reveal the patterns of bands, which are unique for each homologous pair.

After the chromosomes have been photographed, each chromosome is cut out of the photographic print and the homologous pairs are identified and placed together. Chromosomes can then be identified by length, position of the centromere, banding patterns, and other morphological features such as knobs. The largest chromosome is about five times as long as the smallest one, but there are only slight size differences among some of the intermediate-sized ones (see Figure 9–1).

Most Chromosome Abnormalities Are Lethal or Cause Serious Defects

Polyploidy, the presence of multiples of complete chromosome sets, is common in plants but rare in animals. It may arise as a result of failure of chromosome separation during meiosis or fertilization of an egg by more than one sperm. Polyploidy is lethal in humans and many other animals when it occurs in all the cells of the body. Triploidy is sometimes found in embryos that

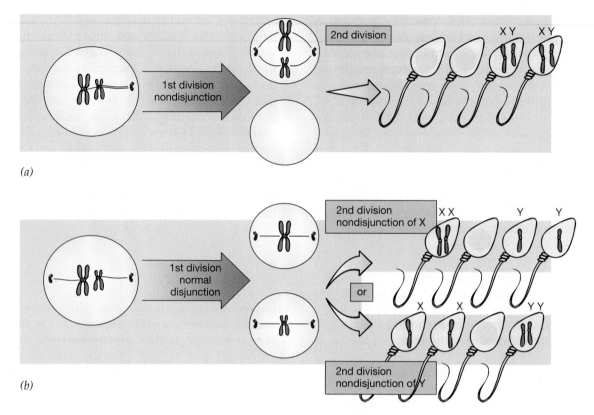

Figure 15–2   Examples of meiotic nondisjunction of the sex chromosomes in the human male. Only the X (red) and Y (brown) chromosomes are shown. (a) Nondisjunction in the first meiotic division results in two XY sperm and two sperm with neither an X nor a Y. (b) Second-division nondisjunction of the X chromosome results in one sperm with two X chromosomes, two with one Y each, and one with no sex chromosomes. Similarly, nondisjunction of the Y results in one sperm with two Y chromosomes, two with one X each, and one with no sex chromosome. By contrast, nondisjunction in the female (not shown) results in the formation of eggs with two X chromosomes or no sex chromosomes, regardless of whether it occurs in the first or second meiotic division.

have been spontaneously aborted in early pregnancy. The few triploid or tetraploid individuals who have been born alive and have lived for a few days have been found to contain a mixture of diploid and polyploid cells.

Abnormalities involving the presence of an extra chromosome or the absence of a chromosome are much more common in humans; these conditions are called **aneuploidies.** Recall that ordinarily there are two of each kind of chromosome; this is the normal **disomic** condition. An individual with an extra chromosome— that is, with three of one kind—is said to be **trisomic** for that kind of chromosome. An individual lacking one member of a pair of chromosomes is said to be **monosomic.**

Aneuploidies generally arise as a result of an abnormal meiotic (or mitotic) division in which chromosomes fail to separate at anaphase; this phenomenon is called **nondisjunction.** In meiosis chromosomal nondisjunction may occur during the first or second meiotic division (or both). For example, two X chromosomes that fail to separate at either the first or the second meiotic division might both enter the egg nucleus. Alternatively, the two joined X chromosomes might go into a polar body, leaving the egg with no X chromosome.

Nondisjunction of the XY pair in the male might lead to the formation of sperm with both an X and a Y chromosome or sperm with neither an X nor a Y chromosome. Similarly, nondisjunction at the second meiotic division can produce sperm with two X's or two Y's. Some of these examples of meiotic nondisjunction are illustrated in Figure 15–2. When an abnormal gamete unites with a normal one, the resulting zygote has a chromosome abnormality that is present in every cell of the body.

Nondisjunction during a mitotic division leads to the establishment of a clone of abnormal cells in an otherwise normal individual; such an individual therefore contains a mixture of normal and abnormal cells.

In some cases part of one chromosome may break off and attach to a nonhomologous chromosome, or two nonhomologous chromosomes may exchange parts. Such an event is called a **translocation.** The consequences of translocations vary considerably but include

Table 15–1 SOME CHROMOSOME ABNORMALITIES

Karyotype	Common Name	Clinical Description
Trisomy 13	Patau syndrome	Multiple defects, with death by age 1 to 3 months
Trisomy 18	Edwards syndrome	Ear deformities, heart defects, spasticity, and other damage; death by age 1 year
Trisomy 21	Down syndrome	Overall frequency is about 1 in 700 live births. True trisomy is most often found among children of older (age 40+) mothers, but translocation resulting in the equivalent of trisomy may occur in children of younger women. A similar, though less marked, influence is exerted by the age of the father. Trisomy 21 is characterized by a fold of skin above the eye, varying degrees of mental retardation, short stature, protruding furrowed tongue, transverse palmar crease, and cardiac deformities.
Trisomy 22		Similar to Down syndrome, but with more skeletal deformities
XO	Turner syndrome (gonadal dysgenesis)	Short stature, webbed neck, sometimes slight mental retardation; ovaries degenerate in late embryonic life, leading to rudimentary sexual characteristics; gender is female; no Barr bodies
XXY	Klinefelter syndrome	Male with slowly degenerating testes, enlarged breasts; one Barr body per cell
XYY		Unusually tall male with heavy acne; some tendency to mild mental retardation
XXX		Despite three X chromosomes, usually fertile, fairly normal females

situations in which some genes are missing (*deletions*) and extra copies of other genes are present (*duplications*). Table 15–1 summarizes some disorders that are produced by aneuploidies (see also Figures 15–4 and 15–7).

Persons with Down syndrome usually have three copies of chromosome 21

Down syndrome is one of the most common chromosomal abnormalities in humans. Affected individuals have abnormalities of the face, eyelids, tongue, hands, and other parts of the body and are mentally and physically retarded (Figure 15–3). They are also unusually susceptible to certain diseases, such as leukemia and Alzheimer's disease. The term **mongolism,** which is no longer used today because of its racist connotations, was originally applied to this condition because of a characteristic fold of the eyelid in affected persons which is superficially similar to that typically found in oriental peoples.

Cytogenetic studies have revealed that most persons with Down syndrome have 47 chromosomes because they are trisomic for chromosome 21, one of the smaller chromosomes (Figure 15–4). Nondisjunction during meiosis is thought to be responsible for the presence of the extra chromosome.

Figure 15–3 Child with Down syndrome participating in the Special Olympics. (Jose Carrillo/Photo Edit)

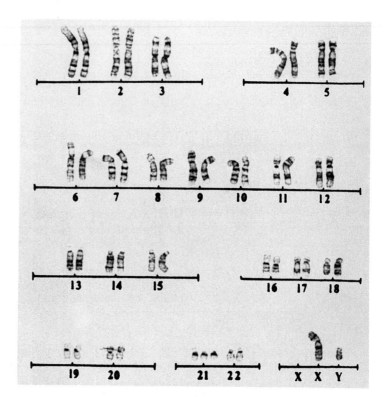

Figure 15–4 Karyotype of an individual with the free trisomy 21 form of Down syndrome. Note the presence of an extra chromosome 21. (Courtesy of Dr. Leonard Sciorra)

Down syndrome occurs in only about 0.15% of all births, but its incidence increases markedly with increasing maternal age (Figure 15–5); it is 100 times more likely in the offspring of mothers who are 45 years of age or older than it is in the offspring of mothers who are under 19 years of age. The occurrence of Down syndrome is affected much less by the age of the father.

Because of this striking correlation of the incidence of Down syndrome with increased maternal age, the condition is thought to be due in most (but certainly not all) cases to meiotic nondisjunction in the mother. The reason for this is not fully understood. One proposed explanation relates to differences in meiosis in human males and females (see Chapter 48). All of the cells in a human female that will ever enter meiosis do so before she is even born. They become arrested in meiotic prophase and remain in that state until she reaches puberty, after which one cell per month resumes meiosis. Therefore, when a woman produces an egg to be fertilized, that egg is essentially as old as she is. In contrast, in human males new cells are continually entering meiosis, and the entire process of sperm production takes only about 50 days.

In about 4% of patients with Down syndrome, only 46 chromosomes are present, but one is abnormal: Extra genetic material from chromosome 21 has been translocated onto one of the larger chromosomes, such as chromosome 14. We refer to the abnormal translocation chromosome as the *14/21 chromosome*. Affected persons

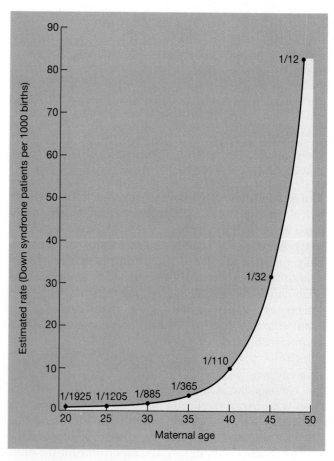

Figure 15–5 Relationship between maternal age and the incidence of Down syndrome.

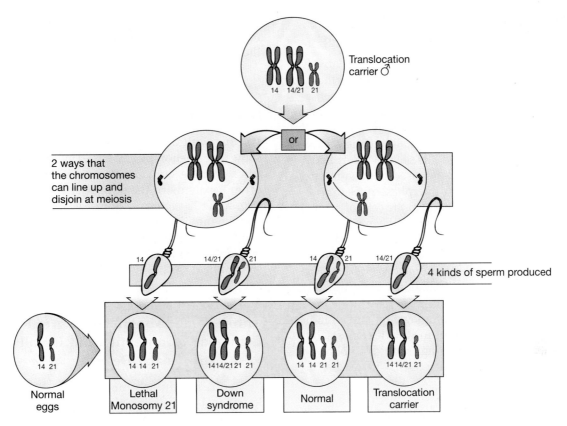

Figure 15–6 The translocation form of Down syndrome. In a carrier individual (either the mother or the father) most of the genetic material from a chromosome 21 has become fused to a chromosome 14, forming a 14/21 translocation chromosome. In this example the father is the carrier; he has 45 chromosomes, with one 14, one 21, and one 14/21. At anaphase I of meiosis, the chromosome 14 and the 14/21 translocation chromosome usually disjoin from one another. The chromosome 21 can go either to the pole with the chromosome 14 or to the pole with the 14/21 translocation chromosome. On average, such a carrier produces four kinds of sperm; when they fertilize normal eggs, these sperm produce four kinds of zygotes. One quarter of the zygotes have only one chromosome 21 (monosomy 21), a lethal condition; one quarter have the translocation form of Down syndrome; one quarter are genotypically and phenotypically normal; and one quarter are translocation carriers like the father.

have one chromosome 14, one 14/21 chromosome, and two copies of chromosome 21. The genetic material from chromosome 21 is thus present in triplicate. When the karyotypes of such an individual's parents are studied, either the mother or the father is usually found to have only 45 chromosomes, although he or she is generally phenotypically normal. Such a person has one chromosome 14, one 14/21 chromosome, and one chromosome 21. Although the karyotype is abnormal, there is no extra genetic material. In contrast to true, or free, **trisomy 21,** this translocation form of Down syndrome can run in families (Figure 15–6), and its incidence does not increase with maternal age.

The presence of this extra chromosomal material leads to the complex physical and mental abnormalities that characterize Down syndrome. Paradoxically, although no genetic information is missing in these individuals, the extra "doses" of chromosome 21 genes bring about some type of genetic imbalance that is responsible for abnormal physical and mental development. Down syndrome is quite variable in its expression, with some individuals far more severely affected than others. Genetic imbalances produced by the addition or deletion of all or part of a chromosome typically result in multiple defects.

When a disease causes multiple symptoms, we refer to it as a **syndrome;** virtually all chromosomal abnormalities fall into this category. Because the nervous system is so complicated in its development, it appears to be quite sensitive to altered gene dosages, and some form of mental retardation commonly accompanies most chromosome abnormalities. Researchers are using genetic engineering methods to attempt to pinpoint genes on chromosome 21 that affect mental development, as well as possible oncogenes (see Focus on Oncogenes and Cancer in Chapter 16) and genes that may be involved in Alzheimer's disease.

In general, chromosome abnormalities involving the autosomes are devastating in their consequences. Other than Down syndrome, very few autosomal trisomies are known (Table 15–1). The condition known as autosomal **monosomy,** in which only one member of a pair is present, is apparently incompatible with life, because it is not seen in live births.

Sex Chromosome Abnormalities Are Usually Less Severe Than Autosomal Abnormalities

Sex chromosome abnormalities appear to be relatively well tolerated (see Table 15–1), apparently owing at least in part to the phenomenon of dosage compensation discussed in Chapter 10. According to the *single active X hypothesis,* mammals compensate for extra X chromosomal material by rendering all but one X chromosome inactive. The inactive X is seen as a Barr body, a region of darkly staining, condensed chromatin next to the nuclear envelope of an interphase nucleus.

The presence of the Barr body in the cells of normal females (but not of normal males) has been used as an initial screen to determine whether an individual is genetically female or male. As we shall see in our discussion of abnormal sex chromosome constitutions, the Barr body test has serious limitations. Unfortunately the test, also known as **nuclear sexing,** has sometimes been misused, particularly in judging eligibility of individuals to participate as females in athletic contests. If it is used at all, any unusual findings should be followed by karyotype analysis and other tests.

Individuals with Klinefelter syndrome have an XXY karyotype

Persons with Klinefelter syndrome have 47 chromosomes, including two X chromosomes and one Y chromosome. They are nearly normal males, but they have small testes and produce few or no sperm. Evidence that the Y chromosome is the major determinant of the male phenotype has been substantiated by the fact that there is at least one gene on the Y chromosome that appears to act as a "genetic switch," directing male development.

Persons with Klinefelter syndrome tend to be unusually tall and to have female-like breasts, and about half show some degree of mental retardation; most live relatively normal lives. However, when their cells are examined they are found to have one Barr body per cell; on the basis of such a test, they would be erroneously classified as females.

Persons with Turner syndrome have only one X chromosome and no Y

We designate the sex chromosome constitution for Turner syndrome as *XO,* the *O* referring to the absence of a second sex chromosome. Because of the absence of the strong male-determining effect of the Y chromosome, these persons develop essentially as females. However, both their internal and external genital structures are undeveloped, and they are sterile. Apparently a second X chromosome is necessary for the normal development of the ovaries in a female embryo. Examination of their cells reveals no Barr bodies, because there is no "extra" X chromosome to be inactivated.

Some essentially normal males have an XYY karyotype

Persons with an X chromosome plus two Y chromosomes are phenotypically fertile males. Other characteristics of these individuals (unusually tall, with severe acne) hardly merit the term *syndrome;* hence the designation *XYY karyotype.* Some years ago there was a widely publicized suggestion that persons with this condition are more likely to display criminal tendencies and be imprisoned, but further studies have failed to substantiate this.

Chromosome Abnormalities Are Relatively Common at Conception but Usually Result in Prenatal Death

Recognizable chromosome abnormalities are seen in less than 1% of all live births, but substantial evidence suggests that the rate at conception is much higher. About 17% to 20% or more of all recognized pregnancies end in a spontaneous abortion ("miscarriage"). Approximately half of these spontaneously aborted embryos have major chromosome abnormalities, including autosomal trisomies (e.g., trisomy 21), triploidy and tetraploidy, and Turner syndrome (XO), the last of which is the most common. Autosomal monosomies are exceedingly rare. It is *unlikely* that they never occur; it is far more probable that autosomal monosomy is so incompatible with life that a spontaneous abortion occurs very early, before the woman is even aware that she is pregnant. Some investigators place surprisingly high estimates (50% or more) on the rate of loss of very early embryos. It is widely assumed that chromosome abnormalities are responsible for a substantial fraction of these.

MANY GENETIC DISEASES SHOW SIMPLE INHERITANCE PATTERNS

Most Genetic Diseases Are Inherited as Autosomal Recessive Traits

Hundreds of human disorders involving enzyme defects have been found to be due to genetic mutations. These disorders, sometimes referred to as *inborn errors of metabolism,* include phenylketonuria (PKU) and alkaptonuria (see Chapter 11). Two other such genetic disorders associated with single gene defects (although not necessarily in genes coding for enzymes) are cystic fibrosis and sickle cell anemia. Not all human genetic diseases have a simple inheritance pattern, but most of those that do are transmitted as autosomal recessive traits and so are expressed only in the homozygous state.

Phenylketonuria (PKU) is due to an enzyme deficiency and can be treated with a special diet

It is not possible today to cure any genetic disease; the best one can hope for is successful treatment of the symptoms. Perhaps the most dramatic success to date has been in the treatment of **phenylketonuria (PKU).** Homozygous recessive individuals lack an enzyme that converts the amino acid phenylalanine to another amino acid, tyrosine. These persons instead convert phenylalanine into toxic products, which accumulate and damage the central nervous system. The ultimate result is severe mental retardation. A homozygous PKU infant is usually healthy at birth because its mother, who is heterozygous, produces enough enzyme to prevent phenylalanine accumulation before birth. However, during infancy and early childhood, the toxic products eventually cause irreversible damage to the central nervous system.

In the early 1950s it was found that if PKU infants are identified and placed on a special low-phenylalanine diet early enough, the symptoms can be dramatically alleviated. Biochemical tests for PKU have been developed, and screening of newborns through a simple blood test is widespread in the United States, with more than 90% of all infants being tested. Because of these screening programs and the availability of effective treatment, thousands of children have been saved from severe mental retardation. Most such children are able to discontinue the diet by adolescence. Although they still accumulate phenylalanine, the sensitive period is past.

Ironically, the success of treatment of PKU in childhood presents a new problem today. If a homozygous female who was saved from mental retardation becomes pregnant, the high phenylalanine levels in her blood can damage the brain of the fetus she is carrying, even though that fetus is only heterozygous. Therefore, she must resume the diet, preferably before becoming pregnant. This procedure is usually (although not always) successful in preventing the effects of **maternal PKU.** Therefore it is especially important that females with PKU be aware of their condition so that they may obtain appropriate counseling and medical treatment during pregnancy.

Sickle cell anemia results from a hemoglobin defect

Sickle cell anemia is inherited as an autosomal recessive trait. The disease is most common in persons of African descent, and about 1 in 12 African-Americans is heterozygous for it. The blood cells of a person with sickle cell anemia are shaped like sickles, or half-moons, whereas normal red blood cells are biconcave discs.

The sickle cell contains abnormal hemoglobin molecules, which have the amino acid valine instead of glutamic acid at position 6 (the sixth amino acid from the amino terminal end) in the beta chain (see Chapter 3). The substitution of an amino acid with a hydrophobic, uncharged side chain (valine) for one with a hydrophilic, charged side chain (glutamate) makes the hemoglobin less soluble, so it tends to form crystal-like structures that change the shape of the red blood cell (Figure 15–7). This occurs in the veins after the oxygen has been released from the hemoglobin. The blood cells' abnormal sickle shape slows blood flow and blocks small blood vessels, with resulting tissue damage and painful episodes; these cells also have short life spans, leading to anemia in affected persons.

Available treatments for sickle cell anemia include measures to relieve pain, transfusions, and some forms of drug therapy, but these are of limited effectiveness, and children with sickle cell anemia generally lead short, painful lives. There is ongoing research directed toward eventually providing gene therapy for these patients.

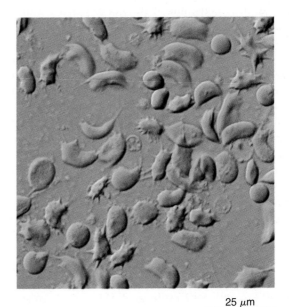

25 μm

Figure 15–7 Red blood cells from a patient with sickle cell anemia. Note the abnormal shape of some of the cells. (G. W. Willis, M.D./Biological Photo Service)

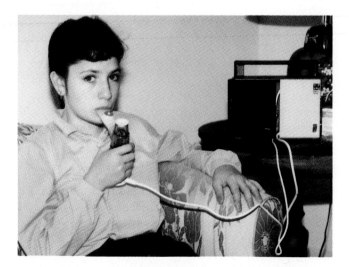

Figure 15–8 A child with cystic fibrosis using a nebulizer, which disperses medications into a fine mist that can then be inhaled. (G. W. Willis, Ochsner Medical Institution/Biological Photo Service)

Cystic fibrosis apparently results from defective ion transport

Cystic fibrosis is the most common autosomal recessive disorder in white children (Figure 15–8). About 1 of every 20 persons in the United States is a heterozygous carrier of the gene for cystic fibrosis, which is characterized by abnormal secretions in the body. The most severe effect of this disorder is on the respiratory system, which produces abnormally viscous mucus. The cilia that line the bronchi (see Chapter 44) cannot easily remove the mucus, and it thus becomes a culture medium for dangerous bacteria. These bacteria or their toxins attack the surrounding tissues, leading to recurring pneumonia and other complications. The heavy mucus also occurs elsewhere in the body (e.g., in the ducts of the pancreas and liver and in the intestines), causing digestive difficulties and other effects.

The cystic fibrosis gene has been cloned. It appears to code for a protein that controls the transport of chloride ions across cell membranes. The malfunction caused by the mutant protein evidently affects sodium ion transport as well and eventually leads to damage in the tissues of the respiratory and digestive systems. Although more than one mutant form exists and these vary somewhat in severity of symptoms, the disease is always serious.

Antibiotics are used to control bacterial infections, and daily physical therapy is required to clear mucus from the respiratory system. Without such treatment, death would occur in infancy. With treatment, about 50% of affected persons live into their 20s, only to die in what should be the prime of life, having spent the equivalent of about 4 years in the hospital. Because of the serious limitations of available treatments, cystic fibrosis has become a prime candidate for the development of gene therapies. These are discussed later in this chapter.

Tay-Sachs disease is a result of abnormal lipid metabolism in the brain

Tay-Sachs disease is an autosomal recessive disease of the central nervous system that results in blindness and severe mental retardation. The symptoms begin within the first year of life and result in death before the age of 5 years. Because of the absence of an enzyme, a normal membrane lipid in the brain fails to break down properly and accumulates in the lysosomes (see Chapter 4). Unfortunately, although this is a matter of ongoing research, no effective treatment for Tay-Sachs disease is available at this time.

The abnormal allele is especially common in the United States among Jews whose ancestors came from Eastern Europe (Ashkenazi Jews). By contrast, Jews whose ancestors came from the Mediterranean region (Sephardic Jews) have a very low frequency of the allele.

Huntington's Disease Is an Autosomal Dominant Disorder That Affects the Nervous System

Huntington's disease (formerly called *Huntington's chorea*) is due to a rare autosomal dominant allele that causes severe mental and physical deterioration, uncontrollable muscle spasms, personality changes, and ultimately insanity. No effective treatment has been found. Every child of an affected individual has a 50% chance of also being affected (and of course passing the abnormal allele to half of his or her offspring).

Ordinarily we would expect a dominant allele with such devastating effects to occur only as a new mutation and not to be transmitted to future generations. However, this disease is characterized by onset relatively late in life (usually between the ages of 35 and 50), so an individual may have children before knowing whether the allele is present.

The chromosome region that contains the Huntington's gene has been identified by recombinant DNA technology and is the subject of intensive research to pin down the precise nature of the biochemical defect. These accomplishments are an excellent illustration of the fact that much of the best biological research today involves a combination of approaches. The complexity of the task requires extensive collaboration among researchers in different disciplines.

One strategy used when trying to isolate a gene is to isolate DNA from persons who carry the abnormal allele and compare it to DNA from closely related persons who do not have the allele. This is generally done by restriction fragment mapping (see Chapter 14). One advantage of studying close relatives is that one can minimize other genetic differences and concentrate on the gene of interest. The optimal approach is to study large families, carefully construct pedigrees, and obtain DNA samples from affected and unaffected individuals across generations. A large extended family with a very high incidence of Huntington's disease was discovered in Venezuela and has been the subject of exhaustive pedigree and DNA analysis. This has made possible the identification of a **DNA marker** for Huntington's disease. A DNA marker is not the DNA of the gene of interest, but it is the next best thing—a piece of DNA that is closely associated with the abnormal allele on the chromosome and is inherited along with it. The Huntington's disease marker is the basis for new tests that allow some persons at risk to learn whether they carry the allele. (See Making the Connection: Probing for Genetic Disease.)

The decision to be tested for any genetic disease is understandably a highly personal one. Certainly, the information can be very useful for those who must make decisions such as whether to have children. However, someone who tests positive for the Huntington's disease allele must then live with the certainty of eventually developing this devastating and incurable disease. It is hoped that identifying affected persons before the onset of symptoms may ultimately contribute to the development of effective treatments. If persons who have the Huntington's allele choose not to reproduce, the frequency of this allele in the population will decrease.

Hemophilia A Is an X-Linked Recessive Disorder That Affects Blood Clotting

Hemophilia A is sometimes referred to as a disease of royalty because of its incidence among male descendants of Queen Victoria, but it is also found in many nonroyal pedigrees. Characterized by the lack of a blood-clotting factor, Factor VIII, it causes severe bleeding from even a slight wound. Because the mode of inheritance is X-linked recessive, affected persons are almost exclusively male, having inherited the abnormal allele on the X chromosome from their heterozygous carrier mothers.

Today, treatments consist of blood transfusions and administration of Factor VIII by injection. Unfortunately, these treatments are costly and have been associated with infection with HIV-1, the virus that causes AIDS. Factor VIII produced using recombinant DNA technology (see Chapter 14) will provide a safer source of the clotting factor.

SOME GENETIC ABNORMALITIES AND OTHER BIRTH DEFECTS CAN BE DETECTED BEFORE BIRTH

Genetic abnormalities may become apparent during early intrauterine life or not until late in adult life. Given that early detection increases the possibilities for prevention or alleviation of the effects of genetic abnormalities, efforts have been made over the years to detect such abnormalities before birth. In the past 20 years physicians have become increasingly successful at prenatal diagnosis and treatment, including transfusion and surgical correction of malformations. Intrauterine diagnosis of a number of genetic abnormalities is now possible.

In one diagnostic technique, known as **amniocentesis,** a sample of the fluid surrounding the fetus (the *amniotic fluid*—see Chapter 49) is obtained (Figure 15–9). A needle is inserted through the lower abdomen of the pregnant woman, through the wall of the uterus, and into the uterine cavity and some of the fluid is drawn into a syringe. Although this procedure carries some risk, it is relatively safe, partly because the positions of the fetus and the needle can be determined through **ultrasound imaging** (Figure 15–10).

The amniotic fluid contains living cells sloughed off the body of the fetus and hence genetically identical to the cells of the fetus. These amniotic fluid cells can then be grown in culture in the laboratory. After 2 to 3 weeks, dividing cells from the culture can be studied for evidence of chromosomal abnormalities and other genetic defects.

Amniocentesis is performed mostly on pregnant women over 35 years of age, whose offspring have a higher than normal risk of Down syndrome. Many other tests have been developed to detect a number of simply inherited genetic disorders, but these disorders are rare enough that the tests are usually done only if a particular problem is suspected. Enzyme deficiencies can often be detected through incubation of cells recovered from amniotic fluid with the appropriate substrate and measurement of the product; this technique has been useful in the prenatal diagnosis of disorders such as Tay-Sachs disease. The tests for a number of other diseases, including sickle cell anemia, Huntington's disease, and cystic fibrosis are less direct, requiring the use of genetic engineering methods. Methods for detecting many more genetic diseases are now being actively sought by researchers. (See Making the Connection: Probing for Genetic Disease.)

Amniocentesis is also useful in detecting a condition known as *spina bifida,* in which the spinal cord does not close properly during development. This is a relatively common (about 1 in 300 births) nongenetic birth defect malformation. Such defects are associated with

MAKING THE CONNECTION

Probing for Genetic Disease

Genetic engineering techniques can be used in characterizing and detecting genetic disease. The earliest studies of this sort were carried out on sickle cell anemia. Carriers and affected individuals can usually be detected by a simple blood test. Because of the great difficulty in obtaining a reliable blood sample from an embryo, prenatal diagnosis is much more difficult. However, through the use of molecular genetic techniques it is possible to examine fetal DNA (obtained from amniocentesis or CVS) and test for the presence of sequences that code for sickle cell hemoglobin.

Hemoglobin (see Chapter 3) contains four polypeptide chains, two identical alpha chains and two identical beta chains. The beta chains of sickle cell hemoglobin differ from those of normal hemoglobin by only a single amino acid at position 6. The base sequence of the normal hemoglobin allele that codes for that amino acid and its two neighbors includes a recognition site for the restriction enzyme MstII. The base sequence of this recognition site is:

CCTGAGG

The sickle cell hemoglobin allele differs by only one base, altering the sequence to read:

CCTGTGG

This change is sufficient to prevent the restriction enzyme from cutting the DNA at that point. This single base change therefore results in a restriction fragment length polymorphism, which can be detected by blot hybridization methods. By synthesizing a radioactive probe complementary to the DNA sequence on one side of the restriction site, it is possible to differentiate that specific fragment of DNA from all of the other DNA fragments in the genome. When normal human DNA is cut with the restriction enzyme MstII, a single radioactive band can be detected on the blotting filter, and that band corresponds to a DNA molecule that is about 1.15 kilobases (1.15 kb, or 1150 bases) long. Because the restriction site is abolished in individuals who have the sickle cell allele, a longer DNA fragment, 1.35 kb in length, is detected. Heterozygous individuals have one copy of the normal allele and one copy of the sickle cell allele. When their DNA is analyzed, two bands can be detected by the probe, corresponding to the 1.15- and 1.35-kb fragments. It is thus possible to distinguish fetuses who are homozygous normal, homozygous recessive, and heterozygous carriers of the trait.

Few genetic diseases are as well understood as sickle cell anemia (see figure). As more human genes are identified and sequenced, an increasing number of abnormal alleles will be detectable in healthy carriers and in fetuses. Even when a gene has been cloned, however, problems can occur in developing screening methods. For example, when the cystic fibrosis gene was cloned, it was found that the mutant alleles in the population are not all identical. The first test to be developed could identify only the most common mutant allele, present in about 70 percent of carriers. It is now possible to identify carriers of some of the less common alleles. The ultimate goal is to develop a test that will detect 95 percent or more of the carriers. With more than 60 different mutant cystic fibrosis alleles detected so far, this is a formidable task.

For many genetic diseases it is not yet possible to detect the actual mutant allele. However, for some of these, including Huntington's disease, it has been possible to identify a particular DNA sequence in some families that is closely linked to the mutant allele and inherited along with it. Such a sequence, called a **DNA marker,** can be detected by blot hybridization methods.

Detecting the sickle cell allele with a genetic probe. (a) The normal ▶ hemoglobin gene has two sites recognized by the restriction enzyme MstII, which cuts the DNA to yield a 1.15-kb DNA fragment. The sickle cell allele has an altered base sequence, so one of these sites is not recognized by MstII. When that DNA is cut by the enzyme, a 1.35-kb fragment is produced. (b) The gene is detected by isolating total DNA from amniotic fluid cells and cutting it with MstII. Fragments from the total DNA are separated by gel electrophoresis (c). DNA from the gel is transferred (blotted) to nitrocellulose filters and hybridized with a radioactive probe (the cloned 1.15-kb MstII fragment derived from the normal hemoglobin gene). (d) DNA sequences complementary to the probe are detected by exposing the filter to x-ray film. Homozygous normal individuals show a single exposed band on the film at a position corresponding to a molecular weight of 1.15 kb. DNA from individuals homozygous for the sickle cell gene displays a single band at 1.35 kb. Heterozygotes have a single copy of each gene; their DNA produces two bands, at the 1.35- and 1.15-kb positions.

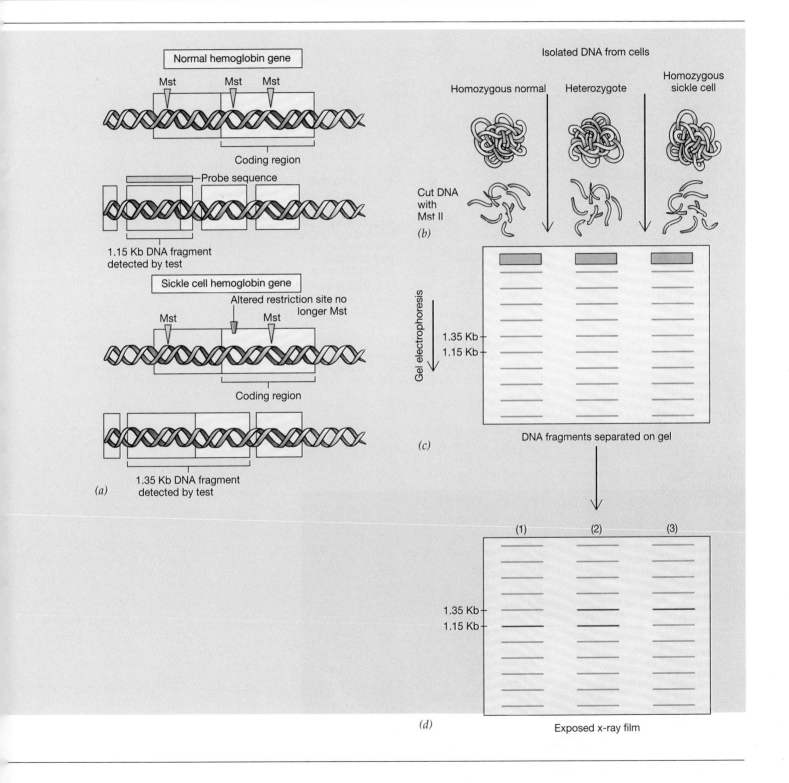

Normal hemoglobin gene

Mst Mst Mst

Coding region

Probe sequence

1.15 Kb DNA fragment detected by test

Sickle cell hemoglobin gene

Mst Altered restriction site no longer Mst Mst

Coding region

1.35 Kb DNA fragment detected by test

(a)

Isolated DNA from cells

Homozygous normal   Heterozygote   Homozygous sickle cell

Cut DNA with Mst II

(b)

Gel electrophoresis

1.35 Kb
1.15 Kb

DNA fragments separated on gel

(c)

(1)   (2)   (3)

1.35 Kb
1.15 Kb

(d)

Exposed x-ray film

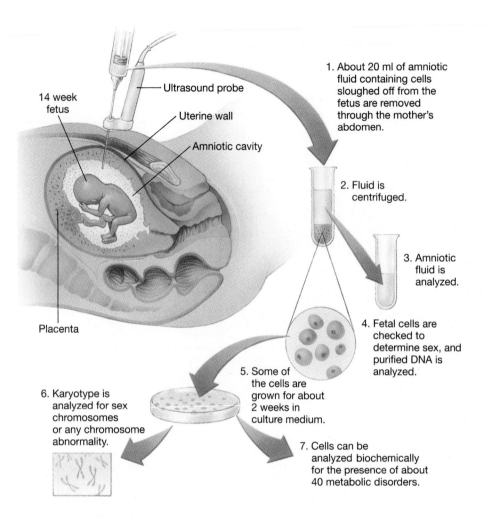

14 week fetus

Ultrasound probe

Uterine wall

Amniotic cavity

Placenta

1. About 20 ml of amniotic fluid containing cells sloughed off from the fetus are removed through the mother's abdomen.

2. Fluid is centrifuged.

3. Amniotic fluid is analyzed.

4. Fetal cells are checked to determine sex, and purified DNA is analyzed.

5. Some of the cells are grown for about 2 weeks in culture medium.

6. Karyotype is analyzed for sex chromosomes or any chromosome abnormality.

7. Cells can be analyzed biochemically for the presence of about 40 metabolic disorders.

Figure 15–9   The process of prenatal diagnosis of genetic disease by amniocentesis.

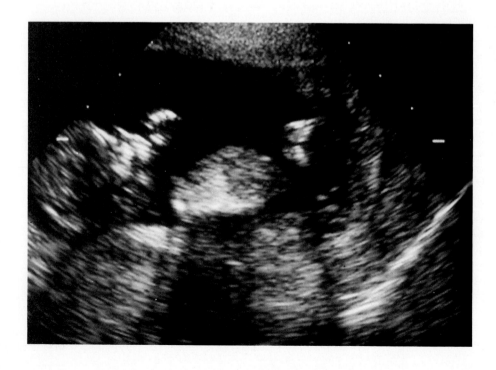

Figure 15–10   Ultrasound image of a 12½-week-old fetus. The head is to the left.   (Courtesy of F. R. Batzer, M.D., Philadelphia Fertility Institute)

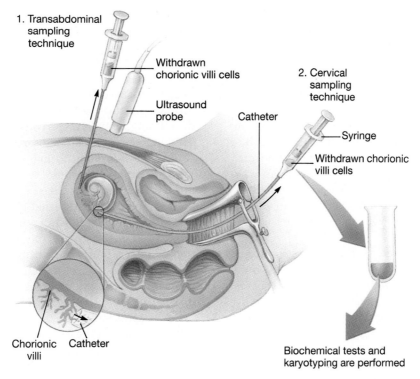

1. Transabdominal
sampling
technique

Withdrawn
chorionic villi cells

Ultrasound
probe

2. Cervical
sampling
technique

Catheter

Syringe

Withdrawn chorionic
villi cells

Chorionic   Catheter
villi

Biochemical tests and
karyotyping are performed

Figure 15–11   Prenatal diagnosis of genetic abnormalities by chorionic villus sampling (CVS). Samples may be obtained by inserting a needle through the uterine wall (1) or through the cervical opening (2).

abnormally high levels of a normally occurring protein, alpha-fetoprotein, in the amniotic fluid. Abnormally low levels are associated with Down syndrome. Alpha-fetoprotein levels can also be measured by testing the mother's blood, but the results are less reliable and any unusual findings should be confirmed by amniocentesis or other tests.

One problem with amniocentesis is that most of the conditions it detects are incurable and the results are generally not obtained until well into the second trimester, when abortion is both psychologically and medically difficult. Therefore, efforts have been made to develop tests that yield results earlier in the pregnancy. One such test, **chorionic villus sampling (CVS)** (Figure 15–11), involves removing and studying cells that will form the fetal contribution to the placenta (and hence should be genetically identical to the fetal cells). CVS may be associated with a slightly higher risk of infection or miscarriage than is amniocentesis, but it has an advantage in that results usually can be obtained within the first trimester.

Although both amniocentesis and CVS can diagnose certain genetic disorders with a high degree of accuracy, they are not foolproof and many disorders cannot be diagnosed; therefore, the lack of an abnormal finding is no guarantee of a normal pregnancy.

GENETIC COUNSELORS EDUCATE PEOPLE ABOUT GENETIC DISEASES AND GIVE THEM INFORMATION TO MAKE REPRODUCTIVE DECISIONS

Couples who have had an abnormal child or who have a relative affected with a hereditary disease and are concerned about the risk of abnormality in their children may seek genetic counseling. Genetics clinics are available in most metropolitan centers.

Advice can be given only in terms of the *probability* that any given offspring will have a particular condition. The geneticist needs complete family histories of both the man and the woman and may use tests for the detection of heterozygous carriers of certain conditions. When a disease involves only a single gene locus, probabilities can usually be easily calculated. For example, if one prospective parent is affected with a trait that is inherited as an autosomal dominant disorder, such as Huntington's disease, the probability that any given child will have the disease is 0.5.

The birth to phenotypically normal parents of a child affected with an autosomal recessive trait, such as albinism or PKU, establishes that both parents are heterozygous carriers; the probability that any subsequent child will be affected is therefore 0.25. (In this context, the term *carrier* is used specifically to refer to an individual who is heterozygous for a recessive allele that causes a genetic disease. Homozygous recessive persons are referred to as *affected* individuals; they are not called *carriers*, even though they also "carry" the disease.)

For a disease inherited through a recessive allele on the X chromosome, such as hemophilia A, the probability depends on the genotypes of the parents. A normal woman and an affected man will have daughters who are carriers and sons who are normal. The probability that a son of a carrier woman and a normal man will be affected is 0.5; the probability that their daughter will be a carrier is also 0.5.

It is now possible to detect carriers of several genetic diseases, so that counseling can be provided when both husband and wife are heterozygous. For diseases that involve an enzyme defect, carriers often show only half the level of enzyme activity characteristic of normal homozygotes. Voluntary screening programs have been set up by synagogues and other organizations to detect couples who are carriers of Tay-Sachs disease among Jews of Eastern European descent. Persons heterozygous for sickle cell anemia can be readily identified with a simple blood test. They have a mixture of normal and abnormal hemoglobins in their red blood cells, with about 45 percent of their total hemoglobin being abnormal. Such persons, said to have **sickle cell trait,** are not ill, and their blood cells do not usually undergo sickling, although they can be made to do so when the amount of oxygen is reduced. Carrier testing for some other diseases, such as cystic fibrosis and hemophilia A, is much more complicated and is usually done only if family history suggests that a person may be a carrier (see Making the Connection: Probing for Genetic Disease).

It is very important that carriers receive appropriate genetic counseling. A genetic counselor is trained not only to give information needed to make reproductive decisions but also to help individuals understand their situation and not feel stigmatized.

Inquiries are commonly made about mental retardation, epilepsy, deafness, congenital heart disease, and other conditions. It is possible that some environmental factor may have played a role in producing the abnormality in the affected child. Did the mother have an infectious disease during pregnancy (e.g., rubella)? Was she receiving some kind of drug therapy, or was she subjected to ionizing radiation? Had the father been exposed to any potentially hazardous agents? By dissecting the environmental contributions, the geneticist can make a better estimate of the probability of recurrence of the trait in subsequent offspring.

THE FEASIBILITY OF GENE REPLACEMENT THERAPY IS BEING EXPLORED

Because many difficulties are inherent in treating most serious genetic diseases, scientists have dreamed of developing actual cures. Today, genetic engineering is bringing these dreams closer to reality. Such therapy could take two main forms.

One approach would be to introduce copies of a normal gene into a fertilized egg, using modifications of the technology already used to produce transgenic animals (see Chapter 14). In some transgenic animals the introduced gene can be stably transmitted from generation to generation, constituting a true "genetic cure." However, this approach raises such complex ethical problems that it is not being actively pursued at this time.

A second strategy—to introduce the normal gene into only some of the cells of the body (somatic cell gene therapy)—is receiving increased attention today. The rationale is that, although a particular gene may be present in all cells, it is expressed only in some (see Chapter 16); expression of the normal allele in only the cells that require it may be sufficient to give a normal phenotype. Needless to say, this approach presents a number of technical obstacles. The solutions to these problems must be tailored to the nature of the gene itself, as well as to its product and the types of cells in which it must be expressed. First the gene must be cloned and the DNA introduced into the appropriate cells. This can be done in a variety of ways; one of the most successful being to use a virus as the vector. Ideally the virus should infect a high percentage of the cells and facilitate the integration of the introduced gene into a chromosome. Most importantly, the virus should do no harm, especially long term. This is a large order, and a great deal of attention is being paid to the development of viral strains with just such desirable characteristics.

The overall process can be illustrated by the gene therapy first approved for clinical trials on patients. A genetic disorder called severe combined immune deficiency (SCID) renders the immune system (see Chapter 43) essentially nonfunctional. Because an affected baby has no defenses, it will die unless isolated from possible sources of infection. Because the cells of the immune system are certain white blood cells that originate in the bone marrow, SCID has been treated successfully in some cases by transplanting healthy bone marrow cells from a normal donor.

About one-quarter of all SCID patients are known to lack a specific enzyme, adenosine deaminase (ADA);

it is the absence of ADA in the immune system cells that causes them to die. These patients have been treated successfully by providing them with ADA, linked to a molecule that makes the enzyme more stable in the bloodstream. This enzyme replacement therapy is not a cure, for the ADA treatments must continue throughout life.

Gene therapy for this condition was thought to be feasible because the normal ADA gene had been cloned and successfully introduced into cells through a viral vector. In the first clinical trials a virus was used to introduce the ADA gene into white blood cells of patients with SCID, and these were transfused back into the patients. The results have been encouraging but, because white blood cells have limited lifetimes, such treatments must be repeated.

Although many obstacles must be overcome, a number of other genetic diseases (including cystic fibrosis and muscular dystrophy) are now considered good candidates for the development of gene therapy. Scientists are currently addressing some of the unique problems presented by each disease. Not all types of cells can be removed from the body, infected with a virus, and then replaced. For example, successful gene therapy for cystic fibrosis will require introduction of normal genes directly into lung cells. A method that has shown some promise is to use as the vector a virus that causes the common cold (Figure 15–12). The field of gene therapy is expected to develop considerably in the future, although such treatments may not become routinely available for some years.

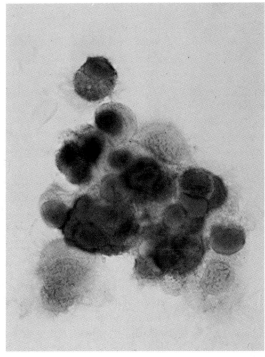

25 μm

Figure 15–12 An approach to gene therapy. The red stain indicates that these lung cells of the cotton rat are expressing the normal human allele of the gene responsible for cystic fibrosis. A modified virus that infects lung cells, but cannot reproduce in them, was used as the vector to introduce the human gene. (Courtesy of Melissa A. Rosenfeld and Ronald G. Crystal, National Heart, Lung and Blood Institute; National Institutes of Health. From *Cell* Vol. 68, no. 1, cover. Copyright by *Cell* Press)

A GREAT DEAL OF NATURAL VARIATION EXISTS IN THE HUMAN POPULATION

One does not need to be a geneticist to recognize that human beings are very diverse, and it is widely acknowledged that much human variation has a genetic basis. However, it is difficult to determine the genetic contribution to characteristics that are hard to assess, such as intelligence and behavior.

Studies on Blood Contribute to Our Understanding of Genetic Diversity in Humans

It is not difficult to understand why so much knowledge of human variation is based on studies of blood. Blood samples are relatively easy to obtain, and blood is a complex tissue consisting of a number of cell types and extracellular molecules that can be studied.

The ABO blood group alleles control the expression of certain red blood cell antigens

The human blood types O, A, B, and AB are inherited through multiple alleles representing a single locus. Allele I^A provides the code for the synthesis of a specific glycoprotein, antigen A, which is expressed on the surface of the red blood cells. (Immunity is discussed in Chapter 43; for now we define antigens simply as substances capable of stimulating an immune response.) Allele I^B leads to the production of a different (but related) glycoprotein, antigen B. The allele i^O does not code for an antigen, although it is allelic to I^A and I^B. Allele i^O is recessive to the other two. Neither allele I^A nor allele I^B is dominant to the other; they are both expressed phenotypically and are therefore **codominant.**

Table 15–2 ABO BLOOD TYPES*

Phenotype (blood type)	Genotypes	Antigen on RBC	Antibodies in Plasma	Frequency in U.S. Population (%)	
				Western European Descent	African Descent
A	$I^A I^A$, $I^A i^O$	A	Anti-B	45	29
B	$I^B I^B$, $I^B i^O$	B	Anti-A	8	17
AB	$I^A I^B$	A, B	None	4	4
O	$i^O i^O$	None	Anti-A, anti-B	43	50

*This table and the discussion of the ABO system have been simplified somewhat. Note that persons produce antibodies against the antigens *lacking* on their own red blood cells (RBCs).

Persons with the genotype $I^A I^A$ or $I^A i^O$ have **blood type A** (Table 15–2); those with genotype $I^B I^B$ or $I^B i^O$ have **blood type B;** and those with genotype $i^O i^O$ have **blood type O.** When both the I^A and I^B alleles are present, both antigen A and antigen B are produced in the red blood cells; persons with this $I^A I^B$ genotype have **blood type AB.**

Antibodies anti-A and anti-B are proteins that appear in the plasma (fluid component of blood) of persons lacking the corresponding antigens on their red blood cells. (Antibodies are proteins produced by the immune system that combine with specific antigens; hence, anti-A combines with antigen A.) Because of their specificity for the corresponding antigens, these antibodies are used in standard tests to determine blood type.

Determining the blood types of the persons involved was one of the traditional ways of settling cases of disputed parentage. However, blood type tests can never prove that a certain person *is* the parent of a particular child; they can determine only whether he or she *could* be. Could a man with blood type AB be the father of a child with blood type O? Could a woman with blood type O be the mother of a child with blood type AB? Could a type-B child with a type-A mother have a type-A father or a type-O father?[1]

More than a dozen other sets of blood types, including the Rh group (discussed in the next section), are inherited through other loci, independently of the ABO blood types. Determining some of these types in a given person may be useful in establishing relationships that could not be made with certainty by ABO blood typing alone.

Today more sophisticated types of genetic tests are used to determine parentage. These include **DNA fingerprinting** (see Chapter 14) and **tissue typing,** which is an examination of inherited antigens found on the surfaces of the cells of the body (see Chapter 43). Theoretically, only identical twins would be expected to have the same DNA fingerprint and the same tissue type. If properly performed, these tests have greater than 99% certainty and can come close to proving parentage.

The Rh alleles are involved in the expression of other red blood cell antigens

Named for the rhesus monkeys in whose blood it was first found, the Rh system consists of at least eight different kinds of Rh antigens, each referred to as an **Rh factor.** By far the most important of these factors is **antigen D.** About 85% of persons living in the United States who are of Western European descent are Rh-positive. This means that they have antigen D on the surfaces of their red blood cells (in addition to the antigens of the ABO system and other blood groups). The 15% or so of this population who are Rh-negative have no antigen D. Unlike the situation discussed for the ABO blood group, Rh-negative persons do not naturally produce antibodies against antigen D (anti-D). However, they produce anti-D antibodies if they are exposed to Rh-positive blood. The allele coding for antigen D is dominant to the allele for the absence of antigen D. Hence, Rh-negative persons are homozygous recessive, and Rh-positive persons are heterozygous or homozygous dominant.

Although several kinds of maternal-fetal blood type incompatibilities are known, **Rh incompatibility** is probably the most important (Figure 15–13). If a woman is Rh-negative and the father of the fetus she is carrying is Rh-positive, the fetus may also be Rh-positive, having inherited the D allele from the father. Ordi-

---

[1] The answer to all these questions is no.

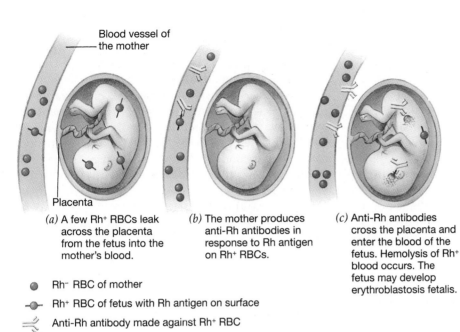

Blood vessel of the mother

Placenta

(a) A few Rh⁺ RBCs leak across the placenta from the fetus into the mother's blood.

(b) The mother produces anti-Rh antibodies in response to Rh antigen on Rh⁺ RBCs.

(c) Anti-Rh antibodies cross the placenta and enter the blood of the fetus. Hemolysis of Rh⁺ blood occurs. The fetus may develop erythroblastosis fetalis.

● Rh⁻ RBC of mother

Rh⁺ RBC of fetus with Rh antigen on surface

Anti-Rh antibody made against Rh⁺ RBC

Hemolysis of Rh⁺ RBC

Figure 15–13 Rh incompatibility can cause serious problems when an Rh-negative woman and an Rh-positive man produce Rh-positive offspring. (*a*) Some antigen D–bearing red blood cells leak across the placenta from the fetus into the mother's blood. (*b*) The mother produces anti-D antibodies in response to the D antigens on the fetal red blood cells. (*c*) In her next pregnancy, some of the mother's anti-D antibodies cross the placenta and enter the blood of her fetus, causing red blood cells to rupture (undergo hemolysis) and release hemoglobin into the circulation. As a result the fetus may develop erythroblastosis fetalis.

narily no mixing of maternal and fetal blood occurs; molecules are exchanged between these two circulatory systems across the placenta. However, late in pregnancy or during the birth process, a small quantity of blood from the fetus may pass through some defect in the placenta.

The fetus's red blood cells, which bear antigen D, sensitize the mother's white blood cells, inducing them to form antibodies to antigen D. When the woman becomes pregnant again, her sensitized white blood cells produce anti-D antibodies that can cross an intact placenta and enter the fetal blood. There they combine with the antigen D molecules on the surface of the fetal red blood cells, causing the cells to rupture. Breakdown products of the hemoglobin released into the circulation damage many organs, including the brain. In extreme cases of this disease, known as **erythroblastosis fetalis,** so many fetal red blood cells are destroyed that the fetus dies before birth.

When Rh-incompatibility problems are suspected, fetal blood can be exchanged by transfusion before birth, but this is a risky procedure. Rh-negative women are now treated just after childbirth (or at termination of pregnancy by miscarriage or abortion) with a preparation of anti-D antibodies known as RhoGAM. These antibodies apparently clear the Rh-positive fetal red blood cells from the mother's blood very quickly, minimizing the chance for her own white blood cells to be sensitized. The antibodies are also soon eliminated from her body. As a result, when she becomes pregnant again her blood does not contain the anti-D that could harm her baby.

Quantitative Traits Are Controlled by Polygenes

Many human characteristics are **quantitative traits**— that is, they represent some measurable quantity such as height. Such characteristics show continuous variation in the population because of the number of loci involved, which can range from a few to a great many (polygenic inheritance), and because of environmental factors, whose role is both significant and difficult to quantify. In addition to height and skin color (see Chapter 10), the inherited components of human intelligence are apparently under polygenic control. It is impossible to specify what these are, given our current inability even to define intelligence in a way that is universally accepted. However, many researchers think that polygenic factors determine the upper limit of mental ability in persons within the normal population; how close each individual comes to that limit depends on a variety of environmental factors, including nutrition and experience.

Many Common Physical Characteristics Are Inherited

We are often curious about the inheritance of certain physical characteristics. Some of these have relatively simple modes of inheritance. For example, dark hair color is due to heavy deposits of the pigment melanin in the hair shaft. There are probably multiple alleles of the locus governing the deposition of melanin, the "darker" alleles being somewhat, but incompletely, dominant to the "lighter" alleles. Red hair color is governed by another unlinked locus with at least two incompletely dominant alleles, one coding for reddish pigment, the other for lack of such pigment. The appearance of red hair is determined by the presence of one or two "red" alleles, but the expression of these alleles can be partially or completely blocked by heavy melanin deposits.

Eye color is determined by the pattern of melanin distribution in the iris. Blue pigment does not exist, only brown or yellowish melanin. If the melanin is deposited in such a way that much of the light is reflected back from the eye, the iris appears blue. Although inheritance of eye color is not simple, the inheritance patterns seen in most families can be explained if we assume that one locus is involved and that the alleles that govern the darker colors are dominant to the alleles that govern the lighter colors (e.g., blue, gray, hazel). It is not uncommon for two dark-eyed parents to have a light-eyed child; it is relatively rare for two light-eyed parents to have a dark-eyed child, but this can occur.

A number of other human characteristics show relatively simple inheritance patterns. For example, the allele for dimples is generally dominant to the allele for no dimples, the allele for freckling is usually dominant to that for no freckles, and the allele for curly hair is usually dominant to that for straight hair.

THE HUMAN GENOME INITIATIVE IS A SYSTEMATIC STUDY OF ALL HUMAN GENES

Along with advances in technology to determine the base sequences of DNA came the realization that it is possible to study the human genome in great depth. Some scientists began to envision a coordinated effort to determine the total informational content of the human genome. They were able to obtain U.S. government funding in the late 1980s to initiate the project, which will take place over a 15-year period. In its most direct sense the information content is the sequence of 3 billion pairs of bases in a human haploid genome. However, only a tiny fraction of human DNA is known to code for protein or RNA; the rest (95 percent or more) either is nonfunctional or has some function that has not yet been identified.

Therefore, the initial emphasis of the project has moved away from sequencing to a more broad-based, multifaceted strategy that will involve scientists from many disciplines. This approach has concentrated on various types of mapping studies that will allow us to understand the physical and functional relationships among genes and groups of genes as revealed by their order on the chromosomes. Comparative mapping studies are being carried out simultaneously in a number of other organisms, especially the laboratory mouse, which has long been the favorite model organism for the study of mammalian genetics. Comparisons of the DNA sequences and the chromosomal organization of related genes and clusters of genes from different organisms are powerful tools for identifying the elements essential for their functions. Analyses of base sequences are also being conducted during this stage of the project, but these are concentrated on currently identifiable genes, such as those implicated in genetic diseases. Automation is making the task of sequencing less laborious, and powerful computer programs manage and analyze the data.

The project has been controversial for many reasons. Some scientists have argued that the conventional approach of first identifying an important gene, then cloning and studying it, is scientifically more interesting and more cost-effective over the long run. Supporters of the project argue that many important genes that might be very difficult to identify will be uncovered in the course of the investigation. Even apparently nonfunctional DNA (sometimes called "junk DNA") may turn out to be important.

Our knowledge of human genetics clearly will be expanding at a great rate over the coming years. The information gained from the comparative mapping studies of other organisms will add greatly to our understanding of evolutionary relationships. Many genes known to be responsible for genetic diseases are being studied, and many more already being uncovered appear to be associated with predispositions to diseases such as heart disease and cancer.

BOTH HUMAN GENETICS AND OUR BELIEFS ABOUT GENETICS HAVE AN IMPACT ON SOCIETY

Many people harbor common misconceptions about genetic diseases and their effect on society. There is a widespread tendency to think of certain individuals or groups as "genetically unfit" and responsible for many of society's ills. Actually abnormal alleles are present in all individuals and all groups; no one is exempt.

As we have seen, abnormal alleles that can lead to certain genetic diseases may be especially common in a particular race or ethnic group. However, this does not mean that the group is especially susceptible to genetic diseases in general; abnormal alleles are found in all populations.

It is not always easy to explain why a certain allele is present at a particularly high frequency in a certain group. To find such answers one must have a great deal of information from many sources. Much must be known about the mutant allele and its effects in both homozygous and heterozygous individuals. Knowledge of the social structure, demographics, and history of a population often provides important clues.

"Heterozygote advantage" in the form of resistance to malaria is the widely accepted explanation for the high frequency of the sickle cell allele among persons of African descent (see Chapter 10). Various hypotheses have been advanced to explain the high frequencies of other genetic diseases in certain populations or ethnic groups.

Sometimes history provides possible explanations. For example, in the Middle Ages Jews in Eastern Europe were subjected to widespread persecution. People were forced into ghettos and there was a decrease in the size of the population (a phenomenon known to population geneticists as a **population bottleneck**—see Chapter 18). A coincidental high frequency of the Tay-Sachs allele in the small surviving population might explain the high frequency (1/28) of this allele in the Ashkenazi Jewish population today. However, molecular analysis has revealed that there are at least two mutant alleles for Tay-Sachs disease in that population. The simplest hypothesis is that these arose independently and were maintained because they conferred some kind of heterozygote advantage. People living in ghettos were vulnerable to a variety of infectious diseases, such as tuberculosis; resistance to one of these diseases could have been the basis of a heterozygote advantage.

Molecular studies have shown that a number of mutant alleles can be responsible for cystic fibrosis, with one main form (the most severe) predominating in northern Europe and another main form, which is somewhat less serious, more prevalent in southern Europe. Presumably these mutant alleles are all independent mutations, maintained by selection. Again, the selective force maintaining heterozygosity for cystic fibrosis may well be an infectious disease; resistance to cholera has been suggested as one possibility.

It is often argued that medical treatment of persons affected with genetic diseases, especially those who are able to reproduce, greatly increases the frequency of abnormal alleles in the population. This is true for autosomal dominant and X-linked diseases, but most genetic diseases that are simply inherited show an auto-

somal recessive inheritance pattern. Only homozygous persons actually have the disease; heterozygous carriers, who are far greater in number, are phenotypically normal. For example, if 1 in 20 persons in the United States is heterozygous for cystic fibrosis, the chance that a husband and wife will both be heterozygous is $(1/20) \times (1/20) = 1/400$. On average, 1/4 of the children of such a couple would have cystic fibrosis, so the frequency of affected individuals in the population would be about $(1/400) \times (1/4) = 1/1600$. Because their numbers are usually very small compared with heterozygotes, reproduction by homozygotes contributes very little to overall frequencies of abnormal alleles.

Each of us is probably heterozygous for several (3 to 15) very harmful alleles, any of which could cause debilitating illness or death in the homozygous state. Why aren't genetic diseases more common? Each of us has many thousands of essential genes, any of which can be mutated. It is very unlikely that the abnormal alleles carried by one person are also carried by that person's mate. Of course, this possibility is more likely if the harmful allele is a relatively common one, such as the allele responsible for cystic fibrosis.

Relatives are more likely than nonrelatives to carry the same harmful alleles, having inherited them from a common ancestor. In fact, a greater than normal frequency of a particular genetic disease among offspring of **consanguineous matings** (matings of close relatives) is often the first clue that the mode of inheritance is autosomal recessive. The offspring of consanguineous matings have a small but significantly increased risk of genetic disease. In fact they can account for a disproportionately high percentage of those individuals in the population with autosomal recessive disorders. Because of this perceived social cost, first-cousin marriages are prohibited in most states in the United States. However, consanguineous marriages are still relatively common in many developing countries, where other factors may outweigh the genetic costs.

As scientists learn more about human genetics, more and more alleles associated with human disease are being identified. It is important that we prepare ourselves to use this knowledge well, not to stigmatize or discriminate, but to improve human health.

SUMMARY

I. Geneticists investigating human inheritance cannot make specific crosses of pure genetic strains; instead, they must rely on studies of populations, analyses of family pedigrees, and molecular studies.

II. Studies of the karyotype (the number and kinds of chromosomes present in the nucleus) permit detection of individuals with various chromosome abnormalities.

A. Such studies can detect trisomy, in which one has an extra chromosome, and monosomy, in which one lacks one member of a pair of chromosomes.

B. The most common form of Down syndrome (trisomy 21) and Turner syndrome (XO) are examples of trisomy and monosomy, respectively.

III. Abnormal alleles of a number of loci are responsible for many inherited diseases, such as PKU, sickle cell anemia, and cystic fibrosis. Most human genetic diseases that show a simple inheritance pattern are transmitted as autosomal recessive traits.

IV. Some genetic diseases and chromosome abnormalities can be diagnosed long before birth by amniocentesis or chorionic villus sampling.

V. Genetic counselors can advise prospective parents who may have a family history of genetic disease regarding the probabilities of their giving birth to affected offspring. It is possible to detect the presence of a number of harmful alleles.

VI. Variation in the human population is exemplified by human blood types, among which are the ABO blood group and the Rh system. The Rh-positive offspring of an Rh-negative mother may develop a very serious disease known as *erythroblastosis fetalis*.

VII. The effect of genetics on society is complex.

A. The fact that a particular abnormal allele is especially common in a certain racial or ethnic group does not mean that that group has a higher frequency of abnormal alleles in general.

B. Some alleles that cause a genetic disease when they are homozygous may be advantageous in heterozygous individuals, at least in a particular environment. For example, the allele responsible for sickle cell anemia in homozygous individuals appears to confer resistance to malaria on heterozygotes.

C. Because most abnormal alleles are recessive, they are manifested phenotypically only in homozygotes, who constitute a tiny fraction of the individuals with the allele. Virtually every individual in the population is a heterozygous carrier of several abnormal alleles.

POST-TEST

1. Standard stocks of genetically identical individuals are called _____ strains.
2. The array of chromosomes present in a given cell is called the _____.
3. An abnormality that is present and evident at birth is called a _____ defect.
4. An abnormality in which there is one more or one fewer than the normal number of chromosomes is called a(n) _____.
5. A person who has an extra chromosome (three of one kind) is said to be _____.
6. A person who is missing a chromosome, having only one member of a pair, is termed _____.
7. The failure of chromosomes to separate normally during cell division is called _____.
8. The transfer of a part of one chromosome to a nonhomologous chromosome is called a _____.
9. Individuals with trisomy 21, or _____ syndrome, are mentally and physically retarded and have abnormalities of the face, tongue, and eyelids.
10. An XXY individual has the disorder known as _____ syndrome; an XO individual has _____ syndrome.
11. An inherited disorder due to a defective or absent enzyme is called an inborn error of _____.
12. The sickle cell allele codes for an altered _____ molecule, which is less soluble than usual and is more likely than normal to crystallize and deform the shape of the red blood cell.
13. In a person with _____ _____, the mucus is abnormally viscous and tends to plug the ducts of the pancreas and liver and to accumulate in the lungs.
14. In the process of _____, a sample of amniotic fluid is obtained by insertion of a needle through the walls of the abdomen and uterus and into the uterine cavity.
15. _____ _____ sampling involves removal and study of cells that will make up the fetal contribution to the placenta.
16. Couples who have some reason to be concerned about the possibility of genetic abnormalities in their offspring may seek _____ _____.

REVIEW QUESTIONS

1. What means have been devised for overcoming some of the difficulties in studying human inheritance?
2. What is meant by *nondisjunction*? What are some human abnormalities that appear to be the result of nondisjunction?
3. Are all birth defects hereditary?
4. What are the relative advantages and disadvantages of amniocentesis and chorionic villus sampling?
5. What are some of the ways that carriers of certain genetic diseases can be identified?
6. What is meant by *inborn errors of metabolism*? Give an example.
7. Mrs. Doe and Mrs. Roe had babies at the same hospital and at the same time. Mrs. Doe took home a girl and named her Nancy. Mrs. Roe took home a boy and named him Richard.

However, she was sure that she had given birth to a girl and brought suit against the hospital. Blood tests showed that Mr. Roe was blood type O, Mrs. Roe was type AB, and Mr. and Mrs. Doe were both type B. Nancy was type A, and Richard was type O. Had an exchange occurred?

8. Imagine that you are a genetic counselor. What advice or suggestions might you give in the following situations?

a. A couple has come for advice because the woman had a sister who died of Tay-Sachs disease.

b. A pregnant woman has learned that as a newborn she suffered a mild case of erythroblastosis fetalis; she is concerned that she might have a similarly affected child.

c. A young man and woman who are not related are engaged to be married. However, they have learned that the man's parents are first cousins. They are worried that they might have an increased risk of genetic defects in their own children.

d. A young woman's paternal uncle (her father's brother) has hemophilia A. Her father is free of the disease and there has never been a case of hemophilia A in her moth-er's family. Should she be concerned about the possibility of hemophilia A in her own children?

e. A 20-year-old man is seeking counseling because his father has just been diagnosed as having Huntington's disease.

RECOMMENDED READINGS

Patterson, D. The causes of Down syndrome. *Scientific American* 257:52–61, August 1987. A discussion of efforts to identify sites on chromosome 21 responsible for the abnormalities associated with Down syndrome.

Sutton, E. P. *Human Genetics*, 4th ed. Harcourt, Brace, Jovanovich, San Diego, 1988. A well-written, comprehensive text on human genetics.

Verma, Inder M. Gene therapy. *Scientific American* 263:68–84, November 1990. A consideration of future prospects for gene therapy and some of the problems to be solved.

Watson, J. D., M. Gilman, J. Witkowski, and M. Zoller. *Recombinant DNA*, 2nd ed. W. H. Freeman, New York, 1992. Chapters 26–30 deal with the uses of recombinant DNA technology in human genetics, including diagnosis, prospects for gene therapy, and the Human Genome Initiative.

CHAPTER 16

❑

Genes and Development

The study of **development,** the process by which cells specialize and organize into a complex organism, encompasses some of the most fascinating and difficult problems in biology today. During the many cell divisions required for a single cell to develop into a multicellular organism, groups of cells become gradually committed to specific patterns of gene activity through a process called **determination.**

A differentiated cell can be recognized by its characteristic appearance and activities. The final step leading to cell specialization is **cellular differentiation.**

Morphogenesis, the development of form, is an even more intriguing piece of the developmental puzzle. It involves a multistep process known as **pattern formation,** by which cells in specific locations become progressively organized into recognizable structures.

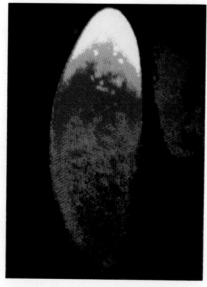

Computer-enhanced photograph of a *Drosophila* egg.   (W. Driever, from W. Driever, C. Nüsslein-Volhard, *Cell* 54, 1988)

Until recently, little was known about how certain genes interact with various signals from other genes and the environment to control development. These networks are too complex to unravel using only traditional methods.

Today scientists interested in development study a variety of carefully chosen mutant organisms with altered developmental patterns. They use the tools of genetic engineering combined with more conventional descriptive and experimental approaches to derive fresh insights into the role of genetic information in the control of development. They are also finding new ways to unravel evolutionary relationships through the study of developmentally important genetic mechanisms that appear to be deeply rooted in the evolutionary history of multicellular organisms.

After you have studied this chapter you should be able to

1. Distinguish between cellular determination and cellular differentiation.
2. Relate the process of pattern formation to morphogenesis.
3. Describe the kinds of experiments that indicate that at least some differentiated plant cells and animal nuclei are totipotent. Discuss how these findings support the idea of nuclear equivalence.
4. Identify the attributes of an organism that would make it especially useful in studies on the genetic control of development.
5. Indicate the features of development and genetics of *Drosophila, Caenorhabditis,* and the mouse (*Mus*) that have made these organisms so valuable to researchers.

6. Distinguish between maternal effect genes, zygotic genes, and homeotic genes in *Drosophila.*
7. Explain the relationship between transcription factors and genes that control development. Provide some examples of genes that are known to function as genetic switches in development.
8. Define the phenomena of induction and programmed cell death and give examples in which they play roles in development.
9. Discuss the value of transgenic organisms in research on the genetic control of development.
10. Describe some examples of homeotic-like transformations in plants.
11. Point out some of the known exceptions to the general phenomenon of nuclear equivalence.

CELLULAR DIFFERENTIATION USUALLY DOES NOT INVOLVE CHANGES IN THE DNA

The human body contains more than 200 recognizably different types of cells (Figure 16–1). Combinations of those cells are organized into remarkably diverse and complex structures such as the eye, the hand, and the brain, each one capable of carrying out many sophisticated activities. Most remarkable of all, however, is the fact that all of the structures of the body and the different cells within them are descended from a single fertilized egg.

All multicellular plants and animals undergo complex patterns of development. The root cells of plants, for example, have structures and functions very different from those of the various types of cells located in plant leaves. Remarkable diversity can also be found at the molecular level; most strikingly, each type of plant or animal cell makes a highly specific set of proteins (Figure 16–2). In some cases, such as the protein hemoglobin in red blood cells, one cell-specific protein may make up more than 90% of the total mass of protein in the cell. Other cells may have a complement of cell-specific proteins that are present in small amounts but still play an essential role. However, because certain proteins are required in every type of cell (all cells, for example, require certain enzymes for glycolysis), cell-specific proteins usually make up only a fraction of the total number of different kinds of proteins.

One explanation for the observation that each type of differentiated cell makes a unique set of proteins might be that during development each group of cells loses the genes it does not need and retains only those genes that are required. With just a few exceptions, however, this does not seem to be true. According to

the concept of **nuclear equivalence,** the nuclei of essentially all differentiated adult cells of an individual are genetically (but not necessarily metabolically) identical to each other and to the nucleus of the fertilized egg cell from which they descended. This means that virtually all the **somatic**[1] cells in an adult have the same genes; they are simply expressed in different tissues in different ways.

The evidence for the idea of nuclear equivalence comes from cases in which differentiated cells or their nuclei have been found to be capable of supporting normal development. Such cells or nuclei are said to be **totipotent.**

A Totipotent Nucleus Contains All the Information Required To Direct Normal Development

In plants it is possible to demonstrate that at least some differentiated cells can be induced to become the equivalent of embryonic cells (Figure 16–3). **Tissue culture** techniques are used to isolate cells from certain plants and allow them to grow in a nutrient medium. In some of the first experiments, single root cells of the carrot were induced to divide in a liquid nutrient medium and to form groups of cells called "embryoid" (embryo-like) bodies. These clumps of dividing cells could then be transferred to an agar medium, which provides nutri-

---

[1] Somatic cells are cells of the body and are distinguished from **germ-line** cells, which ultimately give rise to a new generation. The distinction between somatic cells and germ-line cells is not clear-cut in plants. In animals, however, germ-line cells, whose descendants ultimately undergo meiosis and differentiate as gametes, are generally set aside early in development.

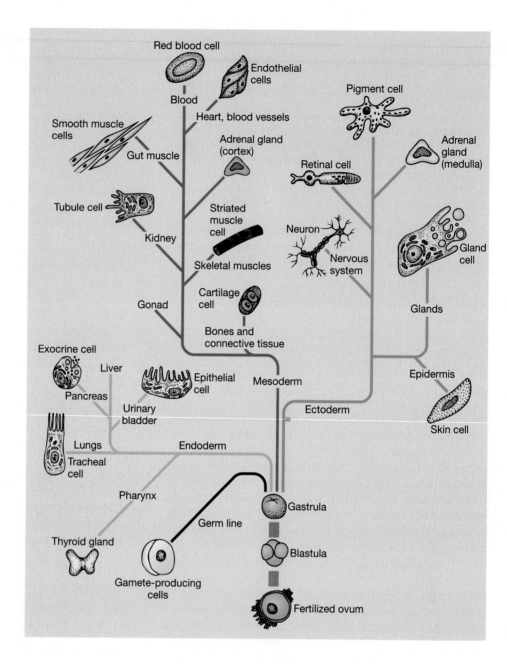

Figure 16–1 Lineages of differentiated cells in animals. Repeated divisions of the fertilized egg result in the formation of tissues (see Chapters 37 and 49 for a discussion of how these are formed) from which groups of specialized cells are produced. Germ-line cells (cells that produce the gametes) are set aside early in development. Somatic cells progress along the developmental pathways, undergoing a series of developmental commitments that progressively determine the fates of different lines of cells.

ents plus a solid supporting structure for the developing plant cells. Upon transfer to the agar, some of the embryoid cells gave rise to roots, stems, and leaves. The resulting "plantlets" could then be transplanted to soil, where they ultimately developed into adult plants capable of producing flowers and viable seeds. The methods of plant tissue culture are now extensively used to produce genetically engineered plants, for they allow the regeneration of whole plants from cells that have incorporated recombinant DNA molecules (see Chapter 31).

Similar experiments have been attempted with animal cells, but so far it has not been possible to induce a fully differentiated somatic cell to behave like a zygote.

Instead, it has been possible to test whether steps in the process of determination are reversible by transplanting the *nucleus* of a cell in a relatively late stage of development into an egg cell whose own nucleus has been destroyed (Figure 16–4). In those experiments, nuclei from amphibian cells at different stages of development were transplanted into egg cells. Some of the transplants proceeded normally through a number of developmental stages, and a few even developed into normal tadpoles. As a rule, the nuclei transplanted from cells at earlier stages were most likely to support development to the tadpole stage. As the fate of the cells became more and more determined, the probability that a transplanted nucleus could control normal development

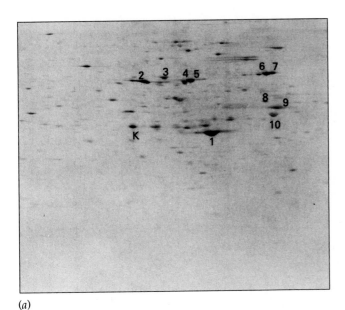

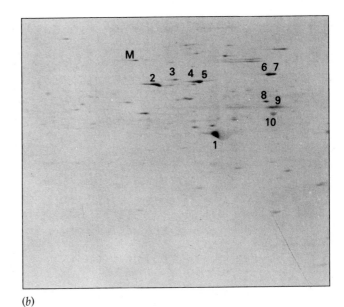

(a)

(b)

Figure 16–2 Proteins from different tissues of the mouse. The spots in the photographs are proteins from (a) kidney, (b) muscle, and (c) liver cells. The proteins were separated by two-dimensional gel electrophoresis, a method that separates the proteins in the horizontal direction by their electric charge followed by a second separation in the vertical direction by molecular weight. Several hundred proteins can be distinguished in each panel. The spots that are labeled with numbers are present in all tissues, but notice that many of them are present in different amounts from one tissue to another. The proteins that are labeled with letters are found only in that specific tissue. (Patrick O'Farrell, from Darnell, Lodish, and Bathmore, *Molecular Cell Biology*, Fig. 12–1, Scientific American Books)

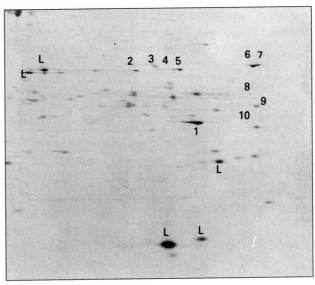

(c)

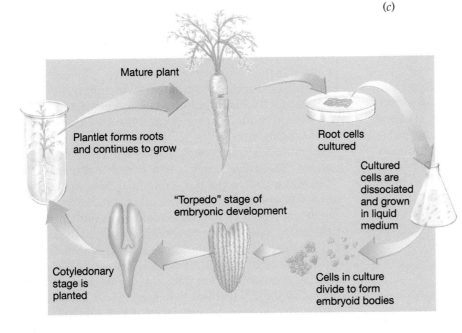

Figure 16–3 Development of a carrot plant from differentiated somatic cells. Discs of phloem cells, which are specialized for nutrient transport, were isolated from carrot root tissues. When the cells were cultured in a liquid nutrient medium, clumps of dedifferentiated cells developed from individual phloem cells. These clumps (embryoids) closely resembled plant embryos in their early stages of development and then progressed to form embryonic shoots and roots. Transferring the embryonic tissue to a solid nutrient medium stimulated the tissues to form plantlets, which could then be grown into mature plants.

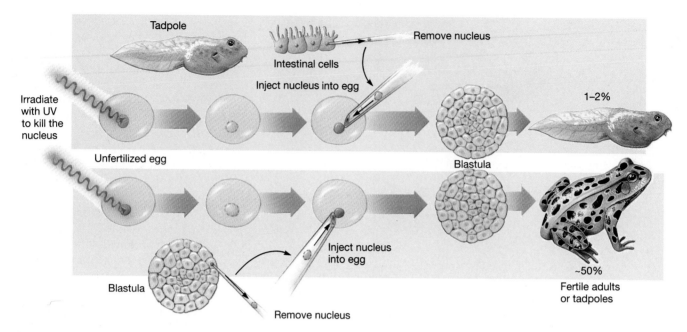

Figure 16–4 Nuclear transplantation experiments. The experiments of Briggs and King and later J. Gurdon showed that a nucleus from a differentiated amphibian cell could program development. This was done by injecting it into an egg whose own nucleus had been destroyed by ultraviolet radiation. The probability of success of the procedure depended on the developmental stage of the transplanted nucleus. As shown in the lower panel, if a nucleus was taken from a cell at the blastula stage of development (when cell division has produced about 1000 cells formed in the shape of a ball), there was a high probability that it would program normal development, resulting in a fertile adult. However, as seen in the upper panel, most trials using nuclei from tadpole intestinal cells (a much later developmental stage) resulted in no growth, probably as a result of damage to the egg or the nucleus by the procedure. In a small number of trials, however, normal development proceeded until the tadpole stage, indicating that the genes necessary to program development to that point were still present.

diminished rapidly. In a few cases, nuclei isolated from the specialized intestinal cells of a tadpole were able to direct development to another tadpole stage. This occurred infrequently, but in such experiments, success counts more than failure, and one can safely conclude that at least some nuclei of differentiated cells are in fact totipotent and have not lost any genetic material.

These results lead to several important interpretations. When specialized plant cells and animal nuclei are totipotent, it is clear that genes have not been lost as a consequence of development. That is, genes that were apparently inactive were, in fact, capable of being reactivated when the cells or nuclei were placed in a new environment. Second, even if no genetic material is lost during development, the nuclei of cells undergo metabolic changes that make it progressively more difficult to remain in a totipotent state. This is especially true of animal nuclei, although various kinds of animals differ considerably in this regard.

Most Differences among Cells Are Due to Differential Gene Expression

Because genes do not appear to be lost regularly during development, the differences in the molecular composition of cells must occur by *regulating the activities of different genes*. This process of developmental gene regulation is often referred to as **differential gene expression.** As discussed in Chapter 13, the expression of eukaryotic genes can be regulated in many different ways and at many levels. For example, a particular enzyme may be produced in an inactive form and then activated at a later time. However, much of the regulation that is important in development occurs at the transcriptional level. The transcription of certain sets of genes is repressed, whereas others are activated. Even expression of genes that are constitutive and active in all cells can be regulated during development so that the *quantity* of each product varies from one tissue type to another.

We can think of differentiation as a series of pathways leading from a single cell to cells in each of the different specialized tissues, arranged in an appropriate pattern. There are times when a cell makes genetic "commitments" to the developmental path its descendants will follow. These commitments gradually *restrict* the development of the descendants to a limited set of final tissue types. This progressive fixation of the fate of a cell's descendants is the process of *determination*.

As the development of a cell is determined along a particular differentiation pathway, those changes may not be obvious. Nevertheless, when a particular stage of determination is complete, the changes in the cell usually become self-perpetuating and are not easily reversed. *Differentiation* is usually the last stage in the developmental process. At this stage, a precursor cell becomes structurally and functionally recognizable as a bone cell, for example, and its pattern of gene activity is different from that in a nerve cell.

MOLECULAR GENETICS IS REVOLUTIONIZING THE STUDY OF DEVELOPMENT

The study of development has been an important area of research for many years, and considerable effort has been expended on studies of development in invertebrate and vertebrate animals. By identifying patterns of tissue development in different animals, researchers have been able to identify similarities, as well as differences, in the basic plan of development from a fertilized egg to an adult in organisms ranging from the sea urchin to mammals (see Chapter 49). In addition to descriptive studies, a number of classic experiments have established important evidence concerning how groups of cells are determined along particular developmental pathways. Today researchers are combining a wide variety of methodologies to identify genes that actually control development in both plants and animals and to determine how those genes work.

Certain Organisms Are Particularly Well Suited for Studies on the Genetic Control of Development

In studies of the genetic control of development, the choice of an organism to use as an experimental system has become increasingly important. One of the most powerful approaches involves the isolation of mutants with arrested or abnormal development at a particular stage. Not all organisms have useful characteristics that allow developmental mutants to be isolated and maintained for future study. The fruit fly, *Drosophila melanogaster,* has such thoroughly understood genetics that it has become one of the most important systems for such studies. Other organisms such as the nematode worm, *Caenorhabditis elegans,* and the laboratory mouse, *Mus musculus,* as well as various plants and some simple eukaryotes, have also become important in the study of developmental genetics. Each of these organisms has attributes that make it particularly useful for examining certain aspects of development.

Drosophila melanogaster *provides researchers with a wealth of developmental mutants*

Undoubtedly the most extensive (and spectacular) examples of genes that control development have been identified in the fruit fly, *Drosophila melanogaster.* One of the main advantages of using *Drosophila* as a research organism is the abundance of mutants (including developmental mutants) available for study and the relative ease with which a new mutation can be directly mapped on the chromosomes. The genetic analysis is greatly facilitated by special chromosomes found in certain tissues with large, metabolically active cells, including the salivary glands of the larvae. These **polytene** ("many-stranded") chromosomes (Figure 16–5) are unusual interphase chromosomes formed when the DNA replicates many times but without mitosis and cytokinesis. A typical polytene chromosome may consist of more than 1000 DNA double helices (along with associated histones and other proteins) aligned side by side. Polytene chromosomes are therefore quite large and show a pattern of bands that is very useful in assigning a particular gene to a particular location on the chromosome. When a gene is active, the chromosome band in which it resides becomes decondensed, forming a **puff,** which is a site of intense RNA synthesis. This evidence of gene activity is similar to that observed in lampbrush chromosomes of certain oocytes (see Chapter 9).

Once the chromosomal position of the mutant gene is determined, the gene can be cloned, using a technique called **chromosome walking,** from a nearby gene that has been previously cloned. Studies of *Drosophila* are also facilitated by the fact that foreign DNA can be injected into eggs and become incorporated into the DNA of the fly in a process called **transformation** (by analogy with transformation in prokaryotes).

The Drosophila **Life Cycle Includes Egg, Larval, Pupal, and Adult Stages**

The life cycle of *Drosophila* consists of several distinct stages (Figure 16–6). After the egg is fertilized, a period of embryogenesis occurs during which the zygote develops into a sexually immature form known as a **larva** (pl. *larvae*). After hatching from the egg, each larva undergoes several molts (times at which the external covering or cuticle is shed). Each molt allows an increase in size until the larva is ready to pupate. **Pupation** involves a molt and the hardening of the new external cuticle, so that the pupa is completely encased. The insect then undergoes a complete metamorphosis (change in form). During that time, most of the larval tissues degenerate and other tissues differentiate to form the body parts of the sexually mature adult fly.

Although the larvae are wormlike in appearance and look nothing like the adult flies, precursor cells of many of the adult structures are organized very early in embryogenesis of the developing larvae as relatively undifferentiated paired structures called **imaginal discs.** This term comes from **imago,** the name given to

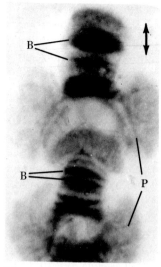

(a)

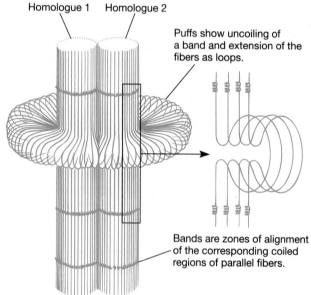

Homologue 1   Homologue 2

Puffs show uncoiling of a band and extension of the fibers as loops.

Bands are zones of alignment of the corresponding coiled regions of parallel fibers.

Homologues are closely paired and each chromosome is of multiple, parallel replicate fibers.

(b)

Figure 16–5   Polytene chromosomes of *Drosophila*. (*a*) A region of a polytene chromosome showing the pattern of stained bands of condensed chromatin (B) and decondensed puffed bands (P), which are the sites of intense gene activity. The chromosome banding patterns in a particular tissue are constant and can be associated with the locations of mutant genes by genetic mapping and DNA hybridization methods. (*b*) In contrast to the chromosomes of most somatic cells, homologous polytene chromosomes are paired and each consists of more than 1000 parallel longitudinal DNA fibers.   (*a*, Courtesy of U. Clever)

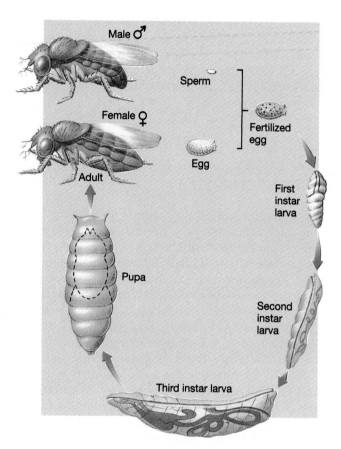

Figure 16–6   Developmental stages of *Drosophila* from the egg to the adult fly.

the adult form of the insect. Each imaginal disc occupies a definite position in the larva and will form a specific structure in the adult body, such as a wing or a leg (Figure 16–7). The discs are formed by the time embryogenesis is complete and the larva is ready to begin feeding.

In some respects the larva can be thought of as a complex developmental stage that is simply used to feed and nurture the precursor cells for the adult fly (which is the only form that can reproduce).

The organization of the precursors of the adult structures, including the imaginal discs, is under complex genetic control. More than 50 different genes have been identified so far that specify the formation of the discs, their positions within the larva, and their ultimate functions within the adult fly. Those genes have been identified through mutations that either prevent certain discs from forming or alter their structure or ultimate fate.

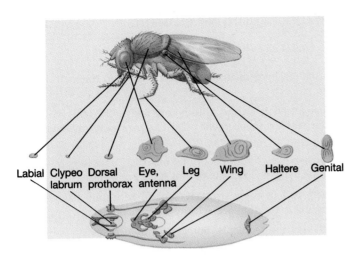

Labial Clypeo Dorsal Eye, Leg Wing Haltere Genital
labrum prothorax antenna

Figure 16–7   A diagram of the imaginal discs in the *Drosophila* larva illustrating the structures they give rise to in the adult fly.

Many *Drosophila* Developmental Mutants Affect the Body Plan

Many types of developmental mutants of *Drosophila* have been identified. Their effects on development in various combinations have been examined and studied extensively at the molecular level. In our discussion we pay particular attention to those that affect the segmented body plan of the organism, both in the larva and in the adult.

Maternal Effect Segmentation Genes Organize the Egg Cytoplasm.

The earliest stages of *Drosophila* development are controlled by maternal genes that act to organize the structure of the egg cell. As the egg develops in the ovary of the female, stores of messenger RNA (mRNA), along with yolk proteins and other cytoplasmic molecules, are passed into it from the surrounding maternal cells. Therefore, all these mRNA molecules are transcribed exclusively from genes found in the mother. The genes that code for these mRNA molecules are referred to as **maternal effect** genes. Analysis of mutants defective in these genes has revealed that many are involved in establishing the polarity of the embryo, by designating which parts of the egg are dorsal or ventral and which are anterior or posterior (see Focus on Body Plan and Symmetry in Chapter 28).

For example, maternal effect mutations are known that produce an embryo with two heads or two posterior ends owing to the absence of specific signals in the egg. The mRNA transcripts from some of the maternal effect genes can be identified by their ability to hybridize with radioactive DNA probes from the cloned genes. Alternatively, their protein products can be identified by antibodies that specifically bind to them. In some cases, the mRNA or its protein product can be seen to form a concentration gradient in the embryo (Figure 16–8). These gradients may provide positional information that specifies the fate of each nucleus or cell within the embryo. That information may then be interpreted by a cell as signals specifying the developmental path it should follow.

In many cases, the effects of maternal effect mutations can be reversed by injecting normal maternal mRNA into the mutant embryo. When this is done, the fly develops normally, indicating that the gene product is needed for a short time only at the earliest stages of development.

Zygotic Segmentation Genes Continue and Extend the Developmental Program.

Immediately after fertilization, the zygote nucleus in the *Drosophila* egg divides, beginning a remarkable series of 13 mitotic divisions (Figure 16–8b). Each of these divisions takes only 5 or 10 minutes, which means that the DNA in the nuclei is replicated constantly at a very rapid rate. During that time, the nuclei do not synthesize RNA. Cytokinesis does not take place, and the several thousand nuclei produced by those divisions remain at the center of the egg until division number eight. At that time, most of the nuclei start to migrate to the periphery of the egg. Membranes begin to form around the nuclei in the periphery. Embryonic mRNA production begins, and some of the **zygotic genes** begin to be expressed. (It is customary to refer to the genes of the embryo itself as zygotic genes, even though the embryo is no longer a zygote.) Certain zygotic genes begin to extend the developmental program beyond the pattern established by the maternal genome.

So far at least 24 **zygotic segmentation genes** have been identified that are responsible for generating a repeating pattern of segments within the embryo (Figures 16–8 to 16–10). The segmentation genes appear to fall into three classes—gap genes, pair-rule genes, and segment polarity genes—representing a rough hierarchy of gene action (Table 16–1).

The **"gap genes"** are apparently the first sets of zygotic genes to act. These genes seem to interpret the maternal anterior-posterior information in the egg and begin the organization of the segments. A mutation in one of the gap genes usually causes one or more missing segments in an embryo.

The other two classes of segmentation genes act not on small groups of segments but rather on all of the segments. For example, mutations in the **"pair-rule"** genes delete every other segment, whereas mutations in the **"segment polarity"** class of genes produce segments in which one part is missing and the remaining part is duplicated as a mirror image. The effects of the

(*Text continued on page 368*)

Table 16-1 CLASSES OF GENES INVOLVED IN PATTERN FORMATION OF EMBRYONIC SEGMENTS IN *DROSOPHILA*

Type of Gene	Site of Gene Activity	Effects of Mutant Alleles and Proposed Function(s) of Genes
Maternal effect genes	Maternal tissues	Initiate pattern formation by activating regulatory genes in nuclei in certain locations in embryo
Gap genes	Embryo	Mutant alleles cause alternate segments to be missing; some may influence activity of pair rule genes, segment polarity genes, and homeotic genes
Pair rule genes	Embryo	When mutated, cause parts of segments to be missing; some may influence activity of segment polarity genes and homeotic genes
Segment polarity genes	Embryo	Mutant alleles delete part of every segment; replace with mirror image of remaining structure; may influence activity of homeotic genes
Homeotic genes	Embryo	Control the identities of the segments; homeotic mutations cause parts of fly to form structures normally formed in other segments

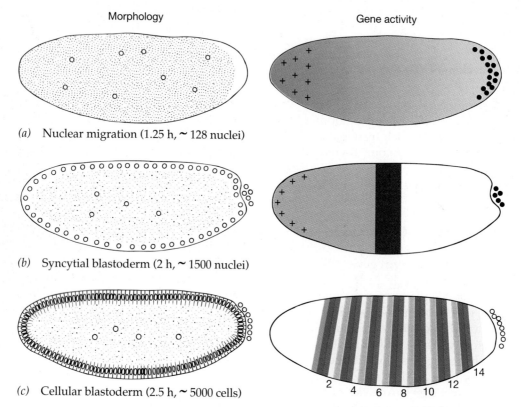

Morphology   Gene activity

(a) Nuclear migration (1.25 h, ~ 128 nuclei)

(b) Syncytial blastoderm (2 h, ~ 1500 nuclei)

(c) Cellular blastoderm (2.5 h, ~ 5000 cells)

Figure 16-8 Early development of the *Drosophila* egg. The diagrams on the left show the structure of the embryo at different times after fertilization. The panels on the right show the patterns of activity of particular genes at each of those stages. (a) At 1.25 hours (about 128 nuclei). Between the seventh and eighth nuclear divisions, the nuclei start to migrate to the periphery of the egg. The products of several maternal genes can be located in different regions of the egg. The crosses mark the location of maternal mRNA transcribed from a gene that defines the anterior (head) end of the egg. The dots represent the location of mRNA transcribed from a gene that specifies how cells located in the posterior of the embryo develop. The pink region represents a concentration gradient of a maternal mRNA extending from the anterior to the posterior end. The protein produced by translation of the mRNA appears to be part of a system of determinants that organize the early pattern of development in the embryo. (b) The pattern at 2 hours (about 1500 nuclei). Most of the nuclei have reached the perimeter of the egg and have started to make their own mRNA. The maternal mRNA shown in pink in the previous panel is now being transcribed from the corresponding zygotic gene by the nuclei in the anterior part of the embryo. The mRNA from a zygotic gap gene is transcribed from cells in only one segment in the middle of the embryo. (c) The pattern at 2.5 hours (about 5000 cells). Membranes start to form around nuclei located at the perimeter of the egg. Messenger RNAs from two *pair-rule genes* can be detected as a series of stripes around the embryo. These stripes mark the prepattern used to form the segments found in the mature larva. The boundaries of each stripe in the prepattern are defined by two or more different genes. The genes that form the prepattern affect another set of genes which defines the actual pattern of segments in the embryo. (After Akam, *Development* 101:1–22.)

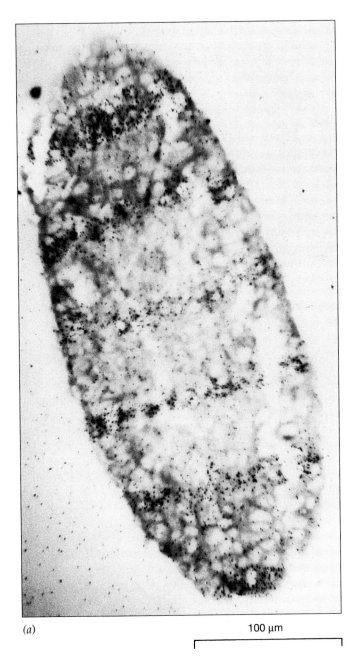

(a)

100 µm

(b)

100 µm

Figure 16–9 The locations of the mRNA molecules transcribed from the engrailed gene, a gene that specifies the boundaries of each segment. The dots in the panels are silver grains produced on x-ray film by radioactive DNA from the cloned engrailed gene sequence that hybridized to its complementary mRNA in the embryo. The autoradiographs are photographed through a microscope in two ways: (a) through normal optics, which cause the silver grains to appear as black dots, or (b) through darkfield optics, which reverse the image. (W. J. Gehring, from A. Fjose, W. J. McGinnis, and W. J. Gehring, 1985, *Nature* 313:284)

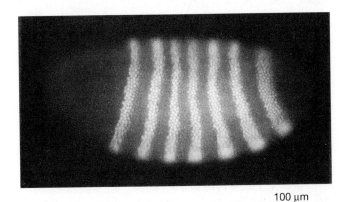

100 µm

Figure 16–10 Locating the pattern of expression of *fushi tarazu* (Japanese for "not enough segments"), one of the zygotic pair-rule genes. The activity of a gene that regulates development can be detected by locating its protein product using fluorescent antibody molecules. In this example the proteins appear to be localized in the nuclei. (W. J. Gehring, from *Science* 236 (1987):1245; 1252)

different classes of mutants are summarized in Figure 16–11.

Each gene can be shown to have distinctive times and places in the embryo in which it is active (Figures 16–9 and 16–10). The observed pattern of expression of the maternal and zygotic genes that control segmentation indicates that cells destined to form adult structures are determined by a progressive series of developmental decisions, according to the following model. First, the anterior-posterior (head to tail) axis and the dorsal and ventral regions of the embryo are determined by maternal segmentation genes that are thought to form gradients of **morphogens** in the egg. (A morphogen is a chemical agent that affects the differentiation of cells and development of form.)

Zygotic segmentation genes then respond to the amounts of various morphogens at each location to control the production of a series of segments from the head to the posterior region. Then, within each segment, other genes are activated that "read" the position of the segment and "interpret" that information to specify which body part that segment should become. Within each compartment, the position of each cell is further specified so that each cell now has a specific "address," which is designated by combinations of the activities of the regulatory genes.

One model for the interaction of the zygotic segmentation genes is that they act in sequence, with the gap genes acting first, then the pair-rule genes, and finally the segment polarity genes. In addition, members of each group can interact with each other. Each time a new group of genes acts, cells of a particular group become more finely restricted in the way that they will develop. As the embryo develops, it is progressively subdivided into smaller specified regions.

Most, if not all, of the segmentation genes (maternal and zygotic) code for *transcription factors* (see Chapter 13). For example, some of the segmentation genes code for a "zinc-finger" type of DNA-binding regulatory protein (see Figure 13–9). Others code for other types of transcription factors, which are discussed in the next section.

Evidence exists that many genes involved in the control of development code for transcription factors that bind to specific DNA sequences. This indicates that those proteins indeed act as genetic "switches" regulating the expression of other genes. Once proteins of this type have been identified, it is possible to use the purified proteins to identify the DNA "target" sequences to which they bind. This approach has been increasingly useful in identifying additional parts of the regulatory pathway involved in different stages of development.

Homeotic Selector Genes Specify the Identity of Each Segment. One function of the zygotic segmentation genes is to regulate the expression of a separate set of genes that actually designate the final adult structure formed by each of the imaginal discs. These genes are called **homeotic** genes. Because of their involvement in segment identity, mutations in homeotic genes cause one body part to be substituted for another and therefore produce some very peculiar changes in the adult. Among the most striking of these are the *Antennapedia* mutants, which have legs that grow from the head at a position where the antennae would normally be found (Figure 16–12).

Homeotic genes in *Drosophila* were originally identified by the altered phenotypes produced by mutant alleles. When the DNA sequences of a number of homeotic genes were analyzed, a short DNA sequence of approximately 180 base pairs was discovered which is characteristic of many homeotic genes as well as some other genes that play a role in development. This sequence has been termed the **homeobox**. Using the homeobox sequence of bases as a molecular probe made it possible to clone new homeotic genes in *Drosophila* that had not been previously identified. Surprisingly, the homeobox probe has detected homologous DNA sequences in a wide range of other organisms, including humans. This finding generated considerable excitement because developmental mutants can be difficult to obtain in many organisms, especially vertebrates. The homeobox has allowed researchers to identify and clone a number of genes that are thought to control development in higher organisms.

The homeobox sequences of a large number of genes have been determined. Comparisons have shown that the DNA sequence itself has been highly conserved during evolution and shows remarkable similarities among organisms as diverse as sea urchins, yeasts, and

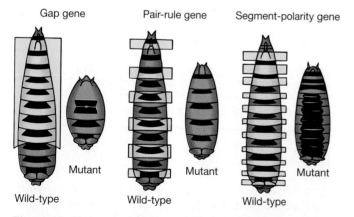

Gap gene   Pair-rule gene   Segment-polarity gene

Mutant   Mutant   Mutant

Wild-type   Wild-type   Wild-type

Figure 16–11   A comparison of mutants representing the three main classes of zygotic segmentation genes.   (After Nüsslein-Volhard and Wieschaus, 1980)

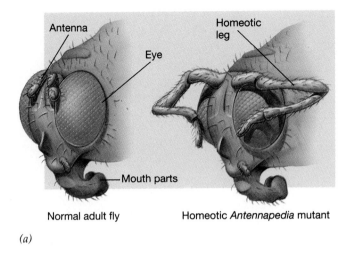

Normal adult fly Homeotic *Antennapedia* mutant

(a)

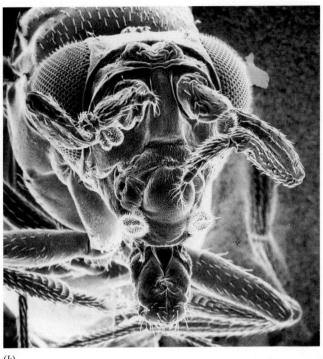

(b)

Figure 16–12 A homeotic mutant of *Drosophila*. (*a*) Head of a normal fly and a fly with the *Antennapedia* mutation. (*b*) Head of a fly with one type of mutation in the *Antennapedia* gene. This particular mutant is one of the more extreme forms of the *Antennapedia* gene. Most of the abnormal alleles produce only incomplete legs in place of the antennal structures. (*b*, Dr. Thomas Kaufman)

humans. Each homeobox codes for a protein functional region called a **homeodomain,** consisting of 60 amino acids that form four alpha helices. One of these serves as a recognition helix, which can bind to specific DNA sequences and affect transcription. Thus the products of the homeotic selector genes, like those of the earlier-acting segmentation genes, are transcription factors. In fact, some of the segmentation genes also contain homeoboxes.

Caenorhabditis elegans *is a roundworm with a very rigid early developmental pattern*

One of the simplest systems for the study of development genes is a roundworm or nematode (see Chapter 28), *Caenorhabditis elegans*. The study of this animal was begun in the 1960s by Sydney Brenner, a molecular biologist. Today it is an important tool for answering basic questions about the development of individual cells within a multicellular organism.

Even as an adult, *Caenorhabditis* is only 1.5 mm long and contains only about 1000 somatic cells (the exact number depends on the sex) and about 2000 germ cells. Individuals can be either **hermaphrodites** (organisms with both sexes in the same individual) or males. Hermaphroditic individuals are self-fertilizing, which makes it easy to obtain offspring homozygous for newly induced recessive mutations. The availability of males that can mate with the hermaphrodites makes it possible to do genetic crosses as well.

Because the body of the worm is transparent, it is possible to follow the development of literally every somatic cell in the worm using a Nomarski differential interference microscope (see Chapter 4) (Figure 16–13). As a result of herculean efforts by several laboratories, the lineage of each somatic cell in the adult has now been determined. Those studies have shown that the nematode has a very rigid developmental pattern. After fertilization, the egg undergoes repeated divisions to produce about 550 cells that make up the small, sexually immature larva. After the larva hatches from the egg case, further cell divisions give rise to the adult worm.

The lineage of each somatic cell in the adult can be traced to a single cell in a small group of **stem cells,** or **founder cells,** that are formed early in development (Figures 16–14 and 16–15). If a particular founder cell is destroyed or removed, the structures that would normally develop from that cell are missing. An embryo with such an invariant developmental pattern is said to be highly **mosaic,** meaning that the fates of cells are largely predetermined.

It was originally thought that each founder cell gives rise to only one organ. The detailed analysis of cell lineages, however, reveals that many of the structures found in the adult, such as the nervous system and the musculature, are in fact derived from more than one founder cell. Conversely, a few lineages have been identified in which a nerve cell and a muscle cell are derived from the division of a single cell. A number

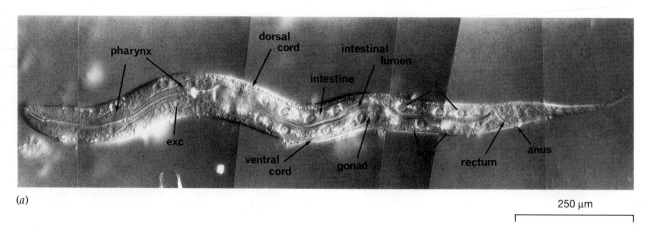

(a)

250 μm

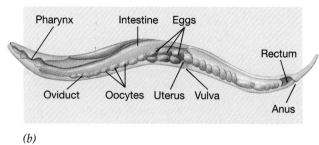

(b)

Figure 16–13 Development of *Caenorhabditis elegans*. (a) A Nomarski interference micrograph of the adult hermaphrodite nematode. (b) Diagram illustrating structures in the adult hermaphrodite. The sperm-producing structures are not shown. (a, Courtesy of Dr. John Sulston, Medical Research Council, from Walbot and Holder, *Developmental Biology* p. 607, figure 22.6a, Random House)

(a)　　(b)　　(c)

(d)　　(e)　　(f)

25 μm

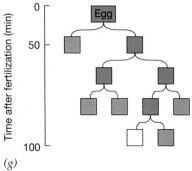

(g)

Figure 16–14 Lineages of the founder cells in *C. elegans* development. (a–f) The early cell divisions of the embryo. (g) A lineage map showing the five somatic founder cells (blue). The cell shown in white will give rise to the germ cells. (a–f, E. Schierenberg, from G. von Ehrenstein and E. Schierenberg, in *Nematodes as Biological Models*, Vol 1, B. Zuckerman, Ed., New York: Academic Press, 1980)

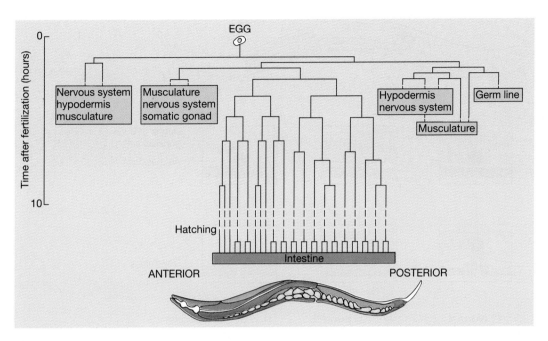

Figure 16–15 A lineage map of the cells in *C. elegans* that form the intestine.

of mutations affecting cell lineages have been isolated, and many of these appear to have properties that would be expected of genes involved in control of developmental decisions.

By using microscopic laser beams small enough to destroy individual cells, it is possible to determine what influence one cell may have on the development of a neighbor. Consistent with the rigid pattern of cell lineages, in most cases destruction of an individual cell in *Caenorhabditis* results in the absence of all of the structures derived from that cell and the normal differentiation of all of the neighboring somatic cells. This suggests that development in each cell is regulated through its own internal program.

However, there are cases in which differentiation of a cell can be influenced by interactions with particular neighboring cells, a phenomenon known as **induction.** One example is the formation of the vulva (pl. vulvae), the structure through which the eggs are laid. A single nondividing cell, called the anchor cell, is a part of the ovary (the structure in which the germ-line cells undergo meiosis to produce the eggs). The anchor cell attaches to the ovary and to a point on the outer surface of the animal, triggering the formation of a passage through which the eggs pass to the outside. When the anchor cell is present, cells on the surface organize to form the vulva and its opening. If the anchor cell is destroyed by a laser beam, however, the vulva does not form and the cells that would normally form the vulva remain as surface cells (Figure 16–16). The anchor cell therefore induces the surface cells to form a vulva.

Analysis of certain cell lineage mutations has been useful in understanding such inductive interactions. For example, several mutations are known that cause more than one vulva to form. In such mutant animals, multiple vulvae form even if the anchor cell is destroyed. Thus, the mutant cells do not require an inductive signal from an anchor cell to form a vulva. Evidently the gene or genes responsible for vulva formation are constitutively expressed in these mutants. Conversely, mutants lacking a vulva are also known. In some of these, the cells that would normally form the vulva appear to be unable to respond to the inducing signal from the anchor cell.

During development in *Caenorhabditis*, a number of instances occur in which cells are produced and die shortly thereafter. Such phenomena have been observed in other organisms as well. For example, the human hand is formed as a webbed structure, but the fingers become individualized when the cells between them die. In *Caenorhabditis*, these **programmed cell deaths** are under genetic control and a number of mutants have been isolated that alter the pattern of these deaths. The loci identified by these mutations are being analyzed at the molecular level and should shed considerable light on the general phenomena of cellular aging and programmed cell death.

Mutations are also known that appear to identify so-called **chronogenes,** that is, genes involved in developmental timing. One such locus has recessive alleles that cause certain cells to adopt fates that would ordinarily be seen later in development. Dominant alleles of

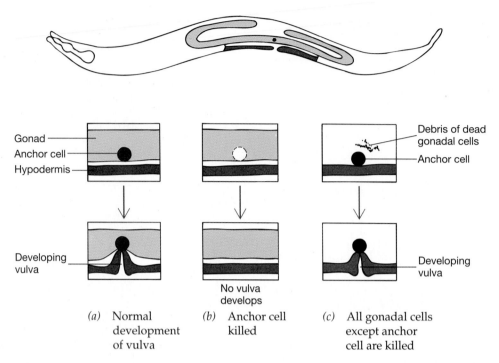

Figure 16–16 A single "anchor cell" induces neighboring cells to form the vulva in *C. elegans*. A schematic diagram showing how laser destruction of single cells or a group of cells can be used to demonstrate the influence of a cell on its neighbors.

the same locus cause certain cells to adopt fates that would usually be expressed earlier. Such genes appear to be good candidates for "switches" that control developmental timing. Many are now being cloned, and important information about these genes and their products should soon be available.

Recently genes that contain homeobox-like sequences have been discovered in *Caenorhabditis*. They are sufficiently different from the *Drosophila* homeobox genes that they were not identified by molecular probes from *Drosophila*. Now that the *Caenorhabditis* sequences can be used as probes, they are expected to allow the identification of additional homeobox genes in it and other organisms.

The mouse is a model for mammalian development

Mammalian embryos develop in markedly different ways from the embryos of *Drosophila* and *Caenorhabditis*. The laboratory mouse, *Mus*, is the best-studied example of early mammalian development.

Cells of Very Early Mouse Embryos Are Totipotent

The early development of the mouse and other mammals is similar in many ways to human development, which is described in detail in Chapter 49. During the early developmental period, the embryo lives free in the reproductive tract of the female. It then implants in the wall of the uterus, after which its needs are met by the mother. Consequently, mammalian eggs are very small and contain little in the way of food reserves. Almost all research on mouse development has concentrated on the stages leading up to implantation because during those stages the embryo is free-living and can be experimentally manipulated. During that period, a number of critical developmental commitments take place that have a significant effect on the future organization of the embryo.

Following fertilization, a series of cell divisions gives rise to a loosely packed group of cells. It has been possible to show that all the cells in the very early mouse embryo are equivalent. For example, at the two-cell stage of mouse embryogenesis, one of the two cells can be destroyed by pricking it with a fine needle. Implanting the remaining cell into the uterus of a foster mother in most cases leads to the development of a normal mouse.

Conversely, two embryos at the eight-cell stage of development can be fused together and implanted into a foster mother, resulting in the development of a normal-sized mouse (Figure 16–17). By using two embryos with different genetic markers (such as coat color), it can be demonstrated that the resulting mouse indeed has four parents. These mice have fur that consists of patches of different colors derived from clusters of genetically different cells. Animals formed in this

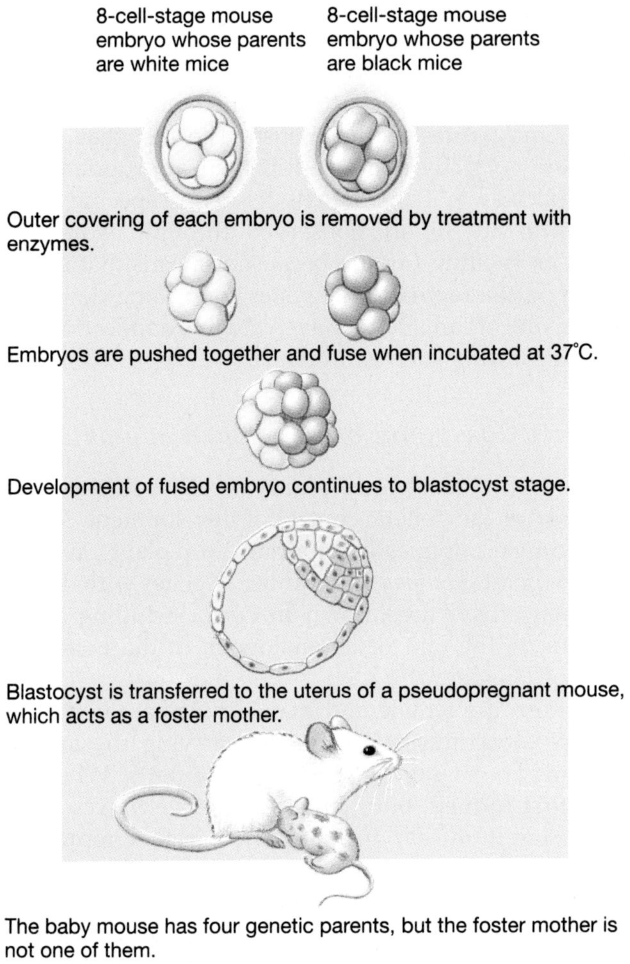

8-cell-stage mouse embryo whose parents are white mice

8-cell-stage mouse embryo whose parents are black mice

Outer covering of each embryo is removed by treatment with enzymes.

Embryos are pushed together and fuse when incubated at 37°C.

Development of fused embryo continues to blastocyst stage.

Blastocyst is transferred to the uterus of a pseudopregnant mouse, which acts as a foster mother.

The baby mouse has four genetic parents, but the foster mother is not one of them.

Figure 16–17 Procedures for the formation of chimeric mice. Embryos from two different strains of mice are removed from females, and the cells are combined in vitro. The resulting aggregate embryo continues to develop and is implanted in the uterus of a foster mother. The offspring has four genetically distinct parents. The foster mother, however, is not genetically related.

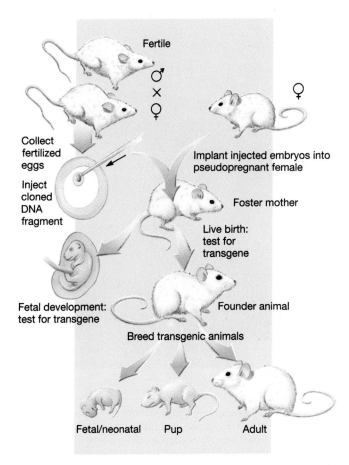

Figure 16–18 The production of transgenic mice. Cloned DNA fragments are injected into the nucleus of a fertilized egg. The eggs are then surgically transferred to a foster mother. The presence of the foreign gene can be examined in the transgenic animal, or the animal can be bred to establish a transgenic line of mice.

way are called **chimeras.** (The term *chimera* is derived from the name of a mythical beast that had the head of a lion, the body of a goat, and the tail of a snake and is used today to refer to any organism that contains two or more kinds of genetically dissimilar cells arising from different zygotes.) Chimeras have been important in allowing the use of genetically marked cells to trace the fates of certain cells during development.

The responses of mouse embryos to these kinds of manipulations are in marked contrast to the mosaic or predetermined nature of early *Caenorhabditis* development, in which the destruction of one of the founder cells results in loss of a significant portion of the embryo. For this reason, we say that very early development of the mouse (and presumably of other mammals) is highly **regulative.** This means that the early embryo

acts as a self-regulating whole that can accommodate missing or extra parts. On the other hand, it has not been possible so far to demonstrate totipotency of either cells or nuclei from slightly later stages of mouse development.

Transgenic Mice Are Used in Studies on Developmental Regulation

In transformation experiments similar to those done with *Drosophila*, foreign DNA injected into fertilized mouse eggs can be incorporated into the chromosomes and expressed (Figures 16–18 and 16–19). The resulting **transgenic** (see Chapter 14) mice have given researchers some insights into how genes are activated during development.

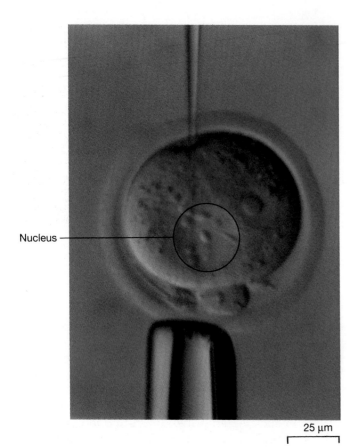

Nucleus

25 μm

Figure 16–19 Technique for microinjection of fertilized mouse eggs. The egg is held by suction on a holding pipet at the bottom. The DNA is injected into the nucleus by the glass needle, shown entering from the top, which is about 1 μm in diameter at the tip. (R. L. Brinster, University of Pennsylvania School of Veterinary Medicine)

Scientists can identify a transgene that has been introduced into a mouse and determine whether it is active by marking the gene in several ways. Sometimes a similar gene from a different species is used, and its protein can be distinguished from the mouse protein by specific antibodies. It is also possible to construct "hybrid genes" that contain the regulatory elements of a mouse gene of interest together with part of another gene that codes for a "reporter" protein, such as an enzyme not normally found in the mouse. For example, such studies have been important in showing which parts of the mouse homeobox genes determine where the gene is expressed in the embryo.

A number of developmentally controlled genes have been introduced into mice and have yielded important information about gene regulation. Most importantly, when developmentally controlled genes from other species such as humans or rats have been introduced into mice, they have been shown to be regulated in the same way as they normally are in the donor animal.

For example, when introduced into the mouse, human genes encoding insulin, globin, and crystallin, which are normally expressed in cells of the pancreas, blood, and eye lens, respectively, are expressed only in those same tissues in the mouse. The fact that these genes are correctly expressed in their appropriate tissues indicates that the signals for tissue-specific gene expression are highly conserved through evolution. This is an exciting finding because it means that information on the regulation of genes controlling development in one organism can have valuable applications to other organisms such as humans.

Homeotic-like mutations are found in plants

Certain well-characterized plants are also being used in the study of the genetic control of development. Many of these are economically important crop plants, such as the corn plant, *Zea mays*. A number of genes with developmental effects are known in corn, including some that can be thought of as analogous to the homeotic genes of *Drosophila*.

In corn the female and male flowers are borne on separate structures, with the ear carrying the female parts and the tassel carrying the male parts. When an ear is first formed, both female and male flower parts are present in the ear, but the male parts are repressed and the female parts continue to develop (Figure 16–20). The reverse happens when a tassel is formed, for only the male parts develop, although both male and female parts are present in the tassel initially. Some mutant alleles of the *tassel seed* locus cause the development of female flower parts on the tassels. Conversely, *anther ear* mutants have male flowers produced on the ear. Like mutations of the *Drosophila* homeotic genes, these mutations may very well identify developmental switch genes that specify alternative fates, in this case male or female structures.

Another plant being used increasingly to study genetics and development in plants is a member of the mustard family, *Arabidopsis* (Figure 16–21). Although *Arabidopsis* itself is of no economic importance, it has a number of advantages for research. The plant is quite small, so thousands of individuals can be grown in limited space. Chemical mutagens can be used to produce mutant strains, and a number of developmental mutants, including some that have "homeotic-like" characteristics, have been isolated. One such mutant transforms the flower petals of the plant into stamens, reproductive structures that contain functional pollen grains. The plant has a very small and simple genome, which greatly facilitates cloning of genes. In addition, cloned foreign genes can be inserted into *Arabidopsis* cells, and these can be integrated into the chromosomes and expressed. These transformed cells can be induced to differentiate into transgenic plants.

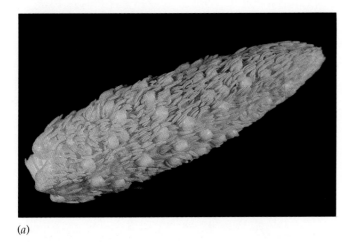

(a)

(b)

Figure 16–20 Homeotic mutations in corn. (*a*) Anther ear. (*b*) Tassel seed. (Carolina Biological Supply Company)

(a)

(b)

Figure 16–21 *Arabidopsis.* (*a*) *A. thaliana*, a normal flower with four petals, four sepals (hidden by the petals), six stamens, and a central ovary. (*b*) A homeotic mutant with only sepals and petals. (Dr. Elliot Meyerowitz, California Institute of Technology)

Several homeotic-like genes in plants have been shown to code for transcription factors, and at least some contain a DNA sequence that may be a counterpart to the homeobox sequences of animals. Now that suitable molecular probes are available from plants, many more such genes should be identified in a wide range of organisms. This information will lead to a deeper understanding of the functions and evolutionary history of these genes (see Making the Connection: Evolution of Gene Complexes That Control the Body Plan).

Some Exceptions to the Principle of Nuclear Equivalence Have Been Found

Although the concept of nuclear equivalence appears to apply to most cells in higher organisms, certain types of developmental regulation can also involve physical changes in the DNA. Such changes in the structure of the genome are not common.

Genomic rearrangements involve structural changes in the DNA

The activity of some genes may be modified during development by different types of **genomic rearrangements** that lead to actual physical changes in the structure of the gene. In some cases, parts of genes are rearranged to make new coding sequences. This is an important mechanism for the development of the immune system (see Chapter 43).

Another type of rearrangement involves the replacement of an active gene with a copy of a "silent" gene located on a different part of the same chromosome. The baker's yeast *Saccharomyces cerevisiae* is a simple eukaryote that has two sexes or mating types called **a** and **α.** The mating type of a cell is determined by an

MAKING THE CONNECTION

Evolution of Gene Complexes That Control the Body Plan

The homeotic genes of *Drosophila* are arranged into two adjacent clusters on the chromosome, the *Antennapedia* complex and the *bithorax* complex. As homeobox-containing genes have been identified in other animals, it has been found that these genes are also clustered and their organization is remarkably similar to that seen in *Drosophila*. The figure compares clusters of homeobox genes in *Drosophila*, the mouse, and *Caenorhabditis,* together with the regions where they are expressed in the animals. Remarkably, the *Drosophila* genes and the equivalent mouse genes are located in the same order along the chromosome, although the correspondence is less clear for *Caenorhabditis*. Furthermore, the order of the genes on the chromosome reflects the order of the corresponding segments they control (from anterior to posterior) in the animal. This organization apparently reflects the need for these genes to be transcribed in a specific sequence.

Although *Drosophila* has only the *Antennapedia/bithorax* complex, vertebrates have four similar complexes, which probably arose through gene duplication and are located in different chromosomes. The fact that extra copies of these genes are present may explain why mutations causing homeotic-like transformations (e.g., the substitution of a leg for an arm) have not been found in vertebrate animals, for it is extremely unlikely that all four complexes would be mutated simultaneously.

It is now thought that the homeobox genes are generally responsible for specifying position in the developing animal embryo, particularly the position along the anterior-posterior axis. The fact that very similar developmental controls are seen in organisms as diverse as insects, unsegmented roundworms, and vertebrates indicates that the basic mechanism evolved early (see Chapters 28, 29, and 30) and has been highly conserved in all animals that have an anterior-posterior axis, even those that are not segmented. Furthermore, the system has apparently been modified in segmented animals such as insects and vertebrates to provide for control of segmentation and specification of segment identity.

The idea that homeobox genes are involved in specifying position in the embryo has been strengthened by recent findings that they not only control the formation of the body axis but also have a role in vertebrate limb development. It is becoming clear that once a successful way of controlling groups of genes and integrating their activities evolved, it was retained, although it has apparently been modified in various ways to provide for alterations of the body plan.

The fact that homeobox-like genes have been found in plants suggests that these genes may have had a very an-

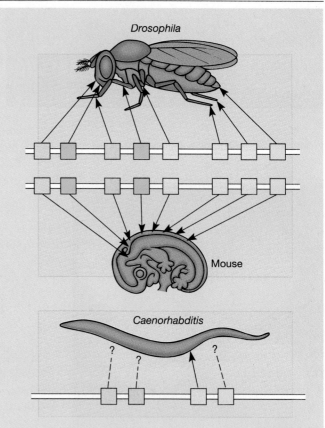

A comparison of the organization of the homeobox gene clusters in *Drosophila* and the laboratory mouse, correlated with the parts of the body in which each gene is expressed. Note that in each organism the order of the genes on the chromosome reflects their spatial order of expression in the embryo. The most anteriorly expressed genes are shown to the left, while those expressed most posteriorly are at the right. *Caenorhabditis* also has clustered homeobox genes that have some similarities to those of *Drosophila* and the mouse.   (After Lenyon et al., *Science* 253:516)

cient origin and may in fact be the genes that made multicellularity possible. Further investigations may allow researchers to develop an overall model of how the rudiments of morphogenesis are controlled in both plants and animals. These systems of master genes that control development are proving to be a rich source of "molecular fossils" that are illuminating evolutionary history in new and exciting ways.

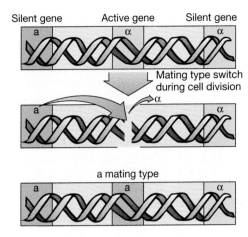

Silent gene   Active gene   Silent gene

a   α   α

Mating type switch
during cell division

α

a   α

a mating type

a   a   α

Figure 16–22 Gene rearrangements involved in the mating type switching of yeast. The active form of the mating type gene resides at the *MAT* locus near the center of the chromosome. Silent copies of the a and α genes are located near either end of the chromosome. During cell division, a copy of the opposite mating type is transferred to the MAT locus, resulting in the reversal of the sex of the cell by the new resident gene.

active gene located at a position close to the middle of one of the yeast chromosomes, called the mating type locus. At some distance on either side of the active gene are two silent genes called *MAT* a and *MAT* α. If a copy of the *MAT* a gene occupies the mating type locus, the mating type is a; if a copy of the *MAT* α gene occupies that site, the mating type of the cell is α. These yeast strains can switch their mating type from one form to the other as frequently as every generation (Figure 16–22). The gene located at the mating type locus is removed and replaced by a DNA sequence copied from the silent gene that corresponds to the opposite mating type.

A somewhat similar system of gene replacement takes place in the unicellular parasite *Trypanosoma brucei,* which causes sleeping sickness in humans and related diseases in other animals (Figure 16–23). When the parasite infects humans, it is able to defeat the immune system by constantly changing the glycoprotein molecules that are exposed on the surface of its cell.

Unlike yeast, which has only two basic copies of the mating type gene per cell, the trypanosome cell contains as many as 1000 different genes for cell surface molecules with sequences so different that an antibody that recognizes one of them would not recognize another. Only one or a few of those copies are expressed at any one time, depending on which copy is present at an **expression site,** which is usually located near the end of a chromosome. The genes in the expression site are exchanged in about one out of every 10^4 to 10^6 cells, providing a constant supply of new cells that cannot be recognized by the immune system, thus maintaining the infection. Although gene replacement clearly offers a mechanism that could serve as a regulatory "genetic switch," it is not known at present whether these mechanisms are relevant to development in higher eukaryotes.

Gene amplification increases the number of copies of specific genes

Some gene products are required in such large quantities during certain stages of development that a single copy of a gene cannot be transcribed and its mRNA translated rapidly enough to fill the needs of the developing cells. In certain cases, the number of copies of a gene may be amplified to meet the demand. For example, the *Drosophila* chorion (eggshell) gene product is a protein made specifically in cells of the insect oviduct. These cells make massive amounts of the particular protein that envelops and protects the fertilized egg. The demand for chorion mRNA in those cells is met by specifically amplifying the gene by DNA replication so that the DNA in that small region of the chromosome is copied many times (Figure 16–24). In other cells of the insect body, however, the gene appears to exist as a single copy on the chromosome.

THE STUDY OF DEVELOPMENTAL BIOLOGY PRESENTS MANY FUTURE CHALLENGES

Scientists are now beginning to learn how genes are activated, inactivated, and modified and how batteries of master regulatory genes interact to control development in a wide variety of organisms. Eventually we hope to understand not only how differentiation and morphogenesis are controlled, but also how the basic control systems have evolved. The identification of certain features common to many organisms, such as homeobox genes, will make the task easier, but we have only scratched the surface. Many complex interactions remain to be explored, and many revelations await us.

A cancer cell lacks normal biological inhibitions. The body is little more to it than a culture medium in which it can grow. Normal cells are tightly regulated by control mechanisms that cause them to divide when necessary and prevent them from growing and dividing at inappropriate times. Cells of many tissues in the adult are normally prevented from dividing and reproduce only to replace a neighboring cell that has died or become damaged. Cancer cells have escaped such controls and can divide continuously.

As a consequence of their abnormal growth pattern, some cancer cells eventually form a mass of tissue called a **tumor.** If the tumor remains at the spot where it originated, it can usually be removed by surgery. One of the major problems with certain forms of cancer is that the cells can escape from the controls that maintain them in their proper location. These cells can **metastasize,** or spread, to different parts of the body, invading other tissues and forming multiple tumors. Lung cancer, for example, is particularly deadly because its cells are highly metastatic and can enter the bloodstream and spread to form tumors in other parts of the lungs or in other organs, such as the liver and the brain. Tumors with cells that can metastasize are referred to as **malignant tumors.**

We now know that cancer is a disease caused by altered gene expression. Using recombinant DNA methods, researchers have identified some of the genes that transform normal cells into cancer cells when they function abnormally (malignant transformation). Each kind of cancer cell apparently owes its traits to at least one, and possibly several, of a relatively small set of genes known as **oncogenes** (cancer-causing genes). Oncogenes arise from changes in the expression of certain genes called **proto-oncogenes,** which are *normal* genes found in all cells and involved in the control of growth and development.

The first oncogenes were found in viruses that can infect mammalian cells and transform them into cancer cells. Such viruses can incorporate DNA sequences of the cellular proto-oncogenes into their own nucleic acid. In some cases, the viruses alter the expression of the proto-oncogenes, converting them into oncogenes. This may happen if the DNA sequences come under the control of viral regulatory elements, which cause the gene to be transcribed at much higher than normal levels, or if the captured gene mutates so that its protein product is more active than the product of the normal proto-oncogene.

A proto-oncogene in a cell that has not been infected by a virus can also mutate and become an oncogene. One of the first oncogenes identified was isolated from a bladder tumor. In the cell that gave rise to the tumor, a proto-oncogene had undergone a single base-pair mutation; the result was that the amino acid glycine was replaced by a valine in the protein product of the gene. This subtle change was apparently a critical factor in the conversion of the normal cell into a cancer cell.

Not all oncogenes, however, code for proteins with amino acid substitutions. The position of the oncogene on the chromosome may also be an important factor in malignant transformation. Some cancers occur more frequently in individuals with certain chromosomal abnormalities. For example, persons with Down syndrome (see Chapter 15) are unusually susceptible to leukemia. It is possible that cellular proto-oncogenes are activated into oncogenes when they become associated with new regulatory regions by chromosome breakage or rearrangements or when they become duplicated, which results in overexpression of the gene.

By means of recombinant DNA technology and other techniques of molecular biology, it has been possible for researchers to identify more than 60 oncogenes and their corresponding proto-oncogenes. Because the fundamental controls of normal cell division and differentiation probably evolved very early in the evolutionary history of eukaryotes, it is not surprising that very similar proto-oncogenes have been found in a diverse array of organisms, ranging from yeasts to humans. For example, the proto-oncogene counterpart of the oncogene found in some bladder tumors (mentioned previously) has also been found in yeast cells.

Some of these controls are illustrated in greatly simplified form in Figure *a.* The growth and division of cells can be triggered by one or more substances known as **growth factors.** These bind to specific **growth factor receptors** associated with the cell surface, initiating a cascade of events inside the cell. Often the growth factor/receptor complex acts as a **protein kinase** (an enzyme that phosphorylates proteins), which then phosphorylates specific amino acids of a number of cytoplasmic proteins. This posttranslational modification usually results in the activation of previously inactive enzymes. These activated enzymes are then able to catalyze the activation of certain nuclear proteins, many of which are **transcription factors.**

Activated transcription factors bind to their DNA targets and stimulate transcription of specific sets of genes that initiate growth and cell division. Even in the simplified scenario presented in the figure it is evident that multiple steps are required to control cell proliferation. Remarkably, the proto-oncogenes that encode the products responsible for a great many of these steps have been identified. The current list of known proto-oncogenes includes genes that code for various growth factors or growth factor receptors and genes that respond to stimulation by growth factors (including a number of transcription factors). When one of these proto-oncogenes is expressed inappropriately, the cell may misinterpret the signal and respond by growing and dividing.

Not all proto-oncogenes are part of a growth control cascade, however. Some are of particular interest because they appear to have similarities to developmental genes involved in pattern formation as well as growth and differentiation. The normal function of some other potential "cancer genes" is apparently to block cell division; these are sometimes referred to as **anti-oncogenes.**

Certain oncogenes appear to be particularly common and are found in a variety of tumors. However, a

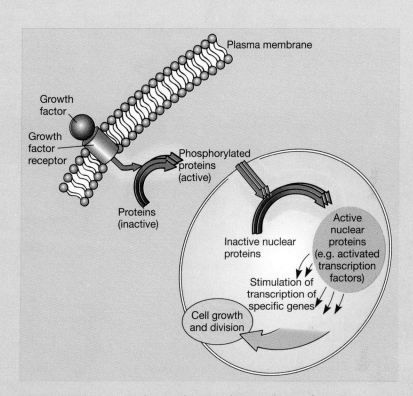

(*a*) A simplified view of part of a growth control cascade.

change in a single proto-oncogene is usually insufficient to cause a cell to become malignant. The development of cancer is usually a multistep process, and scientists are in the process of dissecting the web of events that leads to malignant transformation. As more oncogenes and anti-oncogenes

are discovered and their complex interactions are unraveled, we will gain a fuller understanding of the control of growth and development. It is hoped that this understanding will eventually lead to improved diagnosis and treatment of various cancers.

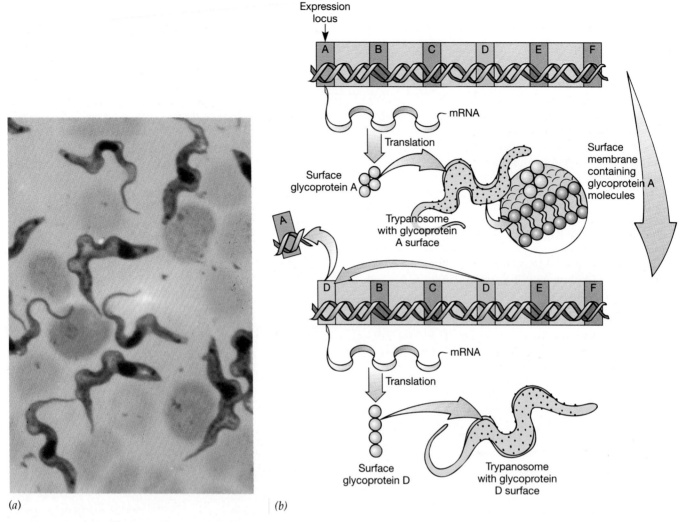

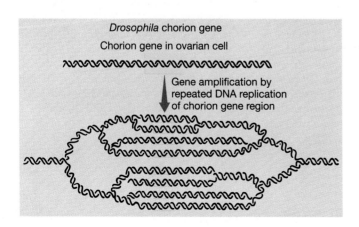

(a)   *(b)*

Figure 16–23   Gene rearrangements in single-celled protozoa (see Chapter 24) called trypanosomes. (*a*) *Trypanosoma brucei,* which is carried by the tsetse fly, causes sleeping sickness in humans and nagana in cattle. (*b*) Trypanosomes coat their surfaces frequently and are thus able to "outrun" the immune system of their human host. Each cell contains as many as a thousand silent genes, each coding for a different surface coat protein. Only one of those genes, which is located at a position near the end of a chromosome, called the expression site, is active at any one time. As the trypanosomes multiply in the bloodstream, occasionally a copy of one of the silent genes replaces the current gene in the expression site, leading to the production of a new group of organisms with a new surface protein. These new trypanosomes appear every 7 to 10 days, preventing the immune system of the body from developing antibodies against the surface protein in time to defeat the infection.   (*a,* Ed Reschke)

Figure 16–24   Amplification of *Drosophila* chorion genes during development. The genes are amplified by multiple replications of a small region of the chromosome containing the chorion protein genes. Replication is initiated at a discrete chromosome origin of replication for each copy of the gene that is produced and is randomly terminated, resulting in series of forked structures on the chromosome.

SUMMARY

I. Development is the process by which the descendants of a single cell specialize and organize into a complex organism.

  A. An organism contains many types of cells that are specialized both structurally and chemically to carry out specific functions. These cells are the product of a process of gradual commitment, called determination, which ultimately leads to the final step in cell specialization, called differentiation.

  B. The development of form, called morphogenesis, occurs through stages, referred to as pattern formation, in which the various specialized cells become organized into structures.

  C. There is no evidence that genes are normally lost during most developmental processes.

    1. At least some nuclei from differentiated plant and animal cells contain all of the genetic material that would be present in the nucleus of a zygote and are therefore said to be totipotent.

    2. The concept of nuclear equivalence is the idea that all (with a few exceptions) of the nuclei of the differentiated somatic cells of an organism are identical to each other and to the nucleus of the single cell from which they descended.

    3. Differences among various cell types are apparently due to differential gene activity.

II. Several organisms have characteristics that make them especially useful in studies of the genetic control of development.

  A. Many types of developmental mutants have been identified in the fruit fly, *Drosophila melanogaster.* Many of these affect the segmented body plan of the organism.

    1. The earliest developmental program to operate in the egg is established by maternal genes; these are active prior to fertilization, and some affect the segmentation pattern that is progressively established in the embryo.

    2. Zygotic segmentation genes do not become active until much later, at a time when the embryo is no longer a zygote. They continue and extend the developmental program initiated by the maternal effect genes.

    3. The zygotic genes and their products interact with each other and with the products of the maternal genes according to a hierarchical pattern, with certain earlier-acting genes controlling particular later-acting genes.

    4. The still later-acting homeotic selector genes are responsible for specifying the identity of each segment.

    5. Many of the segmentation genes are known to code for transcription factors. Some of these contain a DNA sequence called a homeobox, which codes for a protein with a DNA-binding region called a homeodomain.

  B. *Caenorhabditis elegans* is a roundworm that has an extremely rigid developmental pattern in which the fates of cells are largely predetermined.

    1. The lineage of every somatic cell in the adult is known, and each can be traced to a single founder cell in the early embryo.

    2. A number of mutations affecting cell lineages have been identified, and many of these appear to identify genes that control developmental processes such as induction (developmental interactions with neighboring cells), programmed cell death, and developmental timing.

  C. The laboratory mouse, *Mus,* is extensively used in studies of mammalian development.

    1. In contrast to *Caenorhabditis,* mouse development is highly regulative, which means that the very early embryo is a self-regulating whole, and an embryo that contains extra cells or missing cells can still develop normally.

    2. Transgenic mice have been extremely useful in determining how genes are activated and regulated during development.

  D. Genes affecting the developmental pattern have also been identified in certain plants, including *Zea mays* (corn) and *Arabidopsis.* Some of these have been shown to contain homeobox-like sequences or to have other characteristics that make them good candidates for genetic switch genes.

  E. Some homeobox genes are organized into complexes that appear to be systems of master genes specifying the body plan of the organism. Remarkable parallels exist between the homeobox complex of *Drosophila* and those of other animals, including the laboratory mouse and *Caenorhabditis.*

III. A few cases that represent exceptions to the general rule of nuclear equivalence are known. Among these are physical rearrangements of the DNA of the genome and amplification of certain genes to provide more copies for transcription.

POST-TEST

1. Cells become specialized or _____ by a gradual process called _____ .
2. The development of form is called _____ . This occurs through a series of stages known as _____ .
3. The idea that the nuclei of essentially all cells of an organism contain the same genetic information is referred to as the concept of _____ _____ .
4. If a nucleus is found to contain all the information required to support normal development from the embryonic stages to the adult, it is said to be _____ .
5. Differences among differentiated cells with regard to their structures, functions, and molecular compositions are generally attributed to differential _____ .
6. The _____ chromosomes of *Drosophila* make it relatively easy to establish the physical position of a gene.
7. The *Drosophila* egg is organized by the activity of certain _____ _____ genes.
8. _____ genes act after the embryo has formed.
9. Chemical agents that affect cellular differentiation and development of form are generally referred to as _____ .
10. _____ genes are involved in specifying the identities of body parts; when mutated, they generally cause one body part to be substituted for another.
11. Homeodomains are found in proteins that bind to _____ .
12. Cell lineage studies in *Caenorhabditis* are meaningful because the developmental pattern in this organism is highly _____ .
13. When one cell or group of cells influences the differentiation of another, we refer to this phenomenon as _____ .
14. Early embryological development in the mouse is highly _____ , meaning that if cells are lost or added during that time, the embryo still develops normally.
15. _____ mice are important in the study of developmental regulation of certain genes.
16. Mutations that transform one plant part into another are thought to identify genes that are at least somewhat analogous to the _____ genes of *Drosophila*.
17. Physical changes in the structure of a gene (at the DNA level) that may be occasionally important in development are referred to as _____ _____ .
18. _____ _____ sometimes occurs when extra copies of a gene are required to meet a great demand for its product in certain tissues.

REVIEW QUESTIONS

1. Development consists of four main phenomena: cell determination, differentiation of cells, pattern formation, and morphogenesis. How do these processes relate to one another?
2. What lines of evidence support the concept of nuclear equivalence?
3. Why is an understanding of gene regulation in eukaryotes crucial to an understanding of developmental processes?
4. Why is it necessary for scientists to study development in more than one type of organism?
5. What are the relative merits of *Drosophila*, *Caenorhabditis*, the mouse, and *Arabidopsis* as model organisms for the study of development?
6. What is the value of homeotic genes in developmental studies?
7. Describe how transgenic organisms are useful in the study of gene regulation in development.
8. Give some examples of genomic rearrangements that are known to occur as a part of some developmental processes.
9. Under what conditions are examples of gene amplification seen?
10. What are oncogenes and what is their relationship to cellular genes involved in the control of normal growth and development?

RECOMMENDED READINGS

Beardsley, T. Smart genes. *Scientific American,* August 1991. An overview of the role of genes in development.

Browder, L., C. Erickson, and W. Jeffery. *Developmental Biology,* 3rd ed. Saunders College Publishing, Philadelphia, 1991. A thorough coverage of gene expression at the molecular level as well as experimental and descriptive aspects of development.

Darnell, J., H. Lodish, and D. Baltimore. *Molecular Cell Biology,* 2nd ed. Scientific American Books, New York, 1990. Chapters 11 and 24 contain detailed discussions of many of the topics in this chapter.

DeRobertis, E., G. Oliver, and C. Wright. Homeobox genes and the vertebrate body plan. *Scientific American,* July 1990. A discussion of the role of homeobox genes in controlling the body plans of vertebrates and the evolution of such genes.

Watson, J. D., M. Gilman, J. Witkowski, and M. Zoller. *Recombinant DNA,* 2nd ed. W. H. Freeman and Company, New York, 1992. A discussion of the uses of recombinant DNA technology in studies on oncogenes and cancer (Chapter 18) and genes controlling *Drosophila* development (Chapter 20).

Electron Microscopist

LINDA LOPEZ

Linda Lopez says she "took the scenic route to my M.S." After several years of undergraduate foreign language study, she lived abroad before entering the biology program at the University of Texas at Arlington. She earned her B.S. in biology in 1976 and stayed on to do graduate work. Motivated by a graduate course in electron microscopy, Lopez worked in the field for many years—first as an electron microscopy technician at a large medical research center, then as an applications specialist for a microscope manufacturing firm. Since 1989 she has been a research associate and laboratory manager at the University of Texas at Arlington Center for Electron Microscopy. Lopez earned her M.S. in biology in May 1992.

How did your interest in biology—and eventually electron microscopy—develop?

I started out as a Spanish and French major at St. Mary's in San Antonio. After my junior year, I went to live in Mexico City for two years, then traveled to France. When I returned to school, I entered UT at Arlington (UTA) and took two years of science courses to get a degree in biology.

Why did you choose a biology major?

Environmental issues were coming to the forefront at the time, and I thought that they were very interesting and also critical. My M.S. thesis is a study of the air-space system in the leaves of *Eichhornia crassipes*. This plant, the water hyacinth, was brought to the

U.S. about a hundred years ago and, with no natural population control mechanisms, has had an enormous impact on lakes and rivers in southern states. Also, biology is fun. It makes you appreciate things when you go outside—things you might just overlook otherwise.

Did any one person especially influence your decision to focus on microscopy?

As a graduate student, I was influenced by the work of my major professor, Dr. Howard Arnott, a well-known microscopist and now director of the lab where I work. Actually, he was

almost entirely responsible for the beginnings of my career in electron microscopy. He was Dean of Science at the time. When he teaches a course he brings a lot of practical aspects into the classroom. As a major professor, he frequently introduces students to people who can help them later on in a job search. That's how I got my first job at the University of Texas Health Science Center in Dallas.

So your decision to specialize came fairly easily?

I was very lucky. From the first minute of my electron microscopy class in graduate school, I thought the field was absolutely fascinating. It is probably best to begin in a classroom situation to learn what electron microscopy does; you learn basics and how-to's.

Is electron microscopy a course typically offered to biology majors?

UTA offers a course in electron microscopy in the graduate school in biology. The engineering department also has a graduate course in electron microscopy, but a lot of people get into microscopy through biology. In the biology department, you almost invariably have electron microscopes around, and everybody can have the opportunity to learn about them. It's a great skill to know because you can always find a job.

So your job as electron microscopy technician at the University of Texas Health Science Center in Dallas was an extension of your initial interest?

Yes, I actually targeted electron microscopy as a career. Working at a medical school is a valuable way to get a lot of hands-on training with different types of equipment. The huge medical and research facility in Dallas was a real haven for learning techniques, meeting famous people, and learning what is going on in research. I was working in the Department of Anatomy for a cell biologist collaborating with two scientists who later won a Nobel Prize. I worked every day with them and learned a great deal. It was wonderful to see how they attacked a problem. We took the electron micrographs for them, then they would do the biochemistry.

Do medical and research facilities recruit biology majors for laboratory jobs?

Lots of jobs are available, so someone with a bachelor's or master's degree in biology could start as a technician. Job descriptions at the Dallas Health Science Center, for example, are listed on a bulletin board, and you can interview with the research scientists if you think you meet their requirements.

Four years later you became an applications specialist with JEOL U.S.A., an electron microscope manufacturer. How did you do in that position?

I used my knowledge of microscopy to show customers how electron microscopes could meet their needs. They might need help in sample preparation or in operating the microscope and discovering all of its uses. We taught 1-week courses at the Boston facility. Customers would come from all over the country to take the basic instrumentation course. We also had advanced instrumentation courses and would sometimes provide on-site training.

What kinds of businesses are interested in that technology?

Metallurgists require information about the composition and integrity of metal components that go into airplanes, helicopters, oil drilling machinery, and so on. The electron microscope is vital in obtaining this information. Many companies in the food industry use electron microscopes to study their products. What does pasta look like after it's been boiled for 2 minutes? 5 minutes? 10 minutes? Does the surface change? Does it become more porous? In the cosmetics industry, does the size or shape of particles in eyeshadow have anything to do with the way it adheres to the eyelid or the way it reflects light? Manufacturers of integrated circuits require the use of electron microscopes to check the tiny patterns printed on silicon wafers. Other institutions and businesses that value this technology are museums, universities, hospitals, dental schools, paper manufacturers, and contact lens manufacturers, just to name a few.

Now you are the manager of the Center for Electron Microscopy, University of Texas at Arlington. What makes this job a part of a logical progression in your career?

To manage the lab you really must know the equipment, and I do. I have lots of experience with troubleshooting and problem solving. We don't do pure research all the time. Our facility is very powerful, so we often do outside jobs for industry. Setting up an electron microscopy lab is very expensive and time-consuming, so many companies don't have their own facilities. Here at the university lab, we characterize samples for them, so our work is very practical and helpful to industry.

What might be involved in a project?

We often work with geologists, engineers, and chemists. When they see a picture of their sample they are absolutely amazed. Since they aren't used to interpreting micrographs, they rely on me to tell them exactly what they're looking at. An electron microscope is a powerful instrument, flexible and diverse. When you really know how to run the instrument you can do amazing things. You can suggest how to improve a design or an experimental procedure. A lot of electron microscopes have an attachment that does chemical analysis. In the field of environmental contamination, for example, something may look perfectly normal, but chemical analysis will reveal the existence of a contaminant. These microscopes aren't just for taking pictures!

What do you like about your position now?

My work is very, very interesting. I like the academic environment. It's satisfying to be able to do research, study what I want to study, have articles published, and go to professional meetings. I am always learning new things.

What other kinds of work can a career in electron microscopy lead to?

I have mentioned my early interest in the environment. A microscopist can find the abnormal thing among normal things—such as contaminants in water, plants, or animal tissue. You can also do electron microscopy in the food industry. Companies like General Dynamics and Bell Helicopter have electron microscopes. Firms that make artificial limbs use electron microscopes to look at joint surfaces. Also, electron microscopy is used in forensics. I was once asked to take pictures of a piece of fingernail found at a crime scene. Lines on fingernails are just as distinctive as fingerprint patterns, so the evidence was used to solve the crime.

There's a broad spectrum of careers to pursue, not just in biology but in all kinds of industrial settings involving manufactured materials, electronics, fabrics, and the list goes on.

PART IV

▫

Evolution

Individuals are born and die in a matter of years, but the populations of which individuals are members exist for eons. During that time, the characteristics of populations are modified in response to changes in the environment by a process called evolution. Evolution is the central theme of biology and links all fields of the life sciences. Molecular biologists, organismic biologists, and ecologists all attempt to understand their work in the context of evolution. How do evolutionary processes cause change? How has evolution progressed? What evidence is there for evolution?

These are the kinds of questions we consider in Part IV. Chapter 17 discusses the overall mechanism of and evidence for evolution, Chapter 18 examines the evolutionary changes that occur in populations, and Chapter 19 looks at evolutionary changes in species and higher taxa. The evolutionary history of life is considered in Chapter 20 and the evolution of primates in Chapter 21.

Crinoid (a type of marine animal) fossils
from the Cretaceous period.

(Visuals Unlimited/A. J. Copley)

CHAPTER 17

Evolution: Mechanism and Evidence

OUTLINE

Ideas about evolution
Charles Darwin's concept of evolution
Natural selection
The synthetic theory of evolution
Evidence supporting evolution

All of the vast diversity of life forms present on our planet evolved during the Earth's long history from one or a few simple kinds of organisms. This means that seemingly unrelated organisms such as slime molds and blue whales are in fact distantly related to one another and share a common ancestor. All of the organisms that exist today arose from earlier organisms by a process of gradual divergence that Darwin originally described as "descent with modification," or **evolution.**

Evolution is a genetic change in a population of organisms over time. It refers not to changes that occur in an individual organism within its lifetime, but to changes that occur in the characteristics of populations over many generations. The sum total of all the genes present in a given population is its **gene pool.** Another way to think of evolution, using the concept of the gene pool, is that evolution comprises changes in the gene frequencies within a gene pool.

As an example, consider the evolution of bacterial resistance to antibiotics (Figure 17–1). When antibiotics began to be used for human and animal infections, it

Ammonite, a Mesozoic fossil mollusk.
The ammonites became extinct
65 million years ago.
(William E. Ferguson)

was thought that antibiotics would eliminate bacterial diseases, but this has not occurred. Each time penicillin is used, most, but not all, of the bacteria present are killed. The survivors have a genetic resistance to penicillin, and so this trait is passed on to their offspring, resulting in a larger percentage of penicillin-resistant bacteria. The change in the frequency of appearance of certain genes in the bacterial population means that evolution has occurred. If enough of these types of changes occur over time, a new species might arise, but it is important to recognize that evolution may or may not give rise to a new species. (The concept of a species is developed extensively in Chapter 19. Until then, a simple working definition of species is that it comprises a group of similar organisms that are capable of interbreeding.)

The concept of evolution is the cornerstone of biology because it enables us to make sense of the tremendous variety in the living world. Biologists do not question the occurrence of evolution, but the actual mechanisms that cause evolution are under close study and active debate.

After you have studied this chapter you should be able to

1. Discuss the historical foundations of evolution.
2. List the four premises of natural selection as outlined by Darwin.
3. Explain how the synthetic theory of evolution differs from Darwin's original theory of evolution.
4. Summarize the evidence for evolution from the fossil record.
5. Summarize some of the evidence supporting evolution ob-

tained from the fields of comparative anatomy, embryology, biogeography, biochemistry, and molecular biology.
6. Define and give examples of vestigial, homologous, and analogous structures.
7. Distinguish between batesian mimicry and müllerian mimicry.
8. Describe how scientists make inferences about evolutionary relationships from the sequence of amino acids in specific proteins or the sequence of nucleotides in particular genes in organisms.

IDEAS ABOUT EVOLUTION ORIGINATED BEFORE DARWIN

Although Charles Darwin is universally associated with evolution, ideas of evolution were conceived centuries before Darwin was born. Aristotle (384–322 BC) saw much evidence of design and purpose in nature and arranged all of the organisms that were known to him in one "scale of nature" that extended from the very simple to the most complex. He visualized living organisms as being imperfect but moving toward a more perfect state. This has been interpreted by some as the germ of an idea of evolution, but Aristotle is very vague on the nature of this "movement toward the more perfect state" and certainly did not propose any notion of the origin of species.

Long before Darwin, odd fragments resembling bones, teeth, and shells (fossils) had been discovered

embedded in rocks. Some of these corresponded to parts of familiar living animals, but others were strangely unlike any known form. Fossils of marine invertebrates were sometimes found in sedimentary rocks high on mountains! Leonardo da Vinci correctly interpreted these finds in the 15th century as the remains of animals that had existed in previous ages but had become extinct.

During the Renaissance, there was an increased interest in the study of nature and a movement away from simple reliance on the interpretations of early authorities. Modern scientific thought, based on observations, experiments, and rigorous inductive and deductive logic, emerged in the 17th century with the work of Francis Bacon, William Harvey, Isaac Newton, and René Descartes. Only in the 18th century did this new science begin to have much effect on interpretations of the biological world. As new continents were explored, the discovery of new species and more fossils led many to think that the world of life as well as the physical world must be guided by natural laws.

The most thoroughly considered view of evolution before Darwin was expressed by Jean Baptiste de Lamarck in his *Philosophie Zoologique* (1809). Like most biologists of his time, Lamarck thought that all living things were endowed with a vital force that drove them to evolve toward greater complexity. He also thought that organisms could pass on to their offspring traits acquired during their lifetimes. As an example of this line of reasoning, Lamarck suggested that the long neck of the giraffe evolved when a short-necked ancestor took to browsing on the leaves of trees instead of on grass (Figure 17–2). Lamarck theorized that the ancestral giraffe, in reaching up, stretched and elongated its neck. Its offspring, inheriting the longer neck, stretched still further. As the process was repeated over many generations, the long neck of the modern giraffe was achieved.

The mechanism for Lamarckian evolution was an "inner drive" for self-improvement, a notion that was discredited when the mechanisms of heredity were discovered. Lamarck's contribution to science is important,

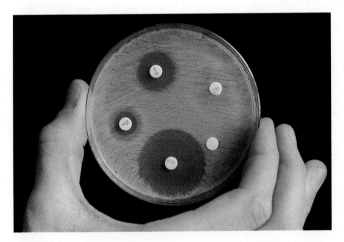

Figure 17–1 Antibiotic resistance in bacteria. An even coating of bacteria covers the surface of this culture dish except where different antibiotics (disks) to which the bacteria are sensitive prevent this growth. Note that certain antibiotics are more effective than others at preventing bacterial growth. The bacteria on this plate are completely resistant to two of the antibiotics (two disks on right). Varieties of bacteria that have developed resistance to certain antibiotics are common today, especially in hospital environments. (Dennis Drenner)

Figure 17–2   How did the giraffe get its long neck? Lamarck hypothesized that giraffes acquired longer necks by continually stretching into the trees to eat leaves unavailable to other large herbivores and that they passed this characteristic on to their offspring. Although Lamarck's mechanism of evolution was incorrect, he was the first scientist to propose that organisms undergo evolution by natural means.   (Visuals Unlimited/Walt Anderson)

Figure 17–3   Charles Darwin as a young man. This portrait was made shortly after Darwin returned to England from his voyage around the world on the *H. M. S. Beagle.* Observations made during this voyage helped him formulate the concept of evolution by natural selection.   (William E. Ferguson)

however, because he was the first to propose that organisms undergo change over time as a result of some natural phenomenon rather than divine intervention. It remained for Charles Darwin (Figure 17–3) to discover the actual mechanism of evolution—natural selection.

CHARLES DARWIN WAS INFLUENCED BY HIS CONTEMPORARIES

Charles Darwin (1809–1882) was sent at the age of 15 to study medicine at the University of Edinburgh. Finding the lectures intolerably dull, he transferred after 2 years to Christ College, Cambridge University, to study theology. At Cambridge he joined a circle of friends interested in natural history and through them became acquainted with Professor John Henslow, a naturalist. Shortly after leaving Cambridge, and upon Henslow's

recommendation, Darwin was appointed "gentleman naturalist" on the *H. M. S. Beagle*, which was taking a 5-year cruise around the world to prepare navigation charts for the British navy.

The *Beagle* left Plymouth, England, in 1831 and cruised slowly down the east coast and up the west coast of South America (Figure 17–4). While other members of the company mapped the coasts and harbors, Darwin had an opportunity to study the animals, plants, fossils, and geological formations of both coastal and inland regions, areas that had not been extensively explored. He collected and catalogued thousands of specimens of plants and animals and kept copious notes of his observations. He experienced first-hand the diverse richness of the flora and fauna of these regions.

The *Beagle* spent some time at the Galapagos Islands, 600 miles west of Ecuador, where Darwin continued his observations and collections of the flora and fauna. He compared the animals and plants of the Galapagos with those of the South American mainland (Figure 17–5). He was particularly impressed by their similarities and wondered why the creatures of the Galapagos should resemble those from South America more than they resembled those from other islands at similar latitudes, for example. Moreover, although there were similarities between Galapagos and South American species, there were distinct differences. There

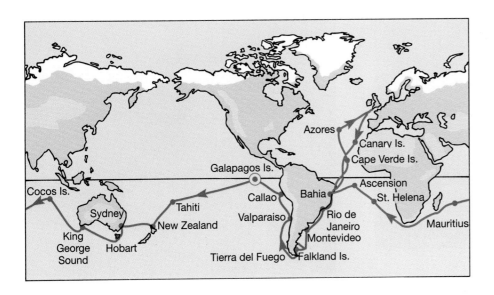

Figure 17–4 Voyage of the *H. M. S. Beagle.*

Figure 17–5 The animals and plants of the Galapagos Islands. (*a*) A land iguana (*Conolophus pallidus*). This animal is endemic (found nowhere else) to the Galapagos. (*b*) The webbed feet of the red-footed booby (*Sula sula*) can grasp tree branches. (*c*) The blue-footed booby is a separate species (*S. nebouxii*) that is distinct from the red-footed booby. (*d*) A tree cactus (*Opuntia echios*). Other *Opuntia* species in the Galapagos are not tree forms. (*e*) A Galapagos tortoise (*Geochelone elephantopus*). (*f*) This cactus (*Brachycereus nesioticus*) grows on recent lava flows. The entire genus is endemic to the Galapagos. (*a,* David Cavagnaro; *b,* E. R. Degginger; *c,* Carolina Biological Supply Company; *d,* William E. Ferguson; *e,* Carolina Biological Supply Company; *f,* William E. Ferguson)

(a)

(b)

(c)

Figure 17–6   Three species of Darwin's famous Galapagos Island finches. These are drab, unremarkable-appearing birds that are derived from a common ancestral population of seed-eating birds from South America. The 14 known species are variously specialized for a variety of lifestyles which are elsewhere filled by birds of different species that never had the opportunity to colonize the Galapagos Islands. The likely derivation of such different birds from a common ancestor suggested to Darwin that species originate by natural selection. (a) Cactus finch, *Geospiza scandens*. The cactus finch feeds on the fleshy parts of cacti. (b) A large ground finch, *Geospiza magnirostra*. This bird has an extremely heavy, nutcracker-type bill adapted for eating heavy-walled seeds. (c) Woodpecker finch, *Camarhyncus pallidus*. This remarkable bird has insectivorous habits similar to those of woodpeckers but lacks the complex beak and tongue adaptations that permit woodpeckers to reach their prey. The adaptations of the woodpecker finch to this lifestyle are almost entirely behavioral. In one of the few known instances of animal tool use, this bird digs insects out of bark and crevices using cactus spines, twigs, or even dead leaves.   (*a*, Jeanne White/Photo Researchers, Inc.; *b* and *c*, Miguel Castro/Photo Researchers, Inc.)

were even differences in the birds (Figure 17–6) and reptiles from one island to the next! Darwin pondered these observations and tried to develop an adequate explanation for their distribution.

The general notion in the mid-1800s was that creatures did not change significantly over time, that they looked the same as the day they were created. True, there were some troubling exceptions to this idea. For one thing, breeders could produce a great deal of variation in domesticated plants and animals in just a few generations (Figures 17–7 and 17–8). This was accomplished by selecting certain traits and breeding only individuals that possessed the desired traits, a procedure known as **artificial selection.**

Evidence found in rocks also was beginning to contradict the accepted view. A number of fossils were discovered that did not have living counterparts. Then, too, geological evidence suggested that the Earth was far older than had been previously suspected. During

the early 19th century, Charles Lyell popularized the geological theory of **uniformitarianism,** first proposed by the English geologist James Hutton during the 18th century. The theory of uniformitarianism states that geological processes and scientific laws that operate today also operated in the past. This means that mountains, valleys, and other physical features of the Earth's surface were not created in their present forms. Instead, they were formed over long periods of time by the slow geological processes of vulcanism, uplift, erosion, and glaciation, processes that still occur today. The slow pace of these geological processes indicated that the Earth is very, very old.

The ideas of Thomas Malthus were another important influence on Darwin. Malthus was a clergyman and economist who noted that populations increase in size geometrically ($2 \rightarrow 4 \rightarrow 8 \rightarrow 16 \rightarrow 32$, and so on) until checked by factors in the environment. In the case of humans, Malthus suggested that wars, famine, and

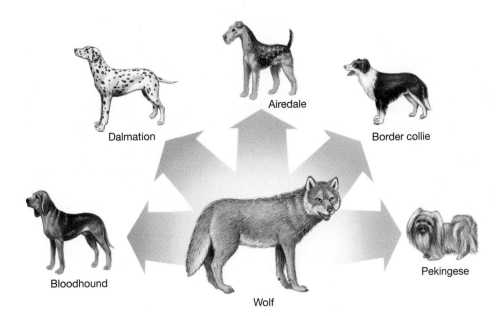

Figure 17–7 Airedales, bloodhounds, border collies, dalmatians, and Pekingese are some of the numerous dog varieties that have been produced by artificial selection. It is likely that dogs evolved from the wolf.

disease serve as the inevitable and necessary brakes on the growth of human populations.

Darwin's years of observing the habits of animals and plants had introduced him to the struggle for existence described by Malthus. It occurred to Darwin that in this struggle favorable variations would tend to be preserved and unfavorable ones eliminated. The result of this would be **adaptation** (evolutionary modification that improves the chances of an organism's survival and reproductive success) of the population to the environment and, eventually, enough modifications to cause the origin of new species. Time was all that was

required in order for new species to originate, and the geologists of the era, including Darwin's friend Lyell, had supplied evidence that the Earth was indeed old enough to provide an adequate amount of time. Darwin had at last obtained a working theory of evolution—that of evolution by natural selection. He spent the next 20 years accumulating a tremendous body of facts to demonstrate that evolution had occurred and formulating his arguments for natural selection.

As Darwin was pondering his ideas, Alfred Russel Wallace, who was studying the flora and fauna of Malaysia and Indonesia, was similarly struck by the diversity of living things and the peculiarities of their distribution. Wallace also arrived at the conclusion that evolution occurred by natural selection. In 1858, he sent a brief essay to Darwin, by then a world-renowned biologist, asking his opinion. Darwin's friends persuaded him to present Wallace's paper along with an abstract of his own views, which he had prepared and circulated to a few friends several years earlier. Both papers were presented in July, 1858, in London at a meeting of the Linnaean Society. Darwin's monumental book, *Origin of Species by Means of Natural Selection*, was published in November, 1859.

Figure 17–8 A number of common vegetables are members of the same species, *Brassica oleracea*, including cauliflower, broccoli, cabbage, brussels sprouts, and kale. Artificial selection is responsible for the variation shown within this species. (Raymond Tschoepe)

NATURAL SELECTION HAS FOUR PREMISES

Darwin's mechanism of natural selection consists of four observations about the natural world. (1) *Overproduction:* Each species produces more offspring than will survive to maturity. (2) *Variation:* There is variation among the offspring. It is important to remember that

Figure 17–9 One of the premises upon which natural selection is based is that sexual reproduction results in offspring that are not identical to one another. A mother cat nurses three kittens, which exhibit variation that is coded in their genes. (E. R. Degginger)

the variation necessary for evolution by natural selection is genetic and can be passed on to offspring (Figure 17–9). (Although Darwin recognized the importance of variation, he did not know about its genetic basis.) (3) *Competition:* Organisms compete with one another for the limited resources available to them (that is, there is a "struggle for existence"). (4) *Survival to reproduce:* Individuals that possess the most favorable combination of characteristics are most likely to survive and reproduce. The process of natural selection thus causes an increase of favorable genes and a decrease of unfavorable genes within a population, which results in the features of that population being better adapted to local conditions. Over time these changes accumulate in geographically separated populations and may be significant enough to cause a new species to arise.

THE SYNTHETIC THEORY OF EVOLUTION COMBINES DARWIN'S THEORY WITH MENDELIAN GENETICS

One of the premises upon which Darwin's theory of evolution by natural selection was based is that individuals pass traits on to the next generation. However, Darwin was unable to explain *how* traits were passed from one generation to another. He was also unable to explain *why* individuals vary within a population. Darwin was a contemporary of Gregor Mendel (see Chapter 10), who worked out the basic patterns of inheritance. However, Darwin was apparently not acquainted with Mendel's work, which was not recognized by the scientific establishment until the early part of the 20th century.

More than 50 years ago, biologists combined Mendelian genetics with Darwin's theory to formulate a comprehensive explanation of evolution, which is known as **neo-Darwinism** or, more commonly, the **synthetic theory of evolution.** (*Synthesis* in this context refers to putting together parts of several previous theories to form a whole.) The synthetic theory of evolution explains Darwin's observation of variation among offspring in terms of mutation and recombination. The synthetic theory of evolution has held up well since it was formulated. It has dominated the thinking and research of many biologists and has resulted in an enormous accumulation of scientific evidence for evolution.

Biologists accept the basic principles of the synthetic theory of evolution but recently have scrutinized certain of its aspects. For example, what is the role of chance in determining the direction of evolution? How rapidly do new species evolve? These questions have arisen in part from a reevaluation of the fossil record and in part from discoveries in molecular aspects of inheritance. These debates are an integral part of the scientific process because they stimulate additional observation and experimentation as well as rethinking of older evidence. Science is an ongoing process, and information obtained in the future may require us to modify certain parts of the synthetic theory of evolution.

MANY TYPES OF EVIDENCE SUPPORT EVOLUTION

The concept of evolution is now supported by an enormous body of scientific observations and experiments. In this text we can report only a small fraction of this wealth of evidence, which is found in the fossil record and in living organisms. Although biologists still do not agree completely on some aspects of the mechanism by which evolutionary changes occur, the concept that evolution has taken place is now well documented and is consistent with all the information that has been brought to bear upon it.

Any scientific theory should lead to observations or testable predictions that, if not true, would require the theory to be modified or rejected. The concept of evolution is testable. For example, suppose our hypothesis is that amphibians evolved from fish ancestors. We would predict that amphibian fossils would not be found in rocks of the same age as those containing the fossils of their fish ancestors. Rather, they would be found in more recent rocks laid down subsequently on top of the older rock strata (layers) containing the ancestral fish.

Likewise, it is possible to test the hypothesis that chimpanzees and gorillas are more closely related to one another than either is to a horse or a whale (meaning that chimpanzees and gorillas shared a common

(a)

(b)

(c)

Figure 17–10 Several types of fossils. (*a*) Impression fossil of a portion of a seed fern leaf. Seed ferns were not closely related to ferns but are an extinct group of gymnosperms. (*b*) Petrifaction of wood from the Petrified Forest National Park in Arizona. Some details of the replaced cell walls may be observable under higher magnification. (*c*) Cast fossil of an ancient echinoderm called a crinoid. (*a*, Carolina Biological Supply Company; *b*, David Muench; *c*, E. R. Degginger)

ancestor more recently in time). One way to test this would be to predict that (1) the sequence of amino acids in chimpanzee hemoglobin is very similar to that in gorilla hemoglobin and that (2) both show greater differences from the amino acid sequences in the hemoglobin of a horse or a whale. If such predictions proved to be untrue, our hypothesis would need modification or replacement. However, all findings to date conform with those predicted by evolution.

The Fossil Record Indicates That Organisms Evolved in the Past

Perhaps the most direct evidence for evolution comes from the sciences of geology and paleontology. Geology deals with studies of the Earth and its history. Paleontology is the science of discovery, identification, and interpretation of **fossils.** The term *fossil* (Latin: *fossilis,* something dug up) refers not only to the parts of an

organism's body that may persist, but also to any impression or trace left by previous organisms.

If the body part has been trapped in sediments without being completely decomposed, the fossil is known as a **compression.** Some organic material still remains in compressions. If the pressure and heat are great during the formation of rock in which the organism is embedded, all of the organic material may be "vaporized." In this case, all that remains is an **impression** (Figure 17–10*a*) of the original plant or animal.

The most common vertebrate fossils are teeth and skeletal parts. From the shapes of the bones and the positions of the bone scars that indicate points of muscle attachment, paleontologists can infer an animal's posture and style of walking, the position and size of its muscles, and the contours of its body. By a careful study of the fossil remains, paleontologists can reconstruct what an animal probably looked like in life.

In some fossils, the original hard parts or even the soft tissues of the body may be replaced by minerals.

Figure 17–11   Dinosaur footprints, each 75 to 90 cm (2.5–3 ft) in length, occur in sedimentary rock in Texas. Dinosaur footprints provide clues about the locomotion, behavior, and ecology of these extinct animals.   (Visuals Unlimited/Scott Berner)

Iron pyrites, silica, and calcium carbonate are some of the common minerals that infiltrate buried tissues. These are known as **petrifactions** (Figure 17–10b). The famous petrified forest of Arizona consists of trees that were buried and infiltrated with minerals.

Molds and **casts** (Figure 17–10c) are fossils produced in a different fashion. Molds are formed by the hardening of the material surrounding the buried organism, followed by the decay and removal of the tissues. The mold may subsequently be filled by minerals that harden to form casts, which are replicas of the original structures.

Footprints or trails made in soft mud that later hardened are a common type of fossil (Figure 17–11). From such remains, the paleontologist can infer something of the structure and locomotion of the animal that made them. Some more recent animal remains have been exceptionally well preserved by being embedded in bogs, tar, amber (Figure 17–12), or ice. The remains of a woolly mammoth deep-frozen in Siberian ice for more than 25,000 years were so well preserved that part of its DNA was able to be analyzed.

Thus, fossils provide a record of animals and plants that lived earlier, some understanding of where and when they lived, and an idea of the kinds of environments in which they lived. When enough fossils of organisms of different geological ages have been found, we can trace the lines of evolution that gave rise to those organisms.

The formation and preservation of a fossil require that an organism be buried under conditions that slow or prevent the process of decay. This is most likely to occur if an organism's remains are covered quickly by fine particles of soil suspended in water. The soil particles are deposited as sediment around the animal or plant and cover it. Remains of aquatic organisms may be trapped in bogs, mud flats, sand bars, or deltas. Remains of terrestrial organisms that lived on a flood plain may also be covered by water-borne sediments or, if the organism lived in an arid region, by wind-blown sand. Animals may be trapped in a tar pit as in La Brea in Los Angeles or covered by volcanic ash as in Pompeii following the eruption of Mount Vesuvius.

Because of the conditions required for preservation, the fossil record is not a random sample of past life. The record is biased toward aquatic organisms and those living in the few terrestrial habitats conducive to fossil formation. For example, relatively few fossils of forest animals have been found. This is because plant and animal remains on the forest floor decay very rapidly, before fossilization can occur. Another reason for bias in the fossil record is that organisms with hard body parts such as bones and shells are more likely to form fossils than organisms with soft body parts.

To be interpreted, the sedimentary layers containing fossils must be arranged in chronological order. The layers of sedimentary rock, if they have not been disturbed, occur in the sequence of their deposition, with the more recent strata on top of the older, earlier ones. However, geological events that occurred after the rocks were initially formed may have changed the relationship of some of the layers. Geologists identify specific sedimentary layers of rock by features such as their

Figure 17–12   A spider embedded in amber. It has been preserved almost perfectly for millions of years.   (Visuals Unlimited/John D. Cunningham)

FOCUS ON

Radioactive Dating

In order to interpret fossil evidence of Earth's past, the rocks in which the fossils appear must be dated. Radioactive isotopes present in rock give us an accurate measure of the rock's age. Radioactive isotopes are said to be radioactive because they emit powerful, invisible radiations. As a radioactive isotope emits radiation, its nucleus changes into the nucleus of a different element; this is known as **radioactive decay.** For example, the radioactive nucleus of one isotope of uranium (^{235}U) decays over time into lead (^{207}Pb).

Each radioactive isotope has its own characteristic rate of decay. The period of time required for one half of a radioactive isotope to change into a different material is known as its **half-life** (see figure). Different radioactive isotopes have enormous variations in their half-lives. For example, the half-life of iodine (^{132}I) is only 2.4 hours, whereas the half-life of uranium (^{235}U) is 704 million years. The half-life of a particular radioactive isotope is constant and never varies; it is not influenced by temperature, pressure, or any other environmental factor.

The age of a fossil is estimated by measuring the proportion of the original radioactive isotope and its decay product. For example, the half-life of a radioactive isotope of potassium (^{40}K) is 1.25 billion years, meaning that in 1.25 billion years half of the radioactive potassium decays into its decay product, argon (^{40}Ar). If the ratio of potassium (^{40}K) to argon (^{40}Ar) in the rock being tested is 1:1, the rock is 1.25 billion years old. (The radioactive clock begins ticking when the rock solidifies. The rock initially contains some potassium, but not argon.)

Several different radioactive isotopes are used in dating fossils. These include potassium (^{40}K; half-life 1.25 billion years), uranium (^{235}U; half-life 704 million years), and carbon (^{14}C; half-life 5730 years). Because of its relatively short half-life, carbon-14 is useful for dating fossils that are 50,000 years old or less.[1] In contrast, ^{40}K, with its long half-life, can be used to date fossils that are hundreds of millions of years old. Whenever possible, the age of a fossil is independently verified using two or more different radioactive isotopes.

[1]Carbon-14 is used to date the carbon remains of anything that was once living, such as wood, bones, and shells. The other isotopes used in radioactive dating are used to date the rock in which fossils may be found.

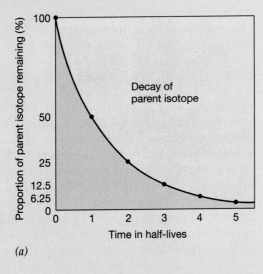

(a)

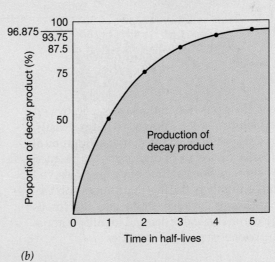

(b)

The decay of radioactive isotopes and subsequent accumulation of decay products. (*a*) At time zero, the radioactive clock begins ticking. At this point a sample is composed entirely of the radioactive isotope. After one half-life, only 50% of the original radioactive isotope remains. (*b*) At time zero, the same sample contains no decay product(s). After one half-life, 50% of the original radioactive isotope has decayed into the decay product(s). During each succeeding half-life, one half of the remaining radioactive isotope is converted to decay product(s).

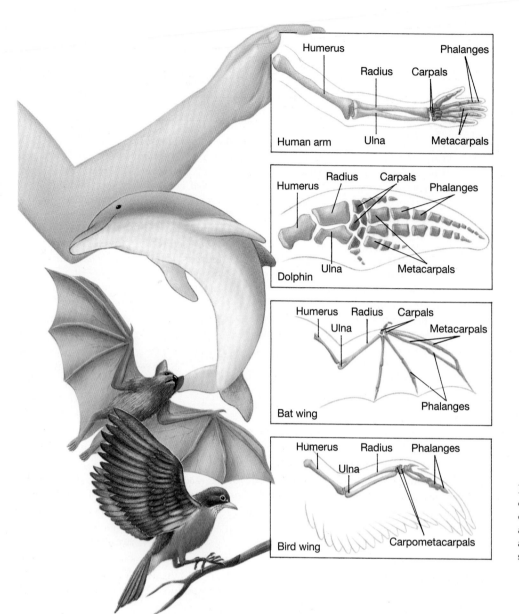

Figure 17–13 Homologous organs. The bird wing, bat wing, dolphin flipper, and human arm are homologous because they have a basic underlying similarity of structure.

mineral content, their position in the layers, and by certain key invertebrate fossils, known as **index fossils,** that characterize a specific layer over large geographical areas. Index fossils are fossils of organisms that existed for a relatively short geological time but were preserved as fossils in large numbers during that time. With this information, geologists arrange strata and the fossils they contain in chronological order and identify comparable layers in widely separated localities.

Comparative Anatomy of Related Species Demonstrates Similarities in Their Structures

Comparing the structural details of any particular organ system in the diverse members of a given phylum reveals a basic similarity of form that is varied to some extent from one class to another. For example, a bird's wing, a dolphin's front flipper, a bat's wing, and a human arm and hand, although superficially dissimilar, are composed of very similar arrangements of bones, muscles, and nerves (see Figure 17–13 for a comparison of their skeletal structure). Each has a single bone, the humerus, in the proximal part of the limb, followed by a radius and ulna, the two bones of the forearm, a group of carpals in the wrist, and a variable number of digits (metacarpals and phalanges). This is particularly striking because wings, flippers, and the human arm are used in different ways for different functions, and there is no mechanical need for them to be so similar. Similar arrangements of parts of the forelimb are evident in ancestral reptiles and amphibians and even in the first fishes that came out of water onto land. Darwin pointed out that such basic structural similarities in organs used in different ways are precisely the expected outcome if evolution has taken place. Or-

(a)

(b)

Figure 17–14 Analogous organs. The wings of birds (a) and insects (b), although used for similar functions, have no underlying structural similarity. (a, Dennis Drenner; b, Skip Moody/Dembinsky Photo Associates)

gans of different organisms that have similar forms due to a common evolutionary origin are termed **homologous.**

With the acceptance that living organisms undergo change over time, biologists came to realize that the homology of organs is due to their common evolutionary origin. Both bird and bat wings evolved from the forelimb of a common vertebrate ancestor. However, the flying surfaces of their wings are quite different. Feathers grow out from the posterior margin on the wings of the bird, whereas the flight surface of the bat's wing is essentially a webbed hand. Flight evolved independently in the two groups. Therefore, although the forelimbs are used as wings in both birds and bats, they are modified in different ways.

Not all species with "similar" structures evolved from a common ancestor. Organs that are not homologous but simply have similar functions in different organisms are termed **analogous** organs. For example, the lungs of mammals and the trachea (air tubes) of insects are analogous organs that have evolved to meet, in quite different ways, the common problem of exchanging gases. The wings of various unrelated flying animals, such as insects and vertebrates, resemble one another superficially (Figure 17–14) but are different in more fundamental aspects. Vertebrate wings are modified forelimbs supported by bones, whereas insect wings are outgrowths of the upper wall of the thorax and are supported by chitinous veins.

Like homologous organs, analogous organs offer crucial proof of evolution and adaptation. Comparisons of organisms with analogous organs indicate they have separate ancestries. Analogous organs are of evolutionary interest because they show how unrelated groups may adapt to common problems as their evolution leads to structural and functional convergence in similar habitats. This is called **convergent evolution** (Figure 17–15).

(a)

(b)

Figure 17–15 Convergent evolution results in structural similarities in two unrelated plant families. These plants evolved in similar desert environments in different parts of the world. (a) *Euphorbia ingens*, a member of the spurge family, which is native to Africa. (b) A member of the cactus family, which is native to North America. (Dennis Drenner)

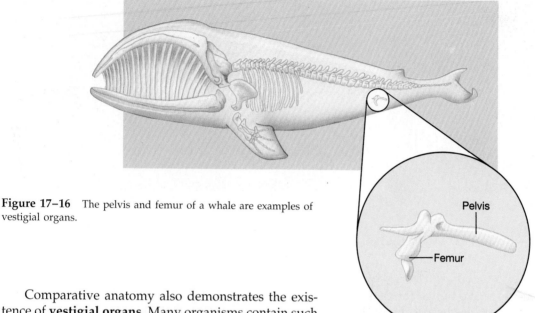

Figure 17–16 The pelvis and femur of a whale are examples of vestigial organs.

Comparative anatomy also demonstrates the existence of **vestigial organs.** Many organisms contain such organs or parts of organs that are seemingly nonfunctional and degenerate, often undersized or lacking some essential part. In the human body more than 100 such structures have been viewed as vestigial, including the appendix, the coccyx (fused tail vertebrae), the third molars, and muscles that move the ears. Whales (Figure 17–16) and pythons have vestigial hind leg bones; wingless birds have vestigial wing bones; many blind, burrowing, or cave-dwelling animals have vestigial eyes; and so on.

Darwin was interested in vestigial organs because they conflicted with the prevailing view of creation. He wondered how organisms that were the product of a "perfect creation" could have useless parts. Evolution, however, easily explained the existence of vestigial structures. The occasional presence of a vestigial organ is to be expected as an ancestral species evolves and adapts to a different mode of life. Some organs become much less important for survival and may end up as vestiges. When an organ loses much or all of its function, it no longer has any selective advantage. Since the presence of the vestigial organ is not hurting the organism, however, selective pressure for completely eliminating the vestigial organ is weak, and the organ tends to remain.

Mimicry Provides an Evolutionary Advantage

Natural selection increases the average fitness of individuals of a species for the environment in which it lives. A subtle example of natural selection is the development of **mimicry,** in which an organism resembles another organism or an inanimate object. **Protective coloration,** which permits an organism to blend into its surroundings, is a type of mimicry. Protective coloration screens an organism from its predators or, in the case of a predator, keeps the prey from noticing it until too late.

Many examples of protective form and coloration come readily to mind (Figure 17–17). Walking-stick insects resemble twigs so closely that one would never guess they are animals—until they start to walk. The chicks of ground-nesting birds are usually colored to blend in with the surrounding weeds and earth so that they cannot be discerned from a distance. Some katydids resemble leaves not only in color but in the pattern of veins in their wings. Pipefish have almost perfect camouflage coloration in green eel grass. Such protective coloration has evidently been preserved and accentuated by means of natural selection.

Batesian mimicry is a type of mimicry in which a harmless or edible species (the mimic) resembles another species (the model) that is dangerous in some way. A harmless moth may look so much like a bee or wasp that even a biologist would hesitate to pick it up (Figure 17–18). Likewise, many butterflies mimic the monarch butterfly. The monarch, having fed while a caterpillar on the poisonous milkweed plant, is toxic to birds. Its imitators, such as the viceroy butterfly, look like the monarch but are nonpoisonous.[1] Birds avoid

---

[1] There is currently much discussion about whether the viceroy is truly a batesian mimic. Some evidence suggests that viceroys are unpalatable, in which case the resemblance between viceroys and monarchs would be an example of müllerian mimicry. A poisonous or offensive chemical that viceroys would possess if they were müllerian mimics has never been identified, however.

(a)

(b)

(c)

Figure 17–17   Examples of mimicry. (*a*) Walking sticks resemble twigs when resting on a plant or other object. Most species occur in the tropics, where some of the largest walking sticks reach a length of more than 30 cm (1 foot)! (*b*) Different katydid species have evolved various forms of protective coloration to blend into their surroundings. The wings of this katydid even have a venation pattern similar to that of leaves. Some katydids are mottled to match partly dead leaves; still others are perfectly camouflaged when resting on rainforest tree trunks. (*c*) Bay pipefish, *Syngnathus leptorhynchus*. The pipefish is closely related to the seahorse. Most species have thin, narrow bodies from 2.5 to 45 cm (1 to 18 inches) in length. In addition to its protective coloration, its habit of holding its body in a position that resembles waving eel grass or algae aids in its camouflage. (*a*, G. R. Roberts; *b*, James L. Castner; *c*, Doug Wechsler)

(a)

(b)

Figure 17–18   Batesian mimicry. (*a*) Few would want to get close enough to this insect to discover that it is actually a moth. (*b*) A genuinely noxious insect, the golden paper wasp.

(*a*, L. E. Gilbert, University of Texas, Austin/Biological Photo Service; *b*, Peter J. Bryant/Biological Photo Service)

Figure 17–19   Müllerian mimicry. These various butterflies are all unpalatable.   (L. E. Gilbert, University of Texas, Austin/Biological Photo Service)

Müllerian mimicry is a type of mimicry in which different species, all of which are poisonous, harmful, or distasteful, resemble one another (Figure 17–19). Although their harmfulness protects them as individual species, their similar coloration works as an added advantage. Potential predators can learn their common warning coloration more easily than if each species had its own distinctive pattern.

Mimicry is evidence of adaptive evolution brought about by natural selection. An organism that is well adapted to its environment has an increased chance of surviving and reproducing, passing some of its genes on to the next generation. Mimicry provides a better chance of survival.

Related Species Have Similar Patterns of Development

The resemblance between embryos of different vertebrates (animals with backbones) is closer than the resemblance between their adults (Figure 17–20). In fact, it is difficult to distinguish among the early embryos of a fish, frog, turtle, chick, pig, and human. Segmented muscles, gill pouches, a tubular heart undivided into left and right sides, a system of aortic arches in the gill

eating the monarch and also avoid eating its imitators. Apparently, natural selection has maintained a resemblance that gives the mimic almost as much protection as the model, for when predators learn to associate the distinctive markings of the model with its undesirable characteristics, they tend to avoid all similarly marked animals.

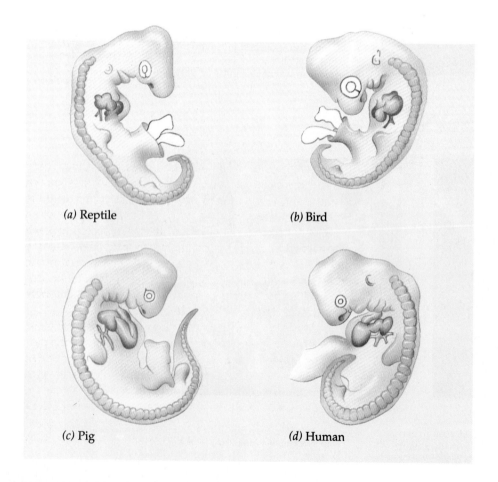

(a) Reptile

(b) Bird

(c) Pig

(d) Human

Figure 17–20   The early stages of embryonic development in several vertebrates. Numerous structural similarities are shared by the early stages, including the presence of a tail and gill pouches.

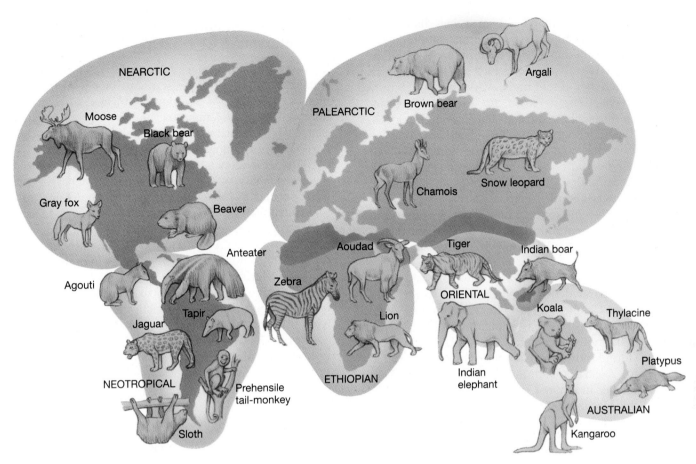

Figure 17–21   Animals and plants are distributed around the world in a distinctive pattern, which reveals the existence of six major biogeographical realms, each characterized by the presence of certain unique species. These biogeographical realms are the direct outcome of the centers of origin of certain species, of their past migrations, and of the barriers they encountered.

region, and many other fishlike features are found in the embryos of all vertebrates. All of these structures are necessary and functional in the developing fish. The small segmented muscles of the embryo give rise to the segmented muscles used by the adult fish in swimming. The gill pouches break through to the surface as gill slits. The adult fish heart remains undivided because it pumps venous blood forward to the gills that develop in association with the aortic arches.

However, none of these fishlike features persists in the adults of reptiles, birds, or mammals. So why are they present in the embryos of reptiles, birds, and mammals? Because the higher vertebrates evolved from fish, they share the fish's basic pattern of development. The accumulation of genetic changes since the fish diverged from the evolutionary line leading to the higher vertebrates modifies the pattern of development of the higher vertebrate embryos (see Chapters 16 and 49).

The Distribution of Plants and Animals Supports Evolution

The study of the distribution of plants and animals is called **biogeography.** One of its basic tenets is that each species of animal and plant originated, or evolved, only once. The particular place where this occurred is known as the species' **center of origin.** The center of origin is not a single point but the range of the population when the new species formed. From its center of origin, each species spreads out until halted by a barrier of some kind—physical, such as an ocean, desert, or mountain; environmental, such as an unfavorable climate; or ecological, such as the presence of organisms that compete with it for food or shelter (Figure 17–21).

Most plant and animal species have their own characteristic geographical distributions. The **range** of a particular species—that is, the portion of Earth over which it is found—may be only a few square miles or, as with humans, almost the entire world. In general, closely related species do not have identical ranges, nor are their ranges far apart. They are usually adjacent but separated by a barrier of some sort, such as a mountain or desert.

We would expect to find a given species distributed everywhere that it could survive if climate and topography were the only factors determining its distribution (that is, if evolution were not a factor). However, species are often not distributed everywhere that they could survive. Central Africa, for example, has elephants, gorillas, chimpanzees, lions, and antelopes, whereas Brazil, with a similar climate and environmental conditions, has none of these. These animals evolved in Africa and could not expand their range into South America because the Atlantic Ocean was an impassable barrier. Likewise, South America has prehensile-tailed monkeys, sloths, and tapirs, none of which is found in Africa. Thus, the natural distribution of organisms on Earth seems understandable only on the basis of evolution.

Regions such as Australia and New Zealand, which have been separated from the rest of the world for a long time (see Chapter 20), have flora and fauna specific to these areas. Australia has populations of egg-laying mammals (monotremes) and pouched mammals (marsupials) found nowhere else. Two hundred million years ago, Australia and the other continents were joined together in a major land mass (see Chapter 20). During the Mesozoic era, the continents drifted apart and Australia became isolated from the rest of the world. The original monotremes and marsupials that were present when Australia broke its connection with the large land mass gave rise to a variety of species able to take advantage of the different habitats available.

The kinds of animals and plants found on oceanic islands in general resemble those of the nearest mainland, yet they include some species found nowhere else. Darwin studied the flora and fauna of the Cape Verde Islands, some 400 miles west of Dakar, Africa, and of the Galapagos Islands, a comparable distance west of Ecuador, South America. On each archipelago, the plants and terrestrial animals were indigenous (native), but those of the Cape Verdes resembled African species and those of the Galapagos resembled South American species. Darwin concluded that organisms from the neighboring continent migrated, or were carried, to the islands and subsequently evolved into new species.

The animals and plants found on oceanic islands are only those that could survive the trip there. There are no frogs or toads on the Galapagos, even though there are woodland spots ideally suited for such creatures, because neither the animals nor their eggs can survive exposure to sea water. There are no native terrestrial mammals either, although there are many bats, as well as land and sea birds. The occurrence in the Galapagos of these particular forms—closely related, yet not identical, to those of the Ecuador coast—suggests strongly that evolution has modified the descendants of the first animals and plants to reach the islands.

Molecules Contain a Record of Evolutionary Change

Evidence for evolutionary relationships is provided by similarities and differences in the biochemistry and molecular biology of different organisms. Also, evolutionary lines of descent based solely on biochemical and molecular characters closely resemble lines of descent based on morphological and fossil evidence.

Further evidence that all life is related comes from the universality of the genetic code (see Chapter 12), that specifies a sequence of three nucleotides in DNA that code for three nucleotides in mRNA that code for a particular amino acid in a polypeptide chain. For example, "AAA" in DNA codes for "UUU" in mRNA, which codes for the amino acid phenylalanine in organisms as diverse as shrimp and tulips; in fact, "AAA" codes for phenylalanine in *all* organisms examined to date. Thus, organisms owe their characteristics to the types of proteins that they possess, which are determined by the *order* of nucleotides in their DNA. The genetic code has been passed along through all branches of the evolutionary tree since its origin in some extremely early form of life.

Immunological data

The blood serum of each species of vertebrate contains specific proteins, coded for by specific genes, whose degree of similarity can be determined by antigen-antibody reactions (see Chapter 43). When serum proteins are compared by this method, our closest relatives are the great apes and then, in descending order, the Old World monkeys, the New World monkeys, and, finally, the tarsiers and lemurs (see Chapter 21 for a description of these primates). The biochemical relationships of a variety of organisms tested in this way correlate with and complement the relationships determined by other means. Cats, dogs, and bears have very similar serum proteins. Cows, sheep, goats, and deer constitute another group with related serum proteins. Similar tests of the sera of crustaceans, insects, and mollusks have shown that species that are regarded as being closely related based on anatomical or fossil evidence have comparably similar serum proteins.

Amino acid sequencing

Darwin's theory that all forms of life are related through descent with modification from earliest organisms has been further verified as we have learned more about molecular biology. Investigations of the sequence of amino acids in proteins obtained from different species have revealed great similarities and certain specific differences.

Even organisms that are very remotely related, such as humans and the bacterium *Escherichia coli*, have

Table 17–1 DIFFERENCES IN NUCLEOTIDE SEQUENCES IN DNA
AS EVIDENCE OF PHYLOGENETIC RELATIONSHIPS

Species Pairs	Percentage Differences in Nucleotide Sequences between Pairs of Species
Human–chimpanzee	2.5
Human–gibbon	5.1
Human–Old World monkey	9.0
Human–New World monkey	15.8
Human–lemur	42.0

From Stebbins, G. L. *Darwin to DNA, Molecules To Humanity*. W. H. Freeman, San Francisco, 1982.

some proteins such as cytochrome *c* (a respiratory protein found in all aerobic organisms) in common. In the course of the long, independent evolution of different organisms, mutations and other evolutionary processes (see Chapter 18) resulted in the substitution of amino acids at various locations in the cytochrome *c* protein. The longer it has been since two organisms diverged, the greater are the differences in the amino acid sequences of their cytochrome *c* molecules.

Despite differences, the cytochrome *c* molecules of all species are clearly similar in structure and function. A diagram that shows lines of descent (evolutionary relationships) can be derived from differences in the amino acid sequence of a common protein like cytochrome *c*. Such a **phylogenetic tree** for vertebrates is depicted in Figure 17–22.

DNA sequencing and hybridization

Because DNA codes for proteins,[1] the differences in amino acid sequences indirectly demonstrate the nature and number of underlying DNA base pair changes that must have occurred during evolution. Such molecular information is determined directly by **DNA sequencing,** which determines the order of nucleotides in strands of DNA that code for a gene shared by several organisms. Generally, the more closely species are thought to be related on the basis of other evidence, the greater is the percentage of nucleotide sequences that their DNA molecules have in common (Table 17–1).

DNA hybridization studies offer a quicker way to evaluate DNA similarities and differences than does DNA sequencing (see Chapter 14). In **DNA hybridization,** DNA is isolated from two different species, con-

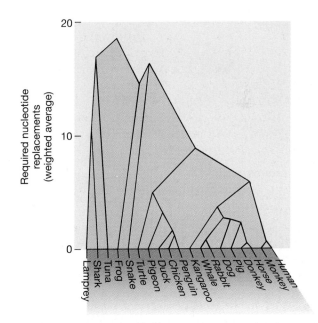

Figure 17–22 A phylogenetic tree of selected vertebrates based on differences in the amino acid sequence of cytochrome *c*. A fairly close resemblance exists between this phylogenetic tree, constructed from molecular evidence, and classic phylogenetic trees based on fossil and morphological evidence. (Adapted from Fitch and Margoliash, in *Evolutionary Biology*, 4:67–109, Plenum Publishing, 1970.)

verted to single strands, mixed together, and allowed to base pair (hybridize). The degree of hybridization is related to how similar the order of base pairs is for the two strands of DNA and can be used to infer evolutionary relationships (Figure 17–23).

DNA base pair changes, which cause differences in the DNA sequences between two different organisms, occur at a more or less constant rate within a given taxonomic group. Using this knowledge, it is possible to develop a **molecular clock** to complement geological estimates of the divergence of species. From the number

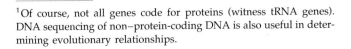

[1]Of course, not all genes code for proteins (witness tRNA genes). DNA sequencing of non–protein-coding DNA is also useful in determining evolutionary relationships.

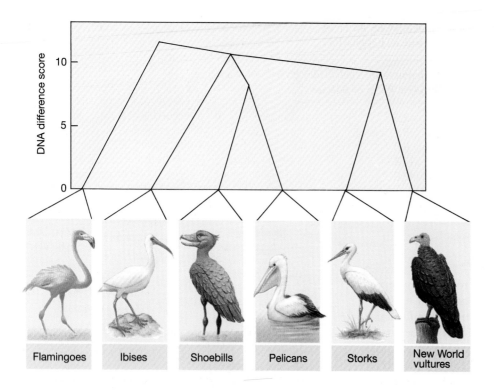

Figure 17–23 A phylogenetic tree of selected birds from the Western Hemisphere. This tree was constructed using data from DNA hybridization studies, in which single-stranded DNA was mixed and reassociated to form double-stranded molecules. The DNA difference score is a measure of the degree of base-pairing. If the DNA difference score between two lines of descent is great, the organisms are less closely related.

of alterations in the DNA nucleotide sequence of one organism compared with another, we can estimate the time of divergence between two closely related species or higher taxonomic groups.

SUMMARY

I. Evolution, the genetic change in a population of organisms over time, is the unifying concept of biology. It enables us to make sense of the tremendous variety of life that exists in the world.

II. Charles Darwin and Alfred Wallace independently proposed essentially identical theories of evolution by natural selection.
   A. *Overproduction:* Each species produces more offspring than will survive to maturity.
   B. *Variation:* Genetic variation exists among these offspring.
   C. *Competition:* Competition occurs among these offspring for the resources needed for life, i.e., food, space, habitat.
   D. *Survival to reproduce:* The offspring with the most favorable combinations of genetic characteristics are most likely to survive and reproduce, passing those characteristics on to the next generation. Over time, changes accumulate in the gene pools of populations and may cause new species to evolve.

III. The synthetic theory of evolution combines Darwin's theory of evolution by natural selection with the genetic mechanisms for explaining evolution (Mendelian genetics).

IV. The concept that evolution has taken place is now well documented.
   A. The most direct evidence of evolution comes from paleontology.
      1. Fossils are remains or traces of ancient organisms.
      2. There are several types of fossils, including compressions, impressions, molds, casts, and petrifactions.
   B. Evidence supporting evolution is derived from comparative anatomy.
      1. Homologous organs have basic structural similarities, even though the organs may be used in different ways. Homologous organs indicate evolutionary ties between the organisms possessing them.
      2. Analogous organs have similar functions but are not homologous and do not indicate close evolutionary ties.
      3. The occasional presence of a vestigial organ is to be expected as an ancestral species adapts to different modes of life and evolves into new species.
   C. Mimicry, which increases the fitness of an organism for a particular environment, provides evidence of evolution.
      1. In batesian mimicry, a harmless or edible species

(the mimic) has evolved to resemble another species (the model) that is dangerous in some way. Predators avoid the mimic as well as the model.

   2. In müllerian mimicry, several different species—all of which are poisonous, harmful, or distasteful—have evolved to resemble one another. Predators easily learn to avoid their common warning coloration.

D. Embryology provides evidence of evolution.
   1. The embryos of related animals are more similar than the adults.
   2. The accumulation of genetic changes since organisms diverged in evolution modifies the pattern of development in higher vertebrate embryos.

E. The distribution of plants and animals (biogeography) supports evolution.
   1. Areas that have been separated from the rest of the world for a long time have organisms specific to those areas.
   2. Each species originated only once (at its center of origin).
   3. From its center of origin, each species spread out until halted by a barrier of some kind.

F. Biochemistry and molecular biology provide compelling evidence of evolution.
   1. Blood sera of closely related vertebrates are more similar than sera of distantly related vertebrates.
   2. The sequence of amino acids in common proteins such as cytochrome c or hemoglobin reveals greater similarities in closely related species.
   3. A greater proportion of the sequence of nucleotides in DNA is identical in closely related organisms.
   4. The universality of the genetic code is further evidence that all life is related.

POST-TEST

1. The fact that all species developed from earlier forms by the accumulation of genetic variation over many successive generations is known as the theory of _____ .

2. The genetic constitution of an entire population of a given organism is termed its _____ _____ .

3. Thomas Malthus believed that _____ increase in size geometrically until checked by factors in the environment.

4. Darwin proposed _____ _____ as the mechanism by which evolutionary change takes place.

5. Inherent in Darwin's theory of evolution by natural selection is the concept that organisms have the potential to produce more offspring than _____ to reproductive maturity.

6. The four premises of natural selection are overpopulation, variation, competition, and _____ to _____ .

7. In natural selection, the selecting agent is the environment, whereas in artificial selection, the selecting agent is _____ .

8. The synthetic theory of evolution is also called _____ .

9. A fossil in which the body part has been trapped in sediments without being completely decomposed is known as a _____ .

10. Geologists can identify specific sedimentary layers of rock by certain key invertebrate fossils, known as _____ _____ .

11. An organ that appears to have little or no function, and is smaller than a similar, fully functional equivalent in the organism's ancestor or relatives, is known as a(n) _____ organ.

12. The wings of butterflies and bats have similar functions but are quite different in structure. This is an example of _____ organs.

13. The portion of Earth over which a given species is found is its _____ .

14. The blood sera of humans match the sera of the _____ _____ most closely.

15. The universality of the _____ _____ is evidence for evolution from a common ancestor.

REVIEW QUESTIONS

1. Explain briefly the concept of biological evolution by natural selection.

2. How can you account for the fact that both Darwin and Wallace independently and almost simultaneously proposed essentially identical theories of evolution by natural selection?

3. In what ways does Lamarck's theory of adaptation not agree with present evidence?

4. Consider the giraffe's long neck. Explain how this came about using Lamarck's concept of evolution. Then explain the giraffe using Darwin's mechanism of evolution by natural selection.

5. Why are only inherited variations important in the evolutionary process?

6. Explain this statement: Natural selection picks from among available variants those best suited to the conditions in which the population finds itself. It does not select based on some view of "best design" or future need. Instead, natural selection provides short-term solutions to immediate environmental challenges.

7. What part of Darwin's theory was he unable to explain? How does the synthetic theory of evolution explain this?

8. Discuss the factors that might interfere with our obtaining a complete and unbiased picture of life in the past from a study of the fossil record.

9. List as many vestigial structures in the human body as you can.

10. Explain why marsupials are widespread in Australia and almost nonexistent elsewhere.

RECOMMENDED READINGS

Amos, W. H. Hawaii's volcanic cradle of life. *National Geographic,* July 1990, pp. 70–87. Depicts the colonization of volcanic lava by a few hardy species and portrays some of the endemic (found nowhere else) species that have evolved in the Hawaiian Islands.

Carson, H. L. The process whereby species originate. *BioScience* Vol. 37, 1987. Discusses the importance of geographical separation in the evolution of species.

Darwin, C. R. *On the Origin of Species by Means of Natural Selection or the Preservation of Favored Races in the Struggle for Life.* Cambridge University Press, New York, 1975. A readily obtainable reprint of one of the most important books of all time. Darwin's long essay is still of great significance to modern readers.

Dawkins, R. *The Blind Watchmaker.* W.W. Norton, New York, 1986. A review of evolution, including the evidence supporting it and the controversies associated with it.

Greene, E. A diet-induced developmental polymorphism in a caterpillar. *Science* 243, 3 February 1989, pp. 643–645. An interesting examination of caterpillars that mimic the food they eat. Those that eat flower clusters on oak trees resemble the flower clusters; those that eat oak leaves resemble twigs to which the leaves are attached.

O'Brien, S. J. The ancestry of the giant panda. *Scientific American,* November 1987. The evolutionary relationship of pandas to raccoons and bears has been clarified using the techniques of molecular biology.

Simpson, G. G. *Fossils and the History of Life.* W.H. Freeman, New York, 1983. An overview of fossil evidence for evolution written by an eminent evolutionary biologist.

Stanley, S. M. *Earth and Life through Time.* W.H. Freeman, San Francisco, 1985. A presentation of evolution for the general public.

Swan, L. W. The concordance of ontogeny with phylogeny. *BioScience* 40:5, May 1990. Examines embryological evidence for evolution.

Thompson, G. R., and J. Turk. *Modern Physical Geology.* Saunders College Publishing, Philadelphia, 1991. Contains informative material on radioactive dating and fossils.

Wallace, A. R. *The Malay Archipelago.* Oxford University Press, New York, 1987. A reprint of Wallace's classic investigation.

Population Genetics

Evolutionary change, which includes modifications of morphology, physiology, ecology, and behavior, is inherited from one generation to the next. Although Darwin recognized that evolution occurs in populations, he did not understand how traits are passed on to successive generations. One of the most significant advances that has occurred in biology since Darwin's time has been the elucidation of the genetic basis of evolution.

As mentioned briefly in Chapter 17, each population possesses an isolated gene pool, which includes all possible alleles at each locus of each chromosome present in the breeding individuals of the population. Because most species are diploid, each individual member of a population contains only two alleles for each locus. Therefore, a single individual has only some of the genes found in its population gene pool (Figure 18–1). Moreover, the genetic variation present in a given population (as illustrated by different phenotypes) indicates that each individual has a different portion of the genes that exist in the gene pool.

If a population is not evolving, the frequencies of each allele remain constant from one generation to the next generation. Changes in allele frequencies over successive generations indicate that evolution has occurred. This type of evolution is sometimes referred to as **microevolution,** because it involves changes that are taking place *within* a population. In this chapter, we examine the factors responsible for microevolution after first considering the genetics of a population that is not evolving.

Bankivia fasciata, an Australian mollusk, exhibits a wide variation in shell colors and patterns. (Barbara J. Miller/Biological Photo Service)

After you have studied this chapter you should be able to

1. Distinguish between the gene pool of a population and the genotype of an individual.
2. Explain the Hardy-Weinberg law and its role in population genetics.
3. Discuss the factors that alter allele frequencies in populations: genetic drift, gene flow (differential migration), mutation, and natural selection.
4. Distinguish between stabilizing selection, directional selection, and disruptive selection and give an example of each.

5. Describe the nature and extent of genetic variation, including genetic polymorphism.
6. Explain how the sickle cell allele illustrates heterozygote advantage.
7. Relate how frequency-dependent selection affects genetic variation.
8. Compare the neutralist and selectionist views on the relative importance of genetic drift and selection in maintaining genetic variation.

THE HARDY-WEINBERG LAW DEMONSTRATES THAT ALLELE FREQUENCIES DO NOT CHANGE IN A POPULATION THAT IS NOT EVOLVING

If we set a trap over a bunch of ripe bananas, we could sample a population of fruit flies, *Drosophila melanogaster*. After we anesthetize and count them, we might find that we have 1000 fruit flies, 910 with gray bodies and 90 with black bodies. After the fruit flies are released, they would mate. If we trapped and counted the next generation of fruit flies, we would find a population that is essentially the same as the previous one, with

roughly nine gray flies to every black fly. If we did this for a succession of generations, we would always get the same result.

The explanation for this stability of populations in successive generations was provided in 1908 by G. H. Hardy, an English mathematician, and W. Weinberg, a German physician. They pointed out that the frequencies of various genotypes in a population can be described mathematically.

Mendel's laws, as we have seen, describe the frequency of genotypes among offspring of a single mating pair. In contrast, the **Hardy-Weinberg law** describes the frequencies of genotypes of an entire breeding population. The Hardy-Weinberg law shows that in large populations, the process of inheritance does not by itself cause changes in allele frequencies, which remain constant from generation to generation. It also explains why dominant phenotypes are not necessarily more common than recessive phenotypes in a population. Thus, knowledge of the Hardy-Weinberg law is essential to understand the mechanisms of evolutionary change in sexually reproducing populations.

We now expand the fruit fly example to explain the Hardy-Weinberg law. A few simple crosses of black and gray fruit flies reveals that the allele for gray body, *B*, is dominant over the allele for black body, *b*. Gray-bodied flies include some that are homozygous, *BB*, and some that are heterozygous, *Bb*. Obviously, all the black flies are homozygous, *bb*. The frequency of either allele, *B* or *b*, is described by a number from zero to one. An allele that is totally absent from the population has a frequency of zero. If in the population all of the alleles at a given locus are the same, then the frequency of that allele is one.

Because only two alleles, *B* and *b*, exist for the gene, the sum of their frequencies must equal one. If we let *p* represent the frequency of the *B* allele, and *q* the frequency of the *b* allele in the population, then we obtain a binomial equation,[1] $p + q = 1$. When we know the

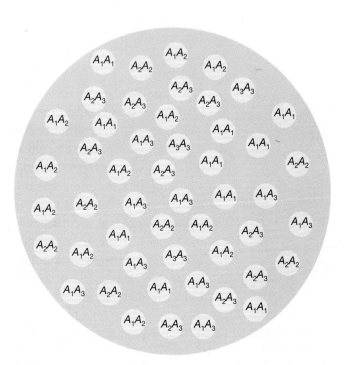

Figure 18–1 A gene pool. This drawing shows only one genetic locus (*A*), with three different alleles possible at that locus (*A₁*, *A₂*, *A₃*). Because each individual (represented by a small circle) is diploid, it possesses only two alleles for each genetic locus. The gene frequencies represented in this drawing are 0.40 for A_1, 0.35 for A_2, and 0.25 for A_3.

---

[1] A binomial equation is an algebraic expression that consists of two quantities connected by a plus or minus sign.

value of either p or q, we can calculate the value of the

[handwritten annotations partially covering text]

... his binomial ... relationship ... the popula- ... frequency of

$$q^2$$

... ency of bb

... in our popula- ... genotype, q^2, is ... is equal to the ... previous discus- ... 3 = 0.7.

... calculate the fre- ... $p^2 = 0.7 \times 0.7 =$ ... gray flies, Bb, ... Thus, approxi- ... ygous and 420 are ... homozygous and ... the number with

... stribution of geno- ... $pq + q^2$, whatever ... be, is in a genetic ... **equilibrium** (Fig- ... ium tells us what to ... olving.

... occurs (that is, the ... enerations in a situ- ... same) when the fol-

... ulation of individu- ... e laws of probability ... drift, to be discussed shortly, ... cy of alleles in a large population as they do in a small population.

2. **Isolation.** There can be no exchange of genes with other populations that might have different allele frequencies—that is, no movement of individuals out of a population (by emigration) or into a population (by immigration).

3. **No mutation.** In this instance, there must be no mutations of B or b.

4. **No selection.** If natural selection is occurring, certain genotypes are favored over others and the allele frequencies change.

5. **Random mating.** In this instance, the individuals represented by BB, Bb, and bb must mate with one another at random; there must be equal probabilities of mating between genotypes. That is, matings between genotypes must occur in proportion to the frequencies of the genotypes. (For example, if BB and Bb flies occur in the proportions of 0.49 and 0.42,

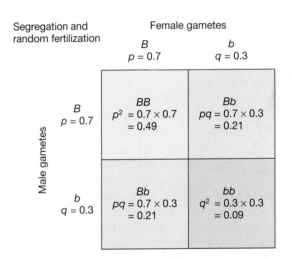

	Gray body	Gray body	Black body
Phenotypes			
Genotypes	BB	Bb	bb
Frequency of genotype in population	0.49	0.42	0.09
Frequency of gametes	$B = 0.49 + 0.21$ $= 0.70$	$b = 0.21 + 0.09$ $= 0.30$	

Segregation and random fertilization

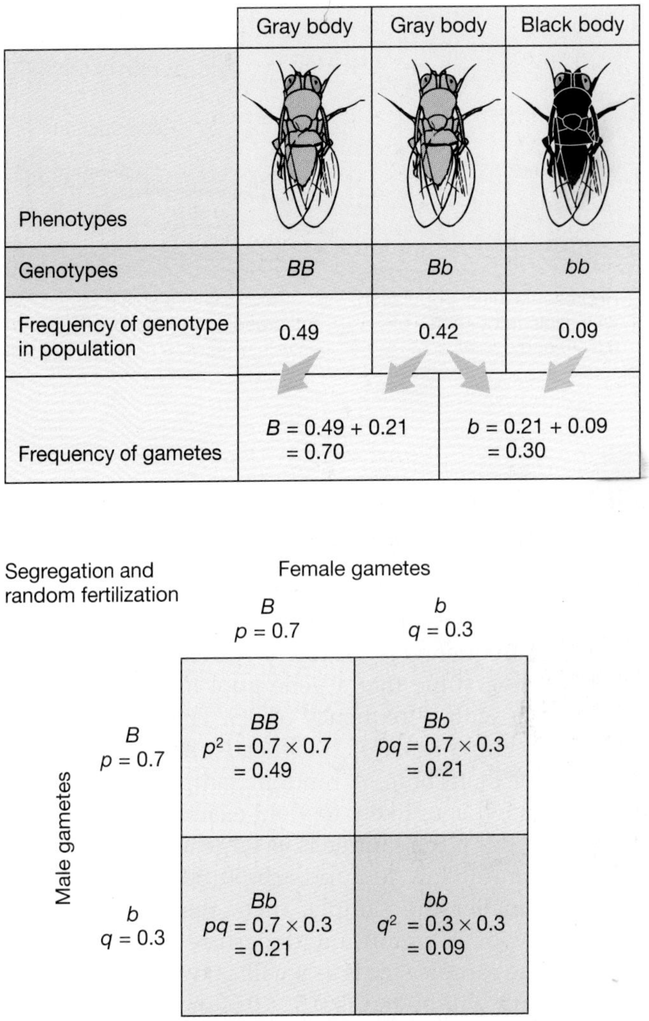

Figure 18–2 The random union of eggs and sperm containing B or b alleles. The frequency of appearance of each of the possible genotypes (BB, Bb, bb) in the offspring is calculated by multiplying the frequencies of the alleles B and b in eggs and sperm.

respectively, $BB \times Bb$ matings should occur at a frequency of $0.49 \times 0.42 = 0.2058$.)

EVOLUTION OCCURS WHEN THERE ARE CHANGES IN ALLELE FREQUENCIES IN A GENE POOL

Allele frequencies are often significantly different from those expected on the basis of the Hardy-Weinberg law. A departure of a population from Hardy-Weinberg equilibrium results from such phenomena as genetic drift (which is greater in small populations), migration, nonrandom mating, mutation, and selection. When one or more of these processes is operating, allele frequencies in a population undergo change from one generation to the next.

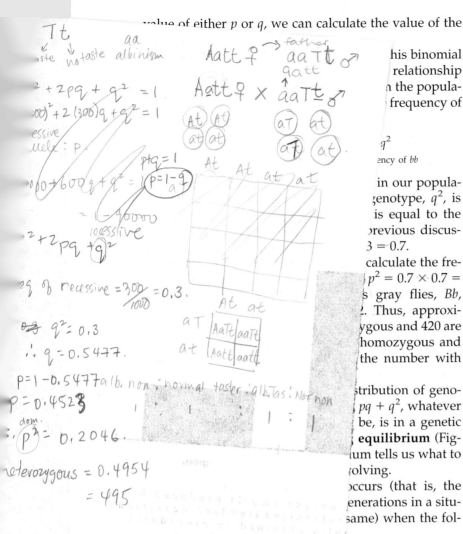

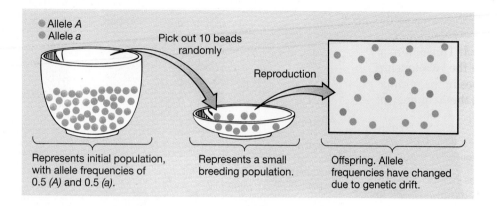

Represents initial population, with allele frequencies of 0.5 (*A*) and 0.5 (*a*).

Represents a small breeding population.

Offspring. Allele frequencies have changed due to genetic drift.

Figure 18–3   Genetic drift. The smaller the breeding population, the more likely it is that allele frequencies will change.

Genetic Drift Causes Changes in Allele Frequencies by Random, or Chance, Events

The size of a population has important effects on allele frequencies because the probability of a departure from the initial frequency is inversely related to population size. Let us assume that a gene pool has the alleles *A* and *a*, each with a frequency of 0.5. This can be simulated by using a bowl of 1000 beads, half of them red and half of them blue. A random sample of ten beads from the bowl is unlikely to yield exactly five reds and five blues. But if the sample is as large as 100, the count is much more likely to approach 50:50.

The smaller the sample, then, the greater is the probability of a significant departure from the true value. If the sample size is as small as two, the probability that both will be red is 0.5 × 0.5, or 0.25. The probability that both will be blue is 0.5 × 0.5 = 0.25. The probability that one will be red and one will be blue is only 0.5.

The effect is similar when a breeding population is very small. The probability of two individuals with the same traits mating is increased, and a reasonable chance exists that the variability of the descendant generation will deviate from that of the parent population (Figure 18–3). (Variability refers to differences in form or quality. In this chapter, variability can be defined in terms of heterozygosity. Variability is highest when allele frequencies are equal.)

If the population remains small for many generations, sampling errors accumulate, and the population's variability drifts in a random way. One allele may be eliminated by chance from the population, even if it determines a trait that has adaptive value. Thus, genetic variation may decrease within a population. Also, in such small populations, a strong tendency exists for all members of the population to become homozygous for one of its alleles. When this occurs, the allele is said to be "fixed" in the gene pool (that is, its frequency becomes 1.0) and the other allele is "lost" (its frequency becomes zero).

The production of random evolutionary changes in small breeding populations is termed **genetic drift.** Genetic drift results in changes in the gene pool of a population from generation to generation. However, genetic drift affects allele frequencies randomly (that is, due to chance). Its direction may or may not be the same as that of other factors that change allele frequencies, such as migration, mutation, and natural selection. As a result, genetic drift may either reinforce or oppose those forces. Although genetic drift can decrease genetic variation *within* a population, it tends to increase the amount of variation *between* local populations.

Genetic bottlenecks cause genetic drift

Because of fluctuations in the environment, such as a depletion in food supply or an outbreak of disease, a population may periodically experience a rapid and marked decrease in the number of individuals. The population is said to go through a **genetic bottleneck** in which genetic drift can occur in the few survivors. As the population again increases in size, the frequencies of many alleles may be quite different from those in the population preceding the decline (Figure 18–4). A genetic bottleneck that took place in the cheetah population about 10,000 years ago is responsible for the low genetic variability that plagues this magnificent animal today (see Focus on The Cheetah: On the Brink of Extinction).

Genetic drift occurs in new colonies of individuals

Genetic drift is also important when one or a few individuals extend beyond the normal range for that species and establish a colony, as in the colonization of oceanic islands. The colonizers carry with them a small and random sample of the alleles of the gene pool from which they came, and their population is small enough initially for genetic drift to operate. The phenomenon

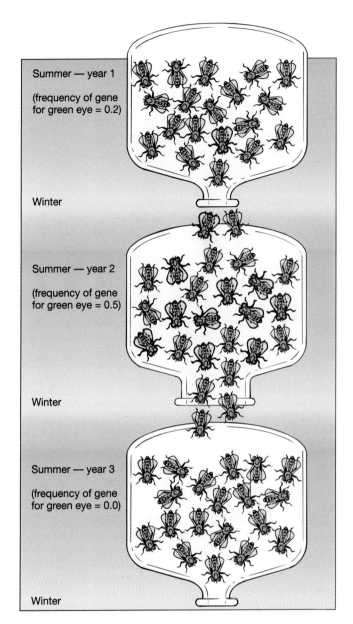

Figure 18–4 The bottleneck effect. Because only a small population of flies survives the winter, its genotypes, not necessarily resulting from natural selection, determine the genetic frequencies of the entire succeeding summer population. (The genotypic frequencies do not match the phenotypic ratios depicted because heterozygous individuals exhibit the dominant phenotype but contribute recessive genes to the allele frequencies.)

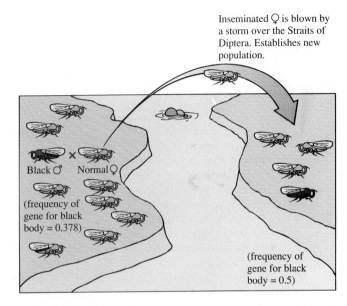

Figure 18–5 The founder effect. In this example, the genetic frequencies of a population have been determined by the genotypes that happened to be possessed by its founders but were not characteristic of frequencies in the population as a whole. (The genotypic frequencies do not match the phenotypic ratios depicted here because heterozygous individuals exhibit the dominant phenotype but contribute recessive genes to the allele frequencies.)

Chapter 15). Apparently the small founder population of humans who colonized Australia, eventually becoming aborigines, lacked the I^B allele. Consequently, Australian aborigines do not have either type B or type AB blood.

Gene Flow, Which Changes the Amount of Variation in the Gene Pool, Is Caused by the Differential Migration of Organisms

Members of a species are not distributed uniformly throughout their range but occur in clusters that are spatially separated to some extent from other clusters. For example, the bullfrogs of one pond form a population separated from those in an adjacent pond (Figure 18–6). Some exchanges occur by migration between ponds, but the frogs in one pond are much more likely to mate with those in the same pond. Members of a species tend to be distributed in such local populations, termed **demes.** Because each deme is more or less isolated genetically from other populations of the species, demes have distinct genetic traits.

The migration of breeding individuals between demes causes a corresponding movement of alleles, or **gene flow,** that can have significant evolutionary consequences. As alleles flow from one population to another, they increase the amount of genetic variability within the population receiving them. If the gene flow

has been termed the **founder effect** (Figure 18–5). As a result, isolated populations may have very different allele frequencies from those characteristic of the species elsewhere, and these differences may very well be random rather than adaptive (see Focus on Evolution of the Africanized Honeybee).

The ABO blood groups in Australian aborigines illustrate the founder effect. Recall that there are three different alleles (I^A, I^B, and i^O) that result in four different phenotypic blood types (A, B, AB, and O) (see

The Cheetah: On the Brink of Extinction

The cheetah is the most specialized member of the cat family. It is the world's fastest animal and has been clocked at 110 kilometers per hour for short distances. Despite its speed, this fascinating creature is a somewhat timid predator that often gives up its prey to more aggressive animals such as lions, vultures, and hyenas.

There are currently about 15,000 cheetahs worldwide, with about 650 of these held in zoos. The cheetah is in danger of becoming extinct, but unlike most endangered animals, the main reason for its declining numbers has little to do with humans. (Many animals are endangered because of habitat destruction and pollution caused by human activities.)

The problems faced by cheetahs, both in zoos and in the wild, are the result of a genetic bottleneck that occurred at the end of the last ice age, approximately 10,000 years ago (see figure). At that time, cheetahs almost became extinct. The few cheetahs that survived had a greatly reduced genetic variability. Thus, the cheetah population today is genetically uniform or homogeneous, a characteristic that causes low reproductive success. The sperm of male

A cheetah and her cub. Genetic variation in the cheetah was considerably reduced by a genetic bottleneck that took place some 10,000 years ago.   (E. R. Degginger)

cheetahs has a very low fertility, and the animals do not have as many offspring as other cat species. Also, many cheetah offspring have health problems and are more susceptible to disease.

A number of scientists are developing a comprehensive strategy to help save the cheetah, including the use of reproductive techniques such as in vitro fertilization, in which an egg is fertilized by sperm in a test tube before being implanted in a female cheetah. These techniques may help scientists to maintain the little bit of genetic diversity that remains in cheetahs today, hopefully increasing their chances of long-term survival.

Figure 18–6   A member of a deme of bullfrogs. The frogs in one pond tend to mate with other frogs in the same pond.   (Dwight Kuhn)

between two demes is great enough, these populations become more similar genetically. Because gene flow has a tendency to reduce the amount of variation between two populations, it tends to counteract the effects of genetic drift and natural selection.

The amount that different species migrate depends on their patterns of breeding and dispersal. Although the migration of certain animals, such as birds, is obvious, many migrations are less apparent. For example, plant pollen may be carried long distances by wind or

FOCUS ON

Evolution of the Africanized Honeybee

Periodically one reads reports in the news about the migration of Africanized honeybees into North America (see figure). The movement of these bees is of great concern for several reasons. First, the Africanized honeybee is dangerous because it attacks as a group at the slightest provocation. Also, it is feared that the Africanized honeybee will interbreed or compete with the European honeybee, which is the type of bee raised commercially in this country. This would adversely affect the honeybees' important roles in pollination and honey production.

Africanized honeybees evolved from a small number of African honeybees that were introduced into Brazil in 1956. Because the number of African honeybees was so small, they contained only a fraction of the genes present in the gene pool of African honeybees. As a result of the founder effect, the few genes present in the introduced population formed the gene pool upon which natural selection would act in its new habitat in South America. Natural selection of this limited gene pool resulted in the Africanized honeybee.

Africanized honeybees have spread beyond their point of origin

Africanized honeybees. (Visuals Unlimited/ D. M. Caron, BES)

in Brazil to occupy large areas of Latin America and Mexico. They passed into Texas in 1990. Wherever they have migrated, decreases in honey production have occurred. Apiculture (beekeeping) in countries occupied by the Africanized bees has also changed because the beekeepers must now use a lot of protective equipment.

How far will Africanized honeybees go? Will they stop because of a climatic barrier, or can they expand their range into more northerly areas of North America? Based on research done in Argentina, climate is thought to pose no barrier to Africanized honeybees. Consequently, they will probably continue to expand their range.

We can take two different approaches to this problem. We can continue to mount expensive pest-control measures whenever populations of Africanized honeybees are discovered in the United States. In Kern County, California, for example, $1 million were spent eradicating Africanized honeybees in 1985. Some biologists advocate a different approach—one that utilizes genetics. Instead of fighting their invasion of our land, we can start selectively breeding Africanized honeybees with African honeybees. The African honeybees have a number of desirable traits that are missing in Africanized honeybees. By selectively breeding African honeybees that possess desirable traits with Africanized honeybees, it would be possible to increase the variation in their gene pool. Artificial selection might even give rise to a variety of honeybee that is as commercially important as the European honeybee.

animals (see Chapter 27). Seeds and fruits, which are formed after sexual reproduction has taken place, are often modified for dispersal, in some cases over long distances (see Chapter 35). Coconut fruits, for example, may be transported hundreds or even thousands of miles by ocean currents.

If the amount of migration by members of a population is large, and if populations differ in their allele frequencies, then significant genetic changes can result. Humans had a long period of relative isolation of different population groups until recently (the past 300 years). The increase in gene flow has significantly altered allele frequencies within various human populations. For example, the United States has been a "melting pot" for racial groups, each of which originally had many of the attributes of a deme. African Americans have a frequency of the Rh^0 allele (one of the alleles of the Rh blood group) of 0.45. In contrast, the frequency of this allele in Africans is 0.63. The lower frequency in African Americans has been attributed to an influx of alleles from the white population, in which the frequency of Rh^0 is very low, 0.03. Allele frequencies have changed in the white population, too, because gene flow has occurred in both directions. The corresponding change in the Rh^0 allele in white populations has not been as dramatic, however, because the white population in the United States is considerably larger than the African American population.

(a)

(b)

Figure 18–7 Fruit flies, *Drosophila melanogaster*. (*a*) A normal fly. (*b*) A mutant with vestigial wings. Hundreds of mutations are known to occur in these little flies, which breed rapidly enough to allow us to follow the transmission of such altered traits from generation to generation. Because mutations are random changes in genetic material, most mutations are harmful to the organism, as is obviously the case in the vestigial wing mutation shown here. Yet for island-dwelling insects, fully developed wings might be more of a disadvantage than an advantage, permitting the insect to be too easily blown away from land. Perhaps for this reason, flies and other insects that dwell on small islands frequently have reduced wings or are entirely wingless. (Peter J. Bryant/Biological Photo Service)

Mutation Increases Variation in the Gene Pool

Variation is introduced into a gene pool through **mutation,** which is the source of all new alleles (Figure 18–7). Although allele frequencies may be changed by mutation, changes in allele frequency by this means are several orders of magnitude smaller than changes caused by other evolutionary forces. As an evolutionary *force,* mutation is negligible, but it is important as the ultimate *source* of variation.

Mutations result from a change in the nucleotide base pairs of a gene, from a rearrangement of genes within chromosomes so that their interactions produce different effects, or from a change in the chromosomes (see Chapter 12). Mutations occur randomly and spontaneously. The rates of mutation are relatively stable for a particular locus but vary by several orders of magnitude between loci within a single species and between different species.

Mutations occurring in somatic (body) cells are not heritable. When an individual with a somatic mutation dies, the mutation dies with it. Some mutations, however, alter the DNA in reproductive cells. These mutations may or may not affect the offspring, because most of the DNA in a cell is "silent" and does not code for specific polypeptides or proteins. If a mutation occurs in the DNA that codes for a polypeptide, it may still have little effect in altering the structure or function of that polypeptide. However, when the polypeptide is altered enough to change how it functions, the mutation is usually harmful.

Mutations produce random changes with respect to the direction of evolution. In a population adapting to a dry environment, mutations appropriate for adapting to dry conditions are no more likely to occur than those for adapting to wet conditions or those that have no relationship to the changing environment. The effect of a random change on the members of a population that is well adapted to its current environment is more likely to be harmful than beneficial.

Most mutations produce small changes in the phenotype that often are detectable only by sophisticated biochemical techniques. By acting against seriously abnormal phenotypes, natural selection eliminates or reduces to low frequencies the most harmful mutations. Small mutations, even those with slightly harmful phenotypic effects, have a better chance of being incorporated into the gene pool, where at some later time they may produce traits that are helpful or adaptive for the population.

Natural Selection Changes Allele Frequencies in a Way That Leads to Adaptation to the Environment

Genetic drift is random change. Gene flow and mutation may occur in a given direction, but the direction is unrelated to the nature of the environment. Only natural selection checks the disorganizing, random effects of the other processes and leads to adaptive evolutionary change.

Natural selection results in the differential reproduction of individuals with different phenotypes (and therefore different genotypes) in response to the environment. Natural selection functions to preserve individuals with favorable genotypes and eliminate individuals with unfavorable genotypes. Individuals have a selective advantage if they are able to survive and produce fertile offspring. Natural environmental pressures, such as competition for food or water or living space, select the individuals that survive to reproduce.

Fitness is the ability of an organism, owing to its genotype, to compete successfully and make a genetic contribution to subsequent generations. Organisms that are favored by natural selection exhibit high fitness, whereas organisms exposed to adverse selection pressure exhibit low fitness.

Natural selection not only explains why organisms are well adapted to the environments in which they live, but also accounts for the astounding diversity of life. Natural selection enables populations to change in order to adapt to different environments and different ways of life.

Natural selection may operate at any number of different times in the life cycle of an organism. There may be selective mating, differential fertility (that is, differences in the number of offspring produced), or differential survival to reproductive age. The last is particularly common and frequently involves subtle interactions between organisms and the environment in which they live.

The forces of natural selection do not cause the development of a "perfect" organism. Rather, natural selection weeds out those phenotypes that are less adapted to environmental challenges so that those that are better adapted survive and pass their genes on to their progeny. Selection is the only process known that brings genetic variation into harmony with the environment and leads to adaptation. By reducing or eliminating alleles that result in the expression of less favorable traits, selection changes the composition of the gene pool in a favorable direction and increases the probability that the favorable alleles responsible for an adaptation will come together in the offspring.

SELECTION INCREASES THE ADAPTEDNESS OF A POPULATION FOR THE ENVIRONMENT IN WHICH IT LIVES

Natural selection does not operate directly on an organism's genotype. Rather, it operates on the phenotype, which is an expression of the genotype. The phenotype represents an interaction of all the alleles in the organism's genetic makeup. It is rare that a single gene pair has complete control over a single phenotypic trait,

such as Mendel originally observed in garden peas. Much more common is the interaction of several genes at different loci for the expression of a single trait, that is, polygenes (see Chapter 10). Many plant and animal characteristics are under this type of control.

Individuals in a population may possess a collection of alleles at different loci called a **coadapted gene complex** that interacts compatibly to produce a phenotype of higher quality. When the alleles of a coadapted gene complex are present together, the organism possessing them is well adapted to its environment. Any alleles that interact unfavorably with the others have been eliminated or their effects have been modified. The genes in a coadapted gene complex, which interact epistatically (see Chapter 10), may be tightly linked, increasing the likelihood that they will be inherited together.

When traits are under polygenic control, such as human height, a range of phenotypes occurs, with most of the population located in the median range and fewer at either extreme. This is a normal distribution or a standard bell curve (Figure 18–8a).

Natural selection involves three main processes—stabilizing, directional, and disruptive selection—that cause changes in the normal distribution of phenotypes in a population. Although we consider each process separately, their influences generally overlap in nature.

Stabilizing Selection Selects against Phenotypic Extremes

The process of natural selection that is associated with a population well adapted to its environment is known as **stabilizing selection.** Most populations are probably under the influence of stabilizing selection most of the time. In stabilizing selection phenotype extremes are selected against. In other words, individuals with a phenotype near the mean are favored.

One of the most widely studied cases of stabilizing selection involves human birth weight, which is under polygenic control and is influenced by environmental factors. Based on extensive data from hospitals, it has been determined that infants born with intermediate weights are more likely to survive (Figure 18–9). Infants at either extreme, i.e., too small or too large, have higher rates of mortality. When infants are too small, their body systems are immature, whereas infants that are too large at birth have difficult deliveries because they cannot pass as easily through the birth canal. Stabilizing selection operates to reduce the variability in birth weight so that it is close to the weight with the minimum mortality rate.

Because stabilizing selection tends to decrease variation by favoring individuals near the mean of the normal distribution at the expense of those at either ex-

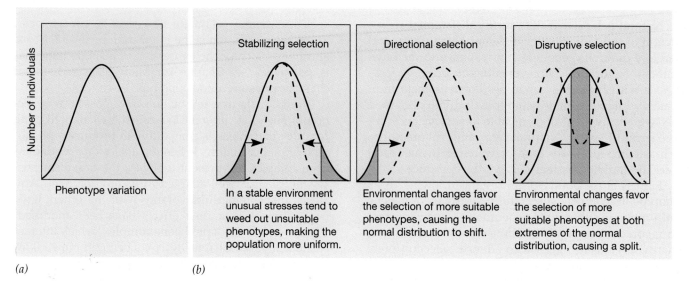

(a)   (b)

Figure 18–8   Different types of natural selection. (a) A trait, such as height, that is under polygenic control exhibits a normal distribution of phenotypes. (b) As a result of stabilizing selection, the curve is narrower. Directional selection moves the curve in one direction. Disruptive selection results in two or more peaks.

treme, the bell curve narrows (Figure 18–8b). Although stabilizing selection decreases the amount of variation in a population, variation is rarely eliminated by this process because other forces act against it. For example, mutation and recombination are continually adding to the variability of a population.

Stabilizing selection is particularly dramatic in an environment that has been stable for an extended period of time. Numerous organisms have remained much the same for the past several million years. Based on fossil evidence, the physical appearance of the ginkgo (see Chapter 27) has not changed appreciably in approximately 200 million years. The appearances of lungfish and horseshoe crabs also have not changed in millions of years.[1] These organisms are well adapted to the environments in which they live.

Directional Selection Favors One Phenotype over Another

If an environment changes over time, **directional selection** may favor phenotypes at one of the extremes of the normal distribution (Figure 18–8b). One phenotype gradually replaces another, resulting in selection of a character in one direction, such as toward larger size. Directional selection can occur, however, only if the appropriate alleles (those that are favored under the new circumstances) are already present in the population.

A classic example of directional selection is the peppered moth population studied in England (see Focus on Evolution in Action in Chapter 1). Recall that most of the peppered moths (*Biston betularia*) in rural England have a light (black and white peppered) wing color and

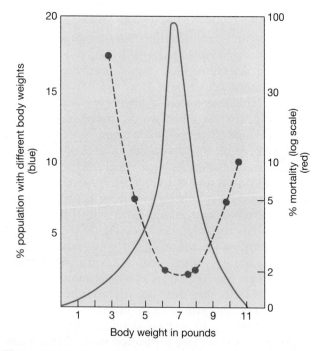

Figure 18–9   Human birth weight is an example of stabilizing selection. Infants with very low or very high birth weights have a higher mortality rate. The blue line indicates number of infants at each birth weight; the red line indicates mortality rate at each birth weight.

---

[1]Although the physical appearance of these organisms has not changed, their physiology, ecology, and behavior may have undergone evolutionary change. These traits are difficult to evaluate from fossil evidence.

only a few are melanic, or all black. In industrial regions, the situation is reversed: Most of the moths are black and only a few are light. Natural selection is shaping the gene pool of each deme of moths to local conditions. In some localities, directional selection operates toward the light phenotype, whereas in other localities, selection occurs in the opposite direction toward the melanic form. Seldom, however, does a population become entirely one type. Male peppered moths fly considerable distances, so gene flow between populations helps to maintain both forms.

Another example of directional selection is the evolution of tolerance to copper in grasses grown on soil contaminated by copper smelting in Lancashire, England (Figure 18–10). Copper in minute amounts is an essential element for plant growth, but high levels of copper in the soil are toxic to plants and inhibit root growth. In an experiment, grasses were taken from soils known to have been contaminated by copper for varying amounts of time. All plants were placed in a nutrient solution that contained a high level of copper, and root growth was measured to give an indication of copper tolerance. When the data were graphed, directional selection was clearly evident, for root growth was less inhibited in grasses from soils contaminated by copper for longer periods of time. These results can be understood if it is assumed that the grass populations growing in areas contaminated with copper for longer periods had had more time to adapt to this environmental condition.

Disruptive Selection Selects for Phenotypic Extremes

Sometimes extreme changes in the environment may favor two or more variant phenotypes at the expense of the mean. That is, more than one phenotype may be favored in the new environment, whereas the average, or intermediate, phenotype is selected against. **Disruptive selection** is a special type of directional selection in which there is a trend in several directions rather than one (Figure 18–8*b*). It results in a divergence, or splitting apart, of distinct groups of individuals within a population.

A clear example of disruptive selection involves batesian mimicry (see Chapter 17). Some localities in Africa are inhabited by three different distasteful species of butterflies. Different females of the edible swallowtail butterfly, *Papilio dardanus*, mimic each of the distasteful models (Figure 18–11). Disruptive selection has favored varieties of the swallowtail that resemble any of the three model species. The initial single population has been disrupted into three different populations that differ in their color patterns as each mimics a different distasteful model.

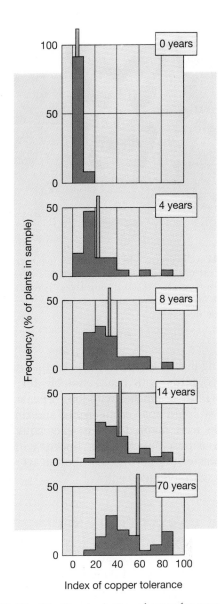

Figure 18–10 Directional selection of genes for copper tolerance in populations of *Agrostis stolonifera*, a grass. Individuals were taken from grass populations growing in areas that had been contaminated by copper (10 to 20 parts per million). Year 0 represents grass growing in uncontaminated soil (the control), and the other graphs represent grasses growing in soil known to be contaminated by copper for the specified time (4 years to 70 years). All plants were grown in a nutrient solution with 0.5 parts per million of copper. Root growth was measured to give an index of copper tolerance: 0 = no growth (complete inhibition) and 100 = maximum growth (no inhibition). The blue bar indicates the mean root growth; note how the arrow progresses in one direction with an increase in time. Copper tolerance is under polygenic control.

Limited food supply during a severe drought imposed disruptive selection on a population of Galapagos finches. The finch population initially exhibited a variety of beak sizes and shapes. Because the only foods available for the finches during the drought were

Figure 18–11   Disruptive selection. Females (*top row*) of the swallowtail butterfly, *Papilio dardanus*, often mimic distasteful species (*bottom row*).   (L. E. Gilbert, University of Texas, Austin/ Biological Photo Service)

Figure 18–12   Genetic variation in European land snails (*Cepaea nemoralis*). Variation in shell color has adaptive value that depends on the habitat in which the snail lives and the time of year. (Visuals Unlimited/John D. Cunningham)

wood-boring insects and seeds from cactus fruits, selection favored birds with beaks suitable for obtaining these types of food. Finches with longer beaks survived because they could open cactus fruits, and finches with wider beaks were favored because they could strip off tree bark to expose insects. Thus, finches with beaks at two extremes of the normal distribution were favored over birds with average beaks.

GENETIC VARIATION IS NECESSARY IF EVOLUTION IS TO OCCUR

Change in the types and frequencies of genes in gene pools, whether by natural selection or other means, is possible only if there is a source of inherited variation. Genetic variation is the raw material for evolutionary change. It provides the diversity upon which natural selection can act. Without genetic variation there can be no heritable differences in the ability to reproduce and therefore no natural selection (Figure 18–12).

The gene pools of populations contain large reservoirs of genetic variation that have been introduced by mutation. Sexual reproduction through meiosis and union of gametes allows the variability introduced by mutation to be combined in new ways, which may be expressed as new phenotypes. This effect can be surprisingly great. Nine different genotypes are generated in a dihybrid cross ($AaBb \times AaBb$) involving only two genes at different loci, each with only two alleles. If we were dealing with five different loci, each with six alleles in the population, the number of different genotypes possible would be 4,084,101! Some of the combinations that are generated may be adaptively superior, and natural selection could favor them.

Genetic polymorphism is the presence in a population of two or more alleles for a given gene. Gene pools contain a tremendous reservoir of genetic polymorphism, much of it present at low frequency and much of it hidden. Until recently, biologists could not estimate the total amount of genetic polymorphism in populations because they could recognize only those genes with different alleles that are conspicuous enough to cause differences in phenotypes in breeding experiments. Biologists now take a random sample of proteins from an organism and, by biochemical techniques such as electrophoresis, measure how many proteins exist in two or more forms as determined by different amino acid sequences. Each variety of a particular protein is coded by a different allele. Using this type of data, 25% of the loci in vertebrate populations are estimated to be genetically polymorphic.

Of what possible significance is a high degree of genetic variation? Populations with genetic variability maintain evolutionary plasticity and can respond better to changing environmental conditions. The reservoir of variability may be large enough for populations to respond to selection pressures in many directions. This has been demonstrated in experiments with the fruit fly, *Drosophila melanogaster*. A population is established from offspring of a single female fly fertilized in the wild. Her progeny have a certain variability and, by appropriate selection procedures, it is possible to either increase or decrease a trait such as the mean number of bristles in a certain part of the thorax. In doing this, the variability is extended beyond that in the initial population (Figure 18–13). Because the changes occur in a few generations and can go in either direction, stored genetic variability rather than new mutations must be the source of the variation.

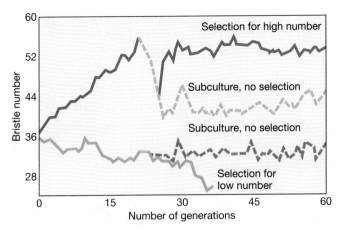

Figure 18–13   One example of inherent genetic variation in *Drosophila melanogaster*. The original female fruit fly had 36 bristles on a part of her thorax. Investigators selected for flies in her offspring with both a low number of bristles (*bottom green*) and a high number of bristles (*top red*). The dashed lines represent subcultures when selection was discontinued.

Genetic Variation Can Be Maintained by Heterozygote Advantage

Often the individuals heterozygous for a specific gene (*Aa*) are more common in the population than would be predicted by the Hardy-Weinberg law. The heterozygous condition, *Aa*, appears to have a higher degree of fitness than either homozygote, *AA* or *aa*. This phenomenon, **heterozygote advantage,** is demonstrated in humans by the selective advantage bestowed on heterozygous carriers of the sickle cell allele.

Heterozygote advantage of the sickle cell allele

Many genes are pleiotropic and affect more than one trait. Whether a mutant allele is harmful or beneficial must be evaluated in the context of all its phenotypic effects in the particular environment in which it is acting.

The mutant allele for sickle cell anemia produces an altered hemoglobin that is less soluble than normal hemoglobin, especially at low oxygen tensions (see Chapter 15). It tends to precipitate as long crystals within the red cell. This deforms or sickles the cell so that it is more likely to be destroyed in the liver, spleen, or bone marrow. Individuals who are homozygous for the sickle cell allele usually die at an early age.

Heterozygous individuals carry alleles for both normal and sickle cell hemoglobin. This heterozygous condition also causes the individual to be more resistant to a particularly virulent type of malaria caused by the protozoon *Plasmodium falciparum* than are individuals who are homozygous for the allele for normal hemoglobin. In certain parts of Africa, India, and southern Asia,

where malaria is prevalent, heterozygous individuals survive in greater numbers than either homozygote (Figure 18–14).

In a heterozygous individual, each allele produces its own specific kind of hemoglobin and the red cells contain the two kinds in roughly equivalent amounts. Such cells do not ordinarily sickle, and the red cells containing altered hemoglobin are more resistant to infection from the malarial organism than are the red cells containing only normal hemoglobin. Each of the two types of homozygous individuals is at a disadvantage. Those homozygous for the sickling allele are likely to suffer or die of anemia, and those homozygous for the normal allele may suffer or die of malaria. The heterozygote is therefore more fit than either homozygote. Both alleles are maintained in the population even though one of the homozygotes is lethal.

Genetic Variation May Be Maintained by Frequency-Dependent Selection

Thus far in our discussion of natural selection, we have assumed that the fitness of particular phenotypes (and their corresponding genotypes) is independent of their frequency in the population. For example, consider copper tolerance in grasses (discussed in the section on directional selection). It little matters whether 1% or 99% of the population is tolerant for copper or sensitive to copper; on soil with high levels of copper, plants with copper tolerance survive whereas those lacking copper tolerance do not.

There are, however, numerous cases of **frequency-dependent selection,** in which the fitness of particular genotypes is proportional to the frequency of their phe-

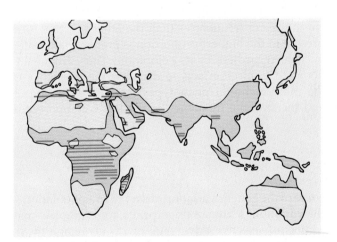

Figure 18–14   Distribution of sickle cell anemia (*bars*) compared with the distribution of falciparum malaria (*dark tan region*). The correlation strongly suggests that the resistance of heterozygous individuals to malaria has served to balance the harmful effects of sickle cell anemia.

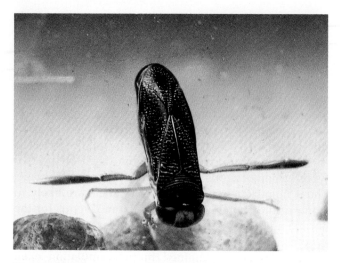

Figure 18–15 Water boatmen (*Sigara distincta*) are aquatic insects that swim in ponds and streams by using their hind legs like oars. Water boatmen occur in three color forms. Frequency-dependent selection operates to maintain all three phenotypes within a given population. (Visuals Unlimited/Glenn Oliver)

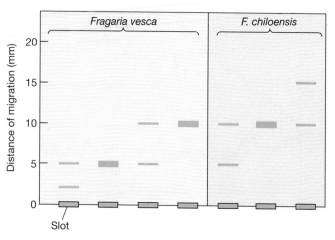

Figure 18–16 Genetic variation in two species of wild strawberry (*Fragaria*) in California. Tissue extracts containing the enzyme peroxidase from separate individuals were placed in slots in a slab of gel (*bottom of drawing*). An electric current was applied to the gel, with the positive side at the top of the slab and the negative side at the bottom. Because peroxidase has a net negative charge, it migrated toward the positive side. Slight variations in amino acid sequence in the peroxidase molecules caused them to have slightly different negative charges and therefore to migrate at different rates. Four different allozymes for peroxidase were found in the individuals studied. Of course, each individual can possess only two different allozymes because strawberries are diploid. Individuals with two different allozymes for peroxidase are heterozygous, whereas those with only one allozyme are homozygous.

notypes in the population. Often, genotypes lose their fitness advantage as they become more common in the population, whereas rare genotypes have a selective edge.

Frequency-dependent selection often acts to maintain genetic variation in populations of prey. The predator catches and consumes the commoner phenotype, while often ignoring the rarer phenotypes. Frequency-dependent selection can be demonstrated with aquatic insects called water boatmen (*Sigara distincta*) (Figure 18–15). Water boatmen have three distinct color phenotypes. When all three phenotypes are present in equal frequencies, fish are more likely to consume the most obvious (least camouflaged) form. However, in populations of water boatmen in which one phenotype is present in greater frequencies than the other two, the form present in the highest proportion is preferentially eaten by fish, regardless of its coloration. Thus, frequency-dependent selection acts to decrease the frequency of the more common phenotypes (and their genotypes) and increase the frequency of the less common types.

Neutral Variation Gives No Selective Advantage or Disadvantage

Some of the genetic variation observed in a population—the variation in human fingerprints, for example—may confer no selective advantage or disadvantage to the individuals possessing it. That is, **neutral variation** does not alter the fitness of an individual to survive and reproduce and is, therefore, not adaptive. Neutral variation arises by mutation, and the frequency of neutral alleles increases or decreases by genetic drift.

The extent of neutral variation in organisms is difficult to determine. It is relatively easy to demonstrate that an allele is beneficial or harmful, provided that its effect is observable. But the variation in alleles that is apparent by protein electrophoresis, often involving very slight differences in their structures, may or may not be neutral. These alleles may be influencing the organism in subtle ways that are difficult to measure or assess. Also, an allele that is neutral in one environment may be beneficial or harmful in another.

The Importance of Selection in Maintaining Genetic Variation Is a Major Question in Population Genetics Today

Molecular techniques have clarified that a substantial pool of genetic variability exists in populations. Most enzymes have several slightly different forms, called **allozymes,** each coded for by a different allele at a given locus. Allozymes are detectable only by electrophoresis; because they appear to function equally well within an organism, allozymes do not cause obvious differences in phenotype (Figure 18–16).

The existence of considerable genetic variation in populations has led to the **neutralist-selectionist con-**

troversy, in which evolutionary biologists disagree about the importance of genetic variation in natural selection. The selectionists take a strictly Darwinian point of view—all genetic variation, even minor differences in allozyme structure, affects the fitness of an organism. As a result, selectionists think that all genetic variation is raw material for adaptive change. The opposing view espoused by neutralists is that much of the genetic variation within an organism is neutral—that is, does not affect an organism's fitness—and is not influenced by natural selection. Neutralists think that neutral alleles accumulate from neutral mutations and genetic drift.

Some evidence indicates that the two opposing views over the importance of selection versus genetic drift may not be mutually exclusive; some allozyme variants appear to affect fitness, whereas others appear to be selectively neutral.

SUMMARY

I. Evolution is a change in allele frequencies in the gene pool of a population. Each individual within a population contains only a portion of the genes in the gene pool.

II. The Hardy-Weinberg law states that genotype frequencies in a population tend to remain constant in successive generations unless certain factors are operating.

III. Allele frequencies may be changed by genetic drift, gene flow (migration), mutation, and natural selection (differential reproduction).
   A. Genetic drift is the random change in allele frequencies of a small breeding population. The changes are usually not adaptive.
   B. The migration of individuals between demes causes a corresponding movement of alleles, or gene flow.
   C. The source of new genes in a gene pool is mutation.
   D. The most important reason for adaptive changes in allele frequencies is natural selection.

IV. Natural selection can change the composition of a gene pool in a favorable direction.
   A. The interactions of genes in a coadapted gene complex produce well-adapted individuals.
   B. Stabilizing selection favors the mean at the expense of phenotypic extremes.
   C. Directional selection favors one phenotype over another, causing a shift in the phenotypic mean.
   D. Disruptive selection favors phenotypic extremes.

V. Most populations have a large reservoir of variability.
   A. Heterozygote advantage occurs when the heterozygote has a higher degree of fitness than either homozygote. Both alleles are maintained in the population.
   B. In frequency-dependent selection, a genotype's selective value varies with its frequency of occurrence.
   C. Variation that confers no detectable selective advantage is called neutral variation.
   D. The neutralist-selectionist controversy is a debate among biologists over the relative importance of selection versus genetic drift in maintaining genetic variability.

POST-TEST

1. _____ is the change in the genetic makeup of a population.

2. The Hardy-Weinberg law demonstrates that the process of inheritance does not, by itself, cause changes in _____ _____ .

3. Random genetic events, called _____ _____, may have a major effect on allele frequencies.

4. The members of a species tend to be distributed in interbreeding populations called _____ .

5. The movement of alleles between demes, called gene flow, is caused by the _____ of breeding individuals.

6. The source of the genetic variability that is the raw material of evolution is _____ .

7. The most important adaptive cause of changes in allele frequencies is _____ _____ .

8. A collection of genes that interact compatibly to affect the same trait or function is called a _____ _____ _____ .

9. In _____ selection, individuals with a phenotype near the mean are favored over those with phenotype extremes.

10. The _____ selection of peppered moths is an indirect consequence of air pollution.

11. _____ selection is a special type of directional selection in which there is a trend in several directions, resulting in a divergence within the population.

12. The presence in a population of two or more alleles for a given gene is known as genetic _____ .

13. A human that has alleles for both normal hemoglobin and sickle cell hemoglobin demonstrates _____ _____ in an area where malaria is prevalent.

14. In _____-_____ selection, the fitness of a particular genotype varies with its frequency of occurrence in the population.

15. Genetic variation that does not confer a selective advantage on the individual possessing it is called _____ variation.

16. Slightly different versions of the same enzyme are called _____ .

17. In the neutralist-selectionist controversy, the _____ view is that most mutations are neutral and do not affect an organism's fitness.

REVIEW QUESTIONS

1. Explain the effect of each of the following on genetic variation:
   a. natural selection
   b. mutation
   c. sexual reproduction
   d. gene flow
   e. genetic drift
2. Explain the distribution of human blood types in Australian aborigines.
3. We have said that mutations are almost always harmful. Why?
4. If a mutation occurs in a somatic cell, can it become established in a population? Explain why or why not.
5. Consider the giraffe. Explain the evolution of the giraffe's long neck by directional selection. Explain how stabilizing selection accounts for the giraffe's long neck today.
6. Insect populations that have been exposed to an insecticide such as DDT develop resistance to the insecticide over time. Would this be an example of stabilizing selection, directional selection, or disruptive selection? Explain.
7. Draw three graphs representing stabilizing, directional, and disruptive selection.
8. Explain this apparent anomaly: We discuss evolution in terms of *genotype* fitness (the selective advantage that a particular genotype confers on an individual), yet natural selection acts on an organism's *phenotype*.
9. The neutralist-selectionist controversy is about genetic variation as represented by allozymes. Does this controversy have any bearing on other kinds of genetic variation (such as variations in color or morphology)? Why or why not?

RECOMMENDED READINGS

Cohn, J. P. Genetics for wildlife conservation. *BioScience* 40:3, March 1990. Genetic analysis of endangered species offers hope for their survival.

Grant, B. R., and P. R. Grant. *Evolutionary Dynamics of a Natural Population.* University of Chicago Press, Chicago, 1990. A study, spanning more than a decade, of the large cactus finch in the Galápagos. Provides insight into the environmental factors affecting directional selection in this population.

Mayr, E. *Population, Species, and Evolution.* Harvard University Press, Cambridge, MA, 1970. A classic discussion of evolution.

Stearns, S. C. The evolutionary significance of phenotypic plasticity. *BioScience* 39:7, July/August 1989. An introduction to environmentally induced phenotypic variation, an important evolutionary phenomenon. This issue of *BioScience* contains several related articles.

CHAPTER 19

Speciation and Macroevolution

The concept of distinct groups of living organisms, known as **species** (from Latin, meaning "kind") is not new. However, every definition of exactly what constitutes a species has some sort of limitation. Linnaeus, an 18th century biologist who is considered the founder of modern taxonomy, classified plants into separate species based on differences in morphology, or physical form (see Chapter 22). This method is still used to help characterize species, but morphology alone is not adequate to explain what constitutes a species. For example, dogs come in a wide variety of sizes and shapes, yet all dogs are classified as members of the same species.

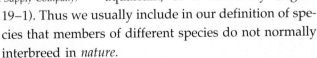

A cheetah concealed in the grass. (Carolina Biological Supply Company)

The discipline of population genetics did much to clarify the concept of species. A species is a group of organisms with a common gene pool. The **biological species concept** is based upon reproductive isolation. Members of a species freely interbreed with other members of the same species to produce fertile offspring and do not interbreed with members of different species. In other words, each species has a gene pool that is isolated from that of other species, and each species is restricted by reproductive barriers from genetic mixing with other species.

One of the problems with the biological species concept is that it applies only to sexually reproducing organisms. Organisms that reproduce asexually do not interbreed so we cannot think of them in terms of reproductive isolation.

Another problem with the biological species concept is classifying extinct forms of life. Fossil remains of extinct organisms are classified on the basis of morphological characteristics because it is impossible to determine whether similar-appearing organisms that lived in the past were able to interbreed. In addition, organisms that are assigned to different species in the wild may interbreed if brought into a zoo, a greenhouse, an aquarium, or a laboratory (Figure 19–1). Thus we usually include in our definition of species that members of different species do not normally interbreed in *nature.*

To summarize, a species is a group of more or less distinct organisms capable of interbreeding with one another in nature but are reproductively isolated from other species. This definition is far from perfect, however, and the biological concept of species has limitations.

After you have studied this chapter you should be able to

1. Define a species and explain the limitations of your definition.
2. Explain the evolutionary significance of biological isolating mechanisms and distinguish between prezygotic and postzygotic isolating mechanisms.
3. List five types of prezygotic isolating mechanisms and distinguish among them.
4. List three types of postzygotic isolating mechanisms and distinguish among them.
5. Explain the mechanism of allopatric speciation and give an example.

6. Explain the mechanism of sympatric speciation and give an example.
7. Take either side in the debate on the pace of evolution by representing the opposing views of gradualism and punctuated equilibrium.
8. Define macroevolution and distinguish among microevolution, speciation, and macroevolution.
9. Discuss macroevolution in the context of novel features, including preaptations, allometric growth, and paedomorphosis.
10. Relate the macroevolutionary significance of evolutionary trends, adaptive radiation, and extinction.

SPECIES HAVE VARIOUS MECHANISMS TO ACHIEVE REPRODUCTIVE ISOLATION FROM ONE ANOTHER

A number of biological mechanisms prevent interbreeding between different species whose ranges overlap. Isolating mechanisms preserve the integrity of each species' gene pool because gene flow between them is prevented. To block a chance occurrence of individuals from two different species overcoming one reproductive isolating mechanism, most species have two or more isolating mechanisms.

Isolating mechanisms that work to restrict the gene flow between species also may be found *within* a species. Each species is composed of local populations that are separated geographically and/or ecologically. This

results in a limited genetic exchange between certain populations. Sometimes local populations, in adapting to local conditions, diverge to the point that they become reproductively isolated from the rest of the species. This may lead to the formation of a new species.

Prezygotic Isolating Mechanisms Interfere with Mating

There are two groups of reproductive isolating mechanisms, prezygotic and postzygotic. **Prezygotic isolating mechanisms** prevent fertilization from ever taking place. Because male and female gametes never come into contact, an interspecific zygote (fertilized egg formed by the union of an egg from one species and a sperm from another species) never forms. Prezygotic

(a)

(b)

Figure 19–1 Lions (*a*) and tigers (*b*) are recognized as separate species. Although their geographical ranges overlap in parts of Asia, a hybrid between a tiger and a lion has never been found in the wild. However, they have been known to crossbreed when brought together in zoos; the offspring of lion–tiger crosses are sterile.   (*a*, Visuals Unlimited/Kjell B. Sandved; *b*, Dominique Braud/Dembinsky Photo Associates)

(a)   (b)   (c)

Figure 19–2 Reproductive isolating mechanisms in closely related flycatcher species in North America. Although the flycatchers are nearly identical in appearance and have overlapping ranges, they remain distinct, reproductively isolated species. They are isolated ecologically because each species is found in a particular habitat within its range during mating. Also, they are isolated behaviorally because each species has its own characteristic song, which serves to identify it to other flycatchers of the same species. (a) The least flycatcher, *Empidonax minimus*, frequents open woods. (b) The acadian flycatcher, *E. virescens*, is found in deciduous forests and swampy woods. (c) The alder flycatcher, *E. alnorum*, prefers groves of willows and alders. (a, Dwight Kuhn; b, J. R. Woodward/VIREO; c, Visuals Unlimited/Tom J. Ulrich)

isolating mechanisms include temporal isolation, ecological isolation, behavioral isolation, mechanical isolation, and gametic isolation.

There are many examples of **temporal isolation,** in which genetic exchange between two groups is prevented because they reproduce at different times of the day, season, or year. The fruit flies *Drosophila pseudoobscura* and *Drosophila persimilis* have ranges that overlap to a great extent, but they do not interbreed. *D. pseudoobscura* is sexually active in the afternoon and *D. persimilis* in the morning. Similarly, there are two species of sage, *Salvia,* with overlapping ranges in southern California. Black sage (*Salvia mellifera*) flowers in early spring, whereas white sage (*S. apiana*) blooms in late spring and early summer.

Although two closely related species may be found in the same geographical area, they usually live and breed in different habitats in that area. This causes **ecological isolation** between the two groups (Figure 19–2). For example, wood frogs breed in temporary woodland ponds, while bullfrogs breed in larger, more permanent bodies of water.

Many animal species have distinctive courtship behaviors, so mating between species is prevented by **behavioral isolation.** Courtship is an exchange of signals between a male and a female. Typically, a male approaches a female and gives a sign or pattern of signals that may be visual, auditory, or chemical. If the female belongs to the same species, she recognizes the signals and returns her own distinctive signals. Further correct exchanges of signals eventually result in mating. If members of two different species begin courtship, one partner does not recognize one of the signals and fails to respond. The courtship behavior stops at that point.

Bowerbirds, for example, exhibit species-specific courtship patterns. The male satin bowerbird of Australia constructs an elaborate bower of twigs, adding decorative blue parrot feathers and white flowers at the entrance (Figure 19–3). When a female approaches the bower, the male dances around her, holding a particularly treasured decoration in his beak. While dancing, he sings a courtship song that consists of a variety of sounds, including buzzes and laughlike hoots. These specific courtship behaviors keep other bird species reproductively isolated from the satin bowerbird.

Morphological or anatomical differences that inhibit mating between species are known as **mechanical isolation.** Sometimes members of different species court and even attempt copulation, but the structures of their genital organs are incompatible, so successful mating is prevented. The interbreeding of certain insect

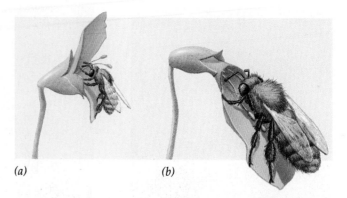

(a) *(b)*

Figure 19-4 Mechanical isolation occurs between black sage (*S. mellifera*) and white sage (*S. apiana*) as a result of differences in floral structure, which evolved to make use of different insect pollinators. Because the two species use different pollinators, interspecific mating is prevented. (*a*) The petal of the black sage is shaped as a landing platform for small bees. Larger bees cannot use this platform. (*b*) The larger landing platform and longer stamens of white sage allow pollination by larger carpenter bees. If smaller bees land on white sage, they do not accomplish pollination because their bodies do not brush against the pollen-bearing stamens.

Figure 19-3 The male satin bowerbird constructs a bower (behind the bird in this photo) to help attract a female. Note the flowers and blue decorations that he has arranged at the entrance to his bower. Different bowerbird species exhibit a variety of highly specialized courtship patterns, which prevent mating between species. (Animals Animals © 1993 Patti Murray)

species such as dragonflies is thwarted in this way. Many flowering plants have physical differences in their flower parts that help them maintain their reproductive isolation from one another. The sage plants presented earlier as an example of temporal isolation also have mechanical isolation. Black sage, which is pollinated by small bees, has a floral structure different from that of white sage, which is pollinated by large carpenter bees (Figure 19–4). Differences in floral structure prevent the insects from cross-pollinating the two species.

If mating has taken place between two species, their gametes may still not combine. Molecular and chemical differences between species cause **gametic isolation,** in which the egg and sperm are incompatible. In aquatic animals that release their eggs and sperm into the surrounding water simultaneously, interspecific fertilization is extremely rare. This is because the surface of the egg contains specific proteins that bind only to complementary molecules on sperm cells of the same species.

Sometimes pollen does not germinate on the stigma (see Chapter 27) of a different plant species. Alternatively, the pollen may germinate and grow a pollen tube, but fertilization still does not occur. Different species, and even different races in the same plant species, have different style lengths and pollen tube lengths. That is, the pollen tube of a particular species is genetically programmed to grow the length of the style that is characteristic for that species. If two races or species have different flower sizes and therefore different style lengths, they may be incompatible. Pollen that is geneti-

cally programmed to grow a short pollen tube cannot grow the entire length of a long style, and fertilization does not occur.

Postzygotic Isolating Mechanisms Prevent Successful Reproduction if Mating Occurs

When prezygotic isolating mechanisms fail, as they occasionally do, **postzygotic isolating mechanisms** come into play. These ensure reproductive failure after fertilization has taken place. Hybrid offspring formed from the union of two separate species usually have numerous problems and are at a severe disadvantage.

Generally, the embryonic development of an interspecific hybrid is aborted. Development is a complex process requiring the precise interaction and coordination of many genes. The genes from parents belonging to different species apparently do not interact properly in regulating the mechanisms for normal embryonic development. In this case, reproductive isolation is achieved by **hybrid inviability.** For example, nearly all of the hybrids die in the embryonic stage when the eggs of a bullfrog are fertilized artificially with sperm from a leopard frog. Plants also exhibit hybrid inviability. For example, in crosses between different species of *Iris*, the hybrid embryo develops but dies before reaching maturity as a result of breakdown of the endosperm in the seed.

If an interspecific hybrid develops successfully, reproduction of the hybrid still may not occur. There

Figure 19–5 Hybrid sterility. Mules are interspecific hybrids formed by mating a female horse with a male donkey. Although the mule exhibits valuable characteristics of each of its parents, it is sterile. (Grant Heilman/Grant Heilman Photography)

are several reasons why this is so. Hybrid animals may exhibit courtship behaviors incompatible with those of either parental species and, as a result, they do not mate. More often, **hybrid sterility** occurs in which the gametes of an interspecific hybrid are abnormal owing to problems during the development of sex organs or the sequence of meiosis. This is particularly true if the two parent species have different chromosome numbers; synapsis, the pairing of homologous chromosomes that occurs during meiosis, cannot occur properly. For example, a mule is the hybrid offspring of a female horse ($2n = 64$) and a male donkey ($2n = 62$). This type of union almost always results in sterile offspring ($32 + 31 = 63$) (Figure 19–5). Many examples of hybrid sterility in plants have been documented. Sometimes the interaction of genes from two species causes a hybrid's anthers (male floral structures that produce pollen) to develop improperly. Such male sterility has been found in hybrids between different tobacco species.

Occasionally, an interspecific hybrid develops that is fertile and produces a second (F_2) generation from a cross between two hybrids or between a hybrid and one of the parent strains. The F_2 hybrid exhibits **hybrid breakdown,** defects that prevent it from successfully reproducing. For example, hybrid breakdown in the F_2 generation of a cross between two sunflower species in the genus *Layia* was 80%. In other words, 80% of the F_2 generation were defective and could not reproduce successfully. Hybrid breakdown can also occur in the F_3 and later generations.

THE KEY TO SPECIATION IS THE DEVELOPMENT OF REPRODUCTIVE ISOLATING MECHANISMS

We are now ready to consider how entirely new species may arise from previously existing ones. The evolution of a new species is known as **speciation.** A required step in speciation is the reproductive isolation of a population from the rest of the species. When a population is so isolated from its ancestral species that no genetic exchange occurs between them, even if the two populations meet, we say that speciation has occurred. There are two main types of speciation, allopatric and sympatric.

Long Physical Isolation and Different Selective Pressures Result in Allopatric Speciation

Speciation that occurs when one population becomes geographically separated from the rest of the species and subsequently evolves is known as geographical speciation, or **allopatric speciation** (*allo,* "different," and *patri,* "fatherland"). Allopatric speciation is thought to be the most common method of speciation, and the evolution of new species of animals has been almost exclusively by allopatric speciation.

The geographic isolation required for allopatric speciation may occur in several ways. Earth's surface is in a constant state of change: Rivers shift their courses; glaciers migrate; mountain ranges form; land bridges develop, separating previously united aquatic populations; large lakes diminish into several smaller, geographically separated pools.

What might be an imposing geographical barrier to one species may be of no consequence to another. For example, as a lake subsides into smaller pools, fish are usually unable to cross the land barriers between the pools and so become reproductively isolated. Birds, on the other hand, can easily fly from one pool to another. Likewise, plants such as cattails, which disperse their fruits by air currents, would not be isolated by this barrier.

Allopatric speciation also occurs when a small population migrates and colonizes a new area away from the original species range. This colony is geographically isolated from its parent species. The Galapagos Islands and the Hawaiian Islands were colonized by individuals of a few species. From these original colonizers, the distinctive groups of unique species characteristic of each island arose (Figure 19–6).

No species is genetically uniform throughout its range. Slight differences within a species occur as a result of adaptations to local conditions, with populations at the periphery of the species range frequently exhibit-

(a)

(b)

Figure 19-6 Allopatric speciation can occur when a small population colonizes a geographically isolated area such as an island. (a) The nene (pronounced "nay-nay"), *Branta sandvicensis*, is a goose found in the Hawaiian Islands. It is thought to have evolved from a small population of geese that originated in North America. Although the nene is an endangered species, strict conservation measures have brought it back from the brink of extinction. (b) The Canada goose, *Branta canadensis*, is a close relative of the Hawaiian goose.   (a, M. J. Rauzon/VIREO; b, R. Villani/VIREO)

ing the most distinct differences. When geographical isolation occurs, it usually separates a small population at the periphery of the species range from the rest of the species. Typically, this population was already genetically different from the species members in the middle of its range, and the genetic divergence is amplified by natural selection and random changes caused by genetic drift.

A population that is geographically isolated does not interbreed with the rest of the species; therefore, no gene flow occurs between it and the parent population. Moreover, the isolated habitat is usually different in several ways from the parent population's habitat. Climate and soil factors are distinct, and usually the isolated population must interact with a different set of organisms. As a result of these habitat differences, the isolated population faces different selective pressures. Most small populations exposed to new selective pressures do not speciate but rather become extinct. However, some isolated populations do survive and, over time, adapt to the new habitat; thus, their gene pools diverge from the gene pool of the original population. Eventually, the differences between the two become so great that they are unable to interbreed even if their range becomes continuous again. (See Focus on The

Kaibab Squirrel: Evolution in Action for an example of allopatric speciation in progress.)

Speciation is more likely to occur if the original isolated population is small. Recall that genetic drift, including the founder effect, is more influential in small populations (see Chapter 18). Genetic drift tends to result in rapid changes in gene frequencies in the isolated population. The genetic divergence caused by genetic drift is further accentuated by the different selective pressures to which the population is exposed.

Occasionally, a geographical barrier disappears after a period of isolation; a river might change its course, or a glacier might retreat. Alternatively, members of an isolated population sometimes migrate back to the habitat of the original species. Three possibilities exist when an isolated population is reunited with the parent species: (1) Speciation has occurred and the divergent population is recognized as a separate and distinct species because it has diverged enough that it is unable to interbreed with the parent species. (2) Speciation has not occurred and the population is able to interbreed successfully with the parent population, restoring gene flow. (3) Sometimes speciation has not quite occurred, but the isolated population is very different from the original population. This results in very

FOCUS ON

The Kaibab Squirrel: Evolution in Action

Many thousands of years ago, the American Southwest was less arid and the forests in the area supported a tree squirrel with conspicuous tufts of hair sprouting from its ears. A small tree squirrel population that lived on the Kaibab Plateau of the Grand Canyon became isolated from the rest of its kind approximately 10,000 years ago when the climate changed, causing areas to the north, west, and east to become desert. Just a few miles to the south were the rest of the squirrels, known as Abert squirrels, but the two groups were separated by the Grand Canyon. With changes in both its appearance and its ecology, the Kaibab squirrel is on its way to becoming a new species.

During its 10,000 years of reproductive isolation, the Kaibab squirrels have diverged in a number of ways. Perhaps most evident are changes in fur color. The Kaibab squirrel now has a white tail, in contrast to the gray tail exhibited by Abert squirrels (see figures). Also, the Kaibab squirrel has a black belly, whereas the

The Kaibab squirrel. (Tom & Pat Leeson)

The Abert squirrel. (Tom & Pat Leeson)

Abert squirrel's belly is white. It is not clear why such striking changes in fur color evolved in Kaibab squirrels.

Coevolution also played a part in the divergence of Kaibab squirrels from Abert squirrels. During its isolation, the Kaibab squirrel has formed a three-way relationship with the ponderosa pine and a fungus called a truffle. In this relationship, the squirrel obtains food (seeds in the summer and bark in the winter) from the pine. The squirrel feeds in one area for a brief time, then moves to another area; thus the trees in one area are not damaged by overfeeding. The truffle is involved in this relationship because it grows on the ponderosa pine's roots as mycorrhizae (see Chapter 25), aiding the tree in mineral and water uptake, and the tree supplies the fungus with organic nutrients. The squirrels eat truffles and excrete the spores, aiding in their dispersal; this helps both the trees and the truffle. Thus a complex, three-way relationship that benefits all three participants has formed.

---

limited gene flow between the two groups. It has been suggested that the two groups diverge even more in this potentially competitive situation by a process known as reinforcement. According to the reinforcement hypothesis, when two populations that are not completely reproductively isolated come into contact, there may be some matings between the two groups. Matings *within* each group are more common, however, and are favored by natural selection because the hybrid offspring are less fit than offspring of parents from the same population. Thus, reinforcement eventually leads to complete reproductive isolation between two populations, at which point they are separate species. Some biologists question the evolutionary significance of reinforcement, and no examples can be cited without reservation.

Examples of allopatric speciation

Many examples of allopatric speciation can be traced to the barriers formed by the glaciers of the Pleistocene epoch (see Chapter 20). A western population of the Pleistocene European bear, *Ursus arctos,* was separated from the rest of the species and evolved into the cave bear, *Ursus spelaeus.* The eastern population remained as *Ursus arctos.* This reconstruction is supported by fossil evidence.

Lakes and pools of water provide the isolation for allopatric speciation of aquatic organisms that islands provide for terrestrial plants and animals. Large lakes formed by glacial melt at the end of the Pleistocene epoch in what is now Nevada were populated by one or several species of pupfish. With the gradual demise of

Figure 19–7 Allopatric speciation is responsible for the various pupfish species that evolved when large glacial lakes dried up, leaving behind smaller pools. Presumably each pool contained a small population of pupfish that gradually diverged from the original population by genetic drift and natural selection. Each species of pupfish is restricted to a single pool.   (Animals Animals © 1993 Mike Andrews)

the large glacial lakes as a result of glacial retreat and a drier climate, isolated pools were left. Today, there are numerous species of pupfish, but each is restricted to a single water hole (Figure 19–7).

Sometimes allopatric speciation occurs quite rapidly. Early in the 15th century, a small population of rabbits was released on Porto Santo, a small island off the coast of Portugal. Because there were no other rabbits or competitors and no carnivorous enemies on the island, the rabbits thrived. By the 19th century, these rabbits were markedly different from their ancestral European stock. They were only half as large, had a different color pattern, and their lifestyle was more nocturnal. Most significantly, they could not produce offspring when bred with members of the ancestral European species. Within 400 years, a very short period of time in geological history, a new species of rabbit had evolved.

In Sympatric Speciation Two Populations Diverge in the Same Physical Location

Although geographical isolation is an important factor in many cases of evolution, it may not be an absolute requirement. When a population forms a new species within the same geographical region as its parent species, **sympatric speciation** (*sym,* "together," and *patri,* "fatherland") has occurred. The divergence of two gene pools which occurs in the same geographical range is

common in plants. Although a few cases of sympatric speciation in parasitic insects have been studied, the role of sympatric speciation in animal evolution is unclear.

Mechanism of sympatric speciation in plants

We have seen that hybrids formed from the union of two species rarely produce robust offspring and that these offspring are usually sterile, like the mule. Before gametes form, meiosis occurs to reduce the chromosome number. In order for the chromosomes to be parcelled correctly into the gametes, the homologous chromosomes pair during prophase I. This cannot occur properly in interspecific hybrid offspring because the chromosomes are not homologous. However, *if* the $2n$ chromosome number is doubled before meiosis, then pairing of homologous chromosomes can occur. This spontaneous doubling of chromosomes has been documented in both plants and animals. It is not a common occurrence, but neither is it rare. It produces nuclei with multiple sets of chromosomes.

Polyploidy, the possession of more than two sets of chromosomes, is a major factor in plant evolution. When it occurs in conjunction with the joining of chromosomes from two different species (brought about by **hybridization,** a crossing of individuals from different species), it is known as **allopolyploidy,** and it can produce an interspecific hybrid that is fertile. This is because the polyploid condition provides the homologous chromosomes that can pair during meiosis. As a result, gametes may be viable (Figure 19–8). Allopolyploids can reproduce with themselves (self-fertilization) or with similar individuals. However, they are reproductively isolated from both parents because the gametes of the allopolyploid have a different number of chromosomes from those of either parent.

If a population of allopolyploids (that is, a new species) becomes established, selective pressures cause one of three outcomes. (1) It is very possible that the population is unable to compete and becomes extinct. (2) The allopolyploid individuals fill a new role in the environment and so coexist with both parent species. (3) The new hybrid species may compete with either of its parent species. If it has a combination of characters that make it more fit than the parent species for all or part of the original range of the parent, the hybrid species replaces the parent.

Although allopolyploidy is extremely rare in animals, it has been a significant factor in the evolution of flowering plants. Almost one half of all flowering plants are thought to be polyploids. Most of these are allopolyploids (Figure 19–9). Moreover, allopolyploidy provides a mechanism for extremely rapid speciation. A single generation is all that is needed to form a new, reproductively isolated species. Allopolyploidy may

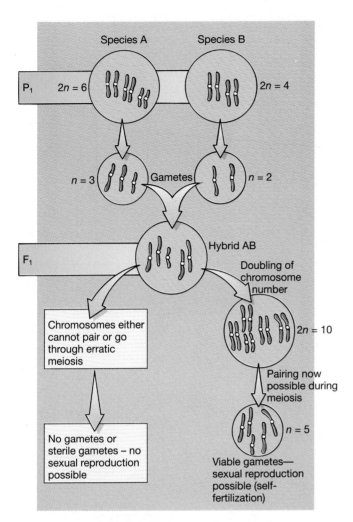

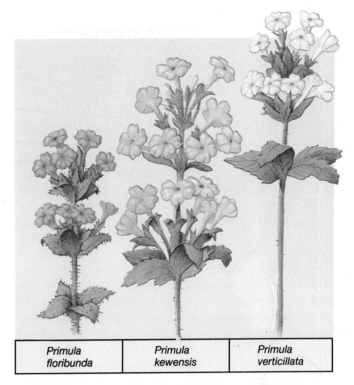

Figure 19–9 An allopolyploid primrose, *Primula kewensis*, arose during the early part of the 20th century. The F₁ hybrid of *P. floribunda* ($2n = 18$) and *P. verticillata* ($2n = 18$) was a diploid perennial ($2n = 18$) and was sterile. Three different times it spontaneously formed a fertile branch, which was *P. kewensis*, a fertile polyploid ($2n = 36$) that produced seeds. (The specific epithet *kewensis* was given in recognition that this species arose accidentally at the Royal Botanic Gardens at Kew, England.)

Figure 19–8 How a fertile allopolyploid is formed. Interspecific hybridization occurs between two species, yielding a hybrid F₁ generation. If doubling of the chromosomes does not occur, they are unable to undergo normal meiosis, and the hybrid is sterile (*left*). If the chromosomes double, the hybrid is able to undergo meiosis and is fertile (*right*).

explain the rapid appearance of flowering plants in the fossil record and the incredible diversity (more than 250,000 species) of flowering plants today.

Mechanism of sympatric speciation in animals

The significance of sympatric speciation in animal evolution is highly disputed among evolutionary biologists. The few examples of sympatric speciation involve parasitic insects. It is thought that a mutation arises in an individual and spreads through a small group of insects as a result of sexual reproduction. The mutation isolates the insects reproductively from the rest of the population, perhaps by allowing them to parasitize a different host species. Further mutations may occur to cause the mutant population to diverge even further

from the original population. The lineage is maintained because these insects either self-fertilize or breed with brothers or sisters (copies of the same mutant alleles are more likely in close relatives). Although the original population and the mutant population continue to occupy the same geographical area, no gene flow occurs between them because the mutant population now lives on a different host; this means that the two groups have separate mating locations.

Examples of sympatric speciation

Several species of hemp nettle occur in temperate parts of Europe and Asia. One of these, *Galeopsis tetrahit* ($2n = 32$), is a naturally occurring allopolyploid that was formed by the hybridization of two species, *G. pubescens* ($2n = 16$) and *G. speciosa* ($2n = 16$). This speciation, which occurred in nature, was experimentally reproduced in the laboratory. *G. pubescens* and *G. speciosa* were crossed to produce F₁ hybrids that were mostly sterile. Nevertheless, both F₂ and F₃ generations were formed. In the F₃ there was a polyploid plant with $2n = 32$ that yielded fertile F₄ offspring. These artificial, allopolyploid plants had the same morphology and chromosome number as the naturally occurring *G. tetrahit*. When the experimentally produced plants were crossed with the naturally occurring *G. tetrahit*, a fertile F_1 generation was formed. Thus, the experiment duplicated the speciation process that occurred in nature.

Many of our important crop plants such as wheat are the result of allopolyploidy. Wheat comprises three groups based on chromosome number: Einkorn wheat and other primitive species are the diploid wheats ($2n = 14$); cultivated emmer and durum are tetraploid wheats ($2n = 28$); bread wheat, possibly the most important of all cultivated plants, is an example of a hexaploid wheat ($2n = 42$). Exactly how bread wheat evolved has been studied extensively (Figure 19–10). It involved two separate hybridizations, the first between two species that each had seven pairs of chromosomes and the second between the resulting tetraploid (14 pairs of chromosomes) and another species with seven pairs of chromosomes. Each hybridization resulted in a sterile hybrid in which the fertilization of nonreduced gametes caused a doubling of chromosomes.

The hawthorn fly, *Rhagoletis*, originally parasitized the North American hawthorn. In the 1860s some hawthorn flies were discovered to be living on apples; by the 1960s another group was infesting cherries. Some studies have indicated that these three groups are reproductively isolated because of their host preference. Also, the time of emergence as a reproductively mature adult has changed for the three groups. No consensus exists about whether hawthorn flies are an example of sympatric speciation. Some biologists contend that the amount of reproductive isolation between these three groups is not clear. It is also possible that these species differentiated allopatrically, with subsequent migration bringing them together.

EVOLUTION IS GRADUAL, OCCURS IN SPURTS, OR IS A COMBINATION OF BOTH PROCESSES

Biologists have long recognized that the fossil record lacks many transitional forms; that is, the starting points and end points are present, but the intermediate stages in the evolution from one species to another are absent. This fact has traditionally been blamed on the incompleteness of the fossil record. Biologists have attempted to fill in the missing parts, much as a writer might fill in the middle of a novel when the beginning and end are already there.

Recently, however, many biologists have begun to question whether the fossil record really is incomplete. The theory of **punctuated equilibrium** proposes that the fossil record accurately reflects evolution as it occurs, with long periods of **stasis** (no change in a species)

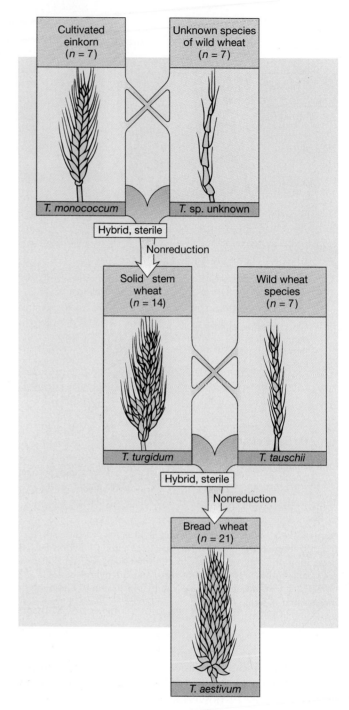

Figure 19–10 The evolution of bread wheat *(Triticum aestivum)* involved two separate hybridizations. Each hybrid was sterile but gave rise to a fertile hybrid when the chromosome number doubled as a result of the nonreduction of chromosome number during meiosis.

punctuated, or interrupted, by short periods of rapid speciation (Figure 19–11). Thus, in evolution by punctuated equilibrium, speciation normally proceeds in "spurts." These relatively short periods of active evolution are followed by long periods of stasis; later, when evolution resumes, new species form, and many old ones are outcompeted and become extinct.

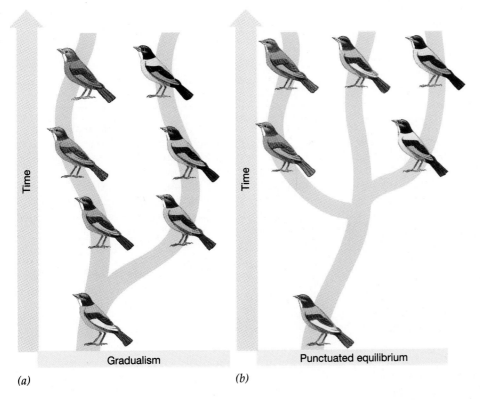

Figure 19–11 There are two theories about the pace of evolution. (*a*) In gradualism there is a slow, steady change in species over time. (*b*) In punctuated equilibrium there are long periods of little evolutionary change (stasis) followed by short periods of rapid speciation.

According to the theory of punctuated equilibrium, most of a species' existence is spent in stasis, and a very small percentage is spent in active evolutionary change. It is important to realize that a "short" amount of time for speciation may mean thousands of years. Such a period of time is short when compared with the several million years that a species exists. Evolutionary biologists who support punctuated equilibrium mention that sympatric speciation and even allopatric speciation can occur in relatively short periods of time.

Punctuated equilibrium accounts for the abrupt appearance of a new species in the fossil record, with little or no record of intermediate forms. That is, proponents think that there are few transitional forms in the fossil record because there were few transitional forms during speciation.

In contrast, the traditional theory of **gradualism** reasons that evolution proceeds at a more or less constant rate, which is not observed in the fossil record because it is incomplete. (Occasionally, a complete fossil record of transitional forms is discovered and cited as a strong case for gradualism; see Focus on Trilobites: Evidence of Gradualism). The theory of gradualism maintains that populations slowly diverge from one another by the gradual accumulation of adaptive characteristics within a population (Figure 19–11). These adaptive characteristics accumulate as a result of different selective pressures brought on by the populations living in different environments.

The abundant evidence in the fossil record of long periods with no change in a species seems to argue against gradualism. Gradualists, however, think that any periods of stasis evident in the fossil record are the result of stabilizing selection (see Chapter 18). They also point out that stasis in fossils is deceptive because fossils do not show all aspects of evolutionary change. Fossils can show changes in external anatomy and skeletal structure, but such characteristics as internal anatomy and changes in physiology, behavior, and ecological roles, which also represent evolution, are not revealed by fossils. Gradualists recognize rapid evolution as taking place only when strong directional selection occurs.

Thus, although evolutionary biologists generally agree that natural selection is the main mechanism responsible for evolution, they are currently evaluating the timing, or pace, of evolutionary change during a species' existence.

MACROEVOLUTION INVOLVES CHANGES IN THE *KINDS* OF SPECIES

In our discussion of evolution, we have examined evolutionary changes within populations (see Chapter 18) and the evolution of new species. But what about the evolution of major groups of living organisms? Evolutionary change above the level of species (i.e., involving

FOCUS ON

Trilobites: Evidence of Gradualism

One of the criticisms of gradualism made by proponents of punctuated equilibrium is that the fossil record shows scant evidence of a gradual transition during the evolution from one species to another. In other words, few intermediate forms exist that would indicate slow, progressive change.

In 1987, a paper was published in *Nature* about an exhaustive study of approximately 15,000 fossil trilobites from a 3-million-year period. Peter Sheldon studied eight lineages (lines of descent) of the small, invertebrate marine organisms, concentrating on the number of ribs in the exoskeleton of each. He found that each lineage showed a gradual increase in the number of ribs during the 3 million years (see figure). There was no evidence of a long period of equilibrium (stasis) followed by a brief period of speciation.

The significance of ribs in trilobites, which are extinct, is unknown. One suggestion is that each rib covered an appendage. Another is that the addition of ribs provided extra strength. It is also possible that extra ribs had a neutral effect but evolved because they were pleiotropically connected to other beneficial traits (see Chapter 10).

The publication of Sheldon's work reignited the discussion about gradualism versus punctuated equilibrium.

Fossil trilobites. (Visuals Unlimited/A. J. Copley)

Some supporters of punctuated equilibrium interpret Sheldon's work quite differently. They say that such minor change as the addition of a few more ribs to the trilobite exoskeleton in 3 million years is equivalent to stasis. They point to two recent studies on bryozoa and clam fossils that clearly support punctuated equilibrium.

Many scientists are of the opinion that both types of evolution, gradualism and punctuated equilibrium, are at opposite ends of a wide spectrum of evolutionary tempos. That is, the pace of evolution may be steady and gradual in certain instances and punctuated in others. Even if that is the case, scientists still want to know which type of evolution is *most* important and why some organisms appear to undergo change in a gradual manner while others have no change followed by sudden, dramatic change.

---

higher taxa such as genera and orders) is known as **macroevolution.** Evolutionary biologists who are interested in macroevolution seek to understand how large phenotypic changes (such as wings with feathers) evolved in major groups of organisms (such as birds). They study significant evolutionary trends through geological time.

Evolutionary Novelties Originate from Mutations That Alter Developmental Pathways

A change in the basic design of an organism can produce something unique. Examples of unusual features include wings of insects, flowers of flowering plants, and feathers of birds. Usually these "new" structures, called **preaptations** (formerly called preadaptations), are variations of some structure already in existence. That is, they evolved to fulfill one role but had enough evolutionary plasticity to be modified for another. Bird feathers are a good example of a preaptation as they evolved from reptilian scales; the mammalian middle ear is a preaptation that evolved from a modified jaw element of reptiles.

How do such novel changes occur? Many are probably due to changes in development. Regulatory genes may exert control over hundreds of other genes. Very slight genetic changes in regulatory genes could cause major structural changes. For example, most organisms have **allometric growth,** varied rates of growth for different parts of the body during development. The size of the head in human newborns is large in proportion to

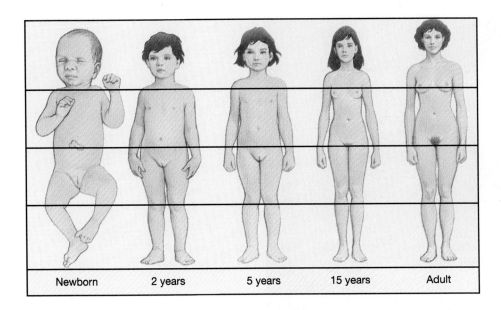

Figure 19–12 Allometric growth in humans. Different stages in the growth of a human are drawn the same size to demonstrate allometric growth. As humans develop, their torsos, hands, and legs grow more rapidly than their heads.

Newborn	2 years	5 years	15 years	Adult

the rest of the body. As a human grows and matures, its torso, hands, and legs grow more rapidly than the head (Figure 19–12). Allometric growth is a phenomenon in many organisms, including the male fiddler crab with its single, oversized claw and the ocean sunfish with its enlarged tail (Figure 19–13). If growth rates are altered even slightly, drastic changes in the shape of the organism may occur. The incredibly large antlers on the extinct Irish elk, *Megaloceros*, an enormous deer that was 10 feet tall and had an antler span of 12 feet, were due to

allometric growth (Figure 19–14). The antlers of the Irish elk grew 2.5 times more rapidly than its skull. The ancestor of the Irish elk did not possess such exaggerated antlers. Allometric growth, then, provides variation that can be selected for or against during the course of evolution.

Sometimes novel changes are the result of changes in the *timing* of development. **Paedomorphosis** is the retention of ancestral juvenile characteristics in an adult descendant. Many salamanders have features as adults

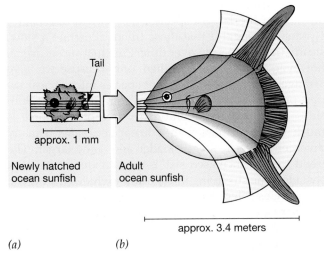

Tail

approx. 1 mm

Newly hatched ocean sunfish

Adult ocean sunfish

approx. 3.4 meters

(a)   *(b)*

Figure 19–13 Allometric growth in the ocean sunfish. The tail end of an ocean sunfish grows faster than its head end, resulting in the unique shape of the adult ocean sunfish. (*a*) A newly hatched ocean sunfish, which is only 1 mm long, has an extremely small tail. (*b*) This allometric transformation can be visualized by drawing rectangular coordinate lines through a picture of the juvenile fish and then changing the coordinate lines mathematically. The adult ocean sunfish is 3.4 meters (11 feet) long and weighs 1 metric ton.

Figure 19–14 Allometric growth is responsible for the huge antlers of the extinct Irish elk. (E. R. Degginger)

Figure 19–15 Paedomorphosis in salamanders. In most salamanders, the external gills found in the larval stage are not present in the adult. Some salamander species retain this juvenile feature as adults. (Jane Burton/Bruce Coleman, Inc.)

that were found only in the immature stages of their ancestors. Retention of gills, an example of paedomorphosis in certain salamanders, obviously alters the salamander's behavioral and ecological characteristics (Figure 19–15).

MACROEVOLUTION IS DEMONSTRATED BY THE FOSSIL RECORD

Macroevolution is concerned with changes in the kinds of species over evolutionary time and includes (1) the origin of evolutionary trends, (2) adaptive radiation, and (3) the effects of extinction on evolution.

Evolutionary Trends Are Indicated in the Fossil Record by Morphological Changes in Hard Body Parts

The fossil record contains a number of examples of changes in a lineage that appear to exhibit an overall trend (Figure 19–16). For example, in the evolution of flowers, the number of floral parts such as stamens and petals tends to become reduced. The mammal lineage shows an evolutionary trend toward an increase in brain size relative to body size, as well as an overall trend toward an increase in body size. Evolutionary trends apply only in a general sense because there are many individual exceptions to an overall trend. Al-

though elephant evolution has revealed a trend in the direction of increased size, a number of extinct elephants were smaller than their ancestors.

Gradualists and punctuationists sometimes disagree over the interpretation of evolutionary trends. The evolution of the horse is an example (Figure 19–17). As it is generally depicted, horse evolution shows a progression from the smallest ancestral species, *Hyracotherium,* to the largest species, the present-day *Equus.* Gradualists suggest that these trends illustrate a slow, steady transformation over time. Punctuationists argue, however, that the trend is there only because we have arranged a number of different species into a linear series, producing an impression of a gradual trend. Both sides agree that the evolutionary tree of the horse is much more complex than a linear series, with many divergent species, some smaller and some larger. The trend toward increased size is most evident when one considers the surviving lineage and excludes the others.

Species selection has been suggested to cause evolutionary trends in much the same way that natural selection alters individuals in a population over time. In natural selection, individuals that survive and produce the largest number of offspring have the greatest effect on evolution. In species selection, the species that survive the longest in evolutionary history and produce the largest number of new species have the greatest effect on an evolutionary trend. But the *direction* of the trend is a consequence of environmental pressure. If environmental conditions change, the trend may reverse direction or simply stop.

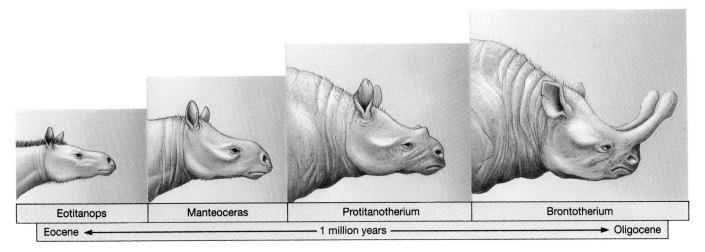

| Eotitanops | Manteoceras | Protitanotherium | Brontotherium |

Eocene ◄───────────── 1 million years ─────────────► Oligocene

Figure 19–16 The titanotheres, an extinct group of mammals, exhibited an evolutionary trend toward increased size. The increase in horn size is an example of allometric growth.

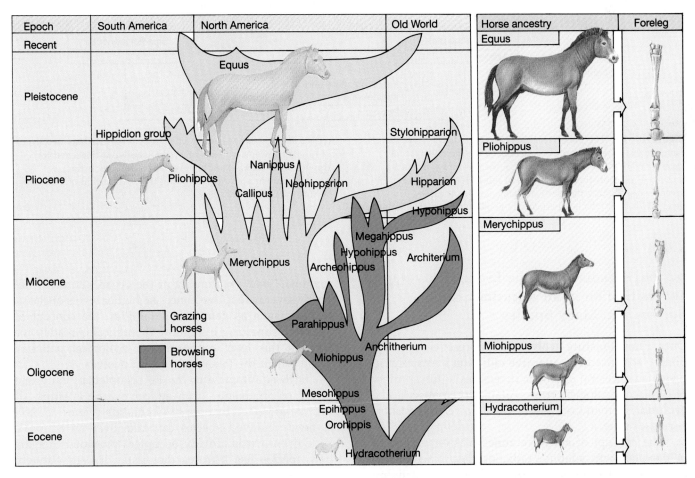

Figure 19–17 The evolution of the horse can be interpreted as evidence for both gradualism and punctuated equilibrium. If one observes the surviving lineage only *(right)*, several trends emerge— a gradual progression toward larger size, a gradual reduction in the number of toes on each foot (from four to one), and a gradual modification of the teeth for grazing (versus browsing). However, each species appears and later disappears in the fossil record without undergoing any appreciable divergence. That is, each new species appears in the fossil record with the changes that distinguish it from its parent species and does not appear to change much during the remainder of its existence.

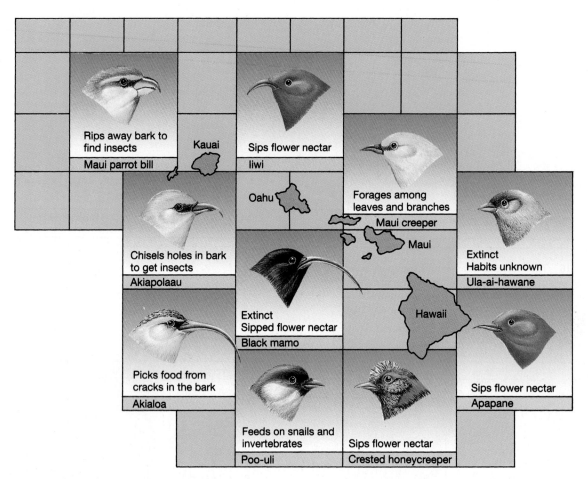

Figure 19–18 The honeycreepers of the Hawaiian Islands are a dramatic example of adaptive radiation. When the honeycreeper ancestor reached the Hawaiian Islands, there were few birds present. The succeeding generations of honeycreepers quickly diversified to occupy the many available ecological niches. The diversity in their bills is a particularly good illustration of adaptive radiation. Some honeycreeper bills are curved to extract nectar out of tubular flowers, whereas others are short and thickened for ripping away bark. Many honeycreepers are now extinct as a result of human activities, including the introduction of predators such as rats, dogs, and pigs.

Adaptive Radiation Is the Evolutionary Diversification of an Ancestral Species into Many Species

Once a novel feature evolves that represents an evolutionary advancement, **adaptive radiation** may occur, in which an ancestral organism diversifies to fill a variety of different ecological roles. Adaptive radiation is the evolution of many related species in a relatively short period of time.

The concept of **adaptive zones** was developed to help explain why adaptive radiations take place. Adaptive zones are new ecological roles or ways of living that were previously not used by an ancestral organism. At the species level, adaptive zones are essentially identical to niches (the ecological role of a species in a community; see Chapter 53); "nocturnal flying to catch insects," "grazing on grass while migrating across a savanna," and "swimming at the ocean's surface" describe several adaptive zones. At higher levels of classification, such as genera and families, the concept of adaptive zones is a little more theoretical. An adaptive zone at this level represents an ecological pathway along which the taxonomic group evolves.

Each adaptive zone can be occupied by only one group of organisms. If an adaptive zone is empty, it may be exploited by adaptive radiation (Figure 19–18). A newly evolved species can take over an adaptive zone even if it is already occupied, provided that the new species has features that make it competitively superior to the original occupants.

Adaptive radiation appears to be more common during periods of major environmental change, but it is difficult to determine if these changes actually trigger adaptive radiation. It is possible that major environmental change has an indirect effect on adaptive radia-

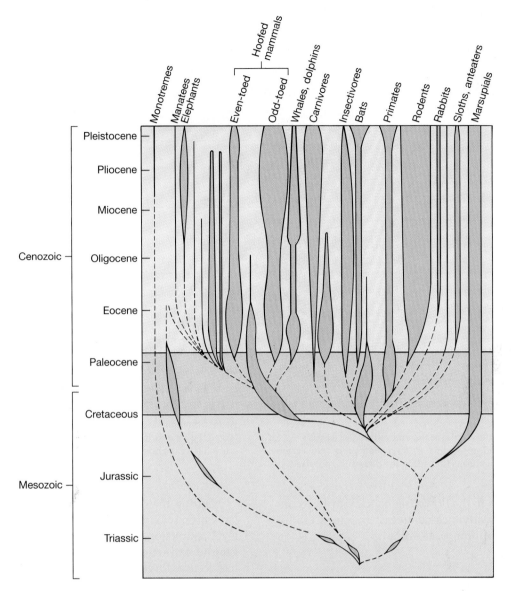

Figure 19–19 Mammals underwent adaptive radiation at the end of the Cretaceous period. The decline of reptiles at this time is thought to have allowed mammals to radiate into many groups in a relatively short period of time. The dashed lines in the diagram indicate hypothetical relationships for which there is no direct fossil evidence, although other evidence (such as comparative anatomy) supports the relationship.

tion by increasing the rate of extinction. Extinction produces empty niches, which are then available for adaptive radiation. Mammals, for example, had evolved millions of years before they underwent adaptive radiation, which is thought to have been triggered by the extinction of the dinosaurs (Figure 19–19). In a relatively short period of time after the dinosaurs' demise, mammals evolved to occupy and exploit a variety of lifestyles; flying, running, burrowing, and swimming mammals evolved.

The appearance of novel evolutionary features is associated with each major period of adaptive radiation. For example, shells and skeletons may have been

the novel features responsible for a period of adaptive radiation at the beginning of the Paleozoic Era (see Chapter 20) in which most animal phyla, both now living and now extinct, evolved.

Care must be taken in interpreting a cause-and-effect relationship between the appearance of a novel evolutionary feature and adaptive radiation. It is tempting to take a simplistic approach and state, for example, that the evolution of the flower triggered adaptive radiation of thousands of species of flowering plants. Perhaps flowering plants exhibited rapid adaptive radiation as a result of the evolution of a more competitive method of sexual reproduction (the flower). However,

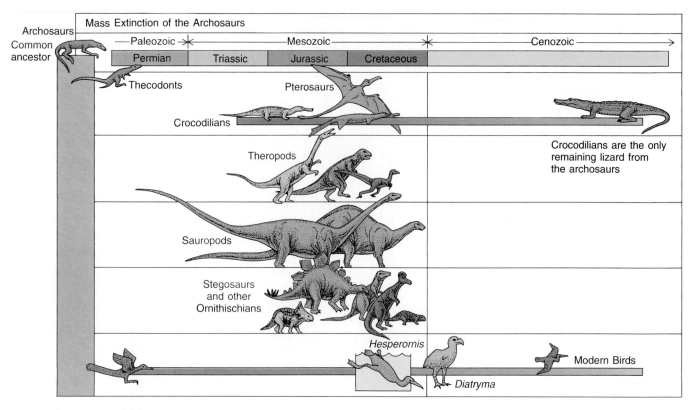

Figure 19–20 Mass extinctions have taken place several times in Earth's history. For example, at the end of the Cretaceous period, which occurred approximately 65 million years ago, a mass extinction of many organisms, including the dinosaurs, occurred. At that time, the archosaurs (one of five main groups of reptiles) largely became extinct. The only lines to survive were the crocodiles and birds, both of which are archosaur descendants.

adaptive radiation in the flowering plants may be a consequence of other advancements that they possess instead of, or in addition to, flowers.

Extinction of Species Is an Important Aspect of Evolution

Extinction, the end of a lineage, occurs when the last individual of a species dies. It is a permanent loss, for once a species is extinct it can never reappear. Extinctions have occurred continually since the origin of life on Earth. By one estimate, there is only one species living today for every 2000 that have become extinct. Extinction is the eventual fate of all species, in the same way that death is the eventual fate of all individual living organisms.

Although extinction has a negative impact on biological diversity, it has a positive evolutionary aspect. As mentioned previously, when species become extinct, the ecological niches that they occupied become vacant. As a result, organisms still living evolve to fill the unoccupied niches. In other words, the extinct species are replaced by new species.

During the course of life on Earth, there appear to have been two types of extinction. The continuous, low-level extinction of species, sometimes called **background extinction,** is one. A second type of extinction has occurred five or six times during Earth's history. At these times, **mass extinctions** of numerous species and higher taxa in both terrestrial and marine environments have taken place (Figure 19–20). The time period over which a mass extinction occurred may have lasted for millions of years, but that is a relatively short period compared with the history of life on Earth. Each period of mass extinction, which appears to have been indiscriminate in which species survived and which became extinct, was followed by a period of "mass speciation," or radiation.

The causes of extinction, particularly mass extinction, are not well understood. Both environmental and biological factors seem to be involved. Major changes in the climate could adversely affect plants and animals that are unable to adapt to them. Marine organisms, in particular, are adapted to a very steady, unchanging climate. If Earth's temperature were to decrease overall by just a few degrees, many marine species would probably perish. Some biologists suggest that climatic changes were responsible for mass extinctions in the past.

Figure 19–21 The dusky seaside sparrow, *Ammodramus maritimus nigrescens*, became extinct in 1987, largely owing to human destruction of its habitat. In an attempt to preserve some of its gene pool, the last six survivors were successfully crossed with a related seaside sparrow subspecies in the mid-1980s. (P. W. Sykes, Jr./VIREO)

It is also possible that mass extinctions were due to changes in the environment triggered by catastrophes. If Earth was bombarded by a large meteorite, for example, the dust going into the atmosphere upon impact could have blocked much of the sunlight. In addition to killing many plants, this would have lowered Earth's temperature, leading to the death of many marine organisms. There is substantial evidence suggesting an impact of a meteorite at the end of the Cretaceous Period (see Chapter 20).

Biological factors also trigger extinction. When a new species evolves, it may be able to outcompete an older species, leading to its extinction. Humans have had a profound impact on extinction (see Chapter 55). The enormous increase in the human population has caused us to spread into areas of Earth that were previously not part of our range. The habitats of many animal and plant species have been altered or destroyed by such large numbers of humans. Habitat destruction can result in an organism's extinction (Figure 19–21). Indeed, some biologists fear that Earth has entered the

largest period of mass extinction in its entire history, and that this has been triggered by human activities.

CAN MICROEVOLUTIONARY CHANGE LEAD TO SPECIATION AND MACROEVOLUTION?

We have seen that such mechanisms as differential reproduction through natural selection, mutation, genetic drift, and migration explain microevolution, the evolutionary changes within a population (see Chapter 18). If this population remains reproductively isolated from its parent species, mutation and selection cause it to diverge more. Given enough changes, the population becomes a new species.

Can these mechanisms be used to explain the evolution of genera, families, and higher taxa? Does natural selection account for macroevolution? Can population genetics help explain major evolutionary events?

The concepts of evolution presented in Chapters 17 to 19 represent the synthetic theory of evolution, in which mutation provides the genetic variation upon which natural selection acts. It combines Darwin's theory with important aspects of genetics and ecology. All aspects of the synthetic theory have been tested and verified at the population and subspecies level. In addition, the synthetic theory is generally accepted by biologists as adequate to explain macroevolution. That is, given enough time, the same processes that lead to speciation produce new genera, new families, new orders, new classes, and new phyla or divisions.

It must be emphasized, however, that the synthetic theory as it relates to macroevolutionary events, although supported by a considerable body of data from many fields, is essentially unproven. Some biologists question whether adaptation is as significant in the evolution of higher taxa as it is in microevolution, for example. It is always possible that other evolutionary mechanisms will be discovered to have an important role in macroevolutionary events. If this occurs, the mechanisms involved in evolution will have to be reevaluated in light of the new evidence.

SUMMARY

I. A biological species is defined as a group of more or less distinct organisms that have the potential to interbreed with one another but not with members of different species.

II. Biological isolating mechanisms restrict the gene flow between species and sometimes between different populations within a species.

A. Prezygotic isolating mechanisms prevent fertilization from taking place.

1. Temporal isolation is due to the two species reproducing at different times of the day, season, or year.

2. Ecological isolation is caused by habitat differences between two closely related species living in the same geographical area.

3. Distinctive courtship behaviors prevent mating between species (behavioral isolation).
4. Mechanical isolation is due to morphological or anatomical differences in the reproductive structures of plants and animals.
5. Molecular and chemical differences may cause gamete incompatibility between species (gametic isolation).

B. Postzygotic isolating mechanisms ensure reproductive failure when fertilization has taken place.
1. Hybrid inviability is abortion of the hybrid embryo.
2. Hybrid sterility prevents hybrids from reproducing.
3. Hybrid breakdown prevents hybrids from reproducing beyond one generation.

III. Speciation is the evolution of a new species.
A. Allopatric speciation occurs when one population becomes geographically isolated from other populations of the species and subsequently evolves.
B. Sympatric speciation, which is extremely rare in animals, does not require geographical isolation. In plants it occurs as a result of allopolyploidy.

IV. The timing of evolutionary change is currently being debated.
A. According to proponents of gradualism, populations slowly diverge from one another by the accumulation of adaptive characteristics within a population.
B. According to proponents of punctuated equilibrium, evolution proceeds in spurts. Short periods of active evolution are followed by long periods of stasis.

V. Macroevolution is the evolution of taxa above the species level.
A. It includes the origin of unusual features, evolutionary trends, adaptive radiation, and extinction.
B. Extinction is the death of a species. Once a species is extinct it can never reappear.

VI. The modern synthesis of evolution is probably adequate to explain macroevolution.

POST-TEST

1. A species is a group of organisms with a common _____ _____.
2. When two closely related species that are found in the same geographical range reproduce at different times of the year, this is known as _____ isolation.
3. If two different species have reproductive structures that prevent mating, they fail to reproduce because of _____ isolation.
4. _____ isolating mechanisms prevent successful reproduction if mating occurs between different species.
5. The most important method of speciation in animal evolution is _____ speciation.
6. An individual that possesses multiple sets of chromosomes, in which one or more of those sets came from a different species, is known as a(n) _____.
7. The facts that (1) the fossil record shows few transitional forms during speciation and (2) long periods of stasis are evident are used to support _____ _____.
8. Evolutionary change that involves taxa above the level of species is called _____.
9. A "new" structure that is a variation of some structure already in existence is called a(n) _____.
10. The incredibly large antlers of the extinct Irish elk were due to _____ _____.
11. The permanent loss of a species that occurs when the last member of a species dies is called _____.
12. _____ extinction is thought to have occurred during five or six periods of Earth's history.
13. The evolution of several to many species from a single ancestral species is known as _____ _____.

REVIEW QUESTIONS

1. Give an example of each of the following:
   a. temporal isolation
   b. ecological isolation
   c. behavioral isolation
   d. mechanical isolation
   e. gametic isolation
2. Describe the three types of postzygotic isolating mechanisms and give an example of each.
3. Identify at least five geographical barriers that might lead to allopatric speciation.
4. Why is speciation more likely to occur if the original isolated population is small than if it is large?
5. Explain how hybridization and polyploidy can cause a new plant species to form in as little time as one generation.
6. If you were in a debate and had to support gradualism, what would you say? How would you support punctuated equilibrium?
7. In macroevolution, how are novel changes in structure related to development?
8. Give an example of each of the following:
   a. preaptation
   b. allometric growth
   c. paedomorphosis
9. What role does extinction play in evolution?

RECOMMENDED READINGS

Alvarez, W., and F. Asaro. An extraterrestrial impact. *Scientific American,* October 1990, pp. 78–84. Evidence that the mass extinction which spelled the demise of the dinosaurs was caused by an asteroid or comet. This issue also contains an article (pp. 85–92) which suggests that a massive volcanic eruption was the cause of this period of extinction.

Bass, T. A. This African lake turns out to be a fine kettle of fish. *Smithsonian,* December 1988, pp. 145–155. An examination of the Cichlicae, fish that evolved into hundreds of different species in Lake Malawi in Africa.

Coyne, J. A. Genetics and Speciation. *Nature* Vol. 355, 6 Feb. 1992, pp. 511–515. A review article on the genetic patterns involved in the speciation process.

Gore, R. Extinctions. *National Geographic,* June 1989, pp. 662–699. Examines the major mass extinctions that occurred on Earth, including the one currently under way.

Grant, V. *The Evolutionary Process: A Critical Study of Evolutionary Theory,* 2nd ed. Columbia University Press, New York, 1991. An authoritative and comprehensive review of evolution.

McDonald, J. F. Macroevolution and retroviral elements. *BioScience* 40:3, March 1990. Examines an unusual hypothesis that transposable elements have a role in the regulatory changes that result in new patterns of development associated with macroevolution.

Mayr, E. *Animal Species and Evolution.* Harvard University Press, Cambridge, MA, 1963. A classic on animal evolution.

Stanley, S. *Macroevolution: Pattern and Process.* W. H. Freeman, San Francisco, 1979. An exposition of punctuated equilibrium and the question of whether it is important in speciation and evolution.

CHAPTER 20

The Origin and Evolutionary History of Life

OUTLINE

Chemical evolution on early Earth
The history of life

The last three chapters have been concerned with how life evolved, but we have not dealt with a fundamental question involving biological evolution: How did life begin? The hypothesis generally accepted by scientists is that life developed from nonliving matter. This process, called **chemical evolution,** involved several stages. First, small organic molecules formed spontaneously and accumulated over time. They were able to accumulate rather than being broken down (as occurs today) because the two things responsible for breaking down organic molecules today—free oxygen and other living things— were absent from early Earth. Second, large macromolecules like proteins and nucleic acids were assembled from smaller molecules. Then, the macromolecules interacted with one another, collecting into more complicated assemblages that could eventually metabolize and replicate. Eventually, these macromolecular

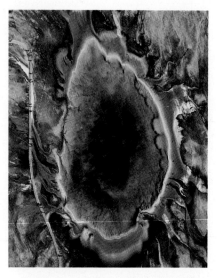

Aerial view of a hot sulfur spring. The last common ancestor of all living organisms may have been a prokaryote that lived in such an environment. Today, hot sulfur springs contain numerous bacteria, which produce the brilliant colors. (Paul Chesley, Photographers/Aspen, Inc.)

assemblages developed into cell-like structures that in the course of time became the first true cells.

After the first cells originated, they evolved over several billion years to produce the rich biological diversity that characterizes our planet today. The development of photosynthesis, aerobic respiration, and eukaryotic cell structure represent several important advances that occurred during early evolution.

It is thought that life originated on Earth only once and that this occurred under environmental circumstances that were quite different from those on Earth today. And so, to understand the origin of life, we must examine the conditions of early Earth. Although we will never be certain of the exact conditions that existed on Earth when life arose, scientific evidence from a number of sources provides us with valuable clues.

LEARNING OBJECTIVES

After you have studied this chapter you should be able to

1. Describe the conditions on early Earth.
2. Outline the major steps that are thought to have occurred in the origin of living cells.
3. Explain how the evolution of photosynthetic autotrophs affected (1) Earth's atmosphere and (2) other life forms.
4. Define the endosymbiont theory and summarize the evidence supporting it.

5. List the four geological eras in chronological order and give approximate dates for each.
6. Briefly describe the geological features and distinguishing living organisms for the Precambrian, Paleozoic, Mesozoic, and Cenozoic eras.
7. Explain how the course of evolution was affected by continental drift.

EARLY EARTH PROVIDED THE CONDITIONS FOR CHEMICAL EVOLUTION

The formation of Earth and the rest of our solar system is tied to the formation of the universe. Evidence suggests that the universe was not always spread out the way it is today. Between 10 and 20 billion years ago, the universe was apparently a dense compaction that exploded (the Big Bang), throwing the matter of the universe into space. This material has been moving outward ever since, so that the universe is continuously expanding. As the materials cooled, atoms of different elements formed, particularly hydrogen and helium.

Our sun is a star that formed 5 to 10 billion years ago. As the solar matter was compressed by gravitational forces, it ignited, producing a tremendous amount of heat. This heat triggered the formation of other elements from hydrogen and helium. Some of this matter was ejected from the sun and coalesced with debris, dust, and gases encircling the sun to form the planets.

Earth is approximately 4.6 billion years old. The matter making up early Earth compacted as a result of gravitational forces, with the heaviest elements—nickel and iron—forming the center core, the medium-weight elements forming the mantle, and the lighter elements remaining near the surface. The first atmosphere, composed largely of the lightest elements, hydrogen and helium, was lost from Earth because Earth's weak gravitational forces could not hold it.

Earth is thought to have been cold originally. As gravitational compaction continued, heat built up and increased by energy from radioactive decay. This heat occasionally escaped in hot springs and volcanoes, which also produced gases. These gases formed the second atmosphere of early Earth. It was a reducing atmosphere with little or no free oxygen present. The gases included carbon dioxide (CO_2), water vapor (H_2O), carbon monoxide (CO), hydrogen (H_2), and nitrogen (N_2). It is also possible that the early atmosphere contained some ammonia (NH_3), hydrogen sulfide (H_2S), and

methane (CH_4), although these reduced molecules may have been rapidly broken down by ultraviolet radiation from the sun. As the temperature of Earth slowly cooled, water vapor condensed and torrential rains fell, forming the oceans. The falling rain eroded Earth's surface, adding minerals to the oceans and making them "salty."

Four requirements existed for the chemical evolution of life: no free oxygen, energy, chemical building blocks, and time. First, life could have begun only in the absence of free oxygen. Oxygen is very reactive and would have broken down the organic molecules that are a necessary step in the origin of life. However, because Earth's atmosphere was strongly reducing, any free oxygen would have formed oxides with other elements. A second requirement for the origin of life was energy. Early Earth was a place of high energy, with violent thunderstorms, widespread vulcanism, bombardment from meteorites, and intense radiation, including ultraviolet radiation from the sun (Figure 20-1). More ultraviolet radiation was probably produced by the "young" sun than is produced today, and Earth had no protective ozone layer to block much of this radiation. Third, the chemicals needed as building blocks for chemical evolution must have been present. These included water, dissolved inorganic minerals (present as ions), and the gases present in the early atmosphere. A final requirement was adequate time for molecules to accumulate and react. The age of Earth, approximately 4.6 billion years, has provided adequate time for chemical evolution.

Organic Molecules Formed on Primitive Earth before Cells Existed

Because organic molecules are the building materials for living organisms, let us consider how they might have originated. The concept that simple organic molecules like sugars, nucleotides, and amino acids could form spontaneously from nonliving raw materials was first hypothesized in the 1920s by two scientists working independently—Oparin, a Russian biochemist, and Haldane, a Scottish physiologist and geneticist.

Figure 20-1 Conditions on early Earth would have been inhospitable for most of today's life forms. The strongly reducing atmosphere lacked oxygen; volcanoes erupted, spewing gases that contributed to the atmosphere; and violent thunderstorms produced torrential rainfall that eroded the land. Meteorites continually bombarded Earth, causing cataclysmic changes in the crust, oceans, and atmosphere.   (Courtesy of Reader's Digest Books. Drawing by H. K. Wimmer)

Their hypothesis was tested in the 1950s by Miller and Urey, who designed an apparatus that simulated conditions then thought to be prevalent on early Earth (Figure 20–2). The atmosphere they started with was rich in hydrogen (H_2), methane (CH_4), water (H_2O), and ammonia (NH_3). They exposed this atmosphere to an electric discharge, which simulated lightning. Their analysis of the chemicals produced in a week revealed that amino acids and other organic molecules had been synthesized.

Recent scientific evidence suggests that Earth's early atmosphere was *not* rich in methane or ammonia, as assumed by Miller and Urey. Similar experiments using different combinations of gases, however, have produced a wide variety of organic molecules, including bases of RNA and DNA.

Oparin envisioned that the organic molecules would, over vast spans of time, accumulate in the shallow seas, as a "sea of organic soup." Under such conditions, he conceived that smaller organic molecules (monomers) would unite to form larger ones (polymers). Based on evidence accumulated since Oparin's time, most scientists think that polymerization to form proteins, nucleic acids, and other large organic molecules would not have occurred in shallow seas. For one thing, many polymerization reactions involve condensation, in which two molecules are joined by the removal of water. It is unlikely that a water-producing reaction would occur in a watery environment without enzymes. Also, it is doubtful that the concentration of organic monomers could have reached high enough levels in the oceans to stimulate their polymerization.

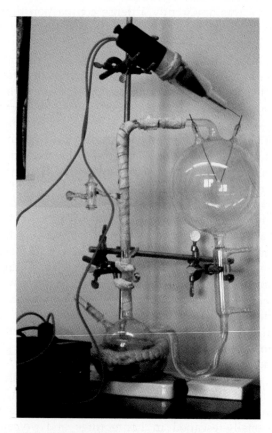

Figure 20-2 Stanley Miller and Harold Urey used an apparatus similar to this to replicate what they thought were the conditions of early Earth. An electric spark was produced in the upper right flask to simulate lightning. The gases present in the flask reacted together, forming a number of basic organic compounds, which accumulated in the flask on the lower left. (Courtesy of Dr. Stanley Miller)

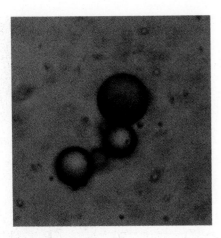

Figure 20–3 Proteinoid microspheres are tiny spheres (1 to 2 μm in diameter) that exhibit some of the properties of life. (From Sidney Fox, Southern Illinois University at Carbondale)

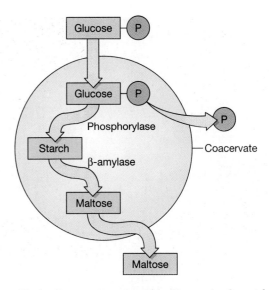

Figure 20–4 Coacervates are capable of very simple metabolic pathways. A coacervate containing phosphorylase and amylase was able to absorb glucose-1-phosphate from the surrounding medium and convert it to maltose, which was detected in the medium.

It is possible that organic polymers were synthesized and accumulated on rock or clay surfaces.[1] Clay is particularly intriguing as a site for polymerization because it contains zinc and iron ions that could act as catalysts. Also, clay binds the exact forms of sugars and amino acids that are found in living organisms. Other amino acids and sugars may be produced but do not bind to clay. To test whether polymers could form on a rock or clay surface, Sidney Fox heated a mixture of dry amino acids and obtained polypeptides. He called the product of this spontaneous polymerization a **proteinoid.**

After polymers are produced, could they assemble into more complex structures? Scientists have worked with several different **protobionts,** spontaneous assemblages of organic polymers. They have been able to make protobionts that resemble simple life forms in several ways, helping us to envision how complex nonliving molecules took that giant leap and became living cells. Protobionts often divide in half after they have "grown." Their internal environment is chemically different from the external environment, and some of them show the rudiments of metabolism. They are amazingly organized, considering their relatively simple composition.

One type of protobiont, the **microsphere,** was formed by adding water to proteinoids (Figure 20–3). Microspheres are spherical and have osmotic properties. Some of them produce an electrical potential across their surfaces, reminiscent of membrane potentials in cells. Microspheres can also absorb materials from their surroundings and respond to changes in osmotic concentration as though they were surrounded by membranes, even though they contain no lipid. **Liposomes** are protobionts made from lipids. In water they form a spherical structure surrounded by a lipid bilayer similar in structure to cell membranes. Another example of a protobiont is the **coacervate,** a particle composed of two or more organic molecules. Oparin formed coacervates from relatively complex mixtures of polypeptides, nucleic acids, and polysaccharides. Coacervates are capable of very simple metabolism (Figure 20–4). When Oparin made a coacervate out of short-chain RNAs and the enzyme responsible for replicating nucleic acids and placed it in a medium that contained nucleoside triphosphates, the coacervate "grew," replicated, and divided.

The First Cells Probably Assembled from Organic Molecules

Studying protobionts helps us appreciate that relatively simple "precells" can exhibit some of the properties of life. However, it is a major step from simple molecular

---

[1] Another possibility is that organic polymerization leading to the origin of life occurred first in **hydrothermal vents,** hot sulfur springs in the deep ocean. Such a location would have been better protected than Earth's surface from the catastrophic effects of bombardment by meteorites. These hot springs produce important precursors of organic molecules and of energy-rich "food," including hydrogen sulfide and methane. Also, molecular evidence suggests that the last common ancestor of all living organisms was most likely a prokaryote that metabolized sulfur and lived in hot springs.

Figure 20–5 Stromatolites at Shark Bay in Western Australia that are approximately 2000 years old. These formations are composed of mats of cyanobacteria and minerals such as calcium carbonate. Some fossil stromatolites are 3.1 to 3.4 billion years old. (William E. Ferguson)

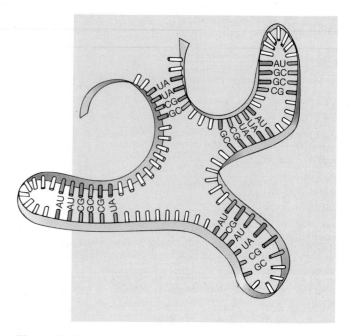

Figure 20–6 Single-stranded RNA can form base pairs with itself, producing a precise conformation that may have catalytic properties. The order of the nucleotides determines the ultimate shape of the molecule.

aggregates such as protobionts to living cells. Yet fossil evidence indicates that prokaryotic cells were thriving 3.5 billion years ago.

Unquestionably, the first cells to evolve were prokaryotic. Australian and South African rocks have yielded microscopic fossils of prokaryotic cells 3.1 to 3.4 billion years old. **Stromatolites** are another type of fossil evidence of Earth's earliest cells. These column-like rocks are composed of many minute layers of prokaryotic cells, usually cyanobacteria. Over time, sediment collects around the cells and gradually becomes mineralized. Meanwhile, a new layer of living cells grows over the older, dead cells. Stromatolites are found in a number of places in the world, including the Canadian Great Slave Lake and the Gunflint Iron Formations along Lake Superior in the United States. Some stromatolites are extremely ancient. One group in Western Australia, for example, is several billion years old. Living colonies still form stromatolites in warm, shallow waters in Yellowstone National Park and in Shark Bay, Australia (Figure 20–5).

We have said that the origin of cells from macromolecular assemblages was a major step in the origin of life. Actually, the evolution of cells probably occurred in a series of small steps. Two crucial parts of that process would have been the origin of molecular reproduction and the development of metabolism.

Molecular reproduction is a requirement of cell evolution

Polynucleotides (RNA and DNA) can form spontaneously on clay in much the same way as polypeptides. It has been suggested that RNA was the first information molecule to evolve in the progression toward the first cell and that proteins and DNA came later. One of the surprising features of RNA is that it often has catalytic properties (Figure 20–6). Catalytic RNAs, or **ribozymes,** function like enzymes in this regard. They are used in present-day cells to help process RNA into rRNA, tRNA, and mRNA. Before the evolution of true cells, this RNA may have catalyzed the formation of more RNA in the clays, shallow rock pools, or hydrothermal vents where life originated. If one adds RNA strands to a test tube containing RNA nucleotides, replication occurs without enzymes. This reaction is increased if zinc is added as a catalyst. (Recall that zinc is bound to clay.)

RNA can also direct protein synthesis. Some of the single-stranded RNA molecules fold back on themselves owing to the interaction of the nucleotides composing the strand. Sometimes the conformation (shape) of the folded molecule is such that it weakly binds to an amino acid. If amino acids are held together closely by RNA molecules, they may bond together, forming a polypeptide.

In living cells, information is transferred from DNA to RNA to proteins. We have considered how RNA and proteins might have evolved. The final step in the evolution of informational molecules would have been to incorporate DNA into the information transfer system. Because DNA is a double helix, it is more stable and less reactive than RNA; this stability would have provided a decided advantage for a molecule that stores genetic information. RNA would still have been needed, however, because DNA is not catalytic.

Several more steps were involved before a true, living cell could develop from macromolecular aggregations. At the present time, we have very little knowledge about how these steps might have occurred. For example, how did the genetic code originate? This must have occurred very early in the origin of life because virtually all living organisms possess the same genetic code. Also, how did a membrane of lipid and protein envelop the macromolecular assemblage, permitting the accumulation of some molecules and the exclusion of others?

Metabolism evolved in a step-wise fashion

Metabolism, all the biochemical reactions performed by a living organism, involves major sequences of reactions which occur in a step-by-step fashion. It is considered likely that metabolism also arose step by step; that is, organisms acquired the enzymes needed for metabolic pathways in successive steps. However, these enzymes most likely would have evolved in the *reverse* order of the sequence in which they were ultimately used for normal metabolism.

For example, let us suppose that our first primitive organism required an organic compound, Z, for its growth (Figure 20–7). This substance and a vast variety of other organic compounds—Y, X, W, V, U, and so forth—were present in the environment, having been synthesized previously. The primitive organism would be able to survive as long as the supply of compound Z lasted. If a mutation occurred for a new enzyme enabling an organism to synthesize Z from compound Y, the organism with this mutation would be able to survive when the supply of compound Z was exhausted. A later mutation that established an enzyme for catalyzing a reaction in which substance Y could be made from substance X would again have survival value when the supply of Y was exhausted. Similar mutations would have set up enzymes enabling the organism to use successively simpler substances, W, V, U, and so on.

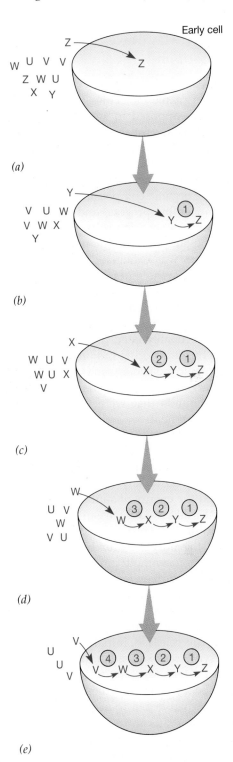

Figure 20–7   The evolution of metabolic pathways probably proceeded backwards. (*a*) Compound Z, required by the primitive cell, was obtained from the environment as long as it was in abundance. (*b*) A mutation produced an enzyme 1 that enabled the cell to use compound Y to make compound Z. Compound Y was obtained from the environment as long as it was available. (*c*) A new mutation produced an enzyme 2 that could convert X to Y. The cell continued to make enzyme 1 that converted Y to Z. (*d*) A new enzyme was added to the pathway, converting compound W to X. (*e*) The final metabolic pathway, starting with compound V and ending with the desired end product, Z, involved the evolution of four enzymes.

Heterotrophy May Have Evolved before Autotrophy

Some of the earliest cells may have been **heterotrophic,** obtaining the organic molecules they needed from the environment as opposed to synthesizing them. These primitive organisms probably consumed many types of organic molecules that had spontaneously formed— sugars, nucleotides, and amino acids, to name a few. They obtained the energy needed to support life by fermenting these organic compounds. Fermentation is, of course, an anaerobic process, and the first cells were almost certainly anaerobic prokaryotes.

Before the supply of spontaneously generated organic molecules was exhausted, mutations may have occurred that gave the mutant organisms a distinct selective advantage. These cells could obtain energy from a new source, sunlight. They were able to store the radiant energy in the form of a chemical such as adenosine triphosphate. Probably later, they were able to expand this process further, storing radiant energy as chemical energy in organic molecules such as sugars. These photosynthetic organisms did not require the energy-rich organic compounds that were of limited availability from the environment.

Photosynthesis requires not only light energy, but also a source of hydrogen, which is used to reduce carbon dioxide when organic molecules are synthesized (see Chapter 8). Most likely the first photosynthetic **autotrophs** used the energy of sunlight to split hydrogen-rich molecules like hydrogen sulfide (H_2S), releasing elemental sulfur in the process. Indeed, the green sulfur bacteria and the purple sulfur bacteria still use H_2S.[1]

The first photosynthetic autotrophs to split water in order to obtain hydrogen were the cyanobacteria. Water is quite abundant on Earth, and the selective advantage that splitting water bestowed on them caused the cyanobacteria to thrive. In the process of splitting water, oxygen (O_2) was released. Initially, the oxygen released from photosynthesis oxidized minerals in the ocean and Earth's crust. Over time, more oxygen was released than could be absorbed by these **sinks** (large reservoirs), and oxygen began to accumulate in the oceans and atmosphere.

The timing of the events just described has been estimated on the basis of geological and fossil evidence. The first autotrophs—prokaryotes, including the cyanobacteria—probably evolved about 3.1 to 3.4 billion years ago. Rocks from that period contain traces of chlorophyll, and evidence such as the stromatolites discussed previously is used to date their appearance. By 2 billion years ago, the cyanobacteria had produced

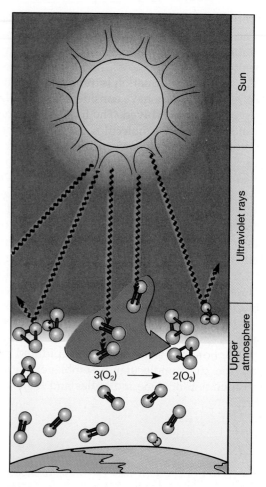

Figure 20–8   Ozone, O_3, is formed in the upper atmosphere when ultraviolet radiation from the sun breaks the double bonds of oxygen molecules.

enough oxygen to begin to change the atmosphere in a significant manner.

As Oxygen Increased in the Atmosphere, Aerobes Evolved That Could Use It

The increase in atmospheric oxygen had a profound effect on Earth and on life. First, oxygen in the upper atmosphere reacted to form **ozone,** O_3 (Figure 20–8). Ozone blanketed Earth, preventing much of the sun's ultraviolet radiation from penetrating to Earth's surface. It enabled living organisms to live closer to the surface in aquatic environments and even on land. Because the energy in ultraviolet radiation had been used to form spontaneously generated organic molecules, their synthesis decreased. Obligate anaerobes were poisoned by the oxygen, and many species undoubtedly perished.

Some anaerobes, however, evolved ways to neutralize the oxygen so that it could not harm them. Some organisms even evolved ways to *use* the oxygen becom-

---

[1] A third group of bacteria, the purple nonsulfur bacteria, uses other organic molecules or hydrogen gas as a hydrogen source.

ing so prevalent in their environment—they evolved the capacity to use oxygen to extract energy from food. Aerobic respiration was tacked onto the existing process of glycolysis. Like other types of metabolism, it probably evolved in a step-by-step fashion.

The evolution of living organisms that could use oxygen had several consequences. Organisms that respire aerobically gain much more energy from a single molecule of glucose than anaerobes do by fermentation. As a result, aerobic organisms were more efficient and more competitive than anaerobes. Coupled with the poisonous nature of oxygen to anaerobes, the efficiency of aerobes forced anaerobes into relatively minor roles on Earth. Today, the vast majority of organisms, including plants, animals, and most protists, prokaryotes, and fungi, use aerobic respiration.

The evolution of aerobic respiration had a stabilizing effect on both oxygen and carbon dioxide in the biosphere. Photosynthetic organisms used carbon dioxide as their carbon source. This raw material would have been depleted from the atmosphere in a relatively short period of time without the advent of aerobic respiration. Aerobic respiration released carbon dioxide as a waste product from the complete breakdown of organic molecules. Carbon thus started cycling in the biosphere, moving from the physical environment to photosynthetic organisms to heterotrophs that ate the plants. Carbon was released back into the physical environment as carbon dioxide by respiration, and the cycle continued. In like manner, oxygen was produced in photosynthesis and used in aerobic respiration.

Eukaryotic Cells Evolved after Prokaryotic Cells

It is logical to consider the ancestors of modern organisms as being very simple. Among modern organisms, the very simplest forms of cellular life are prokaryotes. That is one reason that biologists think the earliest cells were prokaryotic. Recall that prokaryotic cells lack nuclear envelopes as well as other membranous organelles such as mitochondria, endoplasmic reticulum, chloroplasts, and the Golgi complex (see Chapter 4).

Eukaryotes appeared in the fossil record 1.5 to 1.7 billion years ago. How did eukaryotic cells arise from prokaryotes? The **endosymbiont theory,** popularized by Lynn Margulis of the University of Massachusetts, suggests that mitochondria, chloroplasts, and perhaps even centrioles and flagella may have originated from symbiotic relationships between two prokaryotic organisms (Figure 20–9). Thus, chloroplasts are viewed as former photosynthetic bacteria (but generally not cyanobacteria) and mitochondria as former aerobic bacteria (or photosynthetic bacteria that lost the ability to photosynthesize). These endosymbionts were originally ingested by the host cell but were not digested. They

survived and reproduced along with the host cell so that future generations of the host also contained endosymbionts. The two organisms developed a mutualistic relationship, and eventually the endosymbiont lost the ability to exist outside its host.

This theory stipulates that each of these partners brought to the relationship something the other lacked. For example, mitochondria provided the ability to carry out aerobic respiration, which was lacking in the original host cell; chloroplasts provided the ability to use a simple carbon source (carbon dioxide) to produce needed organic molecules. The host cell provided a safe habitat and raw materials or nutrients.

The principal evidence in favor of the endosymbiont theory is that mitochondria and chloroplasts possess some (although not all) of their own genetic apparatus. They have their own DNA (as a circular chromosome, much like prokaryotes) and their own ribosomes (which resemble prokaryotic ribosomes rather than eukaryotic ribosomes). Mitochondria and chloroplasts have some of the machinery for protein synthesis, including tRNA molecules, and are able to conduct protein synthesis on a limited scale. Further, it is possible to poison them with an antibiotic that affects bacteria but not eukaryotic cells. Mitochondria and chloroplasts are enveloped by a double membrane. The outer membrane is envisioned as having developed from the invagination of the host cell's plasma membrane, and the inner membrane developed from the endosymbiont's plasma membrane.

A number of endosymbiotic relationships exist today (Figure 20–10). Many corals have algae living within their cells. This is one of the reasons that coral reefs are so productive. In the gut of the termite lives a protozoon, *Myxotricha paradoxa*, with several different endosymbionts, including spirochete bacteria that are attached to the protozoon and function as flagella. Also, the colonial tunicate, *Diplosoma virens*, has photosynthetic prokaryotes living within its cells. This relationship is particularly intriguing because the prokaryote is a prochlorophyte rather than a cyanobacterium. Prochlorophytes have the same pigment system—chlorophylls *a* and *b* and carotenoids—as plant chloroplasts (Figure 20–11), and it had been suggested that they might be the direct ancestors of chloroplasts. However, molecular sequence data reported in 1992 from the University of Chicago indicate that known prochlorophytes are *not* chloroplast ancestors.

The endosymbiont theory is not the final answer to how eukaryotic cells evolved from prokaryotes. It does not explain how the genetic material in the nucleus came to be surrounded by a membrane, for example. And the evidence supporting the evolution of motile structures such as flagella and cilia from prokaryotes is weak. Further, the 9 + 2 arrangement of the microtubules in flagella has not been found in any prokaryote to date.

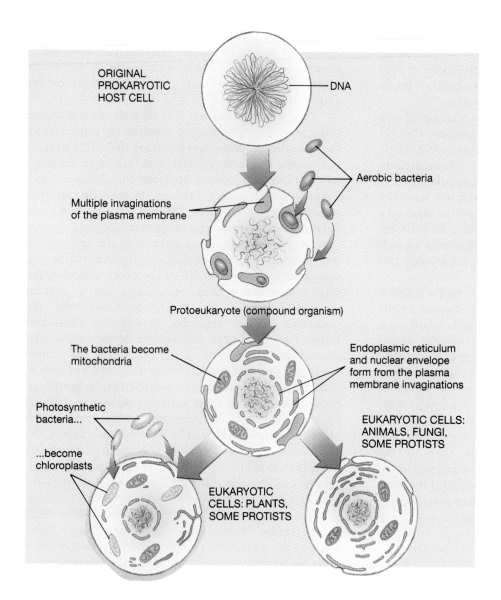

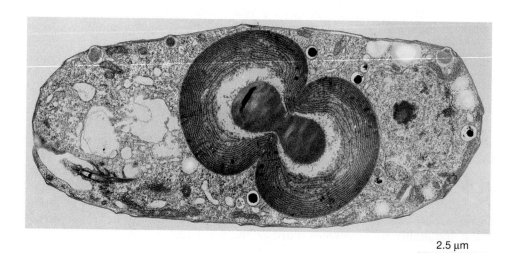

2.5 µm

Figure 20–9 The endosymbiont theory of the origin of the eukaryotes.

Figure 20–10 The flagellate *Cyanophora paradoxa* contains a cyanobacterial endosymbiont (shown in the process of dividing). (Courtesy of Jeremy Pickett-Heaps, University of Melbourne)

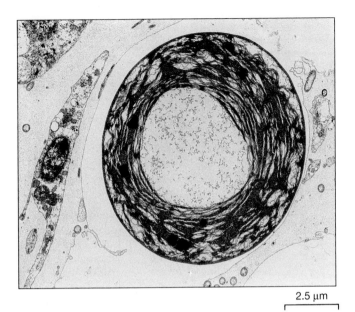

2.5 µm

Figure 20–11   Ultrastructure of *Prochloron*, a prochlorophyte that possesses the pigments found in higher plants. The cells surrounding *Prochloron* are those of its host, the tunicate *Diplosoma virens*.   (E. H. Newcomb, University of Wisconsin/ Biological Photo Service)

THE FOSSIL RECORD PROVIDES US WITH CLUES TO THE HISTORY OF LIFE

The sediments of Earth's crust consist of five major rock strata, each subdivided into minor strata, lying one on top of the other. These sheets of rock were formed by the accumulation of mud and sand at the bottoms of oceans, seas, and lakes. Each contains certain characteristic fossils that serve to identify deposits made at approximately the same time in different parts of the world. Geological time has been divided into **eras,** which are subdivided into **periods,** which in turn are composed of **epochs** (Table 20–1 and Figure 20–12). Between the major eras, and serving to distinguish them, there were widespread geological disturbances, which raised or lowered vast regions of Earth's surface and formed or eliminated shallow inland seas. These disturbances altered the distribution of sea and land

Figure 20–12   A clock may be used to represent biological history. Life began 3.5 billion years ago, at 12:00 midnight. Ten hours later, at 10:04 A.M., the Paleozoic era began. The beginning of the Mesozoic era, 248 million years ago, would be at 11:09 A.M. The Cenozoic era, which began 65 million years ago, would start at 11:47 A.M. The last epoch of the Cenozoic era, the Recent epoch, began 10,000 years ago, which would be represented by the last 0.1 second before 12:00 noon. Representative life forms for each era are included.

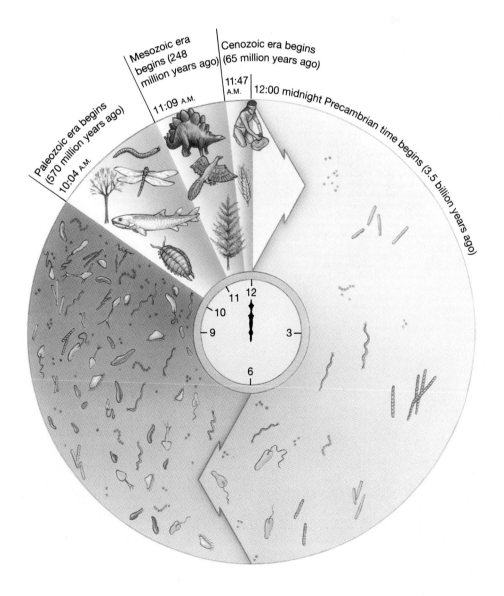

Table 20–1   SOME IMPORTANT BIOLOGICAL EVENTS IN GEOLOGICAL TIME*

Era	Period	Epoch	Million Years B.P.	Geological Conditions	Plants and Microorganisms	Animals
Cenozoic (Age of Mammals)	Quaternary	Recent	0.01	End of last Ice Age; warmer climate	Decline of woody plants; rise of herbaceous plants	Age of *Homo sapiens*
		Pleistocene	2.0	Four Ice Ages; glaciers in Northern Hemisphere; uplift of Sierra Nevada	Extinction of many species	Extinction of many large mammals
	Tertiary	Pliocene	5	Uplift and mountain-building; volcanoes; climate much cooler	Development of grasslands; decline of forests	Large carnivores; many grazing mammals; first known human-like primates
		Miocene	25	Climate drier, cooler; mountain formation	Flowering plants continue to diversify	Many forms of mammals evolve
		Oligocene	38	Rise of Alps and Himalayas; most land low; volcanic activity in Rockies	Spread of forests, flowering plants; rise of monocotyledons	Apes evolve; all present mammal families are represented
		Eocene	55	Climate warmer	Gymnosperms and flowering plants dominant	Beginning of Age of Mammals; modern birds
		Paleocene	65	Climate mild to cool; continental seas disappear	Many now extinct woody flowering plants	Evolution of primitive mammals
Mesozoic (Age of Reptiles)	Cretaceous		144	Continents separate; formation of Rockies; other continents low; large inland seas and swamps	Rise of flowering plants	Dinosaurs reach peak, then become extinct; toothed birds become extinct; first modern birds; primitive mammals
	Jurassic		213	Climate mild; continents low; inland seas; formation of mountains; continental drift begins	Gymnosperms common	Large, specialized dinosaurs; first toothed birds; insectivorous marsupials
	Triassic		248	Many mountains form; widespread deserts	Gymnosperms dominate	First dinosaurs; egg-laying mammals

*You may want to study this table starting from the bottom and working your way up through time.

†Based on Harland et al., *A Geologic Time Scale,* Cambridge University Press, Cambridge, 1982.

Table 20–1   SOME IMPORTANT BIOLOGICAL EVENTS IN GEOLOGICAL TIME* *(continued)*

Era	Period	Epoch	Million Years B.P.	Geological Conditions	Plants and Microorganisms	Animals
Paleozoic (Age of Ancient Life)	Permian		286	Glaciers; formation of Appalachians; continents rise and merge as Pangaea	Conifers diversify; cycads appear	Modern insects appear; mammal-like reptiles; extinction of many Paleozoic invertebrates
	Carboniferous		360	Lands low; great coal swamps; climate warm and humid; later cooler	Forests of ferns, club mosses, horsetails, and gymnosperms; mosses and liverworts	First reptiles; spread of ancient amphibians; many insect forms; ancient sharks abundant
	Devonian		408	Glaciers; inland seas	Plants well established; first forests; gymnosperms appear; bryophytes appear	Age of Fishes; amphibians appear; wingless insects appear; many trilobites
	Silurian		438	Continents mainly flat; flooding	Vascular land plants appear; algae dominant in aquatic environment	Fish evolve; terrestrial arthropods
	Ordovician		505	Sea covers continents; climate warm	Marine algae dominant	Invertebrates dominant; first fish appear
	Cambrian		570	Climate mild; lands low; oldest rocks with abundant fossils	Algae, bacteria, fungi	Age of marine invertebrates; most modern phyla represented
(Precambrian) Proterozoic			1500	Planet cools; glaciers	Bacteria and primitive algae	Toward end, marine invertebrates
Archean			3.5 billion years ago	Mountains form	Evidence of first prokaryotic cells	
Origin of Earth			4.6 billion years ago	Crust forms approx. 4.1 billion years ago		
Origin of the universe			10–20 billion years ago			

organisms and may have triggered the mass extinction of many life forms. The raising and lowering of portions of Earth's crust result from the slow movements of the enormous plates that compose the crust (see Focus on Continental Drift).

Evidence of Living Cells Is Found in Precambrian Times

The richest deposits of fossils date from the beginning of the "explosion of life" that occurred during the Cambrian period, some 570 million years ago. However, there is evidence that life existed long before the Cambrian period. Signs of Precambrian life date back to the **Archean era,** which began about 3.5 billion years ago.

The Archean era began after the formation of Earth's crust, when rocks and mountains already existed and the processes of erosion and sedimentation had begun. Because the rocks of the Archean era are very deeply buried in most parts of the world, they are considered to be some of the most ancient. However, Archean rocks are exposed at the bottom of the Grand Canyon and along the shores of Lake Superior.

The Archean era lasted 2 billion years and was characterized by widespread volcanic activity and giant upheavals that raised mountains. The heat, pressure, and churning associated with these movements probably destroyed most of whatever fossils may have been formed, but some evidence of life still remains. This evidence consists of traces of graphite or pure carbon, which may be the transformed remains of primitive life. These remains are especially abundant in what were the oceans and seas of that era. Fossils of what appear to be cyanobacteria have been recovered from several Archean formations.

The second era, the **Proterozoic era,** which began approximately 1.5 billion years ago, is thought to be almost a billion years in length. It was characterized by the deposition of large quantities of sediment, reflecting massive erosion and perhaps glaciation. The fossils found in the later (more recent) Proterozoic rocks show clear-cut examples of some major groups of bacteria, fungi, protists (including multicellular algae), and animals.

One source of rich deposits of Precambrian fossils is the Ediacaran Hills of South Australia. The forms of life found there—all invertebrates—include jellyfish, segmented worms, soft-bodied arthropods, and several animals with no resemblance to any other known fossil or living form (Figure 20–13). Ediacaran fossils, the oldest known fossils of complex, multicellular animals, are from very late in Precambrian time. Except for an arbitrary geological boundary, they might well be considered early Cambrian.

A Considerable Diversity of Life Forms Evolved during the Paleozoic Era

The **Paleozoic era** began approximately 570 million years ago and lasted approximately 322 million years. It is divided into six periods—**Cambrian, Ordovician, Silurian, Devonian, Carboniferous,** and **Permian.**

The oldest subdivision of the Paleozoic era, the Cambrian period, is represented by rocks rich in fossils.

(a)

(b)

Figure 20–13 These Precambrian fossils were found in the Ediacaran Hills of South Australia. (a) *Spriggina*, a segmented worm, was approximately 4 cm long and is visible on the right-hand side of the ruler. (b) This unidentified fossil organism lived in shallow marine waters. (a, S. M. Awramik, University of California/ Biological Photo Service; b, William E. Ferguson)

Evolution was in such high gear that this period has been nicknamed the **Cambrian explosion,** a period that filled the seas with all kinds of scurrying, slithering, and burrowing creatures. All the present-day animal phyla, except the chordates, are present as Cambrian fossils, at least in marine sediments. There were arachnid-like forms, some of whose descendants (such as the horseshoe crab) exist today. The sea floor was covered with sponges, corals, snails, and other marine animals (crinoid echinoderms, bivalves, primitive cephalopods, brachiopods, and trilobites).

Except for the chordates (the phylum of animals that includes the vertebrates), the major types of body plans were established so early in the history of the eukaryotes that very little further change of a basic nature is seen. This probably indicates that, by the early Cambrian period, animal forms had reached a degree of adaptation that allowed them to exploit Earth and adapt to changes in the environment with only limited modifications in their body plans.

According to geologists, the continents were gradually flooded during the Cambrian period. In the Ordovician period, this submergence reached its maximum, so that much of what is now land was covered by shallow seas. Inhabiting the seas were giant cephalopods, squid- or nautilus-like animals with straight shells 5 to 7 meters long and 30 cm in diameter. The first traces of the early vertebrates, the jawless, bony-armored fish called **ostracoderms,** are also found in Ordovician rocks.

Two life forms of great biological significance appeared in the Silurian period—terrestrial plants and air-breathing animals. The first known land plants resembled ferns in that they possessed vascular (conducting) tissue and reproduced by spores. The evolution of plants allowed terrestrial animals to evolve, as plants provided food and shelter for the first land animals. The only air-breathing land animals that have been discovered in Silurian rocks were arachnids that resembled scorpions.

A great variety of fishes appeared in the Devonian period. In fact, the Devonian period is frequently called the "Age of Fishes." Unlike the jawless ostracoderms, the Devonian fishes typically had jaws, an adaptation that enables a vertebrate to chew and bite. Appearing in Devonian deposits are sharks and the three main types of bony fish: lungfishes, lobe-finned fishes, and the ray-finned fishes. A few lungfishes have survived to the present. The ray-finned fishes later gave rise to the major modern orders of fishes. The lobe-finned fishes, some of which are considered ancestral to the land vertebrates, were thought to have become extinct by the end of the Mesozoic era. However, in 1939 the first living **coelacanth,** a primitive fish with lobed fins, was discovered off the coast of Madagascar (see Figure 30–15). Upper Devonian sediments contain fossil remains of salamander-like amphibians that were often very large, with short necks and heavy, muscular tails. These creatures, whose skulls were encased in bony armor, were quite similar in many respects to the lobe-finned fishes. The early vascular plants diversified during the Devonian period. Ferns, club mosses, horsetails, and seed ferns all flourished. The Devonian was the first period characterized by forests. Wingless insects and millipedes also originated in the late Devonian period.

The Carboniferous period is named for the great swamp forests whose remains persist today as major coal deposits. Much of the land during this time was covered with low swamps filled with horsetails, club mosses, ferns, seed ferns, and gymnosperms (Figure 20–14). The first reptiles, the **cotylosaurs,** appeared in the Carboniferous period, flourished in the Permian period, and became extinct early in the Mesozoic era. Two important groups of winged insects, cockroaches and dragonflies, originated in the Carboniferous period. The dragonflies ranged in size from smaller than today's dragonflies to some with a wingspan of 75 cm (2.5 ft).

The final period of the Paleozoic era, the Permian period, was characterized by great changes in climate and topography. At the end of the Permian period, a general folding of Earth's crust raised a great mountain chain from Nova Scotia to Alabama. These mountains were originally higher than the present Rockies. Other mountain ranges formed in Europe at this time. A glaciation, spreading from the Antarctic, covered most of the Southern Hemisphere, extending almost to the equator in Brazil and Africa.

Many Paleozoic forms of life may have been unable to adapt to the climatic and geological changes and became extinct. Even many marine forms became extinct, perhaps owing to cooler water temperatures. Most of the plants that were dominant in the Carboniferous period became extinct during the Permian period. The seed plants became dominant, with the diversification of conifers and the appearance of cycads.

During the late Carboniferous and early Permian periods, a group of reptiles appeared that are thought to be the ancestors of mammals. These carnivorous reptiles were more slender and lizard-like than the cotylosaurs. In the latter part of the Permian period, mammal-like reptiles called **therapsids** appeared. One of these, *Cynognathus,* the "dog-jawed" reptile, was a slender, lightly built animal with a skull intermediate between that of a reptile and that of a mammal. Its teeth, instead of being conical and all alike, as reptilian teeth are, were differentiated into incisors, canines, and molars. In the absence of information about the animal's soft parts—whether it had scales or hair, whether or not it was endothermic (warm-blooded), and whether it suckled its young—it is called a reptile.

(Text continued on p. 462)

FOCUS ON

Continental Drift

In 1915, Alfred Wegener published a book in which he proposed that the continents moved about. He noted a similarity between the geographical shapes of South America and Africa and proposed that all the land masses had been joined into one huge supercontinent, which he called Pangaea (see figure). He further suggested that Pangaea had subsequently broken apart and the various land masses had separated in a process known as **continental drift.**

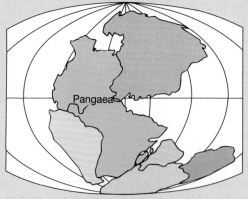

(a)   240 million years ago (Triassic period)

Continental drift, as currently envisioned. (a) The supercontinent Pangaea of the Triassic period, about 240 million years bp (before present). (b) Breakup of Pangaea into Laurasia (Northern Hemisphere) and Gondwana (Southern Hemisphere), 120 million years bp in the Cretaceous period. (c) Further separation of land masses, which occurred in the Tertiary period, 60 million years bp. Note that Europe and North America were still joined and that India was a separate land mass. (d) The continents today. (e) Projected positions of the continents in 50 million years.

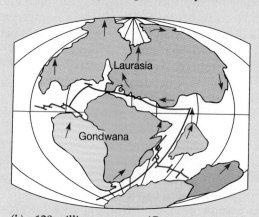

(b)   120 million years ago (Cretaceous period)

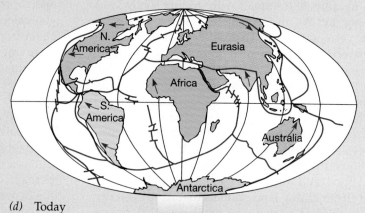

(d)   Today

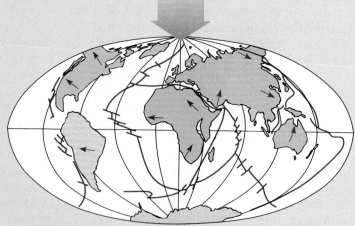

(c)   60 million years ago (early Tertiary period)

(e)   50 million years from now

Wegener did not know of any mechanism that could have caused continental drift, and so his theory, although debated initially, was largely ignored.

By the 1960s, scientific evidence had accumulated that provided the mechanism for continental drift. Earth's crust is composed of seven large plates (plus a few smaller ones) that float on the plastic layer of the mantle. The land masses are situated on some of these plates. As the plates move about, the continents change their relative positions. The movement of the crustal plates is termed **plate tectonics.**

The area where two plates meet is associated with intense geological activity. Earthquakes and volcanoes are common in this region. Both San Francisco, noted for its earthquakes, and the volcano Mount Saint Helens in the state of Washington, which erupted in 1980, are situated where two plates meet. If land masses are on the edges of two meeting plates, mountains may be formed. The Himalayas formed when the plate carrying southern India rammed into the plate carrying Asia. When two plates grind together, one of them is sometimes buried under the other, in a process known as subduction. When two plates move apart, a ridge of lava forms between them that continually expands as the plates move farther apart. The Atlantic Ocean is getting larger because of the buildup of lava along the mid-Atlantic ridge, where two plates are separating.

Knowledge that the continents were at one time connected and have since drifted apart helps explain the geographical distribution of plants and animals, or biogeography (see figure and Chapter 17). Likewise, continental drift has played a major role in the evolution of different life forms. When Pangaea originally formed during the late Permian, it brought together plants and animals that had evolved separately from one another, leading to competition and possible extinctions. Marine life was adversely affected, largely because, with the continents joined as one large mass, there would have been less coastline. Coastal areas are shallower and therefore have high concentrations of marine organisms. Pangaea separated into several land masses approximately 180 million years ago. As the continents began to drift apart, populations became geographically isolated in different environmental conditions, the ideal setting for evolution.

The distribution of fossils of the same animal and plant species on four continents suggests that the continents were once joined.

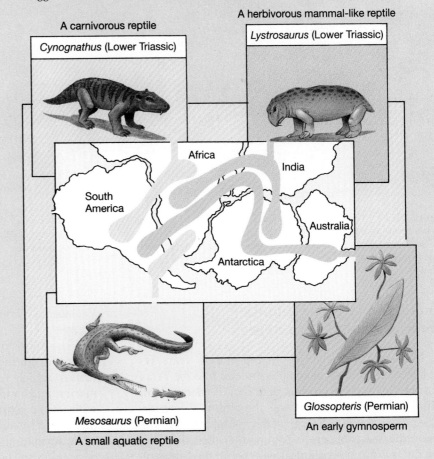

A carnivorous reptile
Cynognathus (Lower Triassic)

A herbivorous mammal-like reptile
Lystrosaurus (Lower Triassic)

Africa

India

South America

Australia

Antarctica

Mesosaurus (Permian)
A small aquatic reptile

Glossopteris (Permian)
An early gymnosperm

1. Giant horsetails (two different species)
2. Seed fern
3. Lycopod trees (two different species)
4. Early seed plant
5. Amphibians (three different species, one an immature tadpole)
6. Reptiles (two different species)
7. Shark
8. Fish (two different species)
9. Horseshoe crab
10. Clam-like mollusk
11. Scorpion
12. Cockroach

Figure 20–14 The Carboniferous period. Swampy and estuarine environments were populated by such plants as giant horsetails and seed ferns. Fish, including sharks, and numerous invertebrates inhabited the water, and insects, scorpions, primitive amphibians, and early reptiles were found on land. The fossilized remains of all organisms pictured here have been identified in a massive deposit in France.

Dinosaurs and Other Reptiles Dominated the Mesozoic Era

The **Mesozoic era** began about 248 million years ago and lasted 183 million years. It is divided into the **Triassic, Jurassic,** and **Cretaceous** periods. The outstanding feature of the Mesozoic era was the origin, differentiation, and extinction of a large variety of reptiles. For this reason, the Mesozoic era is commonly called the "Age of Reptiles." From a botanical viewpoint, the Mesozoic era was dominated by gymnosperms until the mid-Cretaceous period, when the flowering plants replaced them.

The most primitive reptilian line present in the Mesozoic era includes the ancient cotylosaurs and the turtles, which were first seen in Permian strata. Both marine and land turtles have survived to the present with few structural changes since before the time of the dinosaurs. Most of the snakes and lizards found in Mesozoic formations are also similar to their present-day descendants. The marine lizards of the Cretaceous period, which attained a length of 13 meters and pos-

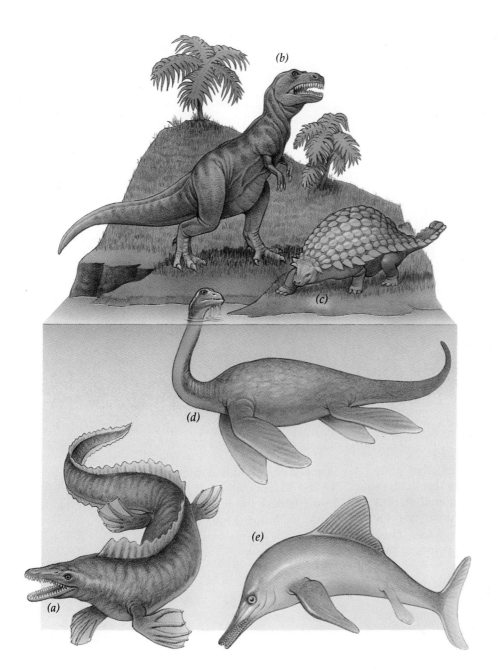

Figure 20–15 Representative reptiles from the Mesozoic era. (*a*) *Tylosaurus*, a large marine reptile, belongs to a group ancestral to modern lizards. (*b*) *Tyrannosaurus*, the largest of the flesh-eating dinosaurs, reached a length of 15 meters and a height of 6 meters. Its head was as much as 2 meters long and was equipped with many sharp teeth, whose edges were serrated like the blades of steak knives. The long tail was probably used as a counterweight to the immense head. (*c*) *Ankylosaurus*, a heavily armored ornithischian. One would not guess from the external appearance of this creature that the ornithischians were so named for their birdlike pelvis. Two types of marine reptiles, (*d*) *Plesiosaurus* and (*e*) *Ichthyosaurus*. Note the similarity of *Plesiosaurus* to animals such as modern seals and the similarity of *Ichthyosaurus* to modern porpoises. During their long reign as the dominant animals on Earth, the reptiles radiated into almost every conceivable environment.

sessed a long tail useful in swimming, did not survive to the present (Figure 20–15*a*).

Of all the reptilian branches, the **dinosaurs** are the most famous. There were two main groups of dinosaurs. The **saurischians** were fast, two-legged forms ranging from the size of a dog to the ultimate representative of this group, the gigantic carnivore of the Cretaceous period, *Tyrannosaurus* (Figure 20–15*b*). Other saurischians had a plant diet and a four-legged form. Some of these were the largest terrestrial animals that ever lived, including *Apatosaurus* (formerly known as *Brontosaurus*), with a length of 21 meters, and *Diplodocus*, with a length of 29 meters.

The other group of dinosaurs, the **ornithischians,** were entirely herbivorous. Although some of them walked upright, the majority had a four-legged form. Some had no front teeth and may have possessed a stout, horny, birdlike beak. In some forms this was broad and ducklike, hence the common name, duck-billed dinosaurs. Webbed feet were characteristic of this type. Other species had great armor plates, possibly as protection against the carnivorous saurischians. *Ankylosaurus*, for example, had a broad, flat body covered with armor plates (actually bones embedded in the skin) and large, laterally projecting spines (Figure 20–15*c*).

Figure 20–16 Reconstruction of representative plants from the Mesozoic era. (*a*) *Matonium*, a fern. A few family representatives survive in the Malay region. (*b*) *Williamsonia*, a cycadeoid. All are extinct. (*c*) *Ginkgoites*, a ginkgo. One ginkgo species survives to the present. (*d*) *Onychiopsis*, a fern. (*e*) *Sphenolepidium*, a conifer. (*f*) *Cycadeoidea*, a cycadeoid. All (*d–f*) are extinct. (From K. Mägdefrau, *Vegetationsbilder der Vorzeit*, Gustave Fischer Verlag, Jena, 1948)

Many classic ideas about dinosaurs—that they were cold-blooded, slow-moving monsters that lived in swamps, for example—have been reconsidered. Recent evidence suggests that many dinosaurs may have been warm-blooded and capable of moving very fast. They may have had complex social behaviors, including caring for their young and hunting in packs.

Two other groups of Mesozoic reptiles were the marine **plesiosaurs** and **ichthyosaurs** (Figure 20–15*d* and *e*). The extremely long neck of the plesiosaurs took up over half of their total length of 15 meters. The ichthyosaurs had a body form superficially like that of a fish or porpoise, with a short neck, large dorsal fin, and shark-type tail.

Although the reptiles were the dominant animals of the Mesozoic era, many other important organisms occur in the same formations. Most of the modern orders of insects appeared during that era. Snails and bivalves increased in number and diversity. Sea urchins reached their peak diversity. Mammals first appeared in the Triassic period, and birds first appear in Jurassic formations. During the early Triassic period, the most abundant plants were gymnosperms (Figure 20–16). By the end of the Cretaceous period, many flowering plants resembling present-day species had evolved and were the dominant vegetation.

Excellent bird fossils, some even showing the outlines of feathers, have been preserved from the Jurassic period. *Archaeopteryx*, a primitive bird, was about the size of a crow and had rather feeble wings (Figures 20–17 and 30–23). Although *Archaeopteryx* was definitely a bird (witness the feathers), it had many reptilian features, including a long bony tail and teeth.

Figure 20–17 A fossil of *Archaeopteryx*, a tailed, toothed, primitive bird from the Jurassic period. Despite many reptilian features, *Archaeopteryx* is clearly a bird, as demonstrated by its feathers. (Dennis Drenner)

Figure 20–18 Was Earth hit by a large meteorite around the time of the dinosaurs' extinction? The dark band of iridium-enriched clay located between Mesozoic and Cenozoic sediments suggests that a meteorite slammed into Earth at that time. The coin on the iridium-rich layer indicates the size of the layer. (Lawrence Berkley Laboratory, University of California)

At the end of the Cretaceous period, a great many animals abruptly became extinct. Most gymnosperms, with the exception of conifers, also perished. Changes in climate may have been a factor in their demise. Other explanations for the mass extinction at the end of the Cretaceous period have been proposed, including the catastrophic collision of Earth with a giant meteorite (see Chapter 19). Scientific evidence exists to support this collision. Sandwiched between the Mesozoic and Cenozoic sediments is a small band of dark clay with a high concentration of iridium (Figure 20–18). Iridium is rare on Earth but abundant in meteorites, leading many to conclude that Earth was hit by a large extraterrestrial object at that time.

The Cenozoic Era Is Known as the "Age of Mammals"

With equal justice the **Cenozoic era** could be called the "Age of Mammals," the "Age of Birds," the "Age of Insects," or the "Age of Flowering Plants." It is marked by the appearance of all these forms in great variety and numbers of species. The Cenozoic era extends from 65 million years ago to the present and is subdivided into two periods, the **Tertiary period,** encompassing some 63 million years, and the **Quaternary period,** which covers the last 2 million years.

The Tertiary period is subdivided into five epochs, named from earliest to latest, **Paleocene, Eocene, Oligocene, Miocene,** and **Pliocene.** The Quaternary period is subdivided into the **Pleistocene epoch** and **Recent epoch.** The Rocky Mountains, formed at the beginning

of the Tertiary period, were considerably eroded by the time of the Oligocene epoch, giving the North American continent a gently rolling topography. In the Miocene epoch, another series of uplifts raised the Sierra Nevada and a new set of Rockies and resulted in the formation of the western deserts.

The uplift begun in the Miocene epoch continued in the Pliocene epoch and, coupled with the ice ages of the Pleistocene epoch, may have killed many of the contemporary mammals and other organisms. The final elevation of the Colorado Plateau, which also caused the cutting of the Grand Canyon, occurred almost entirely in the short Pleistocene and Recent epochs.

During the Tertiary period the appearance of grasses, which served as food, and dense forests, which afforded protection from predators, may have been important factors in leading to changes in the mammalian body pattern. Accompanying the tendency toward increased size, the mammals displayed tendencies toward an increase in the relative size of the brain and toward changes in the teeth and feet.

Evidence of the first known carnivorous mammals, the **creodonts,** appears in Paleocene and Eocene formations. They were replaced in the Eocene and Oligocene epochs by more modern forms ancestral to the present-day carnivores, such as cats, dogs, bears, and weasels, as well as the web-footed marine carnivores, the seals and walruses. One of the most famous ancient carnivores, the saber-toothed cat, became extinct only recently in the Pleistocene epoch (Figure 20–19).

The larger herbivorous mammals, most of which have hooves, are sometimes referred to as the **ungulates.** They do not form a single, natural group, but consist of several independent lines. The molar teeth of

Figure 20–19 Some extinct mammals of the Cenozoic era. (*a*) The woolly mammoth existed during the Pleistocene epoch but disappeared at the end of the Ice Age. (*b*) *Megatherium,* a giant ground sloth that was nearly the size of the modern elephant. (*c*) A *glyptodont,* found in what is now the southern United States, weighed more than 1 ton and resembled a cross between a turtle and an armadillo. (*d*) *Smilodon,* the saber-toothed cat, was found in North and South America.

ungulates are flattened and enlarged to facilitate the chewing of leaves and grass. Their legs are elongated and adapted for the rapid movement necessary to escape predators. Remains of the earliest ungulates appear in Paleocene formations.

The Pleistocene epoch of the Quaternary period was marked by four periods of glaciers. At their greatest extent, these ice sheets covered nearly 4 million square miles of North America, extending south as far as the Ohio and Missouri Rivers. During the Pleistocene glaciers, enough water was removed from the oceans and locked in the ice to lower the sea level by 65 to 100 meters. This formed land bridges, highways for the dispersal of many life forms. Examples include a land bridge that connected Siberia to Alaska at the Bering Strait and one that connected England to the European continent.

The plants and animals of the Pleistocene epoch were similar to those alive today. For this reason, it is sometimes difficult to distinguish between Pleistocene and Recent deposits. A considerable number of mammals, including the saber-toothed cat, the mammoth, and the giant ground sloth, became extinct during the Pleistocene epoch, possibly as a result of early human hunting (Figure 20–19). The Pleistocene epoch was marked by the extinction of many species of plants, especially woody ones, and the appearance of numerous herbaceous plants.

SUMMARY

I. Life began from nonliving matter by chemical evolution.
   A. There are four requirements for chemical evolution.
      1. The absence of oxygen was necessary to prevent it from reacting with and breaking down organic molecules.
      2. Energy was needed to form organic molecules.
      3. Chemical evolution required the chemical building blocks for organic molecules, including water, minerals, and gases present in the atmosphere.
      4. Chemical evolution required sufficient time for molecules to accumulate and react.
   B. Four steps are envisioned in chemical evolution.
      1. First, small organic molecules formed and accumulated.
      2. Macromolecules formed from the small organic molecules.
      3. Macromolecular assemblages (precells) evolved.
      4. Cells evolved from the macromolecular assemblages.

II. The first cells were anaerobic and prokaryotic.
   A. The oldest cells in the fossil record are 3.4 to 3.5 billion years old.

B. The evolution of photosynthesis ultimately changed early life because it generated oxygen, which accumulated in the atmosphere.
C. Aerobic organisms evolved the ability to use oxygen in cell respiration.
D. Certain eukaryotic organelles (mitochondria, chloroplasts, and possibly flagella) probably evolved from prokaryote endosymbionts.

III. Earth's history is divided into eras, periods, and epochs.
A. Life began and different groups of bacteria, protists (including algae), fungi, and animals evolved during the Precambrian era.

B. During the Paleozoic era, all major groups of plants evolved except for flowering plants, and fish and amphibians flourished.
C. The Mesozoic era was characterized by the evolution of flowering plants and reptiles. Insects flourished. Birds and early mammals appeared.
D. In the Cenozoic era, which extends to the present time, there was a diversification of flowering plants and mammals, including humans and their ancestors.

POST-TEST

1. A gas that is common in today's atmosphere but was not part of Earth's atmosphere before living organisms evolved is _____.
2. Energy, the absence of oxygen, chemical building blocks, and _____ were the requirements for chemical evolution.
3. Although Oparin envisioned life as originating in a "sea of organic soup," it may have evolved on _____ surfaces.
4. Protobionts formed from assemblages of polypeptides, nucleic acids, and polysaccharides are called _____.
5. The first autotrophs probably used sunlight to split _____ _____.
6. The _____ theory says that chloroplasts, mitochondria, and possibly other organelles originated as a consequence of symbiotic relationships between two prokaryotic organisms.
7. The correct chronological order of geological eras, starting with the oldest, is Precambrian, _____, _____, and _____.

8. All present-day animal phyla except for the chordates are present as fossils from the _____ period.
9. Terrestrial plants and air-breathing animals appeared during the Silurian period of the _____ era.
10. The Mesozoic era is known as the "Age of _____."
11. The two main groups of dinosaurs are the saurischians and the _____.
12. That the mass extinction at the end of the Mesozoic era was caused by changes when Earth collided with a giant meteorite is supported by the presence of _____ in the layer of sediment marking the boundary between the Mesozoic and Cenozoic eras.
13. Flowering plants diversified and became the dominant land plants during the _____ era.
14. Ice sheets covered much of North America during the _____ epoch of the Quaternary period.
15. Earthquakes, subduction, mountain formation, and _____ may occur where two tectonic plates meet.

REVIEW QUESTIONS

1. If chemical evolution occurred once, why can't it occur again?
2. What are the four requirements for chemical evolution, and why is each essential?
3. Briefly describe one of the contributions of each of these scientists:
   a. Oparin and Haldane
   b. Miller and Urey
   c. Fox
   d. Margulis
   e. Wegener

4. Which informational macromolecule probably evolved first and why?
5. Give at least two pieces of evidence used to support the endosymbiont theory.
6. Explain why fossils of *Mesosaurus,* an extinct reptile that could not swim across open water, are found in the southern parts of both Africa and South America.

RECOMMENDED READINGS

Gifford, E., and A. Foster. *Morphology and Evolution of Vascular Plants,* 3rd ed. W.H. Freeman, New York, 1989. A classic textbook that gives a detailed account of ancient plant structure.

Heyler, D., and C. M. Poplin. The fossils of Montceau-les-Mines. *Scientific American,* September 1988, pp. 70–76. A wonderful collection of fossils from the Carboniferous period provides a glimpse at life 300 million years ago.

Hickman, C. P., L. S. Roberts, and F. M. Hickman. *Biology of Animals*, 5th ed. Times Mirror/Mosby College Publishing, St. Louis, 1990. Provides a detailed overview of animal evolution as well as animal diversity today.

Horgan, J. In the beginning. *Scientific American*, February 1991, pp. 117–125. An overview of our current knowledge about the origin of life. Includes several startling theories that have recently been presented concerning this great scientific puzzle.

McDermott, J. A biologist whose heresy redraws the earth's tree of life. *Smithsonian*, August 1989, pp. 72–80. A look at Dr. Lynn Margulis, the biologist from the University of Massachusetts who popularized the endosymbiont theory.

Storch, G. The mammals of Island Europe. *Scientific American*, February 1992, pp. 64–69. Beautiful fossils of animals from the Eocene epoch are preserved in a mine in Germany.

Wellnhofer, P. Archaeopteryx. *Scientific American*, May 1990, pp. 70–77. Discusses the evolutionary significance of the six fossil specimens of *Archaeopteryx*, the primitive bird that bridges the evolutionary gap between birds and reptiles.

CHAPTER 21

The Evolution of Primates

OUTLINE

Evolution from shrewlike mammals
Trends in hominid evolution
Human cultural evolution

Most people have an interest in their roots. To many of us, this means trying to discover the immediate ancestors of our great grandparents. In this chapter we examine what we might call our "deep roots," as we trace the origin of humans, *Homo sapiens*, back some 65 million years to the earliest primates. For nearly a century after Darwin's *Origin of Species*, fossil evidence on human ancestry was rather sparse and unsatisfactory. However, research over the last four or five decades, especially in East Africa, has provided us with some reasonable answers to the question, "Where did we come from?"

Humans and other primates are mammals, members of the class Mammalia. Mammals are **endothermic** (warm-blooded) animals that produce body hair and feed their young with milk from mammary glands.

Yellow baboons preen in the Amboseli National Park in Kenya. (Stan Osolinski/ Dembinsky Photo Associates)

Most mammals are **viviparous** and bear their young alive as opposed to laying eggs.

Although mammals evolved from reptiles approximately 240 million years ago, they were of secondary importance at that time. It was the "Age of Reptiles," and reptiles were the dominant animals in almost every habitat on Earth.

Three main lines of mammals existed during the Mesozoic era: (1) the multituberculates, which may have given rise to monotremes (mammals that lay eggs) like the duck-billed platypus; (2) the marsupials, which were the ancestors of modern-day kangaroos and opossums; and (3) small shrewlike placental mammals that ate insects and lived a nocturnal existence in the trees. These mammals remained a minor component of life for almost 150 million years.

After you have studied this chapter you should be able to

1. Explain why primates have adaptations for an arboreal existence, even though many primates live on the ground.
2. Describe the morphological adaptations primates possess for life in the trees.
3. List the two suborders in the order Primates and give several distinguishing features and representative examples of each.

4. Distinguish among prosimians, anthropoids, hominoids, and hominids.
5. Describe skeletal and skull differences between apes and hominids.
6. Compare the following hominids: *Australopithecus* spp., *Homo habilis*, *Homo erectus*, and *Homo sapiens*.
7. Describe cultural evolution and its impact on the ecosphere.

PRIMATES EVOLVED FROM SHREWLIKE MAMMALS

Approximately 65 million years ago the dinosaurs and many other reptiles became extinct (see Chapter 20). This provided numerous "empty" niches (ecological roles in a community; see Chapter 53) that the mammals could fill. In addition, the flowering plants, including many trees, underwent adaptive radiation, providing new habitats, sources of food, and protection from predators. During the early Cenozoic era, the mammals underwent adaptive radiation (see Chapter 20). The first primates evolved from the arboreal, shrewlike mammals that had appeared during the "Age of Reptiles." The living organism that most resembles these ancient ancestors is the tree shrew of South America (Figure 21–1).

Because of their ancestry, most primates have adaptations for an arboreal existence. One of the most significant features of primates is that they have five digits on

their hands and feet, four digits plus an opposable thumb. This enables primates to grasp objects, such as tree branches. Nails provide a protective covering for the tips of the digits, and the fleshy pads at the ends of the digits are sensitive. Another arboreal feature is long, slender limbs that rotate freely at hips and shoulders. This allows primates full mobility for climbing and searching for food in the tree tops. The location of the eyes in front of the head, along with a shortened snout, is an adaptation that provides stereoscopic, or three-dimensional, vision. This is essential for arboreal animals, as an error in depth perception might cause a fatal fall. In addition to sharp sight, hearing is acute in primates, although their sense of smell is poor.

Primates share several other characteristics, including complex social behaviors. Some biologists suggest that the learning associated with social interactions in primate societies may have been connected to the increasingly large, more complex brains that evolved. Primates usually bear one offspring, which is helpless and requires a long period of nurturing and protection.

The order Primates has two subgroups, prosimians and anthropoids (Table 21–1). The **prosimians** (which means "before apes") include the lemurs, lorises, and tarsiers, whereas the **anthropoids,** comprising the monkeys, apes, and humans, are primates with larger brains.

Prosimians Are Primitive, Arboreal Primates

The first primates to evolve were the prosimians, which flourished during the Eocene epoch just over 50 million years ago (Figure 21–2). The climate was milder then, and they were widely distributed over much of North America, Europe, and Asia. Recall that North America was still attached to Europe at that time (see Chapter 20). Fossils indicate that primitive prosimians had opposable thumbs, digits with nails, and eyes directed forward. As the climate became cooler and drier toward the end of the Eocene epoch, many of these early prosimians became extinct. Modern prosimians have changed relatively little from their ancestors and occur

Figure 21–1 The common tree shrew most resembles the ancient insectivores that gave rise to the primates. (Doug Wechsler)

Table 21–1　CLASSIFICATION OF THE PRIMATES

Order Primates
　Suborder Prosimii (lower primates)
　　Infraorder Lemuriformes
　　　Family Lemuridae (lemurs)
　　　Family Indriidae (indris)
　　　Family Daubentoniidae (aye-ayes)
　　Infraorder Lorisiformes
　　　Family Lorisidae (lorises, bush babies)
　　Infraorder Tarsiiformes
　　　Family Tarsiidae (tarsiers)
　Suborder Anthropoidea (higher primates)
　　Infraorder Platyrrhini (New World higher primates)
　　Superfamily Ceboidea
　　　Family Callitrichidae (marmosets)
　　　Family Cebidae (New World monkeys)
　　Infraorder Catarrhini (Old World higher primates)
　　Superfamily Cercopithecoidea
　　　Family Cercopithecidae (Old World monkeys)
　　Superfamily Hominoidea[1]
　　　Family Hylobatidae (lesser apes, gibbons)
　　　Family Pongidae (great apes: orangutan, gorilla, chimpanzee)
　　　Family Hominidae (ancient and modern humans)

[1]Molecular data suggest that gorillas, chimps, and humans are more closely related to one another than any of them is to the orangutans, leading some biologists to propose alternative classifications of the superfamily Hominoidea.

in small, isolated populations. Many species are endangered.

All lemurs are restricted to the island of Madagascar off the coast of Africa (Figure 21–3a). Because of extensive habitat destruction, they are endangered. Lorises, which are found in tropical areas of Southeast Asia and Africa, resemble lemurs in many respects. Both have somewhat elongated, pointed faces. This and other primitive features make them most like the ancestral, insectivorous primates.

Tarsiers, which are found in the East Indies and Philippines, are small primates the size of squirrels that are adept climbers and leapers (Figure 21–3b). They are nocturnal tree dwellers that resemble the more advanced anthropoids in a number of ways. Their snouts are shortened and their eyes point forward completely. When the tarsier sits or climbs upright, its head is positioned on the vertebral column at an angle, enabling it to face forward instead of directly upward.

Anthropoids Include Monkeys, Apes, and Humans

The anthropoids evolved from a group of prosimians during the Oligocene epoch, approximately 38 million

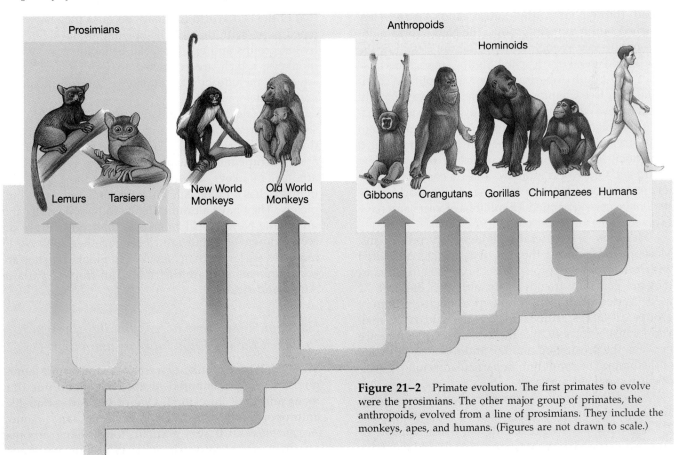

Figure 21–2　Primate evolution. The first primates to evolve were the prosimians. The other major group of primates, the anthropoids, evolved from a line of prosimians. They include the monkeys, apes, and humans. (Figures are not drawn to scale.)

(a)

(b)

Figure 21–3 Prosimians. (a) Lemur. (b) Tarsier. (a, Visuals Unlimited/John D. Cunningham; b, Doug Wechsler)

years ago (Figure 21–2). This took place in Africa or possibly Asia. From there the anthropoids quickly spread throughout Europe, Asia, and Africa. They branched into two main groups, the New World monkeys and the Old World monkeys. It is not clear how the New World monkeys reached South America because Africa and South America had already split by continental drift (see Chapter 20). Originally, it was thought that the New World monkeys had evolved from a separate prosimian line. Various types of comparative biochemistry and molecular biology, including amino acid sequencing of proteins, have indicated that the New World and Old World monkeys share a common ancestor. At any rate, the New World and Old World monkeys have been separated for millions of years and have evolved along different paths.

Monkeys are generally larger than prosimians. Most are active during the day, or *diurnal,* as compared with the nocturnal prosimians. Like the prosimians, they are generally tree dwellers, although their diet is more varied than that of the prosimians. Different groups eat leaves, fruits, buds, insects, and even small vertebrates. Probably the most significant difference between the prosimians and the anthropoids is the size of the brain. The cerebrum, in particular, is more developed in monkeys and apes.

New World monkeys are arboreal and possess long, slender limbs for easy movement in the trees (Figure 21–4a). Many have a **prehensile** tail that is capable of wrapping around branches. Some New World monkeys

have a smaller thumb, and in certain cases the thumb is totally absent. Their facial anatomy is different from that of the Old World monkeys because they have flattened noses with the nostrils opening to the side. They live in groups and exhibit social behavior. New World monkeys, which are restricted to Central and South America, include howler monkeys, squirrel monkeys, and spider monkeys.

Many Old World monkeys are arboreal, although some, such as baboons and macaques, are ground dwellers (Figure 21–4b). The ground dwellers, which are **quadrupedal** and walk on all fours, evolved from arboreal monkeys, however. None of the Old World monkeys has a prehensile tail, and some lack tails completely. They have a thumb that is fully opposable, and unlike the New World monkeys, their nostrils are directed downward and are closer together. Old World monkeys are larger than New World monkeys. They are social animals and are distributed in tropical parts of Africa and Asia.

Hominoids represent a superfamily of primates to which the apes and humans are assigned

The Old World monkeys were ancestral to the hominoids, a group composed of apes and **hominids** (humans and their ancestors). One of the earliest apelike anthropoids was discovered in Egypt and named *Aegyptopithecus.* It was a small, forest-living arboreal ape that existed approximately 35 million years ago.

(a)

(b)

Figure 21–4 New World and Old World monkeys. (*a*) Most New World monkeys have prehensile tails that can function almost as effectively as another limb. Shown here hanging by his tail is a red howler monkey in Venezuela. (*b*) The lion-tailed monkey (*Macaca silenus*) is an Old World monkey native to India.   (*a*, Animals Animals © 1993 Raymond A. Mendez; *b*, Dennis Drenner)

Like other apes, it was quadrupedal. During the Miocene epoch, which began approximately 25 million years ago, the apes and Old World monkeys diversified. Fossils of an early forest-living arboreal ape, *Dryopithecus* (also known as *Proconsul*), are of special interest because it may have given rise to modern apes as well as the human line. The forest ape was arboreal, but it apparently spent part of the time on the ground. Although it was quadrupedal, it lacked the long forearms characteristic of the apes today and had a sloping cranium with bony ridges above the eyes. The dryopithecines were distributed widely across Europe, Africa, and Asia. As the climate gradually cooled and became drier, their range became more limited. By the beginning of the Pliocene epoch, approximately 5 million years ago, the apes that had evolved from the dryopithecines were restricted primarily to tropical rainforests. Unfortunately, moist conditions of the tropics preclude the formation of many fossils, so our knowledge of ape evolution is sketchy. However, sometime between 3.5 and 4 million years ago, human-like primates called hominids arose.

There are four genera of apes classified into two families (Figure 21–5). The gibbons (*Hylobates*) are sometimes known as lesser apes and are placed in a separate family, Hylobatidae. The family Pongidae includes the orangutans (*Pongo*), gorillas (*Gorilla*), and chimpanzees (*Pan*). Gibbons are well adapted for an arboreal existence. They are natural acrobats and can **brachiate,** or swing, with their weight supported by one arm at a time. Orangutans are also tree dwellers, but both gorillas and chimpanzees have adapted to life on the ground. They have retained elongated forearms typical of tree-dwelling primates but use these to assist in quadrupedal walking, sometimes known as **knuckle-walking** because of the way they fold their digits when moving. Apes, like humans, lack tails. They are generally larger than monkeys; gibbons are a notable exception. Ape social organization, particularly in the gorillas and chimpanzees, is more complex. It is thought that this is due, in part, to their larger brains.

Antigen-antibody tests of similarities in serum proteins show that, of all the primates, gorillas and chimpanzees have serum proteins most nearly like those of humans. The amino acid sequence of the chimpanzee's hemoglobin is identical to that of the human; those of the gorilla and rhesus monkey differ from the human's in 2 and 15 amino acids, respectively. Molecular studies of DNA sequences indicate that chimpanzees are our nearest living relatives among the apes. Some of these techniques are further discussed in Chapter 22.

THE FOSSIL RECORD SUGGESTS GENERAL TRENDS IN HOMINID EVOLUTION

The **hominid** line is presumed to have separated from the ape line approximately 4 to 5 million years ago.

Figure 21–5 The apes. (*a*) White-handed gibbons. Gibbons are extremely acrobatic and often move through the trees by brachiation. (*b*) An orangutan in Sumatra. Orangutans are solitary apes that seldom leave the protection of the trees. (*c*) A lowland gorilla in Africa. Gorillas often knuckle-walk. (*d*) A chimpanzee family in West Africa. Chimpanzees live in groups and have complex social behavior. (*a*, Visuals Unlimited/Joe McDonald; *b*, E. R. Degginger; *c*, Animals Animals © 1993 Mella Panzella; *d*, Animals Animals © 1993 Mike Birkhead, Oxford Scientific Films)

General trends in human evolution are evident from the fossil record, but we do not have enough evidence to make specific conclusions. There are simply too few early hominid fossils, and the ones we have are represented by only a few bones. Moreover, it is impossible to determine many aspects about early hominid biology or appearance or behavior from fossilized bones. Nevertheless, it is evident that early hominids evolved a **bipedal** (two-footed) posture before their brains enlarged.

Evolutionary changes from the earliest hominids to modern humans is evident in some of the characteristics of the skeleton and skull. Compared with the ape skeleton, the human skeleton possesses distinct differences that reflect our ability to stand erect and walk on two feet (Figure 21–6). These differences also reflect the change in habitat for early hominids, from an arboreal existence in the forest to spending at least part of the time on the ground. The skeletal differences include a greater curvature of the spine to allow for better balance

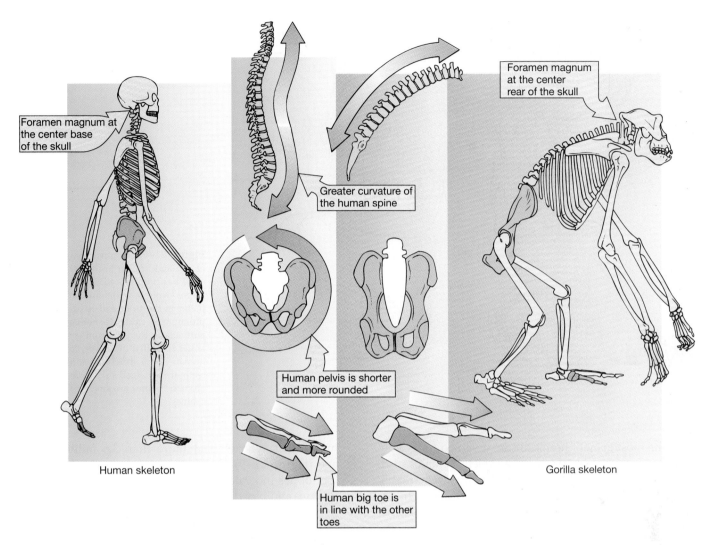

Figure 21–6 Comparison of gorilla and human skeletons. Note the skeletal adaptations for bipedalism in humans.

and weight distribution. The human pelvis is shorter and more rounded, providing a better attachment of muscles used for upright walking. The hole in the base of the skull for the spinal cord, called the **foramen magnum,** is located at the back of the skull in apes. In contrast, the foramen magnum in humans is located in the middle of the bottom of the skull, positioning the head for erect walking. An increase in the length of the legs relative to the arms and movement of the big toe so that it is in line with the rest of the toes further adapted the early hominids for bipedalism.

Another major trend in human evolution is an increase in the size of the brain relative to the size of the body (Figure 21–7). In addition, the ape skull possesses prominent bony ridges above the eye sockets, whereas these **supraorbital ridges** are lacking in human skulls. Human faces are flatter than those of apes, and the jaws are different. The arrangement of teeth in the ape jaw is

somewhat rectangular, compared with a rounded or U-shape in humans. Apes have larger teeth than humans, and their canines are especially large.

The Earliest Hominids Belong to the Genus *Australopithecus*

Hominid evolution began in Africa. The earliest hominids belong to the genus *Australopithecus*, or "southern man ape," which appeared approximately 3.8 million years ago. The actual number of species assigned to this genus is under debate. It is very difficult to decide whether differences in the relatively few skeletal fragments that have been discovered indicate individual variation within a species or separate species. Most biologists recognize two to four species of australopithecines.

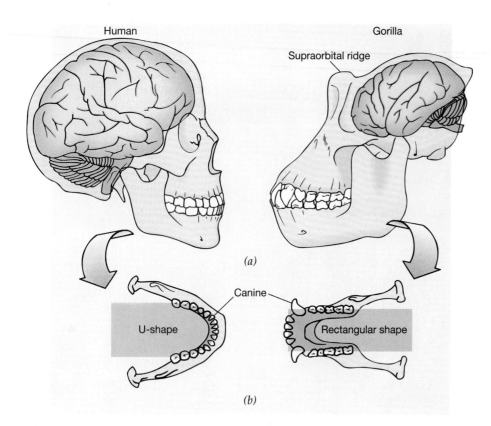

Human

Gorilla

Supraorbital ridge

(a)

Canine

U-shape

Rectangular shape

(b)

Figure 21–7   Comparison of features of ape and human heads. (*a*) The ape skull has pronounced supraorbital ridges. Note how the human skull is flatter in the front and has a more pronounced chin. The human brain, particularly the cerebrum (purple), is larger than that of an ape. (*b*) The human jaw is structured so that the teeth are arranged in a U-shape. Human canines are smaller than ape canines.

The most ancient hominids are assigned to the species *A. afarensis*. Several fossils of skeletal remains of *A. afarensis* have been discovered, including a remarkably complete skeleton named "Lucy" (Figure 21–8). In addition, in 1976 fossil footprints were discovered of three individuals who walked more than 3.6 million years ago (Figure 21–9). The footprints plus pelvis, leg, and foot bones indicate that the development of an upright posture and bipedalism occurred early in human evolution.

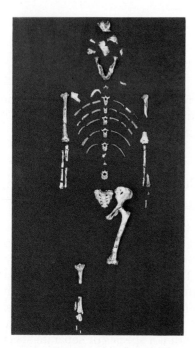

Figure 21–8   The skeletal remains of "Lucy," a hominid approximately 3.5 million years old.   (Institute of Human Origins)

Figure 21–9   Three hominids (*Australopithecus afarensis*) walked across ash scattered by a volcanic eruption more than 3.6 million years ago in Africa. Their footprints were compacted by a rain shower shortly thereafter. The footprints, which were discovered in 1978 by Mary Leakey and her associates, indicate *A. afarensis* had a bipedal gait.   (John Reader/Science Photo Library/Photo Researchers, Inc.)

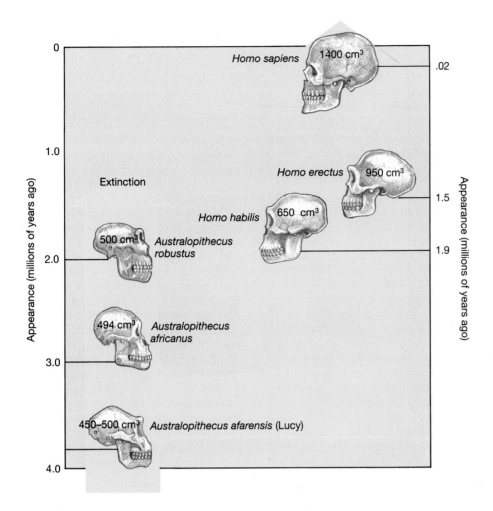

Figure 21–10 A survey of representative hominids, with the approximate dates of their appearance, estimates of their mean cranial capacity, skull features, and possible lineage. Paleoanthropologists are not in complete agreement about the details of our lineage, but many think that the current evidence supports the evolution of *H. habilis* from *A. afarensis*. In this representation, *A. africanus* and *A. robustus* are not in a direct line to *H. sapiens*.

A. afarensis was a small hominid, approximately 3 feet tall. Its face projected forward, and its apelike skull covered a small brain. Although its brain was large in relation to its size, it was small compared with human brain size. The cranial capacity was 450 to 500 cc, compared with a modern human cranial capacity of 1400 cc (Figure 21–10). Its **dentition** (the number and arrangement of teeth) was primitive and included long canines. It is probable that *A. afarensis* and other australopithecines did not talk, did not construct tools, and did not use fire.

Many scientists think *A. afarensis* evolved into the more advanced australopithecine, *A. africanus*, which appeared approximately 3 million years ago. The first *A. africanus* fossil was discovered in South Africa in 1924, and since then a number of others have been found. This rather small hominid walked erect and possessed hands and teeth that were distinctly human-like. Based on characteristics of the teeth, it is thought that *A. africanus* ate both plants and animals. Like *A. afarensis*, it had a small brain, approximately 500 cc. Two larger forms of *Australopithecus* have been identified, *A. robustus* and *A. boisei*, but it is generally agreed that neither is in the direct line to humans.

Homo habilis Is the Oldest Member of the Genus *Homo*

The first hominid to have enough human features to be placed in the same genus as modern humans is *Homo habilis*. *H. habilis* had a larger cranial capacity, an average of 650 cc, than the australopithecines (Figure 21–10). This early human appeared approximately 1.9 million years ago[1] and persisted for more than half a million years. Fossils of *H. habilis* have been found in numerous areas in Africa. These sites contain the first primitive tools, stones that had been chipped to make sharp edges for cutting or scraping. Although primates other than humans occasionally use tools, *H. habilis* represents the first to consciously design them (see Focus on Toolmaking: A Human Activity? for a decidedly different view).

The relationship between the australopithecines and *H. habilis* is not clear. Using physical characteristics

---

[1] In February 1992, Andrew Hill of Yale University announced in *Nature* that part of a human skull that may have been *Homo habilis* was found in Kenya. The skull has been dated at 2.4 million years of age.

FOCUS ON

Toolmaking: A Human Activity?

One of the established notions in paleoanthropology (study of ancient humans) is that the ability to make tools is a strictly human characteristic. Indeed, many authorities have considered toolmaking an indication that an early hominid belonged in the *Homo* genus. Although it is recognized that chimpanzees and other primates can occasionally use items from their environment as tools, the conscious effort to make tools has become ingrained as defining the beginning of human culture. We think that humans can make tools and nonhumans cannot for two reasons. First, our superior brains give us the analytical ability to design and fashion tools. Second, certain characteristics of the human hand enable us to hold objects with the precision required in toolmaking.

We may have to rethink our views about what, if anything, constitutes a specific human activity. In 1988, several fossil hand bones that had been recovered from a cave in South Africa were examined by Randall Susman. A number of fossil skull fragments from the cave had already been studied and identified as belonging to *Australopithecus robustus,* an early hominid from an extinct line that did not give rise to humans. Although *A. robustus* was decidedly apelike in overall appearance and brain size, its hand bones are distinctly modern. They indicate that *A. robustus* would have had the manual dexterity required to fashion stone tools. Additional evidence on the cave floor includes some bone and stone artifacts that could be interpreted as crude tools used by *A. robustus,* a vegetarian, to dig and chop plants. Susman concluded that *A. robustus* may have used tools and that the reason for its extinction was certainly not its inability to use tools. Susman further concluded that the early success of the *Homo* line could not be attributed to its ability to make and use tools.

Not all scholars of human evolution agree with Susman's conclusions. Some point out that the cave also had a few skeletal fragments of *Homo habilis* or *H. erectus* and that these hand bones and the scattered tools could belong to that early human. The final resolution of whether or not *A. robustus* had a human-like hand and used tools may not occur until additional fossil evidence is unearthed. Regardless of the outcome, Susman has succeeded in cautioning paleoanthropologists to be very careful in interpreting evidence about early humans. It will no longer be safe to assume that all stone tools and artifacts are evidence of early human activity.

---

as evidence, some biologists suggest that the australopithecines were ancestors of *H. habilis.* Others think that *H. habilis* and *A. africanus* were contemporaries for much of their existence and that *H. habilis* was in a direct line to humans but *A. africanus* was not. It is hoped that discoveries of additional fossils will help clarify their relationship.

Numerous Fossils of *Homo erectus* Have Been Discovered

There is more agreement on interpretation of the fossils classified as *Homo erectus,* as numerous fossils have been found. *H. erectus* evolved in Africa, as did the other hominids, but migrated into Europe and Asia. For this reason, the oldest fossils of *H. erectus,* 1.5 to 1.6 million years old, are found in Africa, and the later ones are more widely distributed in the Old World. The Peking man and Java man discovered in Asia were later examples of *H. erectus,* which existed until approximately 200,000 years ago.

H. erectus was taller than *H. habilis,* bipedal, and fully erect. Its brain size was larger than that of *H. habilis.* Moreover, during the course of its existence, its brain got progressively larger, evolving from a cranial capacity of 850 cm^3 to between 1000 and 1200 cm^3. Its skull, although larger, did not possess totally modern features, retaining the heavy supraorbital ridge and projecting face that are more characteristic of its ape ancestors (Figure 21–11).

Figure 21–11 A replica of a *Homo erectus* skull. Note the massive bony ridges over the eyes and the receding forehead and protruding jaws. (Dennis Drenner)

The increase in mental faculties associated with an increase in brain size enabled these early humans to make more advanced stone tools, including hand axes and other tools that have been interpreted as choppers, borers, and scrapers. Their intelligence enabled them to survive in areas that were cold. *H. erectus* wore clothing, built fires, and lived in caves or shelters. It is not known for sure whether they were hunters or scavengers. To date, no weapons have been unearthed at their sites.

Homo sapiens Appeared Approximately 200,000 Years Ago

Humans having features modern enough to classify them within our species appeared approximately 200,000 years ago. Their brains continued to enlarge, developing from 850 cm^3 in earliest individuals to the current cranial capacity of 1400 cm^3 (Figure 21–10).

Neandertals may have arisen in Eurasia

One of the earliest groups of *H. sapiens* was the Neandertals. They were first discovered in the Neander Valley in Germany but had a widespread distribution throughout Eurasia. These early humans had a short, sturdy build. Their brains were slightly larger than those of modern *H. sapiens*, their faces projected slightly with less pronounced chins, and they had heavy brow ridges.

Neandertal tools, including spear points, were more sophisticated than those of *H. erectus*. Studies of Neandertal sites indicate that their culture included hunting for large animals. The existence of Neandertal skeletons that were old or had healed fractures demonstrates that they cared for the elderly and sick, which is an example of advanced social cooperation. They apparently had rituals, possibly of religious significance, and buried their dead (Figure 21–12). The presence of food, weapons, and flowers in the graves indicates they had the abstract concept of an afterlife.

The disappearance of the Neandertals is a mystery. Other groups of *H. sapiens* with more modern features coexisted with the Neandertals. It is possible that the Neandertals interbred with these humans, diluting their features beyond recognition, or perhaps that the other humans outcompeted or exterminated them. It is also possible that the Neandertals could not adapt to the climate changes of the Pleistocene epoch and that their disappearance is unrelated to the presence of other humans.

Modern H. sapiens *probably arose in Africa and migrated to Eurasia relatively recently*

H. sapiens with thoroughly modern features existed 40,000 years ago and possibly earlier (some evidence from South Africa indicates that modern *H. sapiens* may

Figure 21–12 The remains of a Neandertal were found buried in Kebara Cave in Israel. (Courtesy of O. Bar-Yosef)

have existed 100,000 years ago). Early *H. sapiens* skulls lacked heavy brow ridges and possessed a distinct chin. The Cro-Magnon culture in France and Spain exemplifies these humans. Their weapons and tools were complex and often made of materials other than stone, including bone, ivory, and wood. They made stone blades that were very sharp. Cro-Magnons developed art, possibly for ritualistic purposes, including cave paintings, engravings, and sculpture (Figure 21–13). The existence of a variety of complex tools and art is an indication

Figure 21–13 The Cro-Magnon people painted animals on cave walls in Europe. These are some of the earliest representations of human art and have been interpreted as having a religious significance, possibly for guaranteeing a successful hunt. (Visuals Unlimited/John D. Cunningham)

FOCUS ON

Molecular Clocks

Molecular data have two related uses in evolutionary biology: (1) to determine which among several existing species are most closely related (see Chapter 17), and (2) to determine how long it has been since two organisms had a last common ancestor. This latter application of molecular biology, to date divergence times, is possible only if changes in DNA are incorporated with some clocklike regularity. Formation of a new allele (by mutation) plus incorporation of the new allele into a population (by genetic drift) appears to occur at a constant rate when averaged over a number of homologous genes. Thus, nucleotide sequences in DNA of different organisms appear to have a specific, constant rate of change over time. By comparing the nucleotide sequences in the same gene for two different species, it is possible to estimate how long it has been since they diverged from a common ancestor.

As you may recall, much DNA codes for the specific order of amino acids in polypeptides, which determines the shape, or conformation, of the polypeptide molecules. A substitution of one nucleotide for another in DNA may or may not result in a different amino acid being inserted in the polypeptide. Recall that a triplet of DNA codes for a single amino acid and that the genetic code common to all organisms specifies that some amino acids are coded for by several possible triplet sequences. Also, even if a different amino acid is substituted in the polypeptide chain, the conformation of the molecule may or may not change. That is, a mutation in DNA does not necessarily cause changes in the polypeptide it codes for. Such changes in DNA are neutral mutations because they do not affect the organism's phenotype. Neutral mutations are important in molecular clocks because natural selection has no effect on them.

Using molecular evidence to calculate a last common ancestor must be done with care. The rate of molecular evolution is generally the same for different species, but there are exceptions. Primates, in particular, have been shown to have a lower mutation rate than other organisms, although the reasons for this are not clear.

When molecular biologists first started using molecular clocks, paleoanthropologists were skeptical. However, evidence from molecular clocks has correlated well with the dating of fossil evidence. Molecular clocks cannot usually be calculated for organisms that are extinct, because we have no DNA from such organisms to analyze (excluding the interesting exception of DNA analysis of frozen carcasses of extinct animals).[1] However, molecular clocks have been used to determine the last common ancestor when no fossil evidence for such an ancestor was known. This information provides clues for locating fossils of such ancestors.

During the late 1980s, the sequences of mitochondrial DNA in various human populations were compared by the molecular clock method in an attempt to determine where modern *Homo sapiens* originated. These data suggest that all humans living today had a last common ancestor who lived 200,000 years ago in Africa. This ancestor was popularly identified as "Eve" because mitochondrial DNA (mtDNA) is a maternal contribution to the next generation. (An egg contains mitochondria, but the head of a sperm, which is the only part to enter the egg during fertilization, does not.) These data do not mean that "Eve" was the only woman living at the time, nor do they mean that "Eve" was the first human; an

---

[1] In 1992 biochemists were attempting to recover DNA from a 50,000-year-old Neandertal skeleton. If successful, anthropologists will be able to test certain hypotheses about human evolution more directly than they previously could.

---

that they may have possessed language abilities, used to transmit their culture to younger generations.

Studies of mitochondrial DNA of different geographical populations of humans today indicate that the first modern *H. sapiens* may have evolved in Africa during the early part of the late Pleistocene epoch (see Focus on Molecular Clocks). Similar studies of nuclear DNA (in the β-globulin cluster) and Y chromosome DNA also support the African origin. Once evolved, these modern humans migrated extensively over Earth. Some crossed the Bering land bridge into North America. Others traveled across water to reach Australia. If modern *H. sapiens* originated in Africa, then it appears that the Neandertal *H. sapiens* was not in a direct line to modern *H. sapiens*.

HUMANS UNDERGO CULTURAL EVOLUTION

Genetically speaking, humans are not very different from other primates. Most of our genes are shared with gorillas and chimpanzees. However, humans do possess a greater intelligence and have been able to

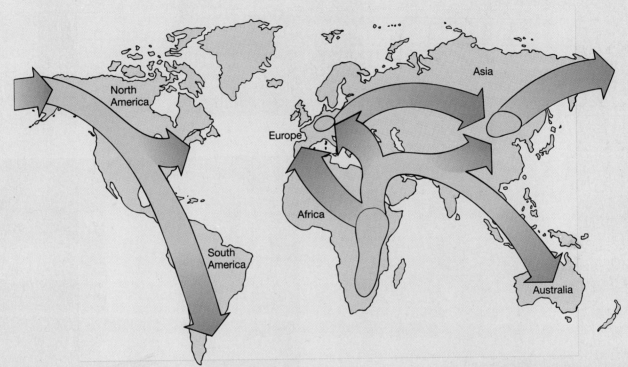

Modern *Homo sapiens* may have evolved in Africa and then expanded their range throughout Earth.

indeterminate number of generations may have preceded her.

"Eve" was determined to have originated in Africa because there were much greater differences in the mtDNA of various African populations than in other groups (see figure). Presumably, the African popula-

tions are older than other humans and had a longer period of time in which to accumulate that diversity because "Eve" originated there. More recently (in 1992), some of the statistical assumptions that the mtDNA study used to reconstruct the human family tree were questioned. How-

ever, both fossil evidence and the great diversity of mtDNA in African populations still seem to many experts to point to an African origin of humans.

maximize this intelligence through **cultural evolution.** Cultural evolution is the progressive addition of knowledge to the human experience. Human culture is dynamic; it is modified as we obtain new knowledge (Figure 21–14). Cultural evolution is generally divided into three stages: (1) the development of hunter/gatherer societies; (2) the development of agriculture; and (3) the Industrial Revolution.

Early humans who were hunter/gatherers relied on what was available in the environment. They were nomadic, and as the resources in a given area were exhausted or as the population increased, they migrated

to a different area. These societies required a division of labor and the ability to make tools and weapons, which are needed not only to kill game but also to scrape hides, dig up roots and tubers, and cook food. Although we are not certain when hunting was incorporated into human society, we do know that it declined in importance approximately 15,000 years ago, possibly owing to a decrease in the abundance of large animals, triggered in part by a change in climate. A few isolated groups of hunter/gatherer societies survived to the 20th century, including the Inuit of polar regions and the Aborigines of Australia.

(a)

(b)

(c)

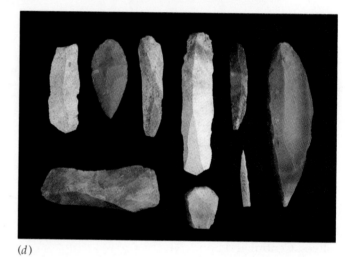

(d)

Figure 21–14 The progressive improvement of stone tools is evidence of cultural evolution. (a) Hand axes appeared approximately 1.5 to 2.0 million years ago. Shown are Oldowan pebble choppers that were used to cut through animal hides to obtain meat. The users of these tools did not kill the animals; instead, they scavenged the remains of animals killed by large predators. (b) These Acheulean hand axes from Europe are more advanced than the earliest axes discovered in Africa. (c) Several Neandertal Mousterian tools. These tools represent more advanced examples of stone tools. Each is specialized for a particular task. (d) Stone blades were fashioned by Cro-Magnon humans. Note that the length of the blade is greater than its width. These are examples of the most advanced tools made from stone.   (a–d, Dennis Drenner)

Development of Agriculture Resulted in a More Dependable Food Supply

Evidence that humans had begun to cultivate crops approximately 10,000 years ago includes the presence of agricultural tools and plant material at archaeological sites. Agriculture, keeping animals as well as cultivating plants, resulted in a more dependable food supply. Recent archaeological evidence suggests that agriculture arose in several steps. Although there is much variation from one site to another, plant cultivation usually occurred first in combination with hunting. Animal domestication followed at a later period. Agriculture, in turn, often led to more permanent dwellings because considerable time was invested in growing crops in one area. Villages and cities often grew up around the farmlands, but connecting the advent of agriculture to the establishment of villages and towns is complicated by recent discoveries. For example, Abu Hureyra in Syria was a village founded *before* agriculture arose. The people subsisted on the rich plant life of the area and migrating herds of gazelle. Once people turned to agriculture, however, they seldom went back to hunting and gathering to obtain food.

Archaeological evidence indicates that agriculture developed independently in several different regions. There were three main centers of agriculture and several minor ones. Each of the main centers was associated with cultivation of a cereal crop, although other foods were grown as well. Cereals are grasses, which

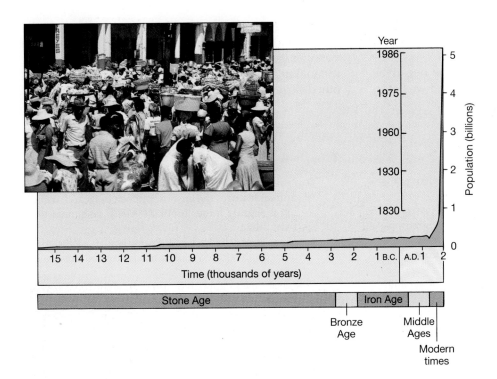

Year

Figure 21–15 The human population is increasing geometrically, as Malthus predicted (see Chapter 17). (Photo from Visuals Unlimited/A. J. Copley)

are members of the monocot group of flowering plants (see Chapter 27). The cereals associated with the three main centers of agriculture are wheat, corn, and rice.

Wheat was cultivated in the semiarid regions along the eastern edge of the Mediterranean. Other crops that originated in this area include peas, lentils, grapes, and olives. Central and South America were the sites of the maize, or corn, culture. Squash, chili peppers, beans, and potatoes were also cultivated there. In the Far East, in southern China, evidence has been found of the early cultivation of rice and other crops such as soybeans. The actual date for the domestication of rice is unknown because rice is cultivated in a wet environment, a condition that prevents preservation of archaeological evidence.

Corn, wheat, and rice are all propagated by seed, which requires fairly sophisticated agricultural practices. It has been suggested that cultivation of plants that could be propagated vegetatively occurred earlier. Plants that are cultivated in this manner, such as bananas, yams, potatoes, and manioc, do not preserve as well as grains because of their high water content. For that reason, we may have no evidence of their cultivation prior to the cereal crops.

Other advances in agriculture include the domestication of animals, which were kept to supply food, milk, and hides. In the Old World animals were also used to prepare fields for planting. Another major advance in agriculture was the use of irrigation, which dates to 7000 years ago in the Near East.

Producing food agriculturally was more time-consuming than obtaining food by hunting and gather-ing, but it was also more productive. In hunter/gatherer societies, everyone shares the responsibility of obtaining food. In agricultural societies fewer people are needed to provide food for everyone. This freed some people to pursue other endeavors, including religion, art, and various crafts.

Cultural Evolution Has Had Profound Impacts on the Ecosphere

Cultural evolution has had far-reaching effects on human society and on other life forms. The Industrial Revolution, which began in the 18th century, resulted in the concentration of people in urban areas where centers of manufacturing are located. Advances in agriculture encouraged this, as fewer and fewer people were needed to provide food for everyone. The spread of industrialization has increased the demand for natural resources to supply the raw materials for industry. The human population has expanded so dramatically that some biologists fear that Earth cannot support our numbers (Figure 21–15). As it is, millions of people are malnourished or undernourished. Almost all the arable land on Earth is under cultivation.

Cultural evolution has resulted in large-scale disruption and degradation of the environment. Tropical rainforests and other natural environments are rapidly being eliminated. Soil, water, and air pollution occur in many places. Desertification (the spread of deserts) is increasing as natural plant cover is removed from arid lands so that they can be cultivated. Many plant and animal species cannot adapt to the rapid changes humans are causing in the environment and are perishing. The decrease in biological diversity due to extinction is alarming.

On a positive note, we are aware of the negative effects we are having on the environment, and we have the intelligence to modify our behavior to improve these conditions. Through education, we can help younger generations develop environmental sensitivity, making cultural evolution our salvation rather than our destruction.

SUMMARY

I. Primates evolved from small, arboreal, shrewlike mammals.
   A. Primates are adapted for an arboreal existence by: the presence of five digits, including an opposable thumb; long, slender limbs that move freely at the hips and shoulders; and eyes located in front of the head.
   B. Primates are divided into two suborders, the prosimians and the anthropoids.
      1. Prosimians include lemurs, tarsiers, and lorises.
      2. Anthropoids include monkeys, apes, and humans.
II. Anthropoids evolved from prosimian ancestors during the Oligocene epoch.
   A. The early anthropoids branched into two groups, the New World monkeys and the Old World monkeys.
   B. Apes evolved from the Old World monkey lineage.
   C. There are four genera of apes: gibbons, orangutans, gorillas, and chimpanzees.
III. The hominid line separated from the ape line approximately 4 to 5 million years ago.
   A. The earliest hominids belong to the genus *Australopithecus*. The australopithecines walked on two feet, a human feature.

B. *Homo habilis* was an early hominid that had some human features the australopithecines lacked, including a slightly larger brain. *H. habilis* fashioned tools from stone.
C. *Homo erectus* had a larger brain than *H. habilis*, made more sophisticated tools, and discovered how to use fire.
D. *Homo sapiens* appeared approximately 200,000 years ago.
   1. Its brain continued to enlarge during its evolution.
   2. Modern *Homo sapiens* may have evolved about 200,000 years ago in Africa. This conclusion is based on a molecular clock estimate.
IV. Cultural evolution is the progressive addition of knowledge to the human experience.
   A. An evolutionary increase in human brain size makes cultural evolution possible.
   B. Two of the most significant advances in cultural evolution were the development of agriculture and the Industrial Revolution.

POST-TEST

1. The three main lines of mammals were the multituberculates, the marsupials, and the _____ mammals.
2. The presence of five digits, including an opposable thumb, is an adaptation for a(n) _____ existence.
3. The two suborders of the order Primates are the _____ and the _____.
4. Tarsiers and lemurs are examples of _____.
5. The anthropoids evolved from a group of _____.
6. Unlike Old World monkeys, New World monkeys possess a _____ tail.
7. One of the earliest apelike anthropoids that evolved 35 million years ago was _____.
8. Apes and humans are collectively called _____.
9. A gibbon _____ by swinging through the trees with its weight supported by one arm at a time.
10. The presence of large supraorbital ridges is more characteristic of _____ (apes or humans).
11. The earliest hominids belong to the genus _____.
12. The first hominid to walk erect on two feet was _____.
13. The earliest hominid to be placed in the genus *Homo* was H. _____.
14. *Homo* _____ made sophisticated tools and discovered how to use fire.
15. *Homo sapiens* appeared approximately _____ years ago.
16. An early group of *Homo sapiens* that had a short, sturdy build and heavy brow ridges was the _____.
17. Both molecular and fossil evidence have recently been used to identify the site where modern humans originated as _____.
18. The _____ _____ center of agriculture was where corn, chili peppers, beans, and potatoes originated.

REVIEW QUESTIONS

1. Distinguish between each of the following:
   a. mammals and primates
   b. prosimians and anthropoids
   c. New World monkeys and Old World monkeys
   d. anthropoids and hominoids
   e. hominoids and hominids
   f. hominids and humans

2. Describe three different adaptations primates have for an arboreal existence.
3. Identify at least three ways an ape skull differs from a human skull.
4. List at least three ways an ape skeleton differs from a human skeleton.
5. Cite one anatomical feature and one behavioral feature that distinguish each of the following from its immediate ancestor:
   a. *Australopithecus afarensis*
   b. *Homo habilis*
   c. *Homo erectus*
   d. *Homo sapiens*—Neandertal
   e. *Homo sapiens*—modern
6. Draw two possible family trees of the hominids listed in question 5.
7. How did the origin of agriculture impact human development?
8. How is cultural evolution related to biological evolution? (*Hint:* The evolution of what biological characteristic contributed to cultural evolution?)
9. How has cultural evolution helped humans?
10. How has cultural evolution affected the rest of Earth besides humans?

RECOMMENDED READINGS

Klein, R. G. *The Human Career: Human Biological and Cultural Origins.* University of Chicago Press, Chicago, 1989. A current summary of the evidence for hominid evolution; written by a paleoanthropologist.

Lewin, R. *In the Age of Mankind.* Smithsonian Institution Press, Washington, D.C., 1988. A beautifully illustrated book that covers the knowledge and controversies about human evolution; written by a well-known scientific journalist.

Martin, R. D. *Primate Origins and Evolution: A Phylogenetic Reconstruction.* Chapman and Hall, New York, 1990. Summarizes the evolutionary relationships among the primates.

Putnam, J. J. The search for modern humans. *National Geographic,* October 1988, pp. 438–477. The rise of *H. sapiens* is examined. This issue of *National Geographic* also includes articles on ice age ancestors, the paintings at Lascaux Cave, and Clovis spearpoints in North America.

Sillen, A., and C. K. Brain. Old flame. *Natural History,* April 1990, pp. 6–10. An examination of archaeological evidence of early hominid use of fire.

Simons, E. L. Human origins. *Science,* Vol. 245, 22 September 1989. A review of recent discoveries of human evolution in Africa.

Tuttle, R. H. The pitted pattern of Laetoli feet. *Natural History,* March 1990, pp. 60–64. Presents the idea that the Laetoli footprints were not made by *Australopithecus afarensis* but by some other hominid that was a contemporary of *A. afarensis.*

Wilson, A. C., and R. L. Cann. The recent African genesis of humans. *Scientific American,* Vol. 266, April 1992, pp. 68–73. One of two articles that appear in this issue debating the origin of humans. Wilson and Cann present molecular evidence in support of an African genesis of modern humans. The other article (by Thorne and Wolpoff) supports the idea that Africans, Asians, Europeans, and Australian Aborigines evolved more or less in their present locations.

Forensic Scientist (Criminalist)

PATRICIA LOUGH

Patricia Lough began her college career as a pre–veterinary medicine major. After graduating from California State College at San Bernardino in 1978, she was drawn to a job performing humoral and cellular immunological research at a veterans hospital. Lough then accepted a position in a crime lab. Since 1982 she has worked as a deputy sheriff criminalist in the Scientific Investigations Division of the San Bernardino County Sheriff's Department. (Although the term "criminalist" is not well known, within the profession it is considered a more formal designation than "forensic scientist.") She first trained in the alcohol and narcotics section and now applies her skills as a forensic scientist to investigations of major crimes that involve sexual assault, contributing special expertise in bloodstain pattern interpretation. Lough earned an M.S. in biology in 1990.

What biology courses particularly interested you as an undergraduate?

I especially enjoyed laboratory sessions and found everything we did there interesting and intriguing. I was fascinated by how the human body functions and the whole life science process.

What courses turned out to be particularly helpful in your career?

My original intention was to go to veterinary school, and the preveterinary program was the same as the premedical or predental curriculum. It was especially fortunate that I took a quantitative analysis chemistry course, because it is a California state prerequisite for performing forensic alcohol analyses. I would advise biology students to take chemistry seriously because so much that we do in biology is chemistry-oriented. A forensic scientist carries out a variety of tests that require knowledge of biology, so my course work in molecular biology, immunology, and genetics has been helpful.

Had you already decided to be a criminalist when you changed your mind about vet school?

I didn't even know this job existed. Watching detective shows on TV, I noticed they were always calling in the crime lab, but I had never heard anything about a crime lab in our area. So I made some inquiries on my own to find out what jobs were available, what duties were involved, and what the qualifications might be. That's how I found out about my career.

What were your early assignments at the San Bernardino crime lab?

Someone new in the field has to learn a lot about the legal requirements for the work. We must have proper documentation and control of the evidence, because if we don't use certain approved techniques, the evidence could be deemed inadmissible in court. We learn how to identify and collect forensic evidence and how to properly preserve it. The new criminalist usually starts work in two areas: the alcohol analysis section for cases involving driving under the influence (DUI), and the narcotics section, where you test drugs confiscated by police during arrests. The alcohol section is a very important place to start because you learn how to handle physical evidence and how to handle multiple samples at the same time. If someone doesn't pay very strict attention to details, the wrong person could go to jail. In our county, we handle about 1000 DUI analyses in a month's time, which means we go to court a lot. It is important to get this early experience as an expert witness.

Time in court, then, is an important part of your job?

It is especially important now that I am in the major assault crime area. The courtroom experience can be demanding and hostile. The jury is looking at you, judging how you walk and how you answer questions, and deciding how much confidence they have in you, because they are going to make decisions based on the work you do.

Forensic serology is a large part of your work. What does this involve?

Serology is the identification and characterization of physiological fluids to identify who could and could not be a source of those fluids. The forensic aspect applies this science to the criminal justice system. Our work is open to review by the defendant's own forensic expert, who may on occasion observe us as we perform tests. For example, if there is only a small bloodstain that will be consumed in our testing, we may contact the defense attorney so he or she can be in on the decisions of what tests to run and whether the defense expert should be present.

What is your role in a sexual assault investigation?

Generally, physical evidence is collected from the victims and suspects by medical personnel. Bedding and clothing are collected by police investigators at the crime scene. All these items are submitted to the crime laboratory for analysis.

In other circumstances, I may be required to collect the evidence. In a recent homicide case in which two women had been killed, there was evidence to suggest that there may have been a sexual assault crime as well as a homicide. My job was to collect the sexual assault kit, which includes obtaining vaginal and rectal samples, as well as other physical evidence at the crime scene, and then analyze them. When a suspect was later identified in the case, I compared the genetic markers from the suspect to the semen found on the two victims. Through routine serology, I was able to include him as a possible semen source. This evidence was later subjected to DNA analysis in our laboratory, which confirmed my findings.

So you are part of the team that is first called to the scene of a crime?

Yes, we do operate as part of a crime scene investigation team. As the criminalist, I would perform crime scene reconstruction and physical evidence collection. Homicide investigators would also be there, and a forensic specialist would process items for fingerprints and take photographs.

What other kinds of investigations are carried out in a crime lab?

We analyze gunshot residue to determine whether someone has recently fired a weapon. We perform hair and fiber analysis of evidence found at a crime scene. We can also examine glass to find out if it is from a windshield or a household product. We do toxicology analyses on blood and urine samples for drugs in under-the-influence investigations. Criminalistics is a comparative science; one is always comparing the known with the unknown. If a person uses a tool to break into a house, we can compare the paint found on that tool to paint on the house. We also do paint comparisons on hit-and-run cases. Arson analyses may involve comparing gas in a can found at a suspect's house with flammable liquids from the crime scene.

What are some of the instruments and techniques you use?

Different types of evidence examinations require different methods. In drug analysis we use chemical microcrystal tests along with thin-layer chromatography, ultraviolet and infrared spectrophotometry, and gas chromatography/mass spectrometry. Antigen-antibody assays and a variety of electrophoretic methods are commonly used in forensic serology. Since 1992 we've had the technology to perform DNA analyses in our laboratory.

What do you find most satisfying about your career choice?

I feel that I provide a benefit to my community, and a real service to that victim sitting at home waiting for tests to be run. Helping people is a very real part of my job.

What kind of biology student would make a good criminalist?

Criminalistics is ideal for a biologist with an interest in law enforcement. Most laboratories require only a bachelor's degree in biology, chemistry, or criminalistics. Not all criminalists perform crime scene investigations. In the laboratory, one must have a certain amount of manual dexterity, pay close attention to details, and like problem solving. Field work can be demanding, with long, irregular hours day or night, in uncomfortable conditions. Yet there is nothing as rewarding as locating a piece of evidence at a crime scene that helps identify the perpetrator. I can't think of any occupation in the sciences that deals so directly with human life. Unfortunately, as populations grow, so does crime. This is one career field in which there will always be job opportunities.

PART V

❑

The Diversity of Life

We do not know exactly how many species exist, but most biologists estimate there are at least 5 to 10 million different species. Each of these organisms has its own unique life history, its own way of obtaining energy, its own place in the world of living things. Certain bacteria, for example, live in the deepest abysses of the ocean, far below where light penetrates, and obtain energy from hydrogen sulfide that spews from cracks in the ocean floor. Stone plants inhabit the desert and live almost entirely underground; the tips of their leaves, which reach to the surface of the soil, resemble tiny stones.

Making sense of the remarkable diversity of life is the focus of Part V. Chapter 22 discusses how organisms are named and classified. The remaining chapters examine the major groups of living things—viruses and prokaryotes (Chapter 23), protists (Chapter 24), fungi (Chapter 25), plants (Chapters 26 and 27), and animals (Chapters 28, 29, and 30).

Biological diversity in a coral reef
ecosystem.
(Susan Blancket/Dembinsky Photo Associates)

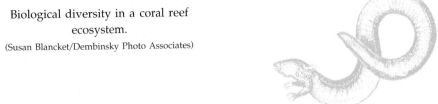

The Classification of Organisms

How would you use what you already know about living things if you wanted to assign them to categories? Would you place insects, bats, and birds in one category because they all have wings and fly? And would you, perhaps, place squid, whales, fish, penguins, and Olympic backstroke champions in another category because they all swim? Or would you classify organisms according to a culinary scheme, placing lobsters and tuna in the same part of the menu, perhaps, as "seafood"?

All of these schemes might be valid, depending on your purpose. Similar methods have been used throughout history. Animals, for example, were classified by St. Augustine in the fourth century as useful, harmful, or superfluous—to human beings. Anthropologists have discovered that some cultures still use a similar system of classification.

In Renaissance times scholars began to develop categories based more on the characteristics of the organisms themselves. These categories were originally arranged roughly in an order that proceeded from the simple to the complex. Out of the many classification schemes that were proposed, the system designed by Carolus Linnaeus in the mid-18th century (described briefly in Chapter 1) has survived with some modification to the present day. Linnaeus probably intended to design a static system of classification, for he had no theory of evolution in mind when he set it up. Neither did he or his colleagues have any concept of the vast number of living and extinct organisms that would later be discovered (Figure 22–1). Yet it is remarkable how flexible and adaptable to new biological knowledge and theory his system has proved to be. Very few other 18th-century inventions survive today in a form that would still be recognizable by their originators.

Harvestman spider (daddy-longlegs) on Jack-in-the-pulpit. (Skip Moody, Dembinsky Associates)

After you have studied this chapter you should be able to

1. Briefly summarize the development of the science of taxonomy and identify the originator of the binomial system.
2. Describe the general scheme of the binomial system of nomenclature.
3. Classify an organism such as a human according to kingdom, phylum or division, class, order, family, genus, and species.
4. List the five kingdoms of organisms recognized by modern biologists, give the rationale for this system of classifica-

tion, and describe the distinguishing traits of the organisms assigned to each.
5. Critically summarize the difficulties encountered in choosing taxonomic criteria.
6. Apply the concept of shared derived characteristics to the classification of organisms.
7. Describe the methods of molecular biology now used by taxonomists, and summarize their advantages.
8. Contrast the three major approaches to classification: phenetics, cladistics, and classical evolutionary taxonomy.

MODERN TAXONOMY IS BASED ON THE WORK OF LINNAEUS

Recall from Chapter 1 that Linnaeus developed a **binomial system** of nomenclature, a system based on a unique *two-part name* for each organism. The first part of the name designates the genus, and the second part is the specific epithet. This is a descriptive word usually expressing some quality of the organism. The specific epithet is always used together with the full or abbreviated generic name preceding it. In each scientific name,

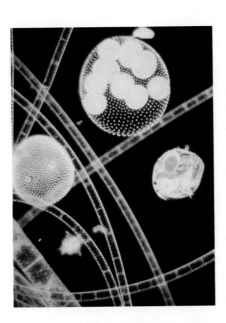

Figure 22–1 Photomicrograph of a concentrated sample of (plankton). Such variety may be bewildering even to the modern graduate student; to Linnaeus, at a time when the microscope was just being developed, the array of microorganisms being viewed for the first time seemed beyond hope of systematic classification. However, a modern marine biologist could identify and completely classify each of the microorganisms (mostly green algae) shown here. (Visuals Unlimited/T.E. Adams)

the genus is given first and is capitalized, whereas the specific epithet is given second and is not capitalized. The same specific epithet can be used as the second name of a species of more than one genus. For example, *Quercus alba* is the name for the white oak and *Salix alba* is the name for the white willow. (Alba is from a Latin word meaning white.) Both parts of the name must be used to ensure that the species is being accurately identified.

The **species** is the basic unit of classification. Recall that a species is a group of organisms with structural, functional, and developmental similarities that breed with one another to produce fertile offspring and do not interbreed with members of other species under natural conditions (see Chapter 19). Members of a species share a common evolutionary ancestry and a common gene pool. Closely related species are grouped together in the next higher unit of classification, the **genus** (plural, *genera*).

In accordance with the binomial system, the scientific name of the domestic dog, *Canis familiaris*, applies to all varieties of tame dogs—collies, German Shepherds, cocker spaniels, Chihuahuas, and so on. They all belong to the same species and all are able to interbreed. Related species of the same genus are *Canis lupus*, the wolf; *Canis latrans*, the coyote; and *Canis aureus*, the golden jackal. The cat, which belongs to a different genus, is named *Felis catus*.

The use of Latin rather than a modern language in naming organisms is a carryover from the days when Latin was the international language of scholars. Why do we continue to use Latin rather than common names for plants and animals? Why call a sugar maple *Acer* (maple) *saccharum* (sugar)? The main reason is to be accurate and to avoid confusion, for in some parts of the United States this same tree is called either hard maple or rock maple. The tree generally called white pine is *Pinus strobus*, but some people refer to other species of pine (for example, *Pinus flexilis* and *Pinus glabra*) as white pines; still other people call *Pinus strobus* northern pine, soft pine, or Weymouth pine. Because many

Table 22–1 CLASSIFICATION OF CORN

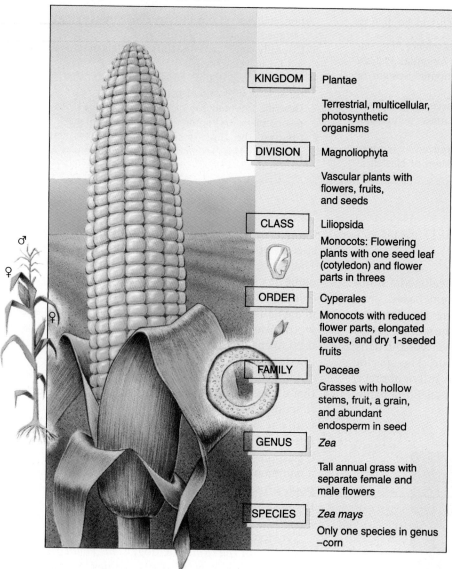

KINGDOM	Plantae
	Terrestrial, multicellular, photosynthetic organisms
DIVISION	Magnoliophyta
	Vascular plants with flowers, fruits, and seeds
CLASS	Liliopsida
	Monocots: Flowering plants with one seed leaf (cotyledon) and flower parts in threes
ORDER	Cyperales
	Monocots with reduced flower parts, elongated leaves, and dry 1-seeded fruits
FAMILY	Poaceae
	Grasses with hollow stems, fruit, a grain, and abundant endosperm in seed
GENUS	*Zea*
	Tall annual grass with separate female and male flowers
SPECIES	*Zea mays*
	Only one species in genus —corn

instances of confusing common names exist, exact scientific names are important for accurate identification of organisms.

Each Taxonomic Level Is More General Than the One Below

Recall from Chapter 1 that classification is hierarchical. One or more related genera constitute a **family,** and families may be grouped into **orders,** orders into **classes,** and classes into **divisions** for plants or fungi or into **phyla** for animals or protists (Table 22–1). Each taxonomic level is more inclusive than the level below. For example, the family Felidae includes all catlike animals—genus *Felis,* the house cat; genus *Panthera,* the leopard genus; and three or four other genera (Figure

22–2). Family Felidae, along with family Ursidae (bears) and several other families of flesh-eating animals, is placed in order Carnivora. Order Carnivora, order Primates (the order to which humans belong), order Rodentia (rodents), and several other orders belong to class Mammalia (mammals), a class of animals with hair, mammary glands that produce milk for the young, and differentiation of teeth into several types. Class Mammalia, class Aves (birds), class Reptilia (reptiles), and several other classes are grouped in subphylum Vertebrata. The vertebrates along with a few other subphyla make up phylum Chordata, which in turn belongs to kingdom Animalia. For a description of human classification, see Focus on Why You Are *Homo sapiens.*

A **taxon** (plural, *taxa*) is a taxonomic grouping of any rank, such as species, genus, or phylum. For exam-

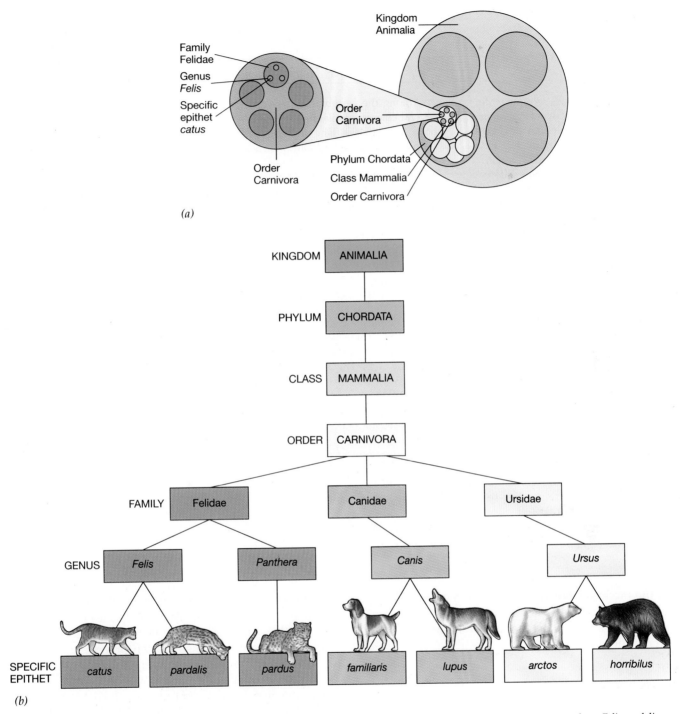

(a)

(b)

Figure 22–2   The principal categories used in classifying an organism. (a) The domestic cat is used to illustrate the hierarchical nature of our taxonomic system. (b) Three of the several families of order Carnivora are illustrated here. Family Felidae, the cats, is made up of four or five genera (two are depicted here), depending on the taxonomic scheme followed. Genus *Felis* includes *Felis catus*, the domestic cat, and several other species such as *Felis pardalis*, the ocelot. Family Canidae—wolves, foxes, jackals, and dogs—includes 12 genera (one is shown). Genus *Canis* includes *Canis familiaris*, the domestic dog, and *Canis lupus*, the timber wolf. Family Ursidae, the bears, is made up of six genera (one is shown here).

FOCUS ON

WHY YOU ARE *Homo sapiens*

At present there are five generally recognized kingdoms of organisms. Because human cells have discrete nuclei surrounded by nuclear envelopes, you belong to the domain Eukaryota. Your cells lack chloroplasts and cell walls, and you are a multicellular heterotroph, with highly differentiated tissues and organ systems. That makes you a member of the kingdom Animalia.

What kind of an animal are you? You possess a spinal column composed of bony vertebrae that has largely replaced a cartilaginous rod you had as an embryo, the notochord. At that time you also had structures that—had you been a fish—would have developed into gill slits. You have a dorsal nerve cord and brain, both of which still retain remnants of their embryonic cavities. These traits mark you as a chordate and a vertebrate—that is, you belong to the phylum Chordata (because you either have or have had a notochord), and to the subphylum Vertebrata (because you have vertebrae that replaced the notochord).

Among the vertebrates there are several classes: cartilaginous fish, bony fish, jawless fish, amphibians, reptiles, mammals, and birds. You are an endotherm (warmblooded) and so must be either a bird or a mammal. Lacking feathers and having teeth and (if you are female) the potential for nursing your young, you are a mammal.

Within the mammals there are three subclasses: the Prototheria, the Metatheria, and the Eutheria. The Prototheria are confined to the Australian continent and its environs. They include the duck-billed platypus and the spiny anteater, both of which, in addition to other unusual traits, lay eggs. The Metatheria, most of which are also from Australia, usually carry their still-embryonic young around in a pouch and totally lack a placenta (an organ of exchange between mother and developing embryo). If you did not hatch from an egg or spend your infancy in a pouch, you can be confident of your status as a eutherian.

A number of orders exist within the subclass Eutheria. The insectivores, for instance, include the moles and shrews, the Chiroptera are the bats, and the Carnivora include the dogs, cats, and ferrets, among others. Your opposable thumbs, frontally directed eyes, flat fingernails, and several other characteristics identify you as a primate, along with monkeys, apes, and tarsiers.

Primates include a number of families. You and the New World monkeys are obviously very different—they have prehensile tails, for instance, which you and all Old World monkeys and apes lack; indeed, you and the apes lack tails altogether. Your posture is upright, you have long legs, short arms, and not much body hair—the family Hominidae.

The family Hominidae has only one living genus—*Homo*. Likewise, the genus *Homo* has only one living species—*Homo sapiens*.

---

ple, the phylum Chordata is a taxon that contains several classes, including Mammalia and Amphibia. Similarly, the class Mammalia is a taxon that includes many different orders.

Subspecies May Become Species

The species is the basic unit of classification, but not the smallest taxon in use. Geographically distinct populations within a species often display certain consistent characteristics that serve to distinguish them from other populations of the same species. If they interbreed, however, they are not truly separate species but are termed instead **subspecies.** For microorganisms such as bacteria, the term **strain** is used.

Although subspecies are usually distinguishable from one another by experts, they may grade imperceptibly into one another at the borders of their geographical ranges, where there is opportunity to interbreed freely. Some of these subspecies may be in the process of becoming reproductively isolated and may, in the course of time, become clear-cut species (Figure 22–3). Thus, they provide an opportunity for field studies of gene pools and of the speciation process.

Although members of various subspecies do not ordinarily differ very much from one another, the differences may be sufficient to affect their behavior, biochemistry, or other characteristics important in biological research. Variations in results can cause problems for scientists attempting to duplicate or extend one another's research findings when they use the same species, but different subspecies, as their experimental organisms. Deer mice, many species of oaks, and numerous other kinds of organisms occur as subspecies.

Taxonomists May Split or Lump

Many organisms fall into easily recognizable, apparently natural groups, and their classification presents

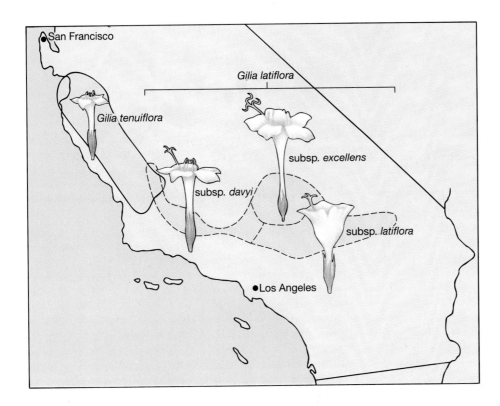

Figure 22–3 The ranges and distinguishing features of the flowers of the subspecies of the California wildflower, *Gilia latiflora*, and of *G. tenuiflora*, a closely related species. From their similarities, it seems probable that *G. tenuiflora* was originally a subspecies of *G. latiflora*. Because it now overlaps geographically with *G. latiflora* without interbreeding, it is now a distinct, separate species. For simplicity, three other subspecies of *G. latiflora* with narrower distributions have been omitted. (The full name of a subspecies includes the genus name, the specific epithet, and the subspecies name, e.g., *Gilia latiflora excellens*.)

no obvious difficulty. Others, however, appear to lie on the borderline between two groups, having some characteristics in common with each. These organisms are difficult to assign to one group or the other.

The number and inclusiveness of the principal groups vary according to the basis used for classification and the judgment of the taxonomist making the decisions. Some taxonomists ignore minor variations and group organisms into already existing taxa; this practice is referred to as **lumping.** Other taxonomists subdivide taxa on the basis of minor differences, establishing separate categories for forms that do not fall naturally into one of the existing classifications; this practice is called **splitting.** "Lumpers" acknowledge as few as 10 animal phyla and four plant divisions, whereas "splitters" may recognize up to 33 animal phyla and up to 12 plant divisions.

Organisms Are Classified in Five Kingdoms

From the time of Aristotle to the mid-20th century, biologists divided the living world into two kingdoms, **Plantae** and **Animalia.** After the development of microscopes, it became increasingly obvious that many organisms could not easily be assigned to either the plant or the animal kingdom. More than a century ago a German biologist, Ernst Haeckel, suggested that a third kingdom be established, the kingdom Protista. Although Haeckel changed the defining characters of this

new kingdom during the course of his work, his goal was to include the most primitive and ambiguous organisms, such as bacteria and most other microorganisms, that did not appear to fit into the plant or animal kingdom.

In 1937, the French marine biologist Edouard Chatton suggested that the term *procariotique* (meaning "before nucleus") be used to describe bacteria and the term *eucariotique* (meaning "true nucleus") be used to describe all other cells. This dichotomy is now universally accepted by biologists as a fundamental evolutionary divergence.

In the 1960s advances in electron microscopy and biochemical techniques revealed basic cellular differences that inspired many new proposals for classifying organisms. In 1969, R. H. Whitaker proposed a five-kingdom classification that has been accepted by the majority of biologists. Whitaker suggested that the fungi be classified as a separate kingdom, kingdom **Fungi,** rather than as part of the plant kingdom. After all, fungi are not photosynthetic and must absorb nutrients produced by other organisms. Fungi also differ from plants in the composition of their cell walls, in their body structure, and in their modes of reproduction.

Kingdom **Prokaryotae** (formerly called Monera) was established to accommodate the bacteria, which are fundamentally different from all other organisms in that they lack distinct nuclei and other membranous organelles. The five kingdoms recognized by most biol-

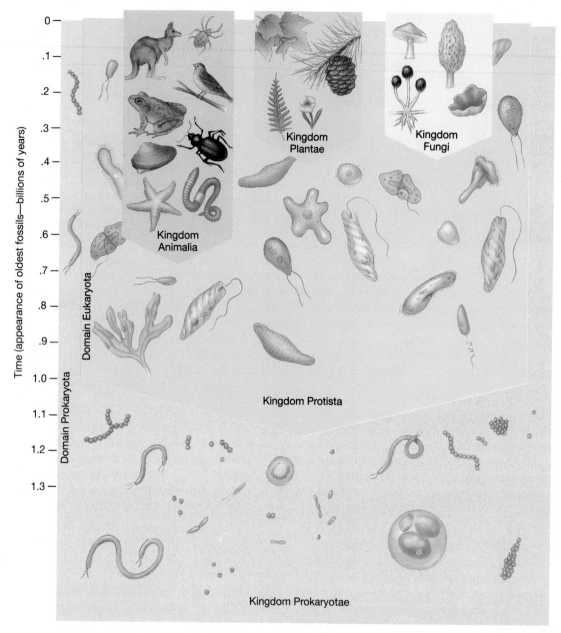

Figure 22–4   The five-kingdom system of classification. The prokaryotes—the bacteria—constitute the domain Prokaryota. Protists, plants, fungi, and animals are included in the domain Eukaryota.

ogists today are illustrated in Figure 22–4 and described in Table 22–2. They include the Prokaryotae (bacteria), Protista (algae, including multicellular forms; protozoa; water molds; and slime molds), Fungi (mushrooms and molds), Plantae, and Animalia.

SYSTEMATICS IS CONCERNED WITH RECONSTRUCTING PHYLOGENY

Modern classification is based on evolutionary relationships. The classification of organisms into groups determined by their evolutionary relationships is called

systematics. A systematist seeks to reconstruct the evolutionary history, or **phylogeny** (literally, production of phyla), of organisms. Once these relationships are defined, the classification of organisms can be based on common ancestry.

Taxa May Be Monophyletic or Polyphyletic

A population of organisms has not only a dimension in space—its range—but also a dimension in time. The populations extend backward in time, merging with populations of other species much like branches of a tree (Figure 22–5). Species have various degrees of evo-

Table 22–2 FIVE KINGDOMS: PROKARYOTAE, PROTISTA, FUNGI, PLANTAE, AND ANIMALIA

Kingdom	Characteristics	Ecological Role and Comments
Prokaryotae	Prokaryotes (lack distinct nuclei and other membranous organelles); single-celled; microscopic	
Bacteria	Cell walls composed of peptidoglycan; cells are spherical (cocci), rod-shaped (bacilli), or coiled (spirilla); metabolically varied	Most are decomposers; some parasitic (and pathogenic); some chemosynthetic autotrophs; some photosynthetic; important in recycling nitrogen and other elements; some utilized in industrial processes
Protista	Eukaryotes; mainly unicellular or colonial	
Protozoa	Microscopic; heterotrophic; move by means of flagella, cilia, or pseudopodia	Important part of zooplankton; near base of many food chains; some are pathogenic
Algae	Photosynthetic; sometimes hard to differentiate from protozoa; some have brown or red pigments in addition to chlorophyll	Very important producers, especially in marine and freshwater ecosystems
Slime molds	Protozoan characteristics during part of life cycle; fungal traits during remainder	
Fungi	Heterotrophic; absorb nutrients; do not photosynthesize; body composed of threadlike hyphae which form tangled masses that infiltrate fungus's food or habitat	Decomposers; some parasites (pathogenic); some used as food; yeast used in making bread and alcoholic beverages; some used to make industrial chemicals or antibiotics; responsible for much spoilage and crop loss
Plantae	Multicellular; complex; adapted for photosynthesis; plants have multicellular reproductive organs; pass through distinct developmental stages and alternation of generations; cell walls of cellulose	Terrestrial biosphere depends upon plants in their role as primary producers; one of most important sources of oxygen in Earth's atmosphere
Animalia	Multicellular heterotrophs, many of which exhibit advanced tissue differentiation and complex organ systems; most able to move about by muscular contraction; extremely and quickly responsive to stimuli, with specialized nervous tissue to coordinate responses	Almost sole consuming organisms in biosphere; some specialized as herbivores, carnivores, or detritus feeders

lutionary relationship with one another, depending on the length of time that has elapsed since their populations diverged. Before diverging, they had a common ancestor. If all of the subgroups within any taxon share the same common ancestor, the grouping is referred to as **monophyletic** (one branch). A taxon containing a common ancestor and all the taxa descended from it is called a **clade.** Many taxa are **polyphyletic,** consisting of several evolutionary lines and not including a common ancestor.

Biologists Consider Homologous Structures

Just how to group species into higher taxonomic groups is sometimes a difficult decision. For example, in Figure 22–5, should species A and B be placed within a single genus or do they represent two distinct genera? If species C and E are distinct genera, should D be part of either of these genera? Similar difficulties exist in determining the assignments to families, orders, classes, and phyla. Most biologists base their judgments about the degree of relationship of organisms on the extent of similarity between living species, and, when available, on the fossil record.

In evaluating similarities, biologists often look for homologous structures in different organisms (see Chapter 17). The presence of such homologous structures implies that divergent evolution has occurred from a common ancestor (Figure 22–6; see p. 499). In contrast, similarities among analogous structures result not from shared ancestry but from convergent evolution. This sometimes occurs when unrelated or distantly related organisms adapt to similar environmental conditions. The shark and the dolphin have similar structures because they adapted to similar environments.

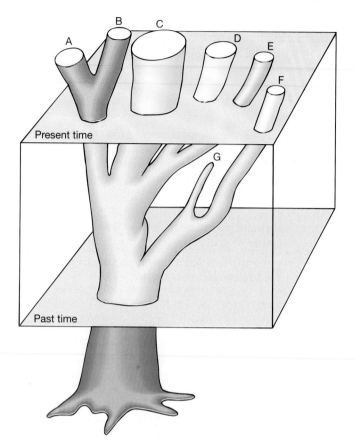

Figure 22-5 The evolutionary relationships of six hypothetical monophyletic species. Circular cross sections of the branches represent the species at the present time. Junctions of the branches represent points of common ancestry. Species G is extinct. If you go far enough back in time, all taxa share a common ancestor. The base of the tree represents the common ancestor of species A, B, C, D, E, F, and G. Which groupings of these species might be considered a genus? A family? Modern taxonomists, working solely with living forms, compare them on the basis of their modern similarities and differences. Paleontologists investigating the fossil record may confirm the findings of the taxonomists if all the organisms classified together taxonomically appear to share their similarities as far back in the fossil record as they can be traced. Many of the groups classified today on the basis of their structural similarities are thought to share a common, although remote, origin and therefore also share genetic similarities.

Derived Characters Have Evolved More Recently Than Primitive Characters

Organisms that are very similar (that is, share many homologous structures) are thought to be closely related, and less similar organisms are viewed as being more remotely related. However, distinguishing between homologous and analogous structures is not always easy. Therefore, the choice of which similarities should be used to show evolutionary relationships is extremely important. How does a systematist interpret the significance of these similarities? In making deci-

sions about taxonomic relationships, the biologist first examines the characteristics common to the largest group of organisms and interprets them as indicating the most remote common ancestry. These **primitive characters,** traits that were present in an ancestral species, remained essentially unchanged.

Derived characters are those traits not present in ancestral species because they evolved more recently. A feature viewed as a derived character in a large taxon may also be considered as a primitive character in a smaller taxon. More recent common ancestry is indicated by classification into smaller and smaller taxonomic groups.

For example, the three small bones in the middle ear are useful in identifying a branching point between mammals and reptiles. The evolution of this derived character was a unique event, and only mammals possess it. However, if we consider only mammals, the three ear bones are a primitive character because all mammals have them. They have no value in distinguishing among mammalian groups. Other derived characters must be used to establish branching points among the mammals.

Biologists Carefully Choose Taxonomic Criteria

Although both fish and porpoises have streamlined body forms, this characteristic is an analogous adaptation and is less important than homologous structures they share with other organisms. For this reason they are not classified together. The porpoise shares important derived characters with mammals such as humans—the ability to breathe air, nurse young, maintain a constant body temperature, and grow hair. Thus, the porpoise is classified as a mammal and is viewed as descending from a mammalian ancestor.

Although the porpoise has more in common with humans than it does with a fish, some characteristics are shared by all three kinds of animals. Among these are a notochord (skeletal rod) and rudimentary gill slits in the embryo stage, and a dorsal tubular nerve cord. These shared primitive characteristics serve as a basis for classification and indicate a common ancestry. This ancestry is more remote between the porpoise and the fish than between the porpoise and human beings. Therefore, fish, humans, and porpoises are grouped together in the large taxon, the phylum Chordata, and humans and porpoises are also classified together in class Mammalia, a smaller taxon indicating their closer relationship (Figure 22-7).

Deciding the appropriate weights for various traits in determining taxonomic categories is not always simple, even in apparently straightforward instances. What, for example, are the most important invariable

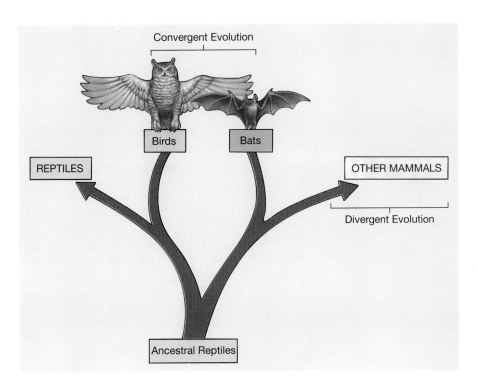

Figure 22–6 Convergent and divergent evolution. In divergent evolution, an ancestral group, for example primitive reptiles, branches and gives rise to two or more lines of evolution in which related taxa acquire dissimilar traits. The presence of homologous structures suggests divergent evolution. In convergent evolution, distantly related groups such as birds and bats may come to resemble one another in structure and function as they evolve to fit similar modes of life.

characteristics of a bird? We might list feathers, beak, wings, absence of teeth, the egg-laying trait, and the fact that they are endotherms (warmblooded). Yet some mammals (the monotremes) also have beaks, lack teeth, and lay eggs, and we do not classify them as birds (Figure 22–8).

No mammal, however, has feathers. Is this trait absolutely diagnostic of birds? According to the conventional taxonomic wisdom, the presence of feathers could be used to decide what is and is not a bird. This applies only to modern birds, however. Some extinct reptiles may have been covered with feathers, while not being birds in any meaningful sense.

Usually, organisms are classified on the basis of a combination of traits rather than on one perhaps superficial trait such as the ability to live in water. The significance of these combinations is determined inductively, that is, by an integration and interpretation of data. Such induction is a necessary first step in all science. The taxonomist proposes, for example, that birds should all have beaks, feathers, no teeth, and so on; this is really a hypothesis. Then he or she reexamines the living world and observes whether there are organisms that might reasonably be called birds that do not fit the current definition of "birdness." If not, the definition is permitted to stand, at least until too many exceptions emerge. Then the definition is modified or abandoned. Sometimes, the taxonomist persuades the world that the apparent exception—the bat, for instance—resembles a bird only superficially and should not be considered one.

Taxonomy is a dynamic science that proceeds by the constant reevaluation of data, hypotheses, and theoretical constructs. As new data are discovered and old data are subjected to reinterpretation, the ideas of taxonomists change. During the 1980s, for example, a type of organism, the Loricifera, was discovered whose combination of traits did not fit those of any existing phylum (Figure 22–9). A new phylum—Phylum Loricifera—was established just to accommodate this single species.

To take another example, as evolutionary concepts about the origin of cellular life have changed, some biologists have considered establishing a new, sixth kingdom for the Archaebacteria, a subgroup of bacteria found in unusual habitats. Although these bacteria do not visibly differ very much from others, they are chemically unique. Archaebacteria branched off very early (*archae* is from the Greek for "ancient") as one of three cell lineages (archaebacteria, eubacteria, and eukaryotes) that evolved from a universal common ancestor. Each of the three cell lineages has a distinct ribosomal RNA structure.

Molecular Biology Provides New Taxonomic Tools

Evolution of new species is not always signaled by obvious structural changes. For example, two distinct species of fruit flies may appear indistinguishable. Some of

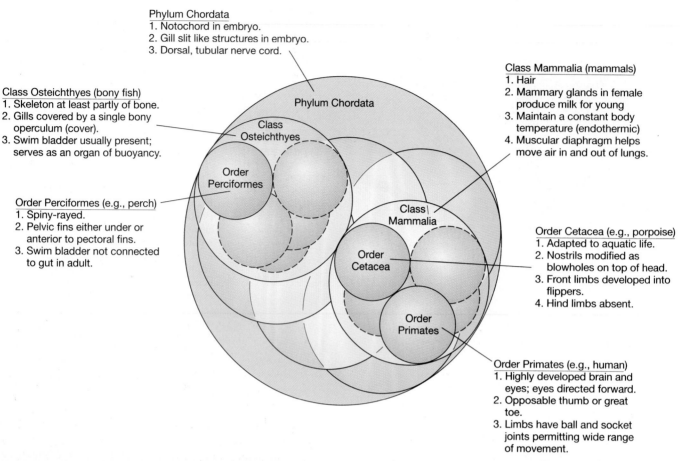

Phylum Chordata
1. Notochord in embryo.
2. Gill slit like structures in embryo.
3. Dorsal, tubular nerve cord.

Class Osteichthyes (bony fish)
1. Skeleton at least partly of bone.
2. Gills covered by a single bony operculum (cover).
3. Swim bladder usually present; serves as an organ of buoyancy.

Order Perciformes (e.g., perch)
1. Spiny-rayed.
2. Pelvic fins either under or anterior to pectoral fins.
3. Swim bladder not connected to gut in adult.

Class Mammalia (mammals)
1. Hair
2. Mammary glands in female produce milk for young
3. Maintain a constant body temperature (endothermic)
4. Muscular diaphragm helps move air in and out of lungs.

Order Cetacea (e.g., porpoise)
1. Adapted to aquatic life.
2. Nostrils modified as blowholes on top of head.
3. Front limbs developed into flippers.
4. Hind limbs absent.

Order Primates (e.g., human)
1. Highly developed brain and eyes; eyes directed forward.
2. Opposable thumb or great toe.
3. Limbs have ball and socket joints permitting wide range of movement.

Figure 22–7   Shared derived characteristics. Members of class Osteichthyes (bony fish) and class Mammalia (the mammals) share many more characteristics with one another and with the members of the other classes of phylum Chordata than they do with members of any other phylum. For example, a perch has more in common with a monkey (a notochord, gill slits, and dorsal nerve cord) than with a sea star or clam. Members of various orders of the same class share more characteristics than members of orders that belong to different classes. Thus, a porpoise has more derived characters in common with a human than with a perch. This indicates a more recent common ancestry for the porpoise and the human.

Figure 22–8   A few mammals share important characteristics with birds. The duck-billed platypus, a monotreme, lays eggs, has a beak, and lacks teeth. Should we classify it as a bird?

their macromolecules, however, are different. Variations in the structure of specific macromolecules among species, just like differences in anatomic structure, result from mutations. Macromolecules that are functionally similar in two different types of organisms are considered homologous if their subunit structure is similar.

Methods that enable biologists to compare the nucleotide sequences of various nucleic acids and the amino acid sequences of proteins have become extremely important taxonomic tools (see Making the Connection: Molecular Biology, Evolution, and Taxonomy). By comparing nucleotide sequences of DNA or amino acid sequences of proteins, we can gain some idea of degree of relatedness of two organisms; the greater the correspondence in their amino acid sequences, the more closely they are thought to be related. The number of differences in nucleotide sequence of DNA or in amino acid sequence of proteins in two groups of organisms reflects the time since the groups

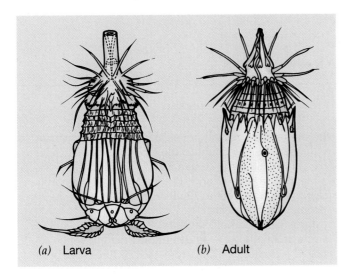

(a) Larva   *(b)* Adult

Figure 22–9 Only one new animal phylum—that for a group of microscopic marine animals—had been added to the animal kingdom since 1900. The recent discovery of the marine animal Loricifera resulted in the proposal that a second new phylum be added. Larvae of Phylum Loricifera propel themselves with a pair of appendages attached to the body by a ball-and-socket joint. The tiny adults, about 0.25 mm long, lack appendages for swimming. Both larvae and adults have head spines and a flexible, retractable tubelike mouth. These animals live between grains of shell gravel in the ocean bottom. They were probably not discovered sooner because they cling so tightly to sediment particles that they were not collected by usual extraction techniques. Are there many other unique organisms yet to be discovered and classified?

branched off from a common ancestor. Thus, specific genes and specific proteins can be used as **molecular clocks** (see Chapter 21). Biologists can use such clocks to help date the divergence of two groups from a common ancestor.

TAXONOMISTS USE THREE MAIN APPROACHES

In constructing a phylogenetic tree, taxonomists consider branch points that indicate the time at which a particular group of organisms evolved. They also consider the extent of divergence between branches, or how different two groups have become since they originated from a common ancestor and evolved along different pathways. Which of these bits of evolutionary data is utilized more in classifying a group of organisms depends upon one's approach to taxonomy. Three major approaches are phenetics, cladistics, and classical evolutionary taxonomy.

Phenetics Is Based on Phenotypic Similarities

Pheneticists do not try to reconstruct evolutionary history. These taxonomists argue that we cannot be sure that our view of phylogeny is correct and we therefore should not base classification on phylogeny. The **phenetic (phenotypic) system** is sometimes called a numerical taxonomy and is based on similarities of many characters. In this system organisms are grouped according to the number of characteristics they share, without trying to determine whether their similarities arise from a common ancestor or from convergent evolution. Pheneticists argue that it is not important to try

to sort homologous and analogous characteristics, because there are many more similarities due to homology rather than analogy. As a result, overall the number of similarities that two organisms have in common reflects the degree of homology.

A taxonomist who follows the phenetic system would explain that porpoises are classified along with humans as mammals rather than fish because they share more similarities with mammals. Pheneticists assign numbers to many arbitrarily chosen traits (more than 100) that are given equal weight. They designate these traits as present (+) or absent (−) in the organisms of a particular taxon. This information is fed into a computer, which indicates which groups have the most traits in common. Phenetics is not used by most taxonomists today because the use of analogous similarities can prevent the formation of accurate conclusions about evolutionary relationships. However, phenetics has made an important contribution to biology because taxonomists have found the phenetic emphasis on quantitative comparisons useful.

Cladistics Emphasizes Phylogeny

The **cladistic** approach to taxonomy emphasizes phylogeny, focusing on how long ago one taxon branched off from another. A clade is a branch. Cladists insist that taxa be monophyletic: Each taxon should contain a common ancestor and its descendants. Thus, common ancestry is the basis for classification rather than data on phenetic similarity. Cladists do not concern themselves with divergence. The significance or magnitude of specific adaptational differences between the descendants of a common ancestor is not important. A cladist would say that porpoises cannot be classified with fish because they evolved much later in time than fish.

MAKING THE CONNECTION

Molecular Biology, Evolution, and Taxonomy

Recent advances in molecular biology have provided the tools for biologists to compare the macromolecules of various organisms. Amino acid sequencing techniques, immunological methods, and DNA sequencing and hybridization techniques are among the procedures now used to compare macromolecules. Such comparisons of molecular structure provide objective, quantifiable measures of evolutionary relationships. Thus, molecular biology and evolution come together in the laboratory to provide important data that can be used by taxonomists.

Cytochrome *c*, the respiratory protein mentioned in Chapter 7, provides a good example of how data gained through amino acid sequencing contribute to taxonomic decisions. In Chapter 17 we learned that although the structure and function of cytochrome *c* are similar in all aerobic organisms, some differences in amino acid sequences exist among species. In fact, the extent of the differences in amino acid sequences reflects the time since two species diverged in their evolutionary history. Human and chimpanzee cytochrome *c* molecules have identical amino acid sequences. In a more distantly related primate, the rhesus monkey, one of the 104 amino acids in the sequence is different from that in human cytochrome *c*. In the dog, a nonprimate, 13 amino acids are different from the amino acid sequence in human cytochrome *c*. Taxonomists use this type of information to help in making decisions about classifying organisms.

We have learned that among related species the DNA sequences for the same structural genes are very similar. Detailed restriction maps within large homologous regions of chromosomes of related organisms are also very similar (see Chapter 15). For example, the DNA region that codes for the equivalent of the human hemoglobin beta chain has been mapped in several primates. Even though the gorilla diverged from humans 4 to 5 million years ago, 65 of the 70 restriction sites are identical.

Morris Goodman of Wayne State University School of Medicine and his coworkers determined the nucleotide sequence of a portion of DNA from each of three species of primates (humans, gorillas, and chimpanzees). From their analysis of the 7000-nucleotide sequence, the investigators inferred a common ancestral gene. The simplest branching pattern that would account for the results suggests that the gorilla first split off from the common ancestor of the chimpanzee and human. Later the chimpanzee and human lines diverged.

Mammalian DNA may contain almost one million copies of a 300-base pair segment, called *alu* DNA, interspersed throughout the genome. The *alu* repeats can be identified because each contains a recognition site for a restriction enzyme (see Chapter 14) known as *alu*I. Although the function of *alu* DNA is unknown, it is a valuable taxonomic character because even closely related species differ somewhat in their *alu* DNA, and much greater differences are seen when the *alu* sequences of more distantly related species are analyzed. Therefore the degree of similarity of *alu* sequences among species can serve as an additional measure of evolutionary relatedness, which can be very useful when combined with other kinds of information.

Cladists develop branching diagrams called cladograms. Each branch on a cladogram represents the divergence, or splitting, of two new groups from a common ancestor. Cladists use carefully defined objective criteria. However, some taxonomists criticize cladists because they ignore later evolutionary changes that take place in groups that have split.

Consider the evolutionary grouping of turtles, lizards, snakes, dinosaurs, crocodiles, and birds. Birds, along with dinosaurs, are thought to be descendants of reptiles that shared a common ancestor with the modern crocodiles and alligators (see Figure 19–20). Crocodiles and birds, then, could be considered sister groups, and some cladists might classify them in the same class. This decision would be made without considering that crocodiles appear to have much more in common adaptationally and ecologically with lizards, snakes, and turtles (all of which descended from a different reptilian ancestor) than they do with birds.

Cladists would classify birds and reptiles in a nested series of monophyletic taxa (Figure 22–10). Birds and reptiles would be assigned to a single taxon (perhaps a class) because they share a common ancestor. Within that taxon birds and crocodilians might be grouped together in one order because they have a common ancestor. Lizards and snakes would be assigned to a different order because they share a different common ancestor. Turtles would be placed in a third order. In this way cladists develop phylogenetic systems of classification.

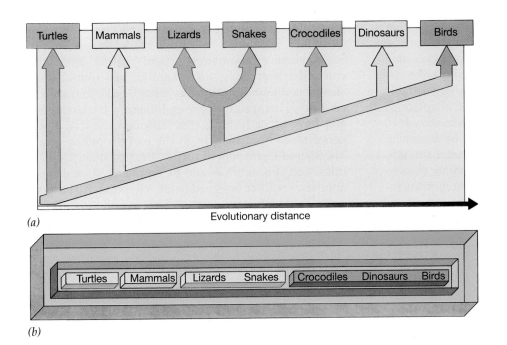

(a)

(b)

Figure 22–10 According to the cladistic approach, birds and reptiles are classified together because they have a common ancestor. (a) A simple cladogram. (b) Sets of nested boxes can be constructed from the cladogram. Each box is equivalent to a taxon.

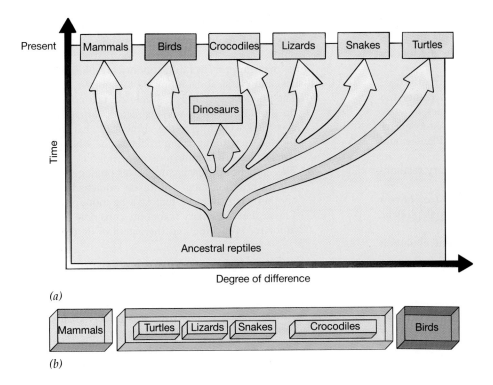

(a)

(b)

Figure 22–11 Classical evolutionary taxonomists consider both common ancestry and extent of divergence that has occurred since two taxa split. (a) The branching points and degrees of difference in the evolution of the major groups of reptiles. Turtles, snakes, lizards, and crocodiles are most similar, but birds, dinosaurs, and crocodiles are most closely related because they branched most recently from a common ancestor. (b) Hierarchical classification of these groups by the classical method.

Classical Evolutionary Taxonomy Uses a Phylogenetic Tree

Classical evolutionary taxonomy is perhaps the most widely accepted approach to classification and is the one used in this book. This traditional approach to taxonomy uses a system of phylogenetic classification and presents evolutionary relationships in a phylogenetic tree. Classical taxonomists consider both evolutionary branching (like cladists) and the extent of divergence that has occurred in a lineage since it branched from a stem group (like pheneticists) (Figure 22–11).

A taxonomist using the classical approach might explain that porpoises are mammals rather than fish because they share many characteristics with other mammals and because these characteristics can be traced to a common ancestor. Organisms are classified in the same taxon according to their shared characteristics only if those traits are derived from a demonstrable common ancestor. The significance of the adaptations possessed by related organisms is also considered. If, for example, egg-laying mammals could be shown to have a very different ancestry from the other mammals, the classical taxonomist might erect a separate class to accommodate them. On the other hand, common ancestry, although necessary for inclusion in the same category, would not by itself be sufficient grounds for inclusion.

A classical taxonomist would classify birds and crocodiles separately, for example, even though they share a common ancestor. The birds would be placed in class Aves because they are endotherms, have feathers, and have other features that indicate extensive divergence since branching from the early reptilian stock. The shared characters of turtles, lizards, snakes, crocodiles, and dinosaurs would be emphasized, and these animals would be assigned to class Reptilia. All of these animals have horny scales and are ectotherms.

SUMMARY

I. The modern system of scientific taxonomy is based on the binomial system first used consistently by Linnaeus.
   A. In this system the basic unit of classification is the species.
   B. The name of each species has two parts: the genus name and the specific epithet. For example, the scientific name for the human is *Homo sapiens* and that for the domestic cat is *Felis catus*.
II. The hierarchical system of classification currently used includes kingdom, phylum (or division, in plants and fungi), class, order, family, genus, and species.
III. The five-kingdom classification in current use recognizes the kingdoms Prokaryotae, Protista, Fungi, Plantae, and Animalia.
IV. Modern classification is based on evolutionary relationships, or phylogeny.
   A. All of the organisms in a monophyletic taxon have a common ancestor; the organisms in a polyphyletic taxon evolved from different ancestors.
   B. Homologous structures imply divergent evolution

from a common ancestor.
   C. Shared primitive characters suggest a distant common ancestor; shared derived characters indicate a more recent common ancestor.
   D. Comparison of DNA and protein structure provides a powerful tool for confirming evolutionary relationships.
V. Three main approaches to taxonomy are phenetics, cladistics, and classical evolutionary taxonomy.
   A. The phenetic system is a numerical taxonomy based on similarities of many characters; organisms are classified according to the number of characteristics they share without trying to determine whether their similarities are homologous or analogous.
   B. The cladistic approach emphasizes phylogeny, focusing on how long ago one taxon branched off from another; cladists insist that taxa be monophyletic.
   C. Classical evolutionary taxonomy considers both evolutionary branching and the extent of divergence.

POST-TEST

1. The science of describing, naming, and classifying organisms is _____.
2. In the binomial system of nomenclature developed by _____, each organism is given a scientific name composed of a _____ name and a _____ epithet.
3. In the hierarchy of taxonomic classification, a number of related genera constitute a _____.
4. The kingdom that includes the algae is _____.
5. Kingdom _____ consists of decomposers such as molds and mushrooms.
6. The members of a monophyletic group have a common _____ that was also a member of that group.
7. The presence of _____ structures in different organisms suggests that divergent evolution has occurred.
8. The porpoise and the human both have the ability to nurse their young, whereas the less closely related fish does not. The ability to nurse their young is a shared _____ character for mammals as compared to fish.
9. The constancy in DNA and _____ evolution permits biologists to use these macromolecules as molecular _____.
10. The _____ system is a numerical taxonomy based on phenotypic similarities.
11. Taxonomists who follow the _____ school of taxonomy might classify crocodiles and birds in the same group based on a common ancestor.
12. A system of classification that attempts to balance data from both phenetics and cladistics is used by _____ _____ taxonomists.

A complete classification of the human would be as follows:

13. Kingdom _____
14. Phylum _____
15. Subphylum _____
16. Class _____
17. Subclass _____

18. Order _____
19. Family _____
20. Genus _____
21. Specific epithet _____

REVIEW QUESTIONS

1. Imagine that you are a biologist in the 17th century (pre-dating Linnaeus). How might you have classified the organisms of our planet?
2. Define (in modern terms) (a) species, (b) class, (c) phylum, (d) division.
3. What are the advantages of a "five-kingdom" system over a "two-kingdom" one? What types of organisms are especially difficult to assign a place in the taxonomic hierarchy?
4. What taxonomic problems was the five-kingdom scheme intended to solve? Has it created new problems?
5. Why are there some difficulties in attempting to use the concept of a species?
6. How can shared derived characteristics be used to determine relationships among organisms?
7. In which kingdom would you classify each of the following?
   a. an oak tree
   b. an amoeba
   c. *Escherichia coli* (a bacterium)
   d. a tapeworm
8. Compare the phenetic, cladistic, and classical evolutionary approaches to taxonomy.
9. Of what use to a taxonomist would be knowledge of the amino acid sequences of the proteins of various organisms?

RECOMMENDED READINGS

Corliss, J. O. Consequences of creating new kingdoms of organisms. *Bioscience*, Vol. 33 (May 1983). The objections of a holdout against the five-kingdom scheme of taxonomy.

Krogmann, D. W. Cyanobacteria (blue-green algae)—their evolution and relation to other photosynthetic organisms. *Bioscience*, Vol. 31, No. 2 (February 1981). A good example of the application of modern taxonomic techniques.

Lewin, R. Molecular clocks scrutinized. *Science*, May 3, 1985. A summary of what is known about molecular clocks.

Margulis, L., and K. V. Schwartz. *Five Kingdoms. An Illustrated Guide to the Phyla of Life on Earth*. W. H. Freeman, San Francisco, 1982. The great diversity of living things, beautifully illustrated.

May, Robert M. How many species inhabit the earth? *Scientific American*, Vol. 267, No. 4 (October 1992), pp. 42–48. An argument for the importance of identifying and classifying the organisms that inhabit our planet; this information impacts on environmental issues.

Mayr, E. Biological classification: Toward a synthesis of opposing methodologies. *Science*, Vol. 214 (October 1981). A discussion of phenetics, cladistics, and evolutionary classification, suggesting that all three methods should be utilized in taxonomy.

Sibley, C. G., and J. F. Ahlquist. Reconstructing bird phylogeny by comparing DNAs. *Scientific American*, February 1986. An interesting account of a modern taxonomic method.

Whittaker, R. H. New concepts of kingdoms of organisms. *Science*, Vol. 163, 1969. A proposal for classifying living things according to a five-kingdom system.

Viruses and Kingdom Prokaryotae

What do AIDS, rabies, and tobacco mosaic disease have in common? These diseases are all caused by viruses, which lie on the threshold between life and nonlife and, as such, are not true living organisms. They exhibit a few of the properties of life, such as reproduction, but carry on no metabolism and are incapable of reproducing outside a host cell.

Bacteria, another important group, are cellular and are assigned their own kingdom, Prokaryotae, because their prokaryotic cell structure is considered a fundamental difference between them and other living organisms. Their contributions include the ability of some bacteria to alter atmospheric nitrogen to a form that can be used by plants. Nitrogen fixation enables plants and animals (because they eat plants) to manufacture essential compounds such as proteins and nucleic acids.

Other bacteria play an essential role in the biosphere as decomposers, breaking down organic molecules into their simpler components. Bacteria, along with fungi, are nature's recyclers. Without bacteria (and fungi), all available carbon, nitrogen, phosphorus, and sulfur would eventually be tied up in the wastes and dead bodies of plants and animals. Life would soon cease to exist because of the lack of raw materials for the synthesis of new cellular components.

We group the viruses and bacteria into a single chapter for convenience; viruses and bacteria are not a natural assemblage of closely related organisms.

Conjugation in *Escherichia coli.* (Dr. L. Card/ Science Photo Library/Custom Medical Stock Photo)

After you have studied this chapter you should be able to

1. Describe the structure of a virus and compare a virus with a free-living cell.
2. Characterize bacteriophages and contrast a lytic infection with a lysogenic infection.
3. Explain how a virus infects an animal cell.
4. Identify two viral infections of plants.
5. Speculate about the evolutionary origin of viruses.
6. Describe the distinguishing characteristics of members of the kingdom Prokaryotae.

7. Characterize the metabolic diversity of bacteria, including autotrophs and heterotrophs, and aerobes, facultative anaerobes, and obligate anaerobes.
8. Summarize the three mechanisms (transformation, conjugation, and transduction) that may lead to genetic recombination in bacteria.
9. Distinguish between each of the following groups of bacteria: archaebacteria, wall-less bacteria, gram-negative bacteria, and gram-positive bacteria. Give examples of each.
10. Discuss the important ecological roles of bacteria.

VIRUSES ARE TINY, INFECTIOUS AGENTS THAT ARE NOT ASSIGNED TO ANY OF THE FIVE KINGDOMS

Viruses are not cellular, cannot move about on their own, and cannot carry on metabolic activities independently. All cellular forms of life contain both DNA and RNA, but a virus contains *either* DNA *or* RNA, not both. Viruses lack ribosomes and enzymes necessary for protein synthesis. They can reproduce, but only within the complex environment of the living cells that they infect. In a sense, viruses come alive only when they infect a cell. They are superbly adapted for their parasitic mode of life.

Because they are not cellular and cannot carry on metabolic activities on their own, viruses are not classified in any of the five kingdoms of living things. Furthermore, no system of virus classification has yet been agreed upon because so little is known about their evolutionary relationships. Although a system has been proposed for dividing them into families and genera, it is not universally accepted. At present viruses are usually grouped on the basis of four main criteria: (1) size, (2) shape, (3) presence or absence of an outer envelope, and (4) the type of nucleic acid—DNA or RNA—they contain, and whether it is single-stranded or double-stranded. They are also sometimes classified according to the types of diseases they cause or their mode of transmission.

A virus is a tiny, infectious particle consisting of a nucleic acid core surrounded by a protein coat called a **capsid.** Some viruses are also surrounded by an outer membranous envelope containing proteins, lipids, carbohydrates, and traces of metals. There are DNA viruses and RNA viruses. Whether the virus contains DNA or RNA, its nucleic acid serves as its genetic material, or **genome.** The viral genome may consist of fewer than five genes or as many as several hundred. However, viruses never have tens of thousands of genes like the cells of more complex organisms.

Only the largest virus, the smallpox virus, can be seen with the light microscope. Most viruses are much smaller than bacteria, and indeed some are scarcely larger than a large molecule. Individual viral particles of all but the smallpox virus are less than 0.25 μm in diameter and can be observed only with an electron microscope. However, accumulations of viruses growing in the cytoplasm of an infected cell can be visible with a light microscope.

The shape of a virus is determined by the organization of protein subunits that make up the capsid. Viral capsids are generally either helical (rod-shaped) or polyhedral in shape, or a complex combination of both (Figure 23–1). Helical viruses, such as the tobacco mosaic virus, appear as long rods or threads; their capsid is a hollow cylinder that encloses or encircles its nucleic acid. Polyhedral viruses appear somewhat spherical in shape. The plant virus known as bushy stunt virus is a polyhedral virus that lacks an outer envelope. Another polyhedral virus, the influenza virus, is surrounded by an outer membranous envelope studded with glycoproteins (protein bonded to carbohydrate molecules) that aid in adhering to the host cell. Adenoviruses have a polyhedral capsid that is distinctive because it is studded with protein spikes. There are about 35 different human adenoviruses that cause a variety of illnesses such as mild respiratory tract infections.

Unlike cells, viruses can be purified and crystallized. In the crystalline form, viruses are arranged in a definite repeating pattern to produce an external shape with symmetrical planar surfaces. For example, viral crystals can be needle-like, rhomboid, or cubic. Later, if the inert crystals are put back into the appropriate host cells, they multiply and produce the symptoms of disease.

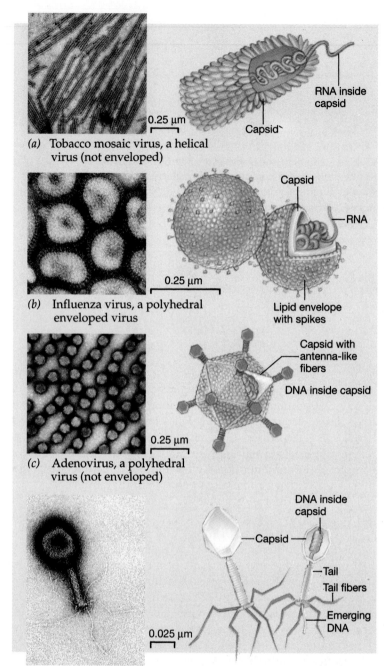

(a) Tobacco mosaic virus, a helical virus (not enveloped)

(b) Influenza virus, a polyhedral enveloped virus

(c) Adenovirus, a polyhedral virus (not enveloped)

(d) T$_4$ bacteriophage, a polyhedral and helical virus (not enveloped)

Figure 23–1 Viruses are generally either helical or polyhedral in shape, or a complex combination of both forms. (*a*) Tobacco mosaic virus has a helical capsid and appears rod-shaped. (*b*) Influenza virus is a polyhedral virus surrounded by a lipid envelope studded with glycoprotein spikes. (*c*) Adenovirus is a polyhedral virus with a capsid that has projecting protein fibers. (*d*) This bacteriophage, known as T$_4$, is a complex combination of helical and polyhedral shapes. (*a, b,* Visuals Unlimited/ K. G. Murti; *c,* Visuals Unlimited/Hans G. Elderblom; *d,* Lee D. Simon/Science Source/Photo Researchers, Inc.)

BACTERIOPHAGES ARE VIRUSES THAT ATTACK BACTERIA

Among the most complex viruses are those that infect bacteria. These viruses are known as **bacteriophages** ("bacteria eaters"), or simply **phages** (Figure 23–1*d*). The most common bacteriophage structure consists of a long nucleic acid molecule coiled within a polyhedral head. Most, but not all, use DNA as their genetic material. Many phages have a tail attached to the head. Fibers extending from the tail may be used to attach to a bacterium.

There are many varieties of phages, and they are usually species-specific (or strain-specific), meaning that one type of phage generally attacks only one species (or strain) of bacteria. Because phages can be easily

FOCUS ON

Culturing Viruses

Because viruses multiply only when they have infected living cells, they cannot be cultured on a nonliving medium. One of the first, and still very useful, methods for culturing animal viruses is growing them in developing chick embryos. A small piece of egg shell is removed about a week or two after fertilization of the egg, and the material containing the virus is injected through the opening. The virus is injected into the embryo itself, or it can be injected onto one of the membranes surrounding the embryo—for example, the yolk sac, which contains food for the embryo, or the amniotic sac, the fluid-filled sac in which the embryo develops (see figure). The opening in the shell is then sealed with paraffin wax, and the egg is incubated at 36°C. The virus multiplies within the living cells and is later separated from the host cells by centrifugation. Cultivation of viruses in developing chick embryos has been used to produce virus for various vaccines, including smallpox, influenza, and yellow fever vaccines. This method is also used for immunological and other research studies.

Currently the most widely used method for culturing animal viruses is tissue culture. Almost any type of animal cell can now be grown and maintained in an appropriate culture medium in glass or plastic dishes.

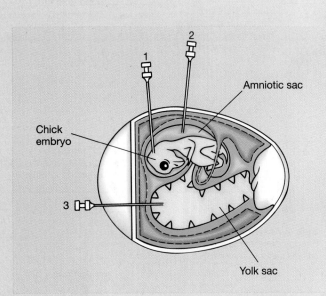

Diagrammatic section through a developing chick embryo from 10 to 12 days old, indicating how viruses can be injected into (1) the head of the embryo, (2) the amniotic sac, and (3) the yolk sac.

Viruses grown in tissue culture may induce characteristic changes in the tissue culture cells just as they do within the body. Thus, tissue culture provides an important model for studying viral infections and their effects on cells. Some vaccines are now prepared from viruses grown in tissue culture. This is advantageous to persons who are allergic to eggs and therefore to the vaccines pre-

pared from viruses cultured in chick eggs.

Some animal viruses cannot be cultured in developing chick embryos or in tissue culture. These must be propagated in living animals, usually mice, guinea pigs, rabbits, or primates. An advantage of animal inoculation is that researchers can study typical symptoms of the infection as they develop.

---

cultured within living bacteria in the laboratory, most of our knowledge of viruses has come from studying phages. They serve as excellent models for the viruses that infect animal cells (see Focus on Culturing Viruses).

Virulent, or **lytic,** bacteriophages **lyse** (destroy) the host cell. **Temperate,** or **lysogenic,** viruses do not kill their host cell during the lysogenic cycle. However, temperate viruses may revert to a lytic cycle and then destroy their host. Some temperate viruses integrate their nucleic acid into the DNA of the host cell so that

when the host cell DNA replicates, the viral DNA is also replicated.

In Lytic Infections, Many New Phages Are Produced and the Host Bacterial Cell Undergoes Lysis

When a lytic virus infects a susceptible host cell, it uses the host cell's metabolic machinery to replicate viral nucleic acid and produce viral proteins. Several steps in

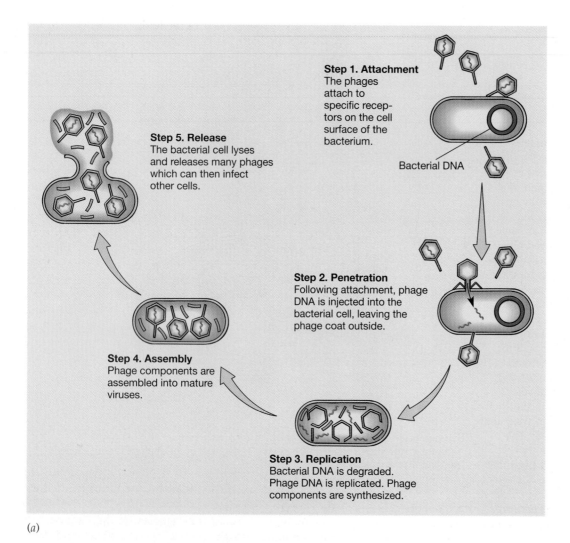

Step 1. Attachment
The phages attach to specific receptors on the cell surface of the bacterium.

Bacterial DNA

Step 2. Penetration
Following attachment, phage DNA is injected into the bacterial cell, leaving the phage coat outside.

Step 3. Replication
Bacterial DNA is degraded. Phage DNA is replicated. Phage components are synthesized.

Step 4. Assembly
Phage components are assembled into mature viruses.

Step 5. Release
The bacterial cell lyses and releases many phages which can then infect other cells.

(a)

(b)

0.25 μm

Figure 23–2   The sequence of events in a lytic infection. (a) The five steps in a lytic infection are attachment, penetration, replication, assembly, and release. (b) Phage infecting *Escherichia coli,* a bacterium. Many phages are attached to the cell wall. (The break in the bacterial cell wall is an artifact produced during preparation for viewing under the electron microscope.)   (b, Lee D. Simon/Science Source/Photo Researchers, Inc.)

the process of viral infection are common to almost all bacteriophages (Figure 23–2):

1. **Attachment.** The phage attaches to specific receptor sites on the surface of the host cell wall. Because each bacterial species (and sometimes each strain within a species) has different receptor sites, a phage attaches only to a specific species (or strain).
2. **Penetration.** After the phage has attached to the cell surface, its tail contracts and pushes a hole through the cell wall, and nucleic acid is injected through the plasma membrane into the cytoplasm of the host cell. The phage capsid remains on the outside. (Most viruses that infect animal cells, in contrast, enter the host cell intact.)
3. **Replication.** Once inside, the phage DNA takes over the metabolic machinery of the cell. The bacterial DNA may be degraded so that the viral genes are free to dictate future biochemical operations. Using the host cell's ribosomes, its energy, and many of its enzymes, the phage replicates its own macromolecules. Phage genes contain all the information necessary to produce new bacteriophages.

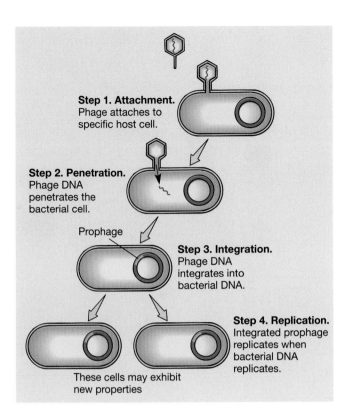

Step 1. Attachment. Phage attaches to specific host cell.

Step 2. Penetration. Phage DNA penetrates the bacterial cell.

Prophage

Step 3. Integration. Phage DNA integrates into bacterial DNA.

Step 4. Replication. Integrated prophage replicates when bacterial DNA replicates.

These cells may exhibit new properties

Figure 23–3 The sequence of events in a lysogenic infection is attachment, penetration, integration into bacterial DNA, and replication when the bacterial DNA replicates.

4. **Assembly.** The newly synthesized viral components are assembled into new bacteriophages.
5. **Release.** In a lytic infection, the phage produces an enzyme that degrades the cell wall of the host cell. The host cell then lyses, releasing about 100 bacteriophages. These new viruses infect other cells, and the process begins anew. An entire lytic cycle, from attachment to release, takes approximately 30 minutes.

In Lysogenic Infections, Phage DNA Is Integrated into the Host Bacterial Chromosome

Unlike virulent viruses that lyse their host cells, temperate viruses do not always destroy their hosts. They can integrate their DNA into the host DNA. When the bacterial DNA replicates, the viral DNA (called a **prophage** when integrated) also replicates (Figure 23–3). The viral genes that code for viral structural proteins may be repressed indefinitely, and the host bacterial cell may behave almost normally. Host cells carrying prophages are said to be lysogenic.

In some cases the bacterial cells containing temperate viruses may exhibit new properties. This is called **lysogenic conversion.** For example, the bacterium that

causes diphtheria produces the toxin responsible for the disease symptoms only when infected by a specific phage. In fact, the toxin is actually encoded by the phage. In the same way, a phage is responsible for producing the toxin associated with scarlet fever; only when scarlet fever bacteria are lysogenic can they cause scarlet fever. *Clostridium botulinum* bacteria synthesize the toxin that causes botulism only when they are lysogenic for certain phages.

Certain external conditions can cause the prophage to enter a lytic phase, releasing new phages and killing the host cell in the process. When a lysogenic cell does lyse, the phages released may contain some bacterial DNA in place of their own genetic material. When such a phage infects a new bacterium, it can introduce this bacterial DNA into the genome of the new bacterial host. Known as **transduction,** this process permits genetic recombination in the new host cell (Figure 23–4). This ability of some viruses to transfer DNA from one cell to another is taken advantage of in recombinant DNA studies in which viruses are used to transport genetic material inside a cell.

SOME VIRUSES INFECT ANIMALS

Hundreds of different viruses infect humans and other animals. Most viruses cannot survive very long outside a living host cell, and so their survival depends on their being transmitted from animal to animal.

The type of receptor molecules on the surface of a virus determines what type of cell the virus can infect. Some viruses, such as the adenoviruses, have fibers that project from the capsid and are thought to help the virus adhere to receptor sites on the host cell. Other viruses, such as those that cause herpes, influenza, and rabies, are surrounded by a lipoprotein envelope with projecting glycoprotein spikes that serve as receptors.

Receptor sites vary with each species and sometimes with each type of tissue. Thus, some viruses can infect only humans, because their receptors combine only with receptor sites found on human cell surfaces. The measles virus and pox viruses can infect many types of tissues because their receptors combine with receptor sites on a variety of cells. However, poliovirus receptors can attach only to cells of certain tissues—spinal cord, throat, and intestinal cells.

Viruses have several ways to penetrate animal cells. When an animal virus that lacks an envelope binds to a receptor site on the surface of a host cell, the cell may engulf it and transport it into the cytoplasm by a process called **adsorptive endocytosis.** In adsorptive endocytosis, the animal cell plasma membrane invaginates to form a membrane-bounded vesicle that contains the virus. Enveloped viruses penetrate animal cells some-

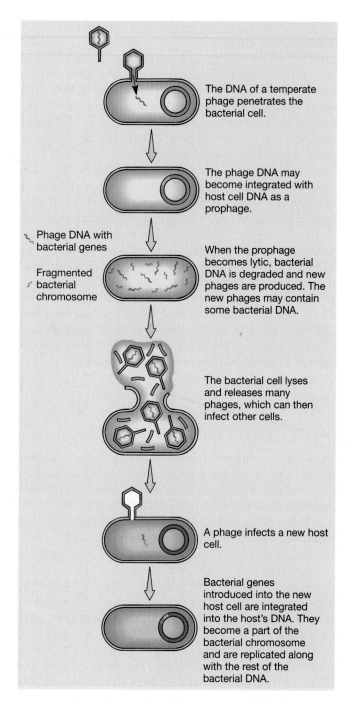

The DNA of a temperate phage penetrates the bacterial cell.

The phage DNA may become integrated with host cell DNA as a prophage.

Phage DNA with bacterial genes

Fragmented bacterial chromosome

When the prophage becomes lytic, bacterial DNA is degraded and new phages are produced. The new phages may contain some bacterial DNA.

The bacterial cell lyses and releases many phages, which can then infect other cells.

A phage infects a new host cell.

Bacterial genes introduced into the new host cell are integrated into the host's DNA. They become a part of the bacterial chromosome and are replicated along with the rest of the bacterial DNA.

Figure 23–4   Transduction. A phage can transfer bacterial DNA from one bacterium to another.

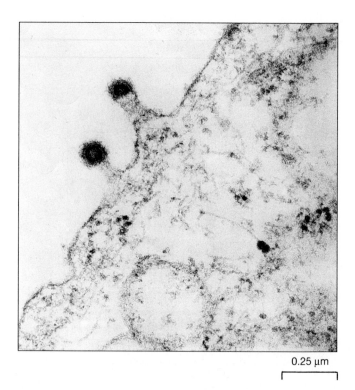

0.25 μm

Figure 23–5   Virus particles budding from the surface of a human cell. Each new virus has incorporated some of the plasma membrane of the host cell. However, the host is able to repair its membrane after the budding is complete.   (N. Salomonsky, University of Virginia/Biological Photo Service)

In DNA viruses, viral DNA and protein synthesis is similar to the processes by which the host cell would normally carry out its own DNA and protein synthesis. In most RNA viruses, transcription takes place with the help of an RNA polymerase. However, **retroviruses** are RNA viruses that use a DNA polymerase called **reverse transcriptase** to transcribe the RNA genome into a DNA intermediate (see Chapter 12, Focus on Reverse Transcription, Jumping Genes, and Pseudogenes). This DNA is then used to synthesize copies of the viral RNA. The virus (HIV) that causes AIDS as well as certain cancer-causing viruses are retroviruses.

After the viral genes are transcribed, the viral structural proteins are synthesized. The capsid is produced and new virus particles are assembled. Viruses that do not have an outer envelope exit by cell lysis; the plasma membrane ruptures, releasing the viral particles. Enveloped viruses receive their lipoprotein envelopes as they pass through the plasma membrane (or, in some types, the nuclear envelope). Because they are released slowly (by a process called budding), these viruses do not usually destroy the host cell when they exit (Figure 23–5).

Viral proteins synthesized within the host cell damage the cell in a variety of ways. Such proteins may alter the permeability of the plasma membrane or may inhibit synthesis of host nucleic acids or proteins. Viruses

what differently. One way is by fusion of the viral envelope with the animal cell's plasma membrane; this allows the viral capsid and nucleic acid to enter the animal cell.

Like other viruses, those that infect animal cells replicate and produce new virus particles. Viral nucleic acid is replicated and viral proteins are synthesized while host DNA, RNA, and protein synthesis are inhibited.

DNA of the host cells, which are then transformed into cancer cells.

Some viruses that cause cancer have one or a few genes, called **oncogenes,** that transform host cells into cancer cells (see Chapter 16). Infection by a retrovirus appears to promote cancer by causing cellular changes that maintain oncogenes in an active state of transcription. Oncogenes code for many different kinds of proteins, including cellular growth factors, membrane receptors, and protein kinases.

Oncogenes or related genes have also been found in normal (uninfected) cells of most species, and studies indicate that activation of cellular oncogenes transforms normal cells into cancer cells. Some viruses that lack oncogenes may cause cancer by activating existing cellular oncogenes.

A class of human retroviruses (the HTLV viruses) has been linked to certain leukemias. This RNA virus enters a T lymphocyte (a type of white blood cell) and triggers a chain of events which leads to leukemia.

No tumor-causing DNA virus has yet been isolated from human tumors, but evidence links several DNA viruses with human cancers. The Epstein-Barr virus apparently infects almost all human beings, causing no symptoms in most. However, in some the Epstein-Barr virus causes infectious mononucleosis (popularly referred to as mono), and this virus has also been linked to Burkitt's lymphoma, a malignant tumor affecting the lymphatic system and most common in young children in Central Africa. The reason for this dramatic difference in virulence—causing no symptoms in most people, infectious mononucleosis in some, and cancer in others—is not known. However, because Burkitt's lymphoma is more common in areas where malaria is prevalent, the possibility exists that an interaction occurs between the agents that cause the two illnesses. The Epstein-Barr virus has also been implicated in the development of another type of cancer, nasopharyngeal carcinoma, among persons of Chinese ancestry.

Both papilloma (wart-causing) virus and herpesvirus have been linked with cervical cancer, and hepatitis B virus has been associated with liver cancer. Viruses may also play a role in Hodgkin's disease (a cancer of the lymphatic system), breast cancer, and Kaposi's sarcoma (a cancer common among AIDS victims).

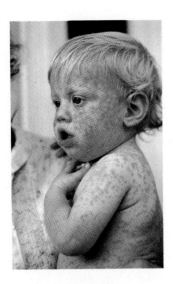

Figure 23–6 Rubella (German measles) is caused by an RNA virus spread by close contact. When contracted during pregnancy, it can cause birth defects. Immunity appears to be lifelong following infection. Vaccination has greatly decreased the incidence of this disease.   (Lowell Georgia/Science Source/Photo Researchers, Inc.)

sometimes damage or kill their host cells by their sheer numbers. A poliovirus may produce 100,000 new viruses within a single host cell!

Viruses Cause Diseases in Animals

Animal viruses contain either DNA or RNA. Animal diseases caused by viruses include hog cholera, foot-and-mouth disease, canine distemper, swine influenza, feline leukemia, and Rous sarcoma in fowl. Humans are susceptible to a variety of viral diseases, including chickenpox, herpes simplex (one type of which is genital herpes), mumps, rubella (German measles; Figure 23–6), rubeola (measles), rabies, warts, infectious mononucleosis, influenza, hepatitis, and AIDS (Table 23–1). Indeed, it has been estimated that each of us suffers from two to six viral infections each year. Fortunately, most of these are relatively benign forms such as the common cold.

The development of effective vaccines has virtually eradicated the smallpox virus, which exists only in a few research laboratories. However, many viral diseases, such as hepatitis B and AIDS, remain serious causes of disease and death.

Viruses Are Linked to Certain Types of Cancer

Both RNA viruses and DNA viruses are known to cause certain types of cancer in animals. The nucleic acid of cancer-causing viruses becomes integrated into the

Prions, Which Appear to Consist Only of Protein Molecules, Are Linked to Certain Animal Diseases

Certain degenerative brain diseases in sheep, cattle, and humans are apparently caused by a virus-like, disease-causing structure called a **prion.** The prion, a protein-like infectious particle, appears to consist only of a

Table 23–1   ANIMAL VIRUSES

Group	Diseases Caused	Characteristics
DNA Viruses		
Poxviruses	Smallpox, cowpox, and economically important diseases of domestic fowl	Large, complex, oval-shaped viruses that replicate in the cytoplasm of the host cell
Herpesviruses	Herpes simplex type 1 (cold sores); herpes simplex type 2 (genital herpes, a sexually transmitted disease); varicella-zoster (chickenpox and shingles). The Epstein-Barr virus causes infectious mononucleosis and Burkitt's lymphoma.	Medium to large, enveloped viruses; frequently cause latent infections; some cause tumors
Adenoviruses	About 40 types known to infect human respiratory and intestinal tracts; common cause of sore throat, tonsillitis, and conjunctivitis; other varieties infect other animals.	Medium-sized viruses
Papovaviruses	Human warts and some degenerative brain diseases; cancer in animals other than humans	Small viruses
Parvoviruses	Infections in dogs, swine, arthropods, rodents	Very small viruses; some contain single-stranded DNA; some require a helper virus in order to multiply
RNA Viruses		
Picornaviruses	About 70 types infect humans including polioviruses; enteroviruses infect intestine; rhinoviruses infect respiratory tract and are main cause of human colds; coxsackievirus and echovirus cause aseptic meningitis.	Diverse group of small viruses
Togaviruses	Rubella, yellow fever, equine encephalitis	Large, diverse group of medium-sized, enveloped viruses; many transmitted by arthropods
Myxoviruses	Influenza in humans and other animals	Medium-sized viruses that often exhibit projecting spikes
Paramyxoviruses	Rubeola, mumps, distemper in dogs	Resemble myxoviruses but somewhat larger
Reoviruses	Vomiting and diarrhea in children	Contain double-stranded RNA
Retroviruses	AIDS, some types of cancer	RNA viruses that contain reverse transcriptase for transcribing the RNA genome into DNA

glycoprotein. The glycoprotein contains at least one polypeptide about 250 amino acids long, and no nucleic acid component may be present. Because nucleic acids are the molecules replicated during cell division and reproduction, exactly how prions replicate is of great biological interest.

SOME VIRUSES INFECT PLANTS

In 1892, a Russian botanist found that tobacco mosaic disease—so called because the infected tobacco leaves have a spotted, mosaic appearance—could be transmitted to healthy plants by daubing their leaves with the sap of diseased plants (Figure 23–7). The sap was infective even after it had been passed through filters fine enough to remove all bacteria. This was the first evidence of viral disease in plants.

Tobacco mosaic virus consists of only an RNA core surrounded by a protein capsid; it is elongate and lacks an outer envelope. After infecting a host cell, the viral RNA attaches to the host's ribosomes and is translated as though it were mRNA. Many types of plant viruses contain RNA that acts like mRNA, including those that cause mosaic diseases such as alfalfa mosaic disease and those that cause stunt diseases such as tomato bushy stunt.

Figure 23–7 Tobacco plant infected with tobacco mosaic virus. The virus produces a yellow and green mottling, or mosaic pattern, on a variety of plants. The disease tends to reduce crop yields rather than killing the plants outright. (Norm Thomas/Photo Researchers, Inc.)

Viral diseases are spread among plants by insects. They are also inherited by way of infected seeds or by asexual propagation. Once a plant is infected, the virus can spread through the plant body by passing through the plasmodesmata, cytoplasmic connections that penetrate the cell walls between adjacent cells.

Plant viruses cause serious agricultural losses. Because cures are not known for viral diseases of plants, it is common to burn plants that have been infected. Some agricultural scientists are focusing their efforts on prevention of viral disease by developing virus-resistant strains of important crop plants.

Viroids Are Infectious Molecules Consisting Only of RNA

Plants may also be infected by virus-like, disease-causing structures called **viroids.** Each viroid consists of a very short strand of RNA (only 250 to 400 nucleotides). No proteins are associated with viroids, and they have no protective coat. Evidence suggests that the viroid genome does not code for any proteins. Host enzymes are used to replicate the viroid's RNA. Viroids are generally found within the host cell nucleus, but how they cause disease is not clear at this time. All viroids that have been identified infect plants, and viroids have been linked to several diseases of plants.

THE ORIGIN OF VIRUSES IS UNCERTAIN

What is the evolutionary origin of the viruses? One hypothesis is that viruses, because of their simplicity, represent a primitive, noncellular form of life. Another

hypothesis is that viruses evolved from cellular ancestors, becoming highly specialized as obligate parasites. During the course of their evolution, they lost all their cellular components—indeed, everything but their genetic material and a few components needed for replication and infection.

The hypothesis currently thought most likely is that viruses are bits of nucleic acid that "escaped" from cellular organisms. According to this view, some viruses may trace their origin to animal cells, others to plant cells, and still others to bacterial cells. Their multiple origins might explain why most viruses are species-specific; perhaps viruses infect only species that are the same as or closely related to the organisms from which they originated. This hypothesis is supported by the genetic similarity between a virus and its host cell—a closer similarity than exists between one virus and another.

BACTERIA ARE PLACED IN THE KINGDOM PROKARYOTAE

All prokaryotes—the bacteria—are assigned to their own kingdom, the Prokaryotae.[1] Prokaryotic cells contain ribosomes but lack membrane-bounded organelles typical of eukaryotic cells. Thus they have no nuclei, no mitochondria, no chloroplasts, no endoplasmic reticulum, no Golgi complex, and no lysosomes (Figure 23–8). The genetic material of a prokaryote is contained in a single circular DNA molecule that lies in the cytoplasm, not surrounded by a nuclear envelope. Most prokaryotic cells have a cell wall surrounding the plasma membrane, but its structure and composition differ from those of eukaryotic cell walls. Some prokaryotes have flagella, but their structure is quite different from that of eukaryotic flagella (see Chapter 24).

Bacterial cells are tiny. Their cell volume is only about one thousandth that of small eukaryotic cells, and their length only about one tenth. Most prokaryotes are unicellular organisms, but some form colonies or filaments containing specialized cells. The plasma membrane, the active barrier between the cell and the external environment, governs the passage of molecules into and out of the cell.

The cell wall surrounding the plasma membrane provides a rigid framework that supports the cell, maintains its shape, and keeps it from bursting because of osmotic pressure. (Most bacteria seem to be adapted

---

[1]The kingdom Prokaryotae is the same as the kingdom Monera in previous editions of this text. The name change was done to conform with the latest edition of *Bergey's Manual of Systematic Bacteriology*, which has been the definitive work on prokaryotes since 1923.

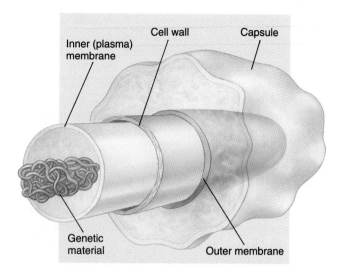

Inner (plasma) membrane

Cell wall

Capsule

Genetic material

Outer membrane

Figure 23–8 Much simpler in their structure than eukaryotes, prokaryotes are distinguished mainly by the things that they lack. The much-folded bacterial chromosome, for instance, floats free in the cytoplasm without a surrounding nuclear envelope. There are no mitochondria or chloroplasts. Most of the functions performed by elaborate systems of internal membranes in eukaryotes are carried out by the plasma membrane of bacteria. This may be surrounded, however, by several layers of material lacking in eukaryotes. The cell wall maintains turgidity and cellular shape, additional membranes may help to confine protons used in chemiosmosis, and a capsule serves for defense.

to hypotonic surroundings.) Normally, bacteria cannot survive without their cell walls. When wall-less forms are produced experimentally, they must be maintained in isotonic solutions to keep them from bursting. However, cell walls are of little help when the bacterium is in a hypertonic environment, as found in food preserved by means of a high sugar or salt content. That is why most bacteria grow poorly in jellies, jams, salted fish, and other foods preserved in this way.

The strength of the bacterial cell wall may be attributed to the properties of **peptidoglycan,** a macromolecule found only in prokaryotes. Peptidoglycan consists of two unusual types of sugars linked with short peptides. The sugars and peptides are linked to form a single macromolecule that surrounds the entire plasma membrane.

A few species of bacteria produce a **capsule** or slime layer that surrounds the cell wall. The capsule may provide the cell with added protection against phagocytosis by other microorganisms (in free-living species) or by their host's white blood cells (in the case of pathogenic—that is, disease-causing—bacteria).

The dense cytoplasm of the bacterial cell contains ribosomes and storage granules that hold glycogen, lipid, or phosphate compounds. Although the membranous organelles of eukaryotic cells are absent, in some bacterial cells the plasma membrane is elaborately

folded inward. Such inner extensions of the plasma membrane, called **mesosomes,** may be involved in cell division. Other internal membranes include those involved with photosynthesis and nitrogen fixation in some bacteria.

Bacterial DNA is found mainly in a single long, circular molecule referred to as a chromosome. Histones and other proteins are not associated with the bacterial chromosome, as they are in eukaryotic chromosomes. When stretched out to its full length, the bacterial chromosome is about 1000 times longer than the cell itself. In addition to the bacterial chromosome, a small amount of genetic information may be present as smaller DNA loops, called **plasmids,** which replicate independently of the chromosome (see Chapter 14). Bacterial plasmids often bear genes involved in resistance to antibiotics.

Bacterial flagella are distinctive in that they consist of a single fibril. At the base of a bacterial flagellum is a complex structure that produces a rotary motion, pushing the cell much as a ship is pushed along by its propeller (Figure 23–9). In this way some bacteria can travel as much as 2000 times their own length in an hour.

Some bacteria have hundreds of hairlike appendages known as **pili.** These structures are organelles of attachment that help the bacteria adhere to certain surfaces, such as the cells they will infect. Some pili are involved in the transmission of DNA between bacteria.

When the environment of a bacterium becomes unfavorable, such as when it becomes very dry, many species become dormant. The cell loses water, shrinks slightly, and remains quiescent until water is again available. Other species form dormant resting cells called **endospores** to survive in extremely dry, hot, or frozen environments or when food is scarce (Figure 23–10). Endospores are not comparable to the reproductive spores of fungi and plants, and endospore formation is not really a kind of reproduction in bacteria; because only one endospore is formed per cell, the total number of individuals does not increase as a result of endospore production. Some endospores are so resistant that they can survive an hour or more of boiling or centuries of freezing. When environmental conditions are again suitable for growth, the endospore absorbs water, breaks out of its inner wall, and becomes an active, growing bacterial cell again.

Bacterial Diversity Is Evident in Their Varied Metabolism

A bacterial cell contains about 5000 different chemical compounds. What each of these does, how they interact, and how the bacterium synthesizes them from the nutrients it takes in are complex biochemical problems

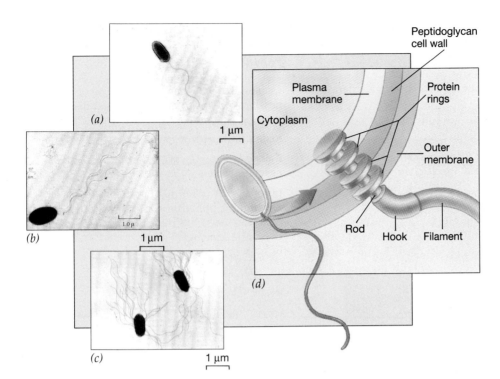

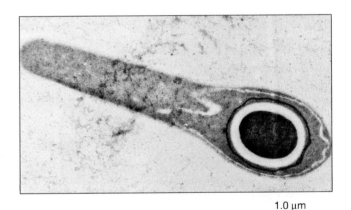

Figure 23–9 Bacterial flagella. (*a*) A single flagellum at the end of the bacterium *Pseudomonas aeruginosa.* (*b*) Some bacteria have a tuft of flagella at one end of the cell. (*c*) In the bacterium *Proteus mirabilis,* flagella project from many surfaces of the cell. (*d*) Structure of a bacterial flagellum. Diffusion of protons into the cell (after they were pumped out of the cell using the energy of ATP) powers the protein motor that spins the flagellum like a propeller. The motor consists of a series of rings that (1) anchor the flagellum to the cell wall and plasma membrane and (2) spin the hook and filament of the flagellum.   (*a, c,* V. Chambers; *b,* E. S. Boatman)

Figure 23–10 Endospore within a cell of *Clostridium tetani,* the bacterium that causes tetanus. Each bacterial cell contains only one endospore, which is a resistant, dehydrated remnant of the original cell.   (T. J. Beveridge, University of Guelph/Biological Photo Service)

that have absorbed researchers for years. Much of the knowledge that has been gained from studying these mechanisms in bacterial cells has been successfully applied to cells of humans and other organisms, for there is surprising uniformity in basic biochemical processes.

Most bacteria are **heterotrophs,** obtaining organic compounds from other organisms. The majority of heterotrophic bacteria are free-living **saprobes,** organisms that get their nourishment from dead organic matter. Other heterotrophic bacteria live in symbiosis with other organisms. These symbionts may be **commensals,** which neither help nor harm their hosts. A few are **parasites** and live at the expense of their host and cause diseases in plants and animals (Table 23–2). Others form **mutualistic** associations in which both the bacterium and partner derive benefits from the association.

Some bacteria are **autotrophic** because they are able to manufacture their own organic molecules. Autotrophic bacteria are either photosynthetic or chemosynthetic. Photosynthetic bacteria obtain energy from light, whereas chemosynthetic bacteria obtain energy from oxidizing inorganic chemicals.

Bacteria that are **chemosynthetic autotrophs,** or **chemoautotrophs,** produce organic molecules from simple inorganic ingredients using energy obtained by oxidizing inorganic compounds. The energy they use to manufacture complex organic molecules comes from the oxidation of ammonia, sulfur compounds, iron compounds, or gaseous hydrogen.

Five groups of photosynthetic bacteria exist: the cyanobacteria, the green sulfur bacteria, the purple sul-

fur bacteria, the green nonsulfur bacteria, and the purple nonsulfur bacteria. The cyanobacteria photosynthesize like algae and plants. Other bacterial photosynthesis differs in two important ways from photosynthesis carried on by algae, plants, and cyanobacteria. First, bacterial chlorophyll absorbs light most strongly in the near-infrared portion of the light spectrum rather than in the visible light range. This enables bacteria to carry on photosynthesis in red light that appears very dim or almost black to human eyes. Second, photosynthesis by bacteria other than cyanobacte-

Table 23–2 SOME BACTERIA THAT INFECT HUMANS

Bacterium	Characteristics	Importance
Chlamydia trachomatis	Gram-negative cocci; obligate parasites	Causes trachoma (the leading cause of blindness); causes a sexually transmitted disease
Clostridium botulinum	Large gram-positive bacilli; anaerobic; form spores	A soil organism that causes botulism; potent toxin affects nervous system
Clostridium tetani	Slender, gram-positive bacilli; strictly anaerobic; form spores	Causes tetanus (lockjaw); potent toxin affects nervous system
Escherichia coli	Gram-negative bacilli; facultative anaerobes	Lives as part of normal intestinal microbial community; opportunistic strains among them can cause diarrhea, urinary tract infections, and meningitis
Haemophilus influenzae	Gram-negative small rods	Causes infections of upper respiratory tract and ear; can cause meningitis
Mycobacterium leprae	Slender, irregular rods	Causes Hansen's disease (leprosy)
Mycobacterium tuberculosis	Slender, irregular rods	Causes tuberculosis of lungs and other tissues
Neisseria gonorrhoeae	Gram-negative cocci that form pairs (diplococci); adhere to cells via pili	Causes gonorrhea
Rickettsia rickettsii	Short rod-shaped; obligate intracellular parasite	Can cause Rocky Mountain spotted fever; transmitted by tick from dog or rodent
Salmonella	Gram-negative bacilli	One species causes food poisoning (diarrhea, vomiting, fever); another species can cause typhoid fever; a third species causes infections of the blood
Staphylococcus aureus	Cocci that often form clusters; gram-positive	Can live harmoniously as part of normal microbial community. Opportunistic; can cause boils. Also toxin is a major cause of food poisoning.
Streptococcus pneumoniae	Cocci that form pairs or chains; gram-positive	Causes pneumonococcal pneumonia and meningitis
Streptococcus pyogenes	Cocci that form pairs and chains; gram-positive	Causes "strep throat," ear infections, scarlet fever. Induces rheumatic fever
Treponema pallidum	Very slender, tightly coiled spirals; move via axial filaments	Causes syphilis

ria does not produce oxygen because water is not used as a hydrogen donor. Instead, the sulfur bacteria use sulfur compounds such as hydrogen sulfide (H_2S) as hydrogen donors. Photosynthetic sulfur bacteria produce free sulfur as a waste product, somewhat as cyanobacteria and plants produce oxygen.

Whether they are heterotrophs or autotrophs, most bacterial cells are **aerobic** (like animal and plant cells), requiring atmospheric oxygen for cellular respiration. Some bacteria are **facultative anaerobes,** meaning that they can use oxygen for cellular respiration if it is available but carry on metabolism anaerobically when necessary. Other bacteria are **obligate anaerobes** and can carry on energy-yielding metabolism only anaerobically. Some obligate anaerobes are actually killed by even low concentrations of oxygen.

Bacteria Reproduce by Fission

Bacteria generally reproduce asexually by **transverse binary fission,** in which one cell divides into two daughter cells. After the circular bacterial chromosome has been replicated, a transverse wall is formed by an ingrowth of both the plasma membrane and the cell wall. The replication of the chromosome and the divi-

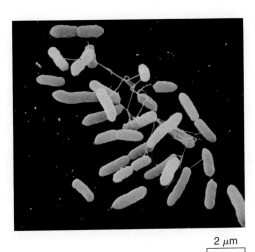

2 μm

Figure 23–11 F pilus connecting *Escherichia coli* bacteria. Plasmid DNA is transferred during conjugation. (Manfred Kage/ Peter Arnold, Inc.)

sion of the cell often get out of phase, so that a bacterial cell may have from one to several identical chromosomes.

Bacterial cell division occurs with remarkable speed; under ideal conditions some species divide every 20 minutes! At this rate, if nothing interfered, one bacterium would give rise to more than 130,000 bacteria within 6 hours. This explains why the entrance of only a few pathogenic bacteria into a human can result so quickly in the symptoms of disease. Fortunately, bacteria cannot reproduce at this rate for very long, because they are soon checked by lack of food or by the accumulation of waste products.

Although sexual reproduction involving the fusion of gametes does not occur in bacteria, genetic material is sometimes exchanged between individuals. This exchange takes place by three different mechanisms: transformation, transduction, and conjugation. In **transformation,** fragments of DNA released by a broken cell are taken in by another bacterial cell. This mechanism was used experimentally to demonstrate that genes can be transferred from one bacterium to another and that DNA is the chemical basis of heredity (see Chapter 11). In the second process of gene transfer, **transduction,** bacterial genes are carried from one bacterial cell into another within a bacteriophage (see section on lysogenic infections).

In **conjugation,** two cells of different mating types come together, and genetic material is transferred from one to another (Figure 23–11). Conjugation has been most extensively studied in the bacterium *Escherichia coli,* in which there are F⁺ strains (varieties that contain a *fertility* factor) and F⁻ strains (varieties that lack a fertility factor). F⁺ individuals contain a plasmid that

codes for the protein used to form special hollow pili called **F pili.** These pili serve as conjugation bridges that pass from the F⁺ to the F⁻ cell. The F pili are long and narrow and have a hole through which fragments of DNA pass from one bacterium to the other. Most strains of *E. coli* never develop F pili, however, and conjugation is probably best viewed as a curiosity with little significance in nature.

THERE ARE TWO FUNDAMENTALLY DIFFERENT GROUPS OF BACTERIA, THE ARCHAEBACTERIA AND THE EUBACTERIA

Under a microscope all bacteria appear fundamentally similar. Their morphological similarities, along with a scant fossil record, have made it difficult to ascertain evolutionary relationships. However, evidence from molecular biology has helped biologists conclude that ancient prokaryotes split into two lineages early in the history of life. The modern descendants of these two ancient lines of bacteria are the Archaebacteria, which include a few genera of prokaryotes able to live in extreme environments, and the Eubacteria, which comprise all other groups of prokaryotes.

THE ARCHAEBACTERIA INCLUDE HALOPHILES, METHANOGENS, AND THERMOACIDOPHILES

Biochemically, members of the **subkingdom Archaebacteria** are very different from other bacteria. One of their most distinguishing features is the absence of peptidoglycan in the cell wall. There are also other important (although quite technical) differences that set the archaebacteria apart from other bacteria—differences in their ribosomal RNA, in their lipids, and in specific enzymes.

The biochemical and metabolic differences between the archaebacteria and other bacteria suggest that these groups may have diverged from each other long ago—relatively early in the history of life. Many of the extreme environments to which the modern archaebacteria are adapted resemble conditions that were common on primitive Earth but are somewhat rare today. These include hot springs whose temperatures may exceed 100°C and deep-sea vents that spew sulfide gases.

The archaebacteria include three groups, the halophiles, the methanogens, and the thermoacidophiles. The **halophiles** live only in extremely salty environments such as salt ponds. Some of the halophiles are

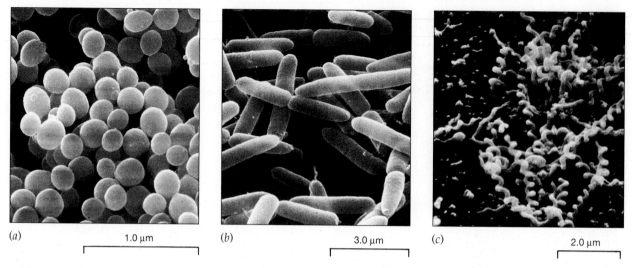

(a)   1.0 μm   (b)   3.0 μm   (c)   2.0 μm

Figure 23–12   Three characteristic bacterial shapes: (a) Cocci. (b) Bacilli. (c) Spirilla.   (a–c, Visuals Unlimited/David M. Phillips)

capable of a type of photosynthesis in which the energy of sunlight is captured by the purple pigment **bacterio-rhodopsin.** The **methanogens** are anaerobes that produce methane from carbon dioxide and hydrogen. They inhabit sewage and swamps and are common in the digestive tracts of humans and other animals. In such habitats, organic material decomposes under anaerobic conditions. The methanogens are probably the most common of the archaebacteria. The **thermoacidophiles** normally grow in hot, acidic environments. One species that is found in the hot sulfur springs of Yellowstone Park flourishes at temperatures near 60°C and pH values of 1 to 2 (the pH of concentrated sulfuric acid).

THE EUBACTERIA ARE DIVIDED INTO THREE GROUPS BASED ON THEIR CELL WALL COMPOSITION

The **subkingdom Eubacteria,** or "true bacteria," contains the classic bacteria studied by the pioneer microbiologists. Most bacteria belong to this group, and when bacteria are casually mentioned, eubacteria are usually what is meant. Early investigators quickly realized that bacteria are present almost universally, being abundant in air, in liquids such as milk, and in and on the bodies of plants and animals, both living and dead. In fact, relatively few places in the world are devoid of eubacteria, for they can be found in fresh and salt water, as far down as several meters deep in the soil, in deep gravel aquifers,[1] in the ice of glaciers, and even in oil deposits far underground.

The eubacteria comprise an extremely wide variety of organisms. Their morphologies and especially their metabolisms are quite diverse. Eubacteria have three main shapes—spherical, rod-shaped, and spiral (Figure 23–12). Spherical bacteria, known as **cocci** (singular, *coccus*), occur singly in some species, in groups of two in others (diplococci), in long chains (streptococci), or in irregular clumps that look like bunches of grapes (staphylococci). Rod-shaped bacteria, called **bacilli** (singular, *bacillus*), may occur as single rods or as long chains of rods. Spiral bacteria are known as **spirilla** (singular, *spirillum*).

Eubacteria May Be Grouped on the Basis of Their Staining Properties

Almost 100 years ago the Danish physician Christian Gram developed the Gram staining procedure. Bacteria that absorb and retain crystal violet stain during laboratory staining procedures are referred to as **gram-positive,** whereas those that do not retain the stain are **gram-negative.** The cell walls of gram-positive bacteria are very thick and consist primarily of peptidoglycan. The cell wall of a gram-negative bacterial cell consists of two layers, a thin peptidoglycan wall, and a thick outer membrane of lipoprotein and lipopolysaccharide (Figure 23–13).

The differences in composition of the cell walls of gram-positive and gram-negative bacteria are of great practical importance. For example, the antibiotic penicillin interferes with peptidoglycan synthesis, ultimately resulting in a fragile cell wall that cannot effectively protect the cell. Penicillin works most effectively against gram-positive bacteria.

Microbiologists recognize three main groups of eubacteria based on differences in cell walls. These are

---

[1] Aquifers are porous layers of underground rock in which groundwater is stored.

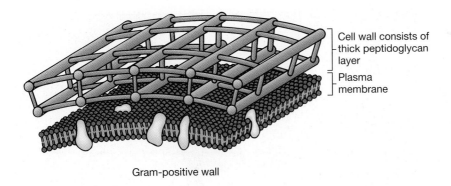

Cell wall consists of thick peptidoglycan layer

Plasma membrane

Gram-positive wall

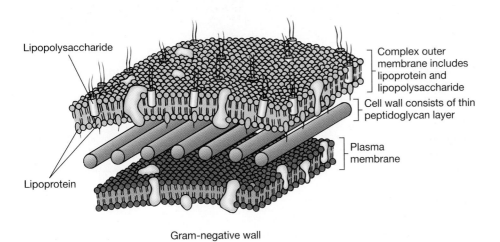

Lipopolysaccharide

Complex outer membrane includes lipoprotein and lipopolysaccharide

Cell wall consists of thin peptidoglycan layer

Plasma membrane

Lipoprotein

Gram-negative wall

Figure 23–13 A simplified, schematic representation of gram-positive and gram-negative bacterial cell walls. The gram-negative bacterium has a membrane outside the cell wall.

the wall-less bacteria, the gram-negative bacteria, and the gram-positive bacteria (Table 23–3).

Mycoplasmas Lack a Rigid Cell Wall

The **mycoplasmas** are tiny bacteria bounded by a plasma membrane but lacking a typical bacterial cell wall. Some are so small that, like viruses, they pass through bacteriological filters. In fact, mycoplasmas are smaller than some viruses. Mycoplasmas may be the simplest form of cellular life. Mycoplasmas are either aerobic or anaerobic, depending on the species. Some live in soil and some in sewage, whereas others are parasitic on plants or animals. Some species of *Mycoplasma* inhabit human mucous membranes but do not generally cause disease. One species causes a type of bacterial pneumonia in humans (Figure 23–14).

Gram-negative Bacteria Have Thin Cell Walls

The gram-negative bacteria exhibit differences in shape, structure, and metabolic processes. Among them are the **nitrogen-fixing aerobic bacteria,** which have the ability to fix atmospheric nitrogen into inorganic com-

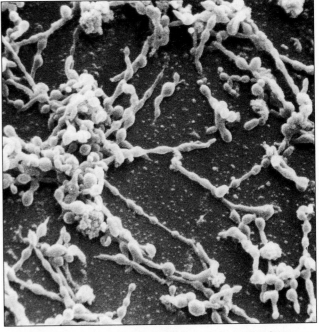

2 μm

Figure 23–14 Scanning electron micrograph of *Mycoplasma pneumoniae,* which causes a type of pneumonia in humans. Notice the irregular, almost filamentous shapes of these prokaryotes. (M. G. Gabridge, cyto Graphics, Inc./Biological Photo Service)

Table 23–3 EXAMPLES OF COMMON EUBACTERIA

Wall-less Bacteria

Mycoplasmas: extremely small cells that lack cell walls

Gram-negative Bacteria

Nitrogen-fixing bacteria: aerobic bacteria that fix nitrogen

Enterobacteria: large group of diverse bacteria, facultatively aerobic, heterotrophic

Spirochetes: spiral-shaped, flexible cell walls, move by means of axial filaments

Cyanobacteria: photosynthetic autotrophs, occur mainly as colonial masses or filaments; some fix nitrogen.

Rickettsias: obligate intracellular parasites; a few cause diseases that are transmitted to humans by arthropods.

Chlamydias: obligate intracellular parasites

Myxobacteria: unicellular bacilli, move by gliding, form upright multicellular reproductive bodies

Gram-positive Bacteria

Lactic acid bacteria: fermenting bacteria that can ferment the sugar in milk

Streptococci: fermenting bacteria

Staphylococci: aerobic bacteria

Clostridia: fermenting bacteria, anaerobic

Actinomycetes: prokaryotes that resemble fungi; most are saprobes that decompose organic material in soil.

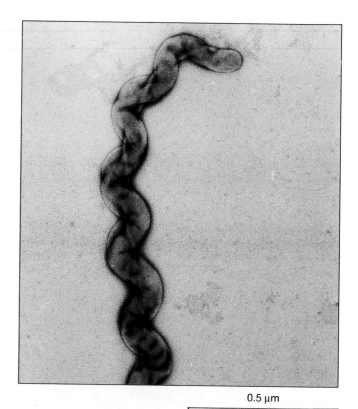

0.5 μm

Figure 23–15 *Leptospira*, a spirochete. The axial filaments are visible as a dark band extending the length of the cell. (S. C. Holt, University of Texas-San Antonio/Biological Photo Service)

pounds that can be used by plants. Other gram-negative bacteria are chemoautotrophs, which, as described earlier, obtain energy from oxidizing inorganic compounds. Many important pathogens are gram-negative eubacteria. For example, the gram-negative coccus *Neisseria gonorrhoeae* causes gonorrhea, and the gram-negative bacillus *Haemophilus influenzae* causes infections of the respiratory tract and ear as well as meningitis.

The **enterobacteria** are a group of gram-negative rods that include free-living saprobes, plant pathogens, and a variety of symbionts that inhabit humans. *Escherichia coli*, a member of this group, inhabits the intestines of humans and other animals as part of the normal microbe population. Some strains of the enterobacterium *Salmonella* cause food poisoning.

Other gram-negative bacteria include the spirochetes, cyanobacteria, rickettsias, chlamydias, and myxobacteria.

Spirochetes are motile bacteria with a corkscrew shape

Spirochetes are slender, spiral-shaped, gram-negative bacteria with flexible cell walls. They move by means of unique internal flagella called **axial filaments** (Figure 23–15). Some species are free-living and inhabit freshwater and marine habitats, whereas other species form symbiotic associations, including a few that are parasitic. The spirochete of greatest medical importance is *Treponema pallidum*, the pathogen that causes syphilis (see Chapter 48). Lyme disease, a tick-borne disease of humans and some other animals, is caused by a spirochete belonging to the genus *Borrelia*.

Cyanobacteria share a number of features with algae and plants

The **cyanobacteria** (formerly known as the blue-green algae) are gram-negative bacteria that are found in ponds, lakes, swimming pools, and moist soil, as well as on dead logs and the bark of trees. Some also occur in the oceans, and a few species inhabit hot springs. A few types are unicellular, and all are microscopic, but most

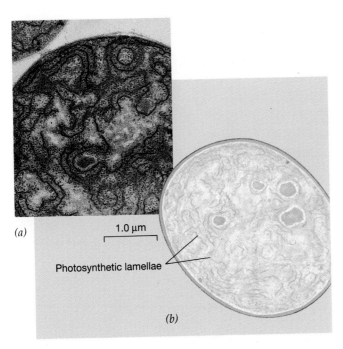

(a)

1.0 μm

Photosynthetic lamellae

(b)

Figure 23–16 Structure of cyanobacteria. (*a*) Electron micrograph and (*b*) drawing of *Anabaena*. The membranous photosynthetic lamellae in the cytoplasm are similar in function to the thylakoid membranes in chloroplasts. (*a*, Norma J. Lang/ Biological Photo Service)

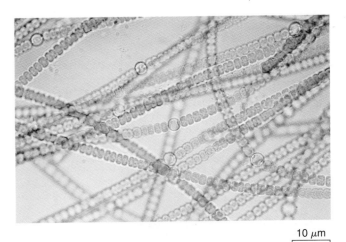

10 μm

Figure 23–17 *Anabaena*, a filamentous cyanobacterium that fixes nitrogen. Nitrogen fixation is localized in *Anabaena*; it occurs in the rounded cells, which are called heterocysts. (Dennis Drenner)

occur as large globular colonies or long filaments united by extracellular materials.

Most cyanobacteria are photosynthetic autotrophs. They contain chlorophyll *a*, which is also found in plants and algae. Cyanobacteria have several varieties of accessory pigments, including carotenoids, **phycocyanin** (a blue pigment), and **phycoerythrin** (a red pigment). These pigments are located on internal membranes called **photosynthetic lamellae** (Figure 23–16).

As producers, cyanobacteria provide oxygen and organic material for other organisms. Many species also fix nitrogen—that is, incorporate atmospheric nitrogen into inorganic compounds that can be used by plants (Figure 23–17). This process enriches the soil. Cyanobacteria form symbiotic relationships with many organisms, including protists, fungi, and some plants. Together with fungi they form some kinds of lichens (see Chapter 25).

Rickettsias and chlamydias are obligate parasites

Rickettsias are small, gram-negative rods. They are obligate intracellular parasites, which means that they must live within cells as parasites in order to survive; it is almost impossible to culture rickettsias on nonliving media. Most rickettsias parasitize arthropods such as fleas, lice, ticks, and mites without causing specific dis-

eases in them. Diseases caused by the few species known to be pathogenic to humans (and other animals) are transmitted by arthropod **vectors** (organisms that transmit parasites), through bites or contact with their excretions. Among these are typhus (transmitted by fleas and lice) and Rocky Mountain spotted fever (transmitted by ticks) (Figure 23–18).

Chlamydias differ from rickettsias in that they are spherical rather than rod-shaped. In addition, these gram-negative bacteria do not depend upon arthropod vectors for transmission. Although they do contain many enzymes and can carry on some metabolic processes, chlamydias are completely dependent on their host for ATP. In other words, they are energy parasites. Studies indicate that chlamydias infect almost every

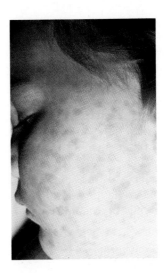

Figure 23–18 Patient suffering with Rocky Mountain spotted fever. (Centers for Disease Control, Atlanta)

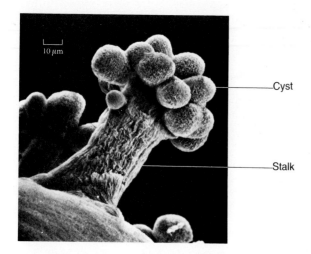

Figure 23–19 The fruiting body of *Stigmatella aurantiaca*, a myxobacterium. Protective resting cells are formed within the cyst that are very resistant to heat and drying. (From Grilicone, P. L., and Pangborn, J., *Journal of Bacteriology* 124:1558, 1975)

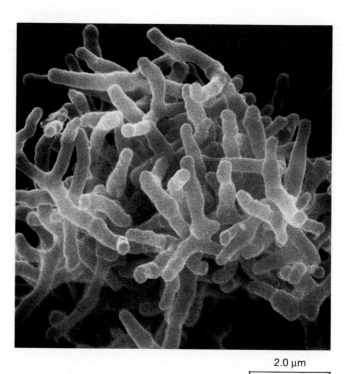

Figure 23–20 Actinomycetes are prokaryotes that resemble fungi. Note the moldlike filamentous structure. (Visuals Unlimited/ David M. Phillips)

species of bird and mammal. Perhaps 10% to 20% of the human population of the world is infected. Interestingly, individuals may be infected for many years without apparent harm. However, sometimes chlamydias do cause acute infectious diseases. For example, trachoma, the leading cause of blindness in the world, is caused by a strain of *Chlamydia*, and the most common sexually transmitted disease in the United States is a genito-urinary infection caused by chlamydia.

Myxobacteria are the most morphologically complex of the prokaryotes

The **myxobacteria** are unicellular gram-negative rods. They excrete slime and when they are cultured in a petri dish, their growth is marked by a spreading layer of slime that they glide or creep along.

Most myxobacteria are saprobes that break down organic matter in the soil, manure, or rotting wood that is their habitat. Some species break down complex substrates such as cellulose and peptidoglycan. A few myxobacteria prey on other bacteria.

Reproduction is more complex in some myxobacteria than in other bacteria. Cells swarm together to form masses, which develop into upright multicellular reproductive structures called **fruiting bodies** (Figure 23–19). During this process, bacterial cells within the fruiting body enter a resting stage equivalent to spores. When conditions are favorable, the spores break open, and the resting cells become active.

Gram-positive Bacteria Have Thick Cell Walls of Peptidoglycan

Gram-positive bacteria have a variety of shapes, including spheres, rods, and filaments. None is photosyn-

thetic. Gram-positive bacteria include the lactic acid bacteria, streptococci, staphylococci, clostridia, and actinomycetes.

The **lactic acid bacteria** are gram-positive bacteria that produce lactic acid as the main end-product of their fermentation of sugars. Lactic acid bacteria may be found in decomposing plant material, milk, yogurt, and other dairy products. They are commonly present in animals and are among the normal inhabitants of the human mouth and vagina.

Streptococci, also gram-positive bacteria, are found in the mouth as well as in the digestive tract. Among the harmful species of streptococci are those that cause "strep throat," scarlet fever, and a variety of infections.

Staphylococci are gram-positive bacteria that normally live in the nose and on the skin. They are opportunistic, which means that they can cause disease when the immunity of the host is lowered. *Staphylococcus aureus* causes boils and skin infections and may infect wounds. Certain strains (varieties) of *S. aureus* cause food poisoning, and some are thought to cause toxic shock syndrome.

The **clostridia** are a notorious group of anaerobic gram-positive eubacteria. One species causes tetanus, another causes gas gangrene, and *Clostridium botulinum* can cause botulism, a potentially fatal type of food poisoning. The clostridia are noted for the production of dangerous toxins. The poison produced by *C. botu-*

linum, for example, is one of the most potent toxins known.

Actinomycetes are gram-positive bacteria that were originally mistaken for fungi

Actinomycetes resemble fungi in that their cells remain together to form branching filaments and many produce moldlike spores called **actinospores** (Figure 23–20). However, they are not fungi because actinomycetes have peptidoglycan in their cell walls, lack nuclear envelopes, and have other prokaryotic characteristics.

The actinomycetes perform much of the decomposition of organic materials in soil. Most members of this group are saprobes, and some are anaerobic. Several species of the genus *Streptomyces* produce antibiotics such as streptomycin, erythromycin, chloramphenicol, and the tetracyclines. In fact, most known antibiotics are derived from actinomycetes.

Some actinomycetes cause diseases such as human tuberculosis and Hansen's disease (leprosy). Other actinomycetes cause serious lung disease or generalized infections in humans and animals.

SUMMARY

I. A virus is a tiny particle consisting of a core of DNA or RNA surrounded by a capsid (protein coat).
   A. Viruses are much smaller than bacteria.
   B. Viruses are not cellular and cannot metabolize on their own.

II. Bacteriophages are viruses that infect bacteria.
   A. Some phages are virulent, or lytic, and destroy the host cell. Other phages are temperate, or lysogenic, and do not kill their host; temperate viruses integrate their DNA into the host DNA.
   B. Viral infection includes attachment to the host cell, penetration, replication, assembly, and release.

III. Many different viruses infect humans and other animals.
   A. Unenveloped animal viruses enter the host cell by adsorptive endocytosis; the outer envelope of an enveloped virus often fuses to the host plasma membrane, allowing the capsid and nucleic acid to pass into the animal cell.
   B. Examples of viral diseases in humans include chickenpox, herpes simplex, infectious mononucleosis, mumps, warts, influenza, hepatitis, and AIDS.
   C. Viruses cause cancers in many types of animals, and there is evidence that they cause certain human cancers.

IV. Plant viruses cause serious agricultural losses.
   A. Viral diseases are spread among plants by insect vectors.
   B. Plants may also be infected by viroids, each of which consists of a strand of RNA without a protective protein coat.

V. Viruses are generally thought to have had multiple evolutionary origins. According to this view, viruses are bits of nucleic acid that escaped from cellular organisms.

VI. Kingdom Prokaryotae contains the bacteria, which have a prokaryotic cell structure.
   A. Prokaryotic cells lack membrane-bounded organelles such as nuclei and mitochondria.
   B. The genetic material of a prokaryote is a single circular DNA molecule.
   C. Most bacteria have cell walls composed of peptidoglycan. Some bacteria also produce a capsule surrounding the cell wall.
   D. Bacterial flagella are different from eukaryotic flagella.
   E. Bacteria are metabolically diverse.
      1. Some bacteria are heterotrophic and must obtain their food from other organisms. Heterotrophic bacteria include saprobes and parasites.
      2. Some bacteria are autotrophic and are able to make their own food. Autotrophic bacteria may be photosynthetic or chemosynthetic, depending on whether their energy source is light or the oxidation of inorganic compounds.
      3. Bacteria may be aerobes, facultative anaerobes, or obligate anaerobes.

VII. Bacteria reproduce asexually by transverse binary fission. Genetic material is sometimes exchanged between individuals by transformation, conjugation, or transduction.

VIII. Bacteria are divided into two groups, the subkingdom Archaebacteria and the subkingdom Eubacteria.

IX. The archaebacteria are anaerobic, have cell walls of unusual chemical composition, and are often adapted to harsh conditions. The three groups of archaebacteria are halophiles, methanogens, and thermoacidophiles.

X. The remaining bacteria are collectively known as the eubacteria; there are three groups based on their cell wall composition.
   A. Mycoplasmas are bacteria that lack cell walls.
   B. Gram-negative bacteria have thin cell walls. They have a thick outer membrane of lipid compounds surrounding the peptidoglycan layer in the cell wall. Gram-negative bacteria include spirochetes, cyanobacteria, rickettsias, chlamydias, and myxobacteria.
   C. Gram-positive bacteria have thick-layered cell walls of peptidoglycan. Gram-positive bacteria include the lactic acid bacteria, streptococci, staphylococci, clostridia, and actinomycetes.

POST-TEST

1. The core of a virus consists of _____ or _____, but never both.
2. The protein coat surrounding the nucleic acid core is the _____.
3. Bacteriophages are viruses that infect _____.
4. The part of a bacteriophage that actually enters the host cell is its _____ _____.
5. Virulent phages cause _____ infections in which the host cell is killed.
6. The five main steps in bacteriophage infection are _____, penetration, replication, assembly, and release.
7. Lysogenic viruses are also known as _____ viruses.
8. Lysogenic phages can transfer nucleic acid from one bacterium to another, resulting in genetic recombination; this process is known as _____.
9. Oncogenes are responsible for the ability of some viruses to transform cells into _____ cells.
10. Smaller and simpler than a virus, a _____ consists of a very short strand of RNA without any sort of protective coat.
11. All of the bacteria are assigned to kingdom _____.
12. Peptidoglycan is found in the eubacterial _____.

13. The majority of heterotrophic bacteria are free-living _____ that get their nourishment from dead organic matter.
14. Bacteria that produce organic molecules from simple organic ingredients using energy obtained from oxidizing inorganic compounds are called _____ _____.
15. In _____, two bacterial cells of different mating types transfer genetic material from one to the other.
16. The _____ are archaebacteria that produce methane from carbon dioxide and hydrogen.
17. Spherical bacteria are referred to as _____, rod-shaped bacteria as _____, and spiral bacteria as _____.
18. Mycoplasmas are eubacteria that lack a _____ _____.
19. The pathogen that causes syphilis is a type of gram-negative bacteria called a _____.
20. Ecologically, the cyanobacteria are important as _____ and as nitrogen fixers.
21. Bacteria that absorb and retain crystal violet stain (the Gram stain) are known as _____ _____ bacteria.
22. The _____ are gram-positive bacteria that were originally mistaken for fungi.

REVIEW QUESTIONS

1. What characteristics does a virus share with a living cell? What characteristics of life are lacking in a virus?
2. List the steps in the process of viral infection, and briefly describe each step.
3. Why is a virus limited in the number of species (or tissue types) that it can infect?
4. What are the differences between the archaebacteria and the eubacteria?
5. Imagine that you discover a new microorganism. After careful study you determine that it should be classified in the kingdom Prokaryotae, with the cyanobacteria. What characteristics might lead you to such a classification?
6. Contrast the cell wall of a gram-positive bacterium with that of a gram-negative bacterium.
7. Give the distinguishing characteristics of each of the following groups: spirochetes, actinomycetes, rickettsias, and mycoplasmas.

RECOMMENDED READINGS

Margulis, L., and K. V. Schwartz. *Five Kingdoms*, 2nd ed. W. H. Freeman & Co., New York, 1988. Discusses the viruses and bacteria in general terms and introduces each bacterial phylum.

Miller, J. A. Diseases for our future. *BioScience* 39:8, September 1989. A discussion of how new human viruses appear and how humans can prepare for them.

Pool, R. Pushing the envelope of life. *Science* 247, 12 January 1990. A research news article that examines the amazing habitats of the archaebacteria.

Prusiner, S. B. Molecular biology of prion disease. *Science* 252, 14 June 1991. Our current understanding of prion diseases, which cause three fatal neurodegenerative conditions in humans.

Radetsky, P. *The Invisible Invaders: The Story of the Emerging Age of Viruses*. Little, Brown, & Company, Boston, 1991. A nontechnical history of viral research from the 19th century development of the smallpox vaccine to present work with AIDS and other viral diseases.

CHAPTER 24

The Protist Kingdom

When the five-kingdom system of classification was proposed by Robert Whittaker in 1969, only unicellular organisms were placed in the protist kingdom. The boundaries of this kingdom have been expanding since that time, although there is no universal acceptance among biologists about what constitutes a "protist." We have interpreted the protist kingdom broadly to include heterotrophic protists (the protozoa, slime molds, and water molds) and autotrophic protists (the algae). Although these groups may superficially resemble animals, plants, or fungi in certain respects, they should not be considered simpler animals, plants, or fungi.

The kingdom Protista consists of a vast assemblage of eukaryotic organisms whose diversity makes them difficult to characterize (Figure 24–1).

Protistologists estimate that there are as many as 200,000 extant (living) species of protists. The major feature they possess, eukaryotic cellular structure, is shared with organisms from three other kingdoms—animals, plants, and fungi. However, eukaryotic cell structure makes the separation between the protists and the kingdom Prokaryotae quite distinct. Eukaryotic cells have true nuclei and other membrane-bounded organelles such as mitochondria and plastids. Their nuclei divide by meiosis and mitosis, although there are variations in the exact process.

The protist kingdom is not a natural assemblage of organisms, and organisms are placed within it for convenience. If natural, phylogenetic relationships were the sole means of classifying organisms into kingdoms, there would be many more than five kingdoms.

Unicellular green algae. (Ed Reschke)

After you have studied this chapter you should be able to

1. Characterize the common features of members of the kingdom Protista.
2. Discuss in general terms the diversity inherent in this kingdom, including modes of nutrition, morphologies, and methods of reproduction.
3. Briefly describe the representative protozoan phyla: amoebas, foraminiferans, actinopods, flagellates, ciliates, and sporozoa.
4. Briefly characterize the representative groups of algae:

dinoflagellates, diatoms, euglenoids, green algae, red algae, and brown algae.
5. Briefly discuss the representative fungus-like protists: plasmodial slime molds, cellular slime molds, and water molds.
6. Describe some of the evolutionary relationships among the various protists.
7. Summarize current theories on the origin of eukaryotic cells and the origin of multicellularity within the protists.
8. Discuss the evolutionary relationships of certain protists with the other kingdoms.

PROTISTS ARE THE "SIMPLE" EUKARYOTES

Size varies considerably within the protist kingdom, from single-celled protozoa to kelps, giant brown algae that can reach 60 meters in length. Although most of the protists are microscopic single-celled organisms, some have a colonial organization, some are **coenocytic** (multinucleate but not multicellular), and some are multicellular. Multicellular protists, however, have relatively simple body forms without specialized tissues.

The word *protist* comes from Greek meaning "the very first." Protists are simple eukaryotic organisms. However, the cellular organization of the single-celled protists is more complex than that of individual plant, animal, or fungal cells, which have different cells, tissues, organs, and organ systems to perform the various functions of a living organism. Single-celled protists

accomplish all of these functions within one cell. For example, water regulation in these organisms is often controlled by special organelles called **contractile vacuoles** (Figure 24–2). Because freshwater protists continually take in water by osmosis, the contractile vacuole is needed to remove excess water. Other protists solve the freshwater challenge with rigid cell walls that limit the amount of water that can be absorbed by osmosis.

Methods of obtaining nutrients in the kingdom Protista are variable. Autotrophic protists have chlorophyll and photosynthesize like plants. Some of the heterotrophic protists obtain their food by absorption, like the fungi, whereas others resemble animals and ingest food derived from the bodies of other organisms. Some protists can switch their mode of nutrition and be autotrophic at certain times and heterotrophic at others.

Many protists are free-living, and some form symbiotic associations with other organisms. These associa-

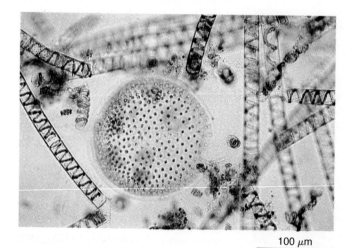

100 µm

Figure 24–1 Various protists in pond water. The protists are an extremely diverse group of organisms. Some are photosynthetic, whereas others are heterotrophic. (E. R. Degginger)

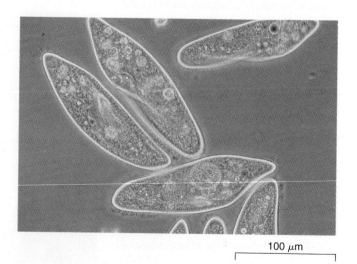

100 µm

Figure 24–2 *Paramecium.* Note the complex internal cellular structure of these single-celled protists. (Visuals Unlimited/Philip Sze)

tions range from mutualism, in which both partners benefit, to parasitism, with some protists being important pathogens (disease-causing agents) of plants or animals (see Chapter 53). Specific examples of symbiotic associations are given throughout this chapter.

Most protists are aquatic and live in oceans or freshwater ponds, lakes, and streams. They make up the **plankton**, the floating microscopic organisms that are the base of the food chain in aquatic ecosystems. Other aquatic protists attach to rocks and other surfaces in the water. Terrestrial (land-dwelling) protists are restricted to damp places like soil and leaf litter. Even the parasitic protists live in the wet environments of plant and animal body fluids.

Reproduction is quite varied in the kingdom Protista. All protists reproduce asexually, and many also reproduce sexually, with sexual reproduction involving both meiosis and **syngamy**, the union of gametes. However, most protists do not develop multicellular reproductive organs, nor do they form embryos like many higher organisms.

Protists, most of which are motile at some point in their life cycle, have various means of locomotion. Movement may be accomplished by amoeboid motion, by flexing individual cells, or by waving cilia or flagella. Many protists use a combination of two or more means of locomotion, as for example, both flagellar and amoeboid. Their cilia and flagella, unlike those of prokaryotes but like those of all eukaryotes, possess a 9 + 2 arrangement of microtubules (i.e., nine outer doublet microtubules encircling two single microtubules) (Figure 24–3).

The relationships among the organisms in the kingdom Protista are currently under study, with ultrastructure (cell structure studied with the aid of electron microscopy), biochemistry, and molecular biology adding critical information about the various groups of protists. To recognize natural relationships among the protists, some protistologists think that as many as 50 phyla are needed. Consideration of all protist groups is beyond the scope of this text, but we will discuss a number of representative groups (Table 24–1).

PROTOZOA ARE ANIMAL-LIKE PROTISTS

The name **protozoa** ("first animals," singular *protozoon*) was originally given to animal-like organisms that are not multicellular. The term *protozoa* is used today to designate an informal grouping of protists that ingest their food (like animals). The protozoa do not represent a natural grouping and their relationships are continually being evaluated as additional evidence becomes available.

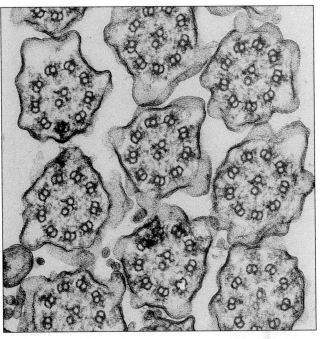

Figure 24–3 Electron micrograph of cross section through several cilia showing the 9 + 2 arrangement of the microtubules that is characteristic of eukaryotes. (W. L. Dentler, University of Kansas/Biological Photo Service)

Single-celled Amoebas Are in the Phylum Rhizopoda

Amoebas are found in soil, fresh water, and oceans. Many members of this group have no definite body shape. Their single cells change form as they move. These organisms reproduce asexually by cell division, and sexual reproduction has not been reported.

A typical example of the phylum Rhizopoda is the amoeba, which moves by pushing out temporary cytoplasmic projections called **pseudopodia** ("false feet") from the surface of the cell. More cytoplasm flows into the pseudopodia, enlarging them until all the cytoplasm has entered and the organism as a whole has moved. Pseudopodia are also used to engulf and capture food (Figure 24–4). A food vacuole encompasses and digests the food particles using digestive enzymes added by lysosomes. The digested materials are absorbed from the food vacuole, which gradually shrinks as it becomes empty.

Parasitic amoebas include *Entamoeba histolytica*, which causes serious amebic dysentery in humans. Some amoebas, like *Acanthamoeba*, are usually free-living but can produce opportunistic infections such as eye infections in contact lens users.

Table 24–1 A COMPARISON OF REPRESENTATIVE PHYLA IN THE PROTIST KINGDOM

Common Name	Phylum	Morphology	Locomotion	Photosynthetic Pigments	Special Features
Amoebas	Rhizopoda	Single cell, no definite shape	Pseudopodia	—	Some have shells (tests)
Foraminiferans	Foraminifera	Single cell	Cytoplasmic projections	—	Pore-studded shells (tests)
Actinopods	Actinopoda	Single cell	Some produce flagellated reproductive cells	—	Axopods protrude through pores in skeleton
Flagellates	Zoomastigina	Single cell	One to many flagella; some amoeboid	—	Symbiotic forms often highly specialized
Ciliates	Ciliophora	Single cell	Cilia	—	Macronuclei; micronuclei
Sporozoa	Apicomplexa	Single cell	None	—	All parasitic; develop resistant spores
Dinoflagellates	Dinoflagellata	Single cell, some colonial	Two flagella	Chlorophylls *a* and *c*; carotenoids, including fucoxanthin	Many covered with cellulose plates
Diatoms	Bacillariophyta	Single cell, some colonial	Most nonmotile; some move by gliding over secreted slime	Chlorophylls *a* and *c*; carotenoids, including fucoxanthin	Silica in shell
Euglenoids	Euglenophyta	Single cell	Two flagella (one of them very short)	Chlorophylls *a* and *b*; carotenoids	Flexible outer covering
Green algae	Chlorophyta	Single cell, colonial, siphonous, multicellular	Most flagellated at some stage in life; some nonmotile	Chlorophylls *a* and *b*; carotenoids	Reproduction highly variable
Red algae	Rhodophyta	Most multicellular, some single cell	None	Chlorophyll *a*; carotenoids; phycocyanin; phycoerythrin	Some reef builders
Brown algae	Phaeophyta	Multicellular	Two flagella on reproductive cells	Chlorophylls *a* and *c*; carotenoids, including fucoxanthin	Differentiation of body into blade, stipe, and holdfast
Plasmodial slime molds	Myxomycota	Multinucleate plasmodium	Streaming cytoplasm, flagellated or amoeboid reproductive cells	—	Reproduce by spores formed in sporangia
Cellular slime molds	Acrasiomycota	Vegetative form— single cell Reproductive form— multicellular (slug)	Pseudopods (for single cells) Cytoplasmic streaming (for multicellular)	—	Aggregation of cells signaled by cyclic AMP
Water molds	Oomycota	Coenocytic mycelium	Biflagellate zoospores	—	Cellulose and/or chitin in cell walls

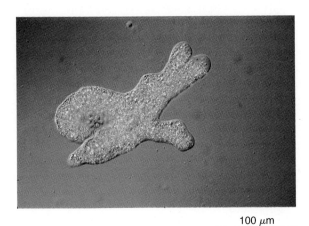

100 µm

Figure 24–4 *Chaos carolinense*, a giant amoeba ingesting a colonial green alga. Note the pseudopodia extending to surround the prey. (Michael Abbey/Photo Researchers, Inc.)

250 µm

Figure 24–5 *Rotaliella*, a foraminiferan. Foraminiferans secrete a shell, or test. Cytoplasm is extruded through the pores, forming a layer outside. (Manfred Kage/Peter Arnold, Inc.)

Species in the Phylum Foraminifera Have Tests Made of Organic Materials Strengthened with Minerals

Members of the phylum Foraminifera are almost all marine organisms that produce shells, or **tests.** The oceans contain vast numbers of foraminiferans, which secrete chalky, many-chambered shells (tests) with pores through which cytoplasmic projections can be extended. Indeed, the group gets its phylum name from this characteristic, as *Foraminifera* is derived from Latin that means "bearing openings." The cytoplasmic projections form a sticky, interconnected net that entangles its prey (Figure 24–5).

Dead foraminiferans sink to the bottom of the ocean, where their shells form a grey mud that is gradually transformed into chalk. With geological uplifting, these chalk formations can become part of the land, like the white cliffs of Dover, England.[1] Because foraminiferan tests are often found in rock layers covering oil deposits, geologists involved in oil exploration look for foraminiferan tests in rock strata.

The Phylum Actinopoda Contains Organisms with Slender Cytoplasmic Projections

Actinopods have long, filamentous cytoplasmic projections called **axopods** that protrude through pores in their skeletons (Figure 24–6). Each axopod is strengthened by a cluster of microtubules. Single-celled algae and other prey become entangled in these axopods and are engulfed outside the main body of the actinopod;

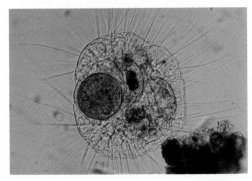

250 µm

Figure 24–6 An actinopod with ingested prey (circular brown cell). Actinopods extrude axopods through their skeletons. (Carolina Biological Supply Company)

cytoplasmic streaming carries the prey back within the shell. Many actinopods contain symbiotic algae that provide them with the products of photosynthesis.

Some actinopods secrete elaborate and beautiful skeletons made of silica. When actinopods die, their skeletons settle and become mud on the ocean floor; eventually, they are compressed into sedimentary rock.

Organisms in the Phylum Zoomastigina Move by Means of Flagella

Flagellates have spherical or elongate bodies, a single central nucleus, and one to many whiplike **flagella** that enable them to move. Flagellates move rapidly, pulling themselves forward by lashing flagella that are usually located at the anterior (front) end. Some flagellates are also amoeboid and engulf food by forming pseudopodia. Others have a definite "mouth" or **oral groove,** a "throat" or **cytopharynx,** and specialized organelles for processing food.

Flagellates in the phylum Zoomastigina are all heterotrophic and obtain their food either by ingesting liv-

[1] The white cliffs of Dover are the remains of a variety of calcareous organisms, including foraminiferans and coccolithophores (not discussed in this text).

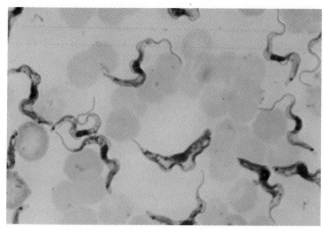

10 μm

Figure 24–7 *Trypanosoma gambiense*, which causes sleeping sickness, in a blood smear. The flagellated trypanosomes are visible as dark, wavy bodies among the paler red blood cells. (Ed Reschke)

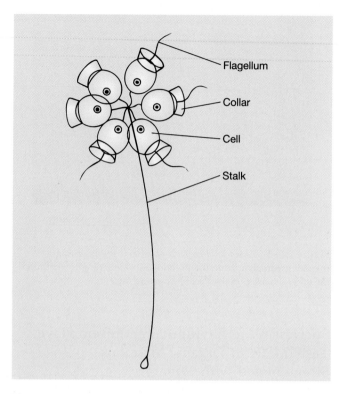

Figure 24–8 A stalked colony of *Codosiga gracilis*, a marine choanoflagellate.

ing or dead organisms or by absorbing nutrients from dead or decomposing organic matter. They may be free-living or symbionts. For example, flagellates with a large number of flagella and very specialized bodies live in the intestines of termites. These flagellates apparently possess the enzymes to digest the cellulose in wood, and both the termite and the flagellates obtain their nutrients from this source.[1] Indeed, termites would starve to death without their endosymbionts. Some parasitic flagellates cause disease (Figure 24–7). For example, a flagellate species in the genus *Trypanosoma* causes African sleeping sickness.

The choanoflagellates (collared flagellates) are one of the classes of flagellates in the phylum Zoomastigina. They are of special interest because their resemblance to certain cells in the sponges is striking (Figure 24–8). Most biologists think the choanoflagellates are related to the sponges, but probably not to other animals. These sedentary flagellates are attached to a substrate by a stalk, and their single flagellum is surrounded by a delicate collar of cytoplasm.

Members of the Phylum Ciliophora Use Cilia for Locomotion

The ciliates are single cells with a definite but somewhat changeable shape caused by a flexible outer covering. In *Paramecium* the surface of the cell is covered with

several thousand fine cilia that extend through pores in the outer covering and permit movement (Figure 24–9). The cilia beat with an oblique stroke so that the animal revolves as it swims. The coordination of the ciliary beating is so precise that the organism not only can go forward but can back up and turn around. Near their surface, many ciliates possess numerous small **trichocysts,** organelles that discharge filaments thought to aid in trapping and holding prey. Most ciliates ingest bacteria or similar food.

Ciliates differ from other protozoa in having two different nuclei, one or more small **micronuclei** that function in the sexual process, and a larger **macronucleus** that controls cell metabolism and growth.

Most ciliates are capable of a sexual phenomenon called **conjugation,** in which two individuals come together and exchange genetic material. *Paramecium* and other ciliate species may have from two to as many as eight different mating types. Although details may vary from strain to strain, during conjugation in *Paramecium*, two individuals of different mating types press their oral surfaces together. Within each individual the macronucleus disintegrates and the micronucleus undergoes meiosis, forming four haploid nuclei. Three of these degenerate, leaving one. This nucleus then divides mitotically, and one of the two identical haploid nuclei remains within the cell. The other nucleus

---

[1]The flagellate symbionts of termites in turn possess symbionts—bacteria that reside within the flagellates. These bacteria, rather than the flagellates, may be responsible for digesting cellulose.

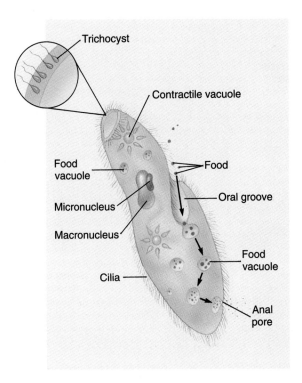

250 μm

Figure 24–9 *Paramecium* is a freshwater protozoon covered with cilia. Food particles, particularly bacteria, are swept into its ciliated oral groove and incorporated into food vacuoles by phagocytosis. Lysosomes fuse with the food vacuoles and the food is digested and absorbed. Undigested wastes are then eliminated through the anal pore by exocytosis. *Paramecium* absorbs water by osmosis from its freshwater surroundings, but it does not swell up because contractile vacuoles fill up with excess water and then contract to void the contents.

Figure 24–10 *Stentor*. Note the numerous cilia that direct food particles into its "mouth," or "gullet." (Eric Gravé/Science Source/Photo Researchers, Inc.)

crosses through the oral region into the other organism and fuses with the haploid nucleus already there. Thus each conjugation yields two cross "fertilizations." This leads to two "new" cells, which are genetically identical but different from the preconjugant cells. Actual cell division need not follow immediately; it is a complex process involving more than simply splitting in half because of the presence of complex organelles that must be replicated. In addition, a new macronucleus must be formed (from a micronucleus) after the micronucleus has divided.

Not all ciliates are motile. Some forms are stalked and others, such as *Stentor*, while capable of some swimming, are more likely to remain attached to the substrate at one spot (Figure 24–10). Their cilia set up currents in the surrounding water to bring them food.

Phylum Apicomplexa Contains Spore-forming Parasites of Animals

The **sporozoa** (singular, *sporozoon*) in the phylum Apicomplexa are a large group of parasitic protozoa, some

of which cause serious diseases such as malaria in humans. Sporozoa have neither organelles for locomotion nor contractile vacuoles. They do move, however, by flexing. At some stage in their life many develop a resistant **spore,** which is the infective agent transmitted to the next host. They often spend part of their life in one host species and part in a different host species.

Malaria, which is caused by a sporozoon, is the world's most common serious infectious disease. From 200 to 300 million people become infected with malaria each year, and 2 to 3 million of them die. *Plasmodium,* the sporozoon that causes malaria, enters human blood through the bite of an infected female *Anopheles* mosquito (Figure 24–11). *Plasmodium* first enters liver cells and then red blood cells, where it multiplies safe from the host's immune system. When each infected cell bursts, many new parasites are released. The released parasites infect new red blood cells and the process is repeated. The simultaneous bursting of millions of red cells causes the symptoms of malaria—a chill followed by fever (as toxic substances are released and affect other organs of the body).

If a mosquito that is not parasitized by *Plasmodium* bites an infected human, it sucks up some malarial parasites along with human blood. A complicated process of sexual reproduction then occurs within the mosquito's stomach, and new malarial parasites develop, some of which migrate into the mosquito's salivary glands to

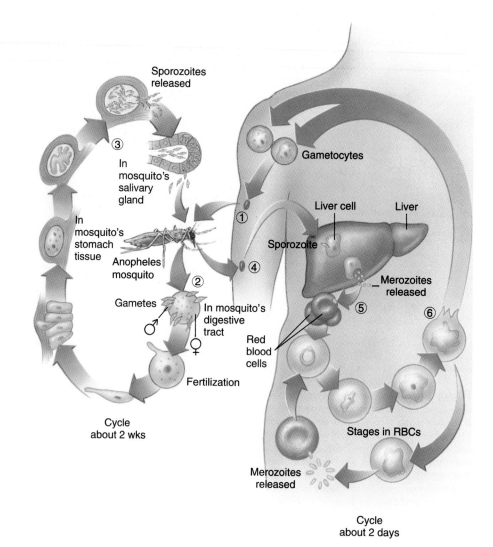

Figure 24–11 *Plasmodium* causes malaria in humans and other mammals. (1) A female *Anopheles* mosquito bites an infected person and obtains gametocytes. (2) In the mosquito's digestive canal the gametocytes develop into gametes, and fertilization occurs. (3) The zygote becomes embedded in the mosquito's stomach lining and produces sporozoites, which are released and migrate to the salivary gland. (4) The mosquito bites an uninfected human and transmits sporozoites to the human's blood. (5) The sporozoites enter the liver cells and divide to produce merozoites that infect red blood cells. (6) In the blood cells merozoites divide to form more merozoites, which infect more red blood cells. Alternatively, the merozoites form gametocytes. The gametocytes can be transmitted to the next mosquito that bites that human, and the process is repeated.

infect the next person bitten. Sexual reproduction of *Plasmodium* does not occur within humans. For this reason, elimination of the mosquito hosts (probably not possible) would eradicate the disease.

ALGAE ARE PLANT-LIKE PROTISTS

The algae represent a diverse group of organisms that are mostly photosynthetic. They range in size from single-celled, microscopic forms to large, multicellular seaweeds. Although photosynthetic, algae are not plants. Unlike plants, the algae lack a cuticle, which is a waxy covering over plants that reduces water loss; algae are therefore restricted to damp or wet environments when actively growing. Also, most algae do not have multicellular **gametangia** (reproductive organs in which gametes are produced); algal gametangia are formed from single cells, whereas plant gametangia are multicellular.

In addition to chlorophyll *a* and yellow and orange **carotenoids,** pigments that are found in all algae, algae possess a variety of other pigments. Classification into phyla, or divisions, is largely by pigment composition and type of storage products. Other characteristics used to classify algae include their cell wall composition, the number and placement of flagella, and their chloroplast morphology.

Most Species in the Phylum Dinoflagellata Are Marine Planktonic Forms

One of the most unusual groups of protists is the dinoflagellates. Most dinoflagellates are unicellular, although a few colonial forms exist. Their cells are often covered with shells of interlocking cellulose plates, impregnated with silicates (Figure 24–12). Each dinoflagellate has two flagella: one flagellum is wrapped around a transverse groove in the center of the cell like a belt; the other flagellum is located in a longitudinal

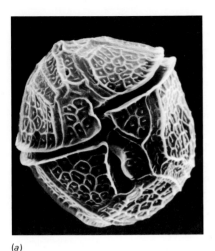 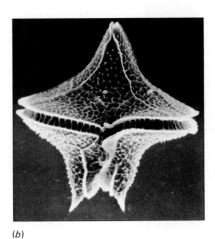

(a)   (b)

Figure 24–12 Scanning electron micrographs of some dinoflagellates. Note the plates that encase the single-celled body. The two flagella are located in grooves. (a) *Gonyaulax*. (b) *Protoperidinium*. (John D. Dodge)

groove (perpendicular to the transverse groove) and projects beyond the cell. The undulation of these flagella propels the dinoflagellate through the water like a spinning top. Indeed, the dinoflagellates' name is derived from the Greek *dinos*, meaning "whirling."

Most dinoflagellates are photosynthetic and possess the photosynthetic pigments chlorophyll *a*, chlorophyll *c*, and carotenoids. However, a number of dinoflagellates are colorless; some of these ingest other microorganisms for food. The storage products of dinoflagellates are usually oils or polysaccharides.

Many dinoflagellates are endosymbionts that reside in marine invertebrates such as jellyfish, corals, and mollusks. These dinoflagellates lack cellulose plates and flagella and are called **zooxanthellae.** Zooxanthellae photosynthesize and provide food for their invertebrate partner. For example, the contribution of zooxanthellae to the productivity of coral reefs is substantial. Some dinoflagellates that reside in other organisms lack pigmentation and do not photosynthesize; these heterotrophs are parasitic on their hosts.

Reproduction in the dinoflagellates is primarily asexual, by longitudinal cell division, although a few genera have been reported to reproduce sexually. The nucleus of dinoflagellates is unusual because the chromosomes are permanently condensed and always evident. Meiosis and mitosis are unique because the nuclear envelope remains intact throughout cell division, and the spindle is located *outside* the nucleus. (The chromosomes do not make direct contact with the spindle microtubules; instead, the chromosomes appear to be attached to the nuclear envelope and the spindle separates new nuclei from each other.) Based on the uniqueness of their chromosome morphology and mitosis, the dinoflagellates are thought to have no close extant relatives.

In terms of ecological contributions, the dinoflagellates are one of the most important groups of producers

Figure 24–13 Red tide in Mexico. The cloudiness in the water is produced by countless billions of dinoflagellates. (Kevin Schafer/Peter Arnold, Inc.)

in marine ecosystems. A few dinoflagellates are known to have occasional population explosions, or **blooms.** These blooms frequently color the water orange, red, or brown and are known as **red tides** (Figure 24–13). It is not known what environmental conditions initiate dinoflagellate blooms, but they are more common in the warm waters of late summer. Some of the dinoflagellate species that form red tides produce a toxin that attacks the nervous system of fish, leading to massive fish kills. A human condition called paralytic shellfish poisoning is caused by eating oysters, mussels, or clams that have fed on certain dinoflagellates; paralytic shellfish poisoning causes respiratory failure.

100 μm

Figure 24–14 Diatoms have strikingly beautiful patterns on their symmetrical shells. (Alfred Pasieka/Peter Arnold, Inc.)

Members of the Phylum Bacillariophyta Have Shells Composed of Two Parts

The diatoms are classified in the phylum Bacillariophyta. Most diatoms are unicellular, although a few colonial forms exist. Diatom shells are composed of two halves that overlap where they fit together, much like a petri dish. Silica is impregnated in the shell, and this glasslike material is laid down in striking, intricate patterns that are useful in classification (Figure 24–14). There are two basic groups of diatoms, those with radial symmetry (wheel-shaped) and those with bilateral symmetry (boat-shaped or needle-shaped). Although most diatoms are part of the floating plankton, some live on rocks and other surfaces, where they move by gliding. This gliding movement is facilitated by the secretion of a slimy material from a small groove along the shell.

Most diatoms are photosynthetic and contain the photosynthetic pigments chlorophyll *a*, chlorophyll *c*, and carotenoids; their pigment composition gives them a yellow or brown color. Food reserves are stored as oils or carbohydrates.

Diatoms most often reproduce asexually by cell division. When a diatom divides, the two halves of its shell separate and each becomes the larger half for a new diatom cell. Therefore, some diatom cells get progressively smaller with each succeeding generation. When diatoms are a fraction of their original size, sexual reproduction is triggered, with the production of shell-less gametes. Sexual reproduction restores the dia-

tom to its original size, because the resulting zygote grows substantially before producing a new shell.

Diatoms are common in both fresh water and oceans, but they are especially abundant in cooler marine habitats. They are major producers in aquatic ecosystems because of their extremely large numbers. When diatoms die, their shells trickle down to the ocean floor and accumulate in layers of what eventually becomes sedimentary rock. After millions of years, some of these deposits have been exposed on land by geological upheaval. These deposits, called **diatomaceous earth,** are mined and used as a filtering, insulating, and soundproofing material.

Most of the Phylum Euglenophyta Are Freshwater Unicellular Flagellates

Most euglenoids are unicellular flagellates (Figure 24–15). They generally possess two flagella, one that is long and whip-like and one that is so short it does not protrude outside the cell. Euglenoids change shape continually as they move through the water because their outer covering is flexible rather than rigid. Euglenoids reproduce asexually by longitudinal cell division; none has ever been observed to reproduce sexually.

The euglenoids are included in our discussion of algal protists because most of them contain chloroplasts and photosynthesize. They have chlorophyll *a*, chlorophyll *b*, and carotenoids, which are the same pigments found in green algae and plants.[1] Their food is stored as paramylon, a polysaccharide. Some photosynthetic euglenoids lose their chlorophyll when grown in the dark and obtain their nutrients heterotrophically by ingesting organic matter. Other species of euglenoids are always colorless and heterotrophic.

Euglenoids inhabit freshwater ponds and puddles, particularly those with large amounts of organic material. For that reason they are used as indicator species of organic pollution. If a body of water has large numbers of euglenoids, it is probably polluted. Marine waters and mud flats are also inhabited by some euglenoids.

Phylum Chlorophyta Contains the Green Algae

If one had to pick a single word to describe the green algae (phylum Chlorophyta), it would be "variety." These protists exhibit many diverse morphologies and methods of reproduction. Their body forms range from single cells to colonial forms to coenocytic, **siphonous**

---

[1] Although the euglenoids have the same pigments as the green algae and plants, they are not thought to be closely related to either group.

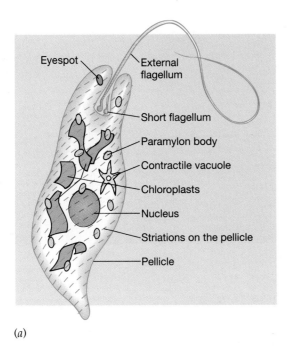

(a)

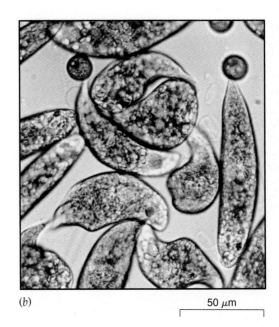

(b)   50 μm

Figure 24-15 *Euglena.* This protist is both plant-like and animal-like. It has at various times been classified in the plant kingdom (with the algae) and in the animal kingdom (when protozoa were considered animals). (*a*) *Euglena* has a complex cellular structure.

The eyespot is a light-sensitive organelle that helps it to react to light. Its outer covering, called a pellicle, is flexible and enables *Euglena* to change shape easily. (*b*) Living euglenoids. Note the red eyespots.   (Visuals Unlimited/T.E. Adams)

Labels on figure (a): Eyespot, External flagellum, Short flagellum, Paramylon body, Contractile vacuole, Chloroplasts, Nucleus, Striations on the pellicle, Pellicle

(tubular) algae to multicellular filaments and sheets (Figure 24–16). The multicellular forms do not have cells differentiated into tissues, however. Most green algae are flagellated during at least part of their life history, although a few are totally nonmotile.

Although the green algae are structurally very diverse, they are biochemically very uniform. Green algae are photosynthetic, with chlorophyll *a*, chlorophyll *b*, and carotenoids present in chloroplasts of a wide variety of shapes. Starch is the main food reserve. Most green algae possess cell walls with cellulose, although some lack walls and some are covered with scales. Many of the green algae are symbionts with other organisms; some live in body cells of invertebrates, whereas others grow together with fungi as a "dual organism" called a lichen (see Chapter 25).

Green algae share a number of characteristics in common with plants. Biochemically, their pigmentation, storage products, and cell walls are identical to those of plants. Because of these and other similarities, it is generally accepted that plants evolved from green alga–like ancestors. Taxonomy of the green algae is currently under study, and research advances in ultrastructure and biochemistry are providing insights into this very diverse group.

Reproduction in the green algae is as varied as their morphology. Both sexual and asexual reproduction occur in the group. Asexual reproduction may be by cell division for unicells or by fragmentation for multicellular forms. Many green algae produce spores asexually by mitosis; if these spores are flagellated and mo-

tile, they are called **zoospores.** Sexual reproduction in the green algae involves the formation of gametes in single-celled gametangia. Three types of sexual reproduction are recognized in green algae—isogamous, anisogamous, and oogamous. If the two flagellated gametes that fuse are identical in size and appearance, sexual reproduction is said to be **isogamous** (Figure 24–17). **Anisogamous** sexual reproduction involves the fusion of two flagellated gametes of different sizes. Some green algae are **oogamous** and produce a nonmotile egg and a flagellated male gamete. In addition to sexual reproduction by the fusion of gametes, some green algae exchange genetic information by conjugation, in which the genetic material of one cell passes into a recipient cell.

Both aquatic and terrestrial forms of green algae occur. Aquatic green algae primarily inhabit fresh water, although a number of marine species also occur. Terrestrial green algae are restricted to damp soil, cracks in tree bark, and other moist places. Regardless of where they live, green algae are ecologically important as the base of the food chain, particularly in freshwater habitats where they are quite common.

Red Algae Are Classified in the Phylum Rhodophyta

The vast majority of red algae in the phylum Rhodophyta are multicellular organisms, although a few unicellular species also occur. The multicellular body form

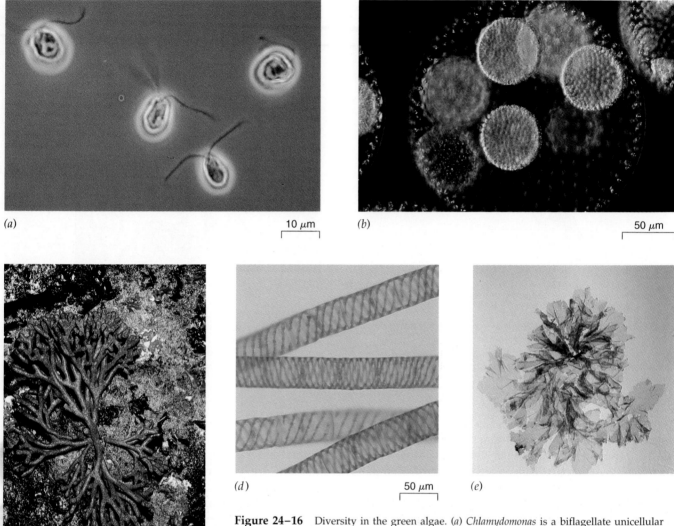

(a)

10 μm

(b)

50 μm

(d)

50 μm

(e)

(c)

Figure 24–16 Diversity in the green algae. (a) *Chlamydomonas* is a biflagellate unicellular organism. (b) *Volvox* is an example of a colonial green alga. A daughter colony can be observed inside the mother colony, which eventually breaks apart to release them. (c) Siphonous green algae like *Codium* are coenocytic, which means their bodies are composed of one giant cell with multiple nuclei. (d) *Spirogyra* is a multicellular green alga with a filamentous body form. Note the spiral-shaped chloroplasts. (e) Some multicellular green algae are sheetlike. The thin, leaflike form has given *Ulva* its common name of "sea lettuce." (a, J. Robert Waaland, University of Washington/Biological Photo Service; b, Carolina Biological Supply Company; c, Doug Wechsler; d, e, Dennis Drenner)

of red algae is commonly composed of complex, interwoven filaments that are delicate and feathery, although a few red algae are flattened sheets of cells (Figure 24–18). Most multicellular red algae attach to rocks or other substrates by a rootlike **holdfast.** The chloroplasts of red algae contain **phycoerythrin,** a red pigment, and **phycocyanin,** a blue pigment, in addition to chlorophyll *a* and carotenoids. Their storage product is floridean starch, a polysaccharide similar to glycogen. The red algae have the same pigment composition as the cyanobacteria, supporting the hypothesis that cyanobacterial endosymbionts evolved into chloroplasts in the red algae (to be discussed shortly).

The cell walls of red algae often contain mucilaginous polysaccharides that are of commercial value. For example, **agar** is extracted from certain red algae and used to make a culture medium for growing microorganisms. A second polysaccharide extracted from red algae is **carrageenan,** which is used to stabilize emulsions in puddings, laxatives, ice creams, and toothpastes. Red algae are an important source of nutrition for humans, particularly in East Asian countries (Figure 24–19).

Reproduction in the red algae has been studied in detail for only a few species, but it is amazingly complex, with an alternation of sexual and asexual stages.

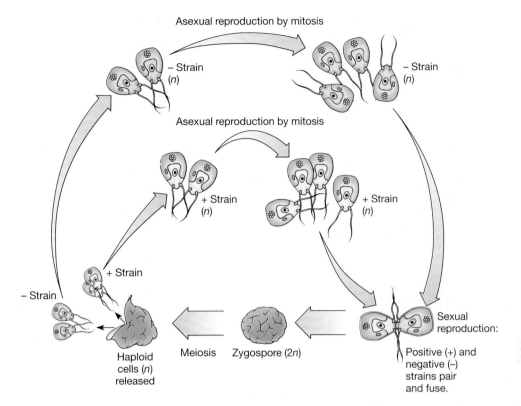

Asexual reproduction by mitosis

− Strain (*n*)

− Strain (*n*)

Asexual reproduction by mitosis

+ Strain (*n*)

+ Strain (*n*)

+ Strain

− Strain

Haploid cells (*n*) released

Meiosis

Zygospore (2*n*)

Sexual reproduction: Positive (+) and negative (−) strains pair and fuse.

Figure 24–17 Life cycle of *Chlamydomonas*. *Chlamydomonas* is a haploid green alga that has two strains, + and −, which are visually indistinguishable. Both strains reproduce asexually by mitosis. At times, single cells behave as gametes. A + strain cell fuses with a − strain cell, forming a diploid zygote that develops into a zygospore. Meiosis occurs within the zygospore, and four haploid cells emerge, two + and two −. This is an example of isogamous sexual reproduction.

Figure 24–18 Most red algae, such as *Plumaria*, are multicellular, many with complex filamentous bodies. (Biophoto Associates)

Figure 24–19 *Porphyra* (nori), a red alga used as food, is grown in seaweed beds such as this one in Japan. The nets are arranged so that the algae are exposed during low tide and submerged during high tide. (Biophoto Associates)

Although sexual reproduction is common, at no stage in the life history of red algae are there any flagellated cells.

The red algae are found primarily in warm tropical oceans, although a few species occur in fresh water as well as in soil. Some red algae incorporate calcium carbonate into their cell walls from the ocean waters. These coralline red algae are very important in building "coral" reefs, possibly more important than are coral animals.

Figure 24–20 *Laminaria,* a typical brown alga. Note the blade, stipe, and holdfast. (J. Robert Waaland, University of Washington/Biological Photo Service)

Figure 24–21 A kelp bed off the coast of California. These underwater forests are ecologically important, supporting large numbers of aquatic organisms. (Richard Herrmann)

The Brown Seaweeds Are Classified in the Phylum Phaeophyta

The phylum Phaeophyta, or brown algae, contains the giants of the protist kingdom. All brown algae are multicellular and range in size from several centimeters to approximately 60 meters in length. Their body forms may be tufts, "ropes," or thick, flattened branches. The largest brown algae, called kelps, are tough and leathery in appearance and have considerable differentiation into leaflike **blades,** stemlike **stipes,** and anchoring holdfasts (Figure 24–20). They often have gas-filled floats to increase buoyancy. It is important to remember that the blades, stipes, and holdfasts of brown algae are not homologous to the leaves, stems, and roots of plants. Brown algae and plants arose from different unicellular ancestors.

Brown algae are photosynthetic and possess chlorophyll *a,* chlorophyll *c,* and carotenoids in their chloroplasts. A special yellow-brown carotenoid, **fucoxanthin,** is found only in brown algae, dinoflagellates, and diatoms. The main food storage reserve in brown algae is a carbohydrate called laminarin.

Brown algae are commercially important for several reasons. They have a polysaccharide, **algin,** in their cell walls, possibly to help cement the cell walls together. It is used as a thickening agent in ice cream, marshmallows, and cosmetics. Brown algae are an important human food, particularly in East Asian countries, and they are rich sources of minerals such as iodine.

Reproduction is varied and complex in the brown algae. They reproduce sexually, and most spend a portion of their lives as haploid organisms and a portion as diploid organisms. Their reproductive cells, both asexual zoospores and sexual gametes, are flagellated.

Brown algae are common in cooler marine waters, especially along rocky coastlines, where they can be found mainly in the intertidal zone or relatively shallow waters. Kelps form extensive underwater "forests" and are essential in that ecosystem as the primary food producer (Figure 24–21). Kelp beds also provide habitats for many marine invertebrates, fish, and mammals. The diversity of life supported by the brown algae is astounding. There is also an extensive colony of floating brown algae in an area of the central Atlantic Ocean called the Sargasso Sea. It is named for the brown alga *Sargassum,* which supports a diverse community by providing food and shelter.

SLIME MOLDS AND WATER MOLDS ARE FUNGUS-LIKE PROTISTS

Some of the fungus-like protists superficially resemble fungi in that they are nonphotosynthetic and their body form is often threadlike hyphae. However, fungus-like protists are not fungi for several reasons. Many fungus-

Figure 24–22 The plasmodium of *Physarum* is colored bright yellow. This naked mass of protoplasm is multinucleate and feeds on bacteria and other microorganisms. (P. W. Grace/Photo Researchers, Inc.)

Figure 24–23 The reproductive structures of plasmodial slime molds such as *Physarum* are often stalked sporangia. (Carolina Biological Supply Company)

like protists have centrioles and flagellated cells, which fungi lack. Unlike fungi, which have cell walls of chitin, many slime molds and water molds produce cellulose as a major component of their cell walls.

The Plasmodial Slime Molds Are Classified in the Phylum Myxomycota

The vegetative (feeding) stage of plasmodial slime molds (phylum Myxomycota) is most unusual. It is a wall-less amoeboid mass that is often brightly colored (Figure 24–22). This **plasmodium** contains many diploid nuclei in its cytoplasm, but it is not divided into separate cells. The cytoplasm streams over damp, decaying logs and leaf litter, often forming a network of channels to cover a larger surface area. As it creeps along, it ingests bacteria, yeasts, spores, and decaying organic matter much as an amoeba does.

When the food supply dwindles or if there is insufficient moisture, the plasmodium crawls to an exposed surface and initiates reproduction. Usually stalked structures of intricate complexity and beauty form from the drying plasmodium (Figure 24–23). Within these structures, called **sporangia,** meiosis occurs to produce haploid nuclei. Later, a wall of cellulose and/or chitin develops around each nucleus, forming **spores.** These spores are extremely resistant to adverse environmental conditions. When conditions are favorable, they crack open, and a haploid reproductive cell emerges from each. It may be a one-celled biflagellate or an amoeboid cell, depending on the moisture available. These two reproductive cells, the flagellated **swarm cell** or the **myxamoeba,** can act as gametes. Eventually two fuse, and the resultant diploid zygote divides by mitosis without cytoplasmic division to form a multinucleate plasmodium.

Phylum Acrasiomycota Contains the Cellular Slime Molds

Although organisms in the phylum Acrasiomycota are called cellular slime molds, their resemblance to the plasmodial slime molds is superficial. Indeed, they have much closer affinities with the amoebas. During its vegetative stage, each cellular slime mold is an individual amoeboid cell that behaves as a separate, solitary organism; it creeps over rotting logs and soil or swims in fresh water, ingesting bacteria and other particles of food. Each cell has a haploid nucleus.

When moisture or food becomes inadequate, the individual cells send out a chemical signal, cyclic AMP (cyclic 3', 5'-*a*denosine *m*ono*p*hosphate) (see Figure 3–31), which causes them to aggregate by the hundreds or thousands for reproduction. During this stage the cells creep about as a multicellular unit, called a **pseudoplasmodium,** or "slug." Each cell of the slug retains its plasma membrane and individual identity. Eventually, the slug settles and constructs a stalked structure. The stalk forms from the cells in the anterior third of the slug, whereas the posterior portion of the slug forms a rounded structure at the top of the stalk, within which spores differentiate. Each spore grows into an individual amoeboid cell, and the cycle repeats itself (Figure 24–24). This reproductive cycle is asexual, although sexual reproduction has been observed occasionally. There are no flagellated stages for most of the cellular slime molds.

Members of the Phylum Oomycota Produce Flagellated Zoospores

The water molds, phylum Oomycota, were once classified as fungi because of their superficial resemblance in

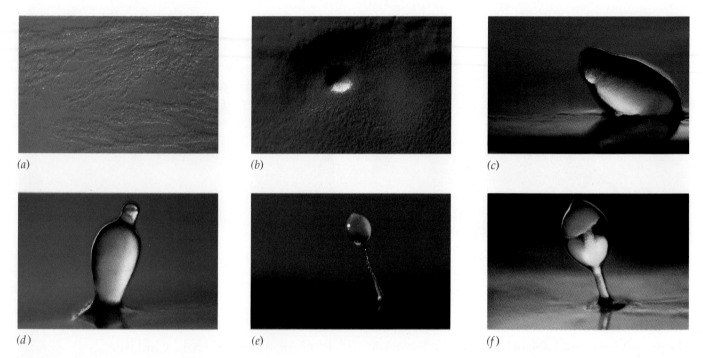

(a) (b) (c)

(d) (e) (f)

Figure 24–24 The life cycle of the cellular slime mold, *Dictyostelium discoideum*. The mature fruiting body releases spores, each of which opens to liberate an amoeba-like one-celled organism that eats, grows, and reproduces by cell division. (1) After their food supply is depleted, the cells stream together. (2) An aggregation of cells. (3) The aggregation organizes into a slug-shaped, multicellular "organism" that migrates for a period of time before forming a stalked fruiting body (4, 5, and 6). Cells making up the anterior third of the slug differentiate into stalk cells, whereas those in the posterior two thirds form the spores. (Carolina Biological Supply Company)

morphology; both water molds and fungi have a vegetative body, termed a **mycelium,** that grows over a substrate, digesting it and then absorbing the predigested nutrients. The threadlike **hyphae** that make up the vegetative mycelium in water molds are coenocytic; there are no cross walls, and the vegetative body is like one giant multinucleate cell. The cell wall of water molds may be composed of cellulose (as in plants) or chitin (as in fungi) or both cellulose and chitin. Because water molds produce flagellated cells at some point in their life cycles, whereas fungi never produce motile cells, most biologists classify the water molds as protists rather than as fungi.

When food is plentiful and environmental conditions are good, water molds reproduce asexually (Figure 24–25). A hyphal tip swells and a cross wall is formed, separating the hyphal tip from the rest of the mycelium. Within this structure, tiny biflagellate zoospores form, each of which can develop into a new mycelium. When environmental conditions worsen, water molds initiate sexual reproduction. After fusion of male and female nuclei, a thick-walled **oospore** develops from the zygote (fertilized egg). Water molds often over-winter as oospores (Figure 24–26).

Some of the water molds have played infamous roles in human history. For example, the Irish potato famine of the 19th century was caused by the water

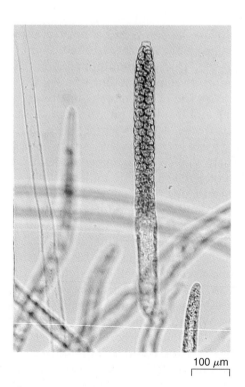

100 μm

Figure 24–25 When *Saprolegnia*, a common water mold, reproduces asexually, it forms sporangia. Within the magnified sporangium shown here, biflagellated zoospores have formed. (Carolina Biological Supply Company)

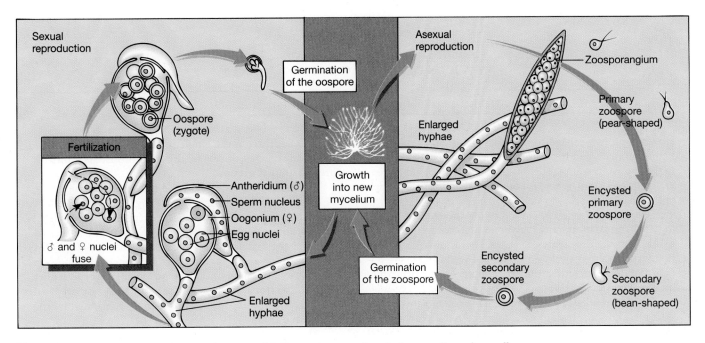

Figure 24–26 The life cycle of a typical water mold. Oomycetes reproduce both asexually and sexually.

mold that causes late blight of potatoes. Owing to several rainy, cool summers in Ireland in the 1840s, the fungus multiplied unchecked. Potato tubers rotted in the fields, and because potatoes were the staple of the Irish peasant's diet, many people starved. Estimates of the number of deaths resulting from the outbreak of this plant disease range from 250,000 to more than 1 million. A mass migration out of Ireland to such places as the United States also ensued.

THE EARLIEST EUKARYOTES WERE PROTISTS

A few protists with hardened shells—for example, the diatoms and foraminiferans—produced abundant fossils. However, most of the protists did not leave extensive fossil records because their bodies are too soft to leave permanent traces. Therefore, evolutionary theories involving the protists are based primarily on comparisons of living organisms. Some of the most useful data for evolutionary interpretations are ultrastructural studies of cell organelles. In addition to electron microscopy, biochemistry and molecular biology also provide important insights.

Protists, thought to have been the first eukaryotic cells, may have originated as early as 1.5 to 2 billion years ago. Compelling evidence exists that several cell organelles, such as mitochondria and chloroplasts, arose from endosymbiotic relationships between various prokaryotic organisms (see Chapter 20). Chloroplasts are thought to have evolved from symbiotic rela-

tionships between photosynthetic prokaryotes and larger single-celled organisms, whereas aerobic bacteria that became endosymbionts may have been the origin of mitochondria.

Multicellularity Arose in the Protist Kingdom

The green algae, red algae, and brown algae are examples of protists that have multicellular species. However, multicellular green algae have more in common with single-celled green algae than with other multicellular protists. Similarly, multicellular forms of both red and brown algae have more in common with different unicellular protists than they do with each other or with the multicellular green algae. Because these groups are so different, it is likely that multicellularity arose in the protist kingdom several different times. That is, the multicellular green algae, red algae, and brown algae probably had different single-celled ancestors.

In fact, the green algae, red algae, and brown algae are so different from one another that they may have come from different *prokaryotic* lines. For example, the green algae possess chlorophyll *a* and chlorophyll *b*. Do any living prokaryotes possess the same pigment composition? In 1975 a bacterium, *Prochloron*, that possesses chlorophyll *a* and chlorophyll *b* was discovered living as an endosymbiont in marine animals. It is possible that an ancient organism similar to *Prochloron* gave rise to chloroplasts in single-celled green algae (and/or euglenoids). Unicellular ancestral green algae then gave rise to multicellular green algae. Likewise, the cyano-

MAKING THE CONNECTION

The Relationship Between Protists and Plants, Animals, and Fungi

How are protists related to the other eukaryotic kingdoms? Plants, animals, and fungi are thought to have their ancestry in the protist kingdom. The protist ancestor of plants is generally agreed upon, whereas both animal and fungal origins are unclear.

The green algae are regarded as the ancestors of plants, in part because of identical pigments and storage products. In addition, some green algae share other traits with plants. Both groups have cellulose in their cell walls and share details of mitosis, including the production of a cell plate during cytokinesis.

The choanoflagellates bear a striking resemblance to the sponges, and some biologists have suggested that an ancient choanoflagellate may be the ancestor of sponges. One or several other flagellates are probably the ancestors of all other animals, which differ from the sponges because they have tissues organized into organs and organs organized into organ systems. However, at this time biologists are not cer-

tain whether there was a single protist ancestor for animals other than sponges, or several different protist ancestors for different animal groups.

The fungi are thought to have had protistan ancestors, but their lineage is uncertain. Both fungi and red algae lack motile cells and share similarities in aspects of their sexual reproduction. The resemblance is strongest between the red algae and the higher fungi,[1] suggesting that fungi evolved from an ancient red alga. However, this opens the question about the evolutionary lineage of the lower fungi: did higher fungi evolve from red algae or from the lower fungi? If an ancient red alga is the ancestor of higher fungi, how did the lower fungi originate?

[1] The higher (more advanced) fungi include the ascomycetes and basidiomycetes, whereas the lower (less advanced) fungi comprise the zygomycetes (see Chapter 25).

bacteria have been implicated as the ancestors of red algae because of similarities in their pigment compositions. Cyanobacteria and red algae are the only organisms to contain chlorophyll *a*, phycoerythrin, and phycocyanin. It is thought than an ancestral unicellular red alga then gave rise to the multicellular red algae. In 1983, *Heliobacterium,* a living prokaryote, was discovered with pigments similar to those of brown algae and diatoms. Prokaryotes similar to *Heliobacterium* may have been the ancestors of these groups.

Multicellular organisms may have evolved from colonial forms

Studying the protists living today provides clues about how multicellularity may have evolved. For example, *Chlamydomonas* (see Figure 24–16*a*) is a unicellular green alga that uses two flagella for motility. The green

algae also include a number of loose aggregations composed of attached *Chlamydomonas*-like cells. These loose aggregations are called **colonies.** For example, *Gonium* is a colony that consists of four *Chlamydomonas*-like cells, whereas *Pandorina* is a colonial organism composed of 16 to 32 *Chlamydomonas*-like cells. The largest colonies—from 1000 to 50,000 *Chlamydomonas*-like cells—are in the genus *Volvox* (see Figure 24–16*b*). As colonies increase in size and number of cells, specialization in cell structure and function occurs, with *Volvox* demonstrating an obvious division of labor among the cells.

The *Chlamydomonas* line is an evolutionary dead-end that did not give rise to further organisms with greater complexity. However, the trend in increasing colony size and cell differentiation within the *Chlamydomonas* line indicates one possible way that multicellularity may have originated: single cells → colonies → multicellular organisms.

SUMMARY

— I. The kingdom Protista is composed of "simple" eukaryotic organisms.
   A. Although most protists are unicellular, their cell structure is more complex than that of animal or plant cells.
   B. Most protists are aquatic.

II. There is significant diversity in the protist kingdom.
   A. Protists range in size from microscopic single cells to multicellular organisms 60 meters in length.
   B. Some protists are autotrophs, while others are heterotrophs.
   C. Protists may be free-living or endosymbiotic, with

relationships ranging from mutualism to parasitism.
- D. Many protists reproduce both sexually and asexually; others reproduce only asexually.
- E. Protists have various means of locomotion, including pseudopodia, flagella, and cilia. Some are nonmotile.
III. Protozoa are the heterotrophic protists.
  - A. Amoebas move and obtain food using cytoplasmic extensions called pseudopodia.
  - B. Foraminiferans secrete many-chambered shells with pores through which cytoplasmic projections are extended to aid in moving and obtaining food.
  - C. The actinopods move and obtain food by means of axopods, slender cytoplasmic projections that extend through pores in their skeletons.
  - D. Flagellates are heterotrophic protists that move by means of flagella.
  - E. The ciliates move by cilia, have micronuclei and macronuclei, and undergo complex reproduction.
  - F. The sporozoa are parasites that produce spores and are nonmotile. A sporozoon causes malaria.
IV. Algae are autotrophic protists.
  - A. Dinoflagellates are mostly unicellular, biflagellate, photosynthetic organisms of great ecological importance.
  - B. Diatoms are major producers in aquatic ecosystems. These are mostly single-celled, with silica impregnated in their shells.
  - C. Euglenoids are single-celled, flagellated protists with pigmentation like green algae and plants. They do

not appear to be close relatives of either group, however.
  - D. Green algae exhibit a wide diversity in size, complexity, and reproduction.
  - E. Red algae are mostly multicellular and lack motile cells.
  - F. All brown algae are multicellular and produce flagellated cells during reproduction.
V. Fungus-like protists were originally classified with the fungi but have features that are clearly protistan.
  - A. The vegetative body of the plasmodial slime molds is a multinucleate plasmodium. Reproduction is by spores.
  - B. The cellular slime molds live vegetatively as individual amoeboid cells. They aggregate for reproduction.
  - C. The water molds have a coenocytic mycelium and reproduce asexually by forming biflagellate zoospores and sexually by forming oospores.
VI. The protists originated 1.5 to 2 billion years ago and were the first eukaryotes.
  - A. Multicellularity arose several times within the kingdom Protista, possibly by following a trend in greater complexity from single cells → colonies → multicellular organisms.
  - B. Plants, animals, and fungi originated from protistan ancestors. Green algae are the probable ancestors of plants, red algae may have given rise to fungi, and choanoflagellates may have been the ancestors of sponges. The ancestor of other animals is probably one or more other flagellates.

POST-TEST

1. In freshwater protozoa the _____ _____ pumps excess water out of the cell.
2. _____ is the union of gametes in sexual reproduction.
3. Cilia and flagella of protists have a 9 + 2 arrangement of _____.
4. Amoebas move and obtain food by means of _____.
5. Foraminiferans secrete many-chambered shells called _____.
6. Some actinopods have long _____ that protrude through pores in their skeletons.
7. The _____ are possibly the ancestors of sponges.
8. Ciliates move by means of cilia, which are structurally similar to _____.
9. The ciliates often display a sexual phenomenon called _____.
10. The _____ are a group of parasitic protozoa that form spores at some stage in their life.
11. Dinoflagellates are photosynthetic, biflagellate, and often

covered by _____ plates.
12. A dinoflagellate bloom is known as a _____ _____.
13. The _____ are photosynthetic protists with shells composed of two halves that fit together like a petri dish.
14. Chlorophyll *a*, chlorophyll *b*, and carotenoids are found in green algae, _____, and plants.
15. _____ sexual reproduction is the fusion of two flagellated gametes of different sizes.
16. The red algae have pigmentation similar to the _____.
17. The multicellular bodies of _____ algae are differentiated into blades, stipes, holdfasts, and gas-filled floats.
18. The vegetative stage of the myxomycetes is a multinucleate _____.
19. The _____ slime molds behave as single-celled organisms until reproduction, when they aggregate.
20. The water molds reproduce asexually by forming biflagellate _____ and sexually by forming _____.

REVIEW QUESTIONS

1. What are the characteristics of a typical protist? Why are protists so difficult to characterize?
2. How are the protists important to humans? How are they important ecologically?

3. Why aren't protozoa considered animals in this text?
4. Some biologists still classify the algae as plants. Why could algae be considered plants? Why do most biologists classify them as protists rather than as plants?

5. Explain why the taxonomic position of *Euglena* is ambiguous.
6. Plasmodial slime molds reproduce sexually, but cellular slime molds do not. What advantages might there be for each organism having the type of reproduction it does?
7. Some biologists still classify the water molds as fungi. Why could water molds be considered fungi? Why do most biologists classify them as protists rather than as fungi?

RECOMMENDED READINGS

Margulis, L., and K. V. Schwartz. *Five Kingdoms,* 2nd ed. W. H. Freeman & Co., New York, 1988. Examines all the phyla into which living organisms are classified and provides a good overview of the protists.

Margulis, L., J. O. Corliss, M. Malkonian, and D. J. Chapman. *Handbook of Protoctista.* Jones & Bartlett, Boston, 1990. Encyclopedic coverage of the protists. This reference book is patterned after *Bergey's Manual of Systematic Bacteriology.*

Round, F. E., R. M. Crawford, and D. G. Mann. *The Diatoms: Biology and Morphology of the Genera.* Cambridge University Press, Cambridge, 1990. A beautifully illustrated reference book on the diatoms. Includes 5000 electron micrographs.

Sharnoff, S. D. Beauties from a beast: Woodland Jekyll and Hydes. *Smithsonian,* July 1991. Beautiful photographs of the sporangia of slime molds.

CHAPTER 25

Kingdom Fungi

OUTLINE

Ecological importance of fungi

Filamentous body plan

Fungal reproduction

Fungal classification

Lichens

Economic importance of fungi

The tasty mushroom—delight of the gourmet—has much in common with the black mold that forms on stale bread and the mildew that collects on damp shower curtains. All of these life forms belong to the kingdom Fungi, a large and diverse group of more than 60,000 known species, most of which are terrestrial.

Although they vary strikingly in size and shape, all of the fungi are eukaryotes; their cells contain membrane-bounded nuclei and mitochondria. Fungi were traditionally classified in the plant kingdom because of superficial resemblances, but biologists today recognize that they are not plants. Fungi are distinct from other eukaryotes in many ways, and thus they are accorded a separate kingdom.

Fungal cells—like plant cells—are encased in cell walls during at least some stage in their life cycle. Fungal cell walls, however, have a

A violet cort mushroom (*Cortinarius*) and two puff balls (*Calostroma*). Both mushrooms and puff balls are fungal reproductive structures. (Dr. Paul A. Zahl/ Photo Researchers, Inc.)

different chemical composition than plant cell walls.

Fungi lack chlorophyll and chloroplasts and are not photosynthetic. They are heterotrophs but do not ingest food. Instead, fungi excrete digestive enzymes and then absorb the predigested food (as small organic molecules) through their cell walls and plasma membranes. They obtain their nutrients from other living organisms (as parasites) or from organic matter (as decomposers). As decomposers, fungi, along with the bacteria (see Chapter 23), play an important ecological role by breaking down dead organic material.

Fungi are nonmotile (at no point in their life cycle do they possess flagellated cells) and reproduce by means of spores, which may be formed sexually or asexually. They are classified into groups mainly on the basis of their sexual reproductive structures.

After you have studied this chapter you should be able to

1. Describe the distinguishing characteristics of the kingdom Fungi.
2. Contrast the body plan of a yeast with that of a mold.
3. Trace the fate of a fungal spore that lands on an appropriate substrate such as an overripe peach, and describe conditions that permit fungal growth.
4. List distinguishing characteristics for each of the four divisions of fungi and give examples of each group.
5. Follow a member of the Zygomycetes (such as black bread mold, *Rhizopus stolonifer*) through the stages of its life cycle.

6. Trace a member of the Ascomycetes (such as *Peziza*) through the stages of its life cycle.
7. Trace a member of the Basidiomycetes (such as a mushroom) through the stages of its life cycle.
8. Explain the ecological role of fungi as decomposers, and discuss the special ecological significance of lichens and mycorrhizae.
9. Summarize the economic significance of the fungi.
10. Identify several fungal diseases of plants and three human fungal diseases.

FUNGI ARE ECOLOGICALLY IMPORTANT

Fungi make important contributions to the ecological balance of our world. Like bacteria, most fungi are decomposers, **saprophytes** that absorb nutrients from organic wastes and dead organisms. Instead of taking food inside its body and then digesting it as an animal would, a fungus digests food outside its body by secreting strong hydrolytic enzymes onto the food. In this extracellular (*extra*, outside) digestion, complex organic compounds are broken down into similar compounds that the fungus can absorb. When fungi degrade wastes and dead organisms in this way, carbon, nitrogen, and mineral components of organic compounds are released, and these elements are recycled through various biogeochemical cycles (see Chapter 54). For example, as decomposition occurs, carbon dioxide is released into the atmosphere and minerals are returned to the soil. Without this continuous decomposition, essential nutrients would soon become locked up in huge mounds of dead animals, feces, branches, logs, and leaves. These nutrients would be unavailable for use by new generations of organisms, and life would cease.

Although most fungi are saprophytes, others form symbiotic relationships with other organisms. Recall that a symbiotic relationship is an intimate relationship between two or more organisms of different species. Some fungi are **parasites,** organisms that live in or on another organism and are harmful to their host. Parasitic fungi absorb food from the living bodies of their hosts. Such fungi cause disease in humans and other animals and are the most important disease-causing organisms of plants. Their activities cost billions of dollars in agricultural damage yearly.

Some types of fungi form mutualistic symbiotic relationships with other organisms. In **mutualism** both symbiotic partners benefit from the relationship. At the same time that a mutualistic fungus absorbs nutrients from its host, it makes some contribution to its host's

Figure 25–1 Mycorrhizae are symbiotic associations between fungi and the roots of plants. An experiment demonstrating that soybeans respond to mycorrhizae: *left*, a control plant; *right*, the other two plants were grown under identical conditions as the control, except that they have mycorrhizal associations.   (Visuals Unlimited/R. Roncadori)

well-being. **Mycorrhizae** (fungus-roots) are symbiotic relationships between fungi and the roots of plants (Figure 25–1). Such relationships occur in more than 90% of all families of plants. The fungus benefits the plant by decomposing organic material in the soil and making the minerals available to the plant, whereas the roots supply the fungus with sugars, amino acids, and some other organic substances.

The importance of mycorrhizae first became evident when horticulturalists observed that orchids do not grow unless they are colonized by an appropriate fungus. Similarly, it has been shown that many forest trees die from mineral deficiencies when transplanted to nutrient-rich grassland soils that lack the appropriate mycorrhizal fungi. When forest soil that contains the appropriate fungi or their spores is added to the soil around these trees, they quickly assume a normal growth pattern.

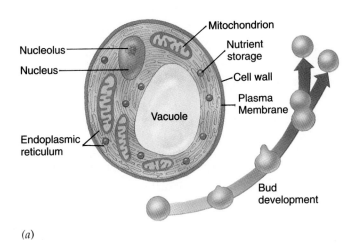

(a)

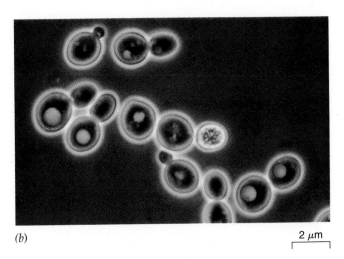

(b)

2 μm

Figure 25–2 Yeasts are unicellular fungi that reproduce asexually, mainly by budding. They may also reproduce sexually. (a) A cell of baker's yeast, *Saccharomyces cerevisiae*, contains a number of eukaryotic organelles. Bud development is also shown.

(b) Micrograph of baker's yeast cells, commonly known as baker's yeast. Note that many of the cells are budding. (b, Manfred Kage/ Peter Arnold, Inc.)

MOST FUNGI HAVE A FILAMENTOUS BODY PLAN

The body structures of fungi vary in complexity, ranging from the single-celled yeasts to the multicellular molds (a term used loosely to include the mildews, rusts and smuts, mushrooms, and many other fungi). In most fungi the rigid cell wall encasing each cell is composed in part of **chitin,** which is also a component of the external skeletons of insects and other arthropods. Chitin, which consists of subunits of a nitrogen-containing sugar called glucosamine (see Chapter 3), is far more resistant to breakdown by microbes than is the cellulose of which plant cell walls are composed.

Yeasts are unicellular fungi that reproduce asexually mainly by **budding,** a process in which a small protuberance (bud) grows and eventually separates from the parent cell (Figure 25–2). Yeasts also reproduce asexually by fission and sexually through spore formation. Some yeast cells group together to form colonies. The yeasts are not classified as a single taxonomic group because many different fungi can be induced to form a yeast stage.

Most fungi are filamentous molds. A mold consists of long, branched, threadlike strings (or filaments) of cells called **hyphae** (singular, *hypha*). Hyphae form a tangled mass or tissue-like aggregation known as a **mycelium** (plural, *mycelia*) (Figure 25–3). The cobweb-like mold sometimes seen on the surface of bread is the mycelium of a fungus. What is not seen is the extensive mycelium that grows down into the substance of the bread. The color of the mold comes from the reproduc-

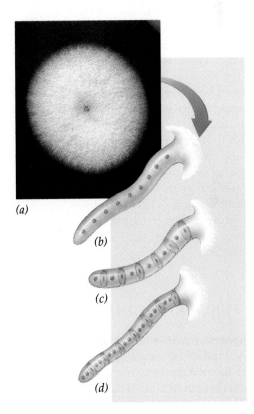

(a)

(b)

(c)

(d)

Figure 25–3 Molds. (a) *Fusarium moniliforme*, a mold that causes disease in many plants. The fuzzy appearance of molds is due to their body form, a collection of filamentous hyphae that are collectively called a mycelium. (b) A coenocytic hypha. (c) A hypha divided into cells by septa; each cell has one nucleus. In some classes the septa are perforated (as shown), permitting cytoplasm to stream from one cell to another. (d) A septate hypha in which each cell has two nuclei. (a, Dennis Drenner)

Table 25–1 DIVISIONS OF KINGDOM FUNGI

Division	Common Types	Asexual Reproduction	Sexual Reproduction
Zygomycota	Black bread mold	Nonmotile spores form in a sporangium	Zygospores
Ascomycota (sac fungi)	Yeasts, powdery mildews, molds, morels, truffles	Conidia pinch off from conidiophores	Ascospores
Basidiomycota (club fungi)	Mushrooms, bracket fungi, puffballs, rusts, smuts	Uncommon	Basidiospores
Deuteromycota (imperfect fungi)	Molds	Conidia	Sexual stage not observed

tive spores, which are produced in large numbers on the mycelium.

Some hyphae are divided by cross walls called **septa** (singular, *septum*) into individual cells containing one or more nuclei. Septa often contain large pores that permit organelles to flow from cell to cell. Other hyphae are **coenocytic,** or undivided by septa, and resemble an elongated, multinucleated giant cell.

Fungi generally grow best in dark, moist habitats, but they are found universally wherever organic material is available. Moisture is necessary for their growth, and they can obtain water from the atmosphere as well as from the medium upon which they live. When the environment becomes very dry, fungi survive by going into a resting stage or by producing spores that are resistant to desiccation (drying out). Although the optimal pH for most species is about 5.6, different fungi can tolerate and grow at pHs ranging from 2 to 9. Many fungi are less sensitive to high osmotic pressures than bacteria and can grow in concentrated salt solutions or sugar solutions such as jelly that discourage or prevent bacterial growth. Fungi may also thrive over a wide temperature range; even refrigerated food is subject to fungal invasion.

MOST FUNGI REPRODUCE BY SPORES

Fungal **spores** are nonmotile reproductive cells dispersed by wind or by animals; both sexual and asexual spores are formed. Spores are usually produced on aerial hyphae that project up into the air above the food source. This arrangement permits the spores to be blown by the wind and distributed to new areas. In some fungi such as mushrooms, the aerial hyphae form large complex reproductive structures in which spores are produced. These structures are called **sporocarps,** or **fruiting bodies.** The familiar part of a mushroom is a large sporocarp. We do not normally see the bulk of the organism, a nearly invisible network of hyphae buried out of sight in the rotting material upon which it grows.

Unlike animal and vascular plant cells, fungal cells usually contain haploid nuclei. In sexual reproduction, fungi often carry out some type of **conjugation,** in which hyphae of two genetically different mating types come together and their nuclei fuse, forming a diploid zygote. In two fungal groups (the ascomycetes and basidiomycetes), the hyphae fuse but the two different nuclei do not fuse immediately; rather, they remain separate within the fungal cytoplasm. Hyphae that contain two distinct, unfused nuclei within each cell are said to be **dikaryotic.** Dikaryotic cells are cytologically described as $n + n$ rather than $2n$. Hyphae that contain only one haploid nucleus per cell are said to be **monokaryotic.**

When a fungal spore comes into contact with an appropriate substrate, perhaps an overripe peach that has fallen to the ground, it germinates and begins to grow. A threadlike hypha emerges from the tiny spore. Soon a tangled mat of hyphae infiltrates the peach while other hyphae extend upward into the air. Cells of the hyphae secrete digestive enzymes into the peach, degrading its organic compounds to small molecules that the fungus can absorb. Fungi are very efficient at converting nutrients into new cell material. If excessive amounts of nutrients are available, fungi are able to store them in the mycelium.

FUNGI ARE CLASSIFIED INTO FOUR DIVISIONS

The classification of fungi is based mainly on the characteristics of the sexual spores and fruiting bodies. Authorities do not unanimously agree on how to classify these diverse organisms, but the current trend is to assign them to four divisions (equivalent to phyla in animal taxonomy): Zygomycota, Ascomycota, Basidiomycota, and Deuteromycota (Table 25–1). The slime molds and the water molds (Oomycota) were traditionally classified as fungi but are now generally considered protists; they are discussed in Chapter 24.

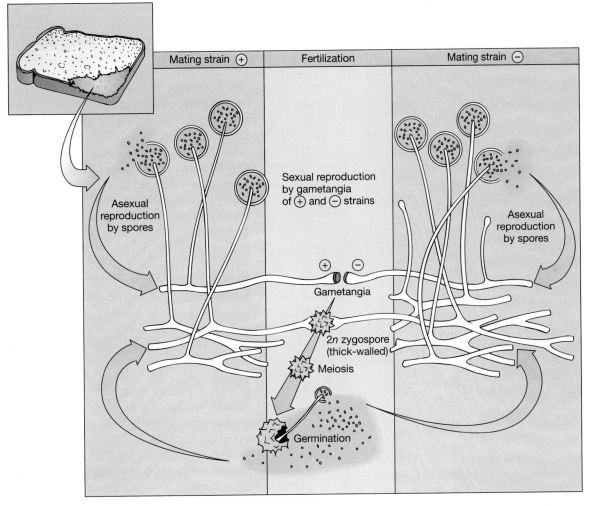

Mating strain ⊕ | Fertilization | Mating strain ⊖

Asexual reproduction by spores

Sexual reproduction by gametangia of ⊕ and ⊖ strains

⊕ ⊖
Gametangia

2n zygospore (thick-walled)

Meiosis

Germination

Asexual reproduction by spores

Figure 25–4 Life cycle of the black bread mold, *Rhizopus stolonifer*. Sexual reproduction takes place only between different mating types, designated (+) and (−).

Zygomycetes Reproduce Sexually by Forming Zygospores

The members of division Zygomycota are referred to as **zygomycetes.** They produce sexual spores called **zygospores** that remain dormant for a time. Their hyphae are coenocytic; that is, they lack septa. However, septa do form to separate the hyphae from reproductive structures. Many zygomycetes live in the soil on decaying plant or animal matter. Some are parasites of plants and animals.

Perhaps the best known zygomycete is the black bread mold, *Rhizopus stolonifer* (Figure 25–4). Bread becomes moldy when a mold spore falls upon it and then germinates and grows into a tangled mass of threads, the mycelium. Hyphae penetrate the bread and absorb nutrients. Eventually certain hyphae grow upward and develop **sporangia** (spore sacs) at their tips. Clusters of black asexual spores develop within each sporangium and are released when the delicate sporangium ruptures.

Sexual reproduction in the black bread mold occurs when the hyphae of two different mating types (designated as plus and minus) grow into contact with one another. The bread mold is **heterothallic,** meaning that an individual fungal mycelium is self-sterile and mates only with an individual of a different mating type. Sexual reproduction occurs only between a member of a plus (+) strain and one of a minus (−) strain. This is a type of physiological sex differentiation, even though there is no morphological sex differentiation. However, it is not appropriate to refer to the two strains as "male" and "female." When hyphae of opposite mating types meet, hormones are produced that cause the tips of the hyphae to come together and to form **gametangia,** structures that produce gametes. These structures become separated from the rest of the mycelium by the formation of septa. Plus and minus nuclei then fuse to form a diploid nucleus, the zygote.

A zygospore forms and provides a thick protective covering around the zygote (Figure 25–5). The zygospore may lie dormant for several months. Meiosis

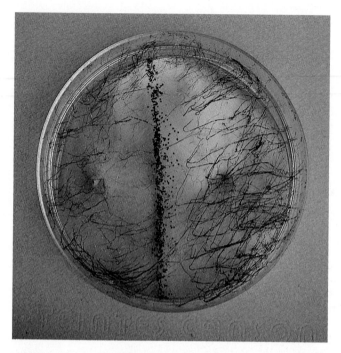

Figure 25–5 Sexual reproduction in the zygomycetes. A petri dish was inoculated with both plus (+) and minus (−) strains of *Rhizopus.* A line of zygospores formed where the two strains came into contact. (Dennis Drenner)

In most ascomycetes, asexual reproduction involves the production of spores called **conidia.** These spores are pinched off at the tips of certain specialized hyphae known as **conidiophores** (conidia-bearers) (Figure 25–6). Sometimes called "summer spores," conidia are a means of rapidly propagating new mycelia. They occur in various shapes, sizes, and colors in different species; the color of the conidia is what gives the characteristic brown, blue, green, pink, or other tint to many of these molds.

Some species of ascomycetes are heterothallic; others are **homothallic,** which means that they are self-fertile and have the ability to mate with themselves. In both heterothallic and homothallic ascomycetes, sexual reproduction takes place after two hyphae grow together and their cytoplasm mingles (Figure 25–7). Within this fused structure the two nuclei come together, but they do not fuse. New hyphae develop from the fused structure; cells of these hyphae are dikaryotic. These $n + n$ hyphae form a fruiting body known as an **ascocarp** that is characteristic of the species. This is where the **asci** (sexual spore sacs) develop (Figure 25–8).

Within a cell that develops into an ascus, the two nuclei fuse and form a diploid nucleus, the zygote. The zygote then undergoes meiosis to form four haploid nuclei. This process is usually followed by one mitotic division of each of the four nuclei, resulting in formation of eight haploid nuclei. Each haploid nucleus (surrounded by cytoplasm) develops into an **ascospore,** so that there are eight haploid ascospores within the ascus. The ascospores are released when the tip of the ascus breaks open.

Division Ascomycota includes more than 300 species of unicellular yeasts. During sexual reproduction, two haploid yeasts fuse, forming a diploid zygote. The zygote undergoes meiosis, and the resulting haploid spores remain enclosed for a time within the original diploid cell wall. This sac of spores corresponds to an ascus and ascospores.

probably occurs at or just before germination of the zygospore. When the zygospore germinates, an aerial hypha develops (by mitosis) with a sporangium at the top. Mitosis within the sporangium forms haploid spores, which eventually germinate to form new hyphae. Only the zygote is diploid; all of the hyphae and the asexual spores of the black bread mold are haploid.

Ascomycetes (Sac Fungi) Reproduce Sexually by Forming Ascospores

Division Ascomycota, the **ascomycetes,** is a large group of fungi consisting of about 30,000 described species. The ascomycetes are sometimes referred to as **sac fungi** because their sexual spores are produced in little sacs called **asci** (singular, *ascus*). Their hyphae usually have septa, but these cross walls are perforated so that cytoplasm can move from one cell to another.

The diverse ascomycetes include most yeasts; the powdery mildews; most of the blue-green, pink, and brown molds that cause food to spoil; saprophytic cup fungi; and the edible morels and truffles. Some ascomycetes cause serious plant diseases such as Dutch elm disease, chestnut blight, ergot disease (on rye), and powdery mildew (on fruits and ornamental plants).

Basidiomycetes (Club Fungi) Reproduce Sexually by Forming Basidiospores

The 25,000 or more species that make up the division Basidiomycota include the most familiar of the fungi—mushrooms, bracket fungi, and puff balls, as well as some important plant parasites such as rusts and smuts (Figure 25–9). Basidiomycetes are also an important part of many cultures' legends and myths.

The **basidiomycetes,** or **club fungi,** derive their name from the fact that they develop a **basidium** (plural, *basidia*), a structure comparable in function to the ascus of ascomycetes. Each basidium is an enlarged, club-shaped hyphal cell, at the tip of which develop

(*Text continues on page 555*)

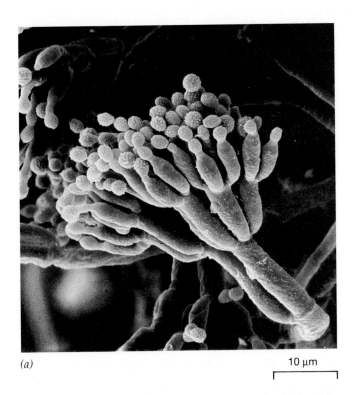

(a)   10 μm

(b)   10 μm

Figure 25–6 Conidia are asexual reproductive cells produced by ascomycetes and most deuteromycetes. The arrangement of conidia on conidiophores varies from species to species and is used to help identify these fungi. (*a*) Scanning electron micrograph (SEM) of *Penicillium* conidiophores, which resemble paintbrushes. (*b*) SEM of *Aspergillus* conidiophores, which produce a tight head of

conidia. The taxonomy of both *Penicillium* and *Aspergillus* is somewhat confusing, as certain species of each genus are classified as ascomycetes (because they produce a sexual stage), whereas other species are classified as deuteromycetes (because they have only been observed to reproduce asexually). (*a*, Biophoto Associates/ Photo Researchers, Inc.; *b*, Visuals Unlimited/David M. Phillips)

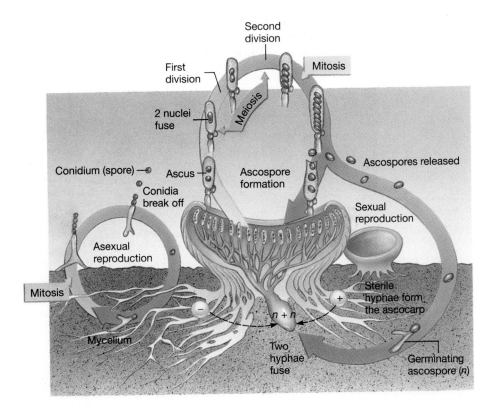

Figure 25–7 Life cycle of an ascomycete. Conidia are produced in asexual reproduction. Sexual reproduction involves the formation of a fruiting body known as an ascocarp in which the saclike asci develop. Ascospores form within the asci. When an ascus breaks open, ascospores are released and can germinate, each forming a hypha.

(a)

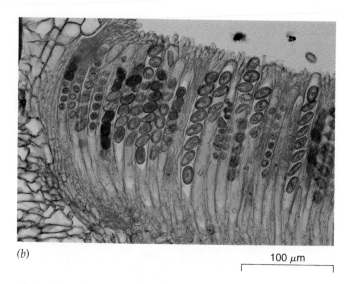

(b)

100 μm

Figure 25–8 Sexual reproduction in the ascomycetes. (a) The ascocarp of *Peziza*, a cup fungus, is saucer- or bowl-shaped.

(b) Asci line the inner portion of the saucer. (a, Ed Reschke; b, Robert and Linda Mitchell)

(a)

Figure 25–9 Diversity in basidiomycete fruiting bodies. (a) Basidia line the gills of the jack-o'-lantern mushroom. (b) At maturity, a dried-out puffball often has a pore through which the basidiospores are discharged as a puff of "smoke." Some puffballs attain remarkable sizes. (c) Bracket fungi, which grow on both dead and living trees, produce shelflike fruiting bodies. Underneath each shelf are many pores, linked with basidia bearing basidiospores. (a, c, Dennis Drenner; b, Connie Toops)

(b)

(c)

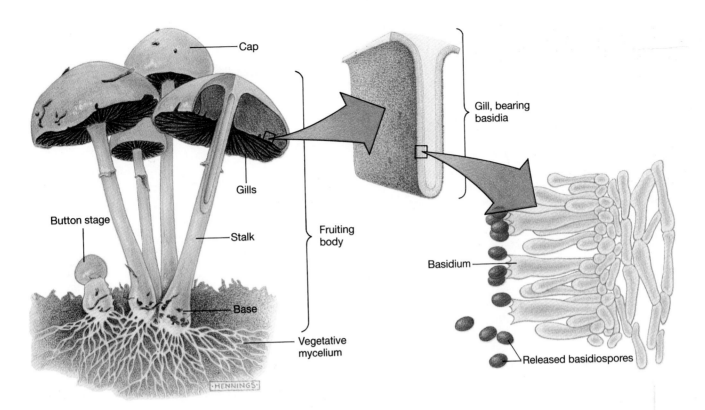

Figure 25–10 Mushroom morphology. Compacted hyphae from the vegetative mycelium form the basidiocarp commonly called a mushroom. Sexual reproduction occurs as dikaryotic cells (at the tips of hyphae in the gills) undergo fusion, followed by meiosis. Haploid basidiospores are the products of meiosis.

four **basidiospores.** Note that basidiospores develop on the *outside* of the basidium, whereas ascospores develop *within* the ascus. The basidiospores are released, and when they come in contact with the proper environment, each develops into a new mycelium.

The mycelium of a basidiomycete such as the cultivated mushroom, *Agaricus campestris,* consists of a mass of white, branching, threadlike hyphae that occur mostly below ground. The hyphae are divided into cells by septa. As in ascomycetes, the septa are perforated and allow cytoplasmic streaming.

Compact masses of hyphae, called buttons, develop along the mycelium. Each button grows into the structure we ordinarily call a mushroom, which consists of a stalk and a cap. More formally, the mushroom is referred to as a sporocarp, or **basidiocarp.** The lower surface of the cap usually consists of many thin perpendicular plates called **gills,** extending radially from the stalk to the edge of the cap. The basidia develop on the surfaces of these gills (Figure 25–10).

Each individual fungus produces millions of basidiospores, and each basidiospore has the potential, should it happen upon an appropriate environment, to give rise to a new **primary mycelium** (Figure 25–11). Hyphae of a primary mycelium consist of monokaryotic cells (cells with a single nucleus). When, in the course of its growth, such a hypha encounters another hypha of a different mating type, the two hyphae fuse. As in the ascomycetes, the two haploid nuclei remain separate within each cell. In this way a **secondary mycelium** with dikaryotic hyphae is produced, in which each cell contains two haploid nuclei.

The $n + n$ hyphae of the secondary mycelium grow extensively and eventually form compact masses, which are the mushrooms or basidiocarps. Each basidiocarp actually consists of intertwined hyphae that are matted together. On the gills of the mushroom the dikaryotic nuclei fuse, forming diploid zygotes. These are the only diploid cells that form in the life history of a basidiomycete. Meiosis then occurs, forming four haploid nuclei. These nuclei move to the outer edge of the basidium. Finger-like extensions of the basidium develop, into which the nuclei and some cytoplasm move; each of these becomes a basidiospore. A cross wall forms that separates the basidiospore from the rest of the basidium by a delicate stalk. When the stalk breaks, the basidiospore is released.

Deuteromycetes (Imperfect Fungi) Are Fungi with No Known Sexual Stage

About 25,000 species of fungi have been assigned to a group referred to as the **deuteromycetes.** They are also

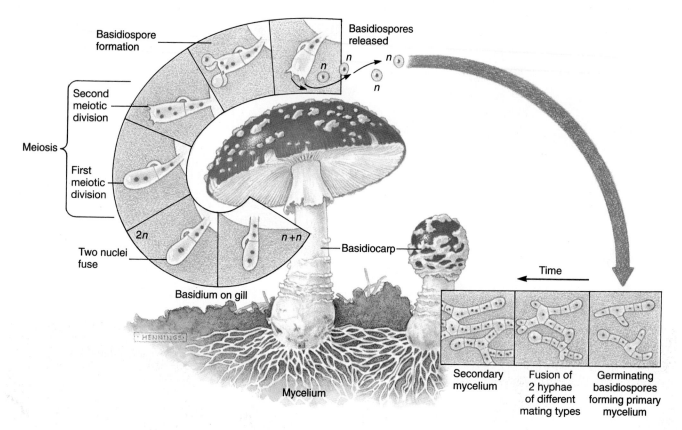

Figure 25–11   Life cycle of a typical basidiomycete.

known as **imperfect fungi** because many have not been observed to have a sexual stage during their life cycle. Should further study reveal a sexual stage, these species will be reassigned to a different division. (Actually, fungi imperfecti with known sexual stages are often dually classified for convenience sake, so the stage encountered in nature—the asexual stage—can be identified.) Most deuteromycetes reproduce only by means of conidia and so are closely related to the ascomycetes; a few appear to be more closely related to the basidiomycetes.

LICHENS ARE DUAL "ORGANISMS" COMPOSED OF A FUNGUS AND A PHOTOTROPH

Although a **lichen** looks like an individual organism, it is actually a symbiotic association between a **phototroph** (an organism that carries on photosynthesis) and a fungus (Figure 25–12). The phototrophic component is usually either a green alga or a cyanobacterium, and the fungus is most often an ascomycete, although in some lichens from tropical regions, the fun-

gal partner is a basidiomycete. The phototrophic organisms found in lichens are also found as free-living species in nature, but the fungal components of lichens are generally found only as part of the lichen.

In the laboratory the fungal and phototrophic components can be separated and grown separately in appropriate culture media. The phototroph grows more rapidly when separated, whereas the fungus grows slowly and requires many complex carbohydrates; generally, the fungus does not produce fruiting bodies when separated in this way. The phototroph and fungus can be reassembled as a lichen, but only if they are placed in a culture medium under conditions incapable of supporting either of them independently.

What is the nature of this partnership? In the past the lichen has been considered a definitive example of mutualism, a symbiotic relationship that is beneficial to both species. The phototroph carries on photosynthesis, producing food for both members of the lichen. It is unclear how the phototroph benefits from the relationship, although it has been suggested that the phototroph obtains water and minerals from the fungus as well as protection against desiccation. Some investigators have more recently suggested that the lichen partnership is not really a case of mutualism but one of controlled parasitism of the phototroph by the fungus.

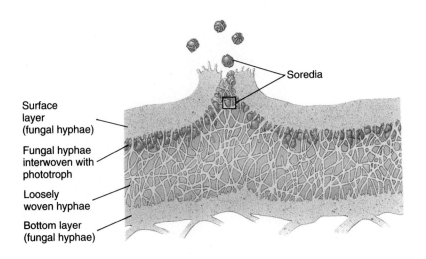

Soredia

Surface layer (fungal hyphae)

Fungal hyphae interwoven with phototroph

Loosely woven hyphae

Bottom layer (fungal hyphae)

Figure 25–12 The lichen, a dual "organism." This cross section of a typical lichen shows distinct layers. The soredium (plural, *soredia*), an asexual reproductive structure, is composed of clusters of algal or cyanobacterial cells enclosed by fungal hyphae.

(a)   *(b)*   *(c)*

Figure 25–13 Lichens vary in their color, shape, and overall appearance. (*a*) Crustose lichens grow tightly attached to rocks or some other substrate. (*b*) Foliose lichens are leaflike in appearance.

(*c*) The British soldier lichen, *Cladonia cristatella*, is a fruticose lichen; it is branching and shrublike. (*a*, M. L. Dembinsky, Jr./Dembinsky Photo Associates; *b*, Dennis Drenner; *c*, E. R. Degginger)

There are some 20,000 species of lichens. They typically possess one of three different growth forms (Figure 25–13). **Crustose** lichens are flat and grow tightly appressed to their substrate (what they are growing on); **foliose** lichens are also flat, but they have leaf-like lobes and are not so tightly appressed to the substrate; **fruticose** lichens grow erect and are branched and shrublike.

Resistant to extremes of temperature and moisture, lichens grow in almost all terrestrial environments, except in polluted industrial cities. They exist farther north than any plants of the Arctic region and are equally at home in the steaming equatorial rain forest. They grow on tree trunks, mountain peaks, and bare rock. In fact, they are often the first organisms to inhabit bare rocky areas and play an important role in the formation of soil (see Chapter 53). Lichens gradually etch tiny cracks in the rocks to which they cling, facilitating disintegration of rocks by wind and rain.

The reindeer mosses of Arctic regions are not mosses but lichens that serve as the main source of food for the caribou of the region. Some lichens produce colored pigments. One of them, orchil, is used to dye woolens, and another, litmus, is widely used in chemistry laboratories as an acid-base (pH) indicator.

Lichens vary greatly in size. Some are almost invisible; others, like the reindeer mosses, may cover kilometers of land with a growth that is ankle deep. Growth proceeds slowly; the radius of a lichen may increase by less than 1 mm each year. Some mature lichens are thought to be thousands of years old.

Lichens absorb minerals mainly from the air and from rainwater, although some may be absorbed directly from their substrate. They have no means of excreting the elements they absorb, and perhaps for this reason they are very sensitive to toxic compounds. A reduction in lichen growth has been used as an indicator of air pollution, especially of sulfur dioxide. Absorption of such toxic compounds results in damage to the chlorophyll of the phototroph. The return of lichens to an area indicates a reduction in air pollution in that vicinity.

When a lichen dries out, photosynthesis stops, and the lichen enters a state of dormancy in which it can tolerate severely adverse conditions such as great extremes of temperatures. Lichens reproduce mainly by asexual means, usually by fragmentation. Generally, bits of the lichen called **soredia** break off and land on a suitable substrate, where they establish themselves as new lichens. Soredia contain cells of both partners. In some lichens, the fungus produces ascospores, which may be carried off by the wind and find an appropriate algal partner only by chance.

FUNGI ARE ECONOMICALLY IMPORTANT

The vital ecological role of fungi as decomposers has already been discussed. Remember that without these organisms, life on Earth eventually would become impossible. The same powerful digestive enzymes that enable fungi to decompose wastes and dead organisms, however, also permit them to reduce wood, fiber, and food to their components with great efficiency. Various molds produce incalculable damage to stored goods and building materials each year. Bracket fungi cause enormous losses by decaying wood, both in living trees and in stored lumber. The timber destroyed each year by these basidiomycetes approaches in value that destroyed by forest fires.

Fungi Provide Food for Humans

The ability of yeasts to produce ethyl alcohol and carbon dioxide from glucose in the absence of oxygen is of great economic importance. The yeasts used in making wine and beer and in baking are cultivated strains carefully kept to prevent contamination. Wine is produced when yeasts ferment fruit sugars. Beer is made when yeasts ferment grain, usually barley. During the process of making bread, carbon dioxide produced by the yeast becomes trapped in the dough as bubbles, which cause

Figure 25–14 Wine, beer, bread, and distinctive cheeses are produced in part by fungi. Yeasts ferment fruits (wine) or grains (beer), producing ethyl alcohol. That same process produces the carbon dioxide bubbles responsible for making bread rise. The bluish splotches in the cheese are patches of conidia. (Courtesy of Raymond Tschoepe)

the dough to rise and give leavened bread its light texture. Both the carbon dioxide and the alcohol produced by the yeast are driven off during baking (Figure 25–14).

The unique flavor of cheeses such as Roquefort, Brie, and Camembert is produced by the action of members of the genus *Penicillium* (Figure 25–14). The mold *P. roquefortii* is found in caves near the French village of Roquefort; only cheeses produced in this area can be called Roquefort cheese.

Fungi have been used in many cultures to improve the nutrient quality of the diet. For example, *Aspergillus tamarii* and other imperfect fungi species are used in the Orient to produce soy sauce by fermenting soybeans. Soy sauce provides other foods with more than its special flavor; it also adds vital amino acids from both the soybeans and the fungi themselves to the low-protein rice diet.

Among the basidiomycetes, there are some 200 kinds of edible mushrooms and about 70 species of poisonous ones, which are sometimes called toadstools. Some edible mushrooms are cultivated commercially: More than 60,000 metric tons are produced each year in the United States alone. Morels, which are gathered and eaten like mushrooms, and truffles, which produce underground fruiting bodies, are ascomycetes (Figure 25–15). These delights of the gourmet are now being commercially cultivated as mycorrhizae on the roots of tree seedlings.

Edible and poisonous mushrooms can look very much alike and may even belong to the same genus.

(a)

(b)

Figure 25–15 Edible ascomycetes. (*a*) *Morchella deliciosa,* commonly called a morel, and (*b*) *Tuber melanosporum,* truffles, are expensive gourmet treats. Both are ascocarps that produce ascospores. Truffles are subterranean ascocarps. Here they are shown entire and sectioned.   (*a,* William E. Ferguson; *b,* Visuals Unlimited/John D. Cunningham)

There is no simple way to distinguish edible from poisonous mushrooms; they must be identified by an expert. For humans, the most toxic substances in mushrooms are cyclopeptides (amatoxins and phallotoxins). One of these cyclopeptides strongly inhibits messenger RNA synthesis in animal cells. Some of the most poisonous mushrooms belong to the genus *Amanita.* Toxic species of this genus have been appropriately called such names as "destroying angel" (*Amanita virosa*) and "death angel" (*Amanita phalloides*); ingestion of a single cap can kill a healthy adult human.

Ingestion of certain species of mushrooms causes intoxication and hallucinations. The sacred mushrooms of the Aztecs, *Conocybe* and *Psilocybe,* are still used in religious ceremonies by Central American Indians and others for their hallucinogenic properties. The chemical ingredient psilocybin, chemically related to lysergic acid diethylamide (LSD), is responsible for the trancelike state and colorful visions experienced by those who eat these mushrooms.

Fungi Produce Useful Drugs and Chemicals

In 1928 Alexander Fleming noticed that one of his petri dishes containing staphylococci bacteria was contaminated by mold. The bacteria were not growing in the vicinity of the mold, leading Fleming to the conclusion that the mold was releasing some substance harmful to them. Within a decade of Fleming's discovery, penicillin produced by the deuteromycete *Penicillium notatum* was purified and used in treating bacterial infections.

Penicillin is still the most widely used and most effective antibiotic. Another fungus, *Penicillium griseofulvicum,* produces the antibiotic griseofulvin, which is used clinically to inhibit the growth of fungi. Cyclosporine, the drug used to suppress immune responses in patients receiving organ transplants, is derived from two strains of deuteromycetes.

The ascomycete *Claviceps purpurea* infects the flowers of rye plants and other cereals. It produces a structure called an **ergot** where a seed would normally form in the grain head (Figure 25–16). When livestock eat

Figure 25–16 The ascomycete *Claviceps purpurea* infecting the flowers of rye. It produces a brownish-black structure called an ergot where a seed would normally form in the grain head. A healthy grain head is shown for comparison.   (Dennis Drenner)

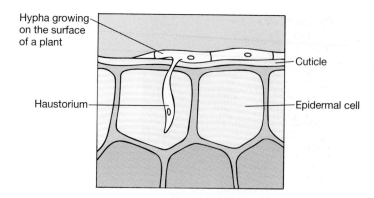

Figure 25–17   Haustoria produced by the powdery mildew fungus penetrate plant epidermal cells.

this grain or when humans eat bread made from ergot-contaminated rye flour, they may be poisoned by the very toxic substances in the ergot. These substances may cause nervous spasms, convulsions, psychotic delusions, and even gangrene. This condition, called ergotism, was known as St. Anthony's fire during the Middle Ages, when it occurred often. In the year 994, an epidemic of St. Anthony's fire caused more than 40,000 deaths. In 1722, the cavalry of Czar Peter the Great was felled by ergotism on the eve of the battle for the conquest of Turkey. This was one of several recorded times that a fungus changed the course of human history. Lysergic acid, one of the constituents of ergot, is an intermediate in the synthesis of lysergic acid diethylamide (LSD). Some of the compounds produced by ergot are now used clinically in small quantities as drugs to induce labor, to stop uterine bleeding, to treat high blood pressure, and to relieve one type of migraine headache.

Fungi can be used as biological control agents to prevent damage by many insect pests without the use of chemical insecticides. Other fungi are grown commercially to produce citric acid and other industrial chemicals. Also, yeasts and certain filamentous fungi are increasingly being manipulated by recombinant DNA techniques to make them produce important biological molecules such as hormones.

Fungi Cause Many Important Diseases of Plants

Fungi are responsible for many serious plant diseases, including epidemic diseases that spread rapidly and often result in complete crop failure, causing great economic loss and human suffering in some cases. All plants are apparently susceptible to some fungal infection. Damage may be localized in certain tissues or structures of the plant, or the disease may be systemic, affecting the entire plant. Fungal infections may cause stunting of plant structures or of the entire plant; they may cause growths like warts; or they may kill the plant.

A plant may become infected after hyphae enter through stomata (pores) in the leaf or stem or through wounds in the plant body. Alternatively, the fungus may produce an enzyme called cutinase that dissolves the plant's cuticle (a waxy covering over the surface of leaves and stems); after dissolving the cuticle, the fungus easily invades the plant tissues. As the fungal mycelium grows, it may remain mainly between the plant cells or it may penetrate the cells. Parasitic fungi often produce special hyphal branches called **haustoria** that penetrate the host cells and obtain nourishment from the cytoplasm (Figure 25–17).

Some important plant diseases caused by ascomycetes are chestnut blight, Dutch elm disease, apple scab, and brown rot, which attacks cherries, peaches, plums, and apricots (Figure 25–18a). Basidiomycete plant pathogens include some 700 species of smuts and 6000 species of rusts that attack that various cereal crops—corn, wheat, oats, and other grains (Figure 25–18b). Some of these parasites, such as the stem rust of wheat and the white pine blister rust, have complex life cycles that involve two or more different plants, during which several kinds of spores are produced. For example, the white pine blister rust must infect a gooseberry or a red currant plant before it can infect another pine. The wheat rust must infect an American barberry plant at one stage in its life cycle.[1] Since this has been known, the eradication of American barberry plants in wheat-growing regions has effectively reduced infection with wheat rust. However, the eradication must be complete, because a single barberry bush can support enough wheat rust organisms to infect hundreds of hectares of wheat. Certain deuteromycetes are also important plant pathogens.

---

[1] The Japanese barberry plant commonly used today in hedges or as a decorative shrub, however, is resistant to infection by rust. Only the American variety is involved in the wheat rust life cycle.

(a) (b)

Figure 25–18 Fungi are important plant pathogens. (a) Brown rot of peaches is caused by *Monilinia fruticola,* an ascomycete. (b) Corn smut on an ear of sweet corn. *Ustilago maydis* is the basidiomycete that causes corn smut. (a, Kathy Merrifield/Photo Researchers, Inc.; b, Runk/Schoenberger from Grant Heilman)

Fungi Cause Certain Diseases of Animals

Although the skin and mucous membranes of healthy animals present effective barriers to fungal penetration, some fungi cause disease in humans and other animals. Some of these cause superficial infections in which the fungi infect only the skin, hair, or nails. Others cause systemic infections, in which fungi infect deep tissues and internal organs and may spread through many regions of the body.

Ringworm and athlete's foot are examples of superficial fungus infections; both are caused by deuteromycetes. Candidiasis (commonly called a yeast infection), also caused by a deuteromycete, is an infection of mucous membranes of the mouth or vagina and is among the most common fungal infections. Histoplasmosis is a serious human systemic infection caused by a fungus that sporulates abundantly in soil containing bird droppings; a person who inhales the spores may then develop the infection. Most pathogenic fungi are opportunists that cause infections only when the body's immunity is lowered. Because the HIV-1 virus disarms the immune system, many AIDS patients have fungal infections that spread throughout their bodies.

SUMMARY

I. Fungi are eukaryotes with cell walls.
  A. Fungi lack chlorophyll and are heterotrophic, absorbing predigested food through the cell wall and plasma membrane.
  B. Fungi reproduce both sexually and asexually by means of spores.
II. Fungi function ecologically as decomposers that break down organic compounds.
  A. Mycorrhizae are symbiotic relationships between fungi and the roots of plants. The fungus supplies minerals to the plant, and the plant secretes organic compounds needed by the fungus.
  B. Lichens are dual "organisms" that play an important role in soil formation.
III. A fungus may be unicellular (the yeast form) or multicellular (the mold form).
  A. The mycelium of a mold consists of long, branched hyphae.
  B. In the zygomycetes, the hyphae are coenocytic (undivided by septa).
  C. In other fungi, perforated septa are present that divide the hyphae into individual cells.
IV. When a fungal spore comes into contact with an appropriate substrate, it germinates and begins to grow.
  A. Some hyphae infiltrate the substrate and digest its organic compounds using hydrolytic enzymes.
  B. Spores are produced on aerial hyphae.
V. Zygomycetes produce sexual resting spores called zygospores. The black bread mold *Rhizopus stolonifer* is a representative member of this group.
VI. Ascomycetes produce asexual spores called conidia at the tips of conidiophores. Sexual (haploid) spores called ascospores are produced in asci. Ascomycetes include yeasts, cup fungi, morels, truffles, and pink and green molds.
VII. Basidiomycetes produce sexual spores called basid-

iospores on the outside of a basidium; basidia develop on the surface of gills in mushrooms. Basidiomycetes include mushrooms, puff balls, rusts, and smuts.

VIII. The deuteromycetes are the imperfect fungi; a sexual stage has not been observed in most deuteromycetes. Most reproduce asexually by forming conidia. Members of this group include *Aspergillus tamarii*, used to produce soy sauce, and deuteromycetes that can cause human fungal infections.

IX. A lichen is a symbiotic combination of a fungus and a phototroph in which the fungus benefits from the photosynthetic activity of the phototroph. Lichens have three main growth forms—crustose, foliose, and fruticose.

X. Fungi have both positive and negative economic importance.

A. Mushrooms, morels, and truffles are used as food; yeasts produce ethyl alcohol and so are vital in production of wine and beer, and they are also used to make bread; certain fungi are used to produce cheeses and soy sauce.

B. Fungi are used to make penicillin and other antibiotics; ergot is used to produce certain drugs; other fungi make citric acid and many other industrial chemicals.

C. Fungi cause many plant diseases including wheat rust, Dutch elm disease, and chestnut blight; they cause human diseases such as ringworm, athlete's foot, histoplasmosis, and candidiasis.

POST-TEST

1. Ecologically, fungi serve as _____.
2. Mycorrhizae are symbiotic relationships between fungi and _____.
3. Fungi were originally classified as plants, in part because they possess _____ _____.
4. Fungi reproduce both sexually and asexually by forming _____.
5. Yeasts reproduce asexually mainly by _____.
6. A mold consists of threadlike strings of cells called _____, which form a tangled mass called a _____.
7. Some hyphae are divided by walls, called _____, whereas other hyphae are _____.
8. The familiar portion of a mushroom is actually a large _____, or fruiting body.
9. *Rhizopus* and other members of the zygomycetes form sexual resting spores called _____.
10. The term _____ means that an individual mycelium is self-sterile and mates only with an individual of a different mating type.
11. In ascomycetes (sac fungi), asexual reproduction involves formation of spores called _____, which are

pinched off at the tips of specialized hyphae called _____.

12. Sexual reproduction in ascomycetes involves production of spores known as _____ within structures called _____.
13. The type of sexual spore produced by a mushroom is a _____.
14. In mushrooms, basidia develop on the surface of perpendicular plates called _____.
15. The deuteromycetes are known as imperfect fungi because only _____ stages are included in the group.
16. A _____ consists of a phototroph and a fungus that are intimately related.
17. A _____ lichen grows flat and tightly appressed to the substrate.
18. When the ascomycete *Claviceps purpurea* infects the flowers of cereals, it produces a structure called an _____ that is toxic.
19. Special hyphae produced by parasitic fungi that can penetrate host cells are known as _____.
20. In order to complete its life cycle, wheat rust must infect both wheat and an American _____ plant.

REVIEW QUESTIONS

1. What characteristics distinguish fungi from other organisms?
2. How does the body plan of a yeast differ from that of a mold? Describe the body structure of a mold.
3. What is the ecological importance of fungi? Of lichens? Of mycorrhizae?
4. What measures can you suggest to prevent bread from becoming moldy?
5. Draw diagrams to illustrate the life cycle of the black bread mold *Rhizopus stolonifer*.
6. Describe the life cycle of a typical mushroom.
7. Briefly describe three important fungal diseases of plants and three fungal diseases of humans.

RECOMMENDED READINGS

Angier, N. A stupid cell with all the answers. *Discover*, November 1986. An interesting report on the usefulness of yeasts in biological experiments.

Bessette, A., and W. J. Sundberg. *Mushrooms: A Quick Reference Guide to Mushrooms of North America*. Macmillan Publishing Company, New York, 1987. A beautifully illustrated guide to common fungi.

Morgan, A. Who put the toad in toadstool? *New Scientist* Vol. 112, 25 December 1986/1 January 1987. An account of some of the myths and folklore associated with mushrooms.

Newhouse, J. R. Chestnut blight. *Scientific American*, July 1990. An account of the chestnut blight fungus that has almost completely eradicated the American chestnut in the United States.

Vogel, S. Taming the wild morel. *Discover*, May 1988. This brief article provides an introduction to the gourmet's delight, morels.

The Plant Kingdom: Seedless Plants

The plant kingdom comprises thousands of different species that live in every conceivable habitat, from the frozen Arctic tundra to lush tropical rain forests. Plants range in size from minute duckweeds to massive giant sequoias. Although plants exhibit great diversity in size, habitat, and form, they are thought to have evolved from common ancestors, the ancient green algae (Figures 26–1 and 26–2). Green algae share a number of biochemical and metabolic traits with plants. Both contain the same photosynthetic pigments—chlorophylls *a* and *b*, carotenes, and xanthophylls. Also, both green algae and plants store their excess carbohydrates as starch. Cellulose is a major component of the cell walls of both, and certain details of cell division, in-cluding the formation of a cell plate during cytokinesis, are shared by plants and many green algae.

There are four major groups of plants living today: bryophytes, ferns and their allies, gymnosperms, and flowering plants (Table 26–1). The mosses and other bryophytes lack a vascular, or conducting, system and are therefore restricted in size. The other three groups of plants possess vascular tissues—**xylem** for water and mineral conduction and **phloem** for food conduction. Ferns and their allies reproduce by spores, whereas gymnosperms and flowering plants primarily reproduce by seeds. Gymnosperms are naked-seed plants, with seeds often produced in a cone, whereas flowering plants produce seeds enclosed within a fruit.

Silver fern with sori on ventral side of frond. (G. R. Roberts)

After you have studied this chapter you should be able to

1. Discuss the environmental challenges faced by plants and give the adaptations that plants evolved to meet these challenges.
2. Name the group of organisms from which plants are thought to have evolved and give several pieces of evidence that support this evolutionary theory.
3. Summarize the features possessed by the bryophytes that distinguish them from green algae.
4. Discuss the advanced features of ferns and fern allies that algae and bryophytes lack.
5. Diagram a generalized plant life cycle, clearly showing the alternation of generations.
6. Compare the generalized life cycles of homosporous and heterosporous plants.

COMPLEX PHOTOSYNTHETIC ORGANISMS ARE PLACED IN THE PLANT KINGDOM

Plants are multicellular organisms that photosynthesize to obtain their energy. Plants use the green pigment chlorophyll to absorb radiant energy, which is then converted to the chemical energy found in carbohydrates (see Chapter 8). In addition to chlorophylls *a* and *b*, all plants have accessory pigments: **xanthophylls** (yellow pigments) and **carotenes** (orange pigments).

One of the most important adaptations plants have in order to survive on land is a waxy covering called a **cuticle** over their aerial parts. A cuticle is essential for existence on land because it helps prevent desiccation, or drying out, of plant tissues by evaporation. Plants are rooted in the ground and, unlike animals, cannot move to wetter areas during dry spells; therefore, a cuticle is critical. In contrast, algae are adapted to an aquatic existence, where water conservation is not important, and do not possess a cuticle.

Algae and the few plants that live in aquatic environments are bathed by water containing dissolved materials, including dissolved carbon dioxide (CO_2) and carbonate ions (CO_3^{2-}). Carbonate moves by diffusion into algal cells and is used as the raw material for photosynthesis. Terrestrial (land) plants obtain their carbon from the atmosphere as CO_2, which must be accessible to the chloroplasts inside green plant cells. Because the external surfaces of plant stems and leaves are covered by a waxy cuticle, however, gas exchange through the cuticle between the atmosphere and the inside of cells is negligible. To overcome this problem, land plants possess tiny openings, or **stomata,** in their surface tissues, which permit the gas exchange that is so essential for photosynthesis.

Plants have multicellular sex organs, or **gametangia** (singular, *gametangium*), each of which possesses a sterile (nonreproductive) layer of cells surrounding the gametes (eggs and sperm). Each female gametangium, called an **archegonium,** produces a single egg. Sperm are produced in the male sex organ, called an **antheridium.** The gametes produced within these organs are

Figure 26–1 The green alga *Coleochaete* resembles a group of green algae that may have been the ancestors of the plants. *Coleochaete* is considered quite primitive because it shares a number of features with its extinct ancestors.   (Courtesy of Linda Graham, University of Wisconsin, Madison)

protected from desiccation by the outer jacket of sterile cells. In contrast, algae lack multicellular gametangia.

Another important difference exists between plants and algae. In plants, after fertilization occurs the fertilized egg develops into a multicellular **embryo** *within* the archegonium. Thus, during its development the embryo is protected. In algae, development of the fertilized egg occurs away from its gametangium. In some algae the gametes are released before fertilization, whereas in others the fertilized egg is released.

A key step in the evolution of vascular plants was the ability to produce **lignin,** a strengthening polymer found in the walls of cells that function for support and conduction. The stiffening property of lignin enabled plants to grow tall and dominate the landscape. The successful occupation of the land by plants in turn made the evolution of large animals on land possible by providing them with both habitat and food. (See Making the Connection: Meeting the Environmental Challenges of Living on Land.)

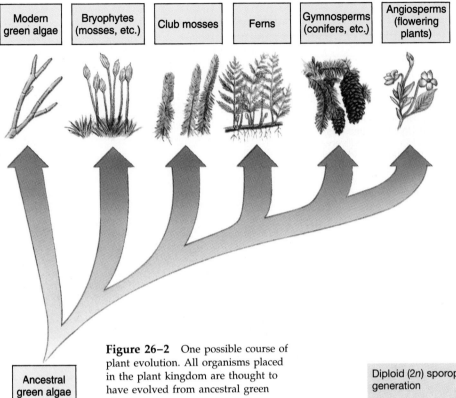

Modern green algae | Bryophytes (mosses, etc.) | Club mosses | Ferns | Gymnosperms (conifers, etc.) | Angiosperms (flowering plants)

Ancestral green algae

Figure 26–2   One possible course of plant evolution. All organisms placed in the plant kingdom are thought to have evolved from ancestral green algae.

THE PLANT LIFE CYCLE ALTERNATES BETWEEN A GAMETOPHYTE GENERATION AND A SPOROPHYTE GENERATION

Plants have a clearly defined **alternation of generations** in which they spend part of their lives in the haploid stage and part in the diploid stage (Figure 26–3).[1] The haploid portion of the life cycle is called the **gametophyte generation** because it gives rise to haploid gametes by mitosis. When two gametes fuse, the diploid portion of the life cycle, called the **sporophyte generation,** begins. The sporophyte generation gives rise to haploid **spores** immediately following meiosis; these spores represent the first stage in the gametophyte generation.

Let us examine alternation of generations more closely. The haploid gametophyte plant produces male sex organs called antheridia in which sperm form. Female gametangia called archegonia, each bearing a single egg, are also formed by the gametophyte plant.

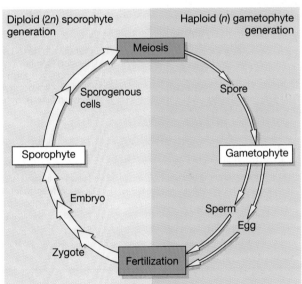

Diploid (2*n*) sporophyte generation — Haploid (*n*) gametophyte generation

Meiosis · Sporogenous cells · Spore · Sporophyte · Gametophyte · Embryo · Sperm · Zygote · Egg · Fertilization

Figure 26–3   The basic plant life cycle. All plants have modifications of this cycle. Note that plants alternate generations, spending part of their life cycle in a multicellular haploid gametophyte stage and part in a multicellular diploid sporophyte stage.

Sperm reach the female gametangium in a variety of ways and swim down the neck of the archegonium. One sperm fuses with the egg in the process known as **fertilization,** which results in a fertilized egg, or **zygote.**

Because the zygote is diploid, it is the first stage in the sporophyte generation. The zygote divides by mitosis and develops into a multicellular embryo, which is supported, nourished, and protected by the gametophyte plant. Eventually, the embryo matures into

---

[1]For convenience we limit our discussion to plants that are not polyploid, although polyploidy is very common in the plant kingdom. We therefore use the terms diploid and 2*n* (and haploid and *n*) interchangeably, although these terms are not actually synonymous.

Table 26–1 THE PLANT KINGDOM

I Nonvascular plants

 I. Nonvascular plants with a dominant gametophyte generation
    Division Bryophyta (bryophytes)
        Class Bryopsida (mosses)
        Class Hepatopsida (liverworts)
        Class Anthoceropsida (hornworts)

II Vascular plants

 II. Vascular plants with a dominant sporophyte generation
  A. Seedless plants
        Division Pterophyta (ferns)
        Division Psilophyta (whisk ferns)
        Division Sphenophyta (horsetails)
        Division Lycophyta (club mosses)

   B. Seed plants
    1. Plants with naked seeds
        Division Coniferophyta (conifers)
        Division Cycadophyta (cycads)
        Division Ginkgophyta (ginkgo)
        Division Gnetophyta (gnetophytes)

   2. Seeds enclosed within a fruit
        Division Magnoliophyta (flowering plants)
        Class Magnoliopsida (dicots)
        Class Liliopsida (monocots)

a sporophyte plant, which has special cells capable of dividing by meiosis. These **sporogenous cells** (spore-producing cells, also called **spore mother cells**) each undergo meiotic division to form four haploid spores. All spores produced by plants are the result of meiosis. This is in contrast to algae and fungi, which may produce spores by meiosis or mitosis.

Because the spores are haploid, they represent the first stage in the gametophyte generation. Each spore divides by mitosis to form a multicellular gametophyte plant, and the cycle continues. Thus, plants have an alternation of generations, alternating between a haploid gametophyte and a diploid sporophyte.

MOSSES AND OTHER BRYOPHYTES ARE NONVASCULAR PLANTS

The bryophytes, which are sometimes divided into three classes—mosses, liverworts, and hornworts—are the only division of nonvascular plants. Because they have no means for extensive transport of water, food, and essential minerals, they are restricted in size. Also, they require a moist environment for active growth and reproduction, although some bryophytes tolerate dry areas. Although these three groups of plants differ in many ways and may or may not be closely related, their life cycles are similar.

Meeting the Environmental Challenges of Living on Land

Life first evolved in the oceans, but many life forms have since adapted to terrestrial life in a sea of air. Every single organism living on land has to meet the same environmental challenges: obtaining enough water, preventing excessive water loss, getting enough energy, and, in temperate and polar regions, tolerating widely varying temperature extremes. How those challenges are met varies from one organism to another and in large part explains the diversity of life encountered on land today. Let us examine how plants and vertebrates (animals with backbones) meet several terrestrial challenges.

1. Obtaining enough water. Animals are motile and walk, slither, fly, run, or crawl to water sources; this requires not only the ability to move (skeletal and muscular systems) but also the ability to sense the presence of water (nervous system). Plants adapted in a much different way to this challenge: They have roots that not only anchor the plant in the soil but also absorb water (and minerals that have dissolved in it).

2. Preventing excessive water loss. The outer layer(s) of terrestrial vertebrates and plants protect(s) the moist inner tissues from drying out. Vertebrates that are adapted to living on land have an accumulation of a water-insoluble protein called keratin in their epithelial cells. Keratin is particularly thick in reptiles, where it forms scales that greatly reduce water loss by evaporation. Plants possess a water-insoluble, waxy coating called a cuticle over their epidermal cells. Plants that are adapted to moister habitats may have a very thin layer of wax, whereas those adapted to drier environments often possess a thick, crusty cuticle.

3. Obtaining sufficient energy. Animals are heterotrophs and eat plants or other animals that eat plants. For this reason animals did not become permanent colonizers of land until plants were established. Plants are autotrophs and must absorb enough sunlight for effective photosynthesis. Some plants have adapted to this challenge by growing tall (to shade out other plants); this approach required the evolution of strong supporting cells such as fibers because plants lack skeletal systems for support. Other plants have adapted to lower light intensities and so are able to grow in the shade of larger plants, albeit more slowly.

4. Tolerating widely varying temperature extremes. Air temperature varies greatly, particularly in temperate and polar regions. Many animals avoid hot temperatures by resting in the shade or by burrowing in the ground during the day when the temperatures are high; these animals become active at night when it is cooler. Sweat glands in mammalian skin produce sweat that cools the body by evaporation. Plants also rely on evaporative cooling; although they don't produce sweat, plants lose large quantities of water through tiny surface pores called stomata. As this water evaporates, it carries heat with it (recall that water has a high heat of vaporization).

   Vertebrates deal with the cold temperatures of winter in several ways. Mammalian hair and bird feathers trap air next to the skin's surface, thereby providing insulation and allowing the body to conserve heat. In addition, some animals avoid colder temperatures by migrating to warmer climates to overwinter, whereas others avoid the cold by passing the winter in a dormant state called hibernation. Many plants also overwinter in a dormant state. The above-ground parts of some plants die during the winter, but the underground parts remain alive; the following spring, these underground parts resume metabolic activity and develop new above-ground shoots. Many trees are deciduous and shed their leaves for the duration of their dormancy. Shedding leaves is actually an adaptation to the "dryness" of winter. Roots cannot absorb water from ground that is cold or frozen; by shedding its leaves, the plant reduces water loss during the cold winter months when obtaining water from the soil is impossible.

Mosses Have a Dominant Gametophyte Generation

Mosses usually live in dense colonies or beds. Each individual plant has tiny rootlike structures called **rhizoids,** which anchor the plant into the soil. Each plant also has an upright stemlike structure that bears leaflike blades. Lacking specialized vascular tissues, mosses do not possess true roots, stems, or leaves. (Some moss species do have water-conducting cells and food-conducting cells, although they are not as specialized or as effective as in the vascular plants.)

The leafy green moss gametophyte (Figure 26–4) bears its gametangia at the top of the plant. Many moss species have separate sexes—male plants that bear antheridia and female plants that bear archegonia. Other mosses produce antheridia and archegonia on the same plant.

In order for fertilization to occur, one of the sperm produced in the antheridia must fertilize the egg held within the archegonium. Sperm transport requires some imagination to envision, particularly if archegonia and antheridia are located on separate plants at some distance from one another. How do the sperm get to the

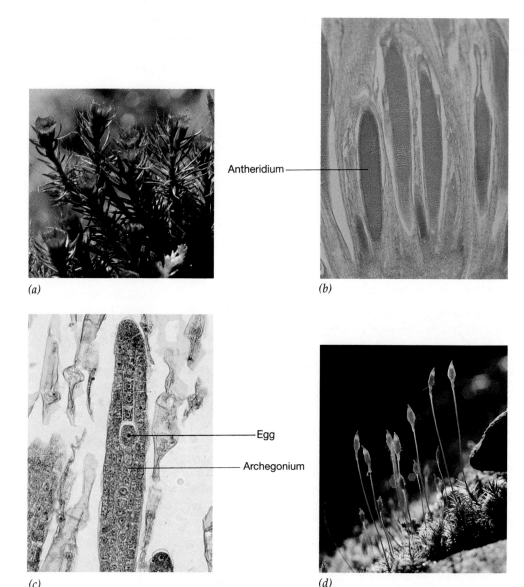

(a)

(b)

Antheridium

Egg

Archegonium

(c)

(d)

Figure 26–4 Mosses. (*a*) The leafy green gametophyte plants of mosses grow in dense clusters. (*b*) Antheridia, located at the top of male gametophyte plants, are the male gametangia. (*c*) The archegonium is the female gametangium. (*d*) The moss sporophyte generation grows out of the top of the gametophyte plant. Each sporophyte is attached to and dependent on the gametophyte plant for nourishment. Spores are produced by meiosis within the capsule at the tip of each sporophyte. (*a, d*, David Cavagnaro; *b, c*, Dennis Drenner)

archegonia? The animal kingdom provides us with a clue. As you may know, the first land animals to evolve from fish were the amphibians. Although frogs, salamanders, and other amphibians are adapted to live on land, they still depend on water to accomplish fertilization and must return to the water to reproduce. The mosses resemble amphibians in this respect: Although they are adapted to life on land, mosses need water to accomplish fertilization, as a transport medium for the sperm. The requirement of water for fertilization is considered a primitive characteristic that mosses have retained from their algal ancestors.

Flagellated **sperm** are transported from antheridia to archegonia by splashing rain droplets. A raindrop lands on the top of a male gametophyte plant, and sperm are released into it from the antheridia. When another raindrop lands on the male plant, it may splash the sperm-laden droplet into the air and onto the top of a nearby female plant. Or insects may touch the sperm-laden fluid and inadvertently carry it for considerable distances. Once in a film of water on the female moss, a haploid sperm swims down the neck of the archegonium and fuses with the haploid egg.

The zygote formed as a result of fertilization grows by mitosis into a multicellular diploid embryo that matures into a moss sporophyte. This sporophyte generation grows out of the top of the female gametophyte, to which it is attached and on which it is nutritionally dependent (Figure 26–4). The sporophyte, which is initially green (and photosynthetic), but becomes a golden brown at maturity, is composed of three parts: a **foot,** which anchors the sporophyte to the gametophyte; a **seta,** or stalk; and a **capsule,** which contains sporogenous cells (spore mother cells).

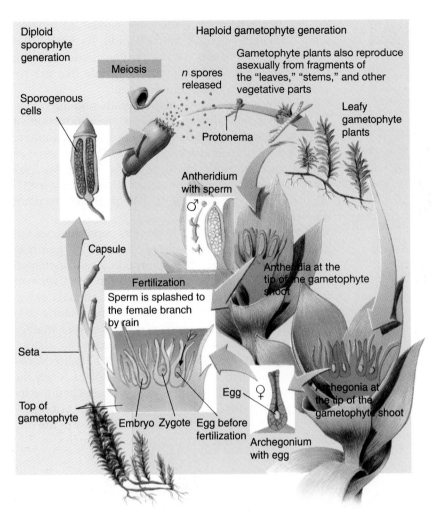

Diploid sporophyte generation

Sporogenous cells

Meiosis

Capsule

Fertilization

Seta

Top of gametophyte

Embryo Zygote

Egg before fertilization

Haploid gametophyte generation

n spores released

Gametophyte plants also reproduce asexually from fragments of the "leaves," "stems," and other vegetative parts

Protonema

Leafy gametophyte plants

Antheridium with sperm ♂

Antheridia at the tip of the gametophyte shoot

Sperm is splashed to the female branch by rain

Egg ♀

Archegonia at the tip of the gametophyte shoot

Archegonium with egg

Figure 26–5 Alternation of generations in mosses. The dominant generation is the gametophyte, represented by the leafy green plants. The sporophyte generation grows out of the top of the gametophyte where the gametangia are located. Mosses require water as a transport medium during fertilization.

The sporogenous cells undergo meiosis to form haploid spores. When the spores are mature, the capsule opens by various mechanisms to release the spores, which are carried by wind or rain to other places. If a moss spore lands in a suitable spot, it germinates and grows into a filamentous thread of green cells called a **protonema.** The protonema, which looks like a filamentous green alga, forms buds, each of which grows into a leafy green gametophyte plant, and the life cycle continues as already described (Figure 26–5).

The haploid gametophyte generation is considered the dominant generation in mosses because it is capable of living independently of the diploid sporophyte. In contrast, the sporophyte generation in mosses is attached to and often nutritionally dependent on the gametophyte plant.

Although all plants evolved from green algal ancestors, the mosses are not in a direct path to the higher plants; that is, higher plants did not have mosslike ancestors. Mosses may represent an evolutionary sideline that developed from ancestral green algae, or alterna-

tively, mosses may have evolved from early vascular plants by regression (that is, by becoming simpler and losing their vascular tissue). The fossil record of ancient mosses can be interpreted in different ways and so does not provide a definitive answer on moss evolution.

Mosses make up an inconspicuous but significant part of their environment. They play an important ecological role in forming soil, especially in primary succession (see Chapter 53). Because they grow tightly packed together in dense colonies, mosses hold the soil in place and help prevent soil erosion. They provide food for animals, especially birds and mammals.

Commercially, the most important mosses are the peat mosses in the genus *Sphagnum*. One of the distinctive features of *Sphagnum* is the presence of large "empty" cells in the "leaves," which apparently function to hold water. This feature makes peat mosses particularly beneficial as a soil conditioner. When added to sandy soils, peat moss helps to hold and retain moisture in the soil. In some countries peat moss is collected, dried, and burned as fuel.

Figure 26–6 Many liverworts have a gametophyte thallus characterized by flattened, ribbon-like lobes. (Dennis Drenner)

The name "moss" is often commonly used for plants that have no affinities to the mosses. For example, reindeer moss is a lichen that is a dominant form of vegetation in the Arctic tundra, Spanish moss is a flowering plant, and club moss is a relative of ferns.

Liverworts Are Either Thallose or Leafy

The gametophytes of some liverworts are quite different from those of mosses. Their body form is often a flattened, leaflike **thallus,** which is lobed (Figure 26–6). Liverworts are so named because the lobes of their thalli superficially resemble the lobes of the human liver. On the underside of the liverwort thallus are root-like rhizoids, which anchor the plant to the soil. Other liverworts have a leafy appearance rather than a lobed

thallus and are superficially very similar to mosses, with "leaves," "stems," and rhizoids. As with other bryophytes, liverworts lack vascular tissue and are small and generally inconspicuous plants that are restricted largely to damp environments.

Liverworts reproduce both sexually and asexually. Their sexual reproduction involves the production of archegonia and antheridia on the haploid gametophyte (Figure 26–7). Their life cycle is basically the same as that of mosses, although some of the structures look quite different. The sporophyte, which is usually somewhat spherical, is attached to the gametophyte plant (Figure 26–8).

One of the ways that liverworts reproduce asexually is by forming tiny balls of tissue called **gemmae** (singular, *gemma*), which are borne in a saucer-shaped structure, the **gemmae cup,** directly on the liverwort thallus. Splashing raindrops and small animals aid in the dispersal of gemmae. When a gemma lands in a suitable place, it grows into a new liverwort thallus. Liverworts may also reproduce asexually by thallus branching and growth. The individual thallus lobes elongate and each becomes a separate plant when the older part of the thallus that originally attached the individual lobes dies. Both of these mechanisms of reproduction—gemmae and thallus branching—are asexual because they do not involve fusion of gametes.

Hornworts Are Inconspicuous Thalloid Plants

Hornworts are a small group of bryophytes whose gametophytes superficially resemble those of the thalloid liverworts. Hornworts may or may not be closely

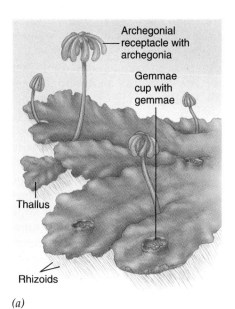

Archegonial receptacle with archegonia

Gemmae cup with gemmae

Thallus

Rhizoids

(a)

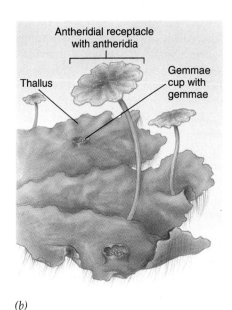

Antheridial receptacle with antheridia

Thallus

Gemmae cup with gemmae

(b)

Figure 26–7 Some liverworts have male and female structures on separate plants. (*a*) This female thallus has stalked structures that terminate in archegonial receptacles with archegonia. (*b*) The male thallus produces antheridial receptacles on stalks. Numerous antheridia are embedded in each antheridial receptacle.

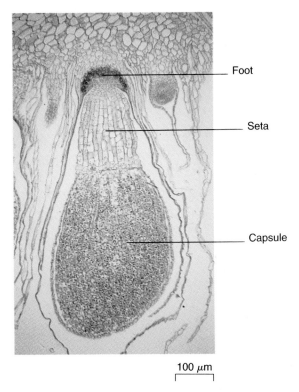

100 µm

Figure 26–8 The liverwort sporophyte, which is always attached to and dependent on the gametophyte plant, has the same basic structure as the moss sporophyte, with its foot, seta (stalk), and capsule. Meiosis occurs in the capsule, producing haploid spores. (Dennis Drenner)

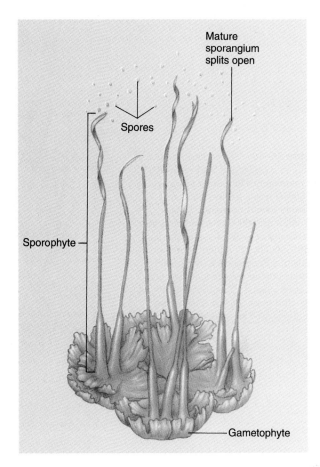

Figure 26–9 *Anthoceros*, a typical hornwort. The leafy green thallus, which is 1 to 2 cm in diameter, is the gametophyte generation. After fertilization the sporophytes project out of the thallus.

related to other bryophytes. For example, their cell structure, particularly the presence of a single large chloroplast in each cell, resembles that of certain algae more than that of plants. Mosses and liverworts, on the other hand, are like all other plants in that they have many disk-shaped chloroplasts per cell. However, hornworts possess stomata, like mosses and all vascular plants (liverworts lack stomata).

In hornworts, archegonia and antheridia are embedded in the gametophyte thallus. After fertilization, the sporophyte projects out of the gametophyte tissue, forming a spike or "horn" (Figure 26–9). A single gametophyte plant often produces a number of sporophytes. Meiosis occurs within each sporangium, and spores are formed.

SEEDLESS VASCULAR PLANTS INCLUDE FERNS AND THEIR ALLIES

Ferns are an ancient group of plants that are still successful today. They are especially common in temperate woodlands and tropical rain forests, where they are found in the greatest variety. Three groups of plants—

whisk ferns, club mosses (lycopods), and horsetails—are considered allies of the ferns because they possess vascular tissue and share similarities in their life cycles.

According to the fossil record, the vascular plants evolved some 420 million years ago. Ferns and fern allies were of considerable importance in past ages, and fossil evidence indicates that many species were immense trees. Many ferns and most fern allies are extinct today (Figure 26–10) except for a few smaller extant (surviving) representatives of the ancient groups.

The most important advancement of the ferns and their allies over algae and bryophytes is the presence of specialized vascular tissues for support and conduction. This system of conduction—xylem and phloem—enables vascular plants to achieve larger sizes than mosses because water, dissolved minerals, and food can be transported over great distances to all parts of the plant. Although ferns in temperate areas are relatively small plants, tree ferns in the tropics may grow to heights of 18 meters (60 feet). The ferns and fern allies all have stems with vascular tissues, and most have vascularized roots and leaves as well.

Figure 26–10   The earliest vascular plants to colonize the land evolved approximately 420 million years ago. (*a*) *Rhynia* was a leafless plant that probably lived in marshes. It had rhizomes, upright stems, and rhizoids. (*b*) *Psilophyton* evolved somewhat later, approximately 375 million years ago. Plants like *Psilophyton* were probably the ancestors of the ferns, horsetails, and seed plants. (*c*) *Asteroxylon* was an early club moss. *Rhynia, Psilophyton,* and *Asteroxylon* are all extinct.

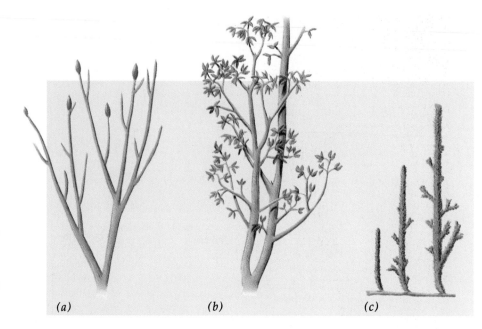

(a)   *(b)*   *(c)*

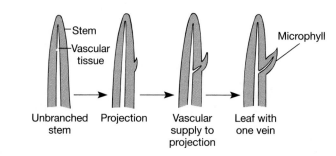

(a)   MICROPHYLL EVOLUTION

Figure 26–11   There are two kinds of leaves. (*a*) Microphylls probably originated as outgrowths of stem tissue that developed a single vascular strand later. Club mosses have microphylls. (*b*) Megaphylls, which are more complex and have multiple veins, probably evolved from a fusion of side branches. Ferns, horsetails, gymnosperms, and flowering plants have megaphylls.

Dichotomously branching stems   Overtopping   Webbing of side branch systems   Leaves with many veins

(b)   MEGAPHYLL EVOLUTION

The evolution of the leaf as the main organ of photosynthesis has been studied extensively. There are two basic types of leaves, microphylls and megaphylls (Figure 26–11). The **microphyll,** which is usually small and possesses a single vascular strand, is thought to have evolved from small, projecting extensions of stem tissue. In contrast, **megaphylls** are thought to have evolved from stem branches, which gradually filled in with additional tissue to form most leaves as we know them today. Megaphylls possess more than one vascular strand, as would be expected if they evolved from branch systems.

Figure 26–12 Tasmanian tree fern. Tree ferns, which are native to tropical rainforests, are found in New Zealand, South Africa, and South America. (Dennis Drenner)

Ferns Have a Dominant Sporophyte Generation

The ferns represent one of the oldest groups of vascular plants. Fossil ferns have been discovered that are 360 million years old. Most ferns are terrestrial, although a few have adapted to aquatic habitats. Although they range from the tropics to the Arctic Circle, most fern species are found in the moist tropics (Figure 26–12). In temperate areas, ferns commonly inhabit moist woodlands and stream banks.

The life cycle of ferns involves a clearly defined alternation of generations (Figure 26–13). The ferns that are grown as house plants (for example, Boston fern, maidenhair fern, and elk's horn fern) are the diploid, or sporophyte, generation. The fern sporophyte is composed of a horizontal underground stem, called a **rhizome,** that bears roots and leaves, called **fronds.** As each young frond first emerges from the ground, it is tightly coiled and resembles the top of a violin, resulting in it being called a **fiddlehead.** As fiddleheads grow, they unroll and expand to form the fronds. Fern fronds are usually compound (that is, the blade is divided into several leaflets), with the leaflets forming beautifully complex leaves. Fronds, roots, and rhizomes are considered true plant organs because of the presence of vascular tissue in each.

The conspicuous plant body of the fern, being the sporophyte generation, forms spores by meiosis. Spore production usually occurs on the fronds, with certain areas on the fronds developing **sporangia,** or spore cases, in which sporogenous cells (spore mother cells) are formed. The sporangia are frequently borne in clusters, called **sori,** on the fronds. Within the sporangia, sporogenous cells undergo meiosis to form haploid spores. When these spores are disseminated and land in suitable places, they germinate and grow by mitosis into mature gametophyte plants.

The gametophyte generation of ferns, which bears no resemblance to the sporophyte generation, is a tiny (about the size of half of one of your fingernails), green, often heart-shaped structure that grows flat against the ground (Figure 26–14). Called a **prothallus,** the fern gametophyte lacks vascular tissue and has tiny rootlike rhizoids to anchor it in the ground. The prothallus produces both archegonia and antheridia on its underside. The archegonia are located near the notch of the prothallus, and each contains a single egg. Numerous sperm are produced in the antheridia, which are found scattered among the rhizoids.

Although ferns are considered more advanced than the mosses because of the presence of vascular tissues, they have still retained the primitive requirement of water for fertilization. A thin film of water on the ground underneath the prothallus provides the transport medium in which the flagellated sperm swim to the neck of an archegonium. After one of the sperm fertilizes the egg in an archegonium, the resulting diploid zygote grows by mitosis into a multicellular embryo. At this stage in its life, the sporophyte embryo is attached to and dependent upon the gametophyte, but as the embryo matures into a sporophyte plant, the prothallus withers and dies.

The fern life cycle has a clearly defined alternation of generations between the diploid sporophyte plant with its rhizome, roots, and fronds, and the haploid prothallus. The sporophyte generation is dominant not only because it is larger than the gametophyte, but also because it persists for an extended period of time, whereas the gametophyte dies soon after reproducing.

Whisk Ferns Are the Simplest Vascular Plants

Psilotum nudum (Figure 26–15a), a representative whisk fern, lacks true roots and leaves but does have a vascularized stem. *Psilotum* has both a horizontal, underground rhizome and vertical, above-ground stems. Whenever the stem forks or branches, it always divides into two equal halves. This **dichotomous** branching (see Figure 26–11) is considered a primitive characteristic. (In contrast, when most plant stems branch, one stem is more vigorous and becomes the main trunk.) The upright stems of *Psilotum* are green and are the main organ

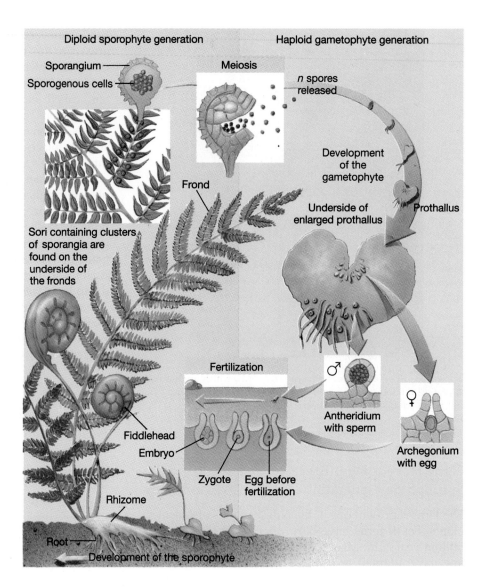

Figure 26–13 The fern life cycle. Note the clearly defined alternation of generations between the gametophyte (prothallus) and sporophyte (leafy plant) stages.

Figure 26–14 The prothallus is the gametophyte generation of a fern. The dark spots near the notch of the heart-shaped prothallus are archegonia. (Carolina Biological Supply Company)

of photosynthesis. Sporangia, which are borne directly on the stems, contain sporogenous cells that undergo meiosis to form haploid spores; after being dispersed, the spores germinate to form haploid prothalli. The prothalli of whisk ferns are difficult to study because they grow underground. They are nonphotosynthetic owing to their subterranean location and apparently have a symbiotic relationship with fungi, which provide them with nourishment.

Most species of whisk ferns are extinct, and the few extant species live mainly in the tropics. Although whisk ferns do not closely resemble ferns in appearance, they are considered fern allies because of similarities in their life cycles. Although their morphology has been carefully studied in recent years, botanists disagree about how to interpret their structures. Most botanists consider whisk ferns to be surviving representatives of very primitive vascular plants.

(a)   (b)

(c)

Figure 26–15 Representative fern allies. (*a*) The growth habit of *Psilotum nudum.* The stem is the main organ of photosynthesis because leaves are absent. (*b*) *Equisetum telematia,* a horsetail with a wide distribution in Eurasia, Africa, and North America. It has unbranched, nonphotosynthetic fertile shoots bearing conelike strobili and separate, highly branched, photosynthetic sterile shoots. Both types of shoots arise from an underground rhizome. (*c*) *Lycopodium,* a club moss. Although the club mosses superficially resemble mosses, they are fern allies. The sporophyte plant has reduced, scalelike leaves that are evergreen. Spores are produced in sporangia on fertile leaves clustered in a conelike strobilus (as shown) or scattered along the stem (other species). (*a, c,* Dennis Drenner; *b,* J. Robert Waaland, University of Washington/Biological Photo Service)

Horsetails Have Hollow, Jointed Stems

Horsetails were very important millions of years ago when they were some of Earth's dominant plants. Ancient horsetails are still significant today because approximately 300 million years ago, these plants were major contributors to the vast coal deposits that we cur-

rently use (see Focus on Ancient Plants and Coal Formation). The few surviving horsetails, all in the single genus *Equisetum,* grow mostly in wet, marshy habitats and are small but very distinctive plants (Figure 26–15*b*).

Horsetails have true roots, stems, and leaves. The hollow, jointed stems are impregnated with silica, which gives them a gritty feeling. Small leaves, which are interpreted as reduced megaphylls, are fused in whorls at each **node** (the area on the stem where leaves attach). The green stem is the main organ of photosynthesis. These plants were named horsetails because certain vegetative (nonreproductive) stems have whorls of branches that give the appearance of a bushy horse's tail. In pioneer days these plants were called "scouring rushes" and were used to scrub out pots and pans along the stream banks.

Each reproductive branch bears a terminal conelike **strobilus.** The strobilus is composed of a number of umbrella-like structures, each bearing 5 to 10 sporangia. The horsetail life cycle is similar in many respects to the fern life cycle.

Club Mosses Are Small Plants with Rhizomes and Short, Erect Branches

Like horsetails, club mosses were dominant plants millions of years ago when species that are now extinct often attained great size. These large trees, like the ancient horsetails, were major contributors to the coal deposits on Earth (see Focus on Ancient Plants and Coal Formation). Extant club mosses, represented by *Lycopodium* (Figure 26–15*c*), are small, attractive plants commonly found in woodlands. They possess true roots, stems (both rhizomes and erect, above-ground stems), and small, scalelike leaves (microphylls). Sporangia are borne on fertile leaves in conelike strobili at the tips of stems or scattered along the stems. Club mosses are evergreen and are often fashioned into Christmas wreaths and other decorations; in some areas they are endangered from overharvesting.

One of the problems with using common names in biology is vividly evident in this group of plants. The most common names for the Division Lycophyta are "club mosses" and "ground pines," yet these plants are neither mosses nor pines and are most closely allied to the ferns.

More Advanced Plants Are Less Dependent on Water as a Transport Medium for Reproductive Cells

Many algae produce flagellated reproductive cells, both spores and sperm, that can swim through the water. Although reproduction by flagellated spores and sperm

FOCUS ON

Ancient Plants and Coal Formation

The plants of the Carboniferous period included giant ferns, horsetails, and club mosses. The early gymnosperms were also present. Recent work suggests that Carboniferous swamps were more open than depicted here.   (No. Geo. 75400C, Field Museum of Natural History, Chicago)

The industrial society in which we live depends on energy from fossil fuels, which formed from the remains of ancient organisms. One of our most important fossil fuels is coal, which is burned to produce electricity and to manufacture items made of steel and iron. Although coal is mined from Earth as a mineral, it is not a mineral like gold or aluminum, but organic, formed from ancient plants.

Much of the coal we use today was formed from the prehistoric remains of primitive vascular plants, particularly those of the Carboniferous period, which occurred approximately 300 million years ago. Five main groups of plants contributed to coal formation. Three were seedless vascular plants—the club mosses, horsetails, and ferns. The other two were seed plants—the seed ferns (now extinct) and primitive gymnosperms.

It is hard to imagine that the small, relatively inconspicuous club mosses, ferns, and horsetails of today could have been so significant in forming the vast beds of coal in the Earth. However, many of the members of these groups that existed during the Carboniferous period were giants by comparison, and they formed vast forests of trees (see figure).

The climate during the Carboniferous period was warm and mild, and plants grew throughout the year because of the favorable weather conditions. Forests of these plants occurred in low-lying areas that were periodically flooded. When the water level receded, these plants became established again.

When these large plants died or were blown over during storms, they decomposed incompletely because they were covered by the swamp water. The anaerobic conditions of the water prevented wood-rotting fungi from decomposing the plants, and anaerobic bacteria do not decompose wood rapidly. Thus, over time the partially decomposed plant material accumulated and consolidated.

Layers of sediment formed over the plant material when the water level rose and flooded the low-lying swamps. Over time, heat and pressure built up in these accumulated layers and converted the plant material to coal and the sediment layers to sedimentary rock. Much later, geological upheavals raised the layers of coal and sedimentary rock. For example, coal is found in seams (layers) in the Appalachian Mountains. The various grades of coal (lignite, bituminous, and anthracite) were formed as a result of different temperatures and pressures to which they were exposed.

Figure 26–16 *Selaginella*. This club moss is heterosporous and produces both microspores and megaspores. Microspores develop into male gametophytes that produce sperm. Megaspores develop into female gametophytes that produce eggs. Heterospory is found in certain ferns and club mosses and in all the gymnosperms and flowering plants. (Dennis Drenner)

is an advantage in aquatic environments, it may be detrimental on land, particularly in locations where extended dry periods occur. In such terrestrial sites, the production of nonmotile, air-borne spores and sperm may be more advantageous. Thus, a general survey of algae and plants shows that algae have *motile spores and sperm*, the relatively primitive mosses and ferns have *nonmotile spores and motile sperm*, and the more advanced gymnosperms and flowering plants have *nonmotile spores and sperm*.

Some Ferns and Club Mosses Are Heterosporous

In the life cycles examined thus far, plants produce only one type of spore as a result of meiosis. This condition, known as **homospory,** is found in bryophytes, horsetails, whisk ferns, and most ferns and club mosses. However, certain ferns and club mosses are **heterosporous** and produce two different types of spores.

Selaginella, a lycopod, is an example of a heterosporous plant (Figure 26–16). Its strobilus bears two kinds of sporangia—microsporangia and megasporangia. **Microsporangia** are sporangia that produce **microsporocytes** (also called **microspore mother cells**), which undergo meiosis to form tiny, haploid **microspores.** Each microspore can develop into a male gametophyte that produces sperm. **Megasporangia** in the *Selaginella* strobilus produce **megasporocytes** (also called **megaspore mother cells**). When megasporocytes undergo meiosis, they form haploid **megaspores,** each of which can develop into a female gametophyte that produces eggs. Refer to Figure 26–17 to help visualize this type of life cycle. The development of male gametophytes from microspores and female gametophytes from megaspores occurs within their respective sporangia. The male and female gametophytes are not truly free-living, unlike the gametophytes of other seedless vascular plants.

Heterospory was a significant development in plant evolution because it was the forerunner of the evolution of seeds. Heterospory is found in the two most successful groups of plants today, the gymnosperms and the flowering plants, both of which produce seeds.

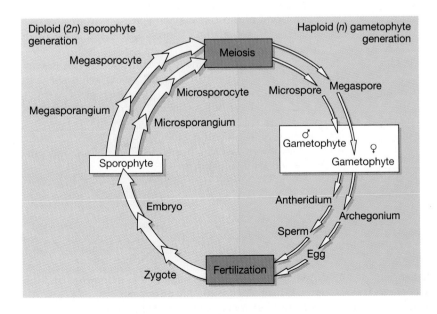

Figure 26–17 A generalized life cycle for heterosporous plants. These plants produce two types of spores, microspores and megaspores.

SUMMARY

I. Plants evolved from green algal ancestors.
  A. Plants and green algae have similar biochemical characteristics: the same photosynthetic pigments, cell wall components, and carbohydrate storage material.
  B. Plants and green algae share similarities in certain fundamental processes like cell division.
II. The colonization of land by plants required the evolution of a number of anatomical, physiological, and reproductive adaptations.
  A. Plants possess a waxy cuticle to protect against water loss and stomata for gas exchange that is necessary for photosynthesis.
  B. A trend in land plants is toward a larger, more dominant sporophyte generation; the gametophyte generation becomes less dominant in more advanced plants.
  C. Plants produce multicellular gametangia with a sterile jacket of cells surrounding the gametes. The male antheridia produce sperm and the female archegonia produce eggs.
  D. Mosses and ferns, although adapted to live on land, require water for fertilization.
III. Plants have an alternation of generations, spending part of their life cycle in the haploid gametophyte stage and part in the diploid sporophyte stage.
  A. The gametophyte generation produces haploid gametes by mitosis.
  B. These gametes fuse in a process known as fertilization, which requires water as a transport medium in both mosses and ferns.

C. The first stage in the sporophyte generation is the zygote, which develops into a multicellular embryo that is protected and nourished by the gametophyte plant.
  D. The mature sporophyte plant has sporogenous cells (spore mother cells) that undergo meiosis, producing haploid spores, which are the first stage in the gametophyte generation.
IV. Mosses and other bryophytes have several advancements over green algae, including the possession of a cuticle, stomata, and multicellular gametangia.
  A. Moss gametophytes are leafy plants that grow from a filamentous protonema.
  B. Liverwort gametophytes are either leafy or thallose.
  C. Hornworts have thalloid gametophytes.
V. Ferns and fern allies have several advancements over algae and bryophytes, including the possession of vascular tissue and a dominant sporophyte generation.
  A. Fern sporophytes have rhizomes, roots, and megaphylls.
  B. Sporophytes of whisk ferns consist of rhizomes and erect branches. They lack true roots and leaves.
  C. Horsetail sporophytes have roots, rhizomes, aerial stems that are hollow and jointed, and leaves that are reduced megaphylls.
  D. Sporophytes of club mosses consist of roots, rhizomes, erect branches, and leaves that are microphylls.
VI. Homospory is the production of one kind of spore, whereas heterospory is the production of two kinds of spores—microspores and megaspores.

POST-TEST

1. The bryophytes lack a _____ system and are therefore restricted in size.
2. The waxy layer that covers aerial parts of plants is the _____.
3. Plants probably evolved from ancient _____ _____.
4. Plants store their carbohydrate reserves as _____.
5. The openings in plants that allow gas exchange for photosynthesis are called _____.
6. The female gametangium, or _____, produces an egg.
7. The male gametangium, or _____, produces sperm.
8. The fusion of gametes is called _____ and results in a diploid fertilized egg, or _____.
9. Meiosis in plants results in the formation of _____.
10. Plants have an _____ of _____ in which they spend part of their life cycle in the gametophyte stage and part in the sporophyte stage.

11. The leafy green moss plant is the _____ generation.
12. The flattened leaflike body form of many liverworts is called a _____.
13. _____ are bryophytes with chloroplasts that are reminiscent of those of certain algae.
14. Clusters of sporangia, termed _____, are often found on fern fronds.
15. A _____ is a leaf that evolved from a branch system.
16. Whisk ferns have vascularized stems but lack true _____ and _____.
17. _____ have hollow, jointed stems that are impregnated with silica.
18. The type of leaf found in club mosses is the _____.
19. Certain lower vascular plants are _____ and produce two kinds of spores.

REVIEW QUESTIONS

1. What are the most important environmental challenges that land plants face, and what adaptations do they possess to meet these challenges?

2. Compare alternation of generations in the mosses and the ferns. Which stage is dominant in each?
3. How does heterospory modify the life cycle?

4. How are mosses, liverworts, and hornworts similar? How is each group distinctive?
5. What features do club mosses, horsetails, and whisk ferns share with ferns? How is each group distinctive?

6. State the advancements that bryophytes have over algae. What advancements do ferns have over algae and bryophytes?

RECOMMENDED READINGS

Gifford, E. M., and A. S. Foster. *Morphology and Evolution of Vascular Plants,* 3rd ed. W. H. Freeman and Company, New York, 1989. An advanced text that discusses the evolutionary significance of plant structures in both living and extinct species.

Mauseth, J. D. *Botany: An Introduction to Plant Biology.* Saunders College Publishing, Philadelphia, 1991. A comprehensive introduction to general botany.

Raven, P. H., R. F. Evert, and S. E. Eichhorn. *Biology of Plants,* 5th ed. Worth Publishers, New York, 1992. A general botany text with an evolutionary emphasis.

CHAPTER 27

The Plant Kingdom: Seed Plants

OUTLINE

Gymnosperms: conifers, cycads, ginkgoes, and gnetophytes
Flowering plants
The evolution of seed plants

The primary means of reproduction and dispersal for the most successful plants is seeds, which develop from the female gametophyte and tissues associated with it. The two groups of seed plants, gymnosperms and flowering plants, show the greatest evolutionary complexity in the plant kingdom and comprise the dominant plants in most habitats. Indeed, one could think of the present time as the "Age of Seed Plants."

Seeds are reproductively superior to spores for several reasons. First, seeds contain a multicellular, well-developed young plant with embryonic root, stem, and leaves already formed, whereas plant spores are composed of a single cell. Second, seeds contain a food supply. After germination, the plant embryo within the seed is nourished by food stored in the seed until it becomes self-sufficient. Because a spore is a single cell, few food reserves exist for the plant that develops from a spore. Third, seeds are protected by a resistant seed coat. Like spores, seeds can live for extended periods of time at reduced rates of metabolism and germinate when conditions become favorable.

Seeds escape from a milkweed fruit.
(Skip Moody/Dembinsky Photo Associates)

Seeds and seed plants have been intimately connected with the development of human civilization. From prehistoric times, early humans collected and used seeds for food. The food supply stored in the seed is a concentrated source of proteins, oils, carbohydrates, and vitamins, which are nourishing for humans as well as for germinating plants. Also, it is easy to store seeds, provided that they are kept dry, so humans could collect seeds during times of plenty and save them for times of need. Few other foods can be stored as conveniently or for as long.

The two groups of seed plants are the **gymnosperms** and the **angiosperms,** or flowering plants. The word *gymnosperm* is adapted from a Greek word meaning "naked seed." These plants produce seeds that are totally exposed or borne on the scales of cones. Pine, spruce, fir, and ginkgo are examples of gymnosperms. The Greek from which the term *angiosperm* is derived translates as "seed enclosed in a vessel or case." Flowering plants, which produce their seeds within a fruit, include such diverse plants as corn, oaks, water lilies, cacti, and buttercups.

Both gymnosperms and flowering plants possess vascular tissue, xylem for the conduction of water and dissolved minerals, and phloem for the conduction of food. Both have alternation of generations and spend a portion of their lives in the diploid sporophyte stage and a portion in the haploid gametophyte stage. The gametophyte generation in each group is significantly reduced. Gymnosperms and flowering plants are heterosporous and produce two types of spores, microspores and megaspores (see Chapter 26).

LEARNING OBJECTIVES

After you have studied this chapter you should be able to

1. Compare the features of seeds with those of spores.
2. Discuss the advantages of plants that reproduce by seeds.
3. Trace the steps in the life cycle of pines.
4. Summarize the features that gymnosperms possess which (1) distinguish them from ferns and (2) distinguish them from flowering plants.
5. Contrast dicots with monocots.
6. Diagram a generalized life cycle of flowering plants.
7. Discuss the evolutionary advancements of the flowering plants.
8. Trace the evolution of gymnosperms from seedless vascular plants and the evolution of flowering plants from gymnosperms.

GYMNOSPERMS ARE VASCULAR PLANTS WITH "NAKED SEEDS"

Some of the most interesting members of the plant kingdom, including a number of record holders, are gymnosperms. For example, the world's most massive organism is the General Sherman tree, a giant sequoia in Sequoia National Park, California, which is over 81.6 meters (272 feet) tall and has a girth of over 23.7 meters (79 feet) at a distance 1.5 meters (5 feet) above ground level. A coastal redwood is the world's tallest tree, measuring almost 114 meters (380 feet) in height (Figure 27–1). The oldest living trees are bristlecone pines, one of which has been dated by tree ring analysis as 4900 years old.

Gymnosperms are usually classified into four divisions. The largest group is the division Coniferophyta, commonly called conifers. Two divisions of gymnosperms represent evolutionary remnants of gymnosperms that were more significant in the past, the Ginkgophyta and the Cycadophyta. The fourth division of gymnosperms, the Gnetophyta, is a collection of some very unusual plants that share certain advancements not found in the other gymnosperms.

Conifers Are Woody Plants That Bear Their Seeds in Cones

The **conifers** (Division Coniferophyta), which includes pines, spruces, hemlocks, and firs, are woody trees or shrubs (there are no herbaceous conifers). Most are evergreen (Figure 27–2), and only a few, such as larch and bald cypress, are **deciduous** and shed their leaves, called **needles,** at the end of the growing season (Figure 27–3). Most conifers are **monoecious,** which means

Figure 27–1　The majestic redwoods are conifers, gymnosperms that produce their seeds in cones. Some of the redwoods are the world's tallest plants.　(Gary R. Bonner)

they have separate male and female reproductive parts in different locations on the same plant. These reproductive parts are generally borne in **cones** (hence their name, *conifer*, which means "bears cones").

Conifers occupy vast areas of Earth today—from the Arctic to the tropics— and are the dominant vegetation in the taiga, the vast forested regions of Canada,

Figure 27–2 Conifers are dominant plants in northern latitudes. Their evergreen needles have special adaptations for surviving in cold environments.   (Dennis Drenner)

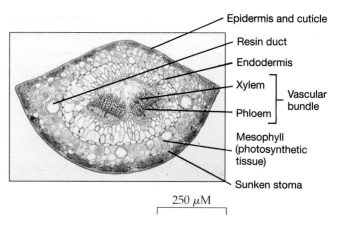

Epidermis and cuticle
Resin duct
Endodermis
Xylem
Phloem   } Vascular bundle
Mesophyll (photosynthetic tissue)
Sunken stoma

250 μM

Figure 27–3 Cross section of a pine needle. The thick, waxy cuticle and sunken stomata (for gas exchange) are two anatomical adaptations that enable the pine tree to retain its needles throughout the winter.   (Dennis Drenner)

Northern Europe, and Siberia (see Chapter 51). In addition, they are important in the Southern Hemisphere, particularly in areas of South America, Australia, and Malaysia. Ecologically, conifers contribute food and shelter to animals and other organisms, and their roots hold the soil in place and help control soil erosion. Humans use conifers for lumber (especially for building materials and paper products) and various substances like turpentine and resins. Because of their attractive appearance, conifers are grown commercially for landscape design and for Christmas trees.

Pine is representative of a typical conifer life cycle

The pine tree is the sporophyte generation and therefore forms spores (Figure 27–4). Pine is heterosporous and produces microspores and megaspores in separate cones. The familiar woody pine cones are female cones, which are usually located on the upper branches of the tree and bear seeds after sexual reproduction has occurred. The male cones are smaller than female cones and are generally produced on the ends of lower branches each spring (Figure 27–5a).

Each male cone is composed of **sporophylls,** leaflike structures that bear sporangia. At the base of each sporophyll are two microsporangia, which contain numerous microsporocytes (also called microspore mother cells). Each of these sporogenous cells undergoes meiosis to form haploid microspores. Microspores then develop into male gametophytes, which are extremely reduced in gymnosperms. The immature male

gametophytes, also called **pollen grains** (Figure 27–5b), are shed from the male cones in great numbers, and some are carried by wind current to the immature female cones.

The woody bracts of the female cones (Figure 27–6) have megasporangia at their bases. Within each megasporangium, meiosis of a megasporocyte (also called a megaspore mother cell) produces four haploid megaspores. One of these develops into a female gametophyte, which produces an egg within each of several archegonia. (The other three megaspores are nonfunctional and soon break down.)

The pollen grain, which initially adhered to the sticky female cone, grows a pollen tube that digests its way through the female gametophyte tissue to the egg within the archegonium. Then a cell within the pollen grain divides to form two nonflagellated sperm (also called pollen grain sperm nuclei, or simply, sperm nuclei). One of these fuses with the egg to form a zygote, or fertilized egg, which grows into a young multicellular pine embryo in the seed.

The haploid female gametophyte tissue surrounding the developing embryo becomes the nutritive tissue in the mature pine seed. The embryo and nutritive tissue are surrounded by a tough protective seed coat, and the mature pine seed has a papery wing that enables it to be carried by wind currents.

There is a long time lapse between the appearance of pine cones on a tree and the maturation of seeds. When **pollination,** the transfer of pollen to the female cone, occurs in the spring, the female cone is immature and meiosis of the megasporocytes (megaspore mother cells) has not occurred. During the ensuing months, the female tissue gradually matures and eggs are formed within archegonia. Meanwhile, the pollen slowly grows a pollen tube through the female tissues to the archegonia. **Fertilization,** the union of the egg and sperm nucleus, occurs during the spring of the year following

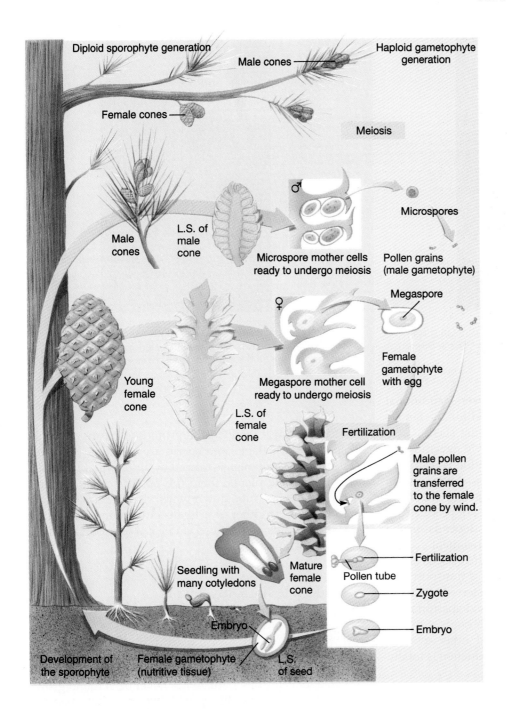

Diploid sporophyte generation

Haploid gametophyte generation

Male cones

Female cones

Meiosis

Male cones

L.S. of male cone

Microspore mother cells ready to undergo meiosis

♂

Microspores

Pollen grains (male gametophyte)

♀

Megaspore

Young female cone

Megaspore mother cell ready to undergo meiosis

L.S. of female cone

Female gametophyte with egg

Fertilization

Male pollen grains are transferred to the female cone by wind.

Fertilization

Pollen tube

Zygote

Embryo

Seedling with many cotyledons

Mature female cone

Embryo

Development of the sporophyte

Female gametophyte (nutritive tissue)

L.S. of seed

Figure 27–4 The life cycle of a pine. One major evolutionary advancement of gymnosperms over the lower vascular plants is the production of wind-borne pollen. Pines and other gymnosperms do not depend on water as a transport medium for sperm.

(a)

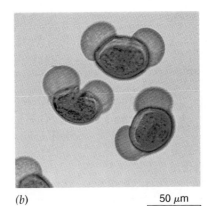

(b)

50 μm

Figure 27–5 Reproduction in pine. (*a*) Male Torrey pine cones produce copious amounts of pollen in the spring. These cones have already shed their pollen and will soon abscise, or detach, from the branch. (*b*) Pine pollen. Note the air bladders that give pollen its buoyancy. Pine pollen is carried by wind to the female cones. (*a*, Dennis Drenner; *b*, Manfred Kage/Peter Arnold, Inc.)

Figure 27–6 Reproduction in pine. Female Torrey pine cone. This cone has not yet opened to shed its seeds. (Dennis Drenner)

Figure 27–7 Cycads growing in South Africa. Cycads are tropical gymnosperms with a palmlike appearance. Most cycads are short plants (under 2 meters tall). (Walter H. Hodge/Peter Arnold, Inc.)

pollination. Seed maturation takes several additional months, although some seeds remain within the female cones for a number of years before being shed.

In the pine life cycle, the sporophyte generation is dominant and the gametophyte generation is restricted to microscopic structures in the cones. Although the female gametophyte produces archegonia, the male gametophyte is so reduced that it does not produce antheridia. The gametophyte generation depends on the parent sporophyte generation for nourishment.

A major advancement in the pine life cycle is elimination of the requirement for water as a transport medium for the sperm. Pine pollen is transferred to female cones by air currents, and nonflagellated sperm nuclei accomplish fertilization by moving through a pollen tube to the egg. Therefore, pine and other gymnosperms are the first plants whose reproduction is totally adapted for life on land.

Cycads Are Gymnosperms with Compound Leaves and Simple Seed Cones

The **cycads** (Division Cycadophyta) were a very important plant group during the Triassic period, which occurred approximately 248 million years ago and is sometimes referred to as the " Age of Cycads." The few remaining extant cycads are tropical plants with compound leaves that give them a palmlike or fernlike appearance (Figure 27–7).

Cycad reproduction is similar to that in pines except that cycads are **dioecious** and therefore have seed cones and pollen cones on separate plants. Their seed structure is most like that of the earliest seeds, and cy-

cads have also retained the primitive feature of motile sperm. These flagellated sperm are a vestige, however, because cycad pollen is carried by air or possibly insects to the female plants; there the pollen germinates and grows a pollen tube down which the sperm pass to get to the egg. In other words, despite having flagellated sperm, cycads do not need water as a transport medium for fertilization.

Ginkgo Is the Only Living Species in Its Division

There is only one living species in the Division Ginkophyta—the ginkgo, or maidenhair tree (Figure 27–8), which is native to China, where it has been cultivated for centuries. Ginkgo has never been found growing wild, and it is likely that it would have become extinct if it had not been cultivated in Chinese monasteries. *Ginkgo* is the oldest genus (and species) of living trees. Fossil ginkgo leaves and wood that are 200 million years old yet nearly identical to the modern-day ginkgo have been discovered.

The ginkgo is common in North America today, particularly in cities, where it is frequently planted because it is somewhat resistant to air pollution. Its leaves are deciduous and turn a beautiful golden color in the fall. Like the cycads, ginkgoes are dioecious, with separate male and female trees, and have flagellated sperm, a vestige that is not required because ginkgoes produce air-borne pollen. Its seeds are completely exposed rather than occurring within cones. Only female trees

Figure 27–8 *Ginkgo biloba*, the ginkgo or maidenhair tree, has separate male and female trees; only the females bear seeds, which are not borne in cones. The unusual leaves of ginkgo resemble those of the maidenhair fern, hence its common name. (William E. Ferguson)

produce seeds, a fact you should remember if you ever wish to plant ginkgoes. As the seeds mature, they produce a disgusting odor, which makes the female trees undesirable. Some cities and towns have passed ordinances making it unlawful to plant female ginkgoes.

Gnetophytes Include Three Unusual Gymnosperms

The Division Gnetophyta is composed of three diverse genera (*Gnetum, Ephedra, Welwitschia*) which share a number of features that make them clearly more advanced than the rest of the gymnosperms. For example, **gnetophytes** have more efficient water-conducting cells, called vessels, in their xylem (see Chapter 31). Flowering plants possess vessels in their xylem, but gymnosperms, with the exception of the gnetophytes, do not. Also, the cone clusters produced by some of the gnetophytes resemble flower clusters.

The genus *Gnetum* contains tropical vines and trees with leaves that resemble those of flowering plants (Figure 27–9*a*). *Ephedra* species (Figure 27–9*b*), shrubs found in deserts and other dry regions, resemble horsetails in appearance and are commonly called joint firs. An Asiatic *Ephedra* is the source of the asthma medicine ephedrine. The third gnetophyte genus, *Welwitschia*, contains a single species found in South African deserts (Figure 27–9*c*). The majority of *Welwitschia*'s body grows underground, and its above-ground stem forms a shallow disk, up to 0.9 meter (3 feet) in diameter, from which two ribbon-like leaves extend. These two leaves

continue to grow from the stem throughout the plant's life, but the ends of the leaves are usually broken and torn by the wind, making it appear as if *Welwitschia* has numerous leaves. When *Welwitschia* reproduces, it forms cones around the edge of its disklike stem.

FLOWERING PLANTS ARE VASCULAR PLANTS THAT PRODUCE FLOWERS, FRUITS, AND SEEDS

The flowering plants, or angiosperms (Division Magnoliophyta), are the most successful plants today, surpassing even the gymnosperms in importance. They have adapted to almost every habitat except Antarctica, and, with approximately 235,000 species, are the dominant plants. Flowering plants reproduce sexually by forming flowers and (after fertilization) seeds within fruits. They possess very efficient water-conducting cells called vessels in their xylem and efficient food-conducting cells called sieve tubes in their phloem (see Chapter 31), and their life cycles have a unique double-fertilization process.

Flowering plants are extremely important to humans, as our very survival as a species depends upon them. All of our major food crops are flowering plants, including important grain crops such as rice, wheat, and corn. Woody flowering plants such as oak, cherry, and walnut provide us with valuable lumber. We use flowering plants to supply us with fibers like cotton, medicines like digitalis, and plant products as diverse as rubber, tobacco, coffee, and aromatic oils for perfumes. Economic botany is the subdiscipline of botany that deals with plants of economic importance, most of which are flowering plants.

There Are Two Classes within the Flowering Plants, Monocots and Dicots

The Division Magnoliophyta is divided into two classes, Liliopsida (commonly called **monocots**) and Magnoliopsida (commonly called **dicots**) (Figure 27–10). Monocots include palms, grasses, orchids, and lilies, and dicots include oaks, roses, cacti, blueberries, and sunflowers. The dicots are more diverse and include more species than the monocots. Table 27–1 provides a comparison of some of the features of the two groups.

Monocots are herbaceous plants with leaves that are usually long and narrow and have parallel venation (the main leaf veins run parallel to one another). The flower parts of monocot flowers occur in three or multiples of three, as for example, three sepals, three petals, three stamens, and three carpels. Monocot seeds have a

(a)

(b)

Figure 27–9 Gnetophytes have a number of advanced features that other gymnosperms lack. (a) The leaves of *Gnetum* are similar to certain flowering plants. (b) *Ephedra*. Species native to desert areas in the southwestern United States were used by pioneers to make a beverage. A common name for this plant is Mormon tea. (c) The most bizarre gymnosperm in the world is *Welwitschia*, which is native to an African desert. Although the plant produces only two leaves, the wind tears them so that it appears to have many. (a, Walter H. Hodge/ Peter Arnold, Inc.; b, Visuals Unlimited/John Cunningham; c, No. Bot. 83024c, Field Museum of Natural History, Chicago)

(c)

Figure 27–10 There are two classes of flowering plants. (a) Monocots such as this *Trillium* have their floral parts in threes. Note the three green sepals, three rose-colored petals, six stamens, and three stigmas (the pistil is composed of three fused carpels). (b) Dicots such as this apple have their floral parts in fours or fives. Note the five petals and the netted venation of the leaves, also a dicot characteristic. (a, Don and Esther Philips/ Tom Stack and Associates; b, John Gerlach/ Dembinsky Photo Associates)

(a)

(b)

Table 27-1 A COMPARISON OF MONOCOTS AND DICOTS

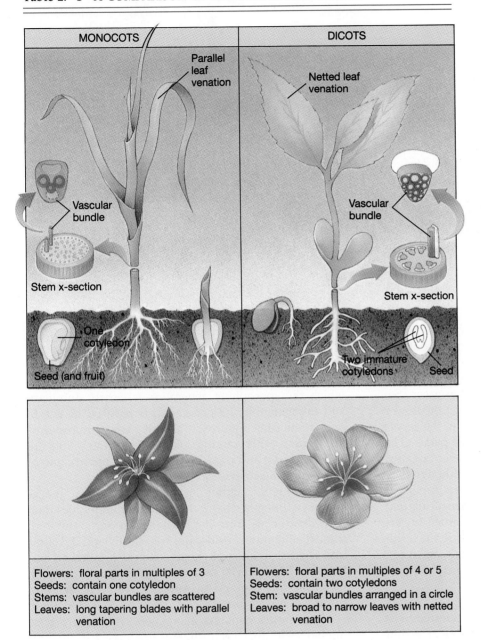

MONOCOTS	DICOTS
Parallel leaf venation	Netted leaf venation
Vascular bundle	Vascular bundle
Stem x-section	Stem x-section
One cotyledon	Two immature cotyledons
Seed (and fruit)	Seed
Flowers: floral parts in multiples of 3 Seeds: contain one cotyledon Stems: vascular bundles are scattered Leaves: long tapering blades with parallel venation	Flowers: floral parts in multiples of 4 or 5 Seeds: contain two cotyledons Stem: vascular bundles arranged in a circle Leaves: broad to narrow leaves with netted venation

single **cotyledon** (embryonic seed leaf), and **endosperm** (nutritive tissue) is usually present in the mature seed.

Dicots may be herbaceous (as for example, tomato) or woody (as for example, hickory). Their leaves are variable in shape, but usually broader than monocot leaves, and have netted venation. Flower parts occur in fours or fives or multiples of four or five. Two cotyledons are present in seeds of dicots, and endosperm is usually absent in the mature seed, having been absorbed by the two cotyledons prior to germination.

Sexual Reproduction in Flowering Plants Involves the Flower

Flowers have four main organs—sepals, petals, stamens, and carpels—that are arranged in whorls (Figure 27–11). A flower that has all four parts is said to be **complete,** whereas an **incomplete** flower lacks one or more of these parts. Although all four parts are important in the reproductive process, only the stamens (the ''male'' parts) and carpels (the ''female'' parts) participate directly in reproduction. A flower that possesses

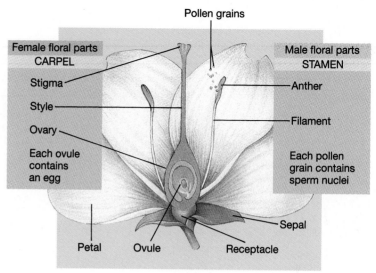

Figure 27–11 Diagram of a "typical" flower. This cutaway view shows the details of basic floral structure.

both stamens and carpels is said to be **perfect,** whereas an **imperfect** flower has stamens *or* carpels, but not both.

Sepals, which are the lowermost and outermost whorl, are leaflike in appearance and often green. Sepals cover and protect the flower parts when the flower is a bud. As the blossom opens from a bud, the sepals fold back to reveal the more conspicuous petals. The collective term for all the sepals of a flower is **calyx.**

Petals are also leaflike in appearance, although they are frequently brightly colored. They play an important role in attracting animal pollinators, thus ensuring that pollination (the transfer of pollen from stamen to carpel) occurs. Petals are not directly involved in the fertilization process, however. Sometimes petals are fused to form a tube or other floral shape; such petals are referred to collectively as a **corolla.**

Just inside the petals are the **stamens,** the "male" reproductive parts, which are collectively referred to as the **androecium.** Each stamen is composed of a thin stalk, called a **filament,** and a saclike **anther,** where meiosis occurs and pollen is produced. Pollen must be transferred to the carpel, usually of another flower of the same species, in order for reproduction to occur.

In the center of most flowers are one or more **carpels,** the "female" reproductive parts. Each carpel has three sections: a **stigma,** where the pollen lands; a **style,** or neck, through which the pollen tube must grow; and an **ovary,** which contains one or more **ovules.** Each ovule contains a female gametophyte and accessory tissues; after fertilization of the egg within, the ovule develops into a seed. The carpels of a flower may be separate or fused together into a single structure called a **pistil.** The collective term for all the carpels of a flower, whether separate or fused, is **gynoecium.**

The Life Cycle of Flowering Plants Includes a Unique Double Fertilization Process

Flowering plants have an alternation of generations in which the sporophyte generation is clearly dominant and the gametophyte generation is reduced in size to only a few cells (Figure 27–12). Like the gymnosperms and certain other vascular plants, flowering plants are heterosporous and produce two kinds of spores, microspores and megaspores.

Each ovule within an ovary contains a megasporocyte (megaspore mother cell) that undergoes meiosis, producing four haploid megaspores. Three of these disintegrate; one divides mitotically and develops into a female gametophyte, which is also called an **embryo sac.** The embryo sac contains eight haploid nuclei, including one egg and two **polar nuclei.** The egg and the polar nuclei are directly involved in fertilization.

The anther contains microsporocytes (microspore mother cells) that each undergo meiosis to form four haploid microspores. Each microspore develops into a male gametophyte, which is also called a pollen grain. Pollen is transferred to the stigma of the carpel and, if compatible, germinates and grows a thin pollen tube down the style and into the ovary. A cell within the pollen grain divides to form two nonflagellated male gametes, called pollen grain sperm nuclei, or simply sperm nuclei. Both sperm nuclei are involved in the fertilization process.

Something happens during sexual reproduction in flowering plants that does not occur anywhere else in the living world. When the sperm nuclei enter the embryo sac, *both* of them participate in fertilization. One sperm nucleus fuses with the egg, forming a zygote that will grow by mitosis and develop into a plant embryo

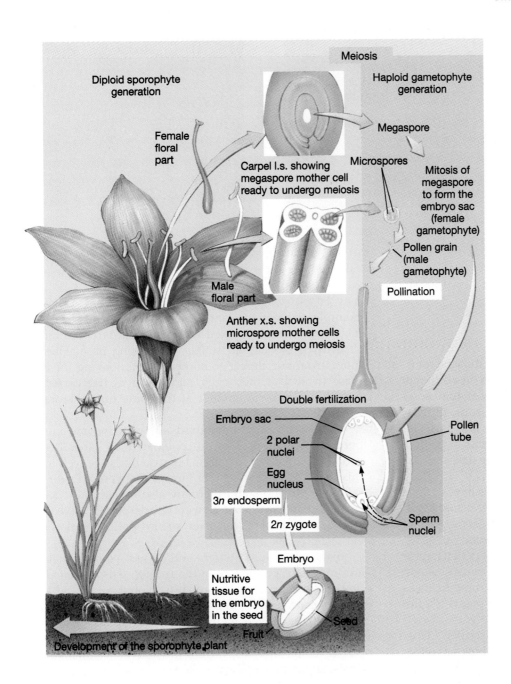

Figure 27–12 Generalized life cycle of a typical flowering plant. The most significant feature of the flowering plant life cycle is double fertilization.

in the seed. The second sperm nucleus fuses with the two haploid polar nuclei, forming a **triploid** (3*n*) cell that grows by mitosis and develops into endosperm in the seed. This process, involving two separate cell fusions, is called **double fertilization** and is, with one exception, unique to flowering plants.[1]

As a result of double fertilization, each seed contains (1) a young plant, (2) food or nutritive tissue (the endosperm), and (3) a seed coat. In monocots the endo-sperm persists and is the main source of food in the mature seed. In most dicots the endosperm is used by the developing embryo, which subsequently stores food in its cotyledons.

As a seed develops from an ovule, the ovary wall surrounding it enlarges and develops into a fruit. In some instances, other tissues associated with the ovary also enlarge to form the fruit. Fruits serve two purposes, to protect the developing seeds from desiccation during maturation and to aid in the dispersal of seeds (see Chapter 35). For example, dandelion fruits have feathery plumes that enable the entire fruit to be carried by air currents. Once a seed lands in a suitable place, it germinates and develops into a mature sporophyte plant, and the life cycle continues as described.

---

[1] In 1990, double fertilization was reported in a gymnosperm, *Ephedra nevadensis*. The first fertilization process, between egg and sperm, results in a zygote as in flowering plants. The second fertilization process produces an additional zygote.

Figure 27–13 Animal pollinators. (*a*) A ruby-throated hummingbird pollinating a trumpet vine flower. (*b*) Bats are important pollinators in the tropics. The pollen grains on the bat's fur will be carried to the next plant, where cross pollination will occur. (*a*, Dan Dempster/ Dembinsky Photo Associates; *b*, Merlin D. Tuttle/Bat Conservation, International)

(*a*) (*b*)

Flowering Plants and Their Animal Pollinators Have Affected One Another's Evolution

Before fertilization can take place, pollen must be transferred from the anther to the stigma, often on a different flower. Flowering plants have evolved a number of mechanisms to ensure this transfer, and some of these involve animals, including insects, birds, and bats. Unrelated species of plants with similar agents of pollination share similar floral features; these features are known as **pollination syndromes.**

Flowers that are pollinated by animals have various methods to attract them, including showy petals (a visual attractant) and scent (an olfactory attractant). One of the rewards for the pollinator is food: nectar (a sugary solution used as an energy-rich food) and pollen (a protein-rich food). As the animal moves from flower to flower searching for rewards, it inadvertently carries pollen, thus facilitating reproduction in plants (Figure 27–13).

Insects are often involved in pollen transfer. Plants that are pollinated by insects often have blue or yellow petals. The insect eye does not perceive color in the same manner as the human eye. Insects see very well in the blue and yellow range of visible light but do not perceive red as a distinct color. Consequently, flowers that are pollinated by insects are not usually red. Insects can also see in the ultraviolet range of the electromagnetic spectrum, an area that is invisible to the human eye; insects see ultraviolet as a color called "bee's purple" (Figure 27–14). Many insect-pollinated flowers have parts that reflect ultraviolet (making them appear purple to insects) and parts that absorb ultraviolet (making them appear other colors such as yellow). This creates patterns on the flower that direct the insect to the center of the flower where the pollen and nectar are located.

Insects have a well-developed sense of smell, and many insect-pollinated flowers have a strong scent that may be pleasant, but not always (Figure 27–15). For example, the carrion plant, which is pollinated by flies, has petals that are dappled with a reddish-brown color (like dried blood) and smells like rotting flesh. Flies move from one flower to another while looking for a place to deposit their eggs, and pollen is transferred from one flower to another at the same time (Figure 27–16).

Birds such as hummingbirds are effective and important pollinators. Flowers pollinated by birds are usually colored red to yellow because birds see well in this region of visible light. In Europe there are no natural bird pollinators and there are also no naturally occurring plants with red flowers. Birds do not have a strong sense of smell, however, so bird-pollinated flowers usually lack a scent.

Bats, which feed at night and do not see very well, are important pollinators in the tropics. Bat-pollinated flowers typically have dusky, dull-colored petals and a strong scent, usually like fermented fruit. Bats are attracted to the flowers by their scent and lap up the nectar. As they move from flower to flower, they transfer pollen. Other animals, including snails and small rodents, sometimes pollinate plants.

Animal pollinators and the plants they pollinate have had such a close association that they have affected one another's evolution. In other words, a strong selective force in the evolution of certain features of flowering plants has been their animal pollinators. Flowering plants have likewise been a strong selective force in the evolution of certain features of those animal pollinators. What is being described here is **coevolution,** a type of evolution in which two different organisms interact so closely that they become increasingly adapted to one another over time.

During the time plants were coevolving specialized features to attract pollinators, the animal pollinators coevolved specialized body parts and behaviors that enable them to both aid pollination and obtain nectar and pollen as a reward. Coevolution is responsible for

(a)

(b)

Figure 27–14 Many insect-pollinated flowers have ultraviolet markings that are invisible to humans but very conspicuous to insects. (*a*) A flower as seen by the human eye is solid yellow. (*b*) The same flower viewed under ultraviolet radiation provides clues about how the insect eye perceives it. The outer, light-appearing portions of the petals reflect both yellow and ultraviolet, which makes them appear purple to the bee's eyes. The inner parts of the flower absorb ultraviolet, which makes them appear yellow to the bee. These differences in coloration draw attention to the center of the flower, where the pollen and nectar are located. (*a, b,* Thomas Eisner)

the long, curved beaks of certain honeycreepers, Hawaiian birds that insert their beaks into tubular flowers to obtain nectar (see Chapter 19). Coevolution is also responsible for the long, tubular corolla of the flowers that honeycreepers visit.

Animal behavior has also coevolved. The flowers of certain orchids, for example, resemble female wasps in coloring and shape. Male wasps, which mature before female wasps, attempt to copulate with the orchid flowers, transferring pollen as they move from flower to flower. When female wasps emerge at a later time, the males finally get to mate for real!

A number of obligate relationships have evolved between animal pollinators and the plants they pollinate. For example, a yucca native to the Southwest can be pollinated only by one species of moth, and the female moth lays her eggs only in the yucca flower's

Figure 27–15 *Amorphophallus*, commonly called devil's tongue, produces a disagreeable floral odor that is visible in this photograph. The floral amines (nitrogen-containing organic compounds) that cause the odor react with HCl on the filter paper wick to produce a chlorine-amine aerosol precipitate that is visible. The devil's tongue is pollinated by beetles and flies. (J. M. Patt and B. J. D. Meeuse)

Figure 27–16 *Stapelia variegata*. This desert flowering plant is sometimes called the carrion plant due to its coloration and unpleasant scent. It is pollinated by flies. (G. J. James/Biological Photo Service)

ovary. Both the yucca and the moth would become extinct if something happened to the other, as neither would be able to reproduce successfully.

Some plants rely on wind rather than animals to transfer pollen (Figure 27–17). Flowering plants that are wind-pollinated produce many, often inconspicuous, flowers. They do not invest their energy in producing large, colorful petals, scent, or nectar. Wind pollination

FOCUS ON

Pollen and Hay Fever

If you suffer from hay fever, you are not alone. Millions of people endure the sneezing and itchy, watery eyes associated with this condition. Everyone knows that one of the causes of hay fever is pollen, but many blame any plant in bloom when they are suffering. For this reason, roses and goldenrod are often unjustly accused.

Hay fever is caused by certain wind-pollinated plants. Plants that produce large, colorful petals are pollinated by animals and do not cause hay fever because their pollen does not get into the air in appreciable quantities. Wind-pollinated plants, on the other hand, must produce large amounts of pollen to ensure that at least some of it lands on the stigmas for successful reproduction. Not all wind-pollinated plants cause an aller-

gic reaction. For example, the conifers are wind-pollinated, yet allergies to conifers are rare.

People with allergies can suffer at different times during the growing season, depending on which plants are pollinating and whether they are sensitized to those plants. In early spring, many trees pollinate before their leaves are fully developed. (Can you explain why pollination at this time would be advantageous to the tree?[1]) Trees that cause allergic reactions in humans include oaks, ashes, walnuts, maples, and elms. If you suffer in late spring and early summer, you are probably allergic to grass pollen, such as bluegrass, timothy, and redtop. It is interesting that most of our major grass crops (e.g., corn, rice, and wheat) do not cause

allergies in humans. In late summer and early fall, people are allergic to different plants, depending on their geographical location. Ragweed is the culprit in the East, whereas saltbush and Russian thistle are problems in the West.

Most people are born with some resistance to pollen allergies, but many become sensitized by repeated contact. For that reason, a move to a different geographical location often temporarily halts the suffering. The biology of the allergic reaction is explained in Chapter 43.

---

[1] If pollination occurred when the leaves were fully formed, the leaves would block the effective dispersal of pollen by the wind.

---

is a "hit or miss" affair, and the likelihood of pollen landing on the stigma of the same species of flower is slim. Wind-pollinated plants therefore produce copious amounts of pollen. Wind-pollinated plants include grasses, ragweed, and many trees (see Focus on Pollen and Hay Fever).

Figure 27–17 Wind is an agent of pollination for a number of flowering plants, including many flowering trees. Shown are clusters of box elder flowers, which lack petals. (David Cavagnaro)

The Evolutionary Advancements of the Flowering Plants Account for Their Success

Why are the flowering plants so successful, both in terms of their ecological dominance and in terms of their large number of different species? Certainly, seed production as their primary means of reproduction and dispersal is significant. The presence of closed carpels and double fertilization increases the reproductive success of flowering plants. However, flowering plants have a number of other advanced features besides their highly successful reproduction. Flowering plants, with few exceptions, have vessels in their xylem and sieve tubes in their phloem, making these vascular tissues very efficient at conduction (see Chapter 31). The leaves of flowering plants, with their broad, expanded blades, are structured for maximum efficiency in photosynthesis (see Chapter 32). Abscission of these leaves during cold or dry spells is also an advantage that has enabled some flowering plants to expand into habitats that would otherwise be too harsh for survival. In addition, the roots of flowering plants are often modified for food or water storage (see Chapter 34).

Probably most crucial to the success of flowering plants, however, is the overall adaptability of the sporophyte generation. This adaptability is evident in the large diversity exhibited by the group. For example, the cactus is marvelously adapted for desert environments, whereas the water lily is well adapted for wet environments. Flowering plants may be so successful, then, because they readily adapt to new habitats and changing environments.

THE FOSSIL RECORD PROVIDES VALUABLE CLUES ABOUT THE EVOLUTION OF SEED PLANTS

One of the groups of plants that evolved from ancestral seedless vascular plants was the **progymnosperms,** all of which are now extinct. Progymnosperms had two advanced features over their immediate ancestors: leaves that were megaphylls (see Chapter 26) and woody tissue that was similar to that of modern gymnosperms. (Recall that ancient club mosses and horsetails included some trees; these plants had woody tissues that differed in several respects from modern woody plants.) Progymnosperms retained a primitive feature, however: They reproduced by spores.

Fossils exist of several advanced progymnosperms that have reproductive structures intermediate between those of spore plants and seed plants. For example, the evolution of microspores into pollen grains and of megasporangia into ovules can be traced in fossil progymnosperms. Plants producing seeds appeared during the late Devonian period over 360 million years ago,

and the fossil record indicates that seed plants apparently evolved independently several times.

Some questions persist about the exact pathway of gymnosperm evolution. The fossil record shows that progymnosperms gave rise to conifers and to another group of extinct plants called **seed ferns.** The seed ferns, which were seed-bearing woody plants with fernlike leaves, in turn gave rise to cycads and possibly ginkgoes, as well as to several plant groups that are now extinct. The origin of gnetophytes remains unclear.

Flowering plants evolved from gymnosperms. By the middle of the Jurassic period, approximately 180 million years ago, a number of gymnosperm lines had evolved with advanced features reminiscent of flowering plants. Among other features, these derived gymnosperms possessed leaves with broad, expanded blades and the first carpels. It is also evident that beetles were visiting these plants; perhaps this was the beginning of coevolution between plants and their pollinators.

The main task facing paleobotanists (scientists who study fossil plants) today is determining which of the ancient gymnosperms with advanced features were in the direct line of evolution to the flowering plants. Most botanists think that flowering plants arose only once; that is, that there is only one line of evolution from the gymnosperms to the flowering plants. The earliest fossils of flowering plants are in Cretaceous rocks approximately 130 million years old. About 50 million years later, during the late Cretaceous period, fossils of flowering plants outnumber those of gymnosperms and ferns, indicating their rapid success once they appeared. The first flowering plants were dicots that were probably weedy shrubs rather than trees or herbaceous plants. Monocots originated from the dicots, possibly along several lines of descent.

SUMMARY

I. Seeds represent an evolutionary advancement over spores.
  A. Each seed contains a well-developed plant embryo and a food supply.
  B. Gymnosperms and flowering plants reproduce by seeds.
II. Gymnosperms are vascular plants with "naked seeds" (that is, seeds that are not enclosed within a fruit).
  A. Gymnosperms are advanced over ferns in several ways, including the production of wind-borne pollen.
  B. There are four divisions of gymnosperms.
    1. Conifers, which are the largest group of gymnosperms, are woody plants that bear needle leaves and produce their seeds in cones.
    2. Cycads are palmlike or fernlike in appearance but reproduce in a manner similar to pines. There are relatively few extant members of this once large division.
    3. *Ginkgo,* the only living species in its division, is a deciduous, dioecious tree. Female ginkgoes produce fleshy seeds directly on branches.
    4. Gnetophytes share a number of advances over other gymnosperms, including vessels in their xylem.
III. Flowering plants (angiosperms) are vascular plants that produce seeds enclosed within a fruit.
  A. The flower, which may contain sepals, petals, stamens, and carpels, functions in sexual reproduction.
  B. There are two classes of flowering plants.

1. Monocots have floral parts in multiples of three, and their seeds contain one cotyledon. The nutritive tissue in their mature seeds is endosperm.
2. Dicots have floral parts in multiples of four or five, and their seeds contain two cotyledons. The nutritive organs in their mature seeds are usually the cotyledons, which have absorbed the nutrients in the endosperm.
C. Flowering plants have several advanced features.
   1. Double fertilization, which results in the formation of both a diploid zygote and triploid endosperm tissue, is unique to the flowering plants.
   2. Flowering plants possess vessels in their xylem.
   3. Various flowering plants use wind or animals to transfer pollen.

IV. Seed plants evolved from seedless vascular plants.
   A. Progymnosperms were seedless vascular plants that had megaphylls and "modern" woody tissue.
      1. Progymnosperms gave rise to conifers.
      2. Progymnosperms gave rise to seed ferns, which in turn gave rise to cycads and possibly ginkgoes.
   B. The evolution of gnetophytes is unclear.
   C. Flowering plants evolved from ancient gymnosperms with advanced features, including leaves with broad, expanded blades and carpels.
      1. Flowering plants probably arose only once.
      2. The first flowering plants were dicot weedy shrubs.
      3. Monocots evolved from dicots, possibly several times.

POST-TEST

1. _____ contain an embryo and food tissue and thus are better than spores for reproduction.
2. Plants that shed their leaves at the end of the growing season are _____.
3. Most conifers are _____ and have male and female reproductive parts at different locations on the same plant.
4. Although conifers bear their seeds in cones, they are considered the "naked seed" plants because their seeds are not enclosed in a _____.
5. The immature male gametophyte of pine is called _____.
6. The nutritive tissue in the pine seed is the _____ _____ tissue.
7. The transfer of pollen from the male to the female reproductive structure is known as _____.
8. Flagellated sperm are found as vestiges in two gymnosperm groups, the _____ and the _____.
9. This class of flowering plants, the _____, includes the palms, grasses, and orchids.
10. The nutritive tissue in flowering plant seeds which is formed as a result of double fertilization is called _____.
11. The _____ is composed of a stigma, style, and ovary.

12. A flower that lacks stamens is said to be both _____ and _____.
13. After fertilization, the _____ develops into a fruit and the _____ develops into a seed.
14. The female gametophyte in flowering plants is also called the _____ _____.
15. Plants with blue petals, nectar, and a strong scent are most likely pollinated by _____.
16. Plants with reduced or absent petals, no nectar, no scent, and copious amounts of pollen are most likely pollinated by _____.
17. The fact that deep tubular flowers are pollinated by insects with long mouthparts, whereas short flowers are pollinated by insects with short mouthparts, is an example of _____.
18. The _____ are extinct seedless vascular plants that had megaphylls and "modern" woody tissue.
19. The progymnosperms gave rise to the _____ and to the seed ferns, which in turn gave rise to the cycads and possibly the _____.
20. Flowering plants evolved from ancient _____ with advanced features.

REVIEW QUESTIONS

1. Why are seeds such a significant evolutionary development?
2. List several ways that conifers are advanced over ferns.
3. What features do cycads, ginkgoes, and gnetophytes share with conifers?
4. How are flowering plants different from gymnosperms?
5. Diagram a flower and label the following parts: anther, calyx, carpel, corolla, filament, ovary, ovule, petal, sepal, stamen, stigma, and style.

6. What are the two classes of flowering plants, and how can one distinguish between them?
7. How does pollination occur in the gymnosperms? In the flowering plants?
8. Describe the evolutionary changes that had to take place as ancient gymnosperms evolved into flowering plants.

RECOMMENDED READINGS

Mauseth, J. D. *Botany: An Introduction to Plant Biology.* Saunders College Publishing, Philadelphia, 1991. A comprehensive introduction to general botany.

Raven, P. H., R. F. Evert, and S. E. Eichhorn. *Biology of Plants,* 5th ed. Worth Publishers, New York, 1992. A general botany text with an evolutionary emphasis.

Stein, B. A. Sicklebill hummingbirds, ants, and flowers. *Bioscience* 42:1, January 1992. Examines two different plant-animal interactions (between ants and flowers, and hummingbirds and flowers) to obtain clues about the structural features of the plants.

Stolzenburg, W. The lonesome flower. *Nature Conservancy* March/April 1992. The only natural pollinator for a flowering plant living in the Hawaiian Islands has disappeared, presumably due to extinction. As a result, the plant is doomed to extinction unless conservation efforts are successful.

Weiss, M. R. Floral color changes as cues for pollinators. *Nature* 354, 21 November 1991. Many plants have flowers that change color from one day to the next, thus guiding the movements of animal pollinators.

The Animal Kingdom: Animals without A Coelom

More than a million species of animals have been classified, and perhaps several million more remain to be identified. Most biologists classify members of kingdom Animalia in about 35 different phyla. The animals most familiar to us—dogs, birds, fish, frogs, snakes—are **vertebrates** (a subphylum of phylum Chordata). A vertebrate is an animal with a backbone. You may be surprised to learn that vertebrates account for only about 5% of the species of the animal kingdom. The majority of animals are the less familiar **invertebrates,** animals without backbones. The invertebrates include such diverse forms as sponges, jellyfish, worms, mollusks, insects, crustaceans, and sea stars.

We have no difficulty identifying a horse as an animal and an oak tree as a plant, but many marine animals that live attached to rocks or docks are often mistaken for plants. For example, early naturalists thought that sponges were plants because they did not move from place to place. So many diverse animal forms exist that exceptions can be found to almost any definition of an animal. Still, there are some characteristics that describe at least most animals (Figure 28–1):

The jellyfish *Gonionemus vertens,* photographed in Friday Harbor, Washington. (C. E. Mills, University of Washington/Biological Photo Service)

1. All animals are multicellular eukaryotes.
2. The cells of an animal are specialized to perform specific functions. In all but the simplest animals, cells are organized to form tissues, and tissues are organized to form organs. In most animal phyla, specialized body systems carry on specific functions.
3. Animals are heterotrophs; they depend on other organisms for nourishment. Most animals ingest their

food first and then digest it inside the body, usually within a digestive system.

4. Most animals are capable of locomotion at some time during their life cycle. However, there are some animals—for example, the sponges—that are **sessile** (firmly attached to the ground or to some object) as adults.

5. Most animals have well-developed sensory and nervous systems and can respond rapidly to changes in their environment.

6. Most animals reproduce sexually, with large, non-motile eggs and small flagellated sperm. Sperm and egg unite to form a fertilized egg, or **zygote,** which develops into a larva or immature form.

LEARNING OBJECTIVES

After you have studied this chapter you should be able to

1. List the characteristics common to most animals; using these characteristics, develop a brief definition of an animal.
2. Identify an ecological role of animals and discuss their distribution; compare the advantages and disadvantages of life in the sea, in fresh water, and on land.
3. Relate the animal phyla on the basis of symmetry, type of body cavity, and pattern of embryonic development, e.g., protostome versus deuterostome.
4. Identify the distinguishing characteristics of phyla Porifera, Cnidaria, Ctenophora, Platyhelminthes, Nemertinea, Nematoda, and Rotifera; compare the level of organization of each of these phyla.

5. Classify a given animal in the appropriate phylum (from among those listed in Objective 4), and identify the class to which it belongs.
6. Trace the life cycle of the following parasites: *Ascaris,* tapeworm, hookworm, and trichina worm. Identify several adaptations that these animals possess for their parasitic lifestyle.
7. Explain the adaptive advantages of each of the following characteristics: bilateral symmetry, cephalization, a motile larva, digestive cavity with two openings, hermaphroditism.

ANIMALS INHABIT MOST ENVIRONMENTS OF THE ECOSPHERE

As consumers, animals depend on producers for their raw materials, energy, and oxygen. Animals also depend upon decomposers for recycling nutrients.

Animals are distributed in virtually every environment of our planet. Animals probably evolved in the Precambrian seas, and most animal phyla still inhabit the sea. Of the three environments—salt water, fresh water, and land—the sea is the most hospitable. Sea water is isotonic to the tissue fluids of most marine animals, so they have little problem maintaining fluid and salt balance. The buoyancy of sea water supports its inhabitants, and the temperature is relatively constant owing to the large volume of water. **Plankton** (the organisms that are suspended in the water and float with its movement) consists of tiny animals and protists that provide a ready source of food.

Life in the sea has certain disadvantages. Although the continuous motion of the water brings nutrients to animals and washes their wastes away, animals must be able to cope with the constant churning and currents that could sweep them away. Fish and marine mammals are strong enough swimmers that they can direct their movements and maintain their location effec-

tively. However, most invertebrates are unable to swim strongly and so have other adaptations. Some are sessile, attaching to some stable structure like a rock, so that they are not wafted about with the tides and currents. Others cling to the substratum or burrow in the sand and silt that cover the sea bottom. Many invertebrates have adapted by maintaining a small body size and becoming part of the plankton. They survive successfully because while they are tossed about, their food supply continues to surround them.

Fresh water offers a much less constant environment than sea water and generally contains less food. Oxygen content and temperature vary, and turbidity (due to sediment suspended in the water) and even water volume fluctuate. Fresh water is hypotonic to the tissue fluids of animals, so water tends to diffuse into the animal; therefore, freshwater animals must have mechanisms for removing excess water while retaining salts. This osmoregulation requires an expenditure of energy. For these reasons, far fewer kinds of animals make their homes in fresh water than in the sea.

Terrestrial life is even more difficult. Dehydration is a serious threat, because water is constantly lost by evaporation and is often difficult to replace. Only a few animal groups, most notably representatives of the arthropods (insects, spiders, and some related forms) and the higher vertebrates, have successfully made their homes on land.

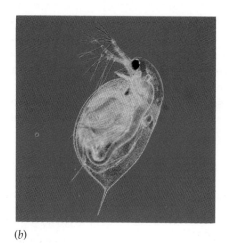

(a)   (b)   (c)

Figure 28–1   Despite their diversity, most members of the animal kingdom share several distinct traits. (a) Some marine animals, like this feather star from the South China Sea, do not move about from place to place and are sometimes mistaken for plants. (b) The nearly transparent body of this freshwater crustacean, *Simocephalus vetulus,* or water flea, shows a complex of organ systems. (c) As heterotrophs, all animals must feed either on producers or on other animals that eat producers. Those that feed on other animals are often highly motile and complex in their behavior. Shown here is a fishing spider feeding on a small fish. The numerous black dots on the dorsal (back) surface of the spider are actually eyes. Although these eyes do not allow the spider to see sharp images, they do serve to make this animal an extremely efficient hunter.   (a, Robert and Linda Mitchell; b, Hermann Eisenbeiss/ Photo Researchers, Inc.; c, Robert Noonan/Photo Researchers, Inc.)

ANIMALS CAN BE CLASSIFIED ACCORDING TO BODY STRUCTURE OR PATTERN OF DEVELOPMENT

Although the evolutionary origin of animals is not clear, many biologists think that most animals evolved from protists, probably from the flagellates. Although the relationships among the various animal phyla are a matter of debate, a few of the more widely held hypotheses are presented in this section.

The animal kingdom may be divided into two large groups, or subkingdoms: **Parazoa,** which consists of sponges, and **Eumetazoa,** which includes all the other animals. This distinction is made because the sponges are so different from all other animals that most biologists think that they are not directly ancestral to any other animal phylum.

In comparing groups of animals, it is convenient to use terms like *lower* and *higher, simple* and *complex,* and *primitive* and *advanced.* Such terms as higher, complex, or advanced do not imply that these animals are better or more nearly perfect than others. Rather, such terms are used in a comparative sense to describe their hypothesized evolutionary relationships. For example, the terms *higher* and *lower* usually refer to the level at which a particular group has diverged from a main line of evolution. It is customary, for instance, to refer to sponges and cnidarians as lower invertebrates because they are thought to have originated near the base of the phylogenetic tree of the animal kingdom. However, neither sponges nor cnidarians are primitive in all structural or physiological characteristics. Each has become highly specialized to its own particular lifestyle.

Animals Can Be Classified According to Body Symmetry

Members of Eumetazoa are often classified in two major branches, partly on the basis of body symmetry. Two phyla, the cnidarians (jellyfish and relatives) and the ctenophores (comb jellies), have **radial symmetry** and are included in the Branch **Radiata.** An animal with radial symmetry has a top and bottom, and similar body parts are arranged as spokes, or radii, from a central body axis. Radial symmetry is considered an adaptation for a sessile lifestyle, for it enables the organism to receive stimuli equally from all directions in the environment.

All of the other eumetazoans have **bilateral symmetry** (at least in their larval stages) and belong to the Branch **Bilateria.** In bilateral symmetry, a plane through the midline of the body divides the body into roughly equivalent right and left halves that are mirror images (Figure 28–2). Bilateral symmetry is considered an adaptation to motility. The front, or **anterior,** end of the animal generally has a head where sense organs are concentrated; this end is positioned to receive most environmental stimuli. The **posterior,** or rear, end of the animal may be equipped with a tail for swimming or may just follow along.

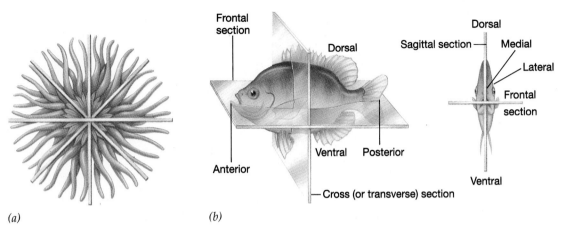

(a)   *(b)*

Figure 28–2 Types of body symmetry in animals. (*a*) In radial symmetry, multiple planes can be drawn through the central axis; each divides the organism into two mirror images. (*b*) Most animals are bilaterally symmetrical. A sagittal cut (lengthwise vertical cut) divides the animal into right and left parts (see figure to right). The head end of the animal is generally its anterior end, and the opposite end is its posterior end. The back of the animal is its dorsal surface; the belly surface is ventral. The diagram also illustrates various ways in which the body can be sectioned (cut) in order to study its internal structure. Many cross sections and sagittal sections are used in illustrations throughout this book to show relationships among tissues and organs.

In order to locate body structures, it is helpful to define some basic terms and directions (Figure 28–2). The back surface of an animal is its **dorsal** surface; the belly side is its **ventral** surface. (In animals that stand on two limbs, such as humans, the term *posterior* refers to the dorsal surface and *anterior* to the ventral surface.) A structure is said to be **medial** if it is relatively closer to the midline of the body and **lateral** if it is toward one side of the body. For example, in a human, the ear is lateral to the nose. The terms **cephalic** and **rostral** (and **superior,** in human anatomy) refer to the head end of the body; the term **caudal** refers to structures closer to the tail. (The term **inferior** is used in human anatomy to mean located below some point of reference, or toward the feet.)

A bilaterally symmetrical organism has three axes, each at right angles to the other two: an anterior-posterior axis extending from head to tail; a dorsoventral axis extending from back to belly; and a left-right axis extending from side to side. We can distinguish three planes (flat surfaces that divide the body into specific parts). A **sagittal plane** divides the body into right and left parts; this plane passes from anterior to posterior and from dorsal to ventral. A **frontal plane** divides a bilateral body into dorsal and ventral parts. A **transverse section,** or **cross section,** cuts at right angles to the body axis and separates anterior and posterior parts.

Animals Can Be Grouped According to Type of Body Cavity

A widely held system for relating the animal phyla to one another is based upon the type of body cavity, or coelom. In the simplest eumetazoans (cnidarians and platyhelminths), the body is essentially a double-walled sac surrounding a digestive cavity with a single opening to the outside—the mouth. There is no body cavity, so these animals are referred to as **acoelomates** (without cavity; Figure 28–3). In order to understand the types of body cavities, we must digress briefly into the animal's embryonic origins.

The structures of most animals develop from three embryonic tissue layers, called **germ layers.** The outer layer, called the **ectoderm,** gives rise to the outer covering of the body and to the nervous system. The inner layer, or **endoderm,** lines the digestive tract. **Mesoderm,** the middle layer, extends between the ectoderm and endoderm and gives rise to most of the other body structures, including the muscles, bones, and circulatory system. The development of the germ layers is described in more detail in Chapter 49.

Complex animals usually have a tube-within-a-tube body plan: The inner tube, the digestive tract, is lined with tissue derived from endoderm and is open at each end—the mouth and the anus. The outer tube or body wall is covered with tissue derived from ectoderm. Between the two tubes is a second cavity, the body cavity. If the body cavity develops between the mesoderm and endoderm, it is called a **pseudocoelom** (false cavity). Animals with this type of body cavity are **pseudocoelomates.**

If the body cavity forms within the mesoderm and is completely lined by mesoderm, the body cavity is a true **coelom.** Animals with a true coelom are **coelomates.** Advantages of having a coelom are discussed in Chapter 29. The phylogenetic tree shown in Figure 28–4 indicates the relationships of the major phyla of animals based on their type of coelom.

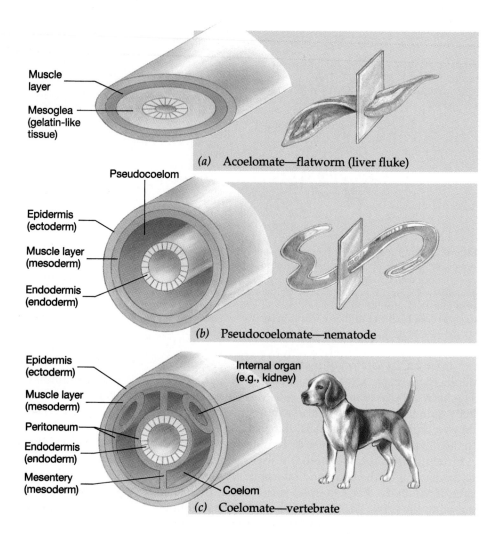

Muscle layer

Mesoglea (gelatin-like tissue)

(a) Acoelomate—flatworm (liver fluke)

Pseudocoelom

Epidermis (ectoderm)

Muscle layer (mesoderm)

Endodermis (endoderm)

(b) Pseudocoelomate—nematode

Epidermis (ectoderm)

Muscle layer (mesoderm)

Peritoneum

Endodermis (endoderm)

Mesentery (mesoderm)

Internal organ (e.g., kidney)

Coelom

(c) Coelomate—vertebrate

Figure 28–3 Three basic animal body plans are illustrated by these cross sections. (*a*) An acoelomate animal has no body cavity. The mesoglea is a gelatin-like tissue. (*b*) A pseudocoelomate animal has a body cavity that develops between the mesoderm and endoderm. The term *body cavity* refers to the space between the body wall and the internal organs. (*c*) In a coelomate animal, the body cavity, called a coelom, is completely lined with tissue derived from mesoderm.

Animals Can Be Classified as Protostomes or Deuterostomes

In another important phylogenetic scheme, complex animals are divided into two groups—the protostomes and deuterostomes—based on their pattern of early embryonic development. These groups reflect two main lines of evolution. Early during embryonic development, a group of cells moves inward to form an opening called the **blastopore.** In most mollusks, annelids, and arthropods, this opening develops into the mouth; these animals comprise the **protostomes** (meaning "first, the mouth"). (Some taxonomists include the flatworms and pseudocoelomates as protostomes.) In echinoderms (e.g., the sea star) and chordates (the phylum that includes the vertebrates), the blastopore develops into the anus; the opening that develops into the mouth forms later in development. These animals are the **deuterostomes** ("second, the mouth").

Another difference in the development of protostomes and deuterostomes is the pattern of **cleavage,** that is, the first several cell divisions of the embryo. In

protostomes, the early cell divisions are oblique to the polar axis, resulting in a spiral arrangement of cells; any one cell is located between the two cells above or below it (Figure 28–5). This pattern of division is known as **spiral cleavage.** In **radial cleavage,** characteristic of the deuterostomes, the early divisions are either parallel or at right angles to the polar axis; the cells are located directly above or below one another.

In the protostomes, the fate of each embryonic cell is fixed very early. For example, if the first four cells of an annelid embryo are separated, each cell develops into only a fixed quarter of the larva; this is referred to as **determinate cleavage.** In deuterostomes, cleavage is **indeterminate:** If the first four cells of a sea star embryo, for instance, are separated, each cell is capable of forming a complete, though small, larva.

Still another difference between protostome and deuterostome development is the manner in which the coelom is formed. In protostomes, the mesoderm splits, and the split widens into a cavity that becomes the coelom (Figure 28–6). This method of coelom formation is known as **schizocoely,** and for this reason the proto-

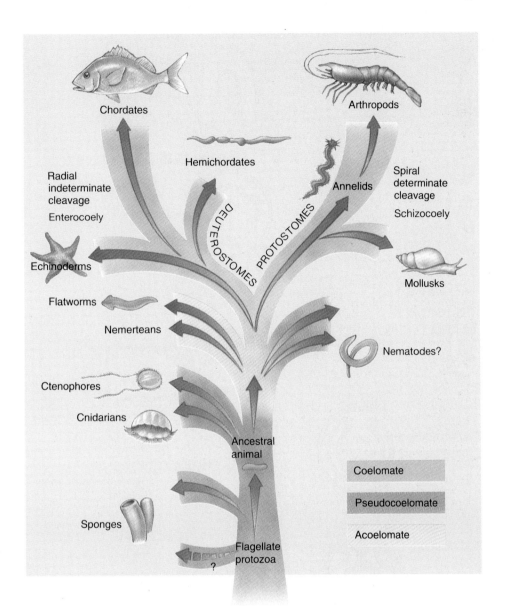

Figure 28–4 Proposed evolutionary relationships are illustrated by this phylogenetic tree indicating acoelomate, pseudocoelomate, and coelomate phyla. The flatworms and nemerteans have a solid body and so are referred to as acoelomate. Nematodes (roundworms) and rotifers do have a body cavity, but it develops from the embryonic cavity, called a blastocoel, and is located between the mesoderm and endoderm. All other bilateral animals and the echinoderms have a true coelom, a body cavity lined by mesoderm. This phylogenetic tree also illustrates protostome-deuterostome relationships. In the protostomes—the mollusks, annelids, and arthropods—the blastopore develops into the mouth, cleavage is generally spiral and determinate, and the coelom develops within the mesoderm when the mesoderm splits. In the deuterostomes—the echinoderms and chordates—the blastopore develops into the anus, and the mouth develops from a second opening. Deuterostomes typically have radial, indeterminate cleavage, and the coelom develops from outpocketings of the gut.

stomes are sometimes called **schizocoelomates.** In deuterostomes, the mesoderm usually forms as "outpocketings" of the developing gut. These outpocketings eventually separate and form pouches; the cavity within these pouches becomes the coelom. This type of coelom formation is called **enterocoely,** and these animals are sometimes referred to as **enterocoelomates.**

PHYLUM PORIFERA CONSISTS OF THE SPONGES

About 5000 species of **sponges** have been identified and assigned to phylum **Porifera.** These simple, multicellular animals occupy aquatic, mainly marine, habitats. Living sponges may be drab or bright green, orange, red, or purple (Figure 28–7). They are usually slimy to the touch and may have an unpleasant odor. Sponges

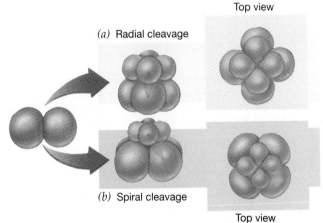

Figure 28–5 Types of cleavage in embryonic development. (*a*) In the radial cleavage characteristic of deuterostomes, the early divisions are either parallel or at right angles to the polar axis so that the cells are stacked in layers. (*b*) Spiral cleavage is characteristic of protostomes. Note the spiral arrangement of the cells. The pattern of cleavage can be appreciated by comparing the position of the green-colored cells in (*a*) and (*b*).

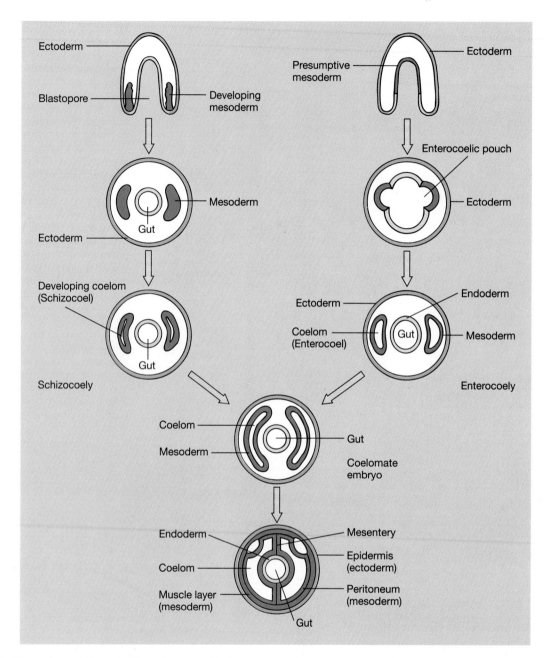

Figure 28–6   The coelom originates in the embryo as a block (or blocks) of mesoderm that splits off from each side of the embryonic gut. In schizocoely, the mesoderm (red) splits; this split widens into a cavity that becomes the coelom. In enterocoely, the mesoderm outpockets from the gut, forming pouches. The cavity within these pouches becomes the coelom. Ectoderm is shown in blue, endoderm in yellow.

range in size from 1 to 200 cm in height and vary in shape from flat, encrusting growths to balls, cups, fans, or vases.

Sponges are usually thought to have evolved from choanoflagellates. Recall that these protozoa have a single flagellum surrounded by a collar of microvilli. Sponges are the only animals that have **collar cells** (choanocytes)—cells that are strikingly similar to the choanoflagellates (see Chapter 24).

In the sense that they apparently did not give rise to any other animal group, sponges seem to represent a dead end in evolution. Of course, sponges themselves continue to change as they are subjected to continual selective pressures from the environment.

Sponges are divided into three main classes on the basis of the type of skeleton they secrete. Members of one class (Calcispongiae) secrete a skeleton composed of small calcium carbonate spikes, or **spicules.** A sec-

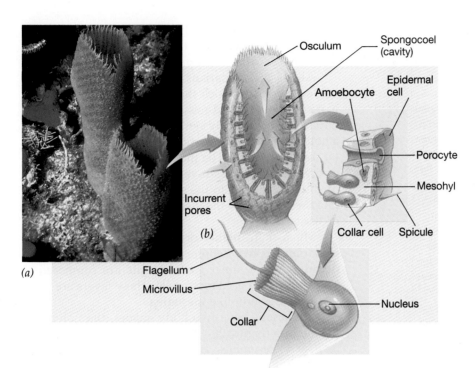

Figure 28-7 Sponge structure. (*a*) Tube sponge, a member of class Demospongiae. (*b*) A simple sponge cut open to expose its cellular organization.

ond class (Hexactinellida), the glass sponges, have a skeleton made of spicules containing silicon. Most sponges belong to a class (Demospongia) characterized by variable skeletons: Some are made of **spongin** (a protein material) fibers, others contain spicules of silicon, and some have a combination of both. A bath sponge consists of a dried spongin skeleton.

Porifera, meaning "to bear pores," aptly describes the sponge body, which resembles a sac perforated with tiny holes. In a simple sponge, water enters through these pores, passes into the central cavity, or **spongocoel** (not a digestive cavity), and finally flows out through the sponge's open end, the **osculum.** Water is kept moving by the action of the flagellated collar cells that line the spongocoel. Each of these cells is equipped with a tiny collar that surrounds the base of the flagellum. The collar is an extension of the plasma membrane and consists of microvilli. The collar cells of some complex sponges can pump a volume of water equal to the volume of the sponge each minute! In some types of sponges, the body wall is extensively folded, and there are complicated systems of canals.

Most sponges are asymmetrical, but some exhibit radial symmetry. Although a sponge is multicellular, its cells are loosely associated and do not form definite tissues. There is a division of labor, with certain cells specialized to perform particular functions such as nutrition, support, or reproduction. The epidermal cells that make up the outer layer of the sponge are capable of contraction. The pores of the sponge are formed by cells called porocytes, which have a ring shape. The collar

cells, which make up the inner layer, create the water current that brings food and oxygen to the cells and carries away carbon dioxide and other wastes; they also trap and phagocytize food particles. Between the outer and inner cellular layers of the sponge body is a gelatin-like layer (the mesohyl) supported by skeletal spicules. Amoeba-like cells, aptly called **amoebocytes,** wander about in this layer; some of these cells secrete the spicules.

Sponge larvae are flagellated and able to swim about. However, the adult sponge remains attached to some solid object on the sea bottom and is incapable of locomotion. Sponges are filter feeders, adapted for trapping and eating whatever food the sea water brings to them. As water circulates through the body, food is trapped along the sticky collars of the choanocytes. Food particles are either digested within the choanocyte or transferred to an amoebocyte for digestion. Undigested food is simply eliminated into the water.

Gas exchange and excretion of wastes depend on diffusion and are carried on by each individual cell. Although cells of the sponge are irritable and can react to stimuli, there are no specialized nerve cells that would enable the animal to react as a whole. Behavior appears limited to the basic metabolic necessities such as capturing food and regulating the flow of water through the body. Pores and the osculum may be closed by the contraction of surrounding cells.

Sponges can reproduce asexually. A multicellular bud may form and then break free from the parent sponge. This sponge fragment can give rise to a new

Table 28–1 CLASSES OF PHYLUM CNIDARIA

Class and Representative Animals	Characteristics
Hydrozoa *Hydra, Obelia,* Portuguese man-of-war	Mainly marine, but some freshwater species; both polyp and medusa stage in many species (polyp form only in *Hydra*); formation of colonies by polyps in some cases
Scyphozoa Jellyfish	Marine; inhabit mainly coastal water; free-swimming jellyfish most prominent forms; polyp stage restricted to small larval stage
Anthozoa Sea anemones Corals Sea fans	Marine; solitary or colonial polyps; no medusa stage; gastrovascular cavity divided by partitions into chambers increasing area for digestion; sessile

sponge or may remain to form a colony with the parent sponge. Sponges also reproduce sexually. Most sponges are **hermaphroditic,** meaning that the same individual can produce both eggs and sperm. Some of the amoebocytes develop into sperm cells, others into egg cells. Fertilization and early development take place within the jelly-like mesohyl. The flagellated larva moves out into the spongocoel and leaves the parent with a stream of excurrent water. After swimming about for a day or two as part of the plankton, the larva finds a solid object, attaches to it, and settles down to a sessile life.

Sponges possess a remarkable ability to repair themselves when injured and to regenerate lost parts. When the cells of a sponge are separated from one another, they can reaggregate, forming a complete sponge again.

CNIDARIANS HAVE STINGING CELLS

Most of the 10,000 or so species of phylum Cnidaria[1] are marine. They are grouped in three classes (Table 28–1). Class **Hydrozoa** includes the hydras, the hydroids, such as *Obelia,* and the Portuguese man-of-war. Class **Scy-**

---

[1] This phylum was formerly known as Coelenterata, a name derived from the fact that the body cavity serves as the digestive cavity: *coel* = hollow; *enteron* = gut.

phozoa includes the jellyfish, and class **Anthozoa** includes the sea anemones, true corals, and alcyonarians (sea fans, sea whips, and precious corals) (Figure 28–8).

All of the cnidarians have stinging cells, called **cnidocytes,** from which they get their name. (Cnidaria is from a Greek word meaning "sea nettles.") The cnidarian body is radially symmetrical and is organized as a hollow sac with the mouth and surrounding tentacles located at one end. The mouth leads into the digestive cavity, called the **gastrovascular cavity.** The mouth is the only opening into the gastrovascular cavity and so must serve for both the ingestion of food and expulsion of wastes.

Much more highly organized than the sponge, a cnidarian has two definite tissue layers. The outer **epidermis** and the inner **gastrodermis** are composed of several types of epidermal cells. These layers are separated by a gelatin-like **mesoglea.**

Cnidarians have two body shapes, the polyp and the medusa (Figure 28–9). The **polyp** form, represented by *Hydra,* resembles an upside-down, slightly elongated jellyfish. Some cnidarians have the polyp shape during their larval stage and later develop into the **medusa** (jellyfish) form. Although many cnidarians live a solitary existence, others form colonies. Some colonies—for example, the Portuguese man-of-war—consist of both polyp and medusa forms.

Class Hydrozoa Includes Solitary and Colonial Forms

Although not really typical, the cnidarian most often studied by beginning biology students is the tiny, solitary animal, *Hydra,* found in freshwater ponds. Hydra appears to the naked eye like a bit of frayed string (Figure 28–10). This animal is named after the multiheaded monster of Greek mythology with the remarkable ability to grow two new heads for each head cut off. The cnidarian hydra also has an impressive ability to regenerate: When cut into several pieces, each piece may grow all the missing parts and become a whole animal.

The hydra's body consists of two layers of cells enclosing a central gastrovascular cavity. The outer **epidermis** serves as a protective layer; the inner **gastrodermis** functions in digestion. The bases of cells in both layers are elongated into contractile muscle fibers; those of the epidermis run lengthwise, and those in the gastrodermis run circularly. By the contraction of one or the other, the hydra can shorten, lengthen, and bend its body.

Hydra typically lives attached to a rock, twig, or leaf by a disk of cells at its base. At the other end is the mouth, connecting the gastrovascular cavity with the outside. The mouth is surrounded by a circlet of tenta-

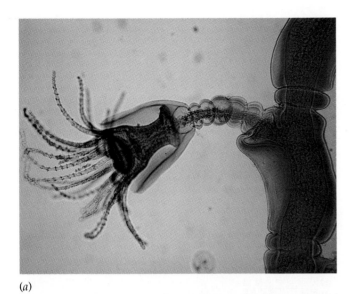

(a)

(b)

(c)

Figure 28–8   Some representatives of phylum Cnidaria. Note the two basic types of body form. (*a*) A member of class Hydrozoa, *Obelia* forms a colony of polyps. (*b*) A Portuguese man-of-war (*Physalia*) with a fish it has captured. (*c*) Coral *Montastrea cavernosa* polyps extended for feeding.   (*a*, Runk/Schoenberger from Grant Heilman; *b*, Animals Animals © 1988 Oxford Scientific Films, Peter Parks; *c*, Charles Seaborn)

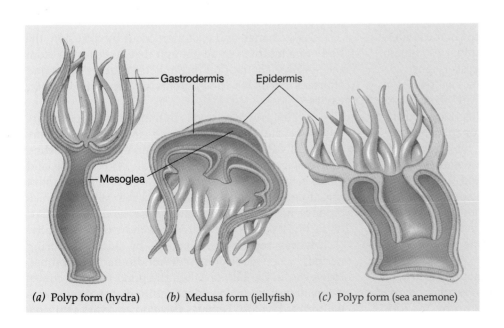

(a) **Polyp form (hydra)**   *(b)* **Medusa form (jellyfish)**   *(c)* **Polyp form (sea anemone)**

Figure 28–9   The polyp and medusa body forms characteristic of phylum Cnidaria are structurally similar. (*a*) The polyp form as seen in *Hydra*. (*b*) The medusa form is basically an upside-down polyp. (*c*) In the anthozoan polyp, the gastrovascular cavity is characteristically divided into chambers by vertical partitions.

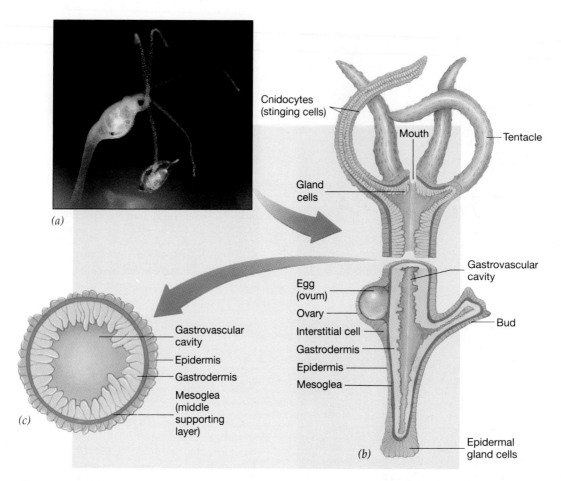

(a)

(c)

Gastrovascular
cavity

Epidermis

Gastrodermis

Mesoglea
(middle
supporting
layer)

Cnidocytes
(stinging cells)

Mouth

Tentacle

Gland
cells

Gastrovascular
cavity

Egg
(ovum)

Ovary

Interstitial cell

Gastrodermis

Epidermis

Mesoglea

Bud

(b)

Epidermal
gland cells

Figure 28–10 *Hydra* body structure. (*a*) A brown hydra, *Hydra oligactis,* capturing a small crustacean. Note the buds present on the hydra's body. One bud has already detached as a separate animal. (*b*) This *Hydra* is cut longitudinally to show its internal structure. Asexual reproduction by budding is represented on the right; sexual reproduction is represented by the ovary on the left. Male hydras develop testes that produce sperm. (*c*) Cross section through the body of a *Hydra*. (*a,* Carolina Biological Supply Company)

cles. Each tentacle may be as much as one and half times as long as the body itself.

Cnidocytes (stinging cells) are located in the epidermis, especially on the tentacles. The cnidocytes contain stinging "thread capsules," or **nematocysts** (Figure 28–11). When stimulated, the nematocysts can release a coiled, hollow thread. Some types of nematocyst threads are sticky; others are long and coil around the prey; a third type is tipped with a barb or spine and can inject a protein toxin that paralyzes the prey. Each cnidocyte has a small projecting trigger (cnidocil) on its outer surface that responds to touch and to chemicals dissolved in the water ("taste") and causes the nematocyst to fire its thread. A nematocyst can be used only once; when it has been discharged, it is released from the cnidocyte and replaced by a new one, produced by a new cnidocyte.

Captured prey is pushed into the mouth by the tentacles. Digestion begins in the gastrovascular cavity. Partially digested fragments are taken up by pseudo-

pods of the gastrodermis cells, and digestion is completed within food vacuoles in these cells.

Gas exchange and excretion occur by diffusion; the body of a hydra is small enough that no cell is far from the surface. The motion of the body as it stretches and shortens circulates the contents of the gastrovascular cavity.

The first true nerve cells in the animal kingdom are found in the cnidarians. These animals have many nerve cells that form irregular **nerve nets** connecting the sensory cells in the body wall with muscle and gland cells. The coordination achieved is of the simplest sort; there is no aggregation of nerve cells to form a brain or nerve cord, and an impulse set up in one part of the body passes in all directions more or less equally.

Hydras reproduce asexually by budding during periods when environmental conditions are optimal. However, in the fall, or when the pond water becomes stagnant and environmental conditions deteriorate, sexual forms develop. Females develop an ovary that pro-

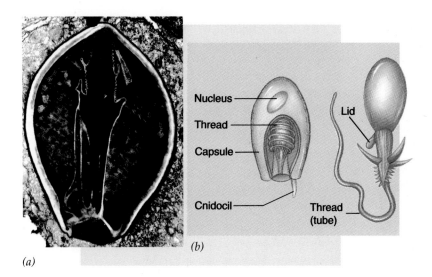

(a)

(b)

Figure 28–11 Nematocysts, the thread capsules within cnidarian cnidocytes. (*a*) Electron micrograph of an undischarged nematocyst of *Hydra* (sagittal section). (*b*) Discharge of a nematocyst. When an object comes in contact with the cnidocil, the nematocyst discharges, ejecting a thread that may entangle the prey or secrete a toxic substance immobilizing the prey. (*a*, G. B. Chapman, Cornell University Medical College)

duces a single egg; males form a testis that produces sperm. After fertilization the egg becomes covered with a shell, leaves the parent, and remains within the protective shell over winter.

Many marine cnidarians form colonies consisting of hundreds or thousands of individuals. A colony begins with a single individual that reproduces asexually by budding. However, instead of separating from the parent, the bud remains attached and continues to form additional buds. Several types of individuals may arise in the same colony, some specialized for feeding, some for reproduction, and others for defense.

The Portuguese man-of-war, *Physalia*, superficially resembles a jellyfish but is actually a colony of polyps and medusae. A modified medusa serves as a float for the colony in the form of a gas-filled sac colored a vivid iridescent purple. The long tentacles of this animal may hang down for several meters below the float. Its cnidocytes are capable of paralyzing a large fish and can severely wound a human swimmer.

Some of the marine cnidarians are remarkable for an alternation of sexual and asexual stages. This alternation of stages differs from the alternation of generations in plants in that both sexual and asexual forms are diploid. Only sperm and egg are haploid. The cnidarian life cycle is illustrated by the colonial marine hydrozoan *Obelia* (Figure 28–12). In this polyp colony, the asexual generation consists of two types of polyps: those specialized for feeding and those for reproduction. Free-swimming male and female medusae bud off from the reproductive polyps. These medusae eventually produce sperm and eggs, and fertilization takes place. The zygote develops into a ciliated swimming larva called a **planula.** The larva attaches to some solid object and begins to form a new generation of polyps by asexual reproduction.

The Jellyfish Belong to Class Scyphozoa

Among the jellyfish the medusa is the more prominent body form. It is like an upside-down hydra with a thick viscous mesoglea that gives firmness to the body. In scyphozoans, the polyp stage is restricted to a small larval stage. The largest jellyfish, *Cyanea*, may be more than 2 meters in diameter and have tentacles 30 meters long. These orange and blue monsters, among the largest of the invertebrate animals, are a real danger to swimmers in the North Atlantic Ocean.

The Corals Belong to Class Anthozoa

The sea anemones and corals have no free-swimming medusa stage, and the polyps may be either individual or colonial forms. These animals have a small ciliated larva, which may swim to a new location before attaching to develop into a polyp.

Anthozoans differ from hydrozoans in that the gastrovascular cavity is divided by a series of vertical partitions into a number of chambers. The partitions increase the surface area for digestion, so that an anemone can digest an animal as large as a crab or fish. Although corals can capture prey, many tropical species depend for nutrition mainly on photosynthetic dinoflagellates that live within their cells (see Chapter 53).

In warm shallow seas, almost every square meter of the bottom is covered with coral or anemones, most of them brightly colored. The reefs and atolls of the South Pacific are the remains of billions of microscopic, cup-shaped calcareous skeletons, secreted during past ages by coral colonies and by coralline plants. Living colonies occur only in the uppermost regions of such reefs, adding their own skeletons to the forming rock.

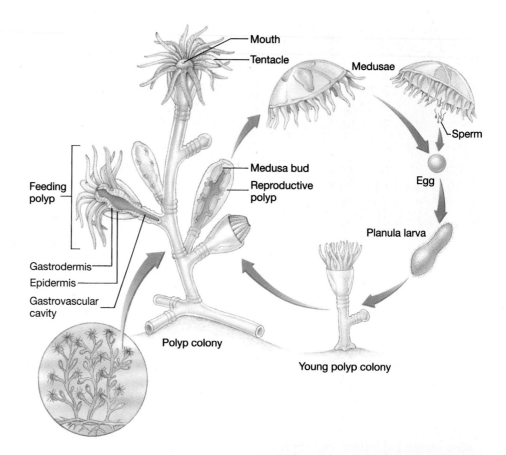

Figure 28–12 Life cycle of *Obelia*, a colonial marine hydrozoan. Note the specialization of individual members of the polyp colony.

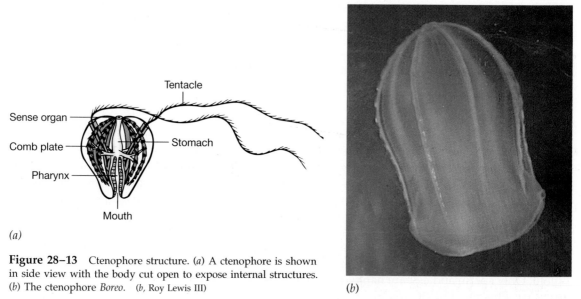

Figure 28–13 Ctenophore structure. (*a*) A ctenophore is shown in side view with the body cut open to expose internal structures. (*b*) The ctenophore *Boreo*. (*b*, Roy Lewis III)

PHYLUM CTENOPHORA INCLUDES THE COMB JELLIES

The **ctenophores,** or comb jellies, are a phylum of about 50 marine species. They are fragile, luminescent animals that may be as small as a pea or larger than a tomato. Ctenophores are biradially symmetrical. You could obtain equal halves by cutting along the long axis or the short axis. Their body plan is somewhat similar to that of a medusa. The body consists of two cell layers separated by a thick jelly-like mesoglea.

The outer surface of a ctenophore is covered with eight rows of cilia, resembling combs (Figure 28–13). The coordinated beating of the cilia in these combs moves the animal through the water. At the upper pole of the body is a sense organ containing a mass of limestone particles balanced on four tufts of cilia connected to sense cells. When the body turns, these particles bear more heavily on the lower cilia, stimulating the sense cells. The cilia in certain combs then beat faster and bring the body back to its normal position. Nerve fibers extending from the sense organ to the cilia control the beating. If these fibers are cut, the beating of the cilia below the incision is disorganized.

Ctenophores have only two tentacles, and most species lack the stinging cells characteristic of the cnidarians. However, their tentacles are equipped with adhesive glue cells, which trap their prey.

FLATWORMS BELONG TO PHYLUM PLATYHELMINTHES

Members of phylum **Platyhelminthes,** the **flatworms,** are flat, elongated, legless animals. They exhibit bilateral symmetry and are the simplest members of the Bilateria. Some zoologists classify them as acoelomate protostomes, whereas others just refer to them as acoelomates and reserve the term *protostomes* for mollusks, annelids, and arthropods. The three classes of Platyhelminthes are **Turbellaria,** the free-living flatworms, including *Planaria* and its relatives; **Trematoda,** the flukes, which are either internal or external parasites; and **Cestoda,** the tapeworms, the adults of which are intestinal parasites of vertebrates (Table 28–2).

Some important characteristics of this phylum follow:

1. **Bilateral symmetry and cephalization.** Along with their bilateral symmetry, flatworms have a definite anterior end and a posterior end. This is a great advantage because an animal with a front end generally moves in a forward direction. With a concentration of sense organs in the part of the body that first meets the environment, an animal is able to detect an enemy quickly enough to escape; it is also more likely to see or smell prey quickly enough to capture it. A rudimentary head, the beginnings of **cephalization,** is evident in flatworms.
2. **Three definite tissue layers.** In addition to an outer epidermis, derived from ectoderm, and an inner endodermis, derived from endoderm, the flatworm has a middle tissue layer that develops from mesoderm.
3. **Well-developed organs.** The flatworms are the simplest animals that have well-developed organs, functional structures made of two or more kinds of tissue. Among their organs is a muscular pharynx for taking in food, eyespots and other sensory organs in the head, a simple brain, and complex reproductive organs.
4. **A simple nervous system.** The simple brain consists of two masses of nervous tissue, called **ganglia,** in the head region. The ganglia are connected to two nerve cords that extend the length of the body. A series of nerves connects the cords like the rungs of a ladder.
5. **Excretory structures called protonephridia** ending in specialized collecting cells called flame cells.
6. **A gastrovascular cavity** in most species. It is often extensively branched and has only one opening, the mouth, usually located on the middle of the ventral surface.

Both groups of parasitic flatworms—the flukes and tapeworms—are highly adapted to and modified by their parasitic life style. They have suckers or hooks for holding onto the host. Their bodies are resistant to the digestive enzymes secreted by their hosts. Many have complicated life cycles that enable them to change hosts (because an individual host eventually dies). To further ensure survival of the species, these worms produce large numbers of eggs. Other adaptations include the loss of unneeded structures such as sense organs or a digestive system.

Table 28–2 CLASSES OF PHYLUM PLATYHELMINTHES

Class and Representative Animals	Characteristics
Turbellaria Planarians	Free-living flatworms; mainly marine, some terrestrial forms living in mud; body covered by ciliated epidermis; usually carnivorous forms that prey on tiny invertebrates or on dead organisms
Trematoda Flukes	All parasites with a wide range of vertebrate and invertebrate hosts; may require intermediate hosts; suckers for attachment to host
Cestoda Tapeworms	Parasites of vertebrates; complex life cycle with one or two intermediate hosts; larval host may be invertebrate; tapeworms have suckers and sometimes hooks on scolex for attachment to host; eggs produced within proglottids, which are shed; no digestive system

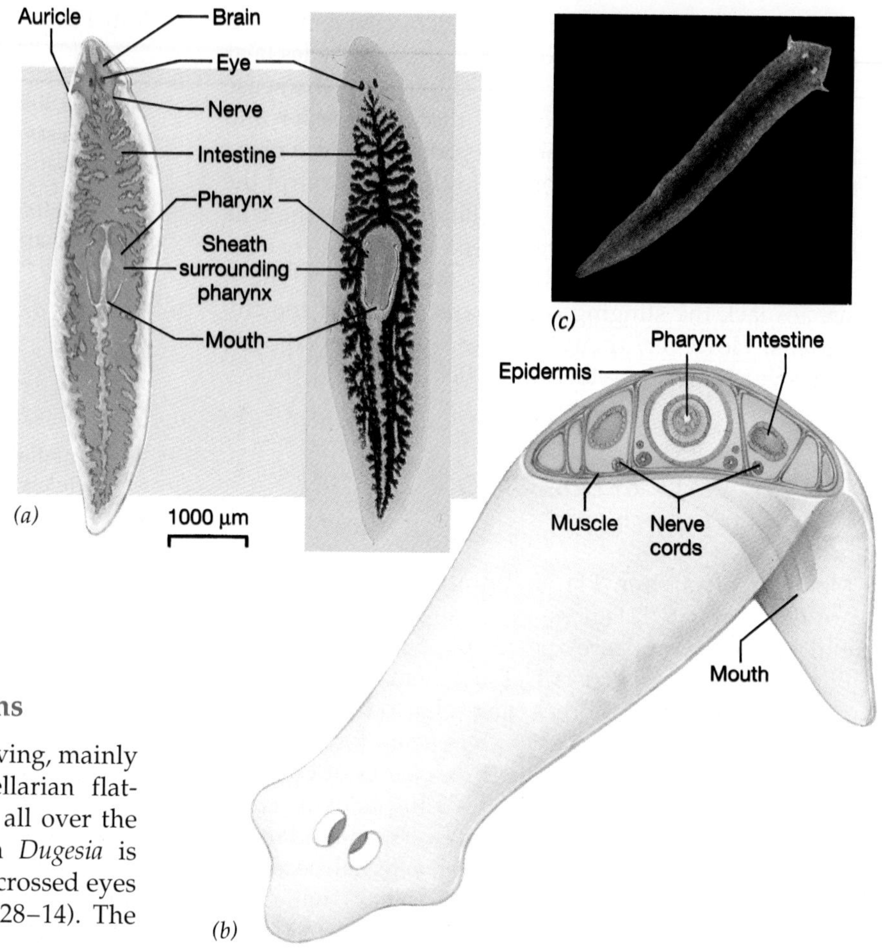

Figure 28–14 The common planarian, *Dugesia*. (*a*) A stained specimen compared with a line drawing. (*b*) Cross section through the body of a planarian. (*c*) A living *Dugesia*. (*a*, Carolina Biological Supply Company; *c*, Visuals Unlimited/T.E. Adams)

Class Turbellaria Includes Planarians

Members of the class Turbellaria are free-living, mainly marine, flatworms. **Planarians** are turbellarian flatworms found in ponds and quiet streams all over the world. The common American planarian *Dugesia* is about 15 mm long, with what appear to be crossed eyes and flapping ears called **auricles** (Figure 28–14). The auricles actually serve as organs of smell.

Planarians are carnivorous, trapping small animals in a mucous secretion. The digestive system consists of a single opening (the mouth), a pharynx, and a branched intestine. A planarian can project its **pharynx** (the first portion of the digestive tube) outward through its mouth, to suck up small pieces of prey. Extracellular digestion takes place in the intestine by enzymes secreted by gland cells. Digestion is completed after the nutrients have been absorbed into individual cells. Undigested food is eliminated through the mouth. The lengthy intestine (actually a highly branched gastrovascular cavity) helps to distribute food to all parts of the body, so that each cell is within range of diffusion. Flatworms can survive without food for months, gradually digesting their own tissues and growing smaller as time passes. Some flatworms confiscate intact nematocysts from the hydras they eat; they incorporate them into their own epidermis and use them for defense.

A planarian's flattened body ensures that gases can reach all of its cells by diffusion. It has no specialized respiratory or circulatory structures. Although some excretion takes place by diffusion, an excretory system is present. It consists of two excretory tubes that extend the length of the body and give off branches called **protonephridia** throughout their length. Each of these tubules ends in a **flame cell**, a collecting cell equipped

with cilia. The beating of the cilia channels water containing wastes into the system of tubules. Planarians are capable of learning; memory is not localized within the brain but appears to be retained throughout the nervous system.

Planarians can reproduce either asexually or sexually. In asexual reproduction, an individual constricts in the middle and divides into two planarians. Each regenerates its missing parts. Sexually, these animals are hermaphroditic. During the warm months of the year, each is equipped with a complete set of male and female organs. Two planarians come together in copulation and exchange sperm cells so that their eggs are cross-fertilized.

The Flukes Belong to Class Trematoda

Although they are parasites, the **flukes,** members of class **Trematoda,** are structurally like the free-living flatworms. They differ in having one or more suckers

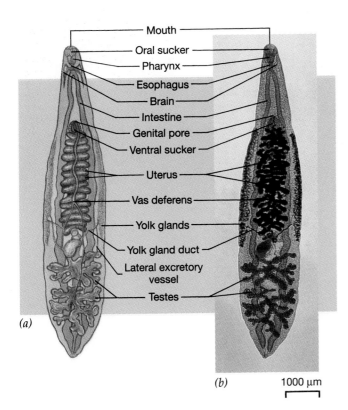

Mouth
Oral sucker
Pharynx
Esophagus
Brain
Intestine
Genital pore
Ventral sucker
Uterus
Vas deferens
Yolk glands
Yolk gland duct
Lateral excretory vessel
Testes

(a)

(b)   1000 μm

Figure 28–15 Flukes are adapted for a parasitic mode of life. (*a*) Internal structure of a fluke. (*b*) The human liver fluke, *Clonorchis sinensis.* (*b,* Carolina Biological Supply Company)

with which to cling to their host (Figure 28–15). Their organs of digestion, excretion, and coordination are like those of the other flatworms, but the mouth is anterior rather than ventral. Trematode reproductive organs are extremely complex.

Among the flukes that are parasitic in humans are the blood flukes, widespread in China, Japan, and Egypt, and the liver flukes, common in China, Japan, and Korea. Blood flukes of the genus *Schistosoma* infect about 200 million people who live in tropical areas. Both blood flukes and liver flukes go through complicated life cycles, involving a number of different forms, alternation of sexual and asexual stages, and parasitism on one or more intermediate hosts, such as snails and fishes (Figure 28–16). When dams are built, the marshy areas formed provide habitats for the aquatic snails that serve as intermediate hosts in the blood fluke life cycle.

The Tapeworms Belong to Class Cestoda

Adult members of the more than 1000 different species of the class Cestoda live as parasites in the intestines of probably every kind of vertebrate, including humans. Tapeworms are long, flat, ribbon-like animals strikingly specialized for their parasitic mode of life. Among their

many adaptations are suckers and sometimes hooks on the head, or **scolex,** which enable the parasite to maintain its attachment to the host's intestine (Figure 28–17). Their reproductive adaptations and abilities are extraordinary. The body of the tapeworm consists of a long chain of segments called **proglottids.** Each segment is an entire reproductive machine equipped with both male and female organs and containing as many as 100,000 eggs. Because an adult tapeworm may possess as many as 2000 segments, its reproductive potential is staggering. A single tapeworm may produce as many as 600 million eggs in a year. Proglottids farthest from the tapeworm's head contain the ripest eggs; these segments are shed daily, leaving the host's body with the feces.

Tapeworms lack certain organs. They absorb their food directly through their body wall from the host's intestine and have no mouth or digestive system of their own. Neither do they possess any sense organs or a brain. Some tapeworms have rather complex life cycles, spending their larval stage within the body of an intermediate host and their adult life within the body of a different, final host. For example, let us consider the life cycle of the beef tapeworm, so named because human beings become infected when they eat poorly cooked beef containing the larvae (Figure 28–18).

The microscopic tapeworm larva spends part of its life cycle encysted within the muscle tissue of a cow. When a human ingests infected meat, the digestive juices break down the cyst, releasing the larvae. The larva attaches itself to the intestinal lining and within a few weeks matures into an adult tapeworm, which may grow to a length of about 15 meters (50 feet). The parasite reproduces sexually within the human intestine and sheds proglottids filled with ripe eggs. Once established within a human host, the tapeworm makes itself very much at home and may remain there for the remainder of its life, as long as 10 years. A person infected with a tapeworm may suffer pain or discomfort, increased appetite, weight loss, and other symptoms or may be totally unaware of its presence.

In order for the life cycle of the tapeworm to continue, its eggs must be ingested by an **intermediate host,** in this case, a cow. (This requirement explains why we are not completely overrun by tapeworms, and why the tapeworm must produce millions of eggs to ensure that at least a few survive.) When a cow eats grass or other foods contaminated with human feces, eggs may be ingested. The eggs hatch in the cow's intestine, and the larvae make their way into muscle. There they encyst and remain until released by a **final host,** perhaps a human eating rare steak.

Two other tapeworms that infect humans are the pork tapeworm, found in poorly cooked, infected pork, and the fish tapeworm, found in raw, or poorly cooked, infected fish. Like most parasites, tapeworms tend to be

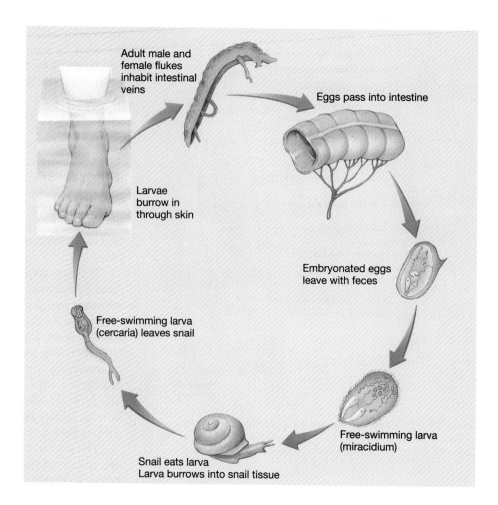

Figure 28–16   Life cycle of a blood fluke, a schistosome. The adult male has a long canal that holds the female during fertilization.

Figure 28–17   False-color scanning electron micrograph of the head (scolex) of the small tapeworm *Acanthrocirrus retrisrostris*, taken in its larval, encysted form from the body of its barnacle host (*Balanus balanoides*). The tapeworm reaches maturity in the intestines of wading birds that eat barnacles. The photograph shows the piston-like rostellum, which can be withdrawn into the head or thrust out and buried in the host's tissue. Beneath the rostellum, two of the four powerful suckers are visible.   (Cath Ellis, Dept. of Zoology, University of Hull/Science Photo Library/Photo Researchers, Inc.)

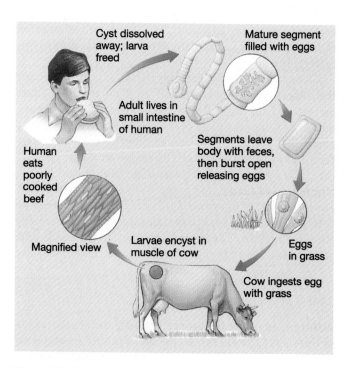

Figure 28–18   Life cycle of the beef tapeworm, a parasitic flatworm.

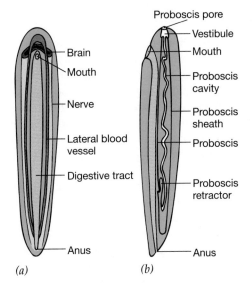

Figure 28–19 Lateral view of a typical proboscis worm or nemertean. Note the complete digestive tract that extends from mouth to anus, giving this animal a tube-within-a-tube body plan. Nemerteans lack a coelom.

An important advance displayed by the nemerteans is the **tube-within-a-tube body plan.** The digestive tract is a complete tube, with a mouth at one end for taking in food and an anus at the other for eliminating undigested food. This is in contrast to the cnidarians and planarians, whose food enters and wastes leave by the same opening.

A second advance exhibited by the nemerteans is the separation of digestive and circulatory functions. These animals are the most primitive organisms to have a separate circulatory system. It is a rudimentary system consisting simply of muscular tubes—the blood vessels—extending the length of the body and connected by transverse vessels. Some of these primitive forms have red blood cells filled with hemoglobin, the same red pigment that transports oxygen in human blood. Nemerteans have no heart to pump the blood; the blood is circulated through the vessels by movements of the body and contractions of the muscular blood vessels.

species-specific; that is, each can infect only certain specific species. For example, the beef tapeworm can only spend its adult life in a human host.

PHYLUM NEMERTINEA HAS EVOLUTIONARY IMPORTANCE

The phylum **Nemertinea** is a relatively small group of animals (about 550 species) that is considered an evolutionary landmark because its members are the simplest animals to possess definite organ systems (Figure 28–19). The nemerteans are not parasitic, and are of no economic importance. Almost all are marine, although a few inhabit fresh water or damp soil. Nemerteans have long narrow bodies, either cylindrical or flattened, varying in length from 5 cm to about 2 m. Some are a vivid orange, red, or green, with black or colored stripes.

Their most remarkable organ—the **proboscis,** from which they get their common name, proboscis worms—is a long, hollow, muscular tube, which can be everted from the anterior end of the body for use in seizing food or in defense. The proboscis secretes mucus, which is helpful in catching and trapping prey. In certain species, the proboscis is equipped with a hard point at its tip and poison-secreting glands at the base of this point. The outward movement of the proboscis is accomplished by the pressure of the surrounding muscular walls on the contained fluid; a separate muscle inside the proboscis retracts it.

ROUNDWORMS BELONG TO PHYLUM NEMATODA

Members of phylum **Nematoda,** the **roundworms,** are of great ecological importance because of their role as consumers of organic matter. They promote nutrient recycling by enhancing bacterial and fungal activity in the soil. By feeding on bacteria and fungi, they eliminate excess individuals and help maintain healthy bacterial and fungal populations. Nematodes are also enormously important parasites. Almost every species of plant and animal can be infected by parasitic nematodes. Among the 30 or so human parasites belonging to phylum Nematoda are the hookworms, the intestinal roundworm *Ascaris,* pinworms, trichina worms, and filaria worms. More than 12,000 species have been named, and perhaps hundreds of thousands of additional species remain to be identified. Nematodes are widely distributed in the soil, the sea, and fresh water. A spadeful of soil may contain more than a million of these tiny white worms, which thrash around, coiling and uncoiling. *Caenorhabditis* is a free-living nematode which has recently found favor among researchers interested in the genetic control of development (Chapter 16).

The elongate, cylindrical, threadlike nematode body is pointed at both ends and covered with a tough **cuticle,** which is molted as it grows (Figure 28–20). Secreted by the underlying epidermis, the cuticle enables nematodes to resist desiccation, permitting them to inhabit dry soils and even deserts. Beneath the epidermis is a layer of longitudinal muscles. No circular muscles are present in the body wall.

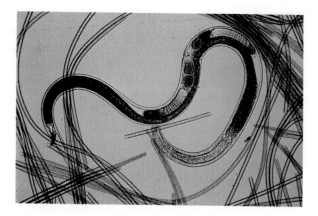

Figure 28–20 A free-living nematode among the cyanobacteria *Oscillatoria*, which it eats. (Visuals Unlimited/T.E. Adams)

Nematodes are the most primitive animals to have a body cavity—a pseudocoelom (Figure 28–21). The fluid-filled pseudocoelom serves as a hydrostatic skeleton that transmits the force of muscle contraction to the enclosed fluid. Characteristic nematode movement is a thrashing motion.

Like the proboscis worms, the nematodes exhibit bilateral symmetry, a complete digestive tract, three distinct tissue layers, and definite organ systems. However, they lack circulatory structures. The sexes are usually separate, and the male is smaller than the female. The characteristics of nematodes and other lower invertebrate phyla are summarized in Table 28–3.

Ascaris Is a Parasitic Roundworm

A common intestinal parasite of humans, *Ascaris* is a white-colored worm about 25 cm long. *Ascaris* spends its adult life in the human intestine, where it makes its living by sucking in partly digested food. Like the tapeworm, it must devote a great deal of effort to reproduction in order to ensure survival of its species. The sexes are separate, and copulation takes place within the host. A mature female may lay as many as 200,000 eggs a day.

Ascaris eggs leave the human body with the feces and, where sanitation is poor (that is, in most of the world), find their way onto the soil. In many parts of the world, human wastes are used as fertilizer—a practice that encourages the survival of *Ascaris* and many other human parasites. People are infected when they ingest *Ascaris* eggs. The eggs hatch in the intestine, and the larvae then take a remarkable journey through the body before settling in the small intestine. The larvae burrow through the intestinal wall into blood vessels or lymph vessels. Then they are carried through the heart to the lungs, where they break through into the air sacs and move up the air passageways to the throat. Finally, the larvae pass through the stomach and into the intestine, where they settle and feed on partly digested food. During their migration, the larvae can damage the lungs and other tissues. Sometimes the worms perforate the intestine and cause serious infection (peritonitis).

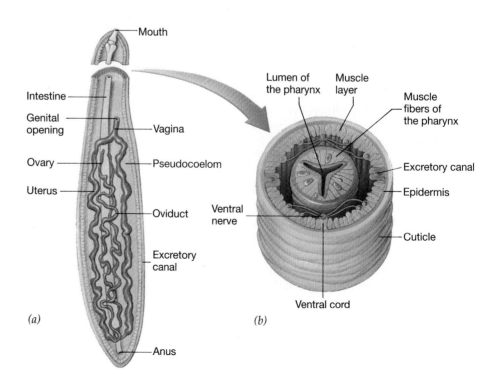

Figure 28–21 Structure of the roundworm *Ascaris*. (*a*) Longitudinal section to show internal anatomy. Note the complete digestive tract that extends from mouth to anus. (*b*) Cross section through the body of *Ascaris*.

Table 28–3 COMPARISON OF SOME LOWER INVERTEBRATE PHYLA

Phylum	Porifera (pore bearers)	Cnidaria	Platyhelminthes (flatworms)	Nemertinea	Nematoda (roundworms)
Representative Animals	Sponges	Hydra Jellyfish Coral	Planarians Flukes Tapeworms	Proboscis worms	Ascarids Hookworms Nematodes
Level of Organization	Multicellular but tissues loosely arranged	Tissues	Organs	Organ systems	Organ systems
Symmetry	Radial or none	Radial	Bilateral; rudimentary head	Bilateral	Bilateral
Digestion	Intracellular	Gastrovascular cavity with only one opening; intra- and extra-cellular digestion	Digestive tract with only one opening	Complete digestive tract with mouth and anus	Complete digestive tract with mouth and anus
Circulation	Diffusion	Diffusion	Diffusion	At least two pulsating longitudinal blood vessels; no heart; blood cells with hemoglobin	Diffusion
Gas Exchange	Diffusion	Diffusion	Diffusion	Diffusion	Diffusion
Waste Disposal	Diffusion	Diffusion	Protonephridia; flame cells and ducts	Two lateral excretory canals with flame cells	Excretory canals
Nervous System	Irritability of cytoplasm	Nerve net; no centralization of nerve tissue	Simple brain; two nerve cords; ladder type system; simple sense organs	Simple brain; two nerve cords; cross nerves; simple sense organs	Simple brain; dorsal and ventral nerve cords; simple sense organs
Reproduction	Asexual, by budding; sexual, most are hermaphroditic; larvae swim by cilia; adults incapable of locomotion	Asexual by budding; sexual, sexes separate	Asexual, by fission; sexual, hermaphroditic, but cross-fertilization in some species	Asexual, by fragmentation; sexual, sexes separate	Sexual, sexes separate
Other Characteristics	Filter feeders; skeleton of chalk, glass, or spongin (a protein material)	Have cnidocytes (stinging cells) along their tentacles	Three definite tissue layers; no body cavity; many parasitic	No body cavity; proboscis for defense and capturing prey	Have pseudocoelom (space between internal organs and body wall); many parasitic

Several Other Parasitic Roundworms Infect Humans

The life cycle of a human **hookworm** is somewhat similar to that of *Ascaris.* Only one host is required. Adult worms, which are less than 1.5 cm (0.5 inch) long, live in the human intestine and lay eggs, which pass out of the body with the feces. Larvae hatch and feed upon bacteria in the soil. After a period of maturation, they become infective. When a potential host walks barefoot on soil containing the microscopic larvae, or otherwise comes in contact with it, the larvae bore through the skin and enter the blood. They migrate through the body before finding their way to the intestine, where they mature.

Humans become infected with **trichina worms** by eating poorly cooked, infected pork or bear. The trichina parasite is adapted to live inside many animals (pigs, rats, bears, and others), and the human is an accidental host. Adult trichina worms live in the small intestine of the host. The females produce larvae, which migrate through the body, making their way to skeletal muscle, where they encyst. Continuation of the life cycle depends upon ingestion by another animal. Because humans are not normally eaten, trichina larvae are not liberated from their cysts and eventually die. The cysts, however, become calcified and permanently remain in the muscles, causing stiffness and discomfort. Other symptoms are caused by the presence of the adults and by the migrating larvae. No cure has been found for this infestation.

Pinworms are the most common worms found in children. Adult worms, less than 1.3 cm (0.5 inch) long, live in the large intestine. Female pinworms often migrate to the anal region at night to deposit their eggs. Irritation and itching caused by this practice induce scratching, which spreads the tiny eggs. Eggs may be further distributed in the air and are in this way scattered throughout the house. The original host or other members of the household may be infected by ingesting the eggs. Eating with dirty hands facilitates the process. Mild infestations may go unnoticed, but those more serious may result in injury to the intestinal wall, discomfort, and irritation.

PHYLUM ROTIFERA ARE WHEEL ANIMALS

Among the more obscure invertebrates are the "wheel animals" of the phylum **Rotifera.** These aquatic, microscopic worms, although no larger than many protozoa, are multicellular. Rotifers have a characteristic crown of cilia on the anterior end, which move rapidly in feeding, giving the appearance of a spinning wheel (Figure 28–22). They have a complete digestive tract, including a **mastax,** a muscular organ for grinding food; a pseudocoelom; an excretory system made up of flame cells and a bladder; and a nervous system with a "brain" and sense organs.

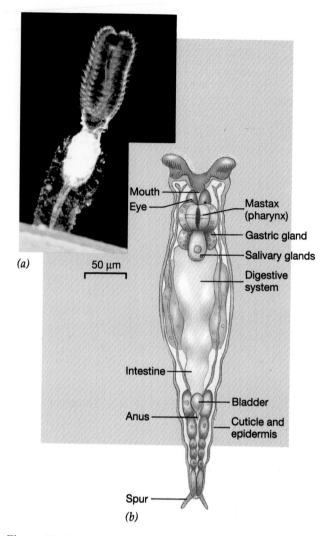

(a) 50 μm

(b)

Figure 28–22 Wheel animals. (*a*) A solitary rotifer, *Stephanboceros,* with cilia extended for feeding. (*b*) Structure of a rotifer. (*a,* Visuals Unlimited/T.E. Adams)

Rotifers are "cell constant" animals: Each member of a given species is composed of exactly the same number of cells; indeed, each part of the body is made of a precisely fixed number of cells arranged in a characteristic pattern. Cell division ceases with embryonic development, and mitosis cannot subsequently be induced; growth and repair are not possible. One of the challenging problems of biological research is discovering the difference between such nondividing cells and the dividing cells of other animals. Do rotifers never develop cancer?

SUMMARY

I. Animals are eukaryotic, multicellular, heterotrophic organisms whose cells exhibit a division of labor. They generally are capable of locomotion at some time during their life cycle, can reproduce sexually, and can respond adaptively to external stimuli.

II. Animals are consumers that inhabit the sea, fresh

water, and the land.

III. Animals may be classified in several different ways.
   A. Subkingdom Parazoa consists of the sponges. All other animals belong to Subkingdom Eumetazoa.
   B. Cnidarians and Ctenophores belong to Branch Radiata. All other eumetazoans belong to Branch Bilateria.
   C. Animals can be classified as acoelomates, pseudocoelomates, or coelomates based on the type of body cavity.
   D. In protostomes, the blastopore develops into the mouth; in deuterostomes, the blastopore becomes the anus.

IV. Phylum Porifera consists of the sponges.
   A. Sponges are divided into three main classes on the basis of the type of skeleton they secrete.
   B. The sponge body is a sac with tiny openings through which water enters, a central cavity (spongocoel), and an osculum.

V. Phylum Cnidaria includes the hydras, jellyfish, and corals.
   A. Cnidarians have radial symmetry, cnidocytes, two definite tissue layers, and a nerve net.
   B. In many types of cnidarians a sessile polyp gives rise to free-swimming medusae.

VI. Phylum Ctenophora consists of the comb jellies, which are fragile, luminescent, biradially symmetrical marine animals.

VII. Phylum Platyhelminthes include the planarians, the flukes, and the tapeworms.
   A. Flatworms are characterized by bilateral symmetry, cephalization, three definite tissue layers, lack of a body cavity, well-developed organs, a simple brain and nervous system, and protonephridia.
   B. The flukes and tapeworms are specialized for a parasitic life style.

VIII. Members of phylum Nemertinea (proboscis worms) have a tube-within-a-tube body plan, no body cavity, a complete digestive tract with mouth and anus, and a separate circulatory system.

IX. Phylum Nematoda, composed of the roundworms, includes species of great ecological importance and species that are parasitic in plants or animals.
   A. Nematodes are characterized by three definite tissue layers, a pseudocoelom, bilateral symmetry, and a complete digestive tract.
   B. Some nematodes parasitic in humans include *Ascaris*, hookworms, trichina worms, and pinworms.

X. Members of phylum Rotifera are aquatic, pseudocoelomate, microscopic worms that exhibit cell constancy.

POST-TEST

1. The majority of animals—those without backbones—are properly referred to as _____.
2. Animals that remain stationary and attached to a substrate are described as _____.
3. Acoelomate animals lack a body _____.
4. The germ layer that gives rise to the outer covering of the body and the nervous system is _____.
5. A true coelom is completely lined with _____.
6. In protostomes the blastopore develops into the _____.
7. _____ symmetry is characteristic of cnidarians.
8. If the first four cells of a protostome embryo are separated, each cell will develop into _____ of a larva.
9. The animal kingdom may be divided into two subkingdoms. Subkingdom Parazoa consists of the _____.
10. Sponges have skeletal elements called _____.
11. In a simple sponge, water enters the body through many pores, passes into the central cavity called a _____, and finally flows out through the sponge's open end, the _____.
12. The two body forms found among cnidarians are the _____ and the _____.
13. The sea anemones and corals belong to phylum _____ and class _____.
14. The simplest animals to exhibit cephalization are the _____.
15. The auricles of a planarian flatworm serve as organs of _____.
16. Humans may become infected with _____ worms by eating poorly cooked pork or bear.
17. Two important advances displayed by the nemerteans are _____ and _____.

Match the characteristics in Column B with the descriptions in Column A:

Column A	Column B
18. Body segments of a tapeworm	a. Cnidocytes
19. Cells that trap food particles in sponges	b. Proglottids
20. Cnidarian nervous system	c. Collar cells
21. Collecting cells in flatworm excretory system	d. Nerve net
22. Cnidarian stinging cells	e. Flame cells

Match the phyla in Column B with the animals or structures in Column A:

Column A	Column B
23. Comb jellies	a. Rotifera
24. Tapeworms	b. Platyhelminthes
25. Proboscis worms	c. Ctenophora
26. Wheel animals; have mastax	d. Nematoda
27. Hookworms, *Ascaris*	e. Nemertinea

REVIEW QUESTIONS

1. For centuries sponges were classified as plants. Justify their current classification as animals.

2. Why is the sea a more hospitable environment for many animals than the land or fresh water?

3. What advances do members of phylum Platyhelminthes exhibit over animals that belong to phylum Cnidaria? In what ways are these animals alike?
4. What are the advantages of bilateral symmetry and cephalization?
5. Identify the phyla (from among those studied in this chapter) that have the following characteristics:
   a. radial symmetry
   b. protonephridia
   c. acoelomate
   d. pseudocoelomate
   e. alternation of sexual and asexual stages
   f. cnidocytes
   g. nerve net
   h. complete digestive tract
   i. circulatory system
6. Describe the alternation of stages exhibited by *Obelia*.
7. How do flatworms survive without specialized structures for gas exchange and internal transport of materials?
8. What special adaptations do tapeworms have to their parasitic mode of life?
9. Describe the life cycle of the following animals:
   a. a beef tapeworm
   b. *Ascaris*
   c. a hookworm

RECOMMENDED READINGS

Barnes, R. D. *Invertebrate Zoology*, 5th ed. Saunders College Publishing, Philadelphia, 1987. This comprehensive textbook discusses the life processes of each invertebrate phylum.

Dorit, R. L., Walker, W. F., and Barnes, R. *Zoology*. Saunders College Publishing, Philadelphia, 1991. A readable, interesting account of animal diversity.

Knoll, A. H. End of the Proterozoic eon. *Scientific American*, Vol. 265, No. 4, October 1991. A discussion of environmental change that may have led to the evolution of large animals.

CHAPTER 29

The Animal Kingdom:
The Coelomate Protostomes

OUTLINE

Adaptations for life on land

Phylum Mollusca: soft-bodied animals with a foot, visceral mass, and mantle

Phylum Annelida: segmented worms

Phylum Arthropoda: animals with jointed appendages and chitinous exoskeletons

What does an earthworm have in common with a clam or a butterfly? All of these animals have a coelom, and all are protostomes. The coelomate protostomes include the annelids, mollusks, and arthropods, as well as several smaller, related phyla. As explained in Chapter 28, in protostomes the mouth develops from the first opening that forms in the embryonic gut. The true coelom is a space completely lined by mesoderm; it lies between the digestive tube and the outer body wall. Coelomate protostomes also have a complete digestive tract with separate mouth and anus, and most have well-developed circulatory, excretory, and nervous systems.

Animals with a coelom, and to a lesser extent those with a pseudocoelom, have certain advantages over those that lack a body cavity. The coelom permits a clear separation between the muscles of the body wall and those in the wall of the digestive tract. This allows the digestive tube to move food along independently of body movements. Perhaps more importantly, the coelom

Luna moth.   (Ed Reschke)

can be used as a hydrostatic skeleton, an enclosed compartment (or series of compartments) of fluid that can be manipulated by surrounding muscles.

In some animals fluid within the coelom helps transport materials such as food, oxygen, and wastes. Cells bathed by the coelomic fluid can exchange materials with it. The cells receive nutrients and oxygen from the coelomic fluid and excrete wastes into it. Some coelomates have excretory structures that remove wastes directly from the coelomic fluid.

The coelom also serves as a space in which many organs develop and function. For example, the heart and blood vessels develop within the coelom and can function freely there without being squeezed by other organs. The pumping action of the heart would not be possible without the surrounding space provided by the coelom. The coelom also provides space for the gonads to develop; in animals with breeding seasons, these reproductive structures enlarge periodically as they fill with ripe gametes.

After you have studied this chapter you should be able to

1. List several advantages of having a coelom.
2. Identify challenges associated with terrestrial living and describe adaptations that enable terrestrial animals to meet those challenges.
3. Describe the distinguishing characteristics of mollusks, annelids, and arthropods and properly classify an animal that belongs to any of these phyla.
4. Describe the principal classes of mollusks and give examples of animals that belong to each.
5. Describe and give examples of each of the three classes of annelids discussed.
6. Distinguish among the subphyla and classes of arthropods and give examples of animals that belong to each class.
7. Discuss factors that have contributed to the great biological success of insects.

LIFE ON LAND REQUIRES MANY ADAPTATIONS

Based on the fossil record, most biologists agree that the first air-breathing land animals were scorpion-like arthropods that came ashore in the Silurian period some 410 million years ago. The first land vertebrates, the amphibians, did not appear until the latter part of the Devonian period, some 60 million years later.

Most modern invertebrate coelomates still inhabit the sea. The earthworm is a terrestrial animal, but most annelids are marine. A few snails inhabit the land, but most mollusks also live in the sea. All echinoderms are marine. Among the arthropods, the crustaceans (crabs, lobsters, and their relatives) and the merostomes (horseshoe crabs) are also largely marine forms. However, certain modern arthropods—including the insects and spiders—are very successful terrestrial animals.

The chief problem of all terrestrial organisms is that of drying out in the absence of a surrounding watery medium. A body covering adapted to minimize fluid loss helps solve this problem in many land animals. Location of the respiratory surface deep within the animal also helps prevent fluid loss. Thus, although gills are located externally, lungs and tracheal tubes (found in insects) are internal.

Supporting the body against the pull of gravity in the absence of the buoyant effect of water is another problem associated with life on land. Some animals, such as earthworms, do not have this problem because they live in the ground and because of their small body size. Larger burrowing animals and those living on the surface of the Earth generally need some sort of supporting skeleton. The vertebrates have an **endoskeleton,** a supporting framework within the body. Arthropods and most mollusks have a tough **exoskeleton,** a supporting armor that covers the body (Figure 29–1).

Reproduction on land poses still another problem. Aquatic forms generally shed their gametes in the water, and fertilization occurs there. The surrounding water serves as an effective shock absorber, protecting the delicate embryos as they develop. Some land ani-

Figure 29–1 The Sally lightfoot crab *Grapsus grapsus* is shown here eating a red tidepool fish. It has a tough exoskeleton composed of chitin.   (William E. Ferguson)

mals, including most amphibians, return to the water for reproduction; their larval forms—tadpoles—develop in the water. Earthworms, snails, insects, reptiles, birds, and mammals engage in internal fertilization. They transfer sperm from the body of the male directly into the body of the female by copulation. The sperm are surrounded by a watery medium or semen. An important adaptation to reproduction on land is the tough, protective shell secreted by the female around her eggs that prevents the developing embryo from drying out. Another adaptation to terrestrial reproduction is the development of the embryo within the moist body of the mother.

MOLLUSKS ARE SOFT-BODIED ANIMALS WITH A FOOT, VISCERAL MASS, AND MANTLE

Mollusks are among the best known of the invertebrates—almost everyone has walked along the shore collecting their shells. With about 60,000 living species and 35,000 fossil species, Phylum **Mollusca,** second

(a)

(b)

Figure 29–2 There are many beautiful forms of mollusks. (*a*) A bay scallop, *Argopecten irradians*, photographed in a seagrass bed in Tampa Bay. Note the many blue eyes looking out from between the hinged shell. (*b*) A cuttlefish (*Sepia officinalis*). Cuttlefish may remain on the sea bottom waiting for passing prey. This cephalopod can change its color to simulate its background. (*a*, Robin Lewis, Coastal Creations; *b*, D. J. Wrobel, Monterey Bay Aquarium/Biological Photo Service)

only to the arthropods in number of species, includes clams, oysters, octopods, snails, slugs, and the largest of all the invertebrates, the giant squid, which may weigh several tons. Although most mollusks are marine, some snails and clams live in fresh water and many species of snails and slugs inhabit the land. Representative mollusks are illustrated in Figure 29–2, and the major classes are listed in Table 29–1.

Although mollusks vary widely in outward appearance, most share certain basic characteristics (Figure 29–3):

1. A soft body, usually covered by a dorsal shell.
2. A broad, flat muscular **foot,** located ventrally, which can be used for locomotion.
3. A **visceral mass,** located above the foot, that contains most of the organs.

Table 29–1 MAJOR CLASSES OF PHYLUM MOLLUSCA

Class and Representative Animals	Characteristics
Polyplacophora Chitons	Primitive marine animals with segmented shells; shell consists of eight separate transverse plates; head reduced; broad foot used for locomotion
Gastropoda Snails Slugs Nudibranchs	Marine, freshwater, or terrestrial; body and shell are coiled; well-developed head with tentacles and eyes
Bivalvia Clams Oysters Mussels	Marine and freshwater; body laterally compressed; two shells hinged dorsally; hatchet-shaped foot; filter feeders
Cephalopoda Squids Octopods	Marine; fast-swimming, predatory; foot divided into tentacles; usually bearing suckers; well-developed eyes

4. A **mantle,** a heavy fold of tissue that covers the visceral mass and usually contains glands that secrete a shell. The mantle generally overhangs the visceral mass, forming a mantle cavity, which may contain gills.
5. A rasplike structure called the **radula,** which is a belt of teeth within the digestive system. (The radula is not present in clams and other bivalves.)

All of the organ systems typical of complex animals are present in the mollusks. The digestive system is a tube, sometimes coiled, consisting of a mouth, buccal cavity, esophagus, stomach, intestine, and anus. The radula, located within the buccal cavity, can be projected out of the mouth and used to scrape particles of food from the surface of rocks or the ocean floor. Sometimes the radula is used to drill a hole in another animal's shell or to break off pieces of a plant.

Most mollusks have an **open circulatory system** in which the blood bathes the tissues directly. (In a closed circulatory system the blood flows within a complete circuit of blood vessels.) In mollusks, the heart pumps blood into a single blood vessel, the **aorta,** which may branch into other vessels. Eventually, blood flows into a network of large spaces called sinuses, where the tissues are bathed directly; this network makes up the **hemocoel,** or blood cavity. From the sinuses, blood drains into vessels that conduct it to the gills, where it is recharged with oxygen. From the gills, the blood returns

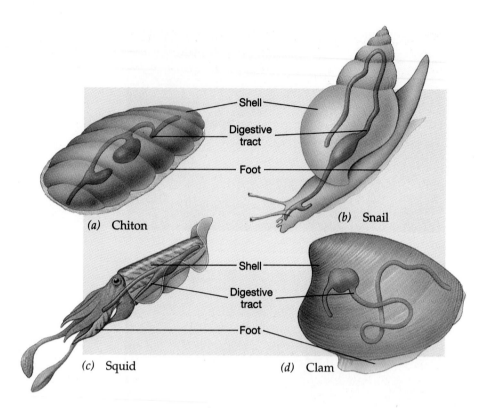

Figure 29–3 Variations in the basic molluskan body plan in chitons, snails, clams, and squids. Note how the foot, shell, and digestive tract have changed their positions in the evolution of the several classes.

(a) Chiton

(b) Snail

(c) Squid

(d) Clam

to the heart. Thus, blood flow in a mollusk follows the pattern

$$\text{heart} \rightarrow \text{aorta} \rightarrow \text{smaller blood vessels} \rightarrow$$
$$\text{sinuses} \rightarrow \text{gills} \rightarrow \text{heart}$$

Open circulatory systems are not very efficient. Blood pressure tends to be low, and tissues are not very efficiently oxygenated. However, because most mollusks are sluggish animals with low metabolic rates, this type of circulatory system is adequate. In the active cephalopods (the class that includes the squids and octopods), the circulatory system is closed.

In mollusks the sexes are usually separate, with fertilization taking place in the surrounding water. Most marine mollusks pass through one or more larval stages. The first larval stage is typically a **trochophore larva,** a free-swimming, ciliated, top-shaped larva characteristic of mollusks and annelids (Figure 29–4). In most of the mollusk classes, the trochophore larva develops into a **veliger larva,** which has a shell and foot. The veliger larva is unique to the phylum Mollusca.

Similarities in the development of mollusks and annelids—the process of spiral cleavage and the trochophore larva—have suggested that these two phyla may have had a common coelomate ancestor. However, many zoologists now think that mollusks and annelids evolved independently from ancestors that resembled the flatworms.

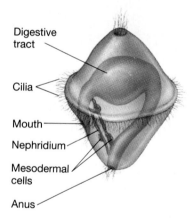

Figure 29–4 Trochophore larva, the first larval stage of a marine mollusk. This type of larva is also characteristic of annelids. Note the characteristic ring of ciliated cells just above the mouth.

Class Polyplacophora Includes the Chitons

Chitons are members of the class **Polyplacophora** (meaning many plates). They are sluggish marine animals with flattened bodies (Figure 29–5). Their most distinctive feature is a shell composed of eight separate but overlapping dorsal plates. The head is reduced in this class, and there are no eyes or tentacles. Chitons inhabit rocky intertidal zones, feeding on algae and other small organisms, which they scrape off rocks and

Figure 29–5 Chitons are sluggish marine animals with shells composed of eight overlapping plates. These living chitons, *Tonicella lineatus*, are from coastal waters off the Pacific Northwest. (Charles Seaborn)

shells with the radula. The broad, flat foot not only functions in locomotion but also helps the animal adhere firmly to rocks. The mantle can also be pressed firmly against the substratum, and the chiton can lift the inner edge of the mantle to produce a partial vacuum. The suction enables the animal to adhere powerfully to its perch.

Class Gastropoda Includes Snails and Their Relatives

Class **Gastropoda,** which includes the snails, conchs, nudibranchs, whelks, limpets, and their relatives, is the largest and numerically the most successful group of mollusks (Figure 29–6). In fact, this class is the second largest class in the animal kingdom—second only to the insects. Most gastropods inhabit marine waters, but others make their home in brackish water, fresh water, or terrestrial areas. Most land snails do not have gills; instead, the mantle is highly vascularized and functions as a lung. These garden snails and slugs are described as **pulmonate.**

We think of snails as having a single, spirally coiled shell, and many do. However, other gastropods, such as limpets and abalones, have shells like flattened dunce caps; still others, such as garden slugs and the beautiful marine snails known as **nudibranchs,** have no shell at all (Figure 29–6).

Many gastropods have a well-developed head with tentacles. Two simple eyes may be located on stalks that extend from the head. The broad flat foot is used for creeping. A unique feature of this group is **torsion,** a twisting of the visceral mass. (This twisting is unrelated to the coiling of the shell.) As the bilateral larva develops, the body twists permanently 180 degrees relative to the head. As a result, the digestive tract becomes somewhat U-shaped, and the anus comes to lie above

(a)

(b)

Figure 29–6 Representative gastropods. (a) A conch, *Strombus gigas,* showing foot, mouth, and eyes. This mollusk grazes on algae. Its large, mobile proboscis sweeps across the bottom of the sea like a vacuum cleaner. (b) Copulating nudibranchs off the Solomon Islands. (a, Charles Seaborn; b, Robert Shupak)

the head (Figure 29–7). Subsequent growth is dorsal and usually in a spiral coil. The twist limits space in the body, and typically the gill, kidney, and gonad are absent on one side.

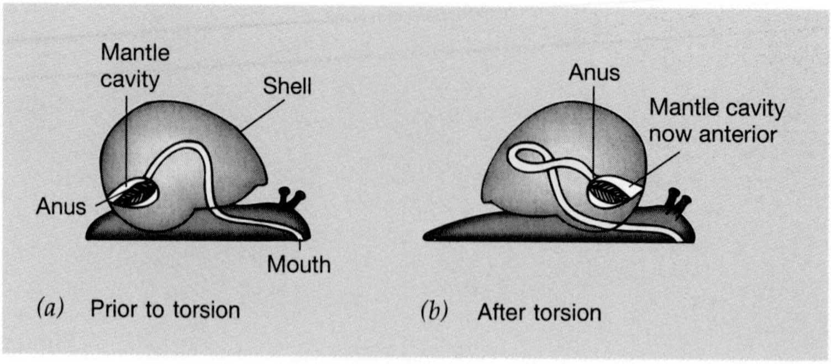

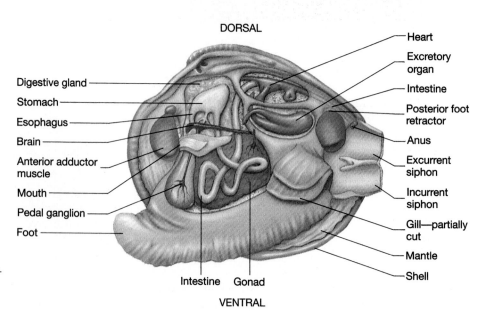

Figure 29–7 Embryonic torsion in the gastropod *Acmaea* (a limpet). As the bilateral larva develops, the visceral mass twists 180 degrees relative to the head.

(a) Prior to torsion — Mantle cavity, Shell, Anus, Mouth

(b) After torsion — Anus, Mantle cavity now anterior

DORSAL

Digestive gland
Stomach
Esophagus
Brain
Anterior adductor muscle
Mouth
Pedal ganglion
Foot

Heart
Excretory organ
Intestine
Posterior foot retractor
Anus
Excurrent siphon
Incurrent siphon
Gill—partially cut
Mantle
Shell

Intestine   Gonad

VENTRAL

Figure 29–8 Internal anatomy of a clam.

Class Bivalvia Includes Clams, Oysters, and Their Relatives

The soft body of members of class **Bivalvia** is laterally compressed and completely enclosed by two shells that hinge dorsally and open ventrally (Figure 29–8). This arrangement allows the hatchet-shaped foot to protrude ventrally for locomotion. Large, strong muscles attached to the shell permit the animal to close its shell.

The inner pearly layer of the bivalve shell is secreted in thin sheets by cells of the mantle. Composed of calcium carbonate, this layer is known as mother-of-pearl and is valued for making jewelry and buttons. When a bit of foreign matter lodges between the shell and the mantle, cells of the mantle secrete concentric layers of calcium carbonate around the intruding particle, forming a pearl.

Some bivalves, such as oysters, attach permanently to the substratum. Others, like clams, burrow slowly through rock or wood, seeking protected dwellings. (The shipworm, *Teredo*, which damages dock pilings and other marine installations, is just looking for a home.) Finally, some bivalves, such as scallops, swim with amazing speed by clapping their two shells to-gether by the contraction of a large adductor muscle (the part of the scallop that is eaten by humans).

Clams and oysters are filter feeders that trap food particles in sea water. They take sea water in through an extension of the mantle called the incurrent siphon. Water leaves by way of an excurrent siphon. As the water passes over the gills, food particles in the water are trapped in mucus secreted by the gills. Cilia move the food to the mouth. An oyster can filter about 3 liters of sea water per hour. Because bivalves are filter feeders, they have no need for a radula, and indeed they are the only group of mollusks that lack this structure.

Most bivalves have two distinct sexes. Gametes are usually discharged into the water, where fertilization takes place. In marine bivalves, a trochophore larva typically develops, which then develops further into a veliger larva with shell and foot. In some marine and nearly all freshwater bivalves, sperm are shed into the water and fertilize the eggs within the mantle cavity of the female. In these species, the female also broods her young within the mantle cavity and development takes place among the gill filaments. Larvae of some freshwater species spend several weeks as parasites on the gills of fishes.

Figure 29–9 *Octopus macropus,* a cephalopod. The octopod lives in a den among the rocks; it may wait near the entrance of its den to seize a passing crustacean, fish, or snail. (Jane Burton/Bruce Coleman, Inc.)

Table 29–2 CLASSES OF PHYLUM ANNELIDA

Class and Representative Animals	Characteristics
Polychaeta Sandworms Tubeworms	Mainly marine; each segment bears a pair of parapodia with many setae; well-developed head; separate sexes; trochophore larva
Oligochaeta Earthworms	Terrestrial and freshwater worms; few setae per segment; lack well-developed head; hermaphroditic
Hirudinea Leeches	Most are blood-sucking parasites that inhabit fresh water; lack appendages and setae; prominent muscular suckers

Class Cephalopoda Includes Squids and Octopods

In contrast to most other mollusks, members of the class **Cephalopoda** (meaning head-feet) are active, predatory animals. They are fast-swimming organisms, adapted for an entirely different lifestyle than their filter-feeding relatives. Some biologists consider cephalopods to be the most advanced of the invertebrates.

The octopus has no shell, and the shell of the squid is reduced to a small "pen" in the mantle. *Nautilus* has a flat, coiled shell consisting of many chambers built up year by year; each year the animal lives in the newest and largest chamber of the series. By secreting a gas resembling air into the other chambers, the *Nautilus* is able to float.

The cephalopod foot is divided into tentacles—ten in squids, eight in octopods. The tentacles, or arms, surround the central mouth of the large head (Figure 29–9). Cephalopods have large, well-developed eyes that form images. Although they develop differently, the eyes are structurally much like vertebrate eyes and function in much the same way.

The tentacles of squids and octopods are covered with suckers for seizing and holding prey. In addition to a radula, the mouth is equipped with two strong, horny beaks used to kill prey and tear it to bits. The mantle is thick and muscular and fitted with a funnel-like structure. By filling the cavity with water and ejecting it through the funnel, the animal can attain rapid jet propulsion in the opposite direction.

Besides its speed, the cephalopod has developed two other important mechanisms that enable it to escape from its predators, which include certain whales and moray eels. One is its ability to confuse the enemy by rapidly changing colors. By expanding and contracting pigment cells in its skin, the cephalopod can display an impressive variety of mottled colors. Another defense mechanism is its ink sac, which produces a thick black liquid. This liquid is released in a dark cloud when the animal is alarmed; while its enemy pauses, temporarily blinded and confused, the cephalopod easily escapes. The ink has been shown to inactivate the chemical receptors of some predators.

The octopus feeds on crabs and other arthropods, catching and killing them with a poisonous secretion of its salivary glands. During the day, the octopus usually hides among the rocks; in the evening, it emerges to hunt for food. Its motion is incredibly fluid, giving little hint of the considerable strength in its eight arms.

Small octopods survive well in aquaria and have been studied extensively. They have a relatively high degree of intelligence and can make associations among stimuli. Their very adaptable behavior resembles more closely that of the vertebrates than the more stereotyped patterns of behavior seen in other invertebrates.

THE SEGMENTED WORMS BELONG TO PHYLUM ANNELIDA

Phylum **Annelida,** the segmented worms, includes earthworms, leeches, and many marine and freshwater worms. The 10,000 or so species are divided into three main classes (Table 29–2 and Figure 29–10). The term *Annelida* means ringed and refers to the series of rings, or segments, that make up the annelid body. Both the body wall and the internal organs are segmented. The

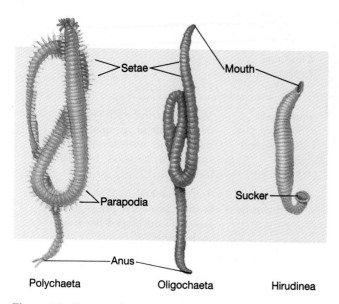

Figure 29–10 Comparison of the classes of the phylum Annelida—Polychaeta, Oligochaeta, and Hirudinea.

segments are separated from one another by transverse partitions called **septa.** The bilaterally symmetrical, tubular body may consist of about 100 segments. Some structures, such as the digestive tract and certain nerves, extend the length of the body, passing through successive segments. Other structures are repeated in each segment (Figure 29–11).

Segmentation is an advantage because not only is the coelom divided into segments, but each segment has its own muscles, enabling the animal to elongate one part of its body while shortening another part. The annelid's hydrostatic skeleton is discussed in Chapter 38. In the annelid, the individual segments are almost all alike. However, in many segmented animals—the arthropods and chordates—different segments and groups of segments are specialized to perform certain functions. In some groups the specialization may be so pronounced that the basic segmentation of the body plan may be obscured.

Bristle-like structures called **setae** anchor the worm to the ground while muscles contract to move the animal along during the process of locomotion. Annelids have a well-developed coelom, a closed circulatory system, and a complete digestive tract extending from mouth to anus. Respiration takes place through the skin or by gills. Typically, a pair of excretory structures called **metanephridia** is found in each segment. The nervous system generally consists of a simple brain composed of a pair of ganglia and a double ventral nerve cord. A pair of ganglia and lateral nerves are repeated in each segment.

Polychaetes Have Parapodia

Class **Polychaeta** includes marine worms that swim freely in the sea, burrow in the mud near the shore, or live in tubes made by cementing bits of shell and sand together with mucus (Figure 29–12). Each body segment has a pair of paddle-shaped appendages called **parapodia** (singular, parapodium) that function in locomotion and in gas exchange. These fleshy structures bear many stiff setae (the name *Polychaeta* means many bristles). Most polychaetes have a well-developed head or **prostomium** bearing eyes and antennae. The prostomium may also be equipped with tentacles, bristles, and palps (feelers). Polychaetes develop from free-swimming trochophore larvae similar to those of mollusks.

Many polychaetes have evolved behavioral patterns that ensure fertilization. By responding to certain rhythmic variations, or cycles, in the environment, nearly all of the females and males of a given species release their gametes into the water at the same time. More than 90% of reef-dwelling *Palolo* worms of the South Pacific shed their eggs and sperm within a single 2-hour period on one night of the year. In this animal the seasonal rhythm limits the reproductive period to November; the lunar rhythm, to a day during the last

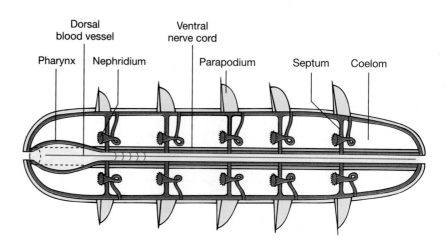

Figure 29–11 A generalized annelid. The body is segmented, and there is serial repetition of many body parts.

(a)

(b)

Figure 29–12   Polychaete annelids. (*a*) The large West Indian fireworm, *Hermodice carunculata,* feeds on corals and sea anemones. (*b*) The Christmas tree worm, *Spiro branchus giganteus,* photographed in the Caribbean. This polychaete bores a protective retreat within living or dead coral or shells. The prostomium has developed to form a crown consisting of several extensions, called radioles, that close together when the worm withdraws into its tube.   (*a*, Charles Seaborn; *b*, Robert Shupak)

quarter of the moon when the tide is unusually low; and the diurnal rhythm, to a few hours just after complete darkness. The posterior half of the *Palolo* worm, loaded with gametes, actually breaks off from the rest, swims backward to the surface, and eventually bursts, releasing the eggs or sperm so that fertilization may occur. Local islanders eagerly await this annual event when they can gather up great numbers of the swarming polychaetes and broil them for dinner.

The Earthworms Belong to Class Oligochaeta

The 3000 or so species of the class **Oligochaeta** are found almost exclusively in fresh water and in moist terrestrial habitats. These worms lack parapodia, have few bristles per segment (the name *Oligochaeta* means few bristles), and lack a well-developed head. All oligochaetes are **hermaphroditic,** meaning that male and female reproductive systems are present in the same individual. Because the earthworm is among the most familiar of all invertebrates, let us examine this animal in more detail.

Lumbricus terrestris, the common earthworm, is about 20 cm long. Its body is divided into more than 100 segments separated externally by grooves and internally by septa. The mouth is located in the first segment, the anus in the last. The earthworm's body is protected from drying by a thin, transparent cuticle, secreted by the cells of the epidermis (Figure 29–13). Mucus secreted by the glandular cells of the epidermis forms an additional protective layer over the body sur-

face. The body wall contains an outer layer of circular muscles and an inner layer of longitudinal muscles.

An earthworm literally eats its way through the soil, ingesting its own weight in soil and decaying vegetation every 24 hours. During this process the soil is turned and aerated, and nitrogenous wastes from the earthworm enrich it. This is why earthworms are vital to the formation and maintenance of fertile soil. The earthworm's soil meal, containing nutritious decaying vegetation, is processed in the complex digestive system. Food is swallowed through the muscular **pharynx** and passes through the **esophagus** to the **stomach.** The stomach consists of two parts: a thin-walled **crop** where food is stored and a thick-walled muscular **gizzard** where food is ground to bits. The rest of the digestive system is a long, straight **intestine,** where food is digested and absorbed. The surface area of the intestine is increased by a dorsal, longitudinal fold (called the typhlosole). Wastes pass out of the intestine to the exterior through the **anus.**

The efficient, closed circulatory system consists of two main blood vessels that extend longitudinally. The dorsal blood vessel, just above the digestive tract, collects blood from blood vessels in the segments. The dorsal blood vessel contracts, pumping blood anteriorly. In the region of the esophagus, five pairs of blood vessels propel blood from the dorsal to the ventral blood vessel. Located just below the digestive tract, the ventral blood vessel carries blood both posteriorly and anteriorly. Small blood vessels branch from it and deliver blood to the various structures in each segment as well as to the body wall. Within these structures blood flows

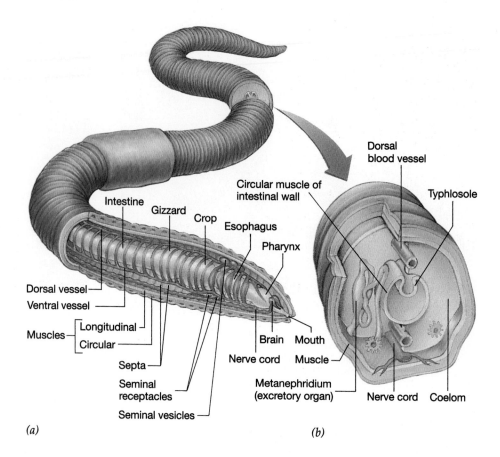

Figure 29–13 Internal structure of an earthworm (an oligochaete). (a) Diagrammatic longitudinal section of the anterior portion. (b) Cross section.

(a)

(b)

through very tiny blood vessels (capillaries) before returning to the dorsal blood vessel.

Gas exchange takes place through the moist skin. Oxygen is transported by the respiratory pigment hemoglobin in the blood plasma. The excretory system consists of paired organs, the metanephridia, repeated in almost every segment of the body. Each metanephridium consists of a ciliated funnel (nephrostome) opening into the next anterior coelomic cavity and connected by a tube to the outside of the body (Figure 29–13). Wastes are removed from the coelomic cavity partly by the beating of the cilia and partly by currents set up by the contraction of muscles in the body wall. The tube of the metanephridium is surrounded by a capillary network that reabsorbs usable materials from the coelomic fluid in the tube.

The metanephridia, open at both ends, are quite different from the protonephridia of the flatworms, which are blind tubules opening only to the exterior. In higher vertebrates, the adults typically have metanephridia, but larval forms usually have protonephridia. The protonephridia generally have a single long flagellum rather than a tuft of cilia. This developmental pattern of excretory structures is often used to support the concept that complex invertebrates (as well as vertebrates) evolved from forms similar to the lower invertebrates.

The nervous system consists of a pair of **cerebral ganglia** that serve as a brain, just above the pharynx,

and a subpharyngeal ganglion, just below the pharynx. A ring of nerve fibers connects these ganglia. From the lower ganglion a double ventral nerve cord extends beneath the digestive tract to the posterior end of the body. In each segment along the nerve cord, there is a pair of fused segmental ganglia. Nerves extend laterally from the segmental ganglia to the muscles and other structures of that segment. The segmental ganglia coordinate the contraction of the muscles of the body wall, so that the worm can creep along.

The subpharyngeal ganglion is the main center controlling movement and vital reflexes. It exerts control over the other ganglia in the chain. When the subpharyngeal ganglion is destroyed, all movement stops. When the brain is removed, the subpharyngeal ganglion is able to control movement, but the worm is no longer able to adjust its actions to conditions in the environment. Earthworm responses are limited to **reflex** (preprogrammed, stereotyped) actions. However, in the laboratory, earthworms can be conditioned to perform simple acts such as contracting when exposed to bright light or vibration. The earthworm has no well-developed sense organs, an adaptation to its subterranean lifestyle.

Like other oligochaetes, earthworms are hermaphroditic. During copulation, the worms exchange sperm. Two worms, heading in opposite directions, press their ventral surfaces together. These surfaces become glued together by thick mucous secretions of the clitellum, a

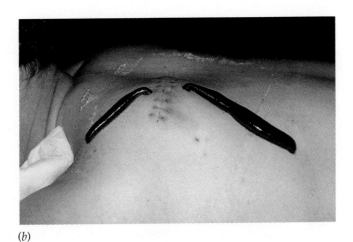

(a)   (b)

Figure 29–14   Class Hirudinea. (a) The leech, *Helobdella stagnalis*. The dark area in its swollen body is recently ingested blood. (b) The medicinal leech, *Hirudo medicinalis*, is used to treat hematoma, an accumulation of blood within body tissues that results from injury or disease. The leech attaches its sucker near the site of injury, makes an incision, and deposits an anticoagulant called hirudin. Hirudin prevents the blood from clotting and dissolves already existing clots.   (a, Visuals Unlimited/T. E. Adams; b, St. Bartholomew's Hospital/Science Photo Library/Photo Researchers, Inc.)

thickened ring of epidermis. Sperm from each worm pass posteriorly to its clitellum and are stored in the seminal receptacles of the other worm. The worms then separate. A few days later the clitellum secretes a membranous cocoon containing a sticky fluid. As the cocoon is slipped over the worm's head, eggs are laid into it from the female pores. Sperm are added as the cocoon passes over the seminal receptacles. When the cocoon is free, its openings constrict so that a spindle-shaped capsule is formed, and the eggs develop into tiny worms within the cocoon. This complex reproductive pattern is an adaptation to terrestrial life.

The Leeches Belong to Class Hirudinea

Most leeches, members of the class **Hirudinea**, inhabit fresh water, but some live in the sea or in moist areas on land. Leeches differ from annelids in having neither setae nor appendages. Many leeches prey on small invertebrates such as oligochaetes or snails. About 75% of the known species of leeches are blood-sucking parasites.

Leeches have muscular suckers at both anterior and posterior ends. Most parasitic leeches attach themselves to a vertebrate host, bite through the skin, and suck out a quantity of blood, which is stored in pouches in the digestive tract. An anticoagulant (hirudin), secreted by glands in its crop, ensures the leech a full meal of blood. Their meals may be infrequent, but they can store enough food from one meal to last a long time. The so-called medicinal leech *(Hirudo medicinalis)*, a freshwater worm about 10 cm long, was used by physicians for bloodletting in the 17th and 18th centuries. Their use

was based on the misconception that fevers and disease were caused by an excess of blood. Interestingly, leeches have found a place in modern medicine (Figure 29–14).

ARTHROPODS HAVE JOINTED APPENDAGES AND AN EXOSKELETON OF CHITIN

The animals that make up phylum **Arthropoda** are the most biologically successful of all animals. There are more of them (about 800,000 described species); they live in a greater variety of habitats; and they can eat a greater variety of foods than the members of any other phylum (Figure 29–15). Among their most important characteristics are the following:

1. **Paired, jointed appendages,** from which they get their name (arthropod means jointed foot). These appendages function as swimming paddles, walking legs, mouth parts, or accessory reproductive organs for transferring sperm.
2. A hard, armor-like **exoskeleton,** composed of chitin, that covers the entire body and appendages. The exoskeleton serves at least four important functions: It provides support, enabling the body to withstand the pull of gravity; it provides protection against drying out; it serves as a coat of armor to protect the animal against predators; and it serves as a point of attachment for muscles. The exoskeleton has certain disadvantages, however. Body movement is somewhat restricted, and in order to grow, the arthropod

(a)

(b)

(c)

(d)

Figure 29–15 The arthropods are considered the most biologically successful animals. (a) Starry-eyed hermit crab photographed in the Virgin Islands. (b) Mayfly *Siphlonisca* emerging from pupation. (c) A pair of horseshoe crabs, *Limulus polyphemus*, mating. (d) Hay mite. (a, Robin Lewis, Coastal Creations; b, Dwight R. Kuhn; c, Peter J. Bryant, University of California, Irvine/ Biological Photo Service)

must shed this outer shell periodically and grow another larger one. This process, called **molting,** leaves the animal temporarily vulnerable to predators.

3. A **segmented body,** like that of the annelid. In some arthropod classes, however, segments become fused together or lost during development.

4. An **open circulatory system** with a simple dorsal heart. A hemocoel (blood cavity) occupies most of the body cavity, and the coelom is small and is filled chiefly by the organs of the reproductive system.

The Arthropod Body Has Three Regions

The bodies of most arthropods are divided into three regions: the **head,** composed of four to six segments; the **thorax;** and the **abdomen.** The thorax and abdomen consist of a variable number of segments. In contrast to most annelids, each arthropod has a fixed number of segments, which remains the same throughout life. The remarkable range of variations in body plan and in the shape of the jointed appendages in the numerous species almost defies description.

The nervous system of the more primitive arthropods, like that of the annelids, consists of a ventral nerve cord connecting segmental ganglia. In the more complex arthropods, the successive ganglia usually fuse together. Arthropods have a variety of well-developed sense organs: complicated eyes, such as the compound eyes of insects; organs of hearing; antennae sensitive to touch and chemicals; and cells sensitive to touch on the surface of the body.

Table 29–3 ARTHROPOD SUBPHYLA AND CLASSES

Subphylum and Classes	Subphylum Characteristics
Subphylum **Chelicerata** Class Merostomata (horseshoe crab) Class Arachnida (spiders, scorpions, ticks, mites)	First pair of appendages are the chelicerae used to manipulate food; body consists of cephalothorax and abdomen; no mandibles; no antennae
Subphylum **Crustacea** Class Crustacea (lobsters, crabs, shrimp, barnacles)	Mandibles; two pairs of antennae; biramous appendages
Subphylum **Uniramia** Class Insecta (grasshopper, roach) Class Chilopoda (centipedes) Class Diplopoda (millipedes)	Mandibles; single pair of antennae; uniramous appendages

The open circulatory system includes a dorsal, tubular heart that pumps blood into a dorsal artery and sometimes several other arteries. From the arteries blood flows into large sinuses, which collectively make up the hemocoel. Blood in the hemocoel bathes the tissues directly. No capillaries or veins are present. Eventually blood finds its way back into the heart through openings, called **ostia,** in its walls.

Most of the aquatic arthropods have a system of gills for gas exchange. The land forms, in contrast, typically have a system of fine, branching air tubes called **tracheae** that conduct air to the internal organs. The digestive system is a simple tube similar to that of the earthworm. Excretory structures vary somewhat from class to class.

Living Arthropods Can Be Assigned to Three Subphyla

Currently, most zoologists divide the living arthropods into three subphyla: Chelicerata, Crustacea, and Uniramia (Table 29–3; also see Table 29–4). Subphylum **Chelicerata** includes the horseshoe crabs and arachnids (spiders, scorpions, ticks, mites). Chelicerates are the only arthropods that lack antennae. These animals have clawlike feeding appendages called **chelicerae.** Mem-

bers of subphylum **Crustacea** (lobsters, crabs, shrimp, and barnacles) and members of subphylum **Uniramia** (insects, centipedes, and millipedes) all have jawlike **mandibles** instead of chelicerae. Other than the extinct trilobites (discussed below), the crustaceans are the only group to have biramous appendages—that is, appendages that have two jointed branches at their ends. They are also the only group to have two pairs of antennae. Members of subphylum Uniramia have uniramous (unbranched) appendages and a single pair of antennae.

Arthropods Are Closely Related to Annelids

Arthropods represent the pinnacle of evolutionary development among the protostomes. Most zoologists think that arthropods evolved either from an ancestor of the annelids or from the annelids directly. The relationship between the arthropods and annelids is evident in the basic body plan. Like annelids, arthropods exhibit **metamerism**; that is, the body is divided into a series of similar segments. Primitive arthropods exhibit metamerism even as adults, but all arthropods are segmented at least as embryos. The basic plan of the nervous system is similar in both annelids and arthropods. A ventral nerve cord extends from a dorsal, anterior brain; ganglia are present in each segment.

Trilobites, the most primitive arthropods, inhabited Paleozoic seas more than 600 million years ago. These arthropods, extinct for 250 million years, lived on the sea bottom and dug into the mud. Covered by a hard, segmented exoskeleton, the trilobite body was a flattened oval divided into three parts: an anterior head bearing a pair of antennae and a pair of compound eyes; a thorax; and a posterior abdomen (Figure 29–16). At right angles to these divisions, two dorsal grooves extended the length of the animal, dividing the body into a median lobe and two lateral lobes. (The name trilobite derives from this division of the body into three longitudinal parts.) Each segment of the body had a pair of segmented biramous (two-branched) appendages; each appendage consisted of an inner walking leg and an outer branch bearing gills.

The trilobites may have given rise to the chelicerates, which also lived in Paleozoic waters. Only five marine species of chelicerates—horseshoe crabs—exist today. Fossil evidence suggests that some extinct marine chelicerates invaded fresh water and may have given rise to the arachnids. The early arachnids were aquatic; the first terrestrial arachnids appeared in the Devonian period. Most living arachnids make their home on the land.

Crustacean fossils have been dated back to the Cambrian period, but neither their origin nor their relationship to other arthropod subphyla is clear. A distinc-

Table 29–4   GENERAL CHARACTERISTICS OF THE PRINCIPAL ARTHROPOD CLASSES

	Class				
	Arachnida (About 60,000 Species)	*Crustacea (About 31,000 Species)*	*Insecta (About 750,000 Species)*	*Chilopoda (About 3000 Species)*	*Diplopoda (About 7500 Species)*
Main habitat	Mainly terrestrial	Marine or fresh water; few on land	Mainly terrestrial	Terrestrial	Terrestrial
Body divisions	Cephalothorax and abdomen	Cephalothorax and abdomen	Head, thorax, and abdomen	Head with segmented body	Head with segmented body
Gas exchange	Book lungs or tracheae	Gills	Tracheae	Tracheae	Tracheae
Appendages **Antennae**	None	2 pairs	1 pair	1 pair	1 pair
Mouth parts	Chelicerae, pedipalps	Mandibles, 2 pairs of maxillipeds (for food handling)	Mandibles, maxillae	Mandibles, 2 pairs maxillae	Mandibles, maxillae
Legs	4 pairs on cephalothorax	1 pair per segment or less	3 pairs on thorax; (+wings)	1 pair per segment	2 pairs (or 1) per segment
Development	Direct, except mites and ticks	Usually larval stages	Usually larval stages; some with complete metamorphosis	Direct	Direct

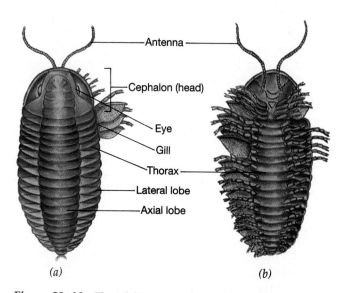

(a)   *(b)*

Figure 29–16   The trilobites are extinct marine arthropods that are considered by many biologists to be among the most primitive members of the phylum. (*a*) Dorsal view of a trilobite from the Ordovician period. (*b*) Ventral view of the same trilobite. Note the biramous appendages.

tive feature of crustaceans is the naupliar larva, which is the first hatching stage in these animals. This larva has only the first three pairs of appendages.

Some zoologists propose that the chelicerates and crustaceans evolved from a marine ancestor and that the uniramians (the subphylum that includes the insects) evolved from a terrestrial ancestor. According to this polyphyletic view, basic arthropod features such as jointed appendages and an exoskeleton of chitin evolved independently at least twice. Zoologists who hold this view suggest that uniramians evolved from members of phylum **Onycophora,** wormlike animals that inhabit humid tropical areas such as rain forests. Onycophorans have some annelid and some arthropod features (Figure 29–17). Like annelids, they are internally segmented, and many organs are duplicated serially. However, the jaws are derived from appendages as in arthropods, and like arthropods, onychophorans have an open circulatory system. The onychophoran respiratory system, which consists of air tubes (tracheal tubes), is also arthropod-like.

Figure 29–17 The velvet worm, *Macroperipatus tarquatus,* an onychophoran from moist forested regions of Trinidad. This animal has features of both arthropods and annelids. Note the soft, sluglike body and the presence of a series of jointed legs. (Raymond A. Mendez © 1993 Animals Animals)

(a)

(b)

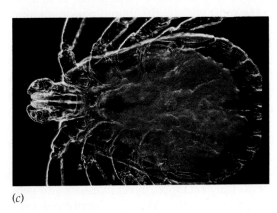
(c)

Figure 29–18 Class Arachnida includes the spiders, scorpions, mites, ticks, and harvestmen. (*a*) A marbled scorpion, *Lychas marmoreus.* (*b*) The red-spotted crab spider, *Misumena vatia,* is a voracious predator. (*c*) A tick, *Dermacentor andersoni.* (*a,* Visuals Unlimited/J. Alcock; *b,* Ed Reschke; *c,* James Solliday/Biological Photo Service)

The earliest fossil insects—primitive, wingless species—date back to the Devonian period more than 360 million years ago. Insect fossils from the Carboniferous period include both wingless and primitive winged species. Cockroaches, mayflies, and cicadas are among the insects that have survived relatively unchanged from the Carboniferous period to the present day.

Subphylum Chelicerata Includes the Horseshoe Crabs and Arachnids

In members of subphylum Chelicerata, the body consists of a cephalothorax and an abdomen. Chelicerates have no antennae and no chewing mandibles (Table 29–3). Instead, the first pair of appendages, which are located immediately anterior to the mouth, are the chelicerae, used to manipulate food and pass it to the mouth. The second pair of appendages, called **pedipalps,** are modified to perform different functions in various groups. Posterior to the pedipalps are four pairs of legs modified for walking.

Class Merostomata includes the horseshoe crabs

Almost all members of the class Merostomata are extinct. The only living merostomes, the **horseshoe crabs,** have survived essentially unchanged for 350 million years or more. *Limulus polyphemus* is the species common in North America. As its common name describes, this animal is horseshoe-shaped. Its long spikelike tail extends posteriorly and is used in locomotion, not for defense or offense. Horseshoe crabs feed on mollusks, worms, and other invertebrates that they find on the ocean floor.

Class Arachnida includes the spiders, scorpions, ticks, harvestmen (daddy long-legs), and mites

Most of the 60,000 or so species of class Arachnida are carnivorous and prey upon insects and other small arthropods (Figure 29–18). The arachnid body consists of a cephalothorax (composed of fused head and thorax) and abdomen. Arachnids have six pairs of jointed appendages. In spiders, the first pair, the chelicerae, are fanglike structures used to penetrate prey and suck out its body fluids. In some species, the chelicerae are used to inject poison into the prey. The second pair of appendages, the pedipalps, are used by spiders to hold and chew food and in some species are modified as sense organs for tasting the food. The other four pairs of appendages are used for walking. Gas exchange in arachnids takes place either by tracheal tubes, by **book lungs,** or by both. Each book lung consists of 15 to 20 plates, like pages of a book, that contain tiny blood vessels. Air enters the body through abdominal slits and circulates between the plates. As air passes over the blood vessels in the plates, oxygen and carbon dioxide are exchanged. An arachnid may have as many as four pairs of book lungs.

The spider has **silk glands** in its abdomen; these glands secrete an elastic protein that is spun into fibers by organs called spinnerets. The silk is liquid as it emerges from the spinnerets but hardens as it is drawn out. Spiders use silk to build nests, to encase their eggs in a cocoon, and in some species, to trap prey. Many spiders lay down a silken dragline as they venture forth. This serves as a safety line and is also a means of communication between members of a species. From a dragline a spider can determine the sex and maturity level of the spinner.

Although spiders do have poison glands for capturing prey, only a few have poison that is toxic to humans. The most widely distributed poisonous spider in the United States is the black widow (*Latrodectus mactans*). Its poison is a neurotoxin that interferes with transmission of messages from nerves to muscles. The brown recluse (*Loxosceles reclusa*) is smaller than the black widow and has a violin-shaped dorsal stripe on its back. Its venom causes death of the tissues surrounding the bite and can occasionally be fatal. Although painful, spider bites cause fewer than five fatalities per year in the United States (usually in children).

Mites and ticks are among the greatest arthropod nuisances. They eat crops, infect livestock and pets, and inhabit our own bodies. Many live unnoticed, owing to their small size, but others cause disease. Certain mites cause mange in dogs and other domestic animals. Chiggers (red bugs), the larval form of red mites, attach themselves to the skin and secrete an irritating digestive fluid that may cause itchy red welts. Larger than mites, ticks are ectoparasites on dogs and other domestic animals. They can transmit diseases such as Rocky Mountain spotted fever, Texas cattle fever, relapsing fever, and Lyme disease.

Subphylum Crustacea Includes the Lobsters, Crabs, Shrimp, and Their Relatives

Crustaceans are vital members of marine food chains. These animals serve as primary consumers of algae and detritus, and as food for the many carnivores that inhabit the oceans. Countless billions of microscopic crustaceans swarm in the ocean and form the food (krill) of many fish and other marine forms such as whales.

As discussed earlier, crustaceans are characterized by mandibles, biramous appendages, and two pairs of antennae (Figure 29–19). Their antennae serve as sensory organs for touch and taste. The mandibles, which are the third pair of appendages, are located on each side of the ventral mouth and are used for biting and grinding food. Posterior to the mandibles are two pairs of appendages, the first and second **maxillae,** used for manipulating and holding food. Several other pairs of appendages are present. Usually five pairs are modified for walking. Others may be specialized for swimming, sperm transmission, carrying eggs and young, or sensation.

As the only class of arthropods that are primarily aquatic, crustaceans generally have gills for gas exchange. Two large **antennal glands** (also referred to as green glands) located in the head remove metabolic wastes from the blood and body fluids and excrete them through ducts opening at the base of each antenna. The crustacean nervous system is somewhat similar to the annelid nervous system but is proportionately larger, and ganglia are fused and large. Most adult members of the class have compound eyes (discussed in Chapter 41). Among the other sense organs present are **statocysts** for detecting the pull of gravity.

Crustaceans characteristically have separate sexes. During copulation, the male uses specialized appendages to transfer sperm into the female. The fertilized eggs are usually brooded. The newly hatched animals pass by successive molts through a series of larval stages until they reach the adult body. The lobster, for example, molts seven times during its first summer; at each molt it gets larger and more closely resembles the adult. After it becomes a small adult, additional molts provide for growth.

Barnacles, the only sessile crustaceans, differ markedly in their external anatomy from other members of the class. They are exclusively marine and secrete complex calcareous cups within which they live. The larvae of barnacles are free-swimming forms that go through several molts and eventually become sessile and develop into the adult form. Barnacles were described by the 19th century naturalist Louis Agassiz as "nothing more than a little shrimplike animal standing on its head in a limestone house and kicking food into its mouth."

The largest order of crustaceans, **Decapoda,** contains more than 10,000 species of lobsters, crayfish, crabs, and shrimp. Most decapods are marine, but a few, such as the crayfish, certain shrimp, and a few crabs, live in fresh water. The crustaceans in general and the decapods in particular show striking specialization and differentiation of parts in the various regions

(a)

(b)

(c)

Figure 29–19 Crustaceans.
(a) Broken-back shrimp from Monterey
Bay. (b) A single barnacle, *Balanus
nubilis*, filtering water for food.
(c) Crab. (a, Frans Lanting/Minden
Pictures; b, c, Charles Seaborn)

of the animal. In the lobster, no two of the 19 pairs of appendages are identical, and the appendages in the different parts of the body differ markedly in form and function (Figure 29–20).

The six segments of the lobster's head and the eight segments of the thorax are fused into a cephalothorax, covered on its top and sides by a shield, the **carapace.** The carapace is composed of chitin impregnated with calcium salts. The two pairs of antennae are the sites of chemoreceptors and tactile sense organs; the second pair of antennae are especially long. The mandibles are short and heavy, with opposing surfaces used in grinding and biting food. Behind the mandibles are two pairs of accessory feeding appendages, the first and second maxillae. The appendages of the first three segments of the thorax are the maxillipeds, which aid in chopping

up food and passing it to the mouth. The fourth segment of the thorax has a pair of large **chelipeds,** or pinching claws. The last four thoracic segments have pairs of **walking legs.**

The appendages of the first abdominal segment are part of the reproductive system and function in the male as sperm-transferring structures. On the following four abdominal segments are paired **swimmerets,** small paddle-like structures used by some decapods for swimming and by the females of all species for holding eggs. Each branch of the sixth abdominal appendages, which are called **uropods,** consists of a large flattened structure. Together with the flattened posterior end of the abdomen (the telson), they form a fan-shaped tail fin used for swimming backwards.

(*Text continued on p. 637*)

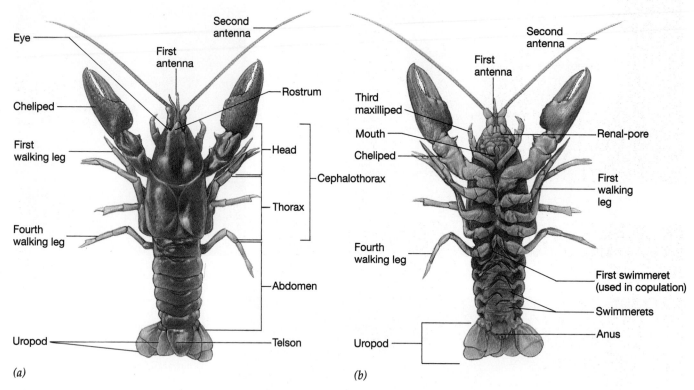

Figure 29–20 Anatomy of a lobster. (*a*) Dorsal view; (*b*) ventral view.

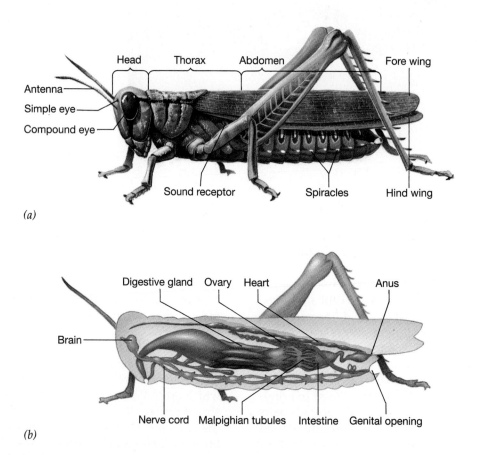

Figure 29–21 Insect body structure. (*a*) External anatomy of the grasshopper. Note the three pairs of segmented legs. (*b*) Internal anatomy of the grasshopper.

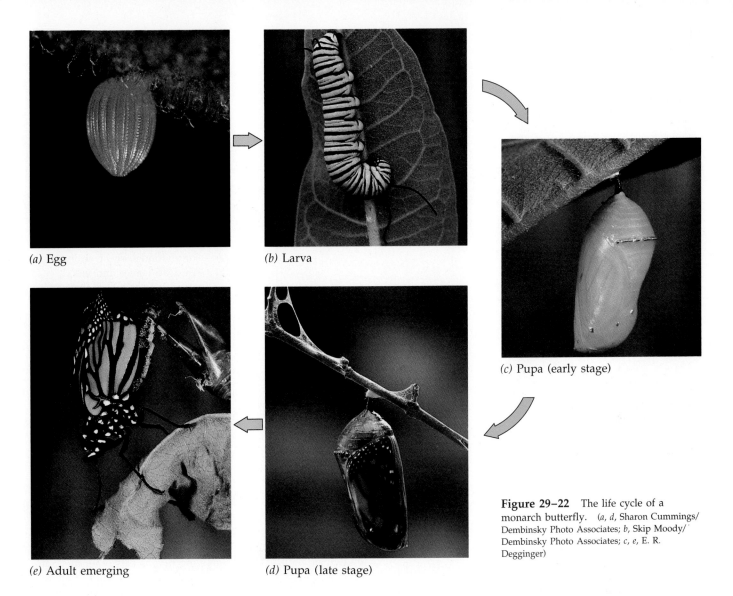

(a) Egg

(b) Larva

(c) Pupa (early stage)

(e) Adult emerging

(d) Pupa (late stage)

Figure 29–22 The life cycle of a monarch butterfly. (*a, d*, Sharon Cummings/ Dembinsky Photo Associates; *b*, Skip Moody/ Dembinsky Photo Associates; *c, e*, E. R. Degginger)

Subphylum Uniramia Includes the Insects, Centipedes, and Millipedes

The insects, centipedes, and millipedes are grouped together in subphylum Uniramia because they all have uniramous (unbranched) appendages. They also have only a single pair of antennae rather than two pairs as in crustaceans.

Insects are the most successful group of animals

With more than 750,000 described species, the class **Insecta** is the most successful group of animals on our planet in terms of diversity, number of species, and number of individuals. More species of insects have been identified than of all other classes of animals combined. What they lack in size, insects make up in sheer numbers. It has been calculated that if all the insects in the world could be weighed, they would weigh more than all of the remaining terrestrial animals. Because they have an extraordinary ability to adapt to changes in the environment, these curious creatures may eventually inherit the earth. Insects are primarily terrestrial animals, but some species live in fresh water, a few are

truly marine, and others inhabit the shore between the tides.

An insect may be described as an **articulated** (jointed), **tracheated** (having tracheal tubes for gas exchange) **hexapod** (having six feet). The insect body consists of three distinct parts—head, thorax, and abdomen (Figure 29–21). Three pairs of legs emerge from the adult thorax, and there may be one or two pairs of wings. One pair of antennae protrudes from the head, and the sense organs include both simple and compound eyes. A complex set of mouth parts is present; these may be adapted for piercing, chewing, sucking, or lapping. Excretion is accomplished by two to many slender **Malpighian tubules,** which receive metabolic wastes from the blood, concentrate the wastes, and discharge them into the intestine.

The sexes are separate, and fertilization takes place internally. Several molts occur during development. In some orders there are several developmental stages called nymphal stages and gradual metamorphosis (change in body form) to the adult form (see Focus on the Principal Orders of Insects). In others there is a complete metamorphosis with four distinct stages in the life cycle: egg, larva, pupa, and adult (Figure 29–22).

(Text continued on p. 640)

FOCUS ON

The Principal Orders of Insects

Order and Examples	Mouth Parts	Wings	Other Characteristics
*Ametabolous Insects**			
Thysanura Silverfish Bristletails	Chewing	None	Long antennae; 3 "tails" extend from posterior tip of abdomen; run fast; live in dead leaves and wood, or in houses where they eat the starch in books and clothing
Collembola Springtails	Chewing	None	Abdominal structure for jumping; live in soil, dead leaves, rotting wood
Hemimetabolous Insects			
Odonata Dragonflies Damselflies	Chewing	2 pairs; long, narrow, membranous	Predators; large compound eyes; aquatic nymph
Ephemeroptera Mayflies	Chewing	2 pairs; membranous; forewings larger than hindwings	Small antennae; vestigial mouth parts in adult; 2 or 3 "tails" extending from tip of abdomen; nymph aquatic
Orthoptera Grasshoppers Crickets Roaches	Chewing	2 pairs or none; leathery forewings, membranous hindwings	Most herbivorous, some cause crop damage; praying mantis eats other insects
Isoptera Termites	Chewing	2 pairs or none; wings shed by sexual forms after mating	Social insects, form large colonies; main diet wood; can be very destructive
Dermaptera Earwigs	Chewing	2 pairs; forewings very short; hindwings large, membranous	Forceps-like appendage on tip of abdomen; nocturnal
Anoplura Sucking lice	Piercing and sucking	None	Ectoparasites of birds and mammals; head louse and crab louse are human parasites; vectors of typhus fever

*Insects may be divided into 3 groups based on their pattern of development. Ametabolous insects do not undergo metamorphosis (egg → immature form → adult). Hemimetabolous insects exhibit incomplete metamorphosis (egg → nymph [resembles adult in many ways but lacks functional wings and reproductive structures] → adult). Holometabolous insects undergo complete metamorphosis (egg → larva → pupa → adult). The wormlike larva, which is very different from the adult, hatches from the egg (Figure 29–22). Typically, an insect spends most of its life as a larva. Eventually, the larva stops feeding, molts, and enters a pupal stage usually within a protective cocoon or underground burrow. The pupa does not feed and cannot defend itself. Its energy is spent remodeling its body form, so that when it emerges it is equipped with functional wings and reproductive organs.

Silverfish, *Lepisma saccharina,* adult and ▶ young. Silverfish are primitive ametabolous insects. (Harry Rogers/Photo Researchers, Inc.)

Order and Examples	Mouth Parts	Wings	Other Characteristics
Hemiptera (true bugs) Chinch bugs Bedbugs	Piercing and sucking	2 pairs; hindwings membranous	Mouth parts form beak; only order of insects properly called bugs
Homoptera Aphids Leaf hoppers Cicadas Scale insects	Piercing and sucking	Usually 2 pairs; membranous	Mouth parts form sucking beak; base of beak near thorax; some very destructive to plants

Holometabolous Insects

Neuroptera Ant lions Dobson flies	Chewing	2 pairs; membranous	Larvae are predators
Lepidoptera Moths Butterflies	Sucking	2 pairs; covered with overlapping scales	Larvae, called caterpillars, have chewing mouth parts; eat plants; adults that feed suck flower nectar
Diptera (true flies) Houseflies Mosquitos Gnats Fruit flies	Usually piercing and sucking	Forewings functional; hindwings small, knoblike halteres	Larvae are maggots or wigglers; may be damaging to domestic animals and food; adults often transmit disease
Siphonaptera Fleas	Piercing and sucking	None	Legs adapted for jumping; lack compound eyes; ectoparasites on birds and mammals; vectors of bubonic plague and typhus
Coleoptera Beetles Weevils	Chewing	Usually 2 pairs; forewings modified as heavy, protective coverings	Largest order of insects (more than 300,000 species); majority herbivorous; some aquatic
Hymenoptera Ants Bees Wasps	Chewing but modified for lapping or sucking in some forms	2 pairs or none; transparent when present	Some are social insects; some sting

◄ An aphid, *Aphis nerii*, giving birth to a live young. (Peter J. Bryant/Biological Photo Service)

An io caterpillar. This larva ► will undergo complete metamorphosis before becoming an adult (see Figure 29–22). (Luci Giglio)

Figure 29–23   A royal cell of the termite *Nasutitermes* sp., from Peru. The queen, with an enlarged abdomen, occupies the center of the chamber. Most of the individuals are workers. A few soldiers with "squirt gun" heads and reduced mandibles are visible.   (James L. Castner)

Figure 29–24   *Cicada*, molting. This insect requires 13 years to mature. The nymphs live in the soil, where they feed on roots. (Chris Simon)

Certain species of bees, ants, and termites exist as colonies or societies made up of several different types of individuals, each adapted for some particular function (Figure 29–23). The members of some insect societies communicate with each other by "dances" and by chemicals called pheromones. Social insects and their communication are discussed in Chapter 50.

Many adaptations contribute to the success of the insects

What are the secrets of insect success? One important feature is their body plan, which can be modified and specialized in so many ways that insects have been able to adapt to a remarkable number of lifestyles. Another reason for their success is the ability to fly. Unlike other invertebrates, which creep slowly along (or under) the ground, most insects fly rapidly through the air. Their wings and small size facilitate their wide distribution. The insect body is well protected by a tough exoskeleton, which also helps to prevent water loss by evaporation. Other protective mechanisms include mimicry, protective coloration, and aggressive behavior (Chapter 17). Metamorphosis divides the insect life cycle into different stages, a strategy that has the advantage of placing larval forms in different life styles so that they do not have to compete with adults for food or habitats (Figure 29–24).

Insects have a great impact on humans

Not all insects compete with us for food or merely cause us to scratch, swell up, or recoil from their presence. Bees, wasps, beetles, and many other insects pollinate flowers of crops and fruit trees. Some insects destroy other insects that are harmful. For example, dragonflies eat mosquitos; some organic farmers even purchase lady beetles, so adept are they at ridding plants of aphids and other insect pests. Insects are important members of many food chains. Many birds, mammals, amphibians, reptiles, and even some fish depend upon insects for food. Many beetles and the larvae (maggots) of flies are detritus feeders; they break down dead plants and animals and their wastes, permitting nutrients to be recycled.

Many insect products are useful to us. Bees produce honey as well as beeswax, which is used in making candles, lubricants, chewing gum, and other products. Shellac is made from lac, a substance given off by certain scale insects that feed on the sap of trees. And the labor of silkworms provides us with silk.

On the negative side, billions of dollars worth of crops are destroyed each year by insect pests. Whole buildings may be destroyed by termites, and clothing can be damaged by moths. Fire ants not only inflict painful stings but cause farmers serious economic loss because of their large mounds, which damage mowers and other farm equipment. Mounds also reduce grazing land because livestock quickly learn to avoid them.

Blood-sucking flies, screwworms, lice, fleas, and other insects annoy and transmit disease in both humans and domestic animals. Mosquitos are vectors of malaria and yellow fever. Body lice may carry the typhus rickettsia, and houseflies sometimes transmit typhoid fever and dysentery. Tsetse flies transmit African sleeping sickness, and fleas may be vectors of bubonic plague.

Table 29–5 COMPARISON OF CHARACTERISTICS OF SOME HIGHER ANIMAL PHYLA*

	Mollusca	*Annelida* (segmented worms)	*Arthropoda* (joint-footed animals)
Representative Animals	Clams Snails Squids	Earthworms Leeches Marine worms	Crustaceans Insects Spiders
Body Symmetry	Bilateral	Bilateral	Bilateral
Gas Exchange	Gills and mantle	Diffusion through moist skin; oxygen circulated by blood	Tracheae in insects; gills in crustaceans; book lungs or tracheae in spider group
Waste Disposal	Metanephridia	Pair of metanephridia in each segment	Malpighian tubules in insects; antennal (green) glands in crustaceans
Nervous System	Three pairs of ganglia; simple sense organs	Simple brain; ventral nerve cord; simple sense organs	Simple brain; ventral nerve cord; well-developed sense organs
Circulation	Open system	Closed system	Open system
Reproduction	Sexual; sexes separate; fertilization in water	Sexual; hermaphroditic but cross-fertilize	Sexual; sexes separate
Other Characteristics	Soft-bodied; usually have shell and ventral foot for locomotion	Earthworms till soil	Hard exoskeleton; most diverse and numerous group of animals

*Members of these phyla are at the organ system level of organization and have a complete digestive tract.

Classes Chilopoda and Diplopoda include centipedes and millipedes

Members of class Chilopoda are called centipedes (meaning hundred-legged), and members of class Diplopoda are known as millipedes (meaning thousand-legged). These animals are all terrestrial and are typically found beneath stones or wood in the soil in both temperate and tropical regions.

While they are not clearly related, centipedes and millipedes are similar in having a head and an elongated trunk with many segments, each bearing legs (Figure 29–25). The centipedes have one pair of legs on each segment behind the head. Most centipedes do not have enough legs to merit their name—the most common number being 30 or so—although in a few species, the number of legs is 100 or more. The legs of centipedes are long, enabling them to run rapidly. Centipedes are carnivorous and feed upon other animals, mostly insects, but the larger centipedes have been known to eat snakes, mice, and frogs. The prey is captured and killed with poison claws located just behind the head on the first trunk segment.

Millipedes have two pairs of legs on most body segments. Diplopods are not as agile as chilopods, and most species can crawl only slowly over the ground, although they can powerfully force their way through earth and rotting wood. Millipedes are generally herbivorous and feed on both living and nonliving vegetation.

(a)

(b)

Figure 29–25 Chilopods and diplopods have uniramous appendages. (a) Centipede, a member of the class Chilopoda. Centipedes have one pair of appendages per segment.

(b) Millipede, a member of the class Diplopoda. Millipedes have two pairs of appendages per segment. (a, b, E. R. Degginger)

SUMMARY

I. The coelomate protostomes include the mollusks, annelids, and arthropods, as well as some minor phyla.

II. The coelom provides space for many organs and permits the digestive tract to move independently of body movements; coelomic fluid helps transport materials and bathes cells that line the coelom.

III. In terrestrial animals, the body covering must prevent fluid loss, some sort of skeleton must be present to withstand the pull of gravity, and there must be reproductive adaptations, such as internal fertilization, development within the mother's body, or shells that prevent drying out of the developing embryo.

IV. Mollusks are soft-bodied animals usually covered by a shell; they possess a ventral foot for locomotion and a mantle that covers the visceral mass.

A. Class Polyplacophora includes the sluggish marine chitons, which have segmented shells.

B. Class Gastropoda, the largest and most successful group of mollusks, includes the snails, slugs, and whelks. In gastropods, the body is twisted, and the shell (when present) is coiled.

C. Class Bivalvia includes the clams and oysters, animals enclosed by two shells, hinged dorsally.

D. Class Cephalopoda includes the squids and octopods, which are active predatory animals; the foot is divided into tentacles that surround the mouth located in the large head.

V. Phylum Annelida, the segmented worms, includes many aquatic worms, earthworms, and leeches.

A. Annelids have conspicuously long bodies that are segmented both internally and externally; their large compartmentalized coelom serves as a hydrostatic skeleton.

B. Class Polychaeta consists of marine worms characterized by bristled parapodia, used for locomotion.

C. Class Oligochaeta, which includes the earthworms, contains segmented worms characterized by a few

setae per segment. The body is divided into more than 100 segments separated internally by septa.

D. Class Hirudinea, the leeches, is composed of animals that lack setae and appendages. They are equipped with suckers for sucking blood.

VI. Phylum Onychophora includes animals with both annelid and arthropod characteristics.

VII. Phylum Arthropoda is composed of animals with jointed appendages and an armor-like exoskeleton of chitin.

A. The trilobites are extinct marine arthropods that were covered by a hard, segmented shell.

B. Subphylum Chelicerata includes class Merostomata (the horseshoe crabs) and class Arachnida (spiders, mites, and their relatives).

1. In the chelicerates the first pair of appendages are chelicerae, used to manipulate food. Chelicerates have no antennae and no mandibles.

2. The arachnid body consists of a cephalothorax and abdomen; there are six pairs of jointed appendages, of which four pairs serve as legs.

C. Subphylum Crustacea includes the lobsters, crabs, and barnacles. The body consists of a cephalothorax and abdomen; often five pairs of walking legs are present. Crustaceans have two pairs of antennae and mandibles for chewing.

D. Subphylum Uniramia includes class Insecta, class Chilopoda, and class Diplopoda; members of this subphylum have unbranched appendages and a single pair of antennae.

1. An insect is an articulated, tracheated hexapod; its body consists of a head, thorax, and abdomen. Insects are the most ecologically successful group of animals.

2. The centipedes have one pair of legs per body segment, whereas the millipedes have two pairs of legs per body segment.

POST-TEST

1. The _____ of arthropods and mollusks provides protection and serves as a point of attachment for muscles.
2. The molluskan _____ is a belt of teeth within the digestive system.
3. A hemocoel is characteristic of animals with an _____ circulatory system.
4. The first larval stage of a mollusk is a free-swimming _____ larva.
5. Segmental, serial repetition of structures within an animal is known as _____.
6. In pulmonate snails, the highly vascularized mantle functions as a _____.
7. Nudibranchs are mollusks that lack a _____.
8. Setae are bristle-like structures that function in _____.
9. _____ animals have both male and female reproductive organs.
10. The earthworm brain consists of a pair of _____.
11. Most members of class Hirudinea are blood-sucking _____.
12. Onychophorans are considered a possible link between the annelids and the _____.
13. Animals with an exoskeleton and paired, jointed appendages are _____.
14. The mandibles of a crustacean are used for _____.
15. Antennal (green) glands in the crustacean are _____ organs.

16. The only sessile crustaceans are the _____.
17. Chelipeds are large _____.
18. Malpighian tubules are _____ organs.

Select the appropriate animal in Column B for the description given in Column A:

Column A	Column B
19. An articulated, tracheated hexapod	a. Trilobite
20. An animal that uses book lungs	b. Insect
21. An animal with two pairs of legs per segment	c. Spider
22. An extinct arthropod with a hard, segmented shell	d. Millipede
	e. None of the above

Select the appropriate animal subphylum or class in Column B for the description given in Column A.

Column A	Column B
23. Largest and most successful group of crustaceans	a. Polychaetes
24. An arthropod subphylum whose members have unbranched appendages	b. Chelicerates
	c. Gastropods
25. Arthropods with no antennae or mandibles	d. Uniramia
	e. None of the above

REVIEW QUESTIONS

1. In what ways are mollusks and annelids alike? In what ways are they different?
2. Give two distinguishing characteristics for each:
   a. mollusks
   b. annelids
   c. arthropods
3. What are the advantages of each of the following?
   a. presence of a coelom
   b. the arthropod exoskeleton
   c. segmentation (metamerism)
4. Contrast the lifestyles of a gastropod and a cephalopod.
5. What is a trochophore larva? A veliger larva?
6. Describe some of the adaptations that have contributed to insect success.
7. Distinguish between insects and spiders.
8. What are the distinguishing features of each of the arthropod subphyla?
9. What are the distinguishing features of the principal arthropod classes?
10. Identify animals that belong to each class of arthropods.

RECOMMENDED READINGS

Brownell, P. H. Prey detection by the sand scorpion. *Scientific American*, Vol. 251, No. 6 (December 1984). The sand scorpion does not see or hear the insects it feeds on. Instead it uses receptors on its legs that are exquisitely sensitive to disturbances of the sand.

Camhi, J. M. The escape system of the cockroach. *Scientific American*, Vol. 243, No. 6 (December 1980). A study of the mechanisms by which a roach rapidly escapes from predators.

Gosline, J. M., and M. E. Demont. Jet-propelled swimming in squids. *Scientific American*, Vol. 252, No. 1 (January 1985). As the squid swims it takes up and expels water by contracting radial and circular muscles in its mantle wall.

Jackson, R. R. A web-building jumping spider. *Scientific American*, Vol. 253, No. 3 (September 1985). Unlike most other jumping spiders, the Australian species, *Portia fimbriata*, builds webs. This predatory spider hunts other spiders.

Moore, J. Parasites that change the behavior of their host. *Scientific American*, Vol. 250, No. 5 (May 1984). Certain parasites, such as thorny-headed worms, which infect pill bugs, make the host more vulnerable to predation by their next host.

Nijhout H. F. The color patterns of butterflies and moths. *Scientific American*, Vol. 245, No. 5 (November 1981). A study of the development of the more than 100,000 different wing patterns of butterflies and moths.

Reid, R. G. B. and F. R. Bernard. Gutless bivalves. *Science*, Vol. 208 (May 1980). A description of a new species of bivalve that lacks internal digestive organs.

Richardson, J. R. Brachiopods. *Scientific American*, Vol. 255, No. 3 (September 1986). One class of these clamlike animals survives by searching out environments suited to an unchanging form; the other class survives by adapting its form or behavior to the local environment.

CHAPTER 30

The Animal Kingdom: The Deuterostomes

OUTLINE

Phylum Echinodermata: spiny-skinned animals of the sea

Phylum Chordata: animals with a notochord, dorsal
tubular nerve cord, and pharyngeal gill slits

I t may seem strange to group the **echinoderms**—the sea stars, sea urchins, and sand dollars—with the **chordates,** the phylum to which we belong. However, evidence exists that echinoderms and chordates evolved from a common ancestor. These groups, along with the hemichordates and Chaetognatha, are classified as deuterostomes, the second main branch of the animal kingdom. As deuterostomes, they share similarities in their patterns of development. In contrast to the protostomes, the mouth forms from a second opening that develops in the embryo; the anus forms from the first opening. As discussed in Chapter 28, deuterostomes are characterized by radial, rather than spiral, cleavage. The fate of their cells is fixed later in development than in protostomes; that is, cleavage is indeterminate. The mesoderm develops from paired pouches that pocket out from the primitive gut. The coelom forms from cavities within the mesodermal out-pocketings.

The red sea star *Fromia ghardagana* on a sponge in the Red Sea. (SharkSong/M. Kazmers/Dembinsky Photo Associates)

Some characteristics of echinoderms and chordates are discussed in this chapter and are compared in Table 30–1 (page 668). Although the echinoderm larva is bilaterally symmetrical, the adult typically exhibits radial symmetry. Its endoskeleton (internal skeleton), consisting of calcium carbonate plates, commonly bears external spines. Echinoderms have a unique water vascular system made up of internal canals and external tube feet. This system functions in locomotion, in obtaining food, and, in some forms, in gas exchange.

During some time in its life cycle, a chordate has a notochord; a dorsal, tubular nerve cord; and pharyngeal gill slits. The largest chordate subphylum is Vertebrata, animals with backbones (vertebral columns). A vertebrate has a well-developed head with sense organs and a brain encased in a bony cranium. The cranium and vertebral column are part of the living endoskeleton.

Two small, related phyla must be mentioned. Phylum **Hemichordata,** a small group of wormlike marine animals, is described in Focus on the Hemichordates. Phylum **Chaetognatha** is comprised of the arrowworms, a group of about 50 species that are found in marine plankton.

After you have studied this chapter you should be able to

1. Discuss the relationship of the echinoderms and chordates, giving specific reasons for grouping them together.
2. Describe the distinguishing characteristics of the echinoderms.
3. Describe and give examples of each of the five main classes of echinoderms.
4. Distinguish among the subphyla of phylum Chordata and describe the characteristics that they have in common; describe the characteristics of subphylum Vertebrata.
5. Distinguish among the classes of vertebrates and assign a given vertebrate to the correct class.
6. Trace the evolution of vertebrates according to current theory.
7. Identify adaptations that reptiles and other terrestrial vertebrates have made to life on land.
8. Contrast monotremes, marsupials, and placental mammals and give examples of members that belong to each group.
9. Identify the major orders of placental mammals and give examples of animals that belong to each order.

ECHINODERMS ARE SPINY-SKINNED ANIMALS OF THE SEA

All of the members of phylum **Echinodermata** inhabit the sea. They are found in all oceans and at all depths. About 6000 living and 20,000 extinct species have been identified. The living species are divided into five principal classes (Figure 30–1): Class **Crinoidea** includes the sea lilies and feather stars; class **Asteroidea**, the sea stars; class **Ophiuroidea**, the basket stars and brittle stars; class **Echinoidea**, the sea urchins and sand dollars; and class **Holothuroidea**, the sea cucumbers.

The echinoderms are in many ways unique in the animal kingdom. The larvae of echinoderms are bilaterally symmetrical, ciliated, and free-swimming. During development the symmetry changes to radial. Echinoderms have an endoskeleton that consists of small calcareous plates (composed of $CaCO_3$), typically bearing

(a)

(b)

(c)

(d)

(e)

Figure 30–1 Some representative echinoderms. (a) A feather star from the Caribbean Sea. (b) Pacific Henricia sea star, *Henricia laeviuscula*. (c) Brittle star on coral in Honduras. (d) Blue spotted sea urchin, *Astropyga radiata*. (e) Basket star living on the surface of a sponge.
(a, Susan Blanchet/Dembinsky Photo Associates; b, Marilyn Kazmers/Dembinsky Photo Associates; c, Robert Shupak; d, Brian Parker/Tom Stack and Associates; e, Harold W. Pratt/Biological Photo Service)

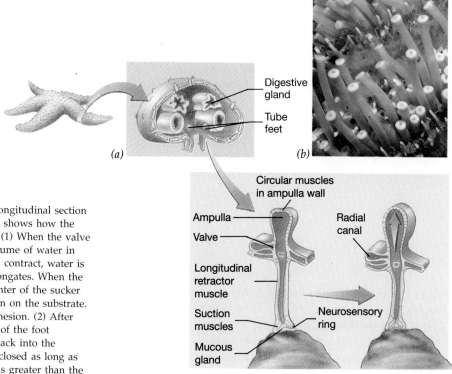

Figure 30–2 Tube feet in echinoderms. (*a*) Longitudinal section through the tube foot of a sea urchin. Sequence shows how the foot works to anchor the animal to a substrate. (1) When the valve to the radial canal is closed, there is a fixed volume of water in the tube foot. When the muscles in the ampulla contract, water is forced into the lower part of the foot, which elongates. When the foot comes in contact with the substrate, the center of the sucker withdraws, producing a near-vacuum, or suction on the substrate. A secretion from the mucous glands aids in adhesion. (2) After adhesion of the sucker, the logitudinal muscles of the foot contract, shortening the foot and forcing fluid back into the ampulla. The valve to the radial canal remains closed as long as the hydrostatic pressure in the tube foot remains greater than the pressure within the canal. (*b*) Tube feet of a sea star.   (*b*, Charles Seaborn)

spines that project outward; the name *Echinodermata*, meaning spiny-skinned, reflects this trait. The endoskeleton is covered by a thin, ciliated epidermis.

Also unique in echinoderms is the **water vascular system**, a network of canals through which sea water circulates. Branches of this system lead to numerous tiny **tube feet**, which extend when filled with fluid. The tube feet serve in locomotion and obtaining food and, in some forms, in gas exchange. The water vascular system serves as a hydrostatic skeleton for the tube feet. To extend a foot, a rounded muscular sac, or **ampulla**, at the upper end of the foot contracts, forcing water through a valve into the tube of the foot. At the bottom of the foot is a suction structure that adheres to the substratum. The foot can be withdrawn by contraction of muscles in its walls, which forces water back into the ampulla (Figure 30–2).

Echinoderms have a well-developed coelom, in which the various internal organs are located. The complete digestive system is the most prominent body system. A variety of respiratory structures are found in the various classes, including dermal gills in the sea stars and respiratory trees in sea cucumbers. Only a rudimentary circulatory system is present, and no specialized excretory structures exist. The nervous system is simple, usually consisting of nerve rings about the mouth with radiating nerves. Echinoderms have no brain. The sexes are usually separate, and eggs and sperm are released into the water, where fertilization takes place externally.

Class Crinoidea Includes the Feather Stars and Sea Lilies

Class Crinoidea, the most primitive class of living echinoderms, includes the feather stars and the sea lilies. The feather stars are free-swimming crinoids, although they often remain in the same location for long periods of time. Sea lilies are sessile and remain attached to the ocean floor by a stalk. Although there are relatively few living species, a great many extinct crinoids are known.

Crinoids differ from other echinoderms in that the oral (mouth) surface is turned upward. A number of branched, feathery arms also extend upward. In all other classes, the mouth is located on the ventral surface. The crinoids are filter feeders. Their tube feet, abundant on the feathery arms, are coated with mucus that traps microscopic organisms.

Class Asteroidea Includes the Sea Stars

Sea stars, or starfish, are members of class Asteroidea. The body of a sea star consists of a central disk from which radiate 5 to 20 or more arms, or rays (Figure 30–3). In the center of the underside of the disk is the mouth. The endoskeleton consists of a series of calcareous plates that permit some movement in the arms. Around the base of the delicate skin gills used in gas exchange are tiny pincer-like spines called pedicellaria; operated by muscles, these keep the surface of the animal free of debris (Figure 30–3).

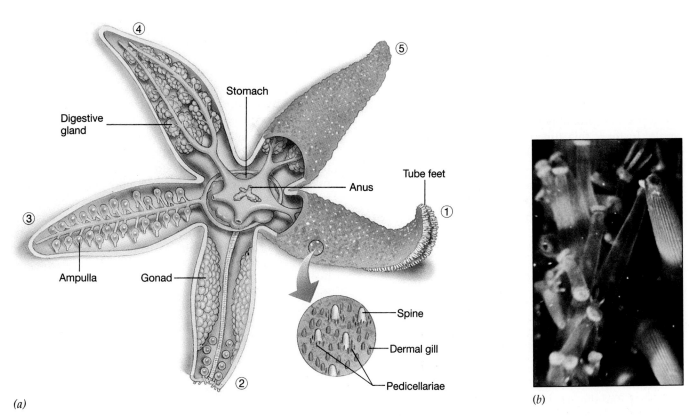

(a)

(b)

Figure 30–3 Structure of the sea star. *(a)* The sea star *Asterias* viewed from above with the arms in various stages of dissection. (1) Upper surface with a magnified detail showing the features of the surface. The end is turned up to show the tube feet on the lower surface. (2) Arm dissected to show well-developed gonads. Gonads are present in each arm. (3) Upper body and digestive glands have been removed, showing the ampullae of some of the hundreds of tube feet (magnified view). (4) Other organs have been removed to show the digestive glands (actually present in each arm). (5) Upper surface. The two-part stomach is in the central disc with the anus dorsal (uppermost) and the mouth beneath on the ventral surface. *(b)* Photomicrograph showing psines and pedicellaria on the surface of an echinoderm.

The undersurface of each arm is equipped with hundreds of pairs of tube feet. The cavities of the tube feet are all connected by radial canals in the arms; these in turn are connected by a circular canal in the central disk. The circular canal is connected by an axial canal to a button-shaped plate on the upper (aboral) surface of the central disk. As many as 250 tiny pores in the aboral plate permit sea water to enter the water vascular system.

Most sea stars are carnivorous and feed upon crustaceans, mollusks, annelids, and even other echinoderms. Occasionally they catch and eat a small fish. To attack a clam or other bivalve mollusk, the sea star mounts it, assuming a humped position as it straddles the edge opposite the hinge (Figure 30–4). Then, with its tube feet attached to the two shells, it begins to pull. The sea star uses many of its tube feet at a time but can change and use new groups as active tube feet get tired. By applying a steady pull on both shells over a long period of time, the sea star succeeds in tiring the powerful muscles of the clam so that they are forced to relax, opening the shell.

To begin its meal, the sea star projects its stomach out through its mouth and into the soft body of its prey.

Figure 30–4 A painted sea star (*Orthiasterias koehleri*) attacking a clam.   (Richard Chesher/Seaphot, Ltd.)

Digestive enzymes are secreted into the clam so that it is partly digested while still in its own shell. The soft parts of the clam are digested to the consistency of a thick soup and pass into the sea star body for further digestion by enzymes secreted from glands located in each arm. The sea star's water vascular system does not enable it to move rapidly, but because it usually preys upon slow-moving or stationary clams and oysters, the speed of attack is not as critical as for most other predators.

The blood circulatory system in sea stars is poorly developed and probably of little help in circulating materials. Instead, this function is assumed by the coelomic fluid, which fills the large coelom and bathes the internal tissues. Metabolic wastes pass to the outside by diffusion. The nervous system consists of a ring of nervous tissue encircling the mouth and a nerve cord extending from this into each arm.

Class Ophiuroidea Includes Basket Stars and Brittle Stars

Basket stars and brittle stars (serpent stars) are members of the class Ophiuroidea. They make up the largest group of echinoderms in number of species and in number of individuals. These animals resemble asteroids in that their bodies also consist of a central disk with arms, but the arms are long and slender and more sharply set off from the central disk (Figure 30–1c). Ophiuroids can move more rapidly than asteroids, using their arms to perform rowing or even swimming movements. The tube feet lack suckers and are not used in locomotion. They are used to collect and handle food and may also serve a sensory function, perhaps that of smell or taste.

Class Echinoidea Includes Sea Urchins and Sand Dollars

The class Echinoidea includes the sea urchins and the sand dollars. Echinoids lack arms, and their skeletal plates are flattened and fused, forming a solid shell called a test. The sea urchin body is covered with spines (Figure 30–1d), which in some species can penetrate flesh and are difficult to remove. So threatening are these spines that swimmers on tropical beaches are often cautioned to wear shoes when venturing off shore, where these animated pincushions lurk in abundance.

Sea urchins use their tube feet for moving and their movable spines for pushing themselves along. Most sea urchins graze, scraping the bottom with their teeth. They eat algae and tiny protists as well as very small animals. Sand dollars have smaller and far fewer spines than sea urchins. Their flattened bodies are adapted for burrowing in the sand, where they feed on tiny organic particles.

Class Holothuroidea Includes Sea Cucumbers

Sea cucumbers are members of the class Holothuroidea. Sea cucumbers are appropriately named, for many species are green and about the size of a small cucumber. The elongated body is a flexible, muscular sac. The mouth is usually surrounded by a circle of tentacles that are modified tube feet. Another characteristic of these holothuroids is the reduction of the endoskeleton to microscopic plates. Like other echinoderms, sea cucumbers have a water vascular system for movement. Their blood circulatory system is more highly developed than that of other echinoderms; it functions to transport oxygen and perhaps nutrients as well.

Sea cucumbers are sluggish animals that usually live on the bottom of the sea, sometimes burrowing in the mud. Some graze on the bottom with their tentacles; others stretch their branched tentacles out in the water and wait for dinner to float by. Algae and other tasty morsels are trapped in mucus along the tentacles; then, one at a time, the tentacles are put into the mouth and the food particles removed and eaten.

An odd habit of some sea cucumbers is evisceration, in which the digestive tract, respiratory tree, and gonads are expelled from the body, usually when environmental conditions are unfavorable. When conditions improve, the lost parts are regenerated. Even more curious, when some species are irritated or attacked, the rear end is directed toward the enemy, and red tubules are shot out of the anus! These unusual weapons are sticky (some release a toxic substance), and the attacking animal may become hopelessly entangled.

CHORDATES HAVE A NOTOCHORD, DORSAL TUBULAR NERVE CORD, AND PHARYNGEAL GILL SLITS DURING SOME TIME IN THEIR LIFE CYCLE

The phylum of animals to which humans belong, **phylum Chordata,** is divided into three subphyla: subphylum **Urochordata,** which consists of marine animals called tunicates; subphylum **Cephalochordata,** which is composed of marine animals called lancelets; and subphylum **Vertebrata,** the animals with backbones.

Chordates are all coelomate animals with bilateral symmetry. They have three well-developed germ layers, a tube-within-a-tube body plan, and a segmented body. Most chordates have a **postanal tail,** an appendage that projects posterior to the anus; an endoskeleton; and a closed circulatory system with a ventral heart.

The Hemichordates

The **hemichordates** are a small group of sedentary, wormlike deuterostomes. These marine animals were once considered a subphylum of the chordates because they possess gill slits in the wall of the pharynx and a structure that was thought to be a notochord. However, it is now agreed that this structure is neither homologous with nor analogous to the chordate notochord but simply an anterior projection of the digestive tract. The hemichordates are now assigned to their own phylum. Hemichordates have a ciliated larva that is very similar to the larva of some echinoderms.

The most common and best-known hemichordates are the acorn worms. Many species of these relatively large animals (up to 2 meters in length) burrow in mud along the shoreline or in shallow water. A distinguishing feature of the acorn worms is a short, conical proboscis that looks something like an acorn in some species. In some species the proboscis is used for burrowing and movement within the burrow. Certain species construct mucus-lined burrows within the mud.

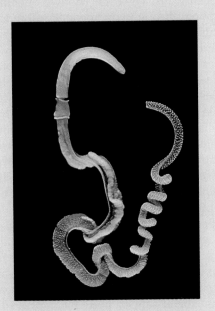

Saccoglossus kowalewskii, an acorn worm about 90 mm long. (C. R. Wyttenbach, University of Kansas/Biological Photo Service)

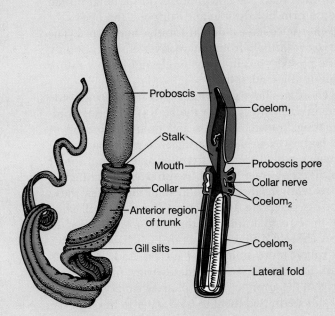

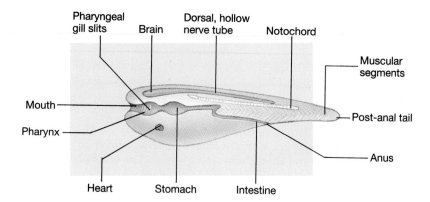

Figure 30–5 A generalized chordate illustrating important chordate characteristics.

Three characteristics distinguish them from all other groups (Figure 30–5).

1. All chordates have a **notochord** during some time in their life cycle. The notochord, a dorsal longitudinal rod, is firm but flexible and supports the body.
2. All chordates have a **dorsal tubular nerve cord.** The nerve cord differs from that of invertebrates not only in its position but in being single and hollow rather than double and solid.
3. All chordates have **pharyngeal gill slits** during some time in their life cycle. In the embryo, a series of alternating branchial arches and grooves develop in the body wall in the pharyngeal region. Pharyngeal pouches extend laterally from the anterior portion of the digestive tract toward the grooves (described in more detail in Chapter 49). In some chordates, these grooves perforate and become functional gill slits, but in terrestrial animals, they become modified to form entirely different structures (such as the outer ear canal) more suitable for life on land. Biologists think that the earliest chordates were filter feeders and that the arrangement of pharyngeal pouches and gill slits permitted them to take water in through the mouth, concentrate small particles of food in the gut, and let the water escape from the body through the gill slits.

No clear fossil record of the ancestors of the chordates exists, but they were probably small, soft-bodied animals. A lancelet-like animal, *Pikaia*, has been found in the Burgess Shale of British Columbia. These rocks date back to the mid-Cambrian period (more than 500 million years old).

Subphylum Urochordata Includes the Tunicates

The tunicates, which comprise the subphylum Urochordata, include the sea squirts, or ascidians, and their relatives. Adult sea squirts are barrel-shaped, sessile, marine animals unlike other chordates; indeed, they are often mistaken for sponges or cnidarians (Figure 30–6). Adult tunicates develop a tunic, quite thick in most species, that covers the entire animal. Curiously, the tunic is composed mainly of cellulose, also the main constituent of plant cell walls. The tunic has two openings: the incurrent siphon, through which water and food enter, and the excurrent siphon, through which water, waste products, and gametes pass to the outside.

Tunicates are filter feeders, removing plankton from the stream of water passing through the pharynx. Food particles are trapped in mucus secreted by cells of the endostyle, a groove that extends the length of the pharynx. Ciliated cells within the pharynx produce a steady current of water that carries food particles down into the eosphagus. Much of the water entering the pharynx passes out of the pharynx through gill slits into an **atrium** (chamber). Water is discharged through the excurrent siphon.

Some species of tunicates form large colonies in which members may share a common mouth and tunic. Colonial forms often reproduce asexually by budding. Sexual forms are usually hermaphroditic. Larval tunicates are typically chordate, superficially resembling frog tadpoles. The expanded body has a pharynx with gill slits, and the long muscular tail contains a notochord and dorsal nerve cord. Eventually the larva becomes attached to the sea bottom and loses its tail, notochord, and much of its nervous system. In the adult, only the gill slits suggest that the tunicate is a chordate.

Subphylum Cephalochordata Includes the Lancelets

Subphylum Cephalochordata consists of the lancelets, which are small, translucent, fish-shaped animals. These segmented animals are 5 to 10 cm long and pointed at both ends. They are widely distributed in shallow seas, either swimming freely or burrowing in the sand near the low-tide line. All three chordate characteristics are highly developed in lancelets. The noto-

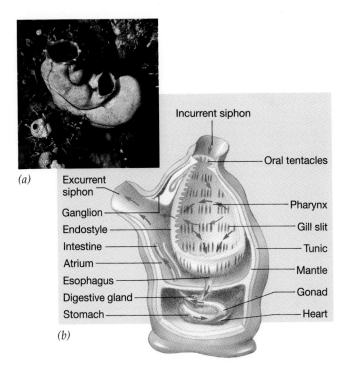

(a)

(b)

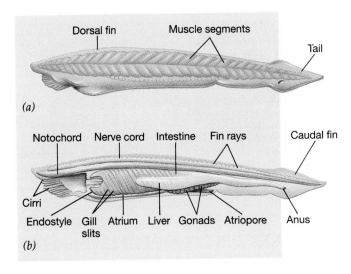

(c)

(d)

Figure 30–6 Structure of a tunicate. (*a*) Incurrent (top) and excurrent (side) siphons of a sea peach tunicate, *Halocynthia auratium*. (*b*) Lateral view of an adult tunicate. The blue arrows represent the flow of water, and the red arrows represent the path of food. The stomach, intestine, and other visceral organs are embedded in the mantle. (*c*) Swimming tadpole stage of a tunicate, *Distaplia occidentalis*. (*d*) Lateral view of a larval tunicate. (*a*, Robert Shupak; *c*, Richard A. Cloney, University of Washington)

chord extends from the tip of the head (hence the name Cephalochordata) to the tip of the tail; many pairs of gill slits are evident in the large pharyngeal region; and a hollow, dorsal nerve cord extends the entire length of the animal (Figure 30–7). The most common genus, *Branchiostoma* (commonly known as Amphioxus), exhibits the basic chordate characteristics so well that it is often the first animal studied in comparative anatomy courses.

Although superficially similar to fishes, lancelets are much more primitive, for they lack paired fins, jaws, sense organs, a heart, and a well-defined brain (Figure 30–8). The straight, rather simple digestive tract begins with the anterior **oral hood,** a vestibule surrounded by delicate tentacles bearing sensory cells. Under the hood and posterior to it, the mouth opening is surrounded by a membrane, or **velum,** equipped with a ring of sensory structures called **cirri.** Like the tunicates, lancelets feed by drawing a current of water into the mouth by the beating of cilia and then straining out the microscopic organisms. Food particles are trapped in mucus in the pharynx and are then carried back to the intestine.

Water passes through the gill slits into the **atrium,** a chamber with a ventral opening, the atriopore, just anterior to the anus. Metabolic wastes are excreted by segmentally arranged, ciliated protonephridia that open into the atrium. In contrast to other invertebrates, the blood flows anteriorly in the ventral vessel and posteriorly in the dorsal vessel. This circulatory pattern is similar to that of fishes.

Figure 30–7 Amphioxus, a member of the suphylum Cephalochordata. (*a*) External view. (*b*) Longitudinal section.

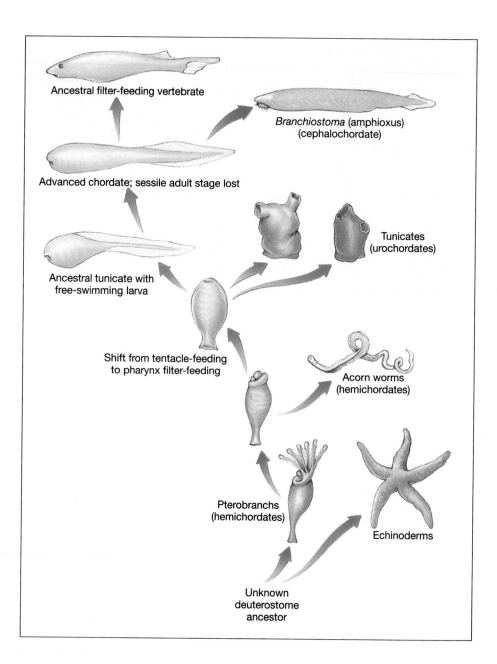

Ancestral filter-feeding vertebrate

Branchiostoma (amphioxus)
(cephalochordate)

Advanced chordate; sessile adult stage lost

Tunicates
(urochordates)

Ancestral tunicate with
free-swimming larva

Shift from tentacle-feeding
to pharynx filter-feeding

Acorn worms
(hemichordates)

Pterobranchs
(hemichordates)

Echinoderms

Unknown
deuterostome
ancestor

Figure 30–8 A diagram illustrating one hypothesis of the evolution of the chordates. (See Focus on the Hemichordates for a discussion of acorn worms.)

The Success of the Vertebrates Is Linked to the Evolution of Key Adaptations

The vertebrates—members of subphylum Vertebrata— are distinguished from other chordates in having a backbone, or **vertebral column,** that forms the skeletal axis of the body. This flexible support develops around the notochord and reinforces or replaces the notochord. The vertebral column consists of cartilaginous or bony segments called **vertebrae.** Dorsal projections of the vertebrae enclose the nerve cord along its length. Anterior to the vertebral column, a **cranium,** or braincase, encloses and protects the brain, the enlarged anterior end of the nerve cord.

The cranium and vertebral column are part of the **endoskeleton.** In contrast to the nonliving exoskeleton of invertebrates, the vertebrate endoskeleton is a living tissue that grows with the animal. Another vertebrate characteristic is *pronounced* **cephalization,** concentration of nerve cells and sense organs in a definite head. All vertebrates share certain other characteristics (which are not necessarily exclusive to these animals): a closed circulatory system with a two-, three-, or four- chambered ventral heart; paired kidneys; a complete digestive tract and large digestive glands (liver and pancreas); muscles attached to the skeleton for move- ment; a brain that is regionally differentiated for spe- cialized functions; 10 or 12 pairs of cranial nerves that

(a)

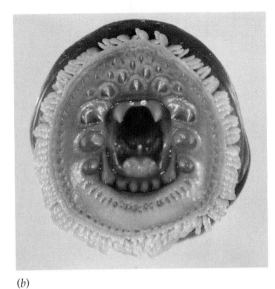

(b)

Figure 30–9   Class Agnatha. (*a*) Three lampreys attached to a carp by their suction cup–type mouths. Note the absence of jaws and paired fins. (*b*) Suction cup–like mouth of adult lamprey,

Estosphenus japonicus. Note the rasplike teeth.   (*a*, Tom Stack/Tom Stack & Associates; *b*, courtesy of Dr. Kiyoko Uehara)

emerge from the brain; an autonomic division of the nervous system that regulates involuntary functions of internal organs; well-developed organs of special sense (eyes; ears, which may serve as organs of equilibrium; organs of smell and taste); two pairs of appendages; and separate sexes.

The vertebrates are less diverse and much less numerous than the insects but rival them in their adaptation to a variety of lifestyles and excel them in the ability to receive and respond to stimuli. The 43,000 or so living species of vertebrates are divided into three classes of fish (sometimes referred to as superclass Pisces) and four classes of land vertebrates (superclass Tetrapoda). The classes of fish include class **Agnatha,** the jawless fish such as lamprey eels; class **Chondrichthyes,** the sharks and rays with cartilaginous skeletons; and class **Osteichthyes,** the bony fish. All fish have highly vascular gills with a large surface for the transfer of oxygen and carbon dioxide.

The four-legged land vertebrates, or tetrapods, are grouped in class **Amphibia**—frogs, toads, and salamanders; class **Reptilia**—lizards, snakes, turtles, and alligators; class **Aves**—birds; and class **Mammalia**—mammals. Not all the tetrapods have four legs (e.g., the snakes), but they all evolved from four-legged ancestors. Not all tetrapods now live on land (e.g., sea turtles, penguins, whales, seals), but all of these aquatic forms evolved from terrestrial ancestors.

The Jawless Fish Are the Most Primitive Vertebrates

The jawless fish comprise class Agnatha (*a*, without; *gnathos*, jaw), which includes the extinct **ostracoderms**

and the living lamprey eels and hagfishes. Fragments of ostracoderm scales have been found in rocks from the Ordovician period, indicating that vertebrates evolved in the sea 450 to 500 million years ago. By the Silurian and Devonian periods, ostracoderms had radiated extensively and were mainly freshwater fish. These freshwater, jawless fish were small, armored, bottom-dwelling filter feeders. The head was covered with thick bony plates, and the trunk and tail were covered with thick scales. Most ostracoderms had poorly developed fins.

Although the ostracoderms became extinct by the end of the Devonian period, they are survived by their descendants—the lampreys and hagfishes. These eel-shaped animals are up to 1 meter long. They are supported by a cartilaginous skeleton. Their smooth skin lacks scales, and they have neither jaws nor paired fins (Figure 30–9). The hagfishes are marine scavengers. They burrow for worms and other invertebrates or prey on dead and disabled fish.

Most lampreys live in fresh water. Some spend their adult life in the ocean and return to fresh water to reproduce. Many species of adult lampreys (e.g., the sea lamprey *Petromyzon*) are parasites on other fish; they are the only parasitic vertebrates. Adult parasitic lampreys have a circular sucking disk around the mouth, which is located on the ventral side of the anterior end of the body. Using this disk to attach to a fish, the lamprey bores through the skin of its host with horny teeth on the disk and tongue. Then the lamprey injects an anticoagulant into its host and sucks the host's blood and soft tissues.

Adult lampreys leave the ocean or lake and swim upstream to spawn. They build a nest, a shallow depression in the gravelly bed of the stream, into which eggs and sperm are shed; after spawning, they die. The

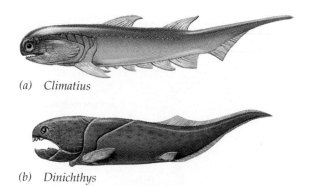

(a) *Climatius*

(b) *Dinichthys*

Figure 30–10 Acanthodians and placoderms from the Devonian period. (a) *Climatius*, a spiny-skinned acanthodian with large fin spines and five pairs of accessory fins between the pectoral and pelvic pairs. (b) *Dinichthys*, a giant placoderm that grew to a length of 9 meters. Its head and thorax were covered by bony armor, but the rest of the body and tail were naked.

fertilized eggs develop into larvae, which drift downstream to a pool and live as filter feeders in burrows in the muddy bottom for up to 7 years. Then they undergo a metamorphosis, become adult lampreys, and migrate back to ocean or lake.

The Earliest Jawed Fishes Are Now Extinct

Fossil evidence suggests that, during the late Silurian and Devonian periods, fish evolved with jaws and fin-like paired appendages. The evolution of jaws from a portion of the gill arch skeleton and the development of fins enabled fish to change from filter-feeding bottom-dwellers to active predators. The success of the jawed vertebrates may have contributed to the extinction of the ostracoderms.

Two classes of extinct jawed fishes are the Acanthodii and the Placodermi. Acanthodians were armored fish with paired spines and pectoral and pelvic fins. The placoderms were armored fish with paired fins (Figure 30–10).

Class Chondrichthyes Includes the Sharks, Rays, and Skates

The ostracoderms and early jawed fishes inhabited mainly fresh water; only a few ventured into the oceans. Members of class **Chondrichthyes,** the cartilaginous fishes, evolved as successful marine forms in the Devonian period. Most species have remained as ocean dwellers, but a few have secondarily returned to a freshwater habitat.

The chondrichthyes—sharks, rays, and skates (Figure 30–11)—retain their embryonic skeleton composed of cartilage. Although this skeleton is not replaced by bone, it may be strengthened by a deposit of calcium salts. The dogfish shark is commonly used in

(a)

(b)

Figure 30–11 Some members of class Chondrichthyes. (a) Dorsal view of a skate, *Raja binoculara*. (b) Ratfish, *Hydrolagua colliei*. (a, b, Charles Seaborn)

biology classes to demonstrate the basic vertebrate characteristics in a simple, uncomplicated form.

All chrondrichthyes have paired jaws and two pairs of fins. The skin contains **placoid scales.** Each of these scales is a toothlike structure composed of an outer layer of enamel and an inner layer of dentine (Figure 30–12). The lining of the mouth contains larger, but essentially similar, scales that serve as teeth. The teeth of the higher vertebrates are homologous with these shark scales. Shark teeth are embedded in the flesh and not attached to the jawbones; new teeth develop continuously in rows behind the functional teeth and migrate forward to replace any that are lost.

Cartilaginous fishes have five to seven pairs of gills. A current of water enters the mouth and passes over the gills and out the gill slits, constantly providing the fish

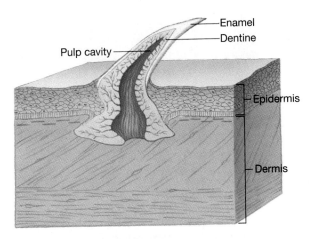

Figure 30–12   Structure of a placoid scale.

with a fresh supply of dissolved oxygen. However, because it has no mechanism for propelling water over the gills, the shark must depend on its forward motion for gas exchange. In some species, the shark suffocates if it stops moving.

Cartilaginous fishes tend to sink unless they are actively swimming, because their bodies are denser than water. The large pectoral fins give a lift component to their forward motion; the sculling action of the tail provides additional lift.

The digestive tract of the shark consists of the mouth cavity; a long pharynx leading to a J-shaped stomach; a short, straight intestine; and a cloaca (Figure 30–13). The liver and pancreas discharge their digestive juices into the intestine. The **cloaca** receives digestive wastes as well as urine from the urinary system and, in the female, sperm from the male. The cloaca, which is characteristic of many vertebrates, opens on the underside of the body.

The shark has a complex brain, which is differentiated both structurally and functionally. The spinal cord is protected by vertebrae. Well-developed sense organs

enable the shark to locate prey by smell and by vibrations in the water, as well as by sight. The **lateral line organ,** found in all fish, is a groove along each side of the body with many tiny openings to the outside. Sensory cells within the canals respond to movement of the water. On its head the shark has **electroreceptors;** these are found in small chambers that connect by sensory canals to pores on the surface of the head. Using these receptors, a shark can sense weak electric currents generated by the muscular activity of animals before it can detect them by sight or smell.

The sexes are separate, and fertilization is internal. In the mature male, each pelvic fin has a slender, grooved section known as a **clasper,** which is used to transfer sperm into the female's cloaca. The eggs are fertilized in the upper part of the female's oviducts. Part of the oviduct is modified as a shell gland, which secretes a protective coat around the egg. Skates and some species of sharks are **oviparous;** that is, they lay eggs. Many species of shark, however, are **ovoviviparous;** that is, they brood their young internally. The young are born alive after hatching from the eggs incubated within a modified portion of the oviduct called the uterus. During development, they depend on stored yolk for their nourishment. A few species of sharks are **viviparous:** Not only do the embryos develop within the uterus, but they receive much of their nourishment from their mother's blood. An intimate relationship is established between the yolk sac surrounding each embryo and the blood vessels in the lining of the uterus.

Most sharks are streamlined predators that swim actively and catch other fish as well as crustaceans and mollusks. The largest sharks, like the largest whales, feed on plankton. They gulp water through the mouth; as the water passes through the pharynx and out the gill slits, food particles are trapped in a branchial sieve. The whale shark, which may reach a length of more than 12 meters, is the largest fish known.

Although books and films portray sharks as monstrous enemies, there are only about 30 unprovoked

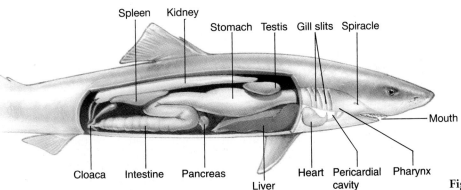

Figure 30–13   Internal anatomy of the shark.

(a)

(c)

(b)

(d)

Figure 30–14 Fish and some of their adaptations. (a) Porcupine fish, *Diodon hysterix,* which has sharp barbs on its skin and can inflate itself with water, as shown in (b), making it look large and unappetizing to its predators. (c) Clownfish, *Amphiprion,* living in a sea anemone. The anemone does not sting a clownfish with a healthy mucous covering. The clownfish receives protection from predators, and it was once thought that the anemone benefited from the association by getting food brought to it by the clownfish. More often, however, the clownfish steals food captured in the tentacles of the anemone. In aquariums, anemones do better without resident clownfish. (d) This member of the scorpionfish family is adapted for bottom living and at first glance looks like debris. The feathery, wormlike tissues near its mouth, however, are able to lure small fish. This slow-moving fish can be deadly to both prey and predators. The first several rays of its dorsal fin are pointed and hollow; when the fish is threatened, the spines stiffen and are filled with a poison similar in action to cobra venom. (a, d, Charles Seaborn; b, Dave B. Fleetham/Tom Stack & Associates; c, Robert Shupak)

shark attacks on humans per year. Sharks are attracted to blood, so a wounded swimmer or a skin diver towing speared fish is a target. Most sharks, however, do not go out of their way to attack humans.

Most rays and skates are sluggish, flattened creatures, living partly buried in the sand. The undulations of its enormous pectoral fins propel the ray or skate along the bottom. These animals feed on mussels and clams. The sting ray has a whiplike tail with a barbed spine at the tip, which can inflict a painful wound. The electric ray has electric organs on either side of the head; these modified muscles can discharge enough electric current (up to 2500 watts) to stun fairly large fish as well as human swimmers.

If members of class Chondrichthyes occasionally inflict injury on humans, relations are strained in both directions. In fact, many species of sharks are endangered. Sharks and rays are eaten by humans. Shark skin is tanned and used in making shoes and handbags, and shark liver oil is an important source of vitamin A.

Bony Fish Belong to Class Osteichthyes

The class Osteichthyes includes more than 24,000 living species of bony fish, both freshwater and saltwater fishes, of many shapes and colors (Figure 30–14). Bony fish range in size from the Philippine goby, which is only about 10 mm (0.4 in) long, to the ocean sunfish (or mola), which may reach 1 metric ton (about 2000 lb). Although cartilaginous and bony fish differ in important ways, they also share sufficient characteristics (e.g.,

Figure 30–15 Ancestors of this coelacanth are thought to have given rise to the amphibians. The paired fins show the basic plan of a jointed series of bones that could evolve into the limbs of a terrestrial vertebrate. This coelacanth, *Latimeria chalumnae*, was photographed near Comoro Island, in deep waters off the coast of Southern Africa. (Peter Scoones/Planet Earth Pictures)

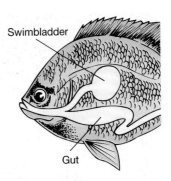

Figure 30–16 The swim bladder is a hydrostatic organ that enables the fish to change the density of its body and so to remain stationary at a given depth.

continuous tooth replacement) to suggest that they evolved from a common ancestor. Both classes evolved about the same time (during the Devonian period).

By the middle of the Devonian period, the bony fishes had diverged into two major groups: the **ray-finned fish** (actinopterygians), which gave rise to most modern osteichthyes, and the sarcopterygians, characterized by fleshy, lobed fins and lungs. During the Devonian period, frequent seasonal droughts caused swamps to become stagnant or even dry up completely. Fishes with lungs had a tremendous advantage for survival under those conditions.

Two lines of sarcopterygians diverged: lungfishes and crossopterygians. Three genera of lungfish have survived to the present day in the rivers of tropical Africa, Australia, and South America. The lobe-finned crossopterygians, generally considered the ancestors of the land vertebrates, were almost extinct by the end of the Paleozoic era. However, one genus (*Latimeria*) belonging to the **coelacanths** (a suborder adapted for marine life) survives in the deep waters off the east coast of Africa near the Comoro Islands (Figure 30–15). Nearly 2 meters long, these giant living fossils have neither lungs nor functional swim bladders.

The ray-finned fish had two important adaptive radiations. The first gave rise during the late Paleozoic era to a group of fish that are now mostly extinct. The second adaptive radiation began during the early Mesozoic era and has given rise to the modern bony fish, the **teleosts.** In them the lungs became modified as **swim bladders,** hydrostatic organs that may also store oxygen (Figure 30–16). By secreting gases into the bladder or absorbing gases from it, the fish can change the density of its body and so hover at a given depth of water without muscular effort.

In addition to having a swim bladder, most bony fish are characterized by a bony skeleton with many vertebrae (Figure 30–17). Bits of the notochord may persist. The body is covered with overlapping bony dermal scales. Most species have both median and paired fins, with fin rays of cartilage or bone. A lateral protective flap of the body wall, the **operculum,** extends posteriorly from the head and covers the gills.

Unlike the sharks, bony fish generally are oviparous. They lay an impressive number of eggs that they fertilize externally. The ocean sunfish, for example, lays over 300 million eggs! Of course, most of the eggs and young become food for other animals. Many species of fish build nests for their eggs and even watch over them.

Class Amphibia Includes Frogs, Toads, and Salamanders

The first successful tetrapods, or land vertebrates, were the **labyrinthodonts** (Figure 30–18), clumsy, salamander-like animals with short necks and heavy muscular tails. These ancient members of class Amphibia resembled their ancestors, the lobe-finned fishes, but had evolved limbs strong enough to support the weight of the body on land. These earliest limbs were five-fingered, a pattern that has generally been kept by the higher vertebrates. The labyrinthodonts ranged in size from small to ones as large as crocodiles. These animals flourished during the late Paleozoic and early Mesozoic eras, but all became extinct during the Mesozoic era. It is probable that the labyrinthodonts gave rise to other primitive amphibians, to modern frogs and salamanders, and to the earliest reptiles, the **cotylosaurs,** or stem reptiles.

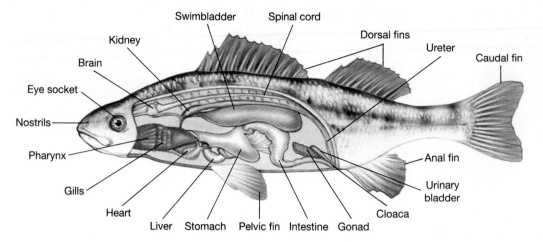

Figure 30–17 Internal anatomy of the perch, a bony fish.

Modern amphibians are classified in three orders: Order **Urodela** includes the salamanders, mud puppies, and newts—animals with long tails. Order **Anura** is made up of the tailless frogs and toads, with legs adapted for hopping; and order **Apoda,** the wormlike, legless caecilians (Figure 30–19). Although some adult amphibians are quite successful as land animals and can live in quite dry places, most return to the water to reproduce. Eggs and sperm are generally released in the water.

The embryos of frogs and toads develop into larvae called **tadpoles** with tails and gills. Tadpoles feed on aquatic plants, and after a time they undergo metamorphosis. The gills and gill slits disappear, the tail is resorbed, the forelegs emerge, the digestive tract shortens (and food preference shifts from eating plant material to a carnivorous diet), the mouth widens, a tongue develops, the tympanic membrane and eyelids appear, and the shape of the eye lens changes. Many biochemical changes occur to provide for the change from a completely aquatic life to an amphibious one.

As in insects, metamorphosis in amphibians is under hormonal control. Amphibian metamorphosis is regulated by thyroid hormones secreted by the thyroid gland. Amphibians undergo a single change from larva to adult. Several species of salamanders, such as the mud puppy *Necturus,* do not undergo complete metamorphosis. They retain many larval characteristics as adults. In this process, known as **neoteny,** animals become sexually mature without completing metamorphosis.

Adult amphibians do not depend solely on their primitive lungs for the exchange of respiratory gases. Their moist, glandular skin, which lacks scales and is plentifully supplied with blood vessels, also serves as a respiratory surface. Many mucous glands within the skin help to keep the body surface moist, which is im-

portant in gas exchange and helps prevent drying out. A number of amphibian species have skin glands that secrete poisonous substances to discourage predators.

The coloration of amphibians may conceal them in their habitat or may be very bright and striking. Many of the brightly colored species are poisonous; their distinctive colors warn predators that they are not encountering an ordinary amphibian. Some frogs have the ability to change color from light to dark. The change in color is controlled by the pituitary gland.

The amphibian heart has three chambers, two **atria** that receive blood and a single **ventricle** that pumps blood into the arteries. A double circuit of blood vessels keeps oxygen-rich and oxygen-poor blood partially separate. Blood passes through the **systemic circulation** to the various tissues and organs of the body. Then,

Figure 30–18 An artist's conception of labyrinthodont life in a carboniferous swamp about 345 million years ago. (Neg. no. 322872, (photo by Logan) courtesy of Department of Library Services, American Museum of Natural History)

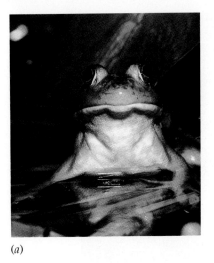

(a)

(b)

Figure 30–19 Modern amphibians. (*a*) Bullfrog (*Rana catesbeina*). (*b*) The red salamander, *Pseudotriton ruber*, belongs to the family Plethodontidae. The plethodonts usually spend their entire lives in fairly moist environments. They have lost their lungs and now rely entirely on their moist skin and the membranes that line their mouth and pharynx as organs for gas exchange. The red salamander is a species commonly found in the eastern United States. (*a*, Dwight Kuhn; *b*, Carolina Biological Supply Company)

after returning to the heart, it is directed through the **pulmonary circulation** to the lungs and skin, where it is recharged with oxygen. The oxygen-rich blood returns to the heart to be pumped out into the systemic circulation again. The comparative anatomy of the heart and circulation of various vertebrate classes is discussed in Chapter 42.

Class Reptilia Includes Turtles, Lizards, Snakes, and Alligators

Members of class Reptilia are true terrestrial animals. Unlike most amphibians, they need not return to water to reproduce. A variety of adaptations make the reptilian lifestyle possible. A protective leathery shell surrounds the egg, which helps to prevent the developing embryo from drying out. Because sperm cannot penetrate this shell, fertilization must occur within the body of the female before the shell is added. This internal fertilization requires additional adaptations, including copulatory organs for transferring sperm from the body of the male into the female reproductive tract.

As the embryo develops within the protective shell, a membrane called the **amnion** forms and surrounds the embryo. The amnion contains fluid, providing the embryo with its own private pond. The amniotic fluid keeps the embryo moist and also serves as a shock absorber should the egg get bounced around. All terrestrial vertebrate embryos have amnions as well as other membranes that protect and support their development (see Chapter 49).

The reptile body is covered with hard, dry, horny scales, which protect the animal from drying out and from predators. This dry, scaly skin cannot serve as an organ for gas exchange; however, reptile lungs are better-developed than the saclike lungs of amphibians.

Divided into many chambers, the reptilian lung provides a greatly increased surface area for gas exchange. Most reptiles have a three-chambered heart but it is more efficient than the amphibian heart because it has a partition, though incomplete, within the ventricle. This partial separation of oxygen-rich and oxygen-poor blood facilitates oxygenation of body tissues. (If the wall within the ventricle were complete, as it is in birds and mammals, the heart would have four separate chambers—two atria and two ventricles—and oxygen-rich and oxygen-poor blood could be kept completely separate.) In the crocodile, the heart *is* four-chambered.

Another adaptation to life on land is a method of waste disposal that conserves water. Little water is removed from the blood with the wastes, and much of what is filtered out by the kidneys is reabsorbed in the kidney tubules and urinary bladder. In aquatic animals, nitrogenous wastes from protein and nucleic acid metabolism are excreted as ammonia. This waste product is quite toxic, and ammonia excretion requires large amounts of water. Reptiles (like birds and terrestrial arthropods) convert ammonia to uric acid, which is much less toxic and can be excreted as relatively insoluble crystals.

Like fish and amphibians, reptiles lack metabolic mechanisms for regulating body temperature. They are **ectothermic,** meaning that their body temperature depends on the temperature of the surrounding environment. However, reptiles do have behavioral adaptations that enable them to maintain a body temperature higher than that of their environment. You may have observed a lizard basking in the sun. Such behavior permits the lizard's body temperature to rise so that its metabolic rate increases and it can actively hunt for food. When the body temperature of a reptile is low, the metabolic rate is low and it is very sluggish. Thus reptiles are much more successful in warm than in cold climates.

(a)

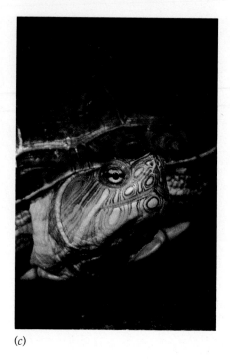

(c)

(b)

Figure 30–20 Modern reptiles. (*a*) The American alligator. (*b*) Eastern hog-nose snakes, *Heterodon platyrhinos*, hatching. (*c*) A red-eared turtle. (*a*, Ed Reschke; *b*, Zig Leszczynski © 1993 Animals Animals; *c*, E.R. Digginger)

Although a few species of turtles, tortoises, and lizards are **herbivores,** animals that eat vegetation, most reptiles are **carnivores** (meat-eaters). Their paired limbs (usually with five toes) are well adapted for running and climbing, and their well-developed sense organs enable them to locate prey.

Modern reptiles belong to three orders

The reptiles living today are assigned to one of three orders: Order **Chelonia** includes turtles, terrapins, and tortoises. Order **Squamata** is composed of lizards, snakes, iguanas, and geckos, and order **Crocodilia** includes crocodiles, alligators, caimans, and gavials.

Members of order Chelonia are enclosed in a protective shell made up of bony plates overlaid by horny scales. Some species can withdraw their heads and legs completely into their shells. Turtles range in size from about 8 cm in length to the great marine species, which measure more than 2 meters in length and may weigh 450 kg. The land species are usually referred to as tortoises, whereas the aquatic forms are called turtles (freshwater types are sometimes called terrapins).

Lizards and snakes are the most common of the modern reptiles (Figure 30–20). These animals have rows of scales that overlap like shingles on a roof, forming a continuous armor that may be shed periodically. Lizards range in size from the gecko, which may weigh as little as 1 gram, to the Komodo dragon of Indonesia, which may weigh 100 kg. Their body size and shape vary greatly. Some—for example, the glass snake, which is really a lizard—are legless. (The glass snake gets its name from its ability to detach from its tail when a predator grabs the tail. The long tail breaks— like glass—into many pieces that writhe around, distracting and confusing the predator while the tailless lizard escapes.) For a discussion of an interesting example of evolution of iguanas in the Caribbean, see Making the Connection (page 662).

Snakes are characterized by a flexible, loosely jointed jaw structure that permits them to swallow animals larger than the diameter of their own jaws. Snakes lack legs, and their bodies are elongated. Their eyes, covered by a transparent cuticle, lack movable eyelids. They also lack an external ear opening, a tympanic membrane (eardrum), and a middle ear cavity.

The forked tongue of the snake, which often darts quickly from the mouth, is not poisonous. It is used as an accessory sensory organ for touch and smell; chemicals from the ground or air adhere to it, and the tip is then projected into a sense organ located in the roof of

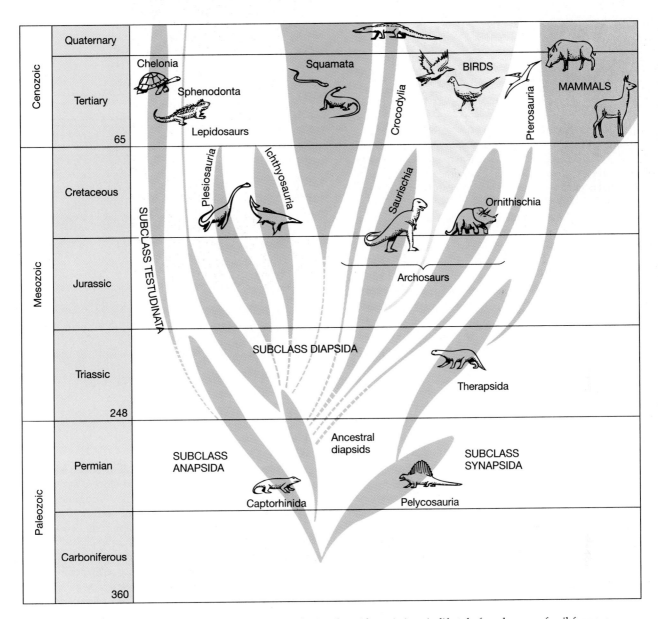

Figure 30–21 Evolutionary tree of the reptiles, drawn to emphasize the wide variations in lifestyle found among fossil forms.

the mouth that detects odors. Pit vipers and some boas also have a prominent **sensory pit** on each side of the head that enables them to detect heat. These sense organs permit them to locate and capture small nocturnal mammals.

Some snakes—for example, king snakes, pythons, and boa constrictors—capture their prey by rapidly wrapping themselves around the animal and squeezing it so that it cannot breathe. Others have fangs, which are hollow teeth connected with poison glands in the mouth. When the snake bites its prey, the poison is pumped through the fangs into the prey's body. Some snake poisons cause the breakdown of red blood cells in the prey; others, such as that of the coral snake, are neurotoxins that interfere with nerve function. Poisonous snakes of the United States include rattlesnakes,

copperheads, cottonmouths, and coral snakes. All except the coral snakes are pit vipers.

Three groups of crocodilians are (1) the crocodiles of Africa, Asia, and America, (2) the alligators of the southern United States and China, and the caimans of Central America, and (3) the gavials of Southeast Asia. Most species live in swamps, in rivers, or along sea coasts, burrowing in the mud and feeding on various kinds of animals. Crocodiles are the largest living reptiles, some measuring more than 7 meters long.

Reptiles were once the dominant land animals

Reptiles, birds, and mammals are thought to have a common ancestor (Figure 30–21). A labyrinthodont ancestor gave rise to vertebrates that evolved the repro-

MAKING THE CONNECTION

The Iguanas of Mona Island, the Galapagos of the Caribbean

In Chapter 17 we discussed the unusual and unique species studied by Charles Darwin on the Galapagos Islands off the Pacific coast of South America. The same evolutionary processes that occurred in the Galapagos Islands have given rise to unique species on other islands.

Consider Mona Island, a small island that is part of Puerto Rico. Mona Island could be considered the "Galapagos of the Caribbean." Located 68 km west of the main island of Puerto Rico and 60 km east of Hispaniola, Mona Island is home to many fascinating animal and plant species.

Mona Island is quite different from the rest of Puerto Rico. The island resembles a great, kidney-shaped white slab of floating limestone, bounded almost completely by towering cliffs rising vertically out of the sea. Although moist tropical trade winds blow over it, its low elevation precludes much precipitation; as a result, it has a semi-arid climate.

In spite of Mona Island's small size (12 km long, 6 km wide), its distance from large land masses, its lack of a deep, fertile soil, and its low rainfall, it supports 417 species of vascular plants and nearly 700 species of land animals. Many of these species are endemic (found nowhere else). Ancestral species are thought to have colonized the island from nearby land areas. Over countless generations, the colonizers became more and more distinctive as they adapted to the local conditions. In time, they evolved into new species.

Like the Galapagos, Mona Island is now a wildlife sanctuary inhabited by unique plant and animal species, including its most striking endemic, the Mona ground iguana (*Cyclura steinegeri*). The genus *Cyclura* consists of 14 living and fossil species, all of which are confined to the Bahamas and the Greater Antilles. These distinctive reptiles are rapidly becoming extinct. In 1916, there were 11 species of iguanas in the Caribbean, but now only 6 species remain; all of these are confined to remote areas uninhabited by humans.

The Mona iguana measures from 1 to 1.3 meters in length and has a heavy body, a large head, and a stout, laterally compressed tail. A dorsal crest extends from its head to its tail. The closest living relative of the Mona iguana is the Rhinoceros iguana (*Cyclura cornuta*) found on Hispaniola. Both species have a distinct series of horns protruding from the snout, but the species can be distinguished by differences in the patterns of their scales.

Mona Island.   (Héctor E. Quintero, Ph.D.)

Mona iguanas are found throughout Mona island, especially along major escarpments, cliff slopes, and sinkholes. In the summer nesting season, they congregate on the coastal plains where soils are deeper and more suitable for building nests. Males are usually solitary and strongly territorial.

In 1977, a study estimated the population of iguanas on Mona Island to be 2000. That study also demonstrated a scarcity of young iguanas, which is characteristic of declining populations. The hazards to which Mona iguanas have been subjected are mostly the result of the introduction of species to the island. Cats, mice, rats, and pigs dig up iguana nests and eat their eggs, whereas goats compete with the iguanas for food. If action is not taken soon to control the introduced species, the Mona island iguana, like many of its nearby relatives, will probably become extinct. Something similar occurred on the Galapagos Islands. Extinction of the Galapagos land iguana first occurred on islands where goats had been living the longest. Currently, stable iguana populations can only be found in the Galapagos on islands without goats.

---

ductive adaptations required to be independent of a watery external environment. Terrestrial vertebrate embryos are enclosed by an amnion, and vertebrates are referred to as amniotes. The earliest reptiles are thought to have somewhat resembled lizards. By the late Carboniferous period (about 290 million years ago)

amniotes had diverged into three groups: One group evolved into the mammals, a second group into the turtles, and a third group into all of the other reptiles and into the birds.

The class Reptilia has many more extinct than living species. The Mesozoic era, which ended about

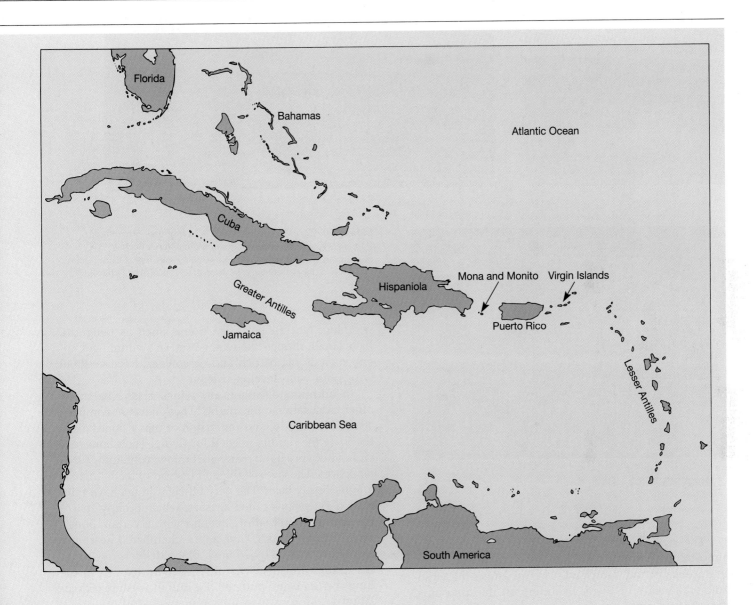

Florida

Bahamas

Atlantic Ocean

Cuba

Greater Antilles

Hispaniola

Mona and Monito   Virgin Islands

Jamaica

Puerto Rico

Lesser Antilles

Caribbean Sea

South America

Essay contributed by Dr. Héctor Quintero, Department of Biology, Inter American University, San German, Puerto Rico.

65 million years ago, is known as the age of reptiles; during that time reptiles were the dominant terrestrial animals (see Chapter 20). They had spread out into an impressive variety of ecological lifestyles (see Figure 30–21). Some were able to fly, others became marine, and many filled terrestrial habitats. Some of the dinosaurs were among the largest land animals that have ever lived. *Tyrannosaurus* was the largest carnivore that has ever walked the Earth. It stood about 6 meters high and had large teeth that looked like daggers. *Diplodocus* was nearly 30 meters long and may have weighed 45 metric tons.

(a)

(b)

(c)

Figure 30–22 Modern birds. (a) A tawny owl, *Strix aluco*. (b) Peacock, a male peafowl, *Pavo cristatus*. (c) A flock of flamingoes in Tanzania. (a, D. Klees/World View/Planet Earth Pictures; b, courtesy of Busch Gardens; c, Jonathan Scott/Planet Earth Pictures)

The reptiles were the dominant land animals for almost 200 million years. Then, toward the end of the Cretaceous period (which was also the end of the Mesozoic era), many of them, including all the dinosaurs, disappeared from the fossil record (see Chapter 20).

The Birds Belong to Class Aves

Birds, which comprise the class Aves, are the only animals that have feathers (Figure 30–22). Thought to have evolved from reptilian scales, feathers are flexible and very strong for their light weight. They protect the body, decrease water loss through the body surface, decrease the loss of body heat, and aid in flying by presenting a plane surface to the air.

The anterior limbs of birds are usually modified for flight; the posterior pair, for walking, swimming, or perching. Not all birds fly. Some, such as penguins, have small, flipper-like wings used in swimming. Others, such as the ostrich and cassowary, have vestigial wings but well-developed legs.

In addition to feathers and wings, birds have many other adaptations for flight. They have a compact, streamlined body, and the fusion of many bones gives the body the rigidity needed for flying. Their bones are strong but very light; many are hollow, containing large air spaces. The jaw is light, and instead of teeth, there is a light, horny beak. The very efficient lungs have thin-walled extensions called air sacs, which occupy spaces between the internal organs and within certain bones. Birds, like mammals, have a four-chambered heart and a double circuit of blood flow. Blood delivers oxygen to the tissues and then is recharged with oxygen in the lungs before being pumped out into the systemic circulation again.

The very effective respiratory and circulatory systems provide enough oxygen to the cells to permit a high metabolic rate. This is necessary for the tremendous muscular activity required for flying. Some of the heat generated by metabolic activities is used to maintain a constant body temperature. Birds and mammals are the only animals that are **endothermic** (sometimes referred to as warmblooded). This ability to maintain a constant body temperature permits metabolic processes to proceed at constant rates and enables birds to remain active in cold climates.

Birds excrete nitrogenous wastes mainly as semisolid uric acid. Because they lack a urinary bladder, these solid wastes are delivered into the cloaca. They leave the body as part of the feces, which are frequently dropped. This adaptive mechanism helps to maintain a light body weight.

Birds have become adapted to a variety of environments, and various species have very different types of beaks, feet, wings, tails, and behavioral patterns. Although all birds must eat frequently (because they have a high metabolic rate but do not store much fat), the choice of food varies widely among species. Many species eat seeds or fruits. Others eat worms, mollusks, or arthropods. Warblers and some other species eat mainly insects. Owls and hawks eat rodents, rabbits, and other small mammals. Vultures feed on dead animals. Pelicans, gulls, terns, and kingfishers catch fish. Some hawks catch snakes and lizards. Grouse and quail eat leafy vegetation. Beaks are specifically adapted to the eating habits.

An interesting feature of the bird digestive system is the **crop,** an expanded, saclike portion of the digestive tract below the esophagus, in which food is temporarily stored. The stomach is divided into a **proventriculus,** which secretes gastric juices, and a thick, muscular **gizzard** where food is ground. The bird swallows small bits of gravel, which act as "teeth" in the gizzard, mechanically breaking down food.

Birds have a well-developed nervous system with a brain that is proportionately larger than that of reptiles. Birds rely heavily on vision; their eyes are larger relative to those of other vertebrates. Hearing is also well developed.

In striking contrast to the silent reptiles, birds sing. Most birds have short, simple calls that signal danger or that influence feeding, flocking, or interaction between parent and young. Songs are usually more complex than calls and are performed mainly by males; songs are related to reproduction, attracting and keeping a mate, and claiming and defending territory.

One of the most fascinating aspects of bird behavior is the annual migration that many species make. Some birds, such as the golden plover and Arctic tern, fly from Alaska to Patagonia, South America, and back each year, flying perhaps 40,250 km (25,000 miles) en route. A discussion of migration and navigation is included in Chapter 50.

Early birds had reptilian characteristics

Birds are thought to have evolved from saurichian dinosaurs. These long-tailed animals moved about on two feet and had forelimbs with three clawed fingers. Feathers may have first evolved as an adaptation that conserved body heat. Bird ancestors became endothermic and more active. According to one hypothesis these animals ran along the ground using their feathered forelimbs as nets to trap insects. Another hypothesis holds

Figure 30–23 *Archaeopteryx,* the earliest known bird. This drawing represents the hypothesis that *Archaeopteryx* was at least a climbing animal that had some ability to use its wings and feathers for gliding. Other hypotheses suggest that *Archaeopteryx* was primarily a land animal whose wings could be used to trap small insects and whose feathers possibly served as insulation. (After a painting by Rudolf Freund, Carnegie Museum of Natural History)

that bird ancestors climbed trees and used their feathered forelimbs for gliding.

Although the bones of birds are fragile and disintegrate quickly, a few fossils of early birds have been found. The first birds looked very much like reptiles. They had teeth (which modern birds lack), a long tail, and bones with thick walls. Unlike reptiles, their jaws were elongated into beaks, and they had feathers and wings.

The earliest known species of bird, *Archaeopteryx* (meaning ancient wing), was about the size of a pigeon and had rather feeble wings. Its jawbones were armed with reptilian-type teeth (so this early bird could get its worm?), and it had a long reptilian tail covered with feathers. Each of its wings was equipped with three digits bearing claws (Figure 30–23). Several specimens of this species have been found in the Jurassic limestone of Bavaria, which was laid down about 150 million years ago (see Figure 20–17).

Cretaceous rocks have yielded fossils of other early birds. *Hesperornis,* which lived in the United States, was a toothed aquatic diving bird with powerful hind legs and vestigial wings. *Ichthyornis* was a toothed flying bird about the size of a seagull. In 1990 a fossil found in the rocky remnants of an ancient lake in China was described as the earliest known example of a bird with modern flying ability. This bird apparently had the adaptations necessary for living in trees. From the tertiary period onward, the fossil record of birds shows an absence of teeth and progressive changes leading to the modern birds.

Modern birds are a very successful group

Even modern birds possess some characteristics in common with the reptiles. For example, they have reptilian-type scales on their legs, and they lay eggs. (Although most male birds lack a copulatory organ, fertilization is internal. Copulation involves contact between male and female cloacas.)

About 9000 species of birds have been described; these have been classified in 27 orders. Birds inhabit a wide variety of habitats and can be found on all of the continents, most islands, and even the open sea. The largest living birds are the ostriches of Africa, which may be up to 2 meters tall and weigh 136 kg, and the great condors of the Americas, with wingspreads of up to 3 meters. The smallest known bird is Helena's hummingbird of Cuba, which is less than 6 cm long and weighs less than 4 grams. Beautiful and striking colors are found among birds. The color is due partly to pigments deposited during the development of the feathers and partly to reflection and refraction of light of certain wavelengths. Many birds, especially females, are protectively colored by their plumage. Brighter colors are often assumed by the male during the breeding season to help him attract a mate.

Mammals Have Hair and Mammary Glands

The distinguishing features of mammals are the presence of hair; **mammary glands,** which produce milk for the young; and the differentiation of teeth into incisors, canines, premolars, and molars. A muscular **diaphragm** helps to move air into and out of the lungs. The nervous system is more highly developed than in any other group. The cerebrum is especially large and complex, with an outer gray region called the cerebral cortex. Like the birds, mammals are endothermic—they maintain a constant body temperature. Endothermy is supported by the covering of hair, which serves as insulation; by the four-chambered heart and separate pulmonary and systemic circulations; and by the presence of sweat glands. Red blood cells without nuclei serve as excellent oxygen transporters.

Fertilization is always internal, and except for the primitive monotremes that lay eggs, mammals are viviparous. Most mammals develop a **placenta,** an organ of exchange between developing embryo and mother, through which the embryo receives its nourishment and oxygen and rids its blood of wastes.

Figure 30–24   A mammal-like reptile, *Lycaenops,* from the late Permian period in South Africa.   (Trans. no. 203–Painting by John C. Germann, courtesy of Department of Library Sciences, American Museum of Natural History)

The limbs of mammals are variously adapted for walking, running, climbing, swimming, burrowing, or flying. In four-legged mammals, the limbs are more directly under the body than in reptiles, which contributes to speed and agility. Life processes of mammals are discussed in detail in Part 7.

Early mammals were small, endothermic animals

Mammals are thought to have evolved from a group of reptiles called **therapsids** (Figure 30–24) during the Triassic period some 200 million years ago. The therapsids were doglike carnivores with differentiated teeth (a mammalian trait) and legs adapted for running. The fossil record indicates that the early mammals were small, about the size of a mouse. They were probably endothermic and produced milk for their young.

How did the mammals manage to coexist with the reptiles during the 160 million or so years that the reptiles ruled Earth? Many adaptations permitted the mammals to compete for a place on the planet. The earliest mammals lived in trees and were nocturnal, searching for food (mainly insects and plant material and perhaps reptile eggs) at night while the reptiles were inactive. The lifestyle is suggested by the large eye sockets in fossil species, which indicate that these animals had the large eyes characteristic of present-day nocturnal primates. By bearing their young alive, mammals avoided the hazards of having their eggs consumed by predators. By nourishing the young and caring for them, the parents could offer both protection and an education—which probably focused on how to obtain food and avoid being eaten.

As reptiles died out, the mammals began to move into their abandoned territories. Numerous varieties of mammals evolved and became widely distributed and adapted to an impressive variety of lifestyles.

Figure 30–25 The spiny anteater, *Tachyglossus aculeatus,* a monotreme.   (Tom McHugh/Photo Researchers, Inc.)

(*a*)

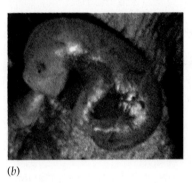

(*b*)

Figure 30–26 The kangaroo, a marsupial native to Australia. (*a*) Adult with a young kangaroo. The young continue to develop in the safety of the marsupium. (*b*) Young marsupials are born in a very immature state.   (*a,* Tom McHugh/Photo Researchers, Inc.; *b,* photo by Robert Anderson, reprinted with permission of Hubbard Scientific Company)

Modern mammals are assigned to three subclasses

Today mammals inhabit virtually every corner of the Earth—on the land, in fresh and salt water, and in the air. They range in size from the tiny pigmy shrew, weighing about 25 grams (less than 1 ounce) to the blue whale, which may weigh more than 90,000 kg and is thought to be the largest animal that ever lived.

By the end of the Cretaceous period, there were three main groups of mammals. Today, these groups are classified in three subclasses: **Prototheria,** which includes the egg-laying mammals, also called **monotremes; Metatheria,** which includes the marsupials, or pouched mammals; and **Eutheria,** the placental mammals.

Monotremes Are Mammals That Lay Eggs

The monotremes are the only living order of subclass Prototheria. The two genera include the duck-billed platypus (*Ornithorhynchus*) and the spiny anteater or echidna (*Tachyglossus*) (Figure 30–25). Both are found in Australia and Tasmania; the spiny anteater is also found in New Guinea. The females lay eggs, which may be carried in a pouch on the abdomen or kept warm in a nest. When the young hatch, they are nourished with milk from the mammary glands. As its name suggests, the spiny anteater feeds on ants, which it catches with its long sticky tongue. The duck-billed platypus lives in burrows along river banks. It has webbed feet and a flat, beaver-type tail, which aids in swimming. For food it catches freshwater invertebrates.

Marsupials Are Pouched Mammals

Marsupials include pouched mammals such as kangaroos and opossums. Embryos begin their development in the mother's uterus, where they are nourished by yolk and by fluid in the uterus. After a few weeks, still in a very undeveloped stage, the young are born. They crawl to the marsupium (pouch), where they complete their development. The young marsupial attaches itself by its mouth to a mammary gland nipple and is nourished by its mother's milk (Figure 30–26).

Like the monotremes, the marsupials are found mainly in Australia. Only the opossum is common in North America. At one time, marsupials probably inhabited much of the world, before they were supplanted by the placental mammals. Australia became geographically isolated from the rest of the world before placental mammals reached it, and there the marsupials remained the dominant mammals. They underwent adaptive radiation, paralleling the evolution of

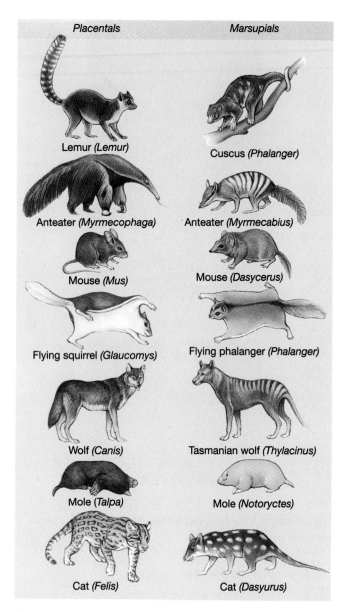

	Placentals	Marsupials
	Lemur *(Lemur)*	Cuscus *(Phalanger)*
	Anteater *(Myrmecophaga)*	Anteater *(Myrmecabius)*
	Mouse *(Mus)*	Mouse *(Dasycerus)*
	Flying squirrel *(Glaucomys)*	Flying phalanger *(Phalanger)*
	Wolf *(Canis)*	Tasmanian wolf *(Thylacinus)*
	Mole *(Talpa)*	Mole *(Notoryctes)*
	Cat *(Felis)*	Cat *(Dasyurus)*

Figure 30–27 Comparison of marsupial and placental mammals. Placental and marsupial mammals have similar lifestyles. For every occupant of a given habitat and lifestyle in one group, there is a counterpart in the other group. This correspondence is not restricted to similarity of habit but also includes structural features.

Table 30–1 COMPARISON OF CHARACTERISTICS OF SOME HIGHER ANIMAL PHYLA[*]

	Echinodermata (Spiny-skinned Animals)	Chordata
Representative animals	Sea stars Sea urchins Sand dollars	Tunicates Lancelets Vertebrates
Body symmetry	Embryo: bilateral; adult: modified radial	Bilateral
Gas exchange	Skin; gills	Gills or lungs
Waste disposal	Diffusion	Kidneys and other organs
Nervous system	Nerve rings; no brain	Dorsal nerve cord with brain at anterior end
Circulation	Open system; reduced	Closed system; ventral heart
Reproduction	Sexual; sexes almost always separate	Sexual; sexes separate
Other characteristics	Water vascular system; tube feet	(1) Notochord; (2) dorsal, tubular nerve cord; (3) pharyngeal gill slits

[*]Members of these phyla are at the organ system level of organization and have a complete digestive tract.

placental mammals elsewhere. Thus, in Australia and adjacent islands, we find marsupials that correspond to our placental wolves, bears, rats, moles, flying squirrels, and even cats (Figure 30–27).

Placental Mammals Complete Embryonic Development within the Mother

Most familiar to us are placental mammals, characterized by development of a **placenta,** an organ of ex-

change. The placenta forms from both embryonic membranes and the uterine wall. In it the blood vessels of the embryo come very close to the blood vessels of the mother, so that materials can be exchanged by diffusion. (The two bloodstreams do not normally mix.) The placenta enables the young to remain within the body of the mother until embryonic development is complete.

Placental mammals are born at a more mature stage than marsupials. Indeed, among some species, the young can walk around and begin to interact with other members of the group within a few minutes of birth. Living (extant) placental mammals are classified into about 17 orders. A brief summary of some of these is given in the Focus on Some Orders of Living Placental Mammals (see page 670). The probable family tree of the vertebrates is illustrated in Figure 30–28.

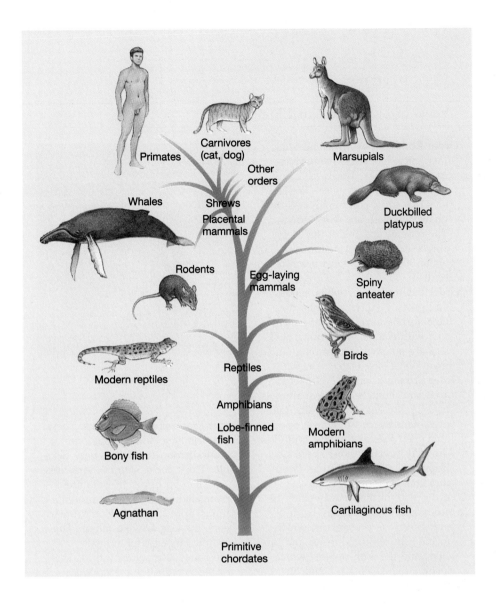

Figure 30–28 A vertebrate family tree.

SUMMARY

I. The echinoderms and chordates are thought to be related; they are both deuterostomes and therefore share many developmental characteristics.

II. Phylum Echinodermata includes marine animals with spiny skins, a water vascular system, and tube feet; the larvae have bilateral symmetry; most of the adults exhibit radial symmetry.

A. Class Crinoidea includes the sea lilies and feather stars; in these animals, the oral surface is turned upward; some are sessile.

B. Class Asteroidea is made up of the sea stars, animals with a central disk from which radiate five or more arms.

C. Class Ophiuroidea includes the brittle stars, which resemble asteroids but have longer, more slender arms, set off more sharply from the central disk.

D. Class Echinoidea includes the sea urchins and sand dollars, animals that lack arms; they have a solid shell, and their body is covered with spines.

E. Class Holothuroidea consists of sea cucumbers, animals with elongated flexible bodies; the mouth is surrounded by a circle of modified tube feet that serve as tentacles.

III. Phylum Chordata consists of three subphyla: Urochordata, Cephalochordata, and Vertebrata. At some time in its life cycle, a chordate has a notochord, a dorsal tubular nerve cord, and pharyngeal gill slits.

A. The tunicates belong to subphylum Urochordata, which are sessile, filter-feeding marine animals that have tunics made of cellulose.

B. Subphylum Cephalochordata consists of the lancelets—small, segmented, fishlike animals that exhibit all three chordate characteristics.

(Summary continued on p. 672)

FOCUS ON

Some Orders of Living Placental Mammals

Order Insectivora: moles, hedgehogs, and shrews. These are nocturnal insect-eating animals, considered to be the most primitive placental mammals and the ones closest to the ancestors of all the placentals. The shrew is the smallest living mammal; some weigh less than 5 grams.

Order Chiroptera: bats. These mammals are adapted for flying; a fold of skin extends from the elongated fingers to the body and legs, forming a wing. Bats are guided in flight by a sort of biologic sonar: They emit high-frequency squeaks and are guided by the echoes from obstructions. These animals eat insects and fruit or suck the blood of other animals. Blood-feeding bats may transmit diseases such as yellow fever and paralytic rabies.

Order Carnivora: cats, dogs, wolves, foxes, bears, otters, mink, weasels, skunks, seals, walruses, and sea lions. Carnivores are flesh-eaters, with sharp, pointed canine teeth and shearing molars. In many species the canines are used to kill the prey. Carnivores have a keen sense of smell and exhibit complex social interactions. Its members are among the fastest, strongest, and smartest of animals. Limbs of the seals, walruses, and sea lions are modified as flippers for swimming. However, these animals are not completely adapted to life in the water; they come ashore to mate and bear their offspring.

Order Edentata: sloths, anteaters, and armadillos. In these animals, the teeth are reduced to molars without enamel in the front part of the jaws, or no teeth are present. Sloths are sluggish animals that hang upside down from branches. They are often protectively colored by green algae that grow on their hair. Armadillos are protected by bony plates; they eat insects and small invertebrates.

Order Rodentia: squirrels, beavers, rats, mice, hamsters, porcupines, and guinea pigs. These are gnawing mammals with chisel-like incisors that grow continually. As they gnaw, the teeth are worn down. The rodents are one of the most successful orders of mammals; about 3000 species have been described.

Order Lagomorpha: rabbits, hares, and pikas. Like the rodents, the lagomorphs have chisel-like incisors with enamel. Their long hind legs are adapted for jumping, and many have long ears.

Order Primates: lemurs, monkeys, apes, and humans. These mammals have highly developed brains and eyes, nails instead of claws, opposable great toes or thumbs, and eyes directed forward. Most species of primates are arboreal (tree-dwelling) and are thought to have evolved from the tree-dwelling insectivores. Primates may be divided into the prosimians, which include the lemurs, lorises, and tarsiers, and the anthropoids, which include monkeys, apes, and humans. (Primate evolution is discussed in Chapter 21.)

Order Perissodactyla: horses, zebras, tapirs, and rhinoceroses. These are herbivorous hoofed mammals with an odd number of digits per foot, usually one or three toes. (Hoofed mammals are often referred to as ungulates.) The teeth are adapted for chewing. These are usually large animals with long legs.

Order Artiodactyla: cattle, sheep, pigs, deer, and giraffes. These herbivorous hoofed mammals have an even number of digits per foot. Most have two toes, but some have four. Many have antlers or horns on the head. Most are ruminants that chew a cud and have a series of stomachs in which bacteria that digest cellulose are incubated; this contributes greatly to their success as herbivores.

(a)

Order Proboscidea: elephants. These animals have a long, muscular trunk (proboscis) that is very flexible. Thick, loose skin is characteristic. The two upper incisors are elongated as tusks. Most are enormous, with large heads and broad ears; the legs are like pillars. These are the largest land animals, weighing as much as 7 tons. This order includes the extinct mastodons and wooly mammoths.

Order Sirenia: sea cows and manatees. These are herbivorous aquatic mammals with finlike forelimbs and no hind limbs. They are probably the basis for most tales about mermaids.

Order Cetacea: whales, dolphins, and porpoises. These mammals have become well adapted for their aquatic life style. They have fish-shaped bodies with broad, paddle-like forelimbs (flippers). Posterior limbs are absent. Many have a thick layer of fat called blubber covering the body. These very intelligent animals mate and bear their young in the water, and the young are suckled like those of other mammals. The blue whale is the largest living animal and probably the largest animal that has ever existed.

(b)   (c)   (d)

(e)   (f)

Representative members of several orders of placental mammals. (*a*) *Trachops cirrhosus*, a frog-eating bat from Panama (order Chiroptera). After the rodents, bats are the largest order of mammals. (*b*) *Ursus maritimus*, a polar bear, photographed in the Kane Basin in the Arctic (order Carnivora). (*c*) *Erethizon dorsatum*, a porcupine (order Rodentia). Porcupine females bear only one offspring in a season. For mammals, young porcupines are unusually able to care for themselves; at the age of 2 days they are able to climb trees and find food. (*d*) *Leontopatheus rosalia*, the golden lion tamarin monkey. Only 150 of these primates survive in their native coastal rainforest in Brazil, which has been reduced to 2% of its original acreage. Thus, even though these animals have been able to breed well in captivity, their future as a species remains uncertain. (*e*) Two giraffes, *Giraffa camelopardalis* (order Artiodactyla), taking a cooling drink at an oasis in South Africa. Special vascular adaptations prevent the dangerous rise in cerebral blood pressure that would otherwise develop when the giraffe lowers its neck to drink. (*f*) A common dolphin, *Delphinus delphis*, photographed in the Sea of Cortez, Mexico. (*a*, Merlin Tuttle/Photo Researchers, Inc.; *b, e, f,* E.R. Degginger; *c, d,* Charles Seaborn)

C. Subphylum Vertebrata includes animals with a vertebral column that forms the chief skeletal axis of the body. Vertebrates also have a cranium that is part of the endoskeleton, pronounced cephalization, differentiated brain, muscles attached to the endoskeleton for movement, and two pairs of appendages.

1. Class Agnatha, the jawless fish, includes the lampreys and hagfishes.
2. Descendants of the ostracoderms (agnathans that are the earliest known fossil vertebrates) are thought to have evolved jaws and paired appendages and to have given rise to the modern jawed fishes.
3. Class Chondrichthyes, the cartilaginous fish, consists of the sharks, rays, and skates.
4. Class Osteichthyes, the bony fish, includes about 20,000 species of freshwater and saltwater fishes. The osteichthyes and chondrichthyes are thought to have evolved from a common ancestor at about the same time. Most modern bony fish are ray-finned fishes with swim bladders.
5. Modern amphibians include the salamanders, frogs and toads, and wormlike caecilians.
   a. Most amphibians return to the water to reproduce; frog embryos develop into tadpoles, which undergo metamorphosis to become adults.
   b. Amphibians use their moist skin as well as lungs for gas exchange; they have a three-chambered heart and systemic and pulmonary circulations; their skin contains mucous glands.
6. Class Reptilia includes turtles, lizards, snakes, and alligators.
   a. Reptiles are true terrestrial animals.
   b. Fertilization is internal; most reptiles secrete a leathery protective shell around the egg; the embryo develops an amnion and other membranes, which protect the embryo and keep it moist.
   c. A reptile has a dry skin with horny scales, lungs with many chambers, and a three-chambered heart (with some separation of oxygen-rich and oxygen-poor blood); reptiles excrete uric acid.
   d. Reptiles dominated Earth during the Mesozoic era; then, during the Cretaceous period, most reptiles, including all of the dinosaurs, became extinct.
7. Birds (class Aves) have many adaptations for flight, including feathers, wings, and light hollow bones containing air spaces; birds have a four-chambered heart, very efficient lungs, a high metabolic rate, and a constant body temperature; they excrete solid wastes (uric acid).
   a. Birds have a well-developed nervous system and excellent vision and hearing.
   b. Birds communicate with simple calls and complex songs.
8. Mammals have hair, mammary glands, differentiated teeth, and maintain a constant body temperature. They have a highly developed nervous system and a muscular diaphragm.
   a. Monotremes, mammals that lay eggs, include the duck-billed platypus and the spiny anteater.
   b. Marsupials are pouched mammals such as kangaroos and opossums. The young are born in an immature stage and complete their development in the marsupium, where they are nourished with milk from the mammary glands.
   c. Placental mammals are characterized by an organ of exchange, the placenta, that develops between the embryo and the mother. Both oxygen and nutrients diffuse across the placenta from mother to embryo, permitting development to take place within the uterus. Living placental mammals are classified into about 17 orders.

POST-TEST

1. Adult echinoderms have _____ symmetry.
2. The _____ _____ system and _____ feet are unique to echinoderms.
3. Echinoids (e.g., sea urchins) lack _____, and their skeletal plates form a solid _____.
4. Three distinguishing characteristics of chordates are a _____, a dorsal, tubular _____ _____, and pharyngeal _____ _____.
5. _____ are sessile, marine chordates often mistaken for sponges.
6. Vertebrates are distinguished from all other animals in having a _____ _____; anterior to this structure a _____ encloses and protects the brain.
7. Vertebrate classes that are tetrapods include _____, _____, and _____.
8. _____ scales are characteristic of sharks.
9. In sharks, the _____ receives digestive wastes, urine, and gametes.
10. The shark's skeleton is composed of _____.
11. Modern fish are thought to have descended from the _____ fish; the lobe-finned fish are thought to be the ancestors of the _____.
12. The operculum covers the _____.
13. The labyrinthodonts are thought to have been the first successful _____.
14. The amnion is an adaptation to _____ life; it secretes a fluid that _____ and _____.
15. The only endothermic animals are the _____ and the _____.
16. Monotremes are mammals that _____ _____.

Match the answer in Column B with the description in Column A; there may be more than one answer for each question.

Column A
17. Have amnion
18. Have hair
19. Have four-chambered heart (two atria and two ventricles)
20. Have tube feet
21. Body covered with hard, dry, horny scales
22. Bones contain air spaces; no teeth
23. Have pharyngeal gill slits at some time in life cycle

Column B
a. Bony fish
b. Amphibians
c. Reptiles
d. Birds
e. Mammals
f. None of the above
g. All of the above (a–e)

Column A
24. Agnathan with circular, sucking disk
25. Earliest known species of bird
26. A cephalochordate
27. A lobe-finned fish

Column B
a. Amphioxus
b. Lamprey
c. *Archaeopteryx*
d. Coelacanth
e. None of the above

REVIEW QUESTIONS

1. Why are echinoderms thought to be more closely related to chordates than to other phyla?
2. What are the three principal distinguishing characteristics of a chordate? How are these evident in a tunicate larva? In an adult tunicate? In a lancelet? In a human?
3. What characteristics distinguish the vertebrates from the rest of the chordates?
4. How do lampreys and hagfish differ from other fish? Of what economic importance are agnathans?
5. What is the function of gills? In general terms, how do they work? Why do you suppose aquatic mammals do not possess them?
6. Compare the skins of sharks, frogs, snakes, and mammals.
7. Identify which organisms possess each of the following and give the location and function of each of the following:
   a. swim bladder
   b. placenta
   c. operculum
   d. amnion
   e. marsupium
8. Give the phylum, subphylum, class (and order if you can) for each of the following animals:

   a. human
   b. turtle
   c. lamprey
   d. *Branchiostoma* (Amphioxus)
   e. dogfish shark
   f. whale
   g. frog
   h. pelican
   i. bat

9. Why are monotremes considered more primitive than other mammals? Some paleontologists consider monotremes to be therapsid reptiles rather than mammals. Give arguments for and against this position.
10. Which vertebrate groups maintain a constant body temperature? How do they accomplish this? Why is this advantageous?
11. Which are more specialized animals, birds or mammals? Explain your answer.
12. According to current evolutionary theory, what is the significance of each of the following:
    a. coelacanths
    b. placoderms
    c. labyrinthodonts
    d. therapsids
    e. *Archaeopteryx*

RECOMMENDED READINGS

Alldredge, A. L., and L. P. Madin. Pelagic tunicates: Unique herbivores in the marine plankton. *Bioscience,* Vol 32, No 8, September 1982. An account of the unique adaptations of pelagic tunicates.

Austad, S. N. The adaptable opossum. *Scientific American,* Vol 258, No 2, February 1988, pp 98–104. The Virginia opossum can adjust the sex ratios of its progeny, an efficient reproductive strategy that helps it adapt quickly to environmental changes.

Griffiths, M. The platypus. *Scientific American,* Vol 258, No 5, May 1988, pp 84–91. Everything you might want to know about this interesting monotreme; the platypus has mechanoreceptors and electroreceptors on its beak for detecting prey.

Gwinner E. Internal rhythms in bird migration. *Scientific American,* Vol 254, No 4, April 1986. Migratory birds have a biological clock that tells them when to begin and end their flight. This clock also helps them find their destinations.

Monastersky, R. The lonely bird. *Science News,* Vol 140, No 7, August 17, 1991, pp 104–105. Debate regarding the earliest fossil bird.

Mossman, D. J., and W. A. S. Sarjeant. The footprints of extinct animals. *Scientific American,* Vol 248, No 1, January 1983. An account of vertebrate evolution with emphasis on information gained from animal tracks.

Rismiller, P. D., and R. S. Seymour. The echidna. *Scientific American,* Vol 264, No 2, pp 96–103, February 1991. A discussion of the natural history and reproductive behavior of the spiny anteater, a mammal that lays eggs.

Vaughan, T. A. *Mammalogy,* 3rd ed. Saunders College Publishing, Philadelphia, 1986. An introduction to the mammals; a systematic approach.

Welty, J. C. *The Life of Birds,* 4th ed. Saunders College Publishing, Philadelphia, 1988. An introduction to the biology of birds.

Zapol, W. M. Diving adaptations in the Weddell seal. *Scientific American,* June 1987. The Weddell seal can swim deeper and hold its breath longer than most other mammals. This adaptation is now thought to be at least in part the result of collapsible lungs and a spleen that functions as a scuba tank.

Medical Illustrator

TODD BUCK

Todd Buck values the opportunity to combine science and art in his growing business as a medical illustrator. He learned about this career while working toward a biology degree at Iowa State University. The biology department there is one of the few in the country to offer a degree in biological/premedical illustration. After earning his B.A. in 1987, Buck entered the University of Illinois at Chicago, where he completed a Master of Associated Medical Sciences in Biomedical Visualization in 1990. Among his recent projects are covers and illustrations for many medical journals and magazines, entries in Encyclopedia Britannica, textbook illustrations, and drawings for private physicians, surgeons, dentists, and attorneys. Buck has won many awards in the Association of Medical Illustrators art competition.

Have you always had competing interests in science and art?

In high school, all my lecture notes were covered with drawings, sketches, and doodles, so I took an art class and loved it. I drew a lot of wildlife because that was something I was interested in then. I have always been interested in the sciences and had some success in life science classes. I assumed that, to make a living, I would have to go into some profession in the sciences, not art. I started out majoring in biology when I entered college because I thought I would like to teach it some day.

Had you planned to attend Iowa State University even before you learned about the special program in biological/premedical illustration?

I went there as a biology major and then heard about the program. I planned to take art classes on my own as electives, anyway. When I talked to people in charge of the biological/premedical illustration (BPMI) program, they referred me to Dean Biechler, who still teaches the illustration courses. Once I was in his class, he offered me a summer job working with other students on a zoology lab manual. We ordered our specimens from a biological supply company—big boxes full of frogs, sharks, crayfish, perch, and everything from jellyfish on up. We had a lab set up in the biology department, and every day we would do dissections and create illustrations. Dr. Warren Dolphin, head of Iowa State's biology department and BPMI program and author of the manual, was always available for consultation. That summer project went on for 2 years. When I graduated, I was the fourth or fifth student to complete the BPMI program at Iowa State University.

What kind of drawings did you do as a student artist?

Doctors often publish articles on new surgical techniques and need illustrations to accompany their articles. We would sit down and review the procedure with the aid of textbooks and sometimes videos. Now I often attend the actual surgery and observe procedures before drawing them.

Have you become very involved in the clinical aspect of medicine, as preparation for your illustrations?

Yes, especially now that I am working professionally, I attend surgeries before doing my illustrations. I bring my camera and stand on risers behind the doctors, taking photographic references, making notes, and even drawing quick sketches.

It sounds as if artistic ability is only half of the requirement for your profession.

Understanding anatomy and functions, such as physiology and pathology, is critical. Biological artists are often asked to illustrate processes they can't see, such as the immune response, and they must have a *conceptual* understanding of the function before they can draw it. Standard shapes and colors have been adopted for certain structures: Nerves are often colored yellow, veins are blue. At other times you must rely on a written description or microscopy to get a sense of shape. In graduate school, the medical artists take anatomy with the medical students. We aren't expected to be medical experts, but we do have to communicate with the doctors we work with.

Have you thought about teaching this highly specialized skill at a college or university?

I feel as if I am teaching now; that is one of the best things about what I do. I am fulfilling both of my desires—to be an artist and to teach biology, which I am doing through my drawings. I am always trying to create drawings that explain structures or concepts in a clear, concise manner, to make a complex process simpler to understand. Every drawing is a teaching tool.

Was your graduate work at the University of Illinois at Chicago highly interdisciplinary?

Yes, and very intense as well. Professionals working in many fields would come into the classroom. For example, I had a course in prosthetics taught by Ray Evenhouse, one of the best medical sculptors in the field. It takes a real artist to create matching prostheses for a missing ear or nose or eye, to sculpt the shapes perfectly and then paint them with translucent colors that look natural. I was also influenced by Dierdre McConathy, the instructor in my color classes, who taught me how to use an airbrush. She also taught me how to push myself further than I thought I could go. Commercial illustrators also came in and gave us assignments, just as if we were working on a deadline in the real world. That was valuable experience for what I do now.

What kind of work did you do at Biomedia Corporation during your internship there?

Biomedia produces medical legal exhibits, big posters that describe accidents or illustrate anatomies of injured parties for use in court. I worked with clients, lawyers, and doctors working on the cases. Because of time constraints and the nonspecialist audience, the artwork is much simpler than it would be for a textbook or journal article.

What are some of the interesting projects you have illustrated as a professional artist?

One of the largest and most exciting is Jones' *Atlas of Liver & Biliary Surgery*, the illustrations for which I produced from beginning to end over 9 months. I attended seven surgical operations, each 10 to 12 hours long, observing surgeons as they transplanted liver sections from parent to child. A small lobe from the parent's liver was placed in the cavity of the child, and it would turn bright pink as soon as the blood was flowing through. The liver regenerates its own tissue and should grow as the child grows. The surgery had tremendous success, and my drawings are some of the first to illustrate the procedure.

What kinds of professional associations and activities are part of your professional life?

The Association of Medical Illustrators is the largest and most important for artists working in the field. Members are willing to share ideas and help each other. This important organization also offers continuing education in the field of medical art, including symposiums on the incredible new computer programs used in illustrations.

What are some of the capabilities of the new software?

I have worked extensively with a program developed by Lewis Sadler, one of my mentors at the University of Illinois. AGEIT simulates aging in the face of a child. You can scan in the photo of a child, and the program allows you to see how the child's face might change over time, up to the age of 18. During a project to locate miss-ing children, my job was to use a computer paint package to fill in details such as thicker eyebrows, changes in dentition, and a wider neck. Two missing children were located based on my renderings.

After working at these interesting jobs, what made you choose to start your own business?

I wanted to control the quality of my work and to be proud to put my name on everything coming out of my studio. One way to do that is to work for yourself. I started free-lancing while still a student, getting most of my early jobs through referrals from my instructors. By sending out samples and by word of mouth, I was able to get clients after I started out on my own, and my business has grown from there. Self-employment allows me to do the best work I possibly can and to feel good about it.

PART VI

Structure and Life Processes in Plants

Rooted to the ground in one place throughout their existence, plants are often mistakenly thought of by students as passive organisms because they do not appear to "do" many of the things that animals do. Plants are far from passive, however, and are interesting in their own right. Although exposed to the same environmental challenges of living on Earth as animals, plants evolved bodies and lifestyles far different from ourselves and other animals. Yet the fundamental features of plants—cell structure, DNA as the main information molecule, and so on—link plants to all the other organisms on Earth.

Part VI considers the structures and life processes of plants in detail. Chapter 31 examines how plants grow and the different kinds of cells and tissues that make up the plant body. Chapter 32 covers leaves and photosynthesis, Chapter 33 covers stems and transport, and Chapter 34 covers roots and mineral nutrition. Chapter 35 examines reproduction in flowering plants, and Chapter 36 looks at how plant hormones affect growth and development.

Close-up of inner leaves of *Neoregelia
carolinae "Tricolor,"* blushing bromeliad.
This plant is an epiphyte that grows on
tree trunks in South American rain forests.

(Connie Toups)

Plant Structure, Growth, and Differentiation

Plants, like animals, are complex multicellular organisms in which there is a division of labor among cells. Plant cells are organized into **tissues,** which are aggregations of specialized cells that perform a specific function or group of functions. Plant tissues are further organized into **organs** such as roots, stems, and leaves. Each organ is composed of different tissues and performs a single function or group of functions very efficiently, while depending on other organs to provide for the remainder of its needs. For example, leaves photosynthesize and provide the converted solar energy of sugar molecules to the rest of the plant body. Leaves in turn depend on roots to absorb water and essential minerals from the soil and on stems to transport these materials to the leaves. Leaves also depend on stems to grow in such a way that leaves are exposed to an optimal amount of sunlight. Thus, the activities of cells, tissues, and organs in a multicellular plant are coordinated with each other in precise ways that contribute to the survival of the entire plant.

Dudleya farinosa, a succulent that grows on coastal bluffs in California. (Ed Reschke)

Plant growth and development are also precise and orderly events. When plants reproduce sexually, a fertilized egg, or zygote, results from the fusion of haploid male and female reproductive cells. This single-celled zygote grows by mitosis into a multicellular embryo. The mature plant that eventually develops from an embryo is composed of millions or even billions of cells that are specialized into tissues and organs. Each stage of growth in plants—from zygote to embryo to seedling to nonreproductive adult to reproductive adult—is under both genetic and environmental controls that interact together in specific ways to regulate growth and development.

LEARNING OBJECTIVES

After you have studied this chapter you should be able to

1. Discuss what is meant by "growth" in plants.
2. Trace the stages in embryo development in flowering plants.
3. Define primary and secondary growth.
4. Distinguish between apical and lateral meristems.
5. Define determinate and indeterminate growth and give an example of each.
6. Describe the simple tissues (parenchyma, collenchyma, and sclerenchyma) of plants.

7. Characterize the vascular tissue systems (xylem and phloem) of plants.
8. Summarize the dermal tissue system (epidermis and periderm) of plants.
9. Discuss the plant body, including the basic features of leaves, stems, and roots.
10. Relate how plant development is different from animal development.
11. Discuss genetic and nongenetic factors that affect plant growth and development.

EMBRYONIC DEVELOPMENT IN PLANTS FOLLOWS AN ORDERLY AND PREDICTABLE PATH

Flowering plants produce a young embryo complete with nutrients in a compact package, the seed (see Chapter 27). The seed develops after fertilization, when an egg nucleus and a sperm nucleus fuse to form a zygote. Mitotic divisions of the zygote to form a multicellular embryo progress in a variety of ways in flowering plants (Figure 31–1). The following paragraphs describe dicot embryonic development.

The two cells formed as a result of the first division of the zygote establish polarity in the embryo. The bottom cell (in reference to Figure 31–1) typically develops into a **suspensor,** a multicellular structure that anchors the embryo and aids in nutrient uptake from the endosperm. The top cell grows into the embryo proper. Initially, the top cell divides to form a chain of cells, called a **proembryo.** As mitosis continues, a small ball of cells, a **globular embryo,** develops. Cells and tissues begin to differentiate (specialize) during this stage. When the embryo begins to lengthen to form its two cotyledons, it resembles a heart: This is called the **heart stage.** As the

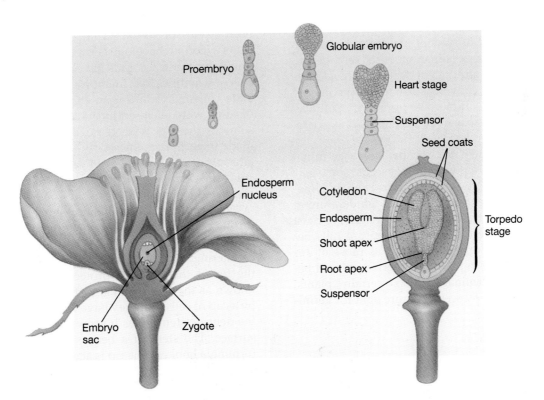

Figure 31–1 Embryonic development in dicots. With the first division of the zygote, polarity is established: The bottom cell develops into the suspensor, and the top cell develops into the plant embryo. In the drawing on the right, the embryo is still immature. In most dicots the endosperm is absent in the mature seed, its reserves having been used for growth and development of the embryo.

cotyledons elongate, the **torpedo stage** develops, which continues to grow into a mature embryo. The embryo continues to enlarge, crushing the suspensor beyond recognition.

The mature embryo consists of an embryonic root called a **radicle,** an embryonic shoot, and two cotyledons (monocots, of course, have a single cotyledon). The embryonic shoot is further differentiated into two parts, an epicotyl and a hypocotyl. The **epicotyl** is the part of the stem above the point of attachment of the cotyledons. The **hypocotyl,** the part of the stem below the cotyledons, is continuous with the embryonic root.

A NUMBER OF EXTERNAL AND INTERNAL FACTORS AFFECT SEED GERMINATION

When a seed is mature, it is often dormant and does not **germinate** (commence growth) immediately. A number of factors influence whether a seed germinates. Many of these are environmental factors, including the presence of water and oxygen, proper temperature, and sometimes the presence of light penetrating the soil surface. For example, no seed germinates unless it has absorbed water because the embryo in the mature seed is dehydrated and a watery medium in cells is necessary for active metabolism. When a seed germinates, its metabolic machinery is turned on, with numerous materials being synthesized and degraded, making water an absolute requirement for germination. Also, seed germination and growth require a great deal of energy. Plants obtain this energy by converting carbohydrate energy into ATP through the same aerobic respiratory pathway as animals, so oxygen is usually needed during germination.[1]

Another environmental factor that affects germination is temperature. In a population of seeds, some germinate at each temperature over a broad range. However, each plant species has an optimal temperature at which the largest number of seeds germinates. For most plants, the optimal germination temperature falls between 25° and 30°C. Some seeds, such as those of apples, require exposure to prolonged periods of cold before their seeds germinate. Also, certain plants, especially those with tiny seeds, require light for germination (see Chapter 35).

Some of the environmental factors that affect seed germination help ensure the survival of the young plant. If seeds were to germinate at extremely low temperatures, the young plants would not likely survive, so the requirement of a prolonged cold period ensures that seeds germinate in the spring rather than the winter. A light requirement ensures that a tiny seed germinates only if it is close to the surface of the soil. If such a seed were to germinate several inches below the soil surface, it might not have enough food reserves to grow to the surface. On the other hand, if this seed were to remain dormant until the soil was disturbed and it was brought to the surface, it would have a much greater likelihood of survival.

Even when external factors are optimal, certain seeds do not germinate because of internal factors. Many plant seeds are dormant either because they are immature and the embryo must develop further or because chemical inhibitors that prevent germination are present. These inhibitors, such as abscisic acid (see Chapter 36), may be leached out of the seed by rain. The presence of such chemical inhibitors helps ensure the survival of the plant. For example, the seeds of desert annuals often contain a high level of abscisic acid that is leached out only when rainfall is sufficient to support the plant's growth after germination.

If the proper combination of external and internal factors is not present, the seed does not germinate. How long can a seed remain dormant? Although there have been stories of seeds germinating after thousands of years when archaeologists excavated the tombs of the Pharaohs, these accounts have not been verified. However, a scientific experiment was conducted at Michigan State University starting in 1879, when different kinds of seeds were enclosed in jars and buried. Periodically, some of the jars were removed, and an attempt was made to germinate the seeds. As late as 1980, 101 years later, some of the seeds still germinated. In a separate study in Denmark in 1978, dormant seeds in the soil excavated from an 850-year-old grave site germinated!

The first part of the plant to emerge from the seed during germination is the radicle, or embryonic root. As the root grows, it forces its way through the soil, encountering considerable friction. The delicate cells at the tip of the root are protected by a layer of cells known as the **root cap.** Plant stem tips are not covered by a cap of cells, but they have different ways to protect the delicate stem tip as it grows through the soil to the surface. The stem of a bean seedling is curved over, forming a hook, so the tip is actually pulled up through the soil (Figure 31–2). Corn and other grasses have a special sheath of cells called a **coleoptile** surrounding the shoot (Figure 31–3). The coleoptile grows up through the soil, and the more delicate shoot then grows up through the middle of the coleoptile sheath.

---

[1]Some plants such as rice are able to respire anaerobically during the early stages of germination and seedling growth. This enables rice to grow and become established in flooded soil, an environment that would suffocate most young plants.

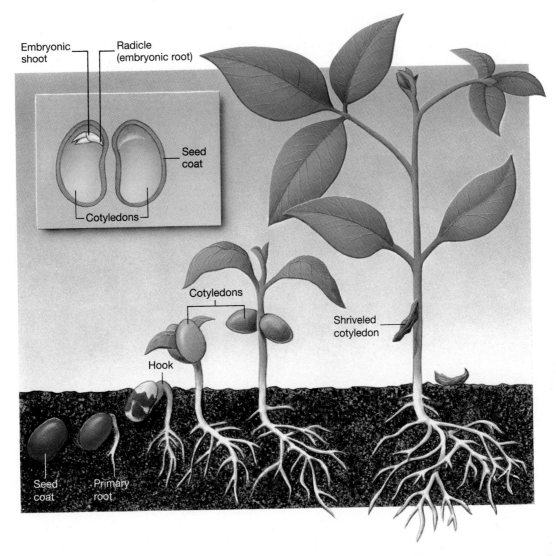

Figure 31–2 Seed germination and growth of a young soybean. Note the hook in the stem of the young seedling, which protects the delicate stem tip as it moves up through the soil. Once the shoot has emerged from the soil, the hook straightens. The stem and roots elongate by growth at their tips. As the stored food in the cotyledons is used by the developing plant, the cotyledons shrivel and fall off the stem. At this point the young plant meets all of its nutritional needs by photosynthesis.

PLANTS EXHIBIT LOCALIZED GROWTH AFTER GERMINATION

The seedling that emerges from the seed continues to grow into an adult plant. Certain parts of the plant grow throughout the life of the plant. This **indeterminate growth** is characteristic of stems and roots. Theoretically, these parts of a plant could continue to elongate forever. Other parts of the plant have **determinate growth** and discontinue growth after reaching a certain size. The size of these structures varies from species to species and from individual to individual depending on the plant's genetic programming and on environmental conditions that may limit its growth. Leaves and flowers are examples of structures that exhibit determinate growth.

Growth is a complex phenomenon involving three different processes: cell division, cell elongation, and cell differentiation. Cell division is an essential part of growth that results in an increase in the number of cells. However, an increase in cell number without a corresponding increase in cell size would contribute little to overall size increase of the plant; thus, cell elongation is an essential part of growth. Plant cells also **differentiate,** or specialize, to perform the various functions required in a complex, multicellular organism (see Chapter 16). Although all diploid cells in a plant contain the same genes, during differentiation some genes are acti-

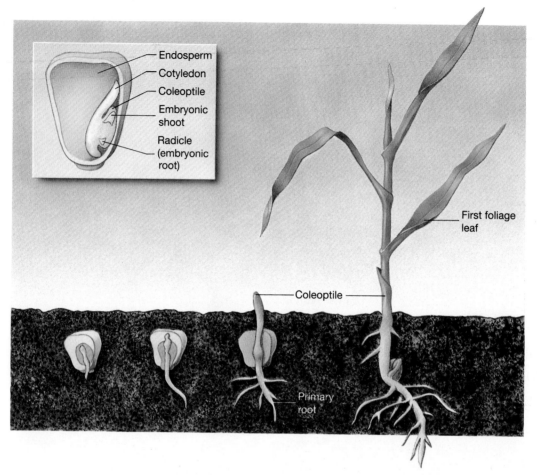

Endosperm
Cotyledon
Coleoptile
Embryonic shoot
Radicle (embryonic root)

First foliage leaf

Coleoptile

Primary root

Figure 31-3   Seed germination and growth of a young corn plant. Note the coleoptile, a sheath of cells that emerges first from the soil. The delicate shoot tip grows up through the middle of the coleoptile.

vated whereas others are repressed, allowing cells to develop differences in structure and physiology that enable them to perform distinct activities.

One difference between plants and animals is the location of growth. When a young animal is growing, all parts of its body grow, although all parts do not necessarily grow at the same rate. However, plant growth is localized into specific areas, called **meristems,** which are composed of cells that remain unspecialized and retain the ability to divide by mitosis.

Primary Growth Takes Place at Apical Meristems

Two kinds of growth occur in plants. One is **primary growth,** which is an increase in the length of the plant. The other is **secondary growth,** an increase in the girth, or width, of the plant. All plants have primary growth, but only woody plants have secondary growth; a plant with primary growth only is said to be **herbaceous.** Primary growth occurs as a result of the activity of **apical meristems,** which are meristematic areas found at the tips of stems and roots.

As discussed previously, the very end of the root is covered by a protective layer of cells called the root cap (Figure 31–4). Directly behind the root cap is the root apical meristem, which contains three areas or zones. Closest to the root cap is the **area of cell division.** A microscopic examination of the area of cell division reveals meristematic cells, which are ''boxy'' in shape and very small. Further back from the tip of the root, just behind the area of cell division, is the **area of cell elongation,** where the cells are no longer dividing but instead are enlarging. It is the elongation of cells in this region that pushes roots through the soil. Some differentiation also occurs in the area of cell elongation, and immature tissues become evident. The immature tissues continue to develop and differentiate into the mature tissues of the adult plant. Further back, behind the area of cell elongation, the cells have completely differentiated and are fully mature. A number of specialized tissues within the root are evident in this region, known as the **area of cell maturation.** For example, root hairs, which are extensions of epidermal cells that increase the absorbing surface of the root in contact with the soil, are found here.

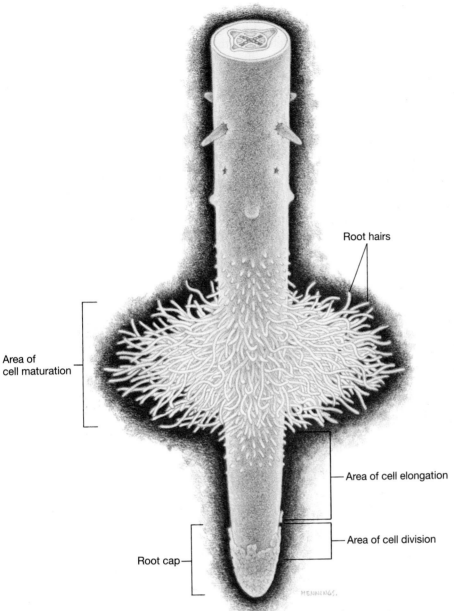

Root hairs

Area of
cell maturation

Area of cell elongation

Area of cell division

Root cap

HENNINGS.

Figure 31–4 The root apical meristem. Just behind the root cap is the area of cell division, where mitosis occurs. Farther from the tip is the area of cell elongation, where cells enlarge and begin to differentiate. The area of cell maturation has fully mature, differentiated cells. Note the root hairs in this region.

The apical meristem of stems is quite different in appearance from the root apical meristem (Figure 31–5). The stem apical meristem has **leaf primordia** (embryonic leaves) and **bud primordia** (embryonic buds) emerging from it. A dome of tiny meristematic cells is located in the center at the very tip of the stem. Further from the tip of the stem, the immature tissues continue to develop into mature tissues that are located farther back from the stem tip. The three areas (cell division, elongation, and maturation) are present in stem tips, although they are not as obvious as in the root.

Figure 31–5 A longitudinal section through a stem apical meristem. Note the leaf primordia and bud primordia. (Dennis Drenner)

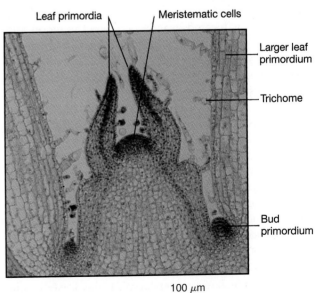

Leaf primordia

Meristematic cells

Larger leaf primordium

Trichome

Bud primordium

100 μm

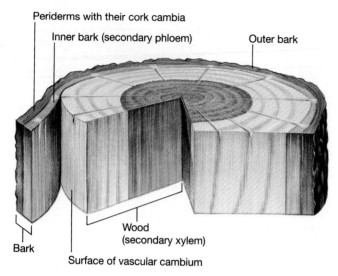

Periderms with their cork cambia

Inner bark (secondary phloem)

Outer bark

Wood (secondary xylem)

Bark

Surface of vascular cambium

Figure 31–6 In secondary growth, plants increase in girth as a result of the activity of two lateral meristems. The vascular cambium produces secondary vascular tissues, the wood and inner bark. The cork cambium produces the outer bark tissues that replace the epidermis in the secondary plant body.

Secondary Growth Takes Place at Lateral Meristems

Woody trees and shrubs have secondary growth in addition to primary growth. That is, the roots and stems of these plants increase in length by primary growth and increase in girth by secondary growth. This increase in girth is due to the cell divisions of **lateral meristems,** which are located on the sides of the stem and root. Actually, two lateral meristems are responsible for secondary growth, the vascular cambium and the cork cambium (Figure 31–6).

The **vascular cambium** is a layer of meristematic cells that forms a ring, or cylinder, around the stem and root trunk. It is located exactly between the wood and bark of the plant, and its cells divide to form more wood toward the inside and more bark toward the outside (the *inner* bark, to be more precise). The **cork cambium** is composed of patches of meristematic cells located in the outer bark region. Cells of the cork cambium divide to form the tissues of the outer bark. A more comprehensive discussion of secondary growth is given in Chapters 33 and 34.

Plants with secondary growth are **perennial,** living year after year. In contrast, many herbaceous plants (which have only primary growth) are **annuals** and grow, reproduce, and die in one season (for example, corn and rice).[1] Some herbaceous plants (for example,

carrots and beets) are **biennials** and take two years to complete growth and reproduction before dying. In temperate climates, herbaceous plants that are perennials (for example, rhubarb and asparagus) live year after year but die back each winter. Their body parts in the soil do not die but remain dormant during the winter and send up new growth above ground each spring. All tropical monocots, including orchids and palms, are herbaceous perennials with persistent above-ground parts.

Why do certain plants have secondary growth and make wood and bark? Secondary growth confers a longer life span than is found in most plants lacking secondary growth. Cells do not live forever. Plants that have primary growth only do not have a way to replace older tissues in the stem and root. Although their tips are continually producing new cells, the older stem and root tissues eventually die. In plants with secondary growth, new stem and root tissues replace the older parts throughout the entire length of the plant, not just at the tips. Therefore, plants with secondary growth are able to have an extended life span, sometimes for thousands of years (see Making the Connection: Is It Better to Be Long-lived or Short-lived?).

CELLS AND TISSUES DIFFERENTIATE IN THE GROWING PLANT

As growth occurs, some cells become specialized and develop into tissues that make up the organs of the plant body. All vascular plants have three tissue systems: a dermal tissue system, a vascular tissue system, and a ground tissue system. The dermal tissue system provides a covering for the plant body. Various substances, including water, dissolved minerals, and dissolved sugar (food), are conducted throughout the plant by the vascular tissue system. The ground tissue system makes up the remainder of the plant body. The three tissue systems are composed of various cell types with a variety of functions (Table 31–1). Some plant tissues are composed of only one cell type (**simple tissues**), whereas other plant tissues have two or more cell types (**complex tissues**).

Parenchyma Cells Have Thin Primary Walls

One type of plant cell, called **parenchyma,** has very thin cell walls (Figure 31–7). Parenchyma tissue, which is a simple plant tissue composed of parenchyma cells, is located throughout the plant's body. The living cells of parenchyma perform a number of important metabolic functions for plants, including photosynthesis, storage, and secretion. Materials stored in parenchyma cells in-

---

[1] Some annuals (for example, sunflowers) have secondary growth, despite the fact that they do not have obvious wood and bark tissues.

Table 31–1 A SUMMARY OF PLANT CELL TYPES

Cell Type		Function	Location
Parenchyma		Secretion Storage Photosynthesis	Throughout the plant body
Collenchyma		Support	Just under stem epidermis Along leaf veins
Sclerenchyma		Support	Throughout the plant body Common in stems and certain leaves
Tracheid		Conduction of water and minerals Also provides support	Xylem
Vessel element		Conduction of water and minerals Also provides support	Xylem
Sieve tube member		Conduction of food	Phloem
Companion cell		Aids sieve tube members in food conduction	Phloem

clude energy-storage molecules (visible as starch grains or oil droplets), water, and salts (visible as crystals). The various functions of parenchyma require living, metabolizing cells.

Like all plant cells, each parenchyma cell is enclosed by a cell wall (see Chapter 4). Cell walls, which provide structural support, often contain several layers.

All plant cells have a **primary cell wall.** Many plant cells, as they mature, deposit additional cell wall material *inside* the primary wall, i.e., between the primary wall and the plasma membrane. This **secondary cell wall** serves to reinforce the primary wall. Parenchyma cells typically have thin primary cell walls and lack secondary cell walls.

MAKING THE CONNECTION

Is It Better to Be Long-Lived or Short-Lived?

It does not necessarily follow that, because individuals belonging to species with secondary growth are able to survive for a long period of time, secondary growth is "better." Comparison of the benefits of a longer versus a shorter life span shows that in some environments, a longer life span is advantageous, whereas in others, a shorter life span is better.

When an environment is relatively constant or stable, it is filled with plants competing for available space. Because such an environment is so crowded, it has few open spots in which new plants can become established. Furthermore, when a plant dies, it creates an empty area that is quickly filled—but not necessarily by the same kind of plant. A plant that has a long life span thrives here, assuming that it has a high competitive ability. In this type of environment, a tree with its longer life span (conferred by secondary growth) has an advantage because it can "hold onto" a piece of soil and continue to produce seeds for many years.

However, in an environment that is undergoing change, many possible sites are usually available. This type of environment is not crowded, and plants usually do not have to compete against large, fully established plants. Thus, an unstable or unpredictable environment is more advantageous for smaller plants that are opportunists—those that grow quickly, have a short life span (that is, no secondary growth), and put all of their resources into producing as many seeds as possible before dying.

Thus, each species has its own life history strategy, with some plants adapted to variable environments and others adapted to stable environments. The longer life span conferred on plants with secondary growth is one of several successful life history plans. We return to the matter of different life history strategies in population ecology (see Chapter 52).

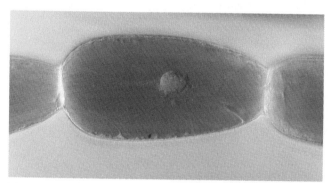

(a)

100 μm

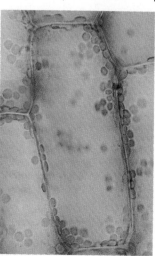

(b)   10 μm

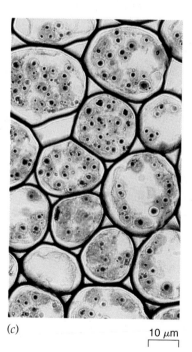

(c)

10 μm

Figure 31–7 Parenchyma are living, relatively unspecialized cells. (a) Parenchyma cells from the stamen hairs of the spiderwort (*Tradescantia virginiana*). The large vacuole contains pigmented material and occupies most of the cell. Note the nucleus and cytoplasmic strands. (b) Some parenchyma cells contain chloroplasts. The primary function of these cells is photosynthesis. (c) Parenchyma cells often function in storage. These parenchyma cells are from the cortex of a *Ranunculus* root. Note the starch grains filling the cells. (a, Phil Gates, University of Durham/Biological Photo Service; b & c, Dennis Drenner)

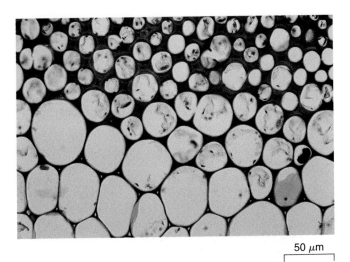

Figure 31–8   Collenchyma cells provide support. Note the unevenly thickened cell walls that are especially thick in the corners. The cells started out as little cubes; as the walls thickened in the corners, the cell contents assumed a spherical shape. (Courtesy of James Mauseth, University of Texas)

Collenchyma Cells Have Unevenly Thickened Primary Walls

Collenchyma tissue, a simple plant tissue composed of collenchyma cells, functions for structural support (Figure 31–8). Support is a crucial function in plants because adequate structural support allows plants to grow upward, enabling them to compete with other plants for available sunlight on a plant-crowded land. Because plants lack a skeletal system typical of animals,

support of plant body parts is provided by individual cells, including the strengthening tissue, collenchyma.

Collenchyma cells are alive at maturity, and their primary cell walls are unevenly thickened, being especially thick in the corners. Collenchyma is not located throughout the plant body; it is found in long strands, often just inside the epidermis in stems and along leaf veins. Collenchyma is an extremely flexible support tissue.

Sclerenchyma Cells Have Both a Primary Wall and a Thick Secondary Wall

A second simple plant tissue specialized for structural support is **sclerenchyma,** cells of which have both primary and secondary cell walls. The word *sclerenchyma* is derived from a Greek term meaning "hard." Their secondary cell walls contain **lignin,** a molecule that imparts strength and rigidity. Sclerenchyma walls are not only strong, or hard, but they become extremely thick (Figure 31–9). At functional maturity, when sclerenchyma is providing support for the plant body, its cells are frequently dead.

One type of sclerenchyma cell is the **sclereid.** Sclereids are short, cubical cells common in the shells of nuts and the "pits" of stone fruits such as cherries and peaches. A second type of sclerenchyma cell is the **fiber** (Figure 31–9b). Fibers are long, tapered cells that are often located in patches or clumps. Fibers are particularly abundant in the wood and bark of flowering plants.

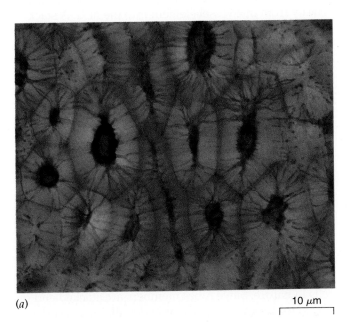

(a)   10 μm

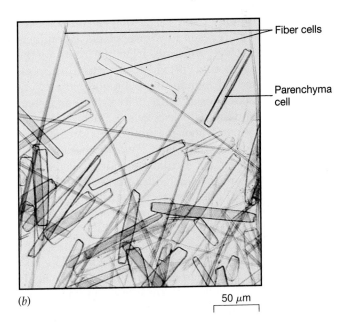

Fiber cells

Parenchyma cell

(b)   50 μm

Figure 31–9   Sclerenchyma cells provide support. (a) Sclerenchyma cells from a cherry pit. The cell walls are extremely thick and hard, providing structural support. (b) Long, tapering fibers (a type of sclerenchyma) and shorter, thicker parenchyma cells from a bamboo stem. The stem was treated with acid to separate the cells. (a, Dennis Drenner; b, courtesy of James Mauseth, University of Texas)

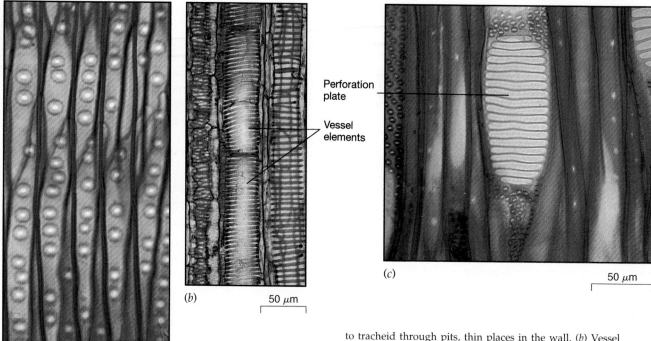

Figure 31–10   Conducting cells in xylem. (*a*) Pine tracheids in longitudinal section. These cells, which occur in clumps, transport water and dissolved minerals. Water passes readily from tracheid to tracheid through pits, thin places in the wall. (*b*) Vessel elements in longitudinal section. These cells are more efficient than tracheids in conducting water. Note how they are stacked end on end. (*c*) The end walls of vessel elements, called perforation plates, have large holes. Water passes through perforation plates from one vessel element to the next.   (*a*, Visuals Unlimited/John D. Cunningham; *b*, J. Robert Waaland, University of Washington/Biological Photo Service; *c*, Visuals Unlimited/J. D. Litvay)

Xylem Has Two Kinds of Conducting Cells, Tracheids and Vessel Elements

Xylem is a complex plant tissue that is composed of four different cell types in flowering plants. It conducts water and dissolved minerals from the roots to the stems and leaves and provides structural support. Xylem is located throughout the plant body; the xylem of the root is continuous with stem xylem, and stem xylem is continuous with leaf xylem. Such continuity is required to move water in a continuous stream from the soil throughout the plant. Two of the four cell types found in xylem actually conduct water and minerals; these are the **tracheids** and **vessel elements** (Figure 31–10). In addition to these cells, xylem also contains parenchyma cells that perform storage functions and fibers that provide support.

Tracheids and vessel elements are specialized for conduction. Both cell types are dead and therefore hollow at maturity; only their cell walls remain. Tracheids are long, tapering cells that are located in patches, or clusters. Water is conducted up through tracheids, passing from one tracheid into another through **pits,** which are thin places in the walls.

The cell diameter of vessel elements is usually wider than that of tracheids; the cells are hollow, and their end walls have holes, or **perforations.** Vessel elements are stacked end on end, and water is conducted readily from one vessel element into the next. A stack of vessel elements is called a **vessel.** Like tracheids, vessel elements also have pits, which permit the lateral transport of water from one vessel to another.[1]

Sieve Tube Members Are the Conducting Cells of Phloem

Conduction of food throughout the plant is accomplished by **phloem.** Like xylem, phloem is a complex tissue that in flowering plants is composed of four cell types—sieve tube members, companion cells, fibers, and parenchyma (Figure 31–11). Fibers are frequently quite extensive in phloem, providing additional support for the plant body.

Food is conducted in solution through the **sieve tube members,** which are among the most specialized cells in nature. Sieve tubes members are stacked end on end to form sieve tubes. Their end walls have a series of

---

[1] Lateral transport between vessel elements is important. For example, if a vessel gets blocked by an air bubble, lateral transport allows water to bypass the obstruction by flowing into neighboring vessels.

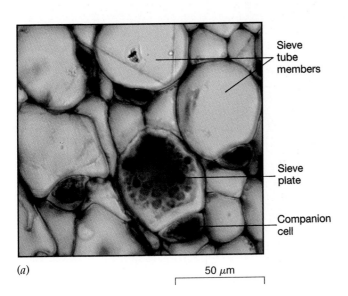

(a)   50 μm

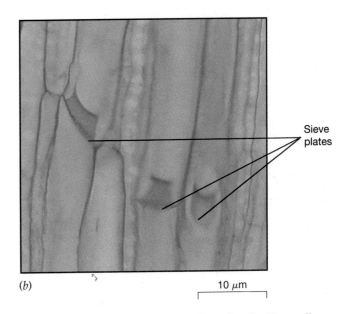

(b)   10 μm

Figure 31–11 Dissolved food is conducted through sieve tube members of the phloem. (*a*) Phloem tissue in cross section. Note the sieve plate, the end wall of the sieve tube member. Most of the sieve tube members appear empty because they were sectioned in the middle of the cells rather than at the end walls. The smaller cells are companion cells. (*b*) Phloem tissue in longitudinal section. (*a*, J. Robert Waaland, University of Washington/Biological Photo Service; *b*, Dennis Drenner)

holes, called **sieve plates,** through which cytoplasmic connections run from one sieve tube member into the next. Sieve tube members are living at maturity, but during maturation many cell organelles disintegrate, including the nucleus, vacuole, and ribosomes.

Few eukaryotic cells can function without nuclei. One example of such cells in mammals is the red blood cell. However, red blood cells function for only a very limited period of time, approximately 120 days in humans, presumably because they lack nuclear control. Sieve tube members typically live for less than a year, although there are notable exceptions. Certain palms have sieve tube members that have remained alive approximately 100 years!

Adjacent to each sieve tube member is a **companion cell,** which assists in the functioning of the sieve tube member. The companion cell is a living cell, complete with nucleus and other organelles. Numerous cytoplasmic connections exist between companion cells and sieve tube members. Although the companion cell does not conduct food throughout the plant, it plays an essential role in moving sugars from the photosynthetic parenchyma cells into the sieve tube members for transport to other parts of the plant (see Chapter 33).

Epidermis Is the Outermost Layer of Cells on a Herbaceous Plant

The dermal tissue system provides a protective covering over plant parts. In plants with primary growth, the dermal covering is a single layer of cells, the **epidermis.**

The epidermis is a complex tissue composed of several types of cells, but most are parenchyma. Epidermal cell walls are somewhat thicker on the outside of the plant for protection. Epidermal parenchyma does not contain chloroplasts; its transparent nature allows light energy to penetrate into the interior of the stem and leaf where photosynthesis occurs.

One of the most important requirements of the above-ground parts of the plant (i.e., stems and leaves) is an ability to control water loss (see Chapter 26). Epidermal cells secrete a waxy layer called a **cuticle** over the surface of their outer walls (Figure 31–12*a*); this wax greatly restricts the loss of water from plant surfaces. (The root epidermis does not produce a cuticle because roots must be permeable to water in order to absorb it from the soil.) Although the cuticle is very efficient at preventing water loss through epidermal cells, it also provides a barrier against the diffusion of carbon dioxide into the leaf, which is a necessary requirement for photosynthesis (see Chapter 8). This diffusion of carbon dioxide is accomplished by **stomata** (singular, *stoma*), tiny pores formed in the epidermis by two rounded cells, called **guard cells** (Figure 31–12*b*). A number of gases pass through stomata by diffusion, including carbon dioxide, oxygen, and water vapor. Stomata are generally open during the day when photosynthesis is occurring and the plant must lose water to cool itself.[1]

---

[1] During drought conditions, the need to conserve water overrides the need to cool the leaves and exchange gases for photosynthesis. This results in the stomata closing during the day.

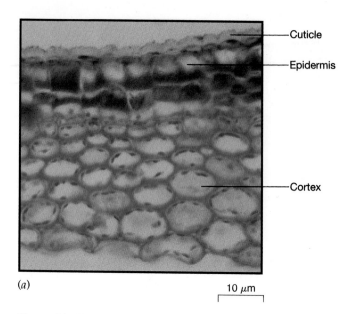

(a)

10 μm

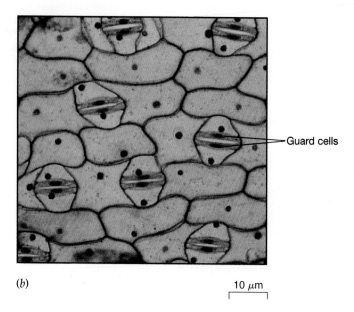

(b)

10 μm

Figure 31–12   Epidermis. (*a*) Cross section of ivy (*Hedera helix*) stem. The cuticle is secreted by the epidermis. (*b*) Surface view of *Tradescantia* leaf epidermis. Note the pink-colored guard cells that form openings for gas exchange.   (*a*, Dennis Drenner; *b*, James Bell/Photo Researchers, Inc.)

They close during the night to conserve water in the plant when photosynthesis is not taking place and cooling is not required (see Chapter 32).

The epidermis also may contain special outgrowths, or hairs, called **trichomes,** which have a variety of functions (see Figure 31–5). Roots hairs are trichomes that increase the surface area of the root that comes into contact with the soil for more effective water and mineral absorption. Plants that can tolerate salty environments often have trichomes on their leaves that are specialized for salt removal. Research indicates that the presence of trichomes on the aerial portions of desert plants may increase the reflection of light off the plants, thereby cooling the internal tissues and decreasing water loss. Other trichomes have a protective function and discourage herbivorous animals from eating the plant.

Periderm Is the Outermost Layers of Cells on a Woody Plant

Plants that increase in girth by secondary growth must produce a dermal covering to replace the epidermis, which gets split apart as the plant expands. **Periderm,** which is a complex tissue, is the functional replacement of the epidermis for plants with secondary growth (see Chapter 33). Periderm is several to many cells thick and forms the outer bark of older stems and roots (Figure 31–13).

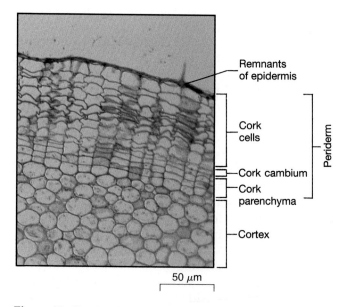

50 μm

Figure 31–13   Periderm is the secondary plant body replacement for epidermis. Formed by the cork cambium, it makes up the outer bark of woody stems and roots. The cells of periderm are always arranged in stacks in cross section.   (Dennis Drenner)

Periderm is continually being formed by a lateral meristem, the cork cambium, located within it. Cork cambium cells divide to form many cork cells to their exterior and one or two layers of cork parenchyma cells to their interior. Cork cells are dead at maturity, and their walls are heavily coated with a waterproof substance to help reduce water loss.

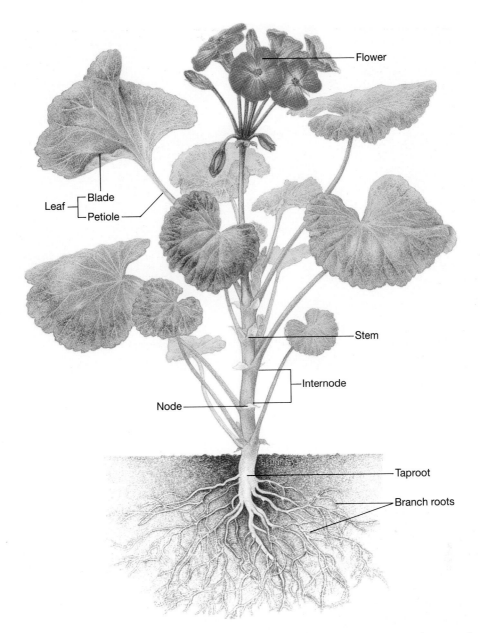

Figure 31–14 The primary plant body of a geranium, a typical herbaceous dicot plant, includes roots, stems, and leaves. Lateral buds grow into either vegetative (nonreproductive) branches or flowering branches.

ROOTS, STEMS, LEAVES, FLOWERS, AND FRUITS MAKE UP THE PLANT BODY

All the cell and tissue types just discussed are organized into a plant body with a root system and a shoot system (Figure 31–14). Plants must have both roots and shoots because they need resources from both the ground (water and minerals) and the air (sunlight and atmospheric CO_2). The root system is generally the below-ground portion of a plant, whereas the above-ground portion, the shoot system, is made up of a vertical stem, which bears leaves, flowers, and fruits. Roots, stems, leaves, flowers, and fruits are considered plant organs because they are composed of several different tissues.[1] Some plant tissues, such as xylem and phloem, are continuous throughout the length of the plant, whereas others, such as fibers, are localized in certain organs.

There are several types of root systems (Figure 31–15). Plants with a **taproot** system have one primary root with many smaller branch roots coming out of it. A taproot develops from the embryonic root (the radicle) that was part of the young plant in the seed. The dande-

---

[1] To be more precise, a flower is a *collection* of organs. Sepals, petals, stamens, and carpels are each considered organs.

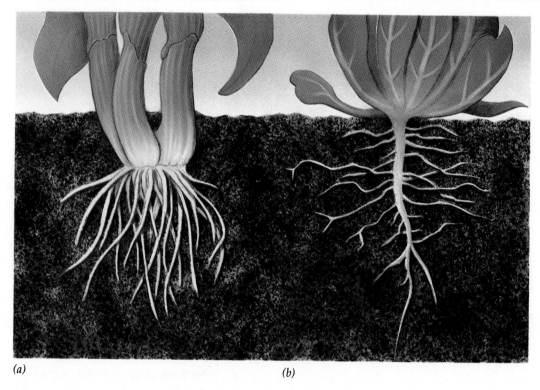

(a)   (b)

Figure 31–15 Root systems in plants. (*a*) The fibrous root system is characteristic of monocots. (*b*) The taproot system is common in dicots. Both fibrous roots and taproots may be modified for food storage.

lion root is a good example of a taproot system. A **fibrous root** system has several to many roots of the same size developing from the end of the stem, with smaller roots branching off these roots. Fibrous root systems form in plants in which the radicle dies during germination. Crabgrass and other grasses have fibrous root systems. Some plants have **storage roots** in which their roots are modified for food storage. Storage roots may be modified taproots (such as the carrot) or fibrous roots (such as the sweet potato).

One way that most stems can be distinguished from roots is that stems bear leaves. The area on the stem where each leaf attaches is called a **node**, whereas the region of the stem between two successive nodes is the **internode.**

Stems also have **buds,** which are undeveloped embryonic shoots. The **terminal bud** includes the apical meristem at the tip of the stem. When the stem apical meristem is not actively growing, it is covered by an outer protective layer of **bud scales,** which are modified leaves. Plants also have **lateral buds** located in the **axils** of leaves. (The axil is the area on the stem directly above where the leaf attaches to the stem.) When buds grow and develop, they form stems that bear leaves or flowers.

A woody twig that has shed its leaves provides a good demonstration of stem structures (Figure 31–16).

The terminal bud is covered by bud scales that protect the embryonic tissues during their dormancy. When the plant resumes growth in the spring, the bud scales fall off, leaving a **bud scale scar.** Because plants form terminal buds once a year (at the end of the growing season), the number of bud scale scars on a twig indicates the age of the twig. A **leaf scar** shows where a leaf was attached on the stem, and the vascular tissue that runs from the stem out into the leaf forms **bundle scars** within the leaf scar. A lateral bud is found directly above the leaf scar. Also, the bark of a woody twig has **lenticels,** sites containing cork cells with large intercellular spaces that allow oxygen to diffuse into the inner tissues of the woody stem. Lenticels look like tiny marks, or specks, on the bark of the twig.

Most leaves are composed of two parts, a blade and a petiole. The broad, expanded portion of the leaf is its **blade,** and the stalk that attaches the blade to the stem is its **petiole** (see Figure 31–14). Leaves may be **simple** (undivided blade) or **compound** (composed of two or more leaflets) (Figure 31–17). Sometimes it is difficult to tell whether a leaf is compound or if it is really a small stem bearing several simple leaves. One easy way to tell if a plant has compound leaves is to look for lateral buds. The lateral buds form at the base of the leaf, whether it is simple or compound, never at the base of leaflets. Also, the leaflets of a compound leaf lie in a

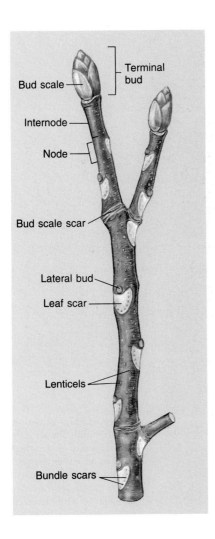

Figure 31–16 The external structure of a woody twig of horse chestnut, *Aesculus hippocastanum.* The age of a woody twig can be determined by counting the number of bud scale scars (don't count side branches). How old is this twig?

entiation is genetic (see Chapter 16). If the genes required for development of a particular characteristic are not present, that characteristic does not develop. The location of a cell during its early development also has a profound effect on what that cell ultimately becomes. Other nongenetic factors, including the external environment, also exert an important influence on gene expression in plants.

One nongenetic factor affecting plant growth and development, including differentiation, is the influence of plant tissues and organs. Much of this control is mediated by **hormones,** substances produced in one part of the plant and transported to another, where they elicit some type of response (see Chapter 36). Unlike animal hormones, which are very specific in the response they elicit, each plant hormone affects a wide variety of growth responses in the plant throughout its lifetime. These hormones interact with one another in both stimulatory and inhibitory ways.

The external environment is a very important nongenetic factor affecting all aspects of plant growth and development. Although it plays a profound role for plants, the physical environment is much less important in animal development. This is not surprising, considering that plants cannot respond to their environment by moving about, as animals can. All aspects of plant growth are intimately connected with environmental cues. For example, in many plants, the initiation of reproduction is controlled by differences in day length and darkness that occur with the changing seasons (see Chapter 35). The environment, then, interacts with the genetic program to modify, and in some cases control, the growth and development of plants.

single plane (you can lay a compound leaf flat on a table), whereas simple leaves are never arranged in one plane on a stem.

Leaves are arranged on a stem in one of several possible ways (Figure 31–18). Plants with an **alternate** leaf arrangement have one leaf at each note; two leaves at each node is an **opposite** leaf arrangement, and three or more leaves per node is a **whorled** leaf arrangement.

Leaf blades have varied vein patterns (Figure 31–19), with monocots having **parallel** venation and dicots having **netted** venation. Netted venation can be **palmate,** in which several major veins radiate out from one point, or **pinnate,** in which the major veins branch off along the entire length of the main vein.

DIFFERENTIATION IN PLANTS IS UNDER BOTH GENETIC AND ENVIRONMENTAL CONTROLS

Differentiation of plant cells and tissues, which occurs throughout the life of the plant, is under a variety of controls. Of course, the ultimate control of plant differ-

One Way to Study Growth and Differentiation Is by Cultivating Cells and Tissues in Sterile, Synthetic Media

Much of our current understanding of plant cell, tissue, and organ differentiation has come from experimental studies involving plant cell and tissue cultures. Plant biologists attempted unsuccessfully to grow isolated plant cells in culture beginning in the early 1900s. Initially, plant cells could be kept alive in a chemically

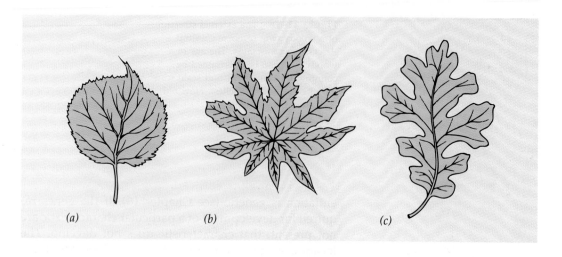

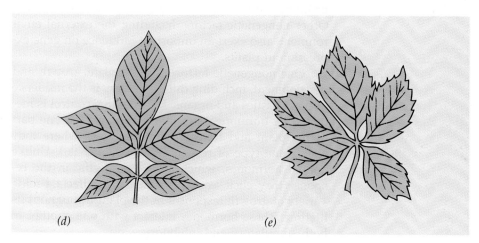

Figure 31–17 Leaves may be simple or compound. Simple leaves (*a, b, c*) have a variety of sizes and shapes. Compound leaves may be pinnately compound (*d*) or palmately compound (*e*). (*a*) Poplar. (*b*) Castor bean. (*c*) Oak. (*d*) Rose. (*e*) Virginia creeper.

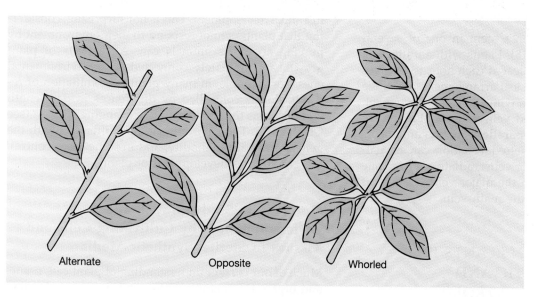

Alternate   Opposite   Whorled

Figure 31–18 Leaf arrangement on the stem may be alternate, opposite, or whorled, depending on the number of leaves at each node.

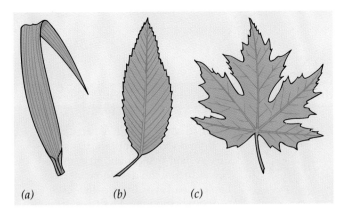

Figure 31–19   Venation patterns in leaves. (*a*) Kentucky bluegrass has parallel veins, which are characteristic of monocot leaves. Siberian elm (*b*) and silver maple (*c*) have netted veins. Siberian elm is pinnately netted and silver maple is palmately netted.

defined, sterile medium, but they did not divide. It was later discovered that the addition of certain natural materials like coconut milk induced cells to divide in culture. Of course, coconut milk has a complex chemical composition, so the division-inducing substance was not chemically identified for some time (see Chapter 36). By the late 1950s, plant cells from a variety of sources could be cultured successfully, dividing to produce a mass of undifferentiated cells, or **callus.**

In 1958, F. C. Steward, a plant physiologist at Cornell University, succeeded in generating an entire carrot plant from a single cell in the carrot root. This demonstrated conclusively that each plant cell contains a genetic blueprint for all features of an entire organism. His work also showed that it is possible to grow an entire plant from a single cell, provided that the proper genes are expressed at the proper times (see Chapter 16).

Since Steward's pioneering work, many plants have been successfully cultured using a variety of cell sources (Figure 31–20). Plants have been regenerated from different tissues, organ explants (an excised organ or part such as a root apical meristem or young embryo), and cells. Under certain conditions, the genes that control embryonic development are expressed in plant tissue culture, and all the embryonic stages can be observed in their normal progression.

Haploid embryos grown from pollen cells in culture may also go through the embryonic stages, demonstrating that the diploid condition is not a requirement for embryo development. The generation of plants from haploid pollen cells has proved to be particularly valuable because every gene, whether dominant or recessive, in a haploid plant is expressed. It is possible to double the chromosomes, thereby producing diploid, homozygous plants, which are needed for breeding important crops. The production of homozygous plants takes very little time (measured in months) using plant

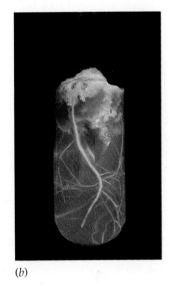
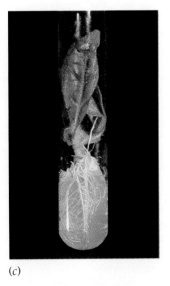

(*a*)   (*b*)   (*c*)

Figure 31–20   Propagating tobacco by tissue culture. A fragment of undifferentiated tissue from the center of a tobacco stem is placed in a culture medium. A complete plant can be formed from the tissue fragment because each cell of the fragment contains all the genetic information for the entire organism. Different kinds of hormones in culture media produce different growth responses. (*a*) Placed on a callus initiation medium, cells begin to proliferate, and undifferentiated tissue (callus) forms. (*b*) The callus produces roots on a root initiation medium. (*c*) By changing the relative levels of several plant hormones, shoots can be initiated. Plants grown by tissue culture techniques can be transferred to soil and grown normally.   (Carolina Biological Supply Company)

FOCUS ON

Some Experimental Methods in Embryogenesis

During the past 50 years, plant biologists have developed increasingly sophisticated methods to study **embryogenesis** (embryo development) in plants. Initially, biologists concentrated on descriptive aspects of embryogenesis, involving light microscope studies of different stages in the developmental process. Even today, important contributions are being made in descriptive embryology.

Autoradiography, in which photographic images show the location of radioactive substances in cells or tissues, is one technique that helps determine where specific chemical events are occurring in an embryo during its development. For example, to monitor RNA in developing cells, one can incubate these cells with radioactively labeled precursors of RNA. After incubation, the cells are stained, sectioned, and placed on slides. The slides are covered with a photographic emulsion and left in the dark. During this time, the radiation emitted from the radioactively labeled RNA exposes the photographic substance. After development of the photograph, the exact location of radioactive RNA in the cell at a particular stage in its development can be determined. Developing a series of such photographs over time can also show the movement of labeled molecules during embryogenesis.

The proteins produced during different stages of embryo development are analyzed in several ways. **Polyacrylamide gel electrophoresis** is an effective way to separate individual proteins from one another. In electrophoresis, protein mixtures are placed into slots cut into a slab of gel. Electricity is applied across the gel for a period of time. Different proteins have different charges, which are determined by their amino acid compositions. As a result of these charge

Gel electrophoresis. The separation of proteins or other large macromolecules can be visualized under ultraviolet radiation if a dye that binds to the organic molecules is added to the gel. The dye fluoresces, giving off pink light when exposed to ultraviolet radiation. (Visuals Unlimited/SIU)

differences, as well as differences in molecular weight, the proteins migrate at different rates across the gel. The proteins may be visualized by using a chemical that changes color in the presence of protein or by autoradiography (if the proteins have first been labeled with radioactive amino acids) (see figure).

Gel electrophoresis of proteins at different stages of development shows changes in the kinds and amounts of various proteins. It demonstrates that certain proteins appear (and disappear) at precise times in the developmental process, indicating when the genes that code for these proteins have been induced (or repressed). Most of these proteins are probably enzymes, but few have been specifically identified, nor have their exact roles in the developmental process been characterized.

Tissue culture techniques have had a great impact on experimental approaches to embryology. It is much

easier to study certain aspects of embryo development in a tissue culture system than in an intact ovule. For example, the development of haploid embryos from pollen cells provides genotypic data that intact diploid embryos within the seed never could. Manipulation of plant hormones in tissue culture has shed some light on hormonal roles in embryology, but many questions remain. It is unclear, for example, how the same plant hormone can have different effects on an embryo at different stages in its development.

Gene expression during development is of great interest to plant biologists. But how does one go about studying which genes affect different stages in embryo development? Corn, also called maize, is one of the most useful organisms to use, in part because much is already known about its biology. Also, a number of maize mutants have abnormalities in their embryonic development. Because most of these mutants have abnormalities in their endosperm development as well, it is relatively easy to identify them by looking for unusual characteristics in the endosperm.

Studying mutants provides useful evidence about how normal development can be interrupted. For example, it is now known that separate genes direct at least some of the developmental processes of root and shoot meristems in embryos. This was determined by studying a mutant with abnormal development in the shoot meristem but normal root meristem development.

Embryo development in plants continues to provide scientists with a fruitful area for future study. With the development of sophisticated molecular techniques, plant biologists have the tools to gain more information than was even dreamed possible a short time ago.

tissue culture methods; to accomplish this using traditional plant breeding techniques requires eight or nine generations (measured in years).

Cell and tissue culture techniques, then, are used to help answer many fundamental questions involving growth and development in plants. The practical potential of these techniques should also be obvious. Using tissue culture, it is possible to regenerate large numbers of genetically identical plants from cells of a single, genetically superior plant. It is possible to alter the genetic composition of a cell while it is in cell culture and then have these changes expressed in the whole plant during regeneration (see Chapter 14). This provides a valuable tool to scientists who practice genetic engineering in an effort to engineer desirable new traits in crop species. Research involving cell and tissue cultures is one of the exciting and fruitful areas of biological research today. (See Focus on Some Experimental Methods in Embryogenesis for a review of other methods used by plant biologists to unravel the secrets of plant development.)

SUMMARY

I. A dicot embryo develops in the seed from proembryo to globular embryo to the heart stage to the torpedo stage.
II. Seed germination is affected by a number of factors.
 A. External environmental factors that may affect seed germination include requirements for oxygen, water, temperature, and light.
 B. Internal factors affecting whether a seed germinates include the maturity of the embryo and the presence or absence of chemical inhibitors.
III. Growth in plants is localized in specific regions called meristems and involves cell division, cell elongation, and cell differentiation.
IV. Plants have two kinds of growth: primary growth, which is an increase in stem or root length; and secondary growth, which is an increase in stem or root girth.
V. Plant cells are organized into tissues.
 A. Parenchyma tissue is composed of relatively unspecialized, living cells that have thin primary walls; the roles of parenchyma include photosynthesis, storage, and secretion.
 B. Collenchyma tissue, which helps support the plant, is composed of living cells with unevenly thickened primary cell walls.
 C. Sclerenchyma tissue, usually composed of dead cells that possess both primary and secondary cell walls, helps support the plant.
 D. Xylem is a complex tissue that functions to conduct water and dissolved minerals. Tracheids and vessel elements are the two kinds of conducting cells in xylem.
 E. Phloem is a complex tissue that functions to conduct food. The food-conducting cells in phloem are sieve tube members.
 F. The epidermis covers the herbaceous plant body and functions primarily for protection. The periderm is the outer covering over the body of woody plants (that is, plants with secondary growth) and serves a protective function.
VI. The plant body is organized into a root system and a shoot system.
 A. There are two main root systems, the taproot system and the fibrous root system. Storage roots may be either modified taproots or modified fibrous roots.
 B. The shoot system is composed of stems and leaves.
  1. Stems bear leaves, terminal buds, and lateral buds.
  2. Leaves may be simple or compound; leaf arrangement on a stem may be alternate, opposite, or whorled; and leaf venation may be parallel or netted (either pinnately netted or palmately netted).
 C. Although separate organs (roots, stems, leaves, flowers, and fruits) exist in a plant, many tissues (for example, xylem and phloem) are integrated throughout the plant body, providing continuity from organ to organ.
VII. Plant development is controlled not only by genetic factors but also by external environmental factors.
 A. Other plant tissues and organs exert a profound influence on plant development, particularly by secreting hormones.
 B. Many factors in the physical environment determine gene expression and thereby affect plant development.

POST-TEST

1. The embryonic stage in dicot development after the heart stage is the _____ stage.
2. The _____ is a multicellular structure that holds a plant embryo in place and aids in nutrient uptake from the endosperm.
3. Stems and roots have _____ growth because they grow throughout the life of the plant.
4. Primary growth, the increase in the length of the plant, is found in localized areas of the plant, the _____ meristems.

5. The _____ _____ is a protective covering over the root tip.
6. Stem apical meristems differ from root apical meristems in bearing embryonic structures, _____ primordia, and _____ primordia.
7. The two lateral meristems responsible for secondary growth are the _____ _____ and the cork cambium.
8. Plants that complete their life cycle in one year are called _____, those that complete it in two years are _____, and those that live year after year are _____.
9. Storage, secretion, and photosynthesis are the functions of _____.
10. The two simple tissues that are specialized for support are _____ and sclerenchyma.
11. Conduction of water and minerals in the xylem occurs in _____ and vessel elements.

12. Conduction of food in the sieve tube members of the phloem is aided by _____ cells.
13. The outer covering of plants with primary growth is _____, whereas plants with secondary growth are covered by _____.
14. Outgrowths of the epidermis are called _____.
15. Plants such as grasses have a _____ root system.
16. Dormant terminal buds are covered by _____ _____.
17. Herbaceous stems have _____ for gas exchange, whereas woody stems have _____.
18. A single leaf composed of several leaflets is said to be _____.
19. Leaf arrangement on the stem may be alternate, _____, or whorled.
20. Monocots have _____ leaf venation and dicots have _____ leaf venation.

REVIEW QUESTIONS

1. Put the following stages of embryonic development for dicots in order and briefly describe each: torpedo stage, globular stage, proembryo, heart stage.
2. What factors influence the germination of seeds? How are these factors advantageous for plants?
3. When seeds germinate, the young root (radicle) *always* emerges before the young shoot. Why?

4. How is growth in plants different from growth in animals?
5. How is plant development different from animal development?
6. Why do you think plant development is so sensitive to nongenetic factors such as environmental influences?
7. How are developmental mutants useful in studying various aspects of plant development?

RECOMMENDED READINGS

Mauseth, J. D. *Botany: An Introduction to Plant Biology.* Saunders College Publishing, Philadelphia, 1991. A comprehensive introduction to general botany.

Raghaven, V. *Embryogenesis in Angiosperms.* Cambridge University Press, Cambridge, 1986. An excellent review of all aspects of embryogenesis in flowering plants. Especially good in reviewing the experimental methods employed.

Raven, P. H., R. F. Evert, and S. E. Eichhorn. *Biology of Plants,* 5th ed. Worth Publishers, New York, 1992. A general botany text with an evolutionary emphasis.

Leaf Structure and Function

Suppose for a moment that you are taking a course in engineering and have been asked to design an efficient solar collector capable of converting the radiant energy it collects into chemical energy. Where would you start with such an assignment? It might be wise to begin by checking books and periodicals in the library to see how solar collectors/energy converters have been designed in the past. In this instance, it would also be wise to ask a biologist, or even a biology student like yourself, whether anything comparable exists in nature. The answer, of course, is yes— plants have organs that are effective solar collectors and energy converters. They are called *leaves.*

The structure of a foliage leaf is adapted for its primary function of photosynthesis, in which plants use light as an energy source for manufacturing organic compounds from carbon dioxide and water. Most leaves have a broad, flattened blade that is very effective in collecting radiant energy and absorbing carbon dioxide; water is obtained from the soil and conducted to the leaf. The leaf's internal structure is composed of several different tissues, all of which are organized to optimize photosynthesis.

In addition to being influenced by the necessity to carry out photosynthesis, the structure of foliage leaves is also affected by the requirement to prevent excessive water loss. Leaves possess several features that help reduce or control water loss, the most important of which is a thin, transparent layer of wax that covers the leaf structure.

However, some features that optimize photosynthesis actually promote water loss. For example, plants need pores to exchange gases for photosynthesis, but these tiny openings allow water to escape into the atmosphere as water vapor. Thus leaf structure represents a trade-off between photosynthesis and water conservation.

Leaves of deciduous trees show brilliant fall colors at Moccasin Lake, Michigan. (John Gerlach/Dembinsky Photo Associates)

After you have studied this chapter you should be able to

1. Describe the major tissues of the leaf.
2. Compare leaf anatomy in dicots and monocots.
3. Relate leaf structure to its function of photosynthesis.
4. Describe the physiological changes that accompany stoma-

tal opening and closing.
5. Discuss transpiration, including its benefits and costs.
6. Discuss leaf abscission, including why it occurs and what physiological and anatomical changes precede it.
7. List several modified leaves and give the function of each.

EPIDERMIS, MESOPHYLL, XYLEM, AND PHLOEM ARE THE MAJOR TISSUES OF THE LEAF

The flattened leaf blade has top and bottom sides, so the leaf has two epidermal layers, an **upper epidermis** and a **lower epidermis** (Figure 32–1). The cells making up this outer covering of the leaf are living parenchyma cells (see Chapter 31). Lacking chloroplasts, they are relatively transparent. One interesting feature of leaf epidermal cells is that the cell wall on the outside of the leaf is somewhat thicker than the cell wall facing inward. This may afford the plant additional protection from injury and water loss.

Leaves have a large surface area exposed to the atmosphere, and water loss by evaporation from the leaf's surface is unavoidable. Although water loss has

some benefits for plants (see below), excessive water loss is harmful. Epidermal cells secrete a noncellular waxy layer called a **cuticle** that helps to reduce water loss. The cuticle varies in thickness in different plants, although on an individual leaf the upper epidermis typically possesses a thicker cuticle than the lower epidermis.

The epidermis of most leaves is covered with various trichomes (hairs) (Figure 32–2). Some leaves have so many trichomes that they feel quite fuzzy. Leaf trichomes perform a variety of functions, such as providing a defense against herbivores and reflecting light, which helps to cool the leaf, thereby decreasing the amount of water lost by evaporation from the leaf's surface.

The leaf epidermis is covered with tiny pores, or **stomata** (singular, *stoma*), flanked by specialized cells in

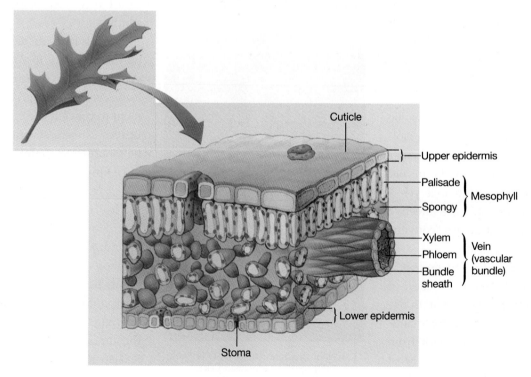

Figure 32–1 The internal arrangement of tissues in a typical leaf blade. The photosynthetic tissue, called mesophyll, is often arranged into palisade and spongy layers. Veins branch throughout the mesophyll. The blade is covered by an upper and lower epidermis.

500 µm

Figure 32–2 Scanning electron micrograph of a nettle leaf. The leaf epidermis is often covered with trichomes that may limit the transpiration of water, discourage herbivores, sting, or perform other functions. The trichomes on nettle leaves and stems readily break off inside the skin of any animal that brushes against the leaf or attempts to eat it. Irritating substances injected into the skin produce a stinging sensation. (Biophoto Associates)

the epidermis called **guard cells** (see Figure 31–12b). Guard cells are usually the only cells in the epidermis that have chloroplasts. Stomata are particularly numerous on the lower epidermis and in many cases are located *only* on the lower surface. This adaptation reduces water loss because these stomata are shielded from direct sunlight. Sunlight warms the leaf surface, causing warm air to rise from the leaf. This convective air current carries a great deal of moisture with it when stomata are located on the upper epidermis. Because air is calmer on the underside of a leaf, less moisture is lost from stomata located in the lower epidermis.

The photosynthetic tissue of the leaf, called the **mesophyll,** is sandwiched between the upper and lower epidermis. The word *mesophyll* comes from Greek, meaning "the middle of the leaf." Mesophyll is composed of parenchyma cells that contain chloroplasts. These cells are very loosely arranged with many air spaces between them. Quite often, mesophyll is divided into two specific regions. Toward the upper epidermis the cells are stacked into a **palisade** layer, whereas in the lower portion the cells are more loosely and irregularly arranged in a **spongy** layer.

The veins of a leaf run throughout the mesophyll. Branching is extensive, so no mesophyll cell is very far from a vein. Each vein contains two types of vascular tissue (see Chapter 31). **Xylem,** which conducts water and dissolved minerals to the leaf, is located on the upper half of the vein (toward the upper epidermis), whereas **phloem,** which conducts dissolved food, is on the lower side of the vein.

Veins are usually surrounded by a **bundle sheath,** which is one or more layers of parenchyma or sclerenchyma cells (see Figure 8–17). Frequently the bundle sheath has support columns called **bundle sheath extensions** that extend through the mesophyll to both the upper and lower epidermis. Bundle sheath extensions may be composed of parenchyma, collenchyma, or sclerenchyma cells.

Leaf Structure Differs in Dicots and Monocots

Dicot leaves are usually composed of a broad, flattened blade and petiole and have netted venation (see Chapter 31). In contrast, monocots often have long, narrow leaves that lack petioles and wrap around the stem in a sheath. Parallel venation is characteristic of monocot leaves.

The internal anatomy of dicot and monocot leaves is different as well (Figure 32–3). Dicot leaves typically have both palisade and spongy layers in the mesophyll,

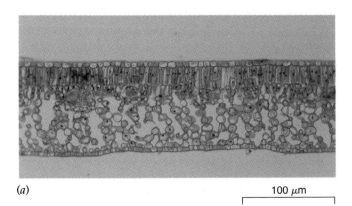

(a)

100 µm

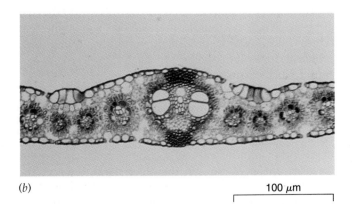

(b)

100 µm

Figure 32–3 Leaf cross sections. (*a*) Privet, a dicot, has a mesophyll with distinct palisade and spongy sections. (*b*) Corn (*Zea mays*), a monocot. Note the absence of distinct regions of

palisade and spongy mesophyll. Also evident is the evenly spaced parallel venation characteristic of monocots. (*a,* Dennis Drenner; *b,* Carolina Biological Supply Company)

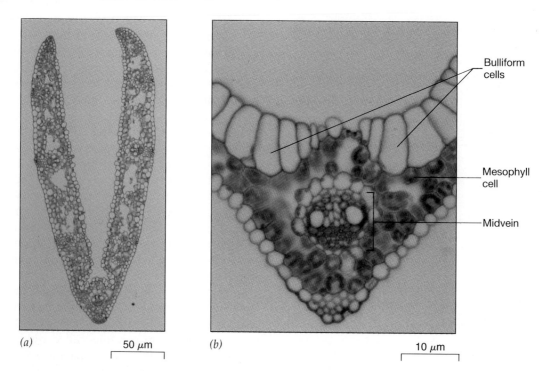

(a)   50 μm   (b)   10 μm

Bulliform cells

Mesophyll cell

Midvein

Figure 32–4 Cross section of bluegrass, a monocot. (*a*) Overall view of a folded leaf. The collapsed bulliform cells in the upper epidermis (on either side of the midvein) are indistinguishable from other cells of the epidermis. (*b*) Higher magnification of the midvein region showing the bulliform cells, which are partially enlarged. When the bulliform cells are fully turgid, the leaf blade is expanded rather than folded up. (Dennis Drenner)

whereas mesophyll in many monocot leaves is not differentiated into palisade and spongy tissues. Because dicots have netted venation, a cross section through a dicot blade shows veins in cross section as well as lengthwise views. In cross section, the parallel venation pattern of monocot leaves produces evenly spaced veins, all of uniform size except the midvein.

The upper epidermis of some monocot leaves has large, thin-walled cells called **bulliform cells** that are located on either side of the midvein (Figure 32–4). These cells may be involved in the folding inward of the leaf during drought. When water is plentiful, the bulliform cells are turgid (swollen with water) and the leaf is open. When the bulliform cells lose water, the leaf edges fold inward, producing a tightly rolled leaf, which reduces its exposure to heat from the sun and thus reduces transpiration.

Monocot and dicot leaves also differ in their guard cells (Figure 32–5). Dicots have guard cells that are shaped like tiny kidney beans, and the epidermal cells adjacent to these guard cells are not noticeably different from other epidermal cells. Some monocot leaves (grasses, for example), on the other hand, have guard cells shaped like dumbbells. Each monocot guard cell is associated with a special epidermal cell called a **subsidiary cell** that is distinctive from all other epidermal cells.

STRUCTURE IS RELATED TO FUNCTION IN LEAVES

The primary function of leaves is to collect radiant energy and convert it to a form that can be used by the plant. This process, photosynthesis, has been examined in detail in Chapter 8. In photosynthesis, plants are able to take relatively simple inorganic molecules—carbon dioxide and water—and convert them into carbohydrate (sugar), with oxygen given off as a waste product. During this process, radiant energy is converted to chemical energy, the energy bonding the atoms in the sugar molecules together. As you may recall, cells have two metabolic purposes for the sugar formed during photosynthesis: (1) It is broken down during cellular respiration to release the chemical energy stored in its bonds. (2) Sugar molecules provide the cell with basic building materials; the cell modifies sugar, converting it into a number of other important compounds such as starch and cellulose.

The tissues of a leaf permit efficient photosynthesis. The epidermis of a leaf, for example, is relatively transparent and allows light to penetrate to the interior of the leaf where the photosynthetic tissue, called the mesophyll, is located. Carbon dioxide diffuses from the atmosphere through the stomata into the leaf's interior, whereas the oxygen produced during photosynthesis

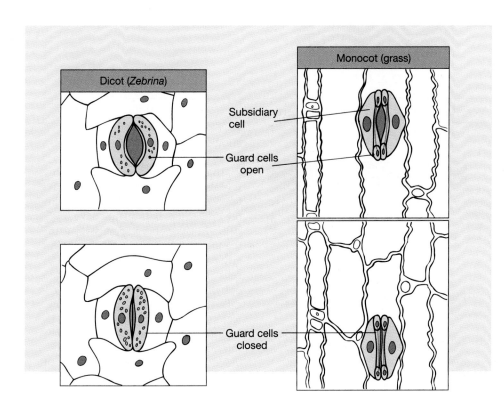

Dicot (*Zebrina*)

Monocot (grass)

Subsidiary cell

Guard cells open

Guard cells closed

Figure 32–5 Variation in guard cells. Dicot guard cells are bean-shaped, whereas many monocot guard cells are narrow in the center and thicker at each end. Each monocot guard cell is associated with a special cell in the epidermis called a subsidiary cell.

diffuses rapidly out of the mesophyll cells and passes through the stomata into the atmosphere. Water is obtained from the soil and transported in the xylem to the leaf, where it moves from the xylem into the intercellular (between cells) spaces of the mesophyll. The loose arrangement of the mesophyll tissue, with its moist cell surfaces and large intercellular spaces between cells, allows for rapid diffusion of both carbon dioxide and water into the mesophyll cells. (Both carbon dioxide and oxygen are dissolved in the water film at the mesophyll cell surface before passing into or out of the cell.)

Veins not only supply water to the photosynthetic tissue of the leaf but also transport the carbohydrate produced during photosynthesis to other parts of the plant. Bundle sheaths and bundle sheath extensions of veins provide additional support to prevent the leaf, which is structurally weak owing to the loose arrangement of cells and the large amount of intercellular space in the mesophyll, from collapsing under its own mass.

The habitat (that part of the environment occupied by an organism) to which a plant is adapted affects characteristics of its leaves. Leaves of both desert plants and swamp plants perform photosynthesis and have the same basic anatomy described in this chapter. However, their leaves are modified to enable them to survive very different environmental conditions (see Figure 32–6 and Focus on Comparative Plant Anatomy).

Figure 32–6 An unusual view of water lily leaves shows their petioles as well as their blades, which float on the water's surface. Water lilies have a number of special adaptations that enable them to thrive in a watery environment. (Frans Lanting/Minden Pictures)

THE POTASSIUM ION MECHANISM CONTROLS STOMATAL OPENING AND CLOSING

Stomata are open during the day when photosynthesis is occurring and closed at night when photosynthesis is shut down. (See Focus on Photosynthesis in Desert Plants in Chapter 8 for an interesting exception.) The opening and closing of stomata are controlled by

FOCUS ON

Comparative Plant Anatomy

Certain modifications in leaf anatomy are characteristic of plants native to certain habitats, particularly habitats with environmental extremes. The figure shows cross sections of leaves from two plant species that grow in entirely different environments. One is a **hydrophyte,** a plant adapted to a very wet habitat, and one is a **xerophyte,** a plant adapted to extremely dry conditions. Let's examine and compare the details of each plant's leaf anatomy to identify the plants.

The epidermis of each plant is quite unusual. You will recall that both the upper and lower epidermis of typical plants are composed of a single layer of cells, with most stomata located on the lower epidermis. Although it is difficult to see at this magnification, plant A has an upper epidermis with many stomata, whereas its lower epidermis lacks stomata entirely! Its cuticle is negligible. Plant B is even stranger, with a multiple-layered upper epidermis, covered by a thick cuticle. Stomata

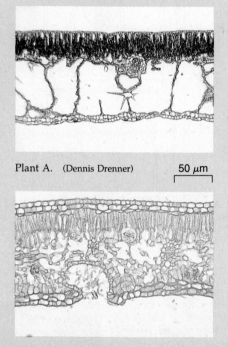

Plant A.   (Dennis Drenner)   50 μm

Plant B.   (Dennis Drenner)   50 μm

are located in cavities of the lower epidermis called **stomatal crypts.** A

number of trichomes are also apparent in the stomatal crypt.

The mesophyll of the plants also reveals differences, although the differences are less pronounced than in the epidermis. Both plants have a palisade layer and a spongy layer in the mesophyll, but plant A has larger air spaces between its mesophyll cells. The large, pink cells in the mesophyll of plant A are sclerenchyma cells that are required to prevent the leaf's collapse because so much of its interior is air space. Support for the interior of the leaf of plant B is provided by bundle-sheath extensions of the veins (not evident in this micrograph). The vascular tissue provides a clue to the identity of the plants as well. Plant A has considerably less vascular tissue than plant B.

Based on your knowledge of leaf anatomy, can you identify which plant is xerophytic and which is hydrophytic? Turn to page 711 to see if you're a good comparative anatomist!

changes in the shape of the guard cells. When water moves into a pair of guard cells from surrounding epidermal cells, the guard cells become turgid and push apart or bend outward at the center, forming a pore. When water leaves the guard cells, they become flaccid and collapse against one another, closing the pore (Figure 32–7).

Opening and closing of stomata are triggered by light and darkness, respectively, although other environmental factors, such as carbon dioxide concentration, are also involved. A low concentration of CO_2 in the leaf induces stomata to open even in the dark. Another important factor that affects stomatal opening and closing is severe water stress. During a prolonged drought, stomata remain closed even during the day; this mechanism is under hormonal control (see Chapter 36).

The opening and closing of stomata also appear to

be under the control of an internal biological clock that approximates the 24-hour cycle. Plants placed in constant darkness continue to open and close their stomata at more or less the same times even in the absence of environmental cues (alternating light and dark periods). This internal biological clock based on a 24-hour cycle is known as a **circadian rhythm.** Other examples of circadian rhythms are cited in Chapter 36.

Data from numerous experiments and observations suggest that stomata open and close by the **potassium ion (K^+) mechanism** (Figure 32–8). The appearance of light triggers an influx of potassium ions into the guard cells from surrounding cells of the epidermis. This movement of K^+ occurs by active transport through specific ion channels in a guard cell's plasma membrane and requires ATP. The ATP supplies energy to pump protons (see Making the Connection box in Chapter 36) out of the guard cells, producing an electrochemical

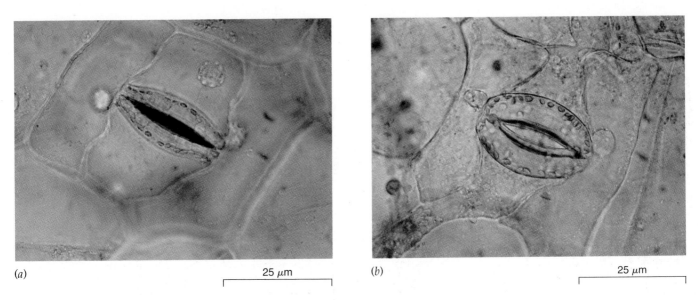

(a)

25 µm

(b)

25 µm

Figure 32–7 Stomatal opening in *Zebrina*. (a) Closed. (b) Open. (Dwight R. Kuhn)

proton gradient that can drive the uptake of potassium through specific K^+ channels. The K^+ accumulates in the vacuoles of the guard cells. Some negatively charged chloride and malate ions also pass into the vacuoles of the guard cells.

The increase of K^+ ions in the guard cells lowers the relative concentration of water in those cells (see Chapter 5). Therefore, water moves into the guard cells from surrounding epidermal cells by osmosis. This in turn changes the shape of the guard cells, and a pore opens.

In the late afternoon or early evening, stomata close by a reversal of this process. The K^+ ions are pumped out of the guard cells into the surrounding epidermal cells, water then leaves the guard cells by osmosis, the cells collapse, and the pore closes. Stomatal closure may not be an *exact* reversal of stomatal opening. Evidence exists that Ca^{2+} triggers stomatal closure but inhibits stomatal opening. The actual mechanism whereby Ca^{2+} exerts this effect is under investigation.

Stomata have varying sensitivities to light of different colors (that is, of different wavelengths). The action spectrum (see Chapter 8) for stomatal opening shows greatest activity in the blue and, to a lesser extent, in the red regions. Also, dim blue light induces stomatal opening, whereas dim red light does not. Any physiological response to light must involve a **photoreceptor,** a pigment that absorbs the light prior to induction of the biological response. These and other data suggest that there are two photoreceptors for stomatal opening and closing, chlorophyll and flavoprotein (a yellow pigment).

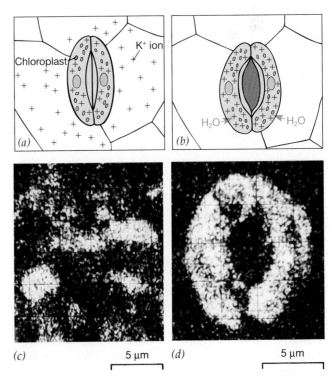

(a)

Chloroplast

K^+ ion

(b)

H_2O → ← H_2O

(c)

5 µm

(d)

5 µm

Figure 32–8 Movement of K^+ ions into and out of the guard cells affects stomatal opening and closing. (a) When the stoma is closed, K^+ ions are randomly distributed throughout the epidermis. (b) With the influx of K^+ ions into the guard cells from surrounding epidermal cells, water moves into the guard cells by osmosis. This changes the shape of the guard cells, and the pore opens. (c) Autoradiograph of a strip of epidermis with a closed stoma. The white spots indicate K^+ ions. Note how they are more or less randomly distributed. (d) Autoradiograph of the same strip of epidermis with the stoma open. Note how the K^+ ions are concentrated within the guard cells. (c, d, Courtesy of Dr. Klaus Raschke, from Humble and Raschke, *Plant Physiology* 48:447–453, 1971, Michigan State University Atomic Energy Plant Research Laboratory)

(a)

(b)

Figure 32–9 Temporary wilting in pumpkin (*Cucurbita pepo*) leaves (*a*) in the late afternoon of a hot day and (*b*) the following morning. Note that wilting helps reduce the surface area from which transpiration occurs. During the night, the plants recovered by absorbing water from the soil while transpiration was negligible. (David Cavagnaro)

LEAVES LOSE WATER BY TRANSPIRATION AND GUTTATION

Despite leaf adaptations such as the cuticle, approximately 99% of the water a plant absorbs from the soil is lost by evaporation from the stems and especially the leaves. Loss of water vapor from land plants is called **transpiration.** Transpiration plays an important role in the upward movement of water in xylem (see Chapter 33) and may provide other benefits to leaves (see below).

The cuticle is effective in reducing excessive water loss: It is estimated that only 1% to 3% of the water lost from a plant passes directly through the cuticle. Most of the water that a plant loses exits through the stomata. The numerous pores that are so effective in gas exchange for photosynthesis also provide openings through which water escapes.

A number of environmental factors influence the rate of transpiration. For example, at higher temperatures more water transpires from plant surfaces. Light increases the transpiration rate, in part because it triggers stomatal opening and in part because it increases leaf temperature, thereby causing more rapid evaporation. Wind also increases transpiration because it carries away the moist air next to the leaf surface and replaces it with dry air. A high relative humidity *decreases* transpiration because the air is already saturated, or nearly so, with water vapor.

Transpiration may seem like a wasteful process, but some benefits may be associated with the large amount of water that plants lose by transpiration. First, like sweating in animals, transpiration has a cooling effect on the plant. When water passes from the liquid to the vapor state, it absorbs a great deal of heat. As water

molecules leave the plant, this heat is carried with them. Thus, the cooling effect of transpiration may prevent leaves from overheating, particularly those in direct sunlight. As a result of transpiration, the internal temperature of leaves on a hot summer day is lower than that of the surrounding air.

A second possible benefit of transpiration is that it provides the plant with essential minerals. Remember that the water a plant transpires is initially absorbed from the soil, where it is not present as pure water but rather as a very dilute solution of dissolved mineral salts. Many of these minerals are required in certain quantities for the plant's life processes. Transpiration may enable plants to take in enough essential minerals; if they did not transpire, plants might not be able to satisfy their mineral requirements.

Despite its perceived benefits, however, transpiration can be harmful to a plant under certain circumstances. On hot summer days, plants may lose more water by transpiration than can be replaced from the soil. As a result, their cells experience a loss of turgor, and the plants wilt (Figure 32–9). If a plant is able to recover overnight, as a result of negligible transpiration (caused by closed stomata) while water is still being absorbed from the soil, the plant is said to have experienced temporary wilting. Most plants recover from temporary wilting with no ill effects. In cases of prolonged drought, the soil may not contain sufficient moisture to permit overnight recovery from wilting. Such a plant is said to be permanently wilted and dies unless water is supplied immediately.

Transpiration appears to be a "mixed blessing" for plants in that it has possible benefits and potential hazards. At any rate, transpiration is an unavoidable trade-off in plants because they must have stomata to allow gas exchange for photosynthesis.

Figure 32–10 Guttation in lady's mantle (*Alchemilla vulgaris*). (Dennis Drenner)

Some Plants Exude Water as a Liquid

Many leaves have special openings at their margins and tips through which liquid water emerges. The loss of water as a liquid, which is known as **guttation,** occurs when transpiration is negligible and available soil moisture is high. Guttation frequently occurs at night when stomata are closed, thereby preventing transpiration, but water continues to move into the roots by osmosis (see discussion of root pressure in Chapter 33). People sometimes wrongly attribute the early morning droplets of water produced on leaves by guttation to dew, which is water condensation from the air (Figure 32–10).

LEAF ABSCISSION ALLOWS PLANTS IN TEMPERATE CLIMATES TO SURVIVE WINTER

In temperate climates (areas that have warm summers and cold winters), the leaves turn color and **abscise,** or fall off, when winter approaches. Most woody flowering plants shed their leaves in order to survive the low temperatures of winter. As you know, leaves lose a tremendous amount of water by transpiration. During the winter, water needs become critical for plants because as the ground chills, the absorption of water by roots is inhibited, and when the ground freezes, *no* absorption can occur. Thus, if a plant kept functional broad leaves during the winter, it would continue to lose water by transpiration but would be unable to replace that water by absorption from the soil. Plants have little need of leaves in winter. In the lower temperatures of winter, a plant's metabolism, including its photosynthetic machinery, slows down a great deal.

Leaf abscission is a complex process that involves many physiological changes in a plant, all of which are orchestrated by changing levels of plant hormones (see Chapter 36). As autumn approaches, the plant reabsorbs many of the essential minerals located in the leaves by moving them to the stems or roots; nitrogen, phosphorus, and possibly potassium move into these tissues from the leaves. The level of sugar in the leaves rises (possibly as a result of starch being converted to sugar for transport out of the leaf). Chlorophyll is broken down so that carotenes and xanthophylls, some of the accessory pigments in the chloroplast, become evident. These orange and yellow accessory pigments were always present in the leaf but were masked by the green chlorophyll. As autumn approaches, water-soluble pigments may also be synthesized and stored in the vacuole. The various combinations of these pigments are responsible for the brilliant colors found in autumn landscapes in temperate climates.

The area where the petiole detaches from the stem during leaf abscission is structurally different from surrounding tissues (Figure 32–11). This area, called the **abscission zone,** is composed primarily of thin-walled parenchyma cells and is anatomically weak because it

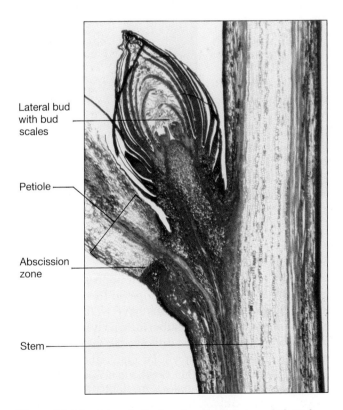

Lateral bud with bud scales

Petiole

Abscission zone

Stem

Figure 32–11 A longitudinal section through a maple branch, showing the base of the petiole. Note the abscission zone where the leaf will abscise from the stem. A lateral bud with its protective bud scales is evident above the petiole. (Dennis Drenner)

(a)

(b)

(c)

(d)

(e)

Figure 32–12 Leaf modifications. (*a*) The leaves of cacti are modified as spines for protection. (*b*) Tendrils, which attach to objects and aid the plant in climbing, may be modified leaves or stems. These pea tendrils are modified leaves. (*c*) Overlapping bud scales protect buds. Shown here is a terminal bud. (*d*) The leaves of bulbs such as the onion are fleshy for storage. (*e*) Some plants, such as *Echeveria* sp., have succulent leaves that are modified for water storage as well as photosynthesis. (*a*, Frank Staats; *b*, *c*, *d*, Dennis Drenner; *e*, Visuals Unlimited/Peter F. Zika)

contains few fibers. When autumn approaches, a protective layer of cork cells develops on the stem side of the abscission zone. These cells have walls permeated by a waxy material called **suberin,** which is impermeable to water. Enzymes then dissolve the middle lamella, which is the layer of intercellular material that cements adjacent cell walls together, in the abscission zone. By this time, only a few xylem cells hold the leaf to the stem. A sudden breeze is enough to make the final break, and the leaf detaches. The protective layer of cork remains on the stem, sealing off the area and forming a leaf scar (see Chapter 31).

LEAVES WITH FUNCTIONS OTHER THAN PHOTOSYNTHESIS EXHIBIT MODIFICATIONS IN STRUCTURE

Although photosynthesis is the primary function of foliage leaves, some leaves have special modifications for functions other than photosynthesis (Figure 32–12). Some plants, for example, have leaves specialized for protection. **Spines,** which are hard and pointed, are found on plants like cacti. In the cactus, the main organ of photosynthesis is the stem rather than the leaf; cactus

(a)

(b)

Figure 32–13 The pitcher plant has leaves modified to form a pitcher that collects water, drowning its prey. (a) Growth habit of a pitcher plant, *Sarracenia purpurea*. (b) A cut-away view of a pitcher reveals accumulated insect bodies and debris. (a, Skip Moody/Dembinsky Photo Associates; b, Carolina Biological Supply Company)

spines are modified leaves that discourage animals from eating the succulent stem tissue.

Many vines have **tendrils,** which are specialized leaves (some tendrils are modified stems) that attach and anchor onto other structures. Because vines have climbing stems that cannot support their own weight, they often possess tendrils that keep the vines attached to the structures on which they are growing.

The winter buds of a dormant woody plant are covered by protective **bud scales,** which are modified leaves (see Chapter 31). Bud scales protect the delicate meristematic tissue of the shoot from injury and desiccation during the cold winter months.

Leaves may also be modified for storage of water or food. For example, a **bulb** is a short stem to which large, fleshy leaves are attached. Onions and tulips form bulbs, which grow underground. Many desert plants have fleshy, succulent leaves for water storage. These leaves are usually green and function for photosynthesis as well.

Some of the most remarkable examples of modified leaves are those of insectivorous plants. These plants use their leaves to trap animal prey, usually insects. Most insectivorous plants grow in poor soil that is deficient in certain essential minerals. These plants obtain some mineral nutrients by digesting insects and other small animals.

Some insectivorous plants have passive traps. For example, the leaves of the pitcher plant are shaped to form a reservoir that collects rainwater (Figure 32–13). An insect that is attracted to the pitcher by its scent or nectar may fall in. It is prevented from crawling out by a row of stiff spines that points downward around the lip of the pitcher. The insect eventually drowns, and enzymes produced by the plant digest part of the insect's body, releasing nutrients that can be absorbed by the plant. In the tropics, pitcher plants may be large enough to hold 1 liter or more of water.

The Venus flytrap is an insectivorous plant with active traps (see Figure 1–5). Its leaves resemble tiny bear traps, and each side of the leaf has three small trichomes located on it. If an insect alights and brushes against two of the hairs, the trap springs shut in less than 0.1 second (see Chapter 36). (The trap is so specialized that it does not shut when raindrops or wind moves the trichomes, however.) After the insect has died and been digested, the trap reopens, and the indigestible remains fall off.

Plants living in unusual environments often have specialized adaptations. The flower pot plant is a small tropical plant that is an **epiphyte;** rather than living on the ground, it lives high in the forest canopy attached to a tree, but it does not parasitize the tree. This plant has leaves that are modified to form a "flower pot"

(a)

(b)

Figure 32–14 The flower pot plant, *Dischidia rafflesiana*. (a) The leaves of the flower pot plant are modified to collect rainwater. (b) A cut-away view of the "pot" reveals a special root produced by the plant to absorb the collected rainwater. (a, b, David A. Steingraeber)

(Figure 32–14). Rainwater and various minerals that are leached out of the tree leaves above collect in the pot. A special root grows into the flower pot leaf and absorbs water and dissolved minerals high above the ground.

SUMMARY

I. Foliage leaf structure is adapted for its primary function, photosynthesis.
   A. The transparent epidermis allows light to penetrate into the mesophyll (the photosynthetic tissue). Stomata in the epidermis permit gas exchange.
   B. The mesophyll has intercellular spaces that permit rapid diffusion of carbon dioxide and water into, and oxygen out of, mesophyll cells.
   C. Leaf veins have xylem to conduct water and essential minerals to the leaf, and phloem to conduct carbohydrate produced by photosynthesis to the rest of the plant.

II. Monocot and dicot leaves can be distinguished on the basis of their external structure and their internal anatomy.

III. Stomata open during the day and close at night.
   A. The K^+ ion mechanism explains the opening and closing of stomata.
      1. Light triggers an influx of K^+ ions into the guard cells, which in turn causes water to move into the guard cells by osmosis. The resulting turgor pressure causes the shape of the guard cells to change, opening a pore.
      2. When stomata close, K^+ ions leave the guard cells,

followed by the diffusion of water out of the guard cells. This closes the pore.
   B. A number of factors affect stomatal opening and closing, including light or darkness, CO_2 concentration, and a circadian rhythm within the plant.

IV. Transpiration is the loss of water vapor from plants.
   A. It occurs primarily through the stomata.
   B. The rate of transpiration is affected by environmental factors such as temperature, wind, and relative humidity.
   C. Transpiration may be both beneficial and harmful to the plant.

V. Guttation is the loss of water as a liquid from leaves.

VI. Leaf abscission (the falling off of leaves) is a complex process involving physiological and anatomical changes.

VII. Leaves may be modified for functions other than photosynthesis.
   A. Spines are leaves modified for protection.
   B. Tendrils attach weak stems to supports.
   C. Bud scales are leaves modified to protect the delicate meristematic tissue of buds.
   D. Bulbs are underground stems with leaves specialized for storage.

POST-TEST

1. The _____ is the photosynthetic tissue in the middle of the leaf.
2. Gas exchange occurs through tiny pores formed by _____ _____.
3. Most stomata are usually located on the _____ epidermis of the leaf.
4. The _____ is a thin, noncellular layer of wax secreted by the epidermis of leaves.
5. The layer of cells that encircles a vein, or vascular bundle, is called a _____ _____.
6. The _____ of a leaf vein transports water and dissolved minerals.
7. Sugars produced in the leaf during photosynthesis are transported to the rest of the plant by the _____.
8. Most of the water that a plant absorbs from the soil is lost from the plant by the process of _____.
9. When transpiration is negligible, plants such as grasses exude excess water by _____.
10. Responses based on an internal, 24-hour biological clock are called _____ _____.
11. The opening and closing of stomata are linked to the movement of _____ ions.
12. When light is involved in a physiological response, the plant must have a _____ to absorb and detect the light prior to the physiological response.
13. The leaves of _____ usually have netted venation, distinct palisade and spongy layers in the mesophyll, and bean-shaped guard cells.
14. _____ cells may be involved in the folding, or rolling, of monocot leaves during periods of drought.
15. The fall of leaves in the autumn is known as leaf _____.
16. The leaf scar formed when a leaf abscises is coated with a waterproof material called _____.
17. _____ are leaves that are modified for climbing.
18. Onion bulbs have fleshy leaves that are modified for _____.
19. Cactus spines are modified _____.
20. The leaves of a pitcher plant are modified as _____ traps for catching insects.

REVIEW QUESTIONS

1. What are the raw materials and products for photosynthesis? Discuss how the leaf's tissues are organized to deliver the raw materials and products of photosynthesis.
2. What leaf structures are important in both photosynthesis and transpiration? How are they modified for each physiological process?
3. Relate the series of physiological changes that occur in the guard cells during stomatal opening.
4. How does the environment influence the rate of transpiration? How does the environment influence stomatal opening and closing?
5. Why do many woody plants in temperate climates lose their leaves in autumn?
6. Discuss the specialized features of leaves of insectivorous plants.

RECOMMENDED READINGS

Mauseth, J. D. *Botany: An Introduction to Plant Biology*. Saunders College Publishing, Philadelphia, 1991. A comprehensive introduction to general botany.

Raven, P. H., R. F. Evert, and S. E. Eichhorn. *Biology of Plants*, 5th ed. Worth Publishers, New York, 1992. A general botany text with an evolutionary emphasis.

Taiz, L., and E. Zeiger. *Plant Physiology*. Benjamin/Cummings Publishing Company, Redwood City, CA, 1991. A plant physiology textbook in which the individual chapters were written by various experts. The mechanism of stomatal opening and closing is considered in detail.

ANSWER TO FOCUS QUESTION

Please refer to the question posed in the Focus on Comparative Plant Anatomy on page 704.

Plant A, a water lily, is a dicot that exhibits hydrophytic characteristics. It has stomata confined to its upper epidermis because the leaf blade floats on water. The water lily's roots and stems, as well as its leaves, have large air spaces because gas exchange is more important than conserving water for such hydrophytic plants. Plant B, oleander, is xerophytic. Xerophytic plants often possess features to reduce transpiration: a thick cuticle, a multiple-layered epidermis, and stomatal crypts. Stomatal crypts reduce the effect of wind currents on transpiration.

Stems and Plant Transport

The vegetative (nonreproductive) body of a vascular plant has three parts: roots, leaves, and stems. Roots serve to anchor the plant and absorb materials from the soil. Leaves are for photosynthesis, converting radiant energy into the chemical energy of carbohydrate molecules. Stems, which exhibit varied forms ranging from massive tree trunks (Figure 33–1) to vines, link the roots to the leaves and are usually located above ground. However, many plants have underground stems.

Stems have three main functions. First, stems bear leaves and reproductive structures at regular intervals. The upright position of most stems and the arrangement of leaves on stems allow each leaf to absorb maximum light for use in photosynthesis. A second function of stems is conduction. Stems conduct water and dissolved minerals from the roots, where they are absorbed from the soil, to the leaves and other

The stem of a Ponderosa pine grows toward the sunlight at Bryce Canyon, Utah. (Doug Locke/Dembinsky Photo Associates)

plant structures. Stems also conduct the food produced in the leaves by photosynthesis to the roots and other parts of the plant. Remember, however, that stems are not the only plant organ in which conduction takes place. The vascular system is continuous throughout all parts of the plant, and conduction occurs in roots, stems, leaves, and reproductive structures. A third main function of stems is to produce new living tissue. Stems continue to grow throughout the life of the plant by both primary and secondary growth (see Chapter 31).

In addition to the main functions of support, conduction, and production of new stem tissue, a number of stems are modified for vegetative propagation (asexual reproduction) (see Chapter 35). Also, some stems are specialized to store food or, if green, to manufacture food by photosynthesis.

After you have studied this chapter you should be able to

1. Compare and contrast the structure of herbaceous dicot and monocot stems.
2. Outline the transition from primary growth to secondary growth in a woody stem.
3. Discuss the structure of woody stems and relate common terms like wood, bark, heartwood, and sapwood to the anatomy of woody plants.

4. List several functions of stems, and discuss how the structure of stems relates to their functions.
5. Describe the pathway of water movement in plants.
6. Discuss root pressure and tension-cohesion as mechanisms to explain the rise of water in xylem.
7. Describe the pathway of sugar transport in plants.
8. Discuss the pressure flow hypothesis for sugar transport in phloem.

HERBACEOUS DICOT AND MONOCOT STEMS CAN BE DISTINGUISHED BY THE ARRANGEMENT OF VASCULAR BUNDLES

Chapter 31 explained the two different types of plant growth. Primary growth is an increase in the length of a plant and occurs in apical meristems, which are found at the tips of stems and roots. Secondary growth is an increase in the girth of a plant and is due to the activity of lateral meristems located along the sides of stems and roots. All plants have primary growth, whereas only some plants have secondary growth.

Stems that have only primary growth are herbaceous. Although all herbaceous stems have the same basic tissues, the arrangement of tissues in the stem is highly varied. For example, consider herbaceous stem structure in the two groups of flowering plants, the dicots and the monocots.

Figure 33–1   Two baobab trees. The baobab stores large volumes of water and starch in its stem tissues. Baobabs are native to Africa, Madagascar, and Australia. The massive trunks have, upon occasion, been hollowed out and used as prison cells. (Frans Lanting/Minden Pictures)

The Vascular Bundles of Herbaceous Dicot Stems Are Arranged in a Circle in Cross Section

The outer covering of primary (herbaceous) stems is the **epidermis.** Inside the epidermis but outside the vascular tissues is a layer that is several cells thick, the **cortex.** The cortex is a complex tissue that may contain parenchyma, collenchyma, and sclerenchyma cells (see Chapter 31).

The vascular tissues of herbaceous dicots are located in patches that are arranged in a circle in cross section (Figure 33–2). Each patch, called a vascular bundle, contains both **xylem** and **phloem.** The xylem is usually located on the inner side of the vascular bundle and the phloem to the outside. Sandwiched between the xylem and the phloem is a single layer of cells, the **vascular cambium.** Sometimes a clump of fibers called a **phloem fiber cap** is found directly outside the phloem. Although vascular bundles are arranged in a circle in cross section, these bundles run as long strands throughout the length of the stem and are continuous with the vascular tissues of both roots and leaves.

The core or center of the dicot stem is **pith,** a tissue composed of large, thin-walled parenchyma cells. The regions between the vascular bundles are usually referred to as **pith rays.** There is no clear distinction between the cortical[1] parenchyma and the pith parenchyma in the pith rays.

Vascular Bundles Are Scattered Throughout Monocot Stems

Monocot stems are also covered by an epidermis. As in dicot stems, the vascular tissues run in strands throughout the length of the stem. However, in cross section these vascular bundles are not arranged in a circle as in dicots. Rather, in cross section the vascular bundles are

---
[1]*Cortical* is the adjective form of cortex.

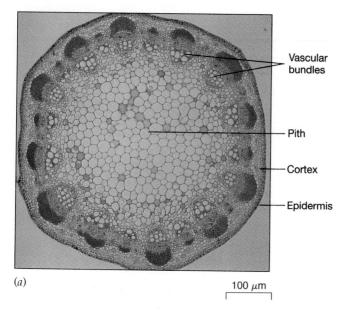

(a)   100 μm

(b)   25 μm

Figure 33–2   Primary growth in a dicot stem. (*a*) Cross section of a *Helianthus* (sunflower) stem showing the organization of tissues. The vascular bundles are arranged in a circle. (*b*) Close-up of the vascular bundles in *Helianthus*. The xylem is to the inside and the phloem to the outside of the bundle. Each vascular bundle is "capped" by a batch of fibers for additional support. (Dennis Drenner)

scattered throughout the stem (Figure 33–3). Therefore, the monocot stem does not have distinct areas of cortex and pith. Instead, the parenchyma tissue in which the vascular tissues are embedded is called **ground tissue** or, sometimes, **ground parenchyma.**

Each vascular bundle in a monocot stem contains xylem toward the inside and phloem toward the outside. Vascular cambium does not occur in monocot stems, however. Recall that vascular cambium gives rise to secondary growth (see Chapter 31). Monocots have primary tissues only and do not produce wood and bark. Although some monocots such as palm trees attain considerable size, most never produce secondary tissues.

Each Tissue in a Herbaceous Stem Has a Specific Function

The epidermis in primary stems provides protection. It is covered by a cuticle, a waxy layer that also covers the leaf epidermis (see Chapter 32). The stem cuticle reduces water loss from the surface of the stem.

As might be expected from the various types of cells they contain, the cortex in dicot stems and ground tissue in monocot stems have several functions. If the stem is green, photosynthesis occurs in parenchyma cells of the cortex. Cortical parenchyma also serves as storage tissue, as evidenced by starch grains and crystals, which are common in cortical parenchyma. (Starch grains are involved in the storage of carbohydrates, whereas crystals store salts.) Collenchyma and scleren-

chyma in the cortex provide strength and support for the stem.

The vascular tissues function not only for conduction but also for support. Xylem transports water and dissolved minerals, and phloem transports dissolved food. Fibers may be found in both xylem and phloem, although they are usually more extensive in phloem. These fibers add considerable strength to the stem body.

The parenchyma cells that make up the pith in the center of dicot stems function primarily for storage. Although monocots lack distinct cortex and pith regions, their ground tissue performs the same functions as cortex and pith in dicots.

GYMNOSPERMS AND WOODY DICOTS HAVE STEMS WITH SECONDARY GROWTH

Secondary growth occurs in plants as a result of the activity of two lateral meristems, vascular cambium and cork cambium (see Chapter 31). Cells in the **vascular cambium** divide and produce secondary xylem and secondary phloem, which become the functional replacements of primary xylem and primary phloem. The second lateral meristem, the **cork cambium,** divides to produce cork cells and cork parenchyma. The cork cambium and the tissues it produces are collectively referred to as **periderm,** which functions as a replacement for the epidermis.

Table 33–1 ANATOMICAL RELATIONSHIPS IN A DICOT STEM[*]

Apical Meristem	Embryonic Tissues	Primary Tissues	Lateral Meristems	Secondary Tissues
Meristematic cells	Procambium	Primary xylem	Vascular cambium	Secondary xylem
		Primary phloem		Secondary phloem
	Ground meristem	Cortex	Cork cambium	Cork parenchyma
		Pith		Cork cells
	Protoderm	Epidermis		

[*]Dashed lines indicate tissues from which the lateral meristems may arise.

Among flowering plants, only certain dicots have secondary growth. Table 33–1 summarizes the anatomical relationships of the various tissues in a dicot stem. Woody plants, such as apple, hickory, and maple, are examples of dicots with secondary growth. Gymnosperms, such as pine, juniper, and spruce, also have secondary growth.

Plants with secondary growth also produce primary growth. That is, a woody plant continues to increase in length (by primary growth) at the tips of its branches and roots, and the older parts of the plant farther back from the tips develop secondary tissues.

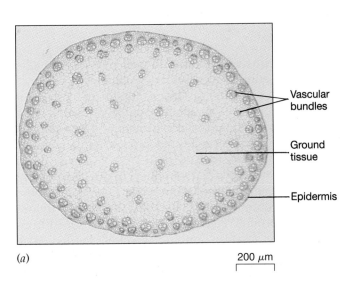

(a)

200 µm

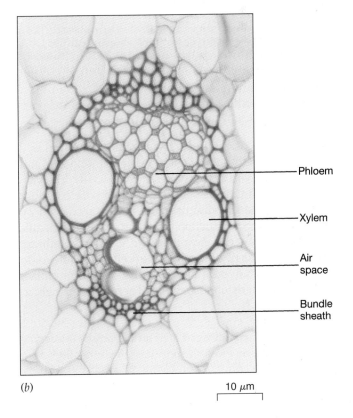

(b)

10 µm

Figure 33–3 Arrangement of stem tissues in *Zea mays* (corn), a monocot. (a) Cross section of stem showing the scattered vascular bundles. (b) Close-up of one of the bundles. The air space is where the first xylem elements were formed. The entire bundle is enclosed in a bundle sheath of sclerenchyma for additional support. (Dennis Drenner)

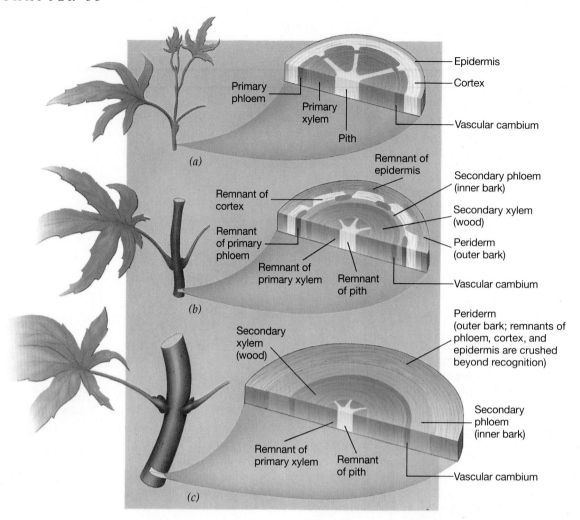

Figure 33–4   Development of secondary growth in the dicot stem is shown in cross section. (*a*) A primary dicot stem. The vascular cambium is sandwiched between the primary xylem and primary phloem in each vascular bundle. (*b*) The vascular cambium, which is a solid cylinder of cells, begins to divide, forming secondary xylem on the inside and secondary phloem on the outside. Note that the primary xylem and primary phloem in the original vascular bundles are split apart in this process. (*c*) A young woody stem. The vascular cambium produces more secondary xylem than secondary phloem. The original primary tissues are no longer functional. The epidermis has been replaced by periderm tissues formed by a second lateral meristem, the cork cambium.

Vascular Cambium Gives Rise to Secondary Xylem and Secondary Phloem

In the primary dicot stem, the vascular cambium is a thin layer of cells sandwiched between the xylem and phloem in the vascular bundles (Figure 33–4). The vascular cambium does not initially form a solid cylinder of cells because the vascular bundles are separated by pith rays. When production of secondary tissues begins in the primary stem, however, the vascular cambium forms an uninterrupted cylinder of cells. It is able to do so because certain cells in each pith ray dedifferentiate and become meristematic again.[1] These cells connect to the vascular cambium cells in each vascular bundle, forming a cylinder of vascular cambium.

When a cell in the vascular cambium divides, one of the daughter cells remains meristematic, that is, it remains a part of the vascular cambium. The other cell may divide again several times, but it eventually develops into mature secondary tissue.

Cells in the vascular cambium divide tangentially (that is, the new cell walls formed between the two new cells are perpendicular to the radius) to produce tissues in two directions (Figure 33–5). The cells formed from the dividing vascular cambium are either located *inside* the ring of vascular cambium or *outside* it. The tissue formed to the inside of the vascular cambium is secondary xylem, which is also known as wood (Figure 33–6). The tissue formed to the outside of the vascular cambium is secondary phloem, which makes up the inner bark of a woody plant. Thus, the vascular cambium is a single layer of cells sandwiched between the two tissues

---

[1] Recall that when growth occurs, cells divide, increase in size, and differentiate into the various cell types found in a mature plant. Cells that have differentiated do not usually retain the ability to divide. However, sometimes mature cells in a plant **dedifferentiate** and revert back to being meristematic (dividing) cells again.

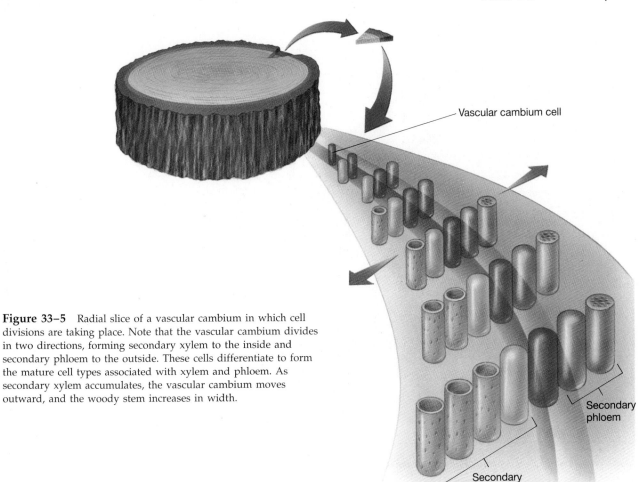

Vascular cambium cell

Secondary phloem

Secondary xylem

Figure 33–5 Radial slice of a vascular cambium in which cell divisions are taking place. Note that the vascular cambium divides in two directions, forming secondary xylem to the inside and secondary phloem to the outside. These cells differentiate to form the mature cell types associated with xylem and phloem. As secondary xylem accumulates, the vascular cambium moves outward, and the woody stem increases in width.

that it produces, secondary xylem (wood) and secondary phloem (inner bark). Besides dividing tangentially to produce secondary xylem and secondary phloem, the vascular cambium divides radially (that is, the new cell walls are parallel to the radius) to form more vascular cambium as the plant increases in girth.

While the secondary xylem and secondary phloem provide vertical transport of materials throughout the plant, materials must also be able to move horizontally (that is, laterally). Lateral movement of materials occurs in **rays,** which are composed of chains of parenchyma cells. The rays are continuous from the secondary xylem to the secondary phloem. Various materials, including water, minerals, and food, are transported laterally in the rays.

What happens to the original primary tissues of the stem once secondary growth commences? As the stem begins to increase in thickness, the orientation of the original primary tissues to one another changes. The secondary tissues (secondary xylem and secondary phloem) are produced between the primary xylem and primary phloem within each vascular bundle. Therefore, as the vascular cambium continues to form secondary tissues, the primary xylem and primary phloem in each vascular bundle are split apart (Figure 33–7).

The primary tissues remaining inside the cylinder of secondary tissue (that is, pith and primary xylem) are under pressure from the changes in growth and soon get crushed beyond recognition. The primary tissues located outside the cylinder of secondary growth (that is, primary phloem, cortex, and epidermis) are also subjected to the pressures produced by secondary growth and are split apart and sloughed off.

Secondary tissues replace the primary tissues in function. Secondary xylem conducts water and dissolved minerals in the woody plant and contains the same cell types found in primary xylem (see Chapter 31). The arrangement of the different cell types in secondary xylem produces distinctive wood characteristics for each species. Secondary phloem transports sugar, and the same types of cells found in primary phloem are also found in secondary phloem, although there are usually more fibers in secondary phloem.

Cork Cambium Produces Periderm, the Functional Replacement for the Epidermis

Cork cambium arises from parenchyma cells in the cortex, epidermis, or phloem. These cells dedifferentiate

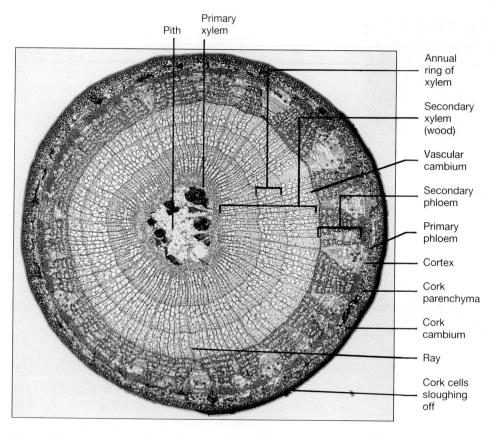

Pith

Primary xylem

Annual ring of xylem

Secondary xylem (wood)

Vascular cambium

Secondary phloem

Primary phloem

Cortex

Cork parenchyma

Cork cambium

Ray

Cork cells sloughing off

Figure 33–6   Cross section of a 3-year-old *Tilia* (basswood) stem.   (Carolina Biological Supply Company)

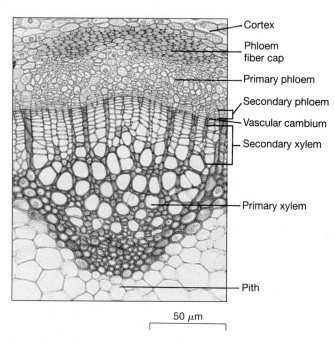

Cortex

Phloem fiber cap

Primary phloem

Secondary phloem

Vascular cambium

Secondary xylem

Primary xylem

Pith

50 µm

Figure 33–7   Cross section through part of a magnolia stem showing a vascular bundle that has been split apart by secondary growth.   (Dennis Drenner)

and become meristematic. Unlike the vascular cambium, the cork cambium does *not* form a continuous cylinder of dividing cells. Instead, it forms a number of small arcs of meristematic cells that cut into successively deeper layers of tissue.

Like the vascular cambium, the cork cambium divides to form new tissue both to its inside and its outside (see Figure 31–13). Cork cells, which are formed to the outside of the cork cambium, are dead at maturity and have heavily suberized (waterproofed) walls. The cork cells produced by the cork cambium protect the plant against mechanical injury, mild fires, temperature extremes, and water loss.

To its inside the cork cambium forms cork parenchyma, which functions for storage. Cork parenchyma is only one to several cells thick, which makes it much thinner than the cork cell layer.

Periderm and any tissues external to it make up the outer portion of the bark (see Figure 31–6). The thickness, patterns, and texture of bark vary considerably from species to species. These differences are due to varying growth rates of the cork cambia of different species, which in turn are under genetic control.

Figure 33–8   Cross section through a tree trunk revealing the darker heartwood in the center of the tree and the lighter sapwood. The sapwood is the functioning xylem that conducts water and dissolved minerals.   (Doug Wechsler)

It is possible to determine the age of a woody stem by counting the **annual rings,** which are concentric circles (in cross section) found in the wood. Examination of annual rings with a magnifying lens reveals that there is actually no ring, or line, separating one year's growth from the next. The appearance of a ring is due to differences in cell size and wall thickness between secondary xylem formed at the end of the preceding year and that formed at the beginning of the following year. In the spring, when water is plentiful, dicot wood formed by the vascular cambium has thin-walled, large-diameter vessels and tracheids and few fibers; it is appropriately called **springwood.** As summer progresses and water becomes less plentiful, the wood that is formed, called **late summerwood,** has thicker-walled, narrower vessels and tracheids and many fibers. The anatomical differences between the late summerwood of the preceding year and the springwood of the following year give the appearance of rings (Figure 33–9).

Plants that grow in temperate climates where there is a growing period and a period of dormancy (that is, winter) exhibit annual rings. In the tropics, environmental conditions determine the presence or absence of rings, but they are not reliable in determining the ages of trees. Much information about climate in past times can be obtained by the study of ancient tree rings (see Focus on Tree Ring Analysis).

Common Terms Associated with Wood Can Be Explained on the Basis of Plant Structure

If you've ever examined different types of lumber, you may have noticed that some trees have wood with two different colors (Figure 33–8). The older wood in the center of the tree is **heartwood.** It typically has a brownish-red color, in contrast to the newer wood closer to the bark, the **sapwood.** A microscopic examination of heartwood reveals the difference. The vessels and tracheids of heartwood are plugged up with various materials so that heartwood cannot function in conduction; the functional secondary xylem is the sapwood. Heartwood is denser than sapwood and provides mechanical support, however. Some evidence exists that heartwood is also more resistant to decay. The materials plugging the cells of heartwood include various pigments, tannins, gums, and resins.

Almost everyone has heard of **hardwood** and **softwood.** Botanically speaking, hardwood is the wood of dicotyledonous flowering plants, whereas softwood is the wood of gymnosperms. Pine and other gymnosperms typically have wood that lacks fibers and vessel elements; the conducting cell in gymnosperm wood is the tracheid. These anatomical differences generally make gymnosperm wood softer than the wood of dicots, although there is much variation from species to species.

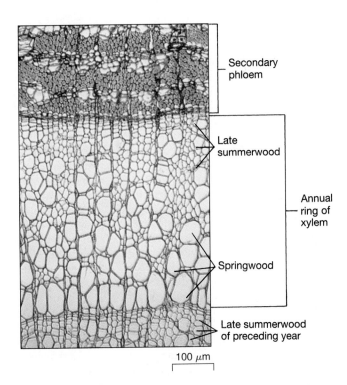

Figure 33–9   Portion of *Tilia* (basswood) stem, in cross section, showing one complete annual ring. Note the differences in cellular sizes between the springwood and the later summerwood. (Dennis Drenner)

FOCUS ON

Tree Ring Analysis

In temperate climates, the age of a tree can be determined by counting the number of annual rings. Other useful information can be determined by analyzing tree rings as well. For example, the size of each ring depends on environmental conditions, including precipitation and temperature. Sometimes the variation in tree rings can be attributed to one factor, and similar patterns appear in the rings of many tree species over a large geographical area. For example, trees in the southwest United States have similar ring patterns due to variations in the amount of annual precipitation. Years with an adequate amount of precipitation produce larger rings of growth, whereas years of drought produce much smaller rings.

It is possible to study the sequence of rings over several thousand years. First a **master chronology**, a complete sample of rings dating back as far as possible, is developed (see figure *a*). One starts with an old tree that is currently living. The oldest rings toward the center of the living tree are matched with the youngest rings toward the outside of a dead tree or even a piece of wood from a house. A master chronology of the area is obtained by using older and older sections of wood, even those found in prehistoric dwellings, and overlapping their matching ring sequences. The longest master chronology is of bristlecone pines in the western United States; it goes back almost 9000 years.

Tree ring analysis, or **dendrochronology**, has been used extensively in several fields. Astronomers have correlated annual tree ring patterns with cycles of sunspots. This work was pioneered by the American astronomer Andrew Douglass during the early years of the 20th century. Tree ring analysis has been extremely useful in dating prehistoric sites of Na-

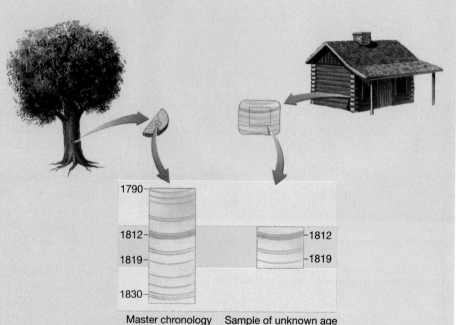

Master chronology   Sample of unknown age

(a) Tree ring dating. A master chronology is developed using progressively older pieces of wood from the same geographical area. By matching the rings of a wood sample of unknown age to the master chronology, the age of the sample can be accurately determined. Ring matching, once a painstakingly tedious job, is usually done by computer today.

tive Americans in the Southwest. For example, the Cliff Palace in Mesa Verde National Park was dated back to AD 1073 using tree rings (see figure *b*). Tree ring analysis also indicates that an extended drought forced the original inhabitants of the Cliff Palace to abandon their homes. Climatologists use tree ring data to study climate patterns in the past. For example, tree ring analysis was used in 1990 to reconstruct the mean summer temperature in Sweden from AD 500 to the present. Tree rings are also being analyzed for other disciplines, including ecology (to study changes in a forest community over time), environmental science (to study the effects of air pollution), and geology (to locate the epicenters and estimate the magnitudes of past earthquakes).

(b) The Cliff Palace in Mesa Verde National Park in Colorado has been dated using tree ring analysis. (Visuals Unlimited/ John Gerlach)

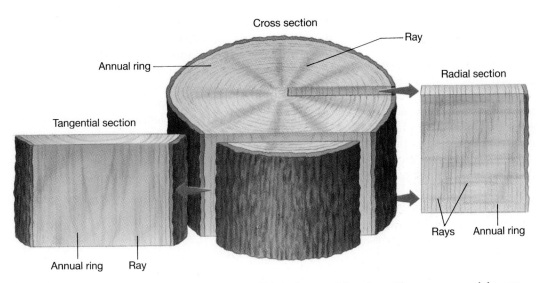

Figure 33–10 A block of wood showing cross, radial, and tangential sections. The appearance of the rays and annual rings is distinctive for each section.

The wood of a tree has quite different appearances depending on the angle at which it is cut (Figure 33–10). These differences are apparent both macroscopically and microscopically. In cross section, annual rings appear as concentric rings, and rays appear as straight lines coming out from the center of the stem. In tangential section, which is a longitudinal section cut perpendicular to the radius, annual rings appear as vertical lines that often come together in a V shape, and rays appear as specks or very short lines. A radial section, which is a longitudinal section cut through the center (along the radius), has annual rings that look like vertical lines running the length of the wood and rays that look like horizontal strips.

As a woody stem increases in width over the years, the branches that it bears grow along with it as long as they are alive. When a branch dies, it no longer continues to grow with the stem. In time the stem grows out and surrounds the base of the branch. The basal portion of an embedded dead branch is called a **knot.** It is possible for a knot to contain bark as well as wood. The presence of knots in wood diminishes its commercial value, except for ornamental purposes. Some trees (knotty pine, for example) are valued for their high production of knots.

TRANSPORT IN PLANTS OCCURS IN XYLEM AND PHLOEM

The movement of food, water, and minerals within a vascular plant is called **translocation.** Water and miner-als are transported in xylem, whereas dissolved food is transported in phloem. Translocation in plants does not resemble the movement of materials in animals because nothing *circulates*. The materials being translocated in xylem travel in one direction only. Although movement in different phloem cells can be in different directions, the materials being transported cannot be said to circulate.

Water and Minerals Are Translocated in Xylem

Water and dissolved minerals form a dilute solution that moves within tracheids and vessel elements, which are hollow, dead cells (see Chapter 31). The movement of water in the xylem is the most rapid of any transport in plants. On a hot summer day, water has been measured moving upward in the xylem at a distance of 60 cm (2 feet) per minute.

Water initially moves horizontally into the roots from the soil, passing through several tissues until it reaches the xylem (see Chapter 34). Once the water is in the tracheids and vessel elements, it travels upward through a continuous system of xylem from root to stem to leaf. The dissolved minerals are carried along passively in the water. The plant does not expend any energy of its own to transport water, which moves as a result of natural physical processes. How does water move to the tops of plants? It might either be pushed up from the bottom of the plant or pulled up from the top of the plant. Actually, both mechanisms exist in plants.

The direction of water movement can be explained by the concept of water potential

In order to understand how water moves, it is helpful to introduce **water potential,** which is defined as the free energy of water. Water potential is important in plant physiology because it is a measure of the ability of a cell to absorb water by osmosis (see Chapter 5). Water potential also provides a measure of the tendency of water to evaporate from cells.

The water potential of pure water is set at 0 bars by convention because it cannot be measured directly (the bar is a metric unit of pressure). It is possible to measure differences in the free energy of water molecules in different situations, however. When solutes are dissolved in water, the free energy of water decreases.[1] This means that dissolved solutes lower the water potential to a negative number. *Water moves from a region of higher (less negative) water potential to a region of lower (more negative) water potential.*

The water potential for the soil varies, depending on how much water is present in the soil. When a soil is very dry, its water potential is very low (very negative). When a soil is moister, its water potential is higher, although it is still a negative number because dissolved minerals are present in very dilute concentrations.

The water potential in root cells is also negative owing to the presence of dissolved minerals, sugars, and other solutes. Roots contain more dissolved materials than soil water, however, unless the soil is very dry (a dry soil has more concentrated solutes). This means that under normal conditions the water potential of the root is more negative than the water potential of the soil. Thus, water moves by osmosis from the soil into the root.

Root pressure pushes water in a root up through the stem

In the **root pressure mechanism** for water transport, water moves into the roots by osmosis because of the differences in water potential between the soil and the cytoplasm of root cells. The accumulation of water in root tissues produces a pressure in the root that forces the water up the xylem toward the top of the plant.

Root pressure is a real phenomenon in plants. Guttation, introduced in Chapter 32, is caused by root pressure. However, plant physiologists have measured root pressure and found that it is not a strong enough force to explain the rise of water to the tops of the tallest trees. Root pressure exerts an influence in smaller plants, particularly in the spring when the soil is very wet, but it clearly does not cause water to rise hundreds of feet in the tallest plants. Further, root pressure is greatest in the spring, when water is plentiful in the soil. It does not occur to any appreciable extent in summer, yet water transport is greatest during hot summer days.

In the tension-cohesion mechanism, transpiration in the leaves pulls water up the stem

A second possible explanation for the rise of water in plants is that a tension is produced at the top of the plant that pulls the water up. This process is much like sucking liquid through a straw. The tension produced at the top of the plant is caused by the evaporative pull of transpiration (see Chapter 32), which in turn is driven by solar energy.

This upward pulling of water is possible only as long as there is a solid, unbroken column of water in the xylem. Water tends to form an unbroken column because of the cohesiveness of water molecules; recall that water molecules are strongly attracted to one another owing to hydrogen bonding (see Chapter 2). Also, the adhesion of water to the walls of the xylem cells is an important factor in maintaining an unbroken column of water.

To summarize, in the **tension-cohesion mechanism,** a tension is produced at the top of the plant by transpiration. This tension pulls the water in the xylem up to the leaves at the top of the plant. The cohesive and adhesive properties of water enable it to form an unbroken column, which can be pulled.

The movement of water in xylem due to the tension-cohesion mechanism can be explained in terms of water potential. The atmosphere has an extremely negative water potential. There is a gradient in water potentials from the least negative (in the soil) up through the plant to the most negative (the atmosphere). This literally pulls the water up through the plant (Figure 33–11).

Is tension-cohesion powerful enough to explain the rise of water in the tallest plants? Plant physiologists have calculated that the tension produced by transpiration is strong enough to pull water up 500 feet in tubes the diameter of xylem vessels. Because the tallest trees are approximately 350 feet high, the tension-cohesion mechanism easily accounts for their water transport. Therefore, botanists think that the tension-cohesion mechanism is the dominant mechanism of xylem translocation in most plants.

---

[1]Solutes induce the formation of hydration layers, in which water molecules surround polar molecules and ions, causing them to remain in solution by preventing them from coming together. The association of water molecules in hydration layers reduces the motion of many water molecules, thereby decreasing their free energy.

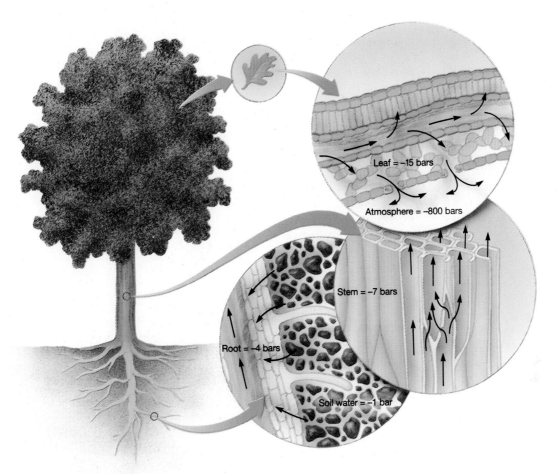

Leaf = −15 bars

Atmosphere = −800 bars

Stem = −7 bars

Root = −4 bars

Soil water = −1 bar

Figure 33–11 The evaporative pull of transpiration is driven by the gradient in water potentials from the soil through the plant to the atmosphere. Water moves from less negative to more negative water potentials.

Sugar Is Translocated in Phloem

The sugar produced during photosynthesis is converted into the disaccharide sucrose before being loaded into the phloem and transported to the rest of the plant. Sucrose, or common table sugar, is the predominant form of food carried in phloem. Transport of solutes in phloem is rapid. Although not as rapid as xylem transport, phloem transport has been measured at approximately 2.5 cm (1 inch) per minute.

Movement within phloem tissue is both upward and downward. Sucrose may be transported from its place of manufacture (the leaf) to a place of storage (the root, fruit, or seed). It may also be transported from the leaf or root to actively growing regions like the root or shoot apical meristems, where it would be quickly used.

The pressure flow hypothesis explains how solutes are transported in phloem

Phloem transport is due to a pressure gradient between the *source*, where the sugar is loaded into the phloem, and the *sink*, where the sugar is removed from the phloem. At the source—for example, a leaf—the dissolved sucrose moves from the mesophyll cells where it was manufactured and is then actively loaded into companion cells in the phloem, through a cotransport system involving hydrogen ions (see Making the Connection box in Chapter 36). ATP energy is apparently used to pump hydrogen ions out of the companion cell, thus forming a concentration gradient across the plasma membrane (Figure 33–12). Evidence for this mechanism is provided by the fact that changes in pH have been observed across the companion cell plasma membrane during sugar loading. Presumably the energy of the hydrogen ion gradient is used to cotransport the sucrose (against its own concentration gradient) as the hydrogen ions flow back across the plasma membrane and into the companion cell.

Once the sugar is in the companion cell, it readily moves into the sieve tube member through the many cytoplasmic connections between the two cells. The increase in dissolved sugars in the sieve tube member decreases (makes more negative) the water potential of

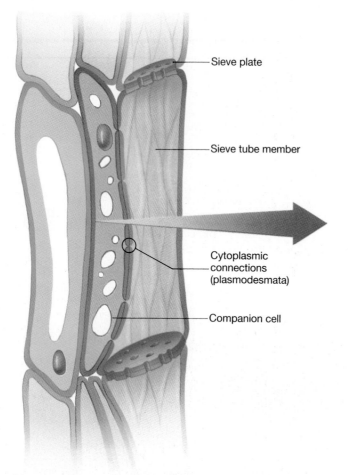

Sieve plate

Sieve tube member

Cytoplasmic connections (plasmodesmata)

Companion cell

(a)

Cell wall | Plasma membrane | Cytoplasm

ADP + P$_i$

H$^+$

ATP

H$^+$

Sucrose

(b)

Figure 33–12   Proposed model of sugar loading into phloem in the leaf. (*a*) The spatial arrangement of the cells involved. (*b*) Enlarged companion cell wall and plasma membrane. The energy of ATP is used to pump protons (H$^+$) out of the companion cell. The return of protons (H$^+$) through a protein channel in the companion cell plasma membrane is accompanied by sucrose. Once the sucrose is loaded into the companion cell, it moves through cytoplasmic connections into the sieve tube member.

that cell. As a result, water moves by osmosis into the sieve tubes, producing a pressure. This pressure pushes the sugar solution through the phloem much as water is forced through a hose.

At its destination, the sink, sugar is actively unloaded from the sieve tube members, with ATP again being required. With a loss in sugar, the water potential in the sieve tube elements at the sink increases (becomes less negative). Therefore, water moves out of the sieve tubes by osmosis and into surrounding cells that have more negative water potentials.

This explanation, called the **pressure flow hypothesis,** explains the movement of solutes in phloem by means of a pressure gradient. It is the difference in sugar concentrations between the source and the sink that causes transport in phloem, as water and solutes flow down the pressure gradient. The actual flow of

solutes in the phloem does not require metabolic energy. However, both loading sugar at the source and unloading sugar at the sink require energy derived from ATP (Figure 33–13).

Although the pressure flow hypothesis adequately explains current data on phloem transport, much remains to be learned about this complex process. Phloem transport is difficult to study in plants. The cells are under hydrostatic pressure, so cutting into the phloem to observe it causes the contents of the sieve tube elements to be sucked against one end wall. Aphids, small wingless insects that insert their mouthparts into phloem sieve tubes for feeding, have been a useful tool in phloem research (Figure 33–14). Much useful information about phloem transport has also been obtained using radioactive tracers. When a leaf is exposed to $^{14}CO_2$, radioactive carbon is fixed into the sugars pro-

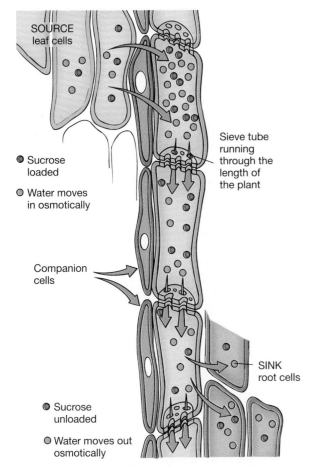

(a)

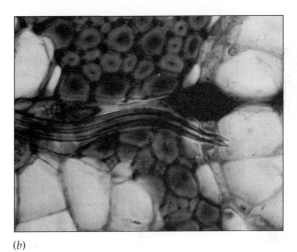

(b)

Figure 33–13 Pressure flow mechanism for phloem transport. Sugar is actively loaded into the sieve tube element at the source. As a result of differences in water potential, water moves osmotically into the sieve tube element. At the sink the sugar is actively unloaded and water leaves the sieve tube element by osmosis. The gradient of sugar from source to sink causes pressure flow through the sieve tube toward the sink.

duced by photosynthesis. The transport of the sugar in phloem can be followed using autoradiographic techniques (see Focus Box in Chapter 31). After exposure to the labeled CO_2, the stem tissue is freeze-dried, sliced into thin sections, and placed on photographic film. The part of the film in contact with radioactive substances is exposed. After development, the exact location of the radioactive sugars can be determined.

Figure 33–14 Mature aphid feeding on a side of a branch. The aphid is about 6 mm long. (*a*) The aphid's mouthpart (stylet) is inserted into the phloem. The pressure in the punctured phloem drives the sugar solution through the stylet and into the aphid's digestive system. (*b*) A microscopic view of basswood (*Tilia americana*) phloem, showing that the aphid stylet has penetrated a sieve tube member. When the aphid's stylet is severed from its body by a laser beam, sugars continue to flow through the stylet at a rate proportional to phloem pressure; this rate can be measured. (*a*, Dwight R. Kuhn; *b*, M. H. Zimmerman, *Science* 133:73–79 (fig. 4), January 13, 1961, Copyright 1988 by the American Association for the Advancement of Science)

SUMMARY

I. The primary functions of stems are support, conduction, and production of new stem tissues.

II. Stems with primary growth have an epidermis, vascular tissue, and cortex and pith, or ground tissue.

A. Dicot stems have the vascular bundles arranged in a circle (in cross section) and have a distinct cortex and pith.

B. Monocot stems have scattered vascular bundles and

ground tissue instead of a distinct cortex and pith.

III. Secondary growth occurs in some dicots and all gymnosperms.

    A. The vascular cambium produces secondary xylem (wood) to the inside and secondary phloem (inner bark) to the outside.

    B. The cork cambium produces cork parenchyma to the inside and cork cells to the outside.

IV. Water and dissolved minerals move upward in the xylem from the root to the stem to the leaves.

    A. Water potential is the free energy of water. Pure water has a water potential of 0 bars, whereas water with dissolved solutes has a negative water potential. Water moves from an area of higher (less negative) water potential to an area of lower (more negative) water potential.

    B. Root pressure, caused by the movement of water into the root (region with lower water potential) from the soil (region with higher water potential), helps explain the rise of water in small plants. Guttation is a consequence of root pressure.

    C. The tension-cohesion mechanism causes the rise of water in even the largest plants.

       1. The evaporative pull of transpiration (powered by the sun) causes a tension at the top of the plant. This tension is due to a gradient in water potentials from the soil (slightly negative) up through the plant to the atmosphere (extremely negative).

       2. An unbroken column of water is pulled up through the plant as a result of the cohesive and adhesive nature of water.

V. Dissolved food is translocated up or down a plant in the phloem.

    A. Sucrose is the main form of food transported in the phloem.

    B. The movement of materials in the phloem is explained by the pressure flow hypothesis.

       1. Sugar is actively loaded (requires ATP) into the sieve tubes at the source. As a result, water moves into the sieve tubes by osmosis.

       2. Sugar is actively unloaded (requires ATP) from the sieve tubes at the sink. As a result, water leaves the sieve tubes by osmosis.

       3. Flow of materials between the source and sink is driven by the pressure gradient produced by additional water entering the phloem at the source and leaving the phloem at the sink.

POST-TEST

1. Vascular tissue arranged in a circle (in cross section) is characteristic of the primary stems of _____.

2. Primary _____ stems lack a distinct pith and cortex.

3. The two lateral meristems responsible for secondary growth are the _____ _____ and the _____ _____.

4. The cork cambium and the tissues it produces are collectively called the _____ and make up the outer region of the bark.

5. Horizontal transport of materials is accomplished by _____ in plants with secondary growth.

6. In plants with secondary growth, the _____ serves as a functional replacement for the epidermis.

7. Botanically speaking, the wood of a tree is _____ _____.

8. The _____ of a tree consists of the inner rings of wood that are nonfunctional and usually pigmented.

9. An annual ring of wood is formed by the difference between the _____ _____ of the preceding year and the _____ of the following year.

10. _____ is the wood of dicotyledonous flowering plants, whereas _____ is the wood of gymnosperms.

11. In wood, the basal portion of an embedded dead branch is called a _____.

12. _____ is the science of tree ring analysis.

13. The movement of food, water, and minerals within a plant is called _____.

14. The free energy of water in a particular situation is referred to as its _____ _____.

15. By convention, the water potential of pure water is set at _____ bars.

16. The presence of dissolved solutes in water _____ the water potential.

17. Water moves from an area of _____ negative water potential to an area of _____ negative water potential.

18. This mechanism of water movement, _____ _____, is not strong enough to explain the rise of water to the tops of the tallest trees.

19. In the tension-cohesion mechanism, the tension is produced at the top of the plant by the evaporative pull of _____.

20. The region of a plant where sugar is loaded into the phloem is known as the _____.

REVIEW QUESTIONS

1. List several functions of stems and describe the tissue(s) responsible for each function.

2. When secondary growth begins, certain cells dedifferentiate and become meristematic. Could a tracheid ever do this? A sieve tube member? Why or why not?

3. What happens to the primary tissues of a stem when secondary growth occurs?

4. What is water potential? How can it be used to explain the movement of water in osmosis? In transpiration?

5. Explain the tension-cohesion mechanism of water trans-

port. Make sure you consider both the "tension" and "cohesion" aspects of the mechanism.

6. Describe the pressure flow hypothesis of sugar movement in phloem, including the activities at the source and sink.

RECOMMENDED READINGS

Mauseth, J. D. *Botany: An Introduction to Plant Biology.* Saunders College Publishing, Philadelphia, 1991. A comprehensive introduction to general botany.

Raven, P. H., R. F. Evert, and S. E. Eichhorn. *Biology of Plants,* 5th ed. Worth Publishers, New York, 1992. A general botany text with an evolutionary emphasis.

Taiz, L., and E. Zeiger. *Plant Physiology.* Benjamin/Cummings Publishing Company, Redwood City, CA, 1991. A plant physiology textbook in which the individual chapters were written by various experts. Transport in plants is thoroughly covered.

Thybony, S. Dead trees tell tales. *National Wildlife* 25:2, Aug-Sept, 1987. Enjoyable account of the potential uses of analyzing annual rings of trees.

Roots and Mineral Nutrition

Roots are underground and out of sight, so most people do not appreciate their importance to plants. Roots are essential plant organs that anchor the plant and absorb water and dissolved minerals from the soil. These materials are then transported throughout the plant. Many roots also serve as storage organs. Surplus sugars produced in the leaves by photosynthesis are transported in the phloem to the roots for storage until they are needed. Most of the sugar that is stored in the root is transported to other parts of the plant when needed. Some plants, like beets and sweet potatoes, have roots that are enormously swollen with food storage tissues (Figure 34–1).

Other roots are modified for additional functions besides anchorage, absorption, conduction, and storage. Some roots are produced at unusual places on plants. These **adventitious roots** grow laterally from a stem and are frequently aerial. **Prop roots,** which are more common in monocots than in dicots, are adven-

The roots of radish seedlings penetrate the soil, anchoring the young plants and absorbing water and minerals.
(Doug Wechsler)

titious roots that provide additional support for the plant (Figure 34–2). Corn is an example of a plant that produces prop roots.

Plants adapted to wet environments where the soil is flooded often have roots modified for aeration. A flooded soil is depleted of oxygen, so aerial roots, which grow down into the soil, may assist in getting oxygen to the belowground roots. Black mangrove and bald cypress are examples of plants with roots modified for aeration (Figure 34–3).

Epiphytes, plants that grow attached to other plants, often have unusual root modifications. For example, certain epiphytic orchids have photosynthetic roots; in some of these the photosynthetic roots comprise the bulk of the plant.

Plants that produce bulbs often have **contractile roots** that contract and pull the bulb and stem deeper into the ground (Figure 34–4). Contractile roots are common in monocots, but certain dicots and ferns also possess them.

LEARNING OBJECTIVES

After you have studied this chapter you should be able to

1. Compare the structures of primary dicot and monocot roots.
2. Outline the transition in a root from primary growth to secondary growth.
3. List several functions of roots and discuss how their structure relates to their functions.
4. Describe several roots that perform unusual functions.
5. Trace the pathway of water movement in roots.
6. List the five components of soil and give the ecological significance of each.
7. Describe the factors involved in soil formation.
8. Outline the criteria an element must satisfy in order to be considered essential for plant growth.
9. List the 16 elements that are essential for plant growth.
10. Give a physiological role in plants for each essential element.

STRUCTURAL DIFFERENCES EXIST BETWEEN PRIMARY ROOTS AND PRIMARY STEMS

All herbaceous roots have certain tissues also found in stems, such as epidermis, cortex, xylem, and phloem. Roots also have several tissues and structures not found in stems, including a root cap and root hairs. Each root tip is covered by a **root cap,** a protective layer many cells thick covering the delicate root apical meristem. As the root grows, pushing its way through the soil, cells of the root cap are sloughed off and replaced by new cells formed from the root apical meristem. **Root hairs** are extensions of epidermal cells located in the area of cell maturation near the root tip (see Chapter 31). Root hairs greatly increase the absorptive capacity

(a)

(b)

Figure 34–2 Prop roots. (*a*) Prop roots in corn (*Zea mays*) arise from the stem. These adventitious roots provide additional support. (*b*) The banyan tree has prop roots that develop from branches. (*a*, Dennis Drenner; *b*, courtesy of James Mauseth, University of Texas)

Figure 34–1 Beets and other root crops are important sources of human food because of the accumulated food that the plant stores in the root. (Dennis Drenner)

Figure 34–3 Many plants living in swampy areas have special roots for aeration. Cypress "knees" may provide oxygen for roots that are buried in anaerobic mud. Cypress trees growing in normal soil do not produce knees.   (Doug Wechsler)

Table 34–1   A COMPARISON OF DICOT ROOTS AND STEMS

Structure or Characteristic	Roots	Stems
Nodes and internodes	No	Yes
Leaves and buds	No	Yes
Photosynthesis	No	Yes
Pith	No	Yes
Cuticle	No	Yes
Root cap	Yes	No
Root hairs	Yes	No
Pericycle	Yes	No
Endodermis	Yes	Seldom
Branch origin	Internal	External

of the root. Although stems and leaves may have various types of hairs, they are distinct from root hairs in structure and function. Table 34–1 summarizes the differences between dicot roots and stems.

Herbaceous Dicot and Monocot Roots Can Be Distinguished by the Arrangement of Vascular Tissues

Like other parts of the plant, dicot roots are covered by a single layer of protective tissue, the **epidermis** (Figure 34–5). Unlike the epidermis of aerial parts of the plant, however, the root epidermis does not secrete a waxy cuticle, which would impede the absorption of water from the soil. The root hairs are another modification enabling the root to absorb water from the soil, as root hairs greatly increase the surface area of the root in contact with moist soil (Figure 34–6). Root hairs are short-lived extensions of epidermal cells and never develop into multicellular root branches. Branches of roots develop in a different manner.

The **cortex** of a dicot root is not composed of the variety of cell types found in stem cortex (see Chapter 33). Rather, parenchyma with many intercellular spaces makes up the bulk of the root cortex. Usually there is no collenchyma in roots, although some sclerenchyma develops as the root ages. The inner layer of the cortex, the **endodermis,** is different from the rest of the cortex. Endodermal cells fit snugly against each other, and each has a special bandlike region on its radial and transverse walls, called a **Casparian strip** (Figure 34–7). The Casparian strip contains suberin, a fatty material that is waterproof. (Recall that suberin is also the waterproof material in cork cell walls.)

(a)   (b)

(c)

Figure 34–4   Plants that produce bulbs often have contractile roots. (a) Germination of the seed. (b) During the first growing season, contractile roots do not pull the bulb appreciably deeper in the soil. (c) During succeeding seasons, contractile roots pull the bulb deeper and deeper until it reaches a depth of temperature stability.

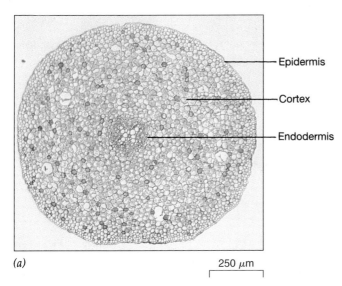

Epidermis

Cortex

Endodermis

(a)

250 μm

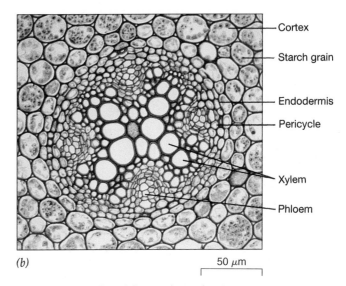

Cortex

Starch grain

Endodermis

Pericycle

Xylem

Phloem

(b)

50 μm

Figure 34–5   Cross section of a buttercup (*Ranunculus*) root. Buttercups are dicots with primary growth. (*a*) Entire root. Note that the bulk of the root is the cortex. (*b*) A close-up of the center

of the root. Note the solid core of vascular tissues.   (Dennis Drenner)

Figure 34–6   Root hairs on a radish seedling. Each delicate hair is a single cell extension of the root epidermis. Root hairs increase the surface area of the root in contact with the soil.   (Dennis Drenner)

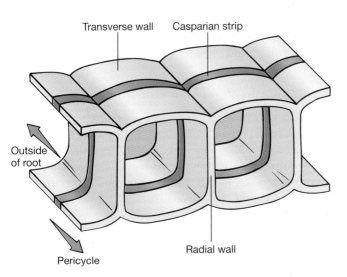

Transverse wall   Casparian strip

Outside
of root

Pericycle

Radial wall

Figure 34–7   A few cells of the endodermis. Note the Casparian strip around the radial and transverse walls. The endodermis controls water uptake by the root.

Just inside the endodermis is a single layer of cells called the **pericycle.** The pericycle is composed of parenchyma cells that retain meristematic properties. The central core of the dicot root is occupied by vascular tissue. **Xylem** is in the center and often has two, three, four, or more extensions, or "arms," in cross section. **Phloem** is located in patches between the xylem arms. The same kinds of cells are in xylem and phloem of the root as in stem xylem and phloem, except that roots typically have fewer fibers for support because the soil supports the root. The **vascular cambium** is sandwiched between the xylem and phloem. Because it possesses an inner core of vascular tissue, the dicot root lacks pith.

The tissues in monocot roots are basically the same as in dicot roots, but they are arranged in a slightly different manner in the center (Figure 34–8). Starting at the outside of the monocot root, there is epidermis, then cortex, endodermis, and pericycle. However, the vascular tissues inside the pericycle do not form a solid cylinder in the center of the root. Instead, the phloem and xylem are located in separate patches arranged in a circle around the centrally located **pith.** Because the vast majority of monocots do not have secondary growth, monocot roots do not contain vascular cambium.

Structure Is Related to Function in Primary Roots

Features of the epidermis, cortex, and endodermis aid in the absorption of water and dissolved minerals from the soil. The lack of a cuticle and presence of root hairs obviously increase absorption. However, most of the

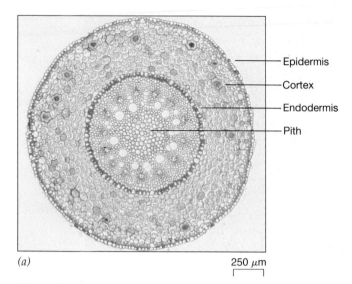

(a)   250 μm

Figure 34–8   Cross section of a greenbriar (*Smilax*) root.
Greenbriar is a monocot. (*a*) Entire root. (*b*) Close-up of a portion

(b)   50 μm

of the center of the root, showing the vascular tissues and the
pith.   (Dennis Drenner)

water that enters the root moves along the cell walls
rather than entering the cells. One of the major components of cell walls is cellulose, which absorbs water like
a wick. As an example of the absorptive properties of
cellulose, consider how cotton balls, which are almost
pure cellulose, soak up water.

When water enters the root cortex, it moves along
the cell walls and intercellular spaces until it reaches the
endodermis (Figure 34–9). Until water reaches the endodermis, most of it has never passed through a plasma
membrane or entered the cytoplasm of a root cell. The
endodermis, with its waterproof Casparian strip running around the radial and transverse walls, blocks
water movement along cell walls; thus, water enters the
endodermal cells after passing through the plasma
membranes. For this reason the endodermis is considered to control the movement of water in the root, even
though it is an internal tissue and water must pass
through other tissues to reach it.

The primary function of the root cortex is storage. A
microscopic examination of the storage parenchyma
that forms the cortex often reveals numerous starch
grains. Starch, which is an insoluble carbohydrate composed of glucose units, is the most common form of
food storage in plants. Another feature of the root cortex, the large intercellular air spaces, allows for aeration
of the root cells.

The pericycle is the origin of multicellular branch
roots (Figure 34–10). Branch roots originate when a portion of the pericycle, usually at the tip of a xylem arm,
becomes meristematic and starts dividing. As it grows,
the branch root breaks through several layers of root
tissue (endodermis, cortex, and epidermis) before entering the soil. Branch roots have all the structures and
anatomical features of the roots from which they

branch. In addition to forming branch roots, the
pericycle is involved in secondary growth in plants
with woody roots.

The xylem and phloem of a root have the same
functions that they do in the rest of the plant. After
passing through the endodermal cells, water enters the
root xylem via the pericycle, often at one of the xylem
arms. Up to this point the pathway of water has been
horizontal from the soil to the center of the root:

root hair → epidermis → cortex → endodermal cells →
pericycle → xylem

Upon entering the xylem, the water is transported up
through root xylem into stem xylem and throughout
the rest of the plant. Phloem conducts food (as sucrose)
to the root, where it is stored, or from the root to other
parts of the plant, where it is used.

Roots selectively absorb minerals

The concentrations of various minerals are different in
the xylem sap than in the soil, a fact which indicates
that plants selectively accumulate certain minerals.
Most minerals are thought to travel through the root
tissues from cell to cell, rather than along the cell walls
as does water. Dissolved mineral ions may pass
through plasma membranes both passively and actively. In active transport, the mineral moves against
the concentration gradient through a special channel in
the membrane (Figure 34–11; also see Making the Connection in Chapter 36). Recall that active transport requires the expenditure of energy, usually in the form of
ATP (see Chapter 5); this is one of many reasons that
roots require sugars for cellular respiration.

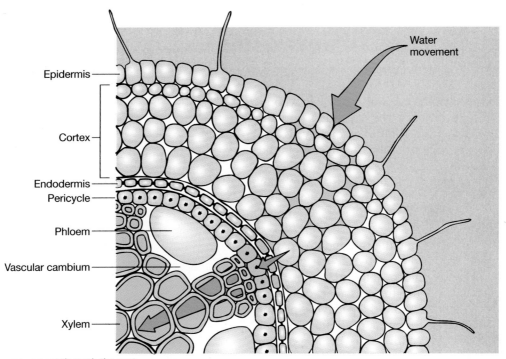

Water movement through the root

Figure 34–9 Most water that enters the root travels along the cell walls and intercellular spaces. When water reaches the endodermis, it can only continue to move if it passes through the plasma membrane and enters the cells because the Casparian strip blocks its passage along the wall. (Individual cells of phloem and vascular cambium are not shown.)

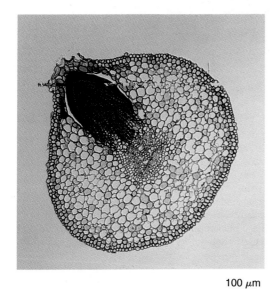

100 μm

Figure 34–10 A multicellular branch root emerges from the root. Branch roots originate at the pericycle. (Ed Reschke)

Figure 34–11 Active transport of mineral ions through plasma membranes. (To keep the figure simpler, the cell wall is not shown.) (*Top*) The energy of ATP is used to pump protons out of the cell, producing a membrane potential (difference in charge) and a pH gradient (difference in pH) on either side of the plasma membrane. (*Middle*) Negatively charged ions tend to pass into the cell through specific channels in association with the positively charged protons. (*Bottom*) Because the proton pump makes the interior of the cell more negative, positively charged ions also tend to move into the cell, usually through other channels.

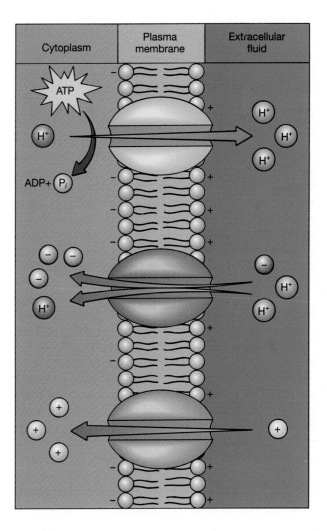

GYMNOSPERMS AND CERTAIN DICOTS HAVE ROOTS WITH SECONDARY GROWTH

Plants that produce woody stems also produce woody roots and have both primary and secondary growth (see Chapter 33). The production of secondary tissues occurs some distance back from the root tips. As in the stem, secondary growth in roots is the result of the activity of two lateral meristems, the vascular cambium and cork cambium. Woody roots have both wood and bark, with the wood being formed in layers, or annual rings, in temperate climates.

Initially, the vascular cambium is found in separate areas of the root sandwiched between the primary xylem and the primary phloem (Figure 34–12). As it produces secondary xylem, the vascular cambium moves outward. When it reaches the pericycle, part of the pericycle joins with it to form a continuous ring of vascular cambium, which continues to divide, producing secondary xylem (wood) to the inside and secondary phloem (inner bark) to the outside.

The primary tissues of the root are gradually destroyed as the root increases in girth. Root epidermis is replaced by periderm, which is composed of cork cells and cork parenchyma produced by the cork cambium. The cork cambium in the root initially arises from regions in the pericycle.

SOIL SUPPORTS TERRESTRIAL PLANTS

Soil is the complex material in which plants are anchored and from which they receive their water and essential mineral elements. Soils are formed from rock that is gradually broken down into smaller and smaller particles by biological, chemical, and physical weathering processes. Except for nitrogen, the minerals that a plant receives from the soil are obtained from this weathered parent rock. Because different rocks are composed of different minerals, soils vary in their mineral composition.

Two very important factors that sometimes work together in the weathering of rock are climate and living organisms. For example, lichens growing on rock surfaces produce acids that etch tiny cracks, or fissures, in the rock surface. Water seeps into these cracks. During winter, the alternate freezing and thawing cause the cracks to enlarge, breaking off small pieces of the rock. Larger plants can then become established and send their roots into the larger cracks, fracturing the rock further. The conversion of solid rock into soil takes a very long period of time, as much as thousands of years.

Another factor involved in soil formation is the topography, or surface features of a region. For exam-

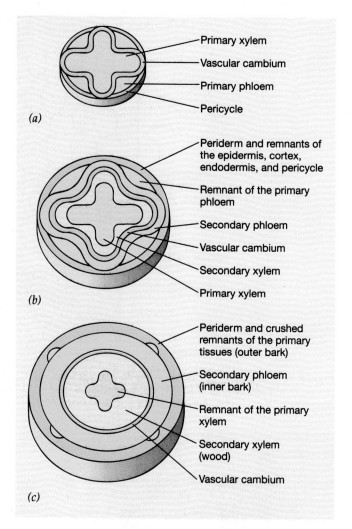

Figure 34–12 Development of secondary growth in a primary root. (*a*) The tissues in a primary dicot root, excluding the epidermis, cortex, and endodermis. The vascular cambium extends out to the pericycle, forming a continuous, noncircular loop. (*b*) The vascular cambium produces secondary xylem to its inside and secondary phloem to its outside. Note that the primary phloem is being pushed outward. (*c*) After a period of time the ring of vascular cambium becomes circular. As it continues to divide, the primary phloem is crushed almost beyond recognition. Meanwhile, the cork cambium forms the outer bark (not shown in detail).

ple, the rate of soil formation depends on whether the soil is located on a mountain top where significant erosion might occur, or in a valley where sedimentation might increase the rate of soil accumulation.

Soil Is Composed of Inorganic Minerals, Organic Matter, Soil Organisms, Soil Atmosphere, and Soil Water

The inorganic minerals that come from weathered rock form the basic soil material. The texture of a soil is determined by the amounts of inorganic soil particles of

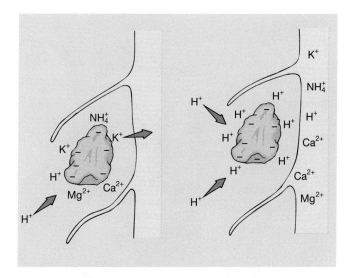

Figure 34–13 Cation exchange in the soil. The negatively charged soil particles bind various positively charged ions, or cations. It is possible for hydrogen ions to replace or be exchanged for these cations, freeing them for absorption by the root. The hydrogen ions for this exchange come from the soil and from the root.

different sizes. The large particles are **sand** (0.02 to 2 mm diameter), the medium are **silt** (0.002 to 0.02 mm diameter), and the small are **clay** (less than 0.002 mm diameter).

The clay component is very important in determining many characteristics of the soil, in part because each clay particle has negative charges on its outer surface. Clay tends to attract and bind positively charged mineral ions, preventing them from being leached out of the soil (Figure 34–13). In contrast, negatively charged mineral ions are repelled by clay particles and usually remain dissolved in soil water, where they are susceptible to leaching.

Different soils have different combinations of soil particle sizes. A loamy soil, which is good for agriculture, has approximately 40% each of sand and silt and about 20% clay. Soils with larger proportions of sand are not as desirable for plant growth because they do not hold water and mineral ions well. Soils with a larger proportion of clay are also not desirable because they tend to get compacted, robbing the soil of spaces that can be filled by water and air.

The remains of plants, animals, and microorganisms provide organic matter, which is decomposed by the microorganisms that inhabit the soil. In the process, essential mineral elements are released into the soil and may be reabsorbed by plants. Organic matter is also important because it alters certain soil characteristics. It increases the water-holding capacity of the soil, acting much like a sponge. For this reason it is an important additive, especially for sandy soils. The partly decayed organic portion of the soil is referred to as **humus.**

The organisms living in the soil form a complex community in numbers too vast to comprehend. A single teaspoon of good agricultural soil may contain millions of living organisms. Soil organisms include bacteria, fungi, algae, protozoa, worms, insects, and larger plants and animals (Figure 34–14). Bacteria and fungi are particularly essential in decomposing dead organic material. They are also important in nutrient cycles. For example, most steps in the nitrogen cycle involve microorganisms (see Chapter 54). Mycorrhizae, symbiotic associations between fungi and the roots of most plants, aid in the uptake of mineral ions. The hyphae come into contact with a large amount of soil and absorb minerals and transfer them to the plant. Food produced by photosynthesis is transferred to the fungus. Plant growth is often enhanced by mycorrhizal associations (see Figure 25–1 and Chapters 25 and 53).

Soil is not a solid. Approximately 30% to 60% of the volume of soil is occupied by space between soil particles. These spaces are filled with varying proportions of soil air and soil water. Soil air has a slightly different composition of gases than atmospheric air. Generally, the level of oxygen is lower and the level of carbon dioxide is higher in soil air. This is due to the respiratory activities of the organisms living in the soil. Both air and water are necessary in soil for good plant growth. Roots use oxygen for respiration. Plants living in swamps and marshes have special adaptations enabling them to survive in anaerobic soil, including large air spaces within the plant tissues and special roots for aeration.

Soil Erosion Is a Serious Threat to Cultivated Soils in Many Regions of the World

Just as the formation of soil from rock is a gradual process, so too soil is gradually worn away, or eroded, from land surfaces. Soil erosion, like soil formation, is a natural process. Two environmental factors that promote erosion are water and wind. Raindrops loosen soil particles, which can then be carried away by running water. Wind is particularly effective in removing soil from bare, dry land. The Dust Bowl in the 1930s was a vivid example of the effect of wind erosion. Soil from states like Oklahoma and Colorado was blown as far east as several hundred miles off the Atlantic coast.

Although soil erosion is a natural process, the effects of water and wind are much reduced when plant cover is sufficient. Plant roots are very effective at holding the soil in place, and stems and leaves cover the ground, lessening the effects of rainfall and wind. Human activities such as agriculture and deforestation accelerate soil erosion by removing the natural plant cover.

Figure 34–14   A large variety of organisms live in the soil. In addition to plant roots, the soil contains bacteria, algae, protozoa, fungi, worms, insects, and an assortment of other animals.

Plains and deserts are particularly vulnerable to soil erosion because they have frequent, prolonged droughts. Plants native to such environments have adaptations that enable them to survive. Crops are usually not adapted to survive droughts, however, and therefore die, leaving the soil exposed and susceptible to erosion.

ROOTS OBTAIN MOST OF THE MINERALS FOUND IN PLANTS

More than 90 naturally occurring elements exist on Earth. More than 60 of these, including elements as common as carbon and as rare as gold, have been found in plant tissues. Not all these elements are considered essential for plant growth, however.

How do biologists determine whether an element is essential? One of the most useful methods is **hydroponics,** growing plants in aerated water with dissolved mineral salts (see Focus on Commercial Hydroponics for another use of hydroponics). It is impossible to conduct mineral nutrition experiments by growing plants in soil because soil is too complex and contains too many elements. However, one can grow plants in a solution of water and all known required mineral salts. If a biologist suspects that a particular element is essential for plant growth, he or she grows plants in a nutrient

FOCUS ON

Commercial Hydroponics

Hydroponics, the practice of growing plants in an aerated solution of chemically defined mineral salts, has been used by scientists to determine which elements are essential. Initially, entrepreneurs hailed hydroponics as the scientific way to grow plants in places where soil was poor or unavailable. However, the expenses involved in commercially growing produce for human consumption prevented hydroponics from becoming more than a curiosity. Recent technical improvements have revived the interest in commercial hydroponics.

Hydroponics has great potential in several places. It is being tried experimentally in desert countries in the Middle East, where the soil is too arid to support cultivation and water is unavailable for irrigation. When plants are grown hydroponically in greenhouses, little water is used compared with traditional agriculture (see figure). Hydroponics is also

Hydroponically grown Boston lettuce. (Grant Heilman, from Grant Heilman Photography)

being tried in temperate latitudes, particularly for winter crops.

Hydroponics has several advantages. First, it is possible to grow these crops under conditions in which pathogens and pests are completely absent. This means that the crops are not exposed to pesticides. Also, hydroponics can be used to

grow crops near their area of use, saving on transportation costs.

The main disadvantage of hydroponics is the expense. The plants must be supplied with nutrient solution, which must be continually monitored and adjusted. Heating and lighting costs are high. Aeration of the roots had been a major expense, although recent developments like the nutrient film technique have cut costs considerably. In the nutrient film technique, the plants are grown in plastic trenches through which a film of nutrient solution is run. In this way, the roots get adequate aeration. The nutrient solution is saved and reused on the plants, cutting down on water and mineral costs.

Although hydroponics will probably never replace traditional agriculture, it has been shown to be a viable alternative in certain situations. As new techniques are developed, hydroponics may become even more common.

---

solution that contains all known essential elements except the one in question. If plants grown in the absence of that element are unable to develop normally or to complete their life cycle, the element may be essential. Additional criteria are used to determine whether an element is essential. The element must be shown to have a direct effect on the metabolism of the plant. Also, the element must be demonstrated to be essential for a wide variety of plant species.

Sixteen Elements Are Essential for Plant Growth

Sixteen elements have been demonstrated to be essential for plant growth (Figure 34–15). Nine of these are required in fairly large quantities (greater than 0.05% dry weight) and are therefore known as **macronutrients:** carbon, hydrogen, oxygen, nitrogen, phosphorus, potassium, sulfur, calcium, and magnesium. The remaining seven **micronutrients** are needed in trace amounts for normal plant growth and development:

iron, boron, manganese, copper, molybdenum, chlorine, and zinc.

Four of the sixteen elements—carbon, oxygen, hydrogen, and nitrogen—come from water or gases in the atmosphere. Carbon is obtained from carbon dioxide in the atmosphere and incorporated during photosynthesis. Oxygen is obtained from atmospheric oxygen (O_2) and water. Water also supplies hydrogen to the plant. Plants get their nitrogen from the soil as ions of nitrogen salts—nitrate (NO_3^-) and ammonium (NH_4^+)—but nitrogen is converted into those forms from atmospheric nitrogen (N_2) by various microorganisms in the soil. The remaining 12 essential elements are obtained from the soil as dissolved mineral ions. Their ultimate source is the parent rock from which the soil was formed.

Some of the roles of the essential elements are summarized in Table 34–2. Carbon, hydrogen, and oxygen are found in all biologically important molecules, including lipids, carbohydrates, nucleic acids, and proteins. Nitrogen is part of proteins, nucleic acids, and chlorophyll. Phosphorus is critical for plants because it

Figure 34–15 Tobacco plants illustrating the effects of deficiencies of specific elements. The plant in the center (Ck.) received all the essential elements. The others were supplied with all essential elements except the one indicated on the label. All plants are the same age and variety. Some of them exhibit chlorosis (breakdown of chlorophyll) and necrosis (death of tissue). (W. R. Robbins, Rutgers University)

is found in nucleic acids, phospholipids (an essential part of cell membranes), and energy transfer molecules like ATP. The middle lamella, which is the cementing layer of the plant cell wall, contains calcium. Calcium has also been implicated in a number of physiological roles in plants, including membrane permeability. Magnesium is part of the chlorophyll molecule (see Figure 8–8). Sulfur is essential because it is found in certain amino acids and vitamins.

Potassium, which plants use in fairly substantial amounts, is not found in a specific compound or group of compounds. Rather, it remains as free K^+ ions in plant cells. Potassium has a very important role in maintaining the turgidity of cells because it promotes the movement of water (by osmosis) into cells. Its role in the opening and closing of stomata through its effect on osmosis in the guard cells has already been discussed (see Chapter 32). In addition to its role in maintaining cell turgidity, chloride (Cl^-) ions, which are present in very minute amounts in plants, are essential for photosynthesis.

Five of the micronutrients (iron, manganese, copper, zinc, and molybdenum) are associated with various enzymes, often as enzyme activators. Potassium is also involved in certain enzymatic reactions. The role of boron in plants is unclear. Recent experiments have suggested that boron is involved in membrane transport, particularly of carbohydrates. Boron also appears to affect calcium utilization.

Besides the sixteen essential elements, several additional elements have been demonstrated to be essential for specific plants. Nickel is involved in enzymatic reactions in legumes such as peas and beans; sodium is probably essential for sugar beets, bluegrass, plants adapted to saline conditions, and plants with C-4 photosynthesis (see Chapter 8); silicon enhances the growth of various grasses. After further evaluation, one or more of these elements may be added to the list of essential elements.

Fertilizers Replace Essential Elements if They Are Missing from the Soil

In a natural ecosystem the minerals removed from the soil by plants are returned when the plants or the animals that eat them die and decompose. However, the agricultural practices of humans prevent this cycle from occurring. The removal of crops from the land gradually depletes the soil of certain essential elements. Likewise, homeowners mow their lawns and remove the

Table 34–2   FUNCTIONS OF ESSENTIAL ELEMENTS

Element	Major Functions
Carbon	Structural–in carbohydrates, lipids, proteins, and nucleic acids
Hydrogen	Structural–in carbohydrates, lipids, proteins, and nucleic acids
Oxygen	Structural–in carbohydrates, lipids, proteins, and nucleic acids
Nitrogen	Structural—in proteins, nucleic acids, chlorophyll, certain coenzymes
Phosphorus	Structural—in nucleic acids, phospholipids, ATP (energy transfer compound)
Calcium	Structural—in middle lamella of cell walls Physiological—role in membrane permeability; enzyme activation
Magnesium	Structural—in chlorophyll Physiological—enzyme activator in carbohydrate metabolism
Sulfur	Structural—in certain amino acids and vitamins
Potassium	Physiological—osmosis and ionic balance; opening and closing of stomata; enzyme activator (for 40+ enzymes)
Chlorine	Physiological—ionic balance; involved in light reactions (oxygen evolution) of photosynthesis
Iron	Physiological—part of enzymes involved in photosynthesis, respiration, and nitrogen fixation
Manganese	Physiological—part of enzymes involved in respiration and nitrogen metabolism; required in oxygen evolution in photosynthesis
Copper	Physiological—part of enzymes involved in photosynthesis
Zinc	Physiological—part of enzymes involved in respiration and nitrogen metabolism
Molybdenum	Physiological—part of enzymes involved in nitrogen metabolism
Boron	Physiological—exact role unclear; involved in membrane transport and calcium utilization

clippings, preventing decomposition and cycling of minerals that were in the grass blades (see Focus on Managing Your Lawn and Garden at Home).

Plant growth is usually limited by the essential material (water, sunlight, or some essential element) that is in shortest supply. This is sometimes called the **concept of limiting factors** (see Chapter 53). The three elements that are most often limiting factors for plants are nitrogen, phosphorus, and potassium. To sustain the productivity of agricultural soils, fertilizers are periodically added to replace those minerals that limit plant growth.

There are two main types of fertilizers, organic and inorganic. Organic fertilizers come from natural sources such as cow manure and ground corncobs. Green manure, another type of organic fertilizer, is actually a crop that is planted in the soil and deliberately plowed under to decompose rather than being harvested. Frequently, the plant that is grown as green manure fixes nitrogen (see Chapter 54) in its roots, thereby increasing the amount of nitrogen in the soil. Using organic fertilizers provides several advantages. First, they increase the amount of organic material in the soil, which improves a soil's water-holding capacity. Organic fertilizers also release the minerals they contain gradually, as decomposers break down the organic material. The addition of organic material to the soil changes the kinds of living organisms in the soil. In ways that are not yet clear to the scientists, this sometimes suppresses microorganisms that cause plant diseases.

Inorganic fertilizer is manufactured and its exact chemical composition is known. Most inorganic fertilizers contain the three elements (nitrogen, phosphorus, and potassium) that are usually the limiting factors in plant growth. The numbers on fertilizer bags (for example, 10, 20, 20) indicate the relative concentrations of each of the three elements (N, P, K). An advantage of inorganic fertilizers over organic fertilizers is that one knows precisely how much of which elements are being applied to the soil. By varying the relative concentra-

FOCUS ON

Managing Your Lawn and Garden at Home

It is possible to put some of what you have learned in this chapter to use when managing your lawn and garden at home. You can maintain and improve your soil by using compost and mulches.

Gardeners often dispose of grass clippings, leaves, and other plant refuse by either bagging it for garbage collection or burning it. Neither is desirable, however: Bagging yard wastes contributes more material to our already overburdened landfills, whereas burning yard wastes contributes to air pollution. Besides, these materials are *not* wastes. They are a valuable resource because they can be used to form a natural soil and humus mixture called **compost** that improves soil fertility and soil structure. Grass clippings, leaves, weeds, sawdust, coffee grounds, animal manure, ashes from the fireplace or grill, shredded newspapers, and egg shells are just some of the materials that can be transformed by microbial action to compost (see figure).

The process of reducing organic debris to compost is called **composting.** To make a compost heap, spread a 6- to 12-inch layer of material in a shady area, sprinkle with garden fertilizer or a layer of manure, and cover with several inches of soil. Additional layers are added as more

Compost is a wonderful soil conditioner that is easily made from yard wastes and kitchen scraps. During the summer, compost is formed in as little as 30 days in the author's backyard in Maryland. One drawback is that microbial action decreases during cool weather.   (Dennis Drenner)

material become available. Water the material thoroughly and turn it over each month to aerate it. Although it is possible to make compost by just heaping it in layers, it is more efficient to construct a compost enclosure. An enclosed compost heap is also less likely to attract animals.

When the compost is uniformly dark in color, crumbly, and has a pleasant, "woodsy" odor, it is ready to be used. The time it takes for de-

composition varies depending on the temperature, the materials you are using, and how often you turn it and water it.

The use of **mulch,** which is any material used as a ground cover around plants, has multiple benefits. It helps control weeds and increases the amount of water in the upper levels of the soil by reducing evaporation. Mulch lowers the soil temperature in the summer and extends the growing season slightly by providing protection against cold in the fall. It decreases erosion by lessening the amount of precipitation runoff.

Although mulches can be of materials such as plastic sheets or gravel, natural mulches such as compost, grass clippings, straw, chopped corncobs, and shredded bark have the added benefit of increasing the organic content of the soil. Grass clippings are a very effective mulch when added around the base of garden plants because they are readily available and they mat together, making it difficult for weeds to become established. Grass mulches must be replaced often, however, because they decay rapidly. Some gardeners prefer mulches of more expensive materials such as shredded bark because they take longer to decompose and are more attractive.

tions of nitrogen, phosphorus, and potassium, a grower can induce different growth responses in plants. For example, when growing a lettuce crop, it is best to use a fertilizer with a high nitrogen content because that stimulates vigorous vegetative growth rather than reproduction. However, the application of a fertilizer with a high nitrogen content when growing tomato plants causes a low production of tomatoes. Although

the tomato plants grow vigorously with a high nitrogen fertilizer, they form few flowers and therefore few fruits.

Obviously, both organic and inorganic fertilizers have advantages. The chemical elements supplied by each are identical, however. Nitrogen from commercial, inorganic fertilizer is the same as nitrogen from organic fertilizer.

SUMMARY

I. Anchorage, absorption, conduction, and storage are the main functions of roots.

A. Roots may be modified for additional functions such as support, aeration, and photosynthesis.

II. Primary roots have an epidermis, cortex, endodermis, pericycle, xylem, and phloem.
   A. The epidermis protects the root and absorbs water and minerals.
   B. The cortex contains storage tissue.
   C. The endodermis controls water uptake by the root.
   D. The pericycle divides to produce branch roots.
   E. The xylem conducts water and dissolved minerals.
   F. The phloem conducts dissolved food.
III. There are some structural differences between monocot and dicot roots.
   A. Monocot roots often have a pith, whereas dicot roots do not.
   B. Dicot roots have a vascular cambium, which monocot roots lack.
IV. Secondary roots have wood and bark.
V. Soil is the complex material in which plants root.
   A. Factors influencing soil formation include parent rock, climate, living organisms, time, and topography.
   B. Soil is composed of inorganic minerals, organic material, living organisms, soil air, and soil water.
   C. Erosion is a natural process that may be accelerated by certain human activities.
VI. Plants require essential elements for normal growth.
   A. Nine elements are macronutrients: carbon, oxygen, hydrogen, nitrogen, potassium, phosphorus, sulfur, magnesium, and calcium.
   B. Seven elements are micronutrients: iron, boron, manganese, copper, zinc, molybdenum, and chlorine.
   C. Essential elements are part of the structure of biological molecules, are important in the ionic balance of cells, and are involved in enzyme reactions.
   D. Some essential elements are added to the soil as organic or inorganic fertilizer.

POST-TEST

1. _____ roots are produced at unusual places on the plant.
2. Plants with bulbs often have _____ roots that pull the bulb deeper into the ground.
3. The waterproof region around the radial and transverse walls of endodermis cells is the _____ _____.
4. The _____ is the origin of branch roots.
5. The center of the dicot root is _____.
6. The center of a monocot root is _____.
7. Minerals may pass through a membrane against the concentration gradient by _____ _____.
8. The largest inorganic soil particles are _____, the medium-sized particles are _____, and the smallest particles are _____.
9. Growing plants in aerated water with dissolved mineral salts is known as _____.
10. _____ are essential elements required in fairly large quantities.
11. Although more than 60 elements have been found in plant tissues, only _____ (how many) are essential for plant growth.
12. _____ is an essential element found in phospholipids, nucleic acids, and energy transfer molecules like ATP.
13. _____ ions and chloride ions have a role in maintaining the turgidity of cells.
14. New cell walls, particularly the middle lamella, could not be synthesized in the absence of _____.
15. _____, along with carbon, oxygen, hydrogen, and nitrogen, is a part of chlorophyll molecules.
16. Green manure is an example of a/an _____ fertilizer.
17. The three elements that most often limit plant growth are potassium, phosphorus, and _____.
18. Grass clippings, leaves, egg shells, and other natural materials can be reduced to a natural soil conditioner called _____.
19. _____ is shredded bark, compost, straw, or some similar material that is placed on the ground around plants.

REVIEW QUESTIONS

1. Trace the pathway of water from the soil through the various root tissues.
2. Compare the uptake of water with the uptake of minerals by the root.
3. How does a root with primary growth develop secondary tissues?
4. List the five components of soil and tell how each is important to plants.
5. Explain how biological, chemical, and physical weathering processes convert rock into soil.
6. How might you design an experiment to determine whether gold is essential for plant growth? What would you use for an experimental control?
7. What criteria have biologists used to determine which elements are essential for plant growth?
8. Give the advantages of both organic and inorganic fertilizers.

RECOMMENDED READINGS

Brown, J. C., and V. D. Jolley. Plant metabolic responses to iron-deficiency stress. *BioScience* 39:8, September 1989. An in-depth discussion of the factors that make iron in the soil available to roots.

Feldman, L. J. The habits of roots. *BioScience* 38:9, October 1988. How roots interact with their soil environment.

Mauseth, J. D. *Botany: An Introduction to Plant Biology.* Saunders College Publishing, Philadelphia, 1991. A comprehensive introduction to general botany.

Moore, P. Upwardly mobile roots. *Nature* 341, 21 September 1989. An essay on unusual root behaviors, including roots that grow out of the soil and up the trunk of a tree to obtain nutrients leaching from the forest canopy.

Raven, P. H., R. F. Evert, and S. E. Eichhorn. *Biology of Plants,* 5th ed. Worth Publishers, New York, 1992. A general botany text with an evolutionary emphasis.

Taiz, L., and E. Zeiger. *Plant Physiology.* Benjamin/Cummings Publishing Company, Redwood City, CA, 1991. A plant physiology textbook in which the individual chapters were written by various experts. Mineral nutrition is thoroughly covered.

❏

Reproduction in Flowering Plants

Many flowering plants are able to reproduce both sexually and asexually. Sexual reproduction involves the formation of flowers and, after fertilization, of seeds and fruits. More specifically, sexual reproduction entails the fusion of haploid male and female gametes, an egg and a sperm nucleus. The union of these cells, which is called fertilization, occurs within the ovary of the flower.

The offspring of sexual reproduction exhibit a great deal of individual variation. Each may resemble one of the parents, both of the parents, or neither of the parents. This variation is due in part to the recombination of genes that occurs during meiosis. (Recall that meiosis must occur in the life cycle if haploid gametes are to be produced.) The union of dissimilar gametes, often from two different parents, is also responsible for variable offspring, as it results in new combinations of genes not found in either parent. Sexual reproduction, then, offers the advantage of new combinations of genes that might make an individual plant better suited to its environment. Also, the seeds and fruits produced as a result of sexual reproduction have various mechanisms for dispersal, which make it possible for a plant species to extend its geographical range.

Asexual reproduction (also called vegetative propagation) in flowering plants does not usually involve the formation of flowers, seeds, and fruits. Instead, the vegetative structures of plants—stems, leaves, and roots—form offspring. In asexual reproduction, part of an existing plant becomes separated from the rest of the plant (by the death of tissues); this part subsequently grows to form a complete, independent plant.

Asexual reproduction always involves only one parent plant, and there is no fusion of gametes. The offspring are formed by mitosis, and meiosis is not involved. This means that the offspring of asexual reproduction are genetically identical to each other and to the parent plant from which they came.

Hepatica americana, liverleaf. This woodland plant flowers in early spring. (Rod Planck/Dembinsky Photo Associates)

After you have studied this chapter you should be able to

1. State the differences between sexual and asexual reproduction.
2. Distinguish between the following plant structures modified for asexual reproduction: rhizomes, tubers, stolons, corms, bulbs, plantlets, and suckers.
3. Explain the difference between seeds produced by apomixis and by sexual reproduction.
4. Define simple, aggregate, multiple, and accessory fruits and give an example of each.

5. Discuss several types of simple fruits (berry, drupe, follicle, legume, capsule, grain, and achene) and give an example of each.
6. Cite several different methods of seed and fruit dispersal.
7. Relate how flowering is induced by variations in the amounts of light and darkness.
8. Discuss phytochrome and its effects on photoperiodism.
9. Explain how temperature affects flowering.

ASEXUAL REPRODUCTION IN FLOWERING PLANTS MAY INVOLVE MODIFIED STEMS, LEAVES, OR ROOTS

Flowering plants have evolved many methods of asexual reproduction. Most of these involve modified vegetative parts. In particular, a number of asexual structures are modified stems—rhizomes, tubers, bulbs, corms, and stolons. These structures become separate plants when the parent tissues from which they arose die.

A **rhizome** is a horizontal underground stem that may or may not be fleshy for storing food. Although rhizomes resemble roots, they are really stems, as indicated by the presence of scalelike leaves, buds, nodes, and internodes. Rhizomes frequently branch in different directions (Figure 35–1). Over time, the older portion of the rhizome dies, eventually separating the two branches into distinct plants. Irises, bamboo, and many grasses are examples of plants that have rhizomes.

Another underground stem is a **tuber**, which is greatly enlarged for food storage. When the connection between a tuber and its parent plant breaks (often as a result of the parent plant dying), the tuber grows into a separate plant. White potatoes and *Caladium* are examples of plants that produce tubers (Figure 35–2). The "eyes" of a potato are actually lateral buds, evidence that the tuber is an underground stem rather than a storage root.

A **bulb** is a shortened underground stem to which fleshy storage leaves are attached (Figure 35–3). Bulbs are globose, or round, and are covered by paper-like bulb scales. They frequently form small daughter bulbs that are initially attached to the parent bulb; when the parent bulb dies and rots away, each daughter bulb can become established as a separate plant. Contractile roots (see Chapter 34) help to pull the daughter bulbs away from the parent. Lilies, tulips, onions, and daffodils form bulbs.

Figure 35–1 Iris. The rhizome is a horizontal underground stem. New shoots arise from buds that develop along the rhizome.

An underground stem that superficially resembles a bulb is a **corm** (Figure 35–3). The storage organ in a corm is the much thickened stem, rather than leaves as in a bulb. An entire corm is stem tissue that is covered with papery scales. These scales are modified leaves that are attached to the corm at nodes. Lateral buds that develop into daughter corms frequently arise on corms; the death of the parent corm separates these daughter corms. Plants that produce corms include crocus, gladiolus, and cyclamen.

Figure 35–2 Potatoes form rhizomes, which enlarge at the ends into tubers. When a parent plant dies, each tuber develops into a separate plant.

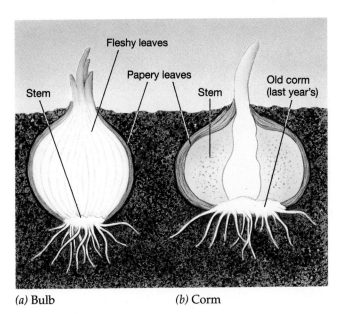

(a) Bulb   *(b)* Corm

Figure 35–3 Bulbs and corms. (*a*) A bulb is an underground stem to which are attached overlapping, fleshy leaves. (*b*) The entire corm is stem tissue, in contrast to the bulb, which is mostly leaf tissue.

Stolons, or runners, are horizontal stems that run above ground (Figure 35–4). They are characterized by having long internodes. Adventitious buds develop along a stolon, and each bud gives rise to a new daughter plant. When the stolon dies, the daughter plants are separated. The strawberry is an example of a plant that produces stolons.

Some plants are capable of forming **plantlets** (small plants) along their leaf margins. *Kalanchoe,* commonly called "mother of thousands," has meristematic tissue in the leaf that gives rise to an individual plantlet at each notch in the leaf (Figure 35–5). When these plantlets attain a certain size, they drop to the ground, root, and grow.

Some roots produce **suckers,** which are aboveground stems that develop from adventitious buds on the roots. (Recall that buds generally originate on stems rather than on roots; hence, buds that develop on roots are described as "adventitious.") Each sucker grows roots at its base and becomes an independent plant when the parent plant dies (Figure 35–6). Plants that form suckers include black locust, pear, apple, cherry, red raspberry, and blackberry. Some weeds are able to produce large numbers of suckers. These plants are difficult to control, because pulling the plant out of the soil seldom removes all the roots. In response to wounding, the roots produce additional suckers, which can be a considerable nuisance.

Figure 35–4 The wild strawberry (*Fragaria virginiana*) reproduces asexually by forming stolons, or runners.

Apomixis Is the Production of Seeds without the Sexual Process

Sometimes plants produce embryos in seeds without meiosis and fusion of gametes. When this occurs, it is known as **apomixis.** For example, an embryo may develop from a diploid cell in the ovule rather than from a diploid zygote that forms from the union of two haploid gametes. The seeds produced by apomixis are a

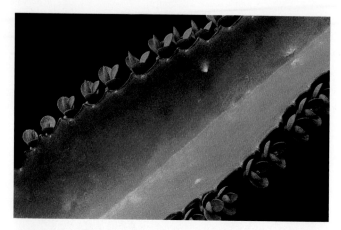

Figure 35–5 The "mother of thousands" (*Kalanchoe*) produces plantlets along the margins of the leaves. When the plantlets attain a certain size, they drop off and root in the ground. (Dennis Drenner)

Figure 35–7 The head of a dandelion. Each individual plumed structure is a fruit that contains a seed. Dandelion seeds are produced asexually by apomixis. The fruits are dispersed by wind currents. (Dennis Drenner)

form of asexual reproduction because there was no fusion of gametes. The embryo is genetically identical to the original parent. However, apomixis has an advantage over other methods of asexual reproduction in that the seeds and fruits produced by apomixis can be dispersed by methods associated with sexual reproduction (to be discussed shortly). Examples of plants that reproduce by apomixis include dandelions, citrus trees, blackberries, garlic, and certain grasses (Figure 35–7).

Figure 35–6 A grove of aspen trees in Utah. Quite often the entire grove is descended from a single plant that reproduced asexually by forming adventitious buds on the roots. These buds developed into suckers, each of which became a separate tree. Because the entire grove is genetically identical, their responses to the environment are uniform. In spring they break dormancy simultaneously, and in the fall their leaves turn color at the same time. (Sharon Cummings/Dembinsky Photo Associates)

SEXUAL REPRODUCTION IN FLOWERING PLANTS INVOLVES FLOWERS, FRUITS, AND SEEDS

The life cycle of flowering plants, including details about the flower, is considered in Chapter 27. After fertilization has occurred within the ovule in the ovary, the ovule develops into a seed, and the ovary surrounding it develops into a **fruit** (Figure 35–8). There are several types of fruits, which vary in structure owing to variations in the flowers from which they were formed. We consider a few representative types.

Fruits Are Mature, Ripened Ovaries

Simple fruits, aggregate fruits, multiple fruits, and accessory fruits are the four basic types of fruits (Table 35–1). A **simple fruit** develops from a single ovary of a single flower. Most fruits are simple fruits. At maturity simple fruits may be fleshy or dry. Two examples of fleshy fruits are berries and drupes (Figure 35–9). A **berry** is a fleshy fruit that has soft tissues throughout. Using this definition, a tomato is a berry, as are grapes and bananas. A **drupe** is a simple, fleshy fruit that has a hard, stony pit surrounding the seed. Examples of drupes include peaches, plums, and avocados.

Many simple fruits are dry at maturity. These fruits fall into two main categories, dehiscent fruits and indehiscent fruits. **Dehiscent fruits** split open at maturity, usually along seams or sutures (Figure 35–10). A milkweed **follicle** is an example of a simple, dry, dehiscent fruit that splits open along *one* seam or suture to release

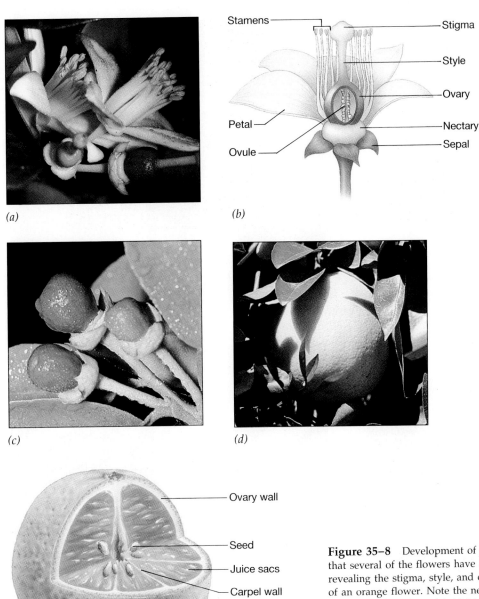

Stamens

Stigma

Style

Ovary

Nectary

Sepal

Petal

Ovule

(a)   *(b)*

(c)   *(d)*

Ovary wall

Seed

Juice sacs

Carpel wall

Figure 35–8   Development of orange fruits. (*a*) Orange flowers. Note that several of the flowers have already lost their petals and stamens, revealing the stigma, style, and ovary of the female structure. (*b*) Diagram of an orange flower. Note the nectary (organ that secretes nectar) in the diagram and in photo (*a*). (*c*) Maturing ovaries. The stigmas and styles have already dropped off. (*d*) Mature fruit. The orange is a modified berry. (*e*) Cross section through an orange. Each section of an orange is a single carpel. The ovary that develops into the fruit is composed of several fused carpels.   (*a, c,* Visuals Unlimited/William J. Weber; *d,* Visual Unlimited/ John D. Cunningham)

its seeds. A **legume** is a simple, dry, dehiscent fruit that splits open along *two* seams or sutures. Pea pods are examples of legumes, as are green beans, although they are harvested before the fruit has dried out and split open. A **capsule** is a simple, dry, dehiscent fruit that splits open along *multiple* seams or pores. Poppy and cotton fruits are capsules.

Indehiscent fruits are simple, dry fruits that do not split open at maturity (Figure 35–11). A **grain** is an ex-

ample of a simple, dry, indehiscent fruit. Kernels of corn and wheat are fruits of this type. Each grain contains one seed and its seed coat is fused to the fruit wall, so that the grain appears to be a seed rather than a fruit. An **achene** is a similar fruit in that it is simple, dry, and indehiscent and contains a single seed. However, the seed coat is not fused to the fruit wall in an achene. Rather, the single seed is attached to the fruit wall at one point only. Therefore, an achene can be separated

Table 35–1 SOME TYPES OF FRUITS*

I. Simple fruit
   A. Fleshy
      1. Berry
      2. Drupe
   B. Dry
      1. Dehiscent
         a. Follicle
         b. Legume
         c. Capsule
      2. Indehiscent
         a. Grain
         b. Achene
II. Aggregate fruit
III. Multiple fruit
IV. Accessory fruit

*The number of specific fruit types is great. This table includes only those types that are discussed in the text.

(a)

(a)

(b)

Figure 35–9 Simple fruits that are fleshy at maturity. (a) The tomato is an example of a berry. Note that the fruit is soft throughout. (b) The peach is a drupe. The hard, stony pit is part of the ovary. A single seed is inside the pit. (a, b, Dennis Drenner)

(b)

(c)

Figure 35–10 Simple, dry, dehiscent fruits. (a) A milkweed fruit is a follicle that splits open along one seam. (b) A bean fruit is a legume that splits open along two seams at maturity. (c) A capsule splits open along multiple seams or pores at maturity. These iris capsules dehisce along three seams. (a, James L. Castner; b, David Cavagnaro; c, G. R. Roberts)

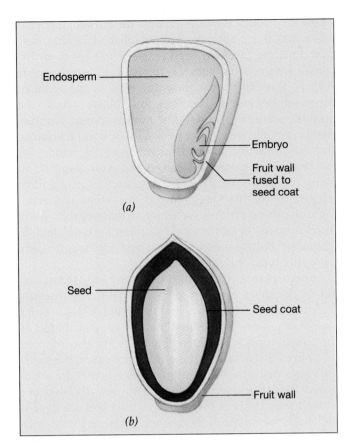

(a)

(b)

Figure 35–11 Simple, dry, indehiscent fruits. (*a*) A corn fruit is a grain. In a grain the fruit wall is fused to the seed coat. (*b*) A sunflower fruit is an achene. Its seed coat is not fused to the fruit wall and it is possible to peel off the fruit wall, separating it from the seed.

(a)

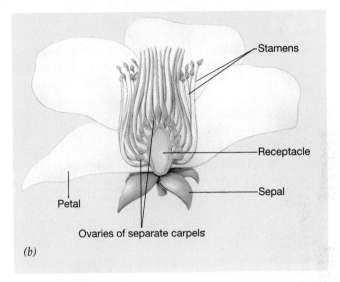

(b)

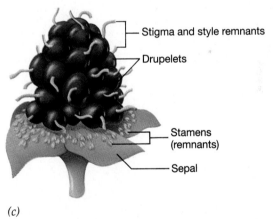

(c)

Figure 35–12 Blackberries are examples of aggregate fruits. (*a*) Developing fruits in various stages of maturity. (*b*) Cutaway view of a blackberry flower, showing the many separate carpels in the center of the flower. (*c*) A developing blackberry fruit is an aggregate of tiny drupelets. (*a*, Dennis Drenner)

from its seed. The sunflower fruit is an example of an achene. One can peel off the fruit wall (the "shell") to reveal the seed within.

Aggregate fruits are a second main type of fruit. An aggregate fruit is formed from a single flower that contains many separate carpels. (Recall from Chapter 27 that the carpel is the female reproductive unit of a flower.) After fertilization each ovary from each individual carpel enlarges. As they enlarge, the ovaries fuse to form a single fruit. Raspberries and blackberries are examples of aggregate fruits (Figure 35–12).

A third type of fruit is the **multiple fruit,** which is formed from the ovaries of many flowers that grow in close proximity on a common axis, or floral stalk. The ovary from each flower fuses with nearby ovaries as it enlarges and develops after fertilization. Pineapples and osage oranges are multiple fruits (Figure 35–13).

Accessory fruits are the fourth type of fruit. They differ from simple, aggregate, and multiple fruits in that other plant tissues, in addition to ovary tissue, make up the fruit. For example, the major edible portion of a strawberry is the red, fleshy **receptacle,** which

is the terminal part of the floral stalk. Apples and pears are also accessory fruits; the outer part of each fruit is an enlarged **floral tube** that surrounds the ovary (Figure 35–14).

Figure 35–13   The pineapple is a multiple fruit, formed from the ovaries of many separate flowers.   (Phil Degginger)

Fruit and Seed Dispersal Is Highly Varied in Flowering Plants

Flowering plants make use of wind, animals, water, and explosive dehiscence to disperse their seeds. Effective methods of seed dispersal have given some plants the opportunity to expand their range. If a seed is carried to

a new environment that is suitable for growth, it germinates and the plant becomes established in that new area. In some cases the seed is the actual agent of dispersal, whereas in others it is the fruit. In tumbleweeds such as Russian thistle, the *entire plant* is the agent of dispersal because it detaches and blows across the ground, scattering seeds as it bumps along. Tumbleweeds are lightweight but have a lot of wind resistance and are sometimes carried for miles by the wind.

Wind is responsible for seed and fruit dispersal in many plants (Figure 35–15). Plants such as maple have winged fruits that are adapted for wind dispersal. Light, feathery plumes are other structures that allow fruits or seeds to be transported, often for considerable distances. Both dandelion fruits and milkweed seeds have this type of adaptation.

Some plants have evolved special structures that aid in dispersal of their seeds and fruits by animals (Figure 35–15). The spines and barbs of cockleburs and similar fruits catch in animal fur and are distributed as the animal moves. Fleshy, edible fruits are also adapted for animal dispersal. As these fruits are eaten, the seeds are either discarded or swallowed. Seeds that are swallowed have thick seed coats and are not digested but instead pass through the digestive tract and are deposited with the animal's feces some distance away from the parent plant. Animals like squirrels and many bird species also help to disperse acorns and other fruits and seeds by burying them for winter use (see Making the

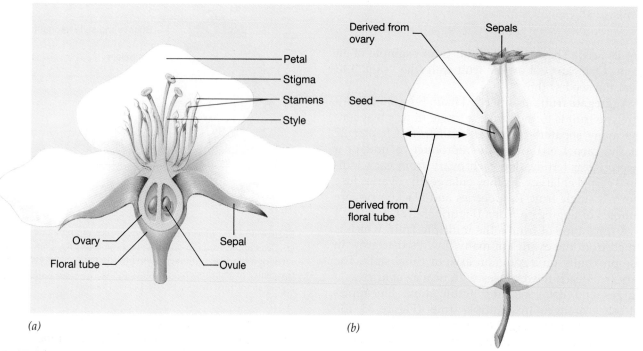

(a)

(b)

Figure 35–14   The pear is an accessory fruit. (*a*) Note the floral tube surrounding the ovary in the pear flower. This tube becomes the major edible portion of the pear. (*b*) Longitudinal section through a pear, showing the fruit tissue derived from both the floral tube and the ovary.

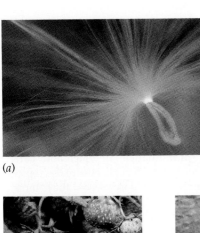
(a)

(b)

(c)

(d)

(e)

Figure 35–15 Methods of seed and fruit dispersal. (*a*) The feathery plumes of a milkweed seed make it buoyant for dispersal by wind. (*b*) The fruits of sugar maple have wings for wind dispersal. (*c*) *Acaena* fruits clinging to sheep wool are carried away from the parent plant. (*d*) Fleshy fruits are eaten by animals such as this meadow vole. The seeds are frequently swallowed whole and pass unharmed through the animal's digestive tract. (*e*) Coconuts are adapted for water dispersal. When it washes ashore, the coconut germinates, often thousands of kilometers from its original home. (*a*, David Cavagnaro; *b*, Dennis Drenner; *c*, G. R. Roberts; *d*, Dwight R. Kuhn; *e*, James L. Castner)

Connection: Seed Dispersal By Ants: An Example of Mutualism). Many buried seeds are never used by the animal and germinate the following spring.

The coconut is an example of a fruit that is adapted for dispersal by water (Figure 35–15). It has air spaces and corky floats that make it buoyant and capable of being carried by ocean currents for thousands of miles. When it washes ashore, the seed within germinates and grows into a coconut palm tree.

Some fruits accomplish dispersal without relying on wind, animals, or water. These fruits use explosive dehiscence to forcibly discharge their seeds. Pressures due to differences in turgor or to drying out cause them to burst open suddenly. The fruits of plants like touch-me-not and bitter cress dehisce so explosively that seeds are scattered several feet (Figure 35–16).

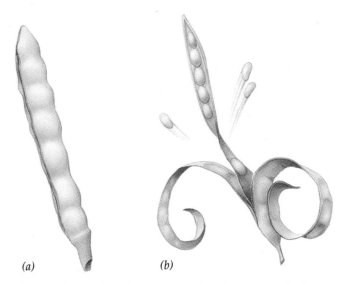
(a)   (b)

Figure 35–16 Explosive dehiscence in bitter cress (*Cardamine*). (*a*) Intact fruit before it has dehisced. (*b*) The fruit dehisces with explosive force, propelling the seeds some distance from the plant.

ENVIRONMENTAL CUES MAY INDUCE FLOWERING IN PLANTS

The initiation of sexual reproduction is often under environmental control, particularly in temperate latitudes. Environmental control is important for the plant's survival, because the timing of sexual reproduction is critical to reproductive success. Plants in temperate climates must flower and form fruits and seeds before dormancy is induced by the onset of winter. A number of plants detect changes in the relative amounts of daylight and darkness that accompany the changing seasons and flower in response to these changes. These plants vary

MAKING THE CONNECTION

Seed Dispersal by Ants: An Example of Mutualism

For a plant species to survive, it must be able to disperse its seeds to places where they can successfully germinate and grow. Natural selection has resulted in a variety of dispersal methods (such as wind, animals, and water) that increase the chances of seeds landing in suitable locations. Regardless of how seeds are dispersed from the parent plant, however, most seeds land in places that are unsuitable for growth, or they are eaten by animals such as mice and squirrels shortly after being dispersed.

The germination of seeds and the subsequent growth of seedlings are favored if the seeds are planted underground. Also, if the seeds are underground, they are less likely to be eaten by animals. The role of burying seeds underground is performed for many plant species by ants, which collect the seeds and take them underground to their nests. Ants disperse and bury seeds for hundreds of different plant species in almost every environment on Earth, from northern coniferous forests to tropical rain forests to deserts.

This remarkable relationship between ants and flowering plants is an example of **mutualism,** in which both partners benefit from the association. The ants ensure the reproductive success of the plants whose seeds they bury, whereas the plants supply food to the ants. A seed that is collected and taken underground by ants often contains a special structure called an oil body that protrudes from the seed. Oil bodies are a nutritious food for ants, which carry seeds underground before removing the oil bodies. Once an oil body is removed from a seed, the ants discard the undamaged seed in an underground refuse pile, which happens to be rich in organic material (such as ant droppings and dead ants) and contains the minerals required by young seedlings. Thus, ants not only bury the seeds away from animals that might eat them but also place the seeds in rich soil that is ideal for seed germination and seedling growth. Other examples of mutualism are considered in Chapter 53.

---

in their response to the duration and timing of light and dark, but the overall mechanism of detection is the same. Other plants have temperature requirements that induce sexual reproduction.

Flowering May Be Initiated by Changes in Light and Dark Periods

Photoperiodism is any response by a plant to the relative lengths of daylight and darkness. Flowering is one of several physiological activities that are photoperiodic in many plants. For example, if one were to plant Biloxi soybeans at 2-week intervals from early May to August, they would all flower at the same time in September, regardless of size or age of individual plants. Biloxi soybeans are photoperiodic and flower only when they are exposed to a specific daylight/darkness course of treatment.

Plants are classified into three main groups on the basis of how photoperiodism affects their flowering. **Short-day plants** were initially defined as plants that flower when exposed to some critical day length or less. However, the important factor in the initiation of flowering in short-day plants is the long, uninterrupted period of darkness rather than the short period of daylight. In other words, *short-day plants flower when the night length is equal to or greater than some critical length.* Examples of short-day plants are chrysanthemum and

Figure 35–17 The chrysanthemum is a short-day plant. Two identical cuttings from the same plant were planted in separate pots. The plant on the left, which flowered, received 8 hours of daylight and 16 hours of darkness. The plant on the right, which remained vegetative, received 16 hours of daylight and 8 hours of darkness.   (Dennis Drenner)

poinsettia, which typically flower in late summer or fall (Figure 35–17). To summarize, short-day plants are able to detect the shortening days of late summer or fall and defer flowering until then.

Long-day plants were initially defined as being able to flower when the day length is equal to or greater than some critical amount. However, a more accurate definition would be that *long-day plants flower when the night length is equal to or less than some critical length.* Plants such as clover, black-eyed Susan, and lettuce flower in late spring or summer and are long-day plants. Thus, these plants are able to detect the lengthening days of spring and summer and defer flowering until that time.

The critical day length (or night length) that initiates flowering varies from species to species, and a long-day plant does not necessarily have a longer critical day length than a short-day plant. For example, cocklebur (a short-day plant) has a critical day length of 15.5 hours, whereas black henbane (a long-day plant) has a critical day length of 11 hours.

Some plants do not initiate flowering in response to changing amounts of daylight and darkness. These **day-neutral plants** flower in response to some other type of stimulus, either external or internal. Tomato, dandelion, string bean, and pansy are examples of day-neutral plants.

Phytochrome detects varying periods of day length and darkness

For plants, or any living organism, to have a biological response to light, there must be a **photoreceptor** (light-sensitive pigment) in that organism to absorb the light. There are often different photoreceptors for different physiological responses. The photoreceptor involved in photoperiodism and a number of other light-initiated physiological responses of plants is a blue-green, proteinaceous pigment called **phytochrome**. Phytochrome, which is present in all vascular plants, has two forms, and it can readily convert from one form to the other upon absorption of light of specific wavelengths. One form of phytochrome, designated P_R (for red-absorbing phytochrome), strongly absorbs red light (at 660 nm). In the process the conformation (shape) of the phytochrome molecule changes to the second form of phytochrome, P_{FR}. This form of phytochrome is so designated because it strongly absorbs red light of longer wavelengths than P_R, described as far-red light (at 730 nm). When P_{FR} absorbs far-red light, it reverts back to the original form, P_R. The P_{FR} form of phytochrome is less stable than the P_R form and so it also reverts spontaneously, albeit slowly, to P_R in the dark. The form of phytochrome that triggers physiological responses such as flowering is P_{FR}.

But what does a pigment that absorbs red light and far-red light have to do with daylight? The sun's light is composed of the entire spectrum of visible light in addition to ultraviolet and infrared radiation. However, sunlight has more red light than far-red light. Therefore, the phytochrome in a plant exposed to the sunlight is a mixture of both P_R and P_{FR}, with P_{FR} predominating. During the night the P_{FR} slowly reverts back to P_R.

Phytochrome affects flowering

In short-day plants the active form of phytochrome, P_{FR}, *inhibits* flowering. In order to flower, these plants need long nights. The long period of darkness allows the P_{FR} to completely revert back to P_R so the plant has some minimum time during the 24-hour period with *no* P_{FR} present. This initiates flowering.

Biologists have experimented with short-day plants by growing them under a short-day/long-night regimen, but interrupting the night with a short burst of red light. Exposure to red light for as brief a period as 10 minutes in the middle of the night prevents flowering in short-day plants (Figure 35–18). This effect occurs because the brief exposure to red light converts some of the phytochrome from the P_R form to the P_{FR} form. Therefore, the plant does not have a sufficient period of time at night without any P_{FR}.

The effect that a short period of red light in the middle of the night has on short-day plants is reversible. That is, if a short-day plant is grown under conditions of short days and long nights, with a night-time brief flash of red light followed by a brief flash of far-red light, that plant will flower. Based on our understanding of the photoreversible nature of phytochrome, this observation is easy to explain. Short-day plants need long nights to allow for complete dark reversion of P_{FR} to P_R to initiate flowering. A brief flash of red light in the middle of the night converts P_R to P_{FR}. However, if this is followed by a brief period of far-red light, the P_{FR} is converted back to P_R. Therefore, flowering occurs.

In long-day plants the active form of phytochrome, P_{FR}, *induces* flowering. Long-day plants exposed to a long-day/short-night regimen flower. The long days cause these plants to produce predominantly P_{FR}. During the short nights some P_{FR} is slowly changed to P_R, but sufficient P_{FR} remains to induce flowering.

Plant biologists are puzzled by the observation that P_{FR}, the active form of phytochrome, inhibits flowering in short-day plants and induces flowering in long-day plants. Why different plants respond in opposite ways to P_{FR} is not known at this time. Biologists are also seeking to understand the exact mechanism of phytochrome action. There is a long period of time—days or even weeks—between the activation of phytochrome by the appropriate light signal and flowering. Once phyto-

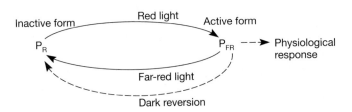

| Long day | Short day | Short day with night interruption |

Short-day plant

Long-day plant

Figure 35–18 Photoperiodic response of a short-day plant (*top row*) and a long-day plant (*bottom row*) to different periods of light and dark. Note that the short-day plant does not flower when exposed to 8 hours of daylight and 16 hours of darkness interrupted with a brief flash of light. This same treatment induces the long-day plant to flower.

chrome has absorbed light and changed into another form, what happens next? Does the activation of phytochrome somehow trigger the production of a hormone, which then initiates flowering? This might be expected, because phytochrome is activated in the leaves but flowering occurs some distance away—in the shoot apical meristem. To date, however, such a chemical messenger has not been identified. Does phytochrome work by affecting membranes or enzymes or gene expression? Does it work by some combination of these mechanisms? Regardless of its mode of action, the universal presence of phytochrome in vascular plants attests to its importance.

Phytochrome is involved in many other plant responses to light

Phytochrome has been implicated in a number of physiological responses besides flowering. For example, it is involved in the light requirement of some seeds for germination (see Chapter 31). This response is photorever-

sible by exposure to red or far-red light. Seeds with a light requirement for germination must be exposed to red light. Exposure to red light converts P_R to P_{FR}, and germination occurs. However, if the seeds are exposed to a brief period of red light followed by a brief period of far-red, they do *not* germinate because P_{FR} is converted back to P_R, the inactive form. Experiments on the photoreversible nature of phytochrome have been conducted in which seeds are exposed to a large number of alternating red and far-red light treatments. Regardless of how many light treatments one gives the seeds, they always respond to the *last* treatment. If the last treatment is red light, the seeds germinate. If the last treatment is far-red light, the seeds remain dormant (Figure 35–19).

Other physiological functions under the influence of phytochrome include sleep movements in leaves (see Chapter 36), shoot dormancy, leaf abscission, and pigment formation in flowers, fruits, and leaves. The importance of light in various plant functions besides photosynthesis cannot be overemphasized. Timing of daylight and darkness is a key way for plants to mea-

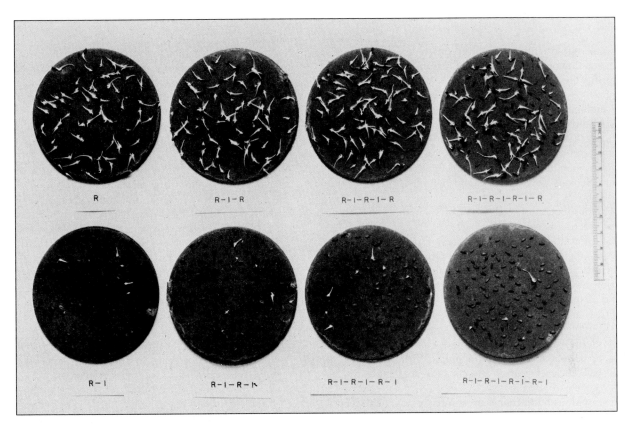

Figure 35–19 The control of lettuce seed germination by red (R) and far-red (I) light. Seeds are moistened and then exposed to red light (for 1 minute each exposure) and far-red light (for 4 minutes each exposure) in the sequences indicated. If the last exposure is red light, most of the seeds germinate. If the last exposure is far-red light, they remain dormant. (Borthwick, H. A., et al., *Proceedings of the National Academy of Science USA* 38:662, 1952)

sure the changes from one season to the next. This measurement is crucial for survival, particularly in environments where the climate fluctuates.

Temperature May Also Affect Reproduction

In certain plants temperature has an effect on flowering. The promotion of flowering by exposure to low temperature is known as **vernalization.** The part of the plant that must be exposed to low temperature varies. For some plants the moist seeds must be exposed to a period of several weeks of low temperature. For other species the young, recently germinated seedlings have a "cold" requirement. Some plants have an absolute requirement for the low-temperature period. That is, they do not flower unless they have been vernalized. Other plants flower sooner if exposed to low temperatures, but they would have flowered at a later time anyway.

Examples of plants with a low-temperature requirement include biennials like carrots and annuals like winter wheat. Carrots and other biennials grow vegetatively the first year, storing surplus food that is produced by photosynthesis in their roots. After remaining dormant during the winter, they flower and reproduce during the second year. Carrots left in a warm environment and not exposed to low temperatures continue vegetative growth indefinitely and do not initiate sexual reproduction.

The external stimulus that a plant responds to (in this case, temperature) is moderated and influenced by internal conditions such as hormone levels within the plant. For example, it is possible to eliminate the low-temperature requirement for flowering in biennials by treatment with a certain plant hormone. You will discover in the next chapter that hormones affect every aspect of plant growth and development.

SUMMARY

I. Asexual reproduction (vegetative propagation) involves the formation of offspring without fusion of gametes. The offspring are genetically identical to the single parent plant.
   A. Rhizomes, tubers, bulbs, corms, and stolons are stems specialized for asexual reproduction.
   B. Some leaves have meristematic tissue along their margins and give rise to plantlets.
   C. Roots may develop adventitious buds that form suckers. Suckers develop roots and may give rise to new plants.
   D. The production of seeds and fruits without sexual reproduction is called apomixis.
II. Sexual reproduction involves the fusion of gametes. The flower is the organ in which sexual reproduction occurs, and fruits and seeds develop as a result of sexual reproduction. Sexual reproduction results in genetic variability in the offspring.
   A. Fruits are mature, ripened ovaries.
      1. Simple fruits develop from a single ovary of a single flower.
         a. Berries and drupes are simple, fleshy fruits.
         b. Follicles, legumes, and capsules are simple, dry, dehiscent fruits.
         c. Grains and achenes are simple, dry, indehiscent fruits.
      2. Aggregate fruits develop from many ovaries within a single flower.
      3. Multiple fruits develop from many ovaries of many flowers growing in close proximity on a common axis.
      4. In accessory fruits the major part of the fruit is tissue other than ovary tissue.
   B. Seeds and fruits of flowering plants are adapted for various means of dispersal—wind, animals, water, and explosive dehiscence.
III. Photoperiodism is the response of plants to the duration and timing of light and dark.
   A. Flowering is a photoperiodic response, with some plants being short-day plants and others long-day plants. Day-neutral plants flower regardless of photoperiod.
   B. The photoreceptor in photoperiodism is a photoreversible pigment, phytochrome.
      1. P_R absorbs red light, converting it to P_{FR}.
      2. P_{FR} absorbs far-red light, converting it to P_R. P_{FR} also reverts slowly back to P_R in darkness.
      3. The active form of phytochrome involved in flowering and other physiological responses is P_{FR}. P_{FR} inhibits flowering in short-day plants, but it induces flowering in long-day plants.
   C. Other physiological responses (such as seed germination in certain plants) are influenced by phytochrome.
IV. Vernalization is the promotion of flowering by exposure to low temperatures.

POST-TEST

1. Genetic variability in offspring is characteristic of _____ reproduction.
2. The _____ is a horizontal, underground stem that is specialized for asexual reproduction.
3. The white potato is an example of an underground stem called a _____.
4. Another name for a runner is a(an) _____, an above-ground, horizontal stem.
5. In apomixis, fruits and seeds are produced by _____ means.
6. A(an) _____ may be defined as a mature, ripened ovary.
7. Grapes, tomatoes, and bananas are simple, fleshy fruits known as _____.
8. The peach is an example of a simple, fleshy fruit called a(an) _____.
9. A simple, dry fruit that splits open to liberate the seeds is said to be _____.
10. Grains and achenes are simple, dry, _____ fruits.
11. A legume is a simple, dry, dehiscent fruit that splits open along _____ seam(s).
12. A(an) _____ fruit forms from many ovaries of a single flower, whereas a(an) _____ fruit develops from many ovaries of many flowers.
13. Apples, strawberries, and pears are examples of _____ fruits.
14. Light, feathery plumes on the seed or fruit signify that it is most likely dispersed by _____.
15. Fleshy, edible fruits are adapted for dispersal by _____.
16. A response of a plant to the relative amounts of daylight and darkness is known as _____.
17. The critical factor in the flowering response of short-day and long-day plants is the amount of _____ (daylight or darkness).
18. The active form of phytochrome, P_{FR}, is formed when _____ light is absorbed.
19. _____ inhibits flowering in short-day plants but induces flowering in long-day plants.
20. _____ is the promotion of flowering by a low-temperature treatment.

REVIEW QUESTIONS

1. Would sexual or asexual reproduction be more beneficial in the following circumstances, and why?
   a. Tree in a stable environment
   b. Annual, herbaceous plant in a rapidly changing environment
   c. Plant with an extremely narrow geographical range
2. Would production of seeds and fruits by apomixis confer any special advantage that other asexual structures such as corms and bulbs lack?
3. Draw pictures to show the kinds of flowers that might form simple, aggregate, multiple, and accessory fruits.
4. Explain some of the features possessed by fruits and seeds that are dispersed by animals.
5. Predict whether flowering would be expected to occur in the following situations. Explain your answer with an emphasis on the involvement of phytochrome.
   a. A short-day plant is exposed to 15 hours of daylight and 9 hours of darkness.
   b. A short-day plant is exposed to 9 hours of daylight and 15 hours of darkness, with a 10-minute flash of red light in the middle of the night.
   c. A short-day plant is exposed to 9 hours of daylight and 15 hours of darkness with the following light treatments in the middle of the night: 10 minutes of red light, 10 minutes of far-red light, 10 minutes of red light, 10 minutes of far-red light.
6. Why is phytochrome described as a photoreversible pigment?

RECOMMENDED READINGS

Beattie, A. J. Ant plantation. *Natural History*, February 1990. Discusses the role that ants play in dispersing certain seeds.

Mauseth, J. D. *Botany: An Introduction to Plant Biology.* Saunders College Publishing, Philadelphia, 1991. A comprehensive introduction to general botany.

Raven, P. H., R. F. Evert, and S. E. Eichhorn. *Biology of Plants,* 5th ed. Worth Publishers, New York, 1992. A general botany text with an evolutionary emphasis.

Taiz, L., and E. Zeiger. *Plant Physiology.* Benjamin/Cummings Publishing Company, Redwood City, CA, 1991. A plant physiology textbook in which the individual chapters were written by various experts. Phytochrome and photoperiodism are thoroughly covered.

Plant Hormones and Responses

I t is generally assumed that plants, being firmly rooted in the ground, are incapable of self-directed movements. However, plants display a variety of movements and growth responses. Some of these are very gradual and subtle, whereas others are quite rapid and spectacular, as when a Venus flytrap snaps its leaf shut in less than 0.1 second after being stimulated (see Chapter 32).

Plants use environmental cues to determine when, whether, and to what extent many aspects of growth and development happen. We have already examined several environmental cues: seed germination is influenced by water, oxygen, temperature, and light (see Chapters 31 and 35); flowering is promoted in certain plants by periods of low temperature (see Chapter 35). Light is a particularly important environmental cue, affecting such diverse physiological responses as photosynthesis (see Chapter 8), stomatal

Dicentra, bleeding heart. The initiation of flowering in plants is under both environmental and hormonal controls. (Dwight R. Kuhn)

opening and closing (see Chapter 32), and flowering (see Chapter 35). Environmental cues often help match a plant's activities with the changing seasons.

Plants, like other complex organisms, respond to internal stimuli as well as external cues. All aspects of plant growth and development are affected by chemical messengers called hormones, which are produced in one part of the plant and transported to another, where they exert their influence. Five different hormones—auxins, gibberellins, cytokinins, ethylene, and abscisic acid—interact in complex ways with one another to produce a variety of responses in plants.

Thus hormones help regulate plant processes. Although plant hormones have been under active scientific investigation for more than a century, much remains to be learned about how they work.

After you have studied this chapter you should be able to

1. Distinguish between a tropism and a turgor movement.
2. Distinguish between phototropism, gravitropism, and thigmotropism.
3. Define circadian rhythm and give an example.
4. List several different ways each of the following hormones affects plant growth and development: auxins, gibberellins, cytokinins, ethylene, and abscisic acid.
5. Outline how the acid-growth hypothesis explains auxin-induced cell elongation.
6. Explain the effect of gibberellins on gene activity in germinating barley seeds.
7. Give an example of a physiological response in plants that may be due to varying ratios of several hormones rather than one specific hormone.
8. Relate which hormones are involved in the following physiological activities and how their functions interact: (a) leaf abscission; (b) seed germination; and (c) apical dominance.

TURGOR MOVEMENTS CAN INDUCE TEMPORARY PLANT MOVEMENTS

Mimosa pudica, the sensitive plant, dramatically folds its leaves and droops in response to a mechanical (touch), electrical, chemical, or thermal stimulus (Figure 36–1). The stimulus spreads throughout the plant even if only one leaflet is initially aroused. When a *Mimosa* leaf is stimulated by touching or some other manner, an electrical signal moves down the leaf to special cells in an organ at the base of the petiole called a **pulvinus** (plural, pulvini). Although it is recognized that plants such as *Mimosa* can use electrical signals for intercellular communication, the actual mechanism of the transmission is imperfectly understood at this time; it is similar to an action potential in animal neurons (see Chapter 39), but it moves much more slowly. Moreover, a chemical messenger is somehow involved. The pulvinus is a somewhat swollen joint that acts as a hinge. When the electrical signal reaches the pulvinus cells, it triggers a loss of turgor in certain of those cells as potassium ions

(a)

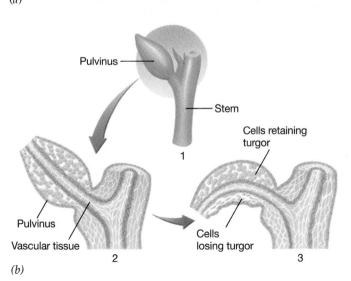

(b)

Figure 36–1 Turgor movements in the sensitive plant, *Mimosa pudica.* (a) *Left, Mimosa* before being disturbed. *Right,* the plant several seconds after being touched. Note how the leaves have folded and drooped. (b) (1) The base of a petiole, showing the pulvinus. (2) Section through a pulvinus, showing cells when leaf is undisturbed. (3) Section through a pulvinus, showing loss of turgor that produces the folding and collapsing of the leaves. (a, Dennis Drenner)

Figure 36–2 Solar tracking in sunflowers. Note how all the flower heads are oriented in the same direction. The orientation of the plants toward light in solar tracking is due to changes in turgor. (Grant Heilman, from Grant Heilman Photography)

(a)

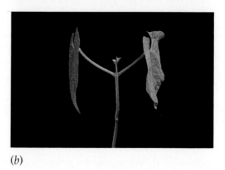

(b)

Figure 36–3 Sleep movements in the common bean, *Phaseolus vulgaris*. (*a*) Leaf position at 12 o'clock noon. (*b*) Leaf position at 12 o'clock midnight. (Dennis Drenner)

and tannins (organic molecules that are common in many plant tissues) leave, causing water to leave by osmosis. The sudden change in turgor is responsible for the leaf movement. Such **turgor movements** are reversible and temporary; the movement of potassium ions and water back into the pulvinus cells causes the plant part to return to its original position.

It is possible that this unusual behavior protects the *Mimosa* from predators; one can imagine the sudden movement of the leaves startling an insect that had alighted to eat the plant tissue. Tannins, which are normally stored in the vacuole, impart a bad taste to the tissue, and some researchers have suggested this as an additional mechanism to avoid predation.

The closure of the Venus flytrap leaf (see Figure 1–5) is similar in its mechanism to that of *Mimosa*. An electrical signal, which moves much more rapidly than in *Mimosa*, induces a movement of potassium out of certain motor cells, followed by the exit of water. This causes the leaf to snap shut.

Changes in turgor are also responsible for **solar tracking,** the ability of leaves or flowers to follow the sun's movement across the sky (Figure 36–2). Frequently, the leaves of these plants are arranged perpendicular to the sun's rays, regardless of the time of day or the sun's position in the sky. This allows for maximal light absorption. Many solar trackers have pulvini at the bases of their petioles; changes in turgor in the cells of the pulvinus help position the leaf in its proper orientation relative to the sun. Sunflower, soybean, and cotton plants are examples of solar trackers.

A BIOLOGICAL CLOCK INFLUENCES MANY PLANT RESPONSES

Plants, animals, and microorganisms appear to have an internal timer, or biological clock, that approximates a 24-hour cycle. These internal cycles are known as **circadian rhythms** (from the Latin words *circum*, around, and *diurn*, daily). Circadian rhythms repeat every 20 to 30 hours, although in nature the rising and setting of the sun resets the biological clock each day. Phytochrome (see Chapter 35) has been implicated as the photoreceptor involved in resetting the biological clock for many plants.

One example of a circadian rhythm in plants is the opening and closing of stomata that occur independently of light and darkness (see Chapter 32). Plants placed in continual darkness for extended periods continue to open and close their stomata. Another example of circadian rhythms in plants is the sleep movements observed in the common bean and other plants (Figure 36–3). During the day, bean leaves are horizontal for optimal light absorption, but at night the leaves fold down or up, which orients them perpendicular to their daytime position. By connecting a leaf to a pen on a rotating disk, the movement can be measured and timed. Results from studies such as this indicate that the plant actually "anticipates" sunrise and sunset, as

Figure 36–4 Plant growth in the direction of light, phototropism, demonstrates that plants respond to their environment. (Dennis Drenner)

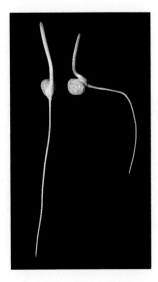

Figure 36–5 Stems exhibit negative gravitropism and roots exhibit positive gravitropism. Two corn seeds were germinated at the same time. The 4-day-old plant on the left served as a control. The plant on the right, also 4 days old, was turned on its side on day 3, making the shoot and root horizontal. In 24 hours, the new root growth was downward and the new shoot growth was upward. (Dennis Drenner)

the movements begin *before* the sun rises or sets. These sleep movements occur independently of Earth's 24-hour cycle; if bean plants are placed in continual darkness or continual light, the movements continue, although on a cycle of approximately 23 hours.

A TROPISM IS PLANT GROWTH IN RESPONSE TO AN EXTERNAL STIMULUS

A plant may respond to an external stimulus such as light, gravity, or touch by differential growth. Such responses are called tropisms and may be positive or negative, depending on whether the plant grows toward or away from the stimulus. **Phototropism** is the growth of a plant caused by the direction of light (Figure 36–4). Most stems exhibit positive phototropism and bend (grow) toward light. A growth in response to the direction of gravity is called **gravitropism** (traditionally called geotropism). Stems generally exhibit negative gravitropism, whereas roots exhibit positive gravitropism (Figure 36–5). **Thigmotropism** is growth in response to a mechanical stimulus, such as contact with a solid object. The twining or curling growth of tendrils, which help attach a plant such as a vine to a support, is an example of thigmotropism (Figure 36–6). Tropisms in plants may also be caused by other stimuli in the environment such as water, temperature, chemicals, and oxygen. Because tropisms are growth responses, they cause permanent changes in the position of a plant part.

HORMONES REGULATE PLANT GROWTH AND DEVELOPMENT

Plants, like animals, use chemical messengers called **hormones** to regulate their development and growth.

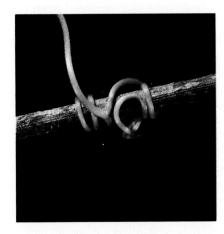

Figure 36–6 The twining motion of a grape tendril is an example of thigmotropism. (Carolina Biological Supply Company)

Plant hormones are organic compounds produced in one part of the plant and transported to another part, where they elicit a physiological response. Hormones are effective in extremely small amounts. For that reason their study is very challenging. In plants the study of hormones is made even more difficult because each plant hormone elicits *many* different responses. In addition, the effects of different plant hormones overlap, so that is it difficult to determine which hormone, if any, is the primary cause of a particular response. Also, plant hormones may be stimulatory or inhibitory, depending on their concentrations. There are five groups of plant hormones: auxins, gibberellins, cytokinins, ethylene, and abscisic acid. Together they control the growth of a plant during all its stages of development.

Charles Darwin First Provided Evidence for the Existence of Auxins, Which Cause a Variety of Physiological Effects

Although he is known primarily for originating the theory of natural selection to explain evolution, Charles Darwin was a gifted naturalist who experimented on a wide variety of biological phenomena. Darwin and his son, Francis, were interested in phototropism, the growth of plants toward light. In the 1880s they experimented with newly germinated canary grass seedlings (Figure 36–7). Recall that the first part of a grass seedling to emerge from the soil is the coleoptile (see Chapter 31).

When the Darwins exposed coleoptiles to unidirectional light, the coleoptiles bent toward the light. The bending occurred close to, but not at the very tip of, the coleoptile. The Darwins tried to influence this bending in several ways. For example, they covered the tip of the coleoptile as soon as it emerged from the soil. The plants treated in this manner did not bend! Likewise, bending did not occur when the coleoptile tip was removed (that is, when the coleoptile was decapitated). When the bottom of an intact coleoptile was shielded from light, however, the coleoptile still bent toward light. From these and similar experiments, the Darwins concluded that "some influence is transmitted from the upper to the lower part, causing it to bend." This conclusion fits the definition of a hormone exactly. Thus, Charles Darwin was the first person to produce data suggesting that plants have hormones. However, it took a number of years before the techniques necessary to extract and identify this substance were available.

In the 1920s Frits Went, a young Dutch scientist, isolated the phototropic hormone from oat coleoptiles. He removed the oat coleoptile tips and placed them on tiny blocks of agar for a period of time. When he put one of these agar blocks on the side of a decapitated coleoptile in the dark, bending occurred (Figure 36–8). This indicated that the substance had diffused from the coleoptile tip into the agar, and later from the agar into the decapitated coleoptile. Went named this substance **auxin** (from the Greek *aux*, grow or increase). The purification and elucidation of auxin's chemical structure were accomplished by a research team led by Kenneth Thimann at the California Institute of Technology.

Auxins are broadly defined as any compounds that stimulate phototropic curvature in oat coleoptiles. The main auxin found in plants is **indoleacetic acid, or IAA** (Table 36–1). Its structure is similar to that of the amino

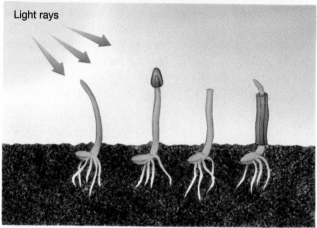

Light rays

Figure 36–7 The Darwins' experiment with coleoptiles of canary grass seedlings. (*Upper row*) Some plants were uncovered, some were covered only at the tip, some had the tip removed, and some were covered everywhere but at the tip. (*Lower row*) After exposure to light coming from one direction, the uncovered plants and the plants with uncovered tips (far right) grew toward the light. The plants with covered tips (left center) or tips removed (right center) did not bend toward light. Darwin and his son concluded that the tip is sensitive to light and produces some "influence" that moves down the plant and causes the bending.

acid tryptophan, from which it is synthesized. A number of synthetic auxins have been made that have similar chemical structures. IAA is synthesized in the shoot apical meristem, young leaves, and seeds. It is not translocated in either xylem or phloem, but instead moves through the plant within the parenchyma cells, at a rate that is too fast to be accounted for by diffusion alone. The movement of IAA is called **polar transport** because it is always unidirectional, or polar, from the top of the shoot toward the roots. Polar transport requires energy and is not due to the influence of gravity. If a section of stem is inverted, the auxins still move toward the root end of the plant.

Auxins cause cell elongation in plants. Recall that cell elongation occurs in apical meristems just behind

Table 36–1 THE FIVE PLANT HORMONES

Hormone	Chemical Structure	Site of Production	Method of Translocation
Auxin (IAA)		Shoot apical meristem, young leaves, seeds	Polar transport in parenchyma cells
Gibberellin (GA$_3$)		Young leaves, root and shoot apical meristems, embryo in seed	Unknown
Cytokinin (Zeatin)		Roots	Xylem
Ethylene		Stem nodes, ripening fruit, senescing tissue	Unknown (diffusion?)
Abscisic acid		Older leaves, root cap, stem	Vascular tissue

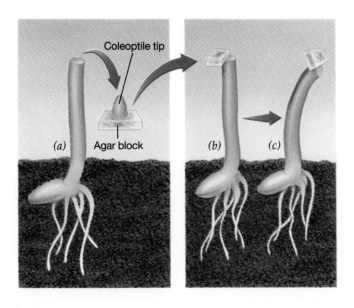

Figure 36–8 Frits Went's experiment. (*a*) Coleoptile tips were placed on agar blocks for a period of time. (*b*) The agar block was transferred to a decapitated coleoptile. It was placed off center, and the coleoptile was left in continuous darkness. (*c*) The coleoptile bent, indicating that a chemical had been transferred from the original coleoptile tip to the agar block and from the agar block to one side of the decapitated coleoptile.

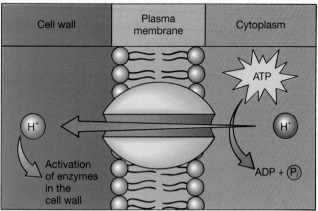

Auxin activated proton pump

| Cell wall | Plasma membrane | Cytoplasm |

Figure 36–9 The acid-growth hypothesis. Auxin activates a proton pump in the plasma membrane. This pumps hydrogen ions out of the cell to the cell wall, changing its pH. The lowered pH of the cell wall activates enzymes that break the cross links holding the cellulose microfibrils together. The pressure caused by increasing turgor then allows the wall to expand.

the area of cell division (see Chapter 31). Auxins apparently change the cell walls in this region so that they can expand. The effect of auxins on cell wall expansion is explained by a mechanism known as the **acid-growth hypothesis** (Figure 36–9). According to the acid-growth hypothesis, auxins trigger a proton pump in the plasma membrane (see Making the Connection: A Comparison

of Proton Pumps in Plants). This causes H^+ ions (protons) to flow from the cytoplasm through the plasma membrane to the cell wall, acidifying it and activating certain enzymes that break bonds between cell wall molecules (Figure 36–10). As result, the cell wall becomes flexible and able to stretch as water accumulates in the vacuole.

Phototropism can be explained by the effect of auxins on cell elongation. When a plant is exposed to a unidirectional source of light, the auxin migrates to the dark side of the stem before being transported down the stem. As a result, the cells on the shaded side of the stem receive more auxin and elongate more than the cells on the lighted side of the stem, causing the stem to bend toward the light (Figure 36–11).

Auxins also influence gravitropism, although the mechanism is incompletely understood at this time. To complicate matters, hormones other than IAA have also been implicated in gravitropism. IAA is thought to be the primary hormone involved in thigmotropism and other plant tropisms, however.

Auxins exert other effects on plants in addition to cell elongation

Certain plants tend to branch out very little. Growth in these plants occurs almost exclusively at the apical meristem, rather than at the lateral meristems. Such

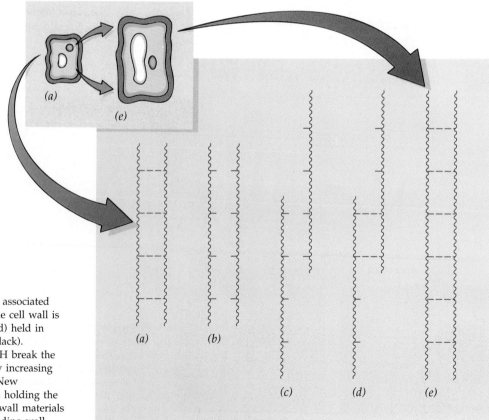

Figure 36–10 How wall expansion associated with cell elongation may occur. (a) The cell wall is composed of cellulose microfibrils (red) held in place by polysaccharide cross links (black). (b) Enzymes activated by a lowered pH break the cross links. (c) The pressure caused by increasing turgor causes the wall to stretch. (d) New polysaccharide cross links are formed, holding the wall in its new position. (e) New cell wall materials are synthesized, completing the expanding wall.

A Comparison of Proton Pumps in Plants

Proton (H^+) pumps are involved in many fundamental physiological processes in plants, including the synthesis of ATP, the transport of materials across membranes, and the expansion of cell walls. Proton pumps, which transport protons so that they accumulate on one side of a membrane, work by establishing an electrochemical gradient across a cell membrane. An electrochemical gradient has both a higher pH and a more negative charge on one side of the membrane (the side with fewer protons) and a lower pH and a more positive charge on the other side (the side with an accumulation of protons). We have discussed proton pumps in several chapters (see Chapters 7, 8, 32, 33, 34, and this chapter), so it might be a good idea to review their various roles.

The energy in an electrochemical gradient established by a proton pump can be used to make ATP from ADP and P_i. In aerobic respiration (see Chapter 7), energy liberated in the electron transport chain is used to establish a proton gradient across the inner mitochondrial membrane. The subsequent flow of these protons through the membrane from the intermembrane space to the matrix of the mitochondrion occurs through special channels associated with the enzyme ATP synthetase. As these protons flow through the channels, their energy is used to synthesize ATP.

ATP is also synthesized during the light-dependent reactions of photosynthesis (see Chapter 8) that take place in chloroplasts. As energized electrons pass along a chain of electron acceptors, some of the energy is used to pump protons across the thylakoid membrane into the interior of the thylakoid. This electrochemical gradient provides the energy to generate ATP when the protons pass through special ATP synthetase channels in the thylakoid membrane.

The energy of an electrochemical gradient can also be used to help transport sugars, amino acids, and mineral ions into plant cells. This occurs in the uptake of potassium ions during the opening of stomata (see Chapter 32), in the loading of sugars into phloem for translocation (see Chapter 33), and in the uptake of mineral ions from the soil (see Chapter 34). First, an electrochemical gradient is established in which the energy of ATP is used to pump protons outside the plasma membrane. You may recall from Chapter 5 that the phospholipid bilayers of cell membranes are impermeable to protons, which means that protons cannot simply diffuse back into the cell. However, the plasma membranes of plant cells have special protein channels that allow protons to diffuse back into cells, usually accompanied by some other molecule. In other words, the potential energy generated by an electrochemical gradient can be used to transport materials such as sugars, amino acids, and negatively charged ions such as chloride (Cl^-) into plant cells. Positively charged ions do not pass through membrane channels accompanied by protons. However, positively charged ions such as potassium (K^+) tend to move into plant cells through special membrane channels because of the more negative charge established in the cell's interior by proton pumps.

As discussed in this chapter, proton pumps are also involved in cell wall acidification that induces the elongation of plant cell walls. The hormone auxin causes young plant cells to pump protons out through plasma membranes, lowering the pH of the cell walls, which in turn activates certain enzymes involved in cell wall expansion.

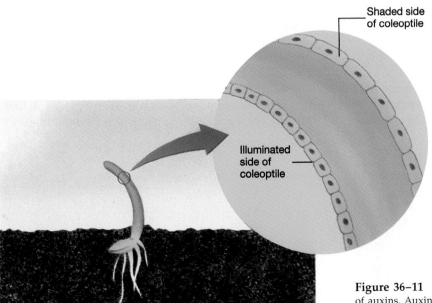

Shaded side of coleoptile

Illuminated side of coleoptile

Figure 36–11 Phototropism is due to the unequal distribution of auxins. Auxins travel down the side of the stem or coleoptile *away* from the light, causing the cells on the shaded side to elongate. Therefore, the stem or coleoptile bends toward light.

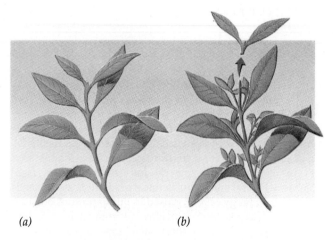

(a)   (b)

Figure 36–12   Auxins inhibit the development of lateral buds. (a) When the tip of the plant (source of auxins) is intact, the lateral buds do not develop. (b) The tip of the plant has been removed. Because there are no auxins moving down from the stem, lateral buds develop into branches.

plants are said to exhibit **apical dominance.** Most plants have apical dominance, but to varying extents. In plants with strong apical dominance (cacti, for example), there is one main stem and few side branches. Auxins promote apical dominance because auxins produced at the terminal apical meristem move down the stem and inhibit the development of the lateral buds (each lateral bud possesses a lateral meristem) (Figure 36–12). When the apical meristem is pinched off, the auxin source is removed and lateral buds develop into branches.

IAA produced by developing seeds stimulates the development of the fruit. When auxins are applied to flowers in which fertilization has *not* occurred, the ovary enlarges and develops into a seedless fruit. Seedless tomatoes have been produced in this manner, for example. Auxins are not the only hormones involved in fruit development, however.

Synthetic auxins have several commercial applications (Figure 36–13). NAA (naphthalenacetic acid) is a synthetic auxin used to stimulate root development on stem cuttings for vegetative propagation, particularly of woody plants. A synthetic auxin, 2,4-D (2,4-dichloro-

phenoxyacetic acid), is used as a selective herbicide. It is applied at concentrations that cause exaggerated growth in some plant parts and growth inhibition in others. For reasons that are not understood at the present time, monocots are less sensitive to 2,4-D. Therefore, an application of 2,4-D to a lawn or a field of corn kills broad-leaf weeds (dicots) but does not harm the grass or corn (both monocots).

Gibberellins, First Discovered in a Fungus, Cause a Variety of Physiological Effects

In the 1920s a Japanese plant scientist, E. Kurosawa, was working on a disease of rice, the so-called "foolish seedling disease," in which the young rice seedlings grow extremely tall and spindly, fall over, and die. The cause of the disease was discovered to be a fungus in the genus *Gibberella* that produces a chemical substance, named **gibberellin,** which causes the symptoms. It wasn't until after World War II that scientists in Europe and North America learned of the exciting work done by the Japanese.

The first gibberellin discovered in healthy plants was isolated from bean seeds in 1960, and they have since been found in many plants. Gibberellins are involved in many normal functions of plants. In the case of the foolish seedling disease of rice, the disease symptoms were caused by an abnormally high gibberellin concentration in the plant tissue.

Gibberellins have a complex chemical structure composed of five rings (Table 36–1). More than 70 naturally occurring gibberellins have been discovered; they all have the same basic structure but differ slightly in the number of double bonds and in the location of certain chemical groups. These structural differences are significant, however, because some gibberellins have pronounced effects on plant growth, whereas others are inactive. Gibberellins are produced in the root and stem apical meristems, in the young leaves, and in the embryos in the seeds. It is not known how gibberellins are translocated through the plant.

As in the foolish seedling disease of rice, gibberellins promote stem elongation in many plants. When a gibberellin is applied to a plant, this elongation may be

Figure 36–13   Commercial applications of synthetic auxins. Honeysuckle (*Lonicera fragrantissima*) cuttings treated with NAA, a synthetic auxin. Many adventitious roots formed on cuttings placed in a higher concentration (*left*), whereas a few roots formed in a lower NAA concentration (*middle*). Cuttings placed in water only (*right*) did not form roots in the same time period.   (Visuals Unlimited/Joe Eakes, Color Advantage)

Figure 36–14 Effect of the continued application of gibberellin on normal and dwarf corn plants. From left to right: dwarf untreated; dwarf treated with gibberellin; normal treated with gibberellin; normal untreated. Note that the dwarf plants respond to gibberellin much more dramatically than the normal plants. In fact, dwarf plants treated with gibberellin resemble normal plants in their growth rate. This dwarf variety is a mutant homozygous for a recessive gene that impairs gibberellin metabolism. (Courtesy of B. O. Phinney, UCLA)

Figure 36–15 Bolting in cabbage. Spectacular stem elongation, often accompanied by flowering, was caused by treatment with gibberellin. (*Left*) Untreated controls. (*Right*) Cabbages treated with gibberellin. (Courtesy of Sylvan Wittwer and Michigan State University)

spectacular, particularly in plants that normally have very short stems. Some dwarf mutants of corn and peas grow to a normal height when treated with gibberellins (Figure 36–14). Gibberellins are also involved in the rapid stem elongation that occurs when many plants initiate flowering. This phenomenon is known as **bolting** (Figure 36–15). Gibberellins cause stem elongation by inducing both cell division and cell elongation. The mechanism of cell elongation is different from that caused by auxins, however.

Gibberellins exert other effects on plants in addition to stem elongation

Gibberellins are involved in several reproductive processes in plants. They stimulate flowering, particularly in long-day plants. In addition, gibberellins can substitute for the low-temperature requirement that biennials have before the initiation of flowering (see Chapter 35). If gibberellins are applied to biennials during their first year of growth, flowering occurs without a period of exposure to low temperatures. Gibberellins, like auxins, also affect the development of fruits. Commercially, gibberellins are applied to several varieties of grapes to produce larger berries.

Gibberellins are involved in the germination process in many plants. The embryo in the seed produces gibberellins that trigger other physiological responses involved in germination. In plants with light or low-temperature requirements for seed germination, treatment with gibberellins can be substituted for the specific environmental requirement. Gibberellins have an important role in the production of enzymes in germinating cereal seeds, and their mechanism of action has been studied in detail in germinating barley seeds. The young barley embryo produces gibberellins, which stimulate the seed to synthesize digestive enzymes. These enzymes digest the stored starch in the seed's endosperm, making it available to the young plant as sugar (Figure 36–16).

Gibberellins appear to be a factor in **hybrid vigor,** the superiority of a hybrid over inbred (and therefore homozygous) plants. For example, inbred strains of corn are not as large or as productive as their hybrid offspring. Until recently, the physiological reason for theses differences was unknown. In 1988 an analysis of gibberellins in hybrid and inbred strains of corn revealed that hybrid strains produce higher levels of gibberellin. When additional gibberellin was applied to inbred strains of corn, their growth approached that of the hybrid strains. Thus, it appears that the production of gibberellins is enhanced in hybrid corn or, alternatively, that inbred corn produces less gibberellin.

Figure 36–16   Mobilization of insoluble storage reserves during germination of a grass seed such as barley. Diagrams (*a*) to (*e*) depict conditions within the seed at the times that appear directly above on the graph. (*a*) Seed in longitudinal section, showing release of gibberellin (GA) from embryo into endosperm after the seed absorbs water. (*b*) Aleurone cells respond to GA by producing digestive enzymes (shown by black dots), secreting these into the starchy endosperm. (*c*) Enzymes break down starch and other molecules in endosperm, releasing soluble nutrients (color dots), which the embryo's cotyledon absorbs (*d*) and delivers to the shoot and root. As the coleoptile appears above ground its tip opens, and the enclosed first foliage leaf emerges. (*e*) By the time storage reserves are depleted, the first foliage leaf has expanded and begun photosynthesis. Although the formation of enzymes to mobilize insoluble storage reserves occurs in many types of seeds, control of enzyme formation by GA seems to be found largely or exclusively in seeds of grasses.

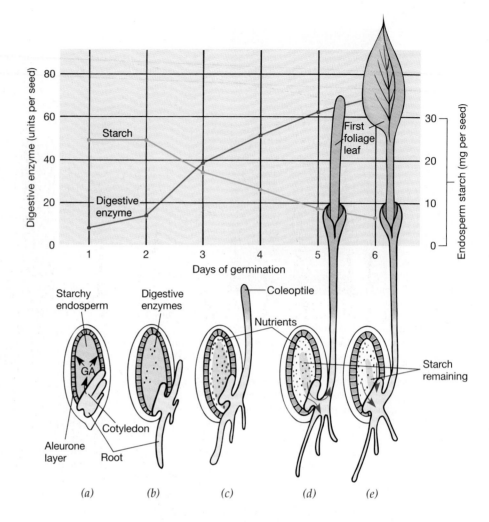

Cytokinins Promote Cell Division and Cause Other Physiological Responses

In the 1940s and 1950s a number of researchers were trying to discover chemical substances that might induce plant cells to divide in tissue culture (see Chapter 31). Folke Skoog and others at the University of Wisconsin discovered that cells would not divide without some substance that was transported in the vascular tissue of plants. This active substance was also found in coconut milk and autoclaved herring sperm DNA. Finally, in 1956 the active substance was isolated from herring sperm and called a **cytokinin** because it induces cell division, or cytokinesis. In 1963 the first naturally occurring cytokinin was identified from corn and named **zeatin.** Since that time several similar molecules have been extracted from other plants.

Cytokinins have an intriguing structure in that they are similar to the purine adenine (Table 36–1). Cytokinins are found as part of certain transfer RNA molecules not only in plants but also in animals and microorganisms. In plants they are produced in the roots and transported in the xylem to all parts of the plant.

Cytokinins promote cell division and differentiation in intact plants. In addition, they are a required ingredient of plant tissue culture media and must be present to induce mitosis. In tissue culture, cytokinins interact with auxin during **organogenesis,** the formation of organs. For example, in tobacco tissue culture a high ratio of cytokinins to auxin induces shoot formation, whereas a low ratio of cytokinins to auxin induces root formation (Figure 36–17).

Cytokinins and auxins also interact in the control of apical dominance. Here their relationship is antagonistic, as auxins inhibit the growth of lateral buds while cytokinins promote it. The situation is reversed in roots, with auxins promoting the growth of branch roots and cytokinins inhibiting it.

One very interesting effect of cytokinins on plant cells is to delay **senescence,** or aging (Figure 36–18). Plant cells, like all living cells, go through a natural aging process. This process is accelerated in plant parts that are cut, such as cut flowers. Cytokinins apparently

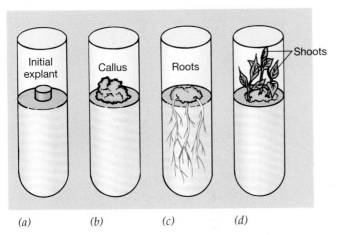

Figure 36–17 Growth responses of tobacco tissue culture to an auxin and a cytokinin. (*a*) The initial explant is a small piece of sterile tissue from the pith of a tobacco stem, which is placed on a nutrient agar medium. After several weeks, the kinds of growth illustrated occur on media supplemented with the varying levels of IAA (auxin) and kinetin (cytokinin). (*b*) 2 mg/L IAA and 0.2 mg/L kinetin produce callus. (*c*) When callus is transplanted to media with 2 mg/L IAA and 0.2 mg/L kinetin, roots differentiate. (*d*) Shoot growth is stimulated by media containing 0.02 mg/L IAA and 1 mg/L kinetin. Thus, a low ratio of kinetin to auxin triggers root growth in tobacco, whereas a low ratio of auxin to cytokinin triggers shoot growth.

Figure 36–18 Senescence was delayed in the green leaf by repeated application of cytokinins. Compare this leaf with the rest of the plant, which was not treated with cytokinins. (A. C. Leopold, Cornell University)

promote cells to maintain their normal levels of protein and nucleic acids, thus delaying the rapid aging associated with cut plant parts. It is thought that intact plants must have a continual supply of cytokinins from the roots. Cut flowers, of course, lose their natural source of cytokinins. Commercially, cytokinins are sprayed on cut flowers to prevent their rapid senescence.

Ethylene, the Only Gaseous Plant Hormone, Causes a Variety of Physiological Effects

The effects of **ethylene** on plants were noted in the 1800s, long before it was recognized as a natural plant hormone. Before electricity was invented, a mixture of various gases called coal gas was used to illuminate homes and streets. It was noted that plants growing near street lights were altered in several ways: trees shed their leaves early, flowers faded quickly and their petals fell off, and newly sprouted seedlings grew horizontally rather than erect. In 1901 a Russian plant physiologist determined that ethylene was the ingredient in coal gas that caused these effects, but it wasn't until 1934 that plant scientists demonstrated that ethylene was also produced by plants.

Ethylene, the only plant hormone that is a gas, is colorless and smells like ether (Table 36–1). Ethylene is produced in several places in plants: in the nodes of

stems, in ripening fruits, and in senescing tissues such as autumn leaves.

Ethylene has a major role in many aspects of senescence, including the ripening process in fruits. A number of physiological changes occur during fruit ripening. Fruits often change color, as chlorophyll is degraded and other pigments are synthesized. Starches and acids stored in the fruit are converted to sugars, giving the fruit a sweet taste. Fruit cell walls are partly broken down, making the fruit tissue softer. Also, flavors characteristic of the particular fruit are synthesized. Ethylene triggers these physiological changes. Further, ethylene has a "domino effect." As a fruit ripens, it produces ethylene, which triggers an acceleration of the ripening process. This induces the fruit to produce more ethylene, which further accelerates ripening. The expression "one rotten apple spoils the lot" is true. A rotten apple is one that is overripe. This apple produces large quantities of ethylene, which diffuse and then trigger the ripening process in nearby apples. Ethylene is used commercially to promote the uniform ripening of bananas. Bananas are picked while green and shipped to their destination. There they are exposed to ethylene before delivery to stores, where they ripen uniformly.

Another effect of ethylene is also related to senescence. Ethylene has been implicated as the hormone that induces leaf abscission (see Chapter 32). However, abscission is actually under the control of two antagonistic plant hormones, ethylene and auxin. As a leaf ages and autumn approaches, the level of auxin in the leaf decreases. This initiates several changes in the abscission zone. Concurrently, cells in the abscission zone begin producing ethylene, which triggers other effects. To further complicate the process, cytokinins may also be involved in abscission. Cytokinins, like auxin, decrease in amount as leaf tissue ages.

Exactly how plants recognize the presence of ethylene or respond in so many diverse ways to its presence is unknown. In 1988 a mutant of *Arabidopsis* (a plant in the mustard family) was reported that lacks sensitivity to ethylene. Subsequent studies of this mutant may provide insight into ethylene's mode of action.

Abscisic Acid Promotes Bud and Seed Dormancy as Well as Causing Other Physiological Responses

Abscisic acid was discovered simultaneously in 1963 by two independent research teams. P. F. Wareing in England was working on a hormone (called dormin) that induced bud dormancy in woody plants, and F. T. Addicott in California was working on a hormone (called abscisic acid) that promoted the abscission of cotton bolls (fruits). Later, when the chemical structures of both hormones were found to be identical, the hormone was given one name, abscisic acid. This was an unfortunate choice because abscisic acid is involved in dormancy, but probably not in abscission.

Abscisic acid (ABA), which is a single compound rather than a family of compounds, has a six-carbon ring with a number of side groups (Table 36–1). It is produced in the leaf, root cap, and stem and is transported in the vascular tissue. Seeds and fruits also contain high levels of ABA, but it is not clear whether it is synthesized or transported there.

Abscisic acid is sometimes referred to as the "stress hormone." It promotes changes in plant tissues that are exposed to unfavorable conditions (that is, stressed). The effect of ABA on plants suffering from water stress is best understood. ABA increases dramatically in the leaves of plants that are exposed to severe drought conditions. The high level of ABA in the leaves triggers an elevation of calcium ions in guard cells, which in turn causes the outflow of potassium ions from the guard cells. This induces water to leave the guard cells by osmosis, and the guard cells collapse. The closing of stomata in water-stressed plants saves a large amount of water that would normally be transpired through the stomata, and this water conservation increases the plant's likelihood of survival. When water is restored to the plant, the stomata do not open immediately, as the level of ABA in leaf cells must decrease before that can occur.

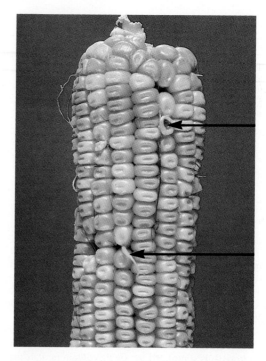

Figure 36–19 Lack of formation of abscisic acid can prevent seed dormancy in corn. Some of the white kernels have germinated prematurely, while still on the ear, to produce white coleoptiles (see arrows). (Courtesy of M. G. Neuffer)

The onset of winter could also be considered a type of stress on plants. Woody plants cease growth and prepare for winter by forming protective coverings of bud scales over their terminal buds. These adaptations are promoted by ABA. Another winter adaptation that involves ABA is dormancy in seeds. If seeds germinated in the autumn, the delicate seedlings would be killed by the first frost. Many seeds have high levels of ABA in their tissues which prevent them from germinating. In a corn mutant that is unable to synthesize ABA, the seeds germinate as soon as the embryos are mature, even while still attached to the ear (Figure 36–19).

The evidence that ABA is the only hormone involved in both bud and seed dormancy is not conclusive, particularly because the addition of gibberellins reverses the effects of dormancy. In seeds the level of ABA decreases during the winter, and the level of gibberellins increases. Cytokinins have also been implicated in breaking dormancy. Once again we see that a single physiological activity in plants may be controlled by the interaction of several hormones (Table 36–2). The actual response made by the plant may be due to changing ratios of hormones rather than to the individual effects of single hormones.

Table 36–2 SOME OF THE INTERACTIONS BETWEEN PLANT HORMONES
DURING VARIOUS ASPECTS OF PLANT GROWTH

Physiological Activity	Auxin	Gibberellin	Cytokinin	Ethylene	Abscisic Acid	Other Factors for Some Plants
Seed germination		Promotes	?		Inhibits	Cold requirement, light requirement
Growth of seedling into mature plant	Cell elongation, organogenesis[1]	Cell division and elongation	Cell division and differentiation, organogenesis[1]			
Apical dominance	Inhibits lateral bud development		Promotes lateral bud development	?		
Initiation of reproduction (flowering)		Stimulates flowering in some plants[2]	?			Cold requirement, photoperiod requirement
Fruit development and ripening	Development	Development		Promotes ripening		Light requirement (for pigment formation)
Leaf abscission	Inhibits		Inhibits	Promotes		Light requirement
Winter dormancy of plant		Breaks	?		Promotes	Light requirement
Seed dormancy		Breaks	?		Promotes	

[1] In plant tissue culture.
[2] Gibberellin cannot be considered *the* flowering hormone. There is evidence for a flowering hormone that has not yet been isolated and characterized.

SUMMARY

I. Plants respond to external stimuli.
   A. Turgor movements are caused by temporary changes in turgor in special cells.
      1. The sensitive plant, *Mimosa pudica*, dramatically folds its leaves in response to various stimuli.
      2. The closure of Venus flytrap leaves is another example of turgor movements, as is solar tracking.
   B. Tropisms are differential growth responses and are permanent.
      1. Phototropism is the growth of a plant caused by the direction of light.
      2. Gravitropism is the growth of a plant due to the influence of gravity.
      3. Thigmotropism is the growth of a plant in response to contact with a solid object.
II. Circadian rhythms are regular rhythms in growth or activities of a plant that approximate the 24-hour day and are reset by an internal biological clock.
III. Hormones regulate plant growth and development and are effective in small amounts.
   A. The functions of hormones overlap.
   B. Many effects of hormones may be due to the interactions of several hormones rather than the effect of a single hormone.
IV. There are five classes of plant hormones.
   A. Auxins are involved in cell elongation, phototropism, gravitropism, apical dominance, and fruit development.
   B. Gibberellins are involved in stem elongation, flowering, and the germination of seeds.
   C. Cytokinins promote cell division and differentiation, delay senescence, and interact with auxins in apical dominance.
   D. Ethylene has a role in the ripening of fruits, leaf abscission, and many other aspects of plant senescence.
   E. Abscisic acid is the stress hormone. It is involved in stomatal closure due to water stress and in bud and seed dormancy.

POST-TEST

1. The _____ is an organ at the base of the petiole in *Mimosa* which can undergo rapid changes in turgor, causing dramatic movements of the leaves.
2. In _____ _____, plants use turgor movements to position organs such as leaves optimally in sunlight.
3. Regularly recurring sleep movements observed in beans are an example of a _____ _____.
4. _____ is the growth of a plant due to the direction of light.
5. Plant roots generally exhibit _____ gravitropism.
6. The twining of tendrils is an example of _____.
7. Cell expansion by _____ is permanent, whereas cell expansion by turgor changes is temporary.
8. _____ are organic compounds produced in one part of the plant and transported to another, where they cause a positive or negative effect.
9. _____ was the first scientist to provide evidence of the existence of hormones in plants.
10. The movement of auxins, called _____ _____, is unidirectional from the top of the shoot to the roots.
11. According to the _____ _____ hypothesis of cell elongation in plants, auxins trigger a proton pump in the plasma membrane that acidifies the cell wall, activating enzymes that break bonds between cell wall molecules.
12. A synthetic _____ known as 2,4-D is used as a selective herbicide.
13. Research on a fungal disease of rice provided the first clues about _____.
14. Gibberellins have an important role in the production of _____ that digest starch in germinating barley seeds.
15. _____ interact with auxins during organogenesis in tissue culture.
16. The relationship between cytokinins and auxins in apical dominance is _____.
17. _____ delay senescence, whereas _____ promotes it.
18. The only plant hormone that is a gas is _____.
19. The stress hormone is _____ _____.
20. Abscisic acid promotes the _____ of woody twigs.

REVIEW QUESTIONS

1. Why might some plants have sleep movements?
2. How might solar tracking *harm* a plant? What types of adaptations might be found in a plant that is a solar tracker to enable it to overcome this potential problem?
3. Of what value is dormancy in seeds?
4. How are auxins involved in phototropism?
5. If sections of coleoptiles are placed in an acidic solution, they elongate as if auxins were present. Explain why this elongation occurs.
6. Could there be any significance to the large number of different gibberellins found in plants?
7. Discuss the hormones that are involved in each of the following: germination of seeds, growth and development of the plant, ripening of fruits, abscission of leaves, and dormancy of seeds.

RECOMMENDED READINGS

Cowen, R. Plant's genetic master switch' subverted. *Science News*, Vol 138, August 11, 1990. Reports on several recent advances in understanding how ABA works at the molecular level.

Mauseth, J. D. *Botany: An Introduction to Plant Biology.* Saunders College Publishing, Philadelphia, 1991. A comprehensive introduction to general botany.

McClure, B. A., and T. Guilfoyle. Rapid redistribution of auxin-regulated RNAs during gravitropism. *Science*, Vol 243, January 6, 1989. How auxin affects gravitropism at the molecular level.

Raven, P. H., R. F. Evert, and S. E. Eichhorn. *Biology of Plants,* 5th ed. Worth Publishers, New York. A general botany text with an evolutionary emphasis.

Rood, S. B., R. I. Buzzell, L. N. Mander, D. Pearce, and R. P. Pharis. Gibberellins: A phytohormonal basis for heterosis in maize. *Science,* Vol 241, September 2, 1988. Plants with hybrid vigor produce more gibberellin than plants that are inbred.

Taiz, L., and E. Zeiger. *Plant Physiology.* Benjamin/Cummings Publishing Company, Redwood City, CA, 1991. A plant physiology textbook in which the individual chapters were written by various experts. Plant hormones and responses are thoroughly covered.

Environmental Lawyer

TIMOTHY R. HENDERSON

Timothy R. Henderson has been setting precedents ever since he began his study of environmental science. After studying biology for two years at Wake Forest University, he transferred to the newly formed environmental science program at the State University of New York (SUNY) at Purchase and graduated in the first class. Combining his interests in biology and policy making, Henderson created a then-unique "joint degree"—an M.S. in Land Resources and a law degree—at the University of Wisconsin, Madison. Since graduating in 1980, he has worked for the Environmental Law Institute, the Environmental Protection Agency, and three law firms. Currently he is an associate with Graham & James in Washington, D.C., where he represents clients on issues such as waste management, recycling, and compliance with environmental law.

What was your career goal when you started college?

In high school, science was my interest, with a special focus on biology, but I wasn't sure what career I wanted. The biology program at Wake Forest University had a premedical orientation. Even though I wasn't keen on going into medicine, I took the courses required for a biology major at Wake Forest. After two years, I looked at different programs in the New York State school system, primarily because my family was from New York State. Many universities had straight biology programs, but SUNY–Purchase had just set up an interdisciplinary program in environmental studies that allowed students to draw courses from

many sciences. I found that to be the most attractive, so I transferred into the new program at Purchase.

What was the appeal of environmental science?

I had a lot of interest in history and politics, and I discovered that studying environmental science was a way to combine my interest in issues of the day with my interest in biological sciences. The nice thing about studying environmental science at SUNY–Purchase was that, except for the required core courses in biology, geology, chemistry, and ecology, students could choose courses and customize their own programs. I directed my program toward biological sciences by taking courses such as wildlife management and ethology. I also took

courses in policy issues, an area I was very interested in. Environmental protection concepts were rather new, and it was exciting to be involved with them, especially in the New York City area, where a lot of the new environmental protection groups had started up.

Will biology majors in more traditional academic programs get the training they need for an environmental science career?

Definitely. The key for any undergraduate degree is to focus and do well in a subject. If you do well in biology, you should have the fundamental understanding of scientific tools to branch out in other fields. One advantage of any science degree is that you have to take fundamental courses in biology, chemistry, and physics. Learn the fundamentals. That sounds like a basketball coach, but it really does apply to biological and environmental studies.

Were you involved in any interesting research projects in undergraduate school?

One of the attractions of the environmental studies program at SUNY–Purchase was the series of challenges it presented, beginning with a senior thesis requirement. My thesis focused on tidal wetlands protection, an issue that I began studying during the summer of my senior year. I was selected, along with a group of students, to work with a professor who had been awarded a National Science Foundation grant to study urban-impacted wetlands on the Long Island Sound. By the end of summer I discovered I didn't have the patience to do laboratory work, which is indispensable for a research scientist. Instead, my interest in policy making asserted itself, so I decided to modify my thesis to evaluate the effectiveness of the new Tidal Wetlands Act that had just been passed in New York State. I ended up essentially critiquing the law's ability to protect the natural-resource values of wetlands.

When did the idea of merging environmental science and law come to you?

While setting up my senior thesis, I chose an "outsider" to be my advisor. He was an attorney who taught a continuing education course in law for scientists and walked the class through some early environmental laws. During my senior year, he provided many of the contacts with government officials that I needed for my research, and he also got me thinking about law school.

What was your first job after graduating from college?

I worked as a research assistant for what is now the Natural Resources Defense Council (NRDC), an environmental advocacy group. I primarily investigated blood-lead levels in children caused by the ingestion of dust containing lead from automobile exhaust. During my year working at NRDC, I also applied to law schools.

What were you looking for in a law school?

I wanted to attend a university that had both a good law school and a graduate program in environmental sciences. The University of Wisconsin–Madison had a graduate program called the Institute of Environmental Studies, and I was able to combine M.S. studies with my law studies. I

essentially created the first joint degree there.

Did you find the disciplines of science and law compatible?

There are clear differences. In an effort to solve problems, scientists share ideas and work toward insights that will lead to the goal of common understanding. Lawyers, on the other hand, are trained to win arguments and to use language to win and to get people to accept "your truth." Sometimes I need to use both sides of my training just to keep two parties talking to one another. My biology background is most helpful when I study unique physical land areas, such as marshes and wetlands. My science background also helps me better select the scientists who assist me on cases.

What are some of your current cases?

I often defend people who are in violation of environmental standards by trying to negotiate settlement. I represent a lot of companies, trying to make sure they understand what their compliance obligations are so they can comply with the environmental law.

Another aspect of my job is to advise buyers or sellers of properties what the environmental law compliance risks are. That activity draws heavily on my science background because I have to work with consultants. They make visual examinations of a site to determine whether it has wetlands, or is near a river, or whether it has evidence of contamination (for example, oil stains or dying vegetation). It is very important for me to understand the reports and to be able to interpret the results of any soil or groundwater samples. Only then can I advise the client of what kind of environmental risk is involved in the purchase.

Will there be a healthy job market for environmental lawyers in the years to come?

The dynamic explosion of the field in recent years is slowing to a steady demand that will continue for the next 30 or 40 years. Of approximately 350 lawyers in my present firm, including our overseas offices, we have around

25 environmental specialists. Fundamental issues abound—such as: Where do we send our garbage? Will the ozone layer disappear? Is the Earth going to warm up so much that the ice caps will melt? What is the best way to use the dwindling undeveloped space that's left? Those issues are not going to go away; they are fundamental to how our society interacts with the environment.

What aspect of your work is most satisfying to you?

Over the years, some jobs and some clients have been frustrating, but the one constant is the intellectual challenge of the kind of work I am involved in. I also feel that in the long run the Earth will be better off because of what environmental attorneys can do.

What kinds of jobs related to the environment, outside law, are available to people with biology degrees?

They can work for the government as staff scientists, developing programs for protecting various types of resources. They can also work with consulting firms that provide technical advice to lawyers like me. Environmental scientists carry the lion's share of the responsibility for cleaning up contaminated areas and ensuring that companies' current practices prevent pollution. One area that will demand a significant amount of scientific analysis and expertise will be the environmental conditions of Eastern Europe and the former Soviet Union.

What changes in environmental law do you foresee for the 1990s?

A tremendous future exists for designing a more "complete-use" economy. Many of the clients I am representing right now are working toward complete use—recycling of consumer wastes, reclamation of industrial materials and scrap metal, and incineration of municipal waste to generate energy—all of which makes common economic sense and also makes sense as a way human beings can live with their environment.

PART VII

Structures and Life Processes in Animals

Like plants and most fungi, animals are **multicellular.** The body of a complex animal is not simply a colony of similar cells but comprises a number of different types of cells, each with a characteristic size, shape, structure, and function. The cells compose tissues, which make up organs, which coordinate in organ systems.

In complex animals, the organ systems work together to maintain life. Each system is responsible for a specific group of activities. Some systems—for example, the integumentary and skeletal systems—are specialized to physically protect the body. The lymphatic system, a subsystem of the circulatory system, defends the body against specific disease organisms.

Animal survival often depends on the ability to move quickly and precisely. In many complex animals, skeletal, muscular, and nervous systems work together to permit effective movement. The nervous system controls movement and regulates most other body processes. Hormones, chemical messengers secreted by the endocrine system, work with the nervous system in regulating metabolic processes.

Recall that animals obtain energy by eating either plants or other organisms that have eaten plants. Food is broken down and absorbed by the digestive system. Nutrients are delivered to each cell by the circulatory system. Cellular respiration requires oxygen; gas exchange is the function of the respiratory system, and in many animals gases are transported by the blood. Wastes are excreted by several systems, principally the urinary system. Perpetuation of the species is the function of the reproductive system.

Mother and young grizzly bears (*Ursus arctos*) photographed at McNeil River, Alaska.
(Jeff Foott/Tom Stack & Associates)

CHAPTER 37

The Animal Body: Tissues, Organs, and Organ Systems

OUTLINE

Epithelial tissue

Connective tissue

Muscle tissue

Nervous tissue

Organs and organ systems

We do not see amoebas the size of whales slithering around because it is inefficient for a cell to become very large (see Chapter 4). Recall that when its size approaches the limits of efficiency, a cell divides to form two cells. In unicellular organisms, cell division results in the production of two new individuals. In multicellular organisms, new cells remain associated to form one individual. Animals can grow to large size because they are composed of many cells.

The number of cells, not their individual sizes, is responsible for the size of an organism (Figure 37–1). The cells of an earthworm, a bird, and an elephant are all about the same size; the elephant is larger because its genes are programmed to provide for a larger number of cells.

Multicellularity also permits the specialization of cells. In a unicellular organism, such as a bacterium

Mountain lion with cub. (Sharon Cummings/Dembinsky Photo Associates)

or a flagellate, the single cell must carry on all the activities necessary for life. In a multi-cellular organism, cells can specialize to perform specific tasks. Recall that a **tissue** consists of a group of closely associated similar cells that are adapted to carry out specific functions. Animal tissues may be classified as epithelial, connective, muscular, or nervous. Each kind of tissue (and subtissue) is composed of cells with a characteristic size, shape, and arrangement. Some tissues are specialized to transport materials, whereas others contract to enable the organism to move. Still others secrete hormones that regulate metabolic processes.

You may recall from Chapter 1 that tissues associate to form **organs** such as the heart or stomach. Groups of tissues and organs form the **organ systems** of the body. Just how cells associate with one another and how tissues, organs, and organ systems perform specialized functions are discussed in this chapter.

After you have studied this chapter you should be able to

1. Discuss the advantages of being multicellular.
2. Define tissue, organ, and organ system.
3. Compare the four principal kinds of animal tissues—epithelial, connective, muscular, and nervous tissues—and give their respective functions.
4. Describe the main types of epithelial tissue and give their functions.

5. Compare the main types of connective tissue and summarize their functions.
6. Contrast the three types of muscle tissue and their functions.
7. Cite the functions of nervous tissue and describe a typical neuron.
8. List the organ systems characteristic of complex animals, describe their functions, and discuss how each system helps maintain homeostasis.

EPITHELIAL TISSUES COVER THE BODY AND LINE ITS CAVITIES

Epithelial tissue (also called **epithelium**) covers body surfaces and lines cavities. It forms the outer layer of the skin; the linings of the digestive, respiratory, and reproductive tracts; and the lining of the kidney tubules. Epithelial tissue consists of cells fitted tightly together, forming a continuous layer, or sheet, of cells. One surface of the sheet is attached to the underlying tissue by a noncellular **basement membrane** composed of tiny fibers and of nonliving polysaccharide material produced by the epithelial cells. Table 37–1 illustrates the main types of epithelial tissue, indicates their locations in the body, and describes their functions.

Epithelial tissues function in protection, absorption, secretion, and sensation. The epithelial layer of the skin covers the entire body and protects it from a variety of threats, including mechanical injury, chemicals, bacte-

ria, and fluid loss. The epithelial tissue lining the digestive tract absorbs nutrients and water into the body.

Everything that enters or leaves the body must cross one or more layers of epithelium. Food that is taken into the mouth and swallowed is not really "inside" the body until it is absorbed through the epithelium of the gut and enters the blood. To a large extent, the permeabilities of the various epithelia regulate the exchange of substances between the different parts of the body and between the organism and the external environment.

Many epithelial membranes are subjected to continuous wear and tear. As outer cells are sloughed off, they must be replaced by new ones from below. Such epithelial tissues generally have a rapid rate of cell division so that new cells are continuously produced to replace those lost.

Three types of epithelial cells can be distinguished on the basis of shape (see Table 37–1). **Squamous** epithelial cells are thin, flattened cells shaped like pancakes or flagstones. **Cuboidal** epithelial cells are short cylinders that from the side appear cube-shaped, resembling dice. Actually, each cell has a complex shape, usually an eight-sided polyhedron. **Columnar** epithelial cells look like tiny columns or cylinders when viewed from the side. The nucleus is usually located near the base of the cell. Viewed from above or in cross section, these cells appear hexagonal. A columnar epithelial cell may have on its free surface cilia that beat in a coordinated way, moving materials in one direction. Most of the respiratory tract is lined with ciliated epithelium that moves particles of dust and other foreign material away from the lungs.

Epithelial tissue may be **simple**—that is, composed of one layer of cells—or **stratified,** composed of two or more layers (see Table 37–1). Simple epithelium is usually located where materials must diffuse through it or where substances are secreted, excreted, or absorbed. Stratified epithelial tissue is located where protection is required. Stratified squamous epithelium is found in the skin and lines the mouth and esophagus of humans and other vertebrates. A third arrangement of epithelial
(*Text continued on p. 781*)

Figure 37–1 All animals are multicellular. A large animal such as this bull elephant from western Kenya is composed of more cells than the much smaller bird riding on its back. (Mike Barlow/Dembinsky Photo Associates)

Table 37–1 EPITHELIAL TISSUES

Nuclei

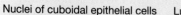

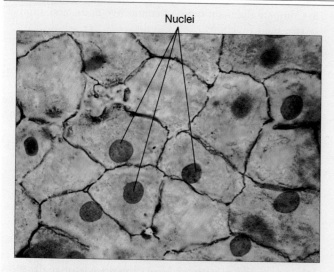

Simple squamous epithelium

Main Locations
Air sacs of lungs, lining of blood vessel

Functions
Passage of materials where little or no protection is needed and where diffusion is major form of transport

Description and Comments
Cells are flat and arranged as single layer

25 μm

Nuclei of cuboidal epithelial cells   Lumen of tubule

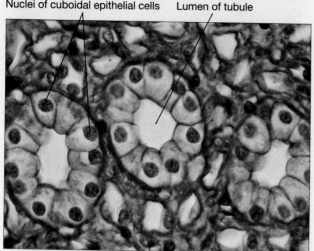

Simple cuboidal epithelium

Main Locations
Linings of kidney tubules, gland ducts

Functions
Secretion and absorption

Description and Comments
Single layer of cells; photograph shows cross-section; from the side each cell looks like short cylinder; sometimes have microvilli for absorption

25 μm

Goblet cell   Nuclei of columnar cells

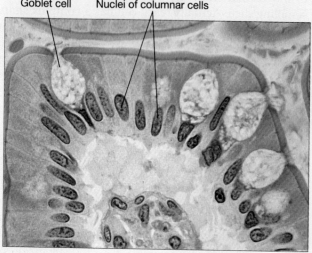

Simple columnar epithelium

Main Locations
Linings of much of digestive tract and upper part of respiratory tract

Functions
Secretion, especially mucus; absorption, protection, movement of mucous layer

Description and Comments
Single layer of columnar cells; sometimes with enclosed secretory vesicles (goblet cells), highly developed Golgi complex; often ciliated

25 μm

Photomicrographs courtesy of Ed Reschke.

Table 37–1   continued

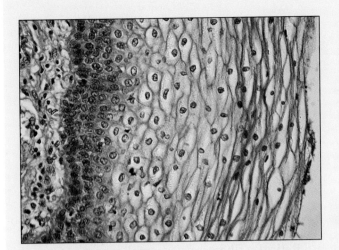

Stratified squamous epithelium

Main Locations
Skin, mouth lining, vaginal lining

Functions
Protection only; little or no absorption or transit of materials; outer layer continuously sloughed off and replaced from below

Description and Comments
Several layers of cells, with only the lower ones columnar and metabolically active; division of lower cells causes older ones to be pushed upward toward surface

25 μm

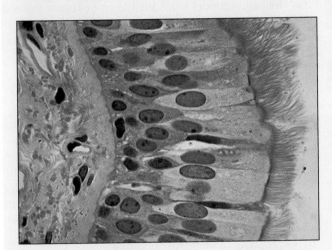

Pseudostratified epithelium

Main Locations
Some respiratory passages, ducts of many glands

Functions
Secretion, protection, movement of mucus

Description and Comments
Comparable in many ways to columnar epithelium except that not all cells are the same height; thus, though all cells contact the same basement membrane, the tissue appears stratified; ciliated, mucus-secreting, or with microvilli

25 μm

cells is **pseudostratified** epithelium, so named because its cells falsely appear to be layered. Although all of its cells rest on a basement membrane, not every cell extends to the free surface of the tissue. This may give the impression that there are two or more cell layers. Some of the respiratory passageways are lined with pseudostratified epithelium equipped with cilia.

The linings of the body cavities and the linings of the blood and lymph vessels develop from **mesenchyme,** a generalized embryonic tissue that gives rise to connective tissues rather than epithelial tissues. Structurally, however, the cells of these linings are in all respects typical epithelial cells. To distinguish them from true epithelia, the linings of blood and lymph vessels are termed **endothelium.**

A **gland** consists of one or more epithelial cells specialized to produce and secrete a product such as sweat, milk, mucus, wax, saliva, hormones, or enzymes (Fig-

ure 37–2). The epithelial tissue lining the cavities and passageways of the body typically contains specialized mucus-secreting cells called **goblet cells.** The mucus lubricates these surfaces and facilitates the movement of materials.

CONNECTIVE TISSUES JOIN AND SUPPORT OTHER BODY STRUCTURES

The main function of **connective tissue** is to join together the other tissues of the body. Connective tissues also support the body and its structures and protect underlying organs. Almost every organ in the body has a supporting framework of connective tissue called **stroma.** The epithelial components of the organ are supported and cushioned by the stroma.

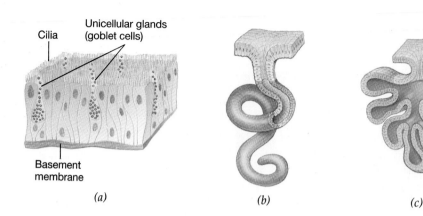

Figure 37–2 A gland consists of one or more epithelial cells. (*a*) Goblet cells are unicellular glands that secrete mucus. (*b*) Sweat glands are simple tubular glands with coiled tubes similar to the one shown here. The walls of the gland are constructed of simple cuboidal epithelium. (*c*) A compound gland has a branched duct. Certain salivary glands are compound glands.

(a)   *(b)*   *(c)*

There are many kinds of connective tissues and many systems for classifying them. Some of the main types of connective tissue are (1) loose and dense connective tissues; (2) elastic connective tissue; (3) reticular connective tissue; (4) adipose tissue; (5) cartilage; (6) bone; and (7) blood, lymph, and tissues that produce blood cells. The tissues vary widely in the details of their structures and in the functions they perform (Table 37–2).

Connective tissues contain relatively few cells, which are embedded in an extensive **intercellular substance** consisting of threadlike microscopic **fibers**. The fibers are scattered throughout a **matrix**—a thin gel composed of polysaccharides—secreted by the cells. The cells of different kinds of connective tissues differ in their shapes and structures and in the kinds of matrices they secrete. The nature and function of each kind of connective tissue are determined in part by the structure and properties of the intercellular substance.

Connective Tissue Contains Collagen, Reticular, and Elastic Fibers

Connective tissue contains three types of fibers: collagen, elastic, and reticular. **Collagen fibers,** the most numerous type, are composed of the protein collagen, the most abundant protein in the body. Collagen is a very tough material, and these fibers impart great strength to the structures in which they occur. The tensile strength of collagen fibers has been compared to that of steel. (Meat is tough because of its collagen content.) When treated with hot water, collagen is converted into the soluble protein gelatin. Collagen fibers are wavy and flexible but resist stretching. Their structure allows them to remain intact when the tissue is stretched.

Elastic fibers branch and fuse to form networks; they can be stretched by a force and then (like a stretched rubber band) return to their original size and shape when the force is removed. Elastic fibers, composed of the protein elastin, are an important component of structures that must stretch.

Reticular fibers are very small branched fibers that form delicate networks not visible in ordinary stained slides. The reticular fibers become apparent when a tissue is stained with silver. Reticular fibers are composed of collagen and some glycoprotein.

Connective Tissue Contains Specialized Cells

Fibroblasts are connective tissue cells that produce the fibers as well as the protein and carbohydrate complexes of the matrix. Fibroblasts release protein components that become arranged to form the characteristic fibers. These cells are especially active in developing tissue and are important in healing wounds. As tissues mature, the number of fibroblasts decreases and they become less active.

Macrophages, the scavenger cells of the body, commonly wander through connective tissues, cleaning up cellular debris and phagocytizing foreign matter, including bacteria. Among the other types of cells seen in connective tissues are mast cells, which release histamine during allergic reactions; adipose (fat) cells; and plasma cells, which secrete antibodies.

Loose Connective Tissue Is Widely Distributed

Loose connective tissue (also called areolar tissue) is the most widely distributed connective tissue in the body. It is found as a thin filling between body parts and serves as a reservoir for fluid and salts. Nerves, blood vessels, and muscles are wrapped in this tissue. Together with adipose tissue, loose connective tissue forms the subcutaneous (below-the-skin) layer that attaches skin to the muscles and other structures beneath. Loose connective tissue consists of fibers running in all directions through a semifluid matrix. Its flexibility permits the parts it connects to move.

Dense Connective Tissue Consists Mainly of Fibers

Dense connective tissue is very strong, though somewhat less flexible than loose connective tissue. Collagen fibers predominate. In **irregular** dense connective tissue, the collagen fibers are arranged in bundles distributed in all directions through the tissue. This type of tissue is found in the lower layer (dermis) of the skin.

In **regular** dense connective tissue, the collagen bundles are arranged in a definite pattern, making the tissue greatly resistant to stress. Tendons, the cable-like cords that connect muscles to bones, consist of this tissue.

Elastic Tissue Is Found in Structures That Must Expand

Elastic connective tissue consists mainly of bundles of parallel elastic fibers. Structures that must expand and then return to their original size, such as the walls of the large arteries and lung tissue, contain elastic connective tissue.

Reticular Connective Tissue Provides Support

Reticular connective tissue is composed mainly of interlacing reticular fibers. It forms a supporting stroma in many organs, including the liver, spleen, and lymph nodes.

Adipose Tissue Stores Energy

Adipose tissue is rich with fat cells, which store fat and release it when fuel is needed for cellular respiration. Adipose tissue is found in the subcutaneous layer and in tissue that cushions internal organs. An immature fat cell is somewhat star-shaped. As fat droplets accumulate within the cytoplasm, the cell assumes a more rounded appearance (Figure 37–3). Fat droplets merge with one another, eventually forming a single large drop of fat that occupies most of the volume of the mature fat-storing cell. The cytoplasm and its organelles are pushed to the cell edges, where a bulge is typically formed by the nucleus. A cross section of such a fat cell looks like a ring with a single stone (cytoplasm forms the ring, and the nucleus the stone).

When you study a section of adipose tissue through a microscope, it may remind you of chicken wire. The rings of cytoplasm are the "wire," and the large spaces indicate where fat drops existed before they were dissolved by chemicals used to prepare the tissue. These spaces may cause the cells to collapse, resulting in a wrinkled appearance of the tissue.

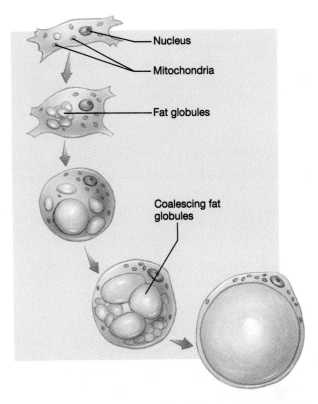

Figure 37–3 Storage of fat in a fat cell. As more and more fat droplets accumulate in the cytoplasm, they coalesce to form a very large globule of fat. Such a globule may occupy most of the cell, pushing the cytoplasm and the organelles to the periphery. See Table 37–2 for a photomicrograph of fat cells filled with fat.

Cartilage and Bone Provide Support

The supporting skeleton of a vertebrate is composed of cartilage or bone. Recall that **cartilage** is the supporting skeleton in the embryonic stages of all vertebrates, but is largely replaced in the adult by bone in all but the sharks and rays. The supporting structure of the external ear, the supporting rings in the walls of the respiratory passageways, and the tip of the nose are examples of human structures composed of cartilage. Cartilage is firm yet elastic. Its cells, called **chondrocytes,** secrete a hard, rubbery matrix around themselves and also secrete collagen fibers, which become embedded in the matrix and strengthen it. Chondrocytes eventually come to lie, singly or in groups of two or four, in small cavities called **lacunae** in the matrix (see Table 37–2). Cartilage cells in the matrix remain alive. Cartilage tissue lacks nerves, lymph vessels, and blood vessels. Chondrocytes are nourished by diffusion of nutrients and oxygen through the matrix.

Bone is the main vertebrate skeletal tissue. It is similar to cartilage in that it consists mostly of matrix mate-

(*Text continued on p. 786*)

Table 37–2   CONNECTIVE TISSUES

Collagen fibers   Nuclei of fibroblasts

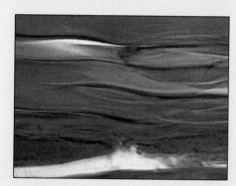

50 μm

Loose (areolar) connective tissue

Main Locations
Everywhere support must be combined with elasticity, e.g., subcutaneous layer

Functions
Support; reservoir for fluid and salts

Description and Comments
Fibers produced by fibroblast cells embedded in semifluid matrix and mixed with miscellaneous group of other cells

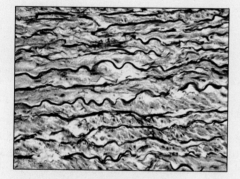

25 μm

Dense connective tissue

Main Locations
Tendons, many ligaments, dermis of skin

Functions
Support; transmission of mechanical forces

Description and Comments
Collagen fibers may be regularly or irregularly arranged

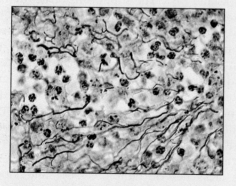

50 μm

Elastic connective tissue

Main Locations
Structures that must both expand and return to their original size, such as lung tissue and large arteries

Functions
Confers elasticity

Description and Comments
Branching elastic fibers interspersed with fibroblasts

Reticular connective tissue

Main Locations
Framework of liver, lymph nodes, spleen

Functions
Support

Description and Comments
Consists of interlacing reticular fibers

50 μm

Photomicrographs for dense connective tissue, adipose tissue, and bone courtesy of Dennis Drenner; all other photomicrographs courtesy of Ed Reschke.

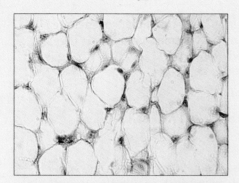

Adipose tissue

Main Locations
Subcutaneous layer; pads around certain internal organs

Functions
Food storage; insulation; support of such organs as mammary glands, kidneys

Description and Comments
Fat cells are star-shaped at first; fat droplets accumulate until typical ring-shaped cells are produced

50 μm

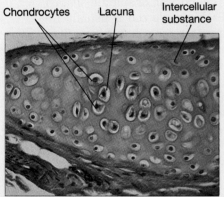

Chondrocytes Lacuna Intercellular substance

Cartilage

Main Locations
Supporting skeleton in sharks, rays, and some other vertebrates; in other vertebrates, ends of bones; supporting rings in walls of some respiratory tubes; tip of nose; external ear

Functions
Flexible support and reduction of friction in bearing surfaces

Description and Comments
Cells (chondrocytes) separated from one another by intercellular substance; cells occupy lacunae

50 μm

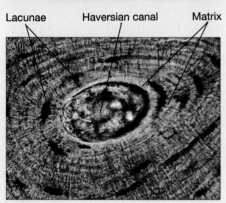

Lacunae Haversian canal Matrix

Bone

Main Locations
Forms skeletal structure in most vertebrates

Functions
Support and protection of internal organs; calcium reservoir; skeletal muscles attach to bones

Description and Comments
Osteocytes in lacunae; in compact bone, lacunae arranged in concentric circles about haversian canals

50 μm

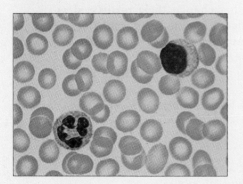

Blood

Main Locations
Within heart and blood vessels of circulatory system

Functions
Transports oxygen, nutrients, wastes, and other materials

Description and Comments
Consists of cells dispersed in fluid intercellular substance

25 μm

rial, containing lacunae, which is inhabited by the cells that secrete and maintain the matrix (Figure 37–4). Unlike cartilage, however, bone is a highly vascular tissue with a substantial blood supply. Diffusion alone would not be sufficient for the nourishment of the bone cells. This is because the matrix consists not only of collagen, mucopolysaccharides, and other organic materials but also of hydroxyapatite crystals, composed mainly of calcium phosphate. Diffusion through such a substance is very slow. Thus, bone cells, or **osteocytes,** communicate with one another and with capillaries by tiny channels called **canaliculi,** which contain fine extensions (cytoplasmic processes) of the osteocytes themselves.

Osteocytes are arranged in concentric layers called **lamellae,** which are formed by the matrix. In turn, the lamellae surround central microscopic channels known as **haversian canals.** Capillaries and nerves run through the haversian canals. Each spindle-shaped unit of bone that consists of a central blood vessel, surrounding lamellae, and osteocytes is called an **osteon.**

Bone tissue contains large multinucleated cells called **osteoclasts,** which can dissolve and remove the bony substance, as can the osteocytes themselves. The shape and internal architecture of the bone can gradually change in response to normal growth processes and physical stress. The calcium salts of bone render the matrix very hard, and collagen prevents the bony matrix from being overly brittle. Bones are amazingly light and strong. Most have a large central **marrow cavity;** this may contain yellow marrow, which is mostly fat, or red marrow, the connective tissue in which red and some white blood cells are produced.

Blood and Lymph Are Circulating Tissues

Blood and **lymph** are circulating tissues that help other parts of the body communicate and interact. Like all connective tissues, they consist of specialized cells dispersed in an intercellular substance. Blood and lymph are discussed in Chapters 42 and 43.

In mammals, blood is composed of red and white cells and platelets suspended within **plasma,** the liquid, noncellular part of the blood. Plasma transports many kinds of substances from one part of the body to another. Some of these substances are simply dissolved in the plasma; others are bound to proteins such as albumins.

The **red blood cells** (erythrocytes) of humans and other vertebrates contain the red respiratory pigment hemoglobin, which transports oxygen. The red blood cells of most mammals are flattened biconcave discs that lack nuclei (Table 37–2); those of other vertebrates are oval and have nuclei.

Human blood contains five different kinds of **white blood cells** (leukocytes), each with distinct size, shape, structure, and functions. The white blood cells constitute an important line of defense against microorganisms that cause disease.

Platelets are small fragments broken off from large cells in the bone marrow. In complex vertebrates they play a key role in blood clotting.

MUSCLE TISSUE IS SPECIALIZED TO CONTRACT

The movements of most animals result from the contraction of the elongated, cylindrical, or spindle-shaped cells of **muscle tissue.** Each muscle cell is usually referred to as a **fiber** because of its length. A muscle fiber contains many small, longitudinal, parallel contractile fibers called **myofibrils.** Two proteins, **myosin** and **actin,** are the chief components of myofibrils. Muscle cells perform mechanical work by contracting.

Three types of muscle tissue are found in vertebrates (Table 37–3). **Skeletal muscle** makes up the large muscle masses attached to the bones of the body. Its fibers are among the exceptions to the rule that cells have only one nucleus; each skeletal muscle fiber has many nuclei. The nuclei of skeletal muscle fibers are also unusual in their position: They lie peripherally, just under the plasma membrane. This is thought to be an adaptation to increase the efficiency of contraction. The entire central part of the skeletal muscle fiber is occupied by the contractile units, the myofibrils. Skeletal muscle cells may be as long as 2 or 3 cm.

Smooth muscle occurs in the walls of the digestive tract, uterus, blood vessels, and certain other internal organs. **Cardiac muscle** is present in the walls of the heart. Whereas skeletal muscle fibers are generally under voluntary control, cardiac and smooth muscle fibers are normally not regulated at will.

By light microscopy, both skeletal and cardiac fibers are seen to have alternate light and dark transverse stripes, or **striations,** that change their relative sizes during contraction. Striated muscle fibers can contract rapidly but cannot remain contracted. A striated muscle fiber must relax and rest momentarily before it can contract again. In invertebrates the distribution of muscle types may be quite different from that in vertebrates, and one or more types may be missing completely.

NERVOUS TISSUE CONTROLS MUSCLES, GLANDS, AND OTHER ORGANS

Nervous tissue is composed of **neurons,** cells specialized for conducting electrochemical nerve impulses, and **glial cells,** cells that support and nourish the neu-

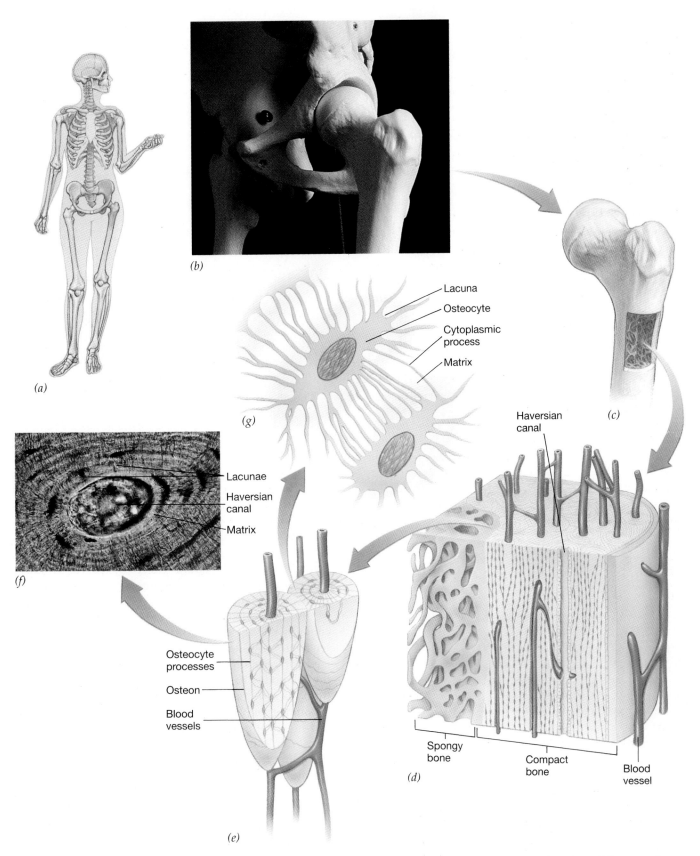

(a)

(b)

(g)

Lacuna
Osteocyte
Cytoplasmic process
Matrix

(c)

Haversian canal

(f)

Lacunae
Haversian canal
Matrix

Osteocyte processes

Osteon

Blood vessels

Haversian canal

Spongy bone

Compact bone

Blood vessel

(d)

(e)

Figure 37–4 Compact bone is made up of units called osteons (three osteons are shown in (*e*)). Blood vessels and nerves run through the haversian canal within each osteon. In bone the matrix is rigid and hard. Bone cells become trapped within lacunae but communicate with one another through tiny canals by way of cytoplasmic processes (extensions). Two bone cells (osteocytes) are illustrated in (*g*). (*b*, Visuals Unlimited/© SIU; *f*, Dennis Drenner)

Table 37–3 THE TYPES OF MUSCLE TISSUES

	Skeletal	*Smooth*	*Cardiac*
Location	Attached to skeleton	Walls of stomach, intestines, etc.	Walls of heart
Type of control	Voluntary	Involuntary	Involuntary
Shape of fibers	Elongated, cylindrical, blunt ends	Elongated, spindle-shaped, pointed ends	Elongated, cylindrical fibers that branch and fuse
Striations	Present	Absent	Present
Number of nuclei per fiber	Many	One	One or two
Position of nuclei	Peripheral	Central	Central
Speed of contraction	Most rapid	Slowest	Intermediate
Ability to remain contracted	Least	Greatest	Intermediate

Nuclei   Striations   Nuclei   Nuclei

Intercalated disks

(a)   Skeletal muscle fibers   (b)   Smooth muscle fibers   (c)   Cardiac muscle fibers

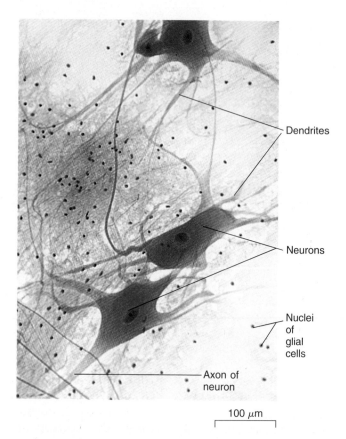

Dendrites

Neurons

Nuclei of glial cells

Axon of neuron

100 μm

Figure 37–5 Nervous tissue consists of neurons and glial cells. (Ed Reschke)

rons (Figure 37–5). Certain neurons receive signals from the external or internal environment and transmit them to the spinal cord and brain; other neurons process and store the information; still others transmit information from the brain and spinal cord to the muscles, glands, and other organs of the body. Neurons communicate at junctions called **synapses**. A **nerve** consists of a great many neurons bound together by connective tissue.

A typical neuron has an enlarged **cell body,** which contains the nucleus, and two types of cytoplasmic extensions (see Chapter 39). **Dendrites** are fibers specialized for receiving impulses and transmitting them to the cell body. The single **axon** transmits impulses away from the cell body. Axons usually are long and smooth but may give off an occasional branch. Axons typically end in a group of fine branches. Axons range in length from a millimeter or two to more than a meter. Those extending from the spinal cord down the arm or leg in the human may be a meter or more in length.

COMPLEX ANIMALS HAVE ORGANS AND ORGAN SYSTEMS

Complex animals have a great variety of organs. Although an animal organ may be composed mainly of one type of tissue, other types are needed to provide

Table 37–4 THE ORGAN SYSTEMS OF A MAMMAL AND THEIR FUNCTIONS

System	*Components*	*Functions*	*Homeostatic Ability*
Integumentary	Skin, hair, nails, sweat glands	Covers and protects body	Sweat glands help control body temperature; as barrier, the skin helps maintain steady state
Skeletal	Bones, cartilage, ligaments	Supports body, protects, provides for movement and locomotion, calcium storage	Helps maintain constant calcium level in blood
Muscular	Organs mainly of skeletal muscle; cardiac muscle; smooth muscle	Moves parts of skeleton, locomotion; movement of internal materials	Ensures vital functions requiring movement, e.g., cardiac muscle circulates the blood
Digestive	Mouth, esophagus, stomach, intestines, liver, pancreas	Ingests and digests foods, absorbs them into blood	Maintains adequate supplies of fuel molecules and building materials
Circulatory	Heart, blood vessels, blood; lymph and lymph structures	Transports materials from one part of body to another; defends body against disease	Transports oxygen, nutrients, hormones; removes wastes; maintains water and ionic balance of tissues
Respiratory	Lungs, trachea, and other air passageways	Exchange of gases between blood and external environment	Maintains adequate blood oxygen content and helps regulate blood pH; eliminates carbon dioxide
Urinary	Kidney, bladder, and associated ducts	Excretes metabolic wastes; removes excessive substances from blood	Helps regulate volume and composition of blood and body fluids
Nervous	Nerves and sense organs; brain and spinal cord	Receives stimuli from external and internal environment, conducts impulses, integrates activities of other systems	Principal regulatory system
Endocrine	Pituitary, adrenal, thyroid, and other ductless glands	Regulates blood chemistry and many body functions	In conjunction with nervous system, regulates metabolic activities and blood levels of various substances
Reproductive	Testes, ovaries, and associated structures	Provides for continuation of species	Passes on genetic endowment of individual; maintains secondary sexual characteristics

support, protection, and a blood supply and to allow transmission of nerve impulses. For example, the heart consists mainly of cardiac muscle tissue, but it is lined and covered by endothelium (a tissue that resembles epithelium), contains blood vessels composed of connective tissue, and is regulated by nervous tissue.

The ten main organ systems of complex animals include the integumentary, skeletal, muscle, nervous, circulatory, digestive, respiratory, urinary, endocrine, and reproductive systems (Figure 37–6). See Table 37–4 for a summary of their principal organs and functions. In the digestive system, for example, organs include the mouth, esophagus, stomach, small and large intestines, liver, pancreas, and salivary glands. This system functions to process food, reducing it to its simple components. The digestive system transfers the products of digestion into the blood for transport to all of the body's cells.

Figure 37–6   The principal organ systems of the human body.

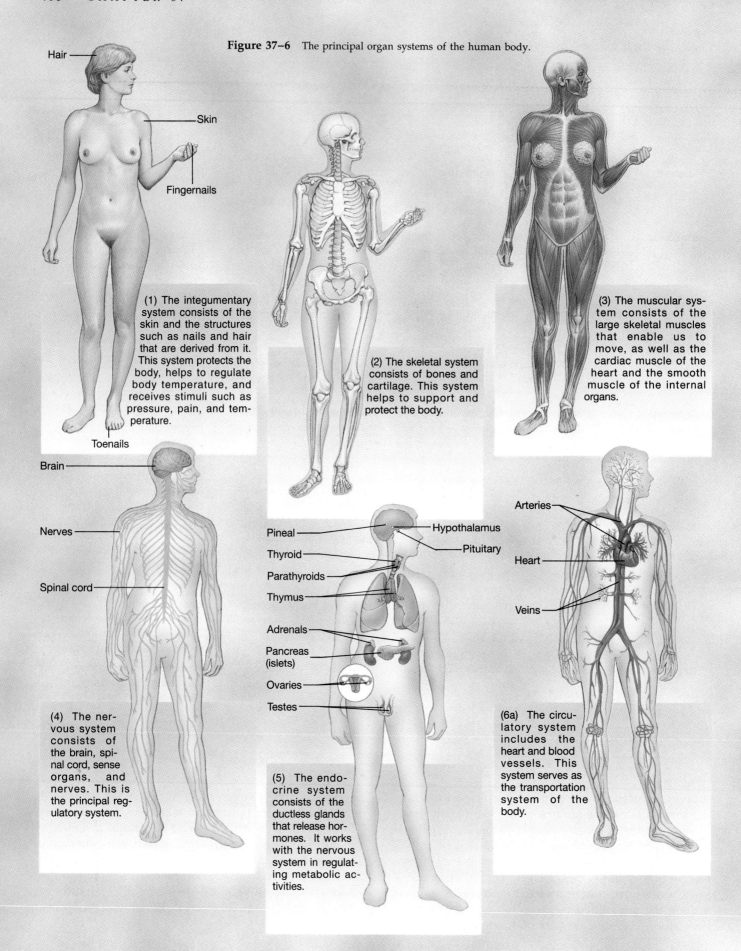

Hair

Skin

Fingernails

Toenails

(1) The integumentary system consists of the skin and the structures such as nails and hair that are derived from it. This system protects the body, helps to regulate body temperature, and receives stimuli such as pressure, pain, and temperature.

(2) The skeletal system consists of bones and cartilage. This system helps to support and protect the body.

(3) The muscular system consists of the large skeletal muscles that enable us to move, as well as the cardiac muscle of the heart and the smooth muscle of the internal organs.

Brain

Nerves

Spinal cord

(4) The nervous system consists of the brain, spinal cord, sense organs, and nerves. This is the principal regulatory system.

Pineal

Thyroid

Parathyroids

Thymus

Adrenals

Pancreas (islets)

Ovaries

Testes

Hypothalamus

Pituitary

(5) The endocrine system consists of the ductless glands that release hormones. It works with the nervous system in regulating metabolic activities.

Arteries

Heart

Veins

(6a) The circulatory system includes the heart and blood vessels. This system serves as the transportation system of the body.

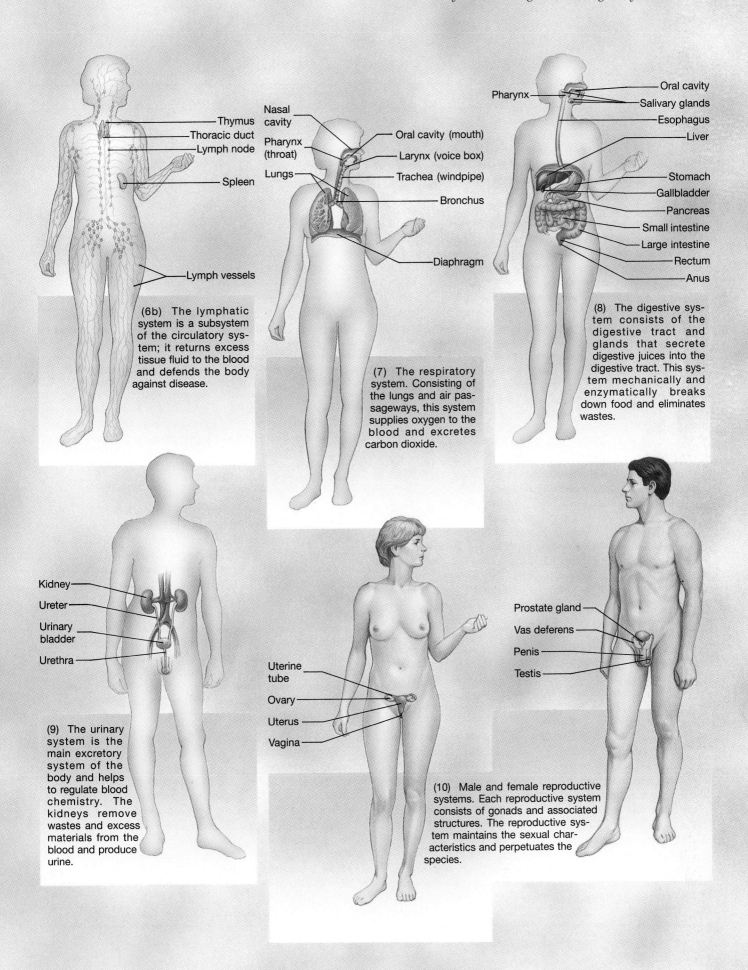

Thymus
Thoracic duct
Lymph node

Spleen

Lymph vessels

(6b) The lymphatic system is a subsystem of the circulatory system; it returns excess tissue fluid to the blood and defends the body against disease.

Nasal cavity
Pharynx (throat)
Lungs

Oral cavity (mouth)
Larynx (voice box)
Trachea (windpipe)

Bronchus

Diaphragm

(7) The respiratory system. Consisting of the lungs and air passageways, this system supplies oxygen to the blood and excretes carbon dioxide.

Pharynx

Oral cavity
Salivary glands
Esophagus
Liver

Stomach
Gallbladder
Pancreas
Small intestine
Large intestine
Rectum
Anus

(8) The digestive system consists of the digestive tract and glands that secrete digestive juices into the digestive tract. This system mechanically and enzymatically breaks down food and eliminates wastes.

Kidney
Ureter
Urinary bladder
Urethra

(9) The urinary system is the main excretory system of the body and helps to regulate blood chemistry. The kidneys remove wastes and excess materials from the blood and produce urine.

Uterine tube
Ovary
Uterus
Vagina

Prostate gland
Vas deferens
Penis
Testis

(10) Male and female reproductive systems. Each reproductive system consists of gonads and associated structures. The reproductive system maintains the sexual characteristics and perpetuates the species.

MAKING THE CONNECTION

Neoplasms Are Unwelcome Tissues

In Focus on Oncogenes and Cancer in Chapter 16, we discussed how normal cells may be transformed into cancer cells. Now that you have learned more about tissues, we can discuss cancer and other abnormal cell growth in the context of the animal body.

A **neoplasm** ("new growth") is an abnormal mass of cells. Neoplasms, or **tumors,** can develop in many species of animals and plants. A benign ("kind") tumor tends to grow slowly, and its cells stay together. Because benign tumors form discrete masses, often surrounded by connective tissue capsules, they can usually be removed surgically. Unless a benign neoplasm develops in a place where it interferes with the function of a vital organ, it is not lethal.

A malignant ("wicked") neoplasm, or **cancer,** usually grows much more rapidly than a benign tumor. Neoplasms that develop from connective tissues or muscle are referred to as **sarcomas,** and those that originate in epithelial tissue are called **carcinomas.** Unlike the cells of benign tumors, cancer cells do not retain normal structural features.

Recall that cancer cells lack the usual regulatory mechanisms due to the presence of at least one, and perhaps several, oncogenes. When a transformed cell multiplies, all the cells derived from it are also abnormal. Membrane proteins that would normally help regulate cell division and interaction with other cells are replaced by tumor-specific proteins.

Two basic defects in behavior that characterize most cancer cells are rapid multiplication and abnormal relations with neighboring cells. Unlike normal cells, which respect one another's boundaries and form tissues in an orderly, organized manner, cancer cells grow helter-skelter upon one another and infiltrate normal tissues. They are apparently no longer able to receive or respond appropriately to signals from surrounding cells; communication is lacking.

Studies indicate that many neoplasms grow to only a few millimeters in diameter and then enter a dormant stage, which may last for months or even years. At some point, cells of the neoplasm release a chemical substance that stimulates nearby blood vessels to develop new capillaries, which grow into the neoplasm. Once a blood supply is ensured, the neoplasm grows rapidly and may soon become life-threatening.

Death from cancer almost always results from **metastasis,** a migration of cancer cells through blood or lymph channels to distant parts of the body. Once there, they multiply, forming new malignant neoplasms; these may interfere with the normal functions of the tissues being invaded. Cancer often spreads so rapidly and extensively that surgeons are unable to locate all the malignant masses.

Why some persons are more susceptible to cancer than others remains a mystery. Some researchers think that cancer cells arise frequently in everyone, but that in most people, the immune system (the system that provides protection from disease organisms **and other** foreign invaders) is capa-

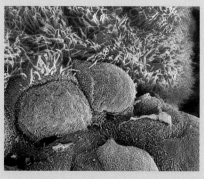

10 μm

Cancer cells multiply rapidly and invade normal tissues, interfering with function. A healthy bronchial passageway is lined with ciliated cells. The cilia (shown in orange) sweep dust and other foreign particles away from the lungs. Cancer cells (shown in green) invade the bronchial wall and crowd out normal cells lining the bronchial passageway. (© Boehringer Ingelheim International GmbH, Photo by Lennart Nilsson, *The Incredible Machine*, National Geographic Society)

ble of destroying them. According to this theory, cancer is a failure of the immune system. Another suggestion is that people have different levels of tolerance to carcinogens (cancer-producing agents). More than 80% of cancer cases are thought to be triggered by carcinogens in the environment.

Cancer is the second greatest cause of death in the United States. One in three persons in the United States gets cancer at some time in his or her life, and two out of three cancer patients die within 5 years of diagnosis. Currently, the key to survival is early diagnosis and treatment with some combination of surgery, hormonal treatment, radiation therapy, and drugs that suppress mitosis (chemotherapy). Because cancer is actually an entire family of closely related diseases (there are more than 100 distinct varieties), it is probable that no single cure exists. Most investigators agree, however, that a greater understanding of the control mechanisms and communication systems of cells is necessary before effective cures can be developed.

Risk of developing cancer can be decreased by following these recommendations:

1. Do not smoke or use tobacco. Smoking is responsible for more than 80% of lung cancer cases.
2. Avoid prolonged exposure to the sun; use sunscreen or sun block. Exposure to the sun is responsible for almost all of the 400,000 cases of skin cancer reported each year.
3. Increase the fiber content of your diet and avoid high-fat, smoked, salt-cured, and nitrite-cured foods.
4. Avoid unnecessary exposure to x rays.
5. Women should examine their breasts each month and obtain annual Pap tests.
6. Men should have prostate examinations yearly after age 50.

SUMMARY

I. Multicellular organisms can attain much larger sizes than can unicellular organisms. Multicellular organisms are composed of a number of cell types, each specialized and adapted to carry out specific functions.

II. A tissue consists of a group of similarly specialized cells that associate to perform one or more functions. Animal tissues are classified as epithelial, connective, muscular, or nervous.

    A. Epithelial tissue may form a continuous layer, or sheet, of cells covering a body surface or lining a body cavity; some epithelial tissue is specialized to form glands.

        1. Epithelial tissue functions in protection, absorption, secretion, or sensation.

        2. Epithelial cells may be squamous, cuboidal, or columnar in shape.

        3. Epithelial tissue may be simple, stratified, or pseudostratified. (Features of each are summarized in Table 37–1.)

    B. Connective tissue joins other tissues of the body, supports the body and its organs, and protects underlying organs. Connective tissue contains cells within an intercellular substance secreted by the cells.

        1. The intercellular substance contains collagen, elastic, and reticular fibers. Connective tissue contains specialized cells such as fibroblasts and macrophages.

        2. Some types of connective tissue are loose and dense connective tissues, elastic connective tissue, reticular connective tissue, adipose tissue, cartilage, bone, and blood. (Features of each are summarized in Table 37–2.)

    C. Muscle tissue is composed of cells specialized to contract. Each cell is an elongated fiber containing many small longitudinal, parallel contractile units called myofibrils. The chief components of myofibrils are the proteins actin and myosin.

        1. Skeletal muscle is striated and is under voluntary control.

        2. Cardiac muscle is striated; its contraction is involuntary.

        3. Smooth muscle contracts involuntarily; it is responsible for movement of food through the digestive tract and for movement of other body organs.

    D. Nervous tissue is composed of neurons, which are cells specialized for conducting impulses, and glial cells, which are supporting cells.

III. Several types of tissue may be united to form an organ; several organs may work together in an organ system. Complex animals have a great variety of organs and ten principal organ systems (see Table 37–4).

POST-TEST

1. A group of cells that fit tightly together to form a continuous sheet covering a body surface or lining a cavity of the body is termed a(n) _____ tissue.

2. The functions of epithelial tissues include _____, _____, _____, and _____.

3. On the basis of their shapes, we can distinguish _____, _____, and _____ epithelial cells.

4. The mammalian respiratory tract is lined with _____ tissue.

5. The outer layer of the skin is composed of _____ _____ epithelial tissue.

6. Epithelial cells specialized to produce and secrete a product are called _____.

7. The supporting connective tissue framework of an organ is called its _____.

8. _____ _____ are small branched fibers forming delicate networks in tissues.

9. The _____ transmits impulses away from the cell body of a neuron.

10. The liquid, noncellular part of the blood is termed _____.

Match the terms in Column A with their definitions in Column B.

Column A
11. Canaliculi
12. Chondrocytes
13. Collagen
14. Fibroblasts
15. Glial cells
16. Macrophages
17. Matrix
18. Myofibrils
19. Red blood cells
20. Platelets

Column B
a. Cells that transport oxygen
b. Scavenger cells that clean up cellular debris
c. The ground substance of connective tissue; intercellular substance
d. A unique protein present in connective tissues, secreted by fibroblasts
e. Connective tissue cells that produce and secrete the proteins and other components of the matrix
f. Cartilage cells that secrete a flexible, rubbery matrix
g. Tiny channels in bone containing extensions of bone cells
h. Fragments of cells that play a role in blood clotting
i. Small, longitudinal, parallel contractile fibers in muscle cells
j. Supporting cells present in nervous tissue

REVIEW QUESTIONS

1. What advantages do multicellular organisms have over unicellular organisms? Can you think of any disadvantages?
2. What are the functions of epithelial tissues? How are the cells adapted to carry out these functions?
3. What is the structure of bone? of adipose tissue? of loose connective tissue? How is each adapted to carry out its special functions?
4. Compare the properties of the three types of muscle.

5. Discuss the structure of a neuron and how this adapts it for its function.
6. Name the kinds of tissues you would expect to find in the following organs: the lung, the heart, the intestines, and the salivary glands.
7. List the principal organ systems found in a complex animal and give the functions of each.
8. How do the cells of a malignant neoplasm differ from those of a normal tissue? What is metastasis?

RECOMMENDED READINGS

Caplan, A. I. Cartilage. *Scientific American,* October 1984, pp. 84–94. Cartilage's basic properties of strength and resilience are explained in terms of the tissue's molecular structure.

Kessel, R. G., and R. H. Kardon. *Tissues and Organs: A Text-Atlas of Scanning Electron Microscopy.* W. H. Freeman Co., San Francisco, 1979. A striking collection of scanning electron micrographs.

National Geographic Society Book Service. *The Incredible Machine.* National Geographic, Washington, D.C., 1986. A beautiful and informative introduction to the human body; features the art of renowned photographer Lennart Nilsson.

Solomon, E. P., R. Schmidt, and P. Adragna. *Human Anatomy and Physiology,* 2d ed. Saunders College Publishing, Philadelphia, 1990. A very readable presentation of human anatomy and physiology.

CHAPTER 38

Protection, Support, and Movement: Skin, Skeleton, and Muscle

OUTLINE

Outer coverings: Protection
Skeletons: Locomotion, protection, and support
Muscles: Movement

Some animals run; some jump; some fly. Others remain rooted to one spot, sweeping their surroundings with tentacles. Many contain internal circulating fluids, pumped by hearts and contained by hollow vessels that maintain their pressure with gentle squeezing. Digestive systems push food along with peristaltic contractions. And in all these cases, each action is powered by muscle, a specialized tissue that, however varied its effects, has but one action: It can contract.

In many animals, the muscle and skeletal systems work together. Muscles responsible for locomotion are anchored to the skeleton, which transmits forces. The skeleton also serves to support the body and protect the delicate organs within.

The epithelial coverings of invertebrates and the skin of vertebrates also protect underlying tissues.

Several body systems—including skeletal and muscular systems—work together to enable this grasshopper to climb and move about with precision. (Chip Clark)

These coverings may be specialized to perform additional functions such as temperature regulation, gas exchange, excretion, or secretion of mucus or other substances.

In our survey of the animal kingdom in Chapters 28–30, we made many references to protective coverings, movement, and skeletal systems in terms of adaptation of individual animal groups. In Chapter 37 we described animal tissues, organs, and systems, laying the foundation for the more detailed discussions in this and later chapters. Here we focus on skin, skeleton, and muscle—systems that are closely interrelated in function and significance. We compare these systems across several animal groups and then focus on their structures and functions in the human body.

After you have studied this chapter you should be able to

1. Describe the external epithelium of invertebrates and summarize its functions.
2. Compare the structure and function of vertebrate skin with those of the external epithelium of invertebrates, and identify the principal derivatives of vertebrate skin.
3. Compare the advantages and disadvantages of different types of skeletal systems, including the hydrostatic skeleton, exoskeleton, and endoskeleton.
4. Identify the main divisions of the vertebrate skeleton and the bones that make up each division.
5. Describe the structure of a typical long bone.

6. Summarize bone development, differentiating between endochondral and intramembranous bone development.
7. Describe the gross and microscopic structures of skeletal muscle.
8. List, in sequence, the events that take place during muscle contraction.
9. Compare the roles of glycogen, creatine phosphate, and ATP in providing energy for muscle contraction.
10. Describe the antagonistic action of muscles.
11. Summarize the functional relationship between skeletal and muscular tissues.

OUTER COVERINGS PROTECT THE BODY

Epithelial tissue covers all external and internal surfaces of the animal body. The outer epithelium forms a protective shield around the body.

The Protective Epithelial Covering of Invertebrates May Function in Secretion or Gas Exchange

In invertebrates, epithelial tissue is simple, rather than stratified, and the external epithelium is generally cuboidal or low columnar. The external epithelium has a protective function and may also be specialized for secretion or gas exchange. Epithelial cells may be modified as sensory cells that are selectively sensitive to light, chemical stimuli, or mechanical stimuli such as contact or pressure.

In many species, the epithelium contains secretory cells that produce a protective cuticle or secrete lubricants or adhesives. In some species, these cells release odorous secretions that are used for communication among members of the species or for marking trails. In other species, the cells produce poisonous secretions that are used for offense or defense. In earthworms, a lubricating mucous secretion serves as a moist slime for diffusion of gases across the body wall and for reduction of friction during movement through the soil.

In some species, an epithelial secretion may be limited to a particular region of the body surface. In the gastropod mollusk, for example, a mucous secretion is released from the foot, producing a slime track through which the snail glides. In some insects—for example, weaver ants—epithelial secretions are released as fine, very strong threads and are used to construct nests. The spinning glands of spiders develop from epithelial

cells. In lepidopteran insects (such as butterflies and moths), silk is synthesized from amino acids in silk-forming glands.

The Vertebrate Skin Functions in Protection and Temperature Regulation

In many fish, in the African ant-eating pangolin (a mammal), and in some reptiles, skin has developed into a set of scales formidable enough to be considered armor. Even human skin has considerable strength. It includes a variety of structures, such as fingernails and toenails, hair, sweat glands, oil (sebaceous) glands, and several types of sensory receptors that give us the ability to feel pressure, temperature, and pain (Figure 38–1).

Human skin and the skin of other mammals contain mammary glands, which are specialized in females for secretion of milk. Oil glands in human skin empty, via short ducts, into hair follicles (Figure 38–2). They secrete a substance called **sebum,** a complex mixture of fats, waxes, and hydrocarbons. In humans these glands are especially numerous on the face and scalp. The oil secreted keeps the hair moist and pliable and prevents the skin from drying and cracking. (At puberty, excessive sebum, produced in response to increased levels of sex hormones, fills the glands and follicles, producing **acne.**)

In humans, the skin functions as a thermostatically controlled radiator, regulating the elimination of heat from the body. About 2.5 million sweat glands secrete sweat, and its evaporation from the surface of the skin lowers the body temperature.

The skin in some other vertebrates differs considerably from ours. Instead of hairs, birds have feathers, which form in a manner comparable to hairs and pro-

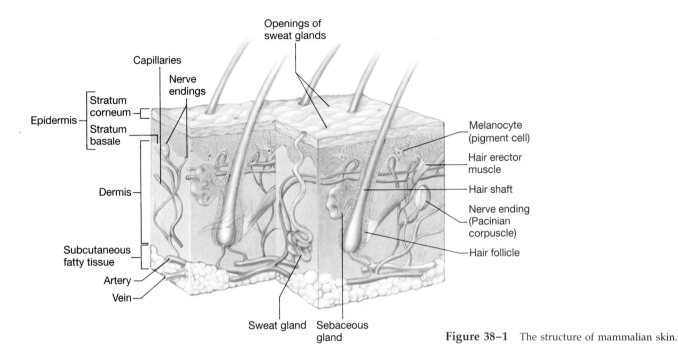

Figure 38-1   The structure of mammalian skin.

vide even more effective insulation than fur. Among the ectothermic vertebrates, one finds epidermal scales (as in reptiles), naked skin covered with mucus (as in many amphibians and fish), and skin with bony or toothlike scales. Some skin, such as that of certain tropical frogs, is even equipped with poison glands. Skin and its derivatives are often brilliantly colored in connection with courtship rituals, territorial displays, and various kinds of communication. The human blush pales alongside the spectacular displays of such animals as peacocks.

The Epidermis Is a Waterproof Protective Barrier

The outer layer of skin, the **epidermis,** is the interface between the delicate tissues within and the hostile environment without. The epidermis consists of several strata, or sublayers. The deepest is **stratum basale,** and the most superficial is **stratum corneum** (see Figure 38-1). In stratum basale, cells continuously divide and are pushed outward as other cells are produced below them. As the epidermal cells move toward the surface of the skin, they mature. In almost all vertebrates the epidermis lacks capillaries, and so the maturing cells receive less and less nourishment and their metabolic activity diminishes.

As they move outward, epidermal cells manufacture **keratin,** an elaborately coiled protein that gives the skin considerable mechanical strength in combination with flexibility. Keratin is quite insoluble and serves to waterproof the body surface. As epidermal cells move

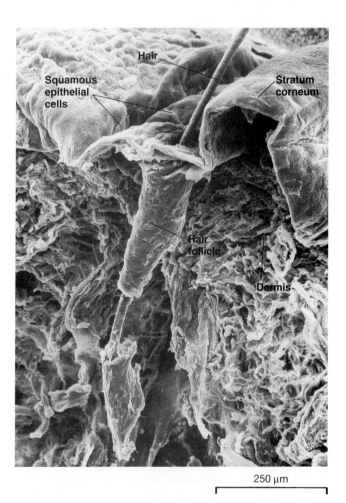

Figure 38-2   Scanning electron micrograph of human skin with a hair follicle.   (Courtesy of Dr. Karen A. Holbrook)

through the stratum corneum, they die. When they reach the outer surface of the skin, they wear off and must be continuously replaced.

The Dermis Contains Blood Vessels and Other Structures

Beneath the epidermis lies the **dermis** (see Figure 38–1), composed of a dense, fibrous connective tissue containing collagen, which imparts strength and flexibility to the skin. Within the dermis are the blood vessels that nourish the skin. The major part of each sweat gland is embedded in the dermis (or in the subcutaneous layer beneath), and the hair follicles reach down into it. Sense organs concerned with touch are also found in this layer. Mammalian skin rests on a subcutaneous layer composed of loose connective tissue and adipose tissue. This fatty tissue insulates the body, conserving heat.

SKELETONS ARE IMPORTANT IN LOCOMOTION, PROTECTION, AND SUPPORT

In some of the simplest animals, muscle acts directly on the jelly-like substance of the body itself or perhaps a fluid-filled body cavity. In more complex animals, however, the skeleton receives, transmits, and transforms the single movement of muscular tissue—contraction—into the variety of motions needed.

In a few instances this skeleton is internal, in the form of plates or shafts of calcium-impregnated tissue. But in most cases the skeleton is not a living tissue but a lifeless deposit atop the epidermis—a shell or **exoskeleton.** In addition to its function in locomotion, the skeleton supports the body and protects the internal organs.

In Hydrostatic Skeletons, Body Fluids Are Used To Transmit Force

Imagine an elongated balloon full of water. If one were to pull on it, it would lengthen, but it would also lengthen if it were squeezed. Conversely, it would shorten if the ends were pushed. In *Hydra* and other cnidarians, cells of the two body layers are capable of contraction that produces similar changes in shape.

The contractile cells in the outer epidermal layer are arranged longitudinally, whereas the contractile cells of the inner layer (the gastrodermis) are arranged circularly around the central body axis (Figure 38–3). The two groups of cells work in **antagonistic** fashion: What one can do, the other can undo. When the epidermal (longitudinal) layer contracts, the hydra shortens. Because of the fluid in the gastrovascular cavity, force is

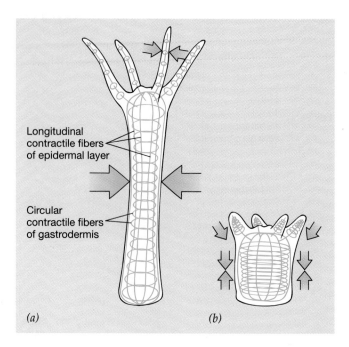

Figure 38–3 Movement in *Hydra*. The longitudinally arranged cells are antagonistic to the cells arranged in circles around the body axis. (*a*) Contraction of the circular muscles elongates the body. (*b*) Contraction of the longitudinal muscles shortens the body.

transmitted so that the hydra thickens as well. On the other hand, when the inner (circular) layer contracts, the hydra thins, and its fluid contents force it to lengthen.

Mechanically, the hydra is little more than a simple bag of fluid. The fluid acts as a hydrostatic skeleton, because it transmits force when the contractile cells contract against it. Hydrostatic skeletons permit only crude mass movements of the body or its appendages. Delicate movements are difficult because, in a fluid, force tends to be transmitted equally in all directions and hence throughout the entire fluid-filled body of the animal. For example, it is not easy for the hydra to thicken one part of its body while thinning another.

The more sophisticated hydrostatic skeleton of the annelid worms enables them to be more versatile in movement. An earthworm may extend its anterior end out of its burrow on damp evenings to feed on bits of decayed vegetation on the surface. The worm may then bring its posterior end out in order to defecate. This practice is not without its hazards, for if the worm waits outside the burrow too long, an equally hungry bird is likely to find it. If the bird is quick enough, the story ends there. If it is not, the giant nerve axons of the worm's ventral solid nerve cord swiftly transmit impulses that stimulate the longitudinal muscles and inhibit the circular muscles. Abruptly the longitudinal muscles contract, pulling the body of the worm toward

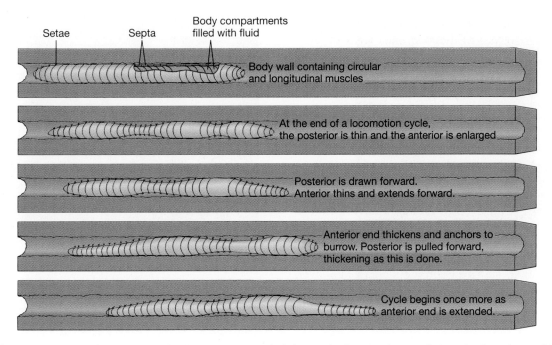

Figure 38–4 Annelid locomotion. Can you infer the segments in which longitudinal or circular muscle is active in each stage? The worm is aided in anchoring itself by bristle-like setae.

the safety of its burrow. If the bird has obtained a firm hold, the worm holds on too, with its swollen, contracted anterior now fitting the burrow like a cork in a bottleneck. If the bird releases its hold, the worm rapidly crawls down the burrow to safety. But how?

If the worm is progressing anterior end first, it must extend a thinned portion of its body into the burrow ahead. Then, while anchored posteriorly by a thickened portion of itself, the worm must swell up its anterior end. Having thus gripped the walls of the burrow, the worm releases its posterior grip and, by longitudinal muscle contraction, drags the whole body toward the anchored anterior end. It repeats this process again and again (Figure 38–4).

All this is made possible by the transverse partitions, or septa (singular, *septum*) that divide the body cavity of the worm. Septa isolate portions of the body cavity and its contained fluid, permitting the hydrostatic skeletons of each segment to be largely independent of one another. Thus, the contraction of the circular muscle in the elongating anterior end need not interfere with the action of the longitudinal muscle in the segments of the still-anchored posterior.

Generally, the hydrostatic skeleton is insufficient for animals that do more than drag themselves along on their bellies. Some examples of it occur in complex invertebrates and even in vertebrates. Among mollusks, for example, the feet of bivalves are extended and anchored by a hydrostatic blood pressure mechanism not too different from that used by the earthworm. The tube feet of echinoderms (such as the sea star and sea urchin)

are moved by an ingenious version of the hydrostatic skeleton, and even the human penis becomes erect and stiff because of the turgidity of pressurized blood in its cavernous spaces.

Mollusks and Arthropods Have Nonliving Exoskeletons

In both mollusks and arthropods, the exoskeleton is a nonliving product of the cells of the epidermis. In mollusks, the exoskeleton basically provides protection, with its major muscle attachments serving the skeleton, rather than the reverse. Thus, the clam has a pair of muscles whose major function is to hold the two valves of the shell tightly shut against the onslaughts of the sea star and chowder maker.

The skeletons of arthropods serve not only to protect but to transmit forces; in that way they are fully comparable to the skeletons of vertebrates. Whereas in mollusks the shell is primarily a retreat to be used in emergencies, with the bulk of the body nakedly and succulently exposed at other times, in arthropods the exoskeleton covers every bit of the body. It even extends inward as far as the stomach on one end and for a considerable distance inward, past the anus, on the other.

Although the arthropod exoskeleton is a continuous one-piece sheath, it varies greatly in thickness and flexibility, with large, thick, inflexible plates separated from one another by thin, flexible joints arranged seg-

Figure 38–5 A greengrocer cicada molting. This insect requires 13 years to mature. (Judy Davidson/Science Photo Library/Photo Researchers)

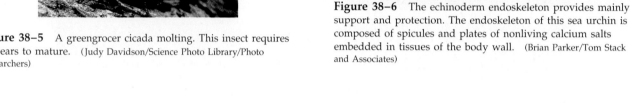

Figure 38–6 The echinoderm endoskeleton provides mainly support and protection. The endoskeleton of this sea urchin is composed of spicules and plates of nonliving calcium salts embedded in tissues of the body wall. (Brian Parker/Tom Stack and Associates)

mentally. Enough joints are provided to make the arthropod's body as flexible as those of many vertebrates. The exoskeleton is also extensively modified to form specialized tools or weapons or otherwise adapted to a vast variety of life styles.

The chief disadvantage of the rigid arthropod exoskeleton is that it prevents growth. To overcome this disadvantage, arthropods must **molt**—that is, cast off their old coverings—from time to time to accommodate new growth (Figure 38–5).

Internal Skeletons Are Living Tissues Capable of Growth

Endoskeletons, or internal skeletons, are extensively developed only in echinoderms and chordates. Echinoderms have spicules and plates of calcium salts embedded in the tissues of their body walls, forming what amounts to an internal shell that provides support and protection (Figure 38–6). Many echinoderm endoskeletons bear spines that project to the outer surface.

The internal skeletons of vertebrates provide support and protection and transmit forces. Composed of living tissue, the vertebrate endoskeleton is light and grows along with the animal, permitting it to grow, potentially, to great size. Compare the largest land vertebrates, elephants and dinosaurs, to the largest land arthropods—beetles a few inches long. If beetles grew to the size of horses, their external armor would weigh so much that it would probably collapse or at least prevent the unfortunate animals from moving. So much for the giant insects of the horror movies!

The endoskeleton probably also permits a greater variety of possible motions than does an exoskeleton. Indeed, in some arthropods, especially the spiders, the hydrostatic action of the body fluid is just as important as the muscles in producing limb movement.

Many vertebrates possess bones that humans lack, such as the skeleton of the gill arches of fish. Careful studies of the embryos of humans and other mammals have shown, however, that a number of elements of the skull originate embryonically in the same way as do the gill arches of fishes; the tiny middle ear bones—malleus, incus, and stapes—are examples.

The vertebrate skeleton has two main divisions. The **axial skeleton,** located along the central axis of the body, consists of the skull, vertebral column, ribs, and sternum (breastbone). The **appendicular skeleton** consists of the bones of the limbs (arms and legs) plus the bones making up the girdles that connect the appendages to the axial skeleton—the shoulder (pectoral) girdle and most of the hip (pelvic) girdle (Figure 38–7).

The **skull,** the bony framework of the head, consists of the cranial and facial bones. In the human, 8 cranial bones enclose the brain, and 14 bones make up the facial portion of the skull. Several cranial bones that are single in the adult human result from the fusion of two or more bones that were separate in the embryo or even in the newborn.

The vertebrate spine, or **vertebral column,** supports the body and bears its weight. In mammals it consists of 24 **vertebrae** and 2 fused bones, the **sacrum** and **coccyx.** The vertebral column consists of the **cervical** (neck) region, composed of 7 vertebrae; the **thoracic** (chest) re-

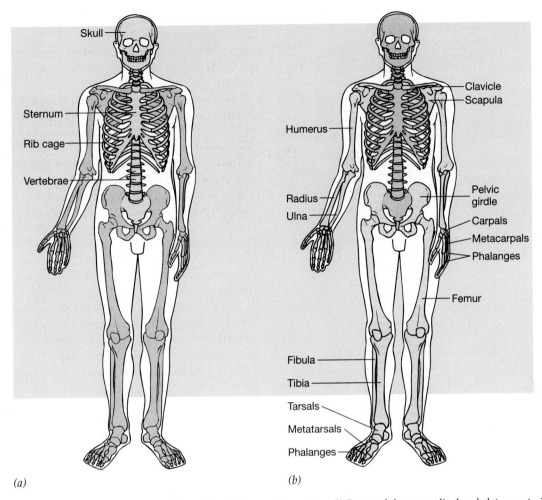

(a)   (b)

Figure 38–7   The human skeleton. (*a*) Bones of the axial skeleton, anterior view. (*b*) Bones of the appendicular skeleton, anterior view.

gion, which consists of 12 vertebrae; the **lumbar** (back) region, composed of 5 vertebrae; the **sacral** (pelvic) region, comprising 5 fused vertebrae; and the **coccygeal** region, consisting of fused vertebrae.

Although vertebrae differ in size and shape in different regions of the vertebral column, a typical vertebra consists of a bony **centrum** (central portion), which bears most of the body weight, and a dorsal ring of bone, the **neural arch,** which surrounds and protects the delicate spinal cord. Vertebrae may also have projections for the attachment of ribs and muscles and for articulating (joining) with neighboring vertebrae. The first vertebra, the **atlas** (named for the mythical Greek who held the world on his shoulders), has rounded depressions on its upper surface into which fit two projections from the base of the skull.

The **rib cage** is a bony basket formed by the **sternum** (breastbone), thoracic vertebrae, and, in mammals, 12 pairs of ribs. The rib cage protects the internal organs of the chest, including the heart and lungs. It also supports the chest wall, preventing it from collapsing as the diaphragm contracts with each breath. The ribs are at-

tached posteriorly to the vertebrae. Of the 12 pairs of ribs in the human, the first 7 are attached anteriorly (ventrally) to the sternum (breastbone); the next 3 are attached indirectly by cartilages; and the last 2, called "floating ribs," have no attachments to the sternum.

The **pectoral girdle** consists of two collarbones, or **clavicles,** and two shoulder blades, or **scapulas.** The **pelvic girdle** consists of a pair of large bones, each composed of three fused hipbones. Whereas the pelvic girdle is securely fused to the vertebral column, the pectoral girdle is loosely and flexibly attached to it by muscles.

The human limbs are comparatively generalized, each terminating in five **digits**—the fingers and toes. The more specialized appendages of other animals may be characterized by four digits (as in the pig), three (as in the rhinoceros), two (as in the camel), or one (as in the horse).

Great apes and humans do have a highly specialized feature: the apposable thumb. (In addition, great apes have an apposable big toe; and although the human big toe is not apposable, it is similar enough in

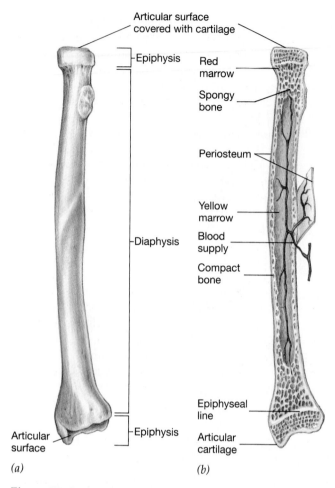

Articular surface
covered with cartilage

Epiphysis
Red
marrow

Spongy
bone

Periosteum

Yellow
marrow

Blood
supply

Compact
bone

Diaphysis

Epiphyseal
line

Articular
surface

Epiphysis

Articular
cartilage

(a)   *(b)*

Figure 38–8   Anatomy of a bone. (*a*) Structure of a typical long bone. (*b*) Internal structure of a long bone.

cle attachments, arranged so that the bone operates as a lever that amplifies the motion they generate. By themselves, muscles cannot shorten enough to produce large movements of the body parts to which they are attached.

Like other bones, the radius is covered by a connective tissue membrane, the **periosteum,** which is capable of laying down fresh layers of bone and thus increasing the bone's diameter. The main shaft of a long bone is its **diaphysis.** The expanded ends of the bone are called **epiphyses.** In children, a disk of cartilage, the **metaphysis,** is found between the epiphyses and the diaphysis. Metaphyses are growth centers that disappear at maturity, becoming vague **epiphyseal lines.** Within the long bone there is a central **marrow cavity** filled with a fatty connective tissue known as yellow bone marrow. The marrow cavity is lined with a thin membrane, the **endosteum.**

The radius has a thin outer shell of **compact bone,** which is very dense and hard. Compact bone is found primarily near the surfaces of a bone, where it provides great strength. Recall from Chapter 37 that compact bone consists of interlocking spindle-shaped units called **osteons** (or haversian systems) (Figure 37–4). Within an osteon, osteocytes (mature bone cells) are found in small cavities called **lacunae.** The lacunae are arranged in concentric circles around central **haversian canals.** Blood vessels that nourish the bone tissue pass through the haversian canals. Threadlike extensions of the cytoplasm of the osteocytes extend through narrow channels called **canaliculi.** These cellular extensions connect the osteocytes.

Interior to the thin shell of compact bone is a filling of **spongy bone** (also called cancellous bone), which, despite its loose structure, provides most of the mechanical strength of the bone. Spongy bone consists of a mesh of thin strands of bone; the spaces in the mesh are filled with bone marrow.

Bones are remodeled throughout life

During fetal development, bones form in two ways. Long bones, such as the radius, develop from cartilage models—a process called **endochondral bone** development. In contrast, the flat bones of the skull, the vertebrae, and some other bones develop from a noncartilage connective tissue scaffold; this is known as **intramembranous bone** development.

Osteoblasts are bone-building cells. They secrete the protein collagen, which forms the strong fibers of bone. The compound hydroxyapatite, composed mainly of calcium phosphate, is present in the tissue fluid. It automatically crystallizes around the collagen fibers, forming the hard matrix of bone. As the matrix forms around the osteoblasts, they become isolated within the lacunae. The trapped osteoblasts are then referred to as osteocytes.

structure to the thumb that it can be used as a surgical substitute.) The opposable thumb can readily be wrapped around objects, such as a tree limb, in climbing, but it is especially useful in grasping and manipulating objects. It can be apposed to each finger singly or to all of them collectively. The muscles that move the thumb are almost as powerful as those of all the other fingers put together.

In humans, the upper appendages (which contain our thumbs) are not used for locomotion as they are in other mammals, including the great apes. Our hands have been emancipated. The combination of apposable thumbs and upright posture enables us to use our hands to shape and build. In this way the human species changes its environment to a greater extent than does any other organism on Earth.

A typical long bone consists of compact and spongy bone

The radius, one of the two bones of the forearm, is a typical long bone (Figure 38–8). It has numerous mus-

Bones are modeled during growth and remodeled continuously throughout life in response to physical stresses and other changing demands. As muscles develop (owing to physical activity), the bones to which they are attached thicken and become stronger. In order for a bone to grow, tissue must be removed from its interior, especially from the walls of the marrow cavity; this process keeps the bone from becoming too heavy. **Osteoclasts** are the very large cells that break down bone in a process referred to as bone resorption. The osteoclasts move about, secreting enzymes that digest bone. Osteoclasts and osteoblasts work side by side to shape bones. Most bone is remade as many as ten times during the course of an average lifetime.

Joints are junctions between bones

At joint surfaces, where two bones meet, the outer layer of each bone consists of articular cartilages. One way to classify joints is according to the degree of movement they allow. The sutures found between bones of the skull are **immovable joints.** In a suture, bones are held together by a thin layer of dense fibrous connective tissue, which may be replaced by bone in the adult. **Slightly movable joints,** found between bodies of vertebrae, are made of cartilage and help absorb shock.

Most joints are **freely movable joints.** Each is enclosed by a joint capsule. The capsule is composed of connective tissue and is lined with a membrane that secretes **synovial fluid,** a lubricant. Generally, the joint capsule is reinforced by ligaments—bands of fibrous connective tissue that connect the bones and limit movement at the joint.

Joints wear down with time and use. In osteoarthritis, a common joint disorder, cartilage repair does not keep up with degeneration, and the articular cartilage wears out. In rheumatoid arthritis, the synovial membrane thickens and becomes inflamed. Synovial fluid accumulates, causing pressure and pain, and the joints become stiff.

MUSCLE IS THE CONTRACTILE TISSUE THAT PERMITS MOVEMENT IN COMPLEX ANIMALS

All eukaryotic cells contain the contractile protein **actin.** It is the major component of microfilaments and is thought to be important in many cell processes, such as amoeboid movement, attachment of cells to an object or surface, and contraction of the cleavage furrow in dividing animal cells. In most cells the contractile protein **myosin** is functionally associated with actin.

The simple cnidarian *Hydra* has only two layers of cells, both consisting of epithelial tissue. Yet these cells are muscular as well as epithelial; their elongated bases contain contractile strands. Some cnidarians have distinct muscle cells specialized for contraction; in a few these are grouped together in conspicuous bands of muscle. In flatworms, muscle occurs as a specialized tissue, organized into definite layers. The contractile proteins, actin and myosin, are most highly organized in muscle cells.

In complex animals the muscles serve as motors that generate mechanical forces and motion. Muscles permit locomotion, manipulation of objects, circulation of blood, movement of food through the digestive tract, and many other movements. The three types of muscle—skeletal, smooth, and cardiac—each specialized for its particular task, were described in Chapter 37. Recall that both skeletal and cardiac muscle are striated (banded).

Bivalve mollusks have both smooth and striated (banded) muscle. The smooth muscle, which is capable of slow, sustained contraction, can be used to keep the two shells tightly closed for long periods, even days. The striated muscle, which contracts rapidly, shuts the shells quickly when the mollusk is threatened. Arthropod muscles are typically striated. (See Making the Connection: Flight Muscles of Insects.)

A Vertebrate Muscle May Consist of Thousands of Muscle Fibers

In vertebrates, each skeletal muscle may be considered an organ. Its fibers are organized in bundles, called **fascicles,** that are wrapped by connective tissue. The biceps in your arm, for example, consists of thousands of individual muscle fibers and their connective tissue coverings.

Recall that each striated muscle fiber is a long, cylindrical cell with many nuclei (Figure 38–9). It is called a fiber because it is elongated. The plasma membrane—known as the **sarcolemma** in a muscle fiber—has multiple inward extensions that form a set of **T tubules** (transverse tubules). The cytoplasm of a muscle fiber is referred to as **sarcoplasm,** and the endoplasmic reticulum as **sarcoplasmic reticulum.**

Threadlike structures called **myofibrils** run lengthwise through the muscle fiber. They are composed of two types of even tinier structures, the **myofilaments.** The thick myofilaments, called **myosin filaments,** consist mainly of the protein myosin, and the thin **actin filaments** consist mostly of the protein actin. Myosin and actin filaments are arranged lengthwise in the muscle fibers so that they overlap. Their overlapping produces the pattern of bands, or striations, characteristic of striated muscle (Figure 38–10). The bands are designated by specific letters, as indicated in Figures 38–9 and 38–11. A **sarcomere** is a unit of thick and thin filaments. Sarcomeres are joined at their ends by an interweaving of filaments called the Z line.

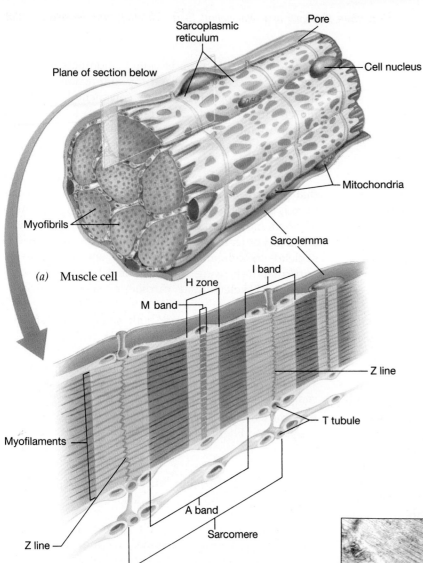

Sarcoplasmic reticulum

Pore

Cell nucleus

Plane of section below

Mitochondria

Myofibrils

Sarcolemma

(a) Muscle cell

Figure 38–9 Structure of skeletal muscle. *(a)* Structure of a skeletal muscle cell. Notice the location of the nuclei, under the sarcolemma. *(b)* Longitudinal section of a myofibril.

I band

H zone

M band

Z line

T tubule

Myofilaments

A band

Sarcomere

Z line

(b) Longitudinal section of myofibril

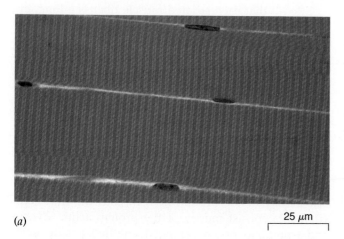

(a)

25 μm

Figure 38–10 Photomicrographs of skeletal muscle. *(a)* Light photomicrograph showing striations. *(b)* Electron micrograph. Note that striations persist at this much higher magnification. The black line indicates 1 micrometer. GLY, glycogen; MY, myosin filaments; ACT, actin filaments; M, mitochondria; TS, transverse tubule or T system; A, H, I, and Z, the zones and bands in the muscle tissue. *(a,* Ed Reschke; *b,* Dr. Lyle Dearden)

(b)

1 μm

MAKING THE CONNECTION

Flight Muscles of Insects

In Chapter 29 we stated that one of the secrets of insect success is their ability to fly. Now that you have learned more about muscle structure and function, we can examine insect flight more closely. Arthropods make up the only invertebrate phylum that possesses a significant amount of striated muscle. In some cases, striated muscle of arthropods may be even more highly differentiated than that of vertebrates. This is seen most easily in the flight muscles of insects, in which many muscle contractions result from a single nervous input.

In most flying insects, the flight muscles are attached not directly to the wings but to the flexible portions of the exoskeleton that articulate with the wings. Each contraction of the muscles produces a dimpling of the exoskeleton in association with a downstroke and sometimes, depending on the exact arrangement of the muscles, on the upstroke as well. When the dimple springs back into its resting position, the muscles attached to it are stretched. The stretching immediately initiates another contraction, and the cycle is repeated. The deformation of the cuticle is transmitted as a force to the wings, and they beat—so fast that we may perceive the sound as a musical tone. In the common blowfly, for instance, the wings may beat at a frequency of 120 cycles *per second*. Yet, in the same blowfly, the neurons that innervate those furiously contracting flight muscles are delivering impulses to them at the astonishingly low frequency rate of three per second. It seems very likely that the mechanical properties of the musculoskeletal arrangement are what provide the stimuli for contraction, by stretching the muscle fibers at the resonant frequency of the system. But the nerve impulses are needed to maintain it.

Insect flight muscle in action has a very high metabolic rate, perhaps the highest of any tissue anywhere. Accordingly, it contains more mitochondria than any known variety of muscle, and it is elaborately infiltrated with tiny air-filled tracheae that carry oxygen directly to each cell (see figure). Many insects have special adaptations to rid the body of the excess heat produced by the flight muscles. The rapidly flying sphinx moth, for example, has in its abdomen what amounts to a "radiator"—that is, a great blood vessel that carries heat from the thorax, where it is generated, and emits it into the cool of the night.

Flight muscles must be kept at appropriate operating temperature if they are to function. You have probably noticed the constant twitching of the wings of such insects as wasps even when they are crawling instead of flying. Probably this behavior is necessary to keep the temperature of the flight muscles high for instant combat readiness. You may also have noticed that the bodies of many moths are quite furry. Moth fur (more properly called pilus) serves the same function as fur in a mammal—to conserve body heat. When the moth awakens and prepares for flight, it shivers its flight muscles at a low frequency to warm them up, constricting its abdominal blood vessel to keep the heat in its thorax. Gradually the frequency of the shivering increases until, at a critical moment, the moth spreads its wings and hums off into the darkness.

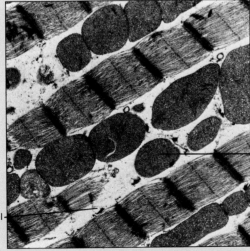

1 μm

Insect flight muscle, such as that of the bumblebee shown here, may be the most powerful muscle found in any organism. Oxygen is brought directly to the muscle by the tracheal tubes, which convey air into the muscle cell itself. Note the prominent striations. (From Heinrich, *Bumblebee Economics,* Harvard University Press, 1978; EM by Mary Ashton, courtesy of Dr. Heinrich, used by permission)

Muscle Contraction Occurs When Actin and Myosin Filaments Slide Past Each Other

The typical pull of a muscle results from the shortening of its cells, which in turn results from the actin and myosin filaments pulling themselves past and between one another (Figure 38–11). Each myosin filament consists of about 200 molecules of the protein myosin in a parallel arrangement. A myosin molecule is made up of six polypeptide chains intertwined to form a double helix. One end of each myosin molecule is folded into two globular structures called heads. The rounded heads of the myosin molecules extend away from the body of the myosin filament; they are positioned on flexible, armlike appendages (Figure 38–12). The heads and armlike appendages together form cross bridges with the actin filaments. The myosin head has the ability to break down ATP in the presence of calcium and use the liberated energy for the contraction process. The head of the myosin molecule bears a binding site that is complementary to binding sites on the actin filament.

Each actin filament is composed of actin and the regulatory proteins **tropomyosin** and **troponin.** The actin component consists of two strands of F-actin, each of which is formed by the interaction of G-actin molecules. One molecule of ADP is attached to each G-actin molecule; these are thought to be the active sites on actin filaments that interact with myosin cross bridges during contraction. When the muscle cell is resting, two tropomyosin molecules block the active sites, preventing interaction with myosin cross bridges. A complex of three troponin molecules binds the tropomyosin to the actin. The troponin complex also binds calcium ions.

During muscle contraction, the actin filaments move toward the middle of the myofibril. As this occurs, the muscle shortens. When many sarcomeres contract simultaneously, they produce the contraction of the muscle as a whole. We can summarize the process of muscle contraction as follows (Figure 38–13):

1. When a nerve impulse passes down a motor neuron (a nerve cell that stimulates a muscle) and arrives at the junction between the neuron and the muscle fiber, the neuron releases a compound known as **acetylcholine** (Figure 38–14).
2. The acetylcholine diffuses across the gap (synaptic cleft) between the neuron and the muscle fiber and combines with receptors on the surface of the muscle fiber.
3. In response, the sarcolemma undergoes an electrical change called **depolarization.** Depolarization may initiate an electrical current, known as an **action potential** or **impulse,** that spreads over the sarcolemma.

4. The action potential spreads through the T tubules and stimulates protein channels in the sarcoplasmic reticulum to open, allowing calcium ions to move out of storage and flow into the sarcoplasm.
5. Calcium combines with the troponin complex. This is thought to cause a change in the shape of the troponin complex that allows the tropomyosin to move deeper into the space between the intertwined G-actin molecules. In this process the active sites on the actin filaments are uncovered.
6. Myosin combines with ATP, then splits ATP. Energy from the ATP is not released until the myosin heads attach to the active sites on the actin filaments. (When attached to the actin filaments, the heads of the myosin molecules are referred to as cross bridges because they bridge the gaps between myosin and actin filaments.)
7. It has been proposed that after the myosin head attaches to the actin filament, it releases the ADP and flexes (bends) about 45 degrees. This flexing motion is the power stroke that pulls the actin filament along. Each myosin head picks up another ATP and releases its hold on the first set of active sites. A new ATP must bind to the myosin head before the cross bridge can detach itself from the actin and begin a new cycle. Energized once again, the myosin heads reach for a second set of active sites. The process is repeated with a third set, and so on (Figure 38–12). This series of stepping motions pulls the myosin and actin filaments past one another. Thus, when the cross bridges attach, move 45 degrees, detach, and then reattach farther along the actin filament, the muscle shortens. (One way to visualize this process is to imagine the myosin heads engaging, "hand over hand," in a kind of tug-of-war on the thin filaments.)
8. When calcium is pumped back into the sarcoplasmic reticulum, ATP is needed and relaxation of the muscle occurs. This entire series of events happens in milliseconds.

Even when we are not moving, our muscles are in a state of partial contraction known as **muscle tone.** At any given moment some muscle fibers are contracted, stimulated by messages from nerve cells. Muscle tone is an unconscious process that helps keep muscles prepared for action. When the motor nerve to a muscle is cut, the muscle becomes limp (completely relaxed), or flaccid.

ATP Powers Muscle Contraction

Muscle cells are often called upon to perform strenuously, and so they must be provided with large

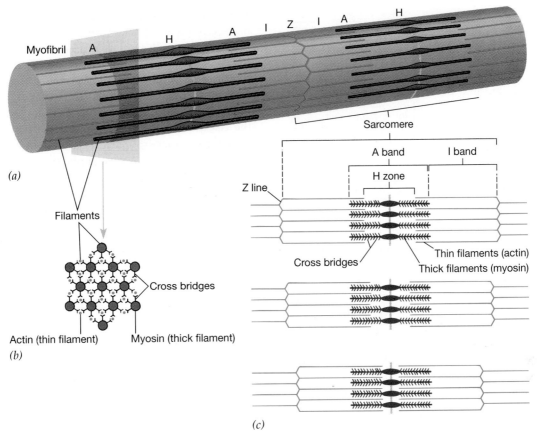

Figure 38-11 A myofibril stripped of the accompanying membranes. (*a*) The Z lines mark the ends of the sarcomeres. (*b*) Cross section of the myofibril shown in (*a*). (*c*) Filaments slide past each other during contraction. Notice the way the filaments overlap. It is the regular pattern of overlapping filaments that gives rise to the striated appearance of skeletal and cardiac muscle. In the top drawing of (*c*), the myofibril is relaxed. In the middle drawing, the filaments have slid toward each other, increasing the amount of overlap and shortening the muscle cell by shortening its sarcomeres. At bottom, maximum contraction has occurred; the sarcomere has shortened considerably. Letters represent zones along the myofibril.

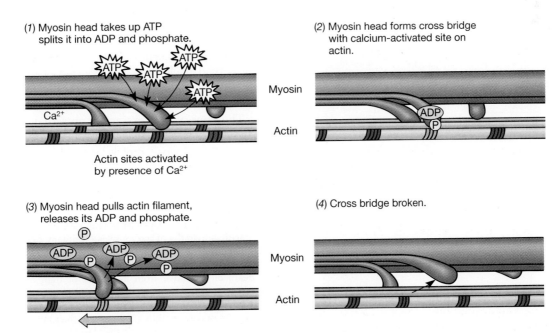

Figure 38-12 A model illustrating the process by which the cross bridges are thought to move the thin and thick filaments past each other in muscle contraction. Parts of this model are still hypothetical.

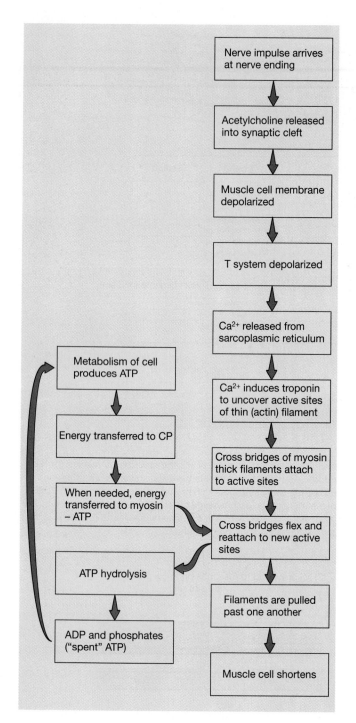

Figure 38–13 Summary of the events of muscular contraction.

amounts of energy. The immediate source of energy necessary for muscle contraction is ATP. ATP is needed both for the pull exerted by the cross bridges and for their release from each active site, as they engage in their tug-of-war on the thin filaments. Rigor mortis, the temporary but very marked muscular rigidity that appears after death, results from ATP depletion following the cessation of cellular respiration upon death.[1]

Sufficient energy can be stored in ATP molecules for only the first few seconds of strenuous activity. Muscle cells also have an energy storage compound, called **creatine phosphate,** that can be stockpiled. The energy stored in creatine phosphate is transferred to ATP as needed. But during vigorous exercise the supply of creatine phosphate does not last very long, either. As ATP and creatine phosphate stores are depleted, muscle cells must replenish their supplies of these energy-rich compounds.

Fuel is stored in muscle fibers in the form of glycogen, a large polysaccharide formed from hundreds of glucose units. Stored glycogen is degraded, yielding glucose, which is then broken down in cellular respiration. When sufficient oxygen is available, enough energy is captured from the glucose to produce needed quantities of ATP.

During strenuous exercise, oxygen may not be available in sufficient quantity to meet the needs of the rapidly metabolizing muscle cells. Under these conditions, muscle cells are capable of breaking down fuel molecules anaerobically (without oxygen) for short periods. Recall from Chapter 7 that lactic acid fermentation is a method of rapidly generating ATP, but not in great quantity. ATP depletion results in weaker contractions and muscle fatigue. Accumulation of the waste product lactic acid also contributes to muscle fatigue. The buildup of lactic acid and depletion of glycogen during muscle exertion make up an **oxygen debt.** The debt is paid back during the period of rapid breathing and aerobic metabolism that typically follows strenuous exercise.

The energy conversion of muscular contraction is not very efficient. Only about 30% of the chemical energy of the glucose fuel is actually converted to me-

---

[1]Rigor mortis does not persist indefinitely, however, for the entire contractile apparatus of the muscles eventually decomposes, restoring pliability. The phenomenon is temperature-dependent, so, given the prevailing temperature, a medical examiner can estimate the time of death of a cadaver from its degree of rigor mortis. Perhaps it should be said that rigor mortis by itself is not muscular contraction; it only tends to freeze the corpse in its position at the time of death. Thus, tales of corpses sitting, pointing to their murderers, and otherwise carrying on posthumously may be entertaining but have no factual basis.

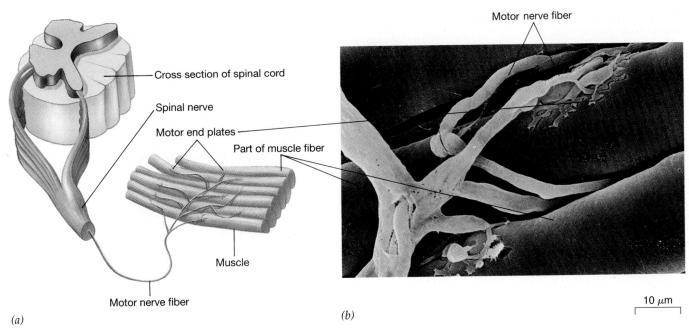

(a)

(b)

Figure 38–14 A motor unit. (*a*) A motor unit typically includes many more muscle fibers than appear here, averaging about 150 muscle fibers each, but some units have less than a dozen fibers, whereas others have several hundred. (*b*) Scanning electron micrograph of some of the cells in a motor unit. Note how the large neuron branches send subdivisions to all the cells in the motor unit. (*b*, Don Fawcett/Science Source/Photo Researchers, Inc.)

chanical work. The remaining energy is accounted for as heat, produced mainly by frictional forces within the muscle cell. That is why we get hot when we work hard physically, and why we shiver when we are cold: The muscle contractions involved in shivering are one way of producing heat to warm the body.

Skeletal Muscle Action Depends on Muscle Pairs That Work Antagonistically

Skeletal muscles produce movements by pulling on tendons, tough cords of connective tissue that anchor muscles to bone. Tendons then pull on bones. Most muscles pass across a joint and are attached to the bones that form the joint. When such a muscle contracts, it draws one bone toward or away from the bone with which it articulates.

Muscles can only pull; they cannot push. Muscles act **antagonistically** to one another; the movement produced by one can be reversed by another. The biceps muscle, for example, permits you to flex your arm, whereas the triceps muscle allows you to extend it once again (Figure 38–15). Thus, the biceps and triceps work antagonistically.

The muscle that contracts to produce a particular action is known as the **agonist.** The muscle that produces the opposite movement is referred to as the **antagonist.** When the agonist is contracting, the antagonist is relaxed. Generally, movements are accomplished

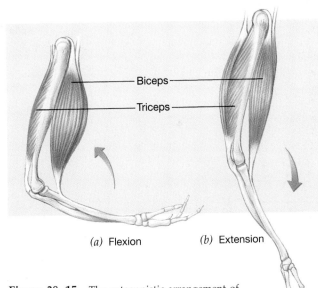

(a) Flexion   *(b)* Extension

Figure 38–15 The antagonistic arrangement of the biceps and triceps muscles.

by groups of muscles working together, so there may be several agonists and several antagonists in any action. Note that muscles that are agonists in one movement may be antagonists in another. The superficial muscles of the human body are shown in Figures 38–16 and 38–17.

Figure 38–16 Superficial muscles of the human body, anterior view.

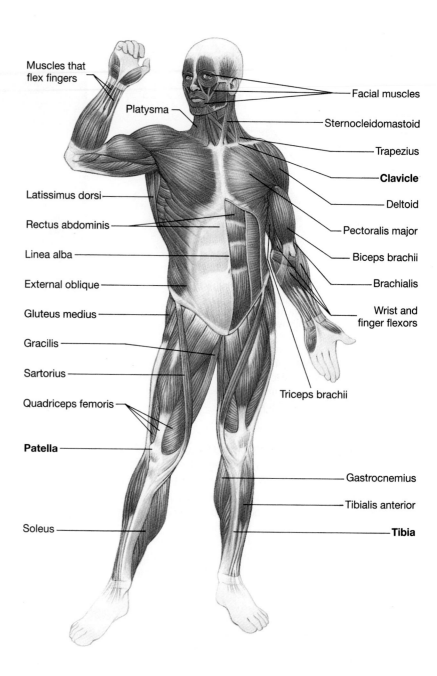

Muscles that flex fingers

Platysma

Facial muscles

Sternocleidomastoid

Trapezius

Clavicle

Latissimus dorsi

Rectus abdominis

Linea alba

External oblique

Gluteus medius

Gracilis

Sartorius

Quadriceps femoris

Patella

Soleus

Deltoid

Pectoralis major

Biceps brachii

Brachialis

Wrist and finger flexors

Triceps brachii

Gastrocnemius

Tibialis anterior

Tibia

Smooth, Cardiac, and Skeletal Muscle Are Specialized for Particular Types of Response

The three types of muscle differ in the ways they respond. Smooth muscle often contracts in response to simple stretching, and its contraction tends to be lengthy. It is well adapted to performing such tasks as the regulation of blood pressure by sustained contraction of the walls of the arterioles. Although smooth muscle contracts slowly, it shortens much more than striated muscle does. Though not well suited for running or flying, smooth muscle squeezes superlatively.

Cardiac muscle contracts abruptly and rhythmically, propelling blood with each contraction. Sustained contraction of cardiac muscle would be disastrous! Skeletal muscle, when stimulated by a single brief stim-

ulus, contracts with a single quick contraction called a **simple twitch.** Simple twitches ordinarily do not occur except in laboratory experiments. In the normal animal, skeletal muscle receives a series of separate stimuli very close together. These produce not a series of simple twitches, however, but a single, smooth, sustained contraction called **tetanus.** Depending upon the identity and number of our muscle cells tetanically contracting, we might thread a needle, haul a rope, or run a mile.

Not all muscular activities are the same. Dancing and, even more so, typing require quick response rather than the long, sustained effort that might be appropriate in hauling a rope. In many animals, entire muscles are specialized for quick or slow responses. In chickens, for instance, the white breast muscles are efficient for

Figure 38–17 Superficial muscles of the human body, posterior view.

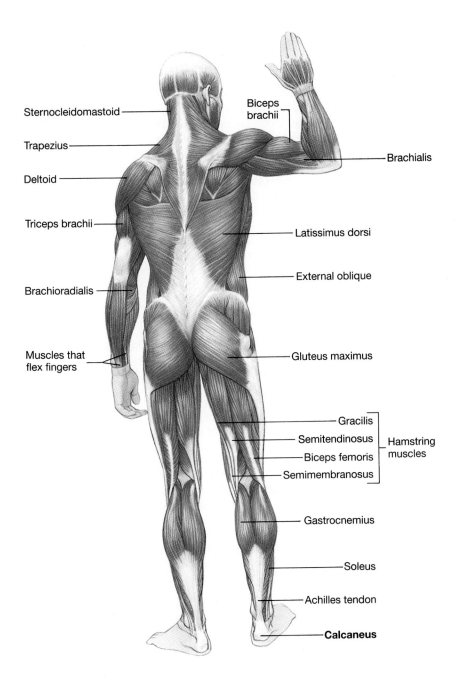

Sternocleidomastoid

Trapezius

Deltoid

Triceps brachii

Brachioradialis

Muscles that flex fingers

Biceps brachii

Brachialis

Latissimus dorsi

External oblique

Gluteus maximus

Gracilis

Semitendinosus

Biceps femoris

Semimembranosus

Hamstring muscles

Gastrocnemius

Soleus

Achilles tendon

Calcaneus

quick responses, because flight is an escape mechanism for chickens. On the other hand, chickens walk about on the ground all day, so the dark meat of the leg and thigh is composed of muscle specialized for more sustained activity.

There is no human equivalent of light and dark meat. However, like other vertebrates, we do possess **fast-twitch fibers,** which are specialized for fast response, and **slow-twitch fibers,** specialized for slow response. We also have intermediate fibers that can be distinguished microscopically with appropriate staining.

Slow-twitch fibers have less sarcoplasmic reticulum than fast-twitch fibers. They have many mitochondria and a rich supply of capillaries. Slow-twitch fibers also have more **myoglobin,** a red pigment similar to hemoglobin. Myoglobin serves as an intermediary responsi-

ble for the transfer of oxygen from hemoglobin to the aerobic metabolic processes of the muscle cell. Myoglobin also may have a modest capacity to store oxygen.

The proportions of slow-twitch and fast-twitch fibers vary from person to person and from muscle to muscle in the same person. The relative proportions of the two appear to be genetically determined and influence the kind of athletic activity at which one has the greatest potential proficiency. A person whose leg and thigh muscles contain a high proportion of fast-twitch fibers could, with proper training, become a good sprinter. An athlete with a greater proportion of slow-twitch fibers may be better suited to marathon activities. Recent evidence, however, suggests that the proportions of the two kinds of fibers can be changed by appropriate training.

SUMMARY

I. In invertebrates, epithelial tissue may contain secretory cells that produce a protective cuticle; secrete lubricants or adhesives; produce odorous or poisonous secretions; or produce threads for nests or webs. Invertebrate epithelium may be specialized for sensory or respiratory functions.

II. Human skin includes nails, hair, sweat glands, oil glands, and sensory receptors.
   A. Cells in the stratum basale of the epidermis continuously divide; as they are pushed upward toward the skin surface, these cells mature, produce keratin, and eventually die.
   B. The dermis, which consists of dense, fibrous connective tissue, rests on a subcutaneous layer composed of loose connective tissue and fat.

III. The skeleton transmits mechanical forces generated by muscle and also supports and protects the body.
   A. *Hydra,* earthworms, and many other invertebrates have a hydrostatic skeleton in which fluid is used to transmit forces generated by contractile cells or muscle.
   B. Exoskeletons are characteristic of mollusks and arthropods. The arthropod skeleton, composed mainly of chitin, is jointed for flexibility. This nonliving skeleton prevents growth, making it necessary for arthropods to molt periodically.

IV. Endoskeletons, found in echinoderms and chordates, are composed of living tissue and therefore are capable of growth.
   A. The human skeleton consists of an axial portion and an appendicular portion.
   B. The radius, a typical long bone, consists of a thin outer shell of compact bone surrounding the inner spongy bone. Within the long bone is a central marrow cavity.
   C. Long bones such as the radius develop from cartilage replicas; this is endochondral bone formation. Other bones, such as the flat bones of the skull, develop from a noncartilage connective tissue model; this is intramembranous bone development.

V. All animals have the ability to move. Specialized muscle tissue is found in most invertebrate phyla and in all of the vertebrates. As muscle tissue contracts (shortens), it moves body parts by pulling on them.
   A. A muscle such as the biceps is an organ made up of hundreds of muscle fibers.
   B. The striations of skeletal muscle fibers reflect the overlapping of their actin and myosin filaments. A sarcomere is a unit of actin and myosin filaments.
   C. During muscle contraction, the actin filaments are pulled inward between the myosin filaments.
      1. Muscle contraction begins when a motor neuron releases acetylcholine into the cleft between the neuron and the muscle.
      2. The acetylcholine combines with receptors on the surface of the muscle fiber.
      3. This results in depolarization of the sarcolemma and transmission of an action potential.
      4. The impulse spreads through the T tubules and stimulates calcium release.
      5. Calcium initiates a process that uncovers the active sites of the actin filaments.
      6. Cross bridges of the myosin filaments attach to the active sites.
      7. The cross bridges flex and reattach to new active sites so that the filaments are pulled past one another and the muscle shortens.
   D. ATP is the immediate source of energy for muscle contraction; muscle tissue has another energy storage compound, creatine phosphate. Glycogen is the fuel stored in muscle fibers.
   E. Muscles act antagonistically to one another.

POST-TEST

1. The vertebrate skin consists of two main layers, the outer _____ and the inner _____.
2. The cells of the stratum _____ of the epidermis are dead and almost waterproof.
3. The protein _____ contributes mechanical strength, flexibility, and waterproofing to the skin.
4. The principal or even sole function of _____ skeletons is transmission of muscular force.
5. Since an exoskeleton tends to limit size, arthropods must _____ from time to time in order to grow.
6. The internal skeletons of echinoderms and chordates are known as _____.
7. The radius has a thin outer shell of _____ bone and a filling of _____ bone.
8. Synovial fluid serves as a _____ in _____.
9. The two types of myofilaments in muscle tissue are _____ filaments and _____ filaments.
10. Creatine phosphate's function is _____ storage in the muscle cell.
11. Fuel is stored in muscle cells in the form of the polysaccharide _____; the immediate source of energy for muscle contraction is _____.
12. Unscramble this list of the events of muscle contraction, putting it into the correct sequence:
   a. calcium release
   b. T-system depolarization
   c. acetylcholine release
   d. nerve impulse
   e. uncovering of the binding sites of the actin filaments
   f. flexing of cross bridges
   g. release of binding sites by cross bridges

REVIEW QUESTIONS

1. Compare vertebrate skin with the external epithelium of invertebrates.
2. What properties does keratin confer on human skin?
3. What is a hydrostatic skeleton? Which functions does it perform?
4. How do the septa in the annelid worm contribute to the flexibility of its hydrostatic skeleton?
5. What are the disadvantages of an exoskeleton? Compare the arthropod exoskeleton to the vertebrate endoskeleton.
6. Describe the divisions of the human skeleton.
7. Draw a typical long bone, such as the radius, and label its parts.
8. Contrast the functions of osteoblasts and osteoclasts. Why is it important that bones be continuously remodeled?
9. Compare the two types of myofilaments in muscle tissue. What is a sarcomere?
10. Outline a model for the sequence of events that causes a muscle cell to contract, beginning with the stimulation of its nerve and including cross bridge action.
11. What is the role of ATP in muscle contraction? What are the functions of creatine phosphate and glycogen?
12. What is the role of agonists? of antagonists? Why is it important that a muscle be able to switch roles?

RECOMMENDED READINGS

Cole, R. P. Myoglobin function in exercising skeletal muscle. *Science,* vol. 216 (April 30, 1982), pp. 523–525. Its function long a mystery, muscle hemoglobin at last yields some of its secrets. Though the details remain unknown, the substance is shown to be necessary for normal muscular oxygen consumption.

Hadley, N. F. The arthropod cuticle. *Scientific American,* vol. 255, no. 1 (July 1986), pp. 104–112. The arthropod cuticle is largely responsible for the adaptive success of the phylum. The author discusses the properties that enable the cuticle to provide protection and support.

Morey, E. R. Spaceflight and bone turnover. *Bioscience* 1984, pp. 168–172. Space flight may become practical only when the demineralization of bone that it produces is stopped. This will require augmentation of our fundamental knowledge of bone mineral turnover mechanisms and their control.

CHAPTER 39

❏

Neural Control: Neurons

OUTLINE

Neurons and glial cells
Neurons transmit information
Synaptic transmission
Neural integration
Neural circuits

Vibrations from approaching footsteps provoke an earthworm to retreat quickly into its burrow. A hungry bird seeks out and devours an insect. A college student learns the principles of biology or calculus. All these activities and countless others are made possible by the nervous system. In complex animals the endocrine system works with the nervous system to regulate many behaviors and physiological processes. The endocrine system generally provides relatively slow and long-lasting regulation, whereas the nervous system permits very rapid responses.

Changes within the body or in the outside world that can be detected by an organism are termed **stimuli.** An organism's ability to survive and to maintain homeostasis depends largely on how effectively it responds to internal and external stimuli.

Thousands of stimuli bombard an organism each day. Appropriate response to a stimulus involves four processes: reception, transmission,

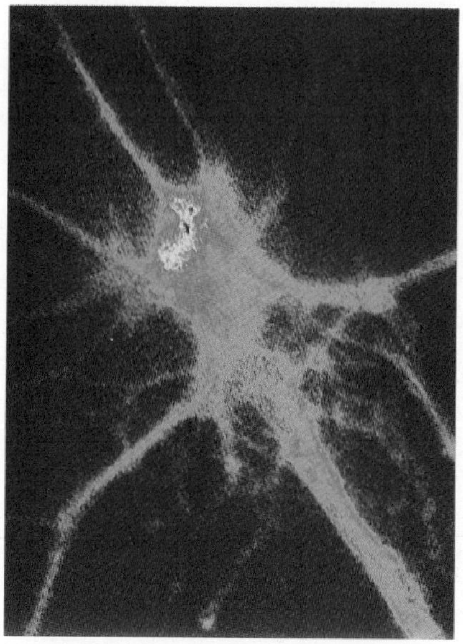

Computer-generated color image of adhesion molecules (CAMs) seen as red and yellow patches on a sensory neuron taken from a sea snail *(Aplysia)*. CAMs may play a role in learning. (Courtesy of Samuel Schacher, Ph.D., Center for Neurobiology and Behavior, College of Physicians & Surgeons of Columbia University)

integration, and response by muscles or glands (Figure 39–1). **Reception,** the process of detecting a stimulus, is the job of the neurons and of specialized sense organs such as the eyes and ears. **Transmission** is the sending of messages along neurons—from one neuron to another or from a neuron to a muscle or gland. A neural message is sent from a receptor to the **central nervous system (CNS)**—the brain or spinal cord. Neurons that transmit information to the CNS are called **afferent neurons** or **sensory neurons.** Afferent neurons generally transmit information to **association neurons** (also called interneurons). **Integration** is the process of sorting and interpreting incoming information and determining the appropriate response. In vertebrates, integration is primarily the function of association neurons in the CNS. Neural messages are transmitted from the CNS by **efferent neurons,** often referred to as **motor neurons.** The **response** is carried out by **effectors,** the muscles and glands.

After you have studied this chapter you should be able to

1. Trace the flow of information through the nervous system (including definitions of the four processes involved in a response to a stimulus—reception, transmission, integration, and response).
2. Draw a typical neuron, label its parts, and give the function of each, including myelin and cellular sheaths.
3. Summarize the process by which an impulse is transmitted along a neuron.
4. Explain the ionic basis of the resting membrane potential.
5. Relate the propagation of an action potential to changes in ion distribution.
6. Compare continuous conduction with saltatory conduction.
7. Trace the events that take place in synaptic transmission. (Draw diagrams to support your description.)
8. Identify the neurotransmitters described in the chapter and describe mechanisms for inactivating neurotransmitters.
9. Identify factors that affect speed of transmission.
10. Describe how a postsynaptic neuron integrates incoming stimuli and "decides" whether or not to fire.
11. Draw diagrams to illustrate convergence, divergence, facilitation, and reverberating circuits, and explain why each is important.

THE CELL TYPES OF THE NERVOUS SYSTEM ARE NEURONS AND GLIAL CELLS

In complex animals the functional unit of the nervous system is the **neuron,** a cell specialized to receive and send information. The neuron works by producing and transmitting rapid electrical signals called **nerve impulses.** A second cell type unique to the nervous system is the **glial cell,** which provides support for the neurons.

Glial Cells Support and Protect Neurons

Some glial cells envelop neurons and form insulating sheaths about them. Others are phagocytic and serve to remove debris from the nervous tissue. A third type of glial cell lines the cavities of the brain and spinal cord. **Schwann cells,** supporting cells found outside the central nervous system, form sheaths about some neurons. Sometimes glial cells are referred to collectively as the **neuroglia,** which literally means "nerve glue."

A Typical Neuron Consists of a Cell Body, Dendrites, and an Axon

Highly specialized to receive and transmit messages in the form of electrical impulses, the neuron is distinguished from all other cells by its long cytoplasmic extensions, or processes. We examine the structure of the common type of neuron, the multipolar neuron (Figure 39–2).

The largest portion of the neuron, the **cell body,** contains the bulk of the cytoplasm, the nucleus, and most of the other organelles. Two types of cytoplasmic extensions project from the cell body of a multipolar neuron: numerous dendrites extend from one end, and a long, single axon projects from the opposite end.

Dendrites are typically short, highly branched fibers specialized to receive nerve impulses and send them to the cell body. The cell body integrates incoming signals and can also receive impulses directly.

Although microscopic in diameter, an **axon** may be 3 feet or more in length and may have branches along its course. It conducts nerve impulses from the cell body to another neuron or to a muscle or gland. At its end the axon branches, forming many **axon terminals.** Each terminal ends in a tiny **synaptic knob.** The knobs release **neurotransmitters,** chemicals that transmit signals from one neuron to another.

The axons of many neurons outside the central nervous system have two coverings—an outer **cellular sheath,** or **neurilemma,** and an inner **myelin sheath** (Figure 39–3). Both are formed by Schwann cells. The cellular sheath is formed by Schwann cells that line up along the axon. The myelin sheath, which lies between the axon and the cellular sheath, is formed when the Schwann cell winds its plasma membrane about the axon several times.

The plasma membrane of the Schwann cell is rich in **myelin,** a white, lipid-rich substance. Myelin is an excellent insulator, and its presence influences transmission of nerve impulses. Gaps in the myelin sheath, called **nodes of Ranvier,** occur between successive Schwann cells. At these points the axon is not insulated with myelin.

Almost all axons more than 2 micrometers in diameter are myelinated; that is, they have myelin sheaths. Those of smaller diameter are generally unmyelinated. In the brain and spinal cord, myelin sheaths are formed by certain glial cells but cellular sheaths are not present.

In **multiple sclerosis,** a neurological disease that affects about 300,000 people in the United States alone, patches of myelin deteriorate at irregular intervals along the lengths of the neurons and are replaced by scar tissue. This damage interferes with conduction of neural impulses, and the victim suffers loss of coordina-

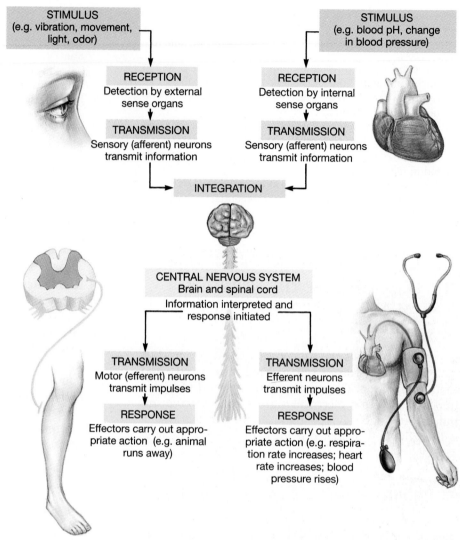

STIMULUS
(e.g. vibration, movement, light, odor)

RECEPTION
Detection by external sense organs

TRANSMISSION
Sensory (afferent) neurons transmit information

STIMULUS
(e.g. blood pH, change in blood pressure)

RECEPTION
Detection by internal sense organs

TRANSMISSION
Sensory (afferent) neurons transmit information

INTEGRATION

CENTRAL NERVOUS SYSTEM
Brain and spinal cord
Information interpreted and response initiated

TRANSMISSION
Motor (efferent) neurons transmit impulses

RESPONSE
Effectors carry out appropriate action (e.g. animal runs away)

TRANSMISSION
Efferent neurons transmit impulses

RESPONSE
Effectors carry out appropriate action (e.g. respiration rate increases; heart rate increases; blood pressure rises)

Figure 39–1 Flow of information through the nervous system.

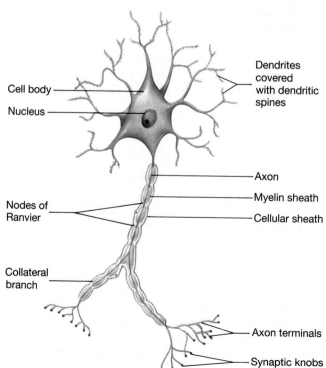

Cell body

Nucleus

Dendrites covered with dendritic spines

Axon

Myelin sheath

Cellular sheath

Nodes of Ranvier

Collateral branch

Axon terminals

Synaptic knobs

Figure 39–2 Structure of a multipolar neuron. The axon of this neuron is myelinated, so the myelin sheath is shown in addition to the cellular sheath.

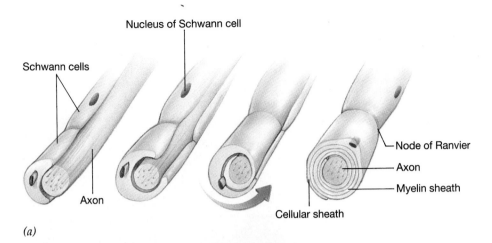

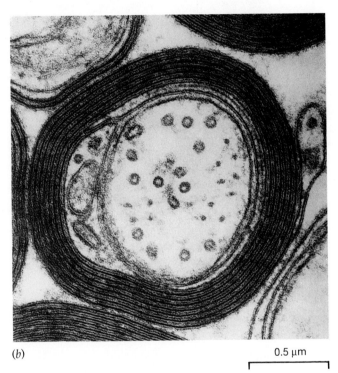

Figure 39–3 The myelin sheath. (*a*) Formation of the myelin sheath around the axon of a peripheral neuron. A Schwann cell wraps its plasma membrane around the axon many times to form the insulating myelin sheath. The rest of the Schwann cell remains outside the myelin sheath, forming the cellular sheath. (*b*) Electron micrograph of a section through a myelinated axon showing the myelin sheath. (Visuals Unlimited/C. S. Raine)

tion, tremor, and partial or complete paralysis of parts of the body. The cause of multiple sclerosis has been a mystery, but some evidence exists that it is an autoimmune disease, in which the body attacks its own tissue (Chapter 43).

The cellular sheath is important in the regeneration of injured neurons. When an axon is cut, the portion separated from the cell body deteriorates and is phagocytized by surrounding cells, but the cellular sheath remains intact. The cut end of the axon grows slowly through the empty cellular sheath, and eventually at least partial neural function may be restored.

A **nerve** is a complex cord consisting of hundreds or even thousands of axons wrapped together in connective tissue (Figure 39–4). We can compare a nerve to a telephone cable. The individual axons correspond to the wires that run through the cable, and the sheaths

and connective-tissue coverings correspond to the insulation. Within the CNS, bundles of axons are referred to as **tracts** or **pathways** rather than nerves. The cell bodies of neurons are usually grouped together in masses called **ganglia.** Inside the CNS, collections of cell bodies are referred to as **nuclei.**

NEURONS CONVEY INFORMATION BY TRANSMITTING RAPIDLY MOVING ELECTRICAL IMPULSES

When a neuron receives a stimulus that is strong enough, its axon fires a nerve impulse. This is an electrical current that travels rapidly down the axon into the

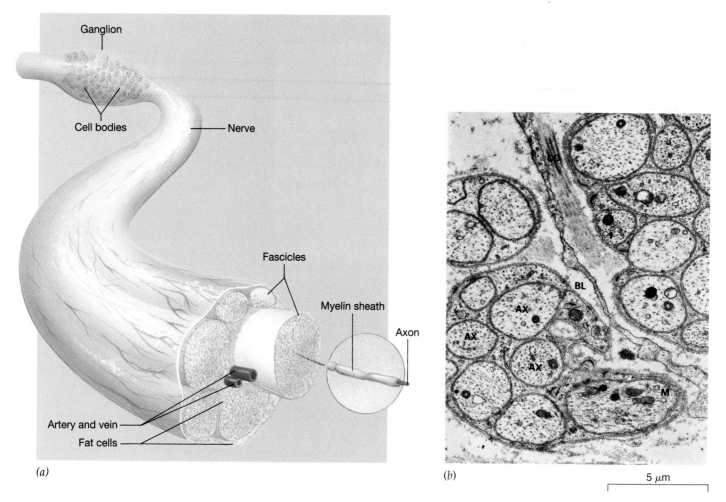

(a)

(b)   5 µm

Figure 39–4   Structure of a nerve and a ganglion. (*a*) A nerve consists of bundles of axons held together by connective tissue. The cell bodies belonging to these axons are grouped together in a ganglion. (*b*) Electron micrograph showing a cross section through a portion of the sciatic nerve. The axons shown here are unmyelinated.   (*b*, Dr. Lyle C. Dearden)

synaptic knobs. Once initiated, the electrical impulse is self-propagating. For a nerve impulse to be fired, however, the plasma membrane has to maintain what is called a resting potential.

The Resting Potential Is the Difference in Electrical Charge across the Plasma Membrane

In a resting neuron—one not transmitting an impulse—the inner surface of the plasma membrane has a negative charge compared with the interstitial fluid surrounding it (Figure 39–5). The plasma membrane is said to be electrically **polarized** (i.e., one side, or pole, has a different charge than the other side). When electric charges are separated in this way, an electrical potential energy difference exists across the membrane. Should the charges be permitted to come together, they have the *potential* of doing work. In resting neurons, the

potential difference across the plasma membrane is called the **membrane potential** or **resting potential.**

The resting potential may be expressed in units called millivolts (mV). (A millivolt equals one-thousandth of a volt and is a unit for measuring electrical potential.) The resting potential of a neuron amounts to about 70 mV. By convention this is expressed as −70 mV because the inner surface of the plasma membrane is negatively charged relative to the interstitial fluid. The potential can be measured by placing one electrode, insulated except at the tip, inside the cell and a second electrode on the outside surface. The two electrodes are connected with an instrument such as a galvanometer, which measures current by electromagnetic action. If both electrodes are placed on the outside surface of the neuron, no potential difference between them is registered; all points on the outside of the membrane are at the same potential. The neuron can be thought of as a biological battery. If its plasma membrane, which is only about one-millionth of a centimeter

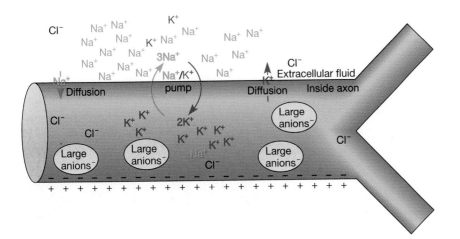

Figure 39–5   Segment of an axon of a resting (nonconducting) neuron. Sodium-potassium pumps in the plasma membrane actively pump sodium out of the cell and pump potassium in. Sodium is unable to diffuse back to any extent, but potassium does diffuse out along its concentration gradient. Negatively charged proteins and other large anions are present in the cell. Because of the unequal distribution of ions, the inside of the axon is negatively charged compared to the surrounding fluid.

thick, were 1 cm thick, the membrane potential would amount to an impressive 70,000 volts!

How does the resting potential develop? It is a direct result of a slight excess of positive ions outside the plasma membrane and a slight excess of negative ions inside the membrane. The distribution of ions inside neurons and in the interstitial fluid surrounding them is similar to that of most other cells in the body. The K^+ concentration is about 30 times greater inside a resting neuron than outside the cell. The Na^+ concentration is about 14 times greater outside than inside the neuron.

This ionic imbalance is brought about by several factors. The neuron plasma membrane has very efficient sodium-potassium pumps that actively transport sodium out of the cell and potassium ions into the cell. Because the pumps work against a concentration gradient and an electrochemical gradient, ATP is required. For every three sodium ions pumped out of the cell, two potassium ions are pumped in. Thus, more positive ions are pumped out than in.

Ions also cross the membrane by facilitated diffusion through membrane proteins that form ion-specific channels. Net movement of ions occurs from an area of higher concentration to an area of lower concentration (Figure 39–6). However, the ease of passage through an ion channel varies according to the type of ion. Sodium ions move through sodium channels much less easily than potassium ions pass through potassium channels. In fact, in the resting neuron the membrane is up to 100 times more permeable to potassium than to sodium. Consequently, sodium ions pumped out of the neuron cannot easily pass back into the cell, but potassium ions pumped into the neuron can diffuse out.

Potassium ions leak out through the membrane along their concentration gradient until the positive charge outside the membrane reaches a level that repels the outflow of more positively charged potassium ions. A steady state is reached when the potassium outflow

equals the inward flow of sodium ions. At this point a potential difference of about -70 mV has developed across the membrane, establishing the resting potential.

Contributing to the overall ion distribution are large numbers of negatively charged proteins and organic phosphates within the neuron that are too large to diffuse out. Some of the potassium ions in the cell help to neutralize these negative charges, but there are not enough potassium ions to neutralize them all. The plasma membrane is permeable to negatively charged chloride ions, but because of the positively charged ions that accumulate outside the membrane, chloride ions are attracted to the outside and tend to accumulate there.

The resting potential is mainly due to the presence of large protein anions inside the cell and to the outward diffusion of potassium ions along their concen-

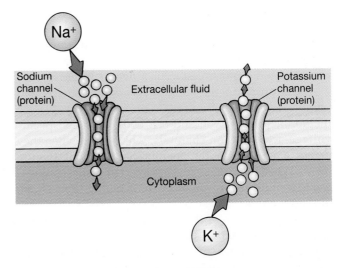

Figure 39–6   Proteins in the plasma membrane form ion-specific channels. Ions diffuse through these channels down their concentration gradient, from a region of higher concentration to a region of lower concentration.

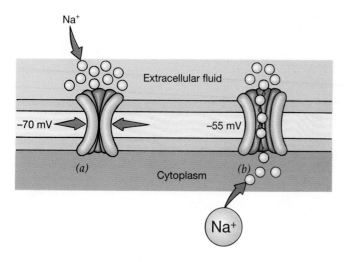

Figure 39–7 Voltage-activated ion channels are present in the plasma membrane of the axon and cell body. (*a*) In the resting state, the voltage-activated Na$^+$ channel is closed. (*b*) When the voltage reaches threshold level, the voltage-activated gate opens, allowing Na$^+$ to flow into the cell. After a certain amount of time elapses, inactivating gates close the channels.

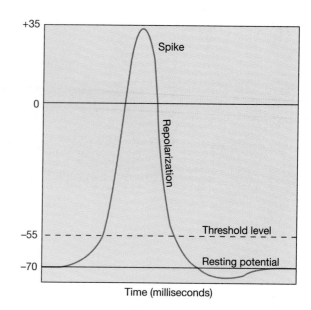

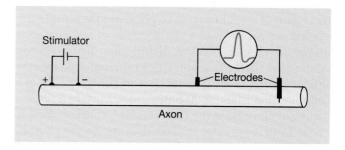

Figure 39–8 An action potential recorded with one electrode inside the cell and one just outside the plasma membrane. When the axon depolarizes to about −55 mV, an action potential is generated. (The numerical values are examples. They vary with different nerve cells.)

tration gradient. However, the conditions for this diffusion must first be set by the action of the sodium-potassium pumps. Remember that the active transport of ions by these pumps is a form of cellular work and therefore requires energy.

The Nerve Impulse Is an Action Potential

Neurons are highly excitable cells. They have the ability to respond to stimuli and to convert stimuli into neural impulses. An electrical, chemical, or mechanical stimulus may alter the resting potential by increasing the permeability of the membrane to sodium. If the neuron membrane is only slightly stimulated, only a local disturbance may occur in the membrane. If the stimulus is sufficiently strong, however, it may result in an **action potential**—the transmission of a **neural impulse.**

In addition to the sodium-potassium pumps and passive ion channels already discussed, the plasma membrane of the axon and cell body contains specific **voltage-activated ion channels,** which open when they detect a change in the membrane potential (Figure 39–7). When the voltage reaches a certain critical point— the **threshold level**—gates open, allowing the passage of specific ions.

The membrane of the neuron can **depolarize** up to about 15 mV—that is, to a resting potential of about −55 mV—without actually initiating an impulse. However, when the extent of depolarization is greater than −55 mV, the threshold level is reached. At that point, the voltage-activated sodium ion channels open and sodium ions pass into the cell. After a certain period of

time, a second set of gates, the inactivating gates, closes the channels. The closing is dependent on time rather than voltage.

K$^+$-sensitive channels also open when the threshold level is reached. They open more slowly and stay open until they sense a particular voltage, that of the resting potential.

An almost explosive action occurs as the action potential is produced. The neuron membrane quickly reaches zero potential and even overshoots to about +35 mV, so a momentary reversal in polarity takes place. The sharp rise and fall of the action potential are referred to as a **spike.** Figure 39–8 illustrates an action potential that has been recorded by placing one electrode inside an axon and one just outside.

The action potential is an electrical current of sufficient strength to induce collapse of the resting potential in the adjacent area of the membrane. The area of depolarization then spreads, like a chain reaction, down the

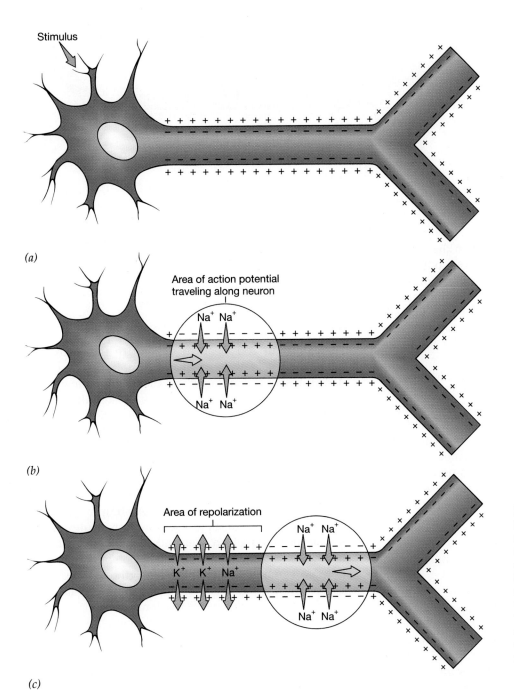

Stimulus

(a)

Area of action potential
traveling along neuron

Na⁺ Na⁺

Na⁺ Na⁺

(b)

Area of repolarization

Na⁺ Na⁺

K⁺ K⁺ Na⁺

Na⁺ Na⁺

(c)

Figure 39–9 Transmission of an impulse along an axon. (*a*) The dendrites (or cell body) of a neuron are stimulated sufficiently to depolarize the membrane to firing level. The axon is shown still in the resting state, with a resting potential. (*b*, *c*) An impulse is transmitted as a wave of depolarization that travels down the axon. At the region of depolarization, sodium ions diffuse into the cell. As the impulse progresses along the axon, repolarization occurs quickly behind it.

length of the axon (at a constant velocity and amplitude for each type of neuron). Thus, a neural impulse is transmitted as a **wave of depolarization** that travels down the neuron.

Conduction of a neural impulse is somewhat analogous to burning a trail of gunpowder. Once the gunpowder is ignited at one end of the trail, the flame moves steadily to the other end by igniting the powder particles ahead of it.

By the time the action potential moves a few millimeters down the axon, the membrane over which it has just passed begins to **repolarize** (Figure 39–9). After a

certain time, the sodium gates close, and the membrane again becomes impermeable to sodium. Potassium gates in the membrane open at this time (due to the threshold level of voltage), allowing potassium to leak out at the point of stimulation. This leakage of potassium ions returns the interior of the membrane to its relatively negative state, repolarizing the membrane. This entire mechanism—depolarization and then repolarization—can take place in less than 1 millisecond.

Even though repolarization takes place very quickly, the redistribution of sodium and potassium to normal resting conditions requires a bit more time.

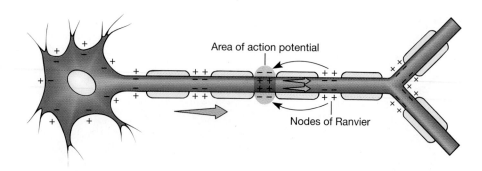

Figure 39–10 Saltatory conduction. In a myelinated axon the impulse leaps along from one node of Ranvier to the next.

Resting conditions are reestablished when the sodium-potassium pump actively transports excess sodium out of the cell. It should be clear that as the wave of depolarization moves down the membrane of the neuron, the normal polarized state is quickly reestablished behind it. We might imagine the action potential as a ring-shaped zone of negative charge traveling along the axon from one end to the other.

During the millisecond or so in which it is depolarized, the axon membrane is in an **absolute refractory period** when it cannot transmit another action potential no matter how great a stimulus is applied. Then, for a few additional milliseconds, while the resting condition is being reestablished, the axon can transmit impulses only when they are more intense than is normally required. This is the **relative refractory period.** Even with the limits imposed by their refractory periods, most neurons can transmit several hundred impulses per second.

Saltatory Conduction Is Rapid

The smooth, progressive impulse transmission just described is characteristic of unmyelinated neurons and is called **continuous conduction.** Conduction in myelinated axons depends upon a similar pattern of current flow. However, in myelinated neurons the myelin acts as an effective insulator around the axon except at the nodes of Ranvier, where the axon membrane makes direct contact with the surrounding interstitial fluid. Sodium channels are concentrated at the nodes. Depolarization jumps along the axon from one node of Ranvier to the next (Figure 39–10). The ion activity at the active node serves to depolarize the next node along the axon. This type of impulse transmission, known as **saltatory conduction,** is faster than the continuous step-by-step type of conduction. A myelinated axon can conduct an impulse up to 50 times faster than the fastest unmyelinated axon.

Saltatory conduction has another advantage over continuous conduction: It requires less energy. Only the nodes depolarize, so fewer sodium and potassium ions

are displaced due to leakage. As a result, the cell does not have to work so hard to reestablish resting conditions each time an impulse is conducted.

The Neuron Obeys an All-or-None Law

Any stimulus too weak to depolarize the neuron to threshold level fails to fire the neuron. It merely sets up a local response that fades and dies within a few millimeters from the point of stimulus. A stimulus strong enough to depolarize the neuron to its critical threshold level results in the propagation of an impulse along the axon.

The threshold level varies with the type of neuron and with the experimental conditions. For example, receptor neurons have lower thresholds to certain stimuli than do other types of neurons. A stimulus stronger than necessary to fire a particular neuron results only in the propagation of an identical action potential. The neuron either propagates an action potential or it does not. No variation exists in the strength of a single impulse. Thus, the neuron obeys an **all-or-none law.**

But how can this be? Sensations, after all, do come in different levels of intensity. We have no difficulty distinguishing between the pain of a severe toothache and that of a minor cut on the hand. This apparent inconsistency is explained by the fact that intensity of sensation depends upon the number of neurons stimulated and upon their frequency of discharge. Suppose you burn your hand. The larger the area burned, the more pain receptors are stimulated and the more neurons are depolarized. Also, the stronger the stimulus, the greater the number of action potentials each neuron transmits per unit of time.

Certain Substances Affect Excitability

Any substance that increases the permeability of the membrane to sodium causes the neuron to become more excitable than normal. Other substances decrease the permeability of the membrane to sodium, making the neuron less excitable.

Calcium balance is essential to normal neural function. When insufficient numbers of calcium ions are present, the sodium gates apparently fail to close completely between action potentials; they thus allow sodium to leak into the cell. This lowers the resting potential, bringing the neuron closer to firing; it fires more easily and sometimes even spontaneously. As a result, the muscle innervated by the neuron may go into spasm. This condition is called **low-calcium tetany.** On the other hand, when calcium ions are too numerous, neurons are less excitable and more difficult to fire.

Many narcotics and anesthetics block conduction of nerve impulses. Local anesthetics such as procaine and cocaine are thought to decrease the permeability of the neuron to sodium. Excitability may be so reduced that the neuron cannot propagate an impulse through the anesthetized region.

DDT and other chlorinated hydrocarbon pesticides interfere with the action of the sodium pump. When nerves are poisoned by such substances, they are unable to transmit impulses. Although the human nervous system can be damaged by these poisons, insects are even more sensitive to them.

SYNAPTIC TRANSMISSION OCCURS BETWEEN NEURONS

Recall that a synapse is the junction between two neurons or between a neuron and an effector. Two types of neuroeffector junctions are known. That between a neuron and a glandular cell is known as a **neuroglandular junction.** That between a neuron and a muscle cell is called a **neuromuscular junction** or **motor end plate.**

A neuron that terminates at a specific synapse is referred to as a **presynaptic neuron;** a neuron that begins at the synapse is known as a **postsynaptic neuron.** Note that these terms are relative to a specific synapse. A neuron that is postsynaptic with respect to one synapse may be presynaptic to the next synapse in the sequence.

Based on how pre- and postsynaptic neurons communicate, two types of synapses have been identified: **electrical synapses** and **chemical synapses.** In electrical synapses, the presynaptic and postsynaptic neurons occur very close together (within 2 nanometers of one another) and form gap junctions (Chapter 5). The two cells are connected by a protein channel called a connexon. Such a synaptic junction allows the passage of ions from one cell to another. Thus, an impulse can be electrically transmitted from the presynaptic neuron to the postsynaptic neuron.

Electrical synapses are found between axons and cell body, axons and dendrites, dendrites and dendrites, and two cell bodies. Such synapses permit rapid communication between cells and help synchronize the activity of many adjacent cells.

Most synapses in the body are thought to be chemical synapses in which the pre- and postsynaptic cells are separated by a relatively wide space (approximately 20 nanometers), the **synaptic cleft.** Because depolarization is a property of the plasma membrane, when an impulse reaches the end of the axon it is unable to jump the gap. An entirely different mechanism—a chemical one—is needed to conduct the "message" across the synaptic cleft to the postsynaptic neuron.

When an impulse reaches a synaptic knob at the end of a presynaptic axon, it stimulates the release of a chemical **neurotransmitter,** also called **transmitter substance,** into the synaptic cleft. This chemical messenger swiftly diffuses across the tiny gap and affects the permeability of the postsynaptic membrane. If sufficient neurotransmitter is present, the postsynaptic membrane may be depolarized to the point of setting off an action potential.

The synaptic knobs continuously synthesize neurotransmitter. Mitochondria in the synaptic knobs provide the ATP required for this synthesis (Figure 39–11). Needed enzymes are produced in the cell body and are transported down the axon to the synaptic knobs. After it is produced, the neurotransmitter is stored in small membrane-bound sacs, **synaptic vesicles,** within the cytoplasm of the synaptic knobs.

Each time an action potential reaches a synaptic knob, the resulting change in membrane potential activates voltage-sensitive calcium channels. Calcium ions from the surrounding tissue fluid then pass into the axon terminal. The Ca^{2+} induces several hundred vesicles to fuse with the presynaptic membrane and release their contents into the synaptic cleft by exocytosis (Figure 39–11).

Each synaptic vesicle releases a fixed number of neurotransmitter molecules. For example, each vesicle containing the neurotransmitter acetylcholine releases about 10,000 molecules. Neurotransmitter molecules then diffuse across the synaptic cleft and combine with specific **receptors** on the dendrites or cell bodies of postsynaptic neurons. These receptors are proteins that control **chemically activated ion channels.** When the neurotransmitter binds with the receptor, the channel opens, permitting the passage of specific ions through the membrane. The resulting redistribution of ions affects the electrical potential of the membrane, causing either depolarization or hyperpolarization. If sufficiently intense, a local depolarization can set off a propagated action potential.

If repolarization is to occur quickly, any excess neurotransmitter in the synaptic cleft must be removed. Some neurotransmitters are inactivated by enzymes. Others are taken back into the presynaptic axon terminal by a pumping mechanism.

Figure 39–11 Transmission of an impulse between neurons or from a neuron to an effector. (*a*) In most synapses the wave of depolarization is unable to jump across the synaptic cleft between the two neurons. (*b*) The problem is solved by chemical transmission across synapses. When an impulse reaches the synaptic knobs at the end of a presynaptic neuron, calcium ions enter the synaptic knob from the interstitial fluid. The calcium ions apparently cause the synaptic vesicles to fuse with the membrane and release neurotransmitter into the synaptic cleft. The neurotransmitter diffuses across the synaptic cleft and may combine with receptors in the membrane of the postsynaptic neuron. This may trigger an impulse in the postsynaptic neuron. It is thought that when neurotransmitter combines with the postsynaptic receptors, the permeability of the postsynaptic membrane to certain ions changes, resulting in either depolarization or hyperpolarization. If depolarization occurs, sodium gates open, permitting sodium to rush into the axon. (*c*) Transmission across a synapse. Electron micrograph of a synaptic knob filled with synaptic vesicles. This is a motor neuron synapsing with a muscle fiber. SC, Schwann cell; M, mitochondria; SV, synaptic vesicle; S, synaptic cleft; MF, membrane of muscle fiber; F, filaments of muscle. (*c*, Visuals Unlimited/T. Reese-D. W. Fawcett)

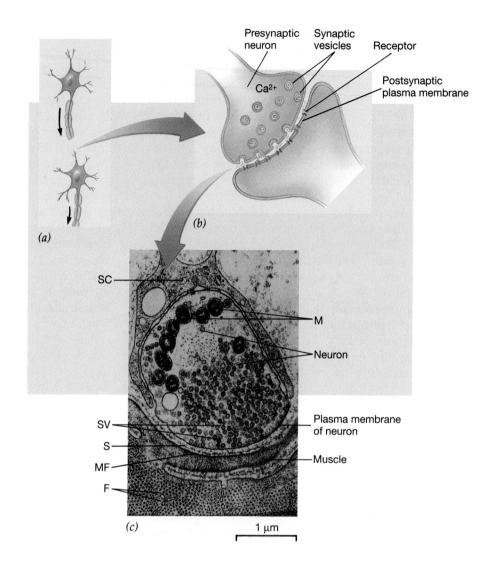

Signals May Be Excitatory or Inhibitory

When neurotransmitter combines with a receptor on the surface of a postsynaptic neuron, the effect can be either to bring the neuron closer to firing or to bring it farther away from firing. If the effect is to partially depolarize the membrane, the neuron is brought closer to firing, and the change in potential is called an **excitatory postsynaptic potential (EPSP).**

Several mechanisms may bring about excitatory transmission. We have discussed chemically activated channels that open when neurotransmitters bind to neurotransmitter receptors on the plasma membrane of the postsynaptic neuron. If a sodium ion channel opens, the resulting influx of sodium ions depolarizes the neuron.

When the neurotransmitter serotonin combines with its receptor, K^+ channels close. This mechanism involves the enzyme **adenylate cyclase.** The activation of the receptor results in activation of adenylate cyclase in the postsynaptic membrane. Adenylate cyclase then converts ATP to **cyclic AMP (cAMP).** Cyclic AMP then activates a protein kinase, which phosphorylates a pro-

tein that closes the K^+ channels. Potassium ions are then unable to diffuse out of the cell, resulting in depolarization.

Some neurotransmitter-receptor combinations *hyperpolarize* the postsynaptic membrane; that is, they make its membrane potential more negative. Because such an action brings the neuron farther away from the firing level, a potential change in this direction is called an **inhibitory postsynaptic potential (IPSP).** Like an EPSP, an IPSP can be produced in several ways. When the neurotransmitter binds to the receptor, K^+ channels may open. As K^+ leaves the cell, it becomes more negative, and the result is hyperpolarization of the membrane. Other receptors that produce IPSPs permit Cl^- to flow into the cell. This increased membrane permeability to Cl^- also hyperpolarizes the membrane.

Graded Potentials Vary in Magnitude

Each EPSP or IPSP is a local response in the neuron membrane. Such responses are referred to as **graded potentials** because they vary in magnitude depending

Table 39–1 SOME NEUROTRANSMITTERS

Substance	Where Secreted	Comments
Acetylcholine	Nerve-muscle junctions; autonomic system;* parts of brain	Inactivated by cholinesterase
Norepinephrine	Autonomic system; reticular activating system and other areas of brain and spinal cord	Inactivated slowly by monoamine oxidase (MAO); mainly inactivated by reabsorption by vesicles in the synaptic knob; norepinephrine level in brain affects mood
Dopamine	Limbic system; cerebral cortex; basal ganglia; hypothalamus	Thought to affect motor function; may be involved in schizophrenia;[†] amount reduced in Parkinson's disease
Serotonin (5-hydroxytryptamine, 5-HT)	Limbic system; hypothalamus; cerebellum; spinal cord	May play role in sleep; LSD antagonizes serotonin; thought to be inhibitory
GABA (gamma-aminobutyric acid)	Spinal cord, cerebral cortex, cerebellum	Acts as inhibitor; may play role in pain perception
Endorphins	CNS and pituitary gland	Neuropeptides that have morphine-like properties and suppress pain; may help regulate cell growth; linked to learning and memory
Enkephalins	Brain and digestive tract	Neuropeptides that inhibit pain impulses by inhibiting release of substance P; bind to same receptors in brain as morphine
Substance P	Brain and spinal cord, sensory nerves, intestine	Transmits pain impulses from pain receptors into CNS

*These and other structures listed in this table will be discussed in Chapter 40.

[†]Studies suggest that the brains of schizophrenics have more dopamine receptors than do those of nonschizophrenics.

on the strength of the stimulus applied. A local change in potential can cause a flow of electric current. The greater the change in potential, the greater the flow of current. Such a local current flow can function as a signal only over a very short distance, because it fades out within a few millimeters of its point of origin. As we will see, however, graded potentials can be added together, resulting in action potentials.

One EPSP is usually too weak to trigger an action potential by itself. Its effect is subliminal, that is, below threshold level. (Even though subthreshold EPSPs do not produce an action potential, they do affect the membrane potential.) EPSPs may be added together in a process known as **summation. Temporal summation** occurs when repeated stimuli cause new EPSPs to develop before previous EPSPs have decayed. By summation of several EPSPs, the neuron may be brought to the critical firing level. When several synaptic knobs release neurotransmitter simultaneously, the postsynaptic neuron is stimulated at several places at the same time. This effect, called **spatial summation,** can also bring the postsynaptic neuron to the threshold level.

Even with summation the postsynaptic neuron may not be depolarized sufficiently to conduct an impulse.

However, the neuron is said to be **facilitated,** meaning that its membrane is nearer the threshold for firing than it would normally be in the resting state. Additional stimulation of the neuron can more easily bring the neuron to the firing level. Facilitation is discussed further later in the chapter.

Many Types of Neurotransmitters Are Known

More than 60 different substances are now known to be or suspected of being neurotransmitters, and a number of neuropeptides have been identified that modulate the effect of neurotransmitters. Many types of neurons secrete two or even three different types of neurotransmitters. Moreover, a postsynaptic neuron may have receptors for more than one type of neurotransmitter. Indeed, some of its receptors may be excitatory and some inhibitory.

Two neurotransmitters that have been studied extensively are acetylcholine and norepinephrine (NE) (Table 39–1). In Chapter 38 we discussed how **acetylcholine** is released from motor neurons that innervate skeletal muscle, and how this neurotransmitter diffuses across the neuromuscular junction to trigger muscle contraction. Acetylcholine is also released by some neurons in the autonomic nervous system (Chapter 40) and by some neurons in the brain. Cells that release this neurotransmitter are referred to as **cholinergic neurons.**

Acetylcholine has an excitatory effect on skeletal muscle, acting to increase the permeability of the muscle fiber membrane to sodium by opening sodium channels. The influx of sodium depolarizes the membrane and ultimately leads to contraction. In contrast, acetylcholine has an inhibitory effect on cardiac muscle, resulting in a decrease in heart rate. Whether a neurotransmitter excites or inhibits is apparently a property of the postsynaptic receptors with which it combines.

After acetylcholine is released by a presynaptic neuron and combines with receptors on the postsynaptic neuron, excess acetylcholine must be removed. This is accomplished by the enzyme cholinesterase, which breaks it down into its chemical components, choline and acetate.

Norepinephrine is released by sympathetic neurons (Chapter 40) and by many neurons in the brain and spinal cord. Neurons that release norepinephrine are called **adrenergic neurons.** Norepinephrine and the neurotransmitters **epinephrine** and **dopamine** belong to a class of compounds called **catecholamines** or **biogenic amines.** After release, most of the excess catecholamines are reabsorbed into the vesicles in the synaptic knobs. Some are degraded by the enzymes catechol-O-methyltransferase and **monoamine oxidase (MAO).** MAO is also thought to help regulate the concentration of catecholamines in the synaptic knobs. Catecholamines affect mood, and many drugs that modify mood do so by altering the levels of catecholamines in the brain.

Other neurotransmitters listed in Table 39–1 include serotonin, gamma-aminobutyric acid (GABA), and the endorphins. GABA is an inhibitory neurotransmitter in the brain and spinal cord.

Nerve Fibers May Be Classified in Terms of Speed of Conduction

In the laboratory it can be demonstrated that an impulse can move in both directions within a single axon. In the body, however, an impulse generally stops when it reaches the dendrites, because there is no neurotransmitter there to conduct it across the synapse. This limitation imposed by neurotransmitter makes neural transmission unidirectional at the synapse. Thus, neural pathways function as one-way streets, with the usual direction of transmission being from the axon of the presynaptic neuron across the synapse to the dendrite or cell body of the postsynaptic neuron.

Compared with the speed of an electrical current or the speed of light, a nerve impulse travels rather slowly. Its speed varies from about 0.5 meter per second to more than 120 meters (400 feet) per second. What factors affect speed of transmission? In general, the greater the diameter of an axon, the greater its speed of conduction. The largest neurons seem also to be the most heavily myelinated, and the more myelin a neuron has, the faster it transmits impulses. In myelinated neurons, the distance between successive nodes of Ranvier is also important: The farther apart the nodes, the faster the axon conducts.

When considering speed of conduction through a sequence of neurons, the number of synapses must be taken into account, because each time an impulse is conducted from one neuron to another there is a slight synaptic delay (about 0.5 millisecond). This delay is due to the time required for the release of neurotransmitter, its diffusion, and its binding to postsynaptic membrane receptors.

NEURAL IMPULSES MUST BE INTEGRATED

Neural integration is the process of sorting and interpreting incoming signals and determining an appropriate response. Each neuron synapses with hundreds of other neurons. Indeed, as much as 40% of a postsynaptic neuron's dendritic surface and cell body may be covered by synaptic knobs of presynaptic neurons. It is the job of the dendrites and cell body of every neuron to integrate the hundreds of messages that continually bombard them.

EPSPs and IPSPs occur continually in postsynaptic neurons; IPSPs cancel the effects of some of the EPSPs. The postsynaptic cell body and dendrites continually tabulate such molecular transactions. When sufficient excitatory neurotransmitter predominates, the neuron is brought to threshold level and an action potential is generated.

It is important to remember that each EPSP or IPSP is not an all-or-none response. Rather, each is a local response (i.e., it does not travel like an action potential) that may be added to or subtracted from other EPSPs and IPSPs. After the neuron membrane has completed its chemical tabulations, the neuron may be inhibited, facilitated, or brought to threshold level. If sufficient EPSPs have been received to bring the neuron to threshold level, an all-or-none action potential is initiated and travels down the axon. This mechanism provides for integration of hundreds of tiny "messages" (EPSPs and IPSPs) before an impulse is actually transmitted along

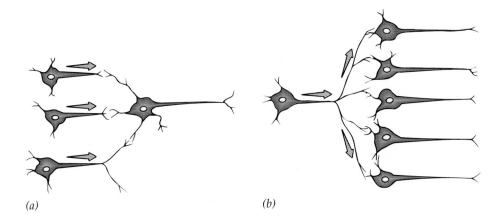

(a) (b)

Figure 39–12 Organization of neural circuits. (*a*) Convergence of neural input. Several presynaptic neurons synapse with one postsynaptic neuron. This organization in a neural circuit permits one neuron to receive signals from many sources. (*b*) Divergence of neural output. A single presynaptic neuron synapses with several postsynaptic neurons. This organization allows one neuron to communicate with many others.

the axon of a postsynaptic neuron. Such an arrangement permits the neuron and the entire nervous system a far greater range of response than would be the case if every EPSP generated an action potential.

Where does neural integration take place? Every neuron acts as a tiny integrator, sorting through (on a molecular level) the hundreds and thousands of bits of information continually bombarding it. Since more than 90% of the neurons in the body are located in the CNS, most neural integration takes place there, within the brain and spinal cord. These neurons are responsible for making most of the "decisions." In the next chapter the brain and spinal cord will be examined in some detail.

NEURONS ARE ORGANIZED INTO CIRCUITS

The CNS contains millions of neurons, but it is not just a tangled mass of nerve cells. Its neurons are organized into separate **neuronal pools,** or networks, and within each pool the neurons are arranged in specific pathways, or **circuits.** Although each pool has some special features, the neural circuits in all of the pools share many organizational features. For example, convergence and divergence are probably characteristic of all of them.

In **convergence,** a single neuron is controlled by converging signals from two or more presynaptic neurons (Figure 39–12*a*). An association neuron in the spinal cord, for instance, may receive converging information from sensory neurons entering the cord, from neurons bringing information from various parts of the brain, and from neurons coming from different levels of the spinal cord. Information from all these sources is integrated before a neural message (action potential) can be sent and an appropriate motor neuron stimulated. Convergence is an important mechanism by

which the CNS can integrate the information that impinges on it from various sources.

In **divergence,** a single presynaptic fiber stimulates many postsynaptic neurons (Figure 39–12*b*). Each presynaptic neuron may branch and synapse with up to 25,000 or more different postsynaptic neurons. For example, a single neuron transmitting an impulse from the motor area of the brain may synapse with hundreds of association neurons in the spinal cord, and each of these may diverge in turn, so that hundreds of muscle fibers may be stimulated.

The mechanism of **facilitation,** discussed earlier in this chapter, is illustrated in Figure 39–13. Neither neuron A nor neuron B by itself can fire neuron 2 or 3. However, stimulation by either A or B does slightly depolarize the neuron. This facilitates the postsynaptic neuron so that, if the other (or any other) presynaptic neuron stimulates it, threshold level is reached more

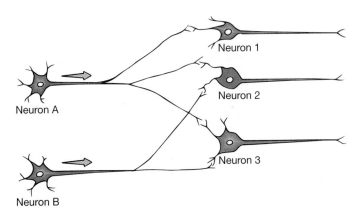

Figure 39–13 Facilitation. Neither neuron A nor neuron B by itself can fire neuron 2 or 3. However, stimulation by either A or B does depolarize the neuron toward the threshold level (if the stimulation is excitatory). This facilitates the postsynaptic neuron so that, if another presynaptic neuron stimulates it, the threshold level may be reached and an action potential generated.

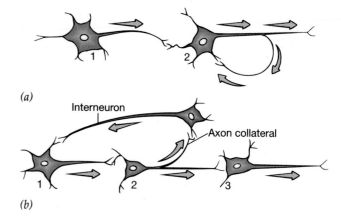

Figure 39–14 Reverberating circuits. (*a*) A simple reverberating circuit in which an axon collateral of the second neuron turns back upon its own dendrites, so the neuron continues to stimulate itself. (*b*) In this neural circuit an axon collateral of the second neuron synapses with an interneuron. The interneuron synapses with the first neuron in the sequence. New impulses are triggered again and again in the first neuron, causing reverberation.

easily and an action potential may be generated. Many neural interactions within the CNS depend upon facilitation.

One of the most important kinds of neural circuits is the **reverberating circuit,** a neural pathway arranged so that a neuron collateral (branch) synapses with an association neuron (Figure 39–14). The association neuron synapses with a neuron earlier in the sequence; that

association neuron can again send new impulses through the circuit. New impulses can be generated over and over until the synapses involved become fatigued (owing to depletion of neurotransmitter) or until they are stopped by some sort of inhibition. Reverberating circuits are thought to be important in rhythmic breathing, in maintaining alertness, and perhaps in short-term memory.

SUMMARY

I. Information flow through the nervous system begins with reception. Information is then transmitted to the CNS, where integration takes place. Appropriate nerve impulses are then transmitted by neurons to the effectors that carry out the response.
II. The neuron is the structural and functional unit of the nervous system.
   A. A typical neuron consists of a cell body from which many branched dendrites and a single, long axon project.
   B. The axon is surrounded by a neurilemma. Many axons are also enveloped in a myelin sheath.
III. A nerve consists of hundreds of axons wrapped in connective tissue; a ganglion is a mass of cell bodies.
IV. A neuron transmits information by firing a neural impulse.
   A. A neuron that is not transmitting an impulse has a resting potential.
      1. The inner surface of the plasma membrane is negatively charged compared to the outside.
      2. Sodium-potassium pumps continuously transport sodium ions out of the neuron and transport potassium ions in.
      3. Potassium ions can leak out more readily than sodium ions can leak in.
   B. Excitatory stimuli are thought to open sodium gates in the plasma membrane. This permits sodium to enter the cell and alter the membrane potential toward depolarization. Inhibitory stimuli hyperpolarize the membrane.

   C. When the membrane potential reaches threshold level, an action potential may be generated.
      1. The action potential is a wave of depolarization that spreads along the axon.
      2. The action potential obeys an all-or-none law.
      3. As the action potential moves down the axon, repolarization occurs very quickly behind it.
   D. Saltatory conduction takes place in myelinated neurons. In this type of transmission, depolarization skips along the axon from one node of Ranvier to the next.
   E. Excitability of a neuron can be affected by calcium concentration and by certain substances such as local anesthetics and pesticides.
V. Synaptic transmission generally depends upon release of a neurotransmitter from vesicles in the synaptic knobs of the presynaptic axon.
   A. The neurotransmitter diffuses across the synaptic cleft and combines with specific receptors on the postsynaptic neuron, resulting in the opening or closing of certain ion channels.
   B. This may cause an excitatory postsynaptic potential (EPSP) or an inhibitory postsynaptic potential (IPSP).
   C. In facilitation, a neuron is brought closer to threshold level by stimulation from various presynaptic neurons; the neuron can then be easily excited by further stimulation.
   D. Temporal or spatial summation may bring the postsynaptic neuron to the threshold level.

VI. The largest, most heavily myelinated neurons conduct impulses most rapidly.

VII. Neural integration is the process of adding and subtracting EPSPs and IPSPs and determining an appropriate response.

VIII. Complex neural pathways are possible because of reverberating circuits and neuronal associations such as convergence and divergence.

POST-TEST

1. The process of conducting neural information is termed _____.

2. Functional connections between neurons are called _____.

3. Changes in the environment that can be detected by an organism are termed _____.

4. A nerve cell is properly referred to as a _____.

5. The supporting cells of nervous tissue are called _____ cells.

6. Dendrites are specialized to _____ _____; the axon functions to transmit impulses from the _____ _____ to a _____.

7. The cellular sheath is important in _____.

8. In some neurons outside the central nervous system, Schwann cells produce both a _____ _____ and a _____ _____.

9. A ganglion consists of a mass of _____ _____.

10. The _____ _____ of a neuron is due mainly to the outward diffusion of potassium ions along their concentration gradient.

11. _____ stimuli are thought to open sodium gates, thereby permitting sodium to rush into the cell.

12. The passage of sodium ions into the neuron causes _____ of the plasma membrane.

13. A wave of depolarization that travels down the axon is called a nerve impulse or _____ _____.

14. Because there is no variation in the intensity of an action potential, the neuron is said to obey an _____ or _____ law.

15. In saltatory conduction, depolarization skips along the axon between the _____ _____ _____.

16. When insufficient calcium ions are present, the _____ _____ is lowered and the neuron fires _____ (*more/less*) easily.

17. When an impulse reaches the synaptic knobs, it stimulates the release of _____.

18. The neurotransmitter that stimulates muscle contraction is _____.

19. Adrenergic neurons release the neurotransmitter _____.

20. In _____, a single presynaptic neuron stimulates many postsynaptic neurons.

21. Label the following diagram. (Refer to Figure 39–2 as necessary.)

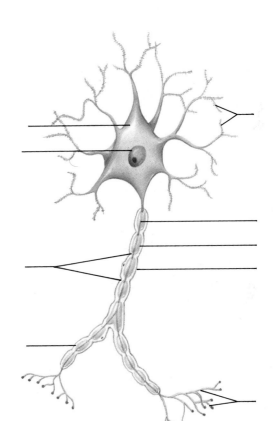

REVIEW QUESTIONS

1. Distinguish between a neuron and a nerve.

2. Imagine that a very unfriendly-looking monster suddenly appears before you. What processes must take place within your nervous system before you can make your escape?

3. What happens when a neuron reaches threshold level?

4. Describe the functions of the following:
   a. myelin   d. dendrites
   b. ganglion e. axon
   c. neuroglia

5. What is meant by the resting potential of a neuron? How do sodium-potassium pumps contribute to the resting potential?

6. What is an action potential? What is responsible for it?

7. What is the all-or-none law?

8. Contrast saltatory conduction with conduction in an unmyelinated neuron.

9. How is neural function affected by the presence of too much calcium? too little calcium?

10. Describe the functions of the following substances:
    a. acetylcholine   c. norepinephrine
    b. cholinesterase

11. Contrast convergence and divergence.
12. What is summation? Describe facilitation.

RECOMMENDED READINGS

Bloom, F. E. Neuropeptides. *Scientific American,* October 1981. An account of the discovery and actions of neuropeptides, which help regulate bodily activities, in some cases acting as both neurotransmitters and hormones.

Fine, A. Transplantation in the central nervous system. *Scientific American,* August 1986. Neurons transplanted from embryos can establish functional connections in the adult brain and spinal cord.

Gottlieb, D. I. Gabaergic neurons. *Scientific American,* February 1988. GABA is an inhibitory neurotransmitter in the brains of all mammals.

Kimelberg, H. K., and M. D. Norenberg. Astrocytes. *Scientific American,* April 1989. A discussion of these interesting glial cells.

Llinas, R. R. Calcium in synaptic transmission. *Scientific American,* October 1982. The role of calcium is studied in the giant synapse of a squid.

Wurtman, R. J. Nutrients that modify brain function. *Scientific American,* April 1982. Increasing the level of neurotransmitter precursors in the blood amplifies signals from some nerve cells. They may eventually be used clinically.

CHAPTER 40

Neural Regulation: Nervous Systems

The type and complexity of an animal's nervous system are closely linked to its lifestyle. The sessile sponge, with its very simple lifestyle, has no nervous system. Whatever responses it makes are at the cellular level. The simplest organized nervous system is the relatively inefficient nerve net found in *Hydra* and other cnidarians (see Figure 40–1). This is an adequate system for an animal that remains rooted in one spot, waiting for dinner to brush by its tentacles.

In a nerve net, neurons are scattered throughout the body. Neither a central control organ nor definite pathways are present. In some neurons and across some synapses, impulses are transmitted in more than one direction. The impulses become less intense as they spread from the region of initial stimulation. More neurons receive the message if the stimulus is strong than if it is weak.

The nerve net produces responses that simultaneously involve large parts of the body. Such a diffuse

The muscular movement that permits this bald eagle (*Haliaeetus leucocephalus*) to fly is directed and coordinated by its very complex nervous system. The nervous system is responsible for regulating most of its life activities and for many internal processes. (Tom and Pat Leeson/Photo Researchers, Inc.)

pattern of transmission is adequate in a radially symmetric animal that moves sluggishly. Responses in cnidarians are limited to discharge of nematocysts and contractions that permit the movements associated with locomotion and feeding. An advantage of the nerve net is that the cnidarian can respond to dinner approaching from any direction. Some cnidarians have two nerve nets. One is a slow-transmitting system that coordinates movement of the tentacles, and the other is faster and is used to coordinate swimming.

With its more highly developed nervous system, a frog can hop about in search of food and eject its tongue with lightning speed to capture a passing fly. However, neither the *Hydra* nor the frog is capable of solving algebra problems or learning about its own biology. An animal's range of possible responses depends in large part on the number of neurons and how they are organized in the nervous system. As animal groups evolved, nervous systems became increasingly complex.

After you have studied this chapter you should be able to

1. Compare nerve nets with bilateral nervous systems.
2. Describe five specific advances characteristic of bilateral nervous systems, and compare them with systems found in radially symmetric animals.
3. Compare the nervous system of a planarian with that of an arthropod and that of a vertebrate.
4. Trace the development of the principal parts of the vertebrate brain (e.g., cerebrum, cerebellum, medulla) from the forebrain, midbrain, and hindbrain.
5. Describe how the relative sizes and functions of the principal parts of the brain differ among fish, amphibians, reptiles, birds, and mammals.
6. Describe the structures that protect the human brain and spinal cord.
7. Describe the spinal cord and its principal functions; diagram a withdrawal reflex.
8. Describe the three functional areas of the human cerebral cortex and give their functions.

9. Give the functions of the reticular activating system and the limbic system.
10. Identify three main types of brain wave patterns, and relate them to specific types of activity.
11. Contrast REM sleep with non-REM sleep.
12. Review current theories of information processing as presented in this chapter.
13. Cite experimental evidence linking environmental stimuli with demonstrable changes in the brain and with learning and motor abilities.
14. Identify the structures and functions of the peripheral nervous system.
15. Describe the functions of the autonomic system and contrast the functions of the sympathetic and parasympathetic systems, giving examples of the effects of these systems on the heart.
16. Discuss the biological actions and effects on mood of the following types of drugs: alcohol, barbiturates, antianxiety drugs, antipsychotic drugs, opiates, stimulants, hallucinogens, and marijuana.

MANY INVERTEBRATES HAVE COMPLEX NERVOUS SYSTEMS

The echinoderm nervous system is a modified nerve net, more complex than the cnidarian nervous system described in the introduction. The echinoderm nervous system consists of a nerve ring around the mouth from which a large radial nerve extends into each arm. Branches of these nerves, which form a network somewhat similar to the nerve net of *Hydra,* coordinate movement of the animal. In sea stars, a nerve net mediates the responses of the dermal gills to touch.

Bilaterally symmetric animals generally have a more complex nervous system than radially symmetric animals. A bilateral form of symmetry usually reflects a more active way of life, with the need to respond to the environment quickly as well as effectively. The following trends can be identified:

1. Increased number of nerve cells.
2. Concentration of nerve cells to form thick cords or masses of tissue, which become nerves, nerve cords, ganglia, and brain.
3. Specialization of function. For example, transmission of nerve impulses in one direction requires both *afferent* nerves, which conduct impulses toward a central nervous system, and *efferent* nerves, which transmit impulses away from the central nervous system and to the effector cells. Certain parts of the central nervous system are also usually specialized to perform specific functions, so distinct structural and functional regions can be identified.

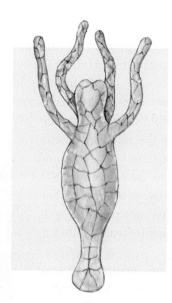

Figure 40–1 The nerve net of *Hydra* and other cnidarians is the simplest organized nervous system. Neither a central control organ nor definite neural pathways are present.

4. Increased number of association neurons and complexity of synaptic contacts. This permits much greater integration of incoming messages, provides a greater range of responses, and allows far more precision in responses.
5. Cephalization, or formation of a head. A bilaterally symmetric animal generally moves in a forward direction. Concentration of sense organs at the front

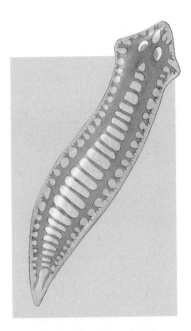

Figure 40–2 Planarian flatworms have a ladder-type nervous system. Cerebral ganglia in the head region serve as a simple brain and, to some extent, control the rest of the nervous system.

end of the body is important either for detection of an enemy quickly enough to escape or for seeing or smelling food in time to capture it. Response can be more rapid if these sense organs are linked by short pathways to decision-making nerve cells nearby. Therefore, nerve cells are also usually concentrated in the head region, and organized to form a brain.

In planarian flatworms, the head region contains concentrations of nerve cells referred to as **cerebral ganglia** (Figure 40–2). These serve as a primitive "brain" and exert some measure of control over the rest of the nervous system. Two solid ventral longitudinal nerve cords extend from the ganglia to the posterior end of the body. Transverse nerves connect the two nerve cords and connect the brain with the eyespots. This arrangement is referred to as a ladder-type nervous system.

In annelids and arthropods, the nervous system also includes a pair of ventrally located longitudinal nerve cords (Figure 40–3). The cell bodies of the nerve cells are massed into pairs of ganglia, each pair located in a body segment. Afferent and efferent neurons are located in lateral nerves, which link the ganglia with muscles and other body structures.

If an earthworm's brain is removed, the animal can move almost as well as before, but when it bumps into an obstacle, it persists in futile efforts to move forward instead of turning aside. This is evidence that the brain is necessary for adaptive movements; it enables the earthworm to respond appropriately to environmental change.

In some arthropods, the cerebral ganglia are somewhat brainlike in that specific functional regions have been identified in them. Mollusks typically have at least three pairs of ganglia: cerebral ganglia, which serve as a coordinating center for complex reflexes and which have a motor function—found dorsal to the esophagus; visceral ganglia, which control shell opening and closing—distributed among the organs; and pedal ganglia, which control the movement of the foot—found in the foot. The visceral and pedal ganglia are connected to the cerebral ganglia by nerve cords.

In cephalopods, such as the octopus, there is a tendency toward concentration of the nerve cells in a central region (Figure 40–4). All the ganglia are massed in the circumesophageal ring, which contains about 168 million nerve cell bodies. With this complex brain, it is no wonder that the octopus is considered to be among the most intelligent of the invertebrates. Octopods have considerable learning abilities and can be taught complex tasks.

KEY FEATURES OF THE VERTEBRATE NERVOUS SYSTEM ARE THE HOLLOW DORSAL NERVE CORD AND THE WELL-DEVELOPED BRAIN

The vertebrate nervous system has two main divisions: the **central nervous system (CNS)** and the **peripheral nervous system (PNS).** The CNS consists of a complex tubular brain that is continuous with the single dorsal tubular spinal cord. Serving as central control, these organs integrate incoming information and determine appropriate responses.

The PNS is made up of the sensory receptors (e.g., touch, auditory, and visual receptors) and the nerves, which are the communication lines. Various parts of the body are linked to the brain by cranial nerves and to the spinal cord by spinal nerves. Afferent neurons in these nerves continuously inform the CNS of changing conditions. Then efferent neurons transmit the "decisions" of the CNS to appropriate muscles and glands, which make the adjustments needed to maintain homeostasis.

For convenience the PNS can be subdivided into **somatic** and **autonomic** portions. Most of the receptors and nerves concerned with changes in the external environment are somatic; those that regulate the internal environment are autonomic. Both systems have sensory (afferent) nerves, which transmit messages from receptors to the CNS, and motor (efferent) nerves, which transmit information back from the CNS to the structures that must respond. In the autonomic system there are two kinds of efferent pathways, **sympathetic** and **parasympathetic** nerves.

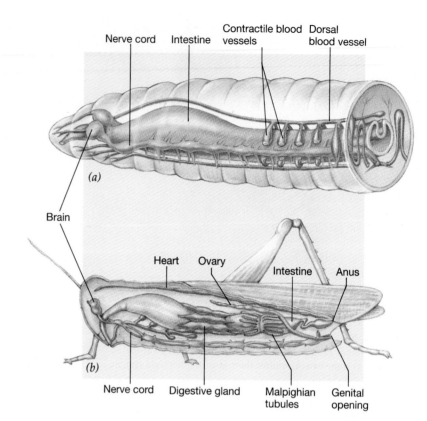

Nerve cord   Intestine   Contractile blood vessels   Dorsal blood vessel

(a)

Brain

Heart   Ovary   Intestine   Anus

(b)

Nerve cord   Digestive gland   Malpighian tubules   Genital opening

Figure 40–3 Annelid and arthropod nervous systems. (*a*) The nervous system of the earthworm is typical of annelids. The cell bodies of the neurons are found in ganglia in each body segment. They are connected by the ventral nerve cord. (*b*) In the insect nervous system, the cerebral ganglia (serving as a simple brain) are connected to two ventral nerve cords.

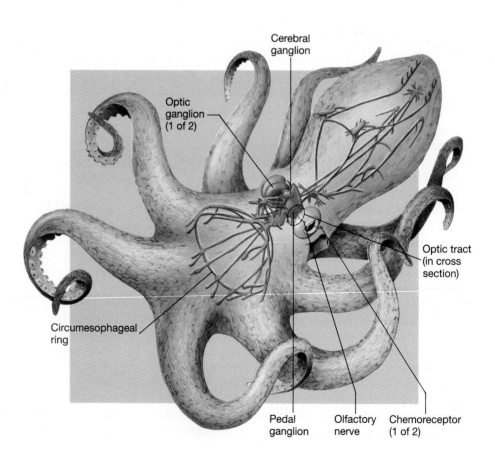

Cerebral ganglion

Optic ganglion (1 of 2)

Optic tract (in cross section)

Circumesophageal ring

Pedal ganglion   Olfactory nerve   Chemoreceptor (1 of 2)

Figure 40–4 The cephalopod nervous system. Several ganglia, including the cerebral, optic, and pedal ganglia, make up the "brain." These structures contain millions of nerve cell bodies.

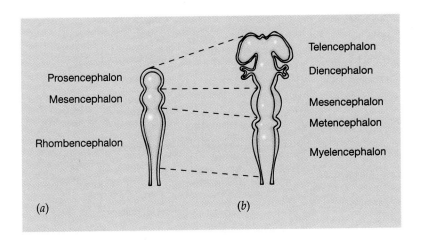

Prosencephalon

Mesencephalon

Rhombencephalon

(a)

Telencephalon

Diencephalon

Mesencephalon

Metencephalon

Myelencephalon

(b)

Figure 40–5 Early in the development of the vertebrate embryo, the anterior end of the neural tube differentiates into the forebrain, midbrain, and hindbrain. These primary divisions subdivide and then give rise to specific structures of the adult brain (see Table 40–1).

THE EVOLUTION OF THE VERTEBRATE BRAIN IS MARKED BY INCREASING COMPLEXITY, ESPECIALLY OF THE CEREBRUM AND CEREBELLUM

In the early vertebrate embryo, the brain and spinal cord differentiate from a single tube of tissue, the **neural tube.** Anteriorly, the tube expands and develops into the brain. Posteriorly, the tube becomes the spinal cord. Brain and spinal cord remain continuous, and their cavities communicate. As the brain begins to differentiate, three bulges become visible—the hindbrain, midbrain, and forebrain (Figure 40–5). All vertebrates, from fish to mammals, have the same basic brain structure. Different parts of the brain may be specialized in different vertebrate classes, and there is an evolutionary trend toward increasing complexity, especially of the cerebrum and cerebellum.

The Hindbrain Develops into the Medulla, Pons, and Cerebellum

The **hindbrain** (rhombencephalon) subdivides to form the metencephalon, which gives rise to the **cerebellum** and **pons,** and the myelencephalon, which gives rise to the **medulla.** The medulla, pons, and midbrain make up the brain stem, the elongated portion of the brain that looks like a stalk holding up the cerebrum.

The medulla, the most posterior part of the brain, is continuous with the spinal cord. Its cavity, the **fourth ventricle,** communicates with the central canal of the spinal cord and with the **cerebral aqueduct,** a channel that runs through the midbrain. The cerebral aqueduct connects the third ventricle (situated within the diencephalon) with the fourth ventricle.

The walls of the medulla are thick and made up largely of nerve tracts that connect the spinal cord with various parts of the brain. In complex vertebrates, the medulla contains discrete nuclei (masses of nerve cell bodies) that serve as vital centers, regulating respiration, heartbeat, and blood pressure. Other reflex centers in the medulla regulate such activities as swallowing, coughing, and vomiting.

The size and shape of the cerebellum vary greatly among the vertebrate classes (Figure 40–6). Development of the cerebellum in different animals is roughly correlated with the extent and complexity of muscular activity. In some fish, birds, and mammals the cerebellum is highly developed, whereas it tends to be small in agnathans, amphibians, and reptiles. The cerebellum coordinates muscle activity and is responsible for muscle tone, posture, and equilibrium.

Injury or removal of the cerebellum results in impaired muscle coordination. A bird without a cerebellum cannot fly, and its wings thrash about jerkily. When the human cerebellum is injured by a blow or by disease, muscular movements are uncoordinated. Any activity requiring delicate coordination, such as threading a needle, is very difficult, if not impossible.

In mammals, a large mass of fibers known as the pons forms a bulge on the anterior surface of the brain stem. The pons is a bridge connecting the spinal cord and medulla with upper parts of the brain. It contains nuclei that relay impulses from the cerebrum to the cerebellum, and centers that help regulate respiration.

The Midbrain Is Most Prominent in Fish and Amphibians

In fish and amphibians, the midbrain, or mesencephalon, is the most prominent part of the brain, serving as

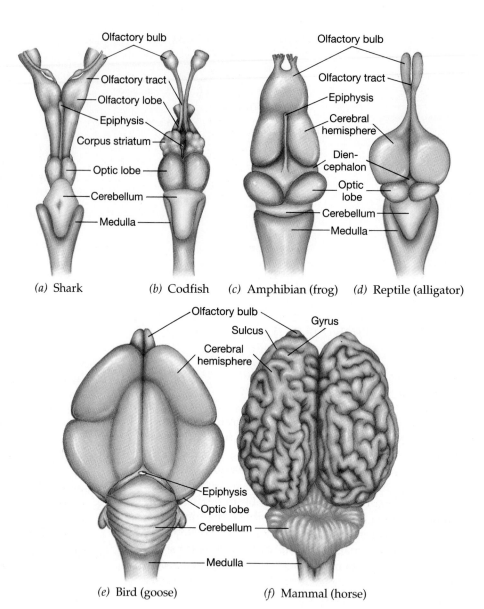

Figure 40–6 Comparison of the brains of members of six vertebrate classes indicates basic similarities and evolutionary trends. Note that different parts of the brain may be specialized in different groups. For example, the large olfactory lobes in the shark brain (*a*) are essential to this predator's highly developed sense of smell. (*a* through *f*) During the course of evolution, the cerebrum and cerebellum have become larger and more complex. In the mammal (*f*), the cerebrum is the most prominent part of the brain; the cerebral cortex, the thin outer layer of the cerebrum, is highly convoluted (folded), which greatly increases its surface area.

the main association area. It receives incoming sensory information, integrates it, and sends decisions to appropriate motor nerves. The dorsal portion of the midbrain is differentiated to some degree in these lower vertebrates. For example, the **optic lobes** are specialized for visual interpretations.

In reptiles, birds, and mammals, many of the functions of the optic lobes are assumed by the cerebrum, which develops from the forebrain. In mammals, the midbrain consists of the **superior colliculi,** which are centers for visual reflexes such as pupil constriction, and the **inferior colliculi,** which are centers for certain auditory reflexes. The mammalian midbrain also contains the **red nucleus,** a center that integrates information regarding muscle tone and posture.

The Forebrain Gives Rise to the Thalamus, Hypothalamus, and Cerebrum

As indicated in Table 40–1, the forebrain, or prosencephalon, further subdivides to form the **telencephalon** and **diencephalon.** The telencephalon gives rise to the **cerebrum,** and the diencephalon to the **thalamus** and **hypothalamus.** The **lateral ventricles** (also called the first and second ventricles) are located within the cerebrum. Each lateral ventricle is connected with the **third ventricle** (within the diencephalon) by way of a channel, the **interventricular foramen.**

The diencephalon contains the thalamus and hypothalamus. In all vertebrate classes, the thalamus is a relay center for motor and sensory messages. In mam-

Table 40–1 DIFFERENTIATION OF CNS STRUCTURES

Early Embryonic Divisions	Subdivisions	Derivatives in Adult	Cavity
Brain Forebrain (prosencephalon)	Telencephalon	Cerebrum	Lateral ventricles (first and second ventricles)
	Diencephalon	Thalamus, hypothalamus, epiphysis (pineal body)	Third ventricle
Midbrain (mesencephalon)	Midbrain	Optic lobes in fish and amphibians; superior and inferior colliculi	Cerebral aqueduct
Hindbrain (rhombencephalon)	Metencephalon	Cerebellum, pons	
	Myelencephalon	Medulla	Fourth ventricle
Spinal cord		Spinal cord	Central canal

mals, all sensory messages except those from the olfactory receptors are delivered to the thalamus before they are relayed to the sensory areas of the cerebrum.

Below the thalamus, the hypothalamus forms the floor of the third ventricle and is the principal integration center for the regulation of the viscera (internal organs). It provides input to centers in the medulla and spinal cord that regulate activities such as heart rate, respiration, and digestive system function. In reptiles, birds, and mammals, the hypothalamus controls body temperature. It also regulates appetite and water balance and is involved in emotional and sexual responses.

The hypothalamus links the nervous and endocrine systems. In fact, the pituitary gland (an important endocrine gland) is connected to the hypothalamus. Certain releasing hormones produced by the hypothalamus regulate the secretion of several other hormones produced by the anterior lobe of the pituitary gland. The hypothalamus also produces the hormones released by the posterior lobe of the pituitary gland.

The telencephalon gives rise to the cerebrum and, in most vertebrate groups, the **olfactory bulbs,** which are concerned with the chemical sense of smell. This is the dominant sense in most aquatic and terrestrial vertebrates. In fact, much of brain development in vertebrates appears to be focused upon the integration of olfactory information. In fish and amphibians, the cerebrum is almost entirely devoted to the integration of such incoming olfactory information.

Birds are an exception among the vertebrates in that their sense of smell is generally poorly developed. In birds, however, a part of the cerebrum called the **corpus striatum** is highly developed. This structure is thought to control the innate, stereotyped, yet complex action patterns characteristic of birds. Just above the corpus striatum is a region thought to govern learning in birds.

In most vertebrates, the cerebrum is divided into right and left **hemispheres.** Most of the cerebrum is made of **white matter,** which consists mainly of axons that connect various parts of the brain. In mammals and most reptiles, a layer of **gray matter** called the **cerebral cortex** makes up the outer portion of cerebral tissue.

Certain reptiles possess a different type of cortex, the **neopallium,** not found in lower vertebrates. It serves as an association area—a region that links sensory and motor functions and is responsible for higher functions such as learning. The neopallium is much more extensive in mammals, making up the bulk of the cerebrum.[1] The cerebrum is the most prominent part of the mammalian brain; during embryonic development, it expands and grows backwards, covering many other brain structures.

In mammals, the cerebrum is responsible for many of the functions that are performed by other parts of the brain in lower vertebrates. In particular, it has many complex association functions that are lacking in reptiles, amphibians, and fish. In small or simple mammals, the cerebral cortex may be smooth. In large complex mammals, the surface area is greatly expanded by numerous folds called **convolutions** or **gyri.** The furrows between them are called **sulci** when shallow and **fissures** when deep.

---

[1] In humans, about 90% of the cerebral cortex is neopallium and consists of six distinct cell layers.

FOCUS ON

Cerebral Dominance

Approximately 90% of us are right-handed. The remaining 10% are left-handed or ambidextrous. In right-handed people, the left cerebral hemisphere is more highly developed for the motor functions related to handedness. In about 95% of adults (regardless of handedness), the left hemisphere is also dominant for language abilities, including the ability to speak, read, learn mathematics, and perform all other intellectual functions associated with language. The speech area in the dominant hemisphere is typically larger than that in the nondominant hemisphere.

In most people, the left cerebral hemisphere is not dominant in all respects; rather, the two hemispheres complement one another. The right hemisphere specializes in functions such as recognizing faces, identifying objects on the basis of shape, and appreciating and recognizing music and form. Some have suggested that creative abilities reside there. The right hemisphere is also responsible for the affective (emotional) aspects of language. For example, this region permits us to express and comprehend tone of voice.

THE HUMAN CENTRAL NERVOUS SYSTEM IS THE MOST COMPLEX BIOLOGICAL MECHANISM KNOWN

As in other vertebrates, the human central nervous system consists of the brain and spinal cord. These soft, fragile organs are carefully protected: Both are encased in bone and wrapped in three layers of connective tissue collectively termed the **meninges.** The three meningeal layers are the tough, outer **dura mater,** the middle **arachnoid,** and the thin, vascular **pia mater,** which adheres closely to the tissue of the brain and spinal cord (Figure 40–7). Meningitis is a disease in which these coverings become infected and inflamed.

Between the arachnoid and the pia mater is the subarachnoid space, which contains **cerebrospinal fluid (CSF).** The fluid is produced by special networks of capillaries, together called the **choroid plexus,** that project from the pia mater into the ventricles. The choroid plexus extracts nutrients from the blood and adds them to the CSF. The choroid plexus and arachnoid serve together as a barrier between blood and CSF; they keep harmful substances in the blood from entering the brain.

CSF is a shock-absorbing fluid that cushions the brain and spinal cord and prevents them from bouncing against the bones of the vertebrae or skull with every movement. CSF also serves as a medium for the exchange of nutrients and waste products between the blood and the brain. CSF circulates down through the ventricles and passes into the subarachnoid space surrounding the brain and spinal cord. It is then reabsorbed into large blood sinuses within the dura mater.

The Spinal Cord Transmits Impulses to and from the Brain and Controls Many Reflex Activities

The tubular spinal cord extends from the base of the brain to the level of the second lumbar vertebra. It has two main functions: (1) to transmit impulses to and from the brain and (2) to control many reflex activities.

The Spinal Cord Consists of Gray and White Matter

A cross section through the spinal cord reveals a small **central canal** surrounded by an area of gray matter shaped somewhat like the letter H (Figure 40–8); outside the gray matter, the spinal cord consists of white matter. The gray matter is composed of large masses of cell bodies, dendrites, and unmyelinated axons as well as glial cells and blood vessels, and is subdivided into sections called **horns.** The white matter consists of myelinated axons arranged in bundles called **tracts** or **pathways.** Long ascending tracts conduct impulses up the cord to the brain. For example, the spinothalamic tracts in the anterior and lateral columns of the white matter conduct pain and temperature information from sensory neurons in the skin. The pyramidal tracts are descending tracts that convey impulses from the cerebrum to spinal motor nerves at various levels in the cord.

Withdrawal Reflexes Are Protective

A **reflex action** is a relatively fixed reaction pattern to a simple stimulus. The response is predictable and auto-

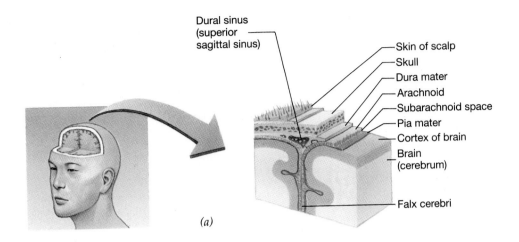

(a)

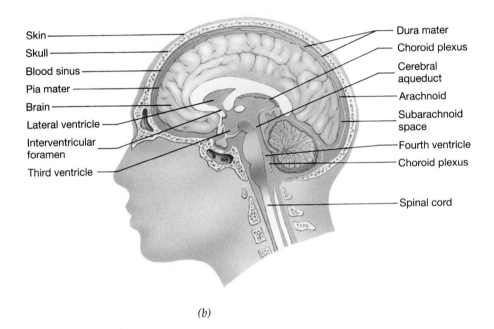

(b)

Figure 40–7   The brain is well protected by several coverings and by the cerebrospinal fluid. (*a*) Frontal section through the superior part of the brain. Note the large sinus shown between two layers of the dura mater. Blood leaving the brain flows into such sinuses and then circulates to the large jugular veins in the neck. (*b*) Circulation of the cerebrospinal fluid in the brain and spinal cord. This cushioning fluid is produced by the choroid plexi in the walls of the ventricles. The fluid circulates throughout the ventricles and subarachnoid space. It is continuously produced and continuously reabsorbed into the blood of the dural sinuses.

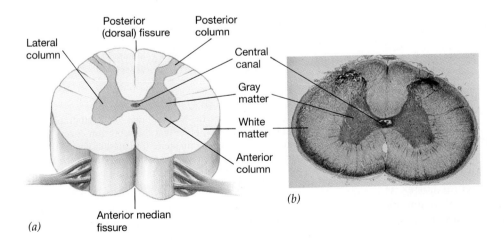

Figure 40–8   The spinal cord consists of gray matter and white matter. (*a*) Cross section through the spinal cord. (*b*) Photomicrograph of a cross section through the spinal cord.   (*b*, M. I. Walker/Photo Researchers, Inc.)

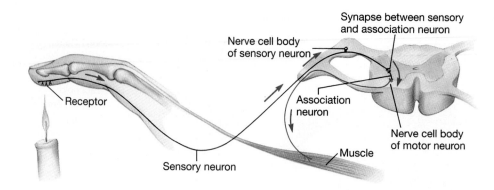

Figure 40–9 The withdrawal reflex involves a chain of three neurons. A sensory neuron transmits the message from the receptor to the central nervous system, where it synapses with an association neuron. Then an appropriate motor neuron (shown in red) transmits an impulse to the muscles that move the hand away from the flame (the response).

matic, not requiring conscious thought. Many of the activities of the body, such as breathing, are regulated by reflex actions.

Although most reflex actions are much more complex, let us consider a **withdrawal reflex,** in which a neural circuit consisting of only three neurons is needed to carry out a response to a stimulus (Figure 40–9). Suppose you touch a hot stove. Almost instantly, and even before you are consciously aware of what has happened, you jerk your hand away from the stove. In this brief instant a message has been carried by a sensory neuron from pain receptors in the skin to the spinal cord. In the tissue of the spinal cord, the message is transmitted from the sensory neuron to an association neuron. Finally, the message is transmitted to an appropriate motor neuron, which conducts it to groups of muscles that respond by contracting and pulling the hand from the stove. Actually, many neurons in sensory, association, and motor nerves participate in such a reaction, and complicated switching is involved. For example, we move our hands *up* from a hot stove but *down* from a hot light bulb. Generally, we are not even consciously aware that all these responding muscles exist.

Quite probably, at the same time that the association neuron sends a message out along a motor neuron, it also sends one up the spinal cord to the conscious areas of the brain. As you withdraw your hand from the hot stove, you become aware of what has happened and feel the pain. This awareness, however, is a feature apart from the reflex response.

The Largest, Most Prominent Part of the Human Brain Is the Cerebrum

The structure and functions of the main parts of the human brain are summarized in Table 40–2. The human brain is illustrated in Figures 40–10 and 40–11. As in other mammals, the human cerebral cortex is functionally divided into three areas: (1) the sensory areas, which receive incoming signals from the sense organs; (2) the motor areas, which control voluntary movement; and (3) the association areas, which link the

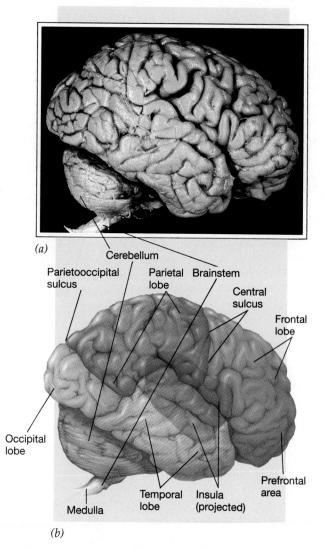

Figure 40–10 Structure of the human brain. (*a*) Photograph of the human brain, lateral view. Note that the cerebrum covers the diencephalon and part of the brain stem. (*b*) Lateral view of the human brain, showing the lobes of the cerebrum. Part of the brain has been made transparent so that the underlying insular lobe can be located. (*a*, Visuals Unlimited/Fred Hossler)

sensory and motor areas and are responsible for thought, learning, language, memory, judgment, and personality.

Table 40–2   THE BRAIN

Structure	Description	Function
Brain stem Medulla	Continuous with spinal cord; primarily made up of nerves passing from spinal cord to rest of brain	Contains vital centers (clusters of neuron cell bodies) that control heartbeat, respiration, and blood pressure; contains centers that control swallowing, coughing, vomiting
Pons	Forms bulge on anterior surface of brain stem	Connects various parts of brain with one another; contains respiratory center
Midbrain	Just above pons; largest part of brain in lower vertebrates; in humans, most of its functions are assumed by cerebrum	Center for visual and auditory reflexes (e.g., pupil reflex, blinking, adjusting ear to volume of sound)
Thalamus	At top of brain stem	Main sensory relay center for conducting information between spinal cord and cerebrum. Neurons in thalamus sort and interpret all incoming sensory information (except olfaction) before relaying messages to appropriate neurons in cerebrum
Hypothalamus	Just below thalamus; pituitary gland is connected to hypothalamus by stalk of neural tissue	Contains centers for control of body temperature, appetite, fat metabolism, and certain emotions; regulates pituitary gland; link between "mind" (cerebrum) and "body" (physiological mechanisms)
Cerebellum	Second largest division of brain	Reflex center for muscular coordination and refinement of movements; when it is injured, performance of voluntary movements is uncoordinated and clumsy
Cerebrum	Largest, most prominent part of human brain; more than 70% of brain's cells located here; longitudinal fissure divides cerebrum into right and left hemispheres, each divided by shallow sulci (furrows) into six lobes; frontal, parietal, temporal, insular, occipital, and limbic	Center of intellect, memory, consciousness, and language; also controls sensation and motor functions
Cerebral cortex (outer gray matter)	Arranged into convolutions (folds) that increase surface area; functionally, cerebral cortex is divided into:	
	1. Motor cortex	Controls movement of voluntary muscles
	2. Sensory cortex	Receives incoming information from eyes, ears, pressure and touch receptors, etc.
	3. Association cortex	Site of intellect, memory, language, and emotion; interprets incoming sensory information
White matter	Within cortex, consists of myelinated axons of neurons that connect various regions of brain; these axons are arranged into bundles (tracts)	Connects: 1. Neurons within same hemisphere 2. Right and left hemispheres 3. Cerebrum with other parts of brain and spinal cord

Investigators have been able to map the cerebral cortex, locating the areas responsible for different functions. The **occipital lobes** contain the visual centers. Stimulation of these areas, even by a blow on the back of the head, causes the sensation of light; their removal causes blindness. The centers for hearing are located in the **temporal lobes** of the brain above the ear; stimulation by a blow causes a sensation of noise. Removal of

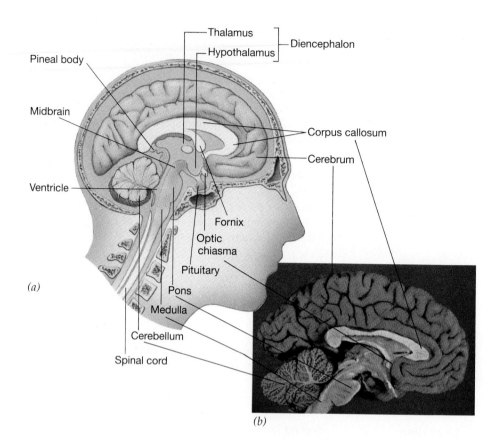

Pineal body
Midbrain
Ventricle

Thalamus
Hypothalamus
Diencephalon

Corpus callosum
Cerebrum

Fornix
Optic chiasma
Pituitary
Pons
Medulla
Cerebellum
Spinal cord

(a)

(b)

Figure 40–11 Midsagittal section through the human brain. Note that in this type of section, half of the brain is cut away so that structures normally covered by the cerebrum are exposed. Compare the diagram (a) with the photograph of the human brain (b). (b, Science Photo Library/Science Source/Photo Researchers, Inc.)

both auditory areas causes deafness. Removal of one does not cause deafness in one ear, but rather produces a decrease in the auditory acuity of both ears.

A groove called the **central sulcus** crosses the top of each hemisphere from medial to lateral edge. This groove partially separates the **frontal lobes** from the **parietal lobes.** The **primary motor areas** in the frontal lobes control the skeletal muscles. The **primary sensory areas** in the parietal lobes receive information regarding heat, cold, touch, and pressure from sense organs in the skin.

The size of the motor area in the brain for any given part of the body is proportional not to the amount of muscle but to the complexity of movement involved. Predictably, areas for the control of the hands and face are relatively large (Figure 40–12). A similar relationships exists between the sensory area and the region of the skin from which it receives impulses. In connections between the body and the brain, not only do the fibers cross so that one side of the brain controls the opposite side of the body, but another "reversal" makes the uppermost part of the cortex control the lower limbs of the body.

When all the areas of known function are plotted, they cover almost all of the rat's cortex, a large part of the dog's, a moderate amount of the monkey's, and only a small part of the total surface of the human cortex (Figure 40–13). The remaining cortical areas are the association areas. Somehow the association regions integrate all the diverse impulses reaching the brain into a meaningful unit so that an appropriate response is made. When disease or accident destroys the functioning of one or more association areas, the ability to recognize certain kinds of symbols may be lost. For example, the names of objects may be forgotten, although their functions are remembered and understood.

The white matter of the cerebrum lies beneath the cerebral cortex. Nerve fibers of the white matter connect the cortical areas with one another and with other parts of the nervous system. A large band of white matter, the **corpus callosum,** connects the right and left hemispheres.

The Reticular Activating System Is an Arousal System

The **reticular activating system (RAS)** is a complex neural pathway within the brain stem and thalamus. It receives messages from neurons in the spinal cord and from many other parts of the nervous system and communicates with the cerebral cortex by complex neural circuits. The RAS is responsible for maintaining consciousness (wakefulness) and for arousal from deep sleep. The RAS continuously filters incoming information and selects only important or unusual information to forward to the higher centers in the cerebrum. When

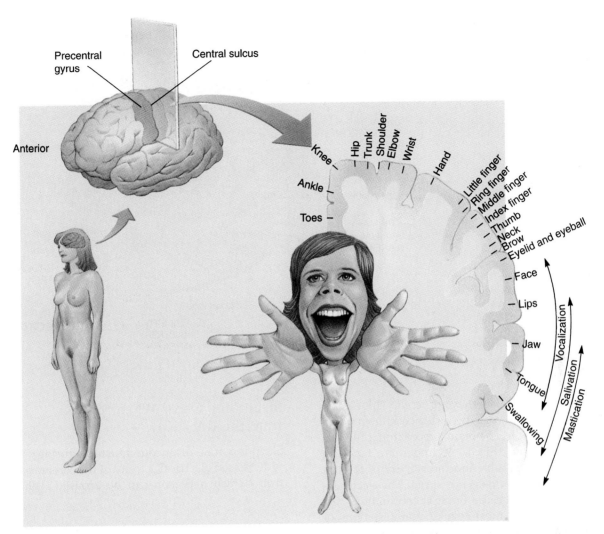

Figure 40–12   A cross section through the primary motor area (precentral gyrus), showing which area of cerebral cortex controls each body part. The figure shown here is proportioned to reflect the amount of cerebral cortex devoted to the control of each body part. Note that more cortical tissue is devoted to controlling those body structures capable of skilled, complex movement.

the RAS is very active and sending many messages into the cerebrum, one feels alert and able to focus attention on specific thoughts. When RAS activity slows, one feels sleepy. If the RAS is severely damaged, the victim may pass into a deep, permanent coma.

The Limbic System Influences Emotional Aspects of Behavior

The **limbic system,** another action system of the brain, consists of certain structures of the cerebrum and diencephalon. It affects the emotional aspects of behavior, sexual behavior, biological rhythms, autonomic responses, and motivation, including feelings of pleasure and punishment. Stimulation of certain areas of the limbic system in an experimental animal results in increased general activity and may cause fighting behavior or extreme rage.

When an electrode is implanted in the so-called reward center of the limbic system, a rat may press a lever that stimulates this area as many as 15,000 times per hour. Stimulation of the reward center is apparently so rewarding that an animal foregoes food and drink and may continue to press the lever until it drops from exhaustion. When an electrode is implanted in the punishment center of the limbic system, an experimental animal quickly learns to press a lever to avoid stimulating that area. The reward and punishment centers are thought to be important in influencing motivation and behavior.

The Brain Exhibits Electrical Activity

Metabolism is accompanied by electrical changes. Brain activity can be studied by measuring and recording the electrical potentials, or "brain waves," given off by var-

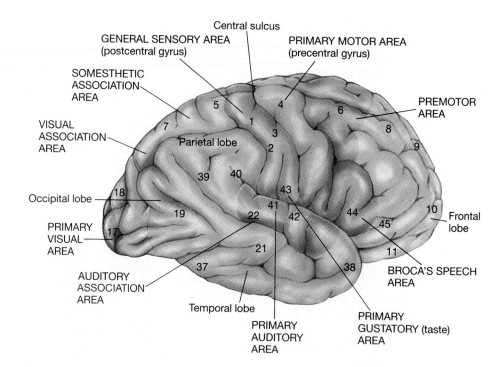

Figure 40–13 Map of the lateral surface of the cerebral cortex, showing some of the functional areas. Areas 4, 6, and 8 are motor areas; areas 1, 2, 3, 17, 41, 42, and 43 are primary sensory areas; and areas 9, 10, 11, 18, 19, 22, 38, 39, and 40 are association areas.

ious parts of the brain when they are active. This electrical activity can be recorded by a device known as an electroencephalograph. To obtain a recording, called an **electroencephalogram (EEG),** electrodes are taped to different parts of the scalp, and the activity of the underlying parts of the cortex is measured. The electroencephalogram shows that the brain is continuously active. On the EEG, the most regular manifestations of activity, called **alpha waves,** are seen to come mainly from the visual areas in the occipital lobes when the person being tested is resting quietly with eyes closed. These waves occur rhythmically at the rate of nine or ten per second (Figure 40–14).

When the eyes are opened, alpha waves disappear and are replaced by more rapid, irregular waves. When some regular stimulus, such as a light blinking at regular intervals, is presented, brain waves with a similar rhythm appear. As you are reading this biology text, your brain is (hopefully) emitting **beta waves.** These have a fast-frequency rhythm characteristic of heightened mental activity, such as information processing. During sleep, brain waves become slower and larger as the person falls into deeper unconsciousness; these slow, large waves associated with certain stages of sleep are called **delta waves.** The dreams of a sleeping person are mirrored in flurries of irregular waves.

Certain brain diseases change the pattern of brain waves. Individuals with epilepsy, for example, exhibit a distinctive, readily recognizable abnormal wave pattern. The location of a brain tumor or the site of brain damage caused by a blow to the head can sometimes be determined by noting the part of the brain that shows abnormal waves.

Sleep May Occur When Signals from the RAS Slow

Sleep is a state of unconsciousness during which there is decreased electrical activity of the cerebral cortex, and from which a person can be aroused. When signals

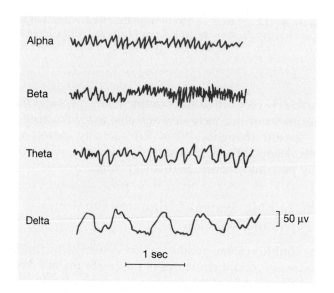

Figure 40–14 Electroencephalograms made while the subject was relaxed, excited, and in various stages of sleep. Theta waves are evoked in some adults when they are under emotional stress. Recordings made during excitement or problem solving show a beta rhythm with brain waves that are rapid and of small amplitude. In sleep the delta waves predominate; these are much slower and of greater amplitude. The regular waves characteristic of the relaxed state are called alpha waves.

from the RAS slow down so that the cerebral cortex is deprived of activating input, a person may lapse into sleep. Consequently, if there is nothing interesting to occupy the mind, we find it easy to go to sleep even when we are not particularly tired. And, although we tend to be wakeful in the presence of attention-holding stimuli, there is a limit beyond which sleep is inevitable.

Two main stages of sleep are recognized: **non-REM** and **REM.** *REM* is an acronym for *rapid eye movements.* During non-REM sleep, sometimes called normal sleep, metabolic rate decreases, breathing slows, and blood pressure decreases. Delta waves, thought to be generated spontaneously by the cerebral cortex when it is not driven by impulses from other parts of the brain, are characteristic of non-REM sleep.

Every 90 minutes or so, a sleeping person enters the REM stage for a time. During this stage, which accounts for about one fourth of total sleep time, the eyes move about rapidly beneath the closed but fluttering lids. Brain waves change to a desynchronized pattern of beta waves. Sleep researchers claim that everyone dreams, especially during REM sleep. Dreams may result from release of norepinephrine within the RAS, which generates stimulating impulses that are fed into the cerebral cortex.

The hypothalamus and brain stem are responsible for the sleep-wake cycle. A nucleus in the hypothalamus is considered the body's biological clock. This nucleus receives input from the retina of the eye regarding light and dark. When stimulated, neurons in the non-REM sleep center release the neurotransmitter serotonin (5-hydroxytryptamine, or 5-HT). Serotonin is thought to inhibit signals passing through the RAS, thus inducing sleep. Neurons in the REM sleep center release norepinephrine.

Why sleep is necessary is not understood. Apparently only higher vertebrates with fairly well-developed cerebral cortices sleep. When a person stays awake for unusually long periods, fatigue and irritability result, and even routine tasks cannot be performed well. Perhaps certain waste products accumulate within the nervous system during waking hours, and sleep gives the nervous system an opportunity to dispose of them.

Not only is non-REM sleep required, but REM sleep is apparently also essential. In sleep deprivation experiments performed with human volunteers, lack of REM sleep makes subjects anxious and irritable. After such experiments, when the subjects are permitted to sleep normally again, they spend more time than usual in the REM stage for a period. Many types of drugs alter sleep patterns and affect the amount of REM sleep. Sleeping pills, for example, may increase the total sleeping time but decrease the time in REM sleep. When a person stops taking such a drug, several weeks may be required before normal sleep patterns are reestablished.

Learning Involves the Storage of Information and Its Retrieval

Learning is a relatively long-lasting adaptive change in behavior resulting from experience. Laboratory experiments have shown that members of every animal phylum can learn, and field observations indicate that learning is important for a wide variety of natural situations. Several types of learning will be discussed in Chapter 50.

Information processing involves three levels of memory

Just how the brain stores information and retrieves the memory on command has been the subject of much speculation. According to current theory, there are three levels of memory—sensory, short-term, and long-term. **Sensory memory** is the persistence of sensory experience for a brief period of time. Sensory memory has a high capacity for information, but that information is lost within about 1 second. Attention is an important component of sensory memory. At any moment we are bombarded with thousands of bits of sensory information. The bits on which we focus our attention are registered in sensory memory. While information is in sensory memory, pattern recognition—the process of identifying the stimuli—can begin.

In order for a sensory memory to be identified or recognized, we must relate it to past experience or past knowledge, and this requires further processing. As pattern recognition and encoding occur, we become aware of stimuli. **Short-term memory** is the information of which we are aware at the moment. Short-term memory can hold only about seven chunks of information (a chunk corresponds to some unit such as a word, syllable, or number).

Short-term memory allows us to recall information for a few seconds or minutes. Usually when we look up a phone number, for example, we remember it only long enough to dial. Should we need the same number the next day, we have to look it up again. Keeping information in short-term memory requires rehearsal. If we redirect our attention, the new stimulus interferes with recall of the information already present, and we forget. Short-term memory is necessary for comprehending speech.

One theory of short-term memory suggests that it is based on reverberating circuits. A memory circuit may continue to reverberate for several minutes until it fatigues or until new signals are received that interfere with the old.

Once we have processed information into **long-term memory,** we no longer have to focus attention on it in order to remember. It is thought that when information is selected for long-term storage, the brain rehearses the material and then stores it in association

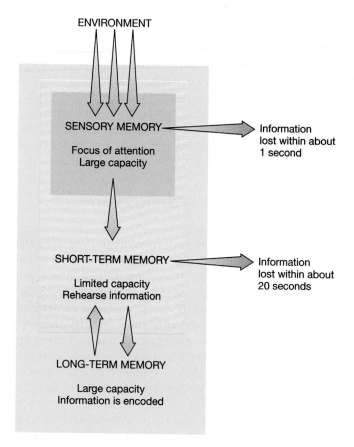

ENVIRONMENT

SENSORY MEMORY

Focus of attention
Large capacity

Information
lost within about
1 second

SHORT-TERM MEMORY

Limited capacity
Rehearse information

Information
lost within about
20 seconds

LONG-TERM MEMORY

Large capacity
Information is encoded

Figure 40–15 Human information processing. Sensory memory is represented here as an activated component of short-term memory. Short-term memory is represented as an activated component of long-term memory.

with similar memories. Long-term memory has an unlimited capacity, and storage may be permanent.

Retrieval of information stored in long-term memory is of considerable interest—especially to students. Some researchers believe that once information is deposited in long-term memory, it remains within the brain permanently. The trick is how to find it when you need it. When you seem to forget something, the problem may be that you have not effectively searched for the memory. Information retrieval can be improved by careful storage. One method is to form strong associations between items when they are being stored.

Sensory memory, short-term memory, and long-term memory are all part of the information processing system. Sensory memory can be viewed as a component of short-term memory, and short-term memory can be thought of as an activated component of long-term memory (Figure 40–15). Information can be transferred back and forth from one component to another. For example, information from long-term memory can be retrieved and temporarily transferred to short-term memory. At that time we are focused on the activated information.

Memory storage involves changes in synaptic function

What physiological changes take place during memory storage? Studies of animal learning have uncovered cellular mechanisms that may also operate in human learning. In at least some types of learning, physical or chemical changes take place in the synaptic knobs or postsynaptic neurons that permanently facilitate or inhibit the transmission of impulses within a newly established circuit. In some cases, specific neurons may become more sensitive to neurotransmitter. Each time a memory is stored, a new neural pathway is facilitated or inhibited. Such an altered circuit is known as a **memory trace** or memory engram.

Habituation is a type of learning in which there is a decrease in response to a repeated stimulus (Chapter 50). The decrease is due to a decrease in synaptic transmission, which results from the inactivation of calcium channels in the presynaptic terminal. The reduction of calcium ion flow into the presynaptic neuron slows down the release of neurotransmitter. In **sensitization,** an increase in response to a stimulus, the responsible cellular mechanism is presynaptic facilitation.

Some investigators think that it is not the location of neurons or the establishment of specific pathways that matters, but the rhythm at which neurons fire. According to this view, each time something new is learned, cells in many parts of the brain acquire a new rhythm of firing. This hypothesis has the advantage of not requiring the localization of memory in the brain—something that no one has been able to demonstrate.

Memory circuits are formed throughout the brain

Researchers have worked with the brains of experimental animals for years without finding specific regions where information is stored. Some forms of learning can take place in association areas within lower brain regions—the thalamus, for example. Even very simple animals that completely lack a cerebral cortex (e.g., worms) are capable of some types of learning.

When large areas of cerebral cortex are destroyed, information is lost somewhat in proportion to the extent of lost tissue. However, no specific area can be labeled the "memory bank." Apparently, memory circuits form throughout the cerebral cortex and also involve many other areas of the brain. Both sensory and motor pathways may be involved in memory.

The association areas of the cerebral cortex, the hippocampal gyri of the limbic system, and the thalamus are involved in learning and remembering. The association areas concerned with interpretation of visual, auditory, and other general sensory information all meet in the **general interpretative area.** This area lies in the posterior portion of the superior temporal lobe and in the anterior portion of the angular gyrus (at the posterior end of the lateral fissure where the parietal, temporal, and occipital lobes all come together). Because impulses from all of the sensory areas are received and integrated in the general interpretative area, this part of the brain is thought to play a very important role in thinking. The temporal portion of the general interpretative area is called **Wernicke's area.** This is an important center for language function because it permits us to recognize and interpret words.

Damage to the general interpretative area may prevent understanding of what we hear or read. We may be able to recognize words but still not be able to arrange them into a coherent thought.

Neurons within the association areas form highly complex pathways that permit complicated reverberation. Several minutes are required for a memory to become consolidated within the long-term memory bank. Should a person suffer a brain concussion or undergo electroshock therapy, for example, memory of what happened immediately prior to the incident may be completely lost. This is known as retrograde amnesia.

The limbic system is important in processing stored information. When portions of the limbic system (the hippocampal gyri) are removed, a person can recall information stored in the past but loses the ability to convert new short-term memories into long-term ones.

Experience Affects the Brain

Studies show that environmental experience may cause physical as well as chemical changes in brain structure. When rats are provided with a stimulating environment and given the opportunity to learn, they exhibit increases in the size of cell bodies and nuclei of brain neurons. A great number of glial cells develop and there is an increased concentration of synaptic contacts. Some investigators have reported that the cerebral cortex becomes thicker and heavier. Characteristic biochemical changes also take place. Other experiments have indicated that animals reared in a complex environment may be able to process and remember information more quickly than animals not given such advantages. Rats provided with basic necessities but deprived of stimulation and/or social interaction do not exhibit these changes.

Early environmental stimulation can also enhance the development of motor areas in the brain. Experiments on rats have shown that the brains of animals that are encouraged to exercise become slightly heavier than those of the control animals. Characteristic changes occur within the cerebellum, including the development of larger dendrites. On the basis of this research, investigators have suggested that physical stimulation may help a young child develop his or her physical potential.

Apparently, during early life certain critical or sensitive periods of nervous system development occur that are influenced by environmental stimuli. For example, when the eyes of young mice first open, neurons in the visual cortex develop large numbers of dendritic spines (structures in which synaptic contact takes place). If the animals are kept in the dark and deprived of visual stimuli, fewer dendritic spines form. If the mice are exposed to light later in life, some new dendritic spines form but never the number that develop in a mouse reared in a normal environment.

Such studies linking the development of the brain with environmental experience support the concept that early stimulation is extremely important for the neural, motor, and intellectual development of children—hence the rapidly expanding educational toy market and widespread acceptance of early education programs. It is also possible that continuing environmental stimulation is needed to maintain the status of the cerebral cortex in later life.

THE PERIPHERAL NERVOUS SYSTEM INCLUDES SOMATIC AND AUTONOMIC SUBDIVISIONS

The **peripheral nervous system (PNS)** consists of the sensory receptors, the nerves that link them with the CNS, and the nerves that link the CNS with the effectors (muscles and glands). The portion of the PNS that helps the body respond to changes in the external environment is the somatic system; the nerves and receptors that maintain homeostasis despite internal changes make up the autonomic nervous system.

The Somatic System Helps the Body Adjust to the External Environment

The **somatic nervous system** includes the receptors that react to changes in the external environment, the sensory neurons that keep the CNS informed of those changes, and the motor neurons that adjust the positions of the skeletal muscles, maintaining the body's well-being. In mammals, 12 pairs of **cranial nerves** emerge from the brain. They transmit information regarding the senses of smell, sight, hearing, and taste from the special sensory receptors, and information from the general sensory receptors, especially in the head region. The cranial nerves also bring orders from the CNS to the voluntary muscles that control movements of the eyes, face, mouth, tongue, pharynx, and larynx. The names of the cranial nerves and the struc-

Table 40–3   THE CRANIAL NERVES OF MAMMALS

Number	Name	Origin of Sensory Fibers	Effector Innervated by Motor Fibers
I	Olfactory	Olfactory epithelium of nose (smell)	None
II	Optic	Retina of eye (vision)	None
III	Oculomotor	Proprioceptors* of eyeball muscles (muscle sense)	Muscles that move eyeball (with IV and VI); muscles that change shape of lens; muscles that constrict pupil
IV	Trochlear	Proprioceptors of eyeball muscles	Other muscles that move eyeball
V	Trigeminal	Teeth and skin of face	Some of muscles used in chewing
VI	Abducens	Proprioceptors of eyeball muscles	Other muscles that move eyeball
VII	Facial	Taste buds of anterior part of tongue	Muscles used for facial expression; submaxillary and sublingual salivary glands
VIII	Auditory (vestibulocochlear)	Cochlea (hearing) and semicircular canals (senses of movement, balance, and rotation)	None
IX	Glossopharyngeal	Taste buds of posterior third of tongue and lining of pharynx	Parotid salivary gland; muscles of pharynx used in swallowing
X	Vagus	Nerve endings in many of the internal organs; lungs, stomach, aorta, larynx	Parasympathetic fibers to heart, stomach, small intestine, larynx, esophagus, and other organs
XI	Spinal accessory	Muscles of shoulder	Muscles of neck and shoulder
XII	Hypoglossal	Muscles of tongue	Muscles of tongue

*Proprioceptors are receptors located in muscles, tendons, or joints that provide information about body position and movement.

tures they innervate are given in Table 40–3. For example, cranial nerve X, the vagus nerve (which forms part of the autonomic system), innervates the internal organs of the chest and upper abdomen.

In humans, 31 pairs of spinal nerves emerge from the spinal cord. Named for the general region of the vertebral column from which they originate, they comprise 8 pairs of cervical spinal nerves, 12 pairs of thoracic, 5 pairs of lumbar, 5 pairs of sacral, and 1 pair of coccygeal spinal nerves.

Each spinal nerve has a **dorsal root** and a **ventral root** (Figure 40–16). The dorsal root consists of sensory (afferent) fibers, which transmit information from the sensory receptors to the spinal cord. Just before the dorsal root joins with the cord, it is marked by a swelling, the **spinal ganglion,** which consists of the cell bodies of the sensory neurons. The ventral root is a grouping of

the motor (efferent) fibers leaving the cord en route to the muscles and glands. Cell bodies of the motor neurons occur within the gray matter of the cord.

Peripheral to the junction of the dorsal and ventral roots, each spinal nerve divides into branches. The dorsal branch serves the skin and muscles of the back. The ventral branch serves the skin and muscles of the sides and ventral part of the body. The autonomic branch innervates the viscera. The ventral branches of several spinal nerves form tangled networks called plexi (singular, *plexus*). Within a plexus, the fibers of a spinal nerve may separate and then regroup with fibers that originated in other spinal nerves. Thus, nerves emerging from a plexus consist of neurons that originated in several different spinal nerves. Among the principal plexi are the cervical plexus, the brachial plexus, the lumbar plexus, and the sacral plexus.

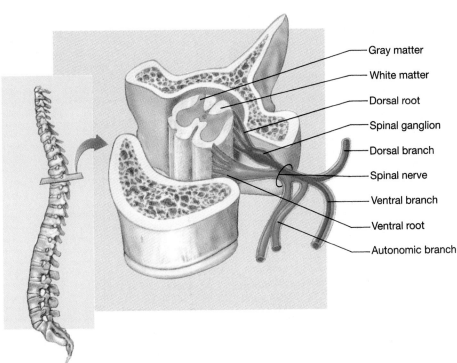

- Gray matter
- White matter
- Dorsal root
- Spinal ganglion
- Dorsal branch
- Spinal nerve
- Ventral branch
- Ventral root
- Autonomic branch

Figure 40–16   Dorsal and ventral roots emerge from the spinal cord and join to form a spinal nerve. The spinal nerve divides into several branches.

The Autonomic System Helps Maintain Homeostasis in Response to Changes in the Internal Environment

The **autonomic system** helps to maintain homeostasis in the internal environment. For instance, it regulates the rate of the heartbeat and maintains a constant body temperature. The autonomic system works automatically and without voluntary input. Its effectors are smooth muscle, cardiac muscle, and glands. Like the somatic system, it is functionally organized into reflex pathways. Receptors within the viscera (internal organs) relay information via afferent nerves to the CNS; the information is integrated at various levels; and the decision is transmitted along efferent nerves to the appropriate muscles or glands.

Information from the organs is transmitted to the CNS by afferent neurons. Some of these, found within cranial or spinal nerves, are thought to synapse with association neurons in the CNS. They bring information about blood pressure, respiration, heartbeat, contractions of the digestive tract, and other visceral activities.

The efferent portion of the autonomic system is subdivided into **sympathetic** and **parasympathetic systems.** In general, the sympathetic nerves operate to stimulate organs and to mobilize energy, especially in response to stress, whereas the parasympathetic nerves influence organs to conserve and restore energy, particularly when one is engaged in quiet, calm activities. Many organs are innervated by both types of nerves,

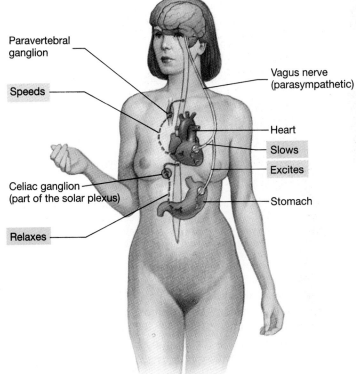

- Paravertebral ganglion
- Speeds
- Vagus nerve (parasympathetic)
- Heart
- Slows
- Excites
- Celiac ganglion (part of the solar plexus)
- Stomach
- Relaxes

Figure 40–17   Dual innervation of the heart and stomach by sympathetic and parasympathetic nerves. (Sympathetic nerves are shown in red; postganglionic fibers are shown as dotted lines.)

which act upon the organ in a complementary way (Figures 40–17 and 40–18, Table 40–4). For example, the heart rate is slowed by impulses from its parasympathetic nerve fibers and speeded up by messages from its sympathetic nerve supply.

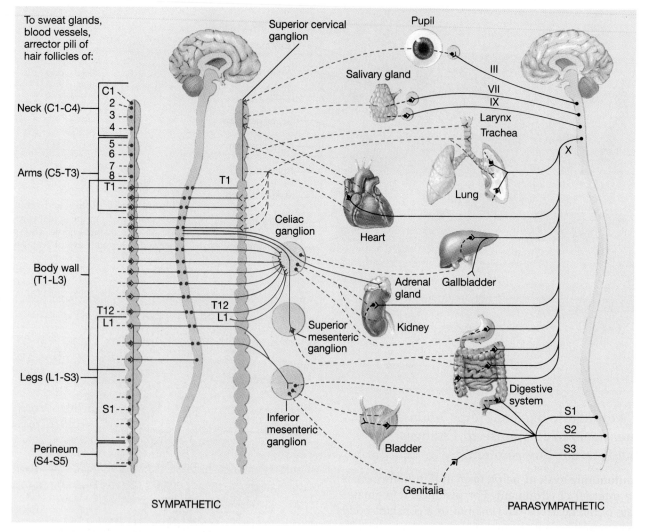

Figure 40–18 Sympathetic and parasympathetic nervous systems. For clarity, peripheral and visceral nerves of the sympathetic system are shown on separate sides of the cord. Complex as it appears, this diagram has been greatly simplified.

(Red lines represent sympathetic nerves, black lines represent parasympathetic nerves, and dashed lines represent postganglionic nerves.) See Table 40–4 for specific actions of the nerves.

Instead of utilizing a single efferent neuron, as in the somatic system, the autonomic system uses a relay of two neurons between the CNS and the effector. The first neuron, called the **preganglionic neuron,** has a cell body and dendrites within the CNS. Its axon, part of a peripheral nerve, ends by synapsing with a **postganglionic neuron.** The dendrites and cell body of the postganglionic neuron are in a ganglion outside the CNS. Its axon terminates near or on the effector. The sympathetic ganglia are paired, and a chain of them—the **paravertebral sympathetic ganglion chain**—occurs on each side of the spinal cord from the neck to the abdomen. Some sympathetic preganglionic neurons do not end in these ganglia but instead pass on to ganglia in the abdomen, close to the aorta and its major branches. These ganglia are known as **collateral ganglia.** Parasympathetic preganglionic neurons synapse with postgangli-

onic neurons in **terminal ganglia** near or within the walls of the organs they innervate.

The sympathetic and parasympathetic systems also differ in the neurotransmitters they release at the synapse with the effector. Both preganglionic and postganglionic parasympathetic neurons secrete acetylcholine. Sympathetic postganglionic neurons release norepinephrine (although their preganglionic neurons secrete acetylcholine). Table 40–5 compares the actions of the sympathetic and parasympathetic systems on selected effectors.

The autonomic system got its name from the original belief that it was independent of the CNS, that is, autonomous. Physiologists have shown that this is not so and that the hypothalamus and many other parts of the CNS help to regulate the autonomic system. Although the autonomic system usually functions auto-

Table 40–4 COMPARISON OF SYMPATHETIC SYSTEM WITH PARASYMPATHETIC SYSTEM

Characteristic	Sympathetic System	Parasympathetic System
General effect	Prepares body to cope with stressful situations	Restores body to resting state after stressful situation; actively maintains normal configuration of body functions
Extent of effect	Widespread throughout body	Localized
Neurotransmitter released at synapse with effector	Norepinephrine (usually)	Acetylcholine
Duration of effect	Lasting	Brief
Outflow from CNS	Thoracolumbar levels of spinal cord	Craniosacral levels (from brain and spinal cord)
Location of ganglia	Chain and collateral ganglia	Terminal ganglia
Number of postganglionic fibers with which each preganglionic fiber synapses	Many	Few

Table 40–5 COMPARISON OF SYMPATHETIC AND PARASYMPATHETIC ACTIONS ON SELECTED EFFECTORS*

Effector	Sympathetic Action	Parasympathetic Action
Heart	Increases rate and strength of contraction	Decreases rate; no direct effect on strength of contraction
Bronchial tubes	Dilates	Constricts
Iris of eye	Dilates pupil	Constricts pupil
Sex organs (male)	Constricts blood vessels; ejaculation	Dilates blood vessels; erection
Blood vessels	Generally constricts	No innervation for many
Sweat glands	Stimulates	No innervation
Intestine	Inhibits motility	Stimulates motility and secretion
Liver	Stimulates glycogenolysis (conversion of glycogen to glucose)	No effect
Adipose tissue	Stimulates free fatty acid release from fat cells	No effect
Adrenal medulla	Stimulates secretion of epinephrine and norepinephrine	No effect
Salivary glands	Stimulates thick, viscous secretion	Stimulates a profuse, watery secretion

*Refer to Figure 40–18 as you study this table. Notice that many other examples could be added to this list.

matically, its activities can be consciously influenced. Biofeedback provides a person with visual or auditory evidence concerning the status of an autonomic body function; for example, a tone may be sounded when blood pressure reaches a desirable level. Using such techniques, subjects have learned to control autonomic activities such as blood pressure, brain wave pattern, heart rate, and blood sugar level. Even certain abnormal heart rhythms can be consciously modified.

MANY DRUGS AFFECT THE NERVOUS SYSTEM

About 25% of all prescribed drugs are taken to alter psychological conditions, and almost all the drugs com-

monly abused affect mood. Many of them act by changing the levels of neurotransmitters within the brain. In particular, levels of norepinephrine, serotonin, and dopamine are thought to influence mood. For example, when excessive amounts of norepinephrine are released in the RAS, we feel stimulated and energetic, whereas low concentrations of this neurotransmitter reduce anxiety. Table 40–6 lists several commonly used and abused drugs and gives their effects. Also see Focus on Alcohol Abuse and Focus on Crack Cocaine.

Habitual use of almost any mood drug may result in **psychological dependence,** in which the user be-

Table 40–6   EFFECTS OF SOME COMMONLY USED DRUGS

Name of Drug	Effect on Mood	Actions on Body	Dangers Associated with Abuse
Barbiturates (e.g., Nembutal, Seconal)	Sedative-hypnotic;* "downers"	Inhibit impulse conduction in RAS: depress CNS, skeletal muscle, and heart; depress respiration; lower blood pressure; cause decrease in REM sleep	Tolerance, physical dependence; death from overdose, especially in combination with alcohol
Methaqualone (e.g., Quaalude, Sopor)	Hypnotic	Depresses CNS; depresses certain polysynaptic spinal reflexes	Tolerance, physical dependence, convulsions, death
Meprobamate (e.g., Equanil, Miltown; "minor tranquilizers")	Antianxiety drug;† induces calmness	Causes decrease in REM sleep; relaxes skeletal muscle; depresses CNS	Tolerance, physical dependence; coma and death from overdose
Valium, Librium ("mild tranquilizers")	Reduce anxiety	May reduce rate of impulse firing in limbic system; relax skeletal muscle	Minor EEG abnormalities with chronic use; very large doses cause physical dependence
Phenothiazines (chlorpromazine; "major tranquilizers")	Antipsychotic; highly effective in controlling symptoms of psychotic patients	Affect levels of catecholamines in brain (block dopamine receptors, inhibit uptake of norepinephrine, dopamine, and serotonin); depress neurons in RAS and basal ganglia	Prolonged intake may result in Parkinson-like symptoms
Antidepressant drugs (e.g., Elavil)	Elevate mood; relieve depression	Block uptake of norepinephrine, so more is available to stimulate nervous system	Cause central and peripheral neurological disturbances, uncoordination; interfere with normal cardiovascular function
Alcohol	Euphoria, relaxation, release of inhibitions	Depresses CNS; impairs vision, coordination, judgment, lengthens reaction time	Physical dependence, damage to pancreas, liver cirrhosis, possible brain damage
Narcotic analgesics (e.g., morphine, heroin)	Euphoria, reduction of pain	Depress CNS; depress reflexes; constrict pupils; impair coordination; block release of substance P from pain-transmitting neurons	Tolerance, physical dependence, convulsions; death from overdose
Cocaine	Euphoria; excitation followed by depression	CNS stimulation followed by depression; autonomic stimulation; dilation of pupils; local anesthesia; inhibits re-uptake of norepinephrine and dopamine	Mental impairment, convulsions, hallucinations, unconsciousness; death from overdose

*Sedatives reduce anxiety; hypnotics induce sleep.

†Antianxiety drugs reduce anxiety but are less likely to cause drowsiness than the more potent sedative-hypnotics.

comes emotionally dependent upon the drug. When deprived of it, the user craves the feeling of euphoria (well-being) that the drug induces. Some drugs induce **tolerance** when they are taken continually for several weeks. This means that increasingly greater amounts are required in order to obtain the desired effect. Toler-

ance often occurs because the liver cells are stimulated to produce more of the enzymes that metabolize and inactivate the drug.

Use of some drugs, such as heroin, tobacco, alcohol, and barbiturates, may also result in **addiction** (physical dependence), in which physiological changes take place

Name of Drug	Effect on Mood	Actions on Body	Dangers Associated with Abuse
Amphetamines (e.g., Dexedrine)	Euphoria, stimulation, hyperactivity ("uppers," "pep pills")	Stimulate release of dopamine and norepinephrine; block re-uptake of norepinephrine and dopamine into neurons; inhibit monoamine oxidase (MAO); enhance flow of impulses in RAS; increase heart rate; raise blood pressure; dilate pupils	Tolerance, possible physical dependence, hallucinations; death from overdose
Caffeine	Increases mental alertness; decreases fatigue and drowsiness	Acts on cerebral cortex; relaxes smooth muscle; stimulates cardiac and skeletal muscle; increases urine volume (diuretic effect)	Very large doses stimulate centers in the medulla (may slow the heart); toxic doses may cause convulsions
Nicotine	Lessens psychological tension	Stimulates sympathetic nervous system; combines with receptors in postsynaptic neurons of autonomic system; has effect similar to that of acetylcholine, but large amounts result in blocking transmission; stimulates synthesis of lipid in arterial wall	Tolerance, physical dependence; stimulates development of atherosclerosis
LSD (lysergic acid diethylamide)	Overexcitation; sensory distortions; hallucinations	Alters levels of transmitters in brain (may inhibit serotonin and increase norepinephrine); potent CNS stimulator; dilates pupils, sometimes unequally; increases heart rate; raises blood pressure	Irrational behavior
Marijuana	Euphoria	Impairs coordination; impairs depth perception and alters sense of timing; inflames eyes; causes peripheral vasodilation; exact mode of action unknown	In large doses, sensory distortions, hallucinations; evidence of lowered sperm counts and testosterone (male hormone) levels

in body cells, making the user dependent upon the drug. When the drug is withheld, the addict suffers physical illness and the withdrawal symptoms that are characteristic of that drug. Addiction can also occur because certain drugs, such as morphine, have components similar to substances that body cells normally manufacture on their own. The continued use of such a drug followed by sudden withdrawal causes potentially dangerous physiological effects, because the body's natural production of these substances has been depressed. It may be some time before homeostasis is reestablished.

FOCUS ON

Alcohol Abuse

Alcohol abuse is responsible for more than 100,000 deaths each year and costs our society more than $100 billion annually. According to pollster Louis Harris, there are 28 million alcoholics in the United States, and about one in three homes includes someone with a serious drinking problem. Alcohol abuse is not limited to adults. About 4.6 million adolescents, or nearly one of every three high school students, experiences negative consequences from alcohol use, including difficulty with parents, poor performance at school, and breaking the law. Alcohol is still the drug most widely abused by youth in the United States.

Alcohol abuse results in physiological, psychological, and social impairment for the abuser and has serious negative consequences for family, friends, and society.

Alcohol abuse has been linked to:

• More than 50% of all traffic fatalities
• More than 50% of violent crimes
• More than 50% of suicides
• More than 60% of cases of child abuse and spouse abuse
• The birth of 15,000 babies with serious birth defects born every year

because their mothers drank alcohol excessively during pregnancy
• Breast cancer: Recent studies suggest that as little as three drinks per week increase risk of breast cancer by 50%
• Greater risk of liver disease and brain impairment for women than males (clinical effects are seen in women consuming about half the alcohol consumed by men)

Alcohol accumulates in the blood because absorption occurs more rapidly than oxidation and excretion. Alcohol causes depression of the CNS. Effects of some blood alcohol levels follow: 50 mg/dL causes sedation; 50 to 150 mg/dL results in loss of coordination; 150 to 200 mg/dL produces intoxication; 300 to 400 mg/dL may result in unconsciousness. Blood levels greater than 500 mg/dL may be fatal.

Alcohol is oxidized to carbon dioxide and water. About 10% is excreted unchanged in expired air, urine, and sweat. Blood alcohol levels are usually estimated from the amount present in expired air.

Alcohol commonly causes cirrhosis of the liver, peripheral nerve degeneration, brain damage, and cardiac

damage accompanied by arrhythmias. Gastritis and damage to the pancreas are also common.

Tolerance in those who drink excessive amounts of alcohol occurs because cells of the CNS adapt to the presence of the drug. Physical dependence develops along with tolerance, and withdrawal may result in serious physiological derangements that can lead to death.

According to one study, children see more than 100,000 beer commercials on television before they are legally old enough to drink. The alcoholic beverage industry is now required to place labels on its products warning that alcohol can cause mental retardation and other birth defects and impairs the ability to drive or operate machinery.

Treatment for alcohol problems includes various forms of psychotherapy, including relapse prevention, a type of cognitive-behavioral modification. The group support offered by Alcoholics Anonymous (AA) has proved effective for many struggling with alcohol abuse.

SUMMARY

I. Among invertebrates, nerve nets and radial nervous systems are typical of radially symmetric animals, and bilateral nervous systems are characteristic of bilaterally symmetric animals.

   A. A nerve net consists of nerve cells scattered throughout the body; no CNS is present. Responses of these animals to stimuli are generally slow and imprecise.

   B. Echinoderms typically have a nerve ring and nerves that extend into various parts of the body.

   C. In a bilateral nervous system, there is a concentration of nerve cells to form nerves, nerve cords, ganglia, and (in complex forms) a brain. There is also an increase in numbers of neurons, especially the association neurons. This permits greater precision and a wider range of responses.

FOCUS ON

Crack Cocaine

The majority of persons seeking treatment for drug abuse are now crack cocaine addicts. Cocaine use by teenagers alone has increased about 400% during the past 10 years, involving an estimated 2 million youngsters. Crack is a very concentrated and extremely powerful form of cocaine—five to ten times as addictive as other forms of cocaine. This drug is produced in illegal, makeshift labs by converting powdered cocaine into small "rocks," which are up to 80% pure cocaine. Crack is smoked in pipes or added to tobacco or marijuana cigarettes.

Use of crack results in an intense, brief high beginning in 4 to 6 seconds and lasting for 5 to 7 minutes. Physiologically, crack stimulates a massive release of catecholamine neurotransmitters (norepinephrine and dopamine) in the brain and blocks re-uptake. Excitation of the sympathetic nervous system occurs, and users report experiencing feelings of self-confidence, power, and euphoria. As the neurotransmitters are depleted, the high is followed by a "crash," a period of deep depression. The abuser experiences an intense craving for another crack "hit" in order to get more stimulation.

Some abusers spend days smoking crack without stopping to eat or sleep. Although a vial of rocks can be obtained for about $20, many abusers develop habits that cost hundreds of dollars a week. Supporting an expensive drug habit leads many abusers to prostitution, drug dealing, and other forms of crime.

Cocaine addicts report problems with memory, fatigue, depression, insomnia, paranoia, loss of sexual drive, violent behavior, and attempts at suicide. Crack can cause respiratory problems, brain seizures, cardiac arrest, and elevation of blood pressure that leads to stroke. Many users have suffered fatal reactions to impurities in the drug or have died as a result of accidents related to drug use.

II. In the vertebrate embryo, the brain and spinal cord arise from the neural tube. The anterior end of the tube differentiates into forebrain, midbrain, and hindbrain.
   A. The hindbrain subdivides into the metencephalon and myelencephalon.
      1. The myelencephalon develops into the medulla, which contains the vital centers and other reflex centers.
      2. The metencephalon gives rise to the cerebellum and pons.
         a. The cerebellum is responsible for muscle tone, posture, and equilibrium.
         b. The pons connects various parts of the brain.
   B. The midbrain is the largest part of the brain in fish and amphibians. It is their main association area, linking sensory input and motor output. In reptiles, birds, and mammals, the midbrain has a lesser function and is used as a center for certain visual and auditory reflexes.
   C. The forebrain differentiates to form the diencephalon and telencephalon.
      1. The diencephalon develops into the thalamus and hypothalamus.
         a. The thalamus is a relay center for motor and sensory information.
         b. The hypothalamus controls autonomic functions; links nervous and endocrine systems; controls temperature, appetite, and fluid balance; and is involved in some emotional and sexual responses.
      2. The telencephalon develops into the cerebrum and olfactory bulbs.
         a. In fish and amphibians, the cerebrum functions mainly to integrate incoming sensory information.
         b. In birds, the corpus striatum controls stereotypical but complex behavior patterns. Another part of the cerebrum is thought to govern learning.
         c. The simplest animals possessing a neopallium are certain reptiles. In mammals, the neopallium accounts for a large part of the cerebral cortex, and the cerebrum has complex association functions.
III. The human brain and spinal cord are protected by bone and three meninges and are cushioned by cerebrospinal fluid.
   A. The spinal cord transmits impulses to and from the brain and controls many reflex activities.
      1. The spinal cord consists of ascending tracts, which transmit information to the brain, and descending tracts, which transmit information from the brain. Its gray matter consists of many nuclei that serve as reflex centers.
      2. A withdrawal reflex involves receptors; sensory, association, and motor neurons; and effectors.
   B. The human cerebral cortex consists of motor areas,

which control voluntary movement; sensory areas, which receive incoming sensory information; and association areas, which link sensory and motor areas and are responsible for learning, language, thought, and judgment.

C. The reticular activating system is responsible for maintaining consciousness.

D. The limbic system affects the emotional aspects of behavior, motivation, sexual behavior, autonomic responses, and biological rhythms.

E. Alpha wave patterns are characteristic of relaxed states, beta wave patterns of heightened mental activity, and delta waves of non-REM sleep.

F. The metabolic rate slows during non-REM sleep. REM sleep is characterized by dreaming.

G. Learning is a change in behavior that results from experience; memory is the storage of knowledge and the ability to retrieve it.

1. Information is transferred from sensory memory to short-term memory and then to long-term memory.

2. Memory storage involves inhibition or facilitation of impulses as a result of changes in synaptic function.

3. Memories appear to be stored throughout the association areas of the cerebrum.

H. The physical structure and chemistry of the brain can be altered by environmental experience.

IV. The peripheral nervous system consists of sensory receptors and nerves, including the cranial and spinal nerves and their branches.

V. The autonomic system regulates the internal activities of the body.

A. The sympathetic system enables the body to respond to stressful situations.

B. The parasympathetic system influences organs to conserve and restore energy.

VI. Some of the types of drugs that affect the nervous system are amphetamines, barbiturates, meprobamate, phenothiazines, antidepressants, narcotic analgesics, and alcohol. Many drugs alter mood by increasing or decreasing the concentrations of specific neurotransmitters within the brain.

POST-TEST

1. In a nerve _____, impulses are transmitted in all directions and there is no central control organ.

2. The cerebral ganglia in a flatworm serve as a simple _____.

3. The nervous system of a mollusk typically contains at least three pairs of _____.

4. The two main divisions of the vertebrate nervous system are the _____ and the _____.

5. In vertebrates, the embryonic neural tube expands anteriorly to form the _____ and develops posteriorly into the _____ _____.

6. The medulla, pons, and midbrain make up the _____ _____.

7. The fourth ventricle, located within the _____, communicates with the _____ _____ of the spinal cord.

For each group, select the most appropriate answer from Column B for the description given in Column A.

Column A
8. Most prominent part of amphibian brain
9. Links nervous and endocrine systems
10. Most prominent part of mammalian brain
11. Coordinates muscle activity
12. Contains vital centers

Column B
a. Cerebellum
b. Cerebrum
c. Midbrain
d. Medulla
e. Hypothalamus

Column A
13. Controls innate, complex action patterns in birds
14. Convey voluntary motor impulses from cerebrum down spinal cord
15. Shallow furrows between gyri
16. Makes up most of human cerebral cortex
17. Layers of connective tissue that protect the CNS

Column B
a. Neopallium
b. Corpus striatum
c. Meninges
d. Pyramidal tracts
e. Sulci

Column A
18. Contains primary motor areas
19. Action system concerned with emotional behavior and with reward and punishment
20. Contains the visual centers
21. Maintains wakefulness

Column B
a. Limbic system
b. RAS
c. Frontal lobe
d. Temporal lobe
e. None of the above

22. As you answer these questions, your brain should be emitting _____ waves.
23. Dreaming takes place during _____ sleep.
24. Cranial nerve X, the _____ nerve, innervates the _____.
25. The sympathetic nervous system mobilizes _____ and helps the body respond to _____.
26. Sensory nerves enter the spinal cord through the _____ root.
27. Some drugs induce tolerance, which means that _____.
28. Label the diagram on the right. (Refer to Figure 40–11 as necessary.)

REVIEW QUESTIONS

1. Contrast the nervous system of a planarian flatworm with that of *Hydra.*
2. What are some characteristics of a bilateral nervous system? What are some advantages of this type of system?
3. Compare the flatworm nervous system with that of a vertebrate. In each case, what is the relationship between the type of nervous system and the animal's lifestyle?
4. Identify the parts of the adult vertebrate brain derived from the embryonic forebrain, midbrain, and hindbrain.
5. Give the function of each of the following structures in the human brain: medulla, midbrain, cerebellum, thalamus, hypothalamus, cerebrum.
6. Compare the midbrain and cerebrum of the fish with those of the mammal.
7. Describe the protective coverings of the human CNS, and give the function of the cerebrospinal fluid.
8. In what sequence is information processed through the levels of memory? What is the importance of the general interpretative area?
9. Cite experimental evidence supporting the view that environmental experience can alter the brain.
10. Contrast the functions of the CNS with those of the PNS.
11. Compare the functions of the somatic and autonomic systems.
12. Contrast the structure and function of the sympathetic system with those of the parasympathetic system.
13. Describe how each of the following drugs affects the CNS: (a) alcohol, (b) phenothiazines, (c) barbiturates, (d) amphetamines.

RECOMMENDED READINGS

Goldstein, G. W., and A. L. Betz. The blood-brain barrier. *Scientific American,* Vol. 255, No. 3 (September 1986), pp. 74–83. A discussion of how brain capillaries regulate the entrance of materials into the brain.

Kalil, R. Synapse formation in the developing brain. *Scientific American,* Vol. 261, No. 6 (December 1989). Developing neurons generate impulses that modify existing synapses and result in the formation of new connections.

Mishkin, M., and T. Appenzeller. The anatomy of memory. *Scientific American,* Vol. 256, No. 6 (June 1987), pp. 80–89. Deep structures in the brain may interact with perceptual pathways in outer layers of the brain to transform sensory stimuli into memories.

Selkoe, D. J. Amyloid protein and Alzheimer's disease. *Scientific American,* Vol. 265, No. 5 (November 1991). Is the accumulation of a protein fragment in the brain a cause of Alzheimer's disease?

Spector, R., and C. E. Johanson. The mammalian choroid plexus. *Scientific American,* Vol. 261, No. 5 (November 1989). The choroid plexus serves an important purpose in nourishing and protecting the nervous system.

Sense Organs

Sense organs link organisms with the outside world and enable them to receive information about their environment. The kinds of sense organs an animal has determine just how it perceives the world. We humans live in a world of rich colors, numerous shapes, and varied sounds. But we cannot hear the high-pitched whistles that are audible to dogs and cats or the ultrasonic echoes by which bats navigate (Figure 41–1). Nor do we ordinarily recognize our friends by their distinctive odors. And although vision is our dominant and most refined sense, we are blind to the ultraviolet hues that light up the world for insects.

A **sense organ** is a specialized structure consisting of one or more **receptor cells** and, sometimes, **accessory cells;** it detects changes in the environment and transmits that information into the nervous system. For example, rod and cone cells in the retina of the human eye are the receptor cells that respond to light. Accessory structures

Simple eyes (ocelli) are visible between the large compound eyes of this green darner dragonfly (*Anax junius*). (Barbara Gerlach/Dembinsky Photo Associates)

(cornea, lens, iris, and ciliary muscles) enhance the versatility of the sense organ but in some instances may limit its performance. The lens, for example, enhances the ability of the eye to see by adjusting the focus of the light rays. However, the lens filters out ultraviolet light before it reaches the retina, so we cannot see it, although the cells in the retina can respond to light of this wavelength.

Receptor cells may be either neuron endings or specialized cells that are in close contact with neurons. Human taste buds, for example, are modified epithelial cells connected to one or more neurons.

Traditionally, humans are said to have five senses: touch, smell, taste, sight, and hearing. In addition, balance is now recognized as a sense, and touch is viewed as a compound sense that involves detection of pressure, pain, and temperature. In this chapter we also consider sense organs known as proprioceptors, which enable us to perceive muscle tension and joint position.

After you have studied this chapter you should be able to

1. Compare exteroceptors, proprioceptors, and interoceptors, and explain the importance of each group.
2. Distinguish among the five types of receptors that are classified according to the types of energy to which they respond. Give examples of sense organs of each type.
3. Describe how a sense organ functions, including definitions of energy transduction, receptor potential, and adaptation in your description.
4. Describe how the following mechanoreceptors work: tactile receptors, statocysts, lateral line organs, and proprioceptors.
5. Compare the function of the saccule and utricle with that of the semicircular canals in maintaining equilibrium.
6. Trace the path taken by sound waves through the structures of the ear, and explain how the organ of Corti functions as an auditory organ.
7. Describe the receptors of taste and smell.
8. Relate the presence of thermoreceptors to the lifestyles of animals that have them.
9. Contrast simple eyes, compound eyes, and the mammalian eye.
10. Label the structures of the mammalian eye on a diagram, and give the function of each of its accessory structures.
11. Compare the two types of photoreceptors in the human retina (include the role of rhodopsin in your explanation).

SENSE ORGANS CAN BE CLASSIFIED ACCORDING TO THE STIMULI TO WHICH THEY RESPOND

By receiving stimuli from the outside environment, **exteroceptors** enable an animal to know and explore the world, search for food, find and attract a mate, recognize friends, and detect enemies. **Proprioceptors** are sense organs within muscles, tendons, and joints that enable the animal to perceive the positions of its arms, legs, head, and other body parts, along with the orientation of its body as a whole. With the help of proprioceptors, humans can get dressed or eat even in the dark.

Interoceptors are sense organs *within* body organs that detect changes in pH, osmotic pressure, body temperature, and the chemical composition of the blood. We are usually not conscious of messages sent to the central nervous system (CNS) by these receptors as they work continuously to maintain homeostasis. We become aware of their activity when they enable us to perceive such diverse internal conditions as thirst, hunger, nausea, pain, and orgasm.

Figure 41–1   Bats navigate with ultrasonic echoes inaudible to the human ear. They emit high-pitched clicking sounds and use the echoes of those sounds to locate objects. California leaf-nosed bat (*Macrotus californicus*).   (Merlin D. Tuttle/ Bat Conservation International/Photo Researchers, Inc.)

Another way sense organs can be classified is according to the *types* of stimuli to which they respond (Table 41–1). **Mechanoreceptors** respond to mechanical energy—touch, pressure, gravity, stretching, and movement. **Chemoreceptors** respond to certain chemical stimuli, and **photoreceptors** detect light energy. **Thermoreceptors** respond to heat and cold. Some fish have well-developed **electroreceptors,** which detect electrical energy.

SENSE ORGANS WORK BY PRODUCING RECEPTOR POTENTIALS

Receptor cells absorb energy, transduce (convert) that energy into electrical energy, and produce a receptor potential. In its capacity as a detector or sensor, a receptor receives a small amount of energy from the environment. Each kind of receptor is especially sensitive to one particular form of energy. For example, photoreceptor cells (rods and cones) in the eye absorb light energy. Temperature receptors respond to radiant energy transferred by radiation, conduction, or convection. Electricity is detected by changes in ion distribution. Taste buds and olfactory cells detect the change in energy accompanying the binding of specific molecules to their chemical receptors.

stimulus (e.g., light energy) → transduction into electrical energy → receptor potential → action potential

Receptor cells are remarkably sensitive to appropriate stimuli. The photoreceptors of the eye, for example, are stimulated by an extremely faint beam of light, whereas only a very strong light can directly stimulate the optic nerve. The negligible amount of vinegar that can be tasted or the amount of vanilla that can be smelled would have no effect if applied directly to a nerve fiber.

Table 41–1   CLASSIFICATION OF RECEPTORS BY STIMULI TO WHICH THEY RESPOND

Type of Receptor	*Examples*	*Effective Stimuli*
Mechanoreceptors	Tactile receptors	Touch, pressure
	Pacinian corpuscles	
	Meissner's corpuscles	
	Proprioceptors	Movement, body position
	Muscle spindles	Muscle contraction
	Golgi tendon organs	Stretch of a tendon
	Joint receptors	Movement in ligaments
	Lateral line organs in fish	Waves, currents in water
	Statocysts in invertebrates	Gravity
	Labyrinth of vertebrate ear	
	Saccule and utricle	Gravity, linear acceleration
	Semicircular canals	Angular acceleration
	Hair cells in the cochlea	Pressure waves (sound)
Chemoreceptors	Taste buds, olfactory epithelium	Specific chemical compounds
Thermoreceptors	Temperature receptors in blood-sucking insects and ticks; pit organs in pit vipers; nerve endings and receptors in skins and tongues of many animals	Heat
Electroreceptors	Organs in skins of some fish	Electrical currents in water
Photoreceptors	Eyespots: ommatidia of arthropods; rods and cones in retinas of vertebrates	Light energy

Multiple kinds of environmental stimuli trigger the receptor cells to perform biological work. The relationship of the stimulus to the work is best exemplified by a very simple sense organ: the tactile hair of an insect. Such a hair and its associated cells constitute a complete sense organ. However, only the bipolar neuron at the base of the hair is a receptor cell. The dendrite of the neuron is attached to the base of the hair near the socket, and the axon passes directly to the CNS without synapsing.

In its unstimulated state, the neuron maintains a steady resting potential; that is, a potential difference exists between the inside and the outside of the neuron. This is because the ionic compositions of the fluids on the two sides of the selectively permeable cell membrane differ. The difference is maintained in part by sodium-potassium pumps powered by ATP. When the hair is touched (a mechanical stimulus), its shaft moves in the socket and mechanically deforms the dendrite. This mechanical energy increases the permeability of the neuron membrane to ions, changing the potential difference between the two sides of the membrane. If the potential difference increases, the cell becomes hyperpolarized. If it decreases or disappears, the cell becomes depolarized.

In a receptor, the state of depolarization caused by a stimulus is called the **receptor potential.** It is a graded response that spreads relatively slowly down the dendrite, fading as it goes. When a special area of the cell near the axon—the axon hillock—becomes depolar-

ized, the threshold level may be reached and an action potential generated. Although an action potential can be initiated in other parts of the neuron if the stimulus is sufficiently strong, the axon hillock is the region of lowest threshold. The action potential travels along the axon to the CNS. The receptor thus performs all the essential functions of a sense organ: (1) It detects an event in the environment (e.g., a force acting on the hair) by absorbing energy; (2) it converts the energy of the stimulus into electrical energy; and (3) it produces a receptor potential, which may result in an action potential that transmits the information to the CNS. With minor variations, this is how all receptors operate.

The amplitude and duration of the receptor potential are related to the strength and duration of the stimulus. A strong stimulus causes a greater depolarization of the receptor membrane than does a weak one. The action potentials are repetitive, and the frequency at which they are generated is related to the magnitude of the receptor potential. In other words, the strength of a stimulus is reflected in the frequency of the action potentials. According to the all-or-none law, the amplitude of each action potential bears no relation to the stimulus; it is characteristic of the particular neuron. In contrast, the receptor potential is a *graded* response.

Once a stimulus has triggered a receptor to generate action potentials, the stimulus has no further control over them. The situation is analogous to lighting a fuse. The heat of the match is the stimulus. When the end of the fuse reaches the combustion point, the fuse begins to burn, and, utilizing its own energy, it ignites adjacent parts of itself. In this way the "message" travels the length of the fuse independently of the temperature of the match flame.

Sensation Depends on Transmission of a "Coded" Message

All action potentials are qualitatively the same. Light of the wavelength 400 nanometers (blue), sugar molecules (sweet), and sound waves of 440 hertz (A above middle C) all cause transmission of similar action potentials. How does the organism know whether it is seeing, hearing, or smelling? Our ability to differentiate stimuli depends on both the sense organ itself and the brain. We can distinguish red from green, a sweet taste from a light breeze, or red from cold because cells of each sense organ are connected to specific neurons in particular parts of the brain. Because a receptor normally responds to only one category of stimuli (e.g., light), a message arriving in the CNS from a particular receptor is interpreted as signifying that a particular stimulus occurred.

Interpretation of the message and the type of sensation is determined by the part of the brain that receives the message. Sensation, when it occurs, take place in the brain. Rods and cones do not see; only the combination of rods, cones, and centers in the brain sees. Artificial stimulation of brain centers (e.g., electrical stimulation) results in sensation. Many sensory messages never give rise to sensations at all. For example, certain chemoreceptors sense internal changes in the body but never stir our consciousness.

When it is stimulated, a sense organ initiates what might be considered a "coded" message, composed of action potentials transmitted by nerve fibers. This coded message is later decoded in the brain. Impulses from the sense organ may differ in (1) the total number of fibers transmitting, (2) the specific fibers carrying action potentials, (3) the total number of action potentials passing over a given fiber, and (4) the frequency of the action potentials passing over a given fiber. For example, the intensity of the stimulus (e.g., softness or loudness) is conveyed by the number of neurons transmitting action potentials and by the frequency of action potentials transmitted by each neuron. Just how the sense organ initiates different codes and how the brain analyzes and interprets them to produce various sensations are not completely understood.

Receptors Adapt to Stimuli

Many receptors do not continue to respond at the initial rate even if the stimulus maintains its intensity. With time, the frequency of action potentials in the sensory neuron decreases. This may occur because the sensory neuron becomes less responsive to stimulation, because the receptor produces a smaller receptor potential, or both. Such a diminishing response to a continued, constant stimulus is called **sensory adaptation.**

Some receptors, such as those for pain or cold, adapt so slowly that they continue to trigger action potentials as long as the stimulus persists. Other receptors adapt rapidly, permitting an animal to ignore persistent unpleasant or unimportant stimuli. For example, when you first pull on a pair of tight jeans, your pressure receptors let you know that you are being squished and you may feel uncomfortable. Soon, though, these receptors adapt, and you hardly notice the sensation of the tight fit. In the same way, we quickly adapt to odors that at first smell seem to assault our senses.

MECHANORECEPTORS RESPOND TO TOUCH, PRESSURE, GRAVITY, STRETCH, OR MOVEMENT

Mechanoreceptors respond to touch, pressure, gravity, stretch, or movement. They are activated when they are mechanically deformed—that is, pushed or pulled so that they change shape. Some mechanoreceptors enable an organism to maintain its body position with respect to gravity (for us, head up and feet down; for a dog, dorsal side up and ventral side down; for a tree sloth, ventral side up and dorsal side down). Other mechanoreceptors are concerned with maintaining postural relations—the position of one part of the body with respect to another. This information is essential for all forms of locomotion and for all coordinated and skilled movements, from spinning a cocoon to completing a reverse one-and-a-half dive with twist.

Mechanoreceptors provide information about the shape, texture, weight, and topographical relations of objects in the external environment. Certain mechanoreceptors affect the operation of internal organs. For example, they supply information about the presence of food in the stomach, feces in the rectum, urine in the bladder, and a fetus in the uterus.

Touch Receptors Are Located in the Skin

The simplest mechanoreceptors are free nerve endings in the skin that are directly stimulated by contact with any object on the body surface. Somewhat more complex is the tactile receptor that lies at the base of a hair or bristle. It is stimulated indirectly when the hair is bent or displaced. A receptor potential then develops, and a few action potentials may be generated. Because this type of receptor responds only when the hair is moving, it is known as a *phasic receptor*. Even though the

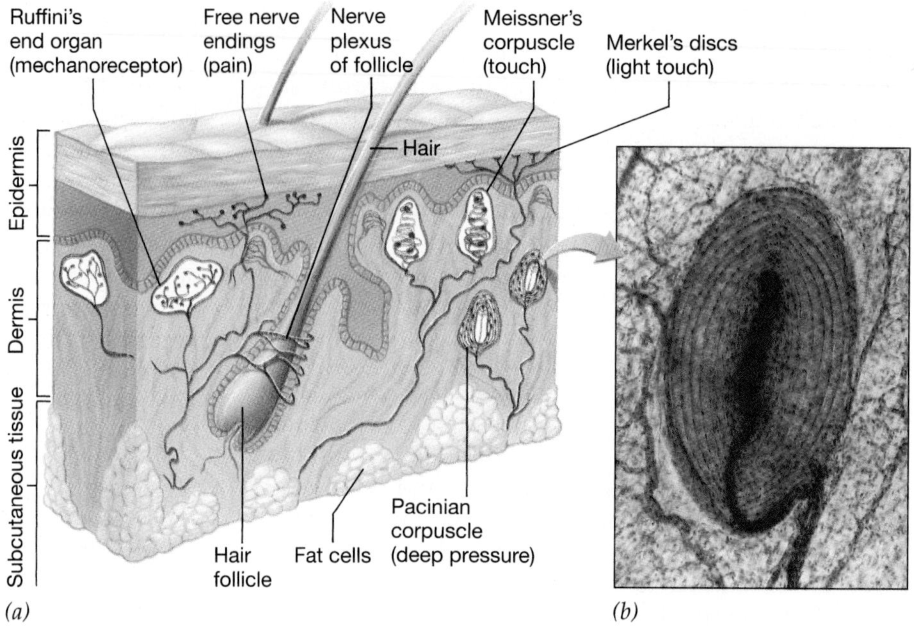

Ruffini's end organ (mechanoreceptor) Free nerve endings (pain) Nerve plexus of follicle Meissner's corpuscle (touch) Merkel's discs (light touch)

Epidermis

Dermis

Subcutaneous tissue

Hair

Hair follicle Fat cells Pacinian corpuscle (deep pressure)

(a)

(b)

Figure 41–2 Sense organs within the human skin. (a) Diagrammatic section through the human skin, showing the types of sense organs present. The free nerve endings respond to pain; tactile hairs, Merkel's disks, Ruffini's end organs, and Meissner's corpuscles respond to touch; Pacinian corpuscles respond to deep pressure. (b) A Pacinian corpuscle, a deep pressure receptor. (b, Ed Reschke)

hair may be maintained in a displaced position, the receptor is not stimulated unless there is motion. Such tactile hairs are found in many invertebrates as well as vertebrates. They function not only in contacts with other objects but also in orientation to gravity, postural orientation, and the reception of vibrations in air and water.

The remarkable tactile sensitivity of human skin, especially of the fingertips and lips, is due to a large number of diverse sense organs (Figure 41–2). By making a careful point-by-point survey of a small area of skin, using a stiff bristle to test for touch, a hot or cold metal stylus to test for temperature, and a needle to test for pain, it has been found that the receptors for these sensations are located at different spots. By comparing the distribution of the types of sense organs and the types of sensations produced, it has been found that the free nerve endings are responsible for pain perception, that a variety of tiny sense organs (e.g., Meissner's corpuscles, Ruffini's end organs, and Merkel's disks) are responsible for touch, and that Pacinian corpuscles mediate the sensation of deep pressure. Naked nerve endings are thought to be responsible for sensations of cold and warmth. (See Focus on Pain Perception.)

The Pacinian corpuscle has been particularly well studied. The nerve ending is surrounded by lamellae (connective tissue layers) interspersed with fluid. Compression causes displacement of the lamellae, which provides the deformation that stimulates the axon. Even though the displacement is maintained under steady compression, the receptor potential rapidly falls to zero and action potentials cease—an excellent example of sensory adaptation. The Pacinian corpuscle is a

phasic receptor responding to velocity (rapid movement of the tissue).

Many Invertebrates Have Gravity Receptors Called Statocysts

Every organism is oriented in a characteristic way with respect to gravity. When displaced from this normal position, it quickly adjusts its body to reassume its nor-

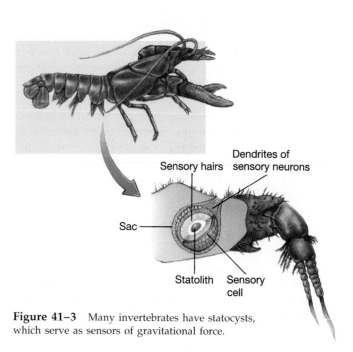

Sensory hairs Dendrites of sensory neurons

Sac

Statolith Sensory cell

Figure 41–3 Many invertebrates have statocysts, which serve as sensors of gravitational force.

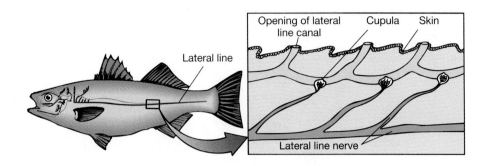

Figure 41–4 The receptor cells of the lateral line organ respond to waves, currents, and disturbances in the water, informing the fish of obstacles and moving objects.

mal orientation. In complex animals, receptors must continually send information to the CNS regarding the position and movements of the body.

Many invertebrates have specialized sense organs, called **statocysts,** that serve as gravity receptors. A statocyst is basically an infolding of the epidermis lined with receptor cells that have hairs (Figure 41–3). The cavity contains a **statolith** (sometimes more than one)—a tiny granule of loose sand grains or calcium carbonate. The particles are held together by an adhesive material secreted by cells of the statocyst. Normally the particles are pulled downward by gravity and stimulate the hair cells. When the position of the statolith changes, the hairs of the receptor cells are bent. This mechanical displacement results in receptor potentials and action potentials that inform the CNS of the change in position. By "knowing" which hair cells are firing, the animal knows where "down" is and so can correct any abnormal orientation.

In a classic experiment, the function of the statocyst was demonstrated by substituting iron filings for sand grains in the statocysts of crayfish. The force of gravity was overcome by holding magnets above the animals: The iron filings were attracted upward toward the magnets, and the crayfish began to swim upside down in response to the new information provided by their gravity receptors.

Lateral Line Organs Supplement Vision in Fish

Lateral line organs are found in fish and in aquatic and larval amphibians. Typically this sense organ consists of a long canal running the length of the body on each side and continuing into the head (Figure 41–4). The canals are lined with receptor cells that have hairs. The tips of the hairs are enclosed by a **cupula,** a mass of gelatinous material secreted by the receptor cells.

The receptor cells are thought to respond to waves, currents, and disturbances in the water. The water moves the cupula and causes the hairs to bend. This

results in messages being dispatched to the CNS. The lateral line organ is thought to supplement vision by informing the fish of obstacles in its way and of moving objects such as prey, enemies, and schooling mates.

Proprioceptors Help Coordinate Muscle Movement

Proprioceptors are sense organs that continually respond to tension and movement in muscles and joints. Vertebrates have three main types of proprioceptors: **muscle spindles,** which detect muscle movement (Figure 41–5); **Golgi tendon organs,** which determine stretch in the tendons that attach muscle to bone; and

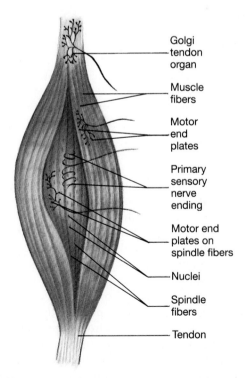

Figure 41–5 A muscle spindle and a Golgi tendon organ. Muscle spindles detect muscle movement; Golgi tendon organs determine stretch in tendons.

Pain Perception

Pain is a protective mechanism that signals an organism to react against a damaging stimulus. Pain receptors are dendrites of certain sensory neurons found in almost every tissue in the human body. An excess of any type of stimulus—pressure, heat, cold—stimulates pain receptors.

When stimulated, pain receptors signal the spinal cord by way of sensory neurons. The message is transmitted to the opposite side of the spinal cord and then sent upward to the thalamus, where pain reception begins (see figure). From there impulses are sent into the parietal lobes of the cerebrum. At that time the individual becomes fully aware of the pain and can assess the situation. How threatening is the stimulus? How intense is the pain? What can be done about it? From the thalamus, messages are also sent to the limbic system, where the emotional aspects of the discomfort are addressed.

Pain can be initiated or facilitated at many levels. How intense one's perception of pain is depends on the particular situation and how one has learned to deal with pain. A child with a bruised knee may emotionally heighten the feeling of pain, whereas a professional fighter may virtually ignore a long series of well-delivered blows.

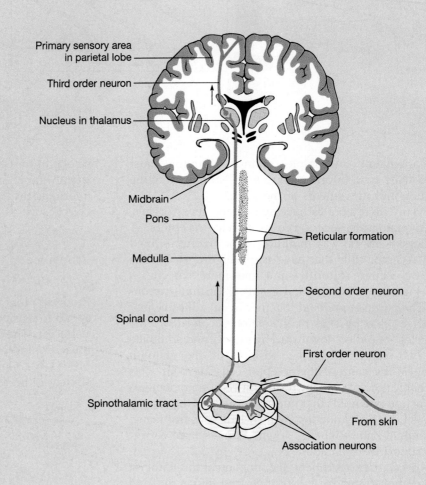

joint receptors, which detect movement in ligaments. These are tonic (static) sense organs rather than phasic receptors. The receptor potential is maintained (though not at constant magnitude) as long as the stimulus is present and action potentials continue to be generated. Thus, information about the position of the organ concerned is continuously supplied.

By means of these sense organs, we can carry out activities such as dressing or playing the piano even with our eyes closed. Impulses from the proprioceptors are important in ensuring the harmonious contractions of the distinct muscles involved in a single movement (without such receptors, complicated, skillful acts would be impossible). These organs are also important in maintaining balance.

Proprioceptors were discovered only a little more than 100 years ago. They are probably more numerous and more continually active than any of the other sense organs, although we are less aware of them than of most of the others. We obtain some idea of what life without proprioceptors would be like when a leg or arm "goes to sleep" and, partly because of a lack of proprioception, grows numb.

The mammalian muscle spindle, one of the more versatile stretch receptors, helps maintain muscle tone. It consists of a bundle of specialized muscle fibers, in the center of which is a region encircled by sensory nerve endings. These neurons respond statically and continue to transmit signals for a prolonged period of time, in proportion to the degree of stretch. Some of the

The brain locates pain on the basis of past experience. Generally, pain at the body surface is accurately projected back to the injured area. For example, when you step on a nail, the pain is perceived by the brain and then subjectively projected back to the injured foot, so that you feel pain at the site of puncture. Artificial stimulation of the leg nerves may produce a sensation of pain in the foot even though the foot is untouched. In fact, after an amputation, the patient may feel **phantom pain** in the missing limb. Phantom pain occurs because when the severed nerve is stimulated and sends a message to the brain, the brain "remembers" the nerve as it originally was—connected to the missing limb.

Most internal organs are poorly supplied with pain receptors. For this reason pain from internal structures is often difficult to locate. In fact, pain is often not projected back to the organ that is stimulated. Instead the pain is *referred* to an area just under the skin that may be some distance from the organ involved. The area to which the pain is referred generally is connected to nerve fibers from the same level of the spinal cord as the organ involved. A person with angina who feels heart pain in his left arm is experiencing **referred pain.** The pain originates in the heart as a result of ischemia (insufficient blood in the blood vessels of the heart muscle) but is actually felt in the arm. One explanation is that neurons from both the heart and the arm converge upon the same neurons in the central nervous system. The brain interprets the incoming message as coming from the body surface because somatic pain is far more common than pain from internal organs; the brain acts on the basis of its past experience. When pain is felt both at the site of the distress and as a referred pain, it may seem to spread, or *radiate*, from the organ to the superficial area.

The physiology of pain is not completely understood. A peptide known as **substance P** functions as a neurotransmitter (or perhaps as a modulator of neural activity) in neurons that transmit pain impulses to the spinal cord and brain. Opiates, such as morphine, are analgesic drugs (drugs that relieve pain). They work by blocking the release of substance P. The body has its own pain control system. The brain and pituitary gland release peptides known as **endorphins** (for "endogenous morphine-like") that are more powerful than the strong opiate morphine. Like the opiate drugs, these peptides are thought to suppress the release of substance P from pain-transmitting neurons. The neurotransmitter GABA (gamma-amino-butyric acid) is also thought to inhibit release of substance P in some areas of the brain. Endorphins are currently being investigated as potential analgesic (pain-killing) drugs.

Some neurobiologists think that endorphins may explain the mechanism of action of acupuncture. For thousands of years acupuncture has been used to relieve pain, but how it works has remained a mystery. There is now some evidence that acupuncture needles stimulate nerves deep within the muscles, which in turn stimulate the pituitary gland and parts of the brain to release endorphins.

Various clinical methods have been developed for relieving pain. Stimulation of the skin over the painful area with electrodes has been successful in some patients. This procedure is called transcutaneous electrical nerve stimulation. In a few patients, electrodes have been implanted in appropriate areas of the brain so that the patient can stimulate the brain at will. This procedure is thought to relieve pain by prompting the release of endorphins.

---

nerve endings also exhibit a strong dynamic response to an increase in length, but only *while* the length is actually increasing.

The Vestibular Apparatus of the Vertebrate Ear Functions To Maintain Equilibrium

When we think of the ear, we think of hearing. However, in vertebrates the main function of the ear is to help maintain equilibrium. Typically the ear also contains gravity receptors. Although many vertebrates do not have outer or middle ears, all have inner ears.

The inner ear consists of a complicated group of interconnected canals and sacs, referred to as the **labyrinth,** which includes a membranous labyrinth that fits inside a bony labyrinth. In mammals the membranous labyrinth consists of two saclike chambers, the **saccule** and the **utricle,** and three **semicircular canals.**

Collectively, the saccule, utricle, and semicircular canals are referred to as the **vestibular apparatus** (Figure 41–6). Destruction of the vestibular apparatus leads to a considerable loss of the sense of equilibrium. A pigeon in which these organs have been destroyed cannot fly but in time can relearn how to maintain equilibrium using visual stimuli. Equilibrium in the human depends not only on stimuli from the organs in the inner ear but also on the sense of vision, stimuli from the proprioceptors, and stimuli from cells sensitive to pressure in the soles of the feet.

The saccule and utricle house gravity detectors in

the form of small calcium carbonate ear stones called **otoliths** (Figure 41–7). The sensory cells of these structures are similar to those of the lateral line organ. Each consists of a group of hair cells surrounded at their tips by a gelatinous cupula. The receptor cells in the saccule and utricle lie in different planes. Normally, the pull of gravity causes the otoliths to press against particular hair cells, stimulating them to initiate impulses, which are sent to the brain by way of sensory nerve fibers at the hair cells' bases. When the head is tilted or in **linear acceleration** (a change in speed when the body is moving in a straight line), the otoliths press on the hairs of other cells and stimulate them. This enables the animal to perceive the directions of gravity and linear acceleration or deceleration when the head is in any position.

Information about turning movements, referred to as **angular acceleration,** is furnished by the three semicircular canals. Each is connected with the utricle and lies at right angles to the other two. Each canal is a hollow ring filled with fluid called **endolymph.** At one of the openings of each canal into the utricle is a small, bulblike enlargement, the **ampulla.** Within each ampulla is a clump of hair cells called a **crista,** similar to the groups of hair cells in the utricle and saccule but lacking otoliths. The receptor cells of the cristae are stimulated by movements of the endolymph in the canals (Figure 41–8).

When the head is turned, a lag in the movement of the fluid within the canals occurs so that the hair cells move in relation to the fluid and are stimulated by its flow. This stimulation produces not only the consciousness of rotation but also certain reflex movements in response to it. These reflexes cause the eyes and head to move in a direction opposite to the original rotation. Because the three canals are in three different planes, a movement of the head in any direction stimulates the movement of the fluid in at least one of the canals.

We humans are used to movements in the horizontal plane, which stimulate certain semicircular canals, but we are unused to vertical movements (parallel to the long axis of the upright body). The motion of an elevator or of a ship pitching in a rough sea stimulates the semicircular canals in an unusual way and may cause seasickness or motion sickness, with resultant nausea or vomiting. When a seasick person lies down, the movement stimulates the semicircular canals in a different way, and nausea is less likely to occur.

Auditory Receptors Are Located in the Cochlea

Some fish hear by means of receptors in the utricle, but hearing does not seem to be important to them. Hearing is important in tetrapods, however, and both birds and mammals have highly developed senses of hearing. Their auditory receptors, found in the **cochlea** of the inner ear, contain mechanoreceptor hair cells that detect pressure waves.

The cochlea is a spiral tube that resembles a snail's shell (Figures 41–9 and 41–10). If the cochlea were uncoiled, it would be seen to consist of three canals separated from each other by thin membranes and coming almost to a point at the apex. Two of these canals, or ducts—the **vestibular canal** (also known as the scala vestibuli) and the **tympanic canal** (scala tympani)—are connected with one another at the apex of the cochlea and are filled with a fluid known as **perilymph.** The middle canal, the **cochlear duct** (scala media), is filled with endolymph and contains the auditory organ, the **organ of Corti.**

Each organ of Corti contains about 24,000 hair cells arranged in rows that extend the entire length of the coiled cochlea. Each cell is equipped with hairlike projections that extend into the cochlear duct. The hair cells rest upon the **basilar membrane,** which separates the

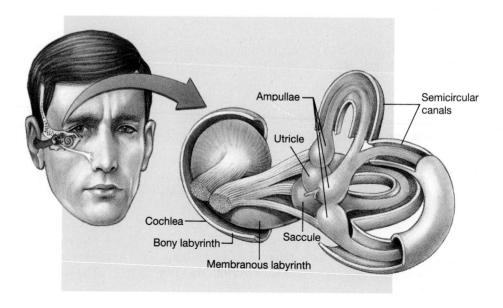

Figure 41–6 The human inner ear with the membranous labyrinth exposed. Because this is a posterior view, the utricle and saccule can be seen.

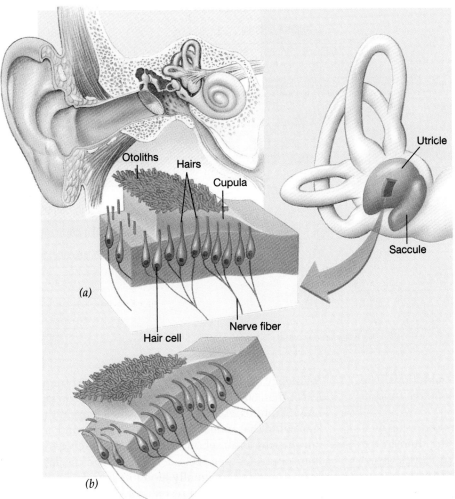

(a)

Otoliths
Hairs
Cupula
Hair cell
Nerve fiber

(b)

Utricle
Saccule

Figure 41–7 The saccule and the utricle. Compare the positions of the otoliths and hairs in (*a*) with those in (*b*). Changes in head position cause the force of gravity to distort the cupula, which in turn distorts the hairs of the hair cells. The hair cells respond by sending impulses down the vestibular nerve (part of the auditory nerve) to the brain.

cochlea from the tympanic canal. Overhanging the hair cells is another membrane, the **tectorial membrane,** which is attached along one edge to the membrane on which the hair cells rest. The hair cells initiate impulses in the fibers of the cochlear nerve.

In terrestrial vertebrates, accessory structures transform sound waves in the air into pressure waves in the cochlear fluid. In the human ear, for example, sound waves pass through the **external auditory meatus** (external ear canal) and set the **tympanic membrane,** or eardrum (the membrane separating the outer ear and the middle ear), vibrating. The vibrations are transmitted across the middle ear by three tiny bones, the **malleus, incus,** and **stapes** (or hammer, anvil, and stirrup, respectively—so called because of their shapes). The hammer is in contact with the eardrum, and the stirrup is in contact with the membrane at the opening of the inner ear, called the **oval window.** The hammer, anvil,

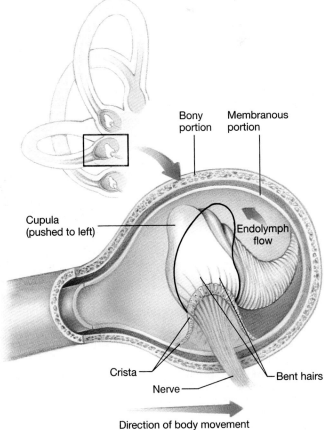

Bony portion
Membranous portion
Cupula (pushed to left)
Endolymph flow
Crista
Nerve
Bent hairs

Direction of body movement

Figure 41–8 Movement of endolymph within the ampulla distorts the cupula. The hair cells of the cupula then are bent, reporting any change to the brain via the vestibular nerve.

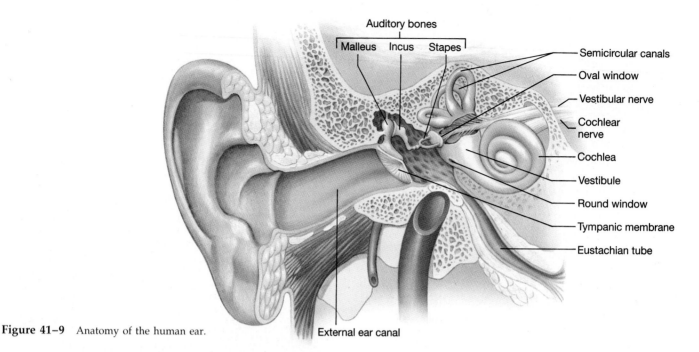

Auditory bones

Malleus   Incus   Stapes

Semicircular canals

Oval window

Vestibular nerve

Cochlear nerve

Cochlea

Vestibule

Round window

Tympanic membrane

Eustachian tube

External ear canal

Figure 41–9   Anatomy of the human ear.

and stirrup act as levers that amplify the vibrations. The vibrations pass through the oval window to the fluid in the vestibular canal.

Because liquids cannot be compressed, the oval window could not cause movement of the fluid in the vestibular duct without an escape valve for the pressure. This is provided by the **round window** at the end of the tympanic canal. The pressure wave presses on the membranes separating the three ducts, is transmitted to the tympanic canal, and causes a bulging of the round window. The movements of the basilar membrane produced by these pulsations cause the hair cells of the organs of Corti to rub against the overlying tectorial membrane. This stimulation initiates nerve impulses in the dendrites of the neurons at the base of each hair cell. We can summarize the sequence of events involved in hearing as follows:

sound waves enter external auditory canal → tympanic membrane vibrates → malleus, incus, and stapes vibrate → intensity of the vibrations is amplified → oval window vibrates → vibrations are conducted through fluid → vibration of basilar membrane → hair cells in the organ of Corti in the cochlea are stimulated → neural impulses are transmitted to the brain by the cochlear nerve

Sounds differ in pitch, loudness, and tone quality. Pitch depends upon frequency of sound waves. Low-frequency vibrations result in the sensation of low pitch, whereas high-frequency vibrations result in the sensation of high pitch. Up to about 4000 cycles per second, the nerve impulses produced have the same frequency as the sounds that cause them. At frequencies lower than 60 cycles per second, the entire basilar membrane vibrates. Action potentials are set up in the cochlear nerve that reflect the rhythm of the sound, and this informs the brain about the pitch. Frequencies greater than 60 cycles per second result in the basilar membrane vibrating unequally along its length. Sounds of a given frequency set up resonance waves in the fluid in the cochlea that cause a particular section of the basilar membrane to vibrate, stimulating the group of hair cells in that section. The brain infers the pitch of a sound by taking note of the particular hair cells that are stimulated. Thus, the brain may recognize a particular pitch by the frequency of the nerve impulses reaching it as well as by the identities of the nerve fibers conducting the impulses.

Loud sounds cause resonance waves of greater amplitude (height). They lead to a more intense stimulation of the hair cells and to the transmission of a greater number of impulses per second by the auditory nerve. Variations in the quality of sound, such as are evident when an oboe, a cornet, and a violin play the same note, depend upon the number and kinds of **overtones,** or **harmonics,** produced. These provide stimulation to different hair cells in addition to the main stimulation common to all three. Thus, differences in quality are recognized in the *pattern* of the hair cells stimulated.

The human ear is equipped to register sound frequencies between about 20 and 20,000 cycles per second, although individuals vary greatly. Some animals— dogs, for example—can hear sounds of much higher frequencies. The human ear is more sensitive to sounds between 1000 and 4000 cycles per second than to higher

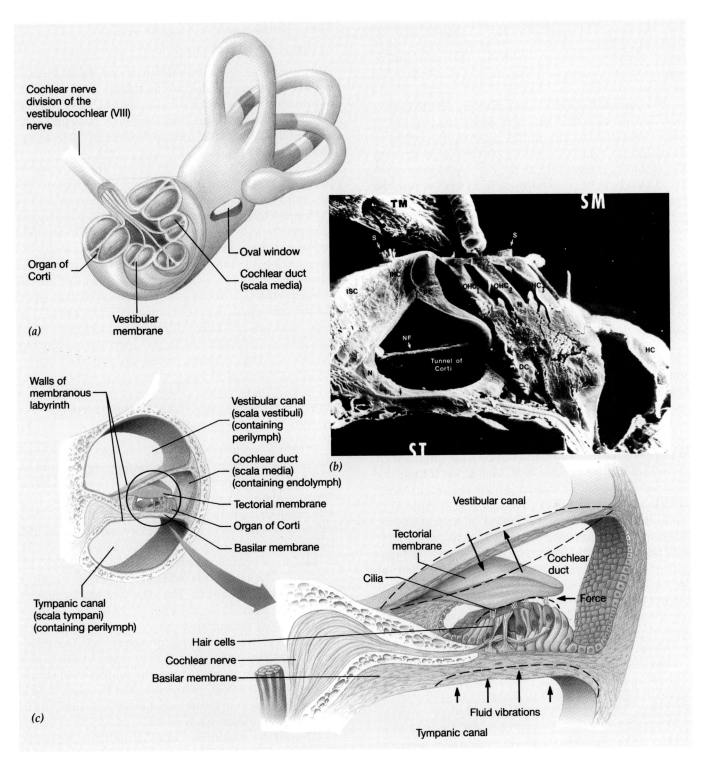

Figure 41–10 The cochlea is the part of the inner ear concerned with hearing. (*a*) Cross section through the cochlea showing the organ of Corti resting on the basilar membrane and covered by the tectorial membrane. (*b*) Scanning electron micrograph of a guinea pig's organ of Corti, showing the inner hair cells, *IHC*, and three rows of outer hair cells, *OHC 1*. *N*, nucleus; *S*, stereocilia; *TM*, tectorial membrane; *SM*, scala media (cochlear duct); *ST*, scala tympani (tympanic duct); *black arrows*, basilar membrane; *HC, DC,* *PC*, various supporting cells. (*c*) How the organ of Corti works. Vibrations transmitted by the hammer, anvil, and stirrup set the fluid in the vestibular canal in motion; these vibrations are transmitted to the basilar membrane, which stimulates the organ of Corti by forcing the hair cells against the tectorial membrane. The hair cells of the organ of Corti, the receptor cells for hearing, are innervated by the cochlear nerve. (*b*, Courtesy of Dr. L. G. Duckert, University of Washington)

or lower ones. Within this intermediate range, the ear is extremely sensitive. In fact, when the energy of audible sound waves is compared with the energy of visible light waves, the ear is ten times more sensitive than the eye.

The normal human ear is extremely efficient. Any more sensitivity would probably be useless, because it would enable us to pick up the random movement of air molecules, which we would perceive as a constant hiss or buzzing. Similarly, if the eye were more sensitive, a steady light would appear to flicker because the eye would be sensitive to the individual photons (light particles) impinging upon it.

There is little fatigue connected with hearing. Even though the ear is constantly assailed by noises, it retains its acuity, and fatigue disappears after a few minutes. When one ear is stimulated for some time by a loud noise, the other ear also shows fatigue (i.e., loses acuity), indicating, not unexpectedly, that some of the fatigue is in the brain rather than in the ear itself.

Deafness may be caused by injury to or malformation of either the sound-transmitting mechanism of the outer, middle, or inner ear, or the sound-perceiving mechanism of the latter. The external ear may become obstructed by wax secreted by the glands in its wall; the middle-ear bones may become fused after an infection; or, more rarely, the inner ear or auditory nerve may be injured by a local inflammation or by a very high fever.

When the ear is subjected to intense sound, the organ of Corti may be injured. This was demonstrated by an experiment in which guinea pigs were exposed to continuous pure tones for a period of several weeks. When their cochleas were examined microscopically, it was found that the guinea pigs subjected to high-pitched tones suffered injury only in the lower part of the cochlea, whereas those subjected to low-pitched tones suffered injury only in the upper part of the cochlea. Rock musicians, boilermakers, and other workers who are subjected to loud, high-pitched noises over a period of years frequently become deaf to high tones because the cells near the base of the organ of Corti become injured.

CHEMORECEPTORS ARE ASSOCIATED WITH THE SENSES OF TASTE AND SMELL

Throughout the animal kingdom, many feeding, social, sexual, and reproductive activities are initiated, regulated, or influenced in some way by specific chemical cues in the environment. Insects, for example, use chemicals to communicate, defend themselves against predators, and recognize specific foods. Many vertebrates employ chemical secretions to mark territory, attract sexual partners, track prey, and defend themselves. Two highly sensitive chemoreceptive systems are the sense of **taste** (gustation) and **smell** (olfaction).

Taste Buds Are the Organs of Taste in Mammals

The organs of taste in mammals are **taste buds**—budlike structures in the mouth, mainly on the tongue. In humans they are found mainly in tiny elevations, or papillae, on the surface of the tongue. A taste bud is an oval epithelial capsule containing several taste receptors (Figure 41–11a).

Traditionally, four basic tastes are recognized: sweet, sour, salty, and bitter. Although the greatest sensitivity to each of these tastes occurs in a given area of the human tongue (Figure 41–11b), not all papillae are restricted to a single category of taste. Flavor depends on the four basic tastes in combination with smell, texture, and temperature. Smell affects flavor because odors pass from the mouth to the nasal chamber via the internal nares. No doubt you have observed that when you are congested, food seems to have little "taste." The taste buds are not affected, but the blockage of nasal passages severely reduces the participation of olfactory reception in the composite sensation of flavor.

The Olfactory Epithelium Is Responsible for the Sense of Smell

In terrestrial vertebrates, olfaction occurs in the nasal epithelium. In humans, the **olfactory epithelium** is found in the roof of the nasal cavity (Figure 41–12). It contains about 20 million specialized olfactory cells with axons that extend upward as the fibers of the olfactory nerves. The end of each olfactory cell on the epithelial surface bears several olfactory hairs that are thought to react to odors (chemicals) in the air.

Unlike the taste buds, which are sensitive to only a few chemical sensations, the olfactory epithelium is thought to react to as many as 50. Mixtures of these primary smell sensations produce the broad spectrum of odors that we are capable of perceiving. The olfactory organs respond to remarkably small amounts of a substance. For example, ionone, the synthetic substitute for the odor of violets, can be detected by most people when it is present in a concentration of only one part to more than 30 billion parts of air.

Despite its sensitivity, smell is perhaps the sense that adapts most quickly. The olfactory receptors adapt about 50% in the first second or so after stimulation, so even offensively odorous air may seem odorless after only a few minutes.

THERMORECEPTORS ARE SENSITIVE TO HEAT

Heat is another form of radiant energy to which organisms respond. Although not much is known about their

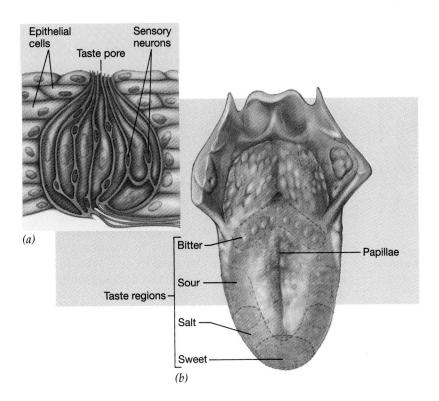

Figure 41–11 Taste buds are located mainly on the surface of the tongue. (*a*) A taste bud is an epithelial capsule containing several taste receptors. (*b*) The surface of the tongue, showing the distribution of taste buds sensitive to sweet, bitter, sour, and salt. A single taste receptor may respond to more than one category of taste.

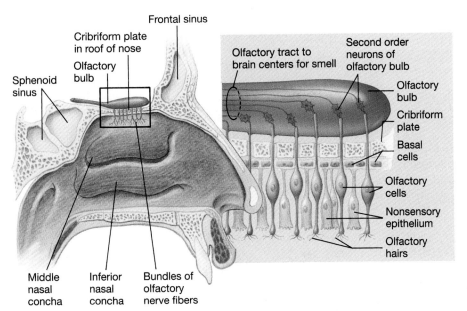

Figure 41–12 Location and structure of the olfactory epithelium. Note that the receptor cells are in the epithelium itself.

specific thermoreceptors, many invertebrates are sensitive to changes in temperature. Mosquitoes, other blood-sucking insects, and ticks use thermoreception in their search for an endothermic host. Some have temperature receptors on their antennae that are sensitive to changes of less than 0.5°C. At least two types of snakes, pit vipers and boas, use thermoreceptors to locate their prey (Figure 41–13).

In mammals, free nerve endings and specialized receptors in the skin and tongue detect temperature changes. Thermoreceptors in the hypothalamus of the brain detect internal changes in temperature and re-

ceive and integrate information from thermoreceptors on the body surface. The hypothalamus then initiates homeostatic mechanisms that ensure a constant body temperature.

ELECTRORECEPTORS DETECT ELECTRICAL CURRENTS IN WATER

Electric organs are found in a few species of rays and bony fishes. Some of these animals have electroreceptors on the body that are linked with the neurons sup-

Figure 41–13   Yellow eyelash viper displaying a pit organ, a sensory structure between each eye and the corresponding nostril. The pit organ can detect the heat from a warm-blooded animal at distances up to 1 to 2 meters.   (G. Dimijian/Photo Researchers, Inc.)

plying the lateral line organs. Electroreceptors are used to detect electrical currents in the water. In species that produce a weak current, the electric organs help in orientation. This is particularly useful in murky water, where visibility and olfaction are poor. Some animals with electric organs can deliver powerful shocks that stun prey or enemies.

PHOTORECEPTORS USE PIGMENTS TO ABSORB LIGHT

Most animals have photoreceptors that use pigments to absorb light energy. **Rhodopsins** are the photosensitive pigments found in the eyes of cephalopod mollusks, arthropods, and vertebrates. Light energy striking a light-sensitive receptor cell triggers chemical changes in the pigment molecules. As a result, the receptor cell may transmit a nerve impulse.

Eyespots, Simple Eyes, and Compound Eyes Are Found among Invertebrates

The simplest true light-sensitive organs are found in certain cnidarians and in flatworms. Their photoreceptor organs are called eyespots or **ocelli.** In planarian flatworms, ocelli are bowl-shaped structures containing black pigment (Figure 41–14). The pigment shades clusters of light-sensitive cells from all light except that coming from above and slightly to the front. This arrangement enables the planarian to detect the direction of the light source. Ocelli can also distinguish light intensity.

Animals with eyespots or very simple eyes can detect light but cannot see objects. Effective image formation, called **vision,** requires a more complex eye, usually with a lens that can focus an image on the light-sensitive cells. A necessary first step in the evolution from photoreceptor to true eye, therefore, was the development of a lens to concentrate light on a group of photoreceptors. As better lens systems evolved, the photoreceptors were able to form images, and true eyes evolved. Two fundamentally different types of complex eyes are the camera eye of vertebrates and some cephalopods (squids and octopods) and the compound eye of the arthropods. (The vertebrate eye and the cephalopod eye are analogous structures. See Chapter 17.)

Compound eyes found in crustaceans and insects are structurally and functionally different from vertebrate eyes (Figure 41–15). The surface of a compound eye appears faceted. Each **facet** is the convex cornea of one of the eye's visual units, called **ommatidia.** The

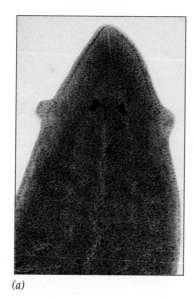
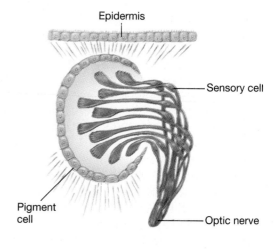

Figure 41–14   Simple invertebrate eye. (*a*) Planarian worm (*Planaria agilis*), showing eyespots. (*b*) Eyespot (ocellus) of a planarian worm.   (*a*, Terry Ashley/Tom Stack & Associates)

(a)   *(b)*

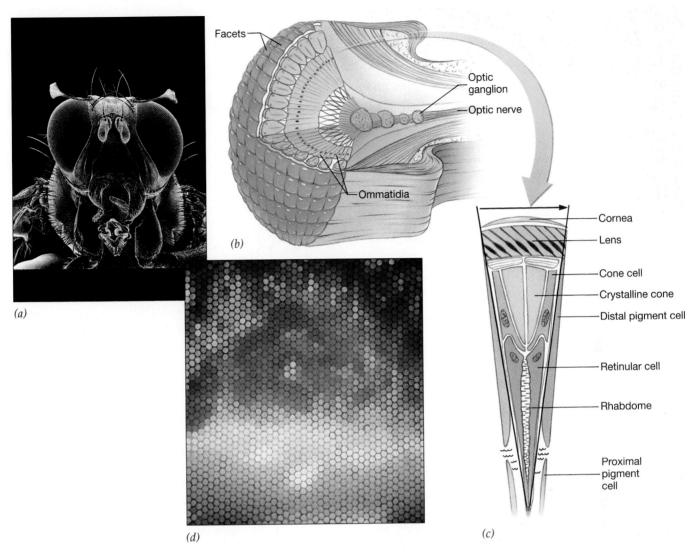

(a)

(b)

(c)

(d)

Figure 41–15   The compound eye. (*a*) The Mediterranean fruit fly (*Ceratitis capitata*). (*b*) Structure of the compound eye, showing several ommatidia. This type of eye registers changes in light and shade so that the animal can detect movement. (*c*) Structure of an ommatidium. The rhabdome is the light-sensitive core of the ommatidium. (*d*) A bee's-eye view of poppies.   (*a*, David Scharf; *d*, John Lithgoe/Seaphot, Ltd.)

number of ommatidia varies with the species. For example, the eyes of certain crustaceans have only 20 ommatidia apiece, whereas the eye of a dragonfly has as many as 28,000.

Each ommatidium consists of a light-sensitive central core, or **rhabdome;** a cornea; and a lens. The rhabdome is surrounded by receptor cells (known as retinular cells) that transmit the sensory stimulus (Figure 41–15). A sheath of pigmented cells envelops each ommatidium. Arthropod eyes usually adapt to different intensities of light. In nocturnal and crepuscular (dark- or dusk-loving) insects and many crustaceans, pigment is capable of migrating proximally and distally. When the pigment is in the proximal position, each ommatidium is shielded from its neighbor, and only light entering directly along its axis can stimulate the receptors. When the pigment is in the distal position, light striking at any angle can pass through several

ommatidia and stimulate many retinal units. As a result, sensitivity of the eye is increased in dim light, and the eye is protected from excessive stimulation in bright light. Pigment migration is under neural control in insects and under hormonal control in crustaceans. In some species it follows a daily rhythm.

Compound eyes do not perceive form well. Although the lens system of each ommatidium is adequate to focus a small inverted image on the retinular cells, there is no evidence that such images are actually perceived as images by the organism. However, all the ommatidia together do produce a composite image. Each ommatidium, in gathering a point of light from a narrow sector of the visual field, is in fact sampling a mean intensity from that sector. All of these points of light taken together form a **mosaic picture.** To appreciate the nature of this mosaic picture, we need only look at a newspaper photograph through a magnifying

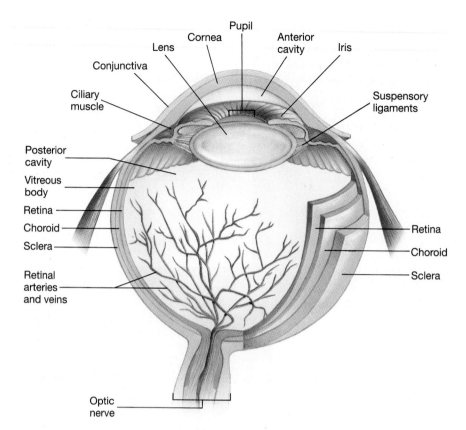

Figure 41–16   Structure of the human eye.

glass; it is a mosaic of many dots of different intensities. The clarity and definition of the picture depend upon how many dots there are per unit area—the more dots, the better the picture. So it is with the compound eye. The image perceived by the animal is probably much better in quality than might be suspected from the structure of the compound eye. The nervous system of an insect is apparently capable of image processing similar to that employed to improve the quality of photographs sent to the Earth by robot spacecraft.

Although the compound eye can form only coarse images, it compensates by being able to follow **flickers** to higher frequencies. Flies are able to detect flickers up to about 265 per second. In contrast, the human eye can detect flickers of only 45 to 53 per second; for us, flickering lights fuse above these values, so we see motion pictures as smooth movement and the ordinary 60-cycle light in the room as steady. To an insect, both motion pictures and room lighting must flicker horribly. However, because the insect has such a high critical flicker fusion threshold, any movement of prey or enemy is immediately detected by one of the eye units. The compound eye is well suited to the arthropod's way of life.

Compound eyes are different from our eyes in two other respects. They are sensitive to different wavelengths of light in the range from red to ultraviolet (UV), and they can analyze the **plane of polarization** of light. Accordingly, an insect can see UV light well, and its world of color is very different from ours. Because different flowers deflect UV light to different degrees,

two flowers that appear identically colored to us may appear strikingly different to insects (see Figure 27–14). How the world appears to an insect with UV vision can be appreciated by viewing the landscape through a television camera with a UV light–transmitting lens.

A sky that appears to us to be equally blue in all quadrants reveals quite different patterns to an insect. This is because the insect's eyes can detect differences in the plane of polarization of the light in various parts of the sky. Honeybees and some other arthropods employ this ability to help them navigate.

Vertebrate Eyes Form Sharp Images

The mammalian eye is like a 35-millimeter camera loaded with extremely sensitive color film. The eye (Figure 41–16) has a **lens** that can be focused for different distances; a diaphragm, the **iris,** which regulates the size of the light opening, the **pupil;** and a light-sensitive **retina** at the rear of the eye, corresponding to the film of the camera. Next to the retina is a sheet of cells filled with black pigment that absorbs extra light and prevents internally reflected light from blurring the image (cameras are also painted black on the inside). This sheet, called the **choroid,** also contains the blood vessels that nourish the retina.

The outer coat of the eyeball, called the **sclera,** is a tough, opaque, curved sheet of connective tissue that protects the inner structures and helps to maintain the rigidity of the eyeball. On the front surface of the eye, this sheet becomes the thinner, transparent **cornea,** through which light enters.

The lens is a transparent, elastic ball just behind the iris. It bends the light rays coming in and brings them to a focus on the retina. The lens is aided by the curved surface of the cornea and by the refractive properties of the liquids inside the eyeball. The **anterior cavity** between the cornea and the lens is filled with a watery substance, the **aqueous fluid.** The larger **posterior cavity** between the lens and the retina is filled with a more viscous fluid, the **vitreous body.** Both fluids are important in maintaining the shape of the eyeball.

At its anterior margin, the choroid is thick and projects medially into the eyeball, forming the **ciliary body.** The ciliary body consists of ciliary processes and the ciliary muscle. The ciliary processes are glandlike folds that project toward the lens and secrete the aqueous fluid. The eye has the power of **accommodation,** meaning it can change focus for near or far vision by changing the curvature of the lens. This is accomplished by the **ciliary muscle,** a part of the ciliary body that is attached to the lens by the suspensory ligaments. When the eye is at rest, the ciliary muscle is relaxed and the ligaments are tense. This pulls the lens into a flattened (ovoid) shape, focusing the eye for far vision. When the ciliary muscle contracts, tension on the suspensory ligaments lessens; the elastic lens then assumes a rounder shape for near vision.

As a person ages, the lens enlarges and becomes less elastic and therefore less able to accommodate for near vision. When this occurs, bifocals—glasses with one portion of each lens ground for distant vision and one portion ground for near vision—may be worn to compensate for what the eye can no longer do.

The amount of light entering the eye is regulated by the **iris,** a ring of smooth muscle that appears as blue, green, gray, or brown, depending on the amount and nature of pigment present. The iris is composed of two mutually antagonistic sets of muscle fibers. One set is arranged circularly and contracts to decrease the size of the pupil. The other is arranged radially and contracts to increase the size of the pupil. The response of these muscles to a change in light intensity is not instantaneous but requires from 10 to 30 seconds. Thus, when a person steps from a light to a dark area, some time is needed for the eyes to adapt to the dark, and when a person steps from a dark room to a brightly lighted area, the eyes are dazzled until the size of the pupil is decreased. The retina of the eye (soon to be discussed) can also adapt to changes in light intensity.

Each eye has six muscles that extend from the surface of the eyeball to various points in the bony socket. These muscles enable the eye as a whole to move and be oriented in a given direction. Cranial nerves innervate the muscles in such a way that the eyes normally move together and focus on the same area.

The positions of the eyes in the heads of humans and certain other higher vertebrates permit both eyes to be focused on the same object (Figure 41–17). This **binocular vision** is important for judging distance and depth.

The retina is the light-sensitive part of the eye

The light-sensitive part of the vertebrate eye is the retina, which lines the posterior two thirds of the eyeball, covering the choroid. The retina contains abundant photoreceptor cells called, according to their shapes, **rods** and **cones.** The human eye has about 125 million rods and 6.5 million cones. Rods function in dim light, allowing us to detect shape and movement; they are not sensitive to colors. Because the rods are more numerous in the periphery of the retina, you can see an object better in dim light if you look slightly to one side of it (allowing the image to fall on the rods).

Cones are responsible for bright-light vision, for the perception of fine detail, and for color vision. They permit color vision by being differentially sensitive to different frequencies (colors) of light. The cones are concentrated in the **fovea,** a small depressed area in the center of the retina. The fovea is the region of sharpest vision. Only those objects more or less directly in front of our eyes can be perceived in color. This can be demonstrated by a simple experiment. Close one eye and focus the other on some point straight ahead. As a colored object is gradually brought into view from the side, you will be aware of its presence and of its size and shape before you are aware of its color. Only when the object is brought closer to the direct line of vision, so that its image falls on a part of the retina containing cones, can its color be determined.

Curiously, light must pass through several layers of connecting neurons in the retina to reach the rods and cones (Figure 41–18). The axons of the sensory neurons extend across the surface of the retina and unite to form the **optic nerve,** which then passes out of the eyeball. This area is called the ''blind spot'' because it has no rods and cones and images falling on it cannot be perceived.

In summary, vision involves the following sequence of events:

light passes through cornea, aqueous humor, lens, and vitreous body → image formed on retina → optic nerve transmits nerve impulses to visual areas of the cerebral cortex

A chemical change in rhodopsin leads to the response of a rod to light

Rhodopsin in the rod cells and some very closely related pigments in the cone cells are responsible for the ability to see. Rhodopsin consists of opsin, a large pro-

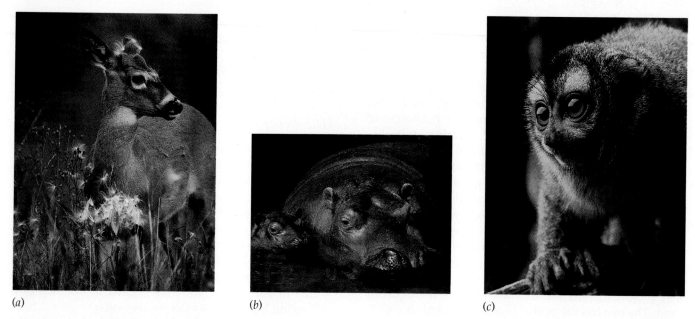

(a)   *(b)*   *(c)*

Figure 41–17 The locations of the eyes vary in different vertebrates, resulting in differences in vision. (*a*) The eyes of the white-tailed deer (*Odocoileus virginianus*) are positioned laterally, enabling the animal to see on both sides; even while grazing, it can spot a predator approaching from behind. This buck is shown with milkweed seed fluff. (*b*) The orbits (bony cavities that contain the eyeballs) of the hippopotamus are elevated, enabling the animal to see even when most of its head is underwater. (*c*) Like many other nocturnal animals, the owl monkey (*Aotus tribirgatus*) has large eyes. They are positioned at the front of the head and give the monkey binocular vision, permitting it to judge distances. (*a*, Carl R. Sams II/Peter Arnold, Inc.; *b*, Gérard Lacz/Peter Arnold, Inc.; *c*, Stephen Dalton © 1993 Animals Animals)

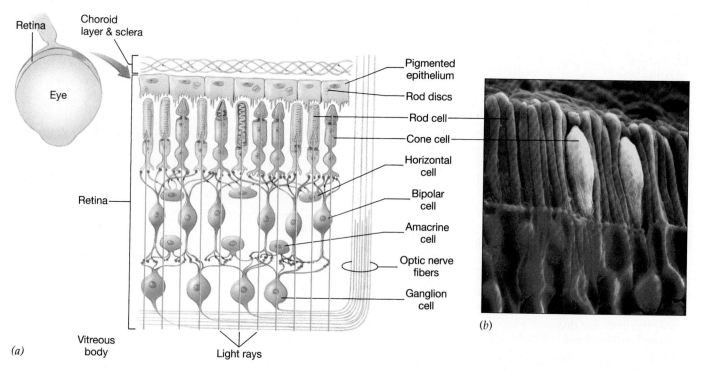

(a)   *(b)*

Figure 41–18 The retina. (*a*) Neuronal connections in the retina. The elaborate interconnections among the various layers of cells allow them to interact and to influence one another in a number of ways. (*b*) Rods (red elongated structures) and two cones (shorter, thicker, yellow structures) make up the top row in this micrograph. The elongated rods permit us to see shape and movement, whereas the shorter cones allow us to view our world in color. (*b*, Lennart Nilsson, from *The Incredible Machine*, p. 279)

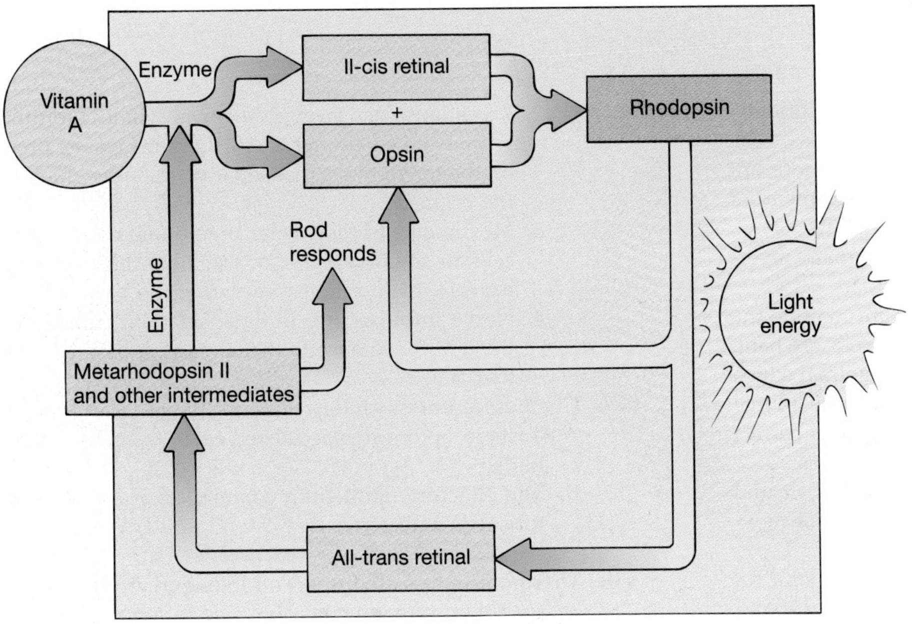

Figure 41–19 The visual cycle. When light strikes rhodopsin, it breaks down, producing a response in the rod cell that contains it.

tein, chemically joined with **retinal,** which is made from vitamin A. Two isomers of retinal exist: the 11-*cis* form and the all-*trans* form.

When light strikes rhodopsin, it transforms 11-*cis* retinal to all-*trans* retinal. This change in shape causes rhodopsin to break down into its components, opsin and retinal. During this process the rhodopsin is converted into a series of intermediate compounds. One of these is **metarhodopsin II,** which is thought to be the key compound in the response of the rod to light. The all-*trans* retinal is converted back to the 11-*cis* form by an enzyme. Then the retinal combines with opsin to produce rhodopsin once again. This sequence of reactions is known as the *visual cycle* (Figure 41–19).

Just how visual images are processed is not certain. The size, intensity, and location of light stimuli determine initial processing in the retina. The pattern of neuron firing in the retina appears to be very important. The optic nerves are thought to transmit information to the brain by way of complex encoded signals.

A single quantum of light can be absorbed by a single molecule of rhodopsin and can lead to the response of a single rod. When the eye is exposed to a flash of light lasting only a millionth of a second, it sees an image of light that persists for nearly a tenth of a second. This is the length of time that the retina remains stimulated following a flash. This persistence of images in the retina enables your eye to fuse the successive flickering images on a motion picture screen, so that what is actually a rapid succession of still pictures is perceived as moving persons and objects.

Color vision depends on three different types of cones

Three different types of cones, each containing a different cone pigment, function in color vision. They are commonly referred to as blue, green, or red cones. Each type of cone can respond to light within a considerable range of wavelengths but is named for the wavelength its pigment responds to most strongly. For example, red light can be absorbed by all three types of cones, but the cones most sensitive to red act as red receptors. By comparing the relative responses of the three types of cones, the brain can detect light colors of intermediate wavelength. Color blindness occurs when one or more of the three types of cones is absent. This is usually an inherited X-linked condition (see Chapter 10).

SUMMARY

I. A sense organ consists of one or more receptor cells and sometimes accessory cells. Receptor cells may be neuron endings or specialized cells in close contact with neurons.

II. Exteroceptors are sense organs that receive information from the outside world. Proprioceptors are sense organs within muscles, tendons, and joints; they enable the animal to perceive orientation of the body and the positions of its parts. Interoceptors are sense organs within body organs.

III. Based on the types of stimuli to which they respond, sense organs also may be classified as mechanoreceptors, chemoreceptors, photoreceptors, thermoreceptors, or electroreceptors.

IV. Receptor cells absorb energy, transduce that energy into electrical energy, and produce receptor potentials.

V. Adaptation of a receptor to a continuous stimulus results in diminished perception. For this reason, adaptation to an unpleasant odor or noise occurs after a few moments.

VI. Mechanoreceptors respond to touch, pressure, gravity, stretch, or movement.
   A. The tactile receptors in the skin are mechanoreceptors that respond to mechanical displacement of hairs or of the receptor cells themselves.
   B. Statocysts are gravity receptors found in many invertebrates.
     1. When the position of the statolith within the statocyst changes, hairs of receptor cells are bent.
     2. Messages sent to the CNS inform an animal which hairs have been stimulated; from this the animal can determine where "down" is and can correct for any abnormal orientation.
   C. Lateral line organs supplement vision in fish and some amphibians by informing the animal of moving objects or objects in its path.
   D. Muscle spindles, Golgi tendon organs, and joint receptors are proprioceptors that continually respond to tension and movement in the muscles and joints.
   E. The saccule and utricle of the vertebrate ear contain otoliths that change position when the head is tilted or when the body is moving forward. The hair cells stimulated by otoliths send impulses to the brain, enabling the animal to perceive the direction of gravity.
   F. The semicircular canals of the vertebrate ear inform the brain about turning movements. Their cristae are stimulated by movements of the endolymph.
   G. In birds and mammals, the organ of Corti within the cochlea contains auditory receptors.
     1. Sound waves pass through the external auditory meatus, cause the eardrum to vibrate, and are transmitted through the middle ear by the hammer, anvil, and stirrup.
     2. Vibrations pass through the oval window to fluid within the vestibular duct. Pressure waves press on the membranes that separate the three ducts of the cochlea.
     3. Movements of the basilar membrane rub the hair cells of the organ of Corti against the overlying tectorial membrane, stimulating the hair cells.
     4. Nerve impulses are initiated in the dendrites of the auditory neurons that lie at the base of each hair cell.
VII. Chemoreceptors include receptors for taste and smell.
   A. Taste receptors are specialized epithelial cells in taste buds.
   B. The olfactory epithelium contains specialized olfactory cells with axons that extend upward as fibers of the olfactory nerves.
VIII. Thermoreceptors are important in endothermic animals because they provide cues about body temperature. In some invertebrates they are used to locate an endothermic host.
IX. Photoreceptors in very simple eyes detect light, but such eyes do not form images effectively. Effective image formation and interpretation are called vision.
   A. The compound eye found in insects and crustaceans consists of ommatidia, which collectively produce a mosaic image.
   B. In the human eye, light enters through the cornea, is focused by the lens, and produces an image on the retina. The iris regulates the amount of light that can enter.
   C. When light strikes rhodopsin in the rod cells, a chemical change in retinal breaks down the rhodopsin, triggering a response in the rod cell.
   D. Rods form images in black and white, whereas cones function in color vision.

POST-TEST

1. A _____ organ detects changes in the environment and transmits that information into the nervous system.
2. _____ are sense organs that receive stimuli from the outside environment; _____ enable an animal to perceive orientation of the body.
3. _____-receptors detect light energy; _____-receptors respond to touch, gravity, or movement.
4. Receptor cells absorb and transduce _____ and produce a _____ _____.
5. The diminishing response of a receptor to a continued, constant stimulus is called _____.
6. Statocysts serve as _____ receptors; their action depends on mechanical displacement of receptor cell hairs by change in position of a _____.
7. The lateral line organ of fishes is thought to supplement _____; its canals are lined with receptor cells that have _____; the receptor cells secrete a mass of gelatinous material called a _____.
8. Three main types of vertebrate proprioceptors are _____ _____, which detect muscle movement; _____ tendon organs, which determine stretch in tendons; and _____ receptors, which detect movement in ligaments.
9. Phasic receptors respond only to _____.
10. The Pacinian corpuscle responds to deep _____.
11. The basic function of the vertebrate ear is to help maintain _____.
12. The inner ear consists of interconnected canals and sacs called the _____; in jawed vertebrates this structure consists of two saclike chambers, the _____ and _____, and three _____ canals.
13. The rocks in your head (within the saccule and utricle), called _____, are actually _____ detectors.
14. Each semicircular canal is filled with fluid called _____; at one of the openings of each canal into the utricle is a small enlargement, the _____.
15. The cochlea, located in the _____ ear, contains mechanoreceptor hair cells that detect _____ waves.
16. The auditory receptor is located within the organ of _____.
17. The senses of taste and smell depend upon _____.
18. The photosensitive pigments in the eyes of vertebrates are _____.

Select the most appropriate answer in Column B for each description in Column A.

Column A
19. Light-sensitive part of human eye
20. Regulates size of pupil
21. Perceive color
22. Region of keenest vision
23. Visual unit in compound eye

Column B
a. Ommatidium
b. Cones
c. Retina
d. Iris
e. Fovea

24. Label the following diagrams. (Refer to Figures 41–9 and 41–16 as necessary.)

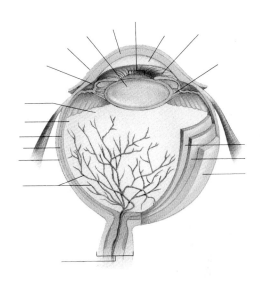

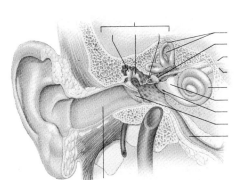

REVIEW QUESTIONS

1. Contrast mechanoreceptors with chemoreceptors.
2. Which sense organs permit us to perform actions such as getting dressed or finding our way into bed when our eyes are closed? Explain how they work.
3. What is the physiological basis of seasickness?
4. Connoisseurs can recognize many varieties of cheese or wine by tasting. How can this be, when there are only four types of taste receptors?
5. Draw a diagram of the human eye, labeling all parts. How are rods and cones distributed in the retina?
6. Discuss the mechanism by which photoreceptors are stimulated by light. What is the function of rhodopsin? How is it regenerated?
7. How does the human eye adjust to near and far vision and to bright and dim lights?
8. Draw a diagram of the human ear, labeling all parts.
9. Discuss the mechanism by which the sensory cells of the ear are stimulated by sound waves.
10. What are otoliths, and what is their role in maintaining equilibrium?
11. Contrast the function of the insect's compound eye with that of the vertebrate eye.

RECOMMENDED READINGS

Abu-Mostafa, Y. S., and D. Psaltis. Optical neural computers. *Scientific American,* Vol. 256, No. 3 (March 1987), pp. 88–94. The arrangement of neurons in the brain can be used as a model for building a computer that can solve problems, such as those involving pattern recognition, that require memorizing all possible solutions.

Borg, E., and S. A. Counter. The middle-ear muscles. *Scientific American,* Vol. 261, No. 2 (August 1989), pp. 74–83. The neuromuscular control system of the middle ear prevents sensory overload and enhances sound discrimination.

Hubel, D. H. *Eye, Brain & Vision.* WH Freeman, New York, 1988. Offers a clear discussion of the process of seeing.

Hudspeth, A. J. The hair cells of the inner ear. *Scientific American,* Vol. 241, No. 1 (January 1983), pp. 54–64. A description of the mechanism by which hair cells in the inner ear respond to convey information about acoustic tones and acceleration. Some of this author's conclusions are controversial.

Long, M. E. The sense of sight. *National Geographic,* Vol. 182, No. 5 (November 1992), pp. 3–41. A beautifully illustrated discussion of vision and new technology for restoring sight.

Nathans, J. The genes for color vision. *Scientific American,* Vol. 260, No. 2 (February 1989), pp. 42–49. The genes that code for the color-detecting proteins of the eye offer clues about the evolution of normal color vision.

Poggio, T., and C. Koch. Synapses that compute motion. *Scientific American,* Vol. 256, No. 5 (May 1987), pp. 46–52. Studies of cells in the eye that interpret movement may help clarify mechanisms involved in other neural processes.

Schnapf, J. L., and D. A. Baylor. How photoreceptor cells respond to light. *Scientific American,* Vol. 256, No. 4 (April 1987), pp. 40–47. How a single photoreceptor cell in the eye registers the absorption of a single photon.

Treisman, A. Features and objects in visual processing. *Scientific American,* Vol. 255, No. 5 (November 1986), pp. 114–125. We perceive meaningful wholes visually by automatically extracting features from a scene and assembling them into objects.

Internal Transport

Most cells require a continuous supply of nutrients and oxygen and removal of waste products. In very small aquatic animals, these metabolic needs can be met by simple diffusion. No specialized circulatory structures are present in sponges, cnidarians, ctenophores, flatworms, or nematodes. Because the bodies of these invertebrates are only a few cells thick, diffusion is an effective mechanism for distributing materials to and from their cells.

In complex animals, whether aquatic or terrestrial, diffusion cannot supply enough raw materials to all of the cells, and specialized circulatory structures are required to transport materials. These structures make up the **circulatory system.**

A circulatory system typically consists of the following:

1. Blood, a fluid connective tissue consisting of cells and cell fragments dispersed in fluid

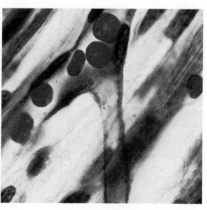

A capillary network where nutrients and gases are exchanged between the blood and the interstitial fluid bathing the cells. (Lennart Nilsson, © Boehringer Ingelheim International GmbH)

2. A pumping organ, generally a heart
3. A system of blood vessels or spaces through which the blood circulates

Arthropods and most mollusks have an **open circulatory system,** in which the heart pumps blood into vessels that have open ends. Bloods spills out of them, filling large spaces that make up the **hemocoel** (blood cavity), bathing the cells of the body directly. Blood re-enters the circulatory system through openings in the heart (in arthropods) or through open-ended vessels that lead to the gills (in mollusks).

Annelids, some mollusks, echinoderms, and vertebrates have a **closed circulatory system.** In them, blood flows through a continuous circuit of blood vessels. The walls of the smallest blood vessels are thin enough to permit diffusion of gases, nutrients, and wastes between blood in the vessels and the extracellular fluid that bathes the cells.

After you have studied this chapter you should be able to

1. Compare internal transport in animals that lack a circulatory system, animals with an open circulatory system, and animals with a closed circulatory system.
2. Relate structural adaptations of the vertebrate circulatory system to each function it performs.
3. Compare the structure and functions of red blood cells, white blood cells, and platelets.
4. Summarize the events involved in blood clotting.
5. Compare the structure and function of different types of blood vessels, including arteries, arterioles, capillaries, and veins.
6. Trace the evolution of the vertebrate heart from fish to mammal.
7. Describe the structure and function of the human heart and label a diagram of the heart.
8. Describe cardiac muscle and describe the conduction system of the heart.

9. Trace the events of the cardiac cycle, and relate normal heart sounds to the events of this cycle.
10. Define cardiac output, describe how it is regulated, and identify factors that affect it.
11. Identify factors that determine blood pressure.
12. Compare blood pressure in different types of blood vessels and summarize how arterial blood pressure is regulated.
13. Trace a drop of blood through the pulmonary and systemic circulations, naming in sequence each structure through which it passes.
14. Identify the risk factors for atherosclerosis, trace the progress of the disorder, and summarize its possible complications (including angina pectoris and myocardial infarction).
15. List the functions of the lymphatic system, and describe how the system operates to maintain fluid balance.

SOME INVERTEBRATES HAVE NO CIRCULATORY SYSTEM

As indicated above, many small, aquatic invertebrates have no circulatory system. In cnidarians, the central gastrovascular cavity serves as a circulatory organ as well as a digestive organ (Figure 42–1). The animal's tentacles capture prey and deliver it through the mouth into the cavity, where digestion occurs. The digested nutrients then pass into the cells lining the cavity, and through them to cells of the outer layer. Movement of the animal's body, as it stretches and contracts, stirs up the contents of the gastrovascular cavity and helps distribute nutrients to all parts of the body.

The flattened body of the flatworm permits effective gas exchange by diffusion. Its branched intestine brings nutrients to all regions of the body. As in cnidarians, circulation is aided by contractions of the muscles of the body wall, which agitate the fluid in the intestine and the tissue fluid. Metabolic rate tends to be higher than in cnidarians, allowing a more active lifestyle. The branching excretory system of planarians provides for internal transport of wastes that are then expelled from the body.

Fluid in the pseudocoelom of nematodes and other pseudocoelomate animals helps to circulate materials. Nutrients, oxygen, and wastes dissolve in this fluid and diffuse through it to and from the individual cells of the body. Body movements of the animal result in movement of the fluid, facilitating distribution of these materials to all parts of the body.

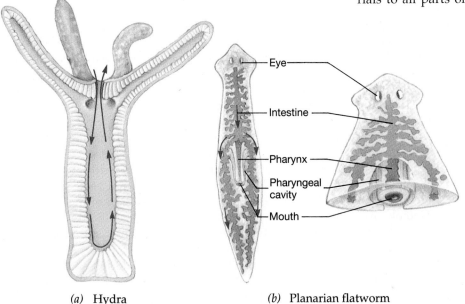

Eye

Intestine

Pharynx

Pharyngeal cavity

Mouth

(a) Hydra *(b)* Planarian flatworm

Figure 42–1 Two invertebrates with no circulatory system. (*a*) In hydra and other cnidarians, the gastrovascular cavity serves a circulatory function, permitting nutrients to come in contact with the body cells. (*b*) In planarian flatworms, the branched intestine conducts food to all regions of the body.

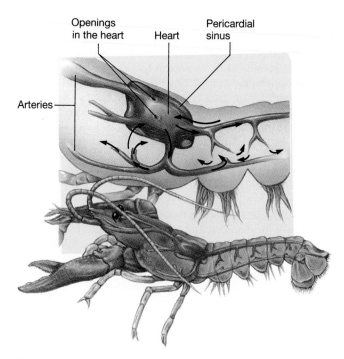

Figure 42–2   Lateral view of a crayfish. Like other arthropods, the crayfish has an open circulatory system.

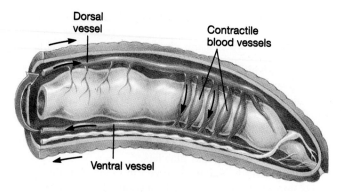

Figure 42–3   The earthworm has a complex closed circulatory system. Five pairs of contractile blood vessels deliver blood from the dorsal vessel to the ventral vessel.

MANY INVERTEBRATES HAVE AN OPEN CIRCULATORY SYSTEM

In the open circulatory system of most mollusks the heart is surrounded by a pericardial cavity. The heart typically consists of three chambers: two atria and a ventricle. The atria receive blood, more appropriately called **hemolymph** in animals with open circulatory systems (because the blood and interstitial fluid are not distinguishable), from the gills. The ventricle pumps this oxygen-rich hemolymph to the tissues. Blood vessels conducting hemolymph from the heart open into large spaces called **sinuses,** enabling the hemolymph to bathe the body cells. Such hemolymph-filled spaces form a **hemocoel.** From the hemocoel, hemolymph passes into vessels that lead to the gills. There it is recharged with oxygen and passes into blood vessels that return it to the heart.

Some mollusks, as well as arthropods, have a blood pigment, **hemocyanin,** that contains copper. Hemocyanin transports oxygen and imparts a bluish color to the hemolymph of these animals (the orginal bluebloods!).

In arthropods a tubular heart pumps hemolymph into blood vessels (arteries) that deliver hemolymph to the sinuses of the hemocoel (Figure 42–2). Hemolymph then circulates through the hemocoel, eventually returning to the pericardial cavity surrounding the heart. Hemolymph enters the heart through tiny openings (called ostia) that are equipped with valves to prevent

backflow. Some insects have accessory "hearts" that help pump hemolymph through the extremities, particularly the wings. Circulation of the hemolymph is faster during muscular movement. Thus, when an animal is active and most in need of nutrients for fuel, its own movement ensures effective circulation. An open circulatory system cannot provide enough oxygen to maintain the active lifestyle of insects. Indeed, insect blood mainly distributes nutrients and hormones. Oxygen is delivered directly to the cells by a system of air (tracheal) tubes that make up the respiratory system.

SOME INVERTEBRATES HAVE A CLOSED CIRCULATORY SYSTEM

A rudimentary closed circulatory system is found in the proboscis worms (phylum Nemertinea). This system consists of a complete network of blood vessels. No heart is present; instead, blood flow depends upon movements of the animal and upon contractions in the walls of the large blood vessels.

Earthworms and other annelids have a complex closed circulatory system (Figure 42–3). Two main blood vessels extend lengthwise in the body. The ventral vessel conducts blood posteriorly, and the dorsal vessel conducts blood anteriorly. Dorsal and ventral vessels are connected by lateral vessels in every segment. Branches of the lateral vessels deliver blood to the surface, where it is oxygenated. In the anterior part of the worm, five pairs of contractile blood vessels (sometimes referred to as hearts) connect dorsal and ventral vessels. Contractions of these paired vessels and of the dorsal vessel, as well as contraction of the muscles of the body wall, circulate the blood. Earthworms have **hemoglobin,** the same red pigment that transports oxygen in vertebrate blood; however, their hemoglobin is not within red blood cells but is dissolved in the blood plasma.

Although other mollusks have an open circulatory system, the fast-moving cephalopods (squid, octopus) require a more efficient means of internal transport. They have a closed system made even more effective by the presence of accessory "hearts" at the base of the gills, which speed the passage of blood through the gills.

THE CLOSED CIRCULATORY SYSTEM OF VERTEBRATES IS ADAPTED TO CARRY OUT A VARIETY OF FUNCTIONS

The circulatory systems of all vertebrates are basically similar, from fishes, frogs, and reptiles to birds and humans. All have a ventral, muscular heart that pumps blood into a closed system of blood vessels. The vertebrate circulatory system consists of heart, blood vessels, blood, lymph, lymph vessels, and associated organs, such as the thymus, spleen, and liver. The tiniest blood vessels, **capillaries,** have very thin walls that permit exchange of materials between blood and extracellular fluid.

The vertebrate circulatory system performs several functions:

1. Transportation of nutrients from the digestive system and from storage depots to each cell of the body
2. Transportation of oxygen from respiratory structures (gills, lungs) to the cells of the body
3. Transportation of metabolic wastes from each cell to organs that excrete them
4. Transportation of hormones from endocrine glands to target tissues
5. Assists maintenance of fluid balance
6. Defends the body against invading microorganisms
7. Helps to distribute metabolic heat within the body and to maintain normal body temperature in endothermic (warm-blooded) animals

VERTEBRATE BLOOD CONSISTS OF PLASMA, BLOOD CELLS, AND PLATELETS

In vertebrates, **blood** consists of a pale yellowish fluid, known as **plasma,** in which red blood cells, white blood cells, and platelets are suspended (Figure 42–4; Table 42–1). In humans the total circulating blood volume is about 8% of the body weight—5.6 liters (6 quarts) in a 70-kg (154-lb) person. This is about the amount of oil in the crankcase of most cars!

About 55% of the blood is plasma; the remaining 45% is made up of blood cells and platelets. Because cells and platelets are heavier than plasma, the two can

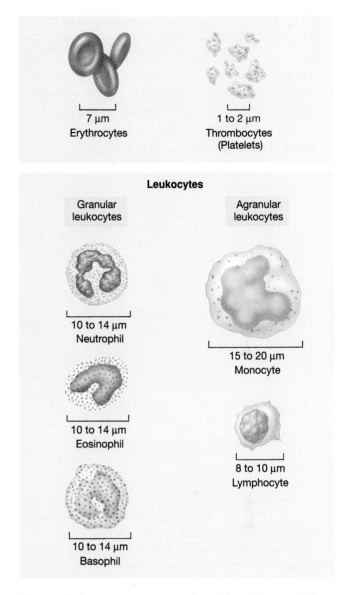

Figure 42–4 Components of vertebrate blood. The principal varieties of blood cells in the circulating blood are illustrated.

be separated from plasma by the process of centrifugation. Plasma does not separate from blood cells in the body because the blood is constantly mixed as it circulates in the blood vessels.

Plasma Is the Fluid Component of Blood

Plasma is composed of water (about 92%), proteins (about 7%), salts, and a variety of materials being transported, such as dissolved gases, nutrients, wastes, and hormones. Plasma is in dynamic equilibrium with the interstitial fluid bathing the cells and with the intracellular fluid within the cells. As blood passes through the capillaries, substances constantly move into and out of the plasma. Changes in its composition initiate re-

Table 42–1 CELLULAR COMPONENTS OF BLOOD

	Normal Range	*Function*	*Pathology*
Red blood cells	Male: 4.2–5.4 million/μL Female: 3.6–5.0 million/μL	Oxygen transport; carbon dioxide transport	Too few: anemia Too many: polycythemia
Platelets	150,000–400,000/μL	Essential for clotting	Clotting malfunctions; bleeding; easy bruising
White blood cells (total)	5000–10,000/μL		
Neutrophils	About 60% of WBCs	Phagocytosis	Too many: may be due to bacterial infection, inflammation, leukemia (myelogenous)
Eosinophils	1–3% of WBCs	Some role in allergic response	Too many: may result from allergic reaction, parasitic infestation
Basophils	1% of WBCs	May play role in prevention of clotting in body	
Lymphocytes	25–35% of WBCs	Produce antibodies; destroy foreign cells	Atypical lymphocytes present in infectious mononucleosis; too many may be due to leukemia (lymphocytic), certain viral infections
Monocytes	6% of WBCs	Differentiate to form macrophages	May increase in monocytic leukemia and fungal infections

sponses on the part of one or more organs of the body to restore its normal steady state.

Plasma contains several kinds of proteins, each with specific properties and functions: fibrinogen; alpha, beta, and gamma globulins; albumin; and lipoproteins. Fibrinogen is one of the proteins involved in the clotting process. When the proteins involved in blood clotting have been removed from the plasma, the remaining liquid is called serum. The gamma globulin fraction contains many types of antibodies that provide immunity to diseases, such as measles and infectious hepatitis. Purified human gamma globulin is sometimes used to treat certain diseases, or to reduce the possibility of contracting a disease. Albumins and globulins help to regulate fluid balance.

Plasma proteins are too large to pass readily through the walls of blood vessels and thus can exert an osmotic pressure, which is important in maintaining an appropriate blood volume. These proteins therefore play a necessary role in regulating the distribution of fluid between plasma and tissue fluid. Plasma proteins (along with the hemoglobin in the red blood cells) are also important acid-base buffers, helping to keep the pH of the blood within a narrow range—at its normal, slightly alkaline pH of 7.4.

Lipoproteins in the blood transport triacylglycerols (triglycerides) and cholesterol. **High-density lipoprotein (HDL)** is thought to prevent cholesterol from clogging the walls of arteries. **Low-density lipoprotein (LDL)** contains a large amount of cholesterol and has been associated with deposit of cholesterol in the arterial wall (atherosclerosis).

Red Blood Cells Transport Oxygen

Erythrocytes, also called **red blood cells (RBCs),** are highly specialized for transporting oxygen. In all vertebrates except mammals, erythrocytes have nuclei. During development of an erythrocyte in a mammal, the nucleus is pushed out of the cell. Each mammalian erythrocyte is a flexible, biconcave disc, 7 to 8 μm in diameter and 1 to 2 μm thick. An internal elastic framework maintains the disc shape and permits the cell to bend and twist as it passes through blood vessels even smaller than its own diameter. In a human, about 30 trillion erythrocytes circulate in the blood—approximately 5.4 million per cubic millimeter (mm^3) in an adult male, 5 million per mm^3 in an adult female.

Erythrocytes are produced within the red bone marrow of certain bones (the vertebrae, ribs, breast bone, skull bones, and long bones). As an erythrocyte develops, it produces great quantities of **hemoglobin,** the oxygen-transporting pigment that gives vertebrate blood its red color. (Oxygen transport is discussed in Chapter 44.) The life span of a human erythrocyte is about 120 days. As blood circulates through the liver and spleen, phagocytic cells remove worn-out erythrocytes from the circulation. These erythrocytes are then disassembled, and some of their components are recycled. In the human body, 2.4 million RBCs are destroyed every second, so an equal number must be produced in the bone marrow to replace them.

Anemia is a deficiency in hemoglobin (often accompanied by a decrease in the number of RBCs). When the amount of hemoglobin is insufficient, the amount of oxygen transported is inadequate to supply the body's needs. An anemic person may complain of feeling weak and may become easily fatigued. Three general causes of anemia are (1) loss of blood due to hemorrhage or internal bleeding, (2) decreased production of hemoglobin or red blood cells as in iron deficiency anemia, and (3) increased rate of RBC destruction—the **hemolytic anemias** such as sickle cell anemia.

White Blood Cells Defend the Body against Disease Organisms

The **leukocytes,** or **white blood cells (WBCs),** are specialized to defend the body against harmful bacteria and other microorganisms. Leukocytes are amoeba-like cells, capable of independent movement. They can move against the current of the bloodstream, and some types routinely slip through the walls of blood vessels and enter the tissues. Human blood contains five kinds of leukocytes, which may be classified as either granular or agranular (Figure 42–4).

The **granular leukocytes** are manufactured in the red bone marrow. These cells are characterized by large distinctive granules in their cytoplasm and lobed nuclei. The three varieties of granular leukocytes are the neutrophils, eosinophils, and basophils. **Neutrophils,** the principal phagocytic cells in the blood, are especially adept at seeking out and ingesting bacteria. They also phagocytize the remains of dead tissue cells, a clean-up task that must be performed after injury or infection. Most of the granules in neutrophils contain enzymes that digest ingested material. **Eosinophils** have large granules that stain bright red with eosin, an acidic dye. These cells increase in number during allergic reactions and during parasitic (e.g., tapeworm) infestations. **Basophils** exhibit deep blue granules when stained with basic dyes. Like eosinophils, these cells are thought to play a role in allergic reactions. Basophils contain large amounts of **histamine,** which they release in injured tissues and in allergic responses. Because

they contain the anticlotting chemical **heparin,** basophils may play a role in preventing blood from clotting inappropriately within the blood vessels.

Agranular leukocytes lack large distinctive granules, and their nuclei are rounded or kidney-shaped. Two types of agranular leukocytes are lymphocytes and monocytes. Some **lymphocytes** are specialized to produce antibodies, whereas others attack foreign invaders such as bacteria or viruses directly. Just how they manage these feats is discussed in the next chapter.

Monocytes are the largest WBCs, reaching 20 μm in diameter. They are manufactured in the bone marrow. After circulating in the blood for about 24 hours, a monocyte leaves the circulation and completes its development in the tissues. The monocyte greatly enlarges and becomes a **macrophage,** a giant scavenger cell. All of the macrophages found in the tissues develop in this way. Macrophages voraciously engulf bacteria, dead cells, and debris.

In human blood there are normally about 7000 WBCs per mm^3 of blood (only one for every 700 RBCs). During bacterial infections the number may rise sharply, so that a WBC count is a useful diagnostic tool. The proportion of each kind of WBC is determined by a differential WBC count. The normal distribution of leukocytes is indicated in Table 42–1.

Leukemia is a form of cancer in which any one of the kinds of white cells multiplies rapidly within the bone marrow. Many of these cells do not mature, and their large numbers crowd out developing RBCs and platelets, leading to anemia and impaired clotting. A common cause of death from leukemia is internal hemorrhaging, especially in the brain. Another frequent cause of death is infection. Although the white cell count may rise dramatically, the cells are immature and abnormal and cannot defend the body against disease organisms. Although no cure for leukemia has been discovered, radiation treatment and therapy with antimitotic drugs can induce partial or complete remissions lasting 15 years or longer in some patients.

Platelets Function in Blood Clotting

In most vertebrates other than mammals, the blood contains small, oval cells called **thrombocytes,** which have nuclei. In mammals thrombocytes are tiny spherical or disc-shaped bits of cytoplasm that lack a nucleus. They are usually referred to as blood **platelets.** About 300,000 platelets per microliter are present in human blood. Platelets are formed from bits of cytoplasm that are pinched off from very large cells (megakaryocytes) in the bone marrow. Thus, a platelet is not a whole cell but a fragment of cytoplasm enclosed by a membrane.

Platelets play an important role in **hemostasis** (the control of bleeding). When a blood vessel is cut, it constricts, reducing loss of blood. Platelets stick to the

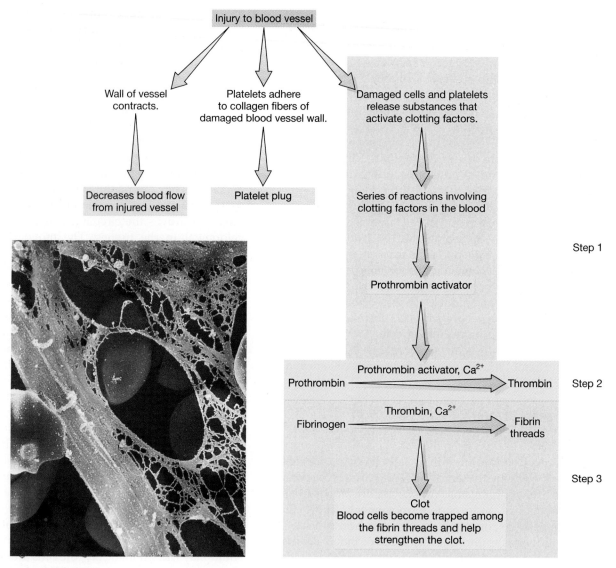

Figure 42–5   Overview of blood clotting. Inse.: Scanning electron micrograph of part of a blood clot, showing red blood cells enmeshed in a network of fibrin.   (SEM by Lennart Nilsson © Boehringer Ingelheim International GmbH)

rough, cut edges of the vessel, physically patching the break in the wall. As platelets begin to gather, they release ADP, which attracts other platelets. Within about 5 minutes after injury a complete platelet patch, or temporary clot, has formed.

At the same time that the temporary clot forms, a stronger, more permanent clot begins to develop. More than 30 different chemical substances interact in this very complex process. The series of reactions that leads to clotting is triggered when one of the clotting factors in the blood is activated by contact with the injured tissue. In **hemophiliacs** (persons with "bleeder's disease") one of the clotting factors is absent as a result of an inherited genetic mutation. The clotting process is summarized in Figure 42–5.

Prothrombin, a plasma protein manufactured in the liver, requires vitamin K for its production. In the presence of clotting factors, calcium ions, and compounds released from platelets, prothrombin is converted to **thrombin.** Then thrombin catalyzes the conversion of the soluble plasma protein **fibrinogen** to an insoluble protein, **fibrin.** Once formed, fibrin polymerizes, producing long threads that stick to the damaged surface of the blood vessel and form the webbing of the clot. These threads trap blood cells and platelets, which help to strengthen the clot.

VERTEBRATES HAVE THREE MAIN TYPES OF BLOOD VESSELS

The vertebrate circulatory system includes three main types of blood vessels: arteries, capillaries, and veins (Figure 42–6). An **artery** carries blood away from the

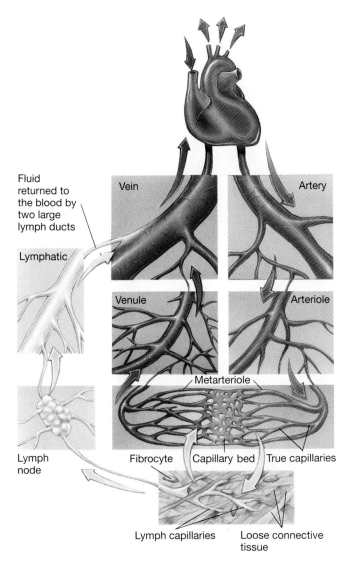

Fluid returned to the blood by two large lymph ducts

Lymphatic

Lymph node

Vein

Venule

Metarteriole

Fibrocyte   Capillary bed   True capillaries

Lymph capillaries

Artery

Arteriole

Loose connective tissue

Figure 42–6   Types of blood vessels and their relationships to one another. Lymphatic vessels return interstitial fluid to the blood by way of ducts that lead into large veins in the shoulder region. Red and blue arrows indicate the direction of blood flow. Yellow arrows indicate flow of interstitial fluid and lymph.

The walls of arteries and veins are thick, which prevents gases and nutrients from passing through them. Materials are exchanged between the blood and tissue fluid bathing the cells through the capillary walls, which are only one cell thick (Figure 42–7). Capillary networks in the body are so extensive that at least one of these tiny vessels is located close to almost every cell in the body. The total length of all capillaries in the body has been estimated to be more than 60,000 miles.

Smooth muscle in the arteriole wall can constrict (vasoconstriction) or relax (vasodilatation), changing the radius of the arteriole. Such changes help maintain appropriate blood pressure and can help control the volume of blood passing to a particular tissue. Changes in blood flow are regulated by the nervous system in response to the metabolic needs of the tissue, as well as by the demands of the body as a whole. For example, when a tissue is metabolizing rapidly, it needs a greater supply of nutrients and oxygen. During exercise, arterioles within the muscles dilate, increasing by more than tenfold the amount of blood flowing to the muscle cells.

If all the blood vessels were dilated at the same time, there would not be sufficient blood to fill them completely. Normally the liver, kidneys, and brain receive the lion's share of the blood. However, if an emergency suddenly occurred requiring rapid action, the blood would be rerouted quickly in favor of the heart and muscles. This would enable rapid, effective action. At such a time the digestive system and kidneys can do with less blood, for they are not critical in responding to the crisis.

The small vessels that directly link arterioles with venules (small veins) are **metarterioles.** The so-called true capillaries branch off from the metarterioles and then rejoin them (Figure 42–8). True capillaries also interconnect with one another. Wherever a capillary branches from a metarteriole, a smooth muscle cell called a precapillary sphincter is present. These sphincters can open or close to regulate passage of blood. Precapillary sphincters open and close continuously, directing blood first to one and then to another section of tissue. These sphincters also (along with the smooth muscle in the walls of arteries and arterioles) regulate the blood supply to each organ and its subdivisions (Figure 42–8).

THE EVOLUTION OF THE VERTEBRATE HEART CULMINATED IN A FOUR-CHAMBERED HEART AND CIRCULATION THROUGH A DOUBLE CIRCUIT OF VESSELS

The vertebrate heart consists of one or two **atria,** chambers that receive blood returning from the tissues, and one or two **ventricles,** chambers that pump blood into

heart, toward other tissues. When an artery enters an organ, it divides into many smaller branches called **arterioles.** The arterioles deliver blood into the microscopic **capillaries.** After coursing through an organ, capillaries eventually merge to form **veins** that transport the blood back toward the heart. Because this basic plan is similar in all vertebrates, much can be learned about the human circulatory system by dissecting an animal such as a shark or a frog.

The blood vessel wall has three layers (Figure 42–7). The innermost layer (tunica intima), which lines the blood vessel, consists mainly of endothelium, a tissue that resembles squamous epithelium. The middle layer (tunica media) consists of connective tissue and smooth muscle cells, and the outer layer (tunica adventitia) is composed of connective tissue rich in elastic and collagen fibers.

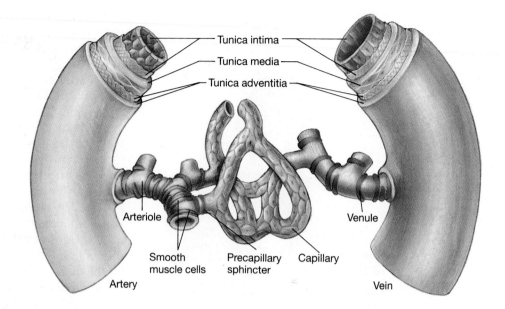

Figure 42–7 Blood vessel structure. Comparison of the three-layered walls of an artery and a vein with the one-cell-thick capillary wall.

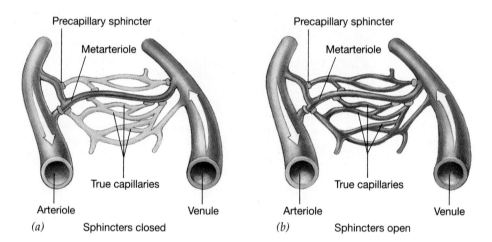

Figure 42–8 Changes in blood flow through a capillary bed as the tissue becomes active. (*a*) When the tissue is inactive, only the metarterioles are open. (*b*) When the tissue becomes active, the decreased oxygen tension in the tissue brings about a relaxation of the precapillary sphincters, and the capillaries open. This increases the blood supply and the delivery of oxygen to the active tissue.

the arteries. Additional chambers are present in some animals. Surveying the vertebrates, we find an evolutionary progression from the relatively simple heart and single-circuit circulation of fish to the complex four-chambered heart and double-circuit circulation of birds and mammals (Figure 42–9).

The Fish Heart Has a Single Atrium and Single Ventricle

Because it has only one atrium and one ventricle, the fish heart can be described as a two-chambered heart. Actually, two accessory chambers are present. A thin-walled **sinus venosus** receives blood returning from the tissues and pumps it into the atrium. The atrium then contracts, sending blood into the ventricle. The ventri-

cle in turn pumps the blood into an elastic **conus arteriosus** (or simply conus), which does not contract. These four compartments are separated by valves that prevent blood from flowing backward. From the conus, blood flows into a large artery, the ventral aorta, which branches to distribute blood to the gills. Because blood must pass through the capillaries of the gills before flowing to the other tissues of the body, blood pressure is low through most of the system. This low-pressure circulatory system permits only a low rate of metabolism in the fish.

Amphibians Have a Three-Chambered Heart

The three-chambered amphibian heart consists of two atria and a ventricle. A thin-walled sinus venosus col-

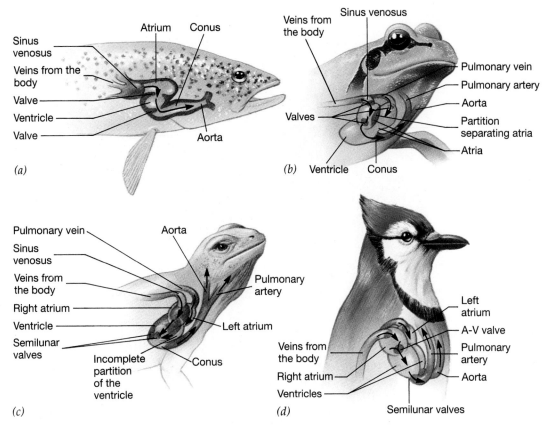

Figure 42–9 The evolution of the vertebrate heart. (*a*) In the fish heart there is one atrium and one ventricle. (*b*) The amphibian heart consists of two atria and one ventricle. (*c*) The reptilian heart has two atria and two ventricles, but the wall separating the ventricles is incomplete so that blood from the right and left chambers mixes to some extent. (*d*) Birds and mammals have two atria and two ventricles, and blood rich in oxygen is kept completely separate from oxygen-poor blood.

lects blood returning from the veins and pumps it into the right atrium. Blood returning from the lungs passes directly into the left atrium. Both atria pump blood into the single ventricle. In the frog heart, oxygen-rich and oxygen-poor blood are kept somewhat separate. Oxygen-poor blood is pumped out of the ventricle first and passes into the tubular conus arteriosus, which has a spiral fold that helps to separate the blood. Much of the oxygen-poor blood is directed to the lungs and skin, where it can be charged with oxygen. Oxygenated blood is delivered into arteries, which conduct it to the various tissues of the body.

In the Reptilian Heart the Wall between the Ventricles Is Incomplete

Although the reptilian heart consists of two atria and two ventricles, the wall between the ventricles is incomplete, so some mixing of oxygen-rich and oxygen-poor blood occurs. Mixing is minimized by the timing of contractions of the left and right sides of the heart and by pressure differences. In the crocodile, the wall between the ventricles is complete so that the heart consists of four separate chambers.

Birds and Mammals Have a Four-Chambered Heart

The hearts of birds and mammals have completely separate right and left sides. The wall between the ventricles is complete, preventing the mixture of oxygen-rich blood in the left side with oxygen-poor blood in the right side. The conus has split and become the base of the aorta and pulmonary artery. No sinus venosus is present as a separate chamber (although a vestige remains as the sinoatrial node, or pacemaker, described later in the chapter).

Complete separation of right and left hearts makes it necessary for blood to pass through the heart twice each time it circulates through the body. As a result, blood in the aorta of birds and mammals contains more oxygen than that in the aorta of the lower vertebrates.

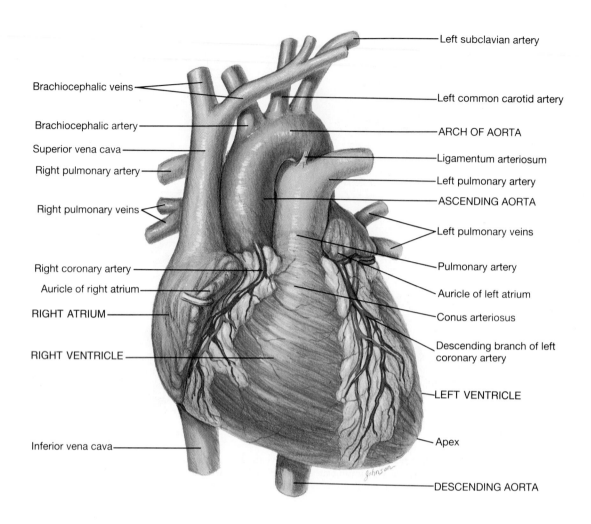

Left subclavian artery

Brachiocephalic veins

Left common carotid artery

Brachiocephalic artery

ARCH OF AORTA

Superior vena cava

Ligamentum arteriosum

Right pulmonary artery

Left pulmonary artery

ASCENDING AORTA

Right pulmonary veins

Left pulmonary veins

Right coronary artery

Pulmonary artery

Auricle of right atrium

Auricle of left atrium

RIGHT ATRIUM

Conus arteriosus

RIGHT VENTRICLE

Descending branch of left coronary artery

LEFT VENTRICLE

Inferior vena cava

Apex

DESCENDING AORTA

(a)

Figure 42–10   The human heart. (a) Anterior view. Note the coronary blood vessels that bring blood to and from the heart muscle itself. (b) Posterior view (*facing page*).

Hence, the tissues of the body receive more oxygen, a higher metabolic rate can be maintained, and the endothermic condition is possible. Birds and mammals can maintain a constant, high body temperature even in cold surroundings.

The pattern of blood circulation in birds and mammals may be summarized as follows:

veins (conduct blood from organs) → right atrium → right ventricle → one of the pulmonary arteries → capillaries in the lung → one of the pulmonary veins → left atrium → left ventricle → aorta → arteries (conduct blood to organs) → capillaries

THE HUMAN HEART IS MARVELOUSLY ADAPTED FOR PUMPING BLOOD

Not much bigger than a fist and weighing less than a pound, the human **heart** is a remarkable organ that

beats about 2.5 billion times in an average lifetime, pumping about 300 million liters (80 million gallons) of blood (Figure 42–10). To meet the body's changing needs, it can vary its output from 5 to more than 20 liters of blood per minute.

The heart is a hollow, muscular organ located in the chest cavity directly under the breastbone. Enclosing it is a tough connective tissue sac, the **pericardium.** The inner surface of the pericardium and the outer surface of the heart are covered by a smooth layer of epithelium-type cells. Between these two surfaces is a small **pericardial cavity** filled with fluid, which reduces friction to a minimum as the heart beats.

The wall of the heart is composed mainly of cardiac muscle attached to a framework of collagen fibers. The right atrium and ventricle are separated from the left atrium and ventricle by a wall, or **septum** (Figure 42–11). Between the atria the wall is known as the **interatrial septum;** between the ventricles it is the **interventricular septum.** On the interatrial septum a shallow

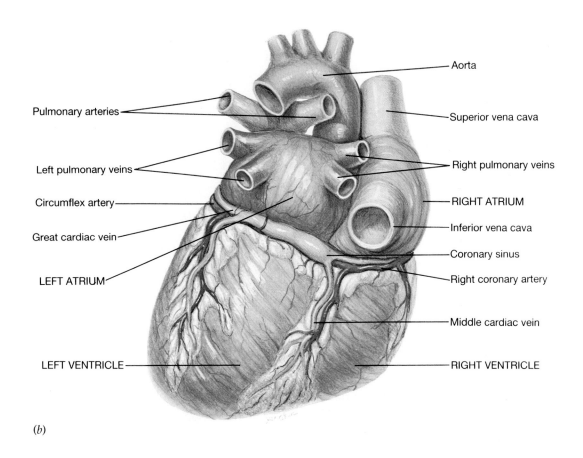

Aorta

Pulmonary arteries

Left pulmonary veins

Circumflex artery

Great cardiac vein

LEFT ATRIUM

LEFT VENTRICLE

Superior vena cava

Right pulmonary veins

RIGHT ATRIUM

Inferior vena cava

Coronary sinus

Right coronary artery

Middle cardiac vein

RIGHT VENTRICLE

(b)

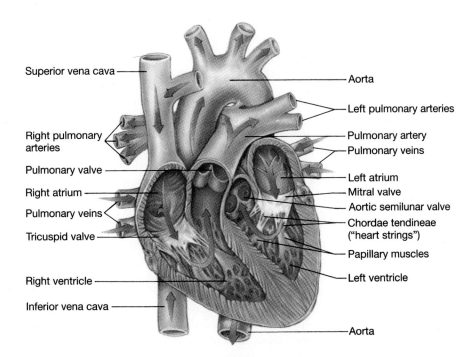

Superior vena cava

Right pulmonary arteries

Pulmonary valve

Right atrium

Pulmonary veins

Tricuspid valve

Right ventricle

Inferior vena cava

Aorta

Left pulmonary arteries

Pulmonary artery

Pulmonary veins

Left atrium

Mitral valve

Aortic semilunar valve

Chordae tendineae ("heart strings")

Papillary muscles

Left ventricle

Aorta

Figure 42–11   Section through the human heart showing chambers, valves, and connecting blood vessels.   (From Guyton, Arthur C., *Textbook of Medical Physiology*, Philadelphia, W. B. Saunders, 1986)

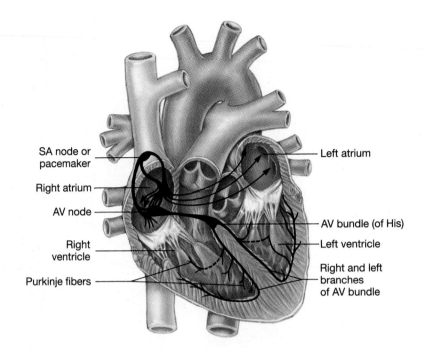

Figure 42–12 The conduction system of the heart. The SA node initiates each heart beat. The action potential spreads through the muscle fibers of the atria, producing atrial contraction. Transmission is briefly delayed at the AV node. Then, the action potential spreads through the AV bundle into the ventricles.

depression, the **fossa ovalis,** marks the place where an opening, the **foramen ovale,** was located in the fetal heart. In the fetus, the foramen ovale permits the blood to move directly from right to left atrium so that very little blood passes to the nonfunctional lungs. At the upper surface of each atrium lies a small muscular pouch called an **auricle.**

To prevent blood from flowing backward, the heart is equipped with valves that close automatically. The valve between the right atrium and ventricle is called the **right atrioventricular (AV) valve** (also known as the tricuspid valve). The left AV valve is referred to as the **mitral valve.** The AV valves are held in place by stout cords, or "heart-strings," the **chordae tendineae.** These cords attach the valves to the **papillary muscles** that project from the walls of the ventricles.

When blood returning from the tissues fills the atria, blood pressure on the AV valves forces them to open into the ventricles. Blood then fills the ventricles. As the ventricles contract, blood is forced back against the AV valves, pushing them closed. Contraction of the papillary muscles and tensing of the chordae tendineae prevent them from opening backward into the atria. These valves are like swinging doors that can open in only one direction.

Semilunar valves (named for their flaps, which are shaped like half-moons) guard the exits from the heart. The semilunar valve between the left ventricle and the aorta is known as the **aortic valve,** and the one between the right ventricle and the pulmonary artery as the **pulmonary valve.** When blood passes out of the ventricle, the flaps of the semilunar valve are pushed aside and offer no resistance to blood flow. But when the ventricles are relaxing and filling with blood from the atria,

the blood pressure in the arteries is higher than that in the ventricles. Blood then fills the pouches of the valves, stretching them across the artery so that blood cannot flow back into the ventricle.

Valve deformities are sometimes present at birth or may result from certain diseases such as rheumatic fever or syphilis. As a consequence of inflammation and scarring, valves may be thickened so that the passageway for blood is narrowed. Sometimes the valve tissues are eroded so that the flaps cannot close tightly, causing blood to leak backward and reducing the efficiency of the heartbeat. Diseased valves can now be surgically replaced with artificial valves.

Each Heartbeat Is Initiated by a Pacemaker

Horror films frequently feature a scene in which a heart cut out of the body of its owner continues to beat. Scriptwriters of these tales actually have some factual basis for their gruesome fantasies, for when carefully removed from the body, the heart does continue to beat for many hours if kept in a nutritive, oxygenated fluid. This is possible because the contractions of cardiac muscle begin within the muscle itself and can occur independently of any nerve supply.

A specialized conduction system ensures that the heart beats in a regular and effective rhythm. Each beat is initiated by the pacemaker, called the **sinoatrial (SA) node** (Figure 42–12). The SA node is a small mass of specialized cardiac muscle in the posterior wall of the right atrium near the opening of a large vein, the superior vena cava. Ends of the SA node fibers fuse with surrounding ordinary atrial muscle fibers so that the

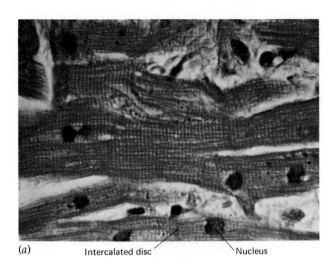

(a)   Intercalated disc   Nucleus

(b)   Intercalated discs

Figure 42–13   Cardiac muscle. (*a*) Cardiac muscle as seen with the light microscope. (*b*) An electron micrograph of cardiac

muscle; A, A band; Z, z line; M, mitochondrion; ID, intercalated disc.   (*b*, Courtesy of Dr. Lyle C. Dearden)

action potential spreads through both atria, producing atrial contraction.

One group of atrial muscle fibers conducts the action potential directly to the **atrioventricular (AV) node,** located in the right atrium along the lower part of the septum. Here transmission is delayed briefly, permitting the atria to complete their contraction before the ventricles begin to contract. From the AV node the action potential spreads into specialized muscle fibers called **Purkinje fibers.** These large fibers make up the **atrioventricular (AV) bundle.** The AV bundle then divides, sending branches into each ventricle. When an impulse reaches the ends of the Purkinje fibers, it spreads through the ordinary cardiac muscle fibers of the ventricles.

At their ends cardiac muscle cells are joined by dense bands called **intercalated discs** (Figure 42–13). Each disc is a type of gap junction (see Chapter 5) in which two cells overlap slightly. This type of junction is of great physiological importance because it offers very little resistance to the passage of an action potential. Ions move easily through the gap junctions, allowing the entire atrial (or ventricular) muscle mass to contract as one giant cell.

Each minute the heart beats about 70 times. One complete heartbeat takes about 0.8 second and is referred to as a **cardiac cycle.** That portion of the cycle in which contraction occurs is known as **systole;** the period of relaxation is **diastole.** Figure 42–14 shows the sequence of events that occur during one cardiac cycle.

You can measure your heart rate by placing a finger over the radial artery in the wrist or the carotid artery in

the neck and counting the pulsations. Arterial **pulse** is the alternate expansion and recoil of an artery. Each time the left ventricle pumps blood into the aorta, the elastic wall of the aorta expands to accommodate the blood. This expansion moves in a wave down the aorta and the arteries that branch from it. When the wave passes, the elastic arterial wall snaps back to its normal size.

Two Main Heart Sounds Can Be Distinguished

When you listen to the heartbeat with a stethoscope you can hear two main heart sounds, lub-dup, which repeat rhythmically. The first heart sound, lub, is low-pitched, not very loud, and fairly long-lasting. It is caused mainly by the closing of the AV valves and marks the beginning of ventricular systole. The lub sound is quickly followed by the higher-pitched, louder, sharper, and shorter dup sound. Heard almost as a quick snap, the dup marks the closing of the semilunar valves and the beginning of ventricular diastole.

The quality of these sounds tells a discerning physician much about the state of the valves. When the semilunar valves are injured, a soft hissing noise ("lub-shhh") is heard in place of the normal sound. This is known as a **heart murmur** and may be caused by any injury that has affected the valves so that they do not close tightly, permitting blood to flow backward into the ventricles during diastole.

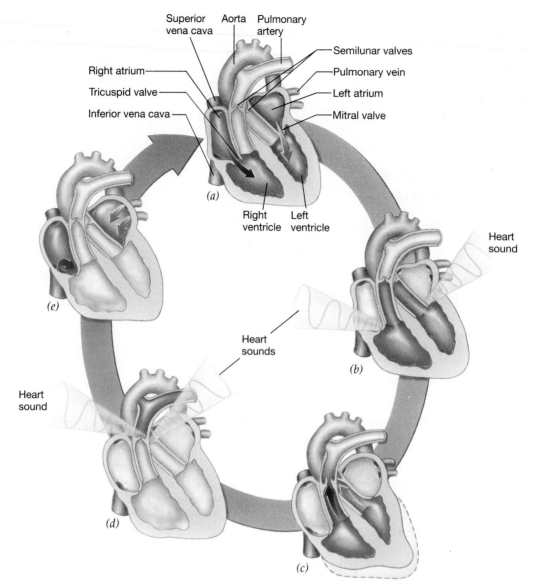

Figure 42–14 The cardiac cycle. Arrows indicate the direction of blood flow; dotted lines indicate the change in size as contraction occurs. (*a*) Atrial systole: Atria contract, and blood is pushed through the open tricuspid (right AV) and mitral valves into the ventricles. The semilunar valves are closed. (*b*) Beginning of ventricular systole: Ventricles begin to contract, and pressure within the ventricles increases and closes the tricuspid and mitral valves, causing the first heart sound. (*c*) Period of rising pressure. (*d*) The semilunar valves open when the pressure within the ventricle exceeds that in the arteries, and blood spurts into the aorta and pulmonary artery. At the beginning of ventricular diastole, the pressure in the relaxing ventricles drops below that in the arteries. The semilunar valves snap shut, causing the second heart sound. (*e*) Period of falling pressure: Blood flows from the veins into the relaxed atria. The tricuspid and mitral valves open when the pressure in the ventricles falls below that in the atria; blood then flows into the ventricles.

The Electrical Activity of the Heart Can Be Recorded

As each wave of contraction spreads through the heart, electrical currents spread into the tissues surrounding the heart and onto the body surface. By placing electrodes on the body surface on opposite sides of the heart, the electrical activity can be amplified and recorded by either an oscilloscope or an electrocardio-graph. The written record produced is called an **electro-cardiogram** (**ECG** or **EKG**). Malfunctioning of the heart causes abnormal action currents, which in turn produce an abnormal ECG.

Cardiac Output Varies with the Body's Need

The volume of blood pumped by one ventricle during one beat is called the **stroke volume.** By multiplying the

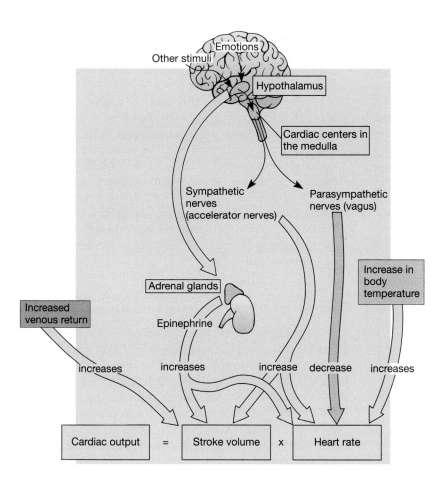

Figure 42–15 Some factors that influence cardiac output.

stroke volume by the number of times the ventricle beats per minute, the **cardiac output** can be computed. In other words, the cardiac output is the volume of blood pumped by one ventricle in 1 minute. For example, in a resting adult the heart may beat about 72 times per minute and pump about 70 mL of blood with each contraction.

cardiac output = stroke volume × heart rate

(number of ventricular contractions per minute)

= 70 mL/stroke × 72 strokes/minute

= 5040 mL/min (about 5 liters/min)

The cardiac output varies dramatically with the changing needs of the body. During stress or heavy exercise, the normal heart can increase its cardiac output fourfold to fivefold, so that 20 to 30 liters of blood can be pumped per minute. Cardiac output varies with changes in either stroke volume or heart rate.

Stroke Volume Depends on Venous Return

Stroke volume depends mainly upon venous return, the amount of blood delivered to the heart by the veins.

According to **Starling's law of the heart,** the greater the amount of blood delivered to the heart by the veins, the more blood the heart pumps (within physiological limits). When extra amounts of blood fill the heart chambers, the cardiac muscle fibers are stretched to a greater extent and contract with greater force, pumping a larger volume of blood into the arteries. This increase in stroke volume increases the cardiac output (Figure 42–15).

The release of norepinephrine by sympathetic nerves also increases the force of contraction of the cardiac muscle fibers. Epinephrine released by the adrenal glands during stress has a similar effect on the heart muscle. When the force of contraction increases, the stroke volume increases, and this in turn increases cardiac output.

Heart Rate Is Regulated by the Nervous System

Although the heart is capable of beating independently of its control systems, its rate is, in fact, carefully regulated by the nervous system (Figure 42–15). Sensory receptors in the walls of certain blood vessels and heart chambers are sensitive to changes in blood pressure.

When stimulated, they send messages to **cardiac centers** in the medulla of the brain. These cardiac centers maintain control over two sets of autonomic nerves that pass to the SA node. Sympathetic nerves release norepinephrine, which speeds the heart rate and increases the strength of contraction. Parasympathetic nerves release acetylcholine, which slows the heart and decreases the force of each contraction.

Hormones also influence heart rate. During stress, the adrenal glands release epinephrine and norepinephrine, which speed the heart. An elevated body temperature can greatly increase heart rate; during fever, the heart may beat more than 100 times per minute. As you might expect, heart rate decreases when body temperature is lowered. This is why a patient's temperature may be deliberately lowered during heart surgery.

BLOOD PRESSURE DEPENDS ON BLOOD FLOW AND RESISTANCE TO BLOOD FLOW

Blood pressure is the force exerted by the blood against the inner walls of the blood vessels. It is determined by the blood flow and the resistance to that flow. Blood flow depends directly upon the pumping action of the heart. When cardiac output increases, blood flow increases, causing a rise in blood pressure. When cardiac output decreases, blood flow decreases, causing a fall in blood pressure. The volume of blood flowing through the system also affects blood pressure. If blood volume is reduced by hemorrhage or by chronic bleeding, the blood pressure drops. On the other hand, an increase in blood volume results in an increase in blood pressure. For example, a high dietary intake of salt causes water retention. This results in an increase of blood volume and leads to higher blood pressure.

Blood flow is impeded by resistance; when the resistance to flow increases, blood pressure rises. **Peripheral resistance** is the resistance to blood flow caused by viscosity of the blood and by friction between the blood and the wall of the blood vessel. In the blood of a healthy person, viscosity remains fairly constant and is only a minor factor influencing changes in blood pressure. More important is the friction between the blood and the wall of the blood vessel. The length and diameter of a blood vessel determine the surface area of the vessel in contact with the blood. The length of a blood vessel does not change, but the diameter, especially of an arteriole, does. A small change in the diameter of a blood vessel causes a big change in blood pressure.

Blood pressure in arteries rises during systole and falls during diastole. Normal blood pressure (measured in the upper arm) for a young male adult is about 120/80 millimeters of mercury, abbreviated mm Hg, as measured by the sphygmomanometer. Systolic pressure is indicated by the numerator, diastolic by the denominator.

When the diastolic pressure consistently measures more than 95 mm Hg, the patient may be suffering from high blood pressure, or **hypertension.** In hypertension, there is usually increased vascular resistance, especially in the arterioles and small arteries. Workload of the heart is increased because it must pump against this increased resistance. As a result, the left ventricle increases in size and may begin to deteriorate in function. Heredity, obesity, and possibly high dietary salt intake are thought to be important factors in the development of hypertension.

Blood Pressure Is Highest in Arteries

As you might guess, blood pressure is greatest in the large arteries and decreases as blood flows away from the heart and through the smaller arteries and capillaries (Figure 42–16). By the time blood enters the veins, its pressure is very low, even approaching zero. Flow rate can be maintained in veins at low pressure because they are low-resistance vessels. Their diameter is larger than that of corresponding arteries, and there is little smooth muscle in their walls. Flow of blood through veins depends upon several factors, including muscular movement, which compresses veins. Most veins larger than 2 mm (0.08 inch) in diameter that conduct blood against the force of gravity are equipped with valves that prevent backflow of blood (Figure 42–17). Such valves usually consist of two cusps formed by inward extensions of the wall of the vein.

When a person stands perfectly still for a long time, as when a soldier stands at attention, blood tends to pool in the veins. This is so because when fully distended with blood, the veins can accept no more blood from the capillaries. Pressure in the capillaries increases, and large amounts of plasma are forced out of the circulation through the thin capillary walls. Within just a few minutes, as much as 20% of the blood volume can be lost from the circulation in this way—with drastic effect. Arterial blood pressure falls dramatically, so that blood flow to the brain is reduced. Sometimes the resulting lack of oxygen in the brain causes fainting, a protective response aimed at increasing blood supply to the brain. Lifting a person who has fainted to an upright position can result in circulatory shock and even death.

Blood Pressure Is Carefully Regulated

Each time you get up from a horizontal position, changes occur in your blood pressure. Several complex mechanisms interact to maintain normal blood pressure

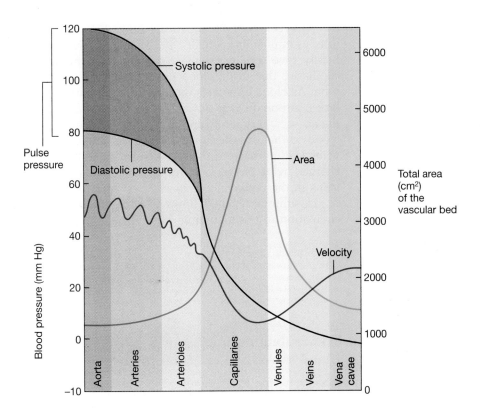

Figure 42–16 Blood pressure in different types of blood vessels of the body. The systolic and diastolic variations in arterial blood pressures are shown. Note that the venous pressure drops below zero (below atmospheric pressure) near the heart.

so that you do not faint when you get out of bed each morning or change position during the day. When blood pressure falls, sympathetic nerves to the blood vessels stimulate vasoconstriction so that pressure rises again.

The **baroreceptors** present in the walls of certain arteries and in the heart wall are sensitive to changes in blood pressure. When an increase in blood pressure stretches the baroreceptors, messages are sent to the cardiac and vasomotor centers in the medulla of the brain. This center stimulates parasympathetic nerves that slow the heart, lowering blood pressure. The vasomotor center inhibits sympathetic nerves that constrict arterioles, thereby lowering blood pressure. These neural reflexes act continuously to maintain blood pressure.

Hormones are also involved in regulating blood pressure. The **angiotensins** are a group of hormones that act as powerful vasoconstrictors. The enzyme **renin** stimulates formation of angiotensins from a plasma protein. Renin is released by the kidneys in response to low blood pressure within the kidneys. The kidneys also act indirectly to maintain blood pressure by influencing blood volume. This is accomplished by hormonal regulation of the rate at which salt and water are excreted.

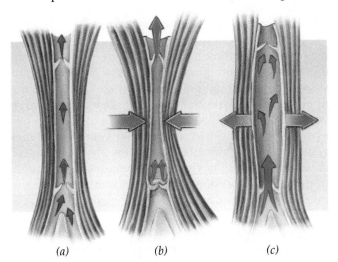

Figure 42–17 The action of skeletal muscles in moving blood through the veins. (*a*) Resting condition. (*b*) Muscles contract and bulge, compressing veins and forcing blood toward the heart. The lower valve prevents backflow. (*c*) Muscles relax, and the vein expands and fills with blood from below. The upper valve prevents backflow.

IN BIRDS AND MAMMALS BLOOD IS PUMPED THROUGH A PULMONARY AND A SYSTEMIC CIRCUIT

One of the main jobs of the circulation is to bring oxygen to all of the cells of the body. In humans, as in other mammals and in birds, blood is charged with oxygen in the lungs. Then it is returned to the heart to be pumped out into the arteries that deliver it to the other tissues

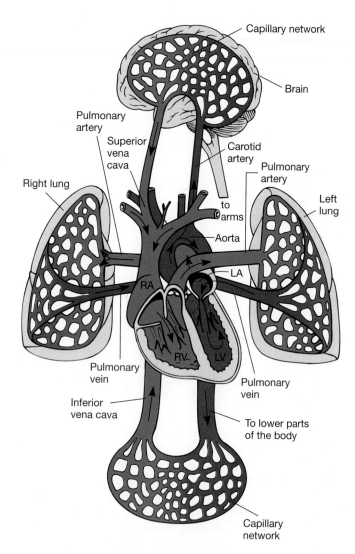

Figure 42–18 Highly simplified diagram showing the pattern of circulation through the systemic and pulmonary circuits. Red represents oxygen-rich blood; blue represents oxygen-poor blood.

and organs of the body. There is a double circuit of blood vessels—(1) the pulmonary circulation, which connects the heart and lungs, and (2) the systemic circulation, which connects the heart with all of the tissues of the body. This general pattern of circulation may be traced in Figure 42–18.

The Pulmonary Circulation Oxygenates the Blood

Blood from the tissues returns to the right atrium of the heart partly depleted of its oxygen supply. This oxygen-poor blood, loaded with carbon dioxide, is pumped by the right ventricle into the pulmonary circulation. As it emerges from the heart, the large pulmonary trunk branches to form the two pulmonary arteries, one going to each lung. These are the only arteries in the body that

carry oxygen-poor blood. In the lungs the pulmonary arteries branch into smaller and smaller vessels, which finally give rise to extensive networks of pulmonary capillaries that bring blood to all of the air sacs of the lung. As blood circulates through the pulmonary capillaries, carbon dioxide diffuses out of the blood and into the air sacs. Oxygen from the air sacs diffuses into the blood so that, by the time blood enters the pulmonary veins leading back to the left atrium of the heart, it is charged with oxygen. Pulmonary veins are the only veins in the body that carry blood rich in oxygen.

In summary, blood flows through the pulmonary circulation in the following sequence:

right atrium → right ventricle → pulmonary artery → pulmonary capillaries (in lung) → pulmonary vein → left atrium

The Systemic Circulation Delivers Blood to All of the Tissues

Blood entering the systemic circulation is pumped by the left ventricle into the **aorta,** the largest artery of the body. Arteries that branch off from the aorta conduct blood to all of the regions of the body. Some of the principal branches include the **coronary arteries** to the heart wall itself, the **carotid arteries** to the brain, the **subclavian arteries** to the shoulder region, the **mesenteric artery** to the intestine, the **renal arteries** to the kidneys, and the **iliac arteries** to the legs (Figure 42–19). Each of these arteries gives rise to smaller branches, which in turn give rise to smaller and smaller vessels, somewhat like branches of a tree that divide until they form tiny twigs. Eventually blood flows into the capillary network within each tissue or organ.

Blood returning from the capillary networks within the brain passes through the **jugular veins.** Blood from the shoulders and arms drains into the **subclavian veins.** These veins and others returning blood from the upper portion of the body merge to form a very large vein that empties blood into the right atrium. In humans this vein is called the **superior vena cava. Renal veins** from the kidneys, iliac veins from the lower limbs, **hepatic veins** from the liver, and other veins from the lower portion of the body return blood to the **inferior vena cava,** which delivers blood to the right atrium.

As an example of blood circulation through the systemic circuit, let us trace a drop of blood from the heart to the right leg and back to the heart:

left atrium → left ventricle → aorta → right common iliac artery → smaller arteries in leg → capillaries in leg → small vein in leg → common iliac vein → inferior vena cava → right atrium

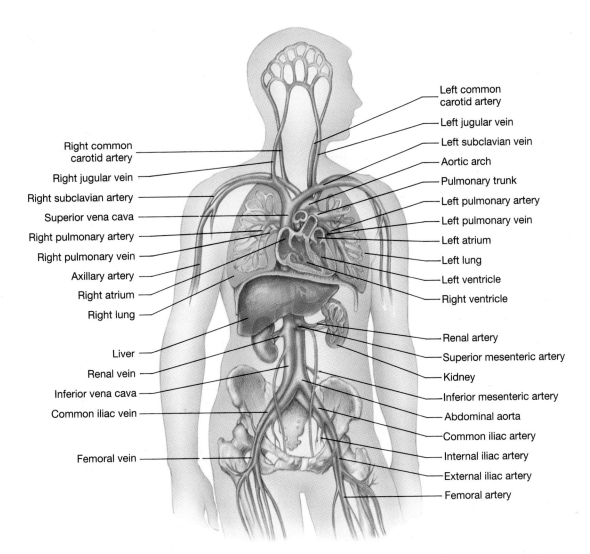

Figure 42–19   Circulation of blood through some of the principal arteries and veins of the human body. Blood vessels carrying oxygen-rich blood are red; those carrying oxygen-poor blood are blue.

The Coronary Circulation Delivers Blood to the Heart

The heart muscle is not nourished by the blood within its chambers because its walls are too thick for nutrients and oxygen to diffuse through them to all of the cells. Instead, the cardiac muscle is supplied by coronary arteries branching from the aorta at the point where that vessel leaves the heart. These arteries branch, giving rise to a network of blood vessels within the wall of the heart. Nutrients and gases are exchanged through the coronary capillaries. Blood from these capillaries flows into coronary veins, which join to form a large vein, the coronary sinus. The coronary sinus empties directly into the right atrium; it does not join either of the venae cavae.

When one of the coronary arteries is blocked, the cells in the area of the heart muscle served by that artery are deprived of oxygen and nutrients and die. The affected muscle stops contracting; if sufficient cardiac muscle is affected, the heart may stop beating entirely. This is a common cause of "heart attack" and is often the result of atherosclerosis (see Focus on Cardiovascular Disease).

Four Arteries Deliver Blood to the Brain

Four arteries—two internal carotid arteries and two vertebral arteries (branches of the subclavian arteries)—deliver blood to the brain. At the base of the brain, branches of these arteries form an arterial circuit called the **circle of Willis.** In the event that one of the arteries serving the brain becomes blocked or injured in some way, this arterial circuit helps ensure blood delivery to the brain cells via other vessels. Blood from the brain returns to the superior vena cava by way of the internal jugular veins at either side of the neck.

Cardiovascular Disease

Cardiovascular disease is the number one cause of death in the United States and in most other industrial societies. Most often death results from some complication of atherosclerosis[1] (hardening of the arteries as a result of lipid and calcium deposition). Although atherosclerosis can affect almost any artery, the disease most often develops in the aorta and in the coronary and cerebral arteries. When it occurs in the cerebral arteries it can lead to a **cerebrovascular accident (CVA),** commonly referred to as a stroke.

Although there is apparently no single cause of atherosclerosis, several major risk factors have been identified:

1. Elevated levels of cholesterol in the blood, often associated with diets rich in total calories, total fats, saturated fats, and cholesterol.
2. Hypertension. The higher the blood pressure, the greater the risk.

[1] Atherosclerosis is the most common form of arteriosclerosis, any disorder in which arteries lose their elasticity.

3. Cigarette smoking. The risk of developing atherosclerosis is two to six times greater in smokers than in nonsmokers and is directly proportional to the number of cigarettes smoked daily.
4. Diabetes mellitus, an endocrine disorder in which glucose is not metabolized normally.

The risk of developing atherosclerosis also increases with age. Estrogen hormones are thought to offer some protection in women until after menopause, when the concentration of these hormones decreases. Other suggested risk factors that are currently being studied are obesity, hereditary predisposition, lack of exercise, stress and behavior patterns, and dietary factors.

In atherosclerosis, lipids are deposited in the smooth muscle cells of the arterial wall. Cells in the arterial wall proliferate and the inner lining thickens. More lipid, especially cholesterol from low-density lipoproteins, accumulates in the wall. Eventually calcium is deposited there, contributing to the slow formation of hard plaque. As the plaque develops,

arteries lose their ability to stretch when they fill with blood, and they become progressively occluded (blocked), as shown in the figure. As the artery narrows, less blood can pass through to reach the tissues served by that vessel and the tissue may become **ischemic** (lacking in blood). Under these conditions the tissue is deprived of an adequate oxygen supply.

When a coronary artery becomes narrowed, **ischemic heart disease** can occur. Sufficient oxygen may reach the heart tissue during normal activity, but the increased need for oxygen during exercise or emotional stress results in the pain known as **angina pectoris.** Persons with this condition often carry nitroglycerin pills with them for use during an attack. This drug dilates veins so that venous return is reduced. Cardiac output is lowered so that the heart is not working so hard and requires less oxygen. Nitroglycerin also dilates the coronary arteries slightly, allowing more blood to reach the heart muscle.

Myocardial infarction (MI) (popularly referred to as heart attack) is a

The Hepatic Portal System Delivers Nutrients to the Liver

Blood almost always travels from artery to capillary to vein. An exception to this sequence occurs in the **hepatic portal system,** which delivers blood rich in nutrients to the liver. Blood is conducted to the small intestine by the superior mesenteric artery. Then, as it flows through capillaries within the wall of the intestine, blood picks up glucose, amino acids, and other nutrients. This blood passes into the mesenteric vein and then into the **hepatic portal vein.** Instead of going directly back to the heart (as most veins would), the hepatic portal vein delivers nutrients to the liver.

Within the liver, the hepatic portal vein gives rise to an extensive network of tiny blood sinuses. As blood courses through the hepatic sinuses, liver cells remove nutrients and store them. Eventually liver sinuses merge to form hepatic veins, which deliver blood to the inferior vena cava. The hepatic portal vein contains blood that, although laden with food materials, has already given up some of its oxygen to the cells of the intestinal wall. Oxygenated blood is supplied to the liver by the hepatic artery.

THE LYMPHATIC SYSTEM IS AN ACCESSORY CIRCULATORY SYSTEM

In addition to the blood circulatory system, vertebrates have an accessory circulatory system, the **lymphatic system** (Figure 42–20). The lymphatic system has three important functions: (1) to collect and return interstitial fluid to the blood, (2) to defend the body against dis-

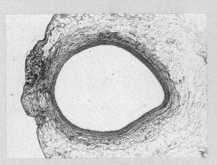

(a)

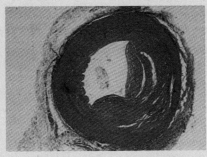

(b)

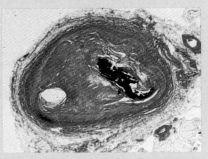

(c)

Progression of atherosclerosis. Cross sections through three arteries showing changes that take place in atherosclerosis. (a) Early stage of atherosclerosis. Inner

lining has thickened slightly. (b) Pronounced changes have taken place in this artery. Note the marked thickening of the wall. (c) This artery is almost

completely blocked with atherosclerotic plaque. (a, Custom Medical Stock Photography; b, c, Visuals Unlimited/Sloop-Ober)

very serious, often fatal, consequence of ischemic heart disease. MI often results from a sudden decrease in coronary blood supply. The portion of cardiac muscle deprived of oxygen dies within a few minutes and is then referred to as an **infarct**. MI is the leading cause of death and disability in the United States. Just what triggers the sudden decrease in blood supply that causes MI is a matter of some debate. It is thought that in some cases an episode of ischemia triggers a fatal arrhythmia such as

ventricular fibrillation, a condition in which the ventricles contract very rapidly without actually pumping blood. In other cases, a **thrombus** (clot) may form in a diseased coronary artery. Because the arterial wall is roughened, platelets may adhere to it and initiate clotting.

If the thrombus blocks a sizable branch of a coronary artery, blood flow to a portion of heart muscle is impeded or completely halted. This condition is referred to as a coronary occlusion. If the coronary occlusion

prevents blood flow to a large region of cardiac muscle, the heart may stop beating—that is, cardiac arrest may occur—and death can follow within moments. If only a small region of the heart is affected, however, the heart may continue to function. Cells in the region deprived of oxygen die and are replaced by scar tissue.

ease organisms by way of immune mechanisms, and (3) to absorb lipids from the digestive tract. In this section we focus upon the first function. Immunity is discussed in Chapter 43, and lipid absorption is discussed in Chapter 45.

The Lymphatic System Consists of Lymphatic Vessels and Lymph Tissue

The lymphatic system consists of (1) an extensive network of **lymphatic vessels** that conduct **lymph,** the clear, watery fluid formed from interstitial fluid, and (2) **lymph tissue,** a type of connective tissue that has large numbers of lymphocytes. Lymph tissue is organized into small masses of tissue called **lymph nodes** and **lymph nodules.** The tonsils, thymus gland, and

spleen, which consist mainly of lymph tissue, are also part of the lymphatic system.

Tiny "dead-end" capillaries of the lymphatic system extend into almost all of the tissues of the body (Figure 42–21). Lymph capillaries join to form larger **lymphatics** (lymph veins). There are no lymph arteries.

Interstitial fluid enters lymph capillaries and then is referred to as lymph. The lymph is conveyed into lymphatics. At certain locations the lymphatics empty into lymph nodes, where lymph is filtered. Bacteria and other harmful matter are removed from the lymph. The lymph then flows into lymphatics leaving the lymph node. Lymphatics from all over the body conduct lymph toward the shoulder region. These vessels join the circulatory system at the base of the subclavian veins by way of ducts—the **thoracic duct** on the left side and the **right lymphatic duct** on the right.

Tonsils are masses of lymph tissue under the lining of the oral cavity and throat. (The pharyngeal tonsils in back of the nose are called **adenoids** when they are enlarged.) Tonsils help protect the respiratory system from infection by destroying bacteria and other foreign matter that enter the body through the mouth or nose. Unfortunately, tonsils are sometimes overcome by invading germs, become the site of frequent infection themselves, and then become prime targets for surgical removal.

Some nonmammalian vertebrates such as the frog have lymph "hearts," which pulsate and squeeze lymph along. However, in mammals the walls of the lymph vessels themselves pulsate, pushing lymph along. Valves within the lymph vessels prevent the lymph from flowing backward. When muscles contract or when arteries pulsate, pressure on the lymph vessels increases lymph flow. The rate at which lymph flows is slow and variable, and the total lymph flow is about 100 mL per hour—very much slower than the 5 liters per minute of blood flowing in the vascular system.

The Lymphatic System Plays an Important Role in Fluid Homeostasis

When blood enters a capillary network it is under rather high pressure, so some plasma is forced out of the capillaries and into the tissues. Once it leaves the blood vessels, this fluid is called **interstitial fluid,** or **tissue fluid.** It is somewhat similar to plasma but contains no red blood cells or platelets and only a few white blood cells. Its protein content is about one fourth of that found in plasma. This is because proteins are too large to pass easily through capillary walls. Smaller molecules dissolved in the plasma do pass out with the fluid leaving the blood vessels. Thus, interstitial fluid contains glucose, amino acids, other nutrients, and oxygen, as well as a variety of salts. This nourishing fluid bathes all the cells of the body.

The main force pushing plasma out of the blood is hydrostatic pressure, that is, the pressure exerted by the blood on the capillary wall, which is caused by the beating of the heart (Figure 42–22). At the venous ends of the capillaries the hydrostatic pressure is much lower. Here the principal force is the osmotic pressure of the blood, which acts to draw fluid back into the capillary. However, osmotic pressure is not entirely effective. Not as much is returned to the circulation as escapes. Furthermore, protein does not return effectively into the venous capillaries and instead tends to accumulate in the interstitial fluid. These potential problems are so serious that fluid balance in the body would be significantly disturbed within a few hours and death would

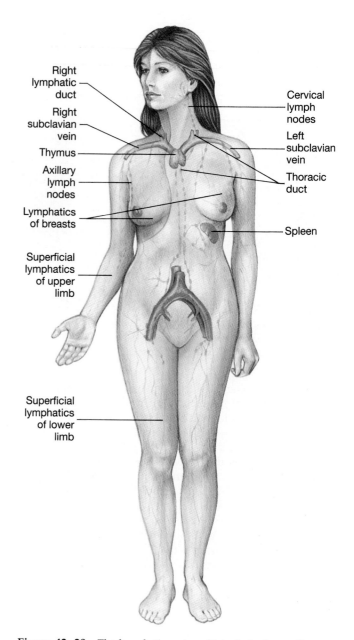

Figure 42–20 The lymphatic system. Note that whereas the lymphatic vessels extend into most tissues of the body, the lymph nodes are clustered in certain regions. The right lymphatic duct drains lymph from the upper right quadrant of the body. The thoracic duct drains lymph from other regions of the body.

occur within about 24 hours if it were not for the lymphatic system.

The lymphatic system preserves fluid balance by collecting about 10% of the interstitial fluid and the protein that accumulates in it. Once it enters the lymph capillaries, the interstitial fluid is called lymph.

The walls of the lymph capillaries are composed of endothelial cells that overlap slightly. When interstitial fluid accumulates, it presses against these cells, pushing

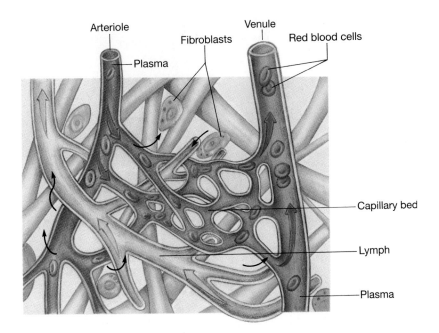

Arteriole
Fibroblasts
Plasma
Venule
Red blood cells
Capillary bed
Lymph
Plasma

Figure 42–21 The relation of lymph capillaries to blood capillaries and tissue cells. Note that blood capillaries are connected to vessels at both ends, whereas lymph capillaries (shown in tan) are "dead-end streets" and contain no erythrocytes. The arrows indicate direction of flow.

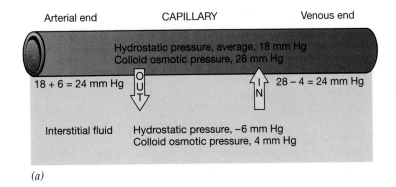

Arterial end   CAPILLARY   Venous end

Hydrostatic pressure, average, 18 mm Hg
Colloid osmotic pressure, 28 mm Hg

18 + 6 = 24 mm Hg   OUT   IN   28 – 4 = 24 mm Hg

Interstitial fluid   Hydrostatic pressure, –6 mm Hg
Colloid osmotic pressure, 4 mm Hg

(a)

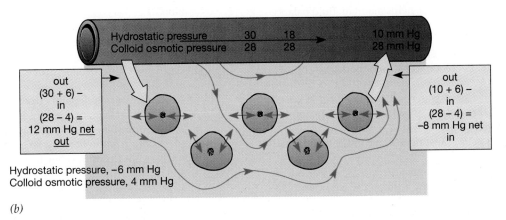

Hydrostatic pressure   30   18   10 mm Hg
Colloid osmotic pressure   28   28   28 mm Hg

out
(30 + 6) –
in
(28 – 4) =
12 mm Hg <u>net</u>
<u>out</u>

out
(10 + 6) –
in
(28 – 4) =
–8 mm Hg net
in

Hydrostatic pressure, –6 mm Hg
Colloid osmotic pressure, 4 mm Hg

(b)

Figure 42–22 Materials are exchanged between blood and tissue fluid through the thin walls of the capillaries. (*a*) Hydrostatic and osmotic pressures are responsible for the exchange of materials between blood and tissue fluid. (*b*) The path by which water flows between capillaries and tissue fluid.

them inward like tiny swinging doors that can swing in only one direction. As fluid accumulates within the lymph capillary, these cell doors are pushed closed.

Obstruction of the lymphatic vessels can lead to **edema,** a swelling that results from excessive accumulation of interstitial fluid. Lymphatic vessels can be blocked as a result of injury, inflammation, surgery, or parasitic infection. For example, when a breast is removed (mastectomy) because of cancer, lymph nodes in the underarm region often are also removed in an effort to prevent the spread of cancer cells. The disrupted lymph circulation may cause the patient's arm to swell greatly. Fortunately, new lymph vessels develop within a few months and the swelling slowly subsides.

Filariasis, a parasitic infection caused by a larval nematode that is transmitted to humans by mosquitoes, also disrupts lymph flow. The adult worms live in the lymph veins, blocking lymph flow. Interstitial fluid then accumulates, causing tremendous swelling. The term elephantiasis has been used to describe the swollen legs sometimes caused by this disease, because they resemble the huge limbs of an elephant (Figure 42–23).

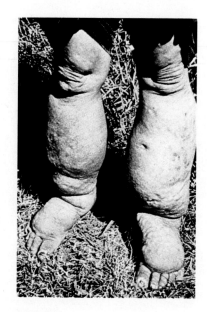

Figure 42–23 Lymphatic drainage is blocked in the limbs of this individual because of the parasitic infection known as filariasis. The condition characterized by such swollen limbs is elephantiasis. (Science VU/Fred Marsik)

SUMMARY

I. Small, simple invertebrates, such as sponges, cnidarians, and flatworms, depend on diffusion for internal transport. More complex animals require a specialized circulatory system.

II. Arthropods and most mollusks have an open circulatory system, in which blood flows into a hemocoel, bathing the tissues directly.

III. Some invertebrates and all vertebrates have a closed circulatory system, in which blood flows through a continuous circuit of blood vessels.

IV. The vertebrate circulatory system consists of a muscular heart that pumps blood into a system of arteries, capillaries, and veins. This system transports nutrients, oxygen, wastes, and hormones; helps maintain fluid balance and body temperature; and defends the body against disease.

V. Vertebrate blood consists of liquid plasma in which red blood cells, white blood cells, and platelets are suspended.

  A. Plasma consists of water, salts, substances in transport, and three types of proteins: albumins, globulins, and fibrinogen.

  B. Red blood cells transport oxygen and carbon dioxide.

  C. Lymphocytes and monocytes are agranular white blood cells; neutrophils, eosinophils, and basophils are granular white cells. White blood cells can leave the blood and wander through the tissues.

  D. Platelets patch damaged blood vessels and release substances essential for blood clotting.

VI. Arteries carry blood away from the heart; veins return blood to the heart.

  A. Arterioles constrict and dilate to regulate blood pressure and distribution of blood to the tissues.

  B. Capillaries are the exchange vessels with thin walls through which materials pass back and forth between the blood and tissues.

VII. The vertebrate heart consists of one or two atria, which receive blood, and one or two ventricles, which pump blood into the arteries.

  A. The four-chambered hearts of birds and mammals have completely separate right and left sides, which separate oxygen-rich blood from oxygen-poor blood.

  B. The heart is enclosed by a pericardium and is equipped with valves that prevent backflow of blood.

  C. The sinoatrial node initiates each heartbeat. A specialized conduction system ensures that the heart beats in a coordinated manner.

  D. Cardiac output equals stroke volume times heart rate.

    1. Stroke volume depends upon venous return and upon neural messages and hormones.

    2. Heart rate is regulated mainly by the nervous system but is influenced by hormones, body temperature, and certain other factors.

    3. The heart rate can be measured by counting the pulse. Arterial pulse is the alternate expansion and recoil of an artery.

VIII. Blood pressure is the force exerted by the blood against the inner walls of the blood vessel.

  A. Blood pressure is greatest in the arteries and decreases as blood flows through the capillaries.

  B. Baroreceptors sensitive to changes in blood pressure

send messages to the cardiac and vasomotor centers in the medulla of the brain. When informed of an increase in blood pressure, the cardiac center stimulates parasympathetic nerves that slow heart rate, and the vasomotor center inhibits sympathetic nerves that constrict blood vessels. These actions reduce blood pressure.

C. Angiotensins raise blood pressure.

IX. The pulmonary circulation connects heart and lungs; the systemic circulation connects the heart with all of the tissues.

A. In the systemic circulation the left ventricle pumps blood into the aorta, which branches into arteries leading to all of the body organs; after flowing through capillary networks within various organs, blood flows into veins that conduct it to the right atrium.

B. The coronary circulation supplies the heart muscle with blood.

C. The hepatic portal system circulates blood rich in nutrients through the liver; it consists of the hepatic portal vein and a network of tiny blood sinuses in the liver, from which blood flows into hepatic veins.

X. Atherosclerosis leads to ischemic heart disease, in which the heart muscle does not receive sufficient blood. Myocardial infarction is a very serious consequence of ischemic heart disease.

XI. The lymphatic system collects interstitial fluid and returns it to the blood. It plays an important role in homeostasis of fluids.

POST-TEST

Select the most appropriate answer or answers from Column B for the description in Column A.

Column A
1. No circulatory system
2. Open circulatory system
3. Closed circulatory system
4. Heart with two atria and two ventricles

Column B
a. Insect
b. Bird
c. Flatworm
d. Earthworm
e. Cnidarian
f. Clam

Select the most appropriate term in Column B to fit the description in Column A.

Column A
5. Transport oxygen
6. Principal phagocytic cells in blood
7. Release histamine in injured tissues
8. Develop from monocytes
9. Initiate clotting

Column B
a. Platelets
b. Red blood cells
c. Macrophages
d. Basophils
e. Neutrophils

10. Hemocyanin is a pigment that transports _____.
11. When the proteins involved in blood clotting are removed from plasma, the remaining fluid is called _____.
12. The _____ _____ fraction of plasma proteins contains many types of antibodies.
13. A deficiency in hemoglobin is referred to as _____.
14. Prothrombin requires vitamin _____ for its production.
15. In the presence of thrombin, fibrinogen is converted to the insoluble protein _____.
16. _____ are blood vessels important in maintaining appropriate blood pressure.
17. Nutrients and other materials are exchanged through the walls of _____.
18. In birds and mammals, blood leaving the right ventricle enters one of the _____ _____.
19. The _____ valves guard the exits of the heart.
20. The portion of the cardiac cycle during which the heart contracts is referred to as _____; the relaxation phase is _____.

21. The cardiac output is the _____.
22. According to Starling's law of the heart, the greater the amount of blood delivered to the heart by the veins, _____
23. The force exerted by the blood against the inner walls of the blood vessels is known as _____ _____.
24. Blood pressure is determined by _____ and by _____.
25. The largest artery in the human body is the _____.
26. The carotid arteries deliver blood to the _____.
27. The renal veins deliver blood from the _____; the hepatic veins deliver blood from the _____.
28. The term *myocardial infarction* (MI) is used as a synonym for _____ _____.
29. Baroreceptors are sensitive to changes in _____ _____.
30. The angiotensins are a group of hormones that are powerful _____.
31. Label the diagram below.

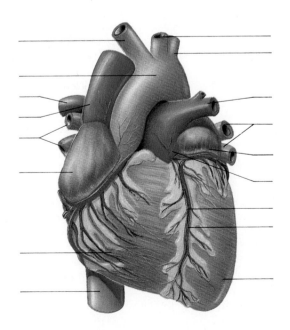

REVIEW QUESTIONS

1. List five functions of the vertebrate circulatory system.
2. Compare the manner in which nutrients and oxygen are transported to the body cells in a hydra, a planarian, an earthworm, an insect, and a frog.
3. Contrast an open with a closed circulatory system.
4. List the functions of the main groups of plasma proteins.
5. Contrast the structure and functions of red and white blood cells.
6. Summarize the process by which blood clots.
7. Compare the functions of arteries, capillaries, and veins. Why are arterioles important in maintaining homeostasis?
8. Compare the hearts of a fish, amphibian, reptile, and bird.
9. Define cardiac output, and describe factors that influence it.
10. What is the relationship between blood pressure and peripheral resistance? What mechanisms regulate blood pressure?
11. Trace the path of a red blood cell from the inferior vena cava to the aorta, and from the jugular vein to the kidney.
12. What is the function of the hepatic portal system? How does its sequence of blood vessels differ from that in most other circulatory routes?
13. List four risk factors associated with the development of atherosclerosis. How is atherosclerosis linked to ischemic heart disease? Describe myocardial infarction.
14. How does the lymph system help maintain fluid balance?
15. What is the relationship between plasma, interstitial fluid, and lymph?

RECOMMENDED READINGS

Cantin, M., and J. Genest. The heart as an endocrine gland. *Scientific American,* Vol. 254, No. 2 (February 1986). In addition to its pumping function, the heart produces a hormone that helps regulate blood pressure and volume.

Golde, D. W. The stem cell. *Scientific American,* Vol. 265, No. 6 (December 1991), pp. 86–93. A discussion of the cells that give rise to the various types of blood cells, with emphasis on implications for developing new treatments for cancer and immune diseases.

Zivin, J. A., and D. W. Choi. Stroke therapy. *Scientific American,* Vol. 265, No. 1 (July 1991), pp. 56–63. New strategies are being evaluated to limit the brain damage that occurs in these cardiovascular accidents.

Zucker, M. B. The functioning of blood platelets. *Scientific American,* Vol. 244, No. 6 (June 1980) pp. 86–103. The interactions of substances in blood platelets and those in blood plasma and tissue play complex roles in health and disease.

Internal Defense

Animals have internal defense mechanisms that protect them against the disease-causing organisms that constantly threaten them. Viruses, bacteria, fungi, and other microorganisms that cause disease are referred to as **pathogens.** Such organisms can enter the body with the air we breathe, with the food or water we ingest, or through wounds in the skin. Internal defense depends upon the ability of an organism to distinguish between *self* and *nonself.* Such recognition is possible because organisms are biochemically unique. Cells have surface macromolecules that are different from the macromolecules on the cells of other species or even other members of the same species. An organism "knows" its own macromolecules and "recognizes" those of other organisms as foreign.

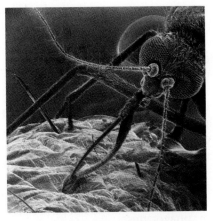

A vector of malaria, encephalitis, and yellow fever, a mosquito feeds on human blood. (Lennart Nilsson, © Boehringer Ingelheim International GmbH)

Pathogens have macromolecules on their cell surfaces that the body recognizes as foreign. A single bacterium may have from 10 to more than 1000 distinct macromolecules on its surface. When a bacterium invades an animal, its distinctive surface macromolecules stimulate the animal's defense mechanisms. A substance capable of stimulating an immune response is called an **antigen.** Many macromolecules are antigenic, including proteins, RNA, DNA, and some carbohydrates.

Nonspecific defense mechanisms prevent pathogens from entering the body and rapidly destroy those that do penetrate the outer defenses. Phagocytosis of invading bacteria is an example of a nonspecific defense mechanism.

Specific defense mechanisms are very precise and highly effective. Their weapons are tailor-made to combat specific antigens associated with each pathogen. Specific defense mechanisms are collectively referred to as **immune responses.** The term *immune* is derived from a Latin word meaning "safe." **Immunology,** the study of specific defense mechanisms, is one of the most exciting fields of medical research today.

Immune responses can be directed to the particular type of pathogen that infects the body. One of the body's most important specific defense mechanisms is the production of **antibodies,** highly specific proteins that help destroy antigens. In complex animals, internal defense includes immunological memory, the capacity to respond more effectively the second time foreign molecules invade the body.

After you have studied this chapter you should be able to

1. Compare in general terms the types of internal defense mechanisms in invertebrates and vertebrates.
2. Distinguish between specific and nonspecific defense mechanisms.
3. Relate the physiological changes and clinical symptoms associated with inflammation to the role of inflammation in the defense of the body.
4. Describe the process of phagocytosis.
5. Contrast T and B lymphocytes with respect to origin, differentiation, and function.
6. Describe the functions of the thymus in immune mechanisms.
7. Define the terms *antigen* and *antibody,* and describe how antigens stimulate immune responses.
8. Give the basic structure of an antibody, and list the five classes of antibodies and their biological roles.
9. Describe the mechanisms of antibody-mediated immunity, including the effects of antigen-antibody complexes upon pathogens; include a discussion of the complement system.

10. Describe the mechanisms of cell-mediated immunity, including development of memory cells.
11. Recount the clonal selection theory, and explain why organisms do not normally develop antibodies to their own tissues.
12. Contrast active and passive immunity, giving examples of each.
13. Contrast a secondary with a primary immune response.
14. Summarize the theory of immunosurveillance, and describe how the body destroys cancer cells.
15. Describe the immunological basis of graft rejection, and explain how the effects of graft rejection can be minimized.
16. Describe the immunological basis of autoimmune diseases, give two examples, and list possible causes.
17. Explain the immunological basis of allergy, and briefly describe the events that occur during (a) a hayfever response and (b) systemic anaphylaxis.
18. Describe the cause of AIDS, the risk factors and the progress of the disease, and summarize the difficulties encountered in developing a vaccine.

INVERTEBRATES HAVE INTERNAL DEFENSE MECHANISMS THAT ARE MAINLY NONSPECIFIC

All invertebrate species that have been studied demonstrate the ability to distinguish between self and nonself. However, most invertebrates are able to make only nonspecific immune responses, such as phagocytosis and the inflammatory response.

Sponge cells possess specific glycoproteins on their surfaces that enable them to distinguish between self and nonself. When cells of two different species of sponges are mixed together, they reaggregate according to species. Hydra and other cnidarians also possess this ability and can reject grafted tissue and cause the death of foreign tissue.

In all invertebrates that have a coelom, phagocytes wander through the tissues and phagocytize bacteria and other foreign matter. Any particle too large to be phagocytized is walled off or encapsulated by the phagocytes. Coelomate invertebrates also have nonspecific substances in the hemolymph that kill bacteria, inactivate cilia in some pathogens, and cause the agglutination (clumping) of some foreign cells. In mollusks these hemolymph substances enhance phagocytosis.

Echinoderms (e.g., sea stars) and tunicates are the simplest animals known to have differentiated white blood cells that perform immune functions. Tunicates also have masses of lymphatic tissue. Among the invertebrates, only certain annelids (e.g., earthworms) and

cnidarians (e.g., corals) are thought to possess specific immune mechanisms and immunological memory. In them and in some echinoderms and simple chordates, the body appears to remember antigens for a short time and can respond to them more effectively in a second encounter.

VERTEBRATES CAN LAUNCH BOTH NONSPECIFIC AND SPECIFIC IMMUNE RESPONSES

All vertebrates can launch both nonspecific and specific immune responses (Figure 43–1). Vertebrates possess many of the basic mechanisms present in invertebrates but have in addition more sophisticated defense mechanisms made possible by the development of a specialized lymphatic system. In the discussion that follows we focus on human internal defense mechanisms, with references to those of other vertebrates.

NONSPECIFIC DEFENSE MECHANISMS INCLUDE MECHANICAL AND CHEMICAL BARRIERS AGAINST PATHOGENS

The outer covering of an animal is the first line of defense against pathogens. The *intact* human skin, for example, presents both a mechanical and a chemical bar-

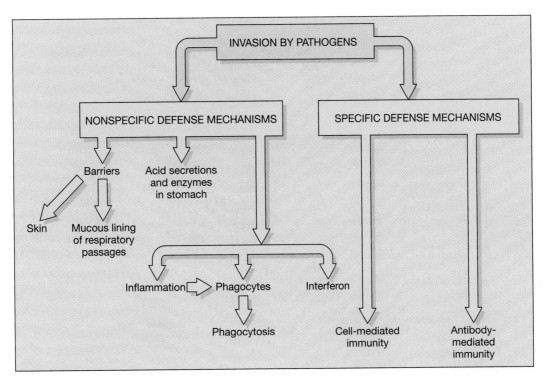

Figure 43–1 Summary of nonspecific and specific defense mechanisms. Nonspecific mechanisms prevent entrance of pathogens and act rapidly to destroy those that manage to cross the barriers. Specific defense mechanisms take longer to mobilize but are highly effective in destroying invaders.

rier to microorganisms. Sweat and sebum contain chemicals that destroy certain kinds of bacteria. **Lysozyme,** an enzyme found in sweat, tears, and saliva, attacks the cell walls of many bacteria.

Microorganisms that enter with food are usually destroyed by the acid secretions and enzymes of the stomach. (The intestine is populated by millions of harmless microorganisms, sometimes referred to as the normal flora. These organisms live quietly in harmony with their host and normally compete successfully with infectious bacteria and fungi.) Nonspecific defense mechanisms also destroy pathogens that enter the body with inhaled air. Such pathogens may be filtered out by hairs in the nose or trapped in the sticky mucous lining of the respiratory passageways, where they may be destroyed by phagocytes.

Interferons Help Defend the Body against Viral Infection

When viruses or other intracellular parasites (some types of bacteria, fungi, and protozoa) infect cells, the cells respond by secreting proteins called **interferons.** These proteins diffuse to neighboring cells and stimulate them to produce antiviral proteins that inhibit viral replication. The virus particles produced in cells exposed to interferon are not very effective at infecting cells. Interferons also mobilize certain lymphocytes known as **natural killer (NK) cells.** NK cells recognize host cells that have been infected by viruses and kill them quickly.

Since its discovery in 1957, drug companies have invested millions of dollars in interferon research. Recombinant DNA techniques are now used to produce large quantities of these compounds. Research has established that interferons are useful in treating some viral infections, and studies suggest that these compounds may be helpful in treating certain forms of cancer. Two nonspecific defense mechanisms that we now consider in some detail are inflammation and phagocytosis.

Inflammation Is a Protective Mechanism

When pathogens invade tissues, they trigger an inflammatory response (Figure 43–2). Injured cells, basophils, and certain other cells release **histamine** and other compounds that dilate blood vessels in the affected area, increasing blood flow to the infected region. The increased blood flow makes the skin look red and feel warm. Capillaries in the inflamed area become more permeable, allowing more fluid to leave the circulation and enter the tissues. As the volume of interstitial fluid increases, **edema** (swelling) occurs. The edema (and

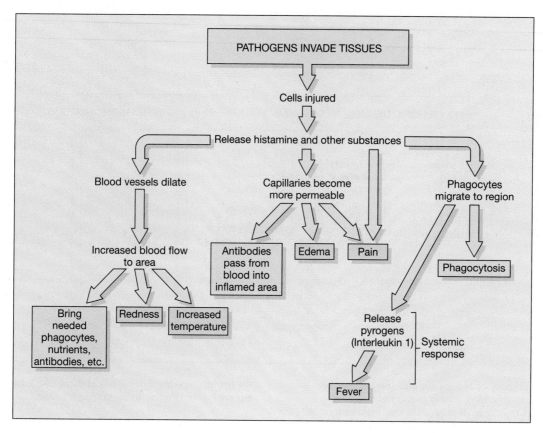

PATHOGENS INVADE TISSUES

Cells injured

Release histamine and other substances

Blood vessels dilate

Capillaries become more permeable

Phagocytes migrate to region

Increased blood flow to area

Antibodies pass from blood into inflamed area

Edema

Pain

Phagocytosis

Bring needed phagocytes, nutrients, antibodies, etc.

Redness

Increased temperature

Release pyrogens (Interleukin 1) | Systemic response

Fever

Figure 43–2 Inflammation is a means by which protective immune mechanisms can be localized at a region where infection occurs. It is a vital process that permits phagocytic cells, antibodies, and other needed compounds to enter the tissue where microbial invasion is taking place.

also certain substances released by the injured cells) causes the pain that is characteristic of inflammation. Thus, the clinical characteristics of inflammation are *redness, heat, edema,* and *pain.*

The increased blood flow that occurs during inflammation brings great numbers of phagocytic cells (first neutrophils and, later, monocytes; see Chapter 42) to the infected area. The increased permeability of the blood vessels allows needed immunoglobulins (antibodies) to leave the circulation and enter the tissues. As fluid leaves the circulation, it also takes with it needed oxygen and nutrients.

Although inflammation is often a local response, sometimes the entire body is involved. **Fever** is a common clinical symptom of widespread inflammatory response. White blood cells (and certain other cells) release cytokines (regulatory proteins) called **pyrogens** that reset the body's thermostat in the hypothalamus, resulting in fever. The most potent pyrogen is a peptide called **interleukin-1** (IL-1), released by macrophages. Prostaglandins (an important group of compounds derived from fatty acids) are also involved in this resetting process. Fever interferes with viral activity and decreases circulating levels of iron. This makes it difficult

for microorganisms to obtain needed iron supplies, placing the invaders at a metabolic disadvantage. Fever also promotes production of certain lymphocytes (T cells) and antibodies. A short-term low fever may therefore help speed recovery.

Phagocytes Destroy Pathogens

One of the main functions of inflammation appears to be increased phagocytosis. Recall from Chapter 5 that a phagocyte ingests a bacterium or other invading organism by flowing around it like an amoeba and engulfing it. As it ingests the organism, the cell wraps it within a membrane-bound vesicle produced from the plasma membrane. The cytoplasmic vesicle containing the bacterium is called a **phagosome.** One or more lysosomes adhere to the phagosome membrane, fuse with it, and release potent digestive enzymes onto the captured bacterium.

After a neutrophil phagocytizes 20 or so bacteria, it becomes inactivated (perhaps by leaking lysosomal enzymes) and dies. A macrophage can phagocytize about 100 bacteria during its life span. Can bacteria counteract the body's attack? Certain bacteria are able

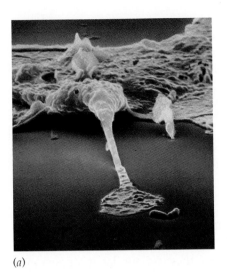

(a)

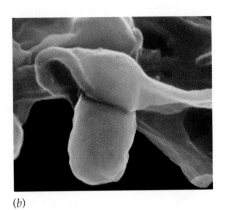

(b)

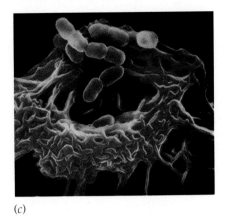

(c)

Figure 43–3 The macrophage is an incredibly efficient warrior. (*a*) A macrophage (grayish green) extends a pseudopod toward an invading *Escherichia coli* bacterium (darker green, *bottom right*) that is already multiplying. (*b*) The bacterium is trapped within the engulfing pseudopod. (*c*) The macrophage sucks the trapped bacteria in along with its own cell membrane. The macrophage plasma membrane will seal over the bacteria, and powerful lysosomal enzymes will destroy them. Colors are artificial.   (Lennart Nilsson, © Boehringer Ingelheim International GmbH)

to release enzymes that destroy the membranes of the lysosomes. The powerful lysosomal enzymes then spill out into the cytoplasm and may destroy the phagocyte. Some bacteria have cell walls or capsules that resist the action of lysosomal enzymes.

Some macrophages wander through the tissue phagocytizing foreign matter and bacteria (Figure 43–3); when it is appropriate, they release antiviral agents. Others stay in one place and destroy bacteria that pass by. For example, air sacs in the lungs contain large numbers of tissue macrophages that destroy foreign matter entering with inhaled air.

SPECIFIC DEFENSE MECHANISMS INCLUDE ANTIBODY-MEDIATED IMMUNITY AND CELL-MEDIATED IMMUNITY

Nonspecific defense mechanisms destroy pathogens and prevent the spread of infection while the specific defense mechanisms are being mobilized. Several days may be required to activate specific immune responses, but once in gear, these mechanisms are extremely effective. Two main types of specific immunity are **cell-mediated immunity,** in which lymphocytes attack the invading pathogen directly, and **antibody-mediated immunity,** in which lymphocytes produce specific antibodies designed to destroy the pathogen. Several types of cells are important in specific immunity.

Cells of the Immune System Include Lymphocytes and Phagocytes

Two cell types important in internal defense are lymphocytes, the warriors in specific immune responses, and phagocytes. The trillion or so lymphocytes are stationed strategically in the lymphatic tissue throughout the body. Two main kinds of agranular lymphocytes are **T lymphocytes,** referred to as **T cells,** and **B lymphocytes,** or **B cells.** One population of lymphocytes has some granules; these are called large granular lymphocytes (LGL). The LGLs include the NK cell mentioned earlier, which destroys virally infected cells and tumor cells.

T cells.   Like macrophages and B cells, T cells originate from stem cells in the bone marrow (Figure 43–4). On their way to the lymph tissues, the future T cells complete their maturation in the thymus gland. The *T* indicates that these cells are *t*hymus-derived; somehow the thymus gland influences the differentiation of lymphocytes, making them **immunocompetent,** that is, capable of immunological response.

T lymphocytes are responsible for cellular immunity. T cells respond to antigens displayed on the surfaces of body cells that have been invaded by viruses or other pathogens that enter cells. The ability to recognize these antigens depends on unique receptor proteins on the plasma membranes of the T cells. These **T-cell receptors** are capable of recognizing and binding with specific antigens.

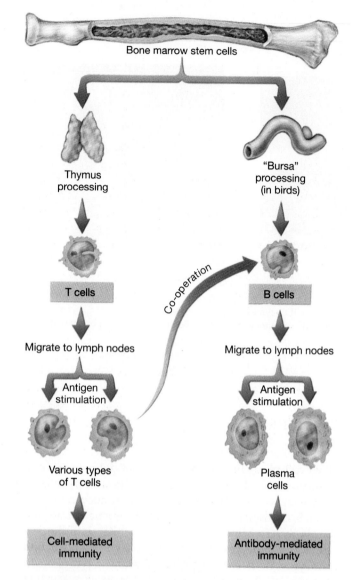

Figure 43–4 Origin and functions of T and B lymphocytes.

Three main types, or subsets, of T cells are recognized:

1. **Cytotoxic T cells,** or killer T cells, recognize and destroy cells with foreign antigens on their surfaces.
2. **Helper T cells** must participate in order for an effective immune response to occur. These cells secrete substances that activate or enhance the immune response.
3. **Suppressor T cells** inhibit the immune response. They release cytokines that inhibit the activity of other T cells and of B cells. Suppressor T cells are thought to have an ongoing function in regulation of the immune response.

B cells.   B cells are responsible for antibody-mediated immunity. In birds, B cells mature in the **bursa of**

Fabricius, a lymphatic organ located near the cloaca. (The *B* denotes bursa-derived.) Other vertebrates do not have a bursa. In most species of mammals, mammalian B cells appear to mature in the bone marrow.

As with T cells, millions of B cells are produced, each with a different antigen-binding specificity. B-cell receptors consist of specific antibodies on the B-cell plasma membrane. When a B cell comes into contact with the specific type of antigen to which it is targeted, it divides rapidly to form a clone of identical cells. These B cells develop into **plasma cells,** the cells that *secrete* the antibodies found in blood and other tissues. Plasma cells have an extensive, highly developed rough endoplasmic reticulum for the synthesis of proteins.

Although T and B lymphocytes have different functions and life histories, they are similar in appearance when viewed with a light microscope. More sophisticated techniques such as fluorescence microscopy, however, have shown that the B and T cells can be differentiated by their unique cell surface macromolecules. They also tend to locate in (or "home" to) separate regions of the spleen, lymph nodes, and other lymph tissues.

Certain diseases provide additional evidence for the existence of separate T and B lymphocyte systems. In DiGeorge syndrome, in which a child is born without a thymus gland, normal B-cell functioning develops, but there are no functional T cells. Conversely, in Bruton's agammaglobulinemia, the victim has normal T-cell immunity but deficient B-cell function.

Macrophages.   Macrophages are important in both nonspecific and specific defense responses. In addition to phagocytizing bacteria, they secrete prostaglandins and almost 100 different proteins, including interferon and enzymes that destroy bacteria. When macrophages are stimulated by bacteria, they secrete interleukin-1, which helps activate B cells and helper T cells. Interleukin-1 also promotes a general response to injury, causing fever and activating a variety of other mechanisms that defend the body against invasion.

When bacteria enter the body, macrophages engulf some of them. Macrophages destroy bacterial cells, but fragments of their bacterial antigens are displayed on the macrophage cell surface. This displayed antigen is necessary to activate helper T cells. The macrophage can be described as an **antigen-presenting cell (APC)** that displays bacterial antigens as well as its own surface proteins.

The Thymus "Instructs" T Cells and Produces Hormones

The **thymus gland,** present in all vertebrates, is thought to have at least two functions. First, in some unknown way the thymus confers immunological competence upon T cells. Within the thymus these cells develop the ability to differentiate into cells that can respond to specific antigens. This "instruction" within the thymus is thought to take place just before birth and during the first few months of postnatal life.

The second function of the thymus is that of an endocrine gland. It secretes several hormones, including one known as **thymosin.** Although not much is known about these hormones, thymosin is thought to affect T cells *after* they leave the thymus, stimulating them to complete their differentiation and to become immunologically active. Thymosin has been used clinically in patients who have poorly developed thymus glands. It is also being tested in patients with certain types of cancer; stimulating cellular immunity in such patients may help inhibit the progression of the disease.

The Major Histocompatibility Complex Permits Recognition of Self

The ability of the vertebrate immune system to distinguish self from nonself depends largely on a group of protein markers (antigens) known as the **major histocompatibility complex (MHC).** These markers are present on the surface of every cell and are slightly different in each individual. In humans the MHC is called the **HLA (human leukocyte antigen) group.** HLA is determined by a cluster of more than a dozen genes. These genes are polymorphic—that is, within the population there are multiple alleles for each locus. Because the HLA group is inherited, the more closely related two individuals are, the more HLAs they have in common. Tissues from the same individual or from identical twins have the same HLA alleles and thus identical HLA antigens.

On the basis of tissue distribution and structure, the MHC is divided into three groups of genes and the proteins for which these genes code. MHC class I antigens are found on most nucleated cells. Class I antigens are important in distinguishing between self and nonself. They bind with foreign antigens produced within cells (for example, by viruses), and the molecular complex formed is displayed on the cell surface. This complex is recognized by cytotoxic T cells (see below).

MHC class II antigens are found only on cells of the immune system, particularly B cells, macrophages, some T cells, and dendritic cells (specialized cells located in the spleen and lymph nodes). Class II antigens regulate the interactions among T cells, B cells, and antigen-presenting cells. MHC class II antigens bind with peptides from proteins that have entered the cell from foreign sources, such as bacteria. The MHC class II and foreign antigen complex is displayed on the cell surface and stimulates helper T cells. MHC class III proteins include components of a group of blood proteins known as complement (discussed in a later section).

Antibody-Mediated Immunity Is a Form of Chemical Warfare

B cells are responsible for antibody-mediated immunity, also called **humoral immunity.** Recall that macrophages display fragments of antigen from a pathogen. The foreign antigen forms a complex with MHC class II antigens of the macrophage. It is the foreign antigen–MHC complex that is displayed on the cell surface (Figure 43–5). Antibodies on the surface of B cells serve as receptors. Only **competent B cells**—the variety of B cell with a matching receptor—can bind with a particular antigen-MHC complex presented by the macrophage.

Helper T cells are essential for many B-cell responses to occur. When a macrophage displaying antigen contacts a helper T cell with complementary receptors, a complex interaction occurs (Figure 43–6). One result of this interaction is that the macrophage secretes interleukins. IL-1 activates helper T cells. The activated helper T cells detect B cells that have bound to the foreign antigen–MHC complex on the macrophage and bind to the same complex. A T cell does not recognize an antigen that is presented alone; the antigen must be presented to the T cell as part of a foreign antigen–MHC complex. Once bound, the activated helper T cell secretes interleukins that activate competent B cells.

Once activated, or sensitized, B cells increase in size. Then they divide by mitosis, each giving rise to a sizable clone of identical cells (Figure 43–7). This cell division in response to a specific antigen is known as **clonal selection.** Some of these B cells mature into plasma cells that secrete antibody. Unlike T cells, most plasma cells do not leave the lymph nodes. Only the antibodies they secrete pass out of the lymph tissues and make their way via the lymph and blood to the infected area.

pathogen invades body → macrophage phagocytizes pathogen → foreign antigen–MHC antigen complex displayed on macrophage cell surface → competent B cell binds with foreign antigen–MHC complex → helper T cell binds with foreign antigen–MHC complex → helper T cell secretes interleukins → competent B cells activated → clone of competent B cells → plasma cells → antibody

Some activated B cells do not differentiate into plasma cells, but instead become memory cells that continue to produce small amounts of antibody long after an infection has been overcome. This antibody, part of the gamma globulin fraction of the plasma, becomes part of the body's arsenal of chemical weapons. Should the same pathogen enter the body again, this circulating

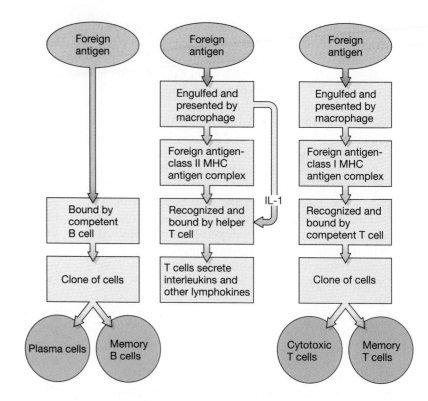

Figure 43–5   Pathways by which antigens stimulate lymphocytes.

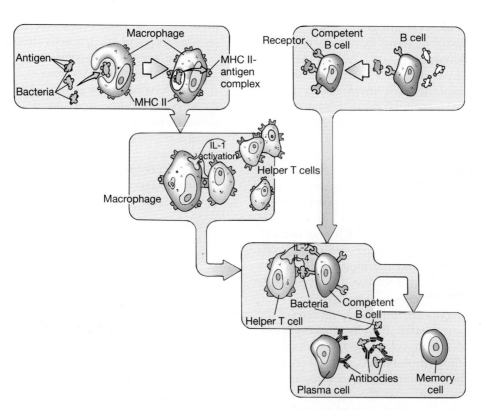

Figure 43–6   B-cell activation. Competent B cells can combine with antibody. However, helper T cells are needed for activation of the B cell. The helper T cell is activated when its receptor combines with the foreign antigen–MHC II complex presented by a macrophage and is stimulated by interleukin-1 secreted by the macrophage. Once activated, the B cell divides, forming a clone of cells. Some of these differentiate to form plasma cells that secrete antibodies. Others develop into memory B cells.

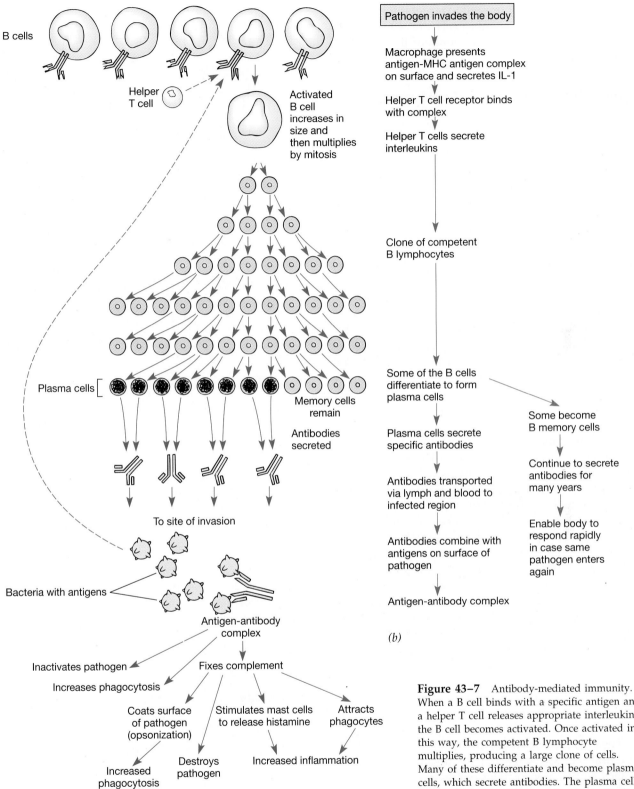

B cells

Helper
T cell

Activated
B cell
increases in
size and
then multiplies
by mitosis

Plasma cells

Memory cells
remain

Antibodies
secreted

To site of invasion

Bacteria with antigens

Antigen-antibody
complex

Inactivates pathogen

Fixes complement

Increases phagocytosis

Coats surface
of pathogen
(opsonization)

Stimulates mast cells
to release histamine

Attracts
phagocytes

Increased
phagocytosis

Destroys
pathogen

Increased inflammation

(a)

Pathogen invades the body

Macrophage presents
antigen-MHC antigen complex
on surface and secretes IL-1

Helper T cell receptor binds
with complex

Helper T cells secrete
interleukins

Clone of competent
B lymphocytes

Some of the B cells
differentiate to form
plasma cells

Plasma cells secrete
specific antibodies

Antibodies transported
via lymph and blood to
infected region

Antibodies combine with
antigens on surface of
pathogen

Antigen-antibody complex

Some become
B memory cells

Continue to secrete
antibodies for
many years

Enable body to
respond rapidly
in case same
pathogen enters
again

(b)

Figure 43–7 Antibody-mediated immunity.
When a B cell binds with a specific antigen and
a helper T cell releases appropriate interleukins,
the B cell becomes activated. Once activated in
this way, the competent B lymphocyte
multiplies, producing a large clone of cells.
Many of these differentiate and become plasma
cells, which secrete antibodies. The plasma cells
remain in the lymph tissues, but the antibodies
are transported to the site of infection by the
blood or lymph. Antigen-antibody complexes
form, directly inactivating some pathogens and
also turning on the complement system. Some of
the B cells become memory cells that persist and
continue to secrete small amounts of antibody
for years after the infection is over.

antibody is immediately present to target it for destruction. At the same time, memory cells are stimulated to quickly divide to produce new clones of the appropriate plasma cells.

A typical antibody has a Y-shaped structure

Antibodies are highly specific proteins called **immunoglobulins,** abbreviated **Ig,** that are produced in response to specific antigens. The function of an antibody is to bind to an antigen. The antibody does not destroy the antigen directly. Rather, it *labels* the antigen for destruction.

How does an antibody "recognize" a particular antigen? In a protein antigen there are specific sequences of amino acids that constitute an **antigenic determinant,** or **epitope.** These amino acids give part of the antigen molecule a specific configuration that can be recognized by an antibody or cell receptor. However, the mechanism is even more complicated. Usually, an antigen has 5 to 10 antigenic determinants on its surface. Some have 200 or even more. These antigenic determinants may differ from one another, so that several different kinds of antibodies can combine with a single complex antigen. Multivalent antigens have the same determinant repeated several times. An example of a multivalent antigen is a virus.

Some substances found in dust and certain drugs are too small to be immunogenic. These substances, called **haptens,** become immunogenic by attaching to the surface of a protein. For example, the antibiotic penicillin is a small molecule, not capable of causing an immune response. However, once penicillin is degraded in the body, it can bind to serum proteins. It can then stimulate an immune response.

A typical antibody is a Y-shaped molecule, in which the two arms of the Y are binding sites (Figure 43–8), permitting the antibody to combine with two antigen molecules. This allows formation of **antigen-antibody complexes.** The tail of the Y performs functions such as binding to cells or activating complement.

The antibody molecule consists of four polypeptide chains: two identical long chains called heavy chains and two identical short chains called light chains (Figure 43–8). Each light chain is made up of approximately 214 amino acids, and each heavy chain of more than 400. The polypeptide chains are held together and their configurations are stabilized by disulfide (—S—S—) linkages and by noncovalent bonds.

Each chain has a constant segment, a junctional segment, and a variable segment. In the **constant segment,** or **C region,** the amino acid sequence is constant within each of the five classes of immunoglobulin. Thus, five types of C regions are known. The C region may be thought of as the handle portion of a door key. The amino acid sequence of the **junctional segment,** or **J**

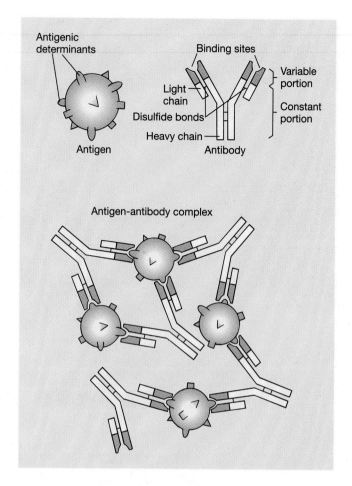

Figure 43–8 Antigen, antibody, and antigen-antibody complex. The antibody molecule is composed of two light chains and two heavy chains, joined together by disulfide bonds. The constant (C) and variable (V) regions of the chains are indicated.

region, is somewhat variable. The **variable segment,** or **V region,** has a highly variable amino acid sequence. In B-cell receptors, the variable region of the immunoglobulin protrudes from the B cell, whereas the constant region anchors the molecule to the cell.

The V region is the part of the key that is unique for a specific antigen (the lock). At its variable regions the antibody folds three-dimensionally, assuming a shape that enables it to combine with a specific antigen. When they meet, antigen and antibody fit together *somewhat* like a lock and key and must fit in just the right way for the antibody to be effective (Figure 43–9). A given antibody can bind with different strengths, or **affinities,** to different antigens. In the course of an immune response, stronger (higher affinity) antibodies are generated.

An antibody molecule has two main functions. Its binding domains combine with the antigen. Its effector domains activate processes that destroy the antigen bound to the antibody. For example, an effector domain may stimulate phagocytosis.

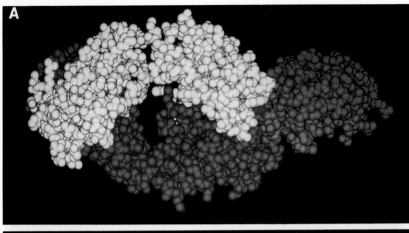

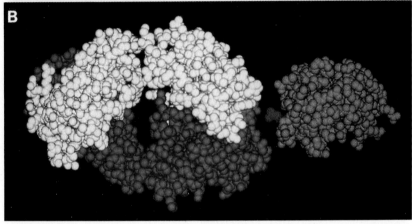

Figure 43–9   An antigen-antibody complex. The antigen lysozyme is shown in green. The heavy chain of the antibody is shown in blue, the light chain in yellow. (*a*) The antigenic determinant, shown in red, fits into a groove in the antibody molecule. (*b*) The antigen-antibody complex has been pulled apart. Note how they fit each other.

Antibodies are grouped in five classes

Immunoglobulins are grouped in five principal classes or isotypes according to their structure. At the constant end, the heavy chains of an antibody have amino acid sequences characteristic of the particular antibody class. Using the abbreviation Ig for immunoglobulin, the classes are designated IgG, IgM, IgA, IgD, and IgE. As more complex animals evolved, it would have been advantageous to have a variety of antibody classes with specialized functions. In the simpler vertebrates, only IgM is present. In the amphibians, IgM and IgG are characteristic. These classes and also IgA are found in birds, and all five classes are produced in humans. The classes of antibodies have different functions determined by their C regions. For example, some antibodies activate complement, whereas others help macrophages phagocytize bacteria.

In humans about 75% of the antibodies in the blood belong to the **IgG** group; these are part of the gamma globulin fraction of the plasma. IgG contributes to immunity against many blood-borne pathogens, including bacteria, viruses, and some fungi. Its small size permits

IgG to leave the blood vessels and participate in defense of body surfaces and tissues. IgG, along with the IgM antibodies, stimulates macrophages and activates the complement system (discussed in the following section). IgM is highly effective against microorganisms such as viruses that have multivalent antigens.

IgA is the principal immunoglobulin found in body secretions, such as mucous secretions of the nose, respiratory passageways, and digestive tract, and in tears, saliva, milk, and vaginal secretions. IgA is important in protecting the body from infections by inhaled or ingested pathogens. **IgD** is a cell-membrane antigen receptor located on the surface of B lymphocytes. **IgE,** the mediator of allergic responses, is discussed in a later section.

Antigen-antibody binding activates other defense mechanisms

Antibodies identify a pathogen as foreign by combining with an antigen on its surface. Often several antibodies combine with several such antigens, creating a mass of clumped antigen-antibody complexes (Figures 43–8 and 43–9). The combination of antigen and antibody activates several defense mechanisms:

1. The antigen-antibody complex may inactivate the pathogen or its toxin. For example, when an antibody attaches to the surface of a virus, the virus may lose its ability to attach to a host cell.
2. The antigen-antibody complex stimulates phagocytosis of the pathogen by macrophages and neutrophils.
3. Antibodies of the IgG and IgM groups work mainly through the complement system. This system consists of at least 19 proteins present in plasma and other body fluids. Normally, complement proteins are inactive. However, an antigen-antibody complex stimulates a series of reactions that activate the system, "fixing" complement. Proteins of the complement system then work to destroy pathogens.

Some complement proteins digest portions of the pathogen cell. Others coat the pathogens, a process called **opsonization.** The coating appears to make the pathogens less "slippery" so that the macrophages and neutrophils can phagocytize them. Complement proteins also increase inflammation. During activation of the complement system, several peptides are produced that attract macrophages and other white blood cells.

Complement proteins are not specific. They act against any antigen, provided that they are activated by antigen-antibody complex. Antibodies identify the pathogen very specifically; then complement proteins complement their action by destroying the pathogens.

Antibodies are extremely diverse

Remarkably, the immune system appears able to recognize every possible antigen, even those that have never before been encountered during the evolution of the species. What is the genetic basis for this extraordinary diversity? Do our cells contain millions of separate antibody genes, each coding for an antibody with a different specificity? Although each human cell has a great deal of DNA, it is insufficient to provide a different gene to code for each specific antibody molecule. This apparent paradox has been largely resolved through the use of molecular techniques. Recombinant DNA technology (Chapter 14) has allowed researchers to make direct comparisons between antibody-coding DNA of the antibody-producing cells and other cells of the body.

Separate DNA segments code for different regions of a heavy or light chain (Figure 43–10). For example, each light chain is coded for by three main DNA segments: a variable (V) segment, a joining (J) segment, and a constant (C) segment. Only one DNA copy of a particular constant segment may be present, but there may be many joining segments and usually very large numbers of different variable segments. During the maturation of a B cell, the DNA segments are shuffled and then joined. One of the many V segments becomes associated with a specific J segment and a specific C segment to produce a complete functional light-chain gene. A similar process takes place for heavy-chain coding.

The production of new combinations of DNA segments is carried out independently during the differentiation of each B cell. The number of potential combinations is so great that, although there are millions of competent B cells, each has the ability to produce a unique antibody molecule. The radical changes that take place in the genes coding for antibodies during the differentiation of lymphocytes make this process a dramatic exception to the principle of nuclear equivalence discussed in Chapter 16.

Additional sources of antibody diversity are known. For example, the variable DNA regions of the mature B lymphocytes mutate very readily (somatic hypermutation), giving rise to genes that code for antibodies with similar but slightly different antigenic specificities.

Cell-Mediated Immunity Provides Cellular Warriors

The T cells and macrophages are responsible for cell-mediated immunity. These cells are especially effective in destroying cells that are infected with viruses and cells that have been altered in some way, such as cancer cells. How do the T cells know which cells to attack? Viral protein is broken down to peptides and transported by MHC protein to the cell surface. The immune system then regards that cell as foreign, and T cells destroy it.

As in antibody-mediated immunity, activated helper T cells are necessary for a response. Recall that T cells have receptors on their surfaces capable of reacting with antigens on the surfaces of altered host cells. As with B cells, only the variety of lymphocyte able to react to the specific antigen presented—that is, a competent lymphocyte—becomes activated. However, as discussed earlier, a T cell cannot recognize an antigen if it is presented alone. The antigen must be presented to the T cell as part of a complex with the class I MHC antigen that the T cell recognizes as "self."

T-cell receptors are molecules with dual specificity; each is specific for one peptide (the foreign antigen) and one MHC molecule. T cells also have co-receptors that bind to MHC molecules but to a different site than the primary receptors. All receptors and co-receptors on a single cell are identical. Cytotoxic T cells are fully acti-

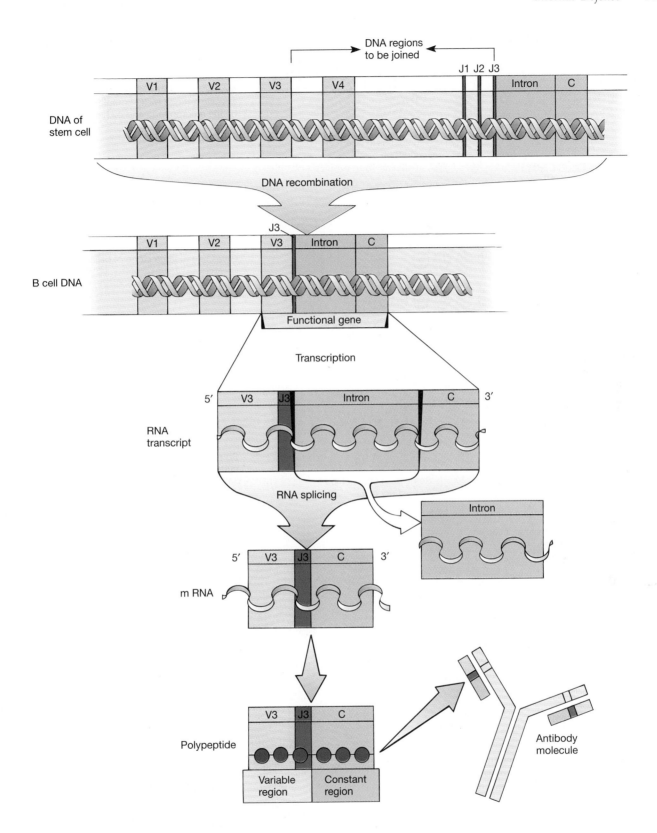

Figure 43–10 DNA rearrangement in production of an antibody. In undifferentiated cells, gene segments are present for a number of different variable (V) regions, for one or more junction (J) regions, and for one or more different constant (C) regions. During differentiation, the segments are rearranged. A gene segment extending from the end of one of the V segments to the beginning of one of the J segments may be deleted. This produces a gene that can be transcribed. The RNA transcript is processed to remove introns and the mRNA produced is translated. Each of the polypeptide chains of an antibody molecule is produced in this way. This diagram is greatly simplified.

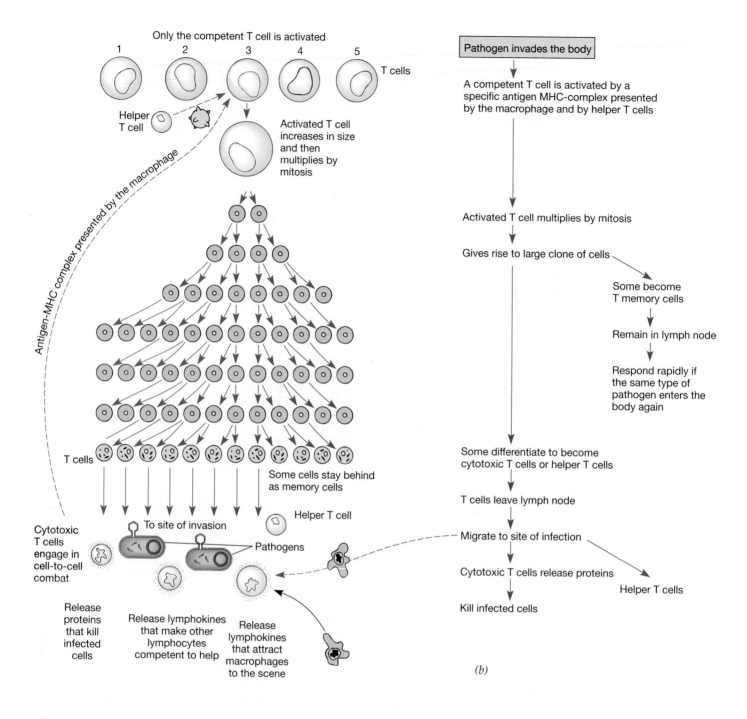

Only the competent T cell is activated

Helper T cell

Antigen–MHC complex presented by the macrophage

Activated T cell increases in size and then multiplies by mitosis

T cells

Some cells stay behind as memory cells

Helper T cell

Cytotoxic T cells engage in cell-to-cell combat

To site of invasion

Pathogens

Release proteins that kill infected cells

Release lymphokines that make other lymphocytes competent to help

Release lymphokines that attract macrophages to the scene

(a)

Pathogen invades the body

A competent T cell is activated by a specific antigen MHC-complex presented by the macrophage and by helper T cells

Activated T cell multiplies by mitosis

Gives rise to large clone of cells

Some become T memory cells

Remain in lymph node

Respond rapidly if the same type of pathogen enters the body again

Some differentiate to become cytotoxic T cells or helper T cells

T cells leave lymph node

Migrate to site of infection

Cytotoxic T cells release proteins

Helper T cells

Kill infected cells

(b)

Figure 43–11 Cell-mediated immunity. When activated by the antigen–MHC complex presented by a macrophage and by a helper T cell, a competent T cell gives rise to a large clone of cells. Many of these differentiate to become cytotoxic T cells, which migrate to the site of infection. There they release proteins such as perforins that destroy invading pathogens.

vated when both receptors and co-receptors bind to the same MHC molecule.

Once stimulated, a T cell increases in size, proliferates, and gives rise to a sizable clone of cytotoxic T cells and memory cells (Figure 43–11). Cytotoxic T cells make up the cellular infantry; they leave the lymph nodes and make their way to the infected area. These

killer cells can destroy a target cell within seconds after contact.

After a cytotoxic T cell combines with antigen on the surface of the target cell, it secretes granules containing a wide variety of cytotoxic proteins. These powerful proteins include perforins and granzymes that can produce lesions in the target cell and cause rapid lysis.

The DNA of the target cell may be broken down into small fragments. Under some conditions, cytotoxic T cells release soluble proteins called **lymphotoxins,** which are especially toxic for cancer cells. After releasing cytotoxic substances, the T cell disengages itself from its victim cell and seeks out a new target cell.

pathogen invades body → macrophage phagocytizes pathogen → foreign antigen–MHC complex displayed on macrophage cell surface → competent T cell activated by specific foreign antigen–MHC complex and helper T cells → clone of competent T cells → cytotoxic T cells → T cells migrate to area of infection → release of proteins that destroy target cells

Helper T cells and macrophages at the site of infection secrete interleukins, interferons, and a variety of other substances that help regulate immune function. Some interleukins confer competence upon other lymphocytes in the area, increasing the ranks of cytotoxic T cells and B cells. Other interleukins enhance the inflammatory reaction, attracting great numbers of macrophages to the site of infection. Interleukins and gamma-interferon stimulate macrophages, making them more active and effective at destroying pathogens.

Suppressor T cells are stimulated by antigen. These cells help regulate immune responses by inhibiting cytotoxic T-cell, B-cell, and macrophage activity. Suppressor T cells also inhibit helper T cells. Suppressor T cells multiply more slowly than cytotoxic T cells. More than a week generally elapses before they are able to suppress an immune response, giving sufficient time for the immune response to effectively defend the body.

A Secondary Immune Response Is More Rapid Than a Primary Response

The first exposure to an antigen stimulates a **primary response.** Injection of an antigen into an immunocompetent animal causes specific antibodies to appear in the blood plasma in 3 to 14 days. After injection of the antigen there is a brief **latent period,** during which the antigen is recognized and appropriate lymphocytes begin to form clones. During the **logarithmic phase** that follows, the antibody concentration rises logarithmically for several days until it reaches a peak (Figure 43–12). IgM is the principal antibody synthesized. Finally, there is a **decline phase,** during which the antibody concentration decreases to a very low level.

A second injection of the same antigen, even years later, evokes a **secondary response.** Because memory cells bearing a living record of the encounter with the antigen persist throughout an individual's life, the secondary response is generally much more rapid than the primary response, with a shorter latent period. The amount of antigen necessary to evoke a secondary response is much less than that needed for a primary re-

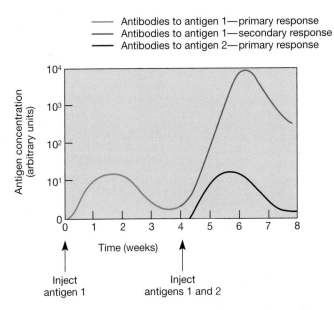

Antibodies to antigen 1—primary response
Antibodies to antigen 1—secondary response
Antibodies to antigen 2—primary response

Figure 43–12 Antibody production in primary and secondary responses to successive doses of antigens. Antigen 1 was injected at day 0, and the immune response was assessed by measuring antibody levels to the antigen. At week 4, the primary response had subsided. Antigen 1 was injected again along with a new protein, antigen 2. Note that the secondary response to antigen 1 was greater and more rapid than the primary response. A primary response was made to the newly encountered antigen 2.

sponse. More antibodies are produced than in a primary response, and the decline phase is slower. In a secondary response the predominant antibody is IgG. The **affinity,** or strength of fit, of the antibody also increases following secondary exposure.

The body's ability to launch a rapid, effective response during a second encounter with an antigen explains why we do not usually suffer from the same disease several times. Most persons get measles or chicken pox, for example, only once. When exposed a second time, the immune system destroys the pathogens before they have time to establish themselves and cause symptoms of the disease. Booster shots of vaccine are given in order to elicit a secondary response, reinforcing the immunological memory of the disease-producing antigens.

You may wonder, then, how a person can get influenza (the "flu") or a cold more than once. Unfortunately, there are many varieties of these diseases, each caused by a virus with slightly different antigens. For example, more than 100 different viruses cause the common cold, and new varieties of "cold" and "flu" virus evolve continuously by mutation (a survival mechanism for them), which may result in changes in their surface antigens. Even a slight change may prevent recognition by memory cells. Because the immune system is so specific, each different antigen is treated by the body as a new immunological challenge.

Table 43–1   ACTIVE AND PASSIVE IMMUNITY

Type of Immunity	When Developed	Development of Memory Cells	Duration of Immunity
Active			
Naturally induced	Pathogens enter the body through natural encounter (e.g., person with measles sneezes on you)	Yes	Many years
Artificially induced	After immunization with a vaccine	Yes	Many years
Passive			
Naturally induced	After transfer of antibodies from mother to developing baby	No	Few months
Artificially induced	After injection with gamma globulin	No	Few months

Active Immunity Follows Exposure to Antigens

We have been considering **active immunity,** immunity developed following exposure to antigens. After you have had chicken pox as a young child, for example, you develop immunity that protects you from contracting chicken pox again. Active immunity can be *naturally* or *artificially* induced (Table 43–1). If someone with chicken pox sneezes near you and you contract the disease, you develop active immunity naturally. Active immunity can also be artificially induced by **immunization,** that is, by injection of a vaccine. In this case, the body launches an immune response against the antigens contained in the vaccine and develops memory cells, so that future encounters with the same pathogen are dealt with swiftly.

Effective vaccines can be prepared in a number of ways. A virus may be attenuated (weakened) by successive passage through cells of nonhuman hosts. In the process, mutations occur that adapt the pathogen to the nonhuman host, so that it can no longer cause disease in humans. This is how polio vaccine, smallpox vaccine, and measles vaccine are produced.

Whooping cough and typhoid fever vaccines are made from killed pathogens that still have the necessary antigens to stimulate an immune response. Tetanus and botulism vaccines are made from toxins secreted by the respective pathogens. The toxin is altered so that it can no longer destroy tissues, but its antigenic determinants are still intact. Most vaccines consist of the entire pathogen, live or killed, or of a protein from the pathogen. In order to reduce potential side effects, researchers are now designing vaccines that consist of synthetic peptides that are only a small part of the anti-

gen. When any of these vaccines is introduced into the body, the immune system actively develops clones, produces antibodies, and develops memory cells.

In **passive immunity,** an individual is given antibodies actively produced by another organism. The serum or gamma globulin containing these antibodies can be obtained from humans or animals. Animal sera are less desirable because their nonhuman proteins can themselves act as antigens, stimulating an immune response that may result in an illness termed serum sickness.

Passive immunity is borrowed immunity, and its effects are not lasting. It is used to boost the body's defense temporarily against a particular disease. For example, during the Vietnam War, in areas where hepatitis was widespread, soldiers were injected with gamma globulin containing antibodies to the hepatitis pathogen. Such injections of gamma globulin offer protection for only a few months. Because the body has not actively launched an immune response, it has no memory cells and cannot produce antibodies to the pathogen. Once the injected antibodies are broken down, the immunity disappears.

Pregnant women confer natural passive immunity upon their developing babies by manufacturing antibodies for them. These maternal antibodies, of the IgG class, pass through the placenta (the organ of exchange between mother and developing child) and provide the fetus and newborn infant with a defense system until its own immune system matures. Babies who are breastfed continue to receive immunoglobulins, particularly IgA, in their milk. These immunoglobulins provide considerable immunity to the pathogens responsible for gastrointestinal infection, and perhaps to other pathogens as well.

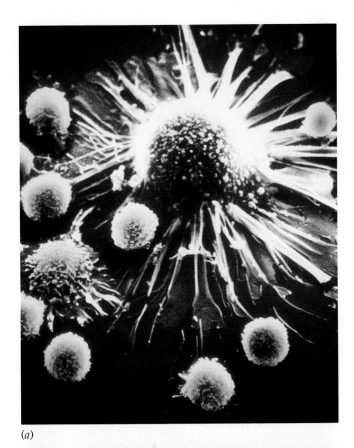

(a)

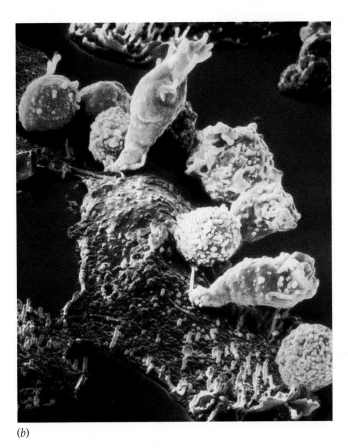

(b)

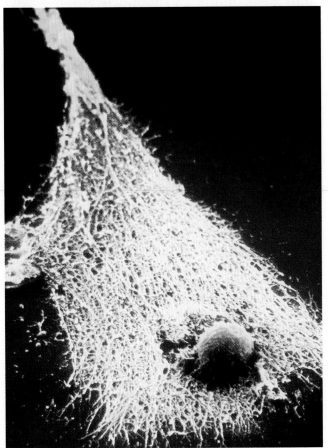

(c)

Figure 43–13 Cytotoxic T cells defend the body against cancer cells. (*a*) An army of cytotoxic T cells surrounds a large cancer cell. The T cells recognize the cancer cell as nonself because it displays altered antigens on its surface. (*b*) Some of the cytotoxic T cells elongate as they chemically attack the cancer cell, breaking down its plasma membrane. (*c*) The cancer cell has been destroyed; only a collapsed fibrous cytoskeleton remains. Photos are artificially colored. (*a–c*, Lennart Nilsson, © Boehringer Ingelheim International GmbH)

The Body Normally Defends Itself against Cancer

Some immunologists think that a few normal cells are transformed into cancer cells every day in each of us in response to viruses, hormones, radiation, or carcinogens in the environment. Because they are abnormal cells, some of their surface proteins are different from those of normal body cells. Such proteins act as antigens, stimulating an immune response. According to the **theory of immune surveillance,** the body's immune system destroys these abnormal cells whenever they arise. Only when these mechanisms fail do abnormal cells divide rapidly, resulting in cancer.

Although many components of the immune system help defend against cancer cells, NK cells and cytotoxic T cells are thought to be most critical (Figure 43–13).

Tumor cells exhibit abnormal surface antigens that trigger immune responses. T cells produce interleukins, which attract macrophages and NK cells and activate them. The T cells also produce interferons, which have an antitumor effect. The macrophages themselves produce factors, including TNF (tumor necrosis factor), that inhibit tumor growth.

NK cells are capable of killing tumor cells or virally infected cells upon first exposure to the foreign antigen. Patients with advanced cancer appear to have lower NK cell activity than healthy persons.

What are the mechanisms by which tumor cells prevent the body from launching an immune response? The cancer cells may be sufficiently similar antigenically to normal cells that the immune system cells may fail to recognize them as foreign. Sometimes cancer cells maintain a "low profile" in this way until a tumor reaches such a large size that the host is unable to destroy it.

Cells of the immune system may recognize cancer cells but be unable to destroy them. Sometimes the presence of cancer cells stimulates B cells to produce IgG antibodies that combine with antigens on the surfaces of the cancer cells. These **blocking antibodies** may block the T cells so that they are unable to adhere to the surface of the cancer cells and destroy them. For some unknown reason, the blocking antibodies are not able to activate the complement system that would destroy the cancer cells. Interestingly, the presence of antibodies in this case is harmful.

An exciting approach in cancer research involves the production of **monoclonal antibodies.**[1] In this procedure, mice are injected with antigens from human cancer cells. After the mice have produced antibodies to the cancer cells, their spleens are removed and plasma cells containing the antibodies are extracted from this tissue. These cells are fused with cancer cells from other mice. The hybrid cells produced have properties of the two "parent" cells. Because of the apparently unlimited ability of cancer cells to divide, these fused hybrid cells continue to divide indefinitely. At the same time they continue to produce antibodies like a plasma cell.

Researchers select hybrid cells that are manufacturing the specific antibody needed and then clone them in a separate cell culture. Cells of this clone produce large amounts of the specific antibody needed—hence the name monoclonal antibodies. Such antibodies can be injected into the very same cancer patients whose cancer cells were used to stimulate their production and are highly specific for destroying the cancer cells. (Monoclonal antibodies specific for a single antigenic deter-

---

[1] Note that use of this technique is not restricted to cancer research. It is used in other contexts to produce large quantities of pure antibodies that react to a specific antigenic determinant.

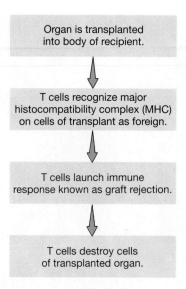

Figure 43–14 Graft rejection.

minant can now be produced.) In trial studies, such antibodies are being tagged with toxic drugs that are then delivered specifically to the cancer cells.

Graft Rejection Is an Immune Response against Transplanted Tissue

Skin can be successfully transplanted from one part of the body to another. However, when skin is taken from one individual and grafted onto the body of another, the skin graft is rejected and it sloughs off. Why?

Recall that tissues from the same individual or from identical twins have identical HLA alleles and thus the same HLA antigens. Such tissues are compatible. Because its HLA antigens are the same, the tissue is not rejected. Tissue transplanted from one location to another in the same individual is called an **autograft.**

Because of the polymorphism (multiple alleles) of the HLA genes, it is difficult to find identical matches among strangers. If a tissue or organ is taken from a donor and transplanted to the body of an unrelated host, several of the HLA antigens are likely to be different. Such a graft made between members of the same species but of different genetic makeup is called an **allograft.** The host's immune system regards the graft as foreign and launches an effective immune response called **graft rejection.** T lymphocytes attack the transplanted tissue and can destroy it within a few days (Figure 43–14).

Before transplants are performed, tissues from the patient and from potential donors must be typed and matched as closely as possible. Cell typing is somewhat similar to blood typing but is more complex. The first obstacle is obtaining the typing sera. For ABO blood typing the sera are readily attainable because A type individuals naturally have anti-B antibodies, B type individuals have anti-A antibodies, and O type individuals have anti-A and anti-B antibodies. In contrast, in order to obtain antibodies directed to antigens of the MHC, an individual must be actively immunized to the foreign proteins. Because some of these antigens are found on all nucleated cells, multiparous females (women who have experienced multiple births) inadvertently become immunized to the histocompatibility antigens of their offspring, and patients undergoing multiple blood transfusions also produce antibodies to the MHC. The antibodies from these serum sources are purified and the specific antibodies generated are used to type tissue.

Recall that antigens of the MHC are described as class I, class II, or class III. Class I antigens, found on all nucleated cells, serve as histocompatibility antigens or transplantation antigens. They are identified by the serological means just described. MHC class II antigens are found mainly on B cells and macrophages. For an organ transplant these differences are significant. If a donor organ is only slighly different from a recipient in its class I antigens but the class II antigens are markedly different, a major immune response to the organ is likely to occur. Conversely, if a donor organ is only slightly different from a recipient in its class I antigens, but the class II antigens are closely matched, only a weak rejection response is generated.

Serologically typing class II antigens is more difficult than typing class I antigens. Identification is often made by an in vitro lymphocyte proliferation test, which takes about 5 days. Therefore, the results of a tissue match may not be known until after the organ has been transplanted. The information is still useful, however, because it gives the physician an idea of how serious the graft rejection may be and how to treat it. If all five of the HLA group of antigens are matched, the graft has about a 95% chance of surviving the first year. Unfortunately, not many persons are lucky enough to have an identical twin to supply spare parts, so perfect matches are difficult to find. Furthermore, some parts such as the heart cannot be spared. Most organs to be transplanted, therefore, are removed from unrelated donors, often from patients who have just died.

To prevent graft rejection in less compatible matches, drugs and x rays have been used to destroy T lymphocytes. These methods do not kill T lymphocytes selectively so all types of lymphocytes are indiscriminately destroyed. Furthermore, lymphocyte destruction suppresses not only graft rejection but other immune responses as well, so that many transplant patients succumb to pneumonia or other infections. Immunosuppressed patients also have an increased incidence of certain types of tumor growths. Cyclosporine, an antibiotic extracted from fungi, is one of several cytotoxic drugs now used to suppress T cells that have been activated by antigens on the graft; cyclosporine has little effect on B cells. Thus, the graft is not rejected and the patient can still resist infection. Virtually all organ graft recipients today are treated with cytotoxic drugs because of their significant effect on organ graft survival.

Certain Body Sites Are Immunologically Privileged

A few immunologically privileged locations exist in the body in which foreign tissue is accepted by a host. The brain and cornea are examples. Corneal transplants are highly successful because the cornea has almost no blood or lymphatic vessels associated with it and so is out of reach of most lymphocytes. Furthermore, antigens in the corneal graft probably would not find their way into the circulatory system, and so would not stimulate an immune response.

Immunological Tolerance Can Be Induced

Immunological tolerance refers to a specific nonresponsiveness to an antigen. The immune system is a highly regulated mechanism that produces strong immune responses that allow us to fight infection and protects us against cancer. Remarkably, this system is selectively tolerant to our own individual tissues and cells.

Tolerance to specific antigens can be generated by eliminating either the T cell or B cell portion of the immune response. Because most antigens have multiple antigenic determinants, it is best to choose simple antigens in these experiments. Stimulating immature cells by low concentrations of antigen can abort the development of either the T cell or the B cell. The absolute absence of T or B cells specific for a particular antigen would result in nonresponsiveness to that antigen.

Another way to generate tolerance is by stimulating suppressor T cells. This can be done with certain antigens, using strictly defined immunization protocols. Then, when the animal comes into contact with the antigen, the suppressor T cells prevent an immune reaction.

Immunological tolerance can be induced in fetal or neonatal animals. If the thymus gland of a newborn animal is removed, the animal's lymph nodes remain small and the animal is deficient in cellular immunity. An animal treated in this way accepts tissue grafts from other animals that differ from it genetically.

In an Autoimmune Disease the Body Attacks Its Own Tissues

Sometimes self-tolerance appears to break down and the body reacts immunologically against its own tissues, causing an **autoimmune disease.** Some of the dis-

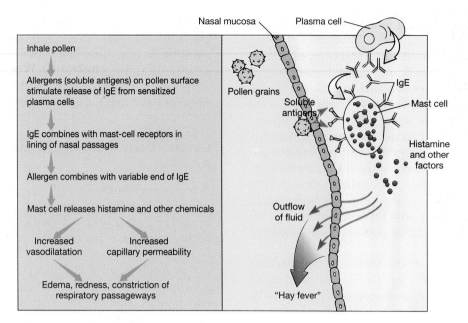

Figure 43–15   A common type of allergic response.

eases that result from such failures in self-tolerance are rheumatoid arthritis, multiple sclerosis, Graves' disease, myasthenia gravis, systemic lupus erythematosus (SLE), and insulin-dependent diabetes (Type I).

Myasthenia gravis is an autoimmune disease in which a circulating antibody combines with acetylcholine receptors in motor neurons. This interaction blocks the receptors and can damage or destroy them. With fewer receptors, the stimulation of the muscle may be reduced to below threshold level. When this happens, muscle contraction cannot occur. Affected persons experience muscle weakness, and respiratory muscles may be affected to a life-threatening extent.

What causes the production of abnormal antibodies in myasthenia gravis and other autoimmune diseases is not known. Some investigators have suggested genetic predisposition, perhaps involving HLA genes. For example, in more than 90% of patients with ankylosing spondylitis, an inflammatory disease of the vertebral joints, a mutation of a particular HLA allele (B27) has been identified.

Certain infections may trigger an autoimmune disease in a genetically susceptible individual. Some studies suggest that a previous viral infection in the tissue involved in autoimmune disease may have stimulated the body to manufacture antibodies against the infected cells. Then, after the virus has been destroyed, the body continues to manufacture harmful antibodies capable of attacking the body cells—even though they are no longer infected. Loss of suppressor cells may also result in autoimmune disease. In some cases, a combination of these factors may be responsible.

Allergic Reactions Are Inappropriate Immune Responses

The immune system normally functions to defend the body against pathogens and to preserve homeostasis, but sometimes the system malfunctions. **Allergy** is a state of altered immune response that is harmful to the body. Allergic persons have a tendency to manufacture antibodies (IgE) against mild antigens, called **allergens,** that do not stimulate a response in nonallergic individuals. About 15% of the population of the United States are plagued by an allergic disorder such as allergic asthma or hayfever. There appears to be an inherited tendency to these disorders.

Let us examine a common allergic reaction—a hayfever response to ragweed pollen (Figure 43–15). When an allergic person inhales the microscopic pollen, allergens stimulate the release of IgE from sensitized plasma cells in the nasal passages. The IgE attaches to receptors on the membranes of mast cells, large connective tissue cells filled with distinctive granules. Each mast cell has thousands of receptors to which the IgE may attach. Each IgE molecule attaches to a mast cell receptor by its C region end, leaving the V region end of the immunoglobulin free to combine with the ragweed pollen allergen.

When the allergen combines with IgE antibody, the mast cell rapidly releases its granules (Figure 43–16). When exposed to extracellular fluid, the granules release histamine, serotonin, and other chemicals that cause inflammation. These substances produce dilation of blood vessels and increased capillary permeability,

Figure 43–16   When an allergen combines with IgE bound to a mast cell receptor, the mast cell releases granules filled with histamine and other chemicals that cause the symptoms of an allergic response.   (Lennart Nilsson, © Boehringer Ingelheim International GmbH)

leading to edema and redness. Such physiological responses cause the victims' nasal passages to become swollen and irritated. Their noses run, they sneeze, their eyes water, and they feel generally uncomfortable.

allergens on pollen → sensitized plasma cells → IgE released → IgE combines with mast cell receptors → bound IgE combines with allergen → mast cell releases granules → histamine and other chemicals released → allergic symptoms

In **allergic asthma,** an allergen-IgE response occurs in the bronchioles of the lungs. Mast cells release SRS-A (slow-reacting substance of anaphylaxis), which causes smooth muscle to constrict. The airways in the lungs sometimes constrict for several hours, making breathing difficult.

Certain foods or drugs act as allergens in some persons, causing a reaction in the walls of the gastrointestinal tract which leads to discomfort and diarrhea. The allergen may be absorbed and cause mast cells to release granules elsewhere in the body. When the allergen-IgE reaction takes place in the skin, the histamine released by mast cells causes the swollen red welts known as **hives.**

Systemic anaphylaxis is a dangerous kind of allergic reaction that can occur when a person develops an allergy to a specific drug such as penicillin, or to compounds present in the venom injected by a stinging insect. Within minutes after the substance enters the body, a widespread allergic reaction takes place. Large amounts of histamine are released into the circulation, causing extreme vasodilation and permeability. So much plasma may be lost from the blood that circulatory shock and death can occur within a few minutes.

The symptoms of allergic reactions are often treated with **antihistamines,** drugs that block the effects of histamine. These drugs compete for the same receptor sites on cells targeted by histamine. When the antihistamine combines with the receptor, it prevents the histamine from combining and thus prevents its harmful effects. Antihistamines are useful clinically in relieving the symptoms of hives and hayfever. They are not completely effective, however, because mast cells release substances other than histamine that cause allergic symptoms.

In serious allergic disorders patients are sometimes given **desensitization therapy.** Very small amounts of the very antigen to which they are allergic are either injected or administered in the form of drops daily over a period of months or years. This stimulates production of IgG antibodies against the antigen. When the patient encounters the allergen, the IgG immunoglobulins combine with the allergen, blocking its antigenic determinants so that the IgE cannot combine with it. In this way a less harmful immune response is substituted for the allergic reaction. Desensitizing injections of the antigen are also thought to stimulate suppressor T-cell activity.

AIDS Is an Immune Disease Caused by a Retrovirus

First recognized in 1981, **acquired immune deficiency syndrome,** or simply **AIDS,** is a deadly disease that is spreading through the human population at an alarming rate. More than 200,000 individuals in the United States have been diagnosed with AIDS. More than 1 million persons in the United States are estimated to be infected with the AIDS virus but do not yet show symptoms. Worldwide, more than 5 million people are thought to be infected with the AIDS virus. Some epidemiologists suggest that these numbers reflect only about 10% the actual number of individuals infected.

AIDS is caused by infection with a retrovirus called **human immunodeficiency virus (HIV-1).** (Recall that a retrovirus is an RNA virus that uses its RNA as a template to make DNA with the help of reverse transcriptase.) The virus infects and destroys helper T cells, resulting in severely depressed immune function (Figures 43–17 and 43–18). The virus apparently selects helper T cells because of a certain component (CD4) of its antigen receptor. (Recall that helper T cells are necessary for both T cell and B cell activation.) Thus, when the helper T cell population is depressed, the ability to resist infection is severely impaired. AIDS patients die within several months to about 5 years from rare forms of cancer, pneumonia, and other opportunistic infections that pose little threat to individuals with fully functioning immune systems.

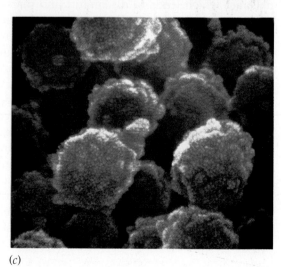

Figure 43–17   HIV-1 virus particles (blue) that cause AIDS attack a helper T cell. HIV-1 seriously impairs the immune system by rapidly destroying helper T cells.   (Lennart Nilsson, © Boehringer Ingelheim International GmbH)

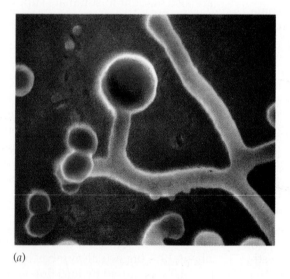

(a)

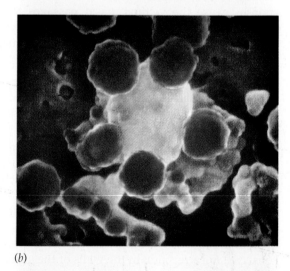

(b)

Figure 43–18   (a) HIV-1 virus particles budding from the ends of branched microvilli. (b) An even higher magnification of virus particles budding from a ''bleb'' (a cytoplasmic extension broader than a microvillus). Note the pentagonal symmetry often evident in other biological branching and flowering structures. (c) HIV-1 virus particles at extremely high magnification. The surfaces are grainy and the outlines slightly blurred because the preparation was coated with coarse-grained heavy metal salt (palladium).

(c)

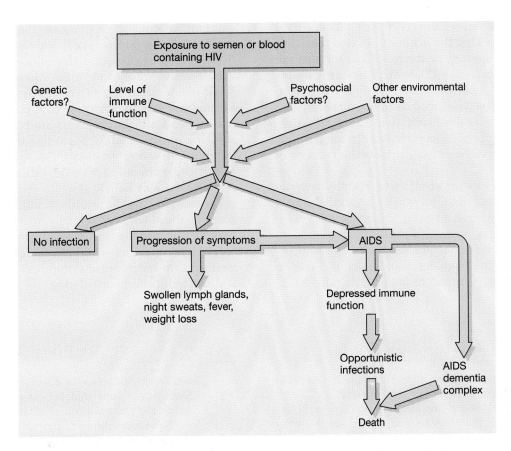

Figure 43–19 Exposure to semen or blood that contains HIV-1 can lead to AIDS. Many factors apparently determine whether a person exposed to the AIDS virus contracts the disease. Some exposed individuals apparently do not become infected. However, the risk increases with multiple exposures.

Symptoms associated with HIV-1 infection may begin with mild infections that resemble infectious mononucleosis. Later, swollen lymph glands may occur throughout the body (Figure 43–19). About one third of AIDS patients develop a neuropsychological disorder known as AIDS dementia complex, which results from direct infection of the central nervous system by the retrovirus. AIDS dementia complex is characterized by progressive cognitive, motor, and behavioral dysfunction that typically ends in coma and death.

Current evidence indicates that AIDS is transmitted mainly by semen during sexual intercourse with an infected person or by direct exposure to infected blood or blood products. Those most at risk are males who engage in homosexual and bisexual behavior (72% of cases) and individuals who use intravenous drugs (20%). The fastest rising risk groups are women and teenagers who contract the virus through heterosexual contact. Heterosexual contact with infected individuals accounts for about one third of HIV infection in women and an increasing number of cases in both men and women. Individuals who require frequent blood transfusions, such as those with hemophilia, and infants born to mothers with AIDS are also at risk.

Effective blood-screening procedures have been developed to safeguard blood bank supplies, so that risk of infection from blood transfusion has been greatly reduced. Use of a latex condom during sexual intercourse provides some protection against the virus. Use of a spermicide containing nonoxynol-9 is thought to provide additional protection. AIDS is not spread by casual contact. People do not contract the disease by hugging, kissing, sharing a drink, or using the same bathroom facilities. Close friends and family members who live with AIDS patients are not more likely to get the disease.

AIDS may be an opportunistic infection that causes disease in individuals with inadequate immune function. Susceptibility to HIV may depend on a combination of genetic, environmental, and psychosocial factors. The latter include personality variables and coping styles that increase susceptibility to environmental stressors.

Research laboratories throughout the world are searching for drugs that will successfully combat the AIDS virus. Because this virus often infects the central nervous system, an effective drug must cross the blood-brain barrier. AZT (azidothymidine) was the first drug developed to treat HIV-1 infection. AZT blocks HIV-1 replication by blocking the action of reverse transcriptase, the enzyme needed by the retrovirus for incorporation into the host cell's DNA. AZT can prolong the period prior to onset of AIDS symptoms. Unfortunately, the virus has developed strains that are resistant to this drug. As other drugs effective against HIV-1 are developed and approved, combination treatment may help slow the development of drug-resistant strains of the virus.

Vaccination is the most effective, simplest way of preventing a disease, and developing a vaccine against HIV-1 has been a most pressing challenge for virologists. Unfortunately, research directed at developing a vaccine against HIV-1 has not yet been successful because the retrovirus mutates rapidly, giving rise to many viral strains. New strains are antigenically differ-

ent. Further slowing progress are the absence of an effective animal model for AIDS and the ethical and practical difficulties associated with finding human volunteers in whom to test the vaccine.

While immunologists work to develop a successful vaccine and effective drugs to treat patients with AIDS, massive educational programs are being developed to slow the spread of AIDS. Spreading the word that having multiple sexual partners increases the risk of AIDS and teaching sexually active individuals the importance of "safe" sex may help to slow the epidemic. Some have suggested that public health facilities offer free condoms to those who are sexually active and free sterile hypodermic needles to those addicted to drugs. The cost of these measures would be far less than the cost of medical care for increasing numbers of AIDS patients and the toll in human suffering.

SUMMARY

I. Immune responses depend upon the ability of an organism to distinguish between self and nonself.
II. Most invertebrates are capable only of nonspecific responses such as phagocytosis and the inflammatory response.
III. Vertebrates can launch both nonspecific and specific responses.
   A. Nonspecific defense mechanisms that prevent entrance of pathogens include the skin, acid secretions in the stomach, and the mucous lining of the respiratory passageways.
   B. Should pathogens succeed in breaking through the first line of defense, other nonspecific defense mechanisms are activated to destroy the invading pathogens.
      1. When pathogens invade tissues, they trigger an inflammatory response, which brings needed phagocytic cells and antibodies to the infected area.
      2. Neutrophils and macrophages phagocytize and destroy bacteria.
   C. Specific immune responses include antibody-mediated immunity and cell-mediated immunity. Both T cells and B cells respond to antigens.
   D. In antibody-mediated immunity, the foreign antigen–major histocompatibility (MHC) complex is presented by a macrophage. Helper T cells must also combine with the foreign antigen–MHC complex; the helper T cells secrete interleukins that activate competent B cells. The activated B cells multiply, giving rise to clones of cells. Some differentiate to become plasma cells, which secrete specific antibodies.
   E. Antibodies are highly specific proteins called immunoglobulins. They are produced in response to specific antigens. Antibodies are grouped in five classes according to their structure.
   F. When antibody combines with a specific antigen to form an antigen-antibody complex, the pathogen may be inactivated, phagocytosis may be stimulated, or the complement system may be activated. The comple-

ment system increases the inflammatory response and phagocytosis; some complement proteins digest portions of the pathogen cell.
   G. In cell-mediated immunity, specific T cells are activated by helper T cells and by a foreign antigen–MHC complex displayed on a macrophage cell surface. Activated T cells multiply, giving rise to a clone of cells.
      1. Some T cells differentiate to become cytotoxic T cells, which migrate to the site of infection and chemically destroy cells infected by pathogens.
      2. Some T cells remain in the lymph nodes as memory cells; others become helper T cells or suppressor T cells.
   H. Second exposure to an antigen evokes a secondary immune response, which is more rapid and more intense than the primary response.
   I. Active immunity develops as a result of exposure to antigens; it may occur naturally or may be artificially induced by immunization. Passive immunity develops when an individual is injected with antibodies produced by another person or animal and is temporary.
   J. NK cells and cytotoxic T cells defend the body against cancer.
   K. Transplanted tissues possess protein markers (MHC) that stimulate graft rejection, an immune response (launched mainly by T cells) that destroys the transplant.
   L. Immunological tolerance to foreign tissues can be induced experimentally under certain conditions.
   M. In autoimmune diseases, the body reacts immunologically against its own tissues.
   N. In an allergic response, an allergen can stimulate production of IgE antibody, which combines with the receptors on mast cells; the mast cells then release histamine and other substances, causing inflammation and other symptoms of allergy.

POST-TEST

1. Molecules capable of stimulating an immune response are called _____.
2. Specific proteins produced in response to specific antigens are called _____.
3. When infected by viruses, some cells respond by producing proteins called _____.
4. The clinical characteristics of inflammation are _____, _____, _____, and _____.
5. T lymphoctyes are thought to originate in the _____ _____; they are processed in the _____ and then proliferate in the _____ tissues.
6. _____ is a cytokine that activates helper T cells.
7. When the body is invaded by the same pathogen a second time, the immune response can be launched more rapidly owing to the presence of _____ cells.
8. The cells that produce antibodies are _____ cells.
9. An antigenic determinant gives the antigen molecule a specific configuration that can be "recognized" by an _____.
10. The _____ confers immunological competence upon T cells.
11. The complement system is activated when an _____ complex is formed.
12. In opsonization, complement proteins _____.
13. Although artificially induced, immunization is a form of _____ immunity.
14. An individual injected with antibodies produced by another organism is receiving _____ immunity.
15. In humans the major histocompatibility complex is called the _____ group.
16. In graft rejection the host launches an effective _____ _____ against _____ tissue.
17. Corneal transplants are highly successful becuase the cornea is an immunologically _____ site.
18. An _____ is a mild antigen that does not stimulate a response in an individual who is not _____.
19. In a typical allergic reaction mast cells secrete _____ and other compounds that cause _____.

REVIEW QUESTIONS

1. How does the body distinguish between self and nonself? Are invertebrates capable of making this distinction?
2. Contrast specific and nonspecific defense mechanisms. Which type confronts invading pathogens immediately? How do the two systems work together?
3. How does inflammation help to restore homeostasis?
4. Contrast cell-mediated with antibody-mediated immune responses.
5. Describe three ways in which antibodies work to destroy pathogens.
6. John is immunized against measles. Jack contracts measles from a playmate in nursery school before his parents have him immunized. Compare the immune responses in the two children. Five years later, John and Jack are playing together when Judy, who is coming down with measles, sneezes on both of them. Compare the immune responses in Jack and in John.
7. Why is passive immunity temporary?
8. What is immunological tolerance?
9. What is graft rejection? What is the immunological basis for it?
10. List the immunological events that take place in a common type of allergic reaction such as hayfever.
11. How does the body defend itself against cancer?
12. What is an autoimmune disease? Give two examples.
13. What public policy decisions would you recommend that might help slow the spread of AIDS?

RECOMMENDED READINGS

Anderson, R. M., and R. M. May. Understanding the AIDS pandemic. *Scientific American*, Vol. 266, No. 5 (May 1992), pp. 58–66. New models are being used to study the transmission of AIDS at the population level.

Boehmer, H. von, and P. Kisielow. How the immune system learns about self. *Scientific American*, Vol. 265, No. 4 (October 1991), pp. 74–81. The thymus destroys T cells that would be harmful to the body.

Cohen, I. R. The self, the world and autoimmunity. *Scientific American*, Vol. 258, No. 4 (April 1988), pp. 52–60. Self-recognition is important for health as well as for certain diseases.

Edelson, R. L., and J. M. Fink. The immunologic function of skin. *Scientific American*, Vol. 252, No. 6 (June 1985), pp. 46–53. Specialized cells in the skin play interacting roles in the response to foreign invaders.

Fischetti, V. A. Streptococcal M protein. *Scientific American*, Vol. 264, No. 6 (June 1991), pp. 58–65. The bacteria that cause strep throat and rheumatic fever depend on a surface protein to evade the body's defenses.

Gallo, R. C. The AIDS virus. *Scientific American*, Vol. 256, No. 1 (January 1987), pp. 46–56. An overview of the discovery of the AIDS virus and a description of the pathogen.

Grey, H. M., Sette, A., and B. Soren. How T cells see antigen. *Scientific American*, Vol. 261, No. 5 (November 1989), pp. 56–64. T cells respond to antigen only when it is presented complexed with MHC antigen by an antigen-presenting cell such as a macrophage.

Johnson, H. M., Russell, J. K., and C. H. Pontzer. Superantigens in human disease. *Scientific American*, Vol. 266, No. 4 (April 1992), pp. 92–101. Superantigens cause food poisoning and toxic shock. The article discusses how superantigens cause disease.

Marrack, P., and J. Kappler. The T cell and its receptor. *Scientific American* (February 1986). The surface proteins on T cells are a vital component of cell-mediated immunity.

Scientific American, Vol. 259, No. 4 (October 1988). A single-topic issue including ten articles on AIDS.

Smith, K. A. Interleukin-2. *Scientific American*, Vol. 262, No. 3 (March 1990), pp. 50–57. A discussion of the regulatory functions of interleukin-2.

Tizard, I. R. *Immunology: An Introduction*, 3rd ed. Saunders College Publishing, Philadelphia, 1992. A basic introduction to immunology.

Gas Exchange

M ost animal cells require a continuous supply of oxygen. Some cells, such as mammalian brain cells, may be damaged beyond repair if their supply is cut off for only a few minutes. Animal cells must also rid themselves of carbon dioxide. The exchange of gases between the organism and its environment is known as **respiration.**

The exchange of gases is a fairly simple process in small, aquatic organisms such as sponges, hydras, and flatworms. Dissolved oxygen from the surrounding water diffuses into the cells, and carbon dioxide diffuses out of the cells and into the water. No specialized respiratory structures are needed.

Oxygen diffuses slowly through tissues. In an organism more than

A wapiti's breath condenses in the frosty air. (Stan Osolinski/Dembinsky Photo Associates)

1 mm thick, diffusion alone does not provide a satisfactory method of gas exchange. Specialized respiratory structures such as gills or lungs are required to ensure adequate exchange of oxygen and carbon dioxide.

Gases move into and out of cells by diffusion. If the air or water supplying the oxygen to the cells can be continuously renewed, more oxygen will be available. For this reason animals carry on **ventilation;** that is, they actively move air or water over their respiratory surfaces. Sponges do this by setting up a current of water through the channels of their bodies by means of flagella. Most fish gulp water, which then passes over their gills. Terrestrial vertebrates ventilate their lungs by inhaling and exhaling air.

After you have studied this chapter you should be able to

1. Describe the following adaptations for gas exchange: the body surface of some animals such as annelids, tracheal tubes, gills, and lungs.
2. Compare gas exchange in various types of animals, e.g., flatworms, earthworms, insects, fishes, and mammals.
3. Compare air and water as sources of oxygen.
4. Describe the function of respiratory pigments.
5. Trace a breath of air through the human respiratory system from external nares to air sacs.
6. Summarize the sequence of events that takes place in breathing.
7. Define tidal volume and vital capacity.

8. Describe how oxygen and carbon dioxide are exchanged in the lungs and in the tissues.
9. Explain the role of hemoglobin in oxygen transport, and identify factors that determine and influence the oxygen-hemoglobin dissociation curve.
10. Outline the mechanisms by which carbon dioxide is transported in the blood.
11. Summarize how respiration is regulated.
12. Describe the physiological effects of each of the following: hyperventilation, sudden decompression at 12,000 meters, and surfacing too quickly from a deep-sea dive.
13. Describe the following effects of breathing polluted air: bronchial constriction, chronic bronchitis, emphysema, and lung cancer.

ANIMALS HAVE EVOLVED SEVERAL DIFFERENT ADAPTATIONS FOR GAS EXCHANGE

Specialized respiratory structures must have thin walls so that diffusion can easily occur. The surface through which gases are exchanged must also be kept moist so that oxygen and carbon dioxide can be dissolved in water. In addition, respiratory structures are generally richly supplied with blood vessels to facilitate transport of respiratory gases. Four principal types of respiratory structures used by animals are the body surface, tracheal tubes, gills, and lungs (Figure 44–1; Table 44–1).

The Body Surface May Be Adapted for Gas Exchange

Gas exchange occurs through the entire body surface in many animals including nudibranch mollusks, most annelids, small arthropods, and a few vertebrates (Figure 44–2). All of these animals are small, with a high ratio of surface to volume. Most animals that exchange gas through the body surface also have a relatively low metabolic rate, so that only small quantities of oxygen are needed.

How does an animal such as the earthworm exchange gases through its body surface? Movements of the worm and air currents ventilate the air so that fresh oxygen-rich air is brought in contact with the body surface. Gland cells in the epidermis secrete mucus, which keeps the body surface moist. Oxygen from tiny air pockets in the loose soil that the earthworm inhabits dissolves in the mucus. Then the oxygen diffuses through the body wall. The oxygen diffuses into blood circulating in a network of capillaries just beneath the outer cell layer. Oxygen is transported by the blood to all of the cells of the earthworm body, diffusing from the blood into the cells. Carbon dioxide from the body cells diffuses into the blood and is transported to the body surface, from which it diffuses out into the environment.

When it rains, water fills the air pockets in the soil and earthworms come to the surface—to come in contact with the air above the ground. Because water holds less oxygen than air, the oxygen available in the soil may not be sufficient at such times.

Tracheal Tube Systems of Arthropods Deliver Air Directly to the Cells

In insects and some other arthropods (e.g., chilopods, diplopods, some mites, and some spiders), the respiratory system consists of a network of **tracheal tubes** (Figure 44–3). Air enters the tracheal tubes through a series of tiny openings called **spiracles** along the body surface. The maximum number of spiracles in an insect is 20—two thoracic pairs and eight abdominal pairs—but the number and position vary in different species. In large or active insects, air moves into and out of the spiracles by movements of the body or by rhythmic movements of the tracheal tubes. For example, the grasshopper draws air into its body through the first four pairs of spiracles when the abdomen expands. Then the abdomen contracts, forcing air out through the last six pairs of spiracles.

Once inside the body, the air passes through the branching tracheal tubes, which extend to all parts of the animal. The tracheal tubes terminate in microscopic, fluid-filled tracheoles. Gases are exchanged between the fluid in these tracheoles and the body cells.

Gills of Aquatic Animals Are Specialized Respiratory Surfaces

Gills are respiratory structures found mainly in aquatic animals, because gills are supported in water but tend

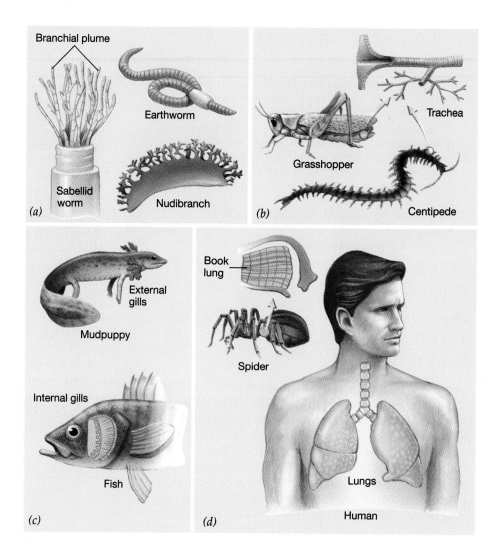

Figure 44–1 Types of respiratory structures found in animals. (*a*) Some animals exchange gases through the body surface (sabellid worms are polychaete annelids; nudibranchs are mollusks). (*b*) Insects and some other arthropods exchange gases through a system of tracheal tubes. (*c*) Many aquatic animals have gills for gas exchange. (*d*) Lungs are adaptations for terrestrial gas exchange.

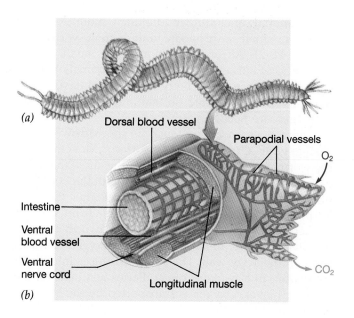

Figure 44–2 Gas exchange across the body surface. (*a*) The clamworm *Nereis virens.* (*b*) Vascular system within a segment of *Nereis virens.* Arrows indicate the direction of blood flow. The limblike parapodium acts as an extension of the body wall in gas exchange with the surrounding water.

Table 44–1 PRINCIPAL TYPES OF RESPIRATORY STRUCTURES

Structure	Animals that Utilize Such Structures	Description	Comment
Body surface	Nudibranch mollusks, most annelids, small arthropods, some vertebrates	In terrestrial forms the body surface is kept moist by mucus secretion. Blood vessels or coelomic fluid present just below the surface receive oxygen and transport it to other body regions.	These animals have high surface-to-volume ratio, low metabolic rate. In some animals (e.g., frogs), other respiratory structures are present.
Tracheal tubes	Insects, some mites, some spiders, millipedes, centipedes	Air enters tracheal tubes through spiracles and passes through the branching tracheal tubes to all parts of the body, terminating in fluid-filled tracheoles. Gas exchange occurs by diffusion between tracheoles and body cells.	In large or active animals ventilation occurs by movements of the body or of tracheal tubes.
Gills	Found mainly in aquatic animals, some annelids, mollusks, crustaceans, fish, and amphibians	Moist, thin structures that grow out from the body surface. In gills of bony fish, each gill consists of many filaments containing blood vessels.	A great deal of energy must be expended in ventilation of the gills.
Lungs	Arachnids, some mollusks, most vertebrates	Respiratory structures that develop as ingrowths of the body surface or from the wall of a body cavity. In vertebrates a series of air passageways may terminate in thin-walled air sacs within the lungs.	Most modern fish lack lungs.

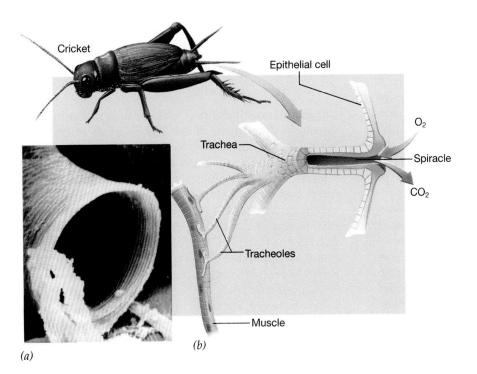

(a)

(b)

Figure 44–3 Tracheal tubes are characteristic of insects and some other invertebrates. (*a*) A scanning electron micrograph of a mole cricket trachea. The corrugations are a very long spiral around the tube, which may strengthen the tracheal wall, somewhat as does the spring within the plastic hoses of many vacuum cleaners and hair dryers. The tracheal wall is composed of chitin. (*b*) Each tracheal tube and its branches conduct oxygen to the body cells of the insect. (*a*, Courtesy of Dr. James L. Nation and Stain Technology Vol. 58, 1983)

Figure 44–4   The gills of the salmon provide an extensive surface for gas exchange.   (G. I. Bernard © 1993 Animals Animals)

to collapse in air. They are moist, thin structures that extend out from the body surface (Figure 44–4). In many animals, the outer surface of the gills is exposed to water, whereas the inner side is in close contact with networks of blood vessels.

Sea stars and sea urchins have **dermal gills** that project from the body wall. Their ciliated epidermal cells ventilate the gills by beating a stream of water over them. Gases are exchanged through the gills between the water and the coelomic fluid inside the body.

Various types of gills are found in some annelids, aquatic mollusks, crustaceans, fish, and amphibians. Molluskan gills are folded, providing a large surface for respiration. In bivalve mollusks and in simple chordates, the gills are adapted for trapping and sorting food. Rhythmic beating of cilia draws water over the gill area, and food is filtered out of the water as gases are exchanged. In mollusks gas exchange also takes place through the mantle.

In chordates, the gills are usually internal. A series of slits perforates the pharynx, and the gills are located along the edges of these gill slits. In bony fish, the fragile gills are protected by an external bony plate, the **operculum.** Movements of the operculum help to pump oxygenated water in through the mouth. The water flows over the gills and then exits through the gill slits.

Each gill in the bony fish consists of many **filaments,** which provide an extensive surface for gas exchange (Figure 44–5). The filaments extend out into the water, which continuously flows over them. A capillary network delivers blood to the gill filaments, facilitating

diffusion of oxygen and carbon dioxide between blood and water. The very impressive efficiency of this system depends on the flow of blood in a direction opposite to the movement of the water. This arrangement, referred to as a **countercurrent exchange system,** maximizes the difference in oxygen concentrations between blood and water.

If blood and water flowed in the *same* direction, the difference between the oxygen concentrations in blood (low) and water (high) would be very large initially and very small at the end. The oxygen concentration in the water would tend to come into equilibrium (balance) with oxygen in the blood. When the concentrations of oxygen in the two fluids became equal, net diffusion of oxygen would stop. A great deal of oxygen would remain in the water.

In the countercurrent exchange system, however, blood low in oxygen comes in contact with water that is partly oxygen-depleted. Then, as the blood becomes more and more oxygen-rich, it comes in contact with water with a progressively higher concentration of oxygen. In this way a high rate of diffusion is maintained, ensuring that a very high percentage (more than 80%) of the available oxygen in the water diffuses into the blood.

Oxygen and carbon dioxide do not interfere with one another's diffusion, and they simultaneously diffuse in opposite directions. This is because oxygen is more concentrated outside the gills than within, but carbon dioxide is more concentrated inside the gills than outside. Thus, the same countercurrent exchange mechanism that ensures efficient influx of oxygen works in reverse fashion to ensure equally efficient outgo of carbon dioxide.

Terrestrial Vertebrates Exchange Gases through Lungs

Lungs are broadly defined as respiratory structures that develop as ingrowths of the body surface or from the wall of a body cavity such as the pharynx (Figure 44–6). Arachnids and some small mollusks (particularly terrestrial snails and slugs, but also some others) have lungs that depend almost entirely on diffusion for gas exchange. The book lungs of spiders are enclosed in an inpocketing of the abdominal wall. These lungs consist of a series of parallel, thin plates filled with blood. The plates are separated by air spaces that are connected to the outside environment through a spiracle.

Larger mollusks and vertebrates with lungs have some means of forcefully moving air across the lung surface, that is, of ventilating the lung. This helps to ensure adequate oxygenation in active animals.

Fossil evidence suggests that crossopterygian fish, thought to be the ancestors of the amphibians, had lungs somewhat similar to those of modern lungfish.

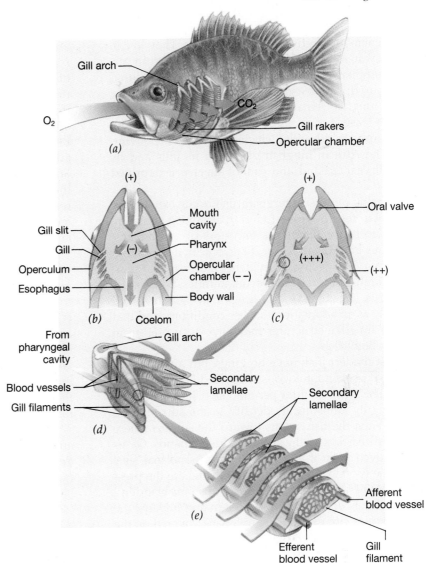

Figure 44–5 Function of the fish gill. (*a*) The gills are located under a bony plate, the operculum, which has been removed in this side view. The gills occupy the opercular chamber and form the lateral wall of the pharyngeal cavity. (*b*) The fish continuously pumps water through its mouth and over the gill arches. In inspiration, the fish enlarges its pharyngeal cavity, seen here from the top. This produces a negative (−) pressure in the pharyngeal cavity and water enters through the mouth. (*c*) When the fish exhales, it closes the mouth and the oral valve behind the lips, so that water is forced between the gills and out. Muscular action produces the high positive (+++) pressure in the pharyngeal cavity that is necessary to force the water between the gills. (*d*) Each gill consists of a cartilaginous gill arch to which two rows of leaflike gill filaments are attached. Blood circulates through the gill filaments as water passes among them. (*e*) Each gill filament has many even smaller extensions called secondary lamellae, which further increase the surface area. The lamellae contain capillaries that receive blood depleted of oxygen. The blood flows through the capillaries in the direction opposite to that of the water washing over the lamellae. As blood flows through the capillaries, it picks up oxygen from the water. In this countercurrent exchange, the blood is charged with oxygen very efficiently.

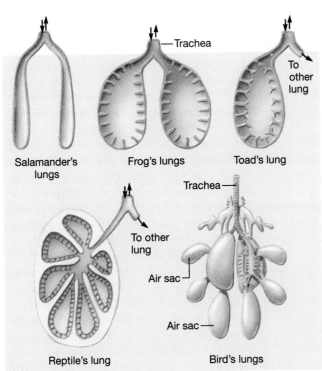

Figure 44–6 The structure of the lung varies in the vertebrate classes. Note the progressive increase in surface area for gas exchange. Salamander lungs are simple sacs, frog lungs have small ridges in the lung wall that help increase surface area, and birds have an elaborate system of lungs and air sacs. Mammalian lungs (Figure 44–7) have millions of air sacs that increase the surface available for gas exchange.

Three genera of lungfish are known today. They live in the headwaters of the Nile, in the Amazon, and in certain Australian rivers. Streams inhabited by the lungfish dry up during seasonal droughts; during these dry periods lungfish remain in the mud of the stream, exchanging gases by means of their lungs. These fish are also equipped with gills, which they use when swimming. The African lungfish uses both its gills and its lungs all year around and cannot survive if deprived of air.

Remains of crossopterygian fish occur extensively in the fossil record. Those found in Devonian strata are thought to be similar to the ancestors of amphibians. Numerous amphibian fossils also occur in adjacent ancient strata. The geological evidence suggests that periodic droughts occurred in Devonian times. Some paleontologists hypothesize that lungs may have evolved originally as an adaptation to these conditions, and that lungs or lunglike structures may have been present in all early bony fish.

Most modern fish have no lungs, but almost all of them do possess homologous swim bladders (see Chapter 30). The swim bladder permits the fish to control its buoyancy by adjusting its density to the surrounding water. When the fish swims toward the surface where the pressure is lower, the swim bladder expands. Gases are removed from it and it returns to its normal size. When the fish swims to greater depths where the pressure is higher, gases are added to the swim bladder.

The lungs of the simplest modern amphibians, the mud puppies, are two long, simple sacs, covered on the outside by capillaries. Frogs and toads have ridges containing connective tissue on the inside of the lung, which increase the respiratory surface somewhat. Because frogs have no diaphragm or rib muscles, their method of breathing is quite different from that of humans; it depends upon the action of valves and muscles in the nostrils and throat—so frogs gulp the air they breathe. Some amphibians have no lungs at all. Among plethodontid (lungless) salamanders (see Figure 30–25), for example, all gas exchange takes place in the pharynx, or across the thin, wet skin.

The lungs of most reptiles are rather simple, with only some folding of the wall to increase the surface for gas exchange. Because gas exchange is not very effective, these reptiles are unable to sustain long periods of activity. In some lizards and in turtles and crocodiles, the lungs are more complex, having many subdivisions that give them a spongy texture. The lungs of some lizards such as African chameleons have supplementary air sacs that can be inflated, enabling the animal to swell up. Such swelling is probably a protective device to frighten would-be predators.

Birds are very active animals with high metabolic rates. They require large amounts of oxygen to sustain their activities and have evolved highly efficient respiratory systems. In them the lungs have developed several extensions (usually nine) called **air sacs,** which reach into all parts of the body and even penetrate some of the bones. The respiratory system is arranged so that there is a one-way flow of air through the lungs, and the air is renewed during each inspiration. Instead of alveoli, the lungs have tiny, thin-walled ducts, the **parabronchi,** which are open at both ends. Gas exchange takes place across the walls of these ducts. The direction of blood flow in the lungs is opposite that of air flow through the parabronchi. This allows for countercurrent exchange that increases the amount of oxygen entering the blood. Avian lungs are efficient because stale air remains in the air sacs, not the parabronchi.

When the bird is at rest, a forward and upward movement of the ribs and a forward and downward movement of the sternum (breast bone) expand the trunk volume, drawing air into the body. When the bird is flying, the chest wall must be held rigid to form an anchor for the flight muscles. However, air sacs lying between certain flight muscles are squeezed and relaxed on each stroke of the wing. These act as bellows to move air into and out of the lungs. The faster the bird flies, the more rapid is the circulation of air through the lungs.

The lungs of mammals are very complex and have an enormous surface area. Using the human respiratory system as an example, we examine gas exchange in mammals in later sections of this chapter.

RESPIRATORY STRUCTURES ARE ADAPTED FOR GAS EXCHANGE IN AIR OR WATER

Animals are adapted to exchange gases in air or water. Some respiratory structures, like tracheal tubes and lungs, are best adapted for gas exchange in air, whereas others, like gills, function best in water. However, even in structures adapted for gas exchange in air, the actual exchange of gases takes place across a moist surface.

In one way a watery medium is optimal for gas exchange because gas molecules must be dissolved in water to pass through plasma membranes. However, water has a much greater density and viscosity (resistance to flow) than air, so a large animal must expend more energy to move water over its respiratory surface than to move air. A fish uses up to 20% of its total energy expenditure to perform the muscular work needed to move water over its gills. An air-breather expends much less energy, only 1% or 2% of the total, to move air in and out of its lungs.

Gas exchange in air has certain advantages over gas exchange in water. Compared with water, air contains far more oxygen. Oxygen also diffuses much faster through air than through water. Moreover, air is not salty, so air-breathers do not have to cope with the dif-

Relating Gas Exchange to Cellular Respiration

Among the important biological concepts discussed in this book are the dependence of most cells on oxygen and the interdependence of producers and consumers, which involves gas exchange. Most cells die quickly without oxygen because this element is required in the process of biological oxidation. It is through this process that cells obtain energy. To provide this supply of oxygen and to rid cells of carbon dioxide, gases must be exchanged continuously between cells and their environment.

Gas exchange between cells and the environment is referred to as **respiration.** When we study respiration in animals, we can think of two phases of respiration: organismic and cellular. During **organismic respiration** oxygen from the environment is taken up by the animal and delivered to its individual cells. At the same time, carbon dioxide generated during cellular respiration is excreted into the environment. The oxygen supplied to the cells by organismic respiration is used in cellular respiration. Recall from Chapter 7 that **cellular respiration** is the complex series of reactions by which cells oxidize organic compounds such as glucose, releasing carbon dioxide and energy. In this process oxygen serves as the final electron acceptor in the electron transport system.

fusion of ions into their body fluids along with oxygen. Aquatic animals also find it difficult to maintain a body temperature that is higher than that of their watery habitat. (Only a few of them do, and most of those, such as whales, actually breathe air.) Thus, breathing air has many advantages: It conserves energy, makes it easier to maintain homeostasis with respect to ion composition, and gives the animal a better opportunity to maintain a body temperature higher than that of the surroundings.

On the other hand, organisms that respire in air struggle continuously with water loss. Air dwellers must have adaptations to help them avoid drying out, and their respiratory surfaces must be kept moist so oxygen and carbon dioxide can pass through the plasma membranes. In addition to having fairly impermeable skin, air-breathing vertebrates have lungs that are located deep within the body, not exposed like gills. This arrangement prevents excessive loss of water from the respiratory surface. Air must pass through a long sequence of passageways before reaching the blood-rich, wet respiratory surfaces of the lung, and expired air must again pass through these passageways before leaving the body. The lungs are thus partially protected from the drying effects of air.

port oxygen by about 75 times. Oxygen enters the pulmonary capillaries and combines with hemoglobin in the red blood cells. Then, as blood circulates through tissues where the concentration of oxygen is low, hemoglobin releases oxygen. This oxygen diffuses out of the blood and into the tissue cells.

Hemoglobin is the respiratory pigment characteristic of vertebrates. It is also present in many invertebrate species from several phyla, including annelids, nematodes, mollusks, and arthropods. In some of these animals the hemoglobin is dispersed in the plasma rather than confined to blood cells.

Hemoglobin is actually a general name for a group of related compounds, all of which consist of an iron-porphyrin, or heme, group bound to a protein, known as a globin (see Figure 3–25). The protein portion of the molecule varies in size, amino acid composition, and physical properties in various species. Three other types of respiratory pigments are hemocyanins, chlorocruorins, and hemerythrins. **Hemocyanins** are blue, copper-containing proteins found in many species of mollusks and arthropods. These do not have a heme (porphyrin) group. When oxygen is combined with the copper, the compound appears blue. Without oxygen, it is colorless. Hemocyanins are dispersed in the blood rather than confined within cells.

RESPIRATORY PIGMENTS INCREASE CAPACITY FOR OXYGEN TRANSPORT

Animals have **respiratory pigments** that combine reversibly with oxygen and greatly increase the capacity of blood to transport oxygen. For example, the hemoglobin in human blood increases its capacity to trans-

THE HUMAN RESPIRATORY SYSTEM IS TYPICAL OF AIR-BREATHING VERTEBRATES

The respiratory system in humans and other air-breathing vertebrates consists of a series of tubes through

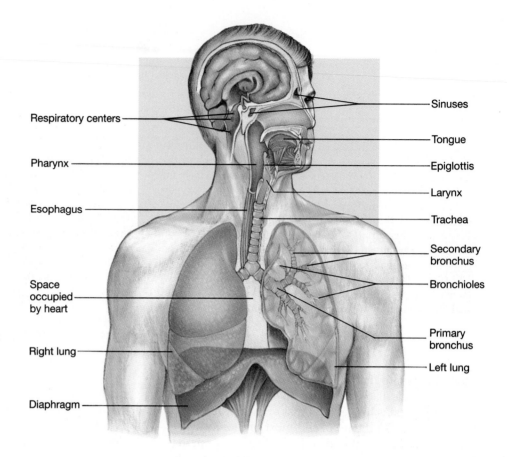

Respiratory centers

Pharynx

Esophagus

Space occupied by heart

Right lung

Diaphragm

Sinuses

Tongue

Epiglottis

Larynx

Trachea

Secondary bronchus

Bronchioles

Primary bronchus

Left lung

Figure 44–7 The human respiratory system. The paired lungs are located in the thoracic cavity. The muscular diaphragm forms the floor of the thoracic cavity, separating it from the abdominal cavity beneath. An internal view of one lung illustrates its extensive system of air passageways. The microscopic air sacs are shown in later figures.

which air passes on its journey from the nostrils to the air sacs of the lungs and back. A breath of air enters the body through the **nose,** flows through the twin compartments of the nasal cavity to the **pharynx** (throat region), through the **larynx** (voice box), and into the **trachea,** or windpipe (Figure 44–7). From the trachea the stream of air divides, first into two streams as the trachea branches into the **bronchi** (one bronchus enters each lung), then into the many branches of the bronchi. These branches give rise to thousands of **bronchioles.** The smallest bronchioles end in clusters of microscopic air sacs, or **alveoli.** From them oxygen diffuses into the blood of the multitude of capillaries enveloping each air sac. At the same time, carbon dioxide diffuses from the capillaries into the air sacs and is exhaled through the respiratory tubes. In summary, the sequence of structures through which air passes after it enters the body is:

nose → pharynx → larynx → trachea → bronchus → bronchiole → alveolus

The Airway Conducts Air into the Lungs

Air finds its way into the pharynx whether one breathes through the nose or the mouth. Nose-breathing is more desirable because as air passes through the nose, it is filtered, moistened, and brought to body temperature. The nostrils are fringed with coarse hair that helps to prevent the entrance of small insects and other foreign matter.

The nostrils open into the **nasal cavities,** which are lined with moist, ciliated epithelium. The lining of the nose has a rich blood supply that warms and humidifies the incoming air. Mucous cells within the epithelium produce more than a pint of mucus a day. Inhaled dirt, bacteria, and other foreign particles are trapped in the layer of mucus and pushed along with the stream of mucus toward the throat by the cilia. In this way foreign particles are delivered to the digestive system, which is far more capable of disposing of such materials than the delicate lungs. A person normally swallows more than a pint of nasal mucus each day, and even more if he or she has an allergy or infection.

The back of the nasal cavities is continuous with the throat region, or pharynx. An opening in the floor of the pharynx leads into the larynx, sometimes called the "Adam's apple." Because the larynx contains the vocal cords, it is also referred to as the voice box. Cartilage embedded in its wall prevents the larynx from collapsing and makes it hard to the touch when felt through the neck.

During swallowing, a flap of tissue, the **epiglottis,** automatically closes off the larynx from the esophagus

F O C U S   O N

Choking

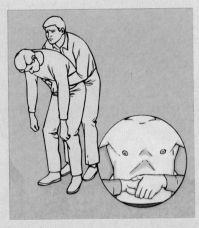

(a)

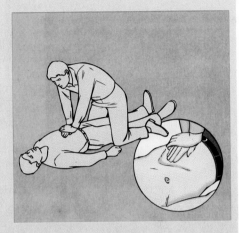

(b)

Choking kills an estimated 8000 to 10,000 people per year in the United States. Many of these have long suffered from some degree of paralysis or other malfunction of the muscles involved in swallowing, often without consciously realizing it. Swallowing is a very complex process in which the mouth, pharynx, esophagus, and vocal cords must be coordinated with great precision. Functional muscular disorders of this mechanism can originate in a variety of ways—as birth defects, for example, or from brain tumors or vascular accidents involving the swallowing center of the brain stem.

Choking is more likely to occur in restaurants, where social interactions and unfamiliar surroundings are likely to distract a person's attention from swallowing and where alcohol is more likely to be taken with the meal. A large number of choking victims have a substantial blood alcohol content upon autopsy, which suggests the possibility that in them a marginally effective swallowing reflex has been further and fatally compromised by the effects of alcohol on the brain.

Anyone who begins to choke and gasp during a meal should be asked if he or she can speak. If not, as indicated by shaking the head or other gestures, the person is probably suffering a laryngeal obstruction rather than a coronary heart attack. If you are present during such an episode, be aware that you can take certain steps that can save the person's life: Stand behind the victim, bring your arms around the person's waist, and clasp your hands just above the beltline. Your thumbs should be facing inward against the victim's body. Then squeeze abruptly and strongly in an upward direction. Repeat the upward thrusts five times. In most instances the residual air in the lungs will pop the obstruction out like a cork from a bottle. If the obstruction is not relieved, reassess the victim's status and reattempt multiple thrusts. This procedure is called the abdominal thrust, or **Heimlich maneuver.**

If the Heimlich maneuver must be performed with the victim lying down, place the victim face up. Kneel astride the victim's hips and, with one of your hands on top of the other, place the heel of your bottom hand on the abdomen slightly above the navel but below the rib cage. Press into the victim's abdomen with a quick upward thrust. This may be repeated if necessary. If there is no response within 15 or 20 seconds, it may be necessary to start cardiopulmonary resuscitation, or CPR. (See Focus on Cardiopulmonary Resuscitation [CPR].)

so that neither food nor liquid can enter the lower airway. Should this defense mechanism fail and foreign matter come in contact with the sensitive larynx, a **cough reflex** is initiated, expelling the material from the respiratory system. Despite these mechanisms, choking sometimes occurs (see Focus on Choking).

From the larynx air passes into the trachea, which divides into two bronchi, one going to each lung. The trachea and bronchi are supported by C-shaped rings of cartilage that prevent the tubes from collapsing as air is drawn in. Both trachea and bronchi are lined by a mucous membrane containing ciliated cells. Many medium-sized particles that have escaped the cleansing mechanisms of the nose and larynx are trapped here. Mucus containing these particles is constantly beaten upward by the cilia to the pharynx, where it is periodically swallowed. This mechanism, functioning as a cilia-propelled mucus elevator, helps keep foreign material out of the lungs.

Gas Exchange Occurs in the Alveoli of the Lungs

The lungs are large, paired, spongy organs occupying the thoracic (chest) cavity. The right lung is divided into

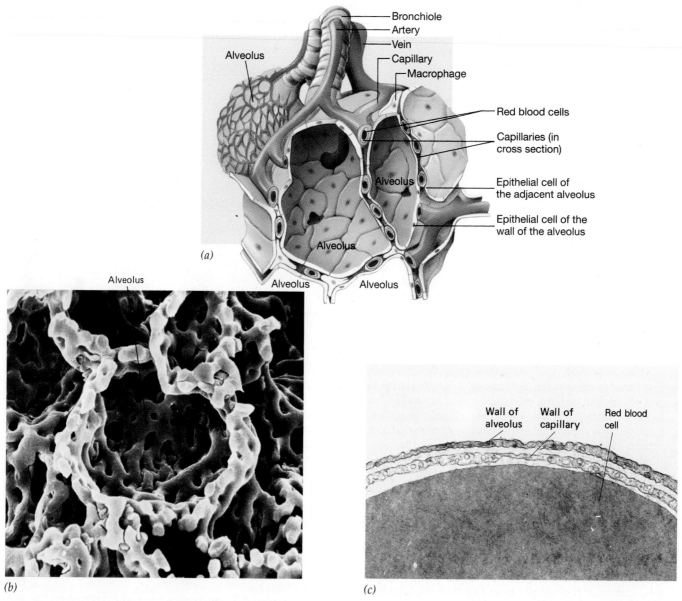

Figure 44–8 Structure of the alveolus. (*a*) The alveolar wall consists of extremely thin squamous epithelium. Each alveolus is enmeshed by a network of capillaries, facilitating free exchange of gases between the alveolus and the blood. (*b*) Scanning electron micrograph showing the capillary network surrounding a portion of two alveoli. (*c*) Oxygen in the lung diffuses the short distance through the thin wall of the alveolus and then through the capillary wall to reach the blood. A portion of a red blood cell (large dark structure) is visible within the capillary. (*b*, Kessel, R. G., and Kardon, R. H.: *Tissues and Organs, A Text-Atlas of Scanning Electron Microscopy.* San Francisco, W. H. Freeman Co., 1979)

three lobes, the left lung into two lobes. Each lung is covered with a membrane, the **pleural membrane,** which forms a continuous sac enclosing the lung and continuing as the lining of the chest cavity. The space between the pleural membranes covering the lung and the pleural membrane lining the chest cavity is called the **pleural cavity.** A film of fluid in the pleural cavity provides lubrication between the lungs and the chest wall.

Inside the lungs the bronchi branch into smaller and smaller airways, the bronchioles. There are more than a million tiny bronchioles in each lung, and each leads into a cluster of tiny air sacs, the alveoli (Figure 44–8). The alveoli are lined by an extremely thin single layer of epithelial cells. Gases diffuse freely through the wall of the alveolus and into the surrounding capillaries. Thus, only two thin membranes separate the air in the alveolus from the blood: the epithelium of the alveolar wall and the capillary wall.

Because the lung consists largely of air tubes and elastic tissue, it is a spongy, elastic organ with a very large internal surface area for gas exchange. In normal

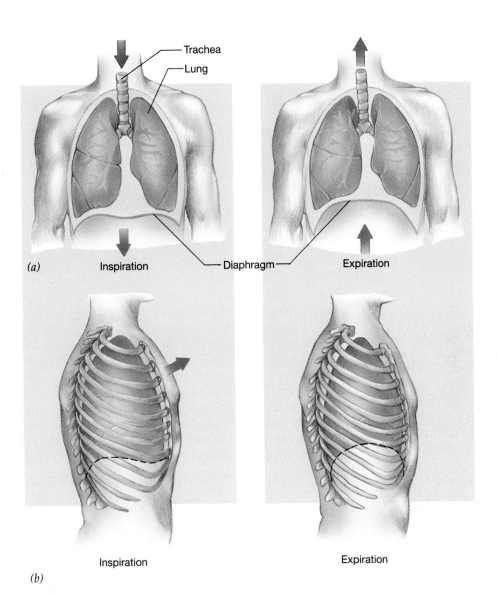

Trachea

Lung

(a) Inspiration — Diaphragm — Expiration

Inspiration

Expiration

(b)

Figure 44–9 The mechanics of breathing. (*a*) Changes in the position of the diaphragm in expiration and inspiration result in changes in the volume of the chest cavity. (*b*) Changes in the position of the rib cage in expiration and inspiration. The elevation of the front ends of the ribs by the chest muscles causes an increase in the front-to-back dimension of the chest and a corresponding increase in the volume of the chest cavity. When the volume of the chest cavity is increased, air moves into the lungs.

adults the surface area of the lungs is estimated to be approximately that of a tennis court.

Ventilation Is Accomplished by Breathing

Breathing is the mechanical process of moving air from the environment into the lungs and of expelling air from the lungs. Inhaling air is referred to as **inspiration;** exhaling air is **expiration.** A resting adult breathes about 12 times each minute. The thoracic (chest) cavity is closed so that no air can enter except through the trachea. (When the chest wall is punctured, for example by a gunshot wound, air enters the pleural space and the lung collapses.)

During inspiration, the chest cavity is expanded by the contraction of the **diaphragm,** the dome-shaped muscle that forms the floor of the thoracic cavity. When the diaphragm contracts, it moves downward, increasing the volume of the thoracic cavity (Figure 44–9). During forced inspiration, when a large volume of air is

inspired, the rib muscles contract as well. This action moves the ribs upward, which also increases the volume of the thoracic cavity. The lungs adhere to the walls of the thoracic cavity, so when the volume of the thoracic cavity increases, the space within each lung is also increased. The air in the lungs now has more space in which to move about, and the pressure of the air in the lungs falls 2 or 3 mm Hg below the pressure of the air outside the body. As a result, air from the outside rushes in through the respiratory passageways and fills the lungs until the two pressures are equal once again.

Expiration occurs when the diaphragm and rib muscles relax. The volume of the chest cavity decreases, increasing the pressure in the lungs (to 2 to 3 mm Hg above atmospheric pressure). The millions of distended air sacs deflate, expelling the air that was inhaled. The pressure returns to normal and the lung is ready for another change of air. Thus, in inspiration, the millions of tiny air sacs fill with air like so many balloons; then, during expiration, the air rushes out of the alveoli, partially deflating the balloons.

Table 44–2 COMPOSITION OF INHALED AIR COMPARED WITH
THAT OF EXHALED AIR

	% Oxygen (O_2)	% Carbon Dioxide (CO_2)	% Nitrogen (N_2)
Inhaled air (atmospheric air)	20.9	0.04	79
Exhaled air (alveolar air)	14.0	5.60	79

As indicated, the body uses up about one third of the inhaled oxygen. The amount of CO_2 increases more than 100-fold because it is produced during cellular respiration.

The Quantity of Air Respired Can Be Measured

The amount of air moved into and out of the lungs with each normal resting breath is called the **tidal volume.** The normal tidal volume is about 500 mL. The **vital capacity** is the maximum amount of air a person can exhale after filling the lungs to the maximum extent.

Vital capacity is greater than tidal volume. This means that the lungs are not completely emptied of stale air and filled with fresh air with each breath. Table 44–2 shows the percentages of oxygen and carbon dioxide present in exhaled air compared with inhaled air. Because carbon dioxide is produced during cellular respiration, there is more of this gas—100 times as much—entering the alveoli from the blood than there is in air inhaled from the environment. Expired air has had only about one third of its oxygen removed and can be breathed over again—a good thing for those in need of mouth-to-mouth resuscitation!

Gas Exchange Takes Place in the Air Sacs

The respiratory system delivers oxygen to the air sacs, but if oxygen were to remain in the lungs, all the other body cells would soon die. The vital link between air sac and body cell is the circulatory system. Each air sac serves as a tiny depot from which oxygen is loaded into blood brought close to the alveolar air by capillaries (Figure 44–10).

Oxygen molecules diffuse from the air sacs into the blood because the air sacs contain a greater concentration of oxygen than does blood entering the pulmonary capillaries. On the other hand, carbon dioxide moves from the blood, where it is more concentrated, to the air sacs, where it is less concentrated. Each gas diffuses through the cells lining the alveoli and the cells lining the capillaries.

The factor that determines the direction and rate of diffusion is the pressure or tension of the particular gas.

According to Dalton's law of partial pressures, in a mixture of gases the total pressure of the mixture is the sum of the pressures of the individual gases. Each gas exerts, independently of the others, the same pressure it would exert if it were present alone. At sea level, the barometric pressure (the pressure of Earth's atmosphere) is able to support a column of mercury (Hg) 760 mm high. Because the atmosphere is made up of about 21% oxygen, oxygen's share of that pressure is $0.21 \times 760 = 160$ mm Hg. Thus, 160 mm Hg is the partial pressure of oxygen, abbreviated P_{O_2}.

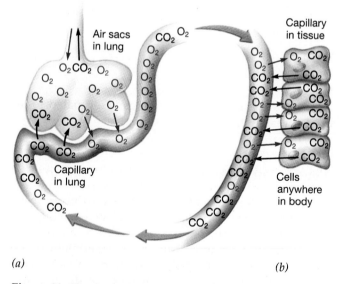

(a)   (b)

Figure 44–10 Gas exchange. (a) Exchange of gases between air sacs and capillaries in the lung. The concentration of oxygen is greater in the alveoli than in the pulmonary capillaries, so oxygen moves from the alveoli into the blood. Carbon dioxide is more concentrated in the blood than in the alveoli, so it moves out of the capillaries and into the alveoli. (b) Exchange of gases between the capillary and body cells. Here, oxygen is more concentrated in the blood than in the cells, so it moves out of the capillary into the cells. Carbon dioxide is more concentrated in the cells, and so it diffuses out of the cells and moves into the blood.

Blood passes through the lung capillaries too rapidly to become completely equilibrated with the alveolar air. The partial pressure of oxygen in arterial blood is about 100 mm Hg. The P_{O_2} in the tissues ranges from 0 to 40 mm Hg, so that oxygen diffuses out of the capillaries and into the tissues. Not all of the oxygen leaves the blood, however. The blood passes through the tissue capillaries too rapidly for equilibrium to be reached; thus, the partial pressure of oxygen in venous blood returning to the lungs is about 40 mm Hg.

Cellular respiration results in the continuous production of carbon dioxide and utilization of oxygen. Consequently, the concentration of oxygen in the cells is lower than that in the capillaries entering the tissues, and the concentration of carbon dioxide is higher in the cells than in the capillaries. Thus, as blood circulates through capillaries of a tissue such as brain or muscle, oxygen moves by diffusion from the blood to the cells, and carbon dioxide moves from the cells into the blood.

Throughout the system, from lungs to blood to tissues, oxygen moves from a region of higher concentration to one of lower concentration: Oxygen moves from the air to the blood, and then to the tissue fluid, and is finally used in the cells. Carbon dioxide also moves from a region of greater to one of lesser concentration. It diffuses from the cells where it is produced through the tissue fluid and blood to the lungs and then out of the body.

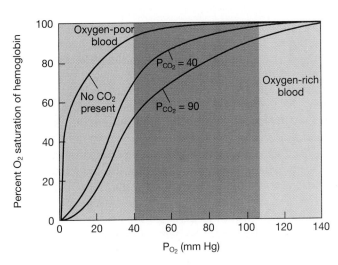

Figure 44–11 Oxygen dissociation curves. These curves show that as oxygen concentration increases, a progressive increase occurs in the amount of hemoglobin that is combined with oxygen. The curves also show how carbon dioxide affects the dissociation of oxyhemoglobin. Look at the vertical axis, labeled percentage saturation. If the blood contains 20% O_2 by volume, which is one fourth of the amount it could contain, it is said to be 25% saturated. The left curve shows what happens if no carbon dioxide is present. The middle curve shows the situation when the P_{CO_2} is 40, which is typical of arterial blood. The right curve indicates P_{CO_2} of 90, which is quite unhealthy. Now find the location on the horizontal axis where the partial pressure of oxygen is 40, and follow the line up through the curves. Notice how the saturation of hemoglobin with oxygen differs among the three curves, even though the partial pressure of oxygen is the same.

Oxygen Is Transported in Combination with Hemoglobin

At rest, the cells of the human body utilize about 250 mL of oxygen per minute, or about 300 liters every 24 hours. With exercise or work this rate may increase as much as 10- or 15-fold. If oxygen were simply dissolved in plasma, blood would have to circulate through the body at a rate of 180 liters per minute to supply enough oxygen to the cells at rest. This is because, as we have seen, oxygen is not very soluble in blood plasma. Actually, the blood of a human at rest circulates at about 5 liters per minute and supplies all of the oxygen the cells need. Why are only 5 liters per minute rather than 180 liters per minute required?

The answer is hemoglobin, the respiratory pigment in red blood cells. Hemoglobin transports about 97% of the oxygen. Only about 3% is dissolved in the plasma. Plasma in equilibrium with alveolar air can take up in solution only 0.25 mL of oxygen per 100 mL, but the properties of hemoglobin enable whole blood to carry some 20 mL of oxygen per 100 mL. The protein portion of hemoglobin is composed of four peptide chains, typically two α and two β chains, each attached to a heme (porphyrin) ring. An iron atom is bound in the center of each heme ring.

Hemoglobin has the remarkable property of forming a loose chemical union with oxygen. An oxygen molecule may attach to the iron atom in each heme. In the lung (or gill), oxygen diffuses into the erythrocyte and combines with hemoglobin (Hb) to form **oxyhemoglobin (HbO$_2$)**:

$$Hb + O_2 \rightleftharpoons HbO_2$$

Hemoglobin would, of course, be of little value to the body if it could only take up oxygen. It must also *release* the oxygen where needed. The reaction shown above goes to the right in the lungs, forming oxyhemoglobin, and to the left in the tissues, releasing oxygen. Oxyhemoglobin is bright scarlet, giving arterial blood its color; deoxygenated hemoglobin is purple, giving venous blood a darker hue.

The ability of oxygen to combine with hemoglobin and to be released from oxyhemoglobin is influenced by several factors, including the pH, the concentrations of carbon dioxide and oxygen, and the temperature. The **oxygen-hemoglobin dissociation curves** shown in Figure 44–11 illustrate that as oxygen concentration increases, there is a progressive increase in the amount of hemoglobin that is combined with oxygen. This is known as the **percent saturation** of the hemoglobin. The percent saturation is highest in the pulmonary capillaries where the concentration of oxygen is greatest. In the capillaries of the tissues where there is less oxygen, the oxyhemoglobin dissociates, releasing oxygen. There, the percent saturation of hemoglobin is correspondingly less.

The extent to which oxyhemoglobin dissociates is determined by oxygen and carbon dioxide concentration. Carbon dioxide reacts with water in the plasma to form carbonic acid, H_2CO_3. An increase in the carbon dioxide concentration increases the acidity and lowers the pH of the blood. Oxyhemoglobin dissociates more readily in a more acidic environment. Lactate released from active muscles also lowers the pH of the blood and has a similar effect on the oxygen-hemoglobin dissociation curve. Displacement of the oxygen-hemoglobin dissociation curve by a change in pH is known as the **Bohr effect.**

Some carbon dioxide is transported by the hemoglobin molecule. Although it attaches to the hemoglobin molecule in a different way and at a different site than oxygen, the attachment of a carbon dioxide molecule causes the release of an oxygen molecule from the hemoglobin. Thus carbon dioxide concentration affects the oxygen-hemoglobin dissociation curve in two ways. This results in an extremely efficient transport system. In the capillaries of the lungs (or gills in fishes), carbon dioxide concentration is relatively low and oxygen concentration is high, so oxygen saturates a very high percentage of hemoglobin. In the capillaries of the tissues, carbon dioxide concentration is high and oxygen concentration is low, so oxygen is released from the hemoglobin.

Carbon Dioxide Is Transported Mainly as Bicarbonate Ions

Carbon dioxide is transported in the blood in three ways. About 23% is carried by the hemoglobin molecule, and 7% is transported in the plasma as carbon dioxide itself. Most of the carbon dioxide (about 70%) is dissolved in the plasma as **bicarbonate ions** (HCO_3^-).

When carbon dioxide enters the blood, most of it enters the red blood cells, where an enzyme called **carbonic anhydrase** catalyzes the following reaction:

$$CO_2 + H_2O \xrightarrow{\text{Carbonic anhydrase}} H_2CO_3 \rightarrow H^+ + HCO_3^-$$

This reaction takes place slowly in the plasma, but the carbonic anhydrase in the red blood cells accelerates the rate of the reaction by about 5000 times. (It also accelerates the reverse reaction in the lungs by the same factor.)

Most of the hydrogen ions released from the carbonic acid combine with hemoglobin, which is a very effective buffer. Many of the bicarbonate ions diffuse into the plasma. Chloride ions diffuse into the red blood cells to replace the bicarbonate ions, a process known as the **chloride shift.**

Some of the carbon dioxide that enters the red blood cell combines with hemoglobin. The bond between the hemoglobin and carbon dioxide is very weak; the reaction, therefore, is readily reversible. By far, most of the carbon dioxide is transported as the bicarbonate ion.

Any condition (such as pneumonia) that interferes with the removal of carbon dioxide by the lungs leads to an increased concentration of carbon dioxide in the form of carbonic acid and bicarbonate ions in the blood. This condition is called **respiratory acidosis.** Although the pH of the blood is not actually acidic in this state, it is lower than normal.

Breathing Is Regulated by Respiratory Centers in the Brain

Respiratory centers are groups of neurons that receive information relevant to respiration, evaluate it, and send messages to the respiratory muscles. Respiratory centers in the medulla regulate the basic rhythm of respiration: one group regulates inspiration, and a second group is concerned with expiration. These centers fire rhythmically so that at rest we breathe 12 to 14 times per minute. Respiratory centers in the pons help control the transition from inspiration to expiration. These centers can stimulate or inhibit the medullary respiratory center that controls inspiration. Nerve impulses from the inspiratory center are delivered to the diaphragm by the phrenic nerves and to the intercostal (chest) muscles by the intercostal nerves. The impulses stimulate contraction of the diaphragm and chest muscles.

The basic rhythm of respiration can be altered in response to changing needs of the body. When you are engaged in a strenuous game of tennis, you require more oxygen than when studying biology. Carbon dioxide concentration is the most important chemical stimulus for regulating the rate of respiration. Recall that an increase in carbon dioxide concentration results in an increase in hydrogen ions from carbonic acid. Thus, an increase in carbon dioxide lowers the pH. Specialized nerve endings called **chemoreceptors** within the medulla and within the walls of the aorta and carotid arteries are sensitive to changes in hydrogen ion concentration. Even a slight increase in carbon dioxide concentration (as might occur, for example, during exercise) stimulates these chemoreceptors and causes an increase in the rate and depth of respiration. As carbon dioxide is removed by the lungs, the hydrogen ion con-

Cardiopulmonary Resuscitation (CPR)

Cardiopulmonary resuscitation, or **CPR,** is a method for aiding victims of accidents or heart attacks who have suffered cardiac arrest and respiratory arrest. Taking a course in CPR could prepare you to save someone's life. CPR should not be used if the victim has a pulse or is able to breathe. It must be started immediately, because irreversible brain damage may occur within about 4 minutes of respiratory arrest. Here are its ABCs:

Airway Clear airway by extending victim's neck. This is sometimes sufficient to permit breathing to begin again.

Breathing Use mouth-to-mouth resuscitation.

Circulation Attempt to restore circulation by using external cardiac compression.

Although not intended to substitute for a CPR course, the procedure for CPR is summarized below:

I. Establish the unresponsiveness of the victim.

II. Procedure for mouth-to-mouth resuscitation:
 1. Place the victim on his or her back on a firm surface.
 2. Clear the throat and mouth, and tilt the head back so that the chin points outward. Make sure that the tongue is not blocking the airway. Pull the tongue forward if necessary.
 3. Pinch the nostrils shut and forcefully exhale into the victim's mouth. Be careful, especially in children, not to over-inflate the lungs.
 4. Remove your mouth and listen for air rushing out of the lungs.
 5. Repeat about 12 times per minute. Do not interrupt for more than 5 seconds.

III. Procedure for external cardiac compression:
 1. Place the heel of one hand on the lower third of the victim's breastbone. Keep your fingertips lifted off the chest. (In infants, two fingers should be used for cardiac compression; in children, use only the heel of the hand.)
 2. Place the heel of the other hand at a right angle to and on top of the first hand.
 3. Apply firm pressure downward so that the breastbone moves about 4 to 5 cm (1.6 to 2 in) toward the spine. Downward pressure must be about 5.4 to 9 kg (12 to 20 lb) with adults (less with children). Excessive pressure can fracture the sternum or ribs, resulting in punctured lungs or a lacerated liver. This rhythmic pressure can often keep blood moving through the heart and great vessels of the thoracic cavity in sufficient quantities to sustain life.
 4. Relax your hands between compressions to allow the chest to expand.
 5. Repeat at the rate of at least 80–100 compressions per minute. (For infants or young children, 100 compressions per minute are appropriate.) Fifteen compressions should be applied, then two breaths, in a ratio of 15:2 (5:1 for children).

---

centration in the blood and other body fluids decreases, and homeostasis is restored. Then, because the respiratory centers are no longer stimulated, the rate and depth of breathing return to normal.

Substantial decreases in oxygen concentration can also affect the rate of breathing. When the partial pressure of oxygen falls markedly, the chemoreceptors in the aorta and carotid arteries are stimulated and send messages to the respiratory centers to increase the rate of respiration. It is interesting that oxygen concentration does not affect the respiratory centers directly, and that in healthy persons living at sea level, oxygen concentration generally does not play an important part in regulating respiration.

Although breathing is an involuntary process, the action of the respiratory centers can be consciously influenced for a short time by either stimulating or inhibiting them. For example, you can inhibit respiration by holding your breath. You cannot hold your breath indefinitely, however, because eventually you feel a strong impulse to breathe. Even if you were able to ignore this, you would eventually pass out and breathing would resume.

Individuals who have stopped breathing because of drowning, smoke inhalation, electric shock, or cardiac arrest can sometimes be sustained by mouth-to-mouth resuscitation until their own breathing reflexes can be initiated again. Cardiopulmonary resuscitation (CPR) is a method for aiding victims who have suffered respiratory or cardiac arrest or both. For an overview of the procedure, see Focus on Cardiopulmonary Resuscitation (CPR).

Hyperventilation Reduces Carbon Dioxide Concentration

Underwater swimmers and some Asiatic pearl divers voluntarily hyperventilate before going under water. By taking a series of deep inhalations and exhalations, you can markedly reduce the carbon dioxide content of the alveolar air and of the blood. As a result, it takes longer before the impulse to breathe becomes irresistible.

When hyperventilation is continued for a long period, dizziness and sometimes unconsciousness may occur. This is because a certain concentration of carbon dioxide is needed in the blood to maintain normal blood pressure. (This mechanism operates by way of the vasoconstrictor center in the brain, which maintains the muscle tone of blood vessel walls.) Furthermore, if divers hold their breath too long, the low concentration of oxygen may result in unconsciousness and drowning.

High Flying or Deep Diving Can Disrupt Homeostasis

The barometric pressure decreases at progressively higher altitudes. Because the concentration of oxygen in the air remains at 21%, the partial pressure of oxygen decreases along with the barometric pressure. At an altitude of 6000 meters (19,500 feet), the barometric pressure is about 350 mm Hg, the partial pressure of oxygen is about 75 mm Hg, and the hemoglobin in arterial blood is about 70% saturated with oxygen. At 10,000 meters, the barometric pressure is about 225 mm Hg, the partial pressure of oxygen is 50 mm Hg, and arterial oxygen saturation is only 20%. Thus, getting sufficient oxygen from the air becomes an ever-increasing problem at higher altitudes.

When a person moves to a high altitude, the body adjusts over a period of time by producing a greater number of red blood cells. In a person breathing pure oxygen at 10,000 meters, the oxygen would have a partial pressure of 225 mm Hg, and the hemoglobin would be almost fully saturated with oxygen. Above 13,000 meters, however, the barometric pressure is so low that even breathing pure oxygen does not permit complete oxygen saturation of arterial hemoglobin.

A person can remain conscious only until the arterial oxygen saturation falls to 40% to 50%. This level is reached at about 7000 meters when the person is breathing air, or 14,500 meters when pure oxygen is used. All high-flying jets have cabins that are airtight and pressurized to the equivalent of the barometric pressure at an altitude of about 2000 meters.

Hypoxia, a deficiency of oxygen, results in drowsiness, mental fatigue, headache, and sometimes euphoria. The ability to think and to make judgments is impaired, and there is a loss of ability to perform tasks requiring coordination. If a jet were flying at about 11,700 meters and underwent sudden decompression, the pilot would lose consciousness in about 30 seconds and become comatose in about 1 minute.

In addition to the problems of hypoxia, a rapid decrease in barometric pressure can cause **decompression sickness** (the bends). Whenever the barometric pressure drops below the total pressure of all gases dissolved in the blood and other body fluids, the dissolved gases tend to come out of solution into a gaseous state and form bubbles. A familiar example of such bubbling occurs each time you uncap a bottle of soda, thus reducing the pressure in the bottle. The carbon dioxide is released from solution and bubbles out into the air. In the body, nitrogen causes the problem because it has such a low solubility in blood and tissues. Nitrogen comes out of solution and forms bubbles that may block capillaries, interfering with blood flow. Other tissues may also be damaged. The clinical effects of decompression sickness are pain, dizziness, paralysis, unconsciousness, and even death.

Decompression sickness is even more common in deep-sea diving than in high-altitude flying. As a diver descends, the surrounding pressure increases tremendously—1 atmosphere for each 10 meters. To prevent the collapse of the lungs, a diver must be supplied with air under pressure, thereby exposing the lungs to very high alveolar gas pressures.

At sea level an adult human has about 1 liter of nitrogen dissolved in the body, with about half of that in the fat and half in the body fluids. After a diver's body has been saturated with nitrogen at a depth of 100 meters, the body fluids contain about 10 liters of nitrogen. To prevent this nitrogen from rapidly bubbling out of solution and causing decompression sickness, the diver must be brought to the surface gradually, with stops at certain levels on the way up. This allows the nitrogen to be expelled slowly through the lungs.

Some mammals can spend rather long periods of time in the ocean depths without coming up for air (see Focus on Adaptations of Diving Mammals).

THE EFFECT OF BREATHING DIRTY AIR IS RESPIRATORY INSULT

We breathe about 20,000 times each day, inhaling about 35 pounds of air—six times more than the food and drink we consume. Most of us breathe dirty urban air laden with particulates, carbon monoxide, and other harmful substances that are damaging to the respiratory system (Figure 44–12).

FOCUS ON

Adaptations of Diving Mammals

The Weddell seal can swim under the ice at a depth of 500 meters for more than an hour without coming up for air. The bottle-nosed whale can remain in the ocean depths for as long as 2 hours. Porpoises, whales, seals, beavers, mink, and several other air-breathing mammals have adaptations that permit them to dive for food or disappear below the water surface for several minutes to elude their enemies.

Diving mammals have about twice the volume of blood, relative to their body weight, as nondivers. Many have high concentrations of myoglobin, an oxygen-binding pigment similar to hemoglobin found in muscles. They do not, however, have larger lungs than those in nondiving mammals.

When a mammals dives to its limit, a group of physiological mechanisms known collectively as the **diving reflex** are activated. Breathing stops. Bradycardia (slowing of the heart rate) occurs. The heart rate may decrease to one tenth of the normal rate, reducing the body's consumption of oxygen and energy. Blood is redistributed, with the lion's share going to the brain and heart, the organs that can least withstand anoxia. Skin, muscles, digestive organs, and other internal organs can survive with less oxygen, and so receive less blood while an animal is submerged. Muscles shift from aerobic to anaerobic metabolism.

Diving mammals do not take in extra air before a dive. In fact, seals

Mother and baby spotted porpoises   *(Tursiops truncatus)*.   (François Gohier/Photo Researchers, Inc.)

exhale before they dive, and the lungs of whales are compressed during diving. These adaptations are thought to reduce the chance of decompression sickness, because with less air in the lungs there is less nitrogen in the blood to dissolve during the dive.

The diving reflex is present to some extent in humans, where it may act as a protective mechanism during birth when an infant may be deprived of oxygen for several minutes. Many cases of near-drownings have

been documented in which the victim had been submerged for several minutes (as long as 45 minutes) in very cold water before being rescued and resuscitated. In many of these survivors there was no apparent brain damage. The shock of the icy water slows the heart rate, increases blood pressure, and shunts the blood to the internal organs of the body that most need oxygen (blood flow in the arms and legs decreases). Metabolic rate decreases so that less oxygen is required.

A Variety of Defense Mechanisms Protect the Lungs

Several defense mechanisms help protect the delicate lungs from the harmful substances we breathe. The hair around the nostrils, the ciliated mucous lining in the nose and pharynx, and the cilia-mucus elevator serve to trap foreign particles in inspired air. One of the body's most rapid defense responses to breathing dirty air is

bronchial constriction. In this process the bronchial tubes narrow. As a result, inhaled particles are more likely to land on their sticky mucous lining. Unfortunately, when the bronchial passageways constrict, less air can pass through them to the lungs. This decreases the amount of oxygen available to body cells. Chain smokers and those who breathe heavily polluted air may remain in a state of chronic bronchial constriction.

Figure 44–12 Air pollution contributes to respiratory disorders. Industry spews tons of pollutants into the atmosphere. (Adam Jones/Dembinsky Photo Associates)

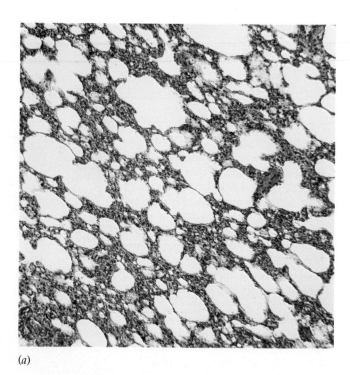

(a)

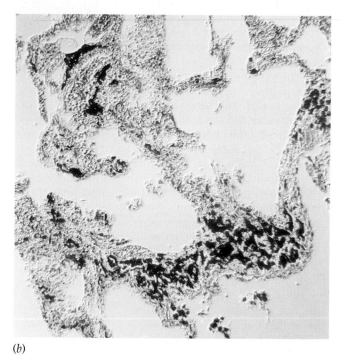

(b)

Figure 44–13 Lung tissue. (a) Normal lung tissue. (b) Lung tissue with accumulated carbon particles. Despite the body's defenses, when we inhale smoky, polluted air, especially over a long period of time, dirt particles do enter the lung tissue and remain lodged there. (Alfred Pasieka/Taurus Photos)

Neither the smallest bronchioles nor the alveoli are equipped with mucus or ciliated cells. Foreign particles that get through other respiratory defenses and find their way into the alveoli may be engulfed by macrophages. The macrophages may then accumulate in the lymph tissue of the lungs. Lung tissue of chronic smokers and those who work in dirty fossil fuel–burning industries contains large blackened areas where carbon particles have been deposited (Figure 44–13).

Continued Respiratory Insult Leads to Respiratory Disease

Continued insult to the respiratory system results in disease. Chronic bronchitis and emphysema are **chronic obstructive pulmonary diseases (COPD)** that have been linked to smoking and breathing polluted air. More than 75% of patients with **chronic bronchitis** have a history of heavy cigarette smoking (see Focus on Facts About Smoking). In chronic bronchitis, irritation from inhaled pollutants causes the bronchial tubes to secrete too much mucus. Ciliated cells, damaged by the pollutants, cannot effectively clear the mucus and trapped particles from the airways. The body resorts to coughing in an attempt to clear the airways. The bronchioles become constricted and inflamed, and the patient is short of breath.

Victims of chronic bronchitis often develop **pulmonary emphysema,** a disease most common in cigarette smokers. In this disorder alveoli lose their elasticity, and walls between adjacent alveoli are destroyed. The

FOCUS ON

Facts About Smoking

- The life of a 30-year-old who smokes 15 cigarettes a day is shortened by an average of more than 5 years.
- If you smoke more than one pack per day, you are about 20 times more likely to develop lung cancer than a nonsmoker. According to the American Cancer Society, cigarette smoking causes more than 75% of all lung cancer deaths.
- If you smoke, you are more likely to develop atherosclerosis, and you double your chances of dying from cardiovascular disease.
- If you smoke, you are 20 times more likely to develop chronic bronchitis and emphysema than a nonsmoker.
- If you smoke, you are seven times more likely to develop peptic ulcers (especially malignant ulcers) than a nonsmoker.
- If you smoke, you have about 5% less oxygen circulating in your blood (because carbon monoxide binds to hemoglobin) than a non-smoker.
- If you smoke when you are pregnant, your baby will weigh about 6 ounces less at birth, and there is double the risk of miscarriage, stillbirth, and infant death than if you did not smoke.
- Workers who smoke one or more packs of cigarettes per day are absent from their jobs because of illness 33% more often than non-smokers.
- Risks increase with the number of cigarettes smoked, inhaling, smoking down to a short stub, and use

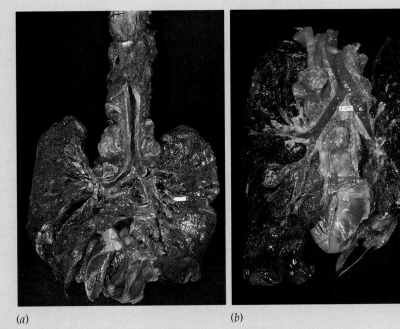

(a)   (b)

A diseased lung compared with a healthy lung. (*a*) Normal human lungs and major bronchi. (*b*) Human lungs and heart showing effects of cigarette smoking.   (Martin M. Rotker/Taurus Photos)

of nonfilter or high-tar, high-nicotine cigarettes. Cigar and pipe smokers have lower risks than cigarette smokers because they do not inhale as much. Cigarette smokers who switch to cigars and continue to inhale actually increase their risks.

- Nonsmokers confined in living rooms, offices, automobiles, or other places with smokers are adversely affected by the smoke. For example, when parents of infants smoke, the infant has double the risk of contracting pneumonia or bronchitis in its first year of life.

- When smokers quit smoking, their risk of dying from chronic pulmonary disease, cardiovascular disease, or cancer decreases. (Precise changes in risk figures depend upon the number of years the person smoked, the number of cigarettes smoked per day, the age of starting to smoke, and the number of years since quitting.)

- If everyone in the United States stopped smoking, more than 300,000 lives would be saved each year.

surface area of the lung is so reduced that gas exchange is seriously impaired. Air is not expelled effectively, and stale air accumulates in the lungs. The emphysema victim struggles for every breath and still the body does not get enough oxygen. To compensate, the right ventricle of the heart pumps harder and becomes enlarged. Emphysema patients frequently die of heart failure.

Cigarette smoking is also the main cause of lung cancer. More than 10 of the compounds in the tar of tobacco smoke have been shown to cause cancer. These carcinogenic substances irritate the cells lining the respiratory passages and alter their metabolic balance. Normal cells are transformed into cancer cells, which may multiply rapidly and invade surrounding tissues.

SUMMARY

I. In very small organisms, gas exchange can occur effectively by diffusion, but in larger and more complex forms, specialized respiratory structures are required.
   A. In nudibranch mollusks, most annelids, small arthropods, and some vertebrates, gas exchange occurs through the entire body surface.
   B. In insects and some other arthropods, the respiratory system consists of a network of tracheal tubes.
   C. Gills are respiratory structures characteristic of aquatic animals.
      1. In echinoderms, simple dermal gills project from the body wall.
      2. In chordates, gills are usually internal, located along the edges of the gill slits.
      3. In bony fish, a countercurrent exchange system promotes diffusion of oxygen into the blood and diffusion of carbon dioxide out of the blood and into the water.
   D. Large mollusks and terrestrial vertebrates have lungs with some means of ventilating them.
   E. Most modern fish do not have lungs but possess homologous swim bladders.
II. Gas exchange with air is more efficient than gas exchange with water because air contains more oxygen than water and because oxygen diffuses more rapidly through air than through water.
III. Respiratory pigments greatly increase the capacity of blood to transport oxygen.
IV. The human respiratory system includes the lungs and a system of tubes through which air reaches them. A breath of air passes in sequence through the nose, pharynx, larynx, trachea, bronchus, bronchioles, and alveoli.
   A. During breathing, the diaphragm and rib muscles contract, expanding the chest cavity. The membranous walls of the lungs move outward along with the chest walls, decreasing the pressure within the lungs. Air from outside the body rushes in through the air passageways and fills the lungs until the pressure once more equals atmospheric pressure.
   B. Tidal volume is the amount of air moved into and out of the lungs with each normal breath. Vital capacity is the maximum volume that can be exhaled after the lungs are filled to the maximum extent.
   C. Oxygen and carbon dioxide are exchanged between alveoli and blood by diffusion.
   D. About 97% of the oxygen in the blood is transported as oxyhemoglobin.
      1. As oxygen concentration increases, there is a progressive increase in the amount of hemoglobin that combines with oxygen.
      2. Owing to lowered pH, oxyhemoglobin dissociates more readily as carbon dioxide concentration increases (Bohr effect).
   E. About 70% of the carbon dioxide in the blood is transported as bicarbonate ions.
   F. Respiratory centers located in the medulla and pons control the basic rhythm of respiration.
      1. The respiratory centers are stimulated by chemoreceptors sensitive to an increase in hydrogen ions, which results from increased carbon dioxide concentration.
      2. The respiratory system can also be stimulated by signals from chemoreceptors sensitive to very low oxygen concentration.
   G. Hyperventilation reduces the concentration of carbon dioxide in the alveolar air and in the blood.
   H. As altitude increases, barometric pressure decreases and less oxygen enters the blood. This situation can lead to hypoxia. A rapid decrease in barometric pressure can cause decompression sickness.
V. Inhaling polluted air results in bronchial constriction, increased mucus secretion, damaged ciliated cells, and coughing. It eventually can lead to chronic bronchitis, emphysema, or lung cancer.

POST-TEST

1. Specialized respiratory structures must have _____ walls so that _____ easily occurs; they must be _____ so that gases can be dissolved; and they are typically richly supplied with _____ _____ to ensure transport of gases.
2. In insects, air enters a network of _____ tubes through openings called _____.
3. The operculum is a bony plate that protects the _____ in _____.
4. Respiratory structures that develop as ingrowths of the body surface are called _____.
5. A fish can rise or sink, or maintain a particular level in the water without muscular effort, by regulating the amount of air in its _____ _____.
6. In birds, the lungs have several extensions referred to as _____ _____.
7. In the mammalian respiratory system, inhaled air passing through the larynx next enters the _____ and then passes into a _____.
8. In the mammalian respiratory system, gas exchange takes place through the thin walls of the _____.
9. In mammals, the floor of the thoracic cavity is formed by the _____.
10. The chief problem with breathing air is _____ _____.

Select the most appropriate answer in Column B for each description in Column A.

Column A	Column B
11. Seals off larynx during swallowing	a. Epiglottis
12. Cavities in bones of skull	b. Larynx
13. Initiates cough reflex	c. Alveoli
14. Covers lung	d. Pleura
15. Gas exchange takes place through their walls	e. None of the above

16. The maximum amount of air a person can exhale after filling the lungs to the maximum extent is the _____ _____.

17. The extent to which oxyhemoglobin dissociates is determined mainly by the _____ concentration.

18. An increase in carbon dioxide concentration lowers the blood pH and results in greater dissociation of _____; this is known as the _____ _____.

19. Most carbon dioxide is transported in the blood as _____ _____.

20. Hypoxia is a deficiency in _____.

21. Bronchial constriction is one of the body's most rapid responses to _____.

22. In _____, the alveolar walls break down so that several air sacs join to form larger, less elastic alveoli.

23. The main cause of lung cancer is _____.

24. Label the diagram shown on the right. (Refer to Figure 44–7 as necessary.)

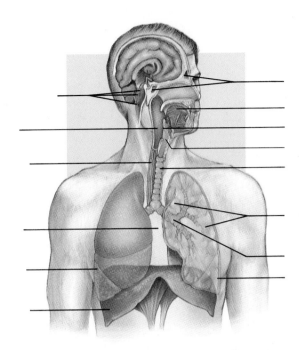

REVIEW QUESTIONS

1. Why are specialized respiratory structures necessary in a tadpole but not in a flatworm?

2. Compare ventilation in a sea star with ventilation in a human.

3. Compare gas exchange in the following animals:
   a. earthworm
   b. grasshopper
   c. fish
   d. frog

4. Why are lungs more suited for an air-breathing vertebrate and gills more effective in a fish? Why are lungs internal?

5. What respiration problem is solved by respiratory pigments? How?

6. Why does alveolar air differ in composition from atmospheric air?

7. What physiological mechanisms bring about an increase in rate and depth of breathing during exercise? Why is such an increase necessary?

8. What is the advantage of having lungs with millions of alveoli rather than lungs consisting of simple sacs, as in the mud puppies?

9. In what way might it be an advantage for a fish to have lungs as well as gills? What function do the "lungs" of most modern fish serve?

10. How does the countercurrent exchange system increase the efficiency of gas exchange between gills and blood?

11. What mechanisms does the human respiratory system have for getting rid of inhaled dirt? What happens when so much dirty air is inhaled that these mechanisms cannot function effectively?

12. What factors affect the dissociation of oxyhemoglobin?

13. What happens to a deep-sea diver who surfaces too quickly? Why?

RECOMMENDED READINGS

Feder, M. E., and W. W. Burggren. Skin breathing in vertebrates. *Scientific American*, Vol. 253, No. 5 (November 1985) pp. 126–142. An interesting account describing how skin functions in gas exchange in some vertebrates.

Kanwisher, J. W., and S. H. Ridgway. The physiological ecology of whales and porpoises. *Scientific American*, Vol. 248, No. 6 (June 1983) pp. 111–119. A discussion of adaptations for deep diving.

Perutz, M. F. Hemoglobin structure and respiratory transport. *Scientific American*, Vol. 239, No. 6 (December 1978) pp. 92–125. Nobel prize winner Perutz describes how hemoglobin changes its shape to facilitate oxygen binding and release.

Zapol, W. M. Diving adaptations of the Weddell seal. *Scientific American*, Vol. 256, No. 6 (June 1987) pp. 100–105. Physiological adaptations enable the seal to swim deeper and hold its breath longer than most other mammals.

Processing Food

Hydra remains rooted in one place waiting for potential prey to come near. When an organism brushes by one of its stinging cells, a long threadlike lasso springs forward, entangling and perhaps paralyzing the prey. Hydra then uses its tentacles to deliver the meal into its mouth. Adapted to an entirely different life style, the lion has strong, quick legs, sharp teeth, and long claws which enable it to actively hunt and kill gazelles and other animals.

Nutrition, the process of taking in and assimilating food, is so vitally important that both individual organisms and ecosystems have evolved around obtaining and processing food. An organism's body plan, as well as its lifestyle, is adapted to its particular mode of nutrition. **Nutrients** are the substances

Giant panda (*Ailuropoda melanoleuca*) eating bamboo. (Tom McHugh/Photo Researchers, Inc.)

present in food that are used by an organism as an energy source to run the machinery of the body, as ingredients to make compounds for metabolic processes, and as building blocks to permit growth and repair of tissues.

All animals are heterotrophs, that is, organisms that must obtain their energy and nourishment from the organic molecules manufactured by other organisms. With only slight variation, all animals require the same basic nutrients: minerals, vitamins, carbohydrates, lipids, and proteins. Carbohydrates, lipids, and proteins can all be used as energy sources. Eating too much of any of these nutrients can result in weight gain, whereas eating too few nutrients or an unbalanced diet can result in malnutrition and death.

After you have studied this chapter you should be able to

1. Correlate the adaptations of herbivores, carnivores, and omnivores with their particular modes of nutrition.
2. Compare how animals with an incomplete digestive system (for example, *Hydra*) and those with a complete digestive system, such as a vertebrate, process food with respect to ingestion, digestion, absorption, and elimination.
3. Identify on a diagram or model each of the structures of the human digestive system described in this chapter, and give the function of each structure.
4. Trace the pathway traveled by an ingested meal.
5. Summarize the functions of the accessory digestive glands of terrestrial vertebrates.
6. Trace the step-by-step digestion of carbohydrate, protein, and lipid.
7. Draw and label a diagram of an intestinal villus, and explain how its structure is adapted to its function.
8. Identify commonly ingested carbohydrates, and trace the fate of glucose after its absorption.

9. Trace the fate of lipids after they are absorbed from the intestine, and summarize the relationship between lipid intake and coronary heart disease.
10. Trace the fate of proteins in the body.
11. Distinguish between water-soluble and fat-soluble vitamins, and describe the effects of specific vitamin deficiencies.
12. Summarize the role of minerals as essential nutrients, giving three specific examples.
13. Contrast basal metabolic rate with total metabolic rate.
14. Write the basic energy equation for maintaining body weight and describe the consequences of altering it in either direction.
15. Summarize the causes of obesity and its treatment.
16. In general terms, describe the problem of world food supply relative to world population, and describe the effects of malnutrition.
17. Summarize the difficulties in obtaining adequate amounts of amino acids in a vegetarian diet, and describe how a nutritionally balanced vegetarian diet could be planned.

FOOD PROCESSING INVOLVES INGESTION, DIGESTION, ABSORPTION, AND ELIMINATION

Most animals have a digestive system that processes the food they eat. Food processing has several steps: **ingestion, digestion, absorption,** and **elimination.** After foods are selected and obtained, they are **ingested,** that is, taken into the body. Ingestion generally involves taking the food into the mouth and swallowing it. Because animals eat macromolecules tailor-made by and for other organisms, their digestive system must break down these molecules and refashion them for their own needs. We cannot incorporate the proteins in steak directly into our own muscles, for example. The body **digests** the steak by mechanically breaking down the large bites of meat into smaller ones and then enzymatically hydrolyzing (breaking down with the addition of water) the proteins into their component amino acids. The amino acids can then be **absorbed** and **transported** to the muscle cells, which incorporate these components into human muscle proteins.

Most animals are equipped with digestive tracts. Nutrients pass through the cells lining the digestive tract and are absorbed into the blood or other body fluids. They are then distributed throughout the body and used for metabolic activities within each cell. Food that is not digested and absorbed is discharged from the body in a process called **egestion** in simple animals and **elimination** in more complex animals.

ANIMALS ARE ADAPTED TO THEIR MODE OF NUTRITION

Some animals are **herbivores,** or primary consumers, which eat exclusively or mainly plant materials (Figure 45–1). Because animals cannot digest the cellulose of plant cell walls, herbivores have evolved many adaptations for extracting nutrients from the plant material they eat. For example, vertebrate herbivores generally have a specialized section of the digestive tract in which bacteria live which are capable of digesting cellulose. In the cud-chewing ruminants (cattle, sheep, deer), the stomach is divided into four chambers. Bacteria inhabiting the first two chambers digest cellulose. Food that is not sufficiently chewed, called cud, is regurgitated into the animal's mouth and chewed again.

Many herbivores eat great quantities of food. Grasshoppers, locusts, elephants, and cattle, for example, all spend a major part of their lives eating. Most of what they eat is not efficiently digested and is eliminated from the body almost unchanged as waste. However, they eat large enough quantities of material to provide the nourishment necessary to sustain their life processes.

Herbivores are sometimes eaten by flesh-eating **carnivores,** which may also eat one another. Carnivores (secondary and higher-level consumers in ecosystems) are adapted for capturing and killing prey. Some carnivores seize their victims and swallow them alive and whole (Figure 45–2). Others paralyze, crush, or shred

Figure 45–1 Adaptations of herbivores. (*a*) An acorn weevil. The impressively long "snout" of this little beetle is used both for feeding and for making a hole in the acorn through which an egg is deposited. When it has hatched, the larva feeds on the contents of the acorn seed. (*b*) The rhinoceros can use its horn to uproot and overturn small trees and bushes; it then eats the leaves. Members of some species use their lips to break off grass. (*a*, Darwin Dale/Photo Researchers Inc.; *b*, Roger de la Harpe/Biological Photo Service)

(*a*)

(*b*)

(*a*)

(*b*)

Figure 45–2 Adaptations of carnivores. (*a*) The long-nose butterfly fish (*Forcipiger longirostris*) has a mouth adapted for extracting small worms and crustaceans from tight spots in coral reefs. (*b*) With lightning speed the Burmese python strikes at its prey, then suffocates it before consuming it whole. (*c*) With its wide field of vision and fast reflexes, the Chinese praying mantis (*Tendora aridifolia sinensis*) is an able carnivore. (*a*, Zig Leszczynski, © 1993 Animals Animals; *b*, courtesy of Mical Solomon and Trudi Segal; *c*, Peter J. Bryant/Biological Photo Service)

(*c*)

their prey before ingesting it. Carnivorous mammals have well-developed canine teeth for stabbing during combat. The digestive juice of the stomach breaks down proteins, and because meat is more easily digested than plant food, their digestive tracts are shorter than those of herbivores.

Omnivores, such as bears and humans, consume both plants and animals. Earthworms ingest large

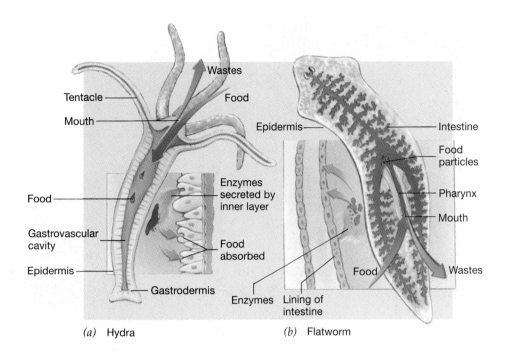

Figure 45–3 Food processing in invertebrates with an incomplete digestive system. The hydra (*a*) and the flatworm (*b*) have a digestive tract with a single opening that serves as both mouth and anus.

(a) Hydra

(b) Flatworm

amounts of soil containing both animal and plant material. The blue whale, the largest animal, is a filter feeder that strains out tiny algae and animals as it swims. Omnivores often possess adaptations that permit them to distinguish among a wide range of smells and tastes and thereby select a variety of foods.

SOME INVERTEBRATES HAVE INCOMPLETE DIGESTIVE SYSTEMS

Some invertebrates, such as sponges, have no digestive system at all, and others have an **incomplete** digestive system with only a single opening. Sponges obtain food by filtering microscopic organisms from the surrounding water. Individual cells phagocytize the food particles, and digestion occurs intracellularly within food vacuoles. Wastes are egested into the water that continuously circulates through the sponge's body.

Cnidarians, such as hydras and jellyfish, capture small aquatic animals by means of their cnidocytes and tentacles (Figure 45–3a). The mouth opens into a large gastrovascular cavity lined by cells that secrete enzymes which break down proteins. During digestion within the gastrovascular cavity, proteins are enzymatically split to polypeptides. Digestion continues intracellularly within food vacuoles, and the digested nutrients are passed to other cells by diffusion. Large undigested food particles are egested through the mouth by contraction of the body.

Free-living flatworms (e.g., planaria) begin to digest their prey even before they ingest it. They extend the pharynx out through their mouth and secrete digestive enzymes onto the prey (Figure 45–3b). When in-

gested, the food enters the branched intestine. Extracellular digestion proceeds as intestinal cells secrete digestive enzymes. Partly digested food fragments are then phagocytized by cells of the intestinal lining, and digestion is completed intracellularly within food vacuoles. As in cnidarians, the flatworm digestive system has only one opening, so undigested wastes are egested through the mouth.

MOST INVERTEBRATES AND ALL VERTEBRATES HAVE COMPLETE DIGESTIVE SYSTEMS

Most other invertebrates and all vertebrates have a **complete digestive system,** in which the digestive tract is a complete tube with two openings (Figure 45–4). Food enters through the mouth, and undigested food is eliminated through the anus. Waves of muscular contractions push the food in one direction, so that more food can be taken in while previously eaten food is being digested and absorbed farther down the tract.

In a complete digestive tract, various regions of the tube are specialized to perform specific functions. In the vertebrate digestive tract, food passes in sequence through the following specialized regions:

mouth → pharynx (throat) → esophagus → stomach → small intestine → large intestine → anus

All vertebrates have accessory glands that secrete digestive juices into the digestive tract at various points. These include the liver, the pancreas, and, in terrestrial vertebrates, the salivary glands.

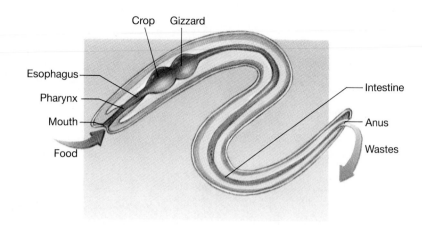

Figure 45–4 The earthworm, like most complex animals, has a complete digestive tract extending from the mouth at one end of the body to the anus at the other end. Various regions of the digestive tract are specialized to perform different food processing functions.

THE HUMAN DIGESTIVE SYSTEM HAS HIGHLY SPECIALIZED STRUCTURES FOR PROCESSING FOOD

In the human digestive system, various regions of the digestive tract have highly specialized structures and functions (Figure 45–5).

The Wall of the Digestive Tract Is Composed of Four Layers

Although its structure varies somewhat in different regions, the wall of the digestive tract is basically similar throughout its length (Figure 45–6). From the **lumen** (inner space) outward, its layers are the mucosa, submucosa, muscularis, and adventitia.

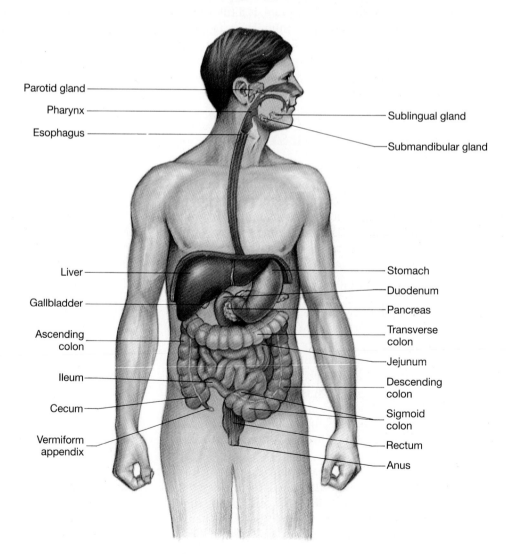

Figure 45–5 The human digestive system. Note the complete digestive tract—a long, coiled tube extending from mouth to anus. Locate the three types of accessory glands.

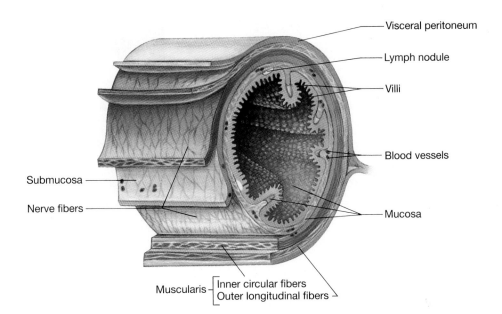

Visceral peritoneum
Lymph nodule
Villi
Blood vessels
Submucosa
Nerve fibers
Mucosa
Muscularis — Inner circular fibers / Outer longitudinal fibers

Figure 45–6 The wall of the digestive tract consists of four layers. The outer layer is known as the visceral peritoneum in the wall of the stomach and intestine. (Above the stomach it is referred to as the serosa, or adventitia.)

The **mucosa,** which lines the digestive tract, consists of epithelial tissue resting upon a layer of connective tissue. Goblet cells in the epithelial tissue secrete mucus, which protects and lubricates the inner surface of the digestive tract. In the stomach and intestine, the mucosa is greatly folded to increase the secreting and absorbing surface of the digestive tube.

The **submucosa,** which is made up of connective tissue, binds the mucosa to the muscle layer beneath. The submucosa is rich in blood and lymph vessels and nerves. Along most of the digestive tract, the **muscularis** consists of two layers of smooth muscle, an inner one with muscle fibers arranged circularly and an outer one with fibers arranged longitudinally (lengthwise). Localized contractions of these muscles mechanically break down food and mix it with digestive juices. Rhythmic waves of contraction of these muscles push food along through the digestive tract in the process of **peristalsis** (see Figure 45–9).

The **adventitia** is the outer connective tissue coat of the digestive tract. Below the level of the diaphragm it is covered by a layer of squamous epithelium and is called the **visceral peritoneum.** By various folds it is connected to the **parietal peritoneum,** a sheet of connective tissues that lines the walls of the abdominal and pelvic cavities. The visceral and parietal peritoneums enclose a potential space (part of the coelom), the **peritoneal cavity.** Inflammation of the peritoneum, called **peritonitis,** can be very serious because infection can spread along the peritoneum to most of the abdominal organs.

Food Processing Begins in the Mouth

The mouth is specialized for ingestion and for beginning the digestive process. Mechanical digestion begins with biting, grinding, and chewing food. Unlike the simple, pointed teeth of fish, amphibians, and reptiles, the teeth of mammals vary in size and shape and are specialized to perform specific functions. The chisel-shaped **incisors** are used for biting, and the long, pointed **canines** are adapted for stabbing and tearing food (Figure 45–7). The flattened surfaces of the **premolars** and **molars** are specialized for crushing and grinding food.

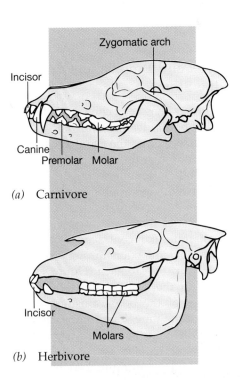

Zygomatic arch
Incisor
Canine
Premolar Molar

(*a*) Carnivore

Incisor
Molars

(*b*) Herbivore

Figure 45–7 Comparison of the teeth of carnivore and herbivore. (*a*) Skull of a coyote. (*b*) Skull of a domestic horse.

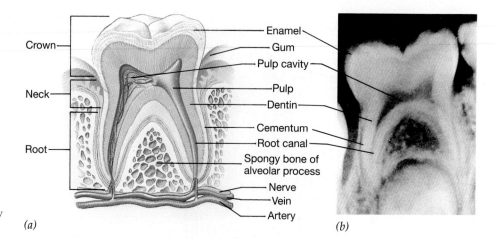

Figure 45–8 Structure of a tooth. (*a*) Sagittal section through a lower human molar. (*b*) Radiograph of a healthy molar.

(a)   *(b)*

A human tooth is illustrated in Figure 45–8. Each tooth is covered by **enamel,** the hardest substance in the body. Most of the tooth consists of **dentin,** which resembles bone in composition and hardness. Beneath the dentin is the **pulp cavity,** a region of soft connective tissue containing blood and lymph vessels and nerves.

While the food is being mechanically disassembled by the teeth, it is also moistened by saliva. Some of the food molecules dissolve, enabling the sense of taste. (Taste buds, which are located on the tongue and other surfaces of the mouth, are discussed in Chapter 41.) Three pairs of **salivary glands** secrete about 1 liter of saliva into the mouth cavity each day. Saliva contains **salivary amylase,** an enzyme that initiates the digestion of carbohydrates. Other substances found in saliva (e.g., immunoglobulin A) reduce the risk of oral infection.

The Pharynx and Esophagus Conduct Food to the Stomach

After a bite of food has been chewed and formed into a lump called a **bolus,** it is swallowed, that is, moved through the **pharynx** into the **esophagus.** The pharynx, or throat, is a muscular tube that serves as the hallway of the respiratory system as well as the digestive system. During swallowing, the opening to the airway is closed by a small flap of tissue, the **epiglottis,** so that food does not enter the respiratory system.

Waves of muscular contraction, called **peristaltic contractions,** move the bolus through the pharynx and esophagus toward the stomach (Figure 45–9). Circular muscle fibers in the wall of the esophagus contract around the top of the bolus, pushing it downward. Almost at the same time, longitudinal muscles around the bottom of the bolus and below it contract, shortening the tube.

When the body is upright, gravity helps to move the food through the esophagus, which is about 25 cm

(10 inches) long, but gravity is not necessary. Astronauts are able to eat in a weightless environment, and food will reach your stomach even if you are standing on your head.

Food Is Mechanically and Enzymatically Digested in the Stomach

The entrance to the stomach is normally closed by a ring of muscle at the lower end of the esophagus. When

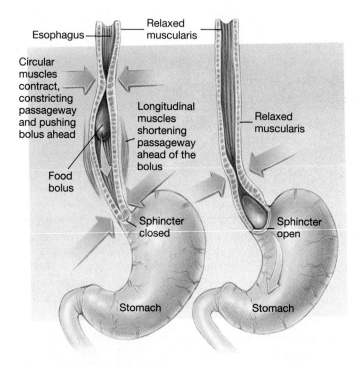

Figure 45–9 Peristalsis. Food is moved through the digestive tract by waves of muscular contraction known as peristalsis.

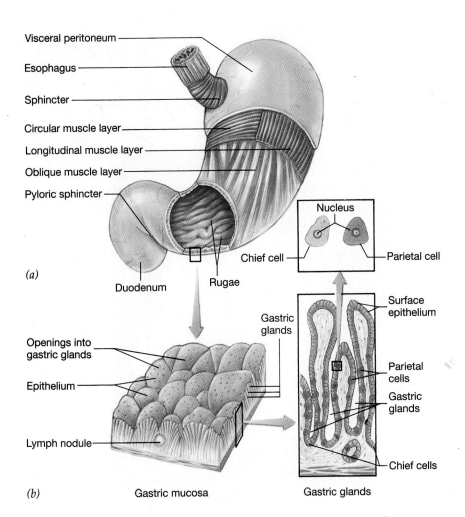

Visceral peritoneum

Esophagus

Sphincter

Circular muscle layer

Longitudinal muscle layer

Oblique muscle layer

Pyloric sphincter

(a)

Duodenum   Rugae

Chief cell

Nucleus

Parietal cell

Openings into
gastric glands

Epithelium

Lymph nodule

Gastric
glands

(b)   Gastric mucosa

Surface
epithelium

Parietal
cells

Gastric
glands

Chief cells

Gastric glands

Figure 45–10   From the esophagus, food enters the stomach, where it is mechanically and enzymatically digested. (*a*) Structure of the stomach. (*b*) The stomach lining and gastric glands.

a peristaltic wave passes down the esophagus, a reflex causes the ring of muscle to relax, permitting the bolus to enter the **stomach** (Figure 45–10). A large muscular organ, the stomach is shaped somewhat like a hot dog. Folds of the stomach wall called **rugae** give the inner lining a wrinkled appearance. As more and more food enters the stomach, the rugae gradually smooth out, stretching the capacity of the stomach to more than a quart (about 1 liter).

The stomach is lined with simple columnar epithelium that secretes large amounts of mucus. Tiny pits mark the entrances to the millions of gastric glands, which extend deep into the stomach wall (Figure 45–10). **Parietal cells** in the gastric glands secrete hydrochloric acid and a substance known as **intrinsic factor,** which is needed for adequate absorption of vitamin B. **Chief cells** in the gastric glands secrete **pepsinogen.** When pepsinogen comes in contact with the acidic gastric juice in the stomach, it is converted to **pepsin,** the main digestive enzyme of the stomach. Pepsin hydrolyzes proteins, reducing them to short polypeptides (see Focus on Peptic Ulcers).

What changes occur in a bite of food during its stay in the stomach? The stomach churns and chemically degrades the food to the consistency of thick soup, called **chyme.** Protein digestion begins, and much of the protein is degraded to polypeptides. Digestion of starch to small polysaccharides and maltose continues until salivary amylase is inactivated by the stomach acid. After 3 or 4 hours of digestion in the stomach, chyme is propelled a few milliliters at a time through the stomach exit, the **pylorus,** and into the small intestine.

Most Enzymatic Digestion Takes Place inside the Small Intestine

Digestion of food is completed in the **small intestine,** and nutrients are absorbed through its wall. The small intestine has three regions: the **duodenum,** the **jejunum,** and the **ileum.** Most chemical digestion takes place in the duodenum (the first portion of the small intestine), not in the stomach, as is commonly believed. Bile from the liver and enzymes from the pancreas are released into the duodenum and act upon the chyme. Then enzymes produced by the epithelial cells lining the duodenum catalyze the final steps of digestion.

The lining of the small intestine appears velvety because of millions of tiny finger-like projections in the

FOCUS ON

Peptic Ulcers

One of the wonders of physiology is that gastric juice does not normally digest the stomach wall itself. Several protective mechanisms prevent this from happening. Cells of the gastric mucosa secrete an alkaline mucus that coats the stomach wall and also neutralizes the acidity of the gastric juice along the lining. In addition, the epithelial cells of the lining are joined by tight junctions, preventing gastric juice from leaking between them and onto the tissue beneath. Should some of the epithelial cells be damaged, they are quickly replaced. In fact, the life span of an epithelial cell in the gastric mucosa is only about 3 days. About 0.5 million of these cells are shed and replaced every minute.

Still, these mechanisms sometimes malfunction or prove inadequate, and a small bit of the stomach lining is digested, leaving an open sore or **peptic ulcer.** Substances such as alcohol and aspirin reduce the resistance of the stomach mucosa to digestion by gastric juice. Peptic ulcers occur more often in the duodenum than in the stomach. They also sometimes occur in the lower part of the esophagus.

Peptic ulcers may bleed, leading to anemia. If the ulcer extends into

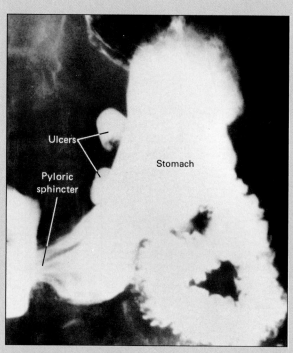

Radiograph of an ulcer in the wall of the stomach. The stomach and intestine have been filled with a contrast medium, making them appear white. This fluid also fills the cavities of the ulcers.

the muscularis, large blood vessels may also be damaged, resulting in hemorrhage. A **perforated ulcer** is one that extends all the way through the wall of the stomach or other affected organ. The opening created may allow bacteria and food to pass through to the peritoneum, leading to peritonitis and shock. Perforation is the main cause of death from ulcers.

---

lining, the intestinal **villi** (Figure 45–11). The villi (singular, *villus*) increase the surface area of the small intestine for digestion and absorption of nutrients. The intestinal surface area is further expanded by thousands of **microvilli,** folds of plasma membrane on the exposed borders of the epithelial cells. About 600 microvilli protrude from the surface of each cell, giving the epithelial lining a fuzzy appearance when viewed with the scanning electron microscope. This fuzzy surface is referred to as a brush border.

If the intestinal lining were smooth like the inside of a water pipe, food would move rapidly through the intestine and many valuable nutrients would not be absorbed. Folds in the wall of the intestine, along with the villi and microvilli, increase the surface area of the small intestine by about 600 times. If the lining of the small intestine of an adult human could be unfolded

and spread out, its surface would be approximately the size of a tennis court.

The Liver Secretes Bile, Which Mechanically Digests Fats

Just below the diaphragm lies the **liver,** the largest and one of the most complex organs in the body (Figure 45–12). A single liver cell can carry on more than 500 separate metabolic activities. The liver's food processing functions include the following:

1. Secretes **bile,** which is important in the mechanical digestion of fats.
2. Helps maintain homeostasis by removing nutrients from the blood.

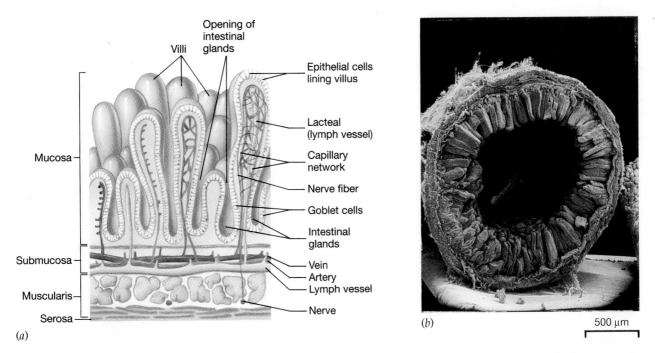

Figure 45–11 The inner wall of the small intestine is studded with villi and tiny openings into the intestinal glands. (*a*) Some of the villi have been opened to show the blood and lymph vessels within. (*b*) Scanning electron micrograph of a cross section of the small intestine. (*b*, Visuals Unlimited/G. Shih-R. Kessel)

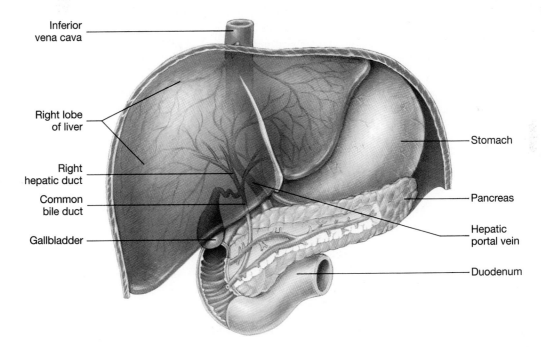

Figure 45–12 Structure of the liver and pancreas. Note the gallbladder and ducts.

3. Converts excess glucose to glycogen and stores it.
4. Converts excess amino acids to fatty acids and urea.
5. Stores iron and certain vitamins.
6. Detoxifies alcohol and many drugs and poisons.

Bile consists of water, bile salts, bile pigments, cholesterol, salts, and lecithin (a phospholipid). Bile produced in the liver is stored in the pear-shaped **gallblad-** **der,** which concentrates bile and releases it into the duodenum as needed. Bile mechanically digests fats by a detergent-like action in which it decreases the surface tension of fat particles. This process, called **emulsification,** disperses the fat molecules, which can then be worked on by lipases (fat-digesting enzymes). Bile contains no digestive enzymes and thus does not digest food material chemically.

Table 45–1 SUMMARY OF DIGESTIVE AGENTS

Agent (Active Form)	Optimal pH	Substrate	Result
Oral cavity			
Salivary amylase	6.9	Carbohydrates	Maltose and small polysaccharides
Mucus		Food	Moistening and lubrication
Stomach			
Hydrochloric acid (HCl)	2.0	Pepsinogen molecular bonds	Pepsin
Pepsin		Proteins	Polypeptides
Mucus		Food and gastric mucosa	Protection
Liver			
Bile salts		Fats	Emulsification
Pancreas			
Pancreatic amylase	7.1	Polysaccharides	Disaccharides
Pancreatic lipase	8.0	Emulsified fats	Fatty acids and glycerol
Trypsin	8.0	Polypeptides	Dipeptides
Chymotrypsin	8.0	Polypeptides	Dipeptides
Carboxypeptidase	8.0	Peptides	Dipeptides and amino acids
Ribonuclease	8.0	RNA	Nucleotides
Deoxyribonuclease	8.0	DNA	Nucleotides
Sodium bicarbonate		Acidic chyme	Neutralizes acidity
Small intestine			
Maltase	8.0	Maltose	Glucose
Sucrase	8.0	Sucrose	Glucose and fructose
Lactase	8.0	Lactose	Glucose and galactose
Aminopeptidase	8.0	Peptides	Amino acids
Dipeptidase	8.0	Dipeptides	Amino acids
Enterokinase	6.9	Trypsinogen	Trypsin (active)
Mucus		Intestinal mucosa	Protection
Intestinal juice		Chyme	Medium for digestion and absorption

The Pancreas Secretes Digestive Enzymes

The **pancreas** is an elongated gland lying behind the stomach which secretes digestive enzymes and hormones that help regulate the level of glucose in the blood. Its principal enzymes are (1) **trypsin** and **chymotrypsin,** which digest polypeptides to dipeptides; (2) **pancreatic lipase,** which degrades neutral fats; (3) **pancreatic amylase,** which breaks down almost all types of carbohydrates, except cellulose, to disaccharides; and (4) **ribonuclease** and **deoxyribonuclease,** which split the nucleic acids ribonucleic acid (RNA) and deoxyribonucleic acid (DNA) to free nucleotides.

Enzymatic Digestion Occurs as Food Moves through the Digestive Tract

As chyme moves through the digestive tract by means of peristalsis, mixing contractions, and motion of the villi, enzymes come into contact with the nutrients and digest them. The various digestive agents are summarized in Table 45–1.

Carbohydrates are digested to monosaccharides

Polysaccharides such as starch and glycogen are important parts of the food ingested by humans and most other animals. The glucose units of these large molecules are connected by glycosidic bonds linking carbon 4 (or 6) of one glucose molecule with carbon 1 of the adjacent glucose molecule. These bonds are hydrolyzed by **amylases,** enzymes that digest polysaccharides to the disaccharide maltose (Table 45–2). Although the amylases of the digestive tract can split the α-glycosidic bonds present in starch and glycogen, they cannot split the β-glycosidic bonds present in cellulose. In most vertebrates, amylase is secreted only by the pancreas. In humans and certain other mammals amylase is also secreted by the salivary glands.

Amylases cannot split the bond between the two glucose units of maltose. Enzymes produced by the cells lining the small intestine break down disaccharides such as maltose to monosaccharides. These enzymes are found in the brush border of the epithelial cells and are thought to catalyze hydrolysis while the disaccharides are being absorbed through the epithelium. **Maltase,** for example, splits maltose into two glucose molecules.

Proteins are digested to amino acids

Several kinds of proteolytic enzymes are secreted into the digestive tract (Table 45–2). Each is specific for peptide bonds at a specific location in a polypeptide chain. Three main groups are exopeptidases, endopeptidases, and dipeptidases.

Exopeptidases split the peptide bond joining a terminal amino acid to a peptide chain. For example, carboxypeptidase cleaves the peptide bond joining the amino acid with the free terminal carboxyl group to the peptide chain. Aminopeptidase splits off the amino acid with a free terminal amino group.

Endopeptidases cleave only peptide bonds *within* a peptide chain. Pepsin, trypsin, and chymotrypsin are endopeptidases. They differ in their requirements for specific amino acids adjacent to the bond to be split. These endopeptidases split peptide chains into smaller fragments, which are then cleaved further by exopeptidases. The combined action of the endopeptidases and exopeptidases results in splitting of the protein molecules to dipeptides and amino acids. **Dipeptidases** in the brush borders of the duodenum then split the remaining small peptides to amino acids. The amino acids and some small peptides are absorbed through the epithelial cells lining the villi and enter the blood.

Fats are digested to fatty acids and monoacylglycerols

Lipids are usually ingested as large masses of triacylglycerols (also referred to as triglycerides) and are digested largely within the duodenum by pancreatic lipase (Table 45–2). Like many other proteins, lipase is water-soluble, but its substrates are not. Thus, the enzyme can attack only the fat molecules at the surface of a mass of fat. The bile salts are detergents that reduce the surface tension of fats, breaking the large masses of fat into smaller droplets. This greatly increases the surface area of fat exposed to the action of lipase and so increases the rate of lipid digestion.

Conditions in the intestine are usually not optimal for the complete hydrolysis of lipids to glycerol and fatty acids. The products of lipid digestion therefore include monoacylglycerols (monoglycerides) and diacylglycerols (diglycerides) as well as glycerol and fatty acids. Undigested triacylglycerols remain as well, and some of these are absorbed without digestion.

Nerves and Hormones Regulate Digestion

Most digestive enzymes are produced only when food is present in the digestive tract. Salivary gland secretion is controlled entirely by the nervous system, but secretion of other digestive juices is regulated by both nerves and hormones (Table 45–3). For example, seeing, smelling, tasting, or even thinking about food causes the brain to send neural messages to the glands in the stomach, stimulating them to secrete gastric juice. In addition, distention of the stomach by food stimulates glands in the stomach wall to release **gastrin.** This hormone is absorbed into the blood and transported to the gastric glands, where it stimulates release of gastric juice.

Absorption Takes Place Mainly through the Villi of the Small Intestine

Only a few substances—water, simple sugars, salts, alcohol, and certain drugs—are composed of molecules small enough to be absorbed through the wall of the stomach. Absorption of nutrients is primarily the job of the intestinal villi. As illustrated in Figure 45–11, the wall of a villus consists of a single layer of epithelial cells. Inside each villus is a network of capillaries and a central lymph vessel called a **lacteal.** To reach the blood (or lymph), a nutrient molecule must pass through an epithelial cell of the intestinal lining and then through a cell lining the blood or lymph vessel.

Absorption occurs by a combination of simple diffusion, facilitated diffusion, and active transport. Glucose and amino acids are absorbed by active transport, which is coupled with the active transport of sodium (see Fig. 5–18). Fructose is absorbed by facilitated diffusion.

After nutrients such as amino acids are transported into the epithelial cells lining the villi, they accumulate within the cells and then diffuse into the blood of the intestinal capillaries. Amino acids and glucose are transported to the liver by the **hepatic portal vein.** In

Table 45–2   SUMMARY OF DIGESTION

Location	Source of Enzyme	Digestive Process*

Carbohydrate digestion

Mouth — Salivary glands — Polysaccharides (e.g., starch) $\xrightarrow{\text{salivary amylase}}$ Maltose + Small polysaccharides

Stomach — — Action continues until salivary amylase is inactivated by acidic pH

Small intestine — Pancreas — Undigested polysaccharides and small polysaccharides $\xrightarrow{\text{pancreatic amylase}}$ Maltose

Intestine — Disaccharides hydrolyzed to monosaccharides as follows:

Maltose (malt sugar) $\xrightarrow{\text{maltase}}$ Glucose + Glucose

Sucrose (table sugar) $\xrightarrow{\text{sucrase}}$ Glucose + Fructose

Lactose (milk sugar) $\xrightarrow{\text{lactase}}$ Glucose + Galactose

Protein digestion

Stomach — Stomach (gastric glands) — Protein $\xrightarrow{\text{pepsin}}$ Short polypeptides

Small intestine — Pancreas — Polypeptides
A—A—A—A—A
|
A—A—A—A—A
$\xrightarrow[\text{chymotrypsin}]{\text{trypsin,}}$ Tripeptides + Dipeptides
A—A—A   A—A

Dipeptides
A—A
$\xrightarrow{\text{carboxypeptidase, aminopeptidase}}$ Free amino acids
A   A
A

Small intestine — Tripeptides + Dipeptides
A—A—A   A—A
$\xrightarrow{\text{peptidases}}$ Free amino acids
A   A
A
A   A
A

Lipid digestion

Small intestine — Liver — Glob of fat $\xrightarrow{\text{bile salts}}$ Emulsified fat (individual triacylglycerols)

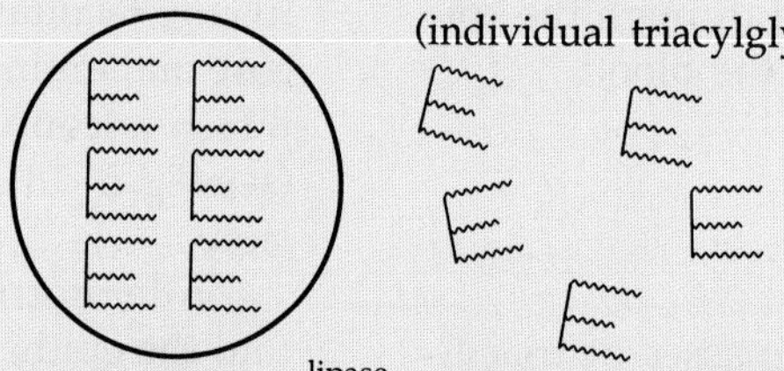

Pancreas — Triacylglycerol $\xrightarrow{\text{lipase}}$ Fatty acids + Glycerol

*◯ = monosaccharide; ⌇ = triacylglycerol; E = glycerol; ∿ = fatty acid; A = amino acid.

Table 45–3 HORMONAL CONTROL OF DIGESTION

Hormone	Source	Target Tissue	Actions	Factors That Stimulate Release
Gastrin	Stomach (mucosa)	Stomach (gastric glands)	Stimulates gastric glands to secrete pepsinogen	Distention of the stomach by food; certain substances such as partially digested proteins and caffeine
Secretin	Duodenum (mucosa)	Pancreas	Stimulates release of alkaline component of pancreatic juice	Acidic chyme acting on mucosa of duodenum
		Liver	Increases rate of bile secretion	
Cholecystokinin (CCK)	Duodenum (mucosa)	Pancreas	Stimulates release of digestive enzymes	Presence of fatty acids and partially digested proteins in duodenum
		Gallbladder	Stimulates contraction and emptying	
Gastrin inhibitory peptide	Duodenum (mucosa)	Stomach	Decreases stomach motor activity, thus slowing emptying	Presence of fatty acids or glucose in duodenum

the liver this vein divides into a vast network of sinusoids (tiny blood vessels similar to capillaries), which allow the nutrient-rich blood to move slowly through the liver tissues, where nutrients and certain toxic substances are removed from the circulation.

The products of lipid digestion are absorbed by a different process and different route (Figure 45–13). Fatty acids and monoacylglycerols combine with bile salts to form soluble complexes called micelles. This greatly facilitates absorption, because the micelles transport the fatty substances to the brush borders. When the micelles come into contact with the epithelial cells of the villi, the monoacylglycerols and fatty acids (both soluble in the lipid of the plasma membrane) diffuse into the cell, leaving the rest of the micelle behind to combine with new fatty acids and monoacylglycerols.

In the epithelial cells, free fatty acids and glycerol are assembled once again by the endoplasmic reticulum into triacylglycerols which are then packaged into globules with absorbed cholesterol and phospholipids and covered with a thin coat of protein. These protein-covered fat globules, called **chylomicrons,** pass out of the epithelial cell and into the lacteal of the villus. They are transported by the lymph and eventually emptied with the lymph into the blood. About 90% of absorbed fat enters the blood circulation in this indirect way. The rest, mainly short-chain fatty acids such as those in butter, are absorbed directly into the blood. After a meal rich in fats, the great number of chylomicrons in the

blood may give the plasma a turbid, milky appearance for a few hours.

Most of the nutrients in the chyme are absorbed by the time the chyme reaches the end of the small intestine. What is left of the chyme (mainly waste) passes through a sphincter, the **ileocecal valve,** into the large intestine.

The Large Intestine Eliminates Wastes

Indigestible material, such as the cellulose of plant foods, along with unabsorbed chyme, passes into the **large intestine.** Although this organ is only about 1.3 meters long (about 4 feet), it is called "large" because it has a larger diameter than the small intestine. The small intestine joins the large intestine about 7 cm (2.8 inches) from the end of the large intestine, thereby forming a blind pouch, the **cecum.** The **vermiform appendix** projects from the end of the cecum. (Appendicitis is an inflammation of the appendix.) The functions of the cecum and appendix in humans are not known; they are generally considered vestigial organs, perhaps important in the vegetarian past of the human species. Herbivores such as rabbits have a large, functional cecum containing bacteria that digest cellulose.

From the cecum to the **rectum** (the last portion of the digestive tract) the large intestine is known as the **colon.** The regions of the large intestine are the cecum, ascending colon, transverse colon, descending colon,

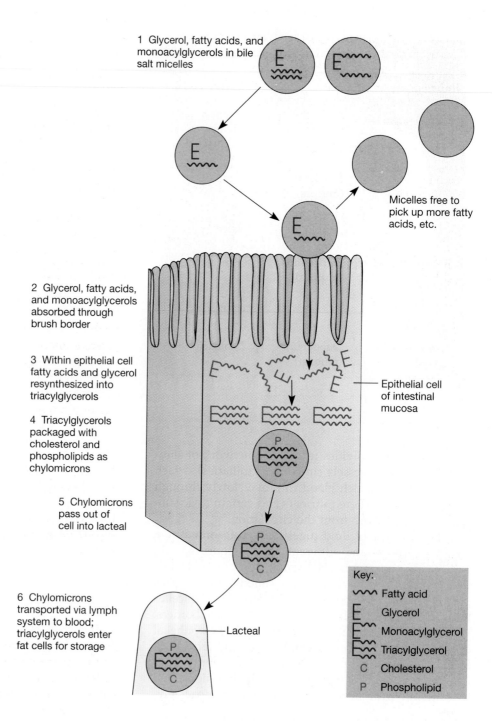

1 Glycerol, fatty acids, and monoacylglycerols in bile salt micelles

Micelles free to pick up more fatty acids, etc.

2 Glycerol, fatty acids, and monoacylglycerols absorbed through brush border

3 Within epithelial cell fatty acids and glycerol resynthesized into triacylglycerols

Epithelial cell of intestinal mucosa

4 Triacylglycerols packaged with cholesterol and phospholipids as chylomicrons

5 Chylomicrons pass out of cell into lacteal

6 Chylomicrons transported via lymph system to blood; triacylglycerols enter fat cells for storage

Lacteal

Key:
- 〰 Fatty acid
- E Glycerol
- E Monoacylglycerol
- 〰 Triacylglycerol
- C Cholesterol
- P Phospholipid

Figure 45–13 Overview of the process of lipid absorption by an epithelial cell lining the intestine.

sigmoid colon, rectum, and anus, the opening for the elimination of wastes.

As the chyme passes slowly through the large intestine, water and sodium are absorbed from it, and it gradually assumes the consistency of normal feces. Bacteria inhabiting the large intestine enjoy the last remnants of the meal and return the favor by producing vitamin K and certain B vitamins that can be absorbed and used.

A distinction must be made between elimination and excretion. *Elimination* is the process of getting rid of

digestive wastes, materials that have never left the digestive tract and did not participate in metabolic activities. *Excretion* is the process of getting rid of metabolic wastes and in mammals is mainly the function of the kidneys and lungs. The large intestine does excrete bile pigments, however.

When chyme passes through the intestine too rapidly, **defecation** (expulsion of feces) becomes more frequent and the feces are watery. This condition, called diarrhea, may be caused by anxiety, certain foods, or disease organisms that irritate the intestinal lining. Pro-

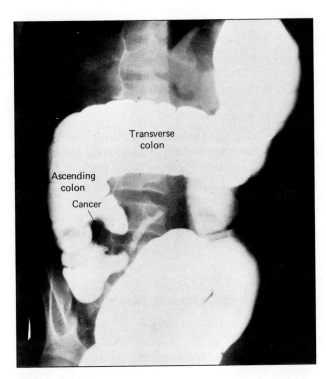

Figure 45–14 Radiographic view of the large intestine of a patient with cancer of the colon. The lumen of the large intestine has been filled with a suspension of barium sulfate, which makes irregularities in the wall visible. The cancer is evident as a mass that projects into the lumen.

longed diarrhea leads to loss of water and salts and eventually to dehydration, a serious condition, especially in infants.

Constipation results when chyme passes through the intestine too slowly. Because more water than usual is removed from the chyme, the feces may become hard and dry. Constipation is often caused by a diet containing insufficient fiber (indigestible materials from plant foods).

Cancer of the colon is one of the most common causes of cancer deaths in the United States (Figure 45–14). Research indicates that this type of cancer may be related to diet because the disease is more common in people whose diets are very low in fiber. Less fiber may result in less frequent defecation, allowing prolonged contact between the mucous membrane of the colon and carcinogens in foods, such as nitrite derivatives.

ADEQUATE AMOUNTS OF REQUIRED NUTRIENTS ARE NECESSARY TO SUPPORT METABOLIC PROCESSES

From about 20 chemical elements that are absorbed in the form of simple compounds and salts, plants are able to produce all the different kinds of organic molecules they need. Although animals require approximately the same 20 chemical elements (see Table 2–1), these elements must already be chemically combined in the form of about 40 chemical nutrients, many of them organic compounds. With only slight variation, all animals require the same basic nutrients—carbohydrates, lipids, proteins, vitamins, and minerals. Although not considered a nutrient in a strict sense, water is a necessary dietary component. Sufficient fluid must be ingested to replace fluid lost in urine, sweat, feces, and breath.

Our discussion focuses on human nutritional needs and on the metabolic fate of these nutrients. Adequate nutrition is an important global concern. Diseases of dietary excess and imbalance are among the leading causes of death. Knowledge about nutrition and commitment to good eating habits would improve health and prevent disease.

Adequate amounts of essential nutrients are necessary for metabolic processes. (Recall that metabolism refers to all of the chemical processes that take place in the body.) Metabolic processes include anabolism and catabolism. Anabolism refers to synthetic processes; catabolism includes breakdown processes such as cellular respiration.

Once nutrients are absorbed from the digestive tract, they are transported by the blood. The blood has been appropriately described as a traveling smorgasbord from which each cell selects whatever nutrients it needs to carry on its metabolic processes. Surplus nutrients are taken up by the liver cells, where they are either stored or converted into other materials. Under normal circumstances blood leaving the liver carries sufficient nutrients to meet the requirements of all the cells of the body.

Carbohydrates Are a Major Energy Source in the Human Diet

Sugars and starches are the principal sources of energy in the ordinary human diet. However, they are not considered essential nutrients because the body can obtain energy from a mixture of proteins and fats. In the average American diet, carbohydrates provide about 50% of the Calories (Cal) ingested daily. Nutritionists measure the energy value of food in Calories per gram of food. (A Calorie, spelled with a capital C, is actually a kilocalorie. It is defined as the amount of heat required to raise the temperature of 1 kg of water from 15°C to 16°C. The physical unit of heat—the calorie [spelled with a lower case c], used by chemists—is 1000 times smaller.)

Carbohydrates are commonly ingested as starch, cellulose, and sucrose

Carbohydrates are ingested primarily as starch and cellulose, both polysaccharides, and sucrose, a disaccharide. (You may want to review the discussion of carbohydrates in Chapter 3.) Nutritionists refer to polysaccharides as complex carbohydrates. Foods rich in complex carbohydrates include rice, potatoes, corn, and other cereal grains. These are the least expensive foods, and for this reason the proportion of carbohydrate in a family's diet often reflects their economic status. Very poor people subsist on diets that are almost exclusively carbohydrate, whereas the more affluent enjoy the more expensive protein-rich foods, such as meat and dairy products.

Fiber is mainly a complex mixture of cellulose and other indigestible carbohydrates of plant origin. The American diet is low in fiber owing to low intake of fruit and vegetables and use of refined flour. As mentioned above, increasing fiber in the diet may decrease the risk of cancer of the colon. Fiber may also stimulate the feeling of being satisfied with the amount of food intake (satiety) and thus may be useful in treating obesity. Nutritionists have suggested that Americans increase their consumption of complex carbohydrates and fiber by eating more fruits, vegetables, and whole grains. They also suggest a reduction in dietary intake of animal products, which are high in fat.

In affluent societies about 25% of the carbohydrate intake (more in children) is in the form of the disaccharide sucrose—cane or beet sugar. Sucrose is the so-called refined sugar put in coffee and desserts. Other important sugars are lactose, the sugar in milk, and fructose, found in fruits.

Glucose is used as fuel by the cells

Monosaccharides are the products of carbohydrate digestion. In the liver the various monosaccharides are converted to glucose. Pancreatic hormones act on the liver to help regulate the concentration of glucose in the blood (blood sugar level). Cells of the body require a constant supply of glucose delivered by the blood. Brain cells are especially dependent because they are unable to store glucose themselves. If deprived of an energy source for even a few minutes, they cease to function. After a meal or rich dessert, when there is an excess of glucose in the blood, the liver cells remove and store it as glycogen. Between meals, when the glucose level begins to fall, the liver cells slowly disassemble glycogen and release glucose back into the blood. In this way the liver maintains a rather steady glucose level in the blood.

The normal blood glucose content during fasting is about 90 mg per 100 mL of blood. After a carbohydrate-rich meal the level may increase briefly to about 140 mg per 100 mL. If the liver did not remove the excess, the level would rise to more than three times normal after a carbohydrate-rich meal and then fall disastrously between meals or during the night.

The amount of glycogen stored in the liver is sufficient to maintain the blood glucose level for several hours. After the glycogen is used up, liver cells convert amino acids and the glycerol portions of fat to glucose (Figure 45–15). Several hormones regulate the various processes by which the liver alters blood glucose level (see Chapter 47).

When excess carbohydrate-rich food is eaten, the liver cells may become fully packed with glycogen and still have more glucose coming in. In this situation liver cells convert excess glucose to fatty acids and glycerol, which solves the excess glucose problem. However, these compounds are then synthesized into triacylglycerols and sent to the fat depots of the body for storage.

Lipids Are Used to Supply Energy and to Make Needed Biological Molecules

Cells use ingested lipids as fuel, as components of cell membranes, and as the building blocks of lipid compounds, such as steroid hormones and bile salts. Lipid accounts for about 40% of the Calories in the average American diet. In poor countries this percentage is less than 10%, because most lipid-rich foods—meats, eggs, and dairy products—are relatively expensive.

Three polyunsaturated fatty acids (linoleic, linolenic, and arachidonic acids) are essential fatty acids that must be included in the human diet because the body cannot synthesize them. Given these and sufficient non-lipid nutrients, the body can make all of the lipid compounds that it needs (including fats, cholesterol, phospholipids, and prostaglandins). For this reason and because lipids are widespread in foods, dietary deficiency of lipids is uncommon.

Most lipids are ingested as triacylglycerols

About 98% of lipids in the diet are ingested in the form of triacylglycerols. (Recall from Chapter 3 that a triacylglycerol is a glycerol molecule chemically combined with three fatty acids; see Figure 3–12.) Triacylglycerols may be saturated, that is, fully loaded with hydrogen atoms. They may be monounsaturated (containing one double bond in the carbon chain of a fatty acid, so two more hydrogen atoms can be added) or polyunsaturated (containing two or more double bonds, so four or more hydrogen atoms can be added).

Generally, animal foods are rich in both saturated fats and cholesterol, and plant foods contain unsaturated fats and no cholesterol. Commonly used polyunsaturated vegetable oils are corn, soya, cottonseed, and safflower oils. Olive and peanut oils contain large amounts of monounsaturated fats. Butter contains mainly saturated fats.

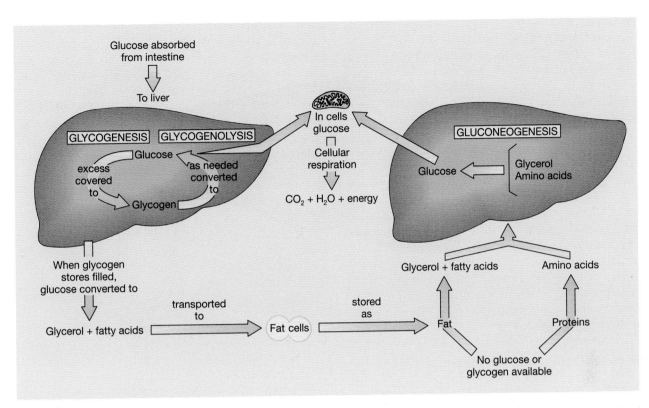

Figure 45–15 The fate of glucose in the body. The liver plays a central role in maintaining an appropriate level of glucose in the blood.

The average American diet provides about 700 mg of cholesterol each day, whereas less than 300 mg is recommended. Cholesterol sources are egg yolks, butter, and meat. The body does not depend upon dietary sources for cholesterol because it is able to synthesize cholesterol from other nutrients. In fact, dietary intake of saturated fats can increase cholesterol level markedly.

Dietary triacylglycerols and cholesterol have been associated with heart disease

Lipids have been the focus of much research because of their role in atherosclerosis, a progressive disease in which the arteries become occluded with fatty material. As discussed in Chapter 42, atherosclerosis leads to circulatory impairment and heart disease.

Cholesterol and triacylglycerols are not transported free in the blood plasma but are bound to proteins and transported as macromolecular complexes called **lipoproteins.** About 70% of plasma cholesterol is transported on **low-density lipoproteins (LDLs).** The remaining cholesterol is transported mainly on **high-density lipoproteins (HDLs).** High levels of LDL have been correlated with increased risk for coronary artery and heart disease. LDL is thought to pick up cholesterol

and deposit it in body cells, sometimes in the smooth muscle cells of the arterial wall. When LDL levels are high, HDL may play a protective role and decrease risk for coronary heart disease. HDL may collect cholesterol from body cells and transport it to the liver. A healthy proportion of HDL and LDL can apparently be promoted by a regular exercise program, by diet (reducing intake of animal fats and cholesterol), by appropriate body weight (obesity has a negative effect on lipoprotein levels), and by not smoking cigarettes.

Unsaturated fats from fish contain fatty acids known as omega-3 fatty acids. These are thought to decrease LDL levels and to play other protective roles in decreasing the risk for coronary heart disease.

A diet high in saturated fats and cholesterol raises the blood cholesterol level by as much as 25%. On the other hand, ingestion of polyunsaturated fats tends to decrease the blood cholesterol level. For these reasons many people now cook with vegetable oils rather than with butter and lard, drink skim milk rather than whole milk, eat ice milk instead of ice cream, and use margarine instead of butter. (In the production of margarines, oils are partially hydrogenated, a process that reduces their degree of polyunsaturation. However, this process can be controlled so that soft margarine is produced which contains a large proportion of polyunsaturated fats.)

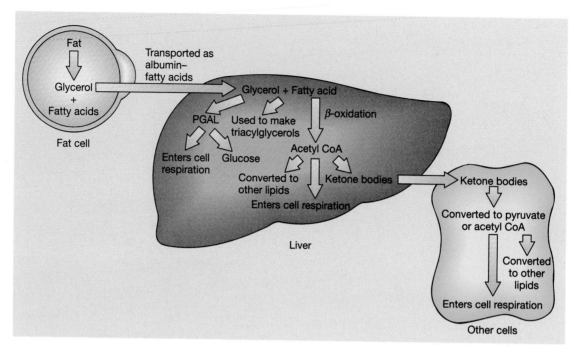

Figure 45–16   Overview of lipid metabolism.

Fat is stored in adipose tissue

Although fats are absorbed into the lymphatic system, they eventually enter the blood. From the blood, fats are taken up by the adipose tissues and stored. When needed, stored fats are hydrolyzed to fatty acids and released into the blood. Before these fatty acids can be used by cells as fuel, they must be broken down into smaller compounds and combined with coenzyme A to form molecules of acetyl coenzyme A (Figure 45–16). This transformation is accomplished in the liver (by a process known as beta-oxidation).

For transport to the cells, acetyl coenzyme A is converted into one of three types of ketone bodies. Normally, the level of ketone bodies in the blood is low, but in certain abnormal conditions, such as starvation and diabetes mellitus, fat metabolism is tremendously increased. Ketone bodies are then produced so rapidly that their level in the blood becomes excessive and causes the blood to become too acidic. Such disruption of normal pH balance can lead to death. (How Eskimos, who live on diets extremely high in fat, manage to maintain acid-base homeostasis is something of a mystery.)

Proteins Serve as Enzymes and Are Essential Structural Components of Cells

Proteins are critical nutrients because they are essential building materials of cells. Proteins also serve as enzymes and are used to make many needed substances such as hemoglobin and myosin. Protein consumption is an index of a country's (or an individual's) economic status, because high-quality protein is the most expensive and least available nutrient. The recommended daily amount of protein is about 56 grams—only about one eighth of a pound. In the United States and other developed countries, most people eat far more protein than required. The average American eats about 300 pounds of meat and dairy products per year. People in some underdeveloped countries consume an average of only 2 pounds per person per year. Protein poverty is one of the world's most pressing health problems; millions of humans suffer from poor health and disease and even die as a consequence of protein malnutrition.

Essential Amino Acids Must Be Ingested in the Diet

Ingested proteins are degraded in the digestive tract to their molecular subunits—amino acids, which are absorbed and used by the cells to make the types of proteins needed. Of the 20 or so amino acids important in nutrition, the body is able to make several by rearranging the atoms of certain organic acids. About eight of the amino acids (nine in children) cannot be synthesized by human body cells at all, or at least not in sufficient quantity to meet the body's needs. Those that must be provided in the diet are called **essential amino acids.**

Not all ingested proteins contain the same kinds or quantities of amino acids, and many proteins lack some of the essential amino acids. Complete proteins, those

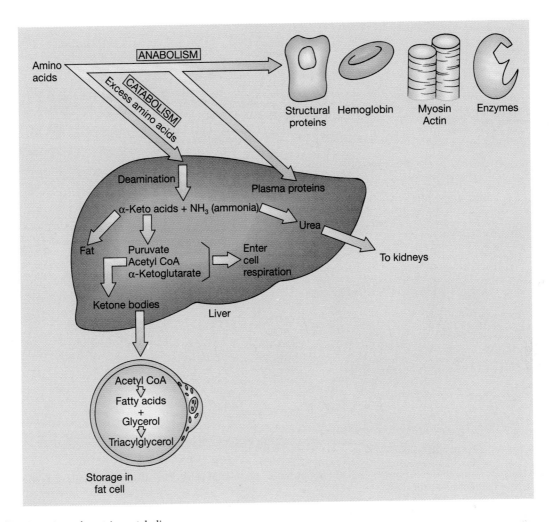

Figure 45–17 Overview of protein metabolism.

that contain the most appropriate distribution of amino acids for human nutrition, are found in eggs, milk, meat, and fish. Some foods, such as gelatin and soybeans, contain a high proportion of protein but lack some essential amino acids or contain them in nutritionally unbalanced proportions. Most plant proteins are deficient in one or more essential amino acids (usually lysine, tryptophan, or threonine).

Most humans depend upon cereal grains as their staple food—usually rice, wheat, or corn (see Focus on Vegetarian Diets). These foods provide neither an adequate proportion of total amino acids nor adequate distribution of essential amino acids, especially not for growing children. In some underdeveloped countries, starchy crops such as sweet potatoes or cassava are the principal food. Total protein content of these foods is less than 2%, far below minimum needs.

Excess amino acids are deaminated, then used as fuel or stored as fat

Amino acids circulating in the blood are removed as needed by individual body cells and used primarily for synthesizing proteins. Excess amino acids are removed from circulation by the liver, where they are deaminated; that is, the amino group is removed. Deamination forms ammonia, which is toxic at high concentrations. The ammonia is converted to urea, which is excreted from the body.

The remaining carbon chain of the amino acid (called a keto acid) may be converted into carbohydrate or lipid and used as fuel or stored (Figure 45–17). Thus, even people who eat high-protein diets can gain weight if they eat too much. Figure 45–18 summarizes the interrelationships of carbohydrate, protein, and lipid metabolism.

Vitamins Are Organic Compounds Essential for Normal Metabolism

Vitamins are organic compounds required by the body for biochemical processes. Many function as components of coenzymes (see Chapter 7). Very small amounts are required in comparison with other dietary constituents. Vitamins may be divided into two main

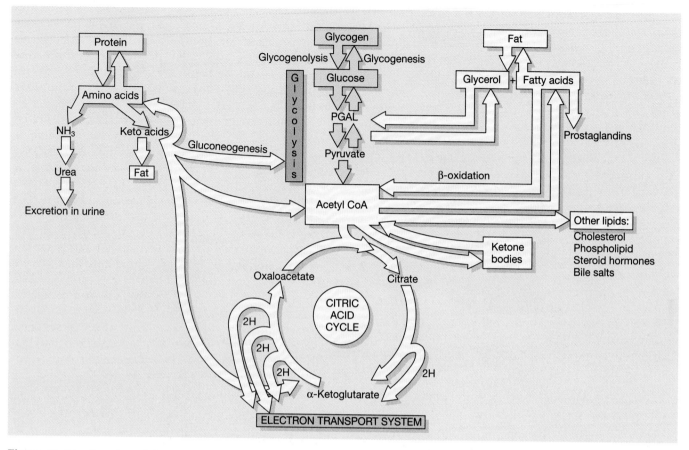

Figure 45–18   Overview of the integrated metabolism of carbohydrates, fats, and proteins. This diagram is greatly simplified and illustrates only a few of the principal pathways.

groups. **Fat-soluble vitamins** include vitamins A, D, E, and K. **Water-soluble vitamins** are the B and C vitamins. Table 45–4 gives the sources, functions, and consequences of deficiency for most of the vitamins.

Debates rage over the advisability of taking large amounts of certain specific vitamins, such as vitamin C to prevent colds or vitamin E to protect against vascular disease. No compelling evidence so far supports claims that massive quantities of any vitamin are beneficial. We do not even understand all the biochemical roles played by vitamins or the interactions between various vitamins and other nutrients. We do know that large overdoses of vitamins, like vitamin deficiency, can be harmful. Moderate overdoses of the B and C vitamins are excreted in the urine, but surpluses of the fat-soluble vitamins are not easily excreted and can accumulate to harmful levels.

Minerals Are Inorganic Nutrients Required by Cells

Minerals are inorganic nutrients generally ingested as salts dissolved in food and water. Essential minerals required in daily amounts of 100 milligrams or more

include sodium, chlorine, potassium, magnesium, calcium, sulfur, and phosphorus (Table 45–5). Several others, such as iron, copper, iodine, fluorine, and cobalt, are required in much smaller amounts and so are known as **trace elements.**

Minerals are necessary components of all body tissues and fluids. Salt content (about 0.9%) is vital in maintaining the fluid balance of the body, and because salts are lost from the body daily in sweat, urine, and feces, they must be replaced by dietary intake. Sodium chloride (common table salt) is the salt needed in largest quantity in blood and other body fluids. A deficiency of this salt results in dehydration.

Energy Metabolism Is Balanced When Energy Input Equals Energy Output

The amount of energy (heat) liberated by the body during metabolism is a measure of the **metabolic rate;** much of the energy expended by the body is ultimately converted to heat. Metabolic rate may be expressed either in Calories of heat energy expended per day or as a percentage above or below a standard normal level.

The **basal metabolic rate (BMR)** is the rate at which the body releases heat as a result of breaking down fuel molecules. BMR is the body's basic cost of metabolic living, that is, the rate of energy used during resting conditions. An individual's **total metabolic rate** is the sum of his or her BMR and the energy used to carry on all daily activities. An athlete or a laborer has a greater total metabolic rate than a teacher or executive who does not exercise regularly.

An average-sized man who does not engage in any exercise program and who sits at a desk all day expends about 2200 Calories daily. If the food he eats each day contains about 2200 Calories, he is in a state of energy balance; that is, his energy input equals his energy output. This is an extremely important concept, for when

$$\text{Energy (Calorie) input} = \text{Energy output}$$

body weight remains constant. When energy output is greater than energy input, stored fat is burned and body weight decreases. On the other hand, people gain weight when they take in more energy (Calories) in food than they expend in daily activity—in other words, when

$$\text{Energy (Calorie) input} > \text{Energy output}$$

Obesity is a serious nutritional problem

Obesity, the excess accumulation of body fat, is a serious form of malnutrition and has become a problem of epidemic proportions in our affluent society. Excess weight places an extra burden upon the heart and may lead to heart disease and other ailments. Obese persons generally die at a younger age than people of normal weight. According to insurance statistics, men who are 20% or more overweight bear a greater risk of dying from heart disease (43%), cerebral hemorrhage (53%), and diabetes (133%) than do men of normal weight. A man who is 20% overweight is 30% more likely to die before retirement age than if his weight were normal. Yet one third of our working population is 25% or more overweight.

Obesity can result from an increase in the size or the number of fat cells, or both. The number of fat cells in the adult is apparently determined mainly by the amount of fat stored during infancy and childhood. When babies or small children are overfed, abnormally large numbers of fat cells are formed. Later in life these fat cells may be fully stocked with excess lipids or may be shrunken, but they are always there. People with such increased numbers of fat cells are thought to be more susceptible to obesity than those with normal numbers.

Most overweight people overeat because of a combination of poor eating habits and psychological factors. Whatever the underlying causes, overeating is the only way to become obese. Although water retention does increase body weight, it does not affect fat storage; water excesses can be diminished more quickly and easily than fat excess. For every 9.3 Calories of excess food taken into the body, 1 gram of fat is stored. (An excess of about 140 Calories per day for a month results in 1 pound of weight gained.)

Because so many people are overweight, dieting has generated a multimillion-dollar industry embracing diet foods, formulas, pills, books, clubs, slenderizing devices, and even surgical procedures such as gastric stapling and insertion of plastic bubbles inside the stomach. Unfortunately, obesity has no magic cure. The only sure (and healthful) way to lose weight is to restrict food (energy) intake to be less than energy output. This forces the body to draw on its fat stores for the missing calories, and as the fat is mobilized and burned, body weight decreases. This can be accomplished best by a combination of increased exercise and decreased caloric intake (a 1000 to 1500 Calorie diet is recommended for the mildly obese). Most nutritionists agree that the best reducing diet is a well-balanced one that provides Calories primarily in the form of complex carbohydrates.

Malnutrition can cause serious health problems

Whereas millions of people eat too much, many others do not have enough to eat or do not eat a balanced diet. Even overweight individuals can be malnourished. Persons suffering from malnutrition may be weak, easily fatigued, and highly susceptible to infection. They are commonly deficient in essential amino acids, iron, calcium, and vitamin A. An estimated 250,000 children become permanently blind every year because their diets are deficient in vitamin A.

Of all the required nutrients, essential amino acids are most often deficient in the diet. Millions of people suffer from poor health and a lowered resistance to disease because of protein deficiency. Children's physical and mental development are retarded when the essential building blocks of cells are not provided in the diet. Because their bodies cannot manufacture antibodies (which are proteins) and cells needed to fight infection, common childhood diseases, such as measles, whooping cough, and chickenpox, are often fatal in children suffering from protein malnutrition.

In young children, severe protein malnutrition results in the condition known as **kwashiorkor.** The term, an African word that means "first-second," refers to the situation in which a first child is displaced from its mother's breast when a younger sibling is born. The older child is placed on a protein-deficient diet of starchy cereal or cassava. Growth becomes stunted, muscles waste away, edema develops (as displayed by a swollen belly), the child becomes apathetic and

(*Text continued on p. 979*)

Table 45-4 THE VITAMINS

Vitamins and U.S. RDA*	Actions	Effect of Deficiency	Sources	Comments
Fat-soluble				
Vitamin A, retinol 5000 IU†	Converted to retinal, a necessary component of retinal pigments, essential for normal vision; essential for normal growth and integrity of epithelial tissue; promotes normal growth of bones and teeth by regulating activity of bone cells	Failure of growth; night blindness; atrophy of epithelium; epithelium subject to infection; scaly skin	Liver, fish-liver oils, egg; yellow and green vegetables	Can be formed from provitamin carotene (a yellow or red pigment); sometimes called anti-infection vitamin because it helps maintain epithelial membranes; excessive amounts harmful
Vitamin D, calciferol 400 IU	Promotes calcium absorption from digestive tract; essential to normal growth and maintenance of bone	Bone deformities; rickets in children; osteomalacia in adults	Liver, fish-liver oils, egg yolk, fortified milk, butter, margarine	Two types: D_2, a synthetic form; D_3, formed by action of ultraviolet rays from sun upon a cholesterol compound in the skin; excessive amounts harmful
Vitamin E, tocopherols 30 IU	Inhibits oxidation of unsaturated fatty acids and vitamin A that help form cell and organelle membranes; precise biochemical role not known	Increased catabolism of unsaturated fatty acids, so that not enough are available for maintenance of cell membranes and other membranous organelles; prevents normal growth	Oils made from cereals, seeds, liver, eggs, fish	
Vitamin K probably about 1 mg	Essential for blood clotting	Prolonged blood clotting time	Normally supplied by intestinal bacteria; green leafy vegetables	Antibiotics may kill bacteria; then supplements needed in surgical patients

Vitamin (RDA)	Function	Deficiency symptoms	Sources	Comments
Water-soluble				
Vitamin C, ascorbic acid 60 mg	Needed for synthesis of collagen and other intercellular substances; formation of bone matrix and tooth dentin, intercellular cement; needed for metabolism of several amino acids; may help body withstand injury from burns and bacterial toxins	Scurvy (wounds heal very slowly and scars become weak and split open; capillaries become fragile; bone does not grow or heal properly)	Citrus fruits, strawberries, tomatoes	Possible role in preventing common cold or in the development of acquired immunity(?); harmful in very excessive dose
B-complex vitamins				
Vitamin B$_1$, Thiamine 1.5 mg	Derivative acts as coenzyme in many enzyme systems; important in carbohydrate and amino acid metabolism	Beriberi (weakened heart muscle, enlarged right side of heart, nervous system and digestive tract disorders)	Liver, yeast, cereals, meat, green leafy vegetables	Deficiency common in alcoholics
Vitamin B$_2$, riboflavin 1.7 mg	Used to make coenzymes (e.g., FAD) essential in cellular respiration	Dermatitis, inflammation and cracking at corners of mouth; mental depression	Liver, cheese, milk, eggs, green leafy vegetables	
Niacin 20 mg	Component of important coenzymes (NAD and NADP) essential to cellular respiration	Pellagra (dermatitis, diarrhea, mental symptoms, muscular weakness, fatigue)	Liver, cheese, milk, eggs, green leafy vegetables	
Vitamin B$_6$, pyridoxine 2 mg	Derivative is coenzyme in many reactions in amino acid metabolism	Dermatitis, digestive tract disturbances, convulsions	Liver, meat, cereals, legumes	
Pantothenic acid 10 mg	Constituent of coenzyme A (important in cellular metabolism)	Deficiency extremely rare	Widespread in foods	
Folic acid 0.4 mg	Coenzyme needed for reactions involved in nucleic acid synthesis and for maturation of red blood cells	A type of anemia	Produced by intestinal bacteria; liver, cereals, dark green leafy vegetables	
Biotin 0.3 mg	Coenzyme needed for carbon dioxide fixation		Produced by intestinal bacteria; liver, chocolate, egg yolk	
Vitamin B$_{12}$ 6 mg	Coenzyme important in nucleic acid metabolism	Pernicious anemia	Liver, meat, fish	Contains cobalt; intrinsic factor secreted by gastric mucosa needed for absorption

*RDA is the recommended dietary allowance, established by the Food and Nutrition Board of the National Research Council, to maintain good nutrition for healthy persons.

†International Unit: the amount that produces a specific biological effect and is internationally accepted as a measure of the activity of the substance.

Table 45–5 SOME IMPORTANT MINERALS AND THEIR FUNCTIONS

Mineral	Functions	Comments
Calcium	Component of bone and teeth; essential for normal blood clotting; needed for normal muscle and nerve function	Good sources: milk and other dairy products, green leafy vegetables. Bones serve as calcium reservoir
Phosphorus	As calcium phosphate, an important structural component of bone; essential in energy transfer and storage (component of ATP) and in many other metabolic processes; component of DNA and RNA	Performs more functions than any other mineral; absorption impaired by excessive intake of antacids
Sulfur	As component of many proteins (e.g., insulin), essential for normal metabolic activity	Sources: high-protein foods such as meat, fish, legumes, nuts
Potassium	Principal positive ion within cells; influences muscle contraction and nerve excitability	Occurs in many foods
Sodium	Principal positive ion in interstitial fluid; important in fluid balance; essential for conduction of nerve impulses	Occurs naturally in foods; sodium chloride (table salt) added as seasoning; too much ingested in average American diet; in excessive amounts, may contribute to high blood pressure
Chlorine	Principal negative ion of interstitial fluid; important in fluid balance and in acid-base balance	Occurs naturally in foods; ingested as sodium chloride
Copper	Component of enzyme needed for melanin synthesis; component of many other enzymes; essential for hemoglobin synthesis	Sources: liver, eggs, fish, whole wheat flour, beans
Iodine	Component of thyroid hormones (hormones that stimulate metabolic rate)	Sources: seafoods, iodized salt, vegetables grown in iodine-rich soils. Deficiency results in goiter (abnormal enlargement of thyroid gland)
Cobalt	As component of vitamin B_{12}, essential for red blood cell production	Best sources are meat and dairy products. Strict vegetarians may become deficient in this mineral
Manganese	Necessary to activate arginase, an enzyme essential for urea formation; activates many other enzymes	Poorly absorbed from intestine; found in whole-grain cereals, egg yolks, green vegetables
Magnesium	Appropriate balance between magnesium and calcium ions needed for normal muscle and nerve function; component of many coenzymes	Occurs in many foods
Iron	Component of hemoglobin, myoglobin, important respiratory enzymes (cytochromes), and other enzymes essential to oxygen transport and cellular respiration	Mineral most likely to be deficient in diet. Good sources: meat (especially liver), nuts, egg yolk, legumes. Deficiency results in anemia
Fluorine	Component of bones and teeth; makes teeth resistant to decay	In areas where it does not occur naturally, fluorine may be added to municipal water supplies (fluoridation). Excess causes tooth mottling
Zinc	Component of at least 70 enzymes, including carbonic anhydrase; components of some peptidases, and thus important in protein digestion; may be important in wound healing	Occurs in many foods

FOCUS ON

Vegetarian Diets

Most of the world's population depends almost entirely upon plants, especially cereal grains—usually rice, wheat, or corn—as the staple food. None of these foods contains adequate amounts of all of the essential amino acids. Besides being deficient in some of the essential amino acids, plant foods contain a lower percentage of protein than do animal foods. Meat contains about 25% protein, whereas even the new high-yield grains contain only 5% to 13%. What protein is available in plant food is also less digestible than that in animal foods. Because most of the protein is encased within indigestible cellulose cell walls, much of it passes right through the digestive tract.

Despite these potential nutritional problems, more and more people are turning to vegetarian diets. Meats are becoming increasingly expensive because they are ecologically expensive to produce. About 21 kg of protein in grain, for example, is required to produce just 1 kg of beef protein. If the human population of our planet continues to expand at a much greater rate than food production, more grain will be diverted for human food and less for animal feed. The price of meat will continue to soar and may become unaffordable for many of us.

Can a vegetarian diet be nutritionally balanced? With an awareness of the special nutritional problems associated with a vegetarian diet (especially in growing children), they can be overcome. The most important rule is to select foods that complement each other. This requires knowledge of which amino acids are deficient in each kind of food. Since the body cannot store amino acids, all of the essential amino acids must be ingested at the same meal. For example, if rice is eaten for dinner, and beans for lunch the next day, the body will not have all of the essential amino acids needed at the same time to manufacture proteins. If beans and rice are eaten together, however, all of the needed amino acids are provided, because one food provides what the other lacks. Similarly, if dairy products are not excluded from the vegetarian diet, then macaroni can be paired with cheese, or cereal with milk, and all of the essential amino acids can be obtained.

anemic, and metabolism is impaired (Figure 45–19). Because the digestive enzymes themselves cannot be manufactured without essential amino acids, eventually what little protein is ingested cannot be digested. Dehydration and diarrhea develop, often leading to death.

Figure 45–19 Children suffering from kwashiorkor, a disease caused by severe protein deficiency. Note the characteristic swollen belly, which results from fluid imbalance. (United Nations, Food and Agricultural Organization photo by P. Pittet)

SUMMARY

I. Food processing includes ingestion, digestion, absorption of nutrients, and elimination of wastes.

II. An organism's body plan and lifestyle are adapted to its mode of nutrition; most animals are either herbivores, carnivores, or omnivores.

III. The simplest invertebrates, the sponges, have no digestive system; digestion is carred on intracellularly. Cnidarians and flatworms have incomplete digestive systems with only one opening, which serves as both mouth and anus.

IV. More complex invertebrates and all vertebrates have a complete digestive system, a tube with an opening at each end.

V. Various regions of the human digestive tract are specialized to perform specific functions.

A. The wall of the human digestive tract consists of four layers: mucosa, submucosa, muscularis, and adventitia.

B. Mechanical digestion and enzymatic digestion of carbohydrates begin in the mouth.

C. As food is swallowed, it is propelled through the pharynx and esophagus. A bolus of food is moved along through the digestive tract by peristalsis.

D. Food is mechanically digested in the stomach by vigorous churning, and proteins are enzymatically digested by the action of pepsin in the gastric juice.

E. Most enzymatic digestion takes place in the duodenum, which receives secretions from the liver and pancreas and produces several digestive enzymes of its own.

F. The liver produces bile, which emulsifies fats.

G. The pancreas releases enzymes that digest protein, lipid, and carbohydrate, as well as RNA and DNA.

H. Chyme is enzymatically digested as it moves through the digestive tract.

1. Polysaccharides are digested to maltose by salivary and pancreatic amylases. Maltase in the brush border of the intestine splits maltose into glucose, the main product of carbohydrate digestion.

2. Proteins are split by pepsin in the stomach and by proteolytic enzymes in the pancreatic juice. The dipeptides produced are then split by dipeptidases in the brush border of the duodenum. The end products of protein digestion are amino acids.

3. Lipids are emulsified by bile salts and then hydrolyzed by lipase in the pancreatic juice.

I. Digestive system activities are regulated by both nerves and hormones.

J. Most nutrients are absorbed through the thin walls of the intestinal villi.

K. The large intestine is responsible for the elimination of undigested wastes. It also incubates bacteria that produce vitamin K and certain B vitamins.

VI. For a balanced diet, humans and other animals require carbohydrates, lipids, proteins, vitamins, and minerals.

A. Most carbohydrates are ingested in the form of polysaccharides—starch and cellulose—and the disaccharide, sucrose.

1. Carbohydrates are used primarily as fuel.

2. Glucose concentration in the blood is carefully regulated; glucose is stored as glycogen and can also be converted to fat.

B. Lipids are used as fuel, as components of cell membranes, and as substrates for the synthesis of steroid hormones and other lipid substances.

1. Most lipids are ingested in the form of triacylglycerols.

2. Cholesterol is transported on low-density lipoproteins; high levels of LDL are associated with increased risk for heart disease.

3. Fatty acids are converted to molecules of acetyl coenzyme A and used as fuel. Excess fatty acids are stored as fat.

C. Proteins serve as enzymes and are essential structural components of cells.

1. The most appropriate distribution of essential amino acids is found in the complete proteins of animal foods.

2. Excess amino acids are deaminated by liver cells. Amino groups are converted to urea and excreted in urine, and the remaining keto acids are converted to carbohydrate and used as fuel or converted to lipid and stored in fat cells.

D. Vitamins are needed for biochemical processes; many serve as components of coenzymes.

1. Vitamins are fat-soluble (A, D, E, K) or water-soluble (B complex and C).

2. Deficiency of each vitamin produces specific physiological disorders.

E. Minerals are inorganic nutrients ingested as salts dissolved in food and water.

VII. Basal metabolic rate (BMR) is the body's cost of metabolic living.

A. Total metabolic rate is the BMR plus the energy used to carry on daily activities.

B. When energy (Calorie) input equals energy output, body weight remains constant.

VIII. Obesity is a serious nutritional problem in which excess fat accumulates in the adipose tissues.

A. A person gains weight by taking in more energy, in the form of Calories, than is expended in activity.

B. Weight may be lost by expending more energy than is taken in. The needed energy is obtained by mobilizing fat and using it as fuel.

IX. Millions of people suffer from malnutrition. Essential amino acids are the nutrients most often deficient in the diet.

POST-TEST

1. The process of taking food into the body and utilizing it is called _____.

2. _____ consists of mechanically and enzymatically breaking down food into molecules small enough to be absorbed.

3. _____ is the process of getting rid of undigested and unabsorbed food.
4. An animal which spends much its time eating and houses bacteria that digest cellulose in its digestive tract is a _____.
5. Carnivorous mammals have well-developed _____ teeth.
6. The most characteristic feature shared by the cnidarian and flatworm digestive systems is that the system is _____.
7. In a complete digestive system the digestive tract has _____ openings.
8. Salivary _____ is an enzyme that initiates the digestion of carbohydrates.
9. A mammalian tooth consists mainly of _____.

Select the most appropriate term in Column B for each description in Column A. Answers may be used more than once or not at all.

Column A
10. Protein digestion begins here
11. Incubates bacteria
12. Receives secretions from pancreas
13. Secretes bile
14. Converts food to chyme
15. Conducts food to stomach

Column B
a. Duodenum
b. Stomach
c. Liver
d. Large intestine
e. None of the above

16. The surface area of the stomach is increased by the presence of _____.
17. Absorption takes place through finger-like projections in the lining of the small intestine called _____.
18. Food leaving the stomach next enters the _____.
19. An open sore in the wall of the stomach or duodenum is called an _____.
20. The function of the gallbladder is to _____.
21. Inorganic nutrients generally ingested as dissolved salts are _____.
22. Vitamins function as _____.

Match the nutrients in Column B with the descriptions in Column A.

Column A
23. Needed for hemoglobin synthesis
24. Used as fuel molecule
25. Deficiency results in goiter
26. Water-soluble vitamin
27. Deficiency results in rickets

Column B
a. Carbohydrate
b. Vitamin D
c. Iron
d. Iodine
e. None of the above

28. Lipids are ingested in the form of _____.
29. In the digestive tract proteins are degraded to _____ _____; most carbohydrates are degraded to _____.
30. Glucose is stored in the liver as _____.
31. In the liver cells excess _____ _____ are deaminated.
32. The _____ _____ _____ is the body's rate of energy use during resting conditions.
33. When energy input is greater than energy output _____ _____ occurs.
34. Kwashiorkor is a disease caused by extreme _____ deficiency.
35. Label the diagram. For correct labeling, see Figure 45–5.

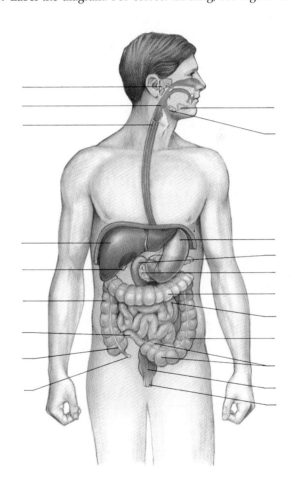

REVIEW QUESTIONS

1. If you were presented with an unfamiliar animal and asked to determine its nutritional lifestyle, how would you go about this task?
2. Compare the advantages of incomplete and complete digestive tracts.
3. How are digestive structures and methods of processing food in sponges, hydras, and flatworms adapted to each group's lifestyle? Give specific examples.
4. Why must food be digested?
5. Trace a bite of food through the human digestive tract, listing each structure through which it passes.
6. What mechanisms prevent gastric juice from digesting the wall of the stomach? What happens when they fail?
7. Give the functions of the three types of vertebrate accessory glands that secrete digestive juices. Identify their secretions.
8. The inner lining of the digestive tract is not smooth like the inside of a water pipe. Why is this advantageous? What structures increase its surface area?

9. Summarize the step-by-step digestion of (a) carbohydrates, (b) lipids, (c) proteins.
10. What happens to ingested cellulose in humans? Why?
11. Draw and label an intestinal villus.
12. How does the absorption of fat differ from the absorption of glucose?
13. What is the adaptive advantage of specialization of different regions in a complete digestive tract?
14. List the nutrients that must be included in a balanced diet.
15. Why, specifically, is each of the following essential? (a) iron, (b) calcium, (c) iodine, (d) vitamin A, (e) vitamin K, (f) essential amino acids.

16. Draw a diagram to illustrate the fate of carbohydrates in the body.
17. Describe the fate of absorbed amino acids.
18. Describe the fate of absorbed fat.
19. Write an equation to describe energy balance and explain what happens when the equation is altered in either direction.
20. What is the most effective way to treat obesity?
21. Summarize the relationship between diet and heart disease.
22. What are some of the difficulties in planning a nutritionally balanced vegetarian diet?

RECOMMENDED READINGS

Brown, M. S., and J. L. Goldstein. How LDL receptors influence cholesterol and atherosclerosis. *Scientific American,* 251(5):58–66, 1984. Many Americans have too few LDL receptors, which normally remove particles carrying cholesterol from the circulation. Absence of these receptors puts individuals at high risk for atherosclerosis and heart attacks.

Krause, M. B., and L. K. Mahan. *Food, Nutrition, and Diet Therapy.* 7th ed. W. B. Saunders Company, Philadelphia, 1984. A comprehensive discussion of the science of nutrition and its application to the maintenance of health.

Sanderson, S. L., and R. Wassersug. Suspension-feeding vertebrates. *Scientific American,* 262(3):96–101, 1990. Animals that filter food out of the surrounding water can grow to large size.

Uvnas-Moberg, K. The gastrointestinal tract in growth and reproduction. *Scientific American* 261(1): 1989. The gastrointestinal tract is the largest endocrine gland in the body, and it helps to readjust metabolism during pregnancy and infant development.

CHAPTER 46

Osmoregulation and Disposal of Metabolic Wastes

Water shapes the basic nature of life and its distribution on Earth. Most organisms consist mainly of water, the medium in which most metabolic reactions take place. The simplest forms of life are small organisms that live in the sea. They obtain their food and oxygen directly from the seawater that surrounds them, and they release waste products into it. Larger, more complex animals and most terrestrial animals have their own internal sea—the blood and interstitial fluid—to bathe their cells and to transport and dissolve nutrients, gases, and waste products.

Terrestrial animals have a continuous need to conserve water. Water must be taken into the body and its loss carefully regulated. Water is ingested with food and drink and also formed in metabolic reactions. Some of this water becomes part of the blood plasma, which transports materials throughout the organism. Then, from the blood plasma, interstitial fluid is formed and bathes all of the cells of the body. Excess water evaporates from the body surface or is excreted by specialized structures.

Two processes that maintain homeostasis of fluids are osmoregulation and excretion of metabolic wastes. **Osmoregulation** is the active regulation of osmotic pressure of body fluids so that they do not become excessively dilute or concentrated. **Excretion** is the process of ridding the body of metabolic wastes, including water. Many animals have evolved efficient **excretory systems** that handle these processes and also rid the body of excess water and ions. Excretory systems maintain homeostasis by selectively adjusting the concentrations of salts and other substances in blood and other body fluids.

A Siberian tiger drinking. Organisms must regulate fluid intake in order to maintain fluid balance. (Dominique Braud/Dembinsky Photo Associates)

After you have studied this chapter you should be able to

1. Relate the principal functions of excretory systems to specific osmoregulatory challenges posed by various environments.
2. Compare the advantages of excreting ammonia, uric acid, and urea.
3. Compare nephridial organs, antennal glands, and Malpighian tubules as osmoregulatory organs.
4. Relate the function of the vertebrate kidney to the success of vertebrates in a wide variety of habitats.
5. Compare the adaptations of freshwater and marine bony fish for solving problems of osmoregulation.

6. Describe adaptations that have solved osmoregulatory problems in sharks, marine animals, and marine birds.
7. Label on a diagram the organs of the mammalian urinary system, and give their functions.
8. Label on a diagram the principal parts of the nephron, including circulatory structures, and give their functions.
9. Trace a drop of filtrate from Bowman's capsule to its release from the body as urine.
10. Summarize the importance of countercurrent exchange in the process of urine formation.
11. Describe the regulatory effects of ADH and aldosterone.

EXCRETORY SYSTEMS HELP MAINTAIN HOMEOSTASIS

Typically, an excretory system helps maintain homeostasis in three ways:

1. It carries on osmoregulation.
2. It excretes metabolic wastes.
3. It regulates the concentrations of most of the components of body fluids.

To carry out these functions, an excretory system collects fluid, generally from the blood or from interstitial fluid. It then adjusts the composition of this fluid by selectively returning needed substances to the body fluid. The adjusted excretory product (urine, for example), containing excess or potentially toxic substances, is released from the body.

The terms *excretion* and *elimination* are sometimes confused (Figure 46–1). Undigested and unabsorbed food materials are **eliminated** from the body in the feces. Such substances never participated in the organism's chemical metabolism or entered body cells, but merely passed through the digestive system.

THE PRINCIPAL METABOLIC WASTE PRODUCTS ARE WATER, CARBON DIOXIDE, AND NITROGENOUS WASTES

As cells carry on metabolic activities, waste products are generated. If allowed to accumulate, metabolic wastes would eventually reach toxic concentrations and threaten the homeostasis of the animal. These wastes must be **excreted** from the body.

The principal metabolic waste products in most animals are water, carbon dioxide, and nitrogenous (nitrogen-containing) wastes. Carbon dioxide is excreted

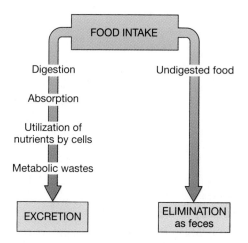

Figure 46–1 Excretion contrasted with elimination.

mainly by respiratory structures (Chapter 44); excretory organs, such as kidneys, remove and excrete most of the water and nitrogenous wastes.

Nitrogenous wastes include ammonia, uric acid, and urea. Recall that amino acids and nucleic acids contain nitrogen. During the breakdown of amino acids, the nitrogen-containing amino group is removed (deamination) and converted to **ammonia** (Figure 46–2). However, ammonia is highly toxic. Some aquatic animals excrete it into the surrounding water before it can build up to toxic levels in their tissues, and a few terrestrial animals vent it directly to the air. But in many organisms, including humans, ammonia is converted to some less toxic nitrogenous waste, such as urea or uric acid.

Uric acid is produced both from ammonia and by the breakdown of nucleotides from nucleic acids. Uric acid forms crystals and can be excreted as a crystalline paste with little fluid loss. This is an important adaptation for conserving water in many terrestrial animals

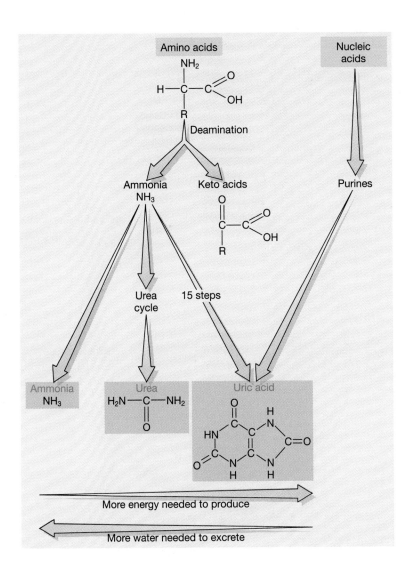

Figure 46–2 Nitrogenous wastes are formed by deamination of amino acids and by metabolism of nucleic acids. Ammonia is the first metabolic product of deamination. Many animals convert ammonia to urea via the urea cycle (see Figure 46–3). Other animals convert ammonia to uric acid. Energy is used in both cases, but less water is required than for the excretion of ammonia.

such as insects, certain reptiles, and birds. In birds, the frequent excretion of uric acid in the feces and the absence of a urinary bladder contribute to the light body weight that is essential for flight. Because uric acid is not toxic, its excretion is an adaptive advantage for species whose young begin their development enclosed in eggs in which wastes accumulate until hatching.

Urea is the principal nitrogenous waste product of amphibians and mammals. It is produced mainly in the liver. The sequence of reactions by which the urea molecule is synthesized from ammonia and carbon dioxide is known as the **urea cycle** (Figure 46–3). These reactions require specific enzymes and the input of energy by the cells. However, urea is far less toxic than ammonia and so can accumulate in higher concentrations without causing tissue damage; thus, it can be excreted in more concentrated form. Because urea is highly soluble, it is excreted dissolved in water. More water is needed to excrete urea than to excrete uric acid.

INVERTEBRATES HAVE SOLVED PROBLEMS OF OSMOREGULATION AND METABOLIC WASTE DISPOSAL WITH A VARIETY OF MECHANISMS

The body fluids of most marine invertebrates are in osmotic equilibrium with the surrounding seawater. These animals are known as **osmotic conformers** because the concentrations of their body fluids vary with salinity changes in the seawater. Fortunately, the sea is a stable environment, and its salt concentration does not vary much over a short period of time.

Marine sponges and cnidarians need no specialized excretory structures. Their wastes pass by diffusion from the intracellular fluid to the external environment. Unlike animals with specialized excretory systems, they expend little or no energy to excrete wastes; energy is provided by the water currents that sweep by or even

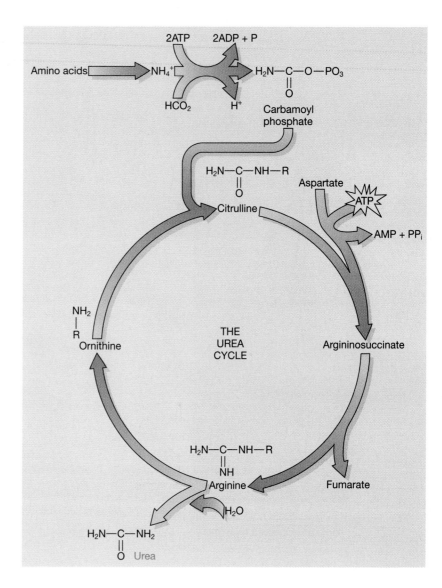

Figure 46–3 The urea cycle is a sequence of enzymatic reactions by which the amino groups from amino acids are converted to urea. Carbon dioxide and ammonia are combined to form carbamoyl phosphate, which then combines with ornithine to form citrulline. Aspartate (the ionic form of the amino acid aspartic acid) then reacts with citrulline to form the intermediate argininosuccinate. This intermediate compound is cleaved to yield arginine and fumarate. Thus, the amino group of aspartate is transferred to arginine. The arginine is hydrolyzed by the enzyme arginase to yield urea and ornithine, which can be used in the next cycle. The energy to drive the cycle and synthesize urea is provided by the two ATPs used in the synthesis of carbamoyl phosphate and the ATP used in the synthesis of argininosuccinate.

through them. When a change in water current or stagnation occurs, aquatic environments such as coral reefs are especially prone to damage from the accumulation of metabolic wastes.

Coastal habitats and brackish water, such as estuaries, are much less stable environments than the open sea. Salt concentrations change frequently with shifting tides. Animals that dwell in these habitats are **osmotic regulators.** In a coastal environment where fresh water enters the sea, the water may have a lower salt concentration than the body fluids of the animal. Water osmotically moves into the animal body, and salt diffuses out. An animal adapted to this environment has excretory structures that actively remove the excess water. Many also have cells in their gills that remove salts from the surrounding water and transport them into the body fluids.

Terrestrial animals have higher water concentrations than the air surrounding them. They tend to lose

water by evaporation from the body surface and from respiratory surfaces. They may also lose water as body wastes are excreted. Adaptation to life on land has required the evolution of structures and processes that conserve water.

Nephridial Organs Are Tubules Specialized for Osmoregulation and/or Excretion in Some Invertebrates

A **nephridial organ** is a common type of specialized excretory structure in invertebrates. It consists of simple or branching tubes that usually open to the outside of the body through nephridial pores. Flatworms and nemerteans are the simplest animals with specialized excretory organs. Although metabolic wastes pass through their body surfaces by diffusion, these animals also have osmoregulatory nephridial organs known as

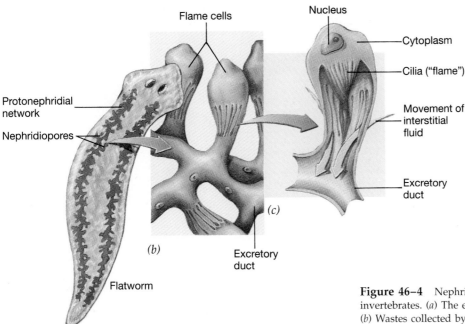

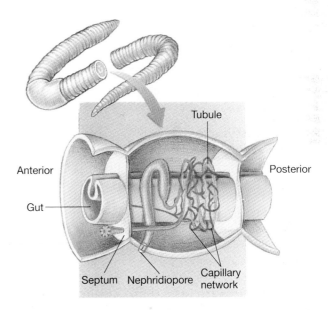

Figure 46–4   Nephridial organs are common among invertebrates. (*a*) The excretory organs of a typical flatworm. (*b*) Wastes collected by flame cells pass through excretory ducts and leave the animal through nephridiopores. (*c*) A single flame cell.

protonephridia, which consist of tubules with enlarged blind ends containing cilia. Protonephridia also have **flame cells** with brushes of cilia (whose constant motion reminded early biologists of flickering flames—hence the name) (Figure 46–4). A system of branching excretory ducts connects protonephridia with the outside. The flame cells lie in the fluid that bathes the body cells; fluid enters the flame cells, passes through the tubules and excretory ducts, and leaves the body through excretory pores.

Annelids and mollusks have nephridial organs called **metanephridia.** Every segment of an earthworm has a pair of metanephridia. Each metanephridium is a tubule open at both ends: The inner end opens into the coelom as a ciliated funnel (Figure 46–5), and the outer end opens to the outside through an excretory pore. Around each tubule is a network of capillaries. Fluid from the coelom (body cavity) passes into the tubule, bringing with it whatever it contains—glucose, salts, or wastes. As the fluid moves through the tubule, needed materials (such as water and glucose) are reabsorbed by the capillaries, leaving the wastes behind. In this way urine that contains concentrated wastes is produced.

Figure 46–5   The excretory structures of the earthworm are a series of paired metanephridia. Each consists of a ciliated funnel opening into the coelom, a coiled tubule, and a nephridiopore opening to the outside. This internal view shows parts of three segments.

Antennal Glands Are Important in Osmoregulation in Crustaceans

Antennal glands, also called **green glands,** are the principal excretory organs of crustaceans (Figure 46–6). A pair of these structures is located in the head, often at the base of the antennae.

Fluid from the blood is filtered into the antennal gland, and its composition is adjusted as it passes through an excretory tubule. Needed materials are reabsorbed into the blood. Wastes can also be actively secreted from the blood into the filtrate within the antennal gland.

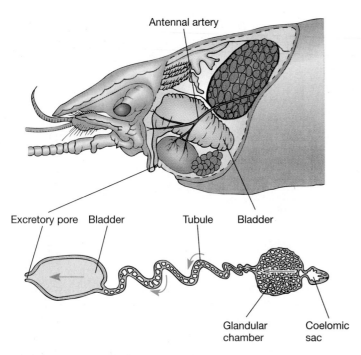

Figure 46–6 Antennal glands are the principal excretory structures of crustaceans. Fluid from the hemolymph is filtered into the coelomic sac, and its composition is adjusted as it passes through the excretory ducts. The exit duct may be enlarged to form a bladder.

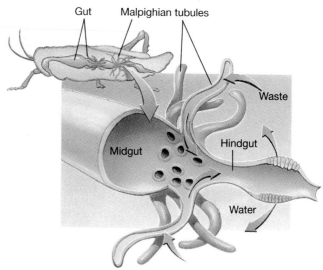

Figure 46–7 The slender Malpighian tubules of insects have blind ends that lie in the hemocoel. Their cells transfer wastes from the hemolymph to the cavity of the tubule. Uric acid, the major waste product, is discharged into the gut.

Malpighian Tubules Are an Important Adaptation for Conserving Water in Insects

The excretory systems of insects and spiders consist of **Malpighian tubules** (Figure 46–7). Two hundred to several hundred tubules may be present, depending upon the species. Malpighian tubules have blind ends that lie in the hemocoel (blood cavity) bathed in blood. Their cells transfer salts and wastes by diffusion or active transport from the blood to the cavity of the tubule. The Malpighian tubules empty into the intestine. Water and some salts are reabsorbed into the blood by specialized rectal glands. Uric acid, the major waste product, is excreted as a semidry paste with a minimum of water. Because Malpighian tubules conserve body fluids, these structures have contributed significantly to the success of insects in terrestrial environments.

THE KIDNEY IS THE KEY VERTEBRATE ORGAN OF OSMOREGULATION AND EXCRETION

Vertebrates live successfully in a wide range of habitats in fresh water, in seawater, in tidal regions, and on land—even in extreme environments such as deserts. In response to the requirements of these environments, vertebrates have evolved adaptations for regulating their salt and water content and for excreting wastes. An example is the desert-dwelling kangaroo rat, which must carefully conserve water. It obtains most of its water metabolically by oxidizing food, and its kidneys are so efficient that it loses little fluid as urine.

The main osmoregulatory and excretory organ in vertebrates is the kidney. Typically, the vertebrate kidney functions by a combination of three processes: **filtration, reabsorption,** and **secretion.** Blood plasma is *filtered* nonselectively, so the initial filtrate that enters the tubules of the kidney contains all the substances present in the blood except blood cells, platelets, and large compounds such as proteins. As the filtrate passes through the coiled tubules of the kidney, needed materials, such as glucose, amino acids, salts, and water, are selectively *reabsorbed* into the blood. Some substances are actively *secreted* from the blood into the filtrate, in the reverse direction from reabsorption. Through reabsorption and secretion, the composition of the filtrate is slowly adjusted. The urine that is finally excreted consists of metabolic waste products and excess water and salts.

In most vertebrates, not only the kidneys but also the skin, lungs or gills, and digestive system function to some extent to maintain fluid balance and dispose of metabolic wastes. The heads of some reptiles and marine birds have salt glands, which excrete salt that has entered the body with ingested seawater. By removing excess water, salts, and other potentially toxic materials, all of these organs help to maintain homeostasis.

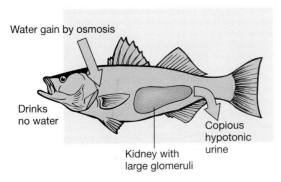

Figure 46–8 Freshwater fish live in a hypotonic medium, so water continuously enters the body by osmosis. These fish excrete large quantities of dilute urine.

Freshwater Animals Must Rid Themselves of Excess Water

As fish began to move into freshwater habitats about 460 million years ago, there was strong selection for the evolution of adaptations for effective osmoregulation. Because the body fluids of freshwater animals have higher salt concentrations than (are hypertonic to) their surroundings, water passes into them osmotically, and they are in constant danger of becoming waterlogged. Freshwater fish are covered by scales and a mucous secretion that retards the passage of water into the body. However, water enters through the gills. The kidneys of these fish have become adapted to filter out excess water, and they excrete large amounts of dilute urine (Figure 46–8).

Water entry, though, is only part of the problem of osmoregulation in freshwater fish. These animals also tend to lose salts to the surrounding fresh water. To compensate, special gill cells have evolved that actively transport salt (mainly sodium chloride) from the water into the body.

Most amphibians are at least semiaquatic, and their mechanisms of osmoregulation are similar to those of freshwater fish. They, too, produce large amounts of dilute urine. Through its urine and skin, a frog can lose an amount of water equivalent to one third of its body weight in a day. Active transport of salt inward by special cells in the skin compensates for salt loss through the skin and urine.

Marine Animals Must Replace Lost Fluid

Freshwater fish have adapted very successfully to their aquatic habitats. Evolution of body fluids more dilute than seawater is one of their chief adaptations. Thus, when some freshwater fish returned to the sea about 200 million years ago, their blood and body fluids were less salty than (hypotonic to) their surroundings. They tended to lose water osmotically and to take in salt. To compensate for fluid loss, many marine bony fish drink seawater (Figure 46–9a). They retain the water and excrete salt by the action of specialized cells in their gills. Very little urine is excreted by the kidneys, and the nephrons (microscopic units of the kidney) have only small or no capillary clusters (glomeruli), which filter the blood in other vertebrates.

Marine chondrichthyes (sharks and rays) have a different set of osmoregulatory adaptations that allows them to tolerate the salt concentrations of their environment. These animals accumulate and tolerate urea (Figure 46–9b). Their tissues are adapted to function at con-

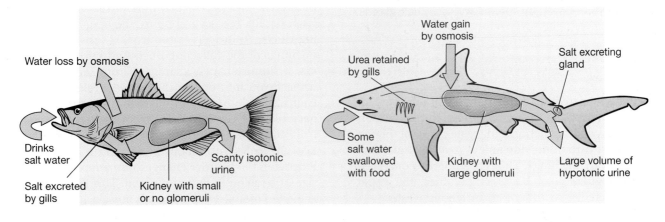

(a)

(b)

Figure 46–9 Osmoregulation in marine bony fish and sharks. (a) Marine fish live in a hypertonic medium and so lose water by osmosis. To compensate, the fish drink salt water, excrete the salt, and produce very little urine. (b) The shark solves its osmotic problem differently. It accumulates urea in high enough concentration to become hypertonic to the surrounding medium. As a result, some water enters the body by osmosis. A large quantity of hypotonic urine is excreted.

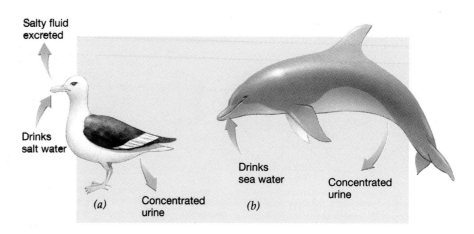

Figure 46–10 Osmoregulation in marine birds and mammals. (*a*) The heads of marine birds have salt glands, which can excrete the excess salt that has entered the body with ingested seawater. They excrete concentrated urine. (*b*) Marine mammals drink seawater along with their food. Their kidneys produce a very salty urine.

centrations of urea that would be toxic in most other animals. The high urea concentration makes the body fluids slightly saltier than (hypertonic to) seawater. This results in a net inflow of water into their bodies. Their well-developed kidneys excrete a large volume of urine. Excess salt is excreted by the kidneys and, in many species, by a rectal gland.

The heads of certain reptiles and marine birds have salt glands, which can excrete the salt that has entered the body with ingested seawater (Figure 46–10*a*). Salt glands are usually inactive; they function only in response to osmotic stress. Thus, when seawater or salty food is ingested, the salt glands excrete a fluid laden with sodium and chloride.

Whales, dolphins, and other marine mammals ingest seawater along with their food. Their kidneys produce a very concentrated urine, much saltier than seawater. This is an important physiological adaptation, especially for marine carnivores (Figure 46–10*b*). The high-protein diet of these animals results in production of large amounts of urea, which must be excreted in the urine or, in some cases, by special accessory salt glands.

The Mammalian Kidney Is Vital in Maintaining Homeostasis

In mammals, as in other terrestrial vertebrates, the kidneys, skin, lungs, and digestive system all play important roles in osmoregulation and waste disposal (Figure 46–11). Most carbon dioxide and a great deal of water are excreted by the lungs. Though primarily concerned with the regulation of body temperature, the sweat glands excrete 5% to 10% of all metabolic wastes.

Most of the deamination of amino acids takes place in the liver, which is also the site of production of both urea and uric acid. In addition, most of the bile pigments produced by the breakdown of red blood cells are normally excreted by the liver into the intestine and then pass out of the body with the feces. However, the

kidneys are the principal excretory organs; they excrete most nitrogenous wastes and help maintain fluid balance by adjusting the salt and water content of the urine.

THE KIDNEYS, URINARY BLADDER, AND THEIR DUCTS MAKE UP THE HUMAN URINARY SYSTEM

The **urinary system** of humans and other mammals consists of the kidneys, the urinary bladder, and associated ducts. The overall structure of the human urinary system is shown in Figure 46–12. Situated just below the diaphragm in the "small" of the back, the kidneys look like a pair of giant, dark-red lima beans, each about the size of a fist. The outer portion of the kidney is called the **renal cortex;** the inner portion, the **renal medulla** (Figure 46–13). The renal medulla contains between 5 and 18 triangular structures called the renal pyramids. The tip of each pyramid is a renal papilla. Each papilla has several pores, the openings of collecting ducts. As urine is produced, it flows through the openings of the collecting ducts and into the **renal pelvis,** a funnel-shaped chamber. From the renal pelvis, urine flows into one of the paired **ureters,** ducts that connect the kidney with the **urinary bladder.** The urinary bladder receives urine from the two ureters, one from each kidney, and is capable of holding (with practice) up to 800 mL (about a pint and a half) of urine. Emptying the bladder changes it in a moment from the size of a melon to that of a pecan. This remarkable feat is made possible by the smooth muscle and transitional epithelium of the bladder wall, which is capable of great shrinkage and stretching.

When urine leaves the bladder, it flows through the **urethra,** a duct leading to the outside of the body. In the male the urethra is lengthy and passes through the penis. Semen and urine are both transported through

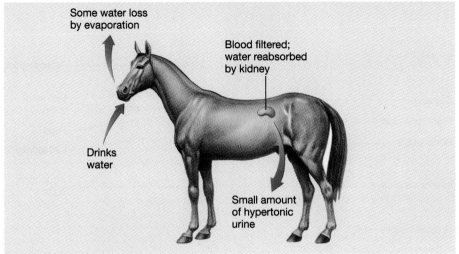

(a) Terrestrial mammal

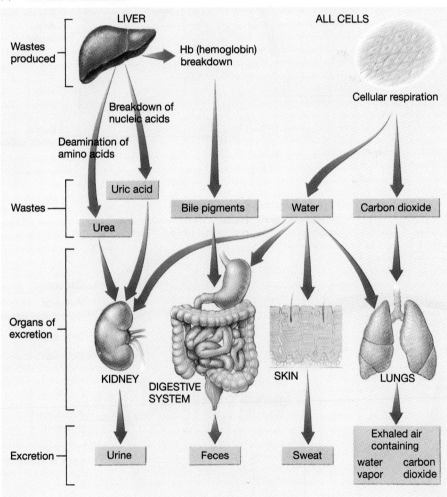

(b)

Figure 46–11 In many terrestrial vertebrates, the kidneys, lungs, skin, and digestive system all participate in disposal of metabolic wastes. (a) The kidney conserves water by reabsorbing it. (b) Disposal of metabolic wastes in humans and other terrestrial mammals. To conserve water, a small amount of hypertonic urine is usually produced. Nitrogenous wastes are produced by the liver and transported to the kidneys. All cells produce carbon dioxide and some water during cellular respiration.

the male urethra. In the female the urethra is short and transports only urine. Its opening to the outside is just above the opening of the vagina. Because the length of the male urethra discourages bacterial invasions of the bladder, such infections are more common in females than in males.

kidney (through renal pelvis) → ureter → urinary bladder → urethra

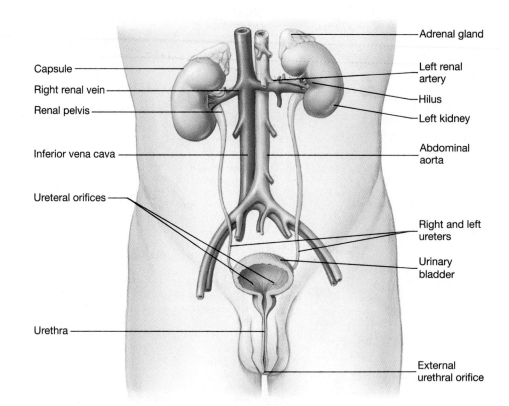

Capsule

Right renal vein

Renal pelvis

Inferior vena cava

Ureteral orifices

Urethra

Adrenal gland

Left renal artery

Hilus

Left kidney

Abdominal aorta

Right and left ureters

Urinary bladder

External urethral orifice

Figure 46–12 The human urinary system. Urine is produced in the kidneys, then conveyed by the ureters to the urinary bladder for temporary storage. The urethra conducts urine from the bladder to the outside of the body.

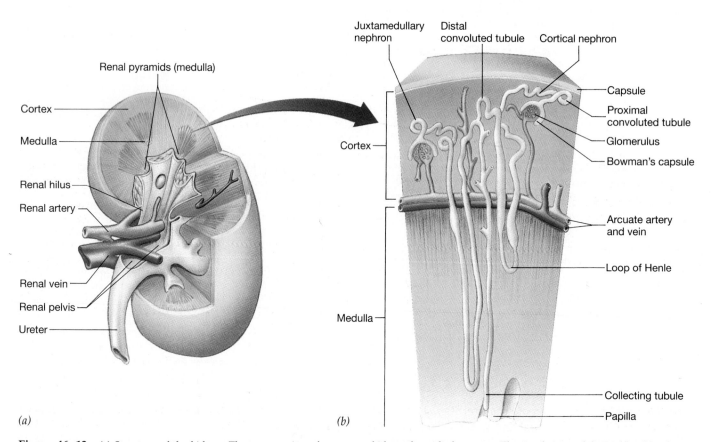

Renal pyramids (medulla)

Cortex

Medulla

Renal hilus

Renal artery

Renal vein

Renal pelvis

Ureter

Juxtamedullary nephron

Distal convoluted tubule

Cortical nephron

Cortex

Medulla

Capsule

Proximal convoluted tubule

Glomerulus

Bowman's capsule

Arcuate artery and vein

Loop of Henle

Collecting tubule

Papilla

(a)

(b)

Figure 46–13 (a) Structure of the kidney. The outer region of the kidney is the cortex; the inner region is the medulla. When urine is produced, it flows into the renal pelvis and leaves the kidney through the ureter. The renal artery delivers blood to the kidney; the renal vein drains blood from the kidney. (b) The locations of the two main types of nephrons (longitudinal view).

The urethra has two muscles called sphincter valves. When the volume of urine in the bladder reaches about 350 mL (10.5 ounces), the sphincter valves open reflexively and **urination,** release of urine from the bladder, occurs. The bladder is not under voluntary nervous control in the way that our skeletal muscles are; what we call bladder control is the ability to facilitate or inhibit the reflex voluntarily. For example, one can voluntarily empty the bladder at a convenient time even before it is full. On the other hand, even when the volume of urine in the bladder has exceeded 350 ml, one can inhibit urination for some time until it becomes convenient. Such voluntary control cannot be exerted by an immature nervous system, however; most babies do not develop urinary control until about age 2, no matter how hard anxious parents try to teach them.

The emptying of the bladder constitutes one of the few normal occurrences of positive feedback in biology. One might think that, with the start of urination, the pressure within the bladder would swiftly fall below the threshold necessary to trigger the urination reflex so that urination would promptly stop, leaving the bladder mostly full. Yet the healthy bladder empties completely. The explanation is that the bladder contracts so strongly that the pressure within it actually rises once urination has begun, which stimulates the urination reflex even more strongly. That is why it is so difficult to stop urination once it has begun.

The Nephron Is the Functional Unit of the Kidney

Each kidney is made up of more than a million functional units called **nephrons.** Each nephron consists of a cuplike **Bowman's capsule** connected to a long, partially coiled **renal tubule** (Figure 46–14). Positioned within Bowman's capsule is a cluster of capillaries known as the **glomerulus.** Three main regions of the renal tubule are the **proximal convoluted tubule,** which conducts the filtrate from Bowman's capsule; the **loop of Henle,** an elongated, hairpin-shaped portion; and the **distal convoluted tubule,** which conducts the filtrate to a **collecting duct.** Thus, filtrate passes through the following structures:

> Bowman's capsule → proximal convoluted tubule → loop of Henle → distal convoluted tubule → collecting duct

The inner wall of Bowman's capsule consists of specialized epithelial cells called **podocytes.** The podocytes possess elongated foot processes, which cover the surfaces of most of the glomerular capillaries (Figure 46–15). Spaces between the "toes" of these foot processes are called **slit pores.** The slit pores are covered by a fine membrane that is thought to have a porous structure.

Blood is delivered to the kidney by the renal artery. Small branches of the renal artery give rise to afferent arterioles. An **afferent arteriole** conducts blood into the capillaries that make up each glomerulus. As blood flows through the glomerulus, some of the plasma is forced into Bowman's capsule.

You may recall that in the usual circulatory pattern capillaries deliver blood into veins. Circulation in the kidneys is an exception in that blood flowing from the glomerular capillaries next passes into an **efferent arteriole,** so called because it conducts blood *away* from the glomerulus. The efferent arteriole delivers blood to a second capillary network, the **peritubular capillaries** surrounding the renal tubule. The first set of capillaries, those of the glomerulus, provides the blood to be filtered; the second set receives materials returned to the blood by the tubule. Blood from the peritubular capillaries enters small veins that eventually lead to the renal vein. In summary, the sequence of blood vessels in which blood circulates through the nephron is

> afferent arteriole → capillaries of glomerulus → efferent arteriole → peritubular capillaries

Urine Is Produced by Filtration, Reabsorption, and Secretion

Urine is produced by a combination of three processes: filtration, reabsorption, and tubular secretion.

Filtration is a nonselective process

Filtration occurs at the junction of the glomerular capillaries and the wall of Bowman's capsule (Figure 46–16). Blood flows through the glomerular capillaries under high pressure, forcing more than 10% of the plasma out of the capillaries and into Bowman's capsule. This process of filtration is somewhat similar to the mechanism whereby tissue fluid is formed as blood flows through other capillary networks in the body. However, much more plasma is filtered in the kidney.

Several factors contribute to this process. First, the glomerular capillaries have higher hydrostatic pressure than other capillaries. This is due in part to the high resistance to flow presented by the efferent arteriole, which is smaller in diameter than the afferent arteriole. Another factor that contributes to the great amount of filtrate is the large surface area for filtration provided by the highly coiled glomerular capillaries. A third factor is the high permeability of the glomerular capillaries. Numerous small pores (fenestrations) are present between the squamous cells that make up the walls of the glomerular capillaries.

Because filtration is not a selective process, it determines the composition of urine only to a minor extent. The **filtration barrier,** which consists of the wall of the glomerular capillaries and the thin membranes cover-

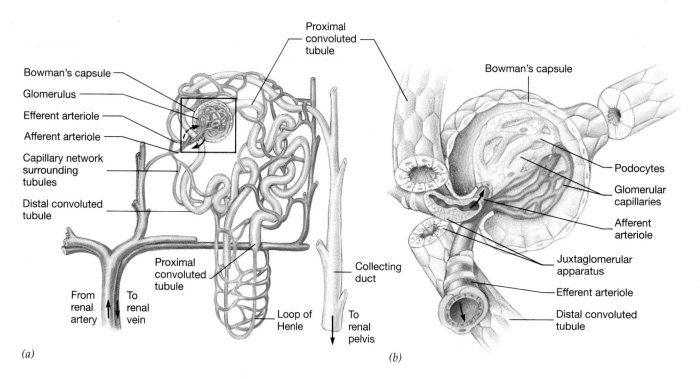

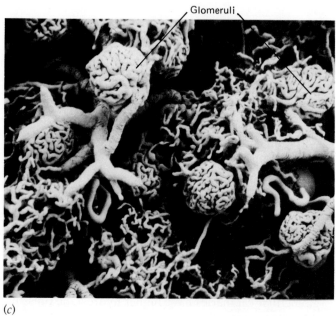

Figure 46-14   Each kidney is composed of more than a million microscopic nephrons. (*a*) Diagrammatic view of the basic structure of a nephron. (*b*) Detailed view of Bowman's capsule. (*c*) Low-power scanning electron micrograph of a portion of the kidney cortex, showing glomeruli and associated blood vessels. Urine forms by filtration from the blood in the glomeruli and by adjustment of the filtrate as it passes through the tubules that drain the glomeruli.   (*c*, CNRI/Science Photo Library/Photo Researchers, Inc.)

ing the slit pores between the podocytes, does hold back blood cells, platelets, and most of the plasma proteins. Small materials dissolved in the plasma—such as glucose, amino acids, sodium, potassium, chloride, bicarbonate, other salts, and urea—pass through this barrier and become part of the filtrate.

The total volume of blood passing through the kidneys is about 1200 mL per minute, or about one fourth of the entire cardiac output. The plasma passing through the glomerulus loses about 20% of its volume to the glomerular filtrate; the rest leaves the glomerulus through the efferent arteriole. The normal glomerular filtration rate amounts to about 180 liters (about 45 gallons) each 24 hours. This is four and a half times the amount of fluid in the entire body! Common sense tells us that urine could not be excreted at that rate. Within a few moments, dehydration would become a life-threatening problem.

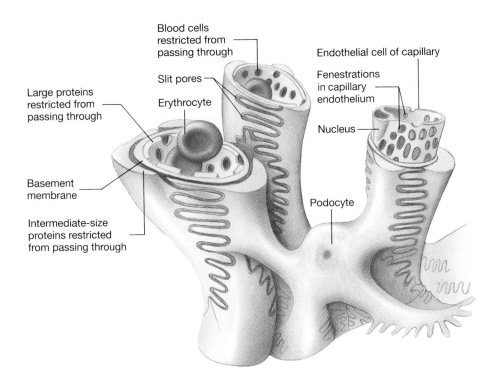

Figure 46–15 Podocytes are part of the filtration barrier of the kidney that separates the blood of the glomerulus from the lumen of Bowman's capsule.

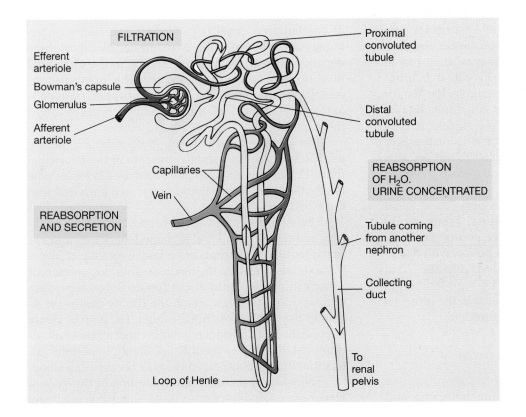

Figure 46–16 Function of the nephron. Diagram shows where filtration, reabsorption, and secretion take place.

Reabsorption is highly selective

The threat to homeostasis posed by the vast amounts of fluid filtered by the kidneys is avoided by **reabsorption.** About 99% of the filtrate is reabsorbed into the blood through the renal tubules, leaving only about 1.5 liters to be excreted as urine. Reabsorption permits precise regulation of blood chemistry by the kidneys. Needed substances such as glucose and amino acids are returned to the blood, while wastes and excess salts and other materials remain in the filtrate and are excreted in the urine. Each day the tubules reabsorb more than 178 liters of water, 1200 g (2.5 lb) of salt, and about 250 g (0.5 lb) of glucose. Most of this, of course, is reabsorbed many times over.

The simple epithelial cells lining the renal tubule are well adapted for reabsorbing materials. They have abundant microvilli, which increase the surface area for reabsorption (and give the inner lining a "brush border" appearance). These cells also contain numerous mitochondria, which provide the energy for running the cellular pumps that actively transport materials.

About 65% of the filtrate is reabsorbed as it passes through the proximal convoluted tubule. Glucose, amino acids, vitamins, and other substances of nutritional value are reabsorbed there, as are many ions, including sodium, chloride, bicarbonate, and potassium. Some of these ions are actively transported; others follow by diffusion. Reabsorption continues as the filtrate passes through the loop of Henle and the distal convoluted tubule. Then the filtrate is further concentrated as it passes through the collecting duct that leads to the renal pelvis.

Normally, substances that are useful to the body, such as glucose or amino acids, are reabsorbed from the renal tubules. If the concentration of a particular substance in the blood is high, however, the tubules may not be able to reabsorb all of it. The maximum rate at which a substance can be reabsorbed is called its **tubular transport maximum (Tm)**. For example, the Tm for glucose averages 320 mg/min for an adult human being. Normally, the tubular load of glucose is only about 125 mg/min, so almost all of it is reabsorbed. However, if glucose is filtered in excess of the Tm, that excess will not be reabsorbed but will instead pass into the urine.

Each substance that has a Tm also has a **renal threshold** concentration in the plasma. When a substance exceeds its renal threshold, the portion not reabsorbed is excreted in the urine. In a person with diabetes mellitus, the concentration of glucose in the blood exceeds its threshold level (about 150 mg glucose per 100 mL of blood), so glucose is excreted in the urine. Its presence there is evidence of this disorder.

Some substances are actively secreted from the blood into the filtrate

Some substances, especially potassium, hydrogen, and ammonium ions, are secreted from the blood into the filtrate. Certain drugs, such as penicillin, are also removed from the blood by secretion. Secretion occurs mainly in the region of the distal convoluted tubule.

Secretion of hydrogen ions, an important homeostatic mechanism for regulating the pH of the blood, takes place through the formation of carbonic acid. Carbon dioxide, which diffuses from the blood into the cells of the distal tubules and collecting ducts, combines with water to form carbonic acid. This acid then dissociates, forming hydrogen ions and bicarbonate ions. When the blood becomes too acidic, more hydrogen ions are secreted into the urine.

The secretion of potassium is also very important. When potassium concentration is too high, nerve impulses are not effectively transmitted and the strength of muscle contraction decreases. The heart can be weakened and even fail. When potassium ions are too highly concentrated, they are secreted from the blood into the renal tubules, and then are excreted in the urine. Secretion results from a direct effect of the potassium ions on the tubules. A high potassium ion concentration in the blood also stimulates the adrenal cortex to increase its output of the hormone aldosterone. This hormone further stimulates secretion of potassium.

Urine Concentration Depends on a Countercurrent Mechanism

When fluid intake is high, a large volume of dilute urine is excreted. When fluid intake is low, wastes must still be excreted, but to conserve fluid, a small volume of concentrated urine is produced. The ability of the kidneys to produce either concentrated or dilute urine depends on a high salt concentration in the interstitial fluid in the medulla of the kidney. This high salt concentration is maintained by salt reabsorption from various regions of the renal tubule and by a countercurrent mechanism.

The salts and urea in the glomerular filtrate are used to increase the osmotic pressure of the interstitial fluid. This causes water to pass from the filtrate into the interstitial fluid. From there, water is reabsorbed into the blood.

There are two types of nephrons: the cortical nephrons and the more internal juxtamedullary nephrons. A **juxtamedullary nephron** has a very long loop of Henle that extends deep into the medulla. This loop consists of a descending loop, into which filtrate flows, and an ascending loop, through which the filtrate passes on its way to the distal convoluted tubule. The loop of Henle is specialized to produce a high concentration of sodium chloride in the medulla. A highly hypertonic interstitial fluid is maintained near the bottom of the loop.

The walls of the descending portion of the loop of Henle are relatively permeable to water but relatively impermeable to salt and urea. As the filtrate passes down the loop of Henle, water passes out by osmosis, leaving a more concentrated filtrate in the loop (Figure 46–17). For reasons to be discussed, the interstitial fluid near the bottom of the descending loop contains a high concentration of sodium chloride and urea; water therefore diffuses out of the filtrate in that region.

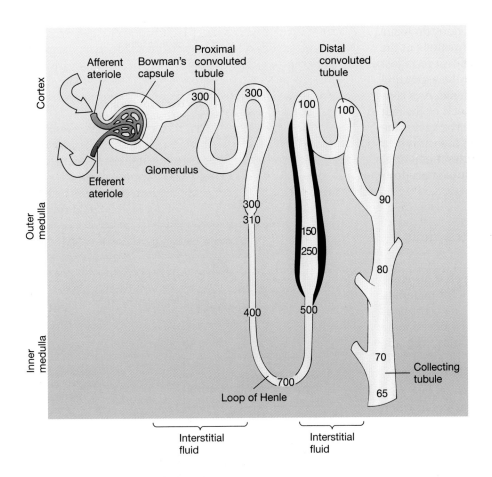

Figure 46-17 Urine formation. Solute concentrations are given in milliosmols per liter. The walls of the descending loop of Henle are relatively permeable to water but impermeable to salt and urea. Water passes out of the descending loop, leaving a more concentrated filtrate inside. At the turn of the loop, the walls of the tubule become more permeable to salt and less permeable to water, so salt moves out into the interstitial fluid; thus, salt concentration is greater in the interstitial fluid at the bottom of the loop. Higher in the ascending loop, chloride pumps transport chloride out into the interstitial fluid, and sodium follows. Urea moves out into the interstitial fluid through the collecting ducts. This countercurrent mechanism establishes a very hypertonic interstitial fluid near the renal pelvis that draws water osmotically from the filtrate in the collecting ducts.

At the turn of the loop of Henle, the walls of the tubule become more permeable to salt and less permeable to water. As the concentrated filtrate begins to move up the ascending portion, salt diffuses out into the interstitial fluid. As a result, salt is concentrated in the interstitial fluid of the medulla. Higher in the ascending part of the loop of Henle, sodium is actively transported through the cells that make up the wall of the tubule.

The collecting ducts are permeable to urea, allowing the concentrated urea in the filtrate to diffuse out into the interstitial fluid. This results in a high urea concentration in the interstitial fluid, which is responsible for water passing out of the descending part of the loop of Henle.

Because water passes out of the descending part of the loop, the salt concentration in the filtrate at the bottom of the loop is high. However, because salt (but not water) is removed in the ascending portion, by the time the filtrate flows through the distal convoluted tubule, it is isotonic or even hypotonic to blood. As the filtrate moves down the collecting duct, water continues to pass by osmosis into the interstitial fluid, where it is collected by blood vessels.

Note that there is a *counterflow* of fluid through the two limbs of the loop of Henle. Filtrate passing down

through the descending portion of the loop is flowing in a direction opposite the filtrate moving upward through the ascending loop. The filtrate is concentrated as it moves down the descending portion of the loop and diluted as it moves up the ascending part of the loop. This **countercurrent mechanism** helps maintain a high salt concentration in the interstitial fluid of the medulla. The hypertonic interstitial fluid draws water osmotically from the filtrate in the collecting ducts.

The collecting ducts are routed so that they pass through the zone of hypertonic interstitial fluid on their way to the renal pelvis. This loss of water from the ducts concentrates the urine to such an extent that it can be hypertonic to blood. *A hypertonic urine has a low concentration of water and so conserves water.* The urine becomes most hypertonic in thirst (in fact, thirst is a signal that the fluid content of the blood is low). In thirst, the permeability of the collecting duct walls becomes very high due to the action of the hormone ADH (to be discussed later).

The water that diffuses from the filtrate into the interstitial fluid is removed by blood vessels known as the vasa recta and carried off in the venous drainage of the kidney. The **vasa recta** are long, looped extensions of the efferent arterioles of the juxtamedullary nephrons. They extend deep into the medulla, only to negotiate a hairpin curve and return to the cortical venous drainage of the kidney. Blood flows in opposite directions in the ascending and descending regions of the vasa recta just as filtrate flows in opposite directions in the ascending and descending portions of the loop of Henle. As a consequence of this countercurrent flow, much of the salt and urea that have entered the blood leave again; the solute concentration of the blood leaving the vasa recta is only slightly higher than that of the blood entering. This mechanism maintains the high solute concentration of the interstitial fluid.

Urine Is Composed of Water, Nitrogenous Wastes, and Salts

By the time the filtrate reaches the renal pelvis, its composition has been precisely adjusted. Useful materials have been returned to the blood by reabsorption. Wastes and excess materials that entered by filtration or secretion have been retained by the tubules. The adjusted filtrate, called **urine,** is composed of about 96% water, 2.5% nitrogenous wastes (primarily urea), 1.5% salts, and traces of other substances, such as bile pigments, which may contribute to the characteristic color and odor.

Healthy urine is sterile and has been used to wash battlefield wounds when clean water was not available. However, when exposed to bacterial action, urine swiftly decomposes, forming ammonia and other products. It is the ammonia that produces diaper rash in infants.

The composition of urine yields many clues to body function and malfunction. **Urinalysis,** the physical, chemical, and microscopic examination of urine, is a very important diagnostic tool and is used to monitor many disorders such as diabetes mellitus.

Urine Volume Is Regulated by the Hormone ADH

The amount of urine produced depends upon the body's need to retain or rid itself of water. We have seen that salt reabsorption and the countercurrent mechanism in the loops of Henle establish a very salty tissue fluid that draws water osmotically from the collecting ducts. Permeability of the collecting ducts to water is regulated by **antidiuretic hormone (ADH).** When the body needs to conserve water, ADH is released from the posterior pituitary gland (Figure 46–18). This hormone acts on the collecting ducts, making them more permeable to water so that more water is reabsorbed, and a small volume of concentrated urine is produced.

Secretion of ADH is stimulated by special receptors in the hypothalamus. When fluid intake is low, the body begins to dehydrate, causing the blood volume to

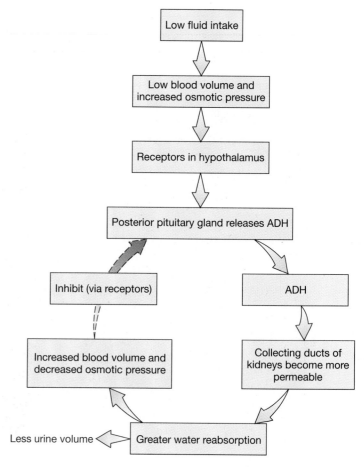

Figure 46–18 Regulation of urine volume. When fluid is low, blood volume decreases and osmotic pressure increases. The posterior lobe of the pituitary gland releases the hormone ADH, which stimulates an increase in water reabsorption.

decrease. As blood volume decreases, the *concentration* of salts dissolved in the blood rises, causing an increase in osmotic pressure. Receptors in the hypothalamus are sensitive to this osmotic change and stimulate the posterior lobe of the pituitary to release ADH. A thirst center in the hypothalamus also responds to dehydration, stimulating an increase in fluid intake.

When one drinks a great deal of water, the blood becomes diluted and its osmotic pressure falls. Release of ADH by the pituitary gland decreases, lessening the amount of water reabsorbed from the collecting ducts. A large volume of dilute urine is produced.

Occasionally, the pituitary gland malfunctions and fails to produce sufficient ADH. This can result in **diabetes insipidus** (not to be confused with the more common disorder, diabetes mellitus). Diabetes insipidus can also result from an acquired unresponsiveness of the kidney to ADH. In this disorder, water is not efficiently reabsorbed from the ducts, and therefore a large volume of urine is produced. A person with severe diabetes insipidus may excrete up to 20 liters of urine each

Kidney Disease, Dialysis, and Transplant

Kidney disease ranks fourth in prevalence among major diseases in the United States. Kidney function can be impaired by infections, poisoning caused by substances such as mercury or carbon tetrachloride, lesions, tumors, kidney stone formation, shock, and many circulatory diseases. One of the most common kidney diseases is *glomerulonephritis*, which is actually a large number of related chronic diseases in which the glomeruli are damaged. The damage is thought to result from an autoimmune response.

In chronic kidney disease, the progressive loss of renal function may eventually reach the stage of **kidney failure,** in which there is a decrease in the glomerular filtration rate and the kidneys are unable to maintain homeostasis of the blood. Homeostatic balance of water, sodium, potassium, calcium, and other salts is no longer possible, and nitrogenous wastes are not excreted. Retention of water causes edema, and as the concentration of hydrogen ions increases, acidosis develops. Nitrogenous wastes accumulate in the blood and tissues, causing a condition referred to as **uremia.** If untreated, the acidosis and uremia can cause coma and eventually death. Chronic kidney failure can be treated by kidney dialysis or by kidney transplant.

Kidney Dialysis Is Used To Treat Patients with Kidney Failure

Dialysis is the process of separating solutes in a solution by diffusion across a semipermeable membrane. A kidney dialysis machine can be used to restore appropriate solute balance to a patient whose kidneys are not functioning.

In extracorporeal dialysis, a plastic tube is surgically inserted into both an artery and a vein in the patient's arm or leg. These tubes can then be connected to a circuit of plastic tubing from a dialysis machine. The patient's blood flows through the tub-

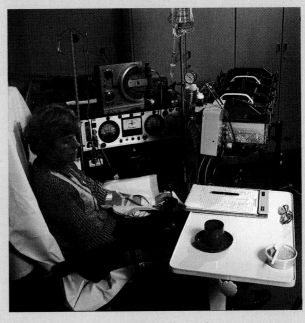

A patient undergoing dialysis in a hospital.   (Werner H. Muller/ Peter Arnold, Inc.)

ing, which is immersed in a solution containing most of the normal blood plasma constituents in their normal proportions. The walls of the plastic tubing constitute a semipermeable membrane. Since the dialysis fluid contains no wastes, nitrogenous wastes such as urea pass from the patient's blood through minute pores in the tubing and into the surrounding solution. As the blood circulates repeatedly through the tubing in the machine, dialysis continues, eventually adjusting most of the values of the patient's blood chemistry to normal ranges. Although much improved by recent engineering advances, machine dialysis is very expensive ($20,000 to $30,000 per year per patient), clumsy, and inconvenient, and it may produce serious side effects such as osteoporosis (a disorder characterized by loss of calcium from the bones).

A different dialysis technique, continuous ambulatory peritoneal dialysis (CAPD), makes use of the fact that the peritoneum (the lining of the abdominal cavity) is a differentially

permeable membrane. A plastic bag containing dialysis fluid is attached to the patient's abdominal cavity, and the fluid is allowed to run into the abdominal cavity. After about 30 minutes, the fluid is withdrawn into the bag and discarded. This process is repeated about three times each day. This type of dialysis is much more convenient but poses the threat of peritonitis, should bacteria enter the body cavity with the dialysis fluid.

Kidney Transplant Is More Effective Than Dialysis

Long-term use of dialysis is not as desirable for the patient as would be a functioning kidney. With a successful kidney transplant a patient can live a more normal life with far less long-term expense. At present more than two thirds of kidney transplants are successful for several years, although physicians must routinely treat the problems of graft rejection (discussed in Chapter 43). Several recipients of kidney transplants have survived for more than 20 years.

day, a serious loss of water from the body. The affected individual become dehydrated and must drink almost continually to offset fluid loss. Diabetes insipidus can often be controlled by injections of ADH or use of an ADH nasal spray.

Sodium Reabsorption Is Regulated by the Hormone Aldosterone

Sodium is the most abundant extracellular ion, accounting for about 90% of all positive ions outside cells. Concentration of sodium is precisely regulated by the hormone **aldosterone,** secreted by the cortex of the adrenal glands. This hormone stimulates the distal tubules and collecting ducts to increase sodium reabsorption.

Aldosterone secretion can be stimulated by a decrease in blood pressure. When blood pressure falls, cells of the **juxtaglomerular complex** secrete the enzyme renin and activate the renin-angiotensin pathway. The juxtaglomerular complex is a small group of cells located in the region where the distal tubule contacts the afferent arteriole (see Figure 46–14b). Renin acts on a plasma protein, converting it to angiotensin, which stimulates aldosterone secretion.

SUMMARY

I. Excretory systems help maintain homeostasis by osmoregulation, excretion of metabolic wastes, and regulation of the concentrations of body fluid components.

II. The principal waste products of animal metabolism are water, carbon dioxide, and nitrogenous wastes, including ammonia, urea, and uric acid.

III. Invertebrate mechanisms of osmoregulation and waste disposal are diverse and are adapted to the body plan and lifestyle of an organism.
   A. Marine sponges and cnidarians have no specialized excretory organs.
   B. Flatworms have nephridial organs characterized by protonephridia with flame cells.
   C. Annelids possess coelomic metanephridia.
   D. Crustaceans employ antennal glands for osmoregulation.
   E. By conserving water, Malpighian tubules contribute to the success of insects on land.

IV. The vertebrate kidney functions in excretion and osmoregulation and is vital in maintaining homeostasis.
   A. Aquatic vertebrates have a continuous problem of osmoregulation. Freshwater fish take in water osmotically; they excrete a large volume of dilute urine.
   B. Marine bony fish lose water osmotically. They compensate by drinking seawater and excreting salt through their gills; only a small volume of urine is produced.
   C. Marine cartilaginous fish retain large amounts of urea, which enables them to take in water osmotically through the gills. This water can be used to excrete a hypotonic urine.
   D. Other aquatic vertebrates have specific adaptations for dealing with osmoregulation. Marine birds and reptiles, for example, have salt glands that excrete excess salt.

V. The urinary system is the principal excretory system in humans and other vertebrates. The vertebrate kidney is a key organ for maintaining homeostasis of body fluids and disposal of metabolic wastes.
   A. The kidneys produce urine, which then passes through the ureters to the urinary bladder for storage. During urination the urine passes through the urethra to the outside of the body.
   B. Each nephron consists of Bowman's capsule, a cluster of capillaries called a glomerulus, and a long, coiled renal tubule.
   C. Urine formation is accomplished by filtration of plasma, reabsorption of needed materials, and secretion of a few substances such as potassium and hydrogen ions into the renal tubule.
      1. Plasma filters out of the glomerular capillaries and into Bowman's capsule. Because filtration is a nonselective process, both needed materials (such as glucose) and wastes become part of the filtrate.
      2. About 99% of the filtrate is reabsorbed from the renal tubules into the blood; this is a highly selective process that returns usable materials to the blood but leaves wastes and excessive quantities of other substances to be excreted in the urine.
      3. In secretion, certain substances are actively transported into the renal tubule to become part of the urine.
   D. The interstitial fluid surrounding the nephrons has a high solute concentration due to a countercurrent mechanism in the loops of Henle. Water is drawn osmotically from the filtrate in the collecting ducts. This permits concentration of urine in the collecting ducts so that urine hypertonic to the blood can be produced.
   E. Urine consists of water, nitrogenous wastes, salts, and excesses of other substances.
   F. Urine volume is regulated by the hormone ADH, which is released by the posterior lobe of the pituitary gland in response to an increase in osmotic pressure of the blood (caused by dehydration). ADH increases the permeability of the collecting ducts. As a result, more water is reabsorbed and only a small volume of concentrated urine is produced.

POST-TEST

1. The process of removing metabolic wastes from the body is called _____.
2. _____ is the ability of an organism to regulate its fluid content.
3. The principal nitrogenous waste product of insects and birds is _____ _____.
4. The principal nitrogenous waste product of amphibians and mammals is _____.
5. Flatworms have excretory structures called _____, which are characterized by _____ cells.

Select the most appropriate answer from Column B for each description in Column A.

Column A	*Column B*
10. Outer portion of human kidney	a. cortex
11. Delivers urine to bladder	b. medulla
12. Part of kidney that receives urine from collecting ducts	c. ureter
	d. urethra
	e. renal pelvis

Column A	*Column B*
13. Site of filtration	a. urethra
14. Site of reabsorption	b. renal tubules
15. Delivers urine to outside of body	c. renal pelvis
	d. Bowman's capsule
	e. ureter

16. The glomerulus consists of a tuft of _____, which project into _____ _____.
17. Blood is delivered to the glomerulus by the _____ _____ and leaves the glomerulus in the _____ _____.
18. Fluid that leaves the glomerular capillaries and enters Bowman's capsule is called _____.
19. When a substance exceeds its renal threshold, the portion not reabsorbed is _____.
20. The countercurrent mechanism helps maintain a high _____ concentration in the interstitial fluid.
21. Antidiuretic hormone (ADH) increases the permeability of the _____ _____ so that more water is _____ and the volume of urine is _____ (increased or decreased).

6. Earthworms have _____ in each of their body segments.
7. The principal excretory organs of crustaceans are _____ _____.
8. The excretory structures of insects are _____ _____.
9. The vertebrate kidney consists of functional units called _____.

22. Label the following diagram.

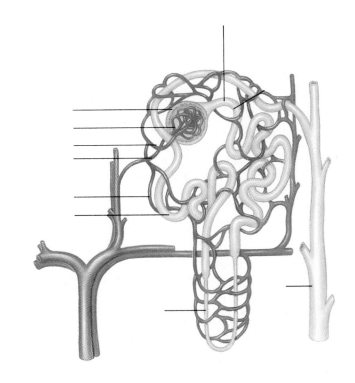

REVIEW QUESTIONS

1. How do excretory systems help maintain homeostasis?
2. The number of protonephridia in a planarian is adjusted to the salinity of the environment. Planaria inhabiting slightly salty water develop relatively few protonephridia, but the number quickly increases as the concentration of salt in the environment is reduced. Can you explain why?
3. What type of osmoregulatory problem is faced by an insect? by a marine fish? by freshwater fish? What adaptations have evolved that enable each of these animals to maintain fluid homeostasis?
4. Name the adaptations that enable each of the following animals to solve its osmoregulatory problems: an amphibian, a marine bird or a reptile, a dehydrated human.

5. Name the structure in the mammalian body that is associated with each of the following: (1) urea formation, (2) urine formation, (3) temporary storage of urine, (4) conduction of urine out of the body.
6. Draw a diagram of a nephron and label its parts.
7. Specify which part of the nephron is associated with each of the following: (1) filtration, (2) reabsorption, (3) secretion.
8. Contrast filtration and secretion.
9. List the sequence of blood vessels through which a drop of blood passes as it makes its way from renal artery to renal vein.

10. Why is glucose normally not present in urine? Why is it present in uncontrolled diabetes mellitus? Why do you suppose diabetics experience an increased output of urine?
11. How is urine volume regulated? Explain. Why must victims of untreated diabetes insipidus drink great quantities of water?
12. How does the countercurrent mechanism in the loops of Henle help concentrate urine?

RECOMMENDED READINGS

Dantzler, W. H. Renal adaptations of desert vertebrates. *Bioscience* 32(2):108–112, 1982. Adaptations in renal physiology are integrated with other physiological and behavioral mechanisms for desert survival.

Solomon, E. P., R. Schmidt, and P. Adragna. *Human Anatomy and Physiology.* Saunders College Publishing, Philadelphia, 1990. Chapters 27 and 28 focus on the human urinary system and fluid balance.

Animal Hormones: Endocrine Regulation

A caterpillar becomes a butterfly. A crustacean changes color. A young girl develops into a woman. An adult copes with chronic stress. These physiological processes and many other adjustments of metabolism, growth, and reproduction are regulated by the endocrine system. The endocrine system works closely with the nervous system to maintain the steady state of the body. **Endocrinology,** the study of endocrine activity, is a very active and exciting field of biomedical research.

The **endocrine system** is a diverse collection of glands and tissues that secrete **hormones,** chemical messengers responsible for the regulation of many body processes. The term *hormone* is derived from a Greek word meaning "to excite." Hormones do indeed affect specific tissues, usually by stimulating a change in some metabolic activity.

Endocrine glands produce hormones and secrete them into the surrounding tissue fluid, from which they diffuse into capillaries. Hormones are then transported

Clown shrimp on anemone. Color changes in crustaceans are regulated by hormones. (Robert Shupak)

throughout the body by the blood but elicit responses only in their **target tissues.** The target tissue may be another endocrine gland, or it may be an entirely different type of organ, such as a bone or a kidney. Often the target tissue is located far from the endocrine gland. Endocrine glands lack ducts; they differ from **exocrine glands** (such as sweat glands and gastric glands), which release their secretions into ducts.

Traditionally, endocrinology focused on the activity of about 10 discrete endocrine glands. We now know that certain neurons and specialized cells in the digestive tract, heart, kidneys, and many other organs also release hormones. Hormones secreted by neurons are called **neurohormones,** and the cells that secrete them are **neurosecretory cells** (Figure 47–1). The scope of endocrinology has been broadened to include the study of chemical messengers produced by neurons, other cells, and organs that are widely distributed in the body, rather than by single, discrete organs.[1]

---

[1] **Pheromones** are chemicals produced by an animal for communication with other animals of the same species (see Chapter 50). Because pheromones are generally produced by exocrine glands and do not regulate metabolic activities within the animal that produces them, most biologists do not classify them as hormones.

After you have studied this chapter you should be able to

1. Define the terms *hormone* and *endocrine gland* and identify sources of hormones other than endocrine glands.
2. Compare two mechanisms of hormone action: Activation of genes and activation of second messengers such as cyclic AMP.
3. Describe the regulation of hormone secretion by negative feedback mechanisms, and draw diagrams illustrating the regulation of secretion of each of the hormones discussed in this chapter.
4. Cite the general sources and actions of invertebrate hormones.
5. Summarize the interaction of hormones that control development in insects.
6. Locate the principal vertebrate endocrine glands, list the hormones secreted by each, and summarize their actions.

7. Support the following concept: The hypothalamus is the link between the nervous and endocrine systems. (Include a description of the mechanisms by which the hypothalamus influences the anterior and posterior lobes of the pituitary gland.)
8. Relate the actions of growth hormone and thyroid hormones to growth; explain the consequences of hyposecretion and hypersecretion of these hormones.
9. Compare the actions of insulin and glucagon in regulating the concentration of glucose in the blood; summarize the physiological problems associated with diabetes mellitus and hypoglycemia.
10. Summarize the roles of the adrenal medulla and the adrenal cortex in helping the body adapt to stress.

HORMONES CAN BE ASSIGNED TO FOUR CHEMICAL GROUPS

Although hormones are chemically diverse, they generally belong to one of four different chemical groups: (1) steroids, (2) amino acid derivatives, (3) peptides or proteins, or (4) fatty acid derivatives (see Figures 47–2 and 47–3).

In vertebrates, the adrenal cortex, testis, ovary, and placenta secrete steroids synthesized from cholesterol. Recall that steroids are a chemical group classified with the lipids (Chapter 3). Progesterone, one of the female sex hormones, is the precursor of the steroid hormones produced by the adrenal cortex, of the male hormone testosterone, and of the female hormone estradiol. The molting hormone of insects is also a steroid.

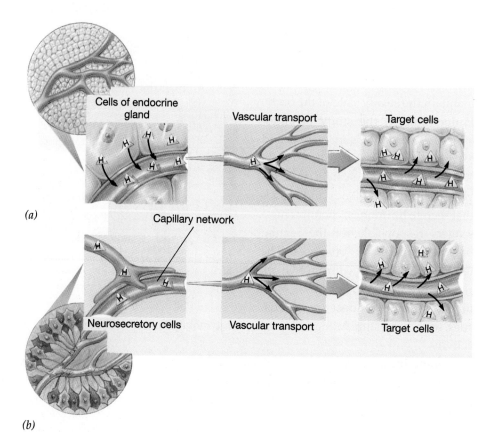

Figure 47–1 Hormones may be secreted by the cells of endocrine glands, as in (*a*), or by neurosecretory cells, as in (*b*). Hormones are generally transported by the blood and are taken up by target cells.

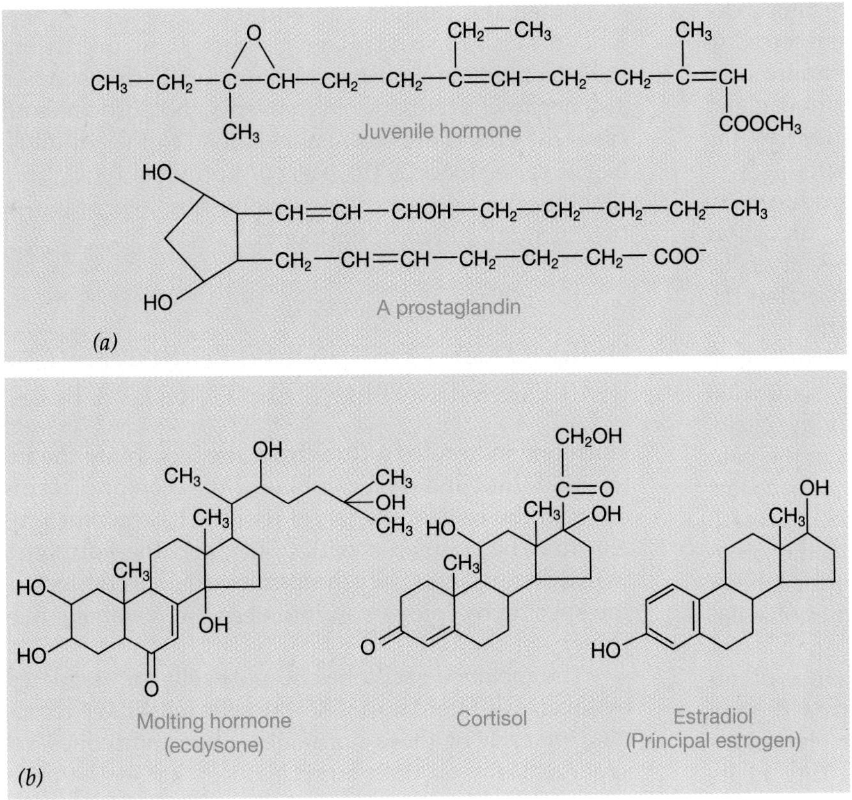

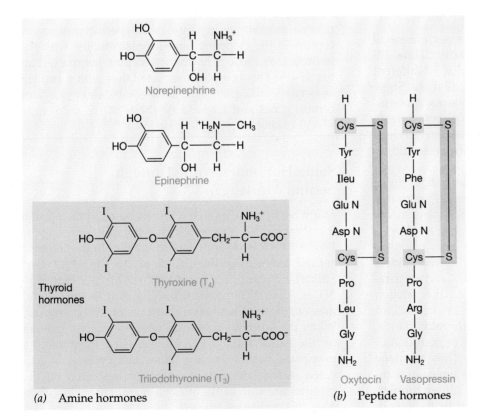

Figure 47–2 Hormones derived from fatty acids and steroids. (*a*) Juvenile hormone and prostaglandins are derived from fatty acids. (*b*) Molting hormone, cortisol, and estradiol are steroid hormones.

Figure 47–3 Hormones belonging to the protein family. (*a*) Some hormones derived from amino acids. Note the presence of iodine in the thyroid hormones. (*b*) Peptide hormones produced in the hypothalamus and secreted by the posterior lobe of the pituitary gland. Oxytocin and antidiuretic hormone are both small peptides containing nine amino acids. Note that the structure of these hormones differs by only two amino acids.

Chemically the simplest hormones are those derived from the amino acid tyrosine; they are referred to as **amines.** Examples of hormones that are amines are the thyroid hormones produced by the thyroid gland and epinephrine and norepinephrine produced by the medulla of the adrenal gland (Figure 47–3a).

Oxytocin and antidiuretic hormone, produced by neurosecretory cells in the hypothalamus, are short **peptides** composed of nine amino acids. Seven of the amino acids are identical in the two hormones, but the actions of these hormones are quite different.

The hormones glucagon, secretin, adrenocorticotropic hormone (ACTH), and calcitonin are somewhat longer peptides with about 30 amino acids in the chain. Insulin, secreted by the islets of Langerhans in the pancreas, is a protein consisting of two peptide chains joined by disulfide bonds (see Figure 3–22). Growth hormone, thyroid-stimulating hormone, and the gonadotropic hormones, all secreted by the anterior lobe of the pituitary gland, are larger proteins with molecular weights of 25,000 or more.

Prostaglandins and the juvenile hormones of insects are hormones derived from fatty acids (Figure 47–2a). Prostaglandins are derivatives of polyunsaturated fatty acids, each with a five-carbon ring in its structure.

HORMONE SECRETION IS REGULATED BY NEGATIVE FEEDBACK MECHANISMS

In vertebrates, most endocrine glands secrete small amounts of their hormones continuously. Thus, although present in minute amounts, about 50 different hormones are circulating in the blood at all times. Some hormones are transported bound to plasma proteins. Hormone molecules are continuously removed from the circulation by target tissues. They are also removed by the liver, which inactivates some hormones, and by the kidneys, which excrete them.

How does an endocrine gland "know" how much hormone to secrete at any given moment? Hormone secretion is regulated by *negative feedback* control mechanisms. Information regarding the hormone level or its effect is fed back to the gland, which then responds homeostatically. For example, the parathyroid glands, located in the neck of tetrapod vertebrates, secrete parathyroid hormone, which helps regulate the calcium level in the blood. Even a slight decrease in calcium concentration is sensed by the parathyroid glands, which respond by increasing their rate of secretion of parathyroid hormone (Figure 47–4). This hormone stimulates release of calcium from the bones and increases reabsorption of calcium by the kidney tubules, increasing the concentration of calcium in the blood.

When the calcium concentration rises above normal, the parathyroid glands respond by decreasing their secretion of parathyroid hormone. Both responses are negative feedback mechanisms, because in both cases the effects are *opposite* (negative) to the stimulus. Negative feedback is the basis of hormonal regulation. Many regulatory processes involve the interaction of two or more different hormones.

HORMONES COMBINE WITH SPECIFIC RECEPTOR PROTEINS OF TARGET CELLS

Hormone molecules diffuse from the blood into the interstitial fluid and then combine with receptor proteins on or in the cells of the target tissue. The receptor protein may be compared with a lock and the hormones with different keys. Only the hormone that fits the lock—the specific receptor—can influence the metabolic machinery of the cell.

The metabolic activities of most cells are regulated by several different hormones, so cells must have receptors for each of these hormones. Some hormones act synergistically on their target tissues; that is, the presence of one hormone enhances the effect of another.

Some Hormones Activate Genes

Steroid hormones and thyroid hormones are relatively small, lipid-soluble molecules that can pass through the plasma membrane. In target cells, specific protein receptors in the cytoplasm or nucleus combine with the hormone to form a hormone-receptor complex (Figure 47–5). This complex then combines with a protein associated with the DNA. This combination activates certain genes and leads to synthesis of the messenger RNAs coding for specific proteins.

Some Hormones Work Through Second Messengers

Many hormones combine with receptors on the plasma membrane of the target cell. The hormonal message is then relayed to the appropriate site within the cell by a **second messenger** (Figure 47–6). In the 1960s Earl Sutherland identified **cyclic AMP** (cAMP; see Figure 3–31) as a hormone intermediary, and it is the second messenger that has been most extensively studied. When the hormone combines with its receptor protein on the extracellular face of the plasma membrane, a membrane-bound enzyme, **adenylate cyclase,** is activated. Adenylate cyclase, however, is located on the cytoplasmic side of the plasma membrane. How then does this activation occur?

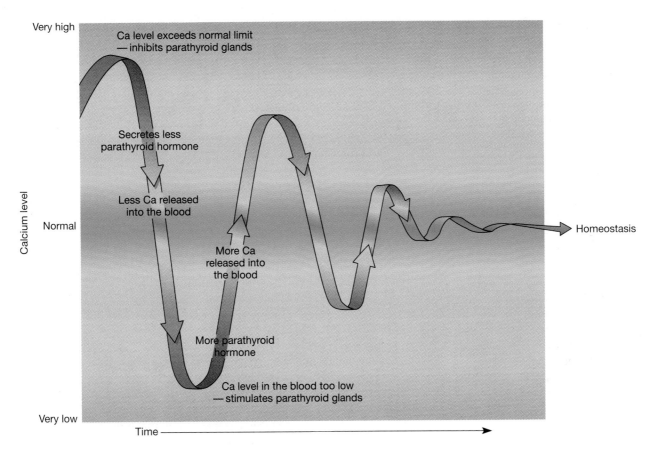

Figure 47–4 Regulation of hormone secretion by negative feedback. When the calcium level in the blood falls below normal, the parathyroid glands are stimulated to release more parathyroid hormone. This hormone acts to increase the calcium level in the blood, thus restoring homeostasis. If the calcium level exceeds normal, the parathyroid glands are inhibited and slow their release of hormone. This diagram has been simplified. Calcitonin, a hormone secreted by the thyroid gland, works antagonistically to parathyroid hormone and is important in lowering blood calcium concentration.

A third protein, known as **G protein,** is also located on the cytoplasmic side of the plasma membrane and acts as a shuttle for communication between the receptor and adenylate cyclase (Figure 47–7). Two types of G protein exist. One type, G_s, stimulates adenylate cyclase, and the other, G_i, inhibits it. When the system is inactive, G protein binds to **guanosine diphosphate,** or **GDP,** which is similar to ADP, the hydrolyzed form of ATP.

Most hormones bind to a stimulatory receptor, resulting in activation of adenylate cyclase. After the receptor-hormone complex is formed, GDP is released from the G protein and the G protein binds to **guanosine triphosphate (GTP).** GTP, like ATP, is an important molecule in energy transfers. The acquisition of GTP produces a conformational change in the G protein that enables the G protein to bind with, and thereby activate, adenylate cyclase.

Once activated, adenylate cyclase catalyzes the conversion of ATP to cyclic AMP (Figure 47–8). The cyclic AMP then activates one or more enzymes known as **protein kinases.** Each type of protein kinase catalyzes the phosphorylation of (addition of a phosphate group to) a specific protein. When the protein is phosphorylated its function is altered; it then triggers a chain of reactions that leads to a specified metabolic effect. Any increase in cyclic AMP is temporary; it is rapidly inactivated by enzymes known as phosphodiesterases, which convert it to AMP.

Protein kinases inhibit or activate other enzymes; each different protein kinase acts on a different type of enzyme. Because different types of protein kinases exist in each kind of target cell (and even within different organelles of the same target cell), protein kinases are able to produce a wide variety of responses. For example, activation of one type of protein kinase may have a metabolic effect on the cell, a second protein kinase may affect membrane permeability, and a third may activate genes (Figure 47–9).

Another important second messenger is the calcium ion. As certain hormones bind to their receptors on the plasma membrane, calcium channels open, resulting in an influx of extracellular calcium. Cyclic AMP can also increase the cellular concentration of calcium

(*Text continued on p. 1010*)

Figure 47–5 Activation of genes by steroid hormones. (1) Steroid hormones are secreted by an endocrine gland and transported to a target cell. (2) Steroid hormones are small, lipid-soluble molecules that pass freely through the plasma membrane. (3) The hormone passes through the cytoplasm to the nucleus. (4) Inside the nucleus, the hormone combines with a receptor. Then the steroid hormone–receptor complex combines with a protein associated with the DNA. (5) This activates specific genes, leading to the mRNA transcription and (6) synthesis of specific proteins. The proteins cause the response recognized as the hormone's action (7).

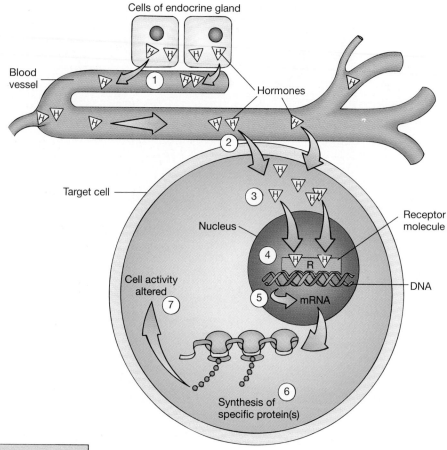

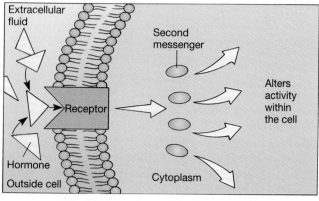

Figure 47–6 Peptide hormones combine with receptors on the plasma membrane of a target cell. The hormonal message is relayed by a second messenger.

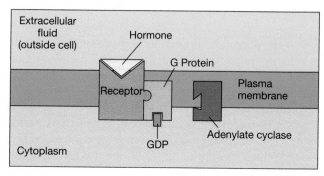

(a)

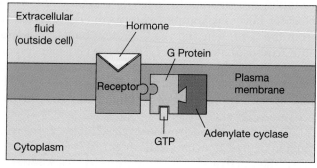

(b)

Figure 47–7 Role of the G protein. (a) A hormone binds to a receptor on the plasma membrane. The hormone-receptor complex binds to a G protein. (b) GDP on the G protein is replaced by GTP. G protein undergoes a conformational change (change in shape), allowing it to bind with adenylate cyclase. The adenylate cyclase is activated and catalyzes the conversion of ATP to cyclic AMP.

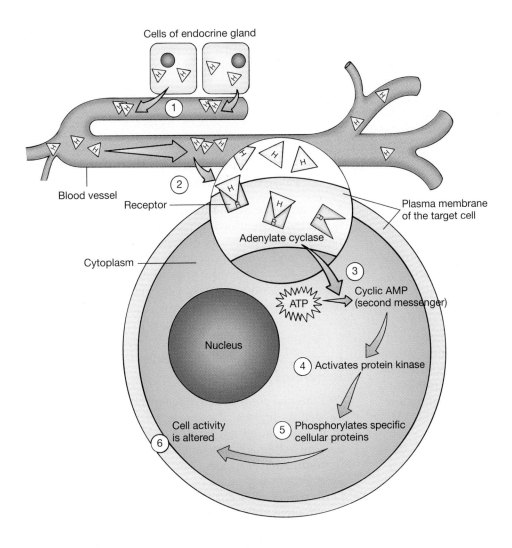

Figure 47–8 Overview of the second messenger mechanism of hormone action. After they are (*1*) secreted by an endocrine gland and transported by the blood to a target cell, peptide hormones (*2*) combine with receptors in the plasma membrane of a target cell. (*3*) The hormone-receptor combination activates an enzyme, adenylate cyclase, located on the inner surface of the membrane. The adenylate cyclase catalyzes the conversion of ATP to cyclic AMP, a second messenger. (*4*) Cyclic AMP then activates one or more protein kinases, which (*5*) phosphorylate specific proteins. (*6*) The activity of the cell is altered.

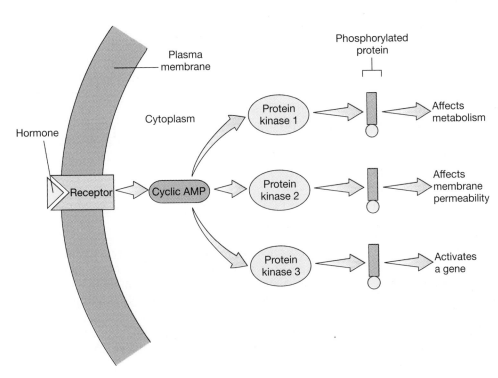

Figure 47–9 When a hormone binds to a receptor on the cell surface and increases the amount of cyclic AMP in the cell, protein kinases are activated. Protein kinases phosphorylate proteins, leading to a variety of effects.

by releasing calcium stored in the smooth endoplasmic reticulum (ER). Once the calcium concentration in the cell is increased, calcium ions bind to the protein **calmodulin.** The calcium-calmodulin complex can then activate certain enzymes. Some cellular processes regulated by this complex include membrane phosphorylation, neurotransmitter release, and microtubule disassembly.

Prostaglandins Are Local Chemical Mediators

Prostaglandins are released by many different tissues, including the prostate gland, lungs, liver, and digestive tract. Although present in very small quantities, prostaglandins exert a wide range of physiological, hormone-like actions on many tissues and body processes. They are often referred to as **local hormones** because they act on cells in their immediate vicinity.

Prostaglandins interact with other hormones to regulate various metabolic activities. Prostaglandins mimic many of the actions of cyclic AMP. Depending upon the specific tissue type, they stimulate or inhibit formation of cyclic AMP. In this way, prostaglandins can modulate cellular response to hormones that use cyclic AMP as a second messenger.

Prostaglandins are classified in several groups, designated PGA, PGB, and so on through PGI on the basis of their chemical structure. A subscript number is used to identify the number of double bonds in their side chains; thus, PGE_1, for example, has one double bond, whereas PGF_2 has two double bonds.

Various prostaglandins have different actions on different tissues. Members of the A and E groups tend to reduce blood pressure; those of the F group raise it. Some prostaglandins cause capillary constriction; others dilate capillaries. Some stimulate smooth muscle to contract, whereas others cause muscle to relax. Various prostaglandins dilate the bronchial passageways, inhibit gastric secretion, increase intestinal motility, stimulate contraction of the uterus, regulate metabolism, affect nerve function, cause inflammation, and affect blood clotting. Those synthesized in the temperature-regulating center of the hypothalamus cause fever. In fact, the ability of aspirin and acetaminophen to reduce fever and decrease pain (long a mystery) depends upon inhibiting prostaglandin synthesis.

Because prostaglandins are involved in the regulation of so many metabolic processes, they have great potential for a variety of clinical uses. At present prostaglandins are used to induce labor in pregnant women, to induce abortion, and to promote healing of ulcers in the stomach and duodenum. Their use as a birth-control drug is being investigated. Some investigators think that these substances may someday be used to treat such illnesses as asthma, arthritis, kidney disease, certain cardiovascular disorders, nasal congestion, and even cancer.

INVERTEBRATE HORMONES REGULATE GROWTH, METABOLISM, REPRODUCTION, MOLTING, AND PIGMENTATION

Most invertebrate hormones are secreted by neurons rather than by endocrine glands. These neurohormones regulate such processes as regeneration in *Hydra*, flatworms, and annelids; molting and metamorphosis in insects; color changes in crustaceans; and gamete production, reproductive behavior, and metabolic rate in many groups.

Color Change in Crustaceans Is Regulated by Hormones

Crustaceans possess true (nonneural) endocrine glands, as well as masses of neurosecretory cells. Their hormonal regulation is complex and affects many activities, including molting, migration of retinal pigment, reproduction, heart rate, and metabolism. One of the most interesting—and novel—activities regulated by hormones is color change.

Pigment cells of crustaceans are located in the integument beneath the exoskeleton. Pigment may be black, yellow, red, white, or even blue. Color changes are produced by changes in the distribution of pigment granules within the cells. Distribution of pigment is regulated by hormones produced by neurosecretory cells. When the pigment is concentrated near the center of a cell, its color is only minimally visible; but when it is dispersed throughout the cell, the color shows to advantage. These pigments provide protective coloration. By appropriate condensation or dispersal of specific types of pigments, a crustacean can approximate the color of its background.

Insect Development Is Regulated by Hormones

Like crustaceans, insects have endocrine glands as well as neurosecretory cells. The various hormones interact with one another to regulate reproduction, metabolism, growth, and development, including molting and morphogenesis.

Hormonal control of development in insects is complex and varies among the many species. Generally,

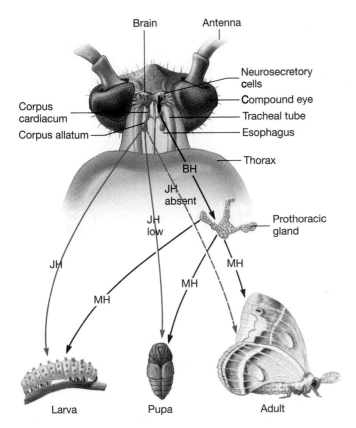

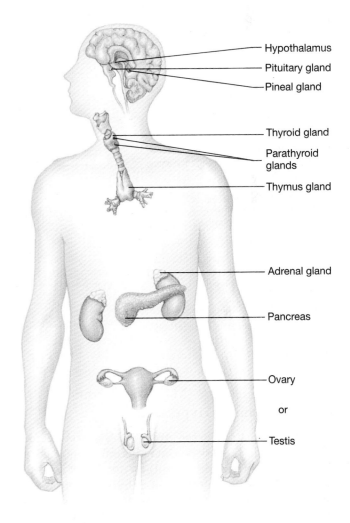

comes an adult. The secretory activity of the corpora allata is regulated by the nervous system, and the amount of juvenile hormone decreases with successive molts.

VERTEBRATE HORMONES REGULATE GROWTH, METABOLISM, AND REPRODUCTION

In vertebrates, hormones regulate such diverse activities as growth, metabolic rate, utilization of nutrients by cells, and reproduction. They are largely responsible for regulating fluid balance and blood homeostasis, and they help the body to cope with stress. The principal human endocrine glands are illustrated in Figure 47–11. Most vertebrates possess similar endocrine glands. Table 47–1 gives the physiological actions and sources of some of the major vertebrate hormones.

Figure 47–10 The neural and endocrine control of growth and molting in a moth. Neurosecretory cells in the brain secrete a hormone, BH, which stimulates the prothoracic glands to secrete molting hormone (MH). In the immature insect, the corpora allata secrete juvenile hormone (JH), which suppresses metamorphosis at each larval molt. Metamorphosis to the adult form occurs when molting hormone acts in the absence of juvenile hormone.

some environmental factor (e.g., temperature change) affects neurosecretory cells in the brain. Once activated, these cells produce a hormone referred to as **brain hormone (BH)** (or ecdysiotropin), which is transported down axons and stored in the paired **corpora cardiaca** (Figure 47–10). When released from the corpora cardiaca, BH stimulates the **prothoracic glands,** endocrine glands in the prothorax, to produce **molting hormone,** also called **ecdysone.** Molting hormone stimulates growth and molting.

In the immature insect, paired endocrine glands called **corpora allata** secrete **juvenile hormone.** This hormone suppresses metamorphosis at each larval molt so that the insect increases in size but retains its immature state (Figure 47–10). After the molt, the insect is still in a larval stage. When the concentration of juvenile hormone decreases, metamorphosis occurs, and the insect is transformed into a pupa (see Chapter 30). In the absence of juvenile hormone, the pupa molts and be-

Figure 47–11 Location of the principal endocrine glands in the human male and female.

Table 47-1 SOME ENDOCRINE GLANDS AND THEIR HORMONES*

Endocrine Gland and Hormone	Target Tissue	Principal Actions
Hypothalamus		
Releasing and release-inhibiting hormones	Anterior lobe of pituitary	Stimulates or inhibits secretion of specific hormones
Hypothalamus (production) *Posterior lobe of pituitary* (storage and release)		
Oxytocin	Uterus	Stimulates contraction
	Mammary glands	Stimulates ejection of milk into ducts
Antidiuretic hormone (vasopressin)	Kidneys (collecting ducts)	Stimulates reabsorption of water; conserves water
Anterior lobe of pituitary		
Growth hormone (GH)	General	Stimulates growth by promoting protein synthesis
Prolactin	Mammary glands	Stimulates milk production
Thyroid-stimulating hormone (TSH)	Thyroid gland	Stimulates secretion of thyroid hormones; stimulates increase in size of thyroid gland
Adrenocorticotropic hormone (ACTH)	Adrenal cortex	Stimulates secretion of adrenal cortical hormones
Gonadotropic hormones (follicle-stimulating hormone, FSH; luteinizing hormone, LH)	Gonads	Stimulate gonad function and growth
Thyroid gland		
Thyroxine (T_4) and tri-iodothyronine (T_3)	General	Stimulate metabolic rate; essential to normal growth and development
Calcitonin	Bone	Lowers blood-calcium level by inhibiting bone breakdown by osteoclasts
Parathyroid glands		
Parathyroid hormone	Bone, kidneys, digestive tract	Increases blood-calcium level by stimulating bone breakdown; stimulates calcium reabsorption by kidneys; activates vitamin D

*The gonadotropic hormones (FSH and LH) and the ovaries and testes and their hormones are discussed in Chapter 48. The digestive hormones are described in Chapter 45.

†For more detailed description see Table 48-2.

‡For more detailed description see Table 48-1.

Endocrine Disorders May Result from Hyposecretion or Hypersecretion

When a disorder or disease process affects an endocrine gland, the rate of secretion may become abnormal. If **hyposecretion** (reduced output) occurs, target cells are deprived of needed stimulation. If **hypersecretion** (abnormal increase in output) occurs, the target cells may be overstimulated. In some endocrine disorders, an appropriate amount of hormone is secreted, but target cells lack receptors (or the receptors may not function properly), so that the cell may not be able to take up the

hormone. Any of these abnormalities leads to predictable metabolic malfunctions and clinical symptoms (Table 47-2).

Nervous System and Endocrine Regulation Are Integrated by the Hypothalamus

Hormonal activity is controlled directly or indirectly by the hypothalamus, which links the nervous and endocrine systems. In response to input from other areas of the brain and from hormones in the blood, neurons of

Endocrine Gland and Hormone	Target Tissue	Principal Actions
Islets of Langerhans of pancreas		
Insulin	General	Lowers glucose concentration in the blood by facilitating glucose uptake and utilization by cells; stimulates glycogenesis; stimulates fat storage and protein synthesis
Glucagon	Liver, adipose tissue	Raises glucose concentration in the blood by stimulating glycogenolysis and gluconeogenesis; mobilizes fat
Adrenal medulla		
Epinephrine and norepinephrine	Muscle, cardiac muscle, blood vessels, liver, adipose tissue	Help body cope with stress; increase heart rate, blood pressure, metabolic rate; reroute blood; mobilize fat; raise blood-sugar level
Adrenal cortex		
Mineralocorticoids (aldosterone)	Kidney tubules	Maintain sodium and phosphate balance
Glucocorticoids (cortisol)	General	Help body adapt to long-term stress; raise blood-glucose level; mobilize fat
Pineal gland		
Melatonin	Gonads, pigment cells, other tissues(?)	Influences reproductive processes in hamsters and other animals; pigmentation in some vertebrates; may control biorhythms in some animals; may help control onset of puberty in humans
Ovary†		
Estrogens (Estradiol)	General; uterus	Develop and maintain sex characteristics in female; stimulate growth of uterine lining
Progesterone	Uterus; breast	Stimulates development of uterine lining
Testis‡		
Testosterone	General; reproductive structures	Develops and maintains sex characteristics of males; promotes spermatogenesis; responsible for adolescent growth spurt
Inhibin	Anterior lobe of pituitary	Inhibits FSH release

the hypothalamus secrete hormones that regulate the release of hormones from the pituitary gland.

Because its secretions control the activities of several other endocrine glands, the **pituitary gland** is often referred to as the master gland of the body. Truly a biological marvel, the pituitary gland is only the size of a large pea and weighs only about 0.5 gram (0.02 ounce), yet it secretes at least nine distinct hormones that exert far-reaching influence over body activities. Connected to the hypothalamus by a stalk of nervous tissue, the pituitary gland consists of two main lobes, the anterior and posterior lobes. In some animals an intermediate lobe secretes hormones that regulate skin color.

The hypothalamus secretes several **releasing** and **release-inhibiting hormones** that regulate the anterior lobe of the pituitary gland. These neurohormones enter capillaries and pass through special portal veins that connect the hypothalamus with the anterior lobe of the pituitary (Figure 47–12). (These portal veins, like the hepatic portal vein, do not deliver blood to a larger vein directly but connect two sets of capillaries.) Within the anterior lobe of the pituitary, the portal veins divide into a second set of capillaries. The hormones pass through the walls of these capillaries into the tissue of the anterior lobe, where they regulate production and secretion of pituitary hormones.

Table 47–2 CONSEQUENCES OF ENDOCRINE MALFUNCTION

Hormone	Hyposecretion	Hypersecretion
Growth hormone	Pituitary dwarfism	Gigantism if malfunction occurs in childhood; acromegaly in adult
Thyroid hormones	Cretinism (in children); myxedema, a condition of pronounced adult hypothyroidism (metabolic rate is reduced by about 40%; patient feels tired all of the time and may be mentally slow); goiter, enlargement of the thyroid gland (see figure)	Hyperthyroidism; increased metabolic rate, nervousness, irritability
Parathyroid hormone	Spontaneous discharge of nerves; spasms; tetany; death	Weak, brittle bones; kidney stones
Insulin	Diabetes mellitus	Hypoglycemia
Adrenocortical hormones	Addison's disease (body cannot synthesize sufficient glucose by gluconeogenesis; patient is unable to cope with stress; sodium loss in urine may lead to shock)	Cushing's disease (edema gives face a full-moon appearance; fat is deposited about trunk; blood glucose level rises; immune responses are depressed)

Goiter resulting from iodine deficiency. (John Paul Kay/Peter Arnold, Inc.)

The Posterior Lobe of the Pituitary Gland Releases Two Hormones

Two peptide hormones, **oxytocin** and **antidiuretic hormone (ADH;** discussed in Chapter 46), are secreted by the **posterior lobe** of the pituitary gland. These hormones are actually produced by specialized nerve cells in the hypothalamus. They reach the posterior lobe of the pituitary by flowing through axons that connect the hypothalamus with the posterior pituitary (Figure 47–13). Enclosed within tiny vesicles, the hormones pass slowly down the axons of these nerve cells. The axons extend through the pituitary stalk and into the posterior lobe. Hormone accumulates in the axon endings until the neuron is stimulated; then it is released and diffuses into surrounding capillaries.

The main target tissue of oxytocin is the female breast. After birth, when an infant sucks at its mother's breast, sensory neurons signal the hypothalamus to release oxytocin. The hormone stimulates contraction of muscle cells surrounding the milk glands so that milk is let down into the ducts and can be sucked by the infant. Psychological factors can influence oxytocin release. For example, the sound of a baby crying can stimulate oxytocin release in a nursing mother.

Oxytocin levels rise toward the end of pregnancy, stimulating the strong contractions of the uterus needed to expel the baby. Oxytocin is sometimes administered clinically (under the name Pitocin) to initiate or speed labor. Because oxytocin also stimulates the uterus to contract, breast feeding promotes rapid recovery of the uterus to nonpregnant size. Males have about the same amount of oxytocin circulating in their blood as nonpregnant females, but its function in them is unknown.

The Anterior Lobe of the Pituitary Gland Regulates Growth and Several Other Endocrine Glands

The **anterior lobe** of the pituitary secretes growth hormone, prolactin, and several **tropic hormones**—hormones that stimulate other endocrine glands (Figure 47–14). **Prolactin** is the hormone that stimulates the cells of the mammary glands to produce milk. Prolactin has no known function in males. Release of each of the anterior pituitary hormones is in some way regulated by a separate releasing hormone from the hypothalamus and sometimes also by a release-inhibiting hormone, also produced in the hypothalamus. When we speak of the pituitary as being stimulated or inhibited, it should be understood that certain receptors in the hypothalamus are generally affected first. They in turn control the pituitary.

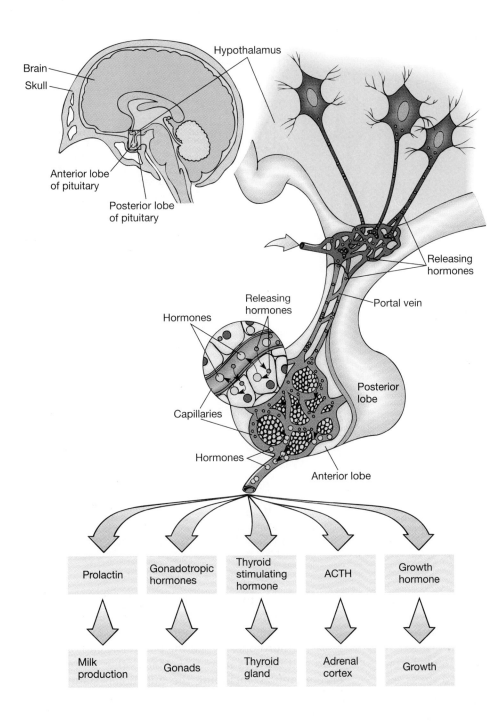

Brain
Skull
Hypothalamus
Anterior lobe of pituitary
Posterior lobe of pituitary

Releasing hormones
Portal vein

Releasing hormones
Hormones
Capillaries
Hormones

Posterior lobe
Anterior lobe

| Prolactin | Gonadotropic hormones | Thyroid stimulating hormone | ACTH | Growth hormone |

| Milk production | Gonads | Thyroid gland | Adrenal cortex | Growth |

Figure 47–12 The hypothalamus secretes several specific releasing and release-inhibiting hormones, which reach the anterior lobe of the pituitary gland by way of portal veins. Each releasing hormone stimulates the synthesis of a particular hormone by the cells of the anterior lobe.

Growth Hormone Stimulates Protein Synthesis

Almost everyone is fascinated by the process of growth. Small children measure themselves periodically against their parents, eagerly awaiting that time when they too will be "big." Whether one will be tall or short depends upon many factors, including genes, diet, hormonal balance, and even emotional nurturance.

Growth hormone (GH) (also called **somatotropin**) stimulates body growth mainly by increasing uptake of amino acids by the cells and by stimulating protein syn-

thesis. Because it prompts cells to build proteins, GH is referred to as an anabolic hormone.

Some of the effects of GH on growth of the skeleton are indirect. GH stimulates the liver to produce peptides called **somatomedins.** These growth factors (1) promote the linear growth of the skeleton by stimulating growth of cartilage in the epiphyseal plates and (2) stimulate general tissue growth and increase in size of organs; this results from stimulation of protein synthesis and other anabolic processes.

GH also affects fat and carbohydrate metabolism. It promotes mobilization of fat from adipose tissues, rais-

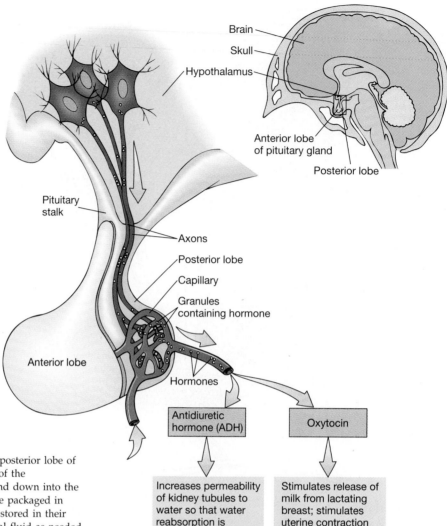

Figure 47–13 The hormones secreted by the posterior lobe of the pituitary are actually manufactured in cells of the hypothalamus. The axons of these neurons extend down into the posterior lobe of the pituitary. The hormones are packaged in granules that flow through these axons and are stored in their ends. The hormone is secreted into the interstitial fluid as needed and transported by the circulatory system.

ing the level of free fatty acids in the blood. In this protein-sparing operation, fatty acids become available for cells to use as fuel. How does this help to promote growth?

Fat mobilization by GH is also important during fasting or when a person is under prolonged stress, situations in which the blood sugar level is low. Can you explain why? Human GH also has several actions that result, directly or indirectly, in raising the blood sugar level.

Growth hormone secretion is regulated by the hypothalamus

In adults as well as in growing children, GH is secreted in pulses throughout the day. Secretion of GH is regulated by both a **growth hormone–releasing hormone (GHRH)** and a **growth hormone–inhibiting hormone (GHIH)** (also called **somatostatin**) released by the hypothalamus. A high level of GH in the blood signals the

hypothalamus to secrete the inhibiting hormone, and the pituitary release of GH slows. A low level of GH in the blood stimulates the hypothalamus to secrete the releasing hormone, so that the pituitary gland is stimulated and releases more GH. Many other factors influence secretion, including the nutritional status of the body and stress. GH secretion is increased by **hypoglycemia** (low blood sugar level) and by a decrease in amino acid concentration in the blood. GH secretion is inhibited by hyperglycemia (high blood sugar concentration), suggesting that a diet very high in carbohydrates may inhibit growth. Physical and emotional stress also stimulate GH secretion.

Remember your parents telling you to get plenty of sleep, eat properly, and exercise in order to grow? These age-old notions are supported by research. Secretion of GH does increase during exercise, probably because rapid metabolism by muscle cells lowers the blood sugar level. GH is also secreted in a series of pulses 2 to 4 hours after a meal. And GH secretion also occurs about 1 hour after the onset of deep sleep.

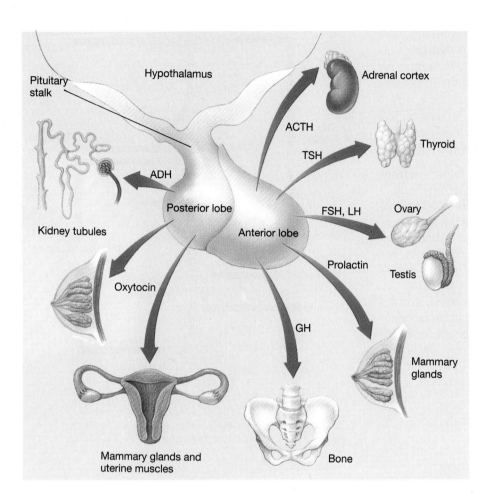

Figure 47–14 The pituitary gland is suspended from the hypothalamus by a stalk of neural tissue. Shown here are the hormones secreted by the anterior and posterior lobes of the pituitary gland and the target tissues they act upon.

Emotional support is also necessary for proper growth. Growth may be retarded in children who are deprived of cuddling, playing, and other forms of nurture, even when their physical needs (food and shelter) are amply met. In extreme cases, childhood stress can produce actual dwarfism (psychosocial dwarfism). Some emotionally deprived children exhibit abnormal sleep patterns, which may be the basis for decreased secretion of GH.

Other hormones also influence growth. Thyroid hormones appear to be necessary for normal GH secretion and function. Sex hormones must be present for the adolescent growth spurt to occur. However, the presence of sex hormones eventually causes the growth centers within the long bones to ossify, fusing the epiphyses to the diaphyses, so that further increase in height is impossible even when GH is present.

Inappropriate amounts of growth hormone secretion result in abnormal growth

Have you ever wondered why circus midgets failed to grow normally? They are probably **pituitary dwarfs,** that is, individuals whose pituitary gland did not produce sufficient GH during childhood. Although minia-

ture, a pituitary dwarf has normal intelligence and is usually well proportioned. If the growth centers in the long bones are still open when this condition is initially diagnosed, it can be treated clinically by injection with GH, which can now be synthesized commercially through the use of recombinant DNA technology.

Can you think of other mechanisms that might fail and result in growth problems? How about the regulating hormones from the hypothalamus? Or suppose GH is secreted normally but somatomedin is not released from the liver? A recent study showed that in a tribe of African pygmies, normal amounts of GH are secreted, but owing to a genetic variance, insufficient amounts of one of the somatomedins are produced. Other forms of dwarfism result from lack of responsiveness of target tissues.

Circus giants and other abnormally tall individuals develop when the anterior pituitary secretes excessive amounts of GH during childhood. This condition is referred to as **gigantism.**

If hypersecretion of GH (or somatomedin) occurs during adulthood, the individual cannot grow taller. However, a condition known as **acromegaly** (large extremities) results in which the bones, especially those in the hands, feet, and face, increase in diameter. Connective tissue also thickens, and body organs may increase in size. An early sign of this disorder may be the need for a wider shoe, or fingers so thickened that rings no longer fit. Another symptom of acromegaly is increase in the diameter of the mandible, causing the lower jaw to protrude.

Thyroid Hormones Stimulate Metabolic Rate

The **thyroid gland** is located in the neck region, in front of the trachea and below the larynx. Two of its hormones, **thyroxine,** also known as T_4, and triiodothyronine, or T_3, are synthesized from the amino acid tyrosine and from iodine. Thyroxine has four iodine atoms attached to each molecule; T_3 has three. Calcitonin, another hormone secreted by the thyroid gland, is discussed in conjunction with the parathyroid glands.

Thyroid hormones are essential for normal growth and development and stimulate the rate of metabolism in most body tissues. They are also necessary for cellular differentiation. Tadpoles cannot develop into adult frogs without thyroxine. This hormone appears to regulate selectively the synthesis of needed proteins.

Thyroid secretion is regulated by negative feedback mechanisms

The principal regulation of thyroid hormone secretion depends upon a negative feedback system between the anterior pituitary and the thyroid gland (Figure 47–15). When the concentration of thyroid hormone in the blood rises above normal, the anterior pituitary is inhibited.

> concentration of thyroid hormones increases - - - →
> inhibits anterior pituitary - - - → secretes less TSH - - - →
> thyroid gland secretes less hormone - - - → thyroid
> hormone concentration decreases

When the level falls, the pituitary secretes more **thyroid-stimulating hormone (TSH).** The TSH acts by way of cyclic AMP to promote synthesis and secretion of thyroid hormones and also to promote increased size of the gland itself.

> low concentration of thyroid hormones → stimulates
> anterior pituitary → secretes more TSH → stimulates
> thyroid gland → secretes more thyroid hormones →
> thyroid hormone concentration increases

Too much thyroid hormone in the blood also affects the hypothalamus, inhibiting secretion of TSH-releasing hormone. However, the hypothalamus is thought to exert its regulatory effects primarily in certain stressful situations, such as extreme weather change. Exposure to very cold weather may stimulate the hypothalamus to increase secretion of TSH-releasing hormone, thereby raising body temperature through increased metabolic heat production.

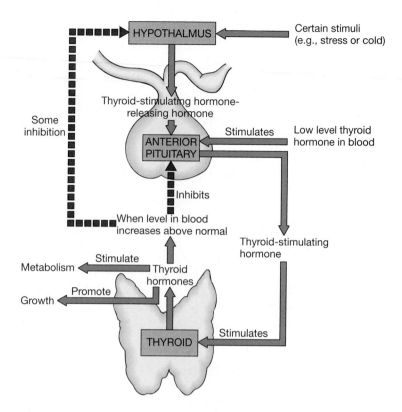

Figure 47–15 Regulation of thyroid hormone secretion. Green arrows indicate stimulation; red arrows indicate inhibition.

Malfunction of the thyroid gland leads to specific disorders

Extreme hypothyroidism during infancy and childhood results in low metabolic rate and can lead to **cretinism,** a condition of retarded mental and physical development. When diagnosed early enough and treated by administration of thyroid hormones, the effects of cretinism can be prevented.

An adult who feels like sleeping all the time, has little energy, and is mentally slow or confused may also be suffering from hypothyroidism. When there is almost no thyroid function, the basal metabolic rate is reduced by about 40% and the patient develops the condition called **myxedema,** characterized by a slowing down of physical and mental activity. Hypothyroidism can be treated by oral administration of the missing hormone.

Hyperthyroidism does not cause abnormal growth but can increase metabolic rate by 60% or even more. This increase in metabolism results in rapid use of nutrients, causing the individual to be hungry and to eat more. But this is not sufficient to meet the demands of the rapidly metabolizing cells, so individuals with this condition often lose weight. They also tend to be nervous, irritable, and emotionally unstable.

Any abnormal enlargement of the thyroid gland is termed a **goiter** and may be associated with either hyposecretion or hypersecretion (see Table 47–2). One cause is dietary iodine deficiency. Without iodine, the gland cannot make thyroid hormones, so their concentration in the blood decreases. In compensation, the anterior pituitary secretes large amounts of TSH. The thyroid gland enlarges, sometimes to gigantic proportions. However, enlargement of the gland cannot increase production of the hormones, because the needed ingredient is still missing. Thanks to iodized salt, goiter is no longer common in the United States. In other parts of the world, however, hundreds of thousands still suffer from this easily preventable disorder.

The Parathyroid Glands Regulate Calcium Concentration

The **parathyroid glands** are embedded in the connective tissue surrounding the thyroid gland. These glands secrete **parathyroid hormone,** which regulates the calcium level of the blood and tissue fluid. Parathyroid hormone stimulates release of calcium from bones and calcium reabsorption from the kidney tubules. It also activates vitamin D, which then increases the amount of calcium absorbed from the intestine.

Calcitonin, secreted by the thyroid gland, works antagonistically to parathyroid hormone. When the concentration of calcium rises above homeostatic levels, calcitonin is released and rapidly inhibits removal of calcium from bone.

The Islets of the Pancreas Regulate Glucose Concentration

Besides secreting digestive enzymes (see Chapter 45), the pancreas serves as an important endocrine gland. Its hormones, insulin and glucagon, are secreted by cells that form little clusters, or islets, dispersed throughout the pancreas. These islets, first described by the German histologist Paul Langerhans, are called the **islets of Langerhans** (Figure 47–16). About a million islets are present in the human pancreas. They are composed of **beta cells,** which secrete **insulin,** and **alpha cells,** which secrete **glucagon.**

Insulin lowers the concentration of glucose in the blood

Insulin stimulates cells, especially skeletal muscle and fat cells, to take up glucose from the blood. Once glucose enters muscle cells, it is either used immediately as fuel or stored as glycogen (the process called glycogenesis). Insulin activity results in *lowering* the glucose level in the blood. It also influences fat and protein metabolism. Insulin reduces the use of fatty acids as fuel and instead stimulates their storage in adipose tissue. In a similar manner, it inhibits the use of amino acids as fuel, thus promoting protein synthesis.

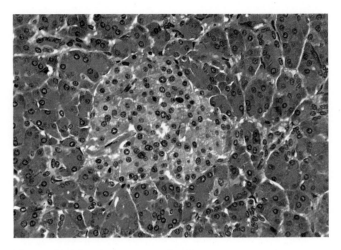

Figure 47–16 Photomicrograph of human pancreas showing an islet of Langerhans (light area in center). (Ed Reschke)

Glucagon raises the concentration of glucose in the blood

Glucagon acts antagonistically to insulin. Its principal effect is to *raise* blood sugar level. It does this by stimulating liver cells to convert glycogen to glucose (the process called glycogenolysis) and by stimulating liver cells to make glucose from other metabolites (gluconeogenesis). Note that these actions are opposite to those of insulin. Glucagon mobilizes fatty acids and amino acids as well as glucose for fuel. Glucagon is thought to be secreted also by certain cells in the wall of the stomach and duodenum.

Insulin and glucagon secretion is regulated by glucose concentration

Secretion of insulin and glucagon is directly controlled by the concentration of glucose in the blood (Figure–47–17). After a meal, when the blood glucose level rises, beta cells increase insulin secretion. Then, as the cells remove glucose from the blood, decreasing its concentration, insulin secretion decreases accordingly.

blood glucose level too high → stimulates beta cells → increased insulin secretion → blood glucose concentration decreases

When one has not eaten for several hours, the concentration of glucose in the blood begins to fall. When it falls from its normal fasting level of about 90 mg of glucose per 100 mL of blood to about 70 mg of glucose, the alpha cells of the islets secrete large amounts of glucagon. Glucose is mobilized from storage in the liver cells, and blood sugar concentration returns to normal.

glucose concentration too low → stimulates alpha cells → increased glucagon secretion → glucose concentration increases

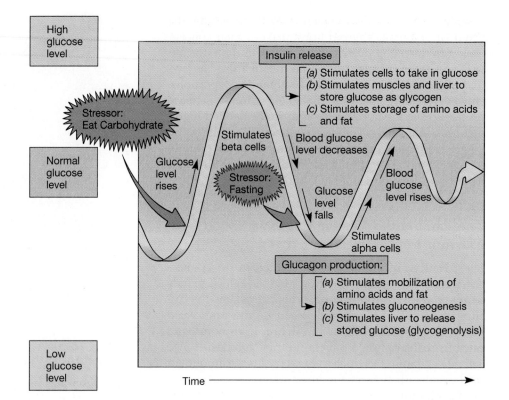

Figure 47–17 Regulation of concentration of glucose in the blood by insulin and glucagon.

The alpha cells respond to the glucose concentration within their own cytoplasm, which is a reflection of the blood sugar level. When blood sugar level is high, there is generally a high level of glucose within the alpha cells, and glucagon secretion is inhibited.

Insulin and glucagon function to maintain the blood sugar concentration within normal limits. When glucose level rises, insulin release brings it back to normal; when it falls, glucagon increases it again. The insulin-glucagon system is a powerful, fast-acting mechanism for keeping blood sugar level normal. Can you think of reasons why it is important to maintain a constant blood sugar level? Brain cells depend upon a continuous supply of glucose because they ordinarily are unable to use other nutrients as fuel. As we will discuss, several other hormones also affect blood sugar concentration.

Diabetes mellitus is a serious disorder of carbohydrate metabolism

The principal disorder associated with pancreatic hormones is **diabetes mellitus.** Of the estimated 10 million diabetics in the United States, about 40,000 die each year as a result of this disorder, making it the third most common medical cause of death. Diabetes is a leading cause of blindness, kidney disorders, disease of small blood vessels, gangrene of the limbs, and various other malfunctions.

More than 90% of diabetes mellitus cases are non–insulin-dependent, often referred to as Type II. (This type was formerly known as maturity-onset diabetes.) Type II diabetes develops gradually, usually in overweight persons over age 30. In many patients with Type II diabetes, the pancreatic islets secrete enough insulin, but receptors on target cells cannot bind it (insulin resistance).

Insulin-dependent diabetes, referred to as Type I (and formerly known as juvenile-onset diabetes), often develops during adolescence. In Type I diabetes there is a marked decrease in the number of beta cells in the pancreas, resulting in insulin deficiency. Daily insulin injections are needed to correct the carbohydrate imbalance that results. Type I diabetes is thought to be an autoimmune disease in which antibodies mark the beta cells for destruction. This disorder may be caused by a combination of genetic predisposition and possibly a virus. Patients with diabetes have a shortened life expectancy because atherosclerotic disease develops as a result of impaired lipid metabolism.

Similar metabolic disturbances occur in both types of diabetes mellitus:

1. Decreased Use of Glucose. In diabetics, cells dependent on and lacking insulin can take in only about 25% of the glucose they require for fuel. Glucose accumulates in the blood, causing **hyperglycemia** (an abnormally high concentration of glucose in the blood).

Instead of the normal fasting level of 90 mg per 100 mL, the level may reach from 300 to more than 1000 mg.

The concentration of glucose is so high in the untreated diabetic that it exceeds the renal threshold: The tubules in the kidneys are unable to return all the glucose in the filtrate to the blood. As a result, glucose is excreted in the urine. The presence of glucose in the urine is a simple screening test for diabetes.

2. Increased Fat Mobilization. Despite the large quantities of glucose in the blood, most cells cannot use it and must turn to other sources of fuel. The absence of insulin promotes the mobilization of fat stores, providing nutrients for cellular respiration. But unfortunately, the blood lipid level may reach five times the normal level, leading to development of atherosclerosis. Also, the increased fat metabolism increases the formation of ketone bodies. These build up in the blood, causing **ketosis,** a condition in which the body fluids and blood become too acidic. If severe, ketosis can lead to coma and death. When the ketone level in the blood rises, ketones appear in the urine, another clinical indication of diabetes. Because of osmotic pressure, when ketone bodies and glucose are excreted in the urine, they take water with them, so that urine volume increases. The resulting dehydration causes the diabetic to feel continually thirsty.

3. Increased Protein Use. Lack of insulin also results in increased protein breakdown relative to protein synthesis, so the untreated diabetic becomes thin and emaciated.

In hypoglycemia the glucose concentration is too low

Hypoglycemia, low blood glucose concentration, is sometimes seen in people who later develop diabetes. It may be an overreaction by the islets to glucose challenge. Too much insulin is secreted in response to carbohydrate ingestion. About 3 hours after a meal the blood sugar concentration falls below normal, making the individual feel very drowsy. If this reaction is severe enough, the patient may become uncoordinated or even unconscious.

Serious hypoglycemia can develop if diabetics receive injections of too much insulin or if the islets, because of a tumor, secrete too much insulin. The blood sugar concentration may then fall drastically, depriving the brain cells of their needed supply of fuel. **Insulin shock** may result, a condition in which the patient may appear to be drunk or may become unconscious, suffer convulsions, or even die.

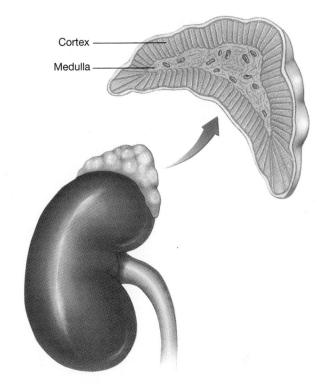

Figure 47–18   The adrenal gland.

The Adrenal Glands Help the Body Adapt to Stress

The paired **adrenal glands** are small, yellow masses of tissue that lie in contact with the upper ends of the kidneys. Each gland consists of a central portion, the **adrenal medulla,** and a larger outer section, the **adrenal cortex** (Figure 47–18). Although joined anatomically, the adrenal medulla and cortex develop from different types of tissue in the embryo and function as distinct glands. Both secrete hormones that help to regulate metabolism, and both help the body deal with stress.

The adrenal medulla initiates an alarm reaction

The adrenal medulla develops from neural tissue, and its secretion is controlled by sympathetic nerves. Two hormones, **epinephrine** (sometimes called adrenaline) and **norepinephrine** (noradrenaline), are secreted by the adrenal medulla. Chemically, these hormones are very similar; they belong to the chemical group known as **catecholamines** (derived from amino acids). Norepinephrine is the same substance secreted as a neurotransmitter by sympathetic neurons and by some neurons in the central nervous system. Its effects on the body are similar but last about ten times longer because the hormone is removed from the blood slowly. About

80% of the hormone output of the adrenal medulla is epinephrine.

Often referred to as the emergency gland of the body, the adrenal medulla prepares us physiologically to deal with threatening situations. During an emergency situation, hormone secretion from this gland initiates an alarm reaction, enabling one to think more quickly, fight harder, or run faster than usual. Metabolic rate increases as much as 100%.

The adrenal medulla hormones cause blood to be rerouted to those organs essential for emergency action. Blood vessels going to the brain, muscles, and heart are dilated, whereas those to the skin and kidneys are constricted. Constriction of blood vessels serving the skin has the added advantage of decreasing blood loss in case of hemorrhage (and explains the sudden paling that comes with fear or rage). At the same time, the heart beats faster and thresholds in the reticular activating system of the brain are lowered, so one becomes more alert. Strength of muscle contraction increases. The adrenal medullary hormones also raise fatty acid and glucose levels in the blood, ensuring needed fuel for extra energy.

Under normal conditions, both epinephrine and norepinephrine are secreted continuously in small amounts. Their secretion is under nervous control. When anxiety is aroused, messages are sent from the brain through sympathetic nerves to the adrenal medulla. Acetylcholine released by these neurons triggers release of epinephrine and norepinephrine.

The adrenal cortex helps the body deal with chronic stress

All the hormones of the **adrenal cortex** are steroids synthesized from cholesterol. Although more than 30 types of steroids have been isolated from the adrenal cortex, this gland produces only three types of hormones in significant amounts: (1) androgen, (2) mineralocorticoids, and (3) glucocorticoids.

An androgen (a hormone that has a masculinizing effect) known as DHEA (dehydroepiandrosterone) is secreted by the adrenal cortex in both sexes. In the tissues it is converted to testosterone, a more powerful androgen and the principal male sex hormone. In males, androgen production by the adrenal cortex is not significant because much more androgen is produced by the testes. However, in females, the androgen produced by the adrenal cortex accounts for most of that circulating in the blood.

The principal **mineralocorticoid** is **aldosterone.** Recall from Chapter 46 that this hormone helps regulate fluid balance by regulating salt balance. In response to aldosterone, the kidneys reabsorb more sodium and excrete more potassium. As a result of increased sodium, extracellular fluid volume increases, which results in greater blood volume and raises blood pressure.

When the adrenal glands do not produce enough aldosterone, large amounts of sodium are excreted in the urine. Water leaves the body with the sodium (because of osmotic pressure), and the blood volume may be so markedly reduced that the patient dies of low blood pressure.

Cortisol, also called hydrocortisone, accounts for about 95% of the **glucocorticoid** activity of the adrenal cortex. Cortisol helps ensure adequate fuel supplies for the cells when the body is under stress. Its principal action is to stimulate liver cells to produce glucose from other nutrients (gluconeogenesis). Cortisol helps provide nutrients for glucose production by stimulating transport of amino acids into liver cells (Figure 47–19). It also promotes mobilization of fats so that fatty acids are available for conversion to glucose. These actions ensure that glucose and glycogen are produced in the liver, and the concentration of glucose in the blood rises. Thus, the adrenal cortex provides an important backup system for the adrenal medulla, ensuring glucose supplies when the body is under stress and in need of extra energy (see Making the Connection: Coping with Stress).

Glucocorticoids are used clinically to reduce inflammation in allergic reactions, infections, arthritis, and certain types of cancer. These hormones help stabilize lysosome membranes so that they do not destroy tissues with their potent enzymes. Glucocorticoids also reduce inflammation by decreasing the permeability of capillary membranes, thereby reducing swelling. They reduce the effects of histamine and so are used to treat allergic symptoms.

When used in large amounts over long periods of time, glucocorticoids can cause serious side effects. They decrease the number of lymphocytes in the body, reducing the patient's ability to fight infections. Other side effects include ulcers, hypertension, diabetes mellitus, and atherosclerosis.

Almost any type of stress stimulates the hypothalamus to secrete **corticotropin-releasing factor, CRF.** This hormone stimulates the anterior pituitary to secrete **adrenocorticotropic hormone, ACTH.** ACTH regulates glucocorticoid secretion (as well as aldosterone secretion). ACTH is so potent that it can result in up to a 20-fold increase in cortisol secretion within minutes. When the body is not under stress, high levels of cortisol in the blood inhibit both CRF secretion by the hypothalamus and ACTH secretion by the pituitary.

Abnormally large amounts of glucocorticoids, whether due to disease or drugs, result in **Cushing's disease.** In this condition, fat is mobilized from the lower part of the body and deposited about the trunk. Edema gives the patient's face a full-moon appearance. Blood sugar level rises to as much as 50% above normal, causing adrenal diabetes. If this condition persists for several months, the beta cells in the pancreas can "burn out" from secreting excessive amounts of insulin. This

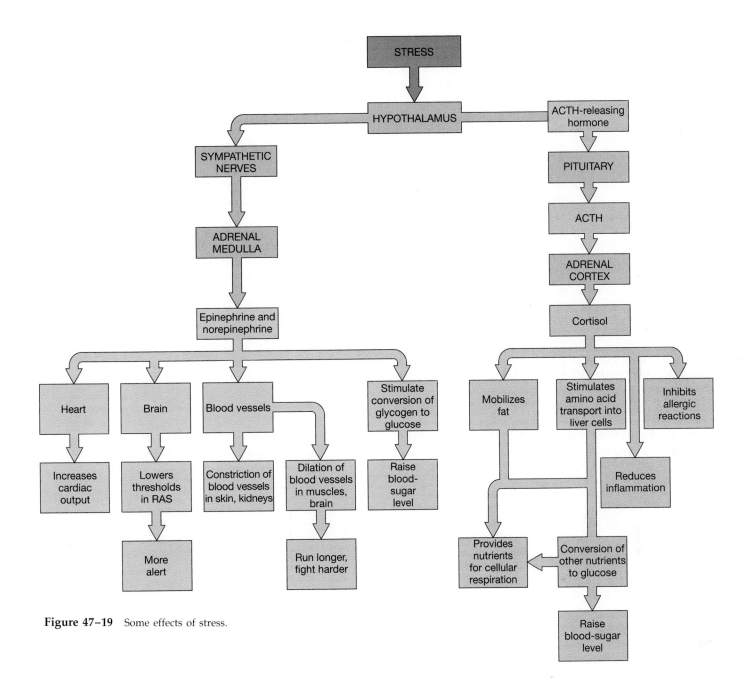

Figure 47–19 Some effects of stress.

can result in permanent diabetes mellitus. Reduction in protein synthesis causes weakness and decreases immune responses, so the patient often dies of infection.

Destruction of the adrenal cortex and the resulting decrease in aldosterone and cortisol secretion cause **Addison's disease.** Reduction in cortisol prevents the body from regulating the concentration of glucose in the blood because it cannot synthesize enough glucose. The cortisol-deficient patient also loses the ability to cope with stress. If cortisol levels are significantly depressed, even the stress of mild infections can cause death.

Many Other Hormones Are Known

Many other tissues of the body secrete hormones. Several hormones secreted by the digestive tract regulate digestive processes. The **thymus gland** produces a hormone (thymosin) that plays a role in immune responses, and the kidneys release hormones, one of which (renin) helps regulate blood pressure. Atrial natriuretic factor (ANF), secreted by the heart, promotes sodium excretion and lowers blood pressure. ANF acts, in part, by inhibiting aldosterone and renin release. The **pineal gland,** located in the brain, produces a hormone called **melatonin,** which influences the onset of sexual maturity. In Chapter 48 we discuss the principal reproductive hormones.

MAKING THE CONNECTION

Coping with Stress

Stressors, whether in the form of noise, infection, or even the anxiety of taking a test for which one is not fully prepared, arouse the body to action. The brain and the adrenal glands work together to help the body cope effectively. Information is transferred by nerves and hormones to many tissues and organs of the body. Neural messages from the brain stimulate the adrenal medulla to release catecholamines (epinephrine and norepinephrine) that prepare the body for fight or flight. Circulating catecholamines produced by the adrenal medulla affect the same target tissues affected by postganglionic sympathetic neurons (see Chapter 40). The hypothalamus also secretes corticotropin-releasing hormone, which signals the anterior pituitary to secrete ACTH. The release of ACTH increases cortisol secretion. Cortisol adjusts metabolism to meet the increased demands of the stressful situation (see Figure 47–19).

Some forms of stress are short-lived. We react to the situation and quickly resolve it. Other stressors may last for days, weeks, or even years—a chronic disease, for example, or an unhappy marriage or job situation. General anxiety and tension are examples of nonspecific stress.

Chronic stress is harmful because of the side effects of long-term elevated levels of glucocorticoids such as cortisol. Although glucocorticoids help reduce inflammation, they also interfere with normal immune responses. These hormones raise blood pressure, which may contribute to heart disease. They increase levels of fat in the blood, which may promote atherosclerosis. When animals receive injections of large amounts of glucocorticoids, such disease states are induced, and similar effects are seen when large doses are administered clinically to human patients. Among the diseases linked to excessive amounts of adrenocortical hormones are ulcers, high blood pressure, atherosclerosis, and arthritis.

Chronic stress has also been shown to damage the brain. Studies indicate that when rodents and monkeys are subjected to prolonged stress, the elevation of glucocorticoids leads to degeneration of neurons, especially in the hippocampus (a part of the brain involved in learning and remembering). Elevated concentration of glucocorticoids also impairs the capacity of neurons in the hippocampus to withstand physiological insult such as reduced blood flow or oxygen to the brain.

Individuals approach stressful situations in their lives differently. A stressor that may result in chronic, damaging levels of glucocorticoids in one person may be coped with more effectively by another. One strategy for reducing psychological and physiological response to stressors is to learn relaxation techniques. A variety of techniques are effective, including meditation, visual imagery, progressive muscle relaxation, and self-hypnosis. Practicing a relaxation technique can result in decreased activity of the sympathetic nervous system and reduced response to norepinephrine. For example, relaxation training has been shown to lower blood pressure in hypertensive patients, decrease the frequency of migraine headaches, and reduce chronic pain.

SUMMARY

I. The endocrine system consists of endocrine glands and tissues that secrete hormones; this system helps regulate many aspects of metabolism, growth, and reproduction. Hormones are transported to their target tissues via the blood.

II. Hormones are steroids; amino acid derivatives; peptides or proteins; or fatty acid derivatives.

III. Hormone secretion is regulated by negative feedback control mechanisms.

IV. Hormones combine with receptor proteins of target cells.

A. Some hormones combine with receptors on the plasma membrane of their target cells and act by way of a second messenger, such as cyclic AMP or calcium.

B. Steroid hormones combine with receptor proteins within the target cell; the hormone-receptor complex may stimulate a particular gene to initiate protein synthesis.

C. Prostaglandins may help regulate hormone action by regulating cyclic AMP formation.

V. Many invertebrate hormones are secreted by neurons rather than by endocrine glands. They help to regulate regeneration, molting, metamorphosis, reproduction, and metabolism.

A. Distribution of pigment in crustaceans is regulated by hormones secreted by neurosecretory cells.

B. Hormones control development in insects.

1. When stimulated by some environmental factor, neurosecretory cells in the insect brain secrete brain hormone (BH).

2. BH stimulates the prothoracic glands to produce molting hormone (ecdysone), which stimulates growth and molting.

3. In the immature insect, the corpora allata secrete juvenile hormone, which suppresses metamorphosis at each larval molt. The amount of juvenile hormone decreases with successive molts.

VI. In vertebrates, hormones help regulate growth, reproduction, salt and fluid balance, and many aspects of metabolism.

VII. Nervous and endocrine system regulation is integrated in the hypothalamus, which regulates the activity of the pituitary gland.
 A. The hormones oxytocin and ADH are produced by the hypothalamus and released by the posterior lobe of the pituitary.
 B. Secretion of anterior pituitary hormones is regulated by releasing and release-inhibiting hormones secreted by the hypothalamus.
 C. The anterior pituitary secretes growth hormone, prolactin, and several tropic hormones.
  1. Growth hormone (GH) stimulates body growth by promoting protein synthesis.
  2. Malfunctions in GH secretion can lead to pituitary dwarfism, gigantism, and acromegaly.

VIII. Thyroid hormones stimulate the rate of metabolism.
 A. Regulation of thyroid secretion depends mainly upon a feedback system between the anterior pituitary and the thyroid gland.
 B. Hyposecretion of thyroxine during childhood may lead to cretinism; during adulthood it may result in myxedema. Goiter is associated with hyposecretion or hypersecretion.

IX. The parathyroid glands regulate the calcium level in the blood.

X. The islets of the pancreas secrete insulin and glucagon.
 A. Insulin stimulates cells to take up glucose from the blood and so lowers blood sugar concentration.
 B. Glucagon raises blood glucose concentration by stimulating conversion of glycogen to glucose and production of glucose from other nutrients.
 C. Insulin and glucagon secretion are regulated directly by blood glucose levels.
 D. In diabetes mellitus, insulin deficiency or insulin resistance results in decreased utilization of glucose, increased fat mobilization, and increased protein utilization.

XI. The adrenal glands secrete hormones that help the body cope with stress.
 A. The adrenal medulla, sometimes referred to as the "emergency gland," secretes epinephrine and norepinephrine.
 B. The adrenal cortex secretes sex hormones; mineralocorticoids, such as aldosterone, which increases the rate of sodium reabsorption and potassium excretion by the kidneys; and glucocorticoids, such as cortisol, which promotes gluconeogenesis.
 C. The hormones of the adrenal medulla help the body respond to stress by increasing heart rate, metabolic rate, and strength of muscle contraction and by causing blood to be rerouted to those organs needed for fight or flight. The adrenal cortex acts as a backup system, ensuring adequate fuel supplies for the rapidly metabolizing cells.

POST-TEST

1. Endocrine glands lack _____; they release their secretions into the surrounding tissue fluid and they are transported by the _____.
2. Endocrine glands produce chemical messengers called _____.
3. A second messenger important in the action of many hormones is cyclic _____.
4. The _____ serves as a link between the nervous and endocrine systems.
5. Hormones bind to specific receptor proteins in cells of their _____ tissues.

Select the most appropriate term in column B for each description in column A.

Column A	*Column B*
6. Located in neck region	a. Anterior lobe of pituitary
7. Secrete insulin	b. Adrenal medulla
8. Sometimes called "emergency gland"	c. Thyroid
9. Regulates other endocrine glands via tropic hormones	d. Islets of pancreas
10. Secretes glucocorticoids	e. None of the above

Column A	*Column B*
11. Stimulates rate of metabolism	a. Thyroid hormones
12. Stimulates release of calcium from bone	b. Glucagon
13. Helps maintain sodium balance	c. Aldosterone
14. Raises blood sugar level	d. Epinephrine
15. Causes heart to beat faster and blood to be rerouted	e. None of the above

16. Cretinism is caused by (hypo or hyper) _____ secretion of _____ during childhood.
17. An abnormal enlargement of the thyroid gland is a _____.
18. The principal action of _____ is to promote production of glucose from other nutrients.

19. Calcitonin is secreted by the _____ gland.
20. In untreated _____, glucose utilization is decreased and ketosis occurs.

REVIEW QUESTIONS

1. What is a hormone? What are some of the important functions of hormones?
2. How are hormones transported? How do they "recognize" their target tissues? What is the role of cyclic AMP in hormone action?
3. How do steroid hormones influence the activity of cells?
4. Why is the hypothalamus considered the link between the nervous and the endocrine systems? Explain.
5. Describe the actions of (1) prolactin, (2) oxytocin, (3) thyroid-stimulating hormone.
6. Draw a diagram to illustrate the regulation of thyroid hormone secretion by the anterior pituitary gland.
7. Explain the hormonal basis for (1) acromegaly, (2) pituitary dwarfism, (3) cretinism, (4) hypoglycemia, (5) Cushing's disease.
8. Explain the antagonistic actions of insulin and glucagon in regulating blood glucose level. What other hormones studied in this chapter affect blood glucose level?
9. Describe several physiological disturbances that result from diabetes mellitus.
10. What are the actions of epinephrine and norepinephrine?
11. How is the adrenal medulla regulated?
12. What three types of hormones are released by the adrenal cortex, and what are the actions of each type?
13. Explain how the adrenal glands help the body deal with stress.
14. What are prostaglandins? What are their functions?

RECOMMENDED READINGS

Cantin, M., and J. Genest. The heart as an endocrine gland. *Scientific American*, 225(5):76–81, 1986. A hormone that helps regulate blood pressure and volume is secreted by the atria.

Lienhard, G. E., J. Slot, D. E. James, and M. M. Mueckler. How cells absorb glucose. *Scientific American*, 266(1):86–91, 1992. A discussion of recent findings on how insulin helps cells transport glucose.

Uvnas-Moberg, K. The gastrointestinal tract in growth and reproduction. *Scientific American*, 261(1):78–83, 1989. The digestive tract secretes hormones that affect not only digestion but also metabolism of ingested nutrients, growth, and behavior.

Reproduction

OUTLINE

The survival of each species requires that its members produce new individuals to replace those that die. At the molecular level, reproduction is a function of the capacity of nucleic acids to replicate themselves. Many invertebrates can reproduce asexually. In **asexual reproduction,** a single parent splits, buds, or fragments, giving rise to two or more offspring that may be identical to it. Asexual reproduction is an adaptation of sessile animals that cannot move about to search for mates. For animals that do move about, this method of reproduction is advantageous when population density is low and mates are not readily available.

Sexual reproduction in animals involves the production and fusion of two types of gametes—sperm and eggs. Generally, a

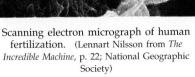

Scanning electron micrograph of human fertilization. (Lennart Nilsson from *The Incredible Machine*, p. 22; National Geographic Society)

male parent contributes the sperm and a female parent contributes the egg. When sperm and egg unite, a fertilized egg, or zygote, forms. The zygote develops into a new organism, similar to both parents but not identical to either one. Sexual reproduction has the biological advantage of promoting genetic variety among the members of a species, because the offspring is the product of a particular combination of genes contributed by both parents, rather than a genetic copy of a single individual. By making possible the combination of the inherited traits of two parents, sexual reproduction gives rise to offspring that may be better able to survive than either parent. In some animals, reproduction involves extremely complex structural, functional, and behavioral processes that are regulated by hormones.

After you have studied this chapter you should be able to

1. Compare asexual and sexual reproduction, giving two examples of asexual reproduction.
2. Compare adaptive advantages of the following reproductive styles: metagenesis, parthenogenesis, and hermaphroditism.
3. Trace the passage of sperm cells through the male reproductive system, from their origin in the seminiferous tubules until they leave the body in the semen.
4. Label the structures of the male reproductive system on a diagram, and describe their functions.
5. Label the structures of the female reproductive system on a diagram, and describe their functions.
6. Trace the development of an ovum and its passage through the female reproductive system until it is fertilized.

7. Describe the actions of testosterone and of the gonadotropic hormones in the male.
8. Describe the hormonal regulation of the menstrual cycle and the timing of important events of the cycle, such as ovulation and menstruation.
9. Identify the physiological changes that occur during sexual response in male and female.
10. Summarize the process of human fertilization, and identify factors that contribute to infertility.
11. Compare the methods of birth control in Table 48–3 with respect to mode of action, effectiveness, advantages, and disadvantages.
12. Identify common sexually transmitted diseases, and describe their symptoms, effects, and treatment.

ASEXUAL REPRODUCTION IS COMMON AMONG SOME ANIMAL GROUPS

In asexual reproduction, a single parent splits, buds, or fragments to give rise to two or more offspring that have hereditary traits similar to those of the parent. Sponges and cnidarians can reproduce by **budding,** in which a small part of the parent's body separates from the rest and develops into a new individual (Figure 48–1). The offspring may split away from the parent and establish an independent existence, or it may remain attached and become a more or less independent member of a colony.

Salamanders, lizards, sea stars, and crabs can grow new tails, legs, arms, and certain other organs if the original ones are lost. Oyster farmers learned long ago that when they tried to kill sea stars by chopping them in half and throwing the pieces back into the sea, the number of sea stars preying on the oyster bed doubled! In fact, a sea star can regenerate an entire new individual from a single arm. In some species, this ability to regenerate a part has become a method of reproduction known as **fragmentation.** The body of the parent may break into several pieces; each piece then regenerates the missing parts and develops into a whole animal. Fragmentation is common among flatworms.

Figure 48–1 *Hydra* reproduces asexually by budding. A part of the body grows outward, separates, and develops into a new individual. The portion of the parent body that buds is not specialized exclusively for performing a reproductive function. (R. D. Campbell, University of California, Irvine Campbell/Biological Photo Service)

SEXUAL REPRODUCTION IS THE MOST COMMON TYPE OF ANIMAL REPRODUCTION

Most animals reproduce sexually. Sexual reproduction, which occurs through the fusion of gametes, generally involves two parents—a male, which produces sperm, and a female, which produces eggs (ova). The egg is typically large and nonmotile, with a store of nutrients that supports the development of the embryo. The sperm is usually small and motile, adapted to propel itself by beating its long, whiplike flagellum. When a sperm cell fertilizes (fuses with) an egg cell, a zygote forms.

(a)

Figure 48–2   External fertilization and internal fertilization.
(a) External fertilization is illustrated by these spawning frogs
(*Rana temporaria*). Most amphibians must return to water for
mating. The female lays a mass of eggs, while the male mounts
her and simultaneously deposits his sperm in the water.
(b) Internal fertilization is practiced by mammals.   (a, Zig
Leszczynski © 1993 Animals Animals; b, Fritz Polking/Dembinsky Photo
Associates)

(b)

In **internal fertilization** the gametes (sperm and egg) fuse inside the body, whereas in **external fertilization** the gametes meet outside the body (Figure 48–2). Most aquatic animals practice external fertilization. Mating partners usually release large numbers of eggs and sperm into the water simultaneously. Although many gametes are lost (to predators, for example), sufficient numbers of sperm and egg cells meet and unite to ensure perpetuation of the species.

In internal fertilization, matters are left less to chance. The male generally delivers sperm cells directly into the body of the female. Her moist tissues provide the watery medium required for movement of sperm. Most terrestrial animals, as well as a few aquatic animals, practice internal fertilization.

ANIMALS HAVE EVOLVED INTERESTING REPRODUCTIVE VARIATIONS

Animals show tremendous diversity in their methods of sexual reproduction. Even members of the same class may differ markedly in their reproductive processes.

Metagenesis Is Characteristic of Some Animal Groups

Some animals exhibit **metagenesis,** in which a species has both asexual and sexual stages (Figure 48–3). For example, in the hydrozoan *Obelia,* a polyp stage gives rise asexually, by budding, to a stage of medusae. The motile medusae produce gametes and reproduce sexually, creating a new generation of polyps. Both stages are diploid organisms.

Fertilization Does Not Occur in Parthenogenesis

Parthenogenesis (virgin development) is a form of asexual reproduction in which an unfertilized egg develops into an adult animal. Parthenogenesis is common among some mollusks, some crustaceans, some insects (especially honeybees and wasps), and some reptiles. Certain species of arthropods (and even some vertebrates—lizards) consist entirely of females that reproduce in this way. More commonly, parthenogenesis occurs for several generations, after which males develop, produce sperm, and mate with the females to fertilize their eggs. In some species, parthenogenesis is advantageous in maintaining the social order; in others, it appears to be an adaptation for survival at times of stress or serious decrease in population.

A special form of parthenogenesis occurs in honeybees. The queen honeybee receives sperm from a male during the "nuptial flight." The sperm she receives are stored in a little pouch separated from her genital tract by a muscular valve. As the queen lays eggs, she can either open this valve, permitting the sperm to escape and fertilize the eggs, or keep the valve closed so that the eggs develop without fertilization. Generally, fertil-

(a)

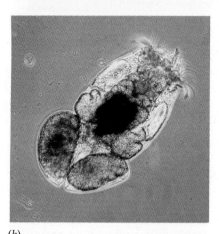

(b)

(c)

Figure 48–3   Reproductive variations. (a) Metagenesis in the hydrozoan *Pennaria tiarelle.* Magnified approximately 3.8 times, this closeup of two polyps shows one bearing two male medusae. (b) Parthenogenesis takes place in *Noteus,* a rotifer, seen with an egg. (c) Hermaphroditic copulation in earthworms.   (a, C. R. Wyttenbach, University of Kansas/Biological Photo Service; b, Visuals Unlimited/Roger Klocek; c, Roger K. Burnard/Biological Photo Service)

ization occurs in the fall; the fertilized eggs are quiescent during the winter. The fertilized become females (queens and workers); the unfertilized eggs become males (drones). Some species of wasps alternately produce a parthenogenetic generation and a generation developed from fertilized eggs.

In Hermaphroditism, One Individual Produces Sperm and Eggs

Sexual reproduction almost always involves two individuals. In **hermaphroditism,** an important exception, a single individual produces both eggs and sperm. A few hermaphrodites are capable of self-fertilization. For parasitic tapeworms, self-fertilization is an adaptation that permits a solitary lifestyle. Reproduction is possible even when only a single tapeworm infects a host.

Most hermaphrodites do not reproduce by self-fertilization; rather, two animals—earthworms, for example—copulate, and each inseminates the other. In some hermaphroditic species, self-fertilization is prevented by the individual's development of testes and ovaries at different times. In the clam *Mercenaria mercenaria,* 98% of the population are males when they first reach maturity; later in their lives they become females and produce eggs. A few continue to produce only sperm and function as males. In the American oyster *Crassostrea virginica,* sperm are produced mainly when the animal first matures. The next year the animal produces eggs.

Certain fish exhibit a somewhat similar reproductive pattern in which sex is related to dominance. In one species of wrasse, the dominant fish is always male, and he lords his position over a harem of females. If he is removed or dies, one of the remaining female fish reverses gender and becomes the new patriarch. In another species of wrasse, the opposite situation exists: The dominant fish is always female, and if she is removed, one of the males becomes female and dominant.

HUMAN REPRODUCTION: THE MALE PROVIDES SPERM

The human male, like other male mammals, has the reproductive role of producing sperm cells and delivering them into the female reproductive tract. When a sperm combines with an egg, it contributes half the chromosomes to the new offspring and determines its sex. The male reproductive system is illustrated in Figure 48–4. Male structures include the testes (which produce sperm and the hormone testosterone), the scrotum (which contains the testes), conducting tubes (which transport sperm from the testes to the outside of the

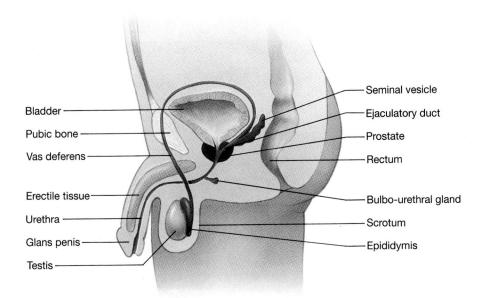

Bladder

Pubic bone

Vas deferens

Erectile tissue

Urethra

Glans penis

Testis

Seminal vesicle

Ejaculatory duct

Prostate

Rectum

Bulbo-urethral gland

Scrotum

Epididymis

Figure 48–4 Anatomy of the human male reproductive system. The scrotum, penis, and pelvic region are shown in sagittal section to illustrate their internal structures.

body), accessory glands (which produce the fluid components of semen), and the penis (the copulatory organ).

The Testes Produce Sperm

In humans and other vertebrates, **spermatogenesis,** sperm cell production, occurs within the walls of a vast tangle of hollow **seminiferous tubules** in each of the paired male gonads, or **testes** (Figure 48–5). The seminiferous tubules are partially lined with undifferentiated stem cells called **spermatogonia.** These cells give rise to sperm cells (Figure 48–6).

During embryonic development and childhood, the spermatogonia divide by mitosis, producing more spermatogonia. At adolescence, some spermatogonia continue to divide by mitosis, but about half of them enlarge and become **primary spermatocytes.** These cells undergo meiosis. (You may want to review the discussion of meiosis in Chapter 9.) In many animals gamete production occurs only in the spring or fall, but humans have no special breeding season. In the human adult male, spermatogenesis proceeds continuously, and millions of sperm are produced every day.

Each primary spermatocyte undergoes a first meiotic division that produces two **secondary spermatocytes** (Figure 48–7). In the second meiotic division, *each* secondary spermatocyte gives rise to two **spermatids.** Thus, four spermatids are produced from the original primary spermatocyte. A spermatid is a fairly large cell with much more cytoplasm than is present in a mature sperm.

spermatogonium → primary spermatocyte → two secondary spermatocytes → four spermatids (haploid) → four spermatozoa (haploid)

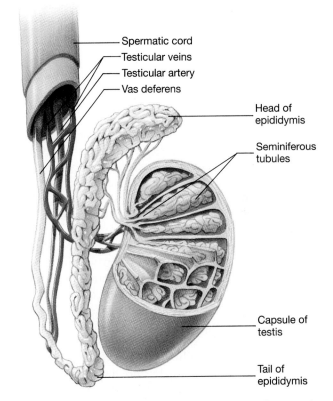

Spermatic cord
Testicular veins
Testicular artery
Vas deferens

Head of epididymis

Seminiferous tubules

Capsule of testis

Tail of epididymis

Figure 48–5 Structure of the testis, epididymis, and spermatic cord. The testis is shown in sagittal section to illustrate the arrangement of the seminiferous tubules.

The haploid spermatid differentiates into a mature sperm consisting of head, midpiece, and flagellum (Figure 48–8). The head consists of the nucleus and, at its front end, an **acrosome** formed from the Golgi complex. The acrosome produces enzymes that help the sperm penetrate the egg. Mitochondria are located in the mid-

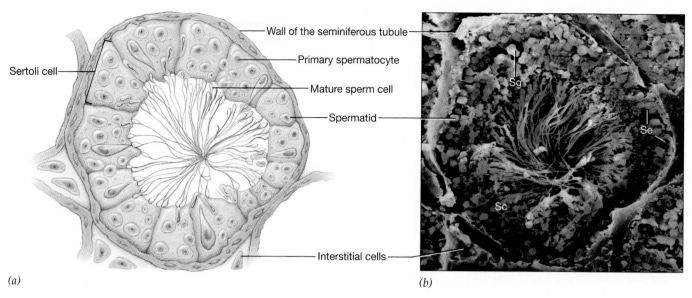

Sertoli cell

Wall of the seminiferous tubule

Primary spermatocyte

Mature sperm cell

Spermatid

Interstitial cells

(a)

Sg

Se

Sc

(b)

Figure 48–6   Structure of a seminiferous tubule, showing developing sperm cells in various stages of spermatogenesis. *(a)* Identify the sequence of sperm cell differentiation. Note the Sertoli cells and the interstitial cells. *(b)* Scanning electron

micrograph of a transverse section through a seminiferous tubule. (*b*, Professor P. Motts/Department of Anatomy/University "La Sapienza," Rome/Science Photo Library/Custom Medical Stock Photo)

piece of the sperm. The two centrioles nestle in a small depression on the nuclear surface. One of these, the distal centriole, gives rise to the flagellum of the sperm. Although relatively long, the sperm flagellum is typical of eukaryotic flagella, with the usual 9 + 2 arrangement of microtubules (Chapter 4). During development of a sperm cell, most of the cytoplasm is discarded and is phagocytized by the large nutritive **Sertoli cells** within the seminiferous tubules.

Human sperm cells cannot develop at body temperature. Although the testes develop within the abdominal cavity of the male embryo, about 2 months before birth they descend into the **scrotum,** a skin-covered sac suspended from the groin that serves as a cooling unit, maintaining sperm at about 2°C below body temperature. In rare cases the testes do not descend. If this condition is not surgically corrected, the seminiferous tubules eventually degenerate and the male becomes **sterile** (because he cannot produce sperm cells).

The scrotum is an outpocketing of the pelvic cavity and is connected to it by the **inguinal canals.** As the testes descend, they pull after them their blood vessels, nerves, and conducting tubes. These structures, encased by muscle and layers of connective tissue, make up the **spermatic cords.** The inguinal region is a weak place in the abdominal wall. Straining the abdominal muscles by lifting heavy objects sometimes results in tearing of the inguinal tissue. A loop of intestine can then bulge into the scrotum through the tear. This condition is called an **inguinal hernia.**

A Series of Ducts Transports Sperm

Sperm cells leave the seminiferous tubules of each testis through a series of small tubules (vasa efferentia) that empty into a larger, highly coiled tube, the **epididymis.** There sperm complete their maturation and are stored.

From each epididymis, sperm pass into the sperm duct, or **vas deferens** (plural, *vasa deferentia*), which extends from the scrotum through the inguinal canal and into the pelvic cavity. Each vas deferens empties into a short **ejaculatory duct,** which passes through the prostate gland and then opens into the urethra. The single **urethra,** which at different times conducts urine and semen, passes through the penis to the outside of the body.

seminiferous tubules → epididymis → vas deferens → ejaculatory duct → urethra → released from body

The Accessory Glands Produce the Fluid Portion of Semen

As sperm are transported through the conducting tubes, they are mixed with secretions from the accessory glands. About 3.5 mL of **semen** are ejaculated during sexual climax. An individual's semen consists of about 400 million sperm cells suspended in the secretions of the seminal vesicles, prostate gland, bulbourethral glands, and small glands in the walls of the ducts.

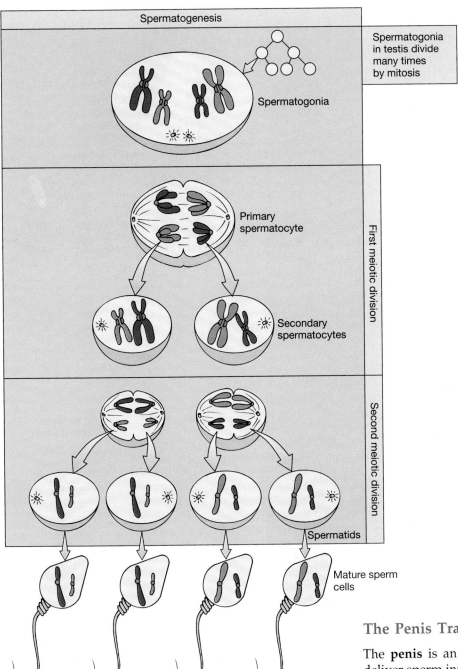

Figure 48–7 Spermatogenesis. The primary spermatocyte undergoes meiosis, giving rise to four spermatids. The spermatids differentiate, becoming mature sperm cells.

The paired **seminal vesicles** empty into the vasa deferentia (Figure 48–4). The single **prostate gland** releases its alkaline secretion into the urethra. During sexual arousal the paired **bulbourethral glands** release a few drops of alkaline fluid, which can neutralize the acidity of the urethra and aid in lubrication.

The Penis Transfers Sperm to the Female

The **penis** is an erectile copulatory organ adapted to deliver sperm into the female reproductive tract. It consists of a long **shaft** with an expanded tip, the **glans.** Part of the loose-fitting skin of the penis folds down and covers the proximal portion of the glans, forming a cuff called the **prepuce** or foreskin. In an operation known as circumcision (commonly performed on male babies for either hygienic or religious reasons), the foreskin is removed.

Under the skin, the penis consists of three parallel columns of **erectile tissue,** sometimes referred to as the **cavernous bodies** (corpora cavernosa) (Figure 48–9). One of these columns surrounds the portion of the urethra that passes through the penis. Erectile tissue consists of large blood vessels called venous sinusoids.

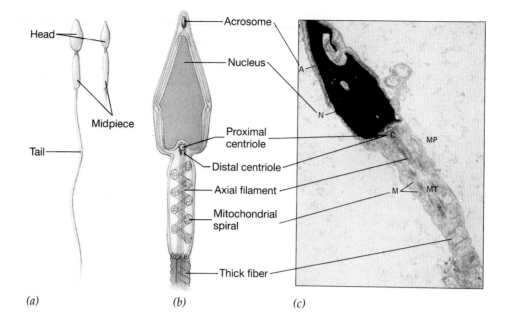

Figure 48–8 Sperm cell structure. (*a*) Top and side views of a sperm (*b*). A head and midpiece. The structures shown would be visible through an electron microscope. (*c*) Electron micrograph of a human sperm cell. *A*, acrosome; *N*, nucleus; *MP*, midpiece; *M*, mitochondria; *MT*, microtubules; *C*, centrioles. (*b*, Dr. Lyle C. Dearden)

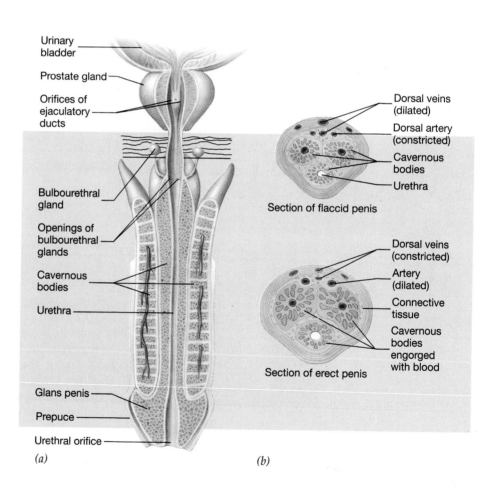

Figure 48–9 Internal structure of the penis. (*a*) Longitudinal section through the prostate gland and penis. (*b*) Cross sections of flaccid and erect penises. Note that in the erect penis the erectile tissues of the corpora cavernosa (cavernous bodies) are engorged with blood.

When the male is sexually stimulated, nerve impulses stimulate the arteries of the penis to dilate. Blood rushes into the venous sinusoids, causing the erectile tissue to swell. This compresses the veins that conduct blood away from the penis, slowing the outflow of blood.

Thus, more blood enters the penis than can leave, further engorging the erectile tissue. The penis becomes erect—that is, longer, larger in circumference, and firm. The human penis contains no bone, but bones do occur in the penises of some other mammals, such as bats.

Table 48–1   PRINCIPAL MALE REPRODUCTIVE HORMONES

Endocrine Gland and Hormones	*Principal Target Tissue*	*Principal Actions*
Hypothalamus Gonadotropin-releasing hormone (GnRH)	Anterior pituitary	Stimulates release of FSH and LH
Anterior pituitary Follicle-stimulating hormone (FSH)	Testes	Stimulates development of seminiferous tubules; may stimulate spermatogenesis
Luteinizing hormone (LH); also called interstitial cell–stimulating hormone (ICSH)	Testes	Stimulates interstitial cells to secrete testosterone
Testes Testosterone	General	*Before birth:* stimulates development of primary sex organs and descent of testes into scrotum *At puberty:* responsible for growth spurt; stimulates development of reproductive structures and secondary sex characteristics (male body build, growth of beard, deep voice, etc.) *In adult:* responsible for maintaining secondary sex characteristics; stimulates spermatogenesis

Reproductive Hormones Promote Sperm Production and Maintain Masculinity

At about age ten, the hypothalamus begins to mature and fulfill its function of regulating sex hormones. It secretes **gonadotropin-releasing hormone (GnRH),** which stimulates the anterior pituitary to secrete the gonadotropic hormones **follicle-stimulating hormone (FSH)** and **luteinizing hormone (LH).** FSH stimulates development of the seminiferous tubules and may promote spermatogenesis (Table 48–1). LH stimulates the **interstitial cells,** which lie between the tubules in the testes, to secrete the hormone testosterone.

Testosterone causes the male adolescent growth spurt, which occurs at about age 13; is responsible for development of the primary male sex characteristics, that is, stimulates growth of the penis and other reproductive organs; and is responsible for the **secondary sexual characteristics** that develop at puberty. These include the growth of the beard and of pubic and axillary hair, muscle development, and increase in length and thickness of the vocal cords, causing the voice to deepen.

What happens when testosterone is absent? If a boy's testes are removed—a procedure known as **castration**—before puberty, he is deprived of testosterone and becomes a eunuch. He retains childlike sex organs and does not develop secondary sexual characteristics.

If castration occurs after puberty, increased secretion of male hormone by the adrenal glands helps maintain masculinity.

HUMAN REPRODUCTION: THE FEMALE PRODUCES OVA AND INCUBATES THE EMBRYO

The female reproductive system produces ova (eggs; singular, *ovum*), receives the penis and its sperm during sexual intercourse, houses and nourishes the embryo during prenatal development, delivers the newborn into the world, and produces milk for the young (lactation). These processes are regulated and coordinated by the interaction of hormones secreted by the hypothalamus, the anterior lobe of the pituitary gland, and the ovaries.

Principal organs of the female reproductive system are the ovaries (which produce ova and hormones), uterine tubes (which transport ova and are the sites of fertilization), uterus (the "incubator" for the developing fetus), vagina (which receives the penis and serves as the canal through which a baby is delivered), vulva (external genital structures), and breasts (which nourish the young) (Figures 48–10 and 48–11).

Figure 48–10 Midsagittal section of female pelvis, showing the reproductive organs. Note the position of the uterus relative to the vagina.

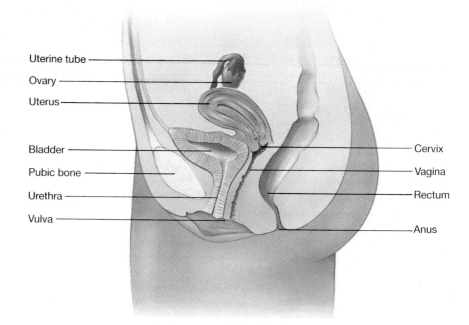

Uterine tube
Ovary
Uterus
Bladder
Pubic bone
Urethra
Vulva
Cervix
Vagina
Rectum
Anus

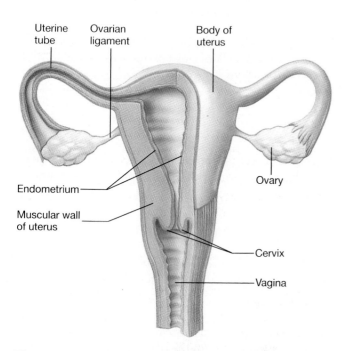

Uterine tube
Ovarian ligament
Body of uterus
Endometrium
Muscular wall of uterus
Ovary
Cervix
Vagina

Figure 48–11 Anterior view of the female reproductive system. Some organs have been cut open to expose the internal structure. The ligaments help to hold the reproductive organs in place.

The Ovaries Produce Ova and Sex Hormones

Like the male gonads, the female gonads, or **ovaries,** produce both gametes and sex hormones. Approximately the size and shape of large almonds, the ovaries are located close to the lateral walls of the pelvic cavity; they are held in position by several connective tissue ligaments. Each ovary is covered with a single layer of epithelium. Internally the ovary consists mainly of connective tissue (called stroma), through which are scattered developing **ova** in various stages of maturation

(Figure 48–12). The process of ovum formation is called **oogenesis.**

Hundreds of thousands of stem cells, termed **oogonia,** are present in the ovaries of a female fetus. During prenatal development the oogonia increase in size and become **primary oocytes.** By the time of birth they are in the prophase of the first meiotic division. All of the female's oocytes are produced during embryonic development; no new oocytes arise after birth. The primary oocytes enter a resting phase that lasts throughout childhood and into adult life. A developing ovum and the cluster of cells surrounding it together constitute a **follicle.**

With the onset of puberty, a pattern is established wherein a few of the follicles develop each month in response to FSH secreted by the anterior pituitary gland. As the follicle grows, the primary oocyte completes its first meiotic division, producing two cells very different in size (Figure 48–13). The smaller one, the **first polar body,** may later divide, forming two polar bodies, but these eventually disintegrate. The larger cell, the **secondary oocyte,** proceeds to the second meiotic division, but halts in metaphase until it is fertilized. When meiosis does continue, the second meiotic division gives rise to a single ovum and a second polar body (Figure 48–13). The polar bodies are small and apparently serve to dispose of unneeded chromosomes with a minimal amount of cytoplasm.

oogonium → primary oocyte → secondary oocyte (+ 1 polar body) (both haploid) → ovum (+ 1 polar body) (both haploid)

Recall that in the male large numbers of sperm are needed, and in spermatogenesis each primary spermatocyte gives rise to four sperm. In contrast, only a few

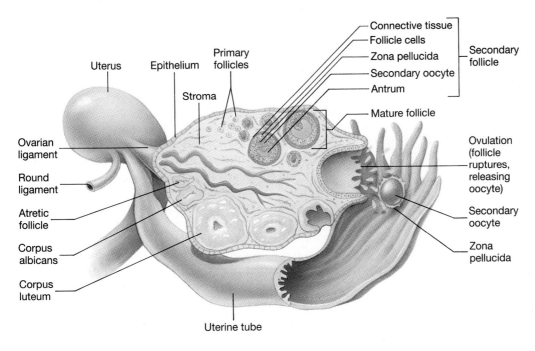

Figure 48–12 Microscopic structure of the ovary. Follicles in various stages of development are scattered throughout the ovary. (Not all of these stages would be present simultaneously in a single ovary.)

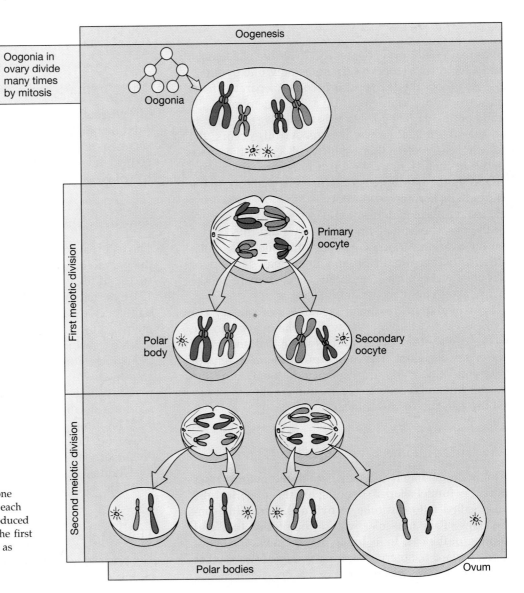

Figure 48–13 Oogenesis. Only one functional ovum is produced from each primary oocyte. The other cells produced are polar bodies that degenerate. The first polar body does not always divide as illustrated here.

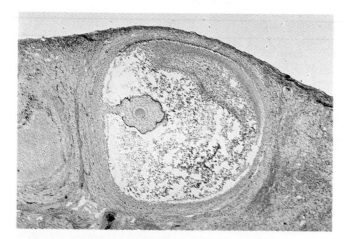

Figure 48–14 A stained section through a developing follicle. The ovum is surrounded by a layer of follicle cells that will be released along with it. These follicle cells become the corona radiata, a layer that acts as a barrier to sperm cells and may help ensure that the egg is fertilized by only one of the many sperm that approach it. (Biophoto Associates)

ova are needed during the reproductive life of a female, and each primary oocyte generates only one ovum.

As an oocyte develops, it becomes separated from its surrounding follicle cells by a thick membrane, the **zona pellucida.** The follicle cells themselves proliferate so that the follicle grows in size. As this occurs, the follicle cells secrete fluid, which collects in the space between them (Figure 48–14). Connective tissue surrounding the follicle cells contains cells that secrete the steroid sex hormone estradiol.

As a follicle matures, it moves closer to the surface of the ovary, eventually resembling a fluid-filled bulge on the ovarian surface. Generally only one follicle matures fully each month. Several others may develop for about a week, then deteriorate. They remain in the ovary as atretic (degenerate) follicles.

At **ovulation** the ovum (actually a secondary oocyte) is ejected through the wall of the ovary into the pelvic cavity. The portion of the follicle that remains in the ovary develops into the **corpus luteum,** a temporary endocrine gland. If pregnancy does not occur, the corpus luteum degenerates, remaining in the ovary as a white scar, the **corpus albicans.**

The Uterine Tube Transports the Ovum

Almost immediately after ovulation, the ovum passes into the funnel-shaped opening of the **uterine tube** (also called fallopian tube or oviduct). Peristaltic contractions of the muscular wall of the uterine tube and beating of the cilia in its lining help to move the ovum along toward the uterus. Within the uterine tube, either fertilization takes place or the ovum degenerates.

The Uterus Incubates the Embryo

The uterine tubes open into the upper corners of the **uterus,** or womb (Figure 48–11). A pear-shaped organ about the size of a fist, the uterus occupies a central position in the pelvic cavity. It has thick walls of smooth muscle and a mucous membrane, the **endometrium,** which thickens each month in preparation for possible pregnancy. If an ovum is fertilized, the tiny embryo is transported into the uterus and implants itself in the endometrium. Here it grows and develops, sustained by nutrients and oxygen delivered by surrounding maternal blood vessels. If fertilization does not occur during a given monthly cycle, the endometrium sloughs off and is discharged in a process known as **menstruation.**

The lower portion of the uterus, called the **cervix,** projects slightly into the vagina. The cervix is a common site of cancer in women. Detection is usually possible with the routine Papanicolaou test (Pap smear), in which, during a regular gynecological examination, a few cells are scraped from the cervix and studied microscopically. If cervical cancer is detected at very early stages of malignancy, the patient can be cured.

The Vagina Receives Sperm

The **vagina** is an elastic, muscular tube that extends from the uterus to the exterior of the body. The vagina serves as a receptacle for sperm during sexual intercourse and as part of the passageway through which a baby leaves the mother's body.

The Vulva Are External Genital Structures

The external female sex organs, collectively known as the **vulva,** include liplike folds, the **labia minora,** which surround the vaginal and urethral openings (Figure 48–15). External to the delicate labia minora are the thicker, hair-covered **labia majora.** Anteriorly the labia minora merge to form the prepuce of the **clitoris,** a very small erectile structure comparable to the male penis. Like the penis, the clitoris contains erectile tissue that becomes engorged with blood during sexual excitement. Rich in nerve endings, the clitoris serves as a center of sexual sensation in the female.

The **mons pubis** is the mound of fatty tissue just above the clitoris, at the junction of the thighs and torso. At puberty it becomes covered by coarse pubic hair. The **hymen** is a thin ring of tissue that may partially block the entrance to the vagina.

The Breasts Function in Lactation

The **breasts,** which contain the **mammary glands,** overlie the pectoral muscles and are attached to them by

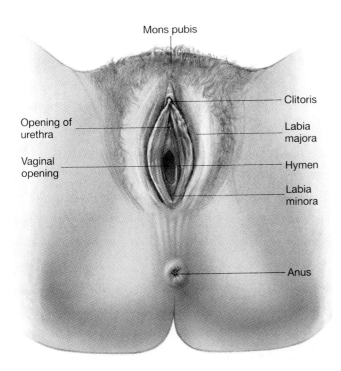

Figure 48–15 The vulva, the external genital structures of the female.

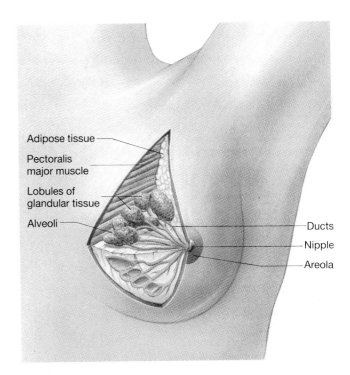

Figure 48–16 The mature human female breast.

connective tissue. Fibrous bands of tissue called **ligaments of Cooper** firmly connect the breasts to the skin. Each breast is composed of 15 to 20 lobes of glandular tissue, further subdivided into lobules, made of connective tissue, in which gland cells are embedded. The secretory cells are arranged in little grapelike clusters called alveoli (Figure 48–16). Ducts from each cluster unite to form a single duct from each lobe, so that the surface of a nipple has 15 to 20 tiny openings. The adipose tissue around the lobe of the glandular tissue determines the size of the breasts and accounts for their softness. The size of the breasts does not affect their capacity to produce milk. The breasts are the most common site of cancer in women (see Focus on Breast Cancer).

Lactation is the production of milk for the nourishment of the young. During pregnancy, high concentrations of female hormones—estrogens and progesterone—produced by the corpus luteum and by the placenta stimulate the glands and ducts of the breast to develop, resulting in increased breast size. For the first couple of days after childbirth, the mammary glands produce a fluid called **colostrum,** which contains protein and lactose but little fat. After birth the hormone **prolactin** (secreted by the anterior lobe of the pituitary gland) stimulates milk production, and usually by the third day after delivery milk itself is produced. When the infant suckles at the breast, a reflex action in the mother results in release of prolactin and **oxytocin** from the pituitary gland. Oxytocin stimulates cells surround-

ing the alveoli to contract so that the alveoli are compressed. This forces milk from the alveoli into the ducts.

Breastfeeding promotes recovery of the uterus following delivery, because the oxytocin released during breastfeeding stimulates the uterus to contract to its nonpregnant size. Breastfeeding offers advantages to the baby, as well. It promotes a close bond between mother and child. Breast milk is tailored to the nutritional needs of the human infant. Furthermore, breast-fed babies receive antibodies in the colostrum and mother's milk that are thought to play a protective role, resulting in a lower incidence of infantile diarrhea and even of respiratory infection during the second 6 months of life.

The Menstrual Cycle Is Regulated by Hormones

As a female approaches puberty, the anterior pituitary secretes the gonadotropic hormones FSH and LH, which signal the ovaries to become active. Interaction of FSH and LH with estrogens and progesterone from the ovaries regulates the **menstrual cycle,** the monthly sequence of events that prepares the body for possible pregnancy. The menstrual cycle runs its course every month from puberty until **menopause,** the end of a woman's reproductive (though not her sexually active) life.

Although wide variation exists, a typical menstrual cycle is 28 days long (Figure 48–17). The first day of the

FOCUS ON

Breast Cancer

Breast cancer is the most common type of cancer among women. Its incidence has increased in recent years, and now the disease strikes about one in every nine women; it is the leading cause of cancer deaths in women. The increased incidence of breast cancer is partly due to increased life expectancy. About 50% of breast cancers begin in the upper outer quadrant of the breast (see figure). As a malignant tumor grows, it may adhere to the deep tissue of the chest wall. Sometimes it extends to the skin, causing dimpling. Eventually the cancer spreads to the lymphatic system. About two thirds of breast cancers have metastasized (spread) to the lymph nodes by the time they are first diagnosed.

Mastectomy (surgical removal of the breast) and **radiation treatment** are common methods of treating breast cancer. **Chemotherapy** is especially useful in preventing metastasis, especially in premenopausal patients. A recent development in cancer treatment is the use of **biological re-**

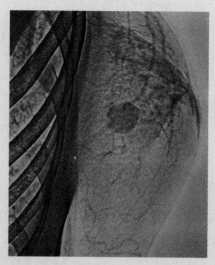

Mammogram showing breast cancer. Note the extensive vascularization. (Visuals Unlimited/SIU)

sponse modifiers, substances such as interferons, interleukins, and monoclonal antibodies.

About one third of breast cancers are estrogen-dependent; that is, their growth depends upon circulating es-

trogens. Removing the ovaries in patients with these tumors relieves the symptoms and may cause remission of the disease for months or even years. Another treatment strategy is administration of the drug tamoxifen, which blocks estrogen receptors. When diagnosis and treatment begin early, 80% of patients survive for 5 years and 62% for 10 years or longer. Untreated patients have only a 20% 5-year survival rate.

Because early detection of these cancers greatly increases the chances of cure and survival, campaigns have been launched to educate women on the importance of self-examination. **Mammography,** a soft-tissue radiological study of the breast, is helpful in detecting very small lesions that might not be identified by palpation. In mammography, lesions show on an x-ray plate as areas of increased density. In **xeromammography** the x-ray image is produced on paper rather than on film. This method requires less radiation and provides excellent detail.

---

cycle is marked by the onset of **menstruation**—the monthly discharge, through the vagina, of blood and tissue from the endometrium. Ovulation occurs on about the 14th day of the cycle.

During the **menstrual phase** of the cycle, lasting about 5 days, the pituitary gland releases FSH, which stimulates a few follicles to develop in the ovary. During the **preovulatory** (before ovulation) **phase** of the menstrual cycle, the ovary secretes **estrogens,** a group of closely related 18-carbon steroid hormones. The principal type of estrogen found in humans is beta-estradiol.

Estrogens stimulate growth of the endometrium, which thickens and develops new blood vessels and glands. The sharp rise in the concentration of estrogens in the blood signals the anterior lobe of the pituitary to secrete LH. Together, LH and FSH stimulate ovulation. LH then stimulates the portion of the follicle remaining in the ovary after the ovum has been ejected to develop into a corpus luteum.

During the **postovulatory phase** the corpus luteum produces both estrogens and **progesterone.** These hormones stimulate the uterus to continue its preparation for pregnancy. Progesterone stimulates tiny glands in the endometrium to secrete a fluid rich in nutrients. If the ovum is fertilized, this nutritive fluid nourishes the early embryo when it arrives in the uterus on about its fourth day of development (Figure 48–18). On about the seventh day after fertilization the embryo begins to implant itself in the thick endometrium. Membranes that develop around the embryo secrete **human chorionic gonadotropin (HCG),** a hormone that signals the mother's corpus luteum to continue to function. (HCG is chemically and functionally related to LH.)

If the ovum is not fertilized, the corpus luteum begins to degenerate and the concentrations of progesterone and estrogens in the blood fall dramatically. Small arteries in the endometrium constrict, reducing the oxygen supply. As cells die and damaged arteries rupture and bleed, menstruation begins once again.

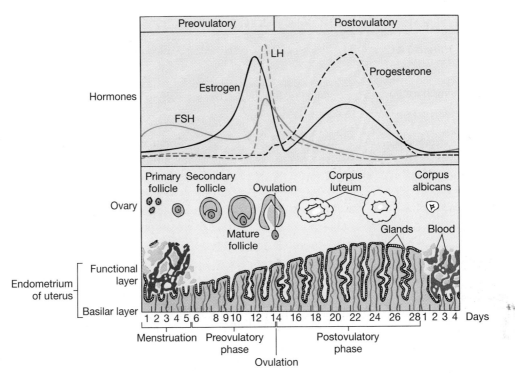

Figure 48–17 The menstrual cycle. The events that take place within the pituitary, ovary, and uterus are precisely synchronized. When fertilization does not occur, the cycle repeats itself about every 28 days. Compare this illustration with Figure 48–18.

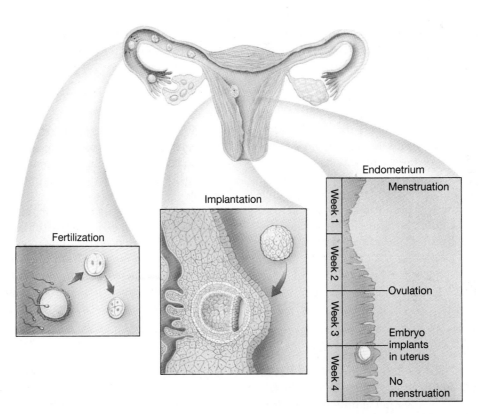

Figure 48–18 The menstrual cycle is interrupted when pregnancy occurs. The corpus luteum does not degenerate, and menstruation does not take place. Instead, the wall of the uterus remains thickened so that the embryo can develop within it.

Table 48–2 PRINCIPAL FEMALE REPRODUCTIVE HORMONES

Endocrine Gland and Hormones	Principal Target Tissue	Principal Actions
Hypothalamus		
Gonadotropin-releasing hormone (GnRH)	Anterior pituitary	Stimulates release of FSH and LH
Anterior pituitary		
Follicle-stimulating hormone (FSH)	Ovary	Stimulates development of follicles; with LH, stimulates secretion of estrogen and ovulation
Luteinizing hormone (LH)	Ovary	Stimulates ovulation and development of corpus luteum
Prolactin	Breast	Stimulates milk production (after breast has been prepared by estrogen and progesterone)
Ovary		
Estrogens (estradiol)	General	Growth of sex organs at puberty; development of secondary sex characteristics (breast development, broadening of pelvis, distribution of fat and muscle)
	Reproductive structures	Maturation; monthly preparation of the endometrium for pregnancy; makes cervical mucus thinner and more alkaline
Progesterone (secreted mainly by corpus luteum)	Uterus	Completes preparation of endometrium for pregnancy
	Breast	Stimulates development

Table 48–2 lists the actions of the pituitary and ovarian reproductive hormones. Note that, like testosterone in the male, estrogens are responsible for the growth of the sex organs at puberty, for body growth, and for the development of secondary sexual characteristics. In the female these include breast development, broadening of the pelvis, and the characteristic development and distribution of muscle and fat that are responsible for the shape of the adult female body.

The female produces some testosterone, mainly in the adrenal cortex. Testosterone is largely responsible for the adolescent growth spurt and for development of pubic hair and hair under the arms in the female (as well as in the male). In the male, some estrogen is produced in the testes.

Hormones of the hypothalamus, anterior pituitary, and ovaries interact to regulate the menstrual cycle

GnRH from the hypothalamus stimulates the anterior pituitary to release FSH and LH (Figure 48–19). FSH stimulates the early maturation of the follicles in the ovary, and FSH and LH together stimulate the final maturation of a follicle. The rise in estrogens secreted by the developing follicles stimulates the anterior pituitary to secrete a surge of LH. This stimulating effect is a positive feedback mechanism. The surge of LH is necessary for the final maturation of the follicle and for ovulation to occur. After ovulation, LH stimulates development of the corpus luteum, which secretes both progesterone and estrogens.

The high constant levels of estrogens and progesterone maintained by the corpus luteum inhibit GnRH and LH secretion. As a result, the corpus luteum begins to degenerate. Once this happens, estrogen and progesterone levels in the blood fall markedly, and menstruation begins. Secretion of FSH and LH increases once again.

Estrogen-progesterone imbalance has been suggested as a cause of **premenstrual syndrome (PMS),** a condition experienced by some women several hours to 10 days before menstruation and ending a few hours after onset of menstruation. Symptoms include fatigue, anxiety, depression, irritability, headache, edema, and skin eruptions.

In Menopause the Ovaries Secrete Less Estrogens and Progesterone

As a woman ages, the ovaries become less responsive to FSH and LH. The number of primary follicles in the ovary decreases, resulting in lowered production of estrogens. By about age 50 the menstrual cycle becomes irregular; eventually it halts.

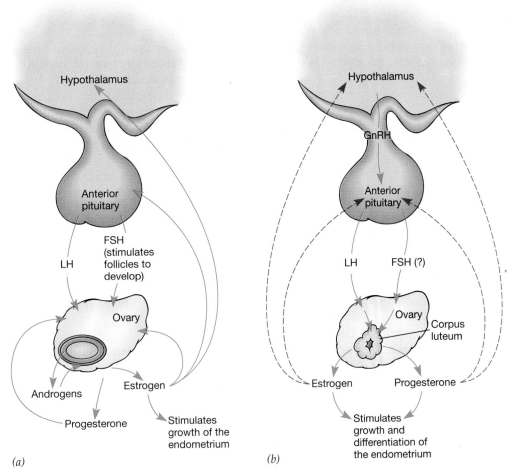

Figure 48–19 (a)

Figure 48–19 (b)

Figure 48–19 Hormonal regulation of the menstrual cycle. (*a*) Hormonal interactions during the preovulatory phase.

(*b*) Hormonal interactions during the postovulatory phase. Red arrows indicate inhibition.

Decreased estrogens affect the temperature-regulating center in the hypothalamus and sometimes lead to hot flashes and episodes of sweating. Estrogen deficiency may also contribute to the depression and headaches experienced by some women during the onset of menopause. In menopausal women some atrophy of the ovaries, vagina, breasts, and other reproductive structures takes place.

Despite these physical changes, menopause does not usually affect a woman's interest or participation in sex. Symptoms of menopause can be alleviated clinically by replacing estrogens. Replacement hormones also appear to reduce the risk of cardiovascular disease and osteoporosis. However, their use is controversial because they may increase the risk for certain types of cancer.

SEXUAL RESPONSE INVOLVES PHYSIOLOGICAL CHANGES

During copulation, also called **coitus** or sexual intercourse in humans, the male deposits semen into the upper end of the vagina. The complex structures of the male and female reproductive systems and the intricate physiological, endocrine, and psychological phenomena associated with sexual activity are adaptations that promote the successful union of sperm and ovum and the subsequent development and nurturing of the embryo.

Sexual stimulation brings about two basic physiological responses: (1) increased blood flow (vasocongestion) to reproductive structures and certain other tissues, such as the skin, and (2) increased muscle tension. During vasocongestion, erectile tissues within the penis and clitoris, as well as in other areas of the body, become engorged with blood.

Sexual response includes four phases: sexual desire, excitement, orgasm, and resolution. The *desire* to engage in sexual activity may be motivated by fantasies or thoughts about sex. Such anticipation can lead to (physical) sexual *excitement* and a sense of sexual pleasure. This excitement phase involves vasocongestion and increased muscle tension. Before the penis can enter the vagina and function in coitus, it must be erect; accordingly, penile erection is the first male response to sexual excitement. In the female, vaginal lubrication is the first response to effective sexual stimulation. During the excitement phase, the vagina lengthens and expands in preparation for receiving the penis; the clitoris and breasts become vasocongested, and the nipples become erect.

If erotic stimulation continues, sexual excitement heightens. Vasocongestion and muscle tension increase markedly. In the female, the inner two thirds of the vagina continue to expand and lengthen. The wall of the outer one third of the vagina becomes greatly vasocongested so that the vaginal entrance is somewhat constricted. In this narrowed state, the outer one third of the vagina is referred to as the orgasmic platform. In the male, the penis increases in circumference. In both sexes, blood pressure increases and heart rate and breathing accelerate.

Coitus may be initiated during the excitement phase. During coitus the penis is moved inward and outward in the vagina in actions referred to as pelvic thrusts, which create friction. Physical and psychological sensations resulting from this friction (and from the entire intimate experience between the partners) may lead to orgasm, the climax of sexual excitement.

Although it lasts only a few seconds, **orgasm** is the phase of maximum sexual tension and its release. In both sexes orgasm is marked by rhythmic contractions of the muscles of the pelvic floor and pelvic reproductive structures. Heart rate and respiration more than double, and blood pressure rises markedly both just before and during orgasm.

In the male, orgasm is marked by a sensation that **ejaculation** (emission) of semen is inevitable, followed by actual ejaculation. Leading up to ejaculation, contractions of the vas deferens propel sperm into the ejaculatory ducts. The accessory glands contract, adding their secretions; then contractions of the ejaculatory ducts, urethra, and certain muscles of the pelvic floor eject the semen from the penis. Muscular contractions continue at about 0.8-second intervals for several seconds. After the first few contractions, their intensity decreases, and they become less regular and less frequent.

In the female, stimulation of the clitoris is important in heightening the sexual excitement that leads to orgasm. Sexual climax is marked by rhythmic contractions of the pelvic muscles and the orgasmic platform, starting at approximately 0.8-second intervals and recurring five to twelve times. After the first three to six contractions, their intensity decreases and the interval between them increases. No fluid ejaculation accompanies orgasm in the female.

Orgasm is followed by the **resolution phase,** a state of well-being during which muscle relaxation and detumescence (reduction of swelling) restore the body to its normal state. In most males a refractory period takes place, during which sexual stimulation brings on no physiological response. Duration of the refractory period varies among individuals and situations. Many women can respond to repeated sexual stimulation, and they may reach orgasm multiple times within a relatively short period.

Sexual dysfunction may be caused by psychological or biological factors. For example, chronic inability to sustain an erection, termed **erectile dysfunction** (formerly called impotence), is often associated with psychological issues. This disorder prevents effective coitus. Vaginismus is a condition in which, during sexual intercourse, a woman experiences painful involuntary spasms of the outer third of the vaginal muscles. Vaginismus is often associated with a history of sexual abuse.

FERTILIZATION IS THE FUSION OF SPERM AND EGG TO PRODUCE A ZYGOTE

In the process of **fertilization,** sperm and ovum fuse, producing a zygote. Fertilization and the subsequent establishment of pregnancy are together referred to as **conception.** When conditions in the vagina and cervix are favorable, sperm begin to arrive at the site of fertilization in the upper uterine tube within 5 minutes after ejaculation. Contractions of the uterus and uterine tubes help transport the sperm. The sperm's own motility is probably the most important factor for success in approaching and fertilizing the ovum.

If only one sperm is needed to fertilize an ovum, why are millions involved in each act of coitus? For one thing, sperm movement is undirected, so many lose their way. Others die as a result of unfavorable pH or of phagocytosis by leukocytes and macrophages in the female tract. Only a few thousand succeed in passing through the correct uterine tube and reaching the vicinity of the ovum. Additionally, large numbers of sperm may be necessary to penetrate the covering of follicle cells (the corona radiata) that surrounds the ovum. Each sperm is thought to release small amounts of enzymes from its acrosome that help break down the cement-like substance holding the follicle cells together.

As soon as one sperm enters the ovum, a rapid electrical change occurs, followed by a slower chemical change in the plasma membrane of the ovum. These changes prevent the entrance of other sperm. As the fertilizing sperm enters the ovum, it usually loses its flagellum (Figure 48–20). Sperm entry stimulates the ovum to complete its second meiotic division. The head of the haploid sperm then swells to form the **male pronucleus** and fuses with the female pronucleus, forming the diploid nucleus of the zygote. The process of fertilization is described in more detail in Chapter 49.

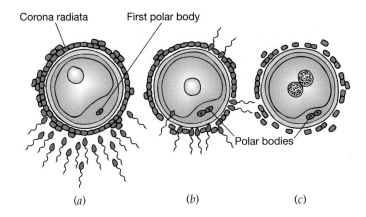

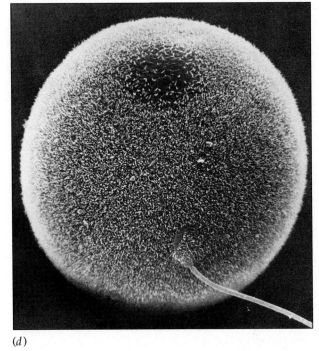

(a)   (b)   (c)

(d)

Figure 48–20 Fertilization. (*a*) Each sperm is thought to release a small amount of enzyme that helps to disperse the follicle cells surrounding the ovum. (*b*) After a sperm cell enters it, the oocyte completes its second meiotic division, producing an ovum and a polar body. (*c*) Pronuclei of sperm and ovum combine, producing a zygote with the diploid number of chromosomes. (*d*) A scanning electron micrograph of a sperm cell fertilizing a hamster ovum. (*d*, David Phillips/Visuals Unlimited)

After ejaculation into the female reproductive tract, sperm remain alive and retain their ability to fertilize an ovum for about 48 hours. The ovum itself remains fertile for only about 24 hours after ovulation. Thus, in a very regular 28-day menstrual cycle, sexual intercourse is most likely to result in fertilization during days 12 to 15. However, many women do not have regular menstrual cycles, and many factors can result in irregularities even in women who generally have regular cycles.

In view of the many factors working against fertilization, it may seem remarkable that it ever occurs! Yet the frequency of coitus and the great number of sperm deposited with each ejaculation enable the human species not only to maintain itself but to increase its numbers at an alarming rate.

INFERTILITY IS THE INABILITY TO ACHIEVE CONCEPTION

Infertility is the inability of a couple to achieve conception after not using contraception for at least 1 year. About 15% of married couples in the United States are affected by infertility. About 30% of cases involve both male and female factors.

A major cause of male infertility is **sterility**—insufficient sperm production. Men with fewer than 20 million sperm per milliliter of semen are usually considered sterile. When a couple's attempts to produce a child are unsuccessful, a sperm count and analysis may be performed in a clinical laboratory. Sometimes semen is found to contain large numbers of abnormal sperm or occasionally none at all. In about one fourth of cases of mumps in adult males, the testes become inflamed; in some of these cases the spermatogonia die, resulting in permanent sterility.

Low sperm counts have been linked to chronic marijuana use, alcohol abuse, and cigarette smoking, and studies show that men who smoke tobacco are more likely than nonsmokers to produce abnormal sperm. Exposure to chemicals such as DDT and PCBs may also result in low sperm count and sterility. Use of anabolic steroids to accelerate muscle development can cause sterility in both males and females.

One cause of female infertility is development of scar tissue in the uterine tubes, which blocks the tubes so that ova can no longer pass to the uterus. Such scarring can be the result of inflammation of the tubes, sometimes from a gonorrhea infection. Occasionally, partial constriction of a uterine tube results in tubal pregnancy, in which the embryo begins to develop in the wall of the uterine tube because it cannot progress to the uterus. Uterine tubes are not adapted to bear the burden of a developing embryo; thus, the uterine tube and the embryo it contains must be surgically removed before the tube ruptures and endangers the life of the mother.

Women with blocked uterine tubes usually can produce ova and can incubate an embryo normally. However, they need clinical assistance in getting the ovum from the ovary to the uterus. The ovum can be removed

Table 48–3 BIRTH CONTROL METHODS

Method	Failure Rate*	Mode of Action	Advantages	Disadvantages
Oral contraceptives	0.3; 5	Inhibits ovulation; may also affect endometrium and cervical mucus and prevent implantation	Highly effective; regulates menstrual cycle	Minor discomfort in some women; possible thromboembolism; hypertension, heart disease in some users; possible increased risk of infertility; should not be used by women who smoke
Depo-Provera (medroxyprogesterone acetate)	About 1	Inhibits ovulation	Effective; long-lasting	Fertility may not return for 6–12 months after use discontinued
Progesterone implantation	About 1	Inhibits ovulation	Effective; long-lasting	Irregular menstrual bleeding in some women
Intrauterine device (IUD)	1; 5	Not known; probably stimulates inflammatory response	Provides continuous protection; highly effective	Cramps; increased menstrual flow; spontaneous expulsion; increased risk of pelvic inflammatory disease and infertility; not recommended for women who have not completed childbearing
Spermicides (sponges, foams, jellies, creams)	3; 20	Chemically kill sperm	No side effects (?); vaginal sponges are effective in vagina for up to 24 hours after insertion; sponges also act as physical barriers to sperm cells	Some evidence linking spermicides to birth defects

*The lower figure is the failure rate of the method; the higher figure is the rate of method failure plus failure of the user to utilize the method correctly. Based on number of failures per 100 women who use the method per year in the United States.

†The failure rate is lower when the diaphragm is used together with spermicides.

‡There are several variations of the rhythm method. For those who use the calendar method alone, the failure rate is about 35. However, if the body temperature is taken daily and careful records are kept (temperature rises after ovulation), the failure rate can be reduced. Also, if a daily record of the type of vaginal secretion is kept, changes in cervical mucus can be noted and used to determine time of ovulation. This type of rhythm contraception is also slightly more effective. When women use the temperature or mucus method and have intercourse *only* more than 48 hours *after* ovulation, the failure rate can be reduced to about 7.

from the ovary, fertilized with sperm in laboratory glassware (a procedure called *in vitro* fertilization), and then placed in the woman's uterus, where it may develop normally.

BIRTH CONTROL METHODS ALLOW INDIVIDUALS TO CHOOSE

Under natural conditions, population sizes of animal species are limited by a variety of mechanisms, even apart from such factors as disease and food shortage. Under conditions of crowding, animals may control their own populations by parental neglect (feeding only the strong offspring) or by cannibalism. In some species, spontaneous abortion, genetic deterioration, or death by stress may occur.

Some use of abortion as a means of birth control has been found in every human population studied. Even infanticide has been practiced, especially in primitive societies. Infanticide is no longer sanctioned anywhere, and abortion remains controversial.

Method	Failure Rate*	Mode of Action	Advantages	Disadvantages
Contraceptive diaphragm (with jelly)†	3; 14	Diaphragm mechanically blocks entrance to cervix; jelly is spermicidal	No side effects	Must be prescribed (and fitted) by physician; must be inserted prior to coitus and left in place for several hours after intercourse
Condom	2.6; 10	Mechanically prevents sperm from entering vagina	No side effects; some protection against STD, including AIDS	Interruption of foreplay to put it on; slightly decreased sensation for male; could break
Rhythm‡	13; 21	Abstinence during fertile period	No side effects (?)	Not very reliable
Douche	40	Flush semen from vagina	No side effects	Not reliable; sperm are beyond reach of douche in seconds
Withdrawal (coitus interruptus)	9; 22	Male withdraws penis from vagina prior to ejaculation	No side effects	Not reliable; contrary to powerful drives present when an orgasm is approached; sperm in the fluid secreted before ejaculation may be sufficient for conception
Sterilization				
Tubal ligation	0.04	Prevents ovum from leaving uterine tube	Most reliable method	Often not reversible
Vasectomy	0.15	Prevents sperm from leaving scrotum	Most reliable method	Often not reversible
Chance (no contraception)	About 90			

Most couples agree that it is best to have babies by choice, not by chance, but unfortunately the majority of couples who engage in sexual intercourse have only vague notions of how to prevent conception. In underdeveloped countries, an estimated 88% of women lack the means to limit family size. Studies indicate that many of these women would use modern birth control methods if they were available and if someone showed them how.

In the United States, more than 1 million teenagers become pregnant every year, and thousands of girls aged 14 or younger have babies each year. Yet only one in five sexually active teenagers consistently uses contraception. In addition, the AIDS epidemic presents an increasing and ominous risk. The number of unwanted babies could be decreased (and risk of sexually trans-mitted disease also lessened) if individuals old enough to produce babies knew how to prevent conception (and lessen the risk of disease).

When a sexually active woman uses no form of birth control, her chances of becoming pregnant during the course of a year are about 90%. Any method for deliberately separating sexual intercourse from production of babies is considered **contraception** (literally, "against conception"). Since ancient times humans have searched for effective contraceptive methods. Modern science has developed a variety of contraceptives with a high percentage of reliability, but the ideal contraceptive has not yet been devised. Some of the more common methods of birth control are described as follows and in Table 48–3. Note that intrauterine devices (IUDs), as well as some types of oral contracep-

Table 48–4 DEATHS IN THE UNITED STATES FROM PREGNANCY AND CHILDBIRTH AND FROM SOME BIRTH CONTROL METHODS

	Death Rate per 100,000
Pregnancy and childbirth	9
Oral contraception	3
IUD	0.5
Legal abortions—first trimester	1.9
Legal abortions—after first trimester (mainly therapeutic abortions)	12.5
Illegal abortions performed by medically untrained individuals	About 100

tives, may not actually prevent fertilization; they probably destroy the embryo or prevent its implantation in the wall of the uterus.

Hormone Contraceptives Prevent Ovulation

More than 80 million women worldwide (more than 8 million in the United States alone) use **oral contraceptives**. The most common preparations are combinations of progestin (synthetic progesterone) and synthetic estrogen. (Natural hormones are rapidly metabolized by the liver, but synthetic ones are chemically modified so that they can be absorbed effectively and metabolized slowly.) When taken correctly, these pills are about 99.9% effective in preventing pregnancy.

Most oral contraceptives prevent pregnancy by preventing ovulation. When postovulatory levels of ovarian hormones are maintained in the blood, the pituitary gland is inhibited and does not produce the surge of FSH and LH that stimulates ovulation. The chief advantage of oral contraceptives is their high rate of effectiveness.

Studies suggest that women over age 35 who smoke or have other risk factors, such as untreated hypertension, should not take oral contraceptives. Women in this category who do use the pill have an increased risk of death from circulatory diseases such as stroke and myocardial infarction. Nonsmokers can take oral contraceptives safely until age 35 with no increased risk of cardiovascular disease. Oral contraceptives result in death in about 3 per 100,000 users. This compares favorably with the rate of about 9 deaths per 100,000 pregnancies (Table 48–4).

Recently, Depo-Provera (medroxyprogesterone acetate) has been approved for contraceptive use in the United States. This hormone prevents ovulation by suppressing anterior pituitary function. It is generally injected intramuscularly every 90 days.

Another technology in contraception involves implantation of progesterone (in the form of levonorgestrel) in the woman's body. Several soft, flexible capsules are inserted under the skin of the upper arm. There the synthetic hormone is continuously released and is transported by the blood. The hormone inhibits ovulation and stimulates thickening of the cervical mucus (which makes it more difficult for the sperm to reach the egg). The capsules are effective for about 5 years, after which they must be replaced. Progesterone implants are one of the most effective, reversible contraceptive procedures available. The failure rate is less than 1 in 100. The most common side effect is irregular menstrual bleeding, which may last up to 1 year.

Use of the Intrauterine Device (IUD) Has Declined

The **intrauterine device (IUD)** is a small plastic loop or coil that must be inserted into the lumen of the uterus by a medical professional. Once in place, some types of IUDs can be left in the uterus indefinitely or until the woman wishes to conceive. Recent IUDs are about 99% effective.

The mode of action of the IUD is not well understood, but it is thought that white blood cells are mobilized in response to the foreign body in the uterus. The white blood cells may produce substances toxic to the fertilized ovum. Some IUDs (copper T and copper 7) contain copper, which is thought to dissolve slowly in the uterine secretions and to interfere with implantation of the embryo. Because IUDs cause changes in the epithelium, their safety has been questioned. They have also been linked with other side effects, such as pelvic inflammatory disease (PID) and increased risk of tubal pregnancy. Currently IUDs are recommended only for women who have completed their childbearing.

Other Common Contraceptive Methods Include the Diaphragm and the Condom

Other common methods of contraception are described and compared in Table 48–3. The **contraceptive diaphragm** mechanically blocks the passage of sperm from the vagina into the cervix. It is covered with spermicidal jelly or cream and inserted just prior to coitus.

The **contraceptive sponge** is also both a mechanical and a chemical method of contraception. This device is made of polyurethane and soaked in nonoxynol-9 spermicide. Once it is inserted into the vagina, intercourse is protected for up to 24 hours. Another advantage of the contraceptive sponge is that it is available without a prescription.

The **condom,** the most commonly used male contraceptive device, contains the semen released from the penis so that sperm cannot enter the female tract. The

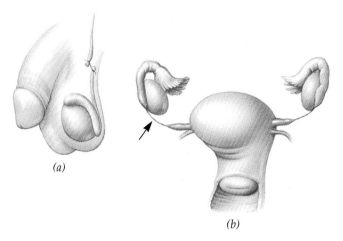

(a)

(b)

Figure 48–21 Sterilization. (*a*) In vasectomy, the vas deferens (sperm duct) on each side is cut and tied. (*b*) In tubal ligation, each uterine tube is cut and tied so that ovum and sperm can no longer meet.

condom is the only contraceptive that provides some protection against AIDS and other sexually transmitted diseases.

Sterilization Renders an Individual Incapable of Producing Offspring

Aside from total abstinence, sterilization is the only foolproof method of contraception. Sterilization is currently the most popular contraceptive method for couples in which the wife is over age 30.

Male sterilization is performed by vasectomy

An estimated 1 million **vasectomies** are performed each year in the United States. After application of a local anesthetic, a small incision is made on each side of the scrotum. Then each vas deferens is cut, and its ends are tied or clipped so that they cannot grow back together (Figure 48–21*a*).

Since testosterone secretion and transport are not affected, a vasectomy in no way affects masculinity. Sperm continue to be produced, though at a much slower rate, and are destroyed by macrophages in the testes. No change in the amount of semen ejaculated is noticed, because sperm account for very little of the semen volume.

In a study of more than 1000 men who had vasectomies, 99% said they had no regrets, and 73% claimed an increase in sexual pleasure, probably because anxiety about pregnancy was erased. By surgically reuniting the ends of the vasa deferentia, doctors can successfully reverse sterilization in about 50% of attempts made. Apparently, some sterilized men eventually develop antibodies against their own sperm and so remain sterile even when their vasectomies are surgically reversed.

An alternative to reversal of vasectomy is the preparatory storage of frozen sperm in sperm banks. If the male should decide to father a child after he has been sterilized, he simply "withdraws" his sperm from the bank so that they can be used to artificially inseminate his wife. Sperm banks have been established in the United States. Not much is known yet about the effects of long-term sperm storage, but there may be an increased risk of genetic defects.

Female sterilization is by tubal ligation

Several techniques are in current use for prevention of ova transport. Most of them involve **tubal ligation,** cutting and tying the uterine tubes (Figure 48–21*b*). This can be done through the vagina but is usually performed through an abdominal incision and requires general anesthesia. As in the male, hormone balance and sexual performance are not affected.

THERE ARE THREE TYPES OF ABORTION

Abortion is termination of pregnancy that results in the death of the embryo or fetus. Worldwide, an estimated 40 million deliberate abortions are performed each year (more than a million in the United States). Three kinds of abortions may be distinguished: spontaneous abortions, therapeutic abortions, and those undertaken as a means of birth control. **Spontaneous abortions** (popularly called miscarriages) occur without intervention and often are a biological mechanism for destroying a defective embryo. **Therapeutic abortions** are performed in order to maintain the health of the mother or when there is reason to suspect that the embryo is grossly abnormal. The third type of abortion, the type performed as a means of birth control, is the most controversial.

Most first-trimester abortions (those performed during the first 3 months of pregnancy) and some later ones are accomplished with suction. After the cervix has been dilated, a suction aspirator is inserted in the uterus, and the embryo and other products of conception are evacuated. In pregnancies of more than 12 weeks, the method most commonly used is dilation and evacuation ("D and E"). The cervix is dilated, the fetus is removed with forceps, and suction is used to aspirate the endometrium.

When abortion is performed during the first trimester by skilled medical personnel, the mortality rate is about 1.9 per 100,000. Most abortions performed after the first trimester are therapeutic abortions; the death rate for them rises to 12.5 per 100,000 (see Table 48–4). The U.S. death rate from illegal abortions performed by medically untrained individuals is about 100 per 100,000. In contrast to these figures, the death rate from pregnancy and childbirth is about 9 per 100,000.

Table 48–5 SOME COMMON SEXUALLY TRANSMITTED DISEASES*

Disease and Causative Organism	Course of Disease	Treatment
Gonorrhea (*Neisseria gonorrhoeae*, a gonococcus bacterium)	Bacterial toxin may produce redness and swelling at infection site; symptoms in males: painful urination and discharge of pus from penis; in about 60% of infected women no symptoms occur in initial stages; can spread to epididymis (in males) or uterine tubes and ovaries (in females), causing sterility; can cause widespread pelvic or other infection, plus damage to heart valves, meninges (outer coverings of brain and spinal cord), and joints	Penicillin, or other antibiotic if penicillin-resistant strain involved
Syphilis (*Treponema pallidum*, a spirochete bacterium)	Bacteria enter body through defect in skin near site of infection and spread throughout the body by lymphatic and circulatory routes; primary chancre (a small, painless ulcer) forms at site of initial infection and heals in about a month; highly infectious at this stage; secondary stage follows, in which a widespread rash and influenza-like symptoms may occur; scaly lesions may occur that teem with bacteria and are highly infectious; latent stage that follows can last 20 years; eventually, lesions called gummae may occur, consuming parts of the body surface or damaging liver, bone, or spleen; serious brain damage may occur; death results in 5–10% of cases	Penicillin
Genital herpes (herpes simplex type 2 virus)	Tiny, painful blisters appear on genitals; may develop into ulcers; influenza-like symptoms may occur; recurs periodically; threat to fetus or newborn infant; may predispose to cervical cancer in females	No effective cure; some drugs may shorten outbreaks or reduce severity of symptoms
Trichomoniasis (a protozoon)	Symptoms include itching, discharge, soreness; can be contracted from dirty toilet seats and towels; may be asymptomatic in males	Drugs
"Yeast" infections (genital candidiasis) (*Candida albicans*)	Irritation, soreness, discharge; especially common in females; may be asymptomatic in males	Drugs
Chlamydia (*Chlamydia trachomatis*, a bacterium)	Discharge and burning with urination, or may be asymptomatic; most common cause of nongonococcal urethritis in males; about 10% of male college students in the United States are infected	Doxycycline (antibiotic)
Pelvic inflammatory disease (PID; caused by gonorrhea or chlamydia)	Generalized infection of reproductive organs and pelvic cavity; usually chronic and difficult to treat; may lead to sterility (more than 15% of cases)	Antibiotics, surgical removal of affected organs
Genital warts (certain strains of human papilloma virus [HPV])	Warty growths may be present on the internal or external genitalia; may predispose to cervical cancer	Difficult to treat; various experimental treatments are being used

A primary syphilitic chancre. This is usually the first symptom of syphilis. (Custom Medical Stock Photo)

*AIDS was discussed in Chapter 43.

MAKING THE CONNECTION

Body Fat and Reproduction

The fat content of the body affects animal reproduction via hormones of the hypothalamus.

In fertile women, the adipose tissue of the breast, abdomen, mesenteries, and bone marrow produces about one third of the circulating estrogen by converting androgen to estrogen. This mechanism is the principal source of estrogen for post-menopausal women. The same process occurs in men, providing them with most of their circulating estrogen.

Chronically undernourished children take longer to achieve the critical body size and fat content required to become fertile than do well-nourished children. The research of Dr. Rose Frisch of Harvard University has shown that humans whose bodies contain too little fat become physiologically infertile. This is well documented in some female athletes, ballet dancers, and anorexic women whose ratio of lean body mass to fat mass increases to about 4:1.

The infertility produced by low body fat levels is a natural means of preventing a female from engaging in the energy-expensive processes of fetal growth and lactation when her body composition is inadequate to support both her own needs and those of her young. Fertility can be regained by appropriate feeding: When a normal lean body mass:fat mass ratio (2.5:1 in humans) is attained, the hypothalamus can begin to direct the release of gonadotropic hormones. This sensitivity to body composition is a fundamental mechanism for adjusting the reproductive output of a population in relation to the amount of food available. Consequently, females with greater reserves of body fat may be able to produce more progeny, and rear them more successfully, than females with smaller fat reserves. This is certainly observed in numerous migratory, arctic-breeding goose populations, which begin nesting on the tundra well before the appearance of spring vegetation, and which depend upon body fat for the energy required to form eggs and stay alive during the incubation period.

Too much fat may impair reproduction as readily as too little body fat. It has long been known that marked obesity is linked to infertility in humans and domesticated animals. Fertility can be resumed by judicious weight loss that brings the absolute and relative amounts of fat in the body to ranges characteristic of the animal's species.

Contributed by Dr. Vernon G. Thomas, Department of Zoology, University of Guelph, Guelph, Ontario, Canada.

SEXUALLY TRANSMITTED DISEASES ARE SPREAD BY SEXUAL CONTACT

Sexually transmitted diseases (STD), also called venereal diseases (VD), are, next to the common cold, the most prevalent communicable diseases in the world.

The World Health Organization has estimated that each year more than 250 million people are infected with gonorrhea and more than 50 million with syphilis. Currently, the most common STD in the United States is chlamydia. Some common sexually transmitted diseases are listed and described in Table 48–5. AIDS was discussed in Chapter 43, Focus on AIDS.

SUMMARY

I. In asexual reproduction, a single parent endows its offspring with a set of genes identical to its own. Sexual reproduction occurs through fusion of gametes; usually each of two parents contributes a gamete containing half of the offspring's genetic endowment.

II. Variations of reproduction among animals include metagenesis (alternation of sexual and asexual stages), parthenogenesis (development of an unfertilized egg into an adult animal), and hermaphroditism (presence of both male and female reproductive organs in a single individual).

III. The human male reproductive system includes the testes (which produce sperm and testosterone), a series of conducting tubes, accessory glands, and the penis.

A. The testes, housed in the scrotum, contain the seminiferous tubules, where the sperm are produced, and the interstitial cells, which secrete testosterone.

B. Sperm complete their maturation and are stored in the epididymis; they may also be stored in the vas deferens.

C. During ejaculation, sperm travel from the vas deferens to the ejaculatory duct and then into the urethra, which passes through the penis.

D. Semen contains about 400 million sperm suspended in the secretions of the seminal vesicles and prostate gland.

E. The penis consists of three columns of erectile tissue; when this tissue is engorged with blood, the penis becomes erect.

F. The gonadotropic hormones FSH and LH stimulate sperm production and testosterone secretion. Testosterone is responsible for establishing and maintaining primary and secondary sex characteristics in the male.

IV. The female reproductive system includes the ovaries (which produce ova and hormones), uterine tubes, uterus, vagina, vulva, and breasts.

A. After ovulation the ovum enters the uterine tube, where it may be fertilized.

B. The uterus serves as an incubator for the developing embryo.

C. The vagina is the lower part of the birth canal, and it receives the penis during coitus.

D. The clitoris is the center of sexual sensation in the female.

E. The first day of menstrual bleeding marks the first day of the menstrual cycle. Ovulation occurs at about day 14 in a typical 28-day menstrual cycle. Events of the menstrual cycle are coordinated by the gonadotropic and ovarian hormones.

1. FSH stimulates follicle development; LH stimulates ovulation and promotes development of the corpus luteum.

2. The developing follicles release estrogens, which stimulate development of the endometrium and are responsible for the secondary female sex characteristics.

3. The corpus luteum secretes estrogens and also progesterone, which stimulates final preparation of the uterus for possible pregnancy.

V. Vasocongestion and increased muscle tension are two basic physiological responses to sexual stimulation. The phases of sexual response include sexual desire, excitement, orgasm, and resolution.

VI. Fertilization is the fusion of egg and sperm to form a zygote.

VII. Effective methods of birth control include hormone contraceptives, intrauterine devices, condoms, contraceptive diaphragms, and sterilization.

VIII. Most first-trimester abortions are performed using suction.

IX. Important types of sexually transmitted diseases are gonorrhea, syphilis, genital herpes, chlamydia, pelvic inflammatory disease, genital warts, and AIDS.

POST-TEST

1. The type of reproduction in which an animal divides into several pieces and then each piece develops into an entire new animal is called _____.

2. In _____ there is an alternation of _____.

3. _____ is a type of asexual reproduction in which an unfertilized egg develops into an adult animal.

4. An individual that can produce both eggs and sperm is described as _____.

5. A sex cell (either egg or sperm) is properly called a(n) _____; a fertilized egg is a(n) _____.

6. An adult who is unable to parent offspring is said to be _____.

For each group, select the most appropriate answer from Column B for each description in Column A.

Column A	Column B
7. Site of sperm production	a. seminiferous tubules
8. Produce testosterone	b. prostate gland
9. Columns of erectile tissue	c. interstitial cells in testes
10. Secretes alkaline fluid into urethra	d. cavernous bodies
11. Sac that holds the testes	e. none of the above

Column A	Column B
12. Produces gametes	a. uterine tube
13. Thickens each month in preparation for pregnancy	b. ovary
14. Lower portion of uterus	c. cervix
15. Site of fertilization	d. endometrium
	e. none of the above

Column A	Column B
16. Produces FSH	a. hymen
17. Produces progesterone	b. corpus luteum
18. Focus of sexual sensation in the female	c. anterior lobe of pituitary
19. Extends from uterus to exterior of body	d. clitoris
	e. none of the above

Column A	Column B
20. Responsible for secondary sexual characteristics in female	a. testosterone
21. Responsible for secondary sexual characteristics in male	b. estradiol (estrogens)
22. Produced by anterior pituitary	c. LH
23. Stimulates glands in endometrium to develop	d. progesterone
	e. none of the above

Column A	Column B
24. Prevents ovulation	a. IUD
25. Prevents sperm from entering vagina	b. contraceptive diaphragm
26. Procedure in which vas deferens is severed	c. oral contraceptive
27. Blocks passage of sperm from vagina into uterus	d. condom
	e. none of the above

28. A _____ abortion is performed in order to maintain the mother's health or when the embryo is thought to be grossly abnormal.

29. Tubal ligation is a common method of _____.

30. The menstrual cycle runs its course every month from puberty until _____.

31. Label the following diagrams. (Refer to Figures 48–4 and 48–11 in the text as necessary.)

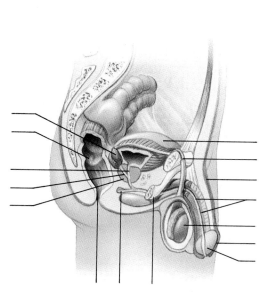
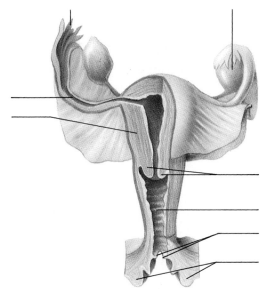

REVIEW QUESTIONS

1. Compare asexual reproduction with sexual reproduction. Give specific examples of asexual reproduction.
2. What are the advantages of metagenesis? Of parthenogenesis? Give an example of each.
3. What are the biological advantages of hermaphroditism? Explain.
4. Compare the functions of ovaries and testes.
5. Trace the passage of sperm from a seminiferous tubule through the male reproductive system until it leaves the male body during ejaculation. Assuming that ejaculation takes place within the vagina, trace the journey of the sperm until it meets the ovum.
6. What are the actions of testosterone? Of estradiol? Of progesterone?

7. What is the function of the corpus luteum? Which hormone stimulates its development?
8. Compare the actions of FSH and LH in the male and the female.
9. Why are so many sperm produced in the male and so few ova produced in the female?
10. Which methods of birth control are most effective? Least effective?
11. Draw a diagram of the principal events of the menstrual cycle, including ovulation and menstruation. Indicate on which days of the cycle sexual intercourse would most likely result in pregnancy.
12. Distinguish among the following terms: erectile dysfunction, infertility, sterility, and castration.

RECOMMENDED READINGS

Duellman, W. E. Reproductive strategies of frogs. *Scientific American* Vol. 267, No. 1 (July 1992) pp. 80–87. In addition to the egg-to-tadpole progression, frogs have other reproductive strategies such as egg to froglet, egg brooding, and tadpoles in the mother's stomach.

Frisch, R. E. Fatness and fertility. *Scientific American* Vol. 258, No. 3 (March 1988), pp. 88–95. Discusses the possibility that fat tissue exerts a regulatory effect on human female reproduction.

Masters, W. H., V. E. Johnson, and R. C. Kolodny, eds. *Human Sexuality.* Little, Brown and Co., Boston, 1985.

Solomon, E. P., R. R. Schmidt, and P. Adragna. *Human Anatomy and Physiology.* Saunders College Publishing, Philadelphia, 1990. This book has an excellent chapter on human reproduction.

Wassarman, P. M. Fertilization in mammals. *Scientific American* Vol. 259, No. 6 (December 1988). A glycoprotein governs many of the events of fertilization, including the process by which the fertilized egg prevents other sperm from entering.

Development

Development is a process that includes all of the changes that take place during the entire life of an organism from conception to death. In this chapter we focus mainly on development of the embryo, but we also touch on growth and maturation of the organism after birth and on the aging process.

Scientists of the 17th century developed the **preformation theory**—the idea that the egg cell contained a completely formed, although miniature, human being. By the end of the 17th century two competing groups of preformationists emerged. One group, the ovists, thought that the preformed organism resided within the egg; the opposing group, the spermists, were certain that the "little man" was housed in the sperm. Using their crude microscopes, some investigators even imagined that they could see a completely formed tiny human being within the head of the sperm (Figure 49–1).

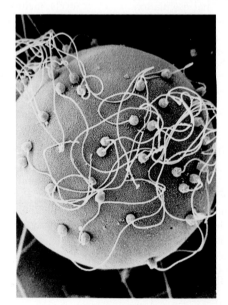

Sperm swarm around an egg of a surf clam in this scanning electron micrograph. (Visuals Unlimited/David M. Phillips)

Some preformationists argued that every woman contained within her body a miniature of every individual who would ever descend from her. Her children, grandchildren, great grandchildren, and so on were thought to be preformed, each within the reproductive cells of the preceding generation. Some investigators even computed mathematically how many generations could fit, one within the other's gametes. They concluded that when all these generations had lived and died, the human species would end. The theory of preformation encompassed all plant and animal species. For almost 200 years this theory was seriously debated by scientists and philosophers.

An opposing view, the **theory of epigenesis,** gained experimental support as better investigative techniques were developed. This theory held that the embryo develops from a formless zygote and that the structures of the body take shape in an orderly sequence, developing their characteristic forms only as they emerge.

Today we know that development is largely epigenetic. No microscopic organism waits preformed in either gamete. Development proceeds from one cell to billions, from a formless mass of cells to an intricate, highly specialized and organized organism. However, a spark of truth can be found in the preformationist view. Although the "little man" itself is not to be found within the zygote, its blueprint *is* there, precisely encoded in the form of chemical specifications within the DNA of the genes.

LEARNING OBJECTIVES

After you have studied this chapter you should be able to

1. Relate the preformation theory and the theory of epigenesis to current concepts of development.
2. Identify the roles of cell proliferation, growth, morphogenesis, and cellular differentiation in the development of an organism.
3. Summarize the functions of fertilization, and describe the four processes involved.
4. Describe the principal characteristics of each of the early stages of development: zygote, cleavage, morula, blastula, gastrula.
5. Contrast cleavage in the sea star (or *Amphioxus*), in the amphibian, and in the bird.
6. Summarize the fate of each of the germ layers and compare gastrulation in *Amphioxus*, the amphibian, and the bird.
7. Define organogenesis and trace the early development of the nervous system.
8. Trace the development of the extraembryonic membranes and placenta, giving the functions of each membrane.
9. Summarize the general course of human development.
10. Identify the principal events of each stage of labor.
11. Contrast postnatal with prenatal life, describing several adaptations that the neonate must make in order to live independently.
12. List specific steps that a pregnant woman can take to promote the well-being of her developing child, and describe how the embryo can be affected by nutrients, drugs, cigarette smoking, pathogens, and ionizing radiation.
13. Trace the stages of the human life cycle.
14. Identify anatomical and physiological changes that occur with aging, and identify current hypotheses of aging.

DEVELOPMENT IS A BALANCED COMBINATION OF SEVERAL PROCESSES

How does a microscopic, unspecialized zygote give rise to the blood, bones, brain, and other complex structures of an organism? As this chapter explains, development is a balanced combination of several processes: cell proliferation (mitosis and cytokinesis), growth, morphogenesis, and cellular differentiation.

The single-celled zygote undergoes mitosis and cytokinesis, forming two cells; each of these cells then divides, giving rise to four cells. The process is repeated again and again, producing the billions of cells of the adult organism. Growth occurs both by increase in the number of cells and by change in the size of these cells. An orderly pattern of proliferation and growth provides the cellular building blocks of the organism. But these processes alone would produce only a formless heap of cells.

Cells must arrange themselves into specific structures and appropriate body forms. The precise cellular movements that bring about the form of a multicellular organism with its intricate pattern of tissues and organs are termed **morphogenesis.**

Not only must cells be arranged into specific structures, but they must also perform specialized functions. In order to function in different ways, body structures

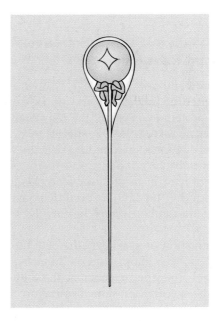

Figure 49–1 The preformed "little man" within the sperm as visualized by 17th-century scientists. (After Hartseeker's drawing from "Essay de Dioptrique," Paris, 1694)

must be made of different components. During early development, cells begin to change from their initial structure and function. They also become different from one another, specializing biochemically and structurally to perform specific tasks. More than 200 distinct types of cells can be found in the adult vertebrate body. The process by which cells become specialized is known as **cellular differentiation.**

As you read the following sections on development, notice how mitosis and cytokinesis, growth, morphogenesis, and cellular differentiation are interrelated. Also note that the pattern of early development is basically similar for all animals.

FERTILIZATION RESTORES THE DIPLOID NUMBER OF CHROMOSOMES

Fertilization is the union of a sperm and an ovum to produce a **zygote,** or fertilized egg. Fertilization serves three functions: (1) The diploid number of chromosomes is restored as the sperm contributes its haploid set of chromosomes to the haploid ovum. (2) In mammals and many other animals, sex of the offspring is determined. (3) Fertilization stimulates reactions in the egg that permit development to take place.

Fertilization involves four steps. First, the sperm must contact the egg and recognition must occur. Second, the sperm enters the egg. Third, the sperm and egg nuclei fuse. Finally, the egg is activated and development begins.

The First Step in Fertilization Involves Contact and Recognition

The plasma membrane of the egg is surrounded by a very thin **vitelline membrane** and, outside of this, by a thick glycoprotein layer called the **jelly coat** (zona pellucida in mammals). In a few species (e.g., some cnidarians) the egg (or a surrounding structure) secretes a chemotactic substance that attracts sperm of the same species. However, in most species no chemical attraction of sperm by the egg has been demonstrated, and meeting of the gametes may be largely a matter of chance.

The activation of sperm by the egg, the **acrosome reaction,** has been most studied in marine invertebrates. When the sperm contacts the jelly coat surrounding the egg, the acrosome (a structure at the head of the sperm) releases enzymes that digest a path through the jelly coat to the vitelline membrane of the egg. Actin molecules join to form actin filaments, which permit the acrosome to extend outward and contact the vitelline membrane of the egg. Recognition that the sperm and egg are of the same species occurs at this time. If the species are the same, a species-specific protein known as **bindin,** located on the acrosome, adheres to a species-specific bindin receptor located on the vitelline membrane.

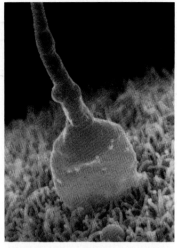

(a)

(b)

Figure 49–2 Fertilization. (a) When the first sperm makes contact with the egg's plasma membrane, microvilli elongate and surround the head of the sperm. This fertilization cone draws the sperm into the cytoplasm of the egg. (b) This computer reconstruction shows the fusion of sperm and egg plasma membranes. (a, Visuals Unlimited/David M. Phillips; b, courtesy of Drs. Gerald and Heide Schatten)

Sperm Entry Is Regulated

Once acrosome–vitelline membrane fusion occurs, enzymes dissolve a bit of the vitelline membrane in the area of the sperm head. The plasma membrane of the egg is covered with microvilli. Several microvilli elongate to surround the head of the sperm, forming a **fertilization cone.** The sperm is then drawn into the egg by contraction of the fertilization cone. As this occurs, the plasma membranes of sperm and egg fuse (Figure 49–2).

As soon as one sperm enters the egg, two reactions occur that prevent additional sperm from entering. Within a few seconds a fast block to polyspermy occurs which involves an electrical change in the plasma membrane of the egg. Ion channels in the plasma membrane open, permitting sodium ions to pass into the cell. The depolarization that occurs prevents other sperm from fusing with the plasma membrane.

A second mechanism preventing entrance of more than one sperm, referred to as the slow block to polyspermy, is the **cortical reaction.** Depolarization of the egg plasma membrane results in calcium ion release from thousands of cortical granules present beneath the membrane. The cortical granules then release enzymes by exocytosis into the area between the plasma membrane and the vitelline membrane. Some of these enzymes dissolve the protein linking the two membranes. Other substances released by the cortical granules result in osmotic passage of water into the space between the membranes. The vitelline membrane becomes elevated and forms the fertilization membrane, a hardened membrane that prevents entry of sperm. (In mammals, a fertilization membrane does not form, but the enzymes released alter the zona pellucida sperm receptors so that no additional sperm can bind to them.) The slow block requires one to several minutes, but it is a complete block. In some species more than one sperm enters the egg, but only the first sperm that enters fertilizes the egg.

Sperm and Egg Pronuclei Fuse

After the sperm nucleus enters the egg through the fertilization cone, it is thought to be guided toward the egg nucleus by a system of microtubules that form within the egg. The sperm nucleus swells, forming the male pronucleus, and the nucleus of the ovum becomes the female pronucleus. Then the haploid pronuclei fuse to form the diploid nucleus of the zygote.

Fertilization Activates the Egg

Release of calcium ions into the egg cytoplasm is necessary for the cortical reaction, and it also triggers metabolic changes within the cell. Oxygen use by the cell increases as certain compounds within the egg cell are oxidized. Within a few minutes after sperm entry a burst of protein synthesis occurs.

In some species sperm penetration initiates rearrangement of the cytoplasm. For example, in the amphibian egg some of the superficial cytoplasm containing dark granules shifts, exposing the underlying lighter-colored cytoplasm. This cytoplasm, which appears gray, is referred to as the gray crescent; it marks the region where gastrulation, an early developmental process, begins in the amphibian embryo.

In some species, the egg can be artificially activated without sperm penetration by swabbing it with blood and pricking the plasma membrane with a needle, by calcium injection, or by certain other treatments. These eggs develop parthenogenetically (that is, without being fertilized).

DURING CLEAVAGE THE ZYGOTE DIVIDES, GIVING RISE TO MANY CELLS

Despite its relatively simple appearance, the zygote has the potential to give rise to all the cell types of the complete individual. Because the sperm cell is quite tiny compared with the egg, the bulk of the zygote cytoplasm comes from the ovum. However, the zygote contains chromosomes contributed by both sperm and egg.

Shortly after fertilization the zygote undergoes a series of rapid mitoses, collectively referred to as **cleavage.** The zygote undergoes mitosis and divides to form a two-cell embryo (Figure 49–3). Each of these cells then undergoes mitosis and divides, bringing the number of cells to four. Repeated divisions continue to increase the number of cells, or **blastomeres,** making up the embryo. At about the 32-cell stage the embryo is referred to as a **morula.** The cells of the morula continue to multiply, eventually forming a hollow ball of several hundred cells, the **blastula,** surrounding a fluid-filled cavity, the **blastocoele.** The stages of early development occur in the following sequence:

$$\text{zygote} \longrightarrow \text{cleavage} \longrightarrow \text{morula} \longrightarrow \text{blastula}$$

Cleavage Provides Building Blocks for Development

During cleavage the cells do not grow, so the mass of cells produced is no larger than the original zygote. The principal effect of early cleavage is to partition the zygote into many small cells that serve as basic building units. Their small size allows the cells to move about with relative ease, arranging themselves into the patterns necessary for further development. Each cell moves by amoeboid motion, probably guided by the proteins of its own cell coat and those of other cell surfaces. Specific properties conferred upon plasma membranes by these surface proteins are important in helping cells to "recognize" one another and therefore in determining which ones adhere to form tissues.

The Amount of Yolk Determines the Pattern of Cleavage

The eggs of many kinds of animals contain yolk, a metabolically inert mixture of proteins, phospholipids, and fats which serves as food for the developing embryo. The amount and distribution of yolk vary among different animal groups. In **isolecithal** eggs, relatively small amounts of yolk are uniformly distributed through the

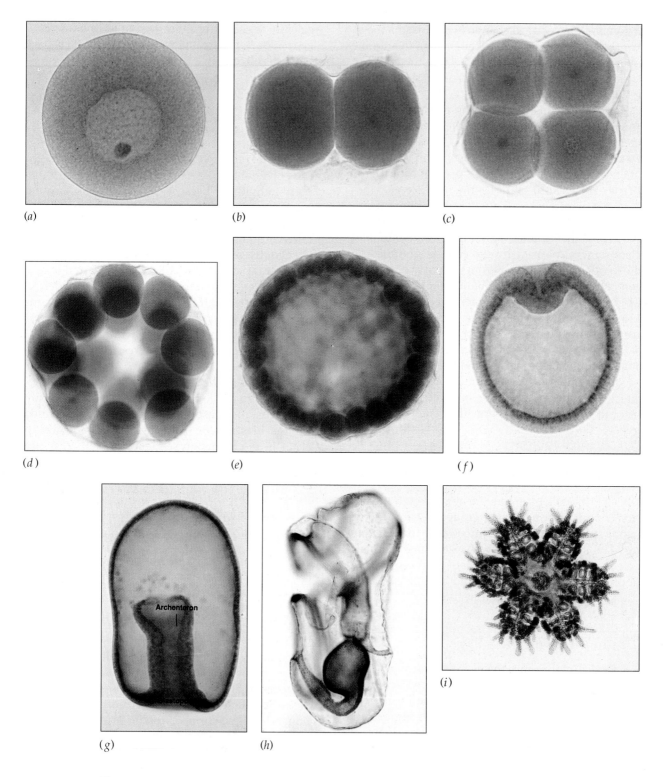

(a) (b) (c)

(d) (e) (f)

Archenteron

(g) (h) (i)

Figure 49–3 Development of a sea star. (a) Unfertilized sea star egg. (b) Two-cell stage. (c) Top view of four-cell stage. (d) Sixteen-cell stage. (e) Cross section through 64-cell blastula. (f) Section through early gastrula. (g) Section through middle gastrula. (h) Sea star larva. (i) Young sea star. In this type of cleavage the entire egg becomes partitioned into cells. The blastopore is the opening into the inner cavity, the archenteron. All views are side views with the animal pole at the top, except (c) and (i), which are top views. (Carolina Biological Supply Company)

cytoplasm. Isolecithal eggs are characteristic of most invertebrates and simple chordates. In **telolecithal** eggs large amounts of yolk are concentrated at one pole of the cell—known as the **vegetal pole.** The opposite, more metabolically active pole is the **animal pole.** Telolecithal eggs are characteristic of many vertebrates.

The amount of yolk in the egg affects the pattern of cleavage. In isolecithal eggs, cleavage is described as **holoblastic** because the entire egg divides, producing cells of roughly the same size. Cleavage of isolecithal eggs can be radial or spiral. Radial cleavage is characteristic of deuterostomes (see Chapter 28).

In **radial cleavage,** the first division passes through both animal and vegetal poles and splits the egg into two equal cells. The second cleavage division passes through both poles of the egg at right angles to the first and separates the two cells into four equal cells. The third division is horizontal, at right angles to the other two, and separates the four blastomeres into eight—four above and four below the third line of cleavage. This holoblastic pattern of radial cleavage occurs in the sea star and in the simple chordate *Amphioxus* (Figures 49–3 and 49–4).

Some protostomes have a pattern of early cell division known as **spiral cleavage** (Figure 49–5). After the first two divisions, the plane of cytokinesis is oblique to the polar axis, resulting in a spiral arrangement of cells, with each cell located between the two cells below it.

The telolecithal eggs of bony fish and amphibians contain a large amount of yolk concentrated toward the vegetal pole. The cleavage divisions in the vegetal hemisphere are slowed by the presence of the inert yolk. As a result, the blastula consists of many small cells in the animal hemisphere and fewer, but larger, cells in the vegetal hemisphere (Figure 49–6). For this reason the lower wall is much thicker than the upper one and the blastocoel is displaced upward.

The telolecithal eggs of reptiles, birds, and some fish have a very large amount of yolk and only a small

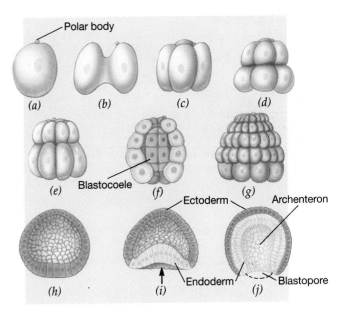

Figure 49–4   Radial cleavage and gastrulation in *Amphioxus* viewed from the side. (*a*) Mature egg with polar body. (*b* to *e*) Two-, four-, eight-, and 16-cell stages. (*f*) Embryo at 32-cell stage cut open to show the blastocoel. (*g*) Blastula. (*h*) Blastula cut open. (*i*) Early gastrula showing beginning of invagination at vegetal pole (*arrow*). (*j*) Late gastrula. Invagination is completed and blastopore has formed.

amount of cytoplasm concentrated at the animal pole. In such eggs, cleavage is said to be **meroblastic** because cell division takes place only in the **blastodisc,** the small disc of cytoplasm at the animal pole (Figure 49–7).

In birds and some reptiles, the blastomeres form two layers, an upper epiblast and below that a thin layer of flat cells, the hypoblast. The epiblast and hypoblast are separated from each other by the blastocoel and from the underlying yolk by another cavity, the subgerminal space. This space appears only under the central portion of the blastodisc.

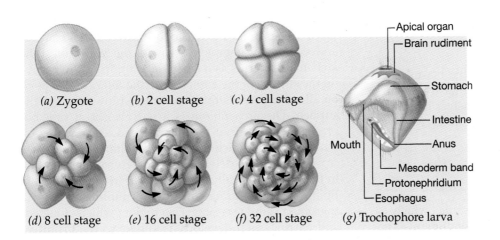

Figure 49–5   Development in annelids. (*a*) through (*f*) are top views of the animal pole. The successive cleavage divisions occur in a spiral pattern as indicated. (*g*) A typical trochophore larva. The upper half of the trochophore develops into the extreme anterior end of the adult worm; all the rest of the adult body develops from the lower half.

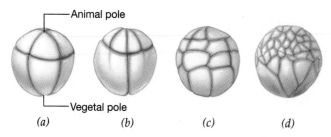

Figure 49–6 Successive stages in cleavage in the telolecithal frog egg, viewed from the side.

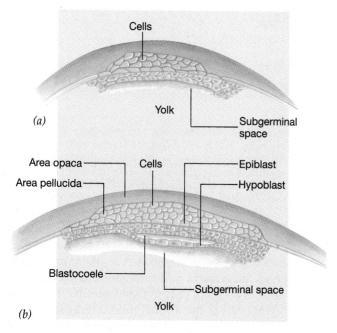

Figure 49–7 Successive stages in the cleavage of a hen's egg. (*a*) Cleavage is restricted to a small disc of cytoplasm on the upper surface of the egg yolk called the blastodisc. A subgerminal space appears beneath the blastodisc, separating it from the unsegmented yolk. (*b*) The blastodisc cleaves into an upper epiblast and a lower hypoblast separated by the blastocoel.

THE GERM LAYERS DEVELOP DURING GASTRULATION

Gastrulation is the process by which the blastula becomes a three-layered embryo, called a **gastrula.** During gastrulation, the cells arrange themselves into three distinct **germ layers,** or embryonic tissue layers—the ectoderm, mesoderm, and endoderm.

Each Germ Layer Has a Specific Fate

The cells lining the cavity of the gastrula, which is called the **archenteron,** make up the **endoderm.** The endoderm gives rise to tissues that eventually line the digestive tract and its outgrowths such as the liver, pancreas, and lungs. The outer wall of the gastrula consists of the germ layer known as **ectoderm.** The ectoderm eventually forms the outer layer of the skin and gives rise to the nervous system and sense organs.

A third layer of cells, the **mesoderm,** proliferates between the ectoderm and endoderm. The mesoderm gives rise to the skeletal tissues, muscle, circulatory system, excretory system, and reproductive system (Table 49–1). The complex morphogenetic movements of cells that result in formation of the germ layers depend upon instructions from the genes of the embryo.

The Pattern of Gastrulation Is Affected by the Amount of Yolk Present

Gastrulation in the sea star and in *Amphioxus* is illustrated in Figures 49–3 and 49–4, respectively. Gastrulation begins when the blastoderm at the vegetal pole flattens and then bends inward. The cells of a section of one wall of the blastula move inward, a process referred to as invagination. The invaginated wall eventually meets the opposite wall, obliterating the original blastocoel. In this way the embryo is converted into a double-walled cup-shaped structure. The cavity of the cup communicates with the exterior on the side that was originally the vegetal pole of the embryo. The internal wall lines the newly formed cavity, the archenteron. The opening of the archenteron to the exterior is the **blastopore.**

In the amphibian, the large yolk-laden cells in the vegetal half of the blastula obstruct the inward movement at the vegetal pole. Instead, cells from the animal pole move down toward the yolk-rich cells and then inward and away from the yolk-rich cells, forming the dorsal lip of the blastopore (Figure 49–8). The blastopore becomes horseshoe-shaped and then ring-shaped as cells lateral and then ventral to the blastopore become involved in the same movements. The yolk-filled cells of the vegetal hemisphere remain as a yolk plug filling the space enclosed by the lips of the blastopore. The rim of the blastopore continues to contract and eventually completely covers the yolk plug. The archenteron forms as a cavity leading from the groove on the surface of the embryo into the interior. It is lined on all sides by cells that have moved inward from the surface. The archenteron is a narrow slit at first but gradually expands at the anterior end, encroaching on the blastocoel, which is eventually obliterated.

Although the details differ somewhat, gastrulation in the bird is basically similar to that in the amphibian. Epiblast cells migrate toward the midline to form a thickened cellular region. This region, which elongates and narrows as it develops, is known as the **primitive streak.** At its center is a narrow furrow, the primitive

Table 49–1   FATE OF THE GERM LAYERS

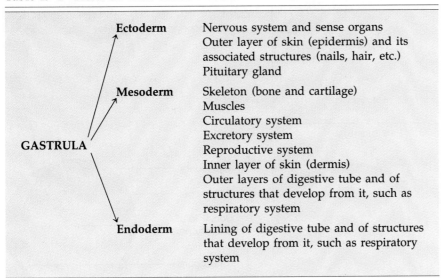

	Ectoderm	Nervous system and sense organs Outer layer of skin (epidermis) and its associated structures (nails, hair, etc.) Pituitary gland
GASTRULA	**Mesoderm**	Skeleton (bone and cartilage) Muscles Circulatory system Excretory system Reproductive system Inner layer of skin (dermis) Outer layers of digestive tube and of structures that develop from it, such as respiratory system
	Endoderm	Lining of digestive tube and of structures that develop from it, such as respiratory system

groove. The primitive streak is a dynamic structure. The cells composing it constantly change as they migrate in from the epiblast, sink down at the primitive streak, then move out laterally and anteriorly in the interior (Figure 49–9). These cells contribute to the endoderm as well as form the mesoderm. The primitive streak is homologous to the blastopore of the sea star, *Amphioxus*, or amphibian embryo. However, the embryo of the chick contains no cavity that is homologous to the archenteron.

At the anterior end of the primitive streak is a thickened knot of cells, **Hensen's node.** Cells destined to form the notochord (supporting rod of cartilage-like cells) become concentrated in Hensen's node and then grow anteriorly as a narrow process from the node just beneath the epiblast. Tissue that will form mesoderm moves laterally and anteriorly from the primitive streak between the epiblast (which becomes ectoderm) and the hypoblast (which becomes endoderm).

ORGANOGENESIS BEGINS WITH THE DEVELOPMENT OF THE NERVOUS SYSTEM

The process of organ formation is called **organogenesis.** The brain, notochord, and spinal cord are among the first organs to develop in the early vertebrate embryo (Figures 49–8*d* and *e* and 49–10). First the notochord, the flexible skeletal axis in all chordate embryos, grows forward along the length of the embryo as a cylindrical rod of cells. The developing notochord **induces** (stimulates) the overlying ectoderm to thicken, forming the

neural plate. Central cells of the neural plate move downward and form a depression called the **neural groove;** the cells flanking the groove on each side form **neural folds.** Continued cell movement brings the folds closer together until they meet and fuse, forming the **neural tube.** In this process, the neural tube comes to lie beneath the surface. The ectoderm overlying it will form the outer layer of skin. The anterior portion of the neural tube grows and differentiates into the brain; the remainder of the tube develops into the spinal cord.

The anterior part of the neural tube is much larger than the posterior part and continues to grow rapidly. At the same time, the neural tube bends down at the anterior end of the embryonic disc. The forebrain, midbrain, and hindbrain differentiate, and the forebrain begins to grow outward on either side, forming the rudiments of the cerebral hemispheres.

Various motor nerves grow out of the developing brain and spinal cord, but sensory nerves have a separate origin. When the neural folds fuse to form the neural tube, bits of nervous tissue known as the **neural crest** arise from the approximate region of fusion on each side of the tube. Neural crest cells migrate downward from their original position and form the dorsal root ganglia of the spinal nerves and the postganglionic sympathetic neurons. From sensory cells in the dorsal root ganglia, dendrites grow out to the sense organ and axons grow in to the spinal cord. Neural crest cells migrate to various locations in the embryo. They give rise to parts of certain sense organs and nearly all pigment-forming cells in the body.

As the nervous system develops, other organs also begin to take shape. The digestive tract is first formed as a separate foregut and hindgut by the growth and fold-

Figure 49–8 Stages in the development of a frog embryo. The diagrams show the embryo cut in half to reveal the inside. (*a*) Late blastula. (*b*) Early gastrula. (*c*) Middle gastrula. (*d*) Late gastrula. (*e*) Nervous system development begins with the formation of the neural plate. This photomicrograph is a cross section, while the diagram represents an embryo cut in half longitudinally.   (*c*, Carolina Biological Supply Company)

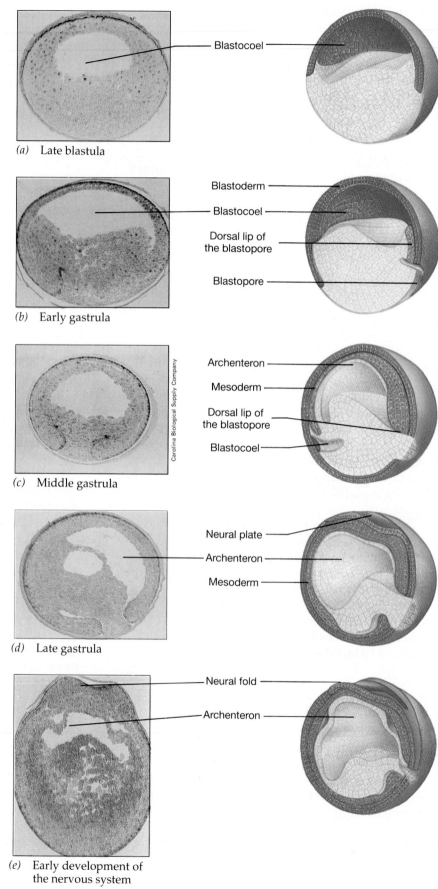

Blastocoel

(*a*)   Late blastula

Blastoderm
Blastocoel
Dorsal lip of the blastopore
Blastopore

(*b*)   Early gastrula

Archenteron
Mesoderm
Dorsal lip of the blastopore
Blastocoel

(*c*)   Middle gastrula

Neural plate
Archenteron
Mesoderm

(*d*)   Late gastrula

Neural fold
Archenteron

(*e*)   Early development of the nervous system

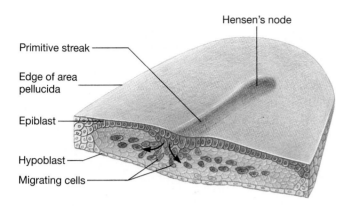

Figure 49–9 Gastrulation in the bird. The anterior half of the area pellucida (a translucent region of cells) of a chick embryo is cut transversely to show the migration of mesodermal and endodermal cells from the primitive streak.

ing of the body wall, which cuts them off as two simple tubes from the original yolk sac (Figure 49–11*a*). As the embryo grows, these tubes, which are lined with endoderm, grow and become greatly elongated. The liver, pancreas, and trachea originate as hollow, tubular out-

growths from the gut. As the trachea grows downward, it gives rise to the paired lung buds, which develop into lungs.

The most anterior part of the foregut becomes the pharynx. A series of small outpocketings of the pharynx, the **pharyngeal pouches,** bud out laterally (Figure 49–11*b*). These pouches meet a corresponding set of inpocketings from the overlying ectoderm, the **branchial grooves.** The arches of tissue formed between the grooves are called **branchial arches.** These arches contain the rudimentary skeletal, neural, and vascular elements of the face, jaws, and neck.

In aquatic vertebrates, the pharyngeal grooves and branchial grooves meet and form a continuous passage from the pharynx to the outside—the gills slits, which function as respiratory organs. In fish and some amphibians, gills develop on the branchial arches. In terrestrial vertebrates, each branchial groove remains separated from the corresponding pharyngeal pouch by a thin membrane of tissue. Structures more appropriate for life on land develop. For example, the first branchial groove becomes the external ear canal, the first pharyngeal pouch becomes the eustachian tube, and the tissue separating the two becomes the eardrum.

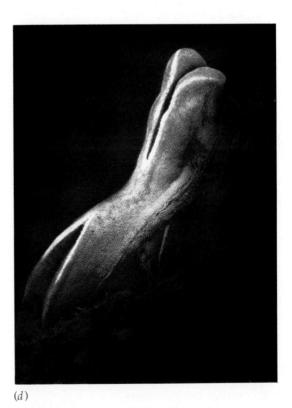

(*d*)

Figure 49–10 Cross sections of human embryos at successively later stages, illustrating the early development of the nervous system. The neural crest cells form the dorsal root ganglia and the postganglionic sympathetic neurons. (*a*) Approximately 19 days. The neural plate has indented to form a shallow groove flanked by neural folds. (*b*) Approximately 20 days. The neural folds approach one another; upon fusing together, they will form

the neural tube. (*c*) Approximately 26 days. The neural tube has now formed and will give rise to the brain at the anterior end of the embryo and the spinal cord posteriorly. (*d*) Photograph of a 20-day-old human embryo, illustrating the developing nervous system. (*d,* Lennart Nilsson © Boehringer Ingelheim International GmbH, from *A Child Is Born,* p. 76)

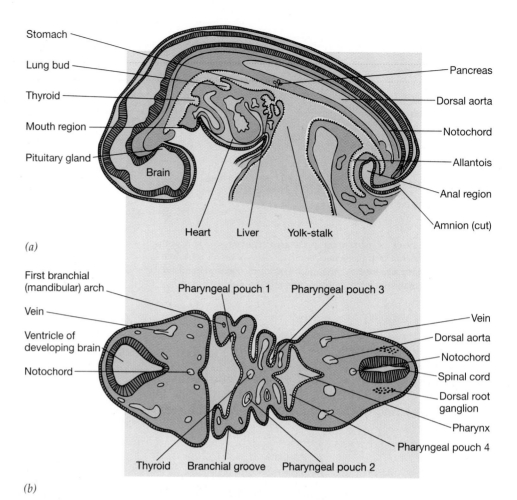

(a)

(b)

Figure 49–11 Organogenesis. (a) Sagittal section through human embryo showing some of the structures developing during the fifth week. Note that the liver, pancreas, and respiratory system develop as outpocketings from the digestive tract. (b) Cross section through a human embryo during the fifth week of development. Note the branchial grooves, pharyngeal pouches, and branchial arches. Because the embryo is flexed, both the brain and spinal cord are seen in the cross section.

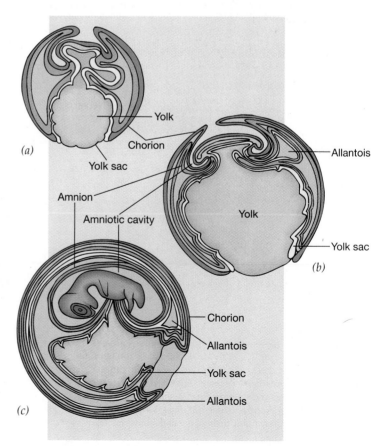

Figure 49–12 Development of extraembryonic membranes. (a to c) Successive stages in the development of the extraembryonic membranes of the chick. Each of the membranes develops from a combination of two germ layers. The chorion and amnion form from lateral folds of the ectoderm and mesoderm that extend over the embryo and fuse. The allantois, an elongated sac consisting of endoderm and mesoderm, develops from an outpocketing of the hindgut. The yolk sac also consists of endoderm and mesoderm.

The heart and circulatory system are among the first structures to take form and must function while still developing. The circulatory organs develop from the mesoderm. Other mesodermal structures include the skeleton, muscles, kidneys, and reproductive structures.

EXTRAEMBRYONIC MEMBRANES AND PLACENTA PROTECT AND NOURISH THE EMBRYO

All terrestrial vertebrates have four **extraembryonic membranes:** the chorion, allantois, yolk sac, and amnion. Although they develop from the germ layers, these membranes are not part of the embryo proper and are discarded at birth. The extraembryonic membranes are adaptations to the challenges of embryonic development on land. During development they protect the embryo, prevent the embryo from drying out, and help it to obtain food and oxygen and eliminate wastes.

The Chorion and Amnion Enclose the Embryo

The **chorion** and **amnion** develop together as folds of the body wall. They grow around the embryo, meeting and fusing above it and eventually enclosing the entire embryo (Figure 49–12). In the eggs of reptiles and birds, the chorion remains in contact with the inner surface of the shell. In mammals it lies next to the cells of the uterine wall.

The space between the embryo and the amnion, the amniotic cavity, becomes filled with clear, watery amniotic fluid secreted by the membrane. Embryos of terrestrial vertebrates develop within this pool of fluid. The amniotic fluid prevents the embryo from drying out and acts as a protective cushion that absorbs shocks and prevents the amniotic membrane from sticking to the embryo. Amniotic fluid also permits the embryo some freedom of motion.

The Allantois Functions in Waste Disposal

The **allantois** is an outgrowth of the developing digestive tract. In reptiles and birds, it stores nitrogenous wastes and so becomes quite large. The products of nitrogen metabolism are excreted as uric acid by the kidney of the developing embryo. The poorly soluble uric acid is deposited as crystals in the cavity of the allantois and is discarded along with the allantois when the young hatches.

The allantois fuses with the chorion to form the **chorioallantoic membrane,** which is rich in blood vessels. In the chick embryo, blood in these vessels provides oxygen and receives carbon dioxide and other wastes from the embryo. Gases are exchanged through the shell. In the human, the allantois is small and nonfunctional except that its blood vessels contribute to the formation of umbilical vessels joining the embryo to the placenta (see below). When the chick hatches or the child is born, most of the allantois, like the other extraembryonic membranes, is discarded. However, the base of the allantois, the portion originally connected to the digestive tract, is converted into part of the urinary bladder.

The Yolk Sac Encloses the Yolk

Like the allantois, the **yolk sac** forms as an outpocketing of the developing digestive tract. In vertebrates with yolk-rich eggs, the yolk sac encloses the yolk, slowly digests it, and makes it available to the embryo. Even in vertebrate embryos with little or no yolk, a yolk sac forms. Its walls serve as temporary centers for blood cell formation.

The Placenta Is an Organ of Exchange

In placental mammals, the **placenta** is the organ of exchange between mother and fetus. The placenta provides nutrients and oxygen for the fetus and removes wastes from the fetus for excretion by the mother. In addition, the placenta serves as an endocrine organ, producing hormones that maintain pregnancy.

The placenta develops from both the embryonic chorion and the maternal uterine tissue. In early development the chorion grows rapidly, invading the endometrium (lining of the uterus) and forming finger-like projections called villi. The villi become vascularized (infiltrated with blood vessels) as the embryonic circulation develops. Enzymes released by the invading embryonic cells destroy some of the endometrial tissue, including many small blood vessels. Small amounts of blood oozing from these damaged vessels form pools around the chorionic villi.

As the human embryo grows, the region on the ventral side from which the folds of the amnion, yolk sac, and allantois grew becomes relatively smaller, and the edges of the amniotic folds come together to form a tube that encloses the other membranes. This tube, the **umbilical cord,** connects the embryo with the placenta (Figure 49–15). In addition to the yolk sac and allantois, the umbilical cord contains the two umbilical arteries and the umbilical vein. The **umbilical arteries** connect the embryo with a vast network of capillaries developing within the villi; blood from the villi returns to the embryo through the **umbilical vein.**

The placenta actually consists of the portion of the chorion that develops villi and the uterine tissue under-

FOCUS ON

Multiple Births

Occasionally, the cells of the two-cell embryo separate and each cell develops into a complete organism. Or sometimes the inner cell mass subdivides, forming two groups of cells, each of which develops independently. Because these cells have identical sets of genes, the individuals formed are exactly alike—**monozygotic, or identical, twins.** Very rarely, the two inner cell masses do not completely separate and give rise to **conjoined (Siamese) twins** (see figure).

Fraternal twins, also called **dizygotic twins,** develop when two eggs are ovulated and each is fertilized by a different sperm. Each zygote has its own distinctive genetic endowment, so the individuals produced are not identical. They may even be of the opposite sex. Triplets (and other multiple births) may similarly be either identical or fraternal (see Figure 49–23). In the United States, twins are born once in about

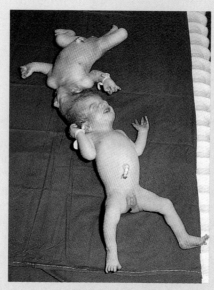

Conjoined or Siamese twins joined at the head. (Biophoto Associates)

80 births (about 30% of twins are monozygotic), triplets once in 80^2 (or 1 in 6400), and quadruplets once in

80^3 (or 1 in 512,000). These statistics appear to be changing. Multiple births have been increasing with increased use of fertility-inducing agents.

A family history of twinning increases the probability of having dizygotic twins. However, giving birth to monozygotic twins does not appear to be influenced by heredity, age of the mother, or other known factors. An estimated two thirds of multiple pregnancies end in birth of a single baby; the other embryo may be absorbed within the first 10 weeks of pregnancy or may be spontaneously aborted. Ultrasonic techniques used early in pregnancy can give valuable information regarding the presence of multiple embryos (see Figure 49–23). Multiple births are associated with increased risk of perinatal mortality and morbidity. An important factor contributing to this risk is low birth rate.

---

lying the villi, which contains maternal capillaries and small pools of maternal blood. The blood of the fetus in the capillaries of the chorionic villi comes in close contact with the mother's blood in the tissues between the villi. The two circulatory systems are always separated by a membrane through which substances may diffuse or be actively transported. *Maternal and fetal blood do not normally mix in the placenta or any other place.*

Several hormones are produced by the placenta. From the time the embryo first begins to implant itself, it releases **human chorionic gonadotropin (HCG),** which signals the corpus luteum that pregnancy has begun. In response, the corpus luteum increases in size and releases large amounts of progesterone and estrogen, which in turn stimulate continued development of the endometrium and placenta. Without HCG, the corpus luteum would degenerate and the embryo would be aborted and flushed out with the menstrual flow. In such a case the woman would probably not even know that she had been pregnant. If the corpus luteum is removed before about the 11th week of pregnancy, the embryo is spontaneously aborted. After that time, how-

ever, the placenta itself produces enough progesterone and estrogens to maintain pregnancy.

HUMAN PRENATAL DEVELOPMENT REQUIRES ABOUT 266 DAYS

In this section we focus on human development as an example of development in placental mammals. Prenatal (before birth) human development normally requires 280 days from the time of the mother's last menstrual period to the birth of the baby, or 266 days from the time of conception (Table 49–2).

Cleavage Takes Place in the Uterine Tube

By about 24 hours after fertilization, the human zygote has become a two-cell embryo. Each of the two cells undergoes mitotic division, bringing the number of cells to four. Cleavage continues as the embryo is pushed along the uterine tube by ciliary action and

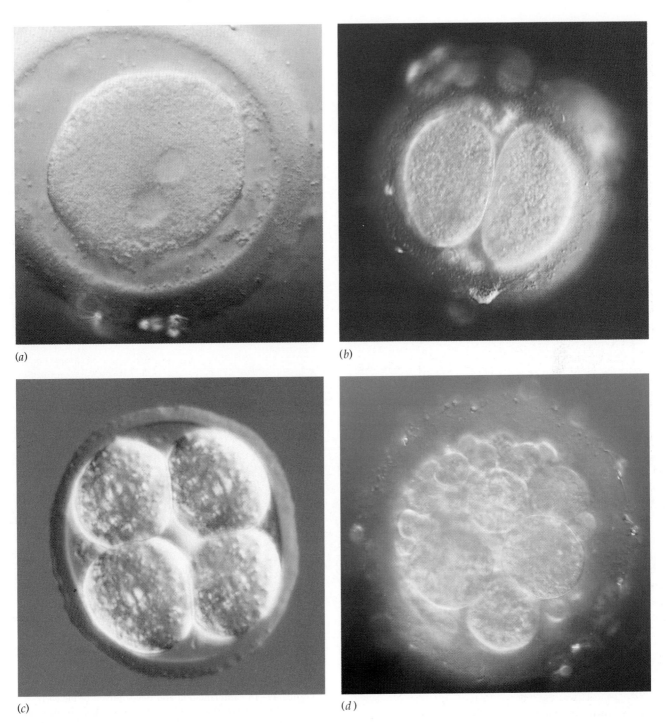

(a)

(b)

(c)

(d)

Figure 49–13 Early human development. (*a*) Human zygote. This single cell contains the genetic instructions for producing a complete human being. (*b*) Two-cell stage. (*c*) Eight-cell stage.

(*d*) Cleavage continues, giving rise to a cluster of cells called the morula. (Lennart Nilsson from *Being Born*, pp. 14, 15, 17)

muscle contraction. By the time the embryo reaches the uterus, it is in the morula stage (Figures 49–13 and 49–14).

When the embryo enters the uterus, the membrane that has surrounded it, the **zona pellucida,** dissolves, and the embryo is bathed in a nutritive fluid secreted by the glands of the uterus. Nourished in this manner, the embryo continues its development for 2 or 3 days, float-

ing free in the uterine cavity. During this period its cells arrange themselves to form a blastula, which in mammals is called a **blastocyst** (Figure 49–15*a*). The outer layer of cells, the **trophoblast,** eventually forms the chorion that surrounds the embryo. A little cluster of cells, the **inner cell mass,** projects into the cavity of the blastocyst. The inner cell mass gives rise to the embryo proper.

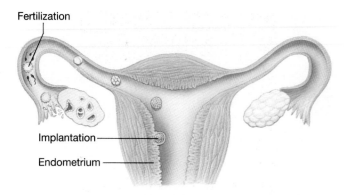

Figure 49-14 Cleavage takes place as the embryo is moved along through the uterine tube to the uterus.

The Embryo Implants in the Wall of the Uterus

On about the seventh day of development, the embryo begins to **implant** in the endometrium of the uterus (Figure 49–15a). The trophoblast cells in contact with the uterine lining secrete enzymes that erode an area just large enough to accommodate the tiny embryo. The embryo slowly works its way down into the underlying connective and vascular tissues. The opening through which the blastocyst enters the uterine lining is closed, first by a blood clot and eventually by overgrowth of regenerated epithelial cells. All further development of the embryo takes place within the endometrium of the uterus (Figure 49–16).

During implantation, enzymes destroy some tiny maternal capillaries in the wall of the uterus. Blood from these capillaries comes in direct contact with the trophoblast of the embryo and temporarily provides a rich source of nutrition.

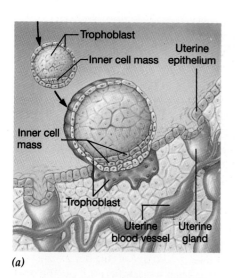

(a)

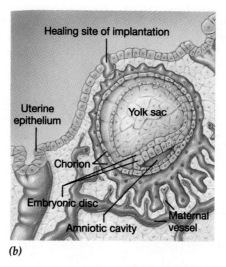

(b)

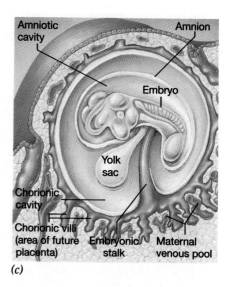

(c)

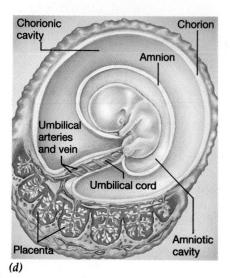

(d)

Figure 49-15 Implantation and development of the early human embryo. (a) About 7 days after fertilization the blastocyst drifts to an appropriate site along the uterine wall and begins to implant itself. The cells of the trophoblast proliferate and invade the endometrium. (b) About 10 days after fertilization. The chorion has formed from the trophoblast. (c) By 25 days intimate relationships have been established between the embryo and the maternal blood vessels. Oxygen and nutrients from the maternal blood are now meeting the embryo's needs. Note the specialized region of the chorion that will soon become the placenta. The embryonic stalk will become part of the umbilical cord. (d) At about 45 days the embryo and its membranes together are about the size of a Ping-Pong ball, and the mother still may be unaware of her pregnancy. The amnion filled with amniotic fluid surrounds and cushions the embryo. The yolk sac has been incorporated into the umbilical cord. Blood circulation has been established through the umbilical cord to the placenta.

Epithelium of uterus   Site of implantation

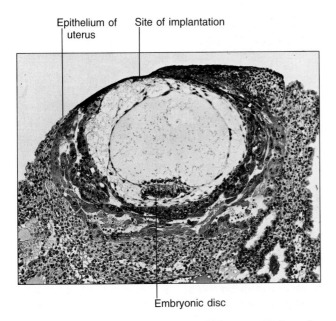

Embryonic disc

Figure 49–16 Photograph of implanted blastocyst 12 days after fertilization. (Courtesy of Carnegie Institution of Washington)

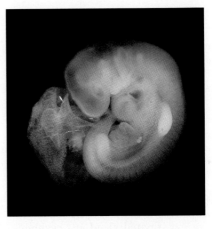

Figure 49–18 Human embryo at 29 days, about 7 mm (0.3 inch) long. Note the slender tail and developing limb buds. The tail will regress during later development. The heart can be seen below the head near the mouth of the embryo. Branchial arches appear as "double chins." (Lennart Nilsson, from *A Child Is Born*)

Implantation is complete by the ninth day of development. This corresponds to about the 23rd day of a woman's menstrual cycle, so that despite all the developmental activities taking place in her uterus, a woman would probably not even know that she was pregnant at this time.

Organ Development Begins during the First Trimester

Gastrulation occurs during the second and third weeks of human development. At that time the notochord begins to form and induces formation of the neural plate. The neural tube develops, and the forebrain, midbrain, and hindbrain are established by the fifth week of development. A week or so later, the forebrain begins to grow outward, forming the rudiments of the cerebral hemispheres.

During the first month of development, the heart begins to take shape and to beat—about 60 times each minute (Figure 49–17). In the pharyngeal region, the pharyngeal pouches, branchial grooves, and branchial arches form. In the floor of the pharynx at the level of the fourth pharyngeal pouches a tube of cells grows downward, forming the primordial trachea, which gives rise to the lung buds. The digestive system also develops outgrowths that will develop into the liver, gallbladder, and pancreas. Near the end of the first month, limb buds begin to differentiate and will eventually give rise to arms and legs (Figures 49–18 and 49–19).

All of the organs continue to develop during the second month. A thin tail becomes prominent during the fifth week, but it does not grow as rapidly as the rest of the body and so becomes inconspicuous by the end of the second month. Muscles develop, and the embryo becomes capable of movement (Table 49–2). The brain begins to send impulses to regulate the functions of some organs, and a few simple reflexes become evident.

Figure 49–17 Ventral views of successive stages in the development of the heart. The heart forms from the fusion of two blood vessels. At first it is upside down, with the end that receives blood from the veins at the bottom. As it develops, the heart twists and turns so as to carry the atrium to a position above the ventricle, and the conus and sinus disappear. The chambers divide to form the four-chambered heart. The heart begins to beat spontaneously without nervous stimulation.

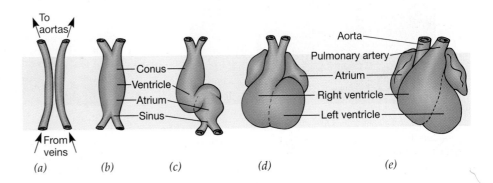

Table 49–2   SOME IMPORTANT DEVELOPMENTAL EVENTS IN THE HUMAN EMBRYO

Time from Fertilization	Event
24 hours	Embryo reaches two-cell stage
3 days	Morula reaches uterus
7 days	Blastocyst begins to implant
2.5 weeks	Notochord and neural plate are formed; tissue that will give rise to heart is differentiating; blood cells are forming in yolk sac and chorion
3.5 weeks	Neural tube forming; primordial eye and ear visible; pharyngeal pouches forming; liver bud differentiating; respiratory system and thyroid gland just beginning to develop; heart tubes fuse, bend, and begin to beat; blood vessels are laid down
4 weeks	Limb buds appear; three primary divisions of brain formed
2 months	Muscles differentiating; embryo capable of movement; gonad distinguishable as testis or ovary. Bones begin to ossify; cerebral cortex differentiating; principal blood vessels assume final positions
3 months	Sex can be determined by external inspection; notochord degenerates; lymph glands develop
4 months	Face begins to look human; lobes of cerebrum differentiate; eyes, ears, and nose look more "normal"
Third trimester	Lanugo appears, then later is shed; neuron myelination begins; tremendous growth of body
266 days (from conception)	Birth

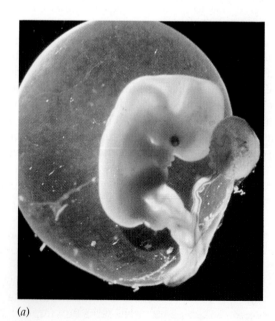

(a)

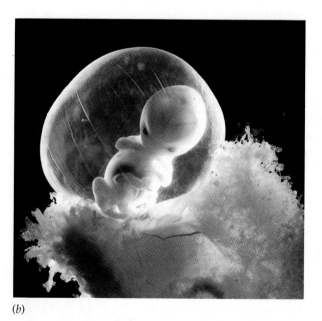

(b)

Figure 49–19 Photographs of developing human embryos. (a) Human embryo at 5½ weeks, 1 cm (0.4 inch) long. Limb buds have lengthened and the eyes have become prominent. (b) In its seventh week of development, the embryo is 2 cm (0.8 inch) long. The dark red object inside the embryo is the liver. (a, Guigoz/Petit Format/Photo Researchers, Inc.; b, Lennart Nilsson, from *A Child Is Born*)

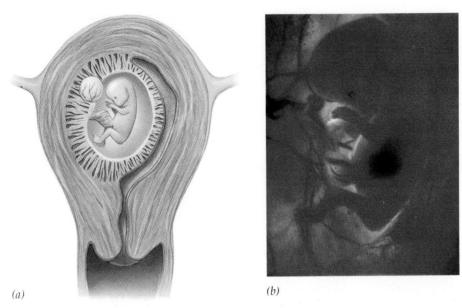

(a)   (b)

Figure 49–20   The human fetus at 10 weeks of development. (*a*) Note position in the uterine wall. (*b*) Photograph at 10 weeks. (*b*, Nestle/Petit Format/Photo Researchers, Inc.)

After the first 2 months of development the embryo is referred to as a **fetus.**

By the end of the **first trimester** (first 3 months of development), the fetus is recognizably human (Figure 49–20). The external genital structures have differentiated, indicating the sex of the fetus. Ears and eyes approach their final positions. Some of the skeleton becomes distinct, and the notochord has been replaced by the developing vertebral column. The fetus performs breathing movements, pumping amniotic fluid into and out of its lungs, and even carries on sucking movements. By the end of the third month, the fetus is almost 56 mm (about 2.2 inches) long and weighs about 14 grams (0.5 ounce).

The Fetus Continues to Develop during the Second and Third Trimesters

During the second trimester, the fetal heart (now beating about 150 times per minute) can be heard with a stethoscope. The fetus moves freely in the amniotic cavity; during the fifth month, the mother usually becomes aware of fetal movements ("quickening").

During the final trimester, the fetus grows rapidly, and final differentiation of tissues and organs occurs. At the beginning of the sixth month the skin has a wrinkled appearance, perhaps because it is growing faster than the underlying connective tissue. If born prematurely at this age the fetus attempts to breathe and is able to move and cry but almost always dies because its brain and lungs are not sufficiently developed to sustain vital functions such as rhythmic breathing and regulation of body temperature.

During the seventh month the cerebrum grows rapidly and develops convolutions. Grasp and sucking reflexes are evident, and the fetus may suck its thumb. Most of the body is covered by a downy hair called **lanugo,** which is usually shed before birth. Occasionally the lanugo is not shed until a few days after birth.

During the last months of prenatal life, a protective creamlike substance, the **vernix,** covers the skin, and hair begins to grow on the scalp. At birth the average full-term baby weighs about 3000 grams (7 pounds) and measures about 52 cm (20 inches) in total length (or about 35 cm from crown to rump).

The Birth Process May Be Divided into Three Stages

The human **gestation period,** the duration of pregnancy, is normally 280 days (40 weeks) from the time of the last menstrual period to the birth of the baby (or 266 days from conception). Babies born as early as 28 weeks or as late as 45 weeks after the last menstrual period may survive. The factors that initiate the process of birth, or **parturition,** after gestation is complete are not well understood. Childbirth begins with a long series of involuntary contractions of the uterus, experienced as the contractions of **labor.**

Labor may be divided into three stages. During the first stage, which typically lasts about 12 hours, the contractions of the uterus move the fetus down toward the cervix. The cervix dilates and becomes effaced, that is, loses its normal shape and flattens so that the fetal head can pass through. During the first stage of labor the

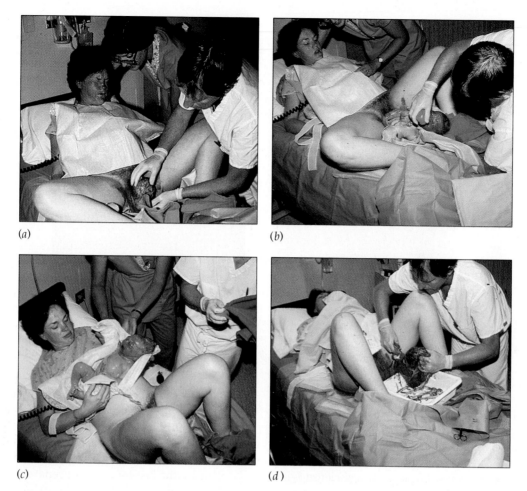

Figure 49–21 Birth of a baby. In about 95% of all human births the baby descends through the cervix and vagina in the head-down position. (*a*) The mother bears down hard with her abdominal muscles, helping to push the baby out. When the head fully appears, the physician or midwife can gently grasp it and guide the baby's entrance into the outside world. (*b*) Once the head has emerged, the rest of the body usually follows readily. The physician gently aspirates the mouth and pharynx to clear the upper airway of any amniotic fluid, mucus, or blood. At this time the neonate usually takes its first breath. (*c*) The baby, still attached to the placenta by its umbilical cord, is presented to its mother. (*d*) During the third stage of labor the placenta is delivered.   (Courtesy of Dan Atchison)

amnion usually ruptures, releasing about 1 liter of amniotic fluid, which flows out through the vagina. In the second stage, which normally lasts between 20 minutes and 1 hour, the fetus passes through the cervix and vagina and is born, or "delivered" (Figure 49–21). With each uterine contraction the woman holds her breath and bears down so that the fetus is expelled from the uterus by the combined forces of uterine and abdominal wall contractions.

After the baby is born, uterine contractions squeeze much of the fetal blood from the placenta back into the infant. After the pulsations in the umbilical cord cease, the cord is tied and cut, severing the child from the mother. The stump of the cord gradually shrivels until nothing remains but the depressed scar, the **navel.**

During the third stage of labor, which lasts 10 or 15 minutes after the birth of the child, the placenta and the fetal membranes are loosened from the lining of the uterus by another series of contractions and expelled. At this stage they are called collectively the **afterbirth.** In humans and certain other mammals in which the placenta forms a very tight connection with the uterine lining, expulsion of the placenta is accompanied by some loss of blood. In mammals in which the connection between the fetal membranes and uterine wall is not close, the placenta can pull away from the uterine wall without causing bleeding. Following birth, the size of the uterus decreases, and its lining is rapidly restored.

During labor an obstetrician may administer drugs such as oxytocin or prostaglandins to increase the contractions of the uterus or may assist with special forceps or other techniques. The opening between the pelvic bones through which the vagina passes normally enlarges during late pregnancy due to the action of hormones on the ligaments of the pubic symphysis. In some women, this opening remains too small to permit the passage of the baby, so the child must be delivered by **cesarean section,** an operation in which an incision is made in the abdominal wall and uterus.

The Neonate Must Adapt to Its New Environment

Important changes take place within a short time after a baby is born. During prenatal life, the fetus received both food and oxygen from the placenta. After birth the newborn's own digestive and respiratory systems must function. Correlated with these changes are several major changes in the circulatory system.

Normally the **neonate** (newborn infant) begins to breathe within a few seconds of birth and cries within half a minute. If anesthetics have been given to the mother, however, the fetus may also have been anesthetized, and breathing and other activities may be depressed. Some infants may not begin breathing for several minutes. This is one of the reasons for the current trend toward childbirth methods that minimize the use of medication.

The neonate's first breath is thought to be initiated by the accumulation of carbon dioxide in the blood after the umbilical cord is cut. This stimulates the respiratory centers in the medulla. The resulting expansion of the lungs enlarges its blood vessels (which previously were partially collapsed). Blood from the right ventricle flows in increasing amounts through the pulmonary vessels instead of through the arterial duct. (Before birth, the arterial duct connected the pulmonary artery and aorta, allowing blood to bypass the lungs during fetal life.)

Environmental Factors Influence the Embryo

Just as a baby's growth and development are obviously influenced by the food he (or she) eats, the air he breathes, the disease organisms that infect him, and the chemicals or drugs to which he is exposed, prenatal development is affected by these environmental influences. Life before birth is, in fact, even more sensitive to environmental changes than it is in the fully formed baby.

About 5% of newborns (about 175,000 babies per year) in the United States have a defect of clinical significance. Such birth defects account for about 15% of deaths among newborns. Birth defects may be caused by genetic or environmental factors or a combination of the two. Genetic factors were discussed in Part 3. In this section we examine some environmental conditions that affect the well-being of the embryo.

Substances or conditions that intrude upon the developing embryo from the outside environment may cause significant damage at one period in development yet appear to be harmless during a later stage. Timing is important. Each developing structure has a critical period during which it is most susceptible to unfavorable conditions. Generally this critical period occurs early in the development of the structure, when interference with cell movements or divisions may prevent formation of normal shape or size, resulting in permanent malformation. Because most structures form during the first 3 months of embryonic life, the embryo is most susceptible to environmental conditions during this early period. During a substantial portion of this time the mother may not even realize that she is pregnant and therefore may take no special precautions to minimize potentially dangerous exposures.

Anything that circulates in the maternal blood—nutrients, drugs, and even gases—may find its way into the blood of the fetus. Some drugs, as well as other types of agents, are **teratogens;** they can interfere with normal development (Figure 49–22). Table 49–3 describes some of the environmental influences upon development. Many of these environmental factors contribute to low birth weight, a condition responsible for a great number of infant deaths.

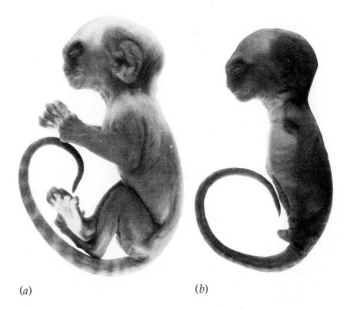

(a) 　　　　　　　　　　　　　　(b)

Figure 49–22 Thalidomide administered to the marmoset (*Callithrix jacchus*) produces a pattern of developmental defects similar to those found in humans. (*a*) Control marmoset fetus obtained from an untreated mother on day 125 of gestation. (*b*) Fetus (same age as control) of marmoset treated with 25 mg/kg of thalidomide from days 38 to 52 of gestation. The drug suppresses limb formation, perhaps by interfering with the function of cholinergic nerves. (Courtesy of Dr. W. G. McBride and P. H. Vardy, Foundation 41; from *Development, Growth and Differentiation* 25(4):361–373, 1983)

Table 49–3   ENVIRONMENTAL INFLUENCES ON THE EMBRYO

Factor	Example and Effect	Comment
Nutrition	Severe protein malnutrition doubles number of defects; fewer brain cells are produced, and learning ability may be permanently affected; vitamin deficiencies linked to CNS defects	Growth rate mainly determined by rate of net protein synthesis by embryo's cells; low birth weight
Excessive amounts of vitamins	Vitamin D essential, but excessive amounts may result in form of mental retardation; an excess of vitamins A and K may also be harmful	Vitamin supplements are normally prescribed for pregnant women, but some women mistakenly reason that if one vitamin pill is beneficial, four or five might be even better
Drugs	Many drugs affect development of fetus: Even aspirin has been shown to inhibit growth of human fetal cells (especially kidney cells) cultured in laboratory; it may also inhibit prostaglandins, which are concentrated in growing tissue	Common prescription and nonprescription drugs are generally taken in amounts based on mother's body weight, which may be hundreds or thousands of times too much for the tiny embryo
Alcohol	When a woman drinks heavily during pregnancy, the baby may be born with fetal alcohol syndrome—that is, deformed and mentally and physically retarded; low birth weight and structural abnormalities have been associated with as little as two drinks a day; some cases of hyperactivity and learning disabilities may be caused by alcohol intake of a pregnant mother	Fetal alcohol syndrome is thought to be one of leading causes of mental retardation in the United States; low birth weight
Cocaine	Premature birth; retarded development; severe cases may be mentally retarded, have heart defects and other medical problems	Thousands of cocaine-addicted babies are being born to mothers who use cocaine during pregnancy; low birth weight
Heroin	High mortality rate and high prematurity rate	Infants that survive are born addicted and must be treated for weeks or months; low birth weight

Factor	Example and Effect	Comment
Thalidomide	Thalidomide, marketed as mild sedative, was responsible for more than 7000 grossly deformed babies born in the late 1950s in 20 countries; principal defect was **phocomelia**, a condition in which babies are born with extremely short limbs, often with no fingers or toes	This drug interferes with cellular metabolism; most hazardous when taken during fourth to sixth weeks, when limbs are developing
Cigarette smoking	Cigarette smoking reduces the amount of oxygen available to the fetus because some of maternal hemoglobin is combined with carbon monoxide; may slow growth and can cause subtle forms of damage; in extreme form carbon monoxide poisoning causes such gross defects as hydrocephaly	Mothers who smoke deliver babies with lower-than-average birth weights and have higher incidence of spontaneous abortions, stillbirths, and neonatal deaths; studies also indicate possible link between maternal smoking and slower intellectual development in offspring
Pathogens	Rubella (German measles) virus crosses placenta and infects embryo; interferes with normal metabolism and cell movements; causes syndrome that involves blinding cataracts, deafness, heart malformations, and mental retardation; risk is greatest (about 50%) when rubella is contracted during first month of pregnancy; risk declines with each succeeding month	Rubella epidemic in the United States in 1963–1965 resulted in about 20,000 fetal deaths and 30,000 infants born with gross defects
	HIV can be transmitted from mother to baby before birth, during birth, or postpartum through breast-feeding	See discussion of AIDS in Chapter 43
	Syphilis is transmitted to fetus in about 40% of infected women; fetus may die or be born with defects and congenital syphilis	Pregnant women are routinely tested for syphilis during prenatal examinations
Ionizing radiation	When mother is subjected to x-rays or other forms of radiation during pregnancy, infant has higher risk of birth defects and leukemia	Radiation was one of earliest teratogens to be recognized

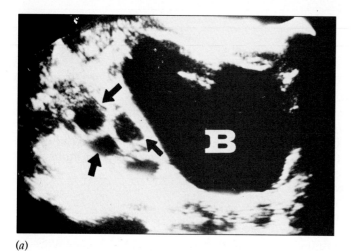

(a)

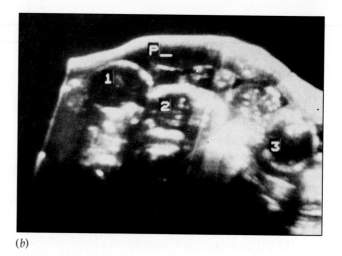

(b)

Figure 49–23 Ultrasonic techniques can be used to monitor follicle maturation and ovulation, as well as to give the physician information about the fetus. (*a*) Sonogram taken with ultrasound techniques, showing three follicles of equal maturation in the left ovary of a human. (*b*) Triplets in the same patient at 16 weeks of pregnancy. P = placenta. Such previews are valuable to the physician in diagnosing defects and predicting multiple births. (Also see Figure 15–10.)   (Courtesy of Biserka Funduk-Kurjak and Asim Kurjak, from *Acta Obstetrics and Gynecology Scan.* 61:1982)

Recent advances in medicine allow physicians to diagnose some defects while the fetus is in the uterus. In some cases treatment is possible before birth. **Amniocentesis,** discussed in Chapter 15, is one technique used to detect certain defects. Figure 49–23 is a **sonogram** of the fetus (a sonogram is a picture taken using ultrasound). Such previews are helpful in diagnosing defects and also in determining the position of the fetus and whether a multiple birth is pending.

THE HUMAN LIFE CYCLE EXTENDS FROM CONCEPTION TO DEATH

Development begins at conception and continues through the stages of the human life cycle until death (Table 49–4). We have examined briefly the development of the embryo and fetus, the birth process, and the adjustments it requires of the neonate. The **neonatal period** is usually considered to extend from birth to the end of the first month of extrauterine life. **Infancy** follows the neonatal period and lasts until the rapidly developing infant can assume an erect posture (i.e., can walk), usually between 10 and 14 months of age. Some regard infancy as extending to the end of the second year. **Childhood,** also a period of rapid growth and development, continues from infancy to adolescence.

Adolescence is the time of development between puberty and adulthood. During adolescence a young person experiences the physical and physiological changes that result in physical and reproductive maturity (Figure 49–24). This is also a time of profound psychological development, as young people make adjustments that help prepare them to assume the responsibilities of adulthood.

Young adulthood extends from adolescence until about age 40. Middle age is usually considered to be the period between ages 40 and 65. Old age begins after age 65.

HOMEOSTATIC RESPONSE TO STRESS DECREASES DURING AGING

Because development in its broadest sense includes any biological change with time, it includes changes that result in the decreased functional capacities of the mature organism, referred to as **aging.** The declining capacities of the various systems in the human body, although most apparent in the elderly, may begin much earlier in life, during childhood or even during prenatal life. The newborn female has only 400,000 oocytes re-

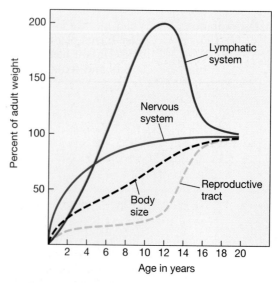

Figure 49–24 Relative rates of growth of several different organ systems during human development.

1076

Table 49–4 STAGES IN THE HUMAN LIFE CYCLE

Stage	*Time Period*	*Characteristics*
Embryo	Conception to end of eighth week of prenatal development	Development proceeds from single-celled zygote to embryo that is about 30 mm long, weighs 1 gram, and has rudiments of all its organs
Fetus	Beginning of ninth week of prenatal development to birth	Period of rapid growth, morphogenesis, and cellular differentiation, changing tiny parasite to physiologically independent organism
Neonate	Birth to 4 weeks of age	Neonate must make vital physiological adjustments to independent life: it must now process its own food, excrete its wastes, obtain oxygen, and make appropriate circulatory changes
Infant	End of fourth week to 2 years of age (sometimes, ability to walk is considered end of infancy)	Rapid growth; deciduous teeth begin to erupt; nervous system develops (myelinization), making coordinated activities possible; language skills begin to develop
Child	Two years to puberty	Rapid growth; deciduous teeth erupt, are slowly shed and replaced by permanent teeth; development of muscular coordination; development of language skills and other intellectual abilities
Adolescent	Puberty (approximately ages 11–14) to adult	Growth spurt; primary and secondary sexual characteristics develop; development of motor skills; development of intellectual abilities; psychological changes as adolescent approaches adulthood
Young adult	End of adolescence (approximately age 20) to about age 40	Peak of physical development reached; individual assumes adult responsibilities that may include marriage, fulfilling reproductive potential, and establishing career; after age 30, physiological changes associated with aging begin
Middle-aged adult	Age 40 to about age 65	Physiological aging continues, leading to menopause in women and physical changes associated with aging in both sexes (e.g., graying hair, decline in athletic abilities, wrinkling skin); this is period of adjustment for many as they begin to face their own mortality
Old adult	Age 65 to death	Period of senescence (growing old); physiological aging continues; maintaining homeostasis more difficult when body is challenged by stress; death often results from failure of cardiovascular or immune system

maining of the 4 million she had 3 months earlier in fetal life!

The aging process is far from uniform among different individuals or in various parts of the body. Various systems of the body generally decline at different times and rates. On the average, a 75-year-old man has lost 64% of the taste buds, 44% of the renal glomeruli, and 37% of the axons in his spinal nerves that he had at age 30. His nerve impulses move 10% more slowly, the blood supply to his brain is 20% less, his glomerular filtration rate has decreased 31%, and the vital capacity of his lungs has declined 44%. The aging process is also marked by a progressive decrease in the body's homeostatic ability to respond to stress.

About 10,000 children born each year are products of **artificial insemination.** Usually this procedure is sought when the male partner of a couple desiring a child is sterile or carries a genetic defect. Although the sperm donor remains anonymous to the couple involved, his genetic qualifications are screened by physicians.

In vitro fertilization is a technique by which an ovum is removed from a woman's ovary, fertilized in a test tube, and then reimplanted in her uterus. Such a procedure may be attempted if a woman's fallopian tubes are blocked or if they have been surgically removed. With the help of this technique a healthy baby was born in England in 1978 to a couple who had tried unsuccessfully for several years to have a child. Since that time, thousands of children have been conceived within laboratory glassware.

Another novel procedure is **host mothering.** In this procedure, a tiny embryo is removed from its natural mother and implanted into a female substitute. The foster mother can support the developing embryo either until birth or temporarily until it is implanted again into the original mother or into another host. This technique has already proved useful to animal breeders. For example, embryos from prize sheep can be temporarily implanted into rabbits for easy shipping by air, and then reimplanted into a foster mother sheep, perhaps of inferior quality.

A newborn bongo and its surrogate mother, an eland. As a young embryo, the bongo was transplanted into the eland's uterus, where it implanted and developed. Bongos are a rare and elusive species inhabiting dense forests in Africa. The larger and more common elands, members of the same genus, inhabit open areas.

Host mothering also has the advantage of allowing an animal of superior quality to produce more offspring than would be naturally possible. Today it is possible to freeze the embryos of many species, including humans, and then to successfully transplant them into host mothers. Host mothering may someday be popular with women who can produce embryos but are unable to carry them to term.

Someday society may have to deal with **cloning** (not yet a reality in the case of humans). In this process the nucleus would be removed from an ovum and replaced with the nucleus of a cell from a person who wished to produce a human copy of himself. Theoretically, any cell nucleus could be used, even a white blood cell nucleus. The fertilized ovum would then be placed into a human uterus for incubation; the resulting baby would be an identical, though younger, twin to the individual whose nucleus was used.

Relatively little is known about the aging process itself, but this is now an active field of scientific investigation. Although marked improvements in medicine and public health have led to survival of a larger fraction of the total human population to an advanced age, there has been no concomitant increase in the maximum life expectancy for either men or women.

A remarkable model of the aging process in humans is provided by a rare, inherited type of abnormal development called **progeria.** In this condition, babies develop more or less normally until they are about 1 year old; they then begin to undergo changes that are considered typical of aging, including loss of hair and arrest of the growth process. The physical appearance becomes that of a wizened old man or woman. The collagen in the connective tissues of the skin becomes highly cross-linked, as seen in old age. Affected children usually die at age 10 to 15 of coronary artery disease secondary to extensive atherosclerosis.

Cells that differentiate and stop dividing appear to be more subject to the changes of aging than those that continue to divide throughout life. Nerve and muscle cells, which lose the capacity for cell division at an earlier age, show a decline in their functional capacities at an earlier age than do tissues such as liver and spleen, which retain the capacity to undergo cell division.

Several hypotheses have been advanced regarding the nature of the aging process—that it is affected by hormonal changes; that it involves the development of autoimmune responses (immune responses against certain components of the organism's own body which result in destruction of those components by antibodies); that it involves the accumulation of specific waste products within the cell; that it involves changes in the molecular structure of macromolecules such as collagen (an increased cross-linkage between the helical chains); that the elastic properties of connective tissues decrease owing to an accumulation of calcium, resulting in stiffening of the joints and hardening of the arteries; that it results from the peroxidation of certain lipids by free radicals; and that cells are destroyed by hydrolases released by the breaking of lysosomes.

Other theories suggest that continued exposure to cosmic radiation and x-radiation leads to the accumulation of somatic mutations, which decrease the ability of the cell to carry out its normal functions. In all likelihood, aging is linked to the same kinds of developmental processes that increase the functional capacities of the systems of the body during earlier development. The processes may be part of the program of timed development built into the genome. Like other developmental processes, aging may be accelerated by certain environmental influences and may occur at different rates in different individuals because of inherited differences. Experimental evidence suggests that aging— at least in rats—can be delayed by caloric restriction: thin rats live longer than fat rats. For now, genetic predisposition may be the best guarantee of a long life.

SUMMARY

I. Development proceeds as a balanced combination of cell proliferation, growth, morphogenesis, and cellular differentiation.

II. Fertilization involves four processes: contact and recognition; regulation of sperm entry; fusion of sperm and egg nuclei; activation of the egg.

III. The zygote undergoes cleavage, forming a morula and then a blastula.
   A. The main effect of cleavage is to partition the zygote into many small cells.
   B. The holoblastic cleavage that takes place in the isolecithal eggs of most invertebrates and simple chordates involves division of the entire egg to form cells that are about equal in size.
      1. In radial cleavage, characteristic of deuterostomes, the blastomeres are arranged somewhat symmetrically in layers.
      2. In spiral cleavage, characteristic of protostomes, each of the blastomeres is located between the two cells above or below it.
      3. In bony fish and amphibians, a concentration of yolk at the vegetal pole slows cleavage so that only a few large cells form there, compared with a large number of smaller cells at the animal pole.
   C. The meroblastic cleavage that occurs in the telolecithal eggs of reptiles and birds is restricted to the blastodisc.

IV. During gastrulation, the ectoderm, mesoderm, and endoderm form; each of these embryonic tissues gives rise to specific adult structures.
   A. In the sea star and in *Amphioxus*, cells from the blastula wall invaginate and eventually meet the opposite wall; the new cavity formed is the archenteron.
   B. In the amphibian, invagination at the vegetal pole is obstructed by the large yolk-laden cells; instead, cells from the animal pole move down over the yolk-rich cells and invaginate, forming the dorsal lip of the blastopore.

C. In the bird, invagination occurs at the primitive streak and no archenteron forms.

V. Organogenesis is the process of organ development. The developing notochord induces nervous system development. The brain and spinal cord develop from the neural tube.

VI. In terrestrial vertebrates, four extraembryonic membranes—chorion, amnion, allantois, and yolk sac— protect the embryo, help supply food and oxygen, and eliminate wastes.
   A. The amnion is a fluid-filled sac that surrounds the embryo and keeps it moist; it also acts as a shock absorber.
   B. In placental mammals, the embryonic chorion and maternal tissue give rise to the placenta, the organ of exchange between mother and developing child.

VII. Early human development follows a fairly typical vertebrate pattern.
   A. Cleavage takes place as the embryo is moved toward the uterus.
   B. In the uterus, the embryo develops into a blastocyst and implants itself in the endometrium.
   C. After the first 2 months of development, the embryo is referred to as a fetus.
   D. Parturition takes place about 280 days after the mother's last menstrual period. During the first stage of labor the cervix becomes dilated and effaced; during the second stage the baby is delivered; and during the third stage the placenta is delivered.

VIII. By controlling environmental factors such as nutrition, vitamin and drug intake, cigarette smoking, and exposure to disease-causing organisms, a pregnant woman can help ensure the well-being of her unborn child.

IX. The human life cycle can be divided into the following stages: embryo, fetus, neonate, infant, child, adolescent, young adult, middle age, and old age.

X. The aging process is marked by a progressive decrease in the body's homeostatic abilities to respond to stress.

POST-TEST

1. Movement of cells to form a tube such as the neural tube is an example of _____; specialization of cells to form neurons or some other cell type is called _____ _____.

2. When the sperm contacts the jelly coat around the egg, the _____ releases enzymes that digest a path to the _____ membrane of the egg.

3. The sperm is drawn into the egg by contraction of the fertilization _____.

4. The fast block to polyspermy involves _____ of the plasma membrane of the egg; the slow block to polyspermy is the _____ reaction.

5. The rapid series of mitoses that converts the zygote to a morula is referred to as _____.

6. In isolecithal eggs the entire egg divides, a type of cleavage referred to as _____ cleavage.

7. In the telolecithal eggs of birds, _____ cleavage is restricted to the _____.

8. The process by which the blastula becomes a three-layered embryo is called _____.

9. The tissue layer that gives rise to the nervous system is the _____; the germ layer that gives rise to the lining of the digestive tract is the _____.

10. In bird gastrulation, invagination takes place at the primitive _____.

11. The notochord induces the overlying ectoderm to form the _____ _____.

12. The neural tube develops into the _____ and _____ _____.

13. The _____ fluid prevents the embryo from drying out and acts as a shock absorber.

14. In humans the _____ is the organ of exchange between mother and fetus.

15. The cluster of cells that projects into the cavity of the blastocyst is the _____ _____ _____; it gives rise to the _____.

16. On about the seventh day of development the human embryo begins to _____ in the _____.

17. After the first 2 months of development, the human embryo is referred to as a _____.

18. The duration of pregnancy is known as the _____ period.

19. The term parturition refers to the _____ process.

20. _____ are agents that can interfere with normal development.

21. The term neonate refers to the _____.

22. Changes that result in decreased functional capacities of the organism are characteristic of the process of _____.

REVIEW QUESTIONS

1. Contrast the preformation theory with the theory of epigenesis, and relate these theories to current concepts of development.

2. How do the mechanisms of fertilization ensure control of both quality (fertilization by a sperm of the same species) and quantity (fertilization by only one sperm)?

3. Trace the development of either a sea star or an *Amphioxus* embryo from zygote to gastrula; draw and label diagrams to illustrate your description.

4. Contrast cleavage and gastrulation in the (a) sea star (or *Amphioxus*), (b) amphibian, and (c) bird.

5. Trace some developmental process such as the formation of the neural tube, and explain how cell proliferation, growth, morphogenesis, and cellular differentiation are integral parts of the process.

6. Give examples of adult structures that develop from each of the germ layers.

7. Why do terrestrial vertebrate embryos develop an amnion? What are its functions?

8. What is the adaptive value of developing a placenta?

9. Describe blastocyst formation and implantation in the human embryo.

10. What happens during each stage of labor?

11. What steps can the pregnant woman take to help ensure the safety and well-being of her developing child?

12. Trace development through the stages of the human life cycle.

13. Describe some of the changes that take place during the aging process.

RECOMMENDED READINGS

Browder, L. W., C. A. Erickson, and W. R. Jeffery. *Developmental Biology,* third edition. Saunders College Publishing, Philadelphia, 1991. A readable introduction to animal development.

Gehring, W. J. The molecular basis of development. *Scientific American,* Vol. 253, No. 4, October 1985. A discussion of how DNA generates a three-dimensional organism.

Hynes, R. O. Fibronectins. *Scientific American,* Vol. 254, No. 6, June 1986. These adhesive proteins serve as organizers in development.

Lagercrantz, H., and T. A. Slotkin. The stress of being born. *Scientific American,* Vol. 254, No. 4, April 1986. The stress hormones released during birth can be important to the neonate's survival.

Wasserman, P. M. Fertilization in mammals. *Scientific American,* Vol. 259, No. 6, December 1988. A glycoprotein governs many of the events of fertilization.

Animal Behavior

Suppose that your instructor were to arm you with a hypodermic syringe full of poison and demand that you find a particular type of insect (that you have never seen and that can fight back) and inject the ganglia of its nervous system (about which you have been taught nothing) with just enough poison to paralyze your victim, but not enough to kill it. You would be hard put to accomplish these tasks, but a solitary wasp no longer than the first joint of your thumb does it all with elegance and surgical precision and without instruction.

The sand wasp *Philanthus* captures bees, stings them, and places the paralyzed insects in burrows excavated in the sand. She then lays an egg on her victim, which is devoured alive by the larva that hatches from that egg. From time to time, the *Philanthus* returns to her hidden nest to reprovision it until the larva

Mother flicker (*Colaptes auratus*) feeding young in nest. What part of this feeding behavior is genetic? What part is modified by learning? (Dwight Kuhn)

becomes a hibernating pupa in the fall. Her offspring will repeat this behavior, doing it perfectly without ever having seen it done.

Behavior refers to the responses of an organism to signals from its environment. Much of what organisms do can be analyzed in terms of specific behavior patterns that occur in response to stimuli (changes) in the environment. A dog may wag its tail, a bird may sing, a butterfly may release a volatile sex attractant. Behavior is just as diverse as biological structure and is just as characteristic of a given species as its structure and biochemistry. Structure, function, and behavior are all parts of the total constellation of adaptations that define an organism and equip it for survival. In this chapter, we consider how behavior enables an organism to live and pass on its heritage to succeeding generations.

After you have studied this chapter, you should be able to

1. Support the theses that behavior is (a) adaptive, (b) homeostatic, and (c) flexible.
2. Cite examples of biological rhythms and suggest some of the mechanisms known or thought to be responsible for them.
3. Summarize the contributions to behavior of heredity, environment, and maturation.
4. Classify learned behaviors as examples of (a) classical conditioning, (b) operant conditioning, (c) sensitization, (d) habituation, or (e) insight learning.
5. Discuss the adaptive significance of imprinting.
6. Suggest biological advantages and disadvantages of migration.
7. Support the hypothesis that optimal foraging behavior is adaptive.

8. Give a description of an animal society, and identify the adaptive advantages of cooperative behavior.
9. Summarize the modes of communication that animals employ.
10. Present the concept of a dominance hierarchy, giving at least one example, and propose a possible adaptive significance and social function for it.
11. Distinguish between home range and territory and give three hypotheses about the adaptive significance of territoriality.
12. Discuss the adaptive value of courtship behavior and describe a pair bond.
13. Compare the society of a social insect with human society.
14. Define kin selection and summarize its proposed role in the maintenance of insect and other animal societies.
15. Describe the focus of sociobiology and summarize the controversy surrounding this approach.

BEHAVIOR IS ADAPTIVE

Biologists study behavior in the laboratory and in natural environments, always keeping in mind that what an animal does cannot be isolated from the way it lives. **Ethology** is the study of behavior in natural environments from the point of view of adaptation. Thus, a particular behavior may help an organism obtain food or water, acquire and maintain territory in which to live, protect itself, or reproduce.

Behavior tends to be homeostatic for the individual organism as well as adaptive in the evolutionary sense. Certain behavioral responses, however, may lead to the death of the individual while increasing the chance that copies of its genes will survive through the enhanced production or survival of the offspring.

BIOLOGICAL RHYTHMS ANTICIPATE ENVIRONMENTAL CHANGES

An organism adapts by synchronizing its metabolic processes and behavior with the cyclic changes in the external environment, so that its behavior can *anticipate* these regular changes. The little fiddler crabs (Figure 50–1) of marine beaches often emerge from their burrows at low tide to engage in social activities such as territorial disputes. They must return to their burrows *before* the tide returns or be washed away. How do the crabs "know" that high tide is about to occur? They cannot consult tide tables!

One might guess that the crabs recognize clues present in the seashore environment. However, when the crabs are isolated in a laboratory away from any known stimulus that could relate to time and tide, their characteristic behavioral rhythms persist.

A Variety of Behavioral Cycles Occur among Organisms

Many types of biological rhythms occur throughout the living world—daily rhythms, monthly cycles, and annual rhythms. In many animals, periods of activity and sleep, feeding and drinking, body temperature, and many other processes have a cycle 24 hours long. This daily rhythmic activity is **circadian** (meaning "approximately one day"; see Chapter 36). Such biological rhythms suggest that organisms have **biological clocks** that are precisely adjusted or reset by environmental cues. Even human physiological processes seem to follow an intrinsic rhythm. Human body temperature, for example, follows a typical daily curve.

Some animals are **diurnal,** exhibiting their greatest activity during the day, whereas others are **nocturnal,** being most active during the hours of darkness. Still others are **crepuscular,** having their greatest activity during the twilight hours—at dawn, sunset, or both. As in the case of the fiddler crabs, these adaptations have ecological reasons. If an animal's food is most plentiful in the early morning, for example, its cycle of activity must be regulated so that it becomes active shortly before dawn.

Some biological rhythms of animals reflect the **lunar (moon) cycle.** The most striking rhythms are those in marine organisms that are tuned to the changes in the tides that match the phases of the moon. For instance, a combination of tidal, lunar, and annual rhythms governs the reproductive behavior of the grunion, a small fish of the Pacific coast of the United States. The grunion swarms from April through June on those three or four nights when the highest tides of the year occur. At precisely the high point of the tide, the fish squirm onto the beach, deposit eggs and sperm in

Figure 50–1 Fiddler crabs run around on the surface of the sand at low tide but must return to their burrows before the tide returns. The males have enlarged claws. (Tom Walker/Photo Researchers, Inc.)

the sand, and return to the sea in the next wave. By the time the next high tide reaches that portion of the beach 15 days later, the young fish have hatched and are ready to enter the sea.

Biological Rhythms Are Controlled by an Internal Clock

Biological rhythms are regulated by internal timing mechanisms referred to as biological clocks. Current evidence suggests that most organisms have no single biological clock but that a number of biochemical processes (possibly involving cellular membranes) interact to govern physiological and behavioral rhythms. The pineal gland is thought to play a role in the timing systems of rats, birds, and some other vertebrates. Regions of the hypothalamus have been shown to be a part of the biological clock in mammals. Although some parts of an organism may coordinate or dominate the function of the biological clock, it is likely that every cell has some type of timing mechanism.

Doubtless, the biological clock has a genetic basis. Normal fruit flies, *Drosophila*, have a clock that has a free-running period of 24.2 hours. (The **free-running period** is the length of the clock's repetitive cycle when the animals are isolated from environmental cycles and kept under constant conditions. It is thought to indicate the rate at which the clock is running.) Mutant fruit flies have been discovered with free-running periods of 19 and 28 hours. Each mutation has been traced to the same locus on the X chromosome.

BEHAVIOR CAPACITY IS INHERITED AND IS MODIFIED BY ENVIRONMENTAL INFLUENCES

All behavior has a genetic basis—the *capacity* for behavior is inherited. Even the capacity to learn is inherited. However, behavior can be modified by the environment, so behavior is a product of the interaction between genetic capacity and environmental influences. Thus, behavior begins with an inherited framework that experience can modify.

The instructions for the honeybee society are inherited and preprogrammed, and the size and structure of the bee's nervous system permit only a limited range of behavior. Yet, these insects are not automatons. Within those limits, the complex bee society can respond flexibly to stimuli in the environment.

Some behavior of vertebrates is also largely predetermined by genes. Several species of the commonly kept cagebird *Agapornis*, better known as the lovebird (an exact English translation of its scientific name), differ not only in appearance but in behavior. These birds build nests of strips of vegetation, but in captivity they accept newspaper instead (Figure 50–2). The birds carry this material to the nests they are building in different ways. Fischer's lovebird (*A. fischeri*) carries the strips of paper to its nest in its bill, one at a time. A peach-faced lovebird (*A. roseicollis*), however, can tuck several such strips among its tail and rump feathers at one time. Thus, it can make fewer trips.

William Dilger cross-bred the peach-faced lovebird and Fischer's lovebird. The hybrids that Dilger bred could tuck the strips in among their feathers, but so ineptly that the strips fell out; they could not successfully build a nest. Eventually, these lovebirds did learn to carry the strips in their beaks but never completely abandoned their futile attempts to tuck them in among their feathers. The method of transportation of nest-building materials is apparently inherited but somewhat flexible.

Behavior Develops

Behavior involves all body systems, but it is influenced primarily by the coordinating mechanisms of the body (that is, the nervous and endocrine systems). The capacity for behavior is therefore subject to whatever genetic characteristics govern the development and range of function of these systems. One may think of a continuous scale of behaviors, ranging from the most rigidly programmed, genetically inherited types, through those that are somewhat modifiable, to those that, although containing a genetic component, are extensively developed through experience.

Before an organism can exhibit any pattern of behavior, it must be physiologically ready to produce the

Figure 50-2 Evidence for the inheritance of behavior may be seen in lovebirds. (*a*) The peach-faced lovebird carries nesting material to the nest by tucking it among its rump feathers. (*b*) Fischer's lovebird carries nesting material in its bill, a strip at a time. (*c*) Hybrids appear confused and try to carry material both ways.

behavior. Breeding behavior does not ordinarily occur among birds or most mammals unless steroid sex hormones are present in their blood at certain concentrations. A human baby cannot walk unless its reflex and muscular development permit it to walk. States of physiological readiness are themselves produced by a continuous interaction with the environment. The level of sex hormones in a bird's blood may be determined by seasonal variations in day length. The baby's muscles develop in response to exercise. Without the trial and error involved in learning how to walk, walking would be retarded.

A good example of such interaction between readiness and environment is afforded by the white-crowned sparrow, which exhibits considerable regional variation in its song. Even if kept in isolation, this bird eventually sings a very poorly developed but recognizable white-crowned sparrow song. If it is allowed to grow up under the care of its parents for the first 3 months of life, however, when it matures it sings in the local "dialect" characteristic of its parents or foster parents. If such learning does not take place in those 3 months, it never does, and if the sparrow consorts with birds of other species after the 3-month period, it does not learn their songs. The white-crowned sparrow seems to hatch with a rough model or pattern of its song built in. The regional details are filled in by learning.

Some Behavior Patterns Have Strong Genetic Components

The term **instinct** refers to innate behavior that is genetically programmed. A classic example of innate behavior in vertebrates is egg-rolling in waterfowl. When an egg is removed from the nest of a goose and placed a few inches in front of her, she reaches out with her neck and pulls the egg back into the nest (Figure 50-3). If the egg veers off to the side while the goose is rolling the egg back toward the nest, the goose steers it back toward the nest. Because this type of behavior appears to have a strong genetic component, ethologists refer to it as a **fixed action pattern (FAP).**

A stimulus that elicits an FAP—such as the egg in egg-rolling behavior or the red-colored "belly" in the

Figure 50–3 Egg-rolling behavior in the European graylag goose is a fixed action pattern.

attack behavior of the stickleback fish (Figure 50–4)—is called a **sign stimulus.** For example, a goose retrieves a wooden egg in the same way as a real egg, so the wooden egg is also by definition a sign stimulus. Yet only the real egg is the "natural" sign stimulus, that is, the one that evolved with the behavior. Stimuli that are used as social signals in communication are known as **releasers.**

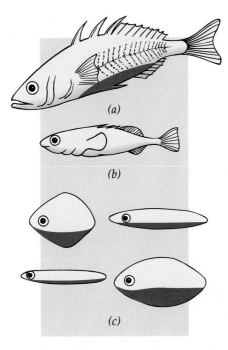

Figure 50–4 A sign stimulus is a particular feature that triggers a fixed action pattern. A male stickleback fish (*a*) does not attack a realistic model of another male stickleback if it lacks a red belly (*b*), but it does attack another model, however unrealistic, that has a red "belly" (*c*). Therefore, it is the specific red sign stimulus, rather than recognition based on a combination of features, that triggers the aggressive behavior.

Behavior Is Modified by Learning

We can define learning as a change in behavior due to experience. The capacity to learn appropriate responses to new situations is adaptive, because learned responses can be shaped to meet the needs of the changing environment that most animals experience. The sand wasp *Philanthus* efficiently carries out a complex, although largely genetically programmed, sequence of behaviors, yet some of her behavior is learned. When *Philanthus* covers a nest with sand, she takes precise bearings on the location of the burrow before flying off again to hunt. There is no way that knowledge of the location of the burrow could be genetically programmed in the wasp. How to dig it, how to cover it, how to kill the bees—these behaviors appear to be genetically programmed. Because a burrow can be dug only in a suitable spot, however, its location must be learned after it is dug. This was determined by the Dutch investigator Niko Tinbergen.

Tinbergen surrounded the wasp's burrow with a circle of pine cones, on which the wasp took her bearings (Figure 50–5). Before she returned with another bee, Tinbergen moved the circles of pine cones. The wasp could not find her burrow because the cones no longer surrounded it. Only when the experimenter restored the cones to their original location could the wasp find her burrow. In contrast, the existence of complex programmed behavior is hard to demonstrate in humans. We owe the complexity of our behavior to a *generalized* ability to learn. The *Philanthus* wasp's intelligence is as narrowly specialized as her stinger.

In Classical Conditioning, a Reflex Becomes Associated with a New Stimulus

In a type of learning called **classical conditioning,** an association is formed between some normal body func-

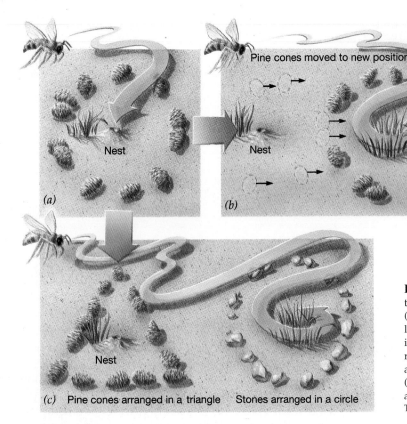

Figure 50–5   Tinbergen's sand wasp experiment. When the ring of pine cones is moved from position (*a*) to position (*b*), the *Philanthus* wasp behaves as if her nest were still located at the center. She has therefore learned its position in relation to the cones. It is the arrangement of the cones rather than the cones themselves that the wasp responds to, as shown by the substitution of a ring of stones for cones in (*c*). The learning ability of *Philanthus* is quite limited but is adequate for situations that normally arise in nature.   (After Tinbergen)

tion and a stimulus. Ivan Pavlov, a Russian physiologist who worked early in this century, discovered that when a bell was rung at the same time that an experimental dog was fed, the dog formed an association between the sound of the bell and the secretion of saliva. Eventually (Figure 50–6), when the bell was rung by itself, the dog salivated. Pavlov called the physiologically meaningful stimulus (food, in this case) the **unconditioned stimulus.** The normally irrelevant stimulus that became a substitute for it (the bell) was the **conditioned stimulus.**

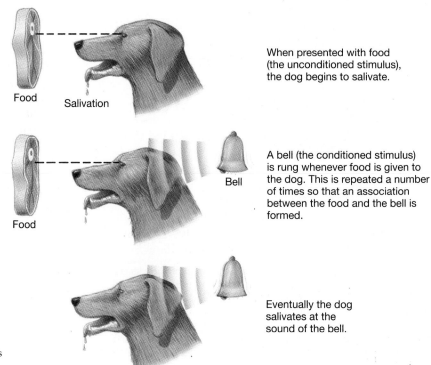

When presented with food (the unconditioned stimulus), the dog begins to salivate.

A bell (the conditioned stimulus) is rung whenever food is given to the dog. This is repeated a number of times so that an association between the food and the bell is formed.

Eventually the dog salivates at the sound of the bell.

Figure 50–6   Pavlov's experiment. The dog learns to salivate at the sound of the bell.

Because a dog does not normally salivate at the sound of a bell, the association was clearly a learned one. It could also be forgotten. If the bell no longer rang at mealtimes, the dog would eventually cease responding to it. Pavlov called this **extinction.**

In Operant Conditioning, Spontaneous Behavior Is Reinforced

In **operant conditioning** (also called instrumental conditioning), the animal must do something to gain a reward **(positive reinforcement)** or avoid a punishment or deprivation. In a typical experiment, a rat is placed in a cage containing a movable bar. When random actions of the rat result in the rat pressing the bar, a pellet of food rolls down a chute and is delivered to the rat. Eventually, the rat learns the association and presses on the bar whenever it is hungry. The rat is positively reinforced for pressing the bar.

In **negative reinforcement** removal of a stimulus increases the probability that a behavior will occur. For example, a rat may be subjected to an aversive stimulus, such as low-level electric shock. When the animal presses a bar, this negative reinforcer is removed and the animal experiences relief.

Many variations of these techniques have been developed. A pigeon might be trained to peck at a lighted circle to obtain food, a chimpanzee might learn to perform some task in order to get tokens that can be exchanged for food, or children might learn to stay quietly in their seats at school to obtain some reward. Operant conditioning is probably the way that animals learn to perform complex tasks like walking or perfecting feeding skills.

Operant conditioning likely plays a large role in the development of behaviors that appear to be preprogrammed. A classic example is the feeding behavior of gull chicks. Herring gull chicks peck the beaks of the parents, which regurgitate partially digested food for them. The chicks are attracted by two stimuli: a red spot on the parent's beak and the beak's shape and downward movement. Like the rat's chance pressing of the bar, this behavior is sufficiently functional to get the chicks their first meal, but they waste much energy in pecking. Some pecks are off target, failing to reach the parent's beak, and are therefore not rewarded. The begging behavior becomes more efficient over time, however. Thus, a behavior that might appear to be entirely instinctive is perfected by learning (Figure 50–7).

Imprinting Is a Form of Learning that Occurs during a Critical Period

Anyone who has watched a mother duck with a swarm of ducklings must have wondered how she can keep track of such a horde of almost identical little creatures,

Figure 50–7   A pelican chick begging food from a parent. (H. Cruickshank/VIREO)

tumbling about in the weeds and grass, let alone differentiate them from those belonging to another mother duck (Figure 50–8). Although she is capable of recognizing her offspring to an extent, basically they have the responsibility of keeping track of her. The survival of the duckling requires extremely rapid establishment of the behavioral bond between it and its parent. This bond, which is usually formed within a few hours of birth (or hatching), forms by a type of learning known as **imprinting.** An early investigator of imprinting, ethologist Konrad Lorenz, discovered that a newly hatched bird may imprint on a human, or even an inanimate object, if its parent is not present. Although the behavior itself is genetically determined, the bird learns the object.

Among many kinds of birds, especially ducks and geese, the older embryos exchange calls with their nest mates and parents right through the porous eggshell. When they hatch, at least one parent is normally on hand, emitting the characteristic vocalizations with which the hatchlings are already familiar. If the parent moves, the chicks follow it. The movement plus the vocalizations produce imprinting, in which, during a brief

Figure 50–8 The formation of parent-offspring bonds. Through imprinting, some young animals follow the first moving object they encounter. Usually, the object is their mother, although it is possible experimentally to imprint many such infants upon unnatural objects. (J. H. Dick/VIREO)

critical period after hatching, the chicks learn the appearance of the parent. Other types of learning are not restricted to such a critical period. Furthermore, imprinting takes place without any external reinforcement and is resistant to negative reinforcement. It seems, therefore, to occupy a special category.

Imprinting establishes the bond between mother and offspring among many mammals as well as among birds. In many species, the mother also establishes a bond with her offspring during a critical period. The mother in some species of hoofed mammals, such as sheep, accepts her offspring for only a few hours after its birth. If they are kept apart past that time, the young are thereafter rejected. Normally, this behavior enables

the mother to distinguish her own offspring from those of others, evidently by olfactory cues. There is no proof that this kind of bonding occurs among humans.

Habituation Enables an Animal to Ignore Irrelevant Stimuli

Habituation is a form of learning in which an animal learns to ignore a repeated or continuing irrelevant stimulus. In Figure 50–9, we see the familiar but extraordinary aggregation of pigeons in a city street. These birds have learned by repeated harmless encounters that humans are no more dangerous to them than cows are to crows and behave accordingly. This is to their advantage. A pigeon intolerant of people might never get enough to eat.

Insight Learning Uses Recalled Events to Solve New Problems

The most complex learning is **insight** learning, the ability to remember past experiences that may involve different stimuli and to adapt these recalled events to solve a new problem. A dog can be placed in a blind alley that it must *circumvent* in order to reach a reward. The difficulty of the problem appears to be that the animal must move *away* from the reward in order to get *to* it. At first the dog typically flings itself at the barrier nearest the food. Eventually, by trial and error, the frustrated dog may find its way around the barrier and reach the reward.

In contrast to the dog, a chimpanzee placed in a similar situation is likely to see the solution instantly (Figure 50–10). Primates appear to be especially good at insight learning, but a broad range of animals seem to have this ability to some degree.

Figure 50–9 In the form of learning known as habituation, an animal's unlearned response to constant or repeated stimulation wanes, as is the case with these pigeons, which are unperturbed by the presence of humans. (Janet Goldwater)

Figure 50-10 Insight learning, and in this case, simple tool use. Confronted with the problem of reaching food hanging from the ceiling, the chimpanzee stacks boxes until it can climb and reach the food. Many other examples of apparent insight are known from the behavior of these animals.

Learning Abilities May Be Biased

Learning capabilities may be biased in that some things are learned more easily than others. One does not really need to teach a baby bird to fly, for instance. Learning language comes very naturally to humans. A child learns the speech of the people who raise it even if no one deliberately instructs it. In general, learning biases reflect the specialized mode of life of an animal. What is most important appears to be most easily learned. The same rat that may have taken a dozen trials to perfect the artificial task of pushing a lever to get an immediate reward learns in a *single* trial to avoid a food that has made it ill as long as 6 hours after the food was eaten. Those who poison rats to get rid of them can readily appreciate the adaptive value of this learning ability. Such quick aversive learning forms the basis of warning coloration, which is found in many poisonous insects and brilliantly colored but distasteful bird eggs. Once made ill by such an egg, predators learn to avoid them.

BEHAVIORAL ECOLOGY EXAMINES INTERACTIONS OF ANIMALS WITH THEIR ENVIRONMENTS

Behavioral ecologists focus on animals' interactions with their environments and on the survival value of their behavior. Two of the many activities that relate behavior and ecology are migration and foraging for food.

Migration Is Triggered by Environmental Changes

Migration is the periodic long-distance movement from one location to another and a subsequent return to the first location. Some migrations involve astonishing feats of endurance and navigation. Ruby-throated hummingbirds cross the vast reaches of the Gulf of Mexico twice each year, and the sooty tern travels across the entire South Atlantic from Africa to its tiny island breeding grounds south of Florida.

Migration is not purposeful, although it can seem carefully planned. Birds may feed heavily weeks before those food reserves will be needed and often fly south even *before* the weather turns cold or food becomes scarce. Salmon swim into fresh water toward the end of their life cycles. Monarch butterflies fly southward, and the *next generation* of butterflies flies north in the spring. Migration appears to be a specific adaptation in the lifestyles of many organisms.

The behavioral trigger that sets off migratory behavior varies. Some animals migrate upon maturation; in others, explicit environmental cues trigger the process. In migratory birds, for example, the pineal gland senses changes in day length. It then triggers characteristic restless behavior called **Zugunruhe,** or migratory restlessness. The bird shows an increased readiness to fly and flies for longer periods of time (Figure 50-11).

The *direction* of travel is also obviously important, and this raises the general problem of animal navigation. Birds appear to navigate by a combination of celestial (sun- and star-related) and geographic and climatic cues. Honeybees and some birds are sensitive to the earth's magnetic field.

Working in the 1950s, Franz and Eleonore Sauer hand reared a number of whitethroats, a species of small European warbler. This ruled out any possibility that the parents had transmitted any information to their offspring. When (and only when) the birds could see the star patterns of the night sky, they attempted to fly in the normal direction of migration for this species, a direction that they had had no opportunity to learn. When the birds were brought into a planetarium and the night sky of a different locale was simulated on the planetarium dome, they attempted to fly in a direction that would have taken them to their normal wintering grounds from that locality. The conclusion seemed ines-

MAKING THE CONNECTION

Cave Bats in Puerto Rico

Among mammals, only rodents have more species than Chiroptera (bats). Bats constitute one of the most diverse groups in terms of feeding habits and reproductive strategies and are the only mammals capable of active flight, as opposed to gliding. The mythical stories that often are associated with bats have resulted in a poor image, which is unwarranted. Their role as insect predators, plant pollinators, and fruit dispersal agents leaves no question as to their important position within ecosystems.

Approximately 31% of Puerto Rico's caves are known to host bat colonies varying in size from a few to hundreds of thousands of individuals. Ten of the 13 species of bats known to the island use these caves as preferred roosting sites. Feeding habits vary widely among these cave-dwelling bats, fruit- and insect-eating bats being the most common, followed by the nectar-feeding and fish-eating bats.

It is common for the layperson to associate bats with caves. This relationship is often attributed to the alleged aversion of bats to light. However, cave-dwelling bats often make use of caves because they provide reliable shelter against climatic variations and predators. Foliage and even trees are perishable, but caves remain almost unchanged for very long periods of time. Factors that are potentially important in the selection of roosts include shelter from wind, local increase in air temperature and/or humidity, and improvement in radiation balance (a reduction of heat loss by electromagnetic energy flow between the bat and objects separated in space).

Some bats are known to select roosting sites that result in entrapment of the metabolic heat they produce. Other bats may reduce their energy expenditure and at the same time stay warm by clustering, or they may resort to torpor (a state of dormancy that results in conservation of energy). In the neotropics, hot caves are used year-round by several species of bats. These so-called hot caves are characterized by a single, reduced entrance, a minimum circulation of air, a high population density of bats, a temperature ranging from 28 to 40°C, and relative humidity exceeding 90%.

Antillean bats that use hot caves exhibit high degrees of gregariousness and roost fidelity. At least one species (probably two) is known to occur exclusively in these caves. Although up to seven species may occupy a single cave in Puerto Rico, different species often maintain spatial separation within the roost. It has been suggested that interspecific competition for access to the roost is what limits the species composition and population sizes in these caves. When several species occupy the same cave, they may compete for roosting sites and access to the exit. Narrow cave mouths may physically restrict the flow of bats during periods of activity and limit the number of individuals in the cave. For example, at Cucaracha cave in western Puerto Rico, three species of bats with a total population of 700,000 individuals share a hot cave with a 1.5 m^2 opening.

Many species of bats inhabiting hot caves are prone to rapid dehydration. These species may roost in large groups because of the benefits derived from a thermoneutral environment (one with an ambient temperature at which energy expenditure is minimal) and reduced dehydration. Also, the development of large colonies may increase both foraging success, by functioning as information centers, and reproductive success, by reducing the exposure of newborns to predation and weather. These benefits are opposed by costs associated with permanent use of caves. For example, large numbers of exiting bats attract concentrations of predators to the cave mouth.

Interspecies differences in patterns of foraging, associated with diet differences, result in spacing of peak exit times. Such spacing may allow larger numbers of cave-warming bodies to be present than would be likely in either a single-species colony or a random assemblage of species, in which peak exit times might coincide. Multispecies colonies of cave-dwelling bats present opportunities for the study of many patterns of behavior.

Contributed by Armando Rodriguez-Durán, Department of Biology, Inter American University, Bayamón, Puerto Rico.

---

capable: Although the direction of migration was unlearned, the birds were able to find it by means of celestial navigation.

Efficient Foraging Behavior Contributes to Survival

Natural selection tends to produce animals that are maximally efficient at propagating their genes, and this is accomplished by making the best choices in mate selection, territory defense, and foraging for food. A topic of current interest to many behavioral ecologists is **optimal foraging,** which refers to the most efficient way for an animal to obtain food. According to current hypotheses, when animals maximize the energy they can obtain per unit of foraging time, they maximize their reproductive success. However, many other factors must be considered, such as avoiding predators while foraging.

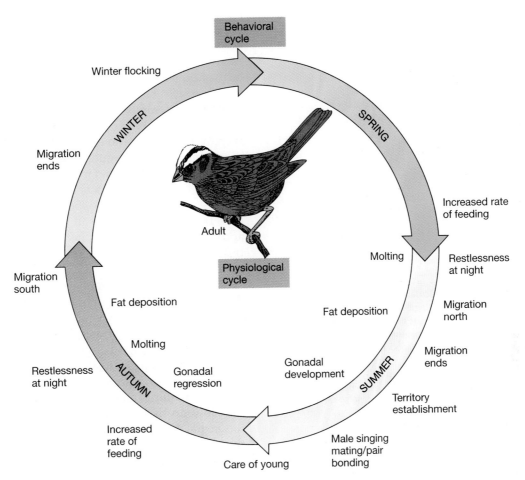

Figure 50–11 Seasonal changes in the physiology and behavior of the white-crowned sparrow. Note the increased rate of feeding and then restlessness (*Zuguruhe*) that precedes each period of migration. (From Alcock, J. *Animal Behavior: An Evolutionary Approach*, 2nd ed. Sunderland, MA, Sinauer Associates, 1979)

Optimal foraging may be illustrated by the following example, which is fictitious for the sake of simplicity. Suppose there exists a monkey that eats only one species of fruit and that this fruit is contained in a husk that is either soft, leathery, or hard. It takes 1 minute to remove a soft husk, 5 minutes to remove a leathery husk, and 10 minutes to remove a hard husk. If the forest contains equal numbers of hard-husked, leathery-husked, and soft-husked fruits, if these three forms are randomly distributed, and if a monkey moves randomly and eats every fruit it encounters, then at the end of a foraging period it should have eaten about the same number of each husk form.

But is it necessarily the best use of the monkey's time and energy to eat all three husk types? Because removing hard husks takes so long, perhaps it is more efficient to pass up these fruits and eat only the soft-husked and leathery-husked fruits. Or maybe the best procedure is to eat only the soft-husked fruits.

These three possible ways of feeding are examples of **foraging strategies.** Two other foraging strategies are to select only the hard-husked fruits or to select the hard-husked fruits and the leathery-husked fruits and pass up the soft-husked fruits. These two strategies are

clearly less efficient ways to forage, because they require a greater expenditure of time and energy for the same amount of food. The term *strategy* used in this context does not imply planning as it does in human behavior but refers to the way an animal locates, procures, and handles food.

Assuming that once husked, all three forms can be eaten in the same brief time, we may ask which of the following strategies is most adaptive, that is, which one permits the monkey to forage optimally:

Strategy I: Select the soft-husked fruits whenever encountered and pass up the other two kinds

Strategy II: Select the soft-husked and leathery-husked fruits whenever encountered, and pass up the hard-husked fruits

Strategy III: Select all three kinds whenever encountered

Strategy I has its trade-offs. Because only every third fruit is soft-husked, the monkey must travel three times as far to get the same number of fruits it would get if it selected leathery-husked and hard-husked fruits as well. Maybe it would be worth traveling far-

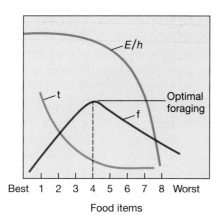

Figure 50–12 Graph illustrating optimal foraging, based on food intake (expressed as energy, E). In any habitat there is a trade-off between travel time (t) and handling time (h). Handling time is graphed here as E/h. Once h and t are determined, the optimal foraging strategy can be calculated. Numbers on the horizontal axis refer to foraging strategies concerning eight different food items, arranged from best to worst. Number 1 refers to selection of only the best food item, number 2 to selection of the best food item plus the second best food item, number 3 to selection of the three best food items, and so forth. In this hypothetical case, an animal that forages optimally (as indicated by the peak of the red curve) would select the four best food items. In better habitats the optimal foraging peak is to the left of 4; in poorer habitats, it is to the right of 4.

ther if it meant spending less time husking, but of course that would depend on *how much* farther.

What do we need to know in order to identify the best foraging strategy? Obviously we need to know how long it takes to get from one fruit tree to the next, and this depends on the density of the fruit trees. If the density of fruit trees is so low that it takes an hour to get from one fruit tree to the next, then common sense would tell us not to pass up a hard-husked fruit just because it takes 10 minutes to husk. On the other hand, if the fruit trees are so dense that it takes only 2 minutes to get to the next tree, then we would certainly pass up all the hard-husked forms and perhaps would even consider passing up both the hard-husked and leathery-husked forms. After all, the next soft-husked fruit is only 6 minutes away, and it takes longer than that to husk a hard-husked fruit.

This relationship between travel time, handling time, and net food intake can be expressed graphically (Figure 50–12). This graph, based on eight rather than three food items, indicates eight possible foraging strategies. Assuming that the caloric value (expressed as E, for energy) of all items is equal, the best item would be the one that requires the least handling time, the worst would be the item that requires the most handling time, and all others would be ranked accordingly.

The numbers on the horizontal axis do not refer to the specific items, but rather to foraging strategies. The number "1" refers to the strategy in which the animal

selects only the best item, the one requiring the shortest handling time (h) per unit of food and hence the highest ratio of energy to handling time (E/h). By being so selective, however, the animal has a long traveling time (t), because it has chosen to pass up the other seven items. In the foraging strategy indicated by "2," the animal selects the best item plus the second best item, thereby decreasing traveling time but increasing handling time (and consequently decreasing E/h). As the animal includes more and more unfavorable food items in its diet, travel time decreases but handling time increases. Thus, the animal spends the least amount of time traveling if it selects all eight food items, but by adding more unfavorable items to its diet to reduce travel time, it must also spend more time handling the items.

In good habitats, where good food items are abundant and the animal does not have to travel far to obtain these items, the optimal foraging strategy tends toward the left of the graph (strategy 1, 2, or 3, depending on how good the habitat is). In contrast, in poor habitats, where it takes longer to find the best food items, the optimal strategy is to select more items, even though doing so requires more handling time.

How do these theoretical considerations apply to the actual behavior of animals? By measuring travel time, handling time, and eating time and relating these values to the theoretical values calculated for optimal foraging, one can test the hypothesis that a particular animal does, in fact, forage optimally. If the actual values do not fit the theoretical values, it may mean that all relevant variables have not been accounted for. The monkey may choose to forage very inefficiently (in terms of consuming a certain number of calories each day) by selecting only hard-husked fruits; but it may do this because it prefers the taste of hard-husked fruits or because they contain a critical nutrient missing from the other two forms. Thus, other hypotheses concerning foraging behavior may come to mind.

If the monkey was indeed observed foraging optimally, according to predicted values, it may have learned to do so through trial and error (operant conditioning), that is, by randomly trying all three strategies and selecting the one associated with the fewest hunger pangs at the end of the day!

SOCIAL INTERACTION HAS BOTH BENEFITS AND COSTS

Many animals benefit from living in groups. Schools of fish are less vulnerable to predators than single fish because large numbers tend to confuse their predators, and some are able to repel predators cooperatively. Flocks of birds may be able to find food better than single individuals. By cooperation and division of labor, some insects are able to construct elaborate nests and raise young by mass-production methods. A pack of wolves and a pride of lions have greater success in hunting than the individual wolves or lions would have if hunting alone. Animals that are hunted may be better able to detect or discourage predators when some individuals in the group are on watch, and they may be able to drive off predators by collective action. Social behavior offers definite benefits that may increase the chances of propagating the genes that produce it.

Social behavior has certain disadvantages as well. Living together means increased competition for food and habitats. Social interaction also increases the risk of transmitting disease.

The mere presence of more than one individual does not mean that their behavior is social. Many factors of the physical environment bring animals together in **aggregations,** but whatever interaction they experience may be circumstantial. A light shining in the dark attracts large numbers of moths. The high humidity under a log may attract aggregations of wood lice. Although it may be adaptive for these organisms to aggregate, their behavior is not truly social unless the presence of some members of the species can be shown to attract others.

We can define **social behavior** as the interaction of two or more animals, usually of the *same species*, that is, **conspecific.** Many species that engage in social behavior form societies. A **society** is an actively cooperating group of individuals belonging to the same species. A hive of bees, a flock of birds, a pack of wolves, and a school of fish are examples of societies. Some societies are loosely organized, whereas others have a complex structure. A well-organized society exhibits cooperation and division of labor among animals of different sexes, age groups, or castes. A complex system of communication reinforces the organization of the society. The members of a society tend to remain together and to resist attempts by outsiders to enter the group.

Communication Is Necessary for Social Behavior

The ability to communicate is an essential element of social behavior, because only by exchanging mutually recognizable signals can one animal influence the behavior of another (Figure 50–13). **Communication** occurs when an animal performs an act that changes the behavior of another organism. Communication may aid in finding food, as in the elaborate dances of honey bees. It may hold a group together, warn a group of danger, indicate social status, ask for or indicate willingness to provide care, identify members of the same species, or indicate sexual maturity.

Figure 50–13 A male hylid frog of Costa Rica calling to locate a mate. (L. E. Gilbert, University of Texas at Austin/Biological Photo Service)

Animals communicate in a wide variety of ways

Methods of animal communication are extremely varied. The singing of birds is an obvious example of auditory communication; it serves to announce the presence of a territorial male. Some animals communicate by scent rather than sound. Antelopes rub the secretions of facial glands on conspicuous objects in their vicinity. Dogs mark territory by frequent urination. Certain fish, the gymnotids, use electric pulses for navigation and communication including territorial threat, in a fashion similar to bird vocalization. As Edward O. Wilson has said, "The fish, in effect, sing electrical songs."

Pheromones are chemical signs used in communication

Pheromones are chemical signals that convey information between members of a species. They are a simple, widespread means of communication. Many types of messages can be conveyed by pheromones. Most pheromones act as releasers that elicit a very specific, immediate, but transitory type of behavior. Others act as primers that trigger hormonal activities that may result in slow, but long-lasting, responses. Some pheromones act in both ways.

An advantage to pheromone communication is that little energy is expended to synthesize the simple, but distinctive, organic compounds involved. Conspecific individuals have receptors that are attuned to the molecular configuration of the pheromone; other species usually ignore it. Pheromones are effective in the dark, can pass around obstacles, and last for several hours or longer. Major disadvantages of pheromone communication are slow transmission and limited information content. Some animals compensate for the latter disadvantage by secreting different pheromones with different meanings.

Figure 50–14 Social animals use many signals to convey messages relating to social dominance. This baboon bares his teeth and screams in an unmistakable show of aggression. (Gerald Lacz, Peter Arnold, Inc.)

Pheromones are important in many species in sex recognition and attraction. Many female insects produce pheromones that attract males of the same species. We have taken advantage of some sex-attractant pheromones to help control such pests as gypsy moths by luring the males to traps baited with synthetic versions of the female pheromone.

Some aspects of the sexual cycle of vertebrates are affected by pheromones. When the odor of a male mouse is introduced among a group of females, their reproductive cycles become synchronized. In some species of mice, the odor of a strange male, a sign of high population density, causes a newly impregnated female to abort. Among humans, some unconsciously perceived body odor seems capable of synchronizing the menstrual cycles of women who associate closely (for instance, college roommates or cellmates in prison). As we shall see, pheromones much more strictly govern the reproduction of many social insects.

Animals Often Form Dominance Hierarchies

In the spring, a paper-wasp nest may be founded cooperatively by females that have survived their winter hibernation. Early in the course of construction, a series of squabbles among the females takes place in which the combatants bite one another's bodies or legs. Finally, one of the wasps emerges as dominant and thereafter she is hardly ever challenged. This queen wasp spends more and more time on the nest and less and

less time out foraging for herself. She takes the food she needs from the others as they return.

The queen then begins to take an interest in raising a family—her family. Because she is almost always at hand, she is able to prevent other wasps from laying eggs in the brood cells by rushing at them, jaws agape. At the same time, she cannot be stopped from laying all the eggs she wants, because she has already demonstrated that she cannot be successfully challenged.

Careful analysis of this aggressive behavior reveals that the queen can bite any other wasp without fear of retaliation. There is usually another wasp, however, that can bite any wasp she chooses (other than the queen) without fear of retaliation. Thus, although the queen can bite any wasp in the nest, the other wasps are not equal to one another. One can arrange the wasps into a definite **dominance hierarchy,** an arrangement of status that regulates aggressive behavior within the society:

Queen > Wasp A > Wasp B > . . . . . . Wasp J > Wasp K

Dominance hierarchies suppress aggression

Once a dominance hierarchy is established, little or no time is wasted in fighting (Figure 50–14). Subordinate wasps, upon challenge, generally exhibit submissive poses that inhibit the aggressive behavior of the queen toward them. Consequently, few or no colony members are lost through wounds sustained in fighting one another.

Many factors affect dominance

In some animals, dominance is a simple function of aggressiveness, which is itself often influenced directly by sex hormones. Among chickens, the rooster is the most dominant; as with most vertebrates, the hormone testosterone increases the aggressiveness of chickens. If a hen receives testosterone injections, her place in the dominance hierarchy shifts upward. Recent tests on rhesus monkeys have shown that when males are dominant, their testosterone levels are much higher than when they have been defeated. Not only can estrogen sometimes reduce dominance and testosterone increase dominance, but dominance may even increase testosterone. It is not always easy to determine cause and effect.

In many species, males and females have separate dominance systems, but in many monogamous animals, especially birds, the female takes on the dominance status of her mate by virtue of their relationship. This is not always the case, however. Like many other fish, some coral reef fish (labrids) are capable of sex reversal. The most dominant individual is always male, and the remaining fish within his territory are always female. If the male dies or is removed, the most dominant female becomes the new male. If anything happens to "him," the next ranking female becomes the new sultan of the harem. Still other fish exhibit the reverse behavior—the most dominant fish becomes a female.

Many Animals Defend Territory

Virtually all animals maintain a minimum personal distance from their neighbors, as one can observe in the even spacing among the members of a flock of birds resting on a telephone line. Most animals have a geographical area that they seldom or never leave. Such an area is called a **home range** (Figure 50–15). Because the animal has the opportunity to become familiar with everything in that range, it has an advantage over both its predators and its prey in negotiating cover and finding food. Some, but not all, animals defend a portion of the home range against other individuals of the same species and even against individuals of other species. Such a defended area is called a **territory.** The tendency to defend such a territory is known as **territoriality.**

Territoriality is easily studied in birds. Typically, the male chooses a territory at the beginning of the breeding season. This behavior results from high concentrations of sex hormones in the blood. The males of adjacent territories fight until territorial boundaries become fixed. Generally, the dominance of a male varies directly with his nearness to the center of his territory. Thus, close to "home" he is a lion, but when invading some other bird's territory he is likely to be a lamb. The interplay of dominance values among territorial males eventually produces a neutral line at which neither is

Figure 50–15 A coral reef has many secluded areas in which a territorial animal can establish a home range. Among the most territorial of coral reef fishes is the moray eel, pictured here, which attacks any animal (including a human diver) that comes too close to its shelter. (IFA-Bilderteam-D. Eichler/Peter Arnold, Inc.)

dominant. That line is the territorial boundary. Bird songs announce the existence of a territory and often serve as a substitute for violence. Furthermore, they announce to eligible females that a propertied male resides in the territory. Typically, male birds take up a conspicuous station, sing, and sometimes display striking patterns of coloration to their neighbors, their rivals, and sometimes their mates (Figure 50–16).

Territoriality among animals may be adaptive in that it tends to reduce conflict among members of the same species, control population growth, and ensure the most efficient use of environmental resources by encouraging dispersion and thus spacing individuals more or less evenly throughout a habitat. Usually, territorial behavior is related to the specific lifestyle of the organism that displays it and to whatever aspect of its ecology is most critical to its reproductive success. For instance, sea birds may range over hundreds of square miles of open water but exhibit territorial behavior restricted to nesting sites on a rock or island, the resource that is in the shortest supply and for which competition is keenest. The adaptive "reason" for territoriality is not always readily evident, however.

Sexual Behavior Is Generally Social

The minimum social contact and, for some species of animals (for example, many species of spiders) the only social contact, is mating. Fertilization and perhaps the rearing of young are, for some animals, the only forms

(a)

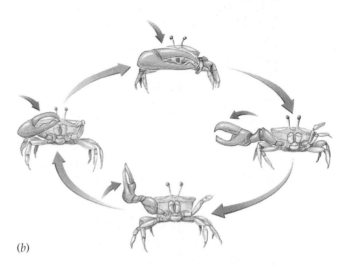

(b)

Figure 50–16 Courtship displays. (*a*) A black-browed albatross couple from the Galapagos Islands. (*b*) Courtship signals by male fiddler crabs are specific to each species. This particular sequence of motions of the large right claw is characteristic of the species *Uca lactae*.   (*a*, Douglas T. Cheeseman, Jr./Peter Arnold, Inc.)

of social behavior (Figure 50–17). Let us consider mating as a basic example of social conduct, for the elements to which it can be reduced are also the least common denominators of most social behavior.

Mating is adaptive in that it is usually necessary for reproduction, at least in animals. It requires *cooperation*, the *temporary suppression of aggressive behavior*, and a *system of communication*. Among some jumping spiders, for example, mating is preceded by a ritual courtship on the part of the male, the effect of which is to produce temporary paralysis in the female. While she is thus enthralled, the male inseminates her. Should she recover before he makes his escape, he becomes the main course at his own wedding feast. Even so, he would be

able to make the ultimate material contribution to the eggs the female will produce and therefore to the perpetuation of his genes. She would otherwise have to bear the metabolic burden of their production all by herself.

Success of a male in dominance encounters with other males indicates his quality to the female. The victorious male courts the female. Species-specific courtship behavior ensures that the male is a member of the same species and also provides the female further opportunity to evaluate the quality of the male. Courtship may also function as a signal to trigger nest building or ovulation. Courtship rituals may be long and complex. The first display of the male releases a counterbehavior

(a)

(b)

Figure 50–17 Male and female jumping spiders, *Phidippus audax*, in the courtship behavior that precedes mating. The male performs an elaborate dance that inhibits the female's natural aggression toward him, allowing him to get close enough to inseminate her.   (Visuals Unlimited/P. Starborn)

Figure 50–18 A pair of nesting albatrosses. In many species pair bonds are maintained by grooming or other displays of attraction. (E. R. Degginger)

of a conspecific female. This, in turn, releases additional male behavior, and so on until the pair are ready for copulation.

Courtship is often strenuous and dangerous, especially for males. Tremendous energy may be expended in the fights that occur among rams, bull seals, and many other mammals and even some birds. Additional energy may be spent in wallowing, roaring, leaping about, and other male acrobatics. These behaviors may be a test of male fitness. The male with the greatest endurance has the opportunity to mate and to propagate his genes.

Pair Bonds Establish Reproductive Cooperation

A **pair bond** is a stable relationship between animals of opposite gender that ensures cooperative behavior in mating and the rearing of the young (Figure 50–18). In some species, a newly arrived female is initially treated as a rival male. Then, through the use of appeasement postures and gestures by both male and female, the initial hostility is dissipated and mating takes place. Such sexual-appeasement behavior may be very elaborate and gives rise to mating dances in some birds. Often, courtship displays continue in modified form throughout the reproductive association of mates, and sometimes, especially in birds, they may persist for life. The releaser mechanisms involved in the establishment and maintenance of the pair bond are often remarkably detailed. Such cues enable courtship rituals to function as

behavioral genetic isolating mechanisms among species (see Chapter 19).

Many organisms care for their young

Care of the young is an important part of successful reproduction in many species; it, too, requires a parental investment (Figure 50–19). The benefit of parental care is the increased likelihood that the offspring will survive, but the cost is a reduction in the number of offspring that can be produced. Because of the time spent carrying the developing embryo, the female has more to lose than the male if the young do not develop. Thus, females are more likely than males to brood eggs and young, and usually the females invest more in parental care.

Investing time and effort in care of the young is usually less advantageous to a male (assuming that the female can handle the job by herself), for time spent in parenting is time lost from inseminating other females. Even worse, it may not be certain who fathered the offspring. Raising some other male's offspring is a genetic disadvantage, which is probably why male lions kill the cubs of former harem masters whose position they have usurped. In some situations, however, it may be to the male's advantage to help rear his own young or even those of a genetic relative. Receptive females may be scarce, and gathering sufficient food may require more effort than one parent can exert. In some habitats, the young may need protection against predators and sometimes against cannibalistic males of the same species.

Play Is Often Practice Behavior

Play is an important aspect of behavior development in many species, especially young mammals. It serves as a means of practicing adult patterns of behavior and perfecting means of escape, prey killing, and even sexual conduct. In true play, the behavior may not be actually consummated. Thus, a kitten pounces upon a dead leaf but of course does not kill it, even though the kitten administers a typical carnivore neck bite. When playing with a littermate, the same kitten may practice the disemboweling stroke with its hind claws, but the littermate is not intentionally injured in the process (Figure 50–20).

Highly Organized Societies Occur Among Insects and Vertebrates

Some animal societies exhibit elaborate and complex patterns of social interactions. Considerable division of labor occurs that is not directly connected with the care of the young.

(b)

Figure 50–19 Examples of parental investment. (*a*) Cougars and black bears are normally mortal enemies and actively avoid each other. This confrontation was initiated when the cougar intruded into the area where a female bear was raising her cubs. (*b*) A chinstrap penguin regurgitating food for her young. Such an investment of time and energy on the part of the parent does not benefit the parent directly, but it does help ensure the transmission of the parent's genes into succeeding generations. (*c*) A baby orangutan rides on its mother's back during early infancy and acquires some of her social status. (*a*, E. R. Degginger; *b*, P. R. Ehrlich, Stanford University/Biological Photo Service; *c*, Schafer and Hill/Peter Arnold, Inc.)

(c)

(a)

Figure 50–20 Young lions playing in southern Africa. Play is behavior that is not consummated and often serves as a means of practicing behavior that will be used in earnest in later life, possibly in hunting, fighting for territory, or competing for mates. (Susan McCartney/Photo Researchers, Inc.)

The social insects include some hymenopterans and termites

Although many insects cooperate socially, such as tent caterpillars, which spin a communal nest, the most elaborate insect societies are found among the bees, ants, wasps, and termites. The first three belong to the order Hymenoptera, which includes many social species. Insect societies are held together by an elaborate system of sign stimuli that are keyed to social interaction; as a result, they tend to be quite rigid. In addition to other modes of communication, the social insects secrete pheromones that accomplish such tasks as suppressing the ovaries of worker honeybees or alerting an ant hill to the presence of an enemy (an "alarm substance" is given off from a special abdominal gland of an excited worker).

The social organization of honeybees has been studied more extensively than that of any other social insect. A honeybee society generally consists of a single adult queen, up to 80,000 worker bees (all female), and, at

Figure 50–21 A queen honeybee inspecting wax cells. Note the numerous workers that surround her. They constantly lick secretions from the queen bee which are transmitted throughout the hive and act to suppress the activity of the workers' ovaries. (Treat Davidson/Photo Researchers, Inc.)

certain times, a few males called drones that fertilize newly developed queens. The queen's job is reproduction; she deposits about 1000 fertilized eggs per day in the wax cells of a comb.

Division of labor in the bee society is determined mostly by age. The youngest worker bees serve as nurse bees. They have special glands on the head that secrete **royal jelly,** which is essential for the nutrition of all larval bees. After about a week as nurse bees, workers begin to produce wax and build and maintain the wax cells. Older workers are foragers, bringing home the vital nectar and pollen. Most worker bees die at the ripe old age of 42—days, that is.

Behavioral cues indicate when there is a labor shortage in any category. If there are too many larvae for the nurse bees, foragers help for the duration of the emergency, redeveloping royal-jelly glands.

The composition of a bee society is controlled by an anti-queen pheromone secreted by the queen. It acts as a releaser, inhibiting the workers from raising a new queen, and it inhibits the development of the ovaries in the workers (Figure 50–21). If the queen dies or the colony becomes so large that the inhibiting effect of the pheromone is dissipated, the workers begin to feed some larvae the special food that promotes their development into new queens.

The most sophisticated known mode of communication among bees is a stereotyped series of body movements known as a **dance.** When a scout locates a rich source of nectar, it communicates to the other bees the direction and distance of the food source relative to the hive. If the food supply is nearby, the scout performs a round dance, which generally excites the other bees and causes them to fly about in all directions (but within a certain distance from the hive) until they find the nectar. If the source is distant, however, the scout performs a waggle dance. This "step" has a figure-eight configuration. As the bee treads the long axis of the figure eight, she emits a series of distinctive sounds and wags her abdomen from side to side. Karl von Frisch, a pioneer in the study of communication in bees, found that the orientation of the circular movements indicates the direction of the food source. The frequency of the waggle indicates the distance. Bees use the angle of the sun and light polarization to orient themselves. The dance locates the food in reference to the position of the sun (Figure 50–22).

Although rudimentary social behavior is widespread among insects, the only elaborate societies with extensive division of labor occur among hymenoptera (bees, wasps, and ants) and termites. The question is not so much why other insects are not social as it is why these particular insects *are* social. We cannot answer this question with assurance for the termites, but the basis of hymenoptera sociality appears to be chromosomal.

Hymenoptera have a system of sex determination in which males are haploid; thus, males develop from unfertilized eggs. Reproductive females store sperm cells from previous matings in a seminal receptacle. If they permit a sperm cell to contact the egg as it is laid, the resulting insect is female; otherwise, it is male. Because a haploid male drone produces sperm that also have a haploid set, each one of those sperm cells has *all* his chromosomes. Because the queen stores this sperm for much, or even all, of her lifetime, the worker bees of a hive are more closely related than sisters born of a diploid father would be. Indeed, they have three-quarters of their genes in common (they share half of the queen's chromosomes and all of the drone's). As a consequence, they are more closely related to the younger sisters they raise than they would be to their own offspring, if they could have any. A worker bee's offspring would have only half of its genes in common with its worker mother.

Vertebrate societies tend to be relatively flexible

Simpler, at least by first impression, but also more flexible than those of insects, vertebrate societies are very common. Great variation exists among vertebrate societies. Hyenas, wolves, red deer, prairie dogs, baboons, and people represent a great range of behaviors, yet a few points of similarity do stand out.

Among vertebrate societies, a far greater range and plasticity of potential behavior exist than among insect societies. Vertebrate societies are far less rigid and much more adaptable to changing needs. Vertebrate societies usually contain nothing comparable to the physically and behaviorally specialized castes of termites or ants. What is more, individual members of vertebrate soci-

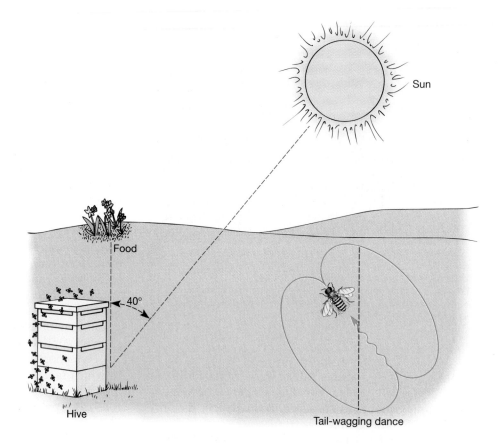

Figure 50–22 Waggle dance of a scout honeybee, indicating a food source located at a 40-degree angle to the left of the sun. The waggle is upward, indicating that the food is toward the sun, and inclined 40 degrees to the left, indicating the angle of the food source to the sun.

eties are not as specialized in their tasks as are the social insects. The very behavioral plasticity of vertebrates makes possible the symbolic transmission of culture, and this opens up possibilities inaccessible to social insects. The only vertebrate society, however, that is based to any great extent on the symbolic transmission of culture is human society (see discussion of cultural evolution in Chapter 21).

Kin Selection Could Produce Altruistic Behavior

In **altruistic behavior,** one individual appears to act in such a way as to benefit others rather than itself. This type of behavior is frequently seen in the more complex social groups (Figure 50–23). Biologists Watts and Stokes observed a particularly clear case of altruistic behavior in the mating of wild turkeys. Several groups of males, each of which has an internal dominance hierarchy, gather in a special mating territory and go through their displays of tail spreading, wing dragging, and gobbling in front of females who come to the area to copulate. One group attains dominance over other groups as a result of cooperation among the males within the group. The dominant member of the dominant group is the one to copulate most frequently with

Figure 50–23 Prairie dog. Low-ranking members of this social rodent group act as sentries. Sentries place their own lives in danger by exposing themselves outside their burrows. However, in this way they protect their siblings and by so doing ensure that the genes they share in common are perpetuated in the population. This is a classic example of kin selection. (Tina Waisman)

the females. Seemingly, the males that helped establish the dominant group but have low status within it gain nothing. Close analysis has shown that members of a group are brothers from the same brood. Because they share many genes with the successful male, they are

MAKING THE CONNECTION

Neural Circuits, Learning, and Behavior

Because innate behavior is a consequence of the biophysical properties of individual neurons and their interconnections, the simpler the nervous system, the simpler the range of behavior. Without the existence of the proper neural circuitry, learned behavior would be impossible. For an organism to learn, its neurons must have a large number of potential interactions with one another—not just the few required by stereotyped preprogrammed behavior, such as the sand wasp's ability to sting its victims.

The kind of learned behavior that the organism typically and most easily develops depends upon the complexity and layout of its neural circuitry. Learning also depends on changes in the readiness of neurons to form circuits with one another.

---

indirectly perpetuating many of their own genes. In this case, altruism is closely related to **kin selection,** vicarious gene propagation among closely related individuals, such as we have seen among the hymenopteran social insects. The nonbreeding turkeys, by promoting the breeding success of a kinsman, propagate copies of many of their own genes.

Among some birds (Florida jays and others), nonreproducing individuals aid in rearing the young. Nests tended by these additional helpers as well as parents produce more young than do nests with the same number of eggs overseen only by parents. The nonreproducing helpers, siblings of the parents, apparently increase their own biological success by ensuring the successful propagation of their genes via their siblings. It has also been suggested that if an organism in a habitat whose carrying capacity is at its limit cannot readily obtain its own territory, it can nevertheless pass on copies of a substantial portion of its genes by aiding an established pair of relatives that do possess a territory.

Sociobiology Attempts to Explain Altruism by Kin Selection

Sociobiology focuses on the evolution of social behavior through natural selection. It represents a synthesis of population genetics, evolution, and ethology. Like many biologists of the past (such as Darwin), Edward O. Wilson and other sociobiologists emphasize the animal roots of human behavior, but they have infused their discipline with population genetics, with particular emphasis on the effect of kin selection on inheritance patterns. Many of the concepts discussed in this chapter, such as altruism and paternal investment in care of the young, are based on contributions made by sociobiologists.

For the sociobiologist, the organism and its adaptations, including its behavior, are ways by which genes make more copies of themselves. The cells and tissues of the body support the functions of the reproductive system. The reproductive system's job is to transmit genetic information to succeeding generations.

Most of the controversy triggered by sociobiology seems related to its possible ethical implications. Sociobiology is often viewed as denying that human behavior is flexible enough to permit substantial improvements in the quality of our social lives. Yet sociobiologists do not disagree with their critics that human behavior is flexible. The debate therefore seems to rest on the *degree* to which human behavior is genetic and the *extent* to which it can be modified.

As sociobiologists acknowledge, people can, through culture, change their way of life far more profoundly in a few years than a hive of bees or a troop of baboons could in hundreds of generations of genetic evolution. This capacity to make changes is indeed genetically determined. How we use it and what we accomplish with it is a responsibility upon which our own well-being and that of other species depend.

SUMMARY

I. Behavior consists of the responses of an organism to signals from its environment.

II. Ethology is the scientific study of behavior in natural environments from the point of view of adaptation.
   A. Behavior tends to be adaptive.
   B. Behavior tends to be homeostatic.

III. Synchronization of an organism's metabolic processes and behavior with cyclical changes in the environment is adaptive.
   A. Some biological rhythms reflect the lunar cycle or the changes in tides due to phases of the moon.
   B. In many species, physiological processes and activity follow circadian rhythms.
   C. No single biological clock has been found. Biological rhythms are thought to be regulated by both internal and external factors.

IV. The capacity for behavior is inherited, and behavior is modified by environmental stimuli.
   A. Before an organism can show any pattern of behavior, it must be physiologically ready to produce the behavior.
   B. Some behavior patterns have strong genetic components. Innate behavior may be triggered by a specific unlearned sign stimulus, or releaser.
   C. Learning is a change in behavior resulting from experience.
   D. The simpler forms of learning are conditioning, both classical and operant, and habituation.
   E. Insight learning is particularly characteristic of the more "intelligent" animals; it involves the ability to see through a problem.
   F. Imprinting is a unique form of learning that establishes a parent-offspring bond during a critical period early in life.

V. Behavioral ecology focuses on interactions between animals and their environment and on the survival value of the behavior.
   A. In some birds, the need to migrate and the direction of migration appear to be genetically programmed, but how to navigate may be learned.
   B. Optimal foraging is theoretically the most efficient strategy for an animal to obtain food.

VI. Social behavior is adaptive conspecific interaction. A society is a group of individuals of the same species that cooperate in an adaptive manner.
   A. A society has a means of communication, cooperation, division of labor, and a tendency to stay together.
   B. Animals form societies because it is adaptive for them to do so.
   C. Animal communication involves the transmission of signals but does not use (as far as is known) symbolic language in the human sense. Pheromones are chemical signals that convey information between members of a species.
   D. Dominance hierarchies result in the suppression of aggressive behavior.
   E. Organisms often inhabit a home range, from which they seldom or never depart. This range, or some portion of it, may be defended against members of the same (or occasionally different) species.
      1. Defended areas are called territories, and the defensive behavior is territoriality.
      2. Territorial defense is often carried out by display behavior rather than by actual fighting.
   F. Courtship behavior ensures that the male is a member of the same species and permits the female to assess the quality of the male.
   G. A pair bond is a stable relationship between a male and a female that ensures cooperative behavior in mating and rearing the young.
   H. Parental care increases the probability that the offspring will survive. A high investment in parenting is often less advantageous to the male than to the female.
   I. Play gives the young animal a chance to practice adult patterns of behavior.
   J. Insect societies depend upon releasers and so tend to be rigid, with the role of the individual narrowly defined.
   K. Vertebrate societies are far less rigid than insect societies. Although innate behavior is important, generally the role of the individual is learned.
   L. In altruistic behavior, one individual appears to behave in such a way as to benefit others rather than itself. Altruism may be closely related to kin selection.
   M. Sociobiology focuses on the evolution of social behavior through natural selection.

POST-TEST

1. _____ may be defined as responses of an organism to signals from its environment.
2. _____ is the study of behavior in natural environments from the point of view of adaptation.
3. A biological rhythm with approximately a 24-hour cycle is a _____ rhythm.
4. Animals that are most active at dawn or twilight are described as _____.
5. A sign stimulus used as a social signal in communication is a _____.
6. _____ behavior is mainly genetic; _____ behavior develops as a result of experience.
7. _____ is a form of learning in which a young animal forms a strong attachment to an individual (usually its parent) within a few hours of birth.
8. In _____ an organism learns to ignore a repeated, irrelevant stimulus.
9. Secretion of saliva by a student when the noon bell rings is an example of _____ conditioning.
10. The term *Zugunruhe* refers to _____ _____.

11. Behavioral ecologists focus on interactions of animals with their _____.
12. A _____ is a group of individuals belonging to the same species that cooperate in an adaptive manner and have a means of communicating with one another.
13. An important difference between human and animal communication is that animal communication is not generally _____.
14. _____ are chemical signals that convey information between members of a species.
15. An arrangement of members of a population by status is called a _____ _____.
16. The geographical area that members of a population seldom leave is the _____ _____.
17. Territoriality tends to reduce _____ and control _____ growth.
18. A _____ _____ is a stable relationship between animals of the opposite sex that ensures cooperative behavior in mating and rearing the young.
19. In a beehive, the youngest bees serve as _____ bees; they secrete _____ _____ on which larvae feed.
20. The extensive behavioral repertoire of the bee is almost entirely _____ (innate or learned).
21. Human society differs from other animal societies in that it depends mainly on the transmission of _____.
22. In _____ behavior, one individual appears to act to benefit others rather than itself.
23. _____ selection favors the indirect perpetuation of an animal's genes by a relative.
24. According to sociobiology, an organism and its adaptations are ways that its genes have of _____.

REVIEW QUESTIONS

1. In what ways is the behavior of *Philanthus*, the sand wasp, adaptive?
2. Why is it adaptive for some species to be diurnal but others nocturnal or crepuscular?
3. Behavior capacity is inherited and is modified by learning. Give an example.
4. When Konrad Lorenz kept a greylag goose isolated from other geese for the first week of its life, the goose persisted in following him about in preference to other geese. How can this behavior be explained?
5. How does physiological readiness affect instinctual behavior? How does it affect learned behavior?
6. What distinguishes an organized society from a mere aggregation of organisms? Cite an example of an organized society, and describe characteristics that qualify the society as organized.
7. How many similarities between the transmission of information by symbolic language and by heredity can you think of? How many differences?
8. Contrast the "language" of bees with human language.
9. How does an organism learn its place in a dominance hierarchy? What determines this place? What are the advantages of a dominance hierarchy?
10. What is territoriality? What functions does it seem to serve?
11. What is kin selection? How is kin selection used by sociobiologists to explain the evolution of altruistic behavior?
12. Why do animals play?
13. What are some advantages of courtship rituals?

RECOMMENDED READINGS

Dilger, W. C. The behavior of lovebirds. *Scientific American,* January 1962. The genetics of nest-material handling in these birds.

Gwinner, E. Internal rhythms and bird migration. *Scientific American,* April 1986. How do birds "know" when to migrate?

Lohmann, K. J. How sea turtles navigate. *Scientific American,* Vol. 266, No. 1, January 1992, pp. 100–106. Research has begun to identify the biological compasses and maps that guide sea turtles as they migrate across hundreds of kilometers of ocean.

Page, R. E., G. E. Robinson, and M. K. Fondrk. Genetic specialists, kin recognition and nepotism in honey-bee colonies. *Nature* 338, 1989.

Sherman, P. W., J. Jarvis, and S. H. Braude. Naked mole rats. *Scientific American,* Vol. 267, No. 2, August 1992, pp. 72–78. These animals have a social structure resembling that of some insects.

Wilson, E. O. *Sociobiology, the New Synthesis.* N. H. Belknap Press, Cambridge, Massachusetts, 1979. A summary of Wilson's proposed mechanisms of the evolution of altruism and his views on kin selection.

CAREER VISIONS

Naturalist

TED WESEMANN

Ted Wesemann enjoys a career that keeps him close to nature and gives him an opportunity to teach other people about the natural world. As director of Wilderness Southeast, a nonprofit educational organization in Savannah, Georgia, he oversees educational nature programs and tours. Wesemann completed his B.S. in biology at Appalachian State University, North Carolina, in 1984 and received his M.S. in 1986. His research on the burrowing owl in southern Florida earned him the best-thesis award and prompted significant ecological action. The Florida Department of Freshwater Fish and Game used his research to begin a species conservation program.

When did you first develop an interest in biology?

When I was about 12, I started watching birds, a hobby that grew out of my natural inclination to be outdoors. I had a pair of binoculars and a bird book, where I kept careful notes, like a junior scientist. Using a small recorder, I started taping birds in the backyard until I had a collection of bird songs—much to the amusement of my family. As I got older, I expanded that interest and rode my bike farther and farther from home. The land just outside south St. Louis was still woodland and truck farms, so there were lots of places to explore.

Did you have a mentor who encouraged your interests?

I had a remarkable high-school biology teacher who helped me decide to make

nature my life's work. His professionalism and enthusiasm for biology eventually helped me develop a scientist's approach to nature and natural history. Roy Pfund is still a biology teacher in St. Louis, and I stay in touch with him. When I began college, I knew I wanted to do something in the field of biology, but I did not succeed right away. I had difficulty focusing on a goal and lacked academic motivation, so I decided to take some time off from school.

Between college studies, how did you maintain your ties to the natural world?

I worked in rural Missouri on horse farms, and then decided to buy some property and build a house in the Ozarks to try my hand at self-sufficiency. When I moved to the moun-

tains of North Carolina, I managed a ski shop at one of the ski resorts during the winter. In summer I started leading white-water canoe trips and hiking and backpacking trips with an outfitter. One of my frustrations with those trips was that they involved more pure sport than natural history. I was spending a lot of time in beautiful outdoor environments, but I had a yearning for a more professional tie with nature, so I returned to school.

Did you know what area of biology you wanted to study?

At that time, the biology department at Appalachian State University offered a naturalist program for people who wanted to be interpretive naturalists.

What kind of work does an interpretive naturalist do? How does it differ from other types of fieldwork?

Naturalist, as that term is generally used, normally means interpretive naturalist—for example, the park ranger who takes people through a natural site and explains how plants adapt or what animals are there. It also describes someone who works in a natural history museum and educates the public through tours and classes.

Usually, people who go into the field to gather data for the government, private enterprise, or a research institution are called wildlife biologists or wildlife technicians. Those people do not necessarily interpret anything for the general public, as a naturalist would. They gather data on species of plants or animals, possibly turning that information into statistical analyses and making decisions about wildlife management. Partly due to federal regulations that require environmental impact statements, companies and government agencies employ biologists or botanists to study an area to determine if plant life or animal life is threatened by a proposed condominium development or city park. The Natural Heritage Program has devised the standard method used to inventory plants and animals.

What kinds of courses did you take in the interpretive naturalist program?

Most of my course work was in ornithology, herpetology, mammalogy, and limnology. I also took courses in biometrics and field techniques. In graduate school, I chose the M.S. track because I wanted to do a thesis, which turned out to be a very important part of my graduate school experience. The results of statistical analyses fascinated me and taught me the valuable lesson that solid research must be thorough, objective, systematic, and precise.

How did you conduct your thesis research?

My research focused on a small owl in southern Florida called the burrowing owl. I looked at factors that would affect the abundance and distribution of the owls. Within a study site, I sampled availability of prey and soil type and recorded percentage of development. Computer analysis then helped me determine the significance of each of these factors in the survival of the owl population.

I expected the owls to stay as far away from people as they could possibly get, but my research proved just the opposite to be true. The owls are actually attracted to areas that have been disturbed by cattle ranching, development, and citrus groves. They are shortgrass prairie birds, so a mowed field, where they can see predators coming and easily spot prey, is a perfect habitat for them.

How did you get your job at Wilderness Southeast?

It was largely a matter of good luck. When I got out of graduate school, I wanted to work in a summer program as an interpretive naturalist. I saw a job announcement in the newsletter *Environmental Opportunities* for a staff member at the summer ecology camp at Wilderness Southeast. I loved working in the program and saw an opportunity to bring together many interests. Fortunately for me, the director of Wilderness Southeast announced his retirement, and the staff encouraged me to apply for the job, which I began in January 1987.

Does Wilderness Southeast still hire students to staff summer programs?

This year we hired four students for our coastal ecology program. They included students working on degrees in marine biology and environmental education, as well as an intern just starting college. We give summer staff the same responsibilities as full-time employees. They work as camp counselors and science teachers for junior-high-school students.

How does Wilderness Southeast operate?

This organization was founded in 1973 by three people who enjoyed conducting natural history trips. It became a nonprofit organization in 1979 and now offers three types of programs—educational nature trips for the general public, summer camps for junior-high-school and high-school students, and customized trips for nature centers, zoos, the Smithsonian Institution, and other organizations.

People who participate in our programs are amateur naturalists or genuinely interested in nature. We guard against becoming merely tour guides by making sure our trips are educational. As we go down the trail or down the river, trip leaders talk about plants, animals, adaptations, and evolutionary strategies, for example. We run programs to the Great Smoky Mountains, Georgia's Barrier Islands, Florida Springs, the Everglades, and many more sites. We also have tropical trips, both coastal and coral reef, as well as rainforest and dry-forest programs, including trips to Costa Rica and Belize. Two years ago we began a

program in Brazil, mostly along the Amazon River.

What are your duties as director of Wilderness Southeast?

Part of my job is administrative, managing six full-time employees and several part-time staff members during the busy season, reporting to the board of directors, and overseeing educational programs. For the interpretive-naturalist side of my job, I am one of four full-time group leaders. From January to May we are usually leading tours at the locations I mentioned. I'd like to emphasize that the guides find this job enormously fulfilling. Nature offers so much that we can continue to learn all our lives, and that is probably the driving force behind our enthusiasm as interpretive naturalists. There is always more to learn, and more to pass on.

How would someone find out about the jobs you have described?

Two informative newsletters are good resources: *Environmental Opportunities* and *Job Scan*. The favorite seems to be *Environmental Opportunities*. It lists job opportunities in categories such as agricultural, administrative, environmental education, fisheries, wildlife, natural resources, environmental engineering, internships, organizational jobs (such as the Audubon Society or Sierra Club), nature centers, and outdoor education.

What are some of the job opportunities for naturalists in your area?

The University of Georgia has a marine education facility here on the coast. Members of the staff offer training and trips, as we do at Wilderness Southeast, but they live at the facility and have access to equipment and laboratories. We rent our building from the 170-acre Environmental Education Center for Chatham County schools. Their staff teaches environmental education to school children who are bused here. Naturalists also work at the science museum in Savannah, preparing educational programs for adults and children as well as carrying out sea turtle research and conservation activities on the islands. I'm certain that similar opportunities exist in most metropolitan areas.

◻

PART VIII

Ecology

There is no isolation in the biosphere—living organisms are inextricably connected to each other and to the physical environment. The organisms of the deepest ocean abyss are linked by atmosphere and water to those of the tropical rain forest, desert, and arctic tundra.

Ecology is the study of the relationships among organisms and between organisms and their environment. Ecologists draw on knowledge from botany, zoology, microbiology, physiology, genetics, evolution, and all the other subdisciplines of biology, in addition to geology, chemistry, and physics. Thus, it is fitting that we examine ecology at the end of our introduction to biology.

Chapter 51 provides an overview of ecology as well as a discussion of the Earth's major life zones. Chapter 52 explores population ecology, and Chapter 53 examines community dynamics. Chapter 54 deals with how the physical environment affects living things. Because the fate of creatures great and small is now decided by human activities, and because the human species in turn depends on other organisms, Chapter 55 deals with humans in the environment.

Arches National Park, Utah.
(David Muench)

CHAPTER 51

Ecology and the Geography of Life

O U T L I N E

The highest levels of biological organization
Geographic distributions of organisms
Major terrestrial life zones
Aquatic life zones
Life zones interact

The concept of ecology was first developed in the 19th century by Ernst Haeckel, who also created its name—*eco* from the Greek word for "household" and *logy* from the Greek word for "study." Ecology, then, means the study of one's house. Nature, viewed from the standpoint of ecology, is like a great estate in which the nonliving environment and organisms interact in an immense and complicated web of relationships. **Ecology** is the study of interactions among organisms and between organisms and their physical environments.

The focus of ecology can be local and very specific or global and quite generalized, depending on the viewpoint of the scientist. Thus, one ecologist might determine the temperature requirements of a single species of oak, another

The complexity of a coral reef community rivals or exceeds that of any terrestrial community. (Susan Blanchet/Dembinsky Photo Associates)

might study species diversity in the forest where the oak is found, and another might examine how energy flows between the forest and surrounding communities.

Ecology is the broadest field within the biological sciences, with explicit links to every other biological discipline. Its universality also brings subjects into view that are not traditionally part of biology. Geology and earth science are extremely important to ecology, especially when scientists examine the physical environment of planet Earth. Because humans are biological organisms, all of our activities have a bearing on ecology; even economics and politics have profound ecological implications.

After you have studied this chapter you should be able to

1. Define ecology and explain which levels of organization in the biological world are studied by ecologists.
2. Distinguish among the following terms: population, community, ecosystem, biosphere, and ecosphere.
3. Briefly describe the principal terrestrial biomes, giving attention to the climate, soil, and characteristic plants and animals of each: tundra, taiga, temperate forest, temperate grassland, desert, chaparral, savanna, and tropical rain forest.
4. Briefly describe the principal aquatic life zones, giving attention to the environmental characteristics and representative organisms of each: fresh water (flowing water, standing water, and freshwater wetlands), estuaries, and oceans (intertidal zone, neritic province, and oceanic province).

ECOLOGISTS STUDY THE HIGHEST LEVELS OF BIOLOGICAL ORGANIZATION

A **population** is a group of members of a single species that live together in the same area at the same time. A population ecologist might study (for example) a population of polar bears or a population of marsh grass.

A **community** consists of all the populations of different species living and interacting together within a certain area. A community ecologist might study how organisms interact with one another—including who eats whom—in a coral reef or in an alpine meadow.

Ecosystem is a more inclusive term than *community* because an **ecosystem** is a community together with its environment. Thus, ecosystems include not only all the interactions among the living organisms of a community but also the interactions between the organisms and their physical environment. An ecosystem ecologist might examine, for example, how temperature, light, precipitation, and soil factors affect the organisms living in a desert or a coastal bay (Figure 51–1).

All the communities of all living things on Earth make up the **biosphere.** These living organisms depend on the Earth's physical environment, which includes the **atmosphere,** the gaseous envelope surrounding the Earth; the **hydrosphere,** the Earth's supply of water (both liquid and frozen, fresh and salty); and the **lithosphere,** the soil and rock of the Earth's crust. The **ecosphere** encompasses the biosphere and its interactions with the atmosphere, hydrosphere, and lithosphere. Ecologists who concentrate their focus on the biosphere/ecosphere level examine the complex interrelationships among the Earth's atmosphere, land, water, and living things.

ORGANISMS HAVE UNIQUE GEOGRAPHIC DISTRIBUTIONS

One would hardly expect to find a penguin in Florida or a palm tree in Alaska—at least, outside of a zoo or botanical garden. Yet we are not surprised to find white-tailed deer in both places, along with black bears, song sparrows, honeybees, dandelions, and daisies. It is obvious that organisms are not uniformly distributed throughout the Earth, but what is it that governs their distribution? Basically, living things are restricted to areas whose available habitats (local environments) and potential lifestyles fit their adaptations. The greater the differences among habitats, the greater the differences among the organisms that inhabit them.

MAJOR TERRESTRIAL LIFE ZONES, CALLED BIOMES, ARE LARGELY DETERMINED BY CLIMATE

A **biome** is a large, relatively distinct ecosystem that is characterized by similar climate, soil, plants, and animals regardless of where it occurs on Earth. Examples of biomes include deserts, tropical rain forests, and tundra. A biome's boundaries are determined by climate

Figure 51–1 Many ecosystem studies require elaborate equipment. Here scientists study the effects of a pollutant on the living organisms in a coastal bay. (Courtesy of Dr. M. R. Reeve, National Marine Fisheries Service, Woods Hole Oceanographic Institute)

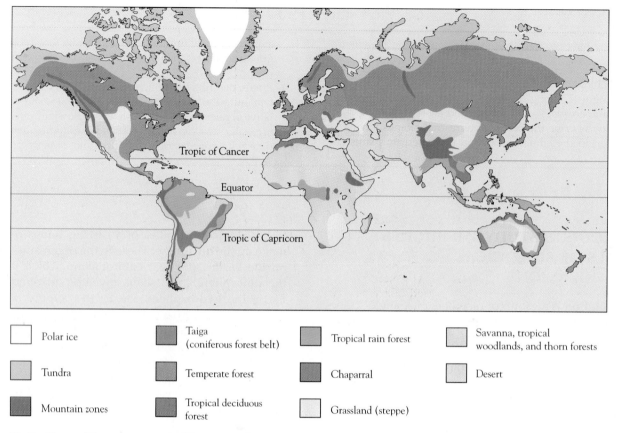

	Polar ice		Taiga (coniferous forest belt)		Tropical rain forest		Savanna, tropical woodlands, and thorn forests
	Tundra		Temperate forest		Chaparral		Desert
	Mountain zones		Tropical deciduous forest		Grassland (steppe)		

Figure 51–2 The world's major terrestrial life zones, or biomes, are distributed primarily in accordance with two factors, temperature and precipitation. In the higher latitudes, temperature is the more important of the two; in temperate and tropical zones, precipitation is a significant determinant of community composition.

more than any other factor (Figure 51–2). For example, because the northernmost biome, the tundra, is colder and has shorter growing seasons than warmer biomes, it has fewer kinds of vegetation (few plants can tolerate the extreme conditions there). As one moves from the poles toward the equator, precipitation becomes a very important climatic factor, producing the temperate communities of desert, grassland, and forest, in increasing order of precipitation.

Tropical and subtropical biomes, which occur in the lower latitudes (near the equator), experience a relatively small range of temperatures throughout the year. They are at least as varied as temperate biomes, and like temperate biomes, they are determined mainly by the amount and seasonality of precipitation they receive. Thus, not only tropical forests exist, but also tropical grasslands and deserts. In the tropics the *seasonal* distribution of rainfall is especially important. Some tropical grasslands would be rain forests (in terms of the *amounts* of precipitation they receive) except that almost all of their rainfall occurs during 2 months of the year. Lush rain forest vegetation could scarcely persist for 10 months without water!

Altitude also affects ecosystems: Changes in vegetation with increasing altitude resemble the changes in vegetation observed in the transition from warmer to colder climates (see Making the Connection: Comparing Altitudes and Latitudes).

Tundra Is the Northernmost Biome

Tundra occurs in the extreme northern latitudes wherever the snow melts seasonally (Figure 51–3). (The Southern Hemisphere has no equivalent of the arctic tundra because it has no land above water in the proper latitudes.) Tundra is exposed to long, harsh winters and very short summers. Although the growing season, with its warmer temperatures, is short (from 50 to 160 days, depending on location), the days are long. In many places the sun does not set at all for many days in midsummer; however, the amount of light at midnight is one tenth that at noon. There is little precipitation (10 to 25 cm, or 4 to 10 in, per year) over much of the tundra, with most of it falling during the summer months.

Tundra soils tend to be geologically young, since most of them were formed after the last ice age. These

MAKING THE CONNECTION

Comparing Altitudes and Latitudes

Hiking up a mountain is similar to traveling toward the North Pole with respect to the major life zones encountered. This is because, as one climbs a mountain, the temperature drops just as it does when one travels north, and the types of plants growing on the mountain change as the temperature changes.

The base of a mountain in Colorado, for example, might be covered by deciduous trees, which shed their leaves every autumn. Above that altitude, where the climate is colder and more severe, one might find a coniferous forest (called a subalpine forest) that resembles the northern taiga. Higher still, where the climate is very cold, a kind of tundra occurs, with vegetation composed of grasses, sedges, and small tufted plants; it is called alpine tundra to distinguish it from arctic tundra. At the very top of the mountain, a per-

manent ice or snow cap might be found, similar to the nearly lifeless polar land areas.

Important environmental differences exist between high altitudes and high latitudes, however, that affect the types of organisms found in each place. Alpine tundra typically lacks permafrost and has more precipitation than arctic tundra. Also, high elevations of temperate mountains do not have the great extremes of day length that are associated with the changing seasons in biomes at high latitudes. Furthermore, the intensity of solar radiation is greater at high elevations than at high latitudes. For example, at high elevations, the sun's rays pass through less atmosphere, which results in a greater amount of ultraviolet radiation than at higher latitudes (because less UV is filtered out by the atmosphere).

soils are usually nutrient-poor and have little organic litter (dead leaves and such). Although the soil surface melts during the summer, tundra has a layer of permanently frozen ground called **permafrost,** varying in depth and thickness, that interferes with drainage and prevents roots of larger plants from becoming established. The limited precipitation, in combination with low temperatures, flat topography (surface features), and the permafrost layer, produces a swampy landscape of broad, shallow lakes, sluggish streams, and bogs.

In the tundra, species are few, but they often exist in great numbers. Tundra is dominated by mosses, lichens (such as reindeer moss), grasses, grasslike sedges, and annuals. No readily recognizable trees or shrubs grow except in very sheltered localities, although dwarf willows and other dwarf trees are common; tundra plants seldom grow taller than 30 cm (12 in).

The year-round animal life of the tundra includes weasels, arctic foxes, snowshoe hares, ptarmigan, snowy owls, and hawks. In the summer, large herbivores such as musk-oxen and caribou migrate north to the tundra to graze on sedges, grasses, and dwarf willows. There are no reptiles or amphibians. Insects such as mosquitos, blackflies, and deerflies survive the winter as eggs or pupae, and adults are present in great numbers during summer weeks.

Tundra regenerates very slowly after it has been disturbed. Even casual use by hikers can damage it.

Figure 51–3 Alaskan tundra in the fall. (David Muench)

Figure 51–4   Taiga, or boreal forest.   (Carolina Biological Supply Company)

Long-lasting injury, likely to persist for hundreds of years, has been done to large portions of the arctic tundra by oil exploration and military use.

Taiga, or Boreal Forest, Is Dominated by Conifers

Just south of the tundra is the **taiga,** or **boreal forest** (northern forest), which stretches across both North America and Eurasia, covering approximately 11 percent of the Earth's land (Figure 51–4). A biome comparable to the taiga is not found in the Southern Hemisphere. Winters are extremely cold and severe, although not as harsh as in the tundra. The growing season of the boreal forest is somewhat longer than that of the tundra. Taiga receives little precipitation, perhaps 50 cm (20 in) per year, and its soil is acidic, mineral-poor, and characterized by a deep layer of partly decomposed pine and spruce needles at the surface. Permafrost is found deep under the soil or is absent. Taiga has numerous ponds and lakes where depressions in the Earth's surface were created by the grinding ice sheets that covered this area during the last ice age.

Deciduous trees such as aspen or birch, which shed their leaves in autumn, may form striking assemblages in taiga, but overall, spruce, fir, and other conifers clearly dominate. Conifers have many drought-resistant adaptations such as needle-like leaves that have minimal surface area for water loss. Such an adaptation enables the conifers to withstand the physiological ''drought'' of the northern winter months (plant roots cannot absorb water when the ground is frozen).

The animal life of the boreal forest includes some larger species such as caribou (which migrate from the tundra to the taiga for the winter), wolves, bears, and moose. However, most of the animals are medium-sized to small; rodents, rabbits, and fur-bearing predators such as lynx, sable, and mink are typical. Most species of birds are seasonally abundant but migrate to warmer climates in the winter. Insects are abundant, but amphibians and reptiles are few except in the southern extensions.

Most of the taiga is not well suited to agriculture because of its short growing season and mineral-poor soil. However, the boreal forest yields vast quantities of lumber and pulpwood (for making paper products), plus furs and other forest products.

Temperate Forests Occur in Temperate Areas Where Precipitation Is Relatively High

In temperate latitudes rainfall varies greatly with longitude (see Chapter 54). Continental interiors tend to be dry, for a variety of reasons. Permanent high-pressure areas, such as those over the Sahara Desert, may nudge moist air masses aside. Air passing over a large land mass also may dry out without having the opportunity to be recharged with fresh moisture. The climate of the North American continent, however, is dominated by rain shadows cast by mountain ranges, especially in the West (Figure 51–5). As prevailing westerly winds push against the bases of the Sierra Nevada and Cascade Range in the Pacific Northwest, masses of moist air from the Pacific Ocean are forced upward, where they cool and precipitate much of their moisture. Thus, the western slopes of the mountains are so well watered that a temperate rain forest has developed. Considerable precipitation also falls in the upper reaches of the eastern slopes, but by the time the air has sunk back to lower altitudes, most of its available moisture has fallen.

Temperate rain forest occurs where temperate-zone precipitation ranges from 200 to 380 cm (80 to 152 in) annually

This is the case on the northwest coast of North America. Similar coniferous temperate rain forests occur in southeastern Australia and in southern South America. In this biome, precipitation is augmented by condensation of water from dense coastal fogs. The proximity of temperate rain forest to the coastline moderates the temperature so that the seasonal fluctuation is narrow; winters are mild and summers are cool. Temperate rain forest has relatively nutrient-poor soil, although its organic content may be high.

The dominant vegetation in the North American temperate rain forest is large evergreen trees, such as

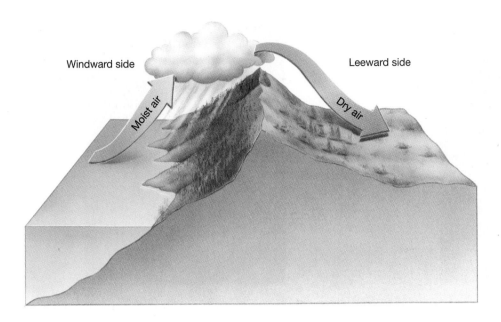

Windward side

Leeward side

Moist air

Dry air

Figure 51–5 When wind blows moist air over a mountain range, precipitation occurs on the windward side of the mountain, causing a dry "rain shadow" on the leeward side. Such a rain shadow occurs in Washington State east of the Cascade Range.

western hemlock, Douglas fir, Sitka spruce, and western arborvitae. Like tropical rain forests, the temperate rain forest is rich in epiphytes—small plants that grow nonparasitically on the large trees (Figure 51–6). The epiphytes in temperate rain forests are mainly mosses, club mosses, lichens, and ferns. Among the animals that live there are squirrels, deer, and numerous bird species.

Temperate rain forest is one of the richest wood producers in the world, supplying us with lumber and pulpwood. It is also one of the most complex ecosystems on Earth. Care must be taken to avoid overharvesting the original old-growth forest. Hundreds of years are required for such an ecosystem to develop. The logging industry typically harvests old-growth forest and replants the area with younger trees that will be harvested in another 100 years or so. Thus, once the old-growth trees are harvested, the ecosystem never has a chance to redevelop.

Figure 51–6 Temperate coniferous rain forest. Note the epiphytes growing on the tree trunks, branches, and leaves. (J. Lotter/Tom Stack & Associates)

Temperate deciduous forest occurs where temperate-zone precipitation ranges from about 75 to 125 cm (30 to 49 in) annually

Hot summers and pronounced winters are characteristic of **temperate deciduous forest.** Typically, the soil of such a forest consists of topsoil, which is rich in organic matter, and a deep, clay-rich lower layer. As organic materials decay, mineral ions are released. If they are not immediately absorbed by the roots of the living trees, these ions leach into the clay, where they may be retained.

Temperate deciduous forests of the northeastern and mideastern United States are dominated by broad-leaved hardwood trees, such as oak, hickory, and beech, that lose their foliage annually (Figure 51–7). In the southern reaches of the temperate deciduous forest, the number of broad-leaved evergreen trees, such as magnolia, increases.

Temperate deciduous forest originally contained such large mammals as puma, wolves, deer, bison, bears, and other species now extinct, plus many small mammals and birds. Both reptiles and amphibians abounded, together with a denser and more varied insect life than exists today. Much of the original temperate deciduous forest was removed by logging and land clearing. Where it has been allowed to regenerate, temperate deciduous forest is often in a seminatural state—that is, highly modified by humans.

Figure 51–7 Seasonal changes during fall in a temperate deciduous forest. (Dennis Drenner)

Figure 51–8 Prairie coneflowers bloom in a grassland in North America. (Willard Clay/Dembinsky Photo Associates)

Worldwide, deciduous forests were among the first communities to be converted to agricultural use. In Europe and Asia, for example, many soils that originally supported deciduous forests have been cultivated by traditional agricultural methods for thousands of years without substantial loss in fertility. However, American farmers of the 18th and 19th centuries perceived land as a limitless resource. They often abandoned the wise soil conservation practices of their ancestors and allowed erosion and other forms of soil depletion to damage the land.

Temperate Grasslands Occur in Temperate Areas of Moderate Precipitation

Summers are hot, winters are cold, and rainfall is often uncertain in **temperate grasslands.** Annual precipitation averages 25 to 75 cm (10 to 30 in). In grasslands with less precipitation, minerals tend to accumulate in a marked layer just below the topsoil instead of washing out of the soil. Grassland soil has considerable organic material because the aboveground portions of many grasses die off each winter, contributing to the organic content, while the roots and rhizomes survive underground. Also, many grasses are sod formers, meaning that their roots and rhizomes form a thick, continuous underground mat.

The North American Midwest is an excellent example of a temperate grassland. Few trees grow except near rivers and streams, but grasses grow in great profusion in the thick, rich soil (Figure 51–8). Formerly, certain species of grass grew as tall as a person on horseback, and the land was covered with herds of grazing animals, particularly bison. The principal predators were wolves, although in sparser, drier areas their place was taken by coyotes. Smaller fauna included prairie dogs and their predators (foxes, black-footed ferrets, and birds of prey), grouse, reptiles (such as snakes and lizards), and great numbers of insects.

Steppes, or shortgrass prairies, are temperate grassland habitats that experience less precipitation than the moister grasslands just described but greater precipitation than deserts. Shortgrass prairies have less grass than the moister grasslands, and occasionally some bare soil. Native grasses are drought-resistant.

The North American grassland is so well suited to agriculture that little of it remains. Almost nowhere can we see even an approximation of what our ancestors encountered as they settled the Midwest. It is not surprising that the American Midwest, the Ukraine, and other temperate grasslands became the breadbaskets of the world. These habitats provide ideal growing conditions for such grasses as the cereal grains.

Chaparral Is a Thicket of Evergreen Shrubs and Small Trees

Some temperate habitats have mild winters combined with very dry summers. Such **Mediterranean climates,** as they are called, occur not only in the area around the Mediterranean Sea but also in California, western Australia, portions of Chile, and South Africa. In the North American Southwest, this community is known as **chaparral.** Chaparral soil is thin and not very fertile. Frequent fires occur naturally in this habitat, particularly in late summer and autumn.

Figure 51–9 Chaparral in the Santa Monica Mountains, California. The chaparral biome consists primarily of drought-resistant evergreen shrubs. Chaparral develops where hot, dry summers alternate with mild, rainy winters. (Visuals Unlimited/John Cunningham)

Chaparral vegetation looks strikingly similar in different areas of the world, even though the individual species are quite different. Chaparral is usually dominated by a dense growth of evergreen shrubs and may contain drought-resistant pine or oak trees (Figure 51–9). During the rainy season the habitat may be lush and green, but the plants lie dormant during the hot, dry summer. Trees and shrubs often have **sclerophyllous leaves**—hard, small, leathery leaves that resist water loss. Many plants are specifically fire-adapted and grow best in the months following a fire. Such growth is possible because fire releases the minerals that were tied up in the aboveground parts of the plants that burned. The underground parts are not destroyed by the fire, however, and with the new availability of essential minerals, the plants sprout vigorously during the winter rains. Mule deer, wood rats, chipmunks, lizards, and many species of birds are common in the chaparral.

The fires that occur at irregular intervals in California chaparral vegetation are often quite costly to humans because they consume expensive homes built on the hilly chaparral landscape. Unfortunately, efforts to control the naturally occurring fires sometimes backfire. Denser, thicker vegetation tends to accumulate when periodic fires are prevented; then, when a fire does occur, it is much more severe.

Desert Occurs Where Little Precipitation Falls

Deserts are very dry areas that are found in both temperate and tropical regions. The low water content of the desert atmosphere leads to daily temperature ex-

tremes. Deserts vary greatly depending upon the amount of precipitation they receive, which is generally less than 25 cm (10 in) per year. A few deserts are so dry that virtually no plant life occurs in them, as is the case in portions of the African Namib Desert and the Atacama-Sechura Desert of Chile and Peru. As a result, desert soil is low in organic material but often has a high mineral content. In some regions, the concentrations of certain soil minerals reach toxic levels.

Plant cover is sparse in deserts, and much of the soil is exposed. Both perennials and annuals (after a rain) grow there. Plants in North American deserts include cacti, yuccas, Joshua trees, and widely scattered bunchgrass (Figure 51–10). Perennial desert plants tend to have reduced leaves or no leaves, an adaptation that enables them to conserve water. Other desert plants shed their leaves for most of the year, growing only in the brief moist season. Desert plants are noted for **allelopathy,** an adaptation in which toxic substances secreted by roots or shed leaves inhibit the establishment of competing plants nearby. Many desert plants are provided with defensive spines, thorns, or toxins to resist the heavy grazing pressure they experience in this food- and water-deficient environment.

Desert animals tend to be small. During the heat of the day they remain under cover or return to shelter periodically. At night they come out to forage or hunt. In addition to desert-adapted insects, there are many specialized desert reptiles—lizards, tortoises, and snakes. Mammals include such rodents as the American kangaroo rat, which does not need to drink water but can subsist solely on the water content of its food plus

Figure 51–10 Inhabitants of deserts are strikingly adapted to the demands of their environment. The moister deserts of North America frequently contain large cacti such as this organ pipe cactus. Photosynthesis is carried out by the stem, which also serves to store water. Leaves are modified into spines, which discourage herbivores from eating cactus tissue. (Stan Osolinski/Dembinsky Photo Associates)

Figure 51–11   The savanna biome of eastern Africa. Such grasslands formerly supported large herds of grazing animals and their predators, which are swiftly vanishing under pressure from pastoral and agricultural land use.   (Visuals Unlimited/Steve McCutcheon)

metabolically generated water. American deserts are also home to jackrabbits, and Australian deserts have kangaroos. Carnivores (such as the African fennec fox and some birds of prey, especially owls) live on the rodents and rabbits.

American deserts have been altered by humans in several ways. Off-road vehicles damage desert vegetation, which sometimes takes years to recover, and certain cacti and desert tortoises are rare as a result of poaching. Also, housing built in desert areas requires the importation of vast quantities of water.

Savanna Is a Tropical Grassland with Scattered Trees

The **savanna** biome is a tropical grassland with widely scattered clumps of low trees (Figure 51–11). Savanna is found in areas of low rainfall or sharply seasonal rainfall with prolonged dry periods; the yearly temperature range is small. Thus, seasons are regulated by precipitation, rather than by temperature as in temperate grasslands. Annual precipitation is 85 to 150 cm (34 to 60 in). Savanna soil is low in essential mineral nutrients, in part because the parent rock from which it is formed is infertile. Savanna soil is often rich in aluminum, and in places the aluminum reaches levels that are toxic to many plants. Although the African savanna is best known, tracts of savanna also occur in South America and northern Australia.

Savanna is characterized by wide stretches of grasses interrupted by occasional trees such as *Acacia*, which bristles with thorns that provide protection against herbivores. Both trees and grasses have features, such as extensive underground root systems, that enable them to survive the periodic fires that sweep through savanna.

In the African savanna lives the largest assemblage of hoofed mammals in the modern world—great herds of herbivores such as wildebeest, antelope, giraffe, and zebra. Large predators, such as lions and hyenas, kill and scavenge the herds. In areas of seasonally varying rainfall, the herds and their predators may migrate annually.

Tropical grasslands are rapidly being converted to rangeland for cattle and other animals, which are replacing the big herds of game animals. In places, severe overgrazing has converted savanna to desert.

Tropical Rain Forests Occur Where Temperatures Are High throughout the Year and Precipitation Falls Almost Daily

The annual precipitation of **tropical rain forests** is 200 to 450 cm (80 to 180 in). Much of this precipitation comes from locally recycled water that enters the atmosphere by transpiration of the forest's own trees.

Tropical rain forests are often found in areas with ancient soil that has been extensively leached by high precipitation, becoming poor in both nutrients and organic material. Because the temperature is high year round, decay organisms, ants, and termites decompose organic litter quite rapidly. Nutrients from the decomposing material are quickly absorbed by highly developed mycorrhizae and then transferred to the roots of plants. Thus, the mineral nutrients of tropical rain forests are tied up in the vegetation, not the soil.

Tropical rain forest is very productive (that is, its plants capture a lot of energy by photosynthesis). Stimulated by the significant solar energy input and the abundant precipitation characteristic of tropical rain forests, productivity is high here despite the scarcity of mineral nutrients in the soil.

Of all the life zones on land, the tropical rain forest is unexcelled in species diversity and variety. No single species dominates; one could travel for 0.4 km (0.25 mi) without encountering two members of the same species of tree.

Despite what you may have seen in Tarzan movies, the vegetation of tropical rain forests is not dense at ground level except near stream banks and in areas that are recovering from logging, fire, or agricultural use. The continuous canopy of leaves overhead produces a dark and extremely humid habitat. A fully developed rain forest has at least three distinct stories of vegetation (Figure 51–12). The topmost story consists of the crowns of occasional very tall trees. It is entirely ex-

Figure 51–12 A broad view of a tropical rain forest on one of the Hawaiian Islands. (David Muench)

posed to direct sunlight. The middle story forms a continuous canopy of leaves that lets in very little sunlight for the support of the sparse understory. The understory consists of both smaller plants that are specialized for life there and the seedlings of taller trees.

The trees of tropical rain forests are usually evergreen flowering plants. Their roots are often shallow and form a mat almost 1 m (about 3 ft) thick on the surface of the soil, which catches and absorbs almost all mineral nutrients released from leaves and litter by decay processes. Swollen bases or braces called buttresses hold the trees upright and aid in the extensive distribution of the shallow roots.

The trees in a tropical rain forest support extensive communities of smaller epiphytic plants that grow in crotches, on bark, or even on the leaves of their hosts. Because little light penetrates to the understory, many of the plants living there are adapted to climb upon already established host trees rather than invest their meager photosynthetic resources in the cellulose tissues of their own trunks. Tropical vines as thick as a human thigh abound.

Rainforest animals include the most abundant and varied insect, reptile, and amphibian fauna on Earth (Figure 51–13). Birds, too, are varied and often brilliantly colored. Most rainforest mammals, such as sloths and monkeys, live only in the trees, although some large ground-dwelling mammals, including elephants, are also found in rain forests.

Human population growth and industrialization in tropical countries may spell the end of most or all rain

Figure 51–13 Some animals of the South American tropical rain forest: (1) howler monkey, (2) scarlet macaw, (3) three-toed sloth, (4) red spider monkey and baby, (5) silky anteater and baby, (6) porcupine, (7) emerald tree boa, (8) tapirs, (9) tawny ocelot, and (10) green leaf frog. Except for the tapirs and ocelot, these animals spend most of their lives in the trees. (Robert Hynes, artist, © National Geographic Society)

forests by the end of the century. It is thought that many rainforest organisms will become extinct in this way before they have even been scientifically described. The ecological impacts of tropical rainforest destruction are discussed in Chapter 55.

•

AQUATIC LIFE ZONES OCCUPY MOST OF THE EARTH'S SURFACE

As you might expect, aquatic life zones are different from terrestrial life zones in almost all respects. For example, in terrestrial biomes, temperature and precipitation are the major determinants of plant and animal inhabitants, and light is relatively plentiful (except in certain habitats, such as the floor of the rain forest). The most significant environmental factors in aquatic life zones are very different. Temperature is less important, and water is obviously not an important limiting factor. The most fundamental division in aquatic ecology is probably between freshwater and saltwater habitats. **Salinity** (the concentration of dissolved salts, such as sodium chloride, in a body of water) affects the kinds of organisms present in aquatic ecosystems, as does the amount of dissolved oxygen. Water also greatly interferes with the penetration of light, so floating aquatic organisms that photosynthesize must remain near the water's surface, and vegetation attached to the bottom can grow only in the shallowest water. In addition, in certain aquatic environments, low levels of essential mineral nutrients limit the number and distribution of living things.

Aquatic habitats contain three main ecological categories of organisms: free-floating plankton, strongly swimming nekton, and bottom-dwelling benthos. **Plankton** are small or microscopic organisms that are relatively feeble swimmers and thus, for the most part, are carried about at the mercy of currents and waves (Figure 51–14). Although they cannot swim far horizontally, some species are capable of large diurnal migrations in a vertical direction and are found at different depths of water at different times of the day or sometimes at different seasons. Plankton are generally subdivided into two major categories: the phytoplankton and the zooplankton. **Phytoplankton**—cyanobacteria and free-floating algae of several types—are the base of most aquatic food chains. **Zooplankton** are nonphotosynthetic protozoa and small animals, including the larval stages of many organisms that are large as adults. **Nekton** are larger, more strongly swimming organisms such as fish, turtles, and whales. **Benthos** are bottom-dwelling creatures that fix themselves to one spot (such as oysters and barnacles), burrow into the sand (such as many worms and echinoderms), or simply walk about on the bottom (such as lobsters and brittle stars).

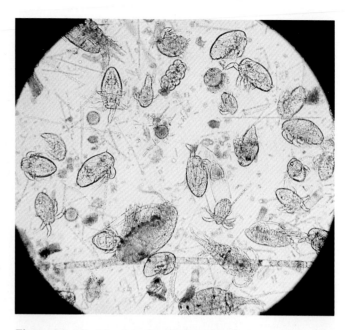

Figure 51–14 Mixed marine plankton. The larger organisms are copepods—very abundant arthropods that graze on diatoms in the plankton and are in turn the food for larger aquatic organisms. (Runk/Schoenberger, from Grant Heilman)

Freshwater Ecosystems Include Rivers, Lakes, and Freshwater Wetlands

The kinds of organisms that can be supported by a freshwater ecosystem are determined by factors such as water depth and current.

Rivers and smaller streams are flowing-water ecosystems

The nature of a flowing-water ecosystem changes greatly from its source (where it begins) to its mouth (where it empties into another body of water). For example, headwater streams (small streams that are the sources of a river) are usually shallow, swiftly flowing, highly oxygenated, and cold. In contrast, rivers downstream from the headwaters are wider and deeper, slower-flowing, less oxygenated, and less cold.

The kinds of organisms found in flowing-water ecosystems vary greatly from one stream to another, depending primarily on the strength of the current. In streams with fast currents, the inhabitants may have adaptations such as suckers to attach themselves to rocks so they are not swept away, or they may have flattened bodies to enable them to slip under or between rocks. Organisms in large, slow-moving streams and rivers do not need such adaptations, although they are typically streamlined (as are most aquatic organisms) to lessen resistance during movement through water. Where the current is very slow, plants and animals of the headwaters are replaced by those characteristic of ponds and lakes.

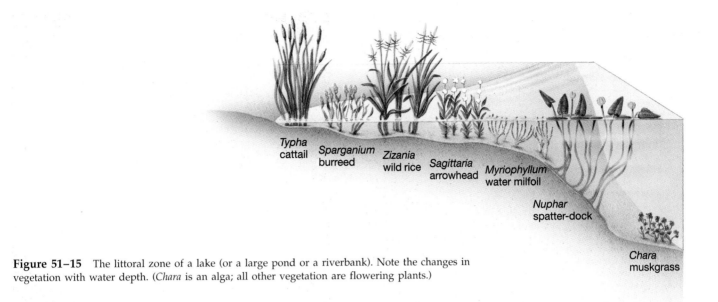

Figure 51–15 The littoral zone of a lake (or a large pond or a riverbank). Note the changes in vegetation with water depth. (*Chara* is an alga; all other vegetation are flowering plants.)

In addition to having currents, flowing-water ecosystems differ from other freshwater ecosystems in that streams depend on the land for much of their energy. In headwater streams, for example, up to 99 percent of the energy input comes from detritus—dead organic material, such as leaves—carried from the land into the stream by wind or surface drainage after precipitation. Downstream, rivers have more photosynthetic organisms, and therefore a slightly lower dependence on detritus as a source of energy, than headwaters.

Lakes and ponds are standing-water ecosystems

A large lake has three basic life zones: the littoral zone, the limnetic zone, and the profundal zone. Ponds and smaller lakes typically lack a profundal zone. The **littoral zone** is the area of shallow water along the shore of a lake or pond. It includes lakeshore vegetation, such as cattails and burreeds, plus several deeper-dwelling aquatic plants and algae (Figure 51–15). The littoral zone is the most highly productive zone of the lake (that is, it is the site of greatest photosynthesis), in part because it receives nutrient inputs from the surrounding land that stimulate the growth of plants and algae. Animals of the littoral zone include frogs and their tadpoles, turtles, worms, crayfish and other crustaceans, insect larvae, and many fish, such as perch, carp, and bass. Here, too, at least in the quieter areas, one finds surface dwellers such as water striders and whirligig beetles.

The **limnetic zone** is the open water away from the shore; it extends down as far as sunlight penetrates. The main organisms of the limnetic zone are microscopic phytoplankton and zooplankton. Larger fish also spend most of their time in this zone, although they may visit the littoral zone to feed and breed. Owing to the depth of the limnetic zone, less vegetation grows there than in the littoral zone.

The deepest zone of a large lake, the **profundal zone,** is beneath the limnetic zone. Because of the lack of light, plants and algae do not live in the profundal zone. Much food drifts in from the littoral and limnetic zones. When dead plants and animals reach the profundal zone, decay bacteria decompose them, liberating the minerals in their bodies. These minerals are not effectively recycled because no photosynthetic organisms are present to absorb them and incorporate them into the food chain. As a result, the profundal habitat tends to be both mineral-rich and anaerobic (without oxygen), with few forms of higher life.

Thermal Stratification and Turnover in Temperate Lakes. The marked layering of lake water caused by how far light penetrates is accentuated by **thermal stratification,** the vertical layering by temperature. Thermal stratification, which is characteristic of large lakes in temperate areas, occurs because the summer sunlight penetrates and warms surface waters, making them less dense.[1] In the summer, cool (and therefore denser) water remains at the lake bottom and is separated from the warm (and therefore less dense) water above by an abrupt temperature transition called the **thermocline.**

In temperate lakes, falling temperatures in autumn cause a mixing of the lake waters called the **fall turnover** (Figure 51–16). (In the tropics, where there is little seasonal temperature variation, such turnovers are uncommon.) As the surface water cools, its density in-

---

[1] Recall that the density of water is greatest at 4°C; both above and below this temperature, water is less dense.

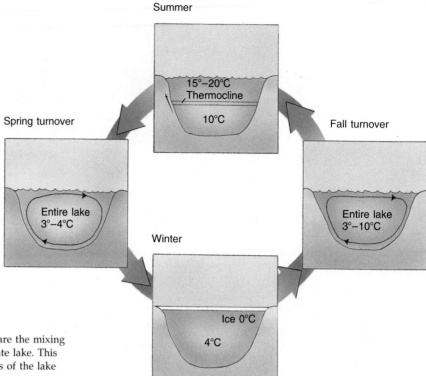

Figure 51–16   Fall turnover and spring turnover are the mixing of the upper and lower layers of water in a temperate lake. This mixing brings oxygen to the oxygen-depleted depths of the lake and minerals to the mineral-deficient surface waters.

creases and it displaces the less dense, warmer, mineral-rich water beneath. The warmer water then rises to the surface where it, in turn, cools and sinks. This cycle of cooling and sinking continues until the lake reaches a uniform temperature throughout.

When winter comes, the surface water cools below 4°C, and if it gets cold enough (0°C), ice forms. Ice is less dense than cold water, so it forms on the surface, and the water on the lake bottom is warmer.

In the spring, a **spring turnover** occurs. Ice melts, and the surface water reaches 4°C, its temperature of greatest density. Consequently, it again sinks to the bottom, and bottom water returns to the surface. As summer arrives, thermal stratification occurs once again.

The mixing of deeper, nutrient-rich water with nutrient-poor surface water during the fall and spring turnovers brings essential minerals to the surface. The sudden presence of large amounts of essential minerals in surface waters encourages the development of large algal populations, which form temporary **blooms** in the fall and spring.

Lands that are transitional between aquatic and terrestrial ecosystems are freshwater wetlands

Wetlands are usually covered by shallow water and have characteristic soils and water-tolerant vegetation. Freshwater wetlands may be marshes, in which grass-like plants dominate, or swamps, in which woody trees or shrubs dominate. Freshwater wetlands also include hardwood bottomland forests (lowlands along streams and rivers that are periodically flooded) in the Southeast, prairie potholes (small, shallow ponds that formed when glacial ice melted at the end of the last ice age) in the Midwest, and peat moss bogs (peat-accumulating wetlands where mosses dominate) in the northern states.

Wetland plants, which are highly productive, provide enough food to support a wide variety of organisms. Wetlands are valuable as habitat for migratory waterfowl and many other bird species, beaver, otters, muskrats, and game fish.

At one time wetlands were thought of as wastelands, areas that needed to be filled in or drained so that farms, housing developments, and industrial plants could be built on them. Wetlands are also breeding places for mosquitoes and therefore were viewed as a menace to public health. Today, however, the crucial environmental services that wetlands provide are widely recognized, and wetlands are somewhat protected by law.

Estuaries Occur Where Fresh Water and Saltwater Meet

Where the sea meets the land there may be one of several kinds of ecosystems: a rocky shore, a sandy beach,

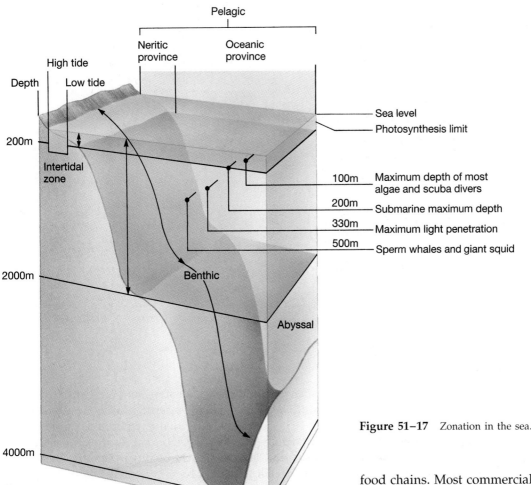

Figure 51–17　Zonation in the sea.

an intertidal mud flat, or a tidal estuary. An **estuary** is a coastal body of water, partly surrounded by land, with access to the open sea and a large supply of fresh water from rivers. It usually contains **salt marshes,** very shallow swampy areas that are dominated by grasses (see Chapter 53 and Figure 53–2), where the salinities fluctuate between those of seawater and fresh water. Many estuaries undergo marked variations in temperature, salinity, and other physical properties in the course of a year. To survive there, organisms must have high tolerance for such wide ranges.

The waters of estuaries are among the most fertile in the world, often having much greater productivity than the adjacent sea or the fresh water upriver. This high productivity is brought about by (1) the action of the ocean's tides, which promote rapid circulation of nutrients and help remove waste products; (2) the transport of nutrients from the land into rivers and creeks that empty into the estuary; and (3) the presence of many plants, which provide an extensive photosynthetic carpet and whose roots and stems also mechanically trap much potential food material. As leaves and plants die, they decay, forming the basis of detritus food chains. Most commercially important fin fish and shellfish spend their larval stages in estuaries among the protecting roots and the tangle of decaying stems.

Salt marshes have often appeared worthless to uninformed people. In consequence, they have been used as dumps, becoming severely polluted, or have been filled with dredged bottom material to form artificial land for residential and industrial development. A large part of the total productivity of the estuarine environment has been lost in this way, along with many other benefits.

Marine Habitats Include the Intertidal Zone, Neritic Province, and Oceanic Province

Although marine (ocean) and freshwater life zones are comparable in many ways, there are many dramatic differences (Figure 51–17). The depths of even the deepest lakes do not approach those of the oceanic abysses, which are extremely deep areas that extend more than 6 km (3.6 mi) below the sunlit surface. Oceans are profoundly influenced by tides and currents. The gravitational pulls of both sun and moon produce two tides per day throughout the oceans, but the heights of those tides vary with the phases of the moon, season, and local topography.

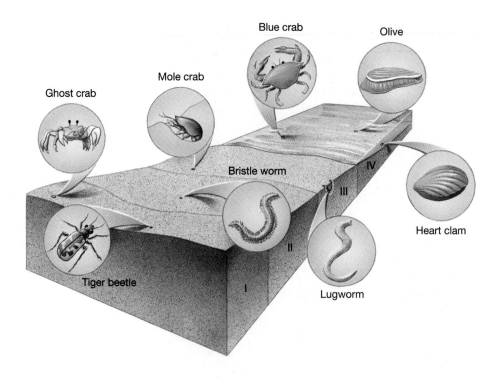

Figure 51–18 Life zones on a sandy beach. I, supratidal zone (above the high tide): ghost crabs and tiger beetles; II, flat beach zone: bristle worms and clams (not shown); III, intertidal zone: mole crabs, lugworms, and sand "crabs" (which follow the retreating or advancing waters; not shown); IV, subtidal zone (always under water): heart clams, olives, and blue crabs.

The shoreline separating low and high tides is called the **intertidal zone.** Although the high levels of light and nutrients, together with an abundance of oxygen, make the intertidal zone a biologically productive habitat, it is also a very stressful one. If an intertidal beach is sandy, the inhabitants must contend with a constantly shifting environment that threatens to engulf them and gives them scant protection against wave action (Figure 51–18). Consequently, most sand-dwelling organisms are continual and active burrowers. They can, however, follow the tides up and down the beach, and so do not usually have any notable adaptations to survive desiccation (drying out) or exposure.

A rocky shore provides a fine anchorage for seaweeds and animals but is exposed to wave action when immersed during high tides and to drying and temperature changes when exposed to the air during low tides. A typical rocky-shore inhabitant has some way of sealing in moisture (perhaps by closing its shell, if it has one) plus a powerful means of anchorage to the rocks. A mussel, for example, has horny, threadlike anchors, and a barnacle has a special cement gland. Rocky-shore intertidal algae (seaweeds) usually have thick, gummy polysaccharide coats, which dry out slowly when exposed, and flexible bodies not easily broken by wave action. Some rocky-shore community inhabitants hide in burrows or crevices at low tide, and some small semiterrestrial crustaceans run about at the splash line, following it up and down the beach.

The **neritic province** is open ocean from the shoreline to a depth of 200 m (650 ft). Nekton (such as sharks, tuna, and porpoises) and larger benthic organisms

(such as corals, spiny lobsters, and starfish) are mostly confined to the shallower neritic waters (less than 60 m, or 195 ft, deep) because that is where their food is. Not only do seaweeds grow on the bottom of shallower areas, but large numbers of phytoplankton live in the water itself.

The upper reaches of the neritic province make up the **euphotic** region, which extends from the surface to a depth of approximately 100 m (325 ft). Light penetrates the euphotic zone in sufficient amounts to support photosynthesis.

The **oceanic province** is the part of the open ocean that is deeper than 200 m (650 ft). It is most of the ocean; in fact, about 88% of the ocean is more than 1.5 km (0.9 mi) deep. Because light cannot penetrate to these depths, the oceanic province has few organisms. Most of the life forms that do survive the tremendous pressure and darkness of the abyss depend upon whatever food drifts down into their habitat from the upper, lighted regions. The principal exceptions are found at the deep-sea hot springs (**thermal vents;** see Chapter 53).

Animals of the abyss are strikingly adapted to darkness and scarcity of food (Figure 51–19). For example, abyssal fish have huge jaws that enable them to swallow large food particles. (An organism that encounters food infrequently needs to eat as much as possible when food is available.) Many have illuminated organs, which enable them to see one another for mating or food capture. A great many abyssal organisms are predators (they have little choice) and live in dispersed populations.

Figure 51–19 A deep-sea fish. Most fish that live at great ocean depths have weak or vestigial eyes. Many have luminous organs that may enable them to locate one another for mating or social display. (Norbert Wu 1991)

ALL TERRESTRIAL AND AQUATIC LIFE ZONES INTERACT WITH ONE ANOTHER

Although we have discussed all terrestrial and aquatic life zones as distinct entities, they do not exist in isolation. When parts of the Amazon rain forest flood annually, for example, fish leave the stream beds and range widely over the forest floor, where they play a role in dispersing the seeds of many species of plants. And in the Antarctic, whose waters are much more productive than its land areas, there is hardly any terrestrial community of organisms, but the many seabirds and seals form a connecting link between the two environments. These animals are supported exclusively by the ocean. Their waste products, cast-off feathers, and the like, when deposited on land, support whatever lichens and insects may occur there.

Inhabitants of different life zones may interact over wide distances—even global distances, in the case of migratory birds and fish. For example, many young albacore tuna migrate across the Pacific Ocean from the California coast to Japan. Flycatchers spend their summers in Canada and the United States and their winters in Central and South America. Many other migratory birds also spend critical parts of their life cycles in entirely different countries, which can make their conservation difficult. It does little good, for instance, to protect a songbird in one country if the inhabitants of the next put it in the cooking pot as soon as it lands in their neighborhood. This concept of large-scale interaction makes ecological concepts difficult for many people to grasp or apply.

SUMMARY

I. The study of the relationships between organisms and their physical environment is called ecology. Ecologists study populations, communities/ecosystems, and the biosphere/ecosphere.
   A. A population is all the members of a particular species that live together in the same area.
   B. A community is all the populations of different species living in the same area. An ecosystem is a community and its environment.
   C. The biosphere is all the communities on Earth—in other words, all of the Earth's living organisms. The ecosphere, the largest ecosystem on Earth, comprises the interactions among the biosphere, atmosphere, lithosphere, and hydrosphere.
II. A biome is a large, relatively distinct ecosystem with characteristic climate, soil, plants, and animals regardless of where it occurs on Earth.
   A. Tundra, the northernmost biome, is characterized by a frozen layer of subsoil (permafrost) and low-growing vegetation that is adapted to extreme cold and a very short growing season.
   B. The taiga, or boreal forest, lies south of the tundra and is dominated by coniferous trees.
   C. Temperate forests occur where precipitation is relatively high. Temperate deciduous forests are dominated by broad-leaved trees that for the most part lose all their leaves seasonally. Temperate rain forest, such as occurs on the northwest coast of North America, is dominated by conifers.
   D. Temperate grasslands typically possess a deep, mineral-rich soil and have moderate but uncertain precipitation.
   E. The chaparral biome is characterized by thickets of small-leaved shrubs and trees and a climate of wet, mild winters and very dry summers.
   F. Deserts, produced by low rates of precipitation, possess communities whose organisms have specialized water-conserving adaptations. Deserts occur in both temperate and tropical areas.
   G. Tropical grasslands, called savannas, have widely scattered trees interspersed with grassy areas.
   H. Tropical rain forests are characterized by mineral-poor

soil and very high rainfall that is evenly distributed throughout the year. Tropical rain forests have high species diversity, with at least three stories of forest foliage and many epiphytes.

III. In aquatic life zones, important environmental factors include salinity, the amount of dissolved oxygen, and the availability of light for photosynthesis.

  A. Aquatic life is ecologically divided into plankton (free-floating), nekton (strongly swimming), and benthos (bottom-dwelling).

  B. The microscopic phytoplankton are photosynthetic and form the base of the food chain in most aquatic communities.

IV. Freshwater ecosystems include flowing water (rivers and smaller streams), standing water (lakes and ponds), and freshwater wetlands.

  A. Flowing-water ecosystems differ from other freshwater ecosystems because the water flows in a current.

    1. Flowing-water ecosystems depend on detritus from the land for much of their energy.

    2. The kinds of organisms found in flowing-water ecosystems vary greatly, mostly due to the current, which is swifter in headwaters than downstream.

  B. Freshwater lakes are divided into zones on the basis of water depth.

    1. The marginal littoral zone contains emergent vegetation and heavy growths of algae. The limnetic

zone is open water away from the shore. The deep, dark profundal zone holds little life other than decomposers.

    2. In summer, temperate lakes exhibit thermal stratification, in which the thermocline separates the warmer water above from the deep, cold water. Annual spring and fall turnovers remix these layers.

  C. Freshwater wetlands, lands that are transitional between freshwater and terrestrial ecosystems, are usually covered by shallow water and have characteristic soils and vegetation.

V. The main marine habitats include estuaries, the intertidal zone, the neritic province, and the oceanic province.

  A. The very productive estuary community receives a high input of nutrients from the adjacent land and serves as an important nursery for the young stages of many aquatic organisms.

  B. Organisms of the intertidal zone possess adaptations that enable them to resist wave action and the extremes of being covered by water (high tide) and exposed to air (low tide).

  C. The neritic province is characterized by rich plankton and benthic organisms.

  D. The oceanic province has no plants or algae; its animal inhabitants are exclusively predators or scavengers subsisting on detritus that drifts in from other areas of the ocean.

POST-TEST

1. Ecology is the study of relationships among organisms and their _____ .

2. All members of the same species that live together in the same place are called a(n) _____ .

3. All the populations of different species interacting in an area compose a(n) _____ .

4. A(n) _____ is the interactions between a community and its environment.

5. The ecosphere takes into account the interactions among the _____ , atmosphere, lithosphere, and hydrosphere.

6. Tundra typically has little precipitation, a short growing season, and a permanently frozen underground layer of _____ .

7. _____ are the dominant vegetation of the taiga.

8. In the temperate zone, the deciding factor in the production of forest versus grassland is usually _____ .

9. In temperate deciduous woodlands, minerals leached from decomposing humus accumulate in a subsurface layer of _____ .

10. The thickest, richest soil in the world occurs in temperate _____ .

11. _____ is a thicket of evergreen shrubs and small trees that is found in areas with dry summers and mild winters.

12. On land, species diversity is exceptionally high in tropical _____ _____ .

13. The _____ is a tropical habitat in which widely spaced trees are interspersed with grassland.

14. Compared with terrestrial habitats, aquatic environments are less variable in temperature and have less available _____ and _____ .

15. Temperate-zone lakes are thermally stratified, with warm and cold layers separated by a transitional _____ .

16. Emergent vegetation grows in the _____ zone of freshwater lakes.

17. _____ occur where fresh water and salt water meet.

18. Organisms in aquatic environments fall into three categories: free-floating _____ , strongly swimming _____ , and bottom-dwelling _____ .

19. The _____ _____ is open ocean from the shoreline to a depth of 200 m.

20. The inhabitants of the dark _____ province are almost entirely heterotrophic, living on an input of dead organisms from other marine habitats.

REVIEW QUESTIONS

1. What climate and soil factors produce the major terrestrial biomes?
2. List the main terrestrial biomes and give the climate, the soil characteristics, and representative living organisms of each.
3. In which biome do you live? If your biome does not match the description given in this text, explain the discrepancy.
4. Which biomes are best suited for agriculture? Explain why each of the biomes you did not mention is unsuitable for agriculture.
5. What environmental factors are most important in determining the adaptations of the organisms found in aquatic habitats?
6. What are plankton? What is their role in aquatic ecosystems?
7. How do the inhabitants of a rocky beach differ from those of a sandy beach?

RECOMMENDED READINGS

Gore, R. Between Monterey tides. *National Geographic* 177:2 (February 1990). An enthralling description of the species diversity and ecosystem complexity of Monterey Bay off the coast of California.

Magnuson, J. J. Long-term ecological research and the invisible present. *BioScience* 40:7 (July–August 1990). One of the challenges of ecological research is that some types require months, years, or even centuries to obtain meaningful data. Much of this issue is devoted to long-term ecological research.

Mares, M. A. Neotropical mammals and the myth of Amazonian biodiversity. *Science*, Vol. 255 (February 21, 1992). Tropical rain forests do not contain as much mammalian diversity as dry lands.

Swan, L. W. The aeolian biome. *BioScience* 42:4 (April 1992). Life in extreme environments, such as barren rock and ice.

CHAPTER 52

❏

Population Ecology

OUTLINE

Density and dispersion
Population growth
Environmental limitations
Reproductive tactics
Human population growth

Populations are made up of individuals but have properties that individuals do not possess. Individuals do not exhibit birth rates, death rates, sex ratios, or median ages. Much of the groundwork for the study of these properties of populations was laid by such people as insurance actuaries, but biologists apply them to the study of all populations.

Communities are composed of populations, but populations have properties that communities lack. Because ecological communities do not share a common gene pool (see Chapter 18), there is no obvious way for natural selection to produce change at the community level. Instead, changes in gene frequencies that are the result of natural selection occur in the populations that make up communities.

A **population** is a group of organisms of a single species living in a particular geographic area at a given time (Figure 52–1). **Population ecology** deals with the numbers of particular organisms that are found in an area and why those numbers change or remain fixed over time. Population ecologists try to determine the processes that are common to all populations. Biologists have additional interests in populations in connection with their biological success or failure (extinction), their evolution, their population genetics, and how they affect the normal functioning of ecosystems. Biologists in applied disciplines must understand populations in order to manage forests, field crops, game, fish, and other populations of economic importance.

Texas bluebonnets. (Willard Clay/
Dembinsky Photo Associates)

After you have studied this chapter you should be able to

1. Define what is meant by a population and discuss what population ecology entails.
2. Define population density and dispersion, and describe the main types of population dispersion.
3. List and explain the factors that produce population change.
4. Define environmental resistance and identify its role in determining population growth and size.
5. Write the logistic equation of population growth and explain what it means. Draw a graph to represent the logistic equation.
6. Distinguish between density-dependent limiting factors and density-independent limiting factors.
7. Distinguish between *K* strategies and *r* strategies, and give an example of each.
8. Explain how developed and developing countries differ in such population characteristics as infant mortality rate, total fertility rate, replacement-level fertility, and age structure.

DENSITY AND DISPERSION ARE IMPORTANT FEATURES OF POPULATIONS

By itself, a population figure tells us relatively little; some context is needed to make the figure meaningful. As a simple example, a thousand mice in a square kilometer is a very different matter from a thousand mice in a hectare (about 2.5 acres). Moreover, sometimes a population is too large to study in its entirety. Such a population is examined by sampling a part of it and then calculating the population density—as, for example, the number of grass plants per square meter or the number of cabbage aphids per cabbage leaf.

Population density, then, is the number of individuals of a species per unit of habitat area at a given time. Different habitats that can sustain a given species vary in the population densities of that species they will support, and the density in a single habitat may also vary from year to year. As an example, consider red grouse populations in northwest Scotland, which were examined at two locations only 2.5 km apart. At one location the population density neither increased nor declined significantly during a 3-year period, but at the other it almost doubled in 2 years and then declined to its initial level once again. The reason was a change in the habitat. The area where the population density increased had been experimentally burned. Young plant growth produced after the burn was beneficial to the grouse. So population density is not an inherent property of a species; it is determined in large part by environmental factors.[1]

---

[1] In Chapter 51, the term *environment* was used to mean the abiotic aspects, both physical and chemical, of an organism's immediate habitat. Throughout the rest of this book, unless specified, an organism's *environment* encompasses its physical, chemical, *and* biological surroundings.

(a)

(b)

(c)

Figure 52–1 A population is a group of organisms of a single species living in a given area at a given time. (*a*) Gooseneck barnacles live on a rocky shore in the subtidal zone. (*b*) A population of *Viguiera* blooms after the winter rains in the Mojave Desert. (*c*) A school of grunts off the Florida Keys. (*a, b,* Dennis Drenner; *c,* Larry Lipsky/Tom Stack & Associates)

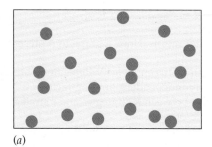

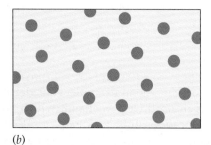

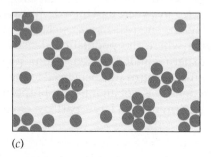

Figure 52–2   The individuals of a population may have different patterns of dispersal in the habitat. (*a*) Random dispersion. (*b*) Uniform dispersion. (*c*) Clumped dispersion.

Figure 52–3   Uniform dispersion. Desert plants such as the creosote bush and the saltbush probably have uniform dispersion due to allelopathy, the production of toxic substances that inhibit the growth of plants nearby.   (William E. Ferguson)

The geographic limit of a population's distribution is its **range.** The individuals within a population's range often exhibit characteristic patterns of **dispersion,** or spacing. Individuals may be dispersed randomly or uniformly, or they may be clumped (Figure 52–2).

Random dispersion occurs when individuals in a population are spaced unpredictably or randomly. Of the three major types of dispersion, random dispersion may seem most likely in nature, but it is actually not common or easy to observe. Perhaps random dispersion occurs infrequently because important environmental factors affecting dispersion usually do not occur at random. Flour beetle larvae in a container of flour are randomly dispersed, for example, but their environment is unusually uniform.

Uniform dispersion occurs when individuals are more evenly spaced than would be expected if occupation of a given habitat were random. A field of soybeans or wheat, artificially produced, exhibits this quality. Sometimes uniform dispersion occurs naturally—for example, when competition between individuals is se-

vere, when they wage chemical warfare on one another by allelopathy (Figure 52–3), and when they exhibit territorial behavior.

Perhaps the most common type of dispersion, **clumped dispersion** (also called **aggregated distribution**), occurs when individuals are concentrated in specific portions of the habitat. In animals it often results from the presence of family groups and pairs. It may also be advantageous to social animals by facilitating mutual aid and kin selection (see Chapter 50). In plants, clumping is commonly the result of inefficient seed dispersal or asexually propagated clones. An entire grove of aspen trees, for example, may originate from a single seed (see Chapter 35, Figure 35–6).

MATHEMATICAL MODELS DESCRIBE POPULATION GROWTH

Part of the progression of scientific knowledge is the discovery of common threads or patterns in separate observations. As mentioned previously, population ecologists wish to understand general processes that are shared by many different populations. To assist them in this endeavor, they develop **models**—mathematical equations that represent population dynamics. No population model is a perfect representation of all populations, but models do serve to illuminate complex processes. Moreover, mathematical modeling enhances the scientific process by providing a framework to which specific population studies can be compared. As more knowledge accumulates, the model is refined and made more precise.

Populations of organisms, be they bacteria, elephants, or humans, change over time. Whether a popu-

Figure 52–4 Emigration (movement away from a specific area) and immigration (movement into a specific area) are important factors in the population sizes of migratory animals. Shown here is a population of monarch butterflies spending the winter in the mountains of central Mexico. Monarch butterflies migrate into the United States and Canada for the summer months and return to Mexico for the winter. A round trip often involves several generations. Somehow, individual monarchs know where to winter in Mexico without having seen the sites before.   (William E. Ferguson)

lation grows, declines, or remains stable depends on the balance of two factors: the rate of arrival and rate of departure of organisms. The arrival rate is determined by the rate at which organisms immigrate into a habitat (enter a population and thus increase its size) along with the rate at which they are born (or hatched, germinated, or otherwise produced). The rate of departure depends on the rate at which individuals emigrate (leave a population and thus decrease its size) and the rate of death. Although exceptions occur, especially in the case of migratory species, immigration and emigration rarely make substantial contributions to population change (Figure 52–4).

The important factors in population dynamics are **natality,** the rate at which organisms produce offspring (that is, the birth rate), and **mortality,** the rate at which organisms die (the death rate). In humans the birth rate is usually expressed as the number of births per 1000 people per year, and the death rate as the number of deaths per 1000 people per year.

Population growth is a special case of population change. To determine its rate, we must also take into account the time interval involved, that is, the change in time. To express these changes, we employ the Greek letter *delta* (Δ):

$$\frac{\Delta N}{\Delta t} = b - d$$

where ΔN is the change in the number of individuals in the population, Δt the change in time, b the natality, and

d the mortality. Thus, the change in a population over time equals the birth rate minus the death rate.

A modification of this equation tells us the rate at which the population is growing at a particular instant in time (rather than the average growth rate during the entire period of study), that is, its **instantaneous growth rate** (dN/dt).[1] Using differential calculus, this growth rate can be expressed as

$$\frac{dN}{dt} = rN$$

where N is the number of individuals in the existing population, t the time, and r the **growth rate** (that is, the change in population size per unit of time; the growth rate equals the birth rate minus the death rate, or $r = b - d$).

Because $r = b - d$, if organisms in the population are born faster than they die, r is a positive value and population size increases. If organisms in the population die faster than they are born, r is a negative value and population size decreases. If r is equal to zero, births and deaths match, and population size is stable despite continued reproduction.

The maximum rate at which a population could increase under ideal conditions is known as its **biotic potential** (r_{max}) or **intrinsic rate of increase.** Different species have different biotic potentials, and several factors influence a particular species' biotic potential. Some of these factors include the age at which reproduction begins, the proportion of the life span during which the organism is capable of reproducing, and the number of offspring produced during each period of reproduction.

Generally, larger organisms, such as blue whales and elephants, have the smallest biotic potentials, whereas microorganisms have the greatest biotic potentials. Under ideal conditions (an environment with unlimited resources), certain bacteria can reproduce by splitting in half every 20 to 30 minutes. At this rate of growth, a single bacterium would increase to a population of over 1 million in just 10 hours and to more than 1 billion in 15 hours!

If one were to plot this increase in number versus time, the graph would have a J shape that is characteristic of **exponential growth,** a type of growth determined by the size of the population (Figure 52–5a). When a population grows exponentially, the larger that population gets, the faster it grows.

Regardless of which organism one considers, whenever biotic potential is plotted versus time, the shape of the curve is the same. The only variable is time; that is, it may take longer for a sea lion population than

---

[1]The symbol *dN* is the differential of *N*; it is not a product, nor should the *d* in *dN* be confused with the death rate, *d*. The same applies to *dt*.

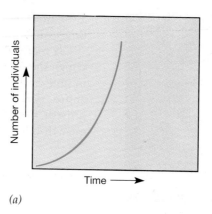

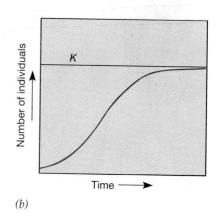

Figure 52–5 Population growth curves. (a) Exponential growth has a characteristic J-shaped curve. Exponential growth cannot occur indefinitely in nature because the environment can only support a finite number of individuals of any species. (b) The logistic model of population growth, when graphed, has a characteristic S-shaped curve. Population growth slows down as the carrying capacity, K, of the environment is approached.

for a bacterial population to reach a certain size, but both populations would invariably increase exponentially under ideal conditions.

In nature, certain populations may exhibit exponential growth for a short period of time. Exponential growth has been experimentally demonstrated in bacterial and protist cultures and in certain insects. However, organisms cannot reproduce at their biotic potential forever because their environment sets limits, which are collectively called **environmental resistance.** Using the preceding example, bacteria would never be able to reproduce unchecked for an indefinite period of time because they would run out of food and living space, and poisonous wastes would accumulate in their vicinity. With crowding, they would also become more susceptible to parasites and predators. As their environment changed, their birth rate (b) would decline and their death rate (d) would increase due to shortages of food, increased predation, increased competition, and other environmental stresses. Conditions might worsen to a point where d would exceed b and the population would decrease. Population size, then, is controlled by the ability of the environment to support it.

Over longer periods of time, the rate of population growth for most organisms decreases to around zero. This leveling out occurs at or near the limits of the environment to support a population. The largest population that can be maintained for an indefinite period of time by a particular environment is the **carrying capacity,** or K, of the environment.

When a graph is made of a population over longer periods of time, the curve has a characteristic S shape that shows the population's initial exponential increase (note the J shape at the start), followed by a leveling out as the carrying capacity of the environment is approached (Figure 52–5b). The S-shaped growth curve can be modeled by a modified growth equation called the **logistic equation.** It describes a population increasing from a very small number of individuals to a larger number of individuals, limited by a finite environment.

The logistic equation takes the carrying capacity of the environment into account.[1]

$$\frac{dN}{dt} = rN\left(\frac{K - N}{K}\right)$$

When the number of organisms (N) is small, the rate of population growth is high, because the expression (K − N/K) has a value of almost 1. But as the population (N) begins to approach the carrying capacity (K), the growth rate falls nearly to zero, despite high population densities, because (K − N/K) approaches 0 in value.

Although the S-shaped curve is a simplification of actual population changes over time, it does appear to fit the population growth observed in many populations that have been studied in the laboratory and a few studied in nature. In a classic experiment, Gause grew a population of *Paramecium caudatum* in a test tube. He supplied a constant but limited amount of food daily, and he occasionally replenished the media to eliminate the buildup of metabolic wastes. Under these conditions, the population of *P. caudatum* increased exponentially at first. The paramecia became so numerous that the water was cloudy with them. But then their rate of increase declined, and the population leveled off.

A population does not always stabilize at K, but may temporarily rise far higher. It may then experience a **population crash,** an abrupt decline from high to very low population density. Such an abrupt change is commonly observed in bacterial cultures and other populations whose resources are nonrenewable or inflexible. When the vital resources are all consumed, the organisms die. A population crash in nature was observed after a small herd of 26 reindeer was introduced on one of the Pribilof Islands of Alaska (in 1910). The herd's population increased exponentially for about 25 years

---

[1] The logistic model of population growth was developed to explain population growth in continually breeding populations. Similar models exist for populations that have specific breeding seasons.

until there were approximately 2000 reindeer, many more than the island could support. The reindeer overgrazed the vegetation until the plant life was almost wiped out. Then, in slightly over a decade, as reindeer died from starvation, their number plunged to eight, one third the size of the original introduced population.

POPULATION GROWTH IS LIMITED BY THE ENVIRONMENT

Population growth is ultimately stopped by limitations on the ability of the environment to support the population. Limiting factors fall into two categories, density-dependent and density-independent, and vary in importance from organism to organism. In many cases, density-dependent and density-independent limiting factors interact to determine a population's size.

Density-Dependent Factors Influence Populations

If a change in population density affects the influence of an environmental factor on that population, then the environmental factor is said to be **density-dependent.** As population density increases, density-dependent factors tend to slow population growth by causing an increase in death rate and/or a decrease in birth rate. The effect of these density-dependent factors increases as population density increases. Density-dependent factors can also exert an enhancing effect on population growth when population density declines, by decreasing death rate and/or increasing birth rate. Density-dependent factors, then, tend to cause a population to maintain itself at a relatively constant number near the carrying capacity of the environment. Examples of density-dependent factors are predation, disease, and competition.

A classic instance of predation as a density-dependent factor is provided by the snowshoe hare and the Canada lynx (Figure 52–6). The Hudson's Bay Company has kept continuous records of the numbers of hare and lynx pelts bought from trappers since about 1800. These records provide an accurate measure of the populations of animals each year. (For example, in a year when the population of hares was large, trappers caught a great number of them.) Consistently, a fluctuation in the number of hare skins was followed, after a brief time lag, by a similar fluctuation in the number of lynx skins. Whenever the hare population increased, for example, a corresponding increase occurred in the lynx population. It is hard to view the lynx as controlling the population of hares in this instance; rather, the predator population seems to be controlled by the size of the prey population. In this example, predation is an im-

portant density-dependent regulator for the predator population. This is true in most, but not all, instances of predator-prey interaction. For example, no obvious density-dependent relationship exists between tawny owls and voles, their chief rodent prey, because the owl population remains relatively constant despite vole population fluctuations. Vole supply does not seem to be an important limiting factor governing the owl population.

As a population becomes denser, the distance between organisms decreases, they meet one another more frequently, and the likelihood of their transmitting disease to one another by direct contact or by animal vectors increases. If the disease is fatal or markedly reduces the chance that its host will reproduce, the population decreases to the level at which disease transmission becomes less likely. If the disease has not killed off all of the host organisms, population density should be fairly constant thereafter.

European hares introduced in colonial times overran parts of the Australian continent, seriously competing with domestic animals and wildlife for forage and other essentials, and doing other ecological damage. Hunting, trapping, poisoning, and huge fences failed to stop their spread. Eventually Australians deliberately imported from Latin America the virus that produces the rabbit disease myxomatosis. This disease is transmitted by parasitic insects, especially mosquitoes. The Australian mosquitoes spread the disease, and the rabbit population declined dramatically. However, a few rabbits developed resistance; in addition, the virus seemed to become less virulent. Rabbits still persist in Australia, although now in more moderate numbers.

Competition for resources of all kinds occurs both within a population (**intraspecific competition**) and among populations of different species (**interspecific competition**). As population density increases, so does competition—possibly to the point where many members of a population fail to obtain the minimum of whatever resource is in shortest supply. This raises the death rate and inhibits further population growth.

It might seem that competition would tend to maintain population density at a constant value, but often this is not the case. Isle Royale is a 5570-square-kilometer (2150-square-mile) island in Lake Superior. It differs from most islands in that large mammals can walk to it when the lake freezes over in winter. The minimum distance to be walked is 15 miles, however, so this has happened infrequently. Around 1900, some moose managed to reach the island for the first time. By 1935 the moose population had increased to about 3000, and consumed almost all the edible vegetation. In the absence of this food resource, nearly 90% of the moose starved. By 1948 the population had recovered to its peak number once again, and again most of the moose starved. Thus, competition (in this case, intraspecific)

(a)

Figure 52–6 A classic case of cyclical oscillation in population density and of dependence of predator upon prey. (*a*) The Canada lynx preys upon the snowshoe hare. (*b*) Changes in the relative abundance of the lynx and the snowshoe hare, as indicated by the numbers of pelts received by the Hudson's Bay Company. (*a*, Ed Cesar/Photo Researchers, Inc.)

(b)

for scarce resources can result in oscillations rather than a constant population.

Competition for resources also includes competition for living space, partly because the living space contains other resources—especially food and concealing cover in the case of animals, or water, minerals, and sunlight in the case of plants. Space is at a premium in certain habitats, such as the ocean floor (Figure 52–7). Favored marine habitats such as abyssal hot springs, rocky intertidal zones, and continental shelves tend to be crowded with sedentary inhabitants.

Whereas space seems a clear-cut limiting factor in sedentary organisms such as barnacles and plants, there have been few experimental demonstrations of its significance for mobile animals such as mammals. The rea-

son is that it is hard to separate limitations of space from consequent limitations of the resources contained by the space.

In complex natural communities, it can be very difficult to separate the effects of different density-dependent factors from one another. In a study reported in 1987, Schoener and Spiller noted that on tropical islands inhabited by lizards, few spiders occur, whereas more spiders and more species of spiders are found on lizard-less islands. Deciding to subject these observations to experimental study, Schoener and Spiller staked out plots of vegetation (mainly sea grape shrubs) and enclosed some of them with lizard-proof screens. Some of the plots were emptied of all lizards, and web-building spiders were introduced into all the plots. At the end of

Figure 52–7 Competition for living space is a density-dependent limiting factor. Shown are barnacles that have attached themselves to the back of a crab shell because living space is scarce on the sea bottom. When the host crab molts, the barnacles will be shed along with the shell.   (E. R. Degginger)

(a)

(b)

Figure 52–8 Density-independent limiting factors are not influenced by changes in population density. Floods caused by hurricanes (a) and forest fires (b) are examples of density-independent limiting factors.   (a, G. R. Roberts; b, Doug Sokell/Tom Stack & Associates)

a 2-year study period, spider population densities averaged 2.5 times higher in the lizard-free enclosures. Moreover, the spider species diversity had greatly increased in the lizard-free areas. These results can probably be explained by a double effect of lizards upon spiders—predation and interspecific competition. Lizards not only eat spiders but also compete with spiders for insect prey.

Density-Independent Factors Influence Populations

Any environmental factor that regulates the size of a population but is not influenced by changes in population density is called a **density-independent factor.** Catastrophic events may serve as density-independent limiting factors. They often affect populations in unpredictable ways: A very severe blizzard, a hurricane, or a fire might cause extreme and irregular reductions in a vulnerable population. Usually the percentage of the population killed is independent of the population density (Figure 52–8).

Consider a density-independent factor that influences mosquito populations in arctic environments. These insects produce several generations per summer and achieve very high population densities by the end of the season. A shortage of food does not seem to be a limiting factor for mosquitoes, nor is there any shortage of ponds in which to breed. What puts a stop to the skyrocketing mosquito population is winter. Not a single adult mosquito survives winter, and the entire population must grow afresh the next summer from the few eggs and hibernating larvae that do survive. Thus, severe winter weather is a density-independent factor that regulates arctic mosquito populations.

It is difficult, however, to find many (so-called) density-independent limiting factors that bear absolutely *no* relationship to population density. Social animals, for example, are often able to resist dangerous weather conditions by means of their collective behavior, as in the case of sheep that huddle together in a snowstorm.

DIFFERENT SPECIES HAVE EVOLVED DIFFERENT REPRODUCTIVE TACTICS

Imagine an organism that possesses the perfect strategy to guarantee it the ability to reproduce at the highest biotic potential possible. In other words, this hypothetical organism produces the maximum number of offspring, the majority of which survive to reproductive maturity. Such an organism would have to mature soon after it was born so that it could begin reproducing at an early age. It would reproduce frequently throughout its life and produce a large number of offspring each time. Further, it would have to be able to care for its young in order to ensure their survival.

In nature, no such organism exists, for the simple reason that an organism that puts all its energy into being a perfect "reproductive machine" would not expend any energy toward its own survival. In reality, animals must use energy to hunt for food, and plants need energy to grow taller than surrounding plants to obtain adequate sunlight. Nature, then, requires organ-

(a)   (b)

Figure 52–9   Two life history strategies, *r* selection and *K* selection. (*a*) Dandelions (*Taraxacum officinale*) are *r* strategists—annuals that mature early and produce many small seeds. A dandelion population fluctuates from year to year but rarely approaches the carrying capacity of its environment. (*b*) Tawny owls (*Strix aluco*) are *K* strategists: They maintain a fairly constant population size at or near the carrying capacity. They mature slowly, delay reproduction, and have a relatively large body size. (*a*, Adam Jones/Dembinsky Photo Associates; *b*, B. Gadsby/VIREO)

isms to compromise in the expenditure of energy. Living things, if they are to be successful, must do what is required to survive as individuals as well as to preserve their species.

Each species has its own life history strategy—reproductive characteristics, body size, habitat requirements, migration patterns, and so on—designed around this energy compromise. Although many different life histories have evolved, their diversity has a pattern. Species are categorized as *r*-selected or *K*-selected, depending on their life history strategies.

Populations described by the concept of **r selection** have a strategy that leads to a high rate of natural increase. (Recall that *r* designates the rate of natural increase. Because such organisms have a high *r*, they are known as **r strategists** or **r-selected species.**) Small body size and production of only one large brood during a lifetime (known as **big bang reproduction**) are typical of many *r* strategists, which are usually opportunists found in variable or unpredictable environments.

Some of the best examples of *r* strategists are common weeds. *Taraxacum officinale*, the dandelion, originated in Europe, but this could hardly be guessed now from its nearly universal distribution (Figure 52–9*a*). Almost everyone knows how dandelions are propagated—by a parachute-like fruit containing little seeds that are scattered widely by any strong breeze or wind. A 3.1-kilometer-per-hour (5-mph) breeze is strong enough to carry the fruits. In temperate climates, any

suitable habitat is colonized as soon as it becomes available.

The seeds of some varieties of dandelions are produced by apomixis, an asexual process for making seeds with a genetic composition identical to that of their parent (see Chapter 35). Upon germination, the new plant uses another form of asexual reproduction. The dandelion has a long taproot that splits longitudinally to form two roots, then four roots, and so on, so that natural clones of plants spread out from the original plant in genetically identical clumps.

Asexual reproduction has several advantages for dandelions and other *r* strategists. In the first place, asexual reproduction in plants does not require insect pollinators or even other plants, both of which may be in short supply in seriously disturbed habitats in the early stages of an *r* strategist's settlement. Second, asexual reproduction is fast. Third, as long as the particular kind of habitat for which an *r* strategist is adapted is common, asexual reproduction preserves without change a phenotype ideally suited to that habitat.

Populations described by the concept of **K selection** have traits that maximize *K* and reduce *r*. (Recall that *K* is the carrying capacity of the environment. A population of a species with *K* selection is maintained at or near *K*, so its individuals have little need for a high reproductive rate.) These organisms, called **K strategists** or **K-selected species,** do not use environmental resources and energy to produce large numbers of off-

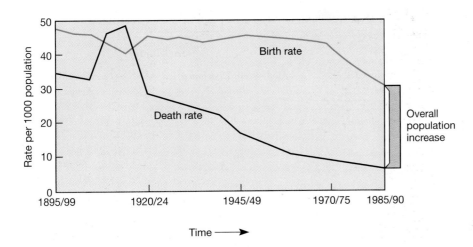

Figure 52–10 In Mexico, the birth and death rates have both declined in this century. The death rate has declined more appreciably, resulting in a large rate of natural increase. (The high death rate prior to 1920 was caused by the Mexican Revolution.)

spring. They characteristically have long life spans with slow development, late reproduction, large size, and repeated reproductive cycles. *K* strategists are found in relatively constant or stable environments, where they have a high competitive ability.

Tawny owls are *K* strategists that pair-bond for life, with both members of a pair living and hunting in adjacent, well-defined territories (Figure 52–9*b*). They regulate their reproduction in accordance with the resources—especially food—in their territories. Even in an average year, 30% of the birds do not breed. If food supplies are unusually limited, many of those that do breed fail to incubate their eggs. Rarely do the owls lay the maximum number of eggs, and often they delay breeding until late in the season, when the rodent populations on which they depend have become large. Thus, tawny owls behaviorally regulate their population size so that it stays at or near the carrying capacity of the environment. Starvation, an indication that the tawny owl population has exceeded *K*, rarely occurs.

HUMAN POPULATION GROWTH HAS THE SAME PARAMETERS AS POPULATION GROWTH IN OTHER ORGANISMS

Now that we have studied some of the basic concepts of population ecology, we can relate what we have learned to the human population. Examine Figure 21–15, which shows the worldwide increase in the human population since the New Stone Age, approximately 10,000 years ago. Now look back at Figure 52–5*a* and observe how the human population is increasing exponentially. The characteristic J curve of exponential growth reflects the decreasing lengths of time it has taken to add still more billions of people to our num-

bers. It took thousands of years for the human population to reach 1 billion, 100 years to reach 2 billion, 30 years to reach 3 billion, 15 years to reach 4 billion, and 12 years to reach 5 billion.

One of the first to recognize that the human population cannot continue to increase indefinitely was Thomas Malthus, an 18th-century British economist (see Chapter 17). He pointed out that human population growth was not always desirable (a view contrary to the beliefs of his day) and that the human population was capable of increasing faster than the food supply. He felt that the inevitable consequences of population growth were famine, disease, and war.

As of 1992, the world population was greater than 5.4 billion, and it is increasing by approximately 93 million humans each year (about 175 people per minute).[1] This increase is not due to an increase in the birth rate (*b*). In fact, the worldwide birth rate has actually declined slightly during the past 200 years. The population increase is due instead to a large *decrease in the death rate (d)* (Figure 52–10), which has occurred primarily because of greater food production, better medical care, and increased sanitation. For example, from about 1920 to 1990, the death rate in Mexico fell from approximately 40 to 6, whereas the birth rate dropped from approximately 40 to 30.

The human population has reached a turning point. Although our numbers continue to increase, the *rate of population increase (r)* has declined over the past several years. Despite this declining growth rate, it will take many years for the world population to stabilize (*r* = 0), primarily because of the momentum provided

---

[1] Unless otherwise noted, all population data in this chapter were obtained from the Population Reference Bureau, a private, nonprofit educational organization that disseminates demographic and population information.

Table 52–1   COMPARISON OF 1992 POPULATION DATA IN DEVELOPED AND DEVELOPING COUNTRIES

	Developed	Developing	
	(Highly Developed) United States	(Moderately Developed) Brazil	(Less Developed) Kenya
Fertility rate	2.0	3.1	6.7
Doubling time at current rate (yr)	89	37	19
Infant mortality rate	9.0	69	62
Life expectancy at birth (yr)	75.5	65	61
Per-capita income (U.S. $)	$21,700	$2680	$370

by the young age structure of our population (to be discussed shortly).

Population experts at the United Nations and the World Bank have projected that the worldwide rate of population growth will continue to slowly decrease until zero population growth is attained. **Zero population growth**—the point at which the birth rate equals the death rate—is projected to occur around A.D. 2089, when it is anticipated that the human population will level off at approximately 10.4 billion. This number is almost twice the 1992 population of the world.

Population projections are "what if" exercises: Given certain assumptions about future tendencies in natality, mortality, and migration, an area's population can be calculated for a given number of years into the future. But such projections must be interpreted with care because they vary depending on the assumptions. For example, in projecting that the population will stabilize at 10.4 billion by the end of the 21st century, population experts assume that the average number of children born to each woman in all countries will have declined to just about 2 by A.D. 2040 (in 1992, the figure was 3.3). If that decline does not occur by A.D. 2040, our population will not stabilize at 10.4 billion people by the end of the 21st century, but will stabilize later and at a greater number. For example, if the population were to continue to grow at its 1992 rate, there would be more than 30 billion humans toward the end of the 21st century.

The main unknown factor in this population growth scenario is the carrying capacity of the environment. No one knows how many humans can be supported by Earth, and projections and estimates vary widely depending on the assumptions made. It is also not clear what will happen to the human population if and when the carrying capacity is approached. Optimists suggest that the human population will stabilize because of a decrease in the birth rate and an increase in the death rate (more people will die because Earth can-

not support them). Some experts take a more pessimistic view, predicting that the widespread degradation of our environment caused by our ever-expanding numbers will make the Earth uninhabitable for humans, and that massive human deaths will occur.[1]

Not All Countries Have the Same Rates of Population Increase

Although worldwide population figures illustrate overall trends, they do not describe other important aspects of the human population story, such as population differences from country to country. The study of **demographics,** the branch of sociology that deals with population statistics, provides interesting information about the populations of countries. As you probably know, not all parts of the world have the same rates of population increase. Countries can be classified into two groups, developed and developing, based on their rates of population growth, degrees of industrialization, and relative prosperity (Table 52–1).

Developed countries (also called highly developed countries), such as the United States, Canada, France, Australia, and Japan, have low rates of population growth, are highly industrialized, and have high per-capita incomes relative to the rest of the world. Developed countries have the lowest birth rates. Indeed, some developed countries (such as Germany) have birth rates just below that needed to sustain the population and are thus declining slightly in numbers. Highly developed countries also have very low **infant mortality rates** (the number of infant deaths per 1000 live births). The infant mortality rate of the United States, for example, was 9.0 in 1992, compared with a 1992 worldwide infant mortality rate of 68. Inhabitants of

---

[1] Some experts think human population has already exceeded the carrying capacity of the environment.

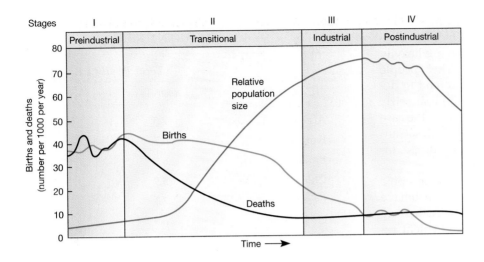

Figure 52–11 The four demographic stages through which a population progresses as its society becomes industrialized.

highly developed countries also have long life expectancies (74.5 years versus 62.5 years) and high average per-capita incomes ($17,900 versus $3790 worldwide in 1992).

Developing countries fall into two subcategories, moderately developed and less developed. Mexico, Turkey, Thailand, and most countries of South America are moderately developed. Both their birth rates and their infant mortality rates are higher than those of highly developed countries. Moderately developed countries have a medium level of industrialization, and their average per-capita incomes are lower than those of highly developed countries. Less developed countries, which include Bangladesh, Niger, Ethiopia, and Laos, have the highest birth rates, the highest infant mortality rates, the lowest life expectancies, and the lowest average per-capita incomes in the world.

One way to represent the population growth of a country is to determine the **doubling time,** the amount of time it would take for its population to double in size, assuming that its current rate of increase does not change. A look at a country's doubling time can reveal its placement as a highly, moderately, or less developed country: The shorter the doubling time, the less developed the country. At 1992 rates of growth, doubling times are 19 years for Togo, 25 years for Ethiopia, 30 years for Mexico, 89 years for the United States, and 347 years for Belgium.

It is also instructive to examine **replacement-level fertility,** the number of children a couple must produce in order to "replace" themselves. Replacement-level fertility is usually given as 2.1 children in developed countries and 2.7 children in developing countries. The number is greater than 2.0 because some children die before they reach reproductive age. Thus, higher infant mortality rates are the main reason that replacement levels in developing countries are greater than in developed countries. Worldwide, the **total fertility rate,** the

average number of children born to a woman during her lifetime, is 3.3, which is well above replacement levels in both developed and developing countries.

Demographers recognize four demographic stages

Based on their observations of Europe as it became industrialized and urbanized, demographers have identified four stages in the transition from relatively high birth and death rates to relatively low birth and death rates. Because all highly developed and moderately developed countries have followed this demographic course, demographers generally assume that the same process will occur in less developed countries as they become industrialized (Figure 52–11).

In the first stage, called the **preindustrial stage,** natality and mortality are high and the population grows at a modest rate. Although women have many children, the infant mortality rate is high. Intermittent famines, plagues, and wars also increase the death rate, so the population grows slowly. Finland in the late 1700s is an example of the first demographic stage.

As a result of improved health care and more reliable food and water supplies that accompany the initiation of an industrial society, the second demographic stage, called the **transitional stage,** is characterized by a lowered mortality. However, because natality is still high, the population grows rapidly. Finland in the mid-1800s was in stage 2, and today large parts of Latin America, Asia, and Africa are in the second demographic stage.

The third demographic stage, the **industrial stage,** characterized by a decline in the birth rate, takes place at some point during the industrialization process. This decline in the birth rate, along with a relatively low death rate, slows population growth. For Finland this occurred in the early 1900s.

The fourth demographic stage, sometimes called the **postindustrial stage,** is characterized by low natality and low mortality. Today countries that are heavily industrialized are generally in this stage. Their people are better educated, are more affluent, and tend to desire smaller families and take steps to limit family size. The population grows slowly or not at all, as is the case in such developed countries as the United States, Canada, Australia, Japan, and most of western Europe, including Finland.

Once a country reaches the fourth demographic stage, is it correct to assume that it will continue to have a low birth rate indefinitely? The answer is that we don't know. Low birth rates may be a permanent response to the socioeconomic factors that are part of an industrialized, urbanized society. On the other hand, low birth rates may be a temporary response to socioeconomic factors such as the changing roles of women in developed countries. No one knows for sure.

The populations in many developing countries are beginning to approach stabilization. Fertility rates must decline in order for a population to stabilize; see Table 52–2 and note the general decline in total fertility rate from the 1960s to 1992 in selected developing countries. Worldwide, the total fertility rate in developing countries has decreased from an average of 6.1 children per woman in 1970 to 3.8 in 1992. In countries such as Brazil, Indonesia, and Mexico, fertility rates have declined by at least 25 percent in the past decade.[1] Fertility rates continue to increase in only a few African countries, including Ethiopia and Cameroon.

The Age Structure of a Country Can Be Used To Predict Its Population Growth

In order to predict the future growth of a population, it is important to know its **age structure,** which is made up of the percentages of the population at different ages. The numbers of males and females at each age, from birth to death, can be represented in an **age structure diagram** (Figure 52–12). Each diagram is divided vertically in half, one side representing the males in a population, and the other side the females. The bottom section of the diagram represents pre-reproductive humans (from 0 to 14 years of age); the middle section, the reproductive ages (15 to 44 years); and the top, post-reproductive humans (45 years and older). The widths of the individual diagrams at any given point are proportional to population sizes; greater width implies a larger population.

[1] Although the fertility rates in these countries have declined, it should be remembered that they still exceed replacement-level fertility. Consequently, the populations in these countries are still increasing.

Table 52–2 FERTILITY CHANGES IN SELECTED DEVELOPING COUNTRIES

Country	Total Fertility Rate*	
	1960–65	1992
Afghanistan	7.0	6.9
Bangladesh	6.7	4.9
Brazil	6.2	3.1
China	5.9	2.2
Egypt	7.1	4.4
Guatemala	6.9	5.2
India	5.8	3.9
Kenya	8.1	6.7
Mexico	6.8	3.8
Nepal	5.9	6.1
Nigeria	6.9	6.5
Thailand	6.4	2.4

*Total fertility rate = average number of children born to each woman during her lifetime.

The overall shape of an age structure diagram indicates whether the population is increasing, stable, or shrinking. The age structure diagram of a country with a very high growth rate (for example, Nigeria or Venezuela) is shaped like a pyramid (Figure 52–13a). The largest percentage of the population is in the pre-reproductive age group. When these children mature, they will become the parents of the next generation, so they provide the momentum for future population growth. Thus, *even if the fertility rate of such a country is at replacement level, the population continues to grow.* In contrast, the less expansive bases of the age structure diagrams of countries with stable and declining populations indicate a smaller proportion of children who will become the parents of the next generation.

The age structure diagram of a stable population, one that is neither growing nor shrinking, demonstrates that the numbers of people at the pre-reproductive age and at the reproductive age are approximately the same (Figure 52–13b). Also, a larger percentage of the population is older (post-reproductive) than in a rapidly increasing population. Many countries in Europe have stable populations.

In a population that is shrinking, the pre-reproductive age group is *smaller* than either the reproductive or post-reproductive group. Germany, Bulgaria, and Hungary are examples of countries with shrinking populations.

It is estimated that one third of the worldwide human population is under age 15. These people have the potential to cause a large increase in the population

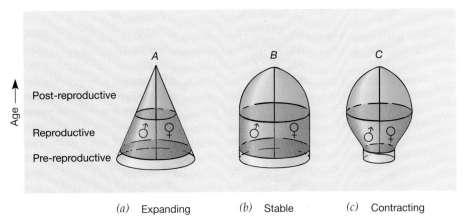

(a) Expanding   *(b)* Stable   *(c)* Contracting

Figure 52–12 Generalized age structure diagrams for *(a)* an expanding population, *(b)* a stable population, and *(c)* a population that is decreasing in size. In each, the left half of the diagram represents the males in the population, and the right half, the females. Each diagram is divided horizontally into age groups.

growth rate when they enter their reproductive years. Even if the birth rate does not increase, the population growth rate will increase simply because there are more females reproducing.

Most of the worldwide population increase that has occurred since 1950 has taken place in developing countries (as a result of the younger age structure and the higher than replacement level fertility rates of their populations). In 1950, 66.8% of the world's population was in developing countries in Africa, Asia (minus Japan), and Latin America; the remaining 33.2% was in developed countries in Europe, the U.S.S.R., Japan, Australia, and North America. Between 1950 and 1992, the world's population more than doubled in size, but most of that growth occurred in developing countries. As a reflection of this, in 1992 the number of people in developing countries had increased to 77.4% of the world's population. Most of the population increase that will occur during the next century will also take place in developing countries.

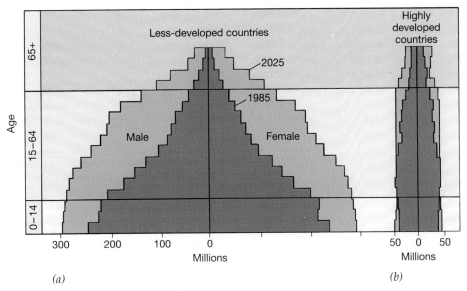

(a)   *(b)*

Figure 52–13 Age structure diagrams for *(a)* less developed and *(b)* highly developed countries. The darker region represents actual age distribution in 1985. The lighter region represents projected age distribution in 2025.

SUMMARY

I. Populations of organisms have certain properties that individual organisms lack, such as birth rates and sex ratios.
   A. Population density is the number of individuals of a particular species per unit of habitat area at a given time.
   B. Population dispersion may be random, uniform, or clumped.
II. Population change results from adjustments in the numbers of births, deaths, immigrants, and emigrants. Usually the most significant factors are birth rate and death rate.
   A. Biotic potential, or intrinsic rate of increase, is the theoretical maximum rate at which a population can grow.
   B. Environmental limitations prevent indefinite population growth. The collective total of all such limitations constitutes environmental resistance.
   C. The carrying capacity of the environment is the highest population that can be maintained for an indefinite period of time by a particular environment.
III. The logistic equation of population growth forms an S-shaped curve when graphed. It shows an initial lag phase (when the population is very small), followed by an exponential phase, followed by a leveling phase as the carrying capacity of the environment is reached.
IV. Limiting factors inhibit population growth.
   A. Density-dependent limiting factors are most effective at limiting population growth when the population density is high. Predation, disease, and competition are examples.
   B. Density-independent limiting factors limit population growth but are not influenced by changes in population density. Hurricanes and fires are examples.

V. Each organism has its own life history strategy, which is part of the total adaptation package of that particular species.
   A. An r strategy emphasizes a high rate of natural increase. These organisms often have small body sizes, bear large numbers of young once per lifetime, and inhabit variable environments.
   B. A K strategy emphasizes maintenance of a population near the carrying capacity of the environment. These organisms often have large body sizes, repetitive reproductive cycles, and long life spans, and inhabit stable environments.
VI. The principles of population ecology apply to humans as well as other organisms.
   A. Currently, human population is increasing exponentially. The rate of population increase has declined slightly over the past several years, however, leading demographers to project that the world population will stabilize ($r = 0$) at approximately 10.4 billion by the end of the 21st century.
   B. Highly developed countries have the lowest birth rates, the lowest infant mortality rates, and the longest life expectancies. They also have the highest per-capita incomes. Developing countries have the highest birth rates, the highest infant mortality rates, and the shortest life expectancies. They also have the lowest per-capita incomes.
   C. The age structure of a population greatly influences population dynamics. It is possible for a country to have replacement-level fertility and still experience population growth if the largest percentage of the population is in the pre-reproductive years.

POST-TEST

1. A _____ is a group of organisms of a single species living in a particular area at a given time.
2. Population _____ is the number of individuals of a species per unit of habitat area at a given time.
3. _____ _____ is when individuals are aggregated, or concentrated, in certain portions of the habitat.
4. Mathematical equations that represent population dynamics are called _____.
5. Birth rate, or _____, increases population size, whereas death rate, or _____, decreases population size.
6. The maximum rate at which a population could increase under ideal conditions is known as its _____ _____.
7. In a graph of population number versus time, a J-shaped curve is characteristic of _____ growth.
8. Populations never remain at their biotic potential indefinitely, because the environment sets limits that are collectively called _____ _____.
9. The _____ _____ is the largest population that

can be maintained by a particular environment for an indefinite period of time.
10. The _____ equation of population growth forms a characteristic S-shaped curve when graphed, because it takes into account the carrying capacity of the environment.
11. An abrupt decline from high population density to very low density is called a _____ _____.
12. Predation, disease, and competition are examples of density-_____ limiting factors.
13. The effect of density-_____ limiting factors on population growth intensifies as population density increases.
14. Density-_____ limiting factors regulate the size of a population but are not influenced by changes in population density.
15. Organisms with _____ selection have traits that allow them to have high rates of natural increase.
16. Organisms that are _____ strategists do not use environmental resources and energy to produce large numbers of offspring.

17. Population experts project that _____ _____ _____, when the human birth rate equals the death rate, will occur around 2089.
18. A developed country has a low _____ _____

_____, which is the number of infant deaths per 1000 live births.
19. The percentages of a population at different ages make up that population's _____ _____.

REVIEW QUESTIONS

1. Give several biological advantages for organisms with clumped dispersion. What are the disadvantages?
2. Explain the S-shaped population growth curve.
3. Give several examples of density-dependent and density-independent factors that limit population growth.
4. Are humans *r* strategists or *K* strategists? Explain the rationale for your answer.

5. Explain how a population can have an increase in its rate of growth when its birth rate is declining.
6. If all the women in the world suddenly started bearing children at replacement-level fertility rates, would the population increase stop immediately? Why or why not?

RECOMMENDED READINGS

Begon, M., and M. Mortimer. *Population Ecology,* 2nd ed. Sinauer Associates, Sunderland, MA, 1986. Numerous plant and animal examples are given for all aspects of single-species populations in this detailed text.

Ehrlich, P. R. Population biology, conservation biology, and the future of humanity. *BioScience* Vol. 37, No. 10, November 1987. Recent advances in population ecology are presented, along with a plea for humans to apply the principles of population ecology to their own populations.

Haub, C. Understanding population projections. *Population Bulletin* Vol. 42, No. 4, December 1987. A comprehensive evaluation of the challenges facing demographers as they calculate population projections.

Odum, E. P. *Ecology and Our Endangered Life-Support Systems.* Sinauer Associates, Sunderland, MA, 1989. Contains a "reader-friendly" chapter on population ecology.

World Population Data Sheet, Population Reference Bureau, Washington, D.C., 1992. A chart that provides current population data for all countries. Includes birth rates, death rates, infant mortality rates, total fertility rates, and life expectancies as well as other pertinent information.

Community Ecology

A **community** is an association of organisms of different species living and interacting together. Thus, you, your dog, and the fleas on your dog are all members of the same community, as are cockroaches, silverfish, dandelions, grasses, maples, and many other organisms.

Organisms form integrated communities of varying sizes, which lack precise boundaries and are rarely completely isolated. Communities interact with and influence one another in countless ways. Furthermore, they are nested within one another like Chinese boxes (Figure 53–1). A forest is a community, but so is a rotting log in that forest; the log contains bacteria, fungi, slime molds, worms, insects, and even mice. The microorganisms living within the gut of a termite in the rotting log also form a community.

Caribou in an open meadow. (Thomas Kitchin/Tom Stack & Associates)

On the other end of the scale, a biome is also a community, as is the entire biosphere of which that biome, in turn, is a part.

Living things exist in a nonliving environment that is as essential to their lives as their interactions with other living organisms. Minerals, air, water, and sunlight are just as much a part of a honeybee's environment, for example, as the flowers that it pollinates and from which it takes nectar and pollen. Together the nonliving environment and the living community it contains make up an **ecosystem.** The physical aspects of ecosystems are considered in Chapter 54, but this separation of community and ecosystem is purely one of convenience. Communities and their physical environments are inseparably linked.

After you have studied this chapter you should be able to

1. Distinguish between a community and an ecosystem.
2. Characterize producers, consumers, and decomposers and give the function of each in a community.
3. Define symbiosis and distinguish among mutualism, commensalism, and parasitism, giving an example of each.
4. Define what is meant by an ecological niche and distinguish between an organism's fundamental niche and its realized niche.
5. Summarize the concept of competitive exclusion and discuss an example that is apparently inconsistent with this concept.

6. Summarize the concept of limiting factors and describe their relationship to the ecological niche.
7. Summarize the main determinants of species diversity in a community.
8. Explain the concept of ecological succession and distinguish between primary succession and secondary succession.
9. Summarize the three main hypotheses that explain succession: the facilitation model, the inhibition model, and the tolerance model.
10. Discuss the two views of the nature of communities: the organismic model and the individualistic model.

A SALT MARSH COMMUNITY EXHIBITS GREAT DIVERSITY

Ecosystems often contain astonishing assortments of organisms that interact with each other and are interdependent in a variety of ways. Consider for a moment a salt marsh in the Chesapeake Bay, on the east coast of the United States. The Chesapeake Bay is the world's richest estuary (a semi-enclosed body of water where fresh water drains into the ocean). Biological diversity and productivity abound wherever fresh water and salt water form a salinity gradient (a gradual change from unsalty fresh water to salty ocean water). The salinity gradient in the bay results in three distinct marsh communities: freshwater marshes at the head of the bay, brackish (moderately salty) marshes in the middle region of the bay, and salt marshes on the ocean side of the bay. Each community has its own characteristic or-

ganisms. Sail to one of the salt marsh islands in the bay, such as South Marsh Island, and you can explore a salt marsh community relatively unaffected by humans (Figure 53–2).

A salt marsh presents a monotonous view: kilometers and kilometers of flooded meadows of cordgrass (*Spartina*). High salinities (although not as high as that of ocean water) and twice-daily tidal inundations produce a challenging environment to which only a few plants have adapted.

Nutrients such as nitrates and phosphates, which drain into the marsh from the land, promote rapid growth of both cordgrass and microscopic algae. These organisms are eaten directly by some animals, and after they die, their remains (called detritus) provide food for many inhabitants of both the salt marsh and the bay.

A casual visitor to a salt marsh would observe two different types of animal life, insects and birds. Insect pests such as saltmarsh mosquitoes and horseflies number in the millions. Birds nesting in the salt marsh include seaside sparrows, laughing gulls, and clapper rails. Migratory birds spend time in the salt marsh as well.

If you studied the salt marsh, you would find it has numerous other species. Large numbers of invertebrates seek refuge in the waters surrounding the cordgrass. There they eat, hide to avoid being eaten, and reproduce. Many of them gather in the intertidal zone because their food (detritus, algae, zooplankton, and worms) is abundant there. A variety of crustaceans live in the salt marsh. The marsh crab, for example, is a common inhabitant that eats cordgrass and small animals as well as detritus. Mollusks include the marsh periwinkle, a snail that moves along the cordgrass, skimming off algae for its food. Marsh periwinkles climb up the cordgrass to avoid becoming prey for larger marsh animals such as terrapins.

Almost no amphibians inhabit salt marshes, because the salty water dries out their skin, but a few

Figure 53–1 Sponges are part of a sea bed community. In addition, each sponge is a community in itself, often harboring a variety of organisms such as this royal gramma and brittle star. (Visuals Unlimited/Marty Snyderman)

PLANTS
   ① Saltmarsh cord grass

ANIMALS
   ② Saltmarsh mosquito
   ③ Saltmarsh greenhead fly (horsefly)

④ Seaside sparrow
⑤ Laughing gull
⑥ Clapper rail
⑦ Marsh crab
⑧ Marsh periwinkles
⑨ Northern diamondback terrapin

⑩ Northern water snake
⑪ Meadow vole
⑫ Spotted sea trout (juvenile)
⑬ Atlantic croaker (juvenile)
⑭ Bay anchovy
⑮ Tidewater silverside

Figure 53–2 Salt marshes, which are found in certain transitional areas between ocean and land, teem with living organisms.

reptiles have adapted, including the northern diamond-back terrapin. It spends its time basking in the sun or swimming in the water in search of food—snails, crabs, worms, insects, and fish. Although a variety of snakes abound in the dry areas adjacent to salt marshes, only the northern water snake (which preys on fish) is adapted to brackish water.

Mammals are represented in the salt marsh by the meadow vole, a small rodent that constructs its nest of cordgrass on the ground above the high tide zone. Meadow voles are excellent swimmers, and they swim and scamper about the salt marsh both day and night. Their diet consists mainly of insects and cordgrass.

The bay is an important nursery for numerous species of marine fish: juvenile forms of spotted sea trout, Atlantic croaker, striped bass, and bluefish, to name just a few. Other fish, such as bay anchovies, bull minnows, and tidewater silversides, never leave the estuary, spending their summers in the salt marsh shallows and their winters burrowed in the mud or swimming in the deeper waters of the bay.

Add to all these visible plant and animal organisms the unseen, microscopic world of the salt marsh, which contains uncountable numbers of protists, fungi, and bacteria, and you can begin to appreciate the complexity of a salt marsh community. The unraveling of the many interactions and interdependencies of organisms living together as a community is one of the goals of community ecologists. This chapter is concerned with making sense of community structure and diversity by finding common patterns and processes in a wide variety of communities.

(a)

(b)

(c)

Figure 53–3 Producers, consumers, and decomposers. (*a*) The trees and epiphytic vegetation of the tropical rain forest are producers. (*b*) The three-toed sloth is a consumer in the tropical rainforest community. It eats mostly leaves; some other consumers eat meat. (*c*) Decomposers such as this cup fungus reduce dead organisms to their mineral constituents plus carbon dioxide and water. (*a*, Frank Staats; *b*, Visuals Unlimited/A. Kerstitch; *c*, James L. Castner)

COMMUNITIES CONTAIN PRODUCERS, CONSUMERS, AND DECOMPOSERS

The organisms of a community can be divided into three categories based on how they get their nourishment: producers, consumers, and decomposers (Figure 53–3). Most communities contain representatives of all three groups, which interact extensively with one another.

Sunlight is the source of energy that powers almost all life processes on Earth. **Producers,** also called **autotrophs** (Greek *auto,* "self," and *tropho,* "nourishment"), manufacture complex organic molecules from simple inorganic substances (carbon dioxide and water), usually using the energy of sunlight. In other words, producers perform photosynthesis. By incorporating the chemicals they manufacture into their own bodies, producers make their bodies or body parts potential food resources for other organisms. Whereas plants are the most significant producers on land, algae and cyanobacteria are important producers in aquatic environments. In the salt marsh community, cordgrass, algae,

and cyanobacteria are all important producers. In abyssal hot spring communities deep in the ocean, nonphotosynthetic bacteria are the producers (see Focus on Life without the Sun).

Animals, animal-like protists, and a very few predatory bacteria and fungi are **consumers;** that is, they use the bodies of other organisms as sources of food energy and body-building materials. Consumers are also called **heterotrophs** (Greek *heter,* "different," and *tropho,* "nourishment"). Consumers that eat producers are called **primary consumers,** which usually means that they are exclusively **herbivores** (plant eaters). Cattle and deer are examples of primary consumers, as is the marsh periwinkle in the salt marsh community. **Secondary consumers** consume primary consumers; they include **carnivores,** which eat other animals. Lions and tigers are examples of carnivores, as are the northern diamondback terrapin and the northern water snake in the salt marsh community. Other consumers, called **omnivores,** eat a variety of organisms, both plant and animal. Bears, pigs, and humans are examples of omnivores; the meadow vole, which eats both insects and

FOCUS ON

Life without the Sun

In 1977 an oceanographic expedition aboard the research submersible *Alvin* studied the Galapagos Rift, a deep cleft in the ocean floor off the coast of Ecuador. The expedition revealed, on the floor of the abyss, a series of hot springs where seawater apparently had penetrated and been heated by the hot rocks below. During its time within the Earth, the water had also been charged with mineral compounds, including hydrogen sulfide, H_2S.

At the tremendous depths (greater than 2500 meters) of the Galapagos Rift, there is no light for photosynthesis. But the hot springs support a rich and bizarre variety of life forms that is in contrast with the surrounding lightless "desert" of the abyssal floor (see figure). Many of the species in these oases of life were new to science. For example, giant blood-red tube worms almost 3 meters in length cluster in great numbers around the vents. Other animals around the hot springs include clams, crabs, barnacles, and mussels.

The mystery is, what do these species live on? Most deep-sea communities depend on the scarce organic matter that drifts down from surface waters; that is, they rely on energy derived from photosynthesis.

Chemosynthetic autotrophic bacteria living in the tissues of these beard worms extract energy from hydrogen sulfide. Thus, they can fix carbon dioxide (dissolved in the water) to manufacture organic compounds. Because beard worms lack digestive systems, they depend on the organic compounds provided by the endosymbiotic bacteria, along with materials filtered from the surrounding water and digested extracellularly. Also visible in the photograph are some filter-feeding mollusks (yellow) and a crab. (Visuals Unlimited/Science VU-WHOI, D. Foster)

The Galapagos Rift community is too densely clustered and too productive to be dependent on chance encounters with organic material from surface waters, however.

The base of the food chain in these aquatic oases is chemosynthetic autotrophic bacteria, which can survive and multiply in water so hot (exceeding 200°C) that it would not even remain in liquid form were it not under such extreme pressure. These bacteria function as producers, but they do not photosynthesize. Instead, they possess enzymes that catalyze the oxidation of hydrogen sulfide to produce water and sulfur or sulfate. Such chemical reactions are exergonic and provide the energy required to fix CO_2 (dissolved in the water) into organic compounds. Thus these bacteria support life in deep-ocean hot springs. Many of the Galapagos Rift animals consume the bacteria directly; others, such as the giant tube worms, get their energy from bacteria that live inside their bodies.

Thus, it is accurate to say that *almost* all organisms on Earth depend on the sun for energy. The organisms in deep-sea hot springs are an interesting and unique exception.

---

cordgrass in the salt marsh community, is also an omnivore.

Many animals do not fit readily into one of these categories because they modify their food preferences to some degree when the need arises. Some consumers, called **detritus feeders** or **detritivores,** consume the organic matter of plant and animal remains. Detritivores are especially abundant in aquatic habitats, where they burrow in bottom muck and consume the organic matter that collects there. Marsh crabs, for example, are detritus feeders in the salt marsh community. Earthworms are terrestrial detritus feeders, as are termites and maggots (the larvae of houseflies). Detritus feeders work together with decomposers to destroy dead organisms and waste products. An earthworm,

for example, actually eats its way through the soil, digesting much of the soil's organic matter. By their extensive tunneling, earthworms also aerate the soil and redistribute its minerals and organic matter.

Decomposers (also called **saprophytes**) are heterotrophs that break down organic material and use the decomposition products to supply themselves with energy. They typically release simple inorganic molecules, such as carbon dioxide and mineral salts, that can then be reused by producers. Bacteria and fungi are important examples of decomposers. For example, dead wood is invaded first by sugar-metabolizing fungi that consume the wood's simple carbohydrates, such as glucose and maltose. When these carbohydrates are exhausted, fungi, often aided by termites and bacteria, complete the digestion of the wood by breaking down cellulose, a complex carbohydrate that is the main component of wood.

Communities such as the Chesapeake Bay salt marsh contain balanced representations of all three ecological categories of organisms—producers, consumers, and decomposers. Producers and decomposers have indispensable roles in ecosystems. Producers provide both food and oxygen for all life. Decomposers are also necessary for the long-term survival of any community, because without them, dead organisms and waste products would accumulate indefinitely. Without decomposers, elements such as potassium, nitrogen, and phosphorus would be permanently placed in dead organisms and therefore unavailable for use by new generations of living things. Although consumers are an important part of most communities, they are not indispensable to the long-term survival of producers or decomposers.

LIVING ORGANISMS INTERACT IN A VARIETY OF WAYS

No organism is independent of other living things. The producers, consumers, and decomposers of a community interact in a variety of complex ways, and each forms associations with other organisms. **Symbiosis** is any intimate, long-term relationship or association between two or more different species. The partners of a symbiotic relationship, called **symbionts,** may benefit from, be unaffected by, or be harmed by the relationship. The thousands, or even millions, of symbiotic associations in nature are all products of coevolution (see Chapter 27). Symbiosis takes three forms: mutualism, commensalism, and parasitism.[1]

In Mutualism, Benefits Are Shared

Mutualism is a symbiotic relationship in which both partners benefit. One example of mutualism is the association between reef-building coral animals and dinoflagellates (algae) called **zooxanthellae.** The zooxanthellae live inside cells of the coral, where they photosynthesize and provide the animal with carbon and nitrogen compounds as well as oxygen. Zooxanthellae have a stimulatory effect on corals, causing them to deposit calcium carbonate shells around their bodies

much faster when the algae are present. Each coral, in turn, supplies its zooxanthellae with waste products such as ammonia, which the algae use to make nitrogen compounds for both partners. The pigments produced by coral animals protect both them and the algae from ultraviolet radiation.

Mycorrhizae are mutualistic associations between fungi and the roots of almost all plants (see Chapters 25 and 34). The fungus absorbs essential minerals from the soil and provides them to the plant, and the plant provides the fungus with organic molecules produced by photosynthesis. Plants grow more vigorously if they have mycorrhizae, and they are better able to tolerate environmental stresses such as drought and high soil temperatures.

Frequently, mutualistic partners are completely dependent on one another. For example, an obligatory relationship exists between the yucca, a plant with stiff leaves found in the southwestern United States, and the yucca moth (discussed in Chapter 27). However, the benefits that a symbiont gets from a mutualistic relationship are sometimes difficult to assess.

Commensalism Is Taking without Harming

Commensalism is a type of symbiosis in which one organism benefits and the other is neither harmed nor helped. One example of commensalism is the relationship between two kinds of insects, silverfish and army ants. Certain kinds of silverfish live with army ants and share the food caught by the ants. The army ants derive no apparent benefit (or harm) from the silverfish. Another example of commensalism is the relationship between a rainforest tree and its epiphytes, smaller plants that live anchored to the bark of its branches. The epiphyte does not obtain nutrients or water directly from the tree, but its location on the tree enables it to obtain adequate light, water (rain dripping down the branches), and required minerals (leached out of the tree's leaves by rain). Thus, the epiphyte benefits from the association, whereas the tree remains largely unaffected.

Parasitism Is Taking at Another's Expense

Parasitism is a symbiotic relationship in which one member, the **parasite,** benefits and the other, the **host,** is adversely affected. The parasite obtains nourishment from its host, but although a parasite may weaken its host, it rarely kills it. (A parasite would have a rough life if it kept killing off its hosts!) Some parasites, such as ticks, live outside the host's body; others, such as tapeworms, live inside the host.

When a parasite causes disease and occasionally death in its hosts, it is called a **pathogen.** For example,

---

[1] Anton de Bary, an important 19th-century biologist, coined the word *symbiosis* and defined it in a very broad way (as a living together of different organisms). de Bary placed mutualism, commensalism, and parasitism under the concept of symbiosis. Although later scientists often equated mutualism and symbiosis, most biologists today define symbiosis more broadly in recognition of de Bary's contributions.

Figure 53–4 Some songbird ecological niches. These species of *Dendroica*, common warblers, spend most of their feeding time in distinct portions of the trees they frequent and also consume somewhat different insect foods. The colored regions indicate where each species spends at least half its foraging time. (After MacArthur.)

humans sometimes get histoplasmosis, a serious and often fatal disease caused by a fungus. Humans become infected when they breathe the spores of the fungus into their lungs. There the spores grow and invade the lung tissue, causing chronic coughing and fever. The spores of the fungus are common in soils that have a high concentration of bird droppings, and the disease is more prevalent in warm tropical regions of the world.

Crown gall disease, which is caused by a bacterium, occurs in many different kinds of plants and results in millions of dollars of damage each year to ornamental and agricultural plants. The bacterium, which lives in the soil, enters plants through small wounds such as those caused by insects. It causes galls (tumorlike growths) to form, often at the crown (between the stem and the roots) of a plant (see Figure 14–15). Although plants seldom die from crown gall disease, they are weakened, grow more slowly, and often succumb to other pathogens.

Many parasites do not cause disease. For example, humans can become infected with the pork tapeworm by eating poorly cooked pork infested with immature tapeworms. Once a tapeworm is inside the human digestive system, it attaches itself to the wall of the small intestine and grows rapidly by absorbing nutrients on their way through the digestive tract. Pork tapeworms that live in the human digestive tract often do not cause any noticeable symptoms.

Parasites may be either facultative or obligate. A **facultative parasite** is an organism that is normally saprophytic but, given the opportunity, becomes parasitic. An **obligate parasite** can exist only as a parasite.

THE NICHE DESCRIBES AN ORGANISM'S ROLE IN THE COMMUNITY

We have seen that a diverse assortment of organisms inhabit each community and that these organisms obtain nourishment in a variety of ways. We have also examined some of the ways that living things interact to form interdependent relationships within the community. Whether an organism is a producer, consumer, or decomposer and the kinds of symbiotic associations it forms help to describe that organism, but other details are needed to provide a complete picture.

Every organism has its own role within the structure and function of a community; we call this role its **ecological niche** (Figure 53–4). An organism's ecological niche encompasses all aspects of its existence—that is, all of the physical, chemical, and biological factors that enable the organism to survive, to remain healthy, and to reproduce. An organism's niche also encompasses what it consumes, what consumes it, the living organisms with which it competes, and how it interacts with and is influenced by the nonliving components of its environment (for example, light, temperature, and moisture). The niche, then, is the totality of an organism's adaptations, its use of resources, and the lifestyle to which it is fitted. Thus, a complete description of an organism's ecological niche involves numerous dimensions.

There are two aspects to an organism's niche in its community: One is the role an organism *could* play in the community, and the other is the role it actually *fulfills*. As an analogy, a person might be capable of be-

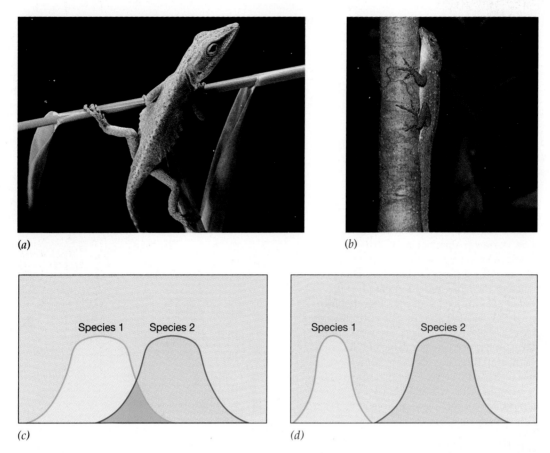

(a)   *(b)*

(c)   *(d)*

Figure 53–5 Competition can restrict an organism's realized niche. (*a*) The green Carolina anole is native to Florida. (*b*) The brown Cuban anole was introduced to Florida. (*c*) The fundamental niches of the two lizards overlap. Species 1 represents the Carolina anole, and species 2 represents the Cuban anole. (*d*) The Cuban anole was able to outcompete the Florida anole, restricting its niche.   (*a*, Runk/Schoenberger, from Grant Heilman; *b*, Connie Toops)

coming a doctor *and* a lawyer, but few people manage to be both. A person's actual lifestyle, including his or her career, is chosen from among many possibilities. Similarly, the potential ecological niche of an organism may be far broader than the role it assumes. Put differently, an organism is usually capable of utilizing much more of its environment's resources or of living in a wider assortment of habitats than it actually does. The potential ecological niche of an organism is its **fundamental niche.** Factors such as competition with other species may exclude it from part of its fundamental niche; thus, the lifestyle that an organism actually pursues and the resources that it actually utilizes make up its **realized niche.**

An example may help to make this distinction clear. The little Carolina anole lizard, which is native to Florida, perches on tree trunks or bushes during the day and waits for insect prey (Figure 53–5*a*). Formerly these lizards were widespread in Florida. Several years ago, however, a related species, the Cuban anole lizard, was introduced into Florida and quickly became common, especially in urban areas (Figure 53–5*b*). Suddenly the Carolina anoles became rare—apparently driven out of their habitat by competition from the larger Cuban lizards. Careful investigation disclosed, however, that Carolina anoles were still around but were now confined largely to the foliated branches of trees, where they were less easily seen. Thus, the habitat portion of the Carolina anole's *fundamental* niche includes the trunks and branches of trees, exterior house walls, and many other locations. But because the Cuban anoles were able to drive them out from all but the tree crowns (environmental competition), the Carolina anoles' *realized* niche became much smaller than their fundamental niche (Figure 53–5*c, d*). Since every natural community consists of numerous species, many of which compete to some extent, the complex interactions among them produce their realized niches.

Competition between Two Species with Identical or Similar Niches Leads to Competitive Exclusion

When two species are very similar, as are the Carolina and Cuban anoles, their fundamental niches may over-

MAKING THE CONNECTION

Character Displacement

Sometimes two similar species have overlapping ranges, being partly sympatric (found together in the same geographic area) and partly allopatric (geographically separated) in their distribution. The two species tend to be morphologically, ecologically, and behaviorally more distinct in places where they occur together than in places where they are allopatric. Such divergence in traits in two sympatric species is known as **character displacement.** It is thought that character displacement prevents the two groups from directly competing, since the differences between them give them different niches in the same environment.

Well-documented examples exist of character displacement between two closely related species. For example, the flowers of two species of *Solanum* in Mexico are very similar in areas where the species occur separately, but in areas where their ranges overlap there is a noticeable difference in flower size; because of this difference, the flowers are pollinated by different bees. In other words, character displacement reduces interspecific competition—in this case, for a particular pollinator.

The body size and bill size of Darwin's finches provide another example of character displacement (see figure). On large islands in the Galapagos where *Geospiza fortis* and *G. fuliginosa* occur together, their bill depths are distinctive: *G. fortis* has a shallower bill that enables it to crack small seeds, whereas *G. fuliginosa* has a deeper bill that enables it to crack medium-sized seeds. However, *G. fortis* and *G. fuliginosa* are also found separately on smaller islands, and where this occurs their bills tend to be the same intermediate size, perhaps because there is no competition from the other species.

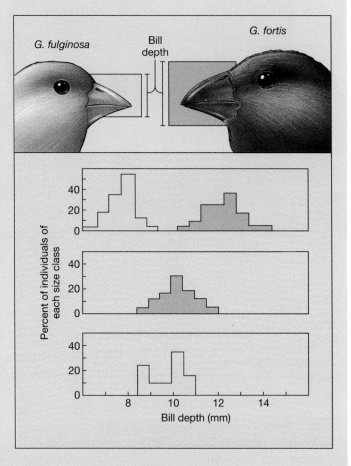

Bill depth exhibits character displacement in two species of finches from the Galapagos, *Geospiza fuliginosa* and *G. fortis*. Birds with deeper bills can crack larger seeds. (*top*) When the two species are found on the same island, character displacement occurs and *G. fuliginosa* (*blue*) has a lesser average bill depth than *G. fortis* (*green*). (*middle*) *G. fortis*. (*bottom*) *G. fuliginosa*. When the species occur on separate islands, their average bill depths are similar.

lap. However, no two species can occupy the same niche in the same community indefinitely, because competitive exclusion occurs. In **competitive exclusion,** one species is excluded from a niche by another as a result of interspecific competition (competition between species) for a resource that is in limited supply. Although it is possible for different species to compete for some necessary resource without being total competitors, two species with absolutely identical ecological niches cannot coexist. Coexistence *can* occur, however, if the overlap of the two species' niches is reduced. In the lizard example, direct competition between the two

species was reduced as the Cuban anole excluded the Carolina anole from most of its former physical habitat until the only place that remained open to it was the tree. Niche overlap between species can also be reduced by character displacement (see Making the Connection: Character Displacement). Indeed, the ecological niches of community members are often mutually compressed, or restricted, in such a way that community members compete minimally with one another. Although many ecologists express some reservations about competitive exclusion, most seem to find much truth in the concept.

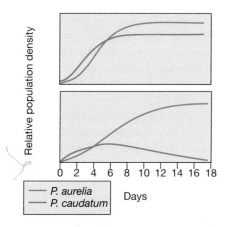

Figure 53–6 Competition between two species of *Paramecium*. The top graph shows how a population of each species of *Paramecium* grows in a single-species environment; the bottom graph shows how they grow in competition with each other.

Interspecific competition, then, determines a species' realized niche. The initial evidence for this came from a series of experiments by the Russian biologist A. F. Gause in 1934. In one study Gause grew populations of two species of the ciliate *Paramecium, P. aurelia* and the larger *P. caudatum,* both in separate test tubes and together (Figure 53–6). When grown alone, each species quickly increased its population to a high level, which it maintained for some time thereafter. When the two were grown together, however, only *P. aurelia* thrived. *P. caudatum* dwindled and eventually died out. Under different sets of culture conditions, *P. caudatum* prevailed over *P. aurelia*. Gause interpreted this to mean that one set of conditions favored one species, and a different set favored the other. Nevertheless, because the two species were similar, one or the other would eventually triumph, given enough time.

Competitive exclusion of a wild mouse (*Mus musculus*) population by voles (small rodents with short tails) apparently occurred in an area of California during the 1960s. The aggressive voles ate much of the mice's food supply, and the voles' continual proximity may have disturbed the mouse population in other ways. The wild mice exhibited less vigor and a lower reproductive rate that eventually resulted in their local extinction.

Apparent contradictions to the competitive exclusion principle sometimes occur. In Florida, for example, native fish and introduced (nonnative) cichlid fish coexist in apparently identical niches. Similarly, botanists have observed closely competitive plant species in the same location. Although such situations seem to contradict the concept of competitive exclusion, the realized niches of these organisms may differ significantly in some way that scientists do not yet understand.

Limiting Factors Restrict an Organism's Realized Niche

What factors actually determine the realized niche of a creature? An organism's lifestyle is basically formed by the total of its structural, physiological, and behavioral adaptations. Such adaptations determine, for example, the tolerance of an organism for environmental extremes. If any feature of its environment lies outside the bounds of its tolerance, then the organism cannot live there. (You would not expect to find a cactus living in a pond, or water lilies in a desert.)

The factors that determine an organism's realized niche can be extremely difficult to identify. For this reason the concept of ecological niche is largely abstract, although some of its dimensions can be experimentally determined. Whatever environmental variable tends to restrict the realized niche of an organism is a **limiting factor.**

Most of the limiting factors that have been investigated are simple variables such as the mineral content of soil, temperature extremes, precipitation, and the like. Such investigations have disclosed that any factor that exceeds an organism's tolerance for it or that is present in quantities smaller than the minimum required by the organism limits the occurrence of that organism in a community. By their interaction, such factors help to define an organism's realized niche.

The concept of limiting factors was originated in the 19th century by the agricultural chemist J. von Liebig. As a result of mineral nutrition studies of plants, von Liebig developed what is now called the **law of the minimum,** which states that plant growth is limited by the shortage of a required nutrient or environmental condition. During the early 1900s, the law of the minimum was expanded and amended to become the **law of tolerance,** which holds that the growth of each organism is limited by whatever essential factor is in shortest supply or is present in harmful excess.

This consideration applies throughout the life cycle of an organism. For instance, although adult blue crabs can live in almost completely fresh water, they cannot become permanently established in such areas because their larvae cannot tolerate fresh water. Similarly, the ring-necked pheasant, a popular game bird, has been widely introduced in North America but does not survive in the southern United States. The adult birds do well, but their eggs do not develop properly in the high temperatures that prevail there.

As a result of more recent studies of limiting factors, ecologists now understand that von Liebig viewed limiting factors much too narrowly. He understood, rightly, that an excess of one limiting factor cannot make up for the deficiency of another. But what he did not realize is that when an organism is near the limit of its tolerance for *several* factors, their interactions collectively limit the organism's realized niche more severely than would be expected from the sum of the effects of the individual limiting factors. (The concept of limiting factors is also discussed in connection with population growth [see Chapter 52] and plant growth [see Chapter 34].)

We have seen that an organism's ecological niche encompasses all aspects of that organism's existence. Now we examine the *number* of niches available in different communities, which in turn determines the number of species those communities contain.

COMMUNITIES VARY IN SPECIES DIVERSITY

Communities vary greatly in the numbers of species they contain. Tropical rain forests and coral reefs are examples of communities with extremely high species diversity. In contrast, small islands and mountaintops exhibit low species diversity.

What determines the number of species in a community? There seems to be no single answer; a number of factors appear to be significant. First, species diversity is related to the abundance of potential ecological niches. An already complex community offers a greater variety of potential ecological niches than a simple community, and for that reason it may become even more complex if organisms potentially capable of filling those niches evolve or migrate into the community.

Species diversity is inversely related to geographical isolation of a habitat. Island communities tend to be much less diverse than continental communities with similar environmental conditions. This is due partly to the difficulty, for many species, of reaching the island to colonize it. Also, sometimes species become locally extinct as a result of random events, and in isolated habitats such as islands or mountaintops, extinct populations cannot be readily replaced. In addition, isolated areas are likely to be small and to possess fewer habitats and potential ecological niches.

Species diversity is inversely related to the environmental stress of a habitat; only those species capable of tolerating extreme environmental conditions can live in an environmentally stressed community. Thus, the species diversity of a polluted stream is low compared to that of a nearby pristine stream. Similarly, the species diversity of high-latitude communities exposed to harsh climates is less than that of lower-latitude communities with milder climates. Although Alaska is by far the largest state in the United States, it contains many fewer species of trees than one would expect in so large a state—only a fraction of the national average. Ecuador, at the opposite extreme, is about the size of the state of Colorado yet has more than 1300 species of

birds—nearly twice as many as the United States and Canada combined. The effect of environmental stress on species diversity is not always clear-cut, however. For example, species diversity is often great in certain desert habitats, which seem to be stressful environments.

Species diversity is usually greater at the margins of distinct communities than in their centers, because the edges contain all or most of the ecological niches of the adjoining communities. This is known as the **edge effect**.

Species diversity is reduced when any one species enjoys a decided position of dominance within a community so that it can appropriate a disproportionate share of available resources, thus crowding out, or outcompeting, many other species.

Species diversity is greatly affected by biotic history. An area recently vacated by glaciers, for instance, has low species diversity because few species have had a chance to enter it and become established. A long-established, stable area may have high diversity even if it is, in other ways, a poor habitat. It is thought that the tropical rain forest is a very ancient habitat that in its entire history has undergone few climatic changes. (In contrast, recall that glaciers have altered temperate and arctic zones.) Having experienced few or no abrupt climatic changes that might have led to their extinction, many species have evolved in tropical rain forests.

Species Diversity Causes Community Stability—Or Does It?

For a long time ecologists thought that community stability—the ability of a community to withstand disturbances—was a consequence of community complexity; that is, a community with considerable species diversity was more stable than a community with less species diversity. According to this view, the greater the species diversity, the less critically important any one species should be. With a multitude of possible interactions within the community, it is unlikely that any single disturbance could affect enough components of the system to make a significant difference in its functioning. Thus, destructive outbreaks of pests are more common in cultivated fields, which are low-diversity communities, than in natural communities with higher species diversity. As another example, the almost complete loss of the American chestnut tree to the chestnut blight fungus has had very little ecological impact on the highly diverse Appalachian woodlands of which it used to be a part.

The greatest objection to the relationship between community stability and complexity arises from mathematical models, which indicate that more complex communities are actually less stable than less complex ones, at least if the assemblage of species in them is random. According to modern views of community structure, this is a reasonable assumption. A few experiments to determine the relationship between community stability and species diversity have been performed, and they suggest that the traditional assumption (that diversity causes stability) is incorrect. A simple relationship between species diversity and community stability apparently does not exist.

SUCCESSION IS COMMUNITY CHANGE OVER TIME

A community of organisms does not spring into existence full-blown but develops gradually, through a series of stages, until it reaches a state of maturity. The process of community development over time, which involves species in one stage being replaced by different species in the next stage, is called **succession.** An area is initially colonized by certain organisms; they are gradually replaced by other organisms, which are themselves replaced, until a more or less stable community in equilibrium with existing environmental conditions develops. This relatively stable stage is called a **climax community** or simply a **climax.** Climax communities represent the major, dominant vegetation of an area, but they are not permanent; they change as environmental conditions change.

Succession in an area is usually described in terms of the changes in the species composition of the vegetation, although each successional stage also has its own characteristic animal life. The time involved in ecological succession is on the order of hundreds or thousands of years, not the millions of years of the evolutionary time scale.

Sometimes a Community Develops in a "Lifeless" Environment

Primary succession is the change in species composition over time in a habitat that has not previously been inhabited by organisms; no soil exists when primary succession begins. A bare rock surface, such as recently formed volcanic lava (Figure 53–7) or rock scraped clean by glacial action, is a site where primary succession might occur. Although the details may vary from one site to another, in such a succession one might first observe a community of lichens, dual organisms composed of a fungus and an alga (see Chapter 25). Because they are the first organisms to colonize bare rock, lichens are called the **pioneer** community. Lichens secrete acids that help to break the rock apart, which is how soil starts to form. Gradually the lichen community is replaced by mosses and drought-resistant ferns,

Figure 53–7   Primary succession. This view shows small plants growing on recently cooled volcanic lava in Hawaii.   (David Muench)

followed in turn by tough grasses and herbs. Once sufficient soil has accumulated, grasses and herbs may be replaced by low shrubs, which in turn would be replaced by forest trees in several distinct stages. Primary succession from a pioneer community to a climax forest community may take hundreds or thousands of years. Primary succession on bare rock might proceed as follows:

lichens → mosses → grasses → shrubs → trees

When lichens colonize rock, they alter their habitat

Few habitats are less hospitable than bare rock. Its temperature may approach 90°C in the sunlight, and unless rain is actually falling on it, it may be totally devoid of moisture. Whatever minerals are present in the rock are locked up in its hard crystalline structure, unavailable to living things. Few animals could do more than briefly rest on such a surface and, in any case, would find nothing there to eat.

Lichens are able to live not only on the surface of many rocks, but beneath the surface of porous rocks in a sheltered and somewhat moister microhabitat (a small, specialized habitat within a larger habitat). Lichens are very resistant to desiccation. They cease to grow in the absence of water but quickly resume active growth when moisture becomes available, and they can absorb their own weight in water within moments of moistening.

As generations of lichen live and die on the rock, several important cumulative changes occur. First, the biomass (amount of living material) of the community increases, so more and more dissolved minerals are stored in the living tissue of the community. Second, fine particles of rock break off from the rock's surface or even within the rock itself. Third, as lichens die, their decomposing remains mix with the rock particles to form a rudimentary soil. Fourth, water is absorbed by the lichens whenever it is available; it is retained in the tissues of the lichens and in the new, thin soil layer for increasingly longer periods. As all these changes occur, a growing number of tiny animals move into the area and make their homes in the lichens and soil.

All these changes—increased biomass, soil development, water retention, and an increased number of life forms—work together to moderate the harsh conditions under which the pioneer community must live, making it possible for mosses to grow there. In fact, because mosses can grow faster than lichens, they tend to replace any lichens that die. The higher productivity of mosses results in a greater accumulation of biomass and, ultimately, of soil. This leads to further habitat change, and grasses, ferns, and herbs move in.

Primary succession occurs on sand dunes

Lake and ocean shores often have extensive sand dunes, which are deposited by wind and water. These dunes are not permanent; they move before the wind. The sand dune environment is severe, with high temperatures during the day and low temperatures at night. The sand may also be deficient in certain mineral nutrients needed by plants. As a result, few plants can tolerate the environmental conditions of a sand dune.

Grasses are a common pioneer plant on sand dunes. As the grasses extend over the surface of the dune, their roots hold the dune in place, helping to stabilize it and enabling mat-forming shrubs to invade the dune, further stabilizing it. Much later the shrubs are replaced by pines, which in turn are replaced by oaks; sometimes the pine stage is skipped. Because the soil fertility remains low, oaks are rarely replaced by other forest trees; they are thus the climax vegetation in primary succession of sand dunes. Primary succession of sand dunes might proceed as follows:

grasses → shrubs → pine trees → oak trees

Sometimes a Community Develops in an Environment Where a Previous Community Existed

Secondary succession is the change in species composition over time in a habitat already substantially modified by a preexisting community; soil is already present at these sites. Areas opened up by forest fires (Figure 53–8) and abandoned agricultural fields are common sites where secondary succession occurs.

(a)

(b)

Figure 53–8 Secondary succession after the Yellowstone fires of 1988. (a) Gray ash covers the forest floor in October 1988. The trees, although dead, remain standing. (b) The same location less than 1 year later, in July 1989, in the beginning stage of secondary succession. Many of the dead trees have fallen over. The dominant plant at this stage is fireweed (*Epilobium*). (a, Ted and Jean Reuther/Dembinsky Photo Associates; b, Stan Osolinski/Dembinsky Photo Associates)

Secondary succession on abandoned farmland has been studied extensively. Although it takes more than 100 years for secondary succession to occur at a single site, it is possible for a single researcher to study old field succession in its entirety by observing different sites in the same area. By examining old court records, the scientist can accurately determine when each field was abandoned.

Abandoned farmland in North Carolina is colonized by a predictable succession of plant communities (Figure 53–9). The first year after cultivation ceases, the

Years after cultivation	Dominant vegetation	
1	Crabgrass	
2	Horseweed	
3	Broomsedge	
5-15	Pine seedlings	
25-50	Pine forest (with developing understory of deciduous hardwoods—not shown)	
150	Oak-hickory climax forest	

Figure 53–9 Secondary succession on an abandoned field in North Carolina.

field is dominated by crabgrass. The following year the dominant species is horseweed, a herbaceous annual. It does not dominate more than a year, however, because decaying horseweed roots inhibit the growth of horseweed seedlings. In addition, horseweed does not compete well with the perennial weeds that become established in the third year—broomsedge, ragweed, and aster. Typically, broomsedge then outcompetes aster because broomsedge is drought-tolerant, whereas aster is not.

In years 5 to 15, the dominant plants in the abandoned farmland are pines such as shortleaf pine and loblolly pine. Through the buildup of litter (pine nee-

dles and branches) on the soil, pines produce conditions that cause the plants that dominated earlier to decline. Eventually pines are replaced by deciduous hardwoods such as oaks. This climax stage of secondary succession depends primarily on the environmental alterations produced by the pines. The pine litter causes changes in the soil, such as an increase in water-holding capacity, that are necessary in order for young hardwood seedlings to become established. Secondary succession on abandoned farmland might proceed as follows:

crabgrass → horseweed → perennial weeds →
pine trees → deciduous hardwood trees

Animal life also changes during secondary succession

As secondary succession proceeds, a progression of wildlife follows the changes in vegetation. Although a few species—the short-tailed shrew, for example—are found in all stages of abandoned farmland succession, most animals appear with certain stages and disappear with others. During the crabgrass and weed stages of secondary succession, the habitat is characterized by open fields that support grasshoppers, meadow mice, cottontail rabbits, and birds such as grasshopper sparrows and meadowlarks. As young pine seedlings become established, animals of open fields give way to animals common in mixed herbaceous and shrubby habitats. Now white-tailed deer, white-footed mice, ruffed grouse, robins, and song sparrows are common, whereas grasshoppers, meadow mice, grasshopper sparrows, and meadowlarks disappear. As the pine seedlings grow into trees, animals of the forest replace those common in mixed herbaceous and shrubby habitats. Cottontail rabbits give way to red squirrels, and ruffed grouse, robins, and song sparrows are replaced by warblers and veeries. Thus, each stage of succession supports its own characteristic wildlife.

Three Different Hypotheses Explain Succession

What causes succession? Ecologists who study succession have developed a number of hypothetical explanations, each of which is supported by some evidence. Three models are older and more established: the facilitation model, the inhibition model, and the tolerance model. The **facilitation model** postulates that succession is due to biological factors; that is, the organisms in each stage change the environment in such a way that it favors a new set of organisms. According to this model, succession is an orderly and predictable process that continues until the climax community (whose composition is determined by climate) is reached. Thus, species in earlier stages of succession *facilitate* their replacement by species in later stages.

The **inhibition model** views succession as an unpredictable, rather than orderly, replacement of species. In this model, succession at a particular location depends on which species get established first, and each species *inhibits* other species from becoming established. Thus, organisms of a given stage of succession retard the species replacement marking the next stage, which takes place only after individuals die or are impaired in some way.

The **tolerance model** asserts that early species are replaced by others that are better able to compete for limiting resources. According to this model, species in later stages of succession are neither facilitated nor inhibited by species in earlier stages. The organisms that eventually dominate the climax community are superior competitors. Thus, species composition at later stages of succession is determined by which organisms can better *tolerate* low levels of resources.

To date, no single model has been proposed that adequately describes the mechanism of succession. It appears that succession at any location is the result of the interaction of all three models just described.

ECOLOGISTS CONTINUE TO STUDY THE NATURE OF COMMUNITIES

F. E. Clements, an ecologist who was professionally active during the first third of this century, was struck by the worldwide uniformity of large tracts of vegetation—for example, tropical rain forest in South America, Africa, and Southeast Asia. He also noted that even though the species composition of a community in a particular habitat might be different from that of a community in a climatically similar habitat elsewhere in the world, overall the components of the two communities were usually analogous. He viewed communities as something like compound organisms—"superorganisms" whose member species cooperated with one another in a manner that resembled the cooperation of the parts of an individual organism's body. Clements' view was that a community went through certain stages of development, like those of an organism, and eventually reached an adult state: The developmental process was succession, and the adult state was the climax community. This cooperative view of the community, called the **organismic model,** stresses the interaction of the members, which tend to cluster in groups within discrete community boundaries.

Opponents of the organismic model, particularly H. A. Gleason, held that biological interactions were less important in the production of communities than climate, soil, and even chance; indeed, the very concept of a community was questionable. It might be a category of classification that had no reality outside the minds of ecologists, reflecting little more than the tendency of organisms with similar environmental requirements to live in similar places. This school of thought, called the **individualistic model,** emphasizes species individuality, with each species having its own particular living requirements. It holds that communities are therefore not interdependent associations of organisms; rather, each species is spread across a continuum of areas that meets its own individual requirements.

Studies testing the organismic and individualistic views of communities do not seem to support Clements' interactive concept. Instead, most studies favor the individualistic model. (However, this does *not* mean that species do not interact or form important associations within a community.)

SUMMARY

I. A biological community consists of a group of organisms of different species that interact and live together. A living community and its nonliving environment make up an ecosystem.

II. The major roles of organisms in communities are those of producer, consumer, and decomposer.
  A. Producers are the photosynthetic organisms that are at the bases of most food chains. They include plants and algae.
  B. Consumers are almost exclusively animals. They feed upon other organisms.
  C. Decomposers are bacteria and fungi that recycle the components of dead organisms and organic wastes by feeding on them.

III. Symbiosis is any intimate association between two or more different species.
  A. Both partners benefit from a mutualistic association.
  B. In commensalism, one organism benefits and the other is unaffected.
  C. In parasitism, one organism (the parasite) benefits and the other (the host) is harmed.

IV. The ecological niche of an organism includes both its distinctive lifestyle and its role in a community. The niche encompasses all aspects of the organism's existence—that is, the physical, chemical, and biological factors that enable it to survive, remain healthy, and reproduce.
  A. Organisms are potentially able to exploit more resources and play a broader role in the life of their community than they actually do.
    1. An organism's potential ecological niche is its fundamental niche; the niche it actually occupies is its realized niche.
    2. Interspecific competition is one of the chief biological determinants of a species' realized niche.
  B. It is thought that no two species can occupy the same niche in the same community for an indefinite period of time, because competitive exclusion occurs. In competitive exclusion, one species is excluded by another as a result of interspecific competition for a resource that is in limited supply.
  C. An organism's limiting factors (such as the mineral content of soil, temperature extremes, and amount of precipitation) tend to restrict its realized niche.

V. Community complexity, expressed in terms of species diversity, is related to a variety of factors. It is often high where the number of potential ecological niches is great, where a community is not isolated or severely stressed, at the edges of adjacent communities, and in communities with long histories.

VI. Succession is the orderly replacement of one community by another.
  A. Primary succession occurs in a habitat that has not previously been inhabited.
  B. Secondary succession begins in an area where a community has already existed and there is a well-formed soil.
  C. Three main hypotheses attempt to explain succession.
    1. The facilitation model postulates that species in a given stage of succession facilitate their replacement by species in the next stage.
    2. The inhibition model asserts that species in a given stage of succession inhibit their replacement by species of the next stage, which takes place only when individuals die or are impaired in some way.
    3. The tolerance model asserts that organisms have no effect on their own species' replacement. Rather, species composition during succession is determined by which organisms can better tolerate existing conditions.

VII. There are two views of the nature of communities.
  A. The organismic model views a community as a "superorganism" that goes through certain stages of development (succession) toward adulthood (climax). In this view, biological interactions are primarily responsible for species composition, and organisms are highly interdependent.
  B. Most ecologists support the individualistic model, which regards the concept of a highly interdependent community as questionable. According to this model, factors other than biological interactions are the primary determinants of species composition in a community.

POST-TEST

1. A _____ is an association of different species living together in one area.

2. Ecologically speaking, mushrooms would be classified as _____, and foxes would be classified as consumers.

3. _____ eat meat, _____ eat plants, and _____ eat a variety of organisms.

4. A symbiotic association in which organisms are beneficial to one another is known as _____.

5. Although _____ adversely affect their hosts, they usually do not kill them.

6. The symbiotic association exemplified by silverfish and army ants that live together and share the food caught by the army ants is _____.

7. An organism's ecological _____ is the totality of its adaptations, its use of resources, and the lifestyle to which it is fitted.

8. The _____ _____ is the ideal ecological niche that an organism could potentially occupy.

9. The interaction of limiting factors and competition from other species helps to determine an organism's _____ _____.

10. "Complete competitors cannot coexist" is a statement of the principle of _____ _____.

11. The _____ _____ signifies that species diversity is higher where two communities meet than at the center of either community.

12. Isolated communities such as islands are likely to be _____ [more/less] diverse than those that are adjacent to large areas of suitable habitat.

13. The replacement of communities over time is called _____.

14. The terminal stage of succession is called a _____.

15. A succession of communities on bare rock is an example of _____ succession.
16. Lichens are called _____ because they are the first inhabitants of bare rock.
17. An abandoned field is a site of _____ succession.
18. According to the _____ model, succession occurs because earlier organisms make the area more suitable for later organisms.

19. F. E. Clements, an early ecologist, viewed communities as _____.
20. Most ecologists today subscribe to the _____ model, which regards the concept of a highly interdependent community as questionable.

REVIEW QUESTIONS

1. Distinguish a community from an ecosystem.
2. How might one distinguish between a decomposer and a detritus feeder?
3. Why is an organism's realized niche usually narrower, or more restricted, than its fundamental niche?
4. Provide some examples of limiting factors that are not mentioned in this chapter.
5. Who was A. F. Gause, and what important ecological concept did he originate?

6. Describe the three hypotheses that purport to explain the process of ecological succession.
7. According to the inhibition model, which are most likely to be the ultimate winners in succession, long-lived plants such as trees or short-lived plants such as crabgrass? Why?
8. Contrast Clements' and Gleason's views on the nature of communities.

RECOMMENDED READINGS

Ahmadjian, V., and S. Paracer. *Symbiosis: An Introduction to Biological Associations.* University Press of New England, Hanover and London, 1986. Covers all types of symbiosis, from viruses in bacteria to plants and their pollinators.

Beardsley, T. Recovery drill. *Scientific American,* November 1990. Some conventional ideas about how communities respond to environmental catastrophes are being challenged by the recovery of Mount St. Helens.

Boucher, D. H. Growing back after hurricanes. *BioScience* Vol. 40, No. 3, March 1990. The significance of periodic environmental catastrophes, such as hurricanes, for communities is causing ecologists to reconsider the notion of a climax community.

Conniff, R. Yellowstone's "rebirth" amid the ashes is not neat or simple, but it's real. *Smithsonian,* September 1989, p. 36. Secondary succession of the forests that were burned during the September 1988 fire in Yellowstone.

Mohlenbrock, R. H. Mount St. Helens, Washington. *Natural History,* June 1990. Secondary succession of areas of devastated by the eruption of Mount St. Helens.

Moore, P. D. Vegetation's place in history. *Nature* Vol. 347, October 25, 1990. A brief discussion of differing views on the nature of communities.

Ecosystems and the Ecosphere

Almost completely isolated from everything in the Universe but sunlight, our planet Earth has often been compared with a vast spaceship whose life-support system consists of the living things that inhabit it. Those living things produce oxygen, cleanse its air, adjust its gases, transfer energy, and recycle waste products with great efficiency. Yet none of these processes would be possible without the nonliving, physical environment of our spaceship Earth.

The science of ecology deals with the abiotic (nonliving) environment as well as with living organisms. Individual communities and their abiotic environments are **ecosystems.** Spaceship Earth, which encompasses the biosphere and its interactions with the hydrosphere, lithosphere, and atmosphere, is the **ecosphere** (see Chapter 51).

Fog is part of the physical environment along the Oregon coast. (Scott Blackman/ Tom Stack & Associates)

This chapter is concerned with three key concepts about ecosystems and the ecosphere. (1) Matter, the material of which living things are composed, cycles from the living world to the abiotic physical environment and back again. All materials vital to life are continually recycled through ecosystems and so become available to new generations of organisms. (2) Although matter is cyclic in ecosystems and the ecosphere, energy flow is not. Energy moves through ecosystems in a linear, one-way direction. Once energy has been used to do biological work for a living organism, it is unavailable to other organisms. Energy cannot be recycled and reused. (3) The abiotic environment, including climate and physical aspects of the soil, causes conditions that determine where species live as well as their distribution and range.

After you have studied this chapter you should be able to

1. Compare how matter and energy work in ecosystems.
2. Diagram the carbon, nitrogen, phosphorus, and hydrologic cycles.
3. Summarize the concept of energy flow through a food chain and compare it with that of a food web.
4. Draw and explain typical pyramids of numbers, biomass, and energy.

5. Distinguish between gross primary productivity and net primary productivity.
6. Summarize the effects of the sun on Earth's climate.
7. Discuss the roles of solar energy and the Coriolis effect in the production of global air and water flow patterns.
8. Give the main causes of precipitation.

MATTER CYCLES THROUGH ECOSYSTEMS

Matter, the material of which living things are composed, cycles from the living world to the abiotic physical environment and back again; we call such cycles **biogeochemical cycles.** Earth is essentially a closed system with respect to matter.[1] The materials used by organisms cannot be "lost," although they can end up in locations that are outside the reach of organisms. Usually, however, materials are reused and often recycled, both within and among ecosystems (see Focus on Microcosms for an example of a closed ecosystem).

Four different biogeochemical cycles of matter—carbon, nitrogen, phosphorus, and water—are representative of all biogeochemical cycles. These four cycles are particularly important to living things. Carbon, nitrogen, and water have gaseous components and so cycle over large distances with relative ease. Phosphorus, however, is completely nongaseous; as a result, only local cycling of phosphorus occurs easily.

Carbon Dioxide Is the Pivotal Molecule of the Carbon Cycle

Carbon must be available to living things because the molecules of life—proteins, nucleic acids, lipids, and carbohydrates—contain carbon. Carbon is present in the atmosphere as a gas, carbon dioxide (CO_2), which makes up approximately 0.03% of the atmosphere. It is also present in the ocean as dissolved carbon dioxide—that is, as carbonate (CO_3^{2-}) and bicarbonate (HCO_3^-)—and in rocks such as limestone. Carbon cycles between the abiotic environment, including the atmosphere, and living organisms (Figure 54–1).

During photosynthesis, plants, algae, and cyanobacteria remove carbon dioxide from the air and **fix,** or incorporate, it into complex chemical compounds such as sugar. These compounds are usually used for fuel for cellular respiration by the producer that made them, by a consumer that eats the producer, or by a decomposer that breaks down the remains of the producer or consumer. Thus, carbon dioxide is returned to the atmosphere by the process of cellular respiration. A similar carbon cycle occurs in aquatic ecosystems between aquatic organisms that photosynthesize (aquatic plants, algae, and cyanobacteria) and dissolved carbon dioxide in the water.

Sometimes the carbon in biological molecules is not recycled back to the abiotic environment for some time. For example, a large amount of carbon is stored in the wood of trees, where it may stay for several hundred years. In addition, millions of years ago, vast coal beds formed from the bodies of ancient trees that did not decay fully before they were buried (see Focus on Ancient Plants and Coal Formation in Chapter 26). Similarly, the oils of diatoms or other unicellular marine organisms probably gave rise to the underground deposits of oil and natural gas that accumulated in the geological past. Coal, oil, and natural gas, called **fossil fuels** because they formed from the remains of ancient organisms, are vast depositories of carbon compounds that were the end products of photosynthesis that occurred millions of years ago.

The carbon in coal, oil, natural gas, and wood may be returned to the atmosphere by the process of burning, or **combustion.** In combustion, organic molecules are rapidly oxidized, converting them into carbon dioxide and water with an accompanying release of light and heat.

Scientists think that most of the carbon that leaves the carbon cycle for millions of years is incorporated into the shells of marine plankton. When these organisms die, their shells sink to the ocean floor and are covered by sediments. These shells, which produce seabed deposits thousands of meters thick, are eventually cemented together to form a sedimentary rock called

---

[1] A closed system with respect to matter is one that does not receive or lose matter.

F O C U S   O N

Microcosms

A favorite illustration of ecosystems has always been a balanced aquarium, that is, an aquarium containing fish and plants, along with decomposer bacteria. If properly set up, the inhabitants of such an aquarium should be able to survive indefinitely, even if it is totally sealed off from the outside world. Unfortunately, whenever this is actually tried, everything usually dies in a very short period of time.

This outcome is of more than academic interest because of the development of space flight. Spacecraft sent on journeys lasting years cannot be expected to carry all the food and oxygen they will need. It is obvious that they should be balanced ecosystems, growing their own food, recy-

cling their own wastes, and producing their own oxygen by photosynthesis. However, in the Soviet Bios experiments in which humans were sealed inside completely closed systems (on Earth) to simulate spacecraft, the walls became covered with green slime and the humans contracted severe diarrhea. Obviously, this situation could not be tolerated in a ship on a long-term mission to Mars.

In 1977 Dr. Joe Hanson of NASA was able to develop the first stable, sealed ecosystem containing algae, shrimp, and bacteria. Engineering Research Associates of Tucson, Arizona, have produced versions of Hanson's systems; by extensive experimentation, they were able to develop

a controlled mixture of as many as 100 species of organisms that worked well (most of these were microorganisms). For example, in addition to shrimp and algae it was necessary to include *Nitrosomonas* bacteria to convert the toxic ammonia excreted by shrimp into nitrite. Nitrite, also toxic, is in turn converted to nitrate by *Nitrobacter*. The nitrate is then used as a nitrogen source by the algae. The entire system, called a **microcosm**, is located inside a sealed glass sphere resembling a paperweight. These little ecosystems may provide us with clues about the management of spacecraft, including our own spaceship, Earth.

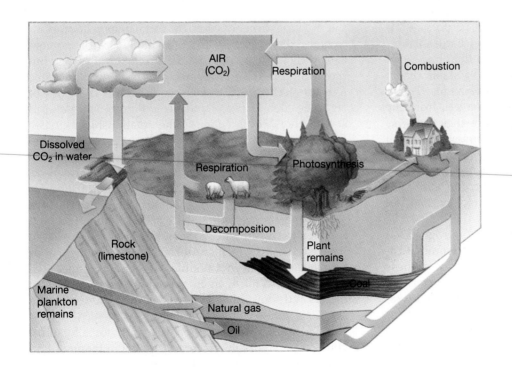

Figure 54–1 Simplified diagram of the carbon cycle. Carbon (as carbon dioxide) enters living things from the abiotic environment when plants and other producers photosynthesize (*violet arrow*). Carbon returns to the environment when living things respire (*green arrows*), when dead organic material is decomposed (*gold arrows*), or when wood or fossil fuels are burned (*light gray arrow*). Movement of carbon also occurs in the abiotic environment (*blue arrows*). Note also that the remains of ancient organisms formed deposits of fossil fuels (oil, natural gas, and coal), which remove carbon from the cycle temporarily. When fossil fuels are burned, the carbon is once again released into the atmosphere.

limestone. Earth's crust is dynamically active, and over millions of years, sedimentary rock on the bottom of the sea floor may be lifted up to form land surfaces (for example, the summit of Mount Everest is composed of sedimentary rock). When limestone is exposed by the

process of geological uplift, it slowly wears away, or disintegrates, by chemical and physical weathering processes. This returns the carbon to the water and atmosphere, where it is available to participate in the carbon cycle once again.

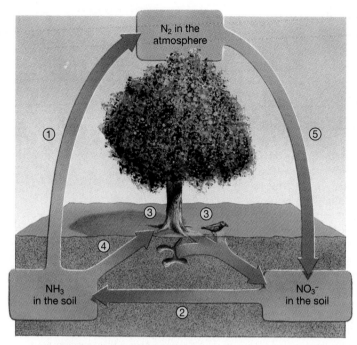

① Nitrogen-fixation
② Nitrification
③ Assimilation
④ Ammonification
⑤ Denitrification

Figure 54–2 The nitrogen cycle has five steps that involve living organisms. Nitrogen-fixing bacteria convert atmospheric nitrogen into ammonia. Ammonia is converted to nitrates by nitrifying bacteria in the soil. Nitrate is the main form of nitrogen absorbed by plants, which assimilate it to produce proteins and nucleic acids; animals eat plant proteins and produce animal proteins as a part of assimilation. When plants and animals die, their nitrogen compounds are broken down by ammonifying bacteria, and ammonia is released. Some nitrogen is returned to the atmosphere by denitrifying bacteria, which convert nitrate to molecular nitrogen.

Bacteria Are Essential to the Nitrogen Cycle

Nitrogen is crucial for all living things because it is an essential part of protein and nucleic acid molecules. At first glance it appears that there could be no possible shortage of nitrogen for living organisms: Earth's atmosphere is about 80% nitrogen gas, N_2, a diatomic molecule. However, molecular nitrogen is so stable that it does not readily combine with other elements. Therefore, living things cannot take nitrogen gas from the atmosphere and use it to manufacture their proteins and nucleic acids. Molecular nitrogen must be broken apart before the nitrogen can combine with other elements to form proteins and nucleic acids. The overall reaction that breaks up molecular nitrogen and combines nitrogen with such elements as oxygen and hydrogen requires a great deal of energy.

The nitrogen cycle has five steps: (1) nitrogen fixation; (2) nitrification; (3) assimilation; (4) ammonification; and (5) denitrification (Figure 54–2). All of these steps except assimilation are performed by bacteria.

The first step in the nitrogen cycle, **nitrogen fixation,** involves the conversion of gaseous nitrogen (N_2) to ammonia (NH_3) or nitrate (NO_3^-). The process is called nitrogen fixation because nitrogen is *fixed* into a form that living things can use. Although considerable nitrogen is fixed as nitrate by combustion, volcanic action, lightning discharges, and industrial means (these processes supply enough energy to break up molecular nitrogen), most nitrogen fixation is biological. Biological fixation, which produces ammonia (NH_3), is carried out by nitrogen-fixing bacteria and cyanobacteria in soil and aquatic environments. These

organisms employ the enzyme **nitrogenase** to break up molecular nitrogen and combine it with hydrogen.

Because nitrogenase functions only in the absence of oxygen, the bacteria that use nitrogen must insulate the enzyme from oxygen by some means. Some nitrogen-fixing bacteria live beneath layers of oxygen-excluding slime on the roots of a number of plants. But the most important nitrogen-fixing bacteria, *Rhizobium*, live in special swellings, or **nodules,** on the roots of legumes such as beans and peas (Figure 54–3) and of some other woody plants. The relationship between *Rhizobium* and the host plants is mutualistic: The bacteria receive carbohydrates from the plant, whereas the plant receives nitrogen in a form that it can use.

In aquatic habitats, most of the nitrogen fixation is done by cyanobacteria. Filamentous cyanobacteria have special oxygen-excluding cells called **heterocysts** that function to fix nitrogen. Some water ferns (Figure 54–4) have cavities in which cyanobacteria live, somewhat as *Rhizobium* lives in root nodules of legumes. Other cyanobacteria fix nitrogen in symbiotic association with cycads and some other terrestrial plants or as the photosynthetic partner of certain lichens.

The reduction of nitrogen gas to ammonia by nitrogenase is a remarkable accomplishment of living organisms that is achieved without the tremendous heat, pressure, and energy required to manufacture the commercial fertilizers. Even so, nitrogen-fixing bacteria must consume the energy in 12 grams of glucose or the equivalent to fix 1 gram of nitrogen biologically.

The conversion of ammonia (NH_3) to nitrate (NO_3^-), called **nitrification,** is accomplished by soil bacteria. Nitrification is a two-step process. First, the

Figure 54–3   Root nodules of a pea plant. Mutualistic *Rhizobium* bacteria live in these nodules, using energy derived from sugars provided by their legume host. The bacteria fix nitrogen, some of which is used by the host plant. The ultimate death and decay of both partners enrich the soil with the fixed nitrogen.   (Hugh Spencer/Photo Researchers, Inc.)

(a)

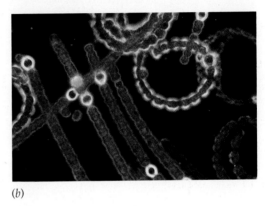

(b)

Figure 54–4   Many cyanobacteria fix nitrogen, often in association with plants. (*a*) *Azolla*, a water fern that harbors nitrogen-fixing cyanobacteria. (*b*) *Anabaena*, a cyanobacterium, has distinctive heterocysts in which nitrogen fixation occurs.   (*a*, Visuals Unlimited/William S. Ormerod; *b*, Dennis Drenner)

soil bacteria *Nitrosomonas* and *Nitrococcus* convert ammonia to nitrite (NO_2^-). Then the soil bacterium *Nitrobacter* oxidizes nitrite to nitrate. The process of nitrification furnishes these bacteria, called nitrifying bacteria, with energy.

In **assimilation,** plant roots absorb the nitrate (NO_3^-) and/or ammonia (NH_3^+) that was formed by nitrogen fixation and nitrification and incorporate the nitrogen into plant proteins and nucleic acids. When animals consume plant tissues, they assimilate nitrogen as well, by taking in plant compounds and converting them to animal compounds.

Living organisms produce nitrogen-containing waste products such as urea (in urine) and uric acid (in the wastes of birds). These substances plus the nitrogen compounds that occur in dead organisms are decomposed, releasing the nitrogen into the abiotic environment as ammonia (NH_3). The conversion of organic nitrogen compounds into ammonia is known as **ammonification,** and the bacteria that perform this process are called ammonifying bacteria. The ammonia produced enters the nitrogen cycle and is available once again for the processes of nitrification and assimilation.

The reduction of nitrate (NO_3^-) to gaseous nitrogen (N_2) is called **denitrification.** Denitrifying bacteria reverse the action of nitrogen-fixing and nitrifying bacteria; that is, denitrifying bacteria return nitrogen to the atmosphere as nitrogen gas. Denitrifying bacteria are anaerobic and therefore prefer to live and grow where little or no free oxygen is present. For example, they are found deep in the soil near the water table, an environment that is nearly oxygen-free.

In summary, the four main groups of bacteria involved in the nitrogen cycle perform, respectively, the following functions: (1) nitrogen fixation—nitrogen-fixing bacteria convert molecular nitrogen to ammonia; (2) nitrification—nitrifying bacteria oxidize ammonia to nitrates; (3) ammonification—ammonifying bacteria produce ammonia from decaying proteins, urea, or uric acid; and (4) denitrification—denitrifying bacteria "defix" nitrogen by liberating it from nitrate as molecular nitrogen.

The Phosphorus Cycle Lacks a Gaseous Component

Phosphorus, which does not exist in a gaseous state and therefore does not enter the atmosphere, cycles from the land to sediments in the oceans and back to the land (Figure 54–5). As water runs over rocks containing phosphorus, it gradually wears away the surface and carries off inorganic phosphate (PO_4^{3-}) molecules.

The erosion of phosphorus-containing rocks releases phosphate into the soil, where it is taken up by

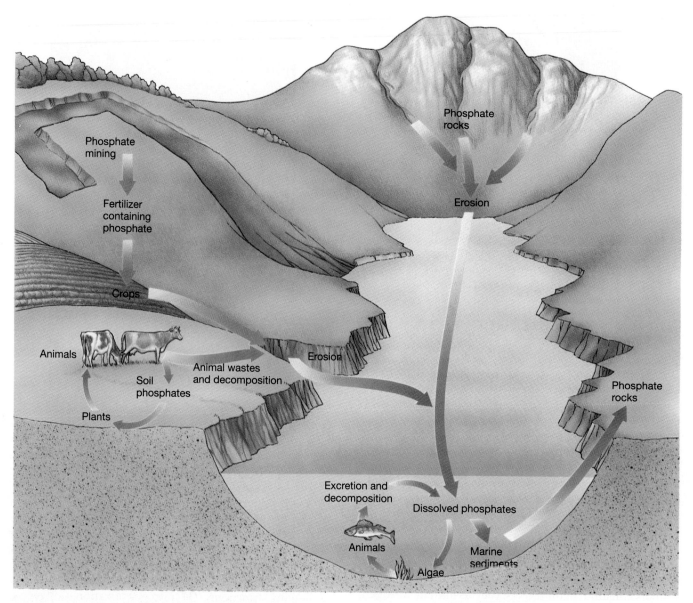

Figure 54–5 The phosphorus cycle in terrestrial and aquatic environments. Recycling of phosphorus (as phosphate, $PO_4{}^{3-}$) is slow because no biologically important form of phosphorus is gaseous. Phosphate that becomes part of marine sediments may take millions of years to solidify into rock, uplift as mountains, and erode again to become available to living things.

plant roots. Once in the plant's cells, phosphate is used in a variety of biological molecules, including nucleic acids. Animals obtain most of their required phosphate from the food they eat, although in some localities drinking water may contain a substantial amount of inorganic phosphate. Thus, as with carbon and nitrogen, phosphorus moves through the food chain as one organism consumes another. Phosphorus released by decomposers becomes part of the pool of inorganic phosphate in the soil that can be reused by plants.

Phosphorus cycles through aquatic communities much as it does through terrestrial communities. Dissolved phosphorus enters aquatic communities through algae and plants, which are in turn eaten by a variety of fin fish and shell fish. Ultimately, decomposers that break down wastes and dead organisms release inorganic phosphorus into the water, available to be used by aquatic producers again.

Phosphate can be lost from biological cycles. Some phosphate is carried from the land by streams and rivers to the ocean, where it can be deposited on the sea floor and remain for millions of years. The geological process of uplift may some day expose these sea floor sediments as new land surfaces, from which phosphate is once again eroded.

Some phosphate in the aquatic food chain finds its way back to the land. A small portion of the fish and aquatic invertebrates are eaten by sea birds, which may defecate on the land where they roost. Guano (manure of sea birds) contains large amounts of phosphate and

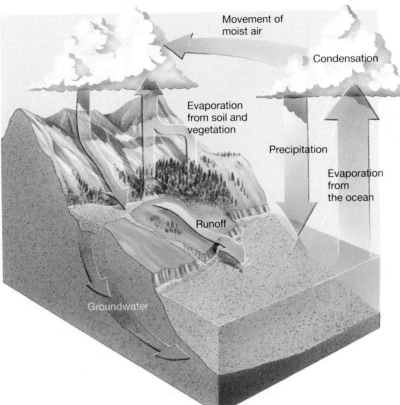

Figure 54–6   The hydrologic cycle. Water cycles from the oceans to the atmosphere to the land and back to the oceans. Although some water molecules are unavailable for thousands of years (locked up in polar ice, for example), all water molecules eventually cycle through the hydrologic cycle.

nitrate; once on land, these minerals may be absorbed by the roots of plants. The phosphate contained in guano may enter terrestrial food chains in this way, although the amounts involved are quite small.

Water Circulates in the Hydrologic Cycle

Water continuously circulates from the oceans to the atmosphere to the land and back to the oceans, providing us with a renewable supply of purified water on land. This complex cycle, known as the **hydrologic cycle,** results in a balance of water in the oceans, on the land, and in the atmosphere (Figure 54–6). When water evaporates from the ocean's surface, it forms clouds in the atmosphere. Water also evaporates from soil, streams, rivers, and lakes on land. Transpiration, the loss of water vapor from land plants, adds more water to the atmosphere.

Water moves from the atmosphere to the land and oceans in the form of precipitation (rain, snow, sleet, or hail). Water may evaporate from land and re-enter the atmosphere directly. Alternatively, it may flow in rivers and streams to coastal **estuaries,** where fresh water meets the oceans. The movement of water from land to oceans is called **runoff.** Or water percolates (seeps) downward in the soil to become **groundwater.** Ground-

water supplies water to the soil, to streams and rivers, and to plants. Ultimately, the water that falls on land from the atmosphere makes its way back to the oceans.

Regardless of its physical form (solid, liquid, or vapor) or location, every molecule of water eventually moves through the hydrologic cycle. Tremendous quantities of water are cycled annually between Earth and its atmosphere. The amount of water entering the atmosphere each year is estimated at 389,500 cubic kilometers (95,000 cubic miles). Approximately three fourths of this water re-enters the ocean directly as precipitation over water; the remaining amount falls on land.

THE FLOW OF ENERGY THROUGH ECOSYSTEMS IS LINEAR

The passage of energy in a one-way direction through an ecosystem is known as **energy flow.** Energy enters an ecosystem as the radiant energy of sunlight, some of which is trapped by producers during photosynthesis. The energy, now in chemical form, is stored in the bonds of organic molecules such as glucose. When these molecules are broken apart by cellular respiration, the energy becomes available to do work such as repairing tissues or pumping protons across membranes. As the work is accomplished, the energy escapes the living organism and dissipates into the environment as low-grade heat. Ultimately, this heat energy radiates into

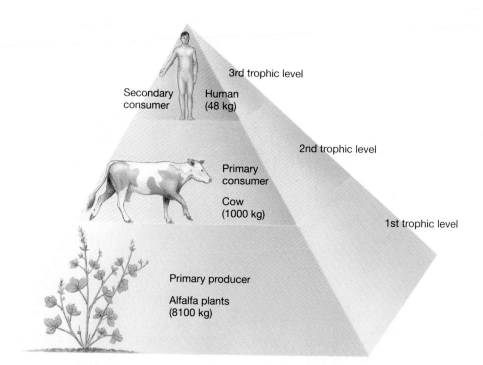

3rd trophic level

Secondary consumer   Human (48 kg)

2nd trophic level

Primary consumer

Cow (1000 kg)

1st trophic level

Primary producer

Alfalfa plants (8100 kg)

Figure 54–7   A hypothetical trophic pyramid. Numbers are illustrative only and are not intended to be exact.

space. Thus, once chemical energy has been degraded to heat, as it is by living things, it becomes unavailable for reuse.[1]

In an ecosystem, both energy flow and the cycling of matter occur in **food chains,** in which energy from food passes from one organism to the next in a sequence. Producers form the beginning of the food chain by capturing the sun's energy through photosynthesis. Herbivores (and omnivores) eat plants, obtaining the chemical energy of the producers' molecules as well as building materials from which they construct their own tissues. Herbivores are in turn consumed by carnivores (and omnivores), who reap the energy stored in the herbivores' molecules. Decomposers are the last links in the food chain. They make their living by extracting energy from organic molecules in the carcasses and body wastes of other members of the food chain.

Each level in a food chain is called a **trophic level** (Figure 54–7). (The word *trophic* comes from a Greek word meaning "to nourish.") The first trophic level is formed by **primary producers** (photosynthesizers), the second by **primary consumers** (herbivores), the third by **secondary consumers** (carnivores), and so on.

Simple food chains like that just described rarely occur in nature, because few organisms eat just one kind of other organism. More typically, the flow of en-

ergy and materials through ecosystems involves a range of choices of food for each organism. In an ecosystem of average complexity, numerous alternative pathways are possible. Thus, a **food web,** a complex of interconnected food chains in an ecosystem, is a more realistic model of the flow of energy and materials through ecosystems (Figure 54–8).

The most important thing to remember about energy flow in ecosystems is that it is *linear,* or one-way. That is, as energy is moved from one trophic level to the next, most (about 90%) of the useful chemical energy is lost as heat. This loss of energy usually limits the number of links in the food chain to fewer than six.

Ecological Pyramids Illustrate How Ecosystems Work

An important feature of energy flow is that most of the energy dissipates into the environment as it moves from one trophic level to another in a food chain or web. The relative energy value at each trophic level is often graphically represented by **ecological pyramids.** The three main types are known as pyramids of numbers, pyramids of biomass, and pyramids of energy.

A **pyramid of numbers** shows the number of organisms (represented by the width of the pyramid) at each trophic level in a given ecosystem (Figure 54–9). In most pyramids of numbers, each successive trophic level is occupied by fewer organisms. For example, in a typical grassland the number of herbivores (such as zebras and wildebeests) is greater than the number of carnivores (such as lions). Inverted pyramids of num-

---

[1]Recall that the second law of thermodynamics (see Chapter 6) stipulates that when energy is converted from one form to another, some of it is degraded into a lower-quality, less useful form—usually heat that disperses into the surroundings. This energy can never be used again by living organisms for biological work.

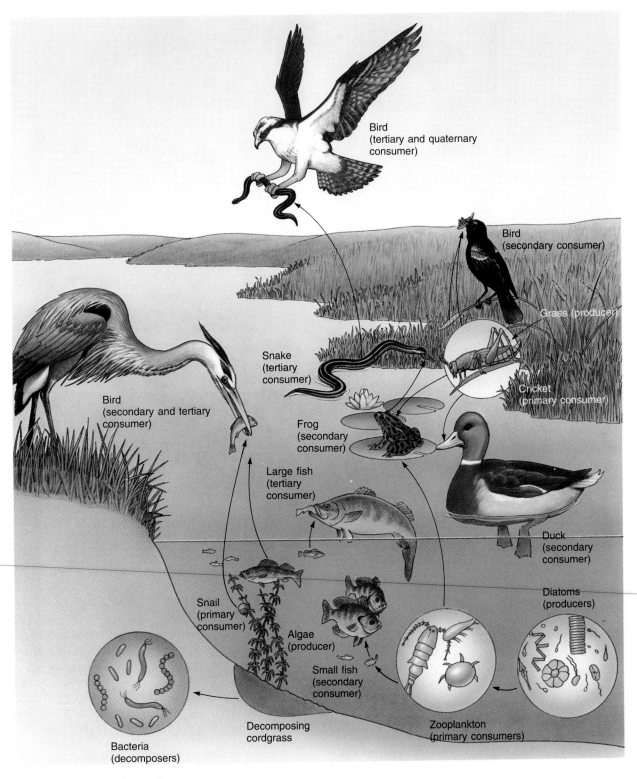

Figure 54–8 A simplified food web.

bers, in which higher trophic levels have *more* organisms than lower trophic levels, are often observed among decomposers, parasites, tree-dwelling herbivorous insects, and similar organisms. One tree can provide food for hundreds of leaf-eating insects, for example.

A **pyramid of biomass** illustrates the total biomass at each successive trophic level per given area at a given time. **Biomass** is a quantitative estimate of the total mass, or amount, of living material; it indicates the amount of fixed energy at a particular time. Biomass units vary; among others, biomass may be represented

Number of individuals   Trophic level

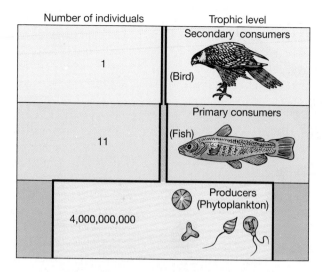

Figure 54–9 A pyramid of numbers is based on the number of organisms at each trophic level.

(a)

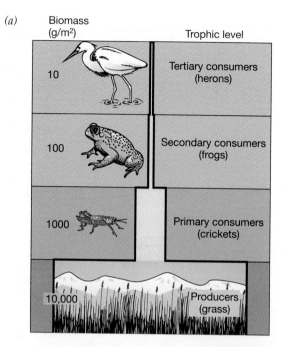

(b)

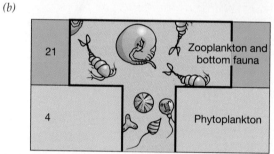

Figure 54–10 Pyramids of biomass. *(a)* A pyramid of biomass for a given area of temperate grassland. *(b)* An inverted biomass pyramid occurs when highly productive lower trophic levels experience very high rates of turnover.

as wet or dry weight of organic matter per unit area or as energy content per unit area. Typically, pyramids of biomass illustrate a progressive reduction of biomass in succeeding trophic levels (Figure 54–10*a*). On the assumption that there is, on the average, about a 90% reduction of biomass for each trophic level,[1] 10,000 kg of grass should be able to support 1000 kg of crickets, which in turn support 100 kg of frogs. By this logic, the biomass of frog-eaters (such as the heron) could only weigh, at the most, about 10 kg. Although carnivores may eat no vegetation, a great deal of vegetation is required to support them.

Occasionally, one finds an inverted pyramid of biomass in which the primary consumers outweigh the primary producers (Figure 54–10*b*). How can this be? In these instances, the producers—usually algae—are highly productive and reproduce quickly despite being rapidly consumed by very efficient herbivores. Thus, although at any point in time relatively few algae are present, the *rate* of biomass production of the primary consumers is much less than that of the primary producers.

A **pyramid of energy** shows the energy relationships of an ecosystem (Figure 54–11). Energy pyramids, which indicate the rate of energy flow from one trophic level to the next, are usually expressed in calories. On the whole, pyramids of energy resemble biomass pyramids in shape but help to make another consequence of the nature of trophic levels clearer: Most food chains are short because of the dramatic reduction in energy content that occurs at each trophic level. This is because most of the energy dissipates into the environment.

---

[1] The 90% reduction in biomass is an approximation; actual biomass reduction varies widely in nature.

Also, pyramids of energy are *never* inverted. They are always larger at the bottom than at the top because of the second law of thermodynamics; more energy always flows into a trophic level than flows out of that level.

Ecosystems Vary in Productivity

The **gross primary productivity** of an ecosystem is the rate at which energy accumulates (as biomass) during photosynthesis. That is, gross primary productivity is the total amount of carbon compounds synthesized by photosynthesis in a given period of time. Of course, plants must respire to provide energy for their life processes, and cellular respiration acts as a drain on photosynthesis. Energy that remains (as biomass) after cellular respiration has occurred is called **net primary productivity;** it is the amount of biomass found in ex-

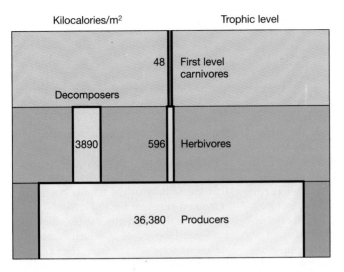

Kilocalories/m²   Trophic level

48 | First level carnivores

Decomposers

3890 | 596 | Herbivores

36,380 | Producers

Figure 54–11 A pyramid of energy. Notice the relatively large role played by bacteria (as decomposers); although not depicted in this figure, decomposers actually operate on all trophic levels.

cess of that broken down by a plant's cellular respiration. Net primary productivity represents the rate at which organic matter is actually incorporated into plant bodies so as to produce growth (Figure 54–12).

net primary productivity =
(*plant growth*)

gross primary productivity − plant respiration
(*total photosynthesis*)

Only the energy represented by net primary productivity is available for the nutrition of heterotrophs, and of

this only a portion is actually used by them. Both gross primary productivity and net primary productivity can be expressed in terms of kilocalories (of energy fixed by photosynthesis) per square meter per year or of dry weight (grams of carbon incorporated into tissue) per square meter per year.

What determines productivity? A number of factors may interact. Some plants are more efficient than others in fixing carbon. Environmental factors are also important. The influx of solar energy, availability of mineral nutrients, availability of water, and other climatic factors are important, as are the degree of maturity of the community, the severity of human modification, and other factors that are difficult to assess. For example, the high productivity of intertidal communities along an ocean shoreline is due largely to wave action. Many intertidal organisms are sedentary detritus filter feeders (such as mussels) whose food is carried to them by wave action so that they expend less energy to obtain food.

Ecosystems differ strikingly in their productivity. Terrestrial communities are generally more productive than aquatic ones, because of the greater availability of light[1] for photosynthesis and higher concentrations of available mineral nutrients. However, lack of water and adverse temperatures tend to limit the productivity of certain terrestrial ecosystems. Aquatic ecosystems have an abundance of water, and temperatures are moderated by the watery environment. Low light intensity and unavailability of mineral nutrients, which are especially scarce in the open sea, usually limit aquatic ecosystems.

The net primary productivity of an ecosystem tells us little about how much biomass is present at any given time. Despite plant growth, under natural conditions a section of prairie contains about as much grass this year as it did last year. The reason is that the **turnover** of plant biomass, which results from its consumption by animals and decomposers, is usually about the same as the net primary productivity of the ecosystem. This balance determines the current plant biomass, or **standing crop**.

ENVIRONMENTAL FACTORS INFLUENCE WHERE AND HOW SUCCESSFULLY AN ORGANISM CAN SURVIVE

In Chapter 53 we discussed some of the biotic interactions among organisms which affect their biological success. We have also seen how living things depend on

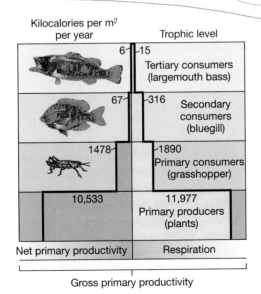

Kilocalories per m² per year   Trophic level

6 | 15 | Tertiary consumers (largemouth bass)

67 | 316 | Secondary consumers (bluegill)

1478 | 1890 | Primary consumers (grasshopper)

10,533 | 11,977 | Primary producers (plants)

Net primary productivity   Respiration

Gross primary productivity

Figure 54–12 A pyramid of energy for a river ecosystem that illustrates gross primary productivity and net primary productivity. Measurements are in kilocalories per square meter per year.

[1] Aquatic environments receive less light than terrestrial environments. When sunlight hits the surface of water, much of it is scattered or reflected. Also, as light penetrates water, some light is absorbed by water molecules, reducing the amount of light at greater depths.

FOCUS ON

The Gaia Hypothesis

One of the most unusual and controversial hypotheses to be advanced in recent years is the Gaia hypothesis,[1] which states that Earth can be viewed as a single living organism. According to the Gaia hypothesis, planet Earth is alive in the sense that it is capable of self-maintenance. Living organisms on Earth interact with the abiotic environment to produce and maintain Earth's chemical composition, temperature, and other characteristics. Thus, the environment and living organisms of Earth depend on one another and work together as a homeostatic mechanism.

As an example of the Gaia mechanism, consider Earth's temperature. It is generally accepted that the temperature of Earth has remained relatively constant at a level suitable for life over the past 3.5 to 4 billion

[1]Gaia is derived from the Greek *gaea*, which means "the Earth."

years that life has existed. Yet there is evidence that the sun has been heating up during that time. Why hasn't Earth increased in temperature? Gaia proponents say that Earth has remained the same temperature because the level of atmosphere-warming CO_2 has dropped during that time. This happened because living Earth compensated for increased sunlight by "fixing" CO_2 into calcium carbonate shells for countless billions of marine plankton. As the plankton died, their shells sank to the ocean floor, thus removing CO_2 from the system. This Gaia planetary temperature mechanism is an example of a feedback loop between the abiotic environment and the living organisms on Earth, which mutually interact to regulate Earth's temperature.

Another example of interactions between the abiotic and living components of Gaia's Earth involves the salinity of the oceans. As terrestrial

rocks are weathered, oceans tend to get saltier and saltier, in time becoming too saline to support life. However, geological evidence indicates that the salinity of the oceans has remained constant for millions of years. Gaia proponents suggest that a feedback loop exists in which bacteria remove excess salt from the ocean in salt flats, which are shallow bays along tropical and subtropical oceans where bacteria grow in such numbers that they form great mats.

Many scientists are reluctant to accept the Gaia hypothesis, although some consider it a useful metaphor. Almost everyone agrees that the environment modifies living organisms and that living organisms modify the environment to some extent, especially on a local scale. However, the idea that Earth's living things *adjust* the physical environment to meet their needs has few backers, in part because it is difficult to test.

---

the physical environment to supply essential materials (in biogeochemical cycles) and energy. Physical factors such as climate and soil also affect living things (see Focus on The Gaia Hypothesis for an interesting view of living organisms and their abiotic environment).

Climate refers to the average weather conditions in a particular place over a period of years and includes temperature and precipitation. Day-to-day variations, day-to-night variations, and seasonal variations in temperature and precipitation are also important aspects of climate. In addition, climate includes wind, humidity, fog, and cloud cover.

The Sun Warms the Earth

The sun is necessary to life. It warms the planet to habitable temperatures. Without the sun's energy, the temperature on planet Earth would approach absolute zero ($-273°C$) and all water would be frozen, even in the oceans. The hydrologic cycle, carbon cycle, and other biogeochemical cycles are powered by the sun, which also determines Earth's climate to a great extent. The

sun's energy is captured by photosynthetic organisms and used to make food molecules that are required by almost all forms of life. Most of our fuels—wood, oil, coal, and natural gas, for example—represent solar energy captured by photosynthetic organisms. Without the sun, life on planet Earth would cease.

The sun's energy, which is the product of a massive nuclear fusion reaction, is emitted to outer space in the form of electromagnetic radiation—especially light, infrared, and ultraviolet radiation. An infinitesimal portion of this energy—one billionth of the sun's total production—strikes Earth's atmosphere, and a minute part of this tiny trickle of energy is used by living things.

In the daytime, 30% of the solar radiation that falls upon Earth is immediately reflected by clouds and surfaces, especially snow, ice, and oceans. The remaining 70% is absorbed by Earth and runs the water cycle, drives winds and ocean currents, powers photosynthesis, and warms the planet. Ultimately, however, all of this energy is lost by the continual radiation of long-wave infrared (heat) energy into space.

These figures are averages for the entire Earth and may vary substantially at different places because of

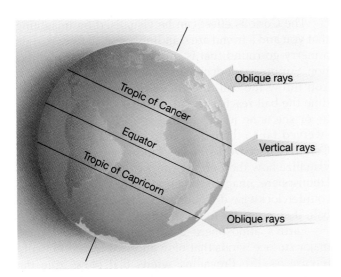

Figure 54–13 The amount of energy per unit area that Earth's surface receives is determined by the angle at which the sun's rays strike Earth. This angle varies from place to place owing to the spherical shape of Earth and the inclination of its axis. In this diagram, which represents the situation in the month of June, solar radiation strikes Earth perpendicularly in the Northern Hemisphere but very obliquely in the Southern Hemisphere. This difference produces summer conditions in the Northern Hemisphere and winter in the Southern Hemisphere.

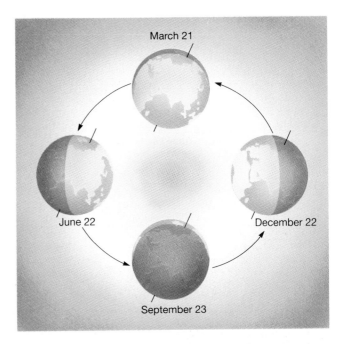

Figure 54–14 As Earth travels around the sun, the inclination of its axis remains the same. As a result, the sun's rays strike the Northern and Southern Hemispheres obliquely at different times of the year. Notice that the absolute angle of the sun's rays at the equator is more nearly the same at all seasons.

local conditions. For example, high clouds increase energy reflection, whereas low clouds increase energy absorption.

Solar energy is more concentrated at the equator and less concentrated at the poles

The most significant local variation in Earth's temperature is produced because the sun's energy does not reach all places on Earth uniformly. A combination of Earth's roughly spherical shape and the tilted angle of its axis produces a great variation in **insolation,** the quantity of energy delivered by sunlight.

As a consequence of Earth's tilting, the sun's rays strike different areas of Earth at different angles at any one time. On the average, the sun's rays hit Earth vertically near the equator, making the energy more concentrated and producing higher temperatures. Near the poles the sun's rays strike more obliquely, and, as a result, they are spread over a larger surface area. Also, rays of light entering the atmosphere obliquely near the poles must pass through a deeper envelope of air than those entering near the equator. This causes more of the sun's energy to be scattered and reflected back into space, which further lowers temperatures near the poles. Thus, the solar energy that reaches polar regions is less concentrated and produces lower temperatures.

Seasons are determined by two main factors: the inclination of Earth's axis (the most important factor) and the distance of Earth from the sun, which varies during the year. Because Earth is always tilted the same on its axis as it circles the sun (23.5 degrees), during half of the year (March 21 to September 22) the Northern Hemisphere tilts *toward* the sun and during the other half (September 33 to March 21) it tilts *away* from the sun (Figures 54–13 and 54–14). (The orientation of the Southern Hemisphere is just the opposite.)

Atmospheric Circulation Is Driven by Uneven Heating by the Sun

In large measure, differences in temperature caused by variations in the amount of solar energy that reaches Earth at different locations drive the circulation of the atmosphere. The very warm surface of Earth near the equator heats the air in contact with it, causing this air to expand and rise. As the warm air rises, it cools and sinks again. Much of it recirculates almost immediately to the same areas it has left, but the remainder flows toward the poles, where eventually it is chilled. Similar upward movements of warm air and its subsequent flow toward the poles occur at higher latitudes (farther from the equator) as well (Figure 54–15). As air cools by contact with the polar ground and ocean, it sinks and flows toward the equator, generally beneath the sheets of warm air flowing toward the pole at the same time. The constant motion of air transfers heat from the equa-

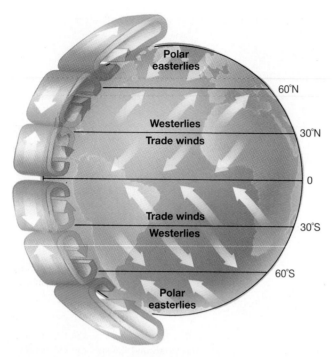

Figure 54–15 Atmospheric circulation transports heat from the equator to the poles. The greatest solar energy input occurs at the equator, heating air most strongly in that area. The air rises and travels poleward, but is cooled in the process so that much of it descends again around 30 degrees latitude in both hemispheres. At higher latitudes the patterns of movement are more complex.

tor toward the poles, and, as the air returns, it cools the land over which it passes. This constant turnover does not equalize temperatures over the surface of Earth, but it does moderate them.

Earth's atmosphere exhibits complex horizontal movements called winds

The nature of wind, with its turbulent gusts, eddies, and lulls, is complex and difficult to understand or predict. It results in part from differences in atmospheric pressure and from the rotation of Earth.

The gases that constitute the atmosphere have weight and exert a pressure that is, at sea level, about 1013 millibars (14.7 pounds per square inch). Air pressure is variable, however, and changes with altitude, temperature, and humidity. Winds tend to blow from areas of high atmospheric pressure to areas of low pressure; the greater the difference between the high and low pressure areas, the stronger the wind.

Earth's rotation influences the direction that wind blows. Earth's rotation from west to east causes wind to swerve to the right in the Northern Hemisphere and to the left in the Southern Hemisphere. This tendency of moving air to be deflected from its path by Earth's rotation is known as the **Coriolis effect.**

The Coriolis effect can be visualized by imagining that you and a friend are standing about 10 feet apart on a merry-go-round that is turning in a clockwise direction. Suppose you decide to throw a ball to your friend. You throw the ball directly at your friend, but by the time the ball reaches the place where your friend was, he or she is no longer in that spot. The ball will have swerved far to the left of your friend. This is how the Coriolis effect works in the Southern Hemisphere. To visualize how the Coriolis effect works in the Northern Hemisphere, imagine the merry-go-round moving in a counterclockwise direction. Now when you throw the ball, it swerves far to the right of your friend.

Earth's atmosphere has three **prevailing winds,** major surface winds that blow more or less continually (Figure 54–15). Prevailing winds that blow from the northeast near the North Pole or from the southeast near the South Pole are **polar easterlies.** Winds that blow in the mid-latitudes from the southwest (Northern Hemisphere) or from the northwest (Southern Hemisphere) are **westerlies.** Tropical winds that blow from the northeast (Northern Hemisphere) or southeast (Southern Hemisphere) are **trade winds.**

Surface Ocean Currents Are Driven by Winds and by the Coriolis Effect

The persistent prevailing winds blowing over the ocean produce mass movements of surface ocean water known as **currents.** The prevailing winds generate *circular* ocean currents called **gyres.** For example, in the North Atlantic, the tropical trade winds tend to blow toward the west, whereas the westerlies in the mid-latitudes blow toward the east. This helps establish a clockwise gyre in the North Atlantic. Thus, surface ocean currents and winds tend to move in the same direction, although many variations to this general rule do occur.

Other factors that contribute to ocean currents include the Coriolis effect, the varying density of water, and the position of land masses. The paths that surface ocean currents travel are partly caused by the Coriolis effect (Figure 54–16). Earth's rotation from west to east causes surface ocean currents to swerve to the right in the Northern Hemisphere, producing a circular, clockwise pattern of water currents. In the Southern Hemisphere, ocean currents swerve to the left, producing a circular, counterclockwise pattern.

The varying **density** (mass per unit volume) of sea water affects deep ocean currents. Sea water that is colder and saltier is denser than sea water that is warmer or more dilute.[1] Thus, colder ocean water sinks

---

[1] Recall that the density of water increases with decreasing temperature down to 4°C.

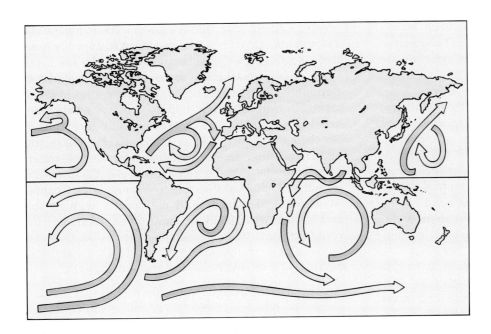

Figure 54–16 The basic pattern of surface ocean currents is caused largely by the action of winds. The main ocean current flow—clockwise in the Northern Hemisphere and counterclockwise in the Southern Hemisphere—results partly from the Coriolis effect.

and flows under warmer water, producing currents far below the surface. Deep ocean currents often travel in different directions and at different speeds than surface currents, in part because the Coriolis effect is more pronounced at greater depths.

The position of land masses also affects oceanic circulation. The oceans are not uniformly distributed over the globe (Figure 54–17). The Southern Hemisphere contains much more water than the Northern Hemisphere. Therefore, the potential circumpolar (around the pole) flow of water in the Southern Hemisphere is almost unimpeded by land masses.

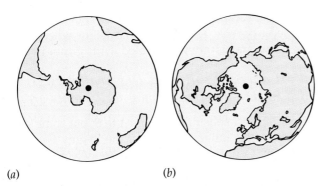

(a)   (b)

Figure 54–17 The Southern (a) and Northern (b) Hemispheres have greatly differing proportions of land and water, with far more water in the Southern Hemisphere. As a result, ocean currents are more free to flow in a circumpolar manner in the Southern Hemisphere.

Climate Results from Patterns of Air and Water Movement

Average temperature, temperature extremes, precipitation, the seasonal distribution of precipitation, day length, and season length are the most important dimensions of climate affecting living organisms. Latitude and the inclination of Earth on its axis determine day length, season length, and, to a large degree, temperature. Differences in precipitation are more subtly determined and depend upon several factors. Variations in these climatic factors produce the biomes such as tundra, desert, rain forest, and grassland (see Chapter 51).

The heavy-rainfall areas of the tropics result mainly from the equatorial upwelling of moisture-laden air. High water surface temperatures encourage the evaporation of vast quantities of water from tropical oceans, and prevailing winds blow the resulting moist air over land masses. Heating of the air by land surfaces warmed by the sun causes moist air to rise. As it rises, the air cools and moisture condenses from water vapor to a liquid and falls as precipitation. The air eventually returns to Earth on either side of the equator between the Tropics of Cancer and Capricorn (between the latitudes 23.5 degrees North and 23.5 degrees South). By then most of its moisture has precipitated, and the dry air returns to the equator. This makes little biological difference over the ocean, but the lack of moisture in this returning air produces some of the great tropical deserts, such as the Sahara Desert.

Air also dries during long journeys over land masses. Near the windward (side from which the wind blows) coasts of continents, rainfall may be heavy. However, in the temperate zones (the areas between the tropics and the polar zones), continental interiors are usually dry, because they are far from oceans that replenish water in the air that passes over them.

Moisture is also removed from air by mountains, which cause air masses to rise. If prevailing winds blow onto a mountain range from the ocean, precipitation occurs primarily on the windward slopes of the mountains. This situation occurs on the North American west coast, where precipitation falls on the western slopes of the mountains. Downwind (in this case, east of the mountain range), a low-precipitation **rain shadow** develops, often producing semi-arid grasslands or deserts (Figure 51–5).

Thus, some of the regional differences in worldwide precipitation result from the drying of air as it returns to more equatorial areas, some from long travel over continents and some from cooling produced by mountainous regions.

Many variations in the overall climatic conditions occur in any habitat

Differences in elevation, in the steepness and direction of slopes, and in exposure to prevailing winds may produce local variations in climate known as **microclimates,** which can be quite different from their overall surroundings. The microclimate is really most important to a living organism, because the microclimate of its habitat is the climate that an organism actually experiences and with which it must cope.

Sometimes it is possible for organisms to substantially modify their own microclimate and make it more favorable for their existence. For instance, trees modify the local climate within a forest so that in the summer the temperature is usually lower and the relative humidity is higher than that outside the forest. The temperature and humidity beneath the litter of the forest floor differ still more; in the summer it is cooler and moister than the surrounding forest. As another example, many desert-dwelling animals burrow to survive surface climatic conditions that would kill them in minutes. The cooler daytime microclimate in their burrows permits them to survive until night, when the surface cools off and they can leave their burrows to forage or hunt.

Soil Factors Affect Living Organisms

Soil is the ground underfoot, a thin layer of Earth's crust that has been modified by the natural action of various agents such as weather and organisms (see Chapter 34). Soil is composed of four distinct elements (mineral particles, organic matter, water, and air). The plants, animals, and microorganisms that inhabit the soil and interact with it continually cycle minerals from the soil to living organisms and back to the soil.

It is easy to take soil for granted. We walk on it throughout our lives, but rarely do we stop to think about how important it is to living things. Vast numbers and kinds of organisms inhabit soil and depend on it for shelter and food. Plants anchor themselves in soil and from it they receive essential minerals and water. Thirteen of the 16 different elements essential for plant growth are obtained directly from the soil (see Chapter 34). Terrestrial plants could not survive without soil and because we depend on plants for our food, humans could not exist without soil either.

Soil occurs in layers called soil horizons

A vertical slice through many soils reveals that they are organized into horizontal layers called **soil horizons,** each of which has a specific composition and special properties. A **soil profile,** which is a section through the soil from the surface to the parent rock, reveals the horizons (Figure 54–18).

The uppermost layer of soil, the **O-horizon,** is rich in organic material. Plant litter, including dead leaves and stems, accumulates in the O-horizon and gradually decays. The O-horizon is often completely absent in desert soils, but it may be the dominant layer in certain organic-rich grassland and deciduous forest soils.

Just beneath the O-horizon is the topsoil, or **A-horizon,** which is dark and rich in accumulated humus. The A-horizon has a granular texture and, in areas with substantial precipitation, is somewhat nutrient-poor as a result of the gradual loss of many nutrients to deeper layers by leaching.

The **B-horizon,** the light-colored subsoil below the A-horizon, is often a zone in which minerals that were leached out of topsoil and litter accumulate. The B-horizon is often rich in iron and aluminum compounds and clay.

Beneath the B-horizon is the layer that borders the solid parent rock, the **C-horizon,** which contains weathered pieces of rock. The C-horizon is below where most roots grow and is often saturated with groundwater.

Soil pH affects a soil's nutrient availability, which in turn determines how well plants grow

The pH of most soils ranges from 4 to 8, but some soils are outside this range. The soil of the Pygmy Forest in Mendocino County, California, is extremely acidic (pH of 2.8 to 3.9). On the other hand, certain saline soils in Death Valley, California, have a pH of 8.5.

Soil pH affects the plants and other organisms living in the soil and is in turn influenced by those organisms. Plants are affected by soil pH, in part because the solubility of different minerals varies with differences

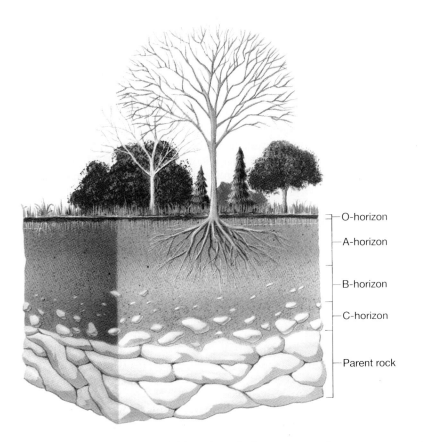

Figure 54–18   A typical soil profile, showing four main layers, or horizons. The O-horizon is accumulated organic litter at the surface, the A-horizon is the topsoil, the B-horizon is the subsoil, and the C-horizon is a transition area between soil and parent rock. Not all soils have all four horizons.

in pH (Figure 54–19). Soluble mineral elements can be absorbed by the plant, whereas insoluble forms cannot. At a lower pH, for example, aluminum and manganese become so soluble in soil water that they are sometimes toxic to plants. (They are absorbed by the roots in greater concentrations than are good for the plant.) Other mineral salts essential for plant growth, such as calcium phosphate, become less soluble at higher pH's.

Soil pH greatly affects the availability of nutrients. An acidic soil has less ability to bind positively charged ions; as a consequence, certain mineral ions essential for plant growth, such as potassium (K^+), are leached more readily from acidic soil. The optimal pH for most plant growth is 6.5 to 7.5, because most nutrients essential for plants are both soluble and available in that pH range.

The soil pH is affected by the type of plants growing in it. Soil litter composed of the needles of conifers, for example, contains acids that leach into the soil, lowering its pH.

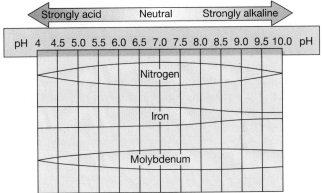

Figure 54–19   The availability of different essential mineral nutrients for absorption by roots of plants varies with changes in pH. For example, nitrogen is most available at neutral pH's, whereas molybdenum is most available at alkaline pH's. Although iron is most available at acidic pH's, if phosphate is present in an acidic soil, it forms an insoluble complex with iron that makes iron unavailable to plants.

SUMMARY

I. Biogeochemical cycles are the cycling of matter from the environment to living things and back to the environment.
   A. Carbon enters plants, algae, and cyanobacteria as CO_2, which is incorporated into organic molecules by photosynthesis. Cellular respiration by plants, by animals that eat plants, and by decomposers returns CO_2 to the

atmosphere, making it available for producers again.
   B. The nitrogen cycle has five steps.
      1. Nitrogen fixation is the conversion of nitrogen gas to ammonia (biological fixation) or nitrate.
      2. Nitrification is the conversion of ammonia to nitrate, one of the main forms of nitrogen used by plants.

3. Assimilation is the biological conversion of nitrates or ammonia to proteins and other nitrogen-containing compounds by plants; the conversion of plant proteins into animal proteins is also part of assimilation.

4. Ammonification is the conversion of organic nitrogen to ammonia.

5. Denitrification converts nitrate to nitrogen gas.

C. The phosphorus cycle has no biologically important gaseous compounds.

1. Phosphorus erodes from rock as inorganic phosphate, which is absorbed from the soil by the roots of plants.

2. Phosphorus enters other living things through the food chain and is released back into the environment as inorganic phosphate by decomposers.

3. Phosphorus can be lost from biological cycles for millions of years when it washes into the ocean and is deposited in sea beds.

D. The hydrologic cycle, which continually renews the supply of water that is so essential to life, involves an exchange of water between the land, the atmosphere, and living things.

1. Water enters the atmosphere by evaporation and transpiration and leaves the atmosphere as precipitation.

2. On land, water filters through the ground or runs off to lakes, rivers, and oceans.

II. Energy flows through an ecosystem in a linear direction, from the sun to producer to consumer to decomposer. Much of this energy is converted to less useful heat as the energy moves from one organism to another.

A. Trophic relationships may be expressed as food chains, or more realistically, as food webs, which show the multitude of alternative pathways that energy may take among the producers, consumers, and decomposers of an ecosystem.

B. Ecological pyramids express the progressive reduction in numbers of organisms, biomass, and energy found in successively higher trophic levels.

C. The gross primary productivity of an ecosystem is the rate at which energy accumulates as biomass during photosynthesis. Net primary productivity is the energy that remains (as biomass) after cellular respiration.

III. The unique planetary environment of Earth makes life possible.

A. Sunlight is the primary (almost the sole) source of energy available to the biosphere.

1. Of the solar energy that reaches Earth, 30% is immediately reflected away and the remaining 70% is absorbed.

2. Ultimately, all absorbed solar energy is radiated into space as infrared (heat) radiation.

B. A combination of Earth's roughly spherical shape and the tilted angle of its axis concentrates solar energy at the equator and dilutes solar energy at the poles.

1. The tropics are therefore hotter and less variable in climate than temperate and polar areas.

2. Seasons are determined by the inclination of Earth's axis and the distance of Earth from the sun, which varies during the year.

C. Atmospheric heat transfer from the equator to the poles produces movement of warm air toward the poles and cool air toward the equator, thus moderating the climate.

D. Surface ocean currents result from prevailing winds. Other factors that contribute to ocean currents include the Coriolis effect, the varying density of water, and the position of land masses.

E. Precipitation is greatest where warm air passes over the ocean, absorbing moisture, and then is cooled, such as when humid air is forced upward by mountains. Deserts develop in the rain shadows of mountain ranges or in continental interiors.

F. Soil organisms are important in recycling nutrients. In a balanced ecosystem, the minerals removed from the soil are returned when plants or animals that eat plants die and are decomposed by microorganisms.

POST-TEST

1. A community and its environment best defines a(an) _____.

2. The movement of matter in ecosystems is _____, whereas the movement of energy is _____.

3. Carbon dioxide enters living organisms by the biological process of _____; carbon dioxide is returned to the atmosphere by the biological process of _____ _____.

4. Most nitrogen fixation is performed by microorganisms, especially mutualistic associations between _____ and _____.

5. Ammonia is oxidized to nitrate by _____ bacteria.

6. The _____ cycle does not have a gaseous component.

7. The global recycling of water is called the _____.

8. Each level in a food chain is called a _____ level.

9. In a food chain, primary producers are eaten by _____ _____.

10. A _____ _____ is a complex of interconnected food chains in an ecosystem.

11. The three types of ecological pyramids are the pyramids of _____, _____, and _____.

12. The quantitative estimate of the total mass, or amount, of living material in an area at a particular time is called _____.

13. Net primary productivity equals gross primary productivity minus _____ _____.

14. Current plant biomass is called the _____ _____.

15. The warmth and constancy of equatorial climates result mostly from the _____ direction at which sunlight falls upon their surface.

16. The _____ _____, which results from the rota-

tion of Earth, displaces the paths of atmospheric and oceanic currents to the right (Northern Hemisphere) and the left (Southern Hemisphere).

17. Mountain ranges may produce downwind arid _____ _____.

18. Local variation in a climate is called a _____.

19. Soil is often organized into layers called _____.

20. The idea that Earth's living things and abiotic environment are able to maintain a climate and chemical composition that are favorable to life is known as the _____ _____.

REVIEW QUESTIONS

1. Why is the cycling of matter essential to the continuance of life on Earth?
2. Why is the concept of a food web generally preferable to that of a food chain?
3. What is the simplest stable ecosystem that you can imagine?
4. Suggest a possible food chain that might have an inverted pyramid of numbers (that is, greater numbers of living organisms at higher trophic levels than at lower trophic levels).
5. Is it possible to have an inverted pyramid of energy? Why or why not?
6. What determines the temperature of Earth? How might this temperature balance be disturbed?
7. What basic forces determine the circulation of Earth's atmosphere? Describe the general directions of atmospheric circulation.
8. What forces produce the main ocean currents?
9. What conditions produce precipitation? What are some of the factors that produce areas of precipitation extremes such as rain forests and deserts?
10. Why might industrial polluters think the Gaia hypothesis provides justification for them to pollute the air, water, and soil indefinitely?

RECOMMENDED READINGS

Brewer, R. *The Science of Ecology.* Saunders College Publishing, Philadelphia, 1988. A readable general textbook on the principles of ecology, including ecosystem ecology.

Cousins, S. Ecologists build pyramids again. *New Scientist,* Vol. 106, 4 July 1985. An analysis of the value of ecological pyramids in understanding energy flow through ecosystems.

Gilliland, M. W. A study of nitrogen-fixing biotechnologies for corn in Mexico. *Environment,* Vol. 30, No. 3, April 1988. Explains the potential benefit of engineering nitrogen-fixing bacteria to provide nitrogen for crops such as corn.

Joseph, L. E. *Gaia: The Growth of an Idea.* St. Martin's Press, New York, 1990. Explains the Gaia hypothesis.

Pimm, S. L., J. H. Lawton, and J. E. Cohen. Food web patterns and their consequences. *Nature,* Vol. 350, April 25, 1991. A review article on current ecological knowledge of food webs.

Schneider, S. H. Debating Gaia. *Environment,* Vol. 32, No. 4, May 1990. Reviews the Gaia view of a self-regulating Earth.

❏

Humans in the Environment

Homo sapiens has been present on Earth for only the past 200,000 years, which is a brief span of time compared with the age of our planet (some 4.6 billion years). Despite our relatively short tenure on Earth, our biological success has been unparalleled. Our numbers have increased dramatically—the human population is expected to surpass 6 billion by 1998—and we have expanded our biological range, moving into almost every habitat on Earth.

Wherever we have gone, we have altered the environment and shaped it to meet our needs. In only a few generations we have transformed the face of Earth, placed a great strain on Earth's resources and resilience, and profoundly affected other life forms. Thus, the impact of humans on the environment merits

Earth Day 1990, Washington, D.C.
(Joanna Pinnes)

special study in biology, not merely because we ourselves are humans but because our impact on the rest of the biosphere has been so extensive.

Humans do not live alone on Earth, nor are we above the laws of nature—our actions do have consequences. We have many partners who share Earth with us, and we would not live long without them. Thus, one of our principal goals is to identify ways to avoid upsetting the delicate balance of the biological systems that support us.

Many environmental concerns exist today—too many to be considered in a single chapter. We therefore focus our attention on four very serious environmental issues—declining biological diversity, deforestation, global climate change, and ozone depletion in the stratosphere.

After you have studied this chapter, you should be able to

1. Distinguish between threatened, endangered, and extinct species.
2. List six causes of declining biological diversity and tell which one is most important.
3. Give examples of in situ and ex situ conservation measures.
4. State at least three reasons why forests are disappearing today.
5. Discuss the ecological benefits of forests.
6. Explain how greenhouse gases contribute to global warming.

7. Describe how global warming may affect sea level, precipitation patterns, living organisms (including humans), and food production.
8. Give examples of ways to prevent, mitigate, and adapt to global warming.
9. Distinguish between ozone in the troposphere and ozone in the stratosphere.
10. Explain how CFCs and other industrial chemicals destroy stratospheric ozone.
11. Cite the potential effects of ozone destruction in the stratosphere.

SPECIES ARE DISAPPEARING FROM EARTH AT AN ALARMING RATE

Extinction, the death of a species, occurs when the last individual member of a species dies (see Chapter 19). Extinction is an irreversible loss, because once a species is extinct it can never reappear. Biological extinction is the eventual fate of all species, much as death is the eventual fate of all individual organisms.

Although extinction is a natural biological process, it can be greatly accelerated by human activities. The burgeoning human population has forced us to spread into almost all areas of Earth, and whenever humans invade an area, the habitats of many plants and animals are disrupted or destroyed, which can lead to their extinction. For example, recall the dusky seaside sparrow, a small bird that became extinct in 1987 largely because of the destruction of its habitat (see Chapter 19).

Currently, Earth's biological diversity is decreasing at an alarming rate (Table 55–1). Conservation biologists estimate that at least one species becomes extinct each day, and a substantial portion of Earth's biological diversity is likely to be eliminated within the next few decades. As many as one fourth of the higher plant families[1] may be extinct by the end of the 21st century, and countless animal species that depend upon those plants for food and habitat will probably become extinct as well.

Some biologists fear that we are entering the greatest period of mass extinction in Earth's history, but the current mass extinction differs from those of previous periods in several respects. First, it is directly attributable to human activities. Second, it is occurring in a tremendously compressed period of time (just a few decades as opposed to millions of years). Perhaps even more sobering, larger numbers of plant species are becoming extinct than in previous mass extinctions. Because plants are the base of the food chain, the extinction of animals that depend on plants cannot be far behind.

A species is **endangered** when its numbers are so severely reduced that it is in danger of becoming extinct. When extinction is less imminent but the population of a particular species is still quite small, the species is said to be **threatened.** Endangered and threatened species represent a decline in biological diversity because their genetic variability is severely diminished. Because long-term survival and evolution depend upon genetic diversity, endangered and threatened species are at greater risk of extinction than species with greater genetic variability.

Species Become Endangered and Extinct for a Variety of Reasons

A number of human activities contribute to species endangerment and extinction. These include the destruction or modification of a habitat and pollution of the environment. Humans also upset the delicate balance of living organisms in a given area by introducing new, exotic species or by controlling pests or predators. Hunting and commercial harvest are also factors.

The majority of species facing extinction today are endangered because of destruction of their habitats by human activities (Figure 55–1). We demolish habitats when we build roads, parking lots, and buildings; clear forests to grow crops or graze domestic animals; and log forests for timber. We drain marshes to build on and thus convert aquatic habitats to terrestrial ones, and we flood terrestrial habitats when we build dams. Because most organisms depend completely on a particular type of environment, habitat destruction reduces their biological range and ability to survive.

---

[1] Recall that a family is a level of organization in classification. A family consists of a number of related genera, each of which consists of a number of related species. When a family becomes extinct, all the species of all the genera comprising that family cease to exist.

Table 55–1

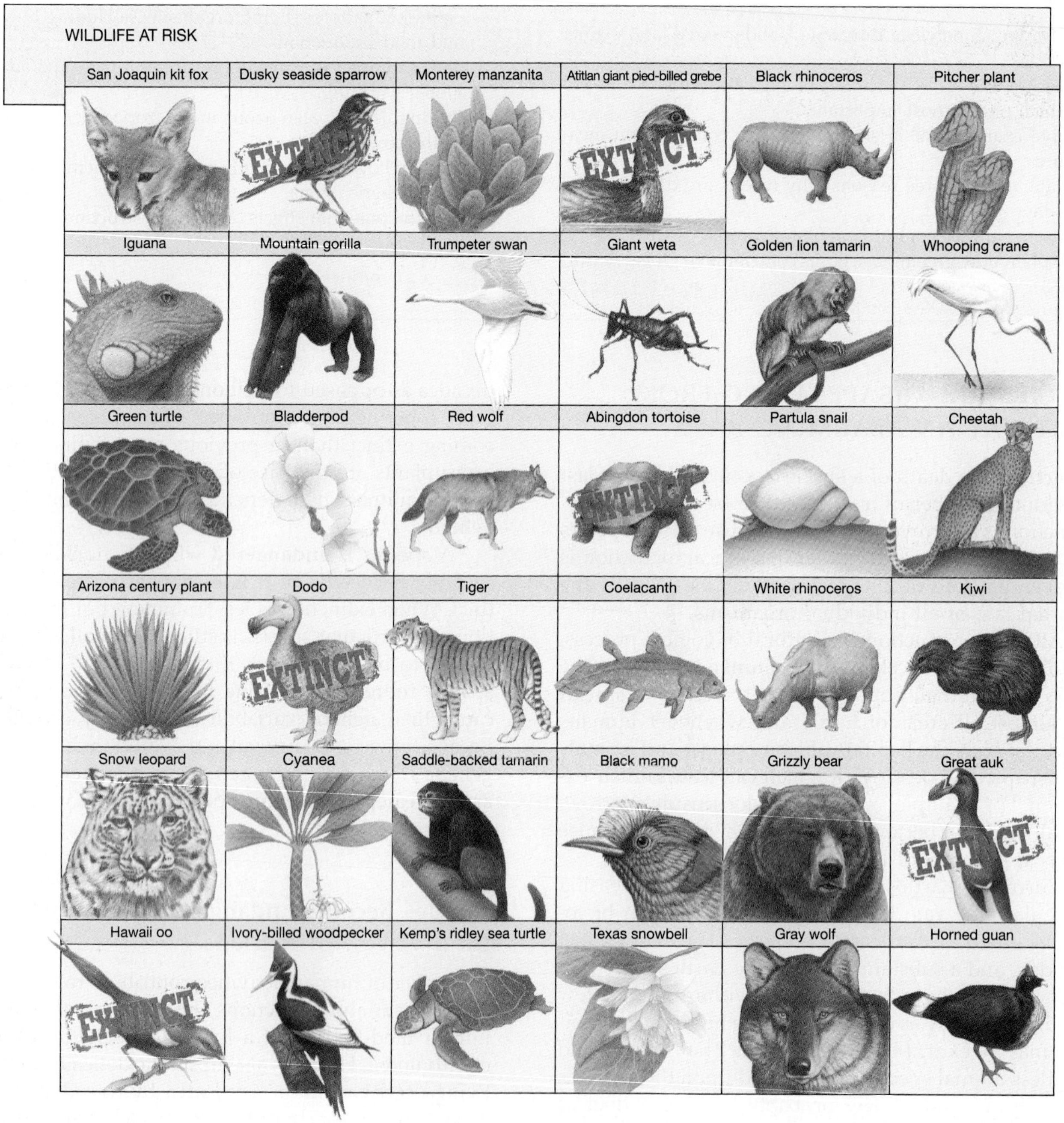
WILDLIFE AT RISK
San Joaquin kit fox
Dusky seaside sparrow
EXTINCT
Monterey manzanita
Atitlan giant pied-billed grebe
EXTINCT
Black rhinoceros
Pitcher plant
Iguana
Mountain gorilla
Trumpeter swan
Giant weta
Golden lion tamarin
Whooping crane
Green turtle
Bladderpod
Red wolf
Abingdon tortoise
EXTINCT
Partula snail
Cheetah
Arizona century plant
Dodo
EXTINCT
Tiger
Coelacanth
White rhinoceros
Kiwi
Snow leopard
Cyanea
Saddle-backed tamarin
Black mamo
Grizzly bear
Great auk
EXTINCT
Hawaii oo
EXTINCT
Ivory-billed woodpecker
Kemp's ridley sea turtle
Texas snowbell
Gray wolf
Horned guan

Even habitats that are left undisturbed and natural are modified by human activities that produce acid precipitation, ozone depletion, and climate change. Acid precipitation is thought to have contributed to the decline of large stands of forest trees and to the biological death of many freshwater lakes. Because ozone in the upper atmosphere shields the ground from large amounts of the sun's harmful ultraviolet radiation, ozone depletion in the upper atmosphere represents a very real threat to all terrestrial life. Global climate change, which is caused in part by carbon dioxide released when fossil fuels are burned, is another threat. Such habitat modifications particularly reduce the biological diversity of species with extremely narrow and rigid environmental requirements. The production of other types of pollutants also adversely affects wildlife (Figure 55–2). Such pollutants include industrial and agricultural chemicals, organic pollutants from sewage,

Figure 55–1 Baby loggerhead sea turtles crawl toward the ocean after hatching. Loggerheads are endangered because development of coastal shorelines in the southeastern United States has destroyed their nesting sites. Female loggerheads come ashore on sandy beaches in South Carolina to lay their eggs. (Connie Toops)

(*a*)

Figure 55–2 A common loon gives her chicks a ride. Pollution, including mercury contamination, has been strongly implicated in the decline of the common loon. (Jean F. Stoick/Dembinsky Photo Associates)

(*b*)

Figure 55–3 The introduction of exotic species often threatens native species. (*a*) *Euglandina rosea* hunting for prey, which may include (*b*) *Partula aurantia*. After this carnivorous snail was introduced on Moorea, it unexpectedly started consuming native *Partula* species. (*a*, Dr. James J. Murray, University of Virginia; *b*, Robert Thorne, Claremont Graduate School Botanical Gardens)

acid wastes seeping from mines, and thermal pollution from the heated waste water of industrial plants.

The introduction of a foreign, or exotic, species into an area where it is not native often upsets the balance among the organisms living in that area. The foreign species may compete with native species for food or habitat or may prey on them. Generally, an introduced competitor or predator causes a greater negative effect on local organisms than do native competitors or predators. Although exotic species may be introduced into new areas by natural means, humans are usually responsible for such introductions, either knowingly or accidentally.

Many examples exist of the introduction of exotic species that have caused local organisms to become endangered or extinct. In 1977 a carnivorous snail was introduced in Moorea, an island in French Polynesia, as

a way to control another snail species that had been introduced by humans and had become a pest (Figure 55–3). The newly introduced species unexpectedly started consuming native snail species in large numbers. As a result, six of the seven native species originally present in Moorea are no longer found in the wild and exist only as small captive populations.

Islands are particularly susceptible to the introduction of exotic species (see Focus on the Lesson of New Zealand). For example, Abingdon Island, one of the Galapagos Islands off the coast of South America, was home to an endemic (found nowhere else) giant tortoise. In 1957 several fishermen introduced goats to Abingdon Island, and within 5 years the Abingdon tortoise was extinct. The goats, with no natural predators on the island, had greatly increased in number and had eaten the tortoises' food. In Hawaii, the introduction of

FOCUS ON

The Lesson of New Zealand

Although the effect of humans on the environment is acknowledged to be considerable, few places exist in the world where human occupation is recent and where the history and impact of our occupation are well known. New Zealand provides an interesting exception. This large archipelago was first occupied by the Maoris about 1000 years ago, and their invasion was followed some 800 years later by European colonization. As a result, we know much about the impact of human settlement on the living organisms of New Zealand.

New Zealand separated from the ancient southern continent of Gondwana before it could be invaded by snakes and placental mammals, about 70 million years ago (see Chapter 20). As a result, the animal life of New Zealand became dominated by birds. During their evolution in this isolated environment, the birds became trusting in nature, many became weak fliers, and others became large and flightless (for example, the moas and kiwis). Thus, when the first Maori settlers arrived, they found a land that contained a unique assemblage of animals that were easily hunted.

The arrival of these first humans had a dramatic impact on New Zealand. Not only did they introduce hunting to the islands, but they also brought dogs, rats, and agriculture. For the first time the birds had to contend with mammalian predation, against which they were poorly adapted, and human-induced habitat modification. The birds had little chance to adapt. By the time Europeans arrived, at least 35 species (39%) of New Zealand's unique birds had become extinct.

With active European settlement, which began in the 1840s, forest clearance accelerated so that now only 23% of New Zealand's original forest remains. The newly cleared land was given over to a pastoral, European style of agriculture. In addition, a huge range of exotic biota was purposely introduced to New Zealand; at present some 800 species of plants, 39 species of birds, and 33 species of mammals are established. Extinctions of endemic birds continued in the face of increased hunting pressure and the efficiency of European firearms, the further reduction of the forests, the damaging impact of browsing mammals on the surviving native vegetation, and the introduction of a larger array of predatory mammals. During the period of European settlement, a further nine species (10%) of New Zealand's endemic land birds have become extinct.

New Zealand has not been alone in its experience. But because its history is so well known, it provides a dramatic example of how completely and rapidly humans can alter major ecosystems. The biological lessons of New Zealand are clear. Ecosystems are complex, dynamic entities that have their own unique evolutionary history. However, major disruption can often lead to the unraveling of their fabric. Increasingly, humans have become the primary cause of such disruptions so that now our species has become a major force in shaping the future of Earth and its ecosystems. Although we have the necessary knowledge to safeguard the ecological integrity of our planet, do we have the wisdom and will to use it responsibly? Only time will tell.

Contributed by Alex L. A. Middleton, Department of Zoology, University of Guelph, Guelph, Ontario, Canada.

---

mouplan sheep has imperiled both the mamane tree (because the sheep eat it) and a species of honeycreeper, an endemic bird that relies on the tree for food.

Sometimes species become endangered or extinct as a result of deliberate efforts to eradicate or control their numbers. Many of these species prey on game animals or sometimes on livestock. Populations of large predators like the wolf, mountain lion, and grizzly bear have been decimated by ranchers, hunters, and government agents. Predators of game animals and livestock are not the only animals vulnerable to human control efforts. Some animals are killed because their lifestyles cause problems for humans. The Carolina parakeet, a beautiful green, red, and yellow bird endemic to the southeastern United States, was extinct by 1920, exterminated by farmers because it ate fruit. Prairie dogs and pocket gophers, other examples of animals killed by humans because of their lifestyles, have been poisoned and trapped because their burrows weaken the ground on which unwary cattle graze. If the cattle step into the burrows, they may be crippled. As a result of sharply decreased numbers of prairie dogs and pocket gophers, the black-footed ferret, the natural predator of these animals, has not been found in the wild in the United States since 1986. (A successful captive breeding program enabled scientists to release 50 black-footed ferrets to the Wyoming prairie in September 1991.)

In addition to hunting as a means of predator and pest control, hunting is done for three other reasons: (1) **commercial hunters** kill animals for profit, for example, by selling their fur; (2) **sport hunters** kill animals for recreation; and (3) **subsistence hunters** kill

Figure 55–4 A game warden in Kenya carries one of many elephant tusks confiscated from poachers. The tusks were later destroyed by the Kenyan government. (Steve Turner/Oxford Scientific Films © 1993 Animals Animals)

animals for food. Subsistence hunting caused the extinction of certain species in the past but is not a major cause of extinction today, mainly because so few human groups still rely on subsistence hunting for their food supply. Sport hunting, also a major factor in the extinction of animals in the past (for example, the passenger pigeon), is now strictly controlled in most countries.

Commercial hunting, however, continues to endanger a number of larger animals such as the tiger, cheetah, and snow leopard, whose beautiful furs are quite valuable. Rhinoceroses are slaughtered for their horns (used for dagger handles in the Middle East and as a medicine and an aphrodisiac in Asia) and bears for their gallbladders (used in Asian medicine to treat ailments ranging from indigestion to hemorrhoids). Although these animals are protected by law, the demand for their products on the black market has caused them to be hunted illegally (Figure 55–4).

In contrast to commercial hunting, in which the target organism is killed, **commercial harvest** is the removal of the *live* organism from the wild. Organisms that are commercially harvested end up in zoos, aquaria, and pet stores. Several million birds are commercially harvested each year for the pet trade, but, unfortunately, many of them die in transit and many more die from improper treatment after they are in their owners' homes. At least nine bird species are now threatened or endangered because of commercial harvest. Although it is illegal to capture endangered animals from the wild, a thriving black market exists, mainly because collectors in the United States, Europe, and Japan pay extremely large amounts to obtain rare

tropical birds. Imperial Amazon macaws, for example, fetch up to $30,000 each.

Animals are not the only organisms threatened by commercial harvest. A number of unique or rare plants have been collected from the wild to the point that they are classified as endangered. These include carnivorous plants, certain cacti, and orchids.

The Two Types of Efforts to Save Wildlife Are In Situ and Ex Situ Conservation

In situ conservation, which includes the establishment of parks and reserves, concentrates on preserving biological diversity *in the wild*. A high priority of in situ conservation is the identification and protection of sites with a great deal of biological diversity. With increasing demands on land, however, in situ conservation cannot guarantee the preservation of all types of biological diversity. **Ex situ conservation** involves conserving biological diversity *in human-controlled settings*. Breeding captive species in zoos and storing seed of genetically diverse plant crops are examples of ex situ conservation.

Protecting wildlife habitats helps preserve biological diversity

Many nations are beginning to appreciate the need to protect their biological heritage and have set aside areas for wildlife habitats. There are currently more than 3000 national parks, sanctuaries, refuges, forests, and other protected areas throughout the world. Some of these areas have been set aside to protect specific endangered species. The first such refuge, established in 1903 at Pelican Island, Florida, was set aside to protect the brown pelican. Today the National Wildlife Refuge System of the United States has land set aside in more than 400 refuges, although most of the land lies in Alaska.

Many protected areas have multiple uses. National parks may serve recreational needs, for example, whereas national forests may be open for logging, grazing, and farming operations. The mineral rights to many refuges are privately owned, and some have had oil, gas, and other mineral development. For example, the D'Arbonne Wildlife Refuge in Louisiana, which is a sanctuary for 145 species of birds, has soil and water pollution from natural gas wells. Hunting is allowed in more than half of the wildlife refuges in the United States, and military exercises are conducted in several of them. The Air Force, for example, conducts low-flying jet exercises and live fire exercises over portions of the Prieta Wildlife Refuge, an Arizona refuge established for bighorn sheep.

Certain parts of the world are critically short of protected areas. In addition to tropical rain forests, pro-

(a)

(b)

Figure 55–5   The University of Wisconsin–Madison Arboretum has pioneered restoration ecology. (*a*) The restoration of the prairie was at an early stage in November, 1935. (*b*) The prairie as it looks today. This picture was taken at approximately the same location as the 1935 photograph.   (Courtesy of Virginia Kline, University of Wisconsin–Madison Arboretum)

tected areas are needed in the tropical grasslands and savannahs of Brazil and Australia and in dry forests widely scattered around the world. The wildlife in tropical deserts is underprotected in northern Africa and Argentina, and the wildlife of many islands and lakes needs protection.

Restoring damaged or destroyed habitats is the goal of restoration ecology

Scientists can reclaim disturbed lands and convert them into areas with high levels of biological diversity. One of the most famous examples of ecological restoration has been carried out since 1934 by the University of Wisconsin–Madison Arboretum (Figure 55–5). During that time, several different communities native to Wisconsin were carefully developed on damaged agricultural land. These native communities include a tallgrass prairie, a xeric (dry) prairie, and several types of pine and maple forests.

Restoration ecology establishes wildlife habitats but also has additional benefits such as the regeneration of soil damaged by agriculture or mining. The disadvantages of restoration ecology include the amount of time it requires to restore an area and the expense. Nonetheless, restoration ecology is an important aspect of wildlife conservation.

Zoos, aquaria, and botanical gardens often make attempts to save species on the brink of extinction

Eggs may be collected from the wild, or the remaining few animals may be captured and bred in zoos and other research environments. Special techniques, such as artificial insemination, embryo transfer, and foster parenting, are used to increase the number of offspring (Figure 55–6).

A few spectacular successes have occurred in captive breeding programs, in which large enough num-

Figure 55–6 A gaur calf and its surrogate mother, a Holstein cow. The gaur, a wild ox native to India, is an endangered species. This young calf was transferred as an embryo to the uterus of the Holstein, where it completed development. The young animal is cared for by its foster mother. (Photo by King's Island Wild Animal Habitat, courtesy of Dr. Betsy L. Dresser, Cincinnati Zoo and Botanical Garden)

bers of a species have been produced to re-establish small populations in the wild. Whooping cranes, which had reached the critically low population of 15 in 1941, have increased in number to over 100. Conservation biologists are hoping to remove the whooping crane from the endangered species list and classify it as only threatened by the year 2000.

Attempting to save a species on the brink of extinction is extremely expensive. Moreover, zoos, aquaria, and botanical gardens do not have the space to try to save all endangered species. This means that conservation biologists must set priorities as to which species to attempt to save. Clearly, maintaining the natural habitat so that different species never become endangered in the first place is more cost effective.

Seed banks help preserve biological diversity of plants

A number of seed collections, called **seed banks,** have been established around the world. Such collections are able to store a large amount of genetic material in a very small amount of space. Seeds stored in seed banks are safe from habitat destruction. Such seeds have even been used to reintroduce to the wild a plant species that had been eliminated by habitat destruction.

Seed banks do have some disadvantages, however. First, many types of plants, such as potatoes and orchids, cannot be stored as seeds. Second, seeds do not remain viable (alive) indefinitely, so the seeds must be periodically germinated and new seeds harvested.

Also, accidents such as fires or power failures can result in the permanent loss of the genetic diversity represented by the seeds. But perhaps the most important disadvantage of seed banks is that plants stored in this manner remain stagnant in an evolutionary sense; they do not adapt in response to changes in their natural environments. As a result, they may be less fit when they are reintroduced into the wild.

DEFORESTATION IS OCCURRING AT AN UNPRECEDENTED RATE

The destruction of all tree cover in an area is **deforestation.** When forests are harvested or destroyed, they no longer make valuable contributions to the environment or to the people who depend upon them. Tropical forest destruction particularly threatens native people whose cultures and ways of life depend upon the forests. When these people come into conflict with developers and colonizers of forests, they have little political strength or legal recourse and are usually forced off their land. Aside from their own right to exist, when such indigenous tribes are lost, fields as diverse as anthropology and botany suffer. Ethnobotanists, for example, learn medicinal and other uses of plants from native peoples.

Deforestation results in decreasing soil fertility and increasing soil erosion (see Chapter 34). Because poor rural people, both natives and colonizers, depend upon the soil for their livelihood, tropical deforestation contributes to the downward spiral of poverty in which many of these people find themselves. Uncontrolled soil erosion, particularly on steep slopes, can also affect the production of hydroelectric power if silt builds up behind dams. The increased sedimentation of waterways caused by soil erosion can harm fisheries. In drier areas, deforestation can lead to the formation of deserts.

When forest is removed, the total amount of surface runoff into rivers and streams actually increases. However, because this water flow is no longer moderated by forest, the affected region experiences alternating periods of flood and drought.

Deforestation causes the extinction of many plant and animal species. In particular, tropical species often have very limited ranges within a forest, so they are quite vulnerable to habitat destruction or modification. Wildlife in temperate areas, including migratory birds and butterflies, also suffer because of tropical deforestation.

Regional and global climate changes are induced by deforestation. Transpiring trees release substantial amounts of moisture into the air (see Chapter 32). This moisture falls back to Earth in the hydrologic cycle (see Chapter 54). When forest is removed, rainfall declines and droughts become common in that region. Deforestation contributes to an increase in global temperature (discussed below) because deforestation results in release of stored carbon into the atmosphere as carbon dioxide, which causes the air to retain solar heat.

Where and Why Are Forests Disappearing?

During the past 1000 years, forests in temperate areas were slowly cleared for housing and agriculture. Today, however, deforestation in the tropics is occurring much more rapidly and over a much larger area. Most of the remaining undisturbed tropical forest, which is located in the Amazon and Congo River basins of South America and Africa, respectively, is being cleared and burned at a rate unprecedented in human history. Tropical forests are also being destroyed at an extremely rapid rate in southern Asia, Indonesia, Central America, and the Philippines. Ten countries account for 76% of tropical deforestation: Brazil, Indonesia, Zaire, Burma, Colombia, India, Malaysia, Mexico, Nigeria, and Thailand.

The three main causes of deforestation of tropical rainforests are subsistence agriculture, commercial logging, and cattle ranching. **Subsistence agriculture,** in which enough food is produced to feed oneself and one's family, is by far the most important cause, accounting for 60% of tropical deforestation. Other reasons for the destruction of tropical forests include the development of hydroelectric dams and mining.

Subsistence farmers do not own the land that they farm

In many developing countries where tropical rain forests are located, the majority of people do not own the land on which they live and work. Land ownership (and therefore profit) is in the hands of a few. Most subsistence farmers were displaced from traditional farmlands because of the inequitable distribution of land ownership. They have no place to go except into the forest, which they clear to grow food.

Subsistence farmers often follow access roads for loggers. These poor rural people first cut down the forest and allow it to dry, then they burn the area and plant crops immediately after burning; this is known as **slash-and-burn agriculture.** The yield from the first crop is often quite high because the nutrients that were in the trees are available in the soil after the trees are burned. However, soil productivity declines at a rapid rate, so subsequent crops are poor. In a very short time, the people farming the land must move to new forest and repeat the process. Often, cattle ranchers then claim the land for grazing because land that is not rich enough to support crops can support livestock.

Slash-and-burn agriculture done on a small scale with long periods—20 to 100 years—between cycles is actually sustainable. But when *several hundred million people* try to obtain a living in this way, the land cannot lie uncultivated for an adequate recovery period.

Vast tracts of tropical rain forests are being removed by commercial logging

Twenty-one percent of tropical deforestation is the result of commercial logging, mostly for export abroad. Most tropical countries allow commercial logging to proceed at a much faster rate than is sustainable. For example, in Sabah and Sarawak (both part of Malaysia), current logging is removing the forest almost twice as fast as the sustainable rate. If this continues, Malaysia will soon experience shortages of timber and will have to start importing logs. When that happens, Malaysia will have lost future revenues, both from logging and from other forest products.

Cattle ranching also causes deforestation

Approximately 12% of tropical forest destruction occurs to provide open rangeland for cattle (Figure 55–7). After the forests are cleared, cattle can be raised on the land for 6 to 10 years, after which time shrubby plants, known as **scrub savannah,** take over the range. Much of the beef raised on these ranches, which are often owned by foreign companies, is exported to fast-food chains.

Dry tropical forests are being destroyed primarily for use as fuel

Wood—perhaps half of the wood consumption worldwide—is used by much of the developing world for heating and cooking fuel (Figure 55–8). Fuel wood consumption is a greater concern in dry tropical forests—tropical areas subjected to a wet season and a prolonged dry season—than in humid forests.

Often the wood cut for fuel is converted to charcoal,[1] which is then used to power steel, brick, and cement factories. Charcoal production is extremely wasteful; 3.6 metric tons (4 tons) of wood produce only enough charcoal to fuel an average-sized iron smelter for 5 minutes.

---

[1] Partially burning wood in a large kiln from which air is excluded converts the wood into charcoal.

Figure 55–7   Tropical forests are often burned to provide grazing land for cattle exported to countries such as the United States.   (David Cavagnaro)

Figure 55–8   A woman in India lights a cooking fire. Half of the people in the world use wood fires to cook food.   (Inga Spence/Tom Stack & Associates)

THE PRODUCTION OF ATMOSPHERIC POLLUTANTS THAT TRAP SOLAR HEAT IN THE ATMOSPHERE MAY AFFECT EARTH'S CLIMATE

Imagine a world in which beautiful tropical islands, such as the Maldives in the Indian Ocean, disappear forever under the waves. Closer to home, consider the permanent flooding of Louisiana's bayous and the Florida Keys. Imagine the forests in the southern United States dying from high temperatures and drought. Think of the effects of an annual hurricane season that is 1 month longer than it is now. Consider the consequences of tropical pests and diseases spreading northward into the United States and remaining throughout the winter.

Although none of these events has occurred, the possibility exists that some or all of them will take place, possibly even during your lifetime. This is because Earth may become warmer during the next century than it has been for the past 1 million years. Unlike climate changes in the past, which occurred over thousands of years or longer, this change would take place in a matter of decades.

Although most scientists agree that the world will continue to warm, they disagree over how rapidly the warming will proceed, how severe it will be, and where warming will be most pronounced. One of the complications that makes global warming difficult to predict is that certain air pollutants from both natural and human sources actually exert a cooling influence. As a result of these uncertainties, many people, including policymakers, are confused about what should be done.

Greenhouse Gases Cause Global Warming

Carbon dioxide (CO_2) and certain other trace gases, including methane (CH_4), ozone[1] (O_3), nitrous oxide

---

[1] Ozone in the lower atmosphere, the troposphere, is a greenhouse gas as well as a component of smog. Ozone in the upper atmosphere, the stratosphere, provides an important planetary service that is discussed below.

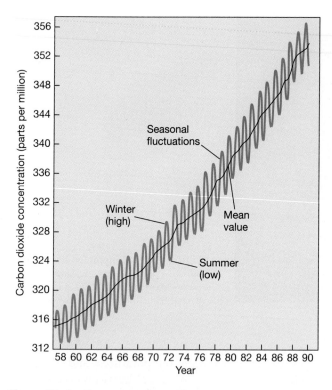

Figure 55–9   The concentration of carbon dioxide in the atmosphere has shown a slow but steady increase for many years. These measurements were taken at the Mauna Loa Observatory, far from urban areas where CO_2 is emitted by factories, power plants, and motor vehicles. (The seasonal fluctuation each year corresponds to winter—a high level of CO_2—and summer—a low level of CO_2—and is caused by greater photosynthesis in summer.)

(N_2O), and chlorofluorocarbons (CFCs), are accumulating in the atmosphere as a result of human activities. The concentration of atmospheric CO_2 has increased from about 280 parts per million (ppm) approximately 200 years ago (before the Industrial Revolution began) to 360 ppm today (Figure 55–9). And it is still increasing, as are the levels of the other trace gases associated with global warming.

For example, every time you drive your car, the combustion of gasoline in the car's engine releases CO_2 and N_2O and triggers the production of tropospheric O_3. Every day as tracts of rain forest are burned in the Amazon, CO_2 is released. CFCs get into the atmosphere from old, leaking refrigerators and air conditioners, and decomposition in landfills is a major source of CH_4.

Global warming occurs because these gases are able to retain infrared radiation (that is, heat) in the atmosphere that normally would dissipate into space from Earth. Thus, the atmosphere warms (Figure 55–10). Some of the heat from the atmosphere is transferred to the oceans and raises their temperature as well. As the atmosphere and oceans warm, the overall temperature of Earth increases. Because CO_2 and other gases trap the

sun's radiation in much the same way that glass does in a greenhouse, the global warming produced in this manner is known as the **greenhouse effect.**

Global Warming Could Alter Food Production, Destroy Forests, Submerge Coastal Areas, and Displace Millions of People

Because the interactions among the atmosphere, the oceans, and the land are too complex and too large to study in the laboratory, climatologists develop models using computer simulations. A model, however, is only as good as the data and assumptions upon which it is based (recall the discussion of ecological models in Chapter 52), and a number of uncertainties are built into our models of global warming. For example, if global warming causes more low-lying clouds to form, they will block some sunlight and decrease the warming trend. On the other hand, global warming may cause more high, thin cirrus clouds to form, which would actually increase the greenhouse effect. As new data about these uncertainties become available, they are used to make the model's predictions more precise.

Current models predict that a doubling of the concentration of CO_2 in the atmosphere will cause the average temperature of Earth to increase by 2°C to 5°C before the end of the next century, although the warming will not be uniform from region to region. At current rates of fossil fuel combustion and deforestation, scientists expect the doubling of CO_2 to occur within the next 50 years. However, the warming trend will be slower than the increasing CO_2 might indicate because the oceans take longer than the atmosphere to absorb heat. The second half of the next century will probably experience greater warming than the first half.

The sea level is expected to rise

If the overall temperature of Earth increases by just a few degrees, major thawing of glaciers and the polar icecaps could occur. In addition, thermal expansion of the oceans will probably occur because water, like other substances, expands when it heats up. These two changes may cause the sea level to rise by as little as 0.2 meter or as much as 2.2 meters by 2050, flooding low-lying coastal areas. Coastal areas that are not actually inundated will be more likely to suffer damage from hurricanes and typhoons. These effects are certainly a cause for concern.

The countries most vulnerable to a rise in the sea level have dense populations that inhabit low-lying river deltas—countries such as Bangladesh, Egypt, Vietnam, and Mozambique. For example, a rising sea level could cause Bangladesh to lose perhaps 25% of its land. Since 1970, at least 300,000 people in Bangladesh

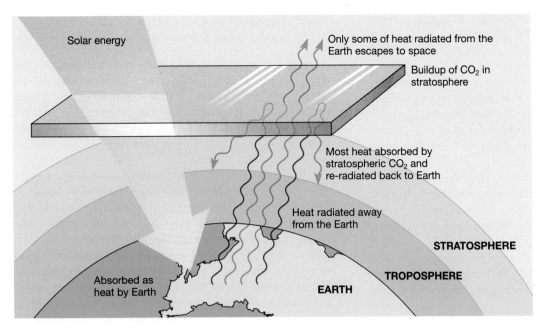

Figure 55–10   How carbon dioxide and the greenhouse effect promote global warming.

have been killed by tropical storms caused by increased flooding and high waves lashing the land. A rising sea level caused by global warming would put even more people at risk in this densely populated nation.

may be more likely to have flooding. The frequency and intensity of storms may also increase. All of these factors could affect the availability and quality of fresh water in many locations. It is projected that arid and semi-arid regions will become even drier and have the greatest water-shortage problems.

Precipitation patterns will probably change

Global warming is also expected to change precipitation patterns, causing some areas to have more frequent droughts (Figure 55–11). At the same time, other areas

Living organisms will probably be affected

Biologists have started to examine some of the potential consequences of global warming on wildlife. Each spe-

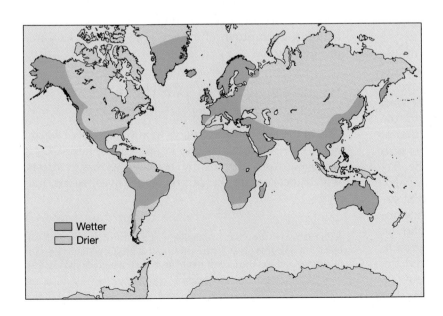

Figure 55–11   One scenario of how precipitation might be altered by warmer global temperatures. This map is based on precipitation rates that occurred thousands of years ago when Earth was warmer.

cies reacts to changes in temperature differently. Some species will undoubtedly become extinct, particularly those with narrow temperature requirements, those confined to small reserves or parks, and those living in fragile ecosystems, whereas other species may survive in greatly reduced numbers and range. Ecosystems considered to be at greatest risk of species loss in the short term are polar seas, coral reefs, mountain ecosystems, coastal wetlands, tundra, and boreal and temperate forests.

Some species may be able to migrate to new environments or adapt to the changing conditions in their present habitat. Also, some species may be unaffected by global warming, whereas others may come out of global warming as winners, with greatly expanded numbers and range. Those considered most likely to prosper include weeds, pests, and disease-carrying organisms that are already common and found in a wide range of environments.

Biologists generally agree that global warming will have an unusually severe impact on plants because they are unable to move about when conditions change. Although their seeds are dispersed, sometimes over long distances, seed dispersal has definite limits in terms of how fast a plant species can migrate. Moreover, soil characteristics, water availability, competition with other species, and human alterations of natural habitats all affect the rate at which plants can move into a new area.

The increase in CO_2 in the atmosphere and the resulting increase in temperature will probably not have a direct adverse effect on human health. Human health will be indirectly affected, however, as such disease carriers as malarial mosquitoes and encephalitis-infected flies expand their range into the newly warm areas. People can also expect more frequent and severe heat waves during summer months.

Agriculture will probably be affected

Global warming will increase problems for agriculture, which is already beset with the challenge of providing enough food for a hungry world without doing irreparable damage to the environment. The rise in sea level will inundate river deltas, which are some of the world's best agricultural land. Certain agricultural pests and disease-causing organisms will probably proliferate. Global warming will also increase the frequency and duration of droughts. To get an idea of how devastating droughts can be, consider the drought experienced in the American grain belt during the summer of 1988. Wheat yields were reduced by 40% and the United States, which is usually the world's largest exporter of grain, used more grain than it produced.

How Should We Deal with Global Warming?

Even if we were to immediately stop polluting the atmosphere with greenhouse gases, Earth would still experience some climate change because of the greenhouse gases that have accumulated during the past 100 years. The amount and severity of global warming depend upon how much additional greenhouse gas we add to the atmosphere.

Three basic ways exist to manage global warming—prevention, mitigation, and adaptation. *Prevention* of global warming can be accomplished by developing ways to prevent the buildup of greenhouse gases in the atmosphere. Prevention is the ultimate and best solution to global warming because it is permanent. *Mitigation*, which involves ways to moderate or postpone global warming, gives us time to pursue other, more permanent solutions to global warming. Further, it gives us time to understand more fully how global warming operates so we can avoid some of its worst consequences. *Adaptation* is responding to changes brought about by global warming. Developing strategies to adapt to climate change assumes that global warming is unavoidable.

We can respond to the threat of global warming by preventing the buildup of greenhouse gases

The development of alternatives to fossil fuels (such as solar energy) offers a permanent solution to the global warming challenge caused by increased CO_2 emissions.[1] Technological innovations that trap CO_2 being emitted from smokestacks would help prevent global warming and yet allow us to use fossil fuels for energy.

Incentives may be required to encourage the development of technological innovations to prevent CO_2 emissions. A tax on greenhouse gases, for example, has been imposed by several nations. Such a tax stimulates emitters to improve efficiency and develop CO_2-free technologies.

We can respond to the threat of global warming by mitigating its effect

One of the most effective ways to mitigate global warming involves forests. As you know, atmospheric CO_2 is removed from the air by actively growing forests, which incorporate the carbon into leaves, stems, and

---

[1] Alternatives to the other greenhouse gases will also have to be developed, but we focus on CO_2 here because it is produced in the greatest quantities and has the largest total effect of all the greenhouse gases.

roots by the process of photosynthesis. On the other hand, deforestation releases CO_2 into the atmosphere as trees decompose or are burned. We can mitigate global warming by planting and maintaining new forests, and some environmentalists have even suggested that developed nations should pay developing nations to maintain their tropical forests. In addition to planting new forests, increasing the energy efficiency of automobiles and appliances would help mitigate global warming by reducing the output of CO_2.

We can respond to the threat of global warming by adapting to its reality

Government planners and social scientists are developing a number of strategies to help us adapt to global warming. People living in coastal areas can be moved inland, away from the dangers of storm surges. This solution has high societal and economic costs, however. An alternative, which is also extremely expensive, is building dikes and levees to protect coastal land. Rivers and canals that spill into the ocean will have to be channeled to protect freshwater and agricultural land from salt water intrusion. The Dutch, who have been doing this sort of thing for several hundred years, are offering their technical expertise to several developing nations threatened by a rise in sea level.

We will also have to adapt to shifting agricultural zones. A number of countries with temperate climates are in the process of evaluating semi-tropical crops to determine the best ones to substitute for traditional crops if/when the climate warms. Drought-resistant strains of lumber trees are being developed by large lumber companies now, because the trees planted today will be harvested in the middle of the next century when global warming may already be well advanced.

OZONE IS DISAPPEARING IN THE STRATOSPHERE

Ozone (O_3) is a form of oxygen that is a human-made pollutant in the troposphere, but a naturally produced, essential component in the stratosphere. The stratosphere, which encircles our planet some 10 to 45 kilometers (6 to 28 miles) above Earth's surface, contains a layer of ozone that shields Earth from much of the ultraviolet radiation coming from the sun (Figure 55–12). If the ozone disappeared from the stratosphere, Earth would become uninhabitable for most forms of life.

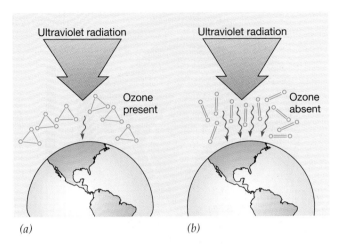

Figure 55–12   Ultraviolet radiation and the ozone layer. (*a*) Ozone absorbs ultraviolet radiation, effectively shielding Earth. (*b*) When ozone is absent, more high-energy ultraviolet radiation penetrates the atmosphere to Earth's surface, where its presence harms living things.

(However, ozone is a problem when it accumulates closer to the ground. Tropospheric ozone is a human-made pollutant; it is a component of photochemical smog, not naturally produced as in the stratosphere. Ozone in the lower atmosphere does not replenish the ozone that has been depleted from the stratosphere because it is converted back to oxygen in a few days.)

The problem of ozone depletion was dramatically demonstrated beginning in 1984 with the discovery of a large hole, or thin spot, in the ozone layer over Antarctica (Figure 55–13). Ozone levels decrease by as much as 67% there each year. A smaller thin spot, or hole, in the stratospheric ozone layer also exists over the Arctic, but probably the most disquieting news is that worldwide levels of stratospheric ozone have been decreasing for several decades. In 1991 a United Nations panel of experts reported that during the 1980s the ozone shield was significantly depleted in the mid-latitudes, even during the summer (when the rate of ozone depletion is lowest). The rate of ozone depletion during the 1980s was roughly three times the rate in the 1970s.

Chemical Destruction of Ozone in the Stratosphere Is Caused by CFCs and Other Industrial Chemicals

The primary culprit responsible for ozone loss in the stratosphere is a group of commercially important compounds called chlorofluorocarbons, or CFCs. CFCs are used as propellants in aerosol cans, as coolants in air conditioners and refrigerators (example—Freon), as

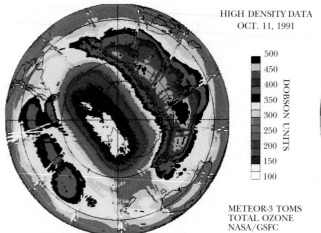

HIGH DENSITY DATA
OCT. 11, 1991

DOBSON UNITS

500
450
400
350
300
250
200
150
100

METEOR-3 TOMS
TOTAL OZONE
NASA/GSFC

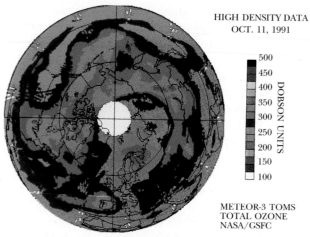

HIGH DENSITY DATA
OCT. 11, 1991

DOBSON UNITS

500
450
400
350
300
250
200
150
100

METEOR-3 TOMS
TOTAL OZONE
NASA/GSFC

Figure 55–13 Maps of the Southern Hemisphere (*left*) and Northern Hemisphere (*right*) show ozone concentrations measured October 11, 1991. The Antarctic ozone hole is located in the lavender and dark purple area at the center of the map on the left. Successively higher ozone concentrations are shown in yellow, green, blue, red, and black (highest). (NASA)

foam for insulation and packaging (example—Styrofoam), and as cleaners in the electronics industry. Additional compounds that also attack ozone include halons (found in many fire extinguishers); methyl bromide (used as a fumigant in agriculture); methyl chloroform (used to degrease metals); and carbon tetrachloride (used in many industrial processes, including the manufacture of pesticides and dyes).

CFCs and similar human-made compounds drift up to the stratosphere, where ultraviolet radiation breaks them down into chlorine, fluorine, and carbon. Under certain conditions found in the stratosphere, chlorine is capable of reacting with ozone, converting it into oxygen (Figure 55–14). The chlorine is not altered by this process; as a result, a single chlorine atom can break down many thousands of ozone molecules.

Ozone Depletion Adversely Affects Living Organisms

Ozone molecules in the stratosphere absorb incoming solar ultraviolet radiation. With depletion of the ozone layer, higher levels of ultraviolet radiation reach the surface of Earth. Excessive exposure to ultraviolet radiation is linked to a number of health problems in humans, including cataracts, skin cancer, and weakened immunity. Substantial scientific evidence also documents crop damage from high levels of ultraviolet radiation.

Scientists are concerned that the ozone hole over Antarctica could possibly damage the plankton that forms the base of the food chain for the oceans of the Southern Hemisphere. A 1992 study confirmed that increased ultraviolet radiation is penetrating the surface waters around Antarctica and that the productivity of

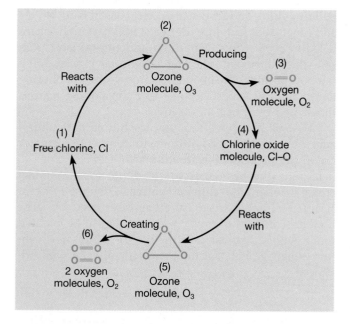

Figure 55–14 The destruction of ozone by free chlorine. Chlorine (1) pulls one of the oxygen atoms away from ozone (2), producing an oxygen molecule, O_2 (3), and a molecule of chlorine oxide (4). The chlorine oxide then reacts with a second molecule of ozone (5) to form two molecules of oxygen (6) and free chlorine (1), which is then available to attack yet another ozone molecule. Thus, for every two ozone molecules that chlorine destroys, three oxygen molecules are produced. Although ozone is continually being formed by natural processes, its rate of formation does not equal its faster rate of destruction.

Antarctic phytoplankton has declined by at least 6% to 12% as a result. If the phytoplankton continues to decline, the food chain of Antarctica, which includes fish, seals, penguins, whales, and vast populations of birds, will collapse.

ENVIRONMENTAL PROBLEMS ARE INTERRELATED

Several connections have been pointed out among the four environmental problems discussed in this chapter. For example, deforestation, global warming, and ozone depletion will likely cause future extinctions. Similarly, any environmental problem you can think of—even if it was not discussed in this chapter—is related to other environmental concerns.

Consider solid waste, which threatens to bury us under mountains of garbage. Solid waste is placed in sanitary landfills, large areas of land that can no longer provide wildlife habitat except for a few species such as rats and gulls. Toxic substances in solid waste often escape into surrounding soil, water, and air, thereby harming wildlife. As organic material decays in landfills, it releases methane, a potent greenhouse gas. Solid waste further contributes to global warming because it contains materials that were discarded rather than reused or recycled. (It requires a great deal of energy to make more materials to replace those that were discarded, and burning fossil fuels to supply that energy produces more greenhouse gases.) Solid waste contributes to both ozone depletion and global warming in that old refrigerators and air conditioners leak CFCs into the atmosphere.

Worldwide environmental deterioration is connected to overpopulation. We have seen that the rate of human population growth is greatest in developing countries (see Chapter 52). However, developed nations are overpopulated as well because they have a high per capita consumption of resources. A single child born in a developed country such as the United States causes a greater impact on the environment and on resource consumption than do a dozen or more children in a developing country. Many natural resources are needed to provide the air conditioners, disposable diapers, cars, video cassette recorders, and other "comforts" of life in developed nations. Thus, the disproportionately large consumption of resources by developed countries affects natural resources and the environment as much as the population explosion in the developing world.

As living organisms, we share much in common with the fate of other life forms on this planet. We are not immune to the environmental damage we have produced. We differ from other organisms, however, in our capacity to reflect on the consequences of our actions and to alter our behavior accordingly. This talent is the key to any hope of ensuring the biosphere's survival.

SUMMARY

I. A reduction in biological diversity is occurring worldwide.
   A. When the last individual member of a species dies, the species is said to be extinct. A species whose numbers are severely reduced so that it is in danger of extinction is said to be endangered. When extinction is less imminent but numbers are quite low, a species is said to be threatened.
   B. Human activities that contribute to a reduction in biological diversity include habitat loss and disturbance, pollution, introduction of foreign species, pest and predator control, hunting, and commercial harvest. Of these, habitat loss is the most significant factor in declining biological diversity.
   C. Efforts to preserve biological diversity in the wild are known as in situ conservation. Ex situ conservation, which includes captive breeding and the establishment of seed banks, occurs in human-controlled settings.
II. Forests provide us with many ecological benefits, including watershed protection, soil erosion prevention, climate moderation, and wildlife habitat.
   A. The greatest problem facing world forests today is tropical deforestation.
   B. In the tropics, forests are destroyed to (1) provide colonizers with temporary agricultural land, (2) produce timber, particularly for developed nations, (3) provide open rangeland for cattle, and (4) supply people with fuel wood.

III. Carbon dioxide and other greenhouse gases cause the air to retain heat (infrared radiation), which warms Earth.
   A. The increase in CO_2 and other greenhouse gases in the atmosphere is causing concerns about major climate changes that may occur during the next century.
      1. The combustion of fossil fuels produces pollutants, especially CO_2.
      2. Other greenhouse gases are methane, nitrogen oxide, chlorofluorocarbons (CFCs), and tropospheric ozone.
   B. Global warming may cause a rise in sea level, changes in precipitation patterns, death of forests, extinction of animals and plants, and problems for agriculture. It could result in the displacement of thousands or even millions of people.
   C. The challenge of global warming can be met by prevention (stop polluting the air with greenhouse gases), mitigation (slow down the rate of global warming), and adaptation (make adjustments to live with global warming).
IV. The ozone layer in the stratosphere helps to shield Earth from damaging ultraviolet radiation.
   A. The total amount of ozone in the stratosphere is slowly declining, and large ozone holes develop over Antarctica and the Arctic each year.
   B. The attack on the ozone layer is caused by CFCs and similar chlorine-containing compounds.

POST-TEST

1. _____ is the permanent loss of a species from Earth.
2. A(an) _____ species is severely reduced in number and is in danger of becoming extinct.
3. A(an) _____ species is not in imminent danger of extinction, but its numbers are low enough for concern.
4. _____ hunting is done for profit, _____ hunting is done for recreation, and _____ hunting is done for food.
5. Although declining biological diversity has many causes, _____ _____ is the most important.
6. _____ _____ conservation concentrates on preserving biological diversity in the wild.
7. The loss of forests is known as _____.
8. Poor rural people living in the tropics practice a type of agriculture known as _____ and _____.
9. The area of the world where deforestation is most acute is the _____.
10. The five greenhouse gases are _____, _____, _____, _____, and _____.
11. Driving a gasoline-powered automobile produces three greenhouse gases: _____, _____, and _____.
12. Greenhouse gases are able to retain _____ radiation in the atmosphere.
13. Current models predict that a doubling of atmospheric CO_2 will cause an increase in temperature of _____ °C to _____ °C.
14. Biologists think that global warming will have the greatest impact on _____ (plants, animals, or fungi).
15. _____ is a human-made pollutant in the troposphere but a natural (and beneficial) gas in the stratosphere.
16. _____ is/are a human-made pollutant that causes global warming *and* ozone depletion in the stratosphere.
17. Stratospheric ozone is beneficial because it absorbs incoming _____ radiation from the sun.
18. Worldwide, the amount of stratospheric ozone is _____. (increasing, decreasing, or remaining the same)

REVIEW QUESTIONS

1. Give at least three good reasons why we should protect biological diversity.
2. Would controlling the growth of the human population have any effect on biological diversity? Why or why not?
3. Give at least five environmental benefits that forests provide.
4. Explain the relationship between eating a hamburger at a fast-food restaurant and tropical deforestation.
5. How do commercial logging, cattle ranching, and other forms of agribusiness in Central and South America deprive local people of land and income?
6. If all of the world's tropical forests were destroyed, how would it affect your life?
7. It has been suggested that the wisest way to "use" fossil fuels would be to leave them in the ground. How would this affect global warming? Energy supplies?
8. Discuss and give examples of the three approaches—prevention, mitigation, and adaptation—to deal with global warming.
9. This statement was overheard in an elevator: "CFCs cannot cause the stratospheric ozone depletion over Antarctica because there are no refrigerators in Antarctica." Criticize the reasoning behind this statement.
10. Distinguish between the benefits of the ozone layer in the stratosphere and the harmful effects of ozone at ground level.

RECOMMENDED READINGS

Brough, H. B. A new lay of the land. *World Watch*, Vol. 4, No. 1, Jan./Feb. 1991. How land reform in the developing world would stem environmental degradation, including deforestation.

Gradel, T. E., and P. J. Crutzen. The changing atmosphere. *Scientific American*, Vol. 261, No. 3, September 1989. How trace gases in the atmosphere are altered by human activities and what their short- and long-term effects are.

Jones, P. D., and T. M. L. Wigley. Global warming trends. *Scientific American*, Vol. 263, No. 2, August 1990. An evaluation of global temperatures and projections for global warming.

Potten, C. J. America's illegal wildlife trade: A shameful harvest. *National Geographic*, Vol. 180, No. 3, September 1991. Illegal hunting and the black market for animal products are decimating America's wildlife.

Repetto, R. Deforestation in the tropics. *Scientific American*, Vol. 262, No. 4, April 1990. Examines government policies that encourage the destruction of tropical forests.

Schneider, S. *Global Warming*. Sierra Club Books, San Francisco, 1989. Examines the causes of global warming and projects what the future may hold for our planet.

Shell, E. Seeds in the bank could stave off disaster on the farm. *Smithsonian*, January 1990. How seed banks are used to improve important crop plants.

Wilson, E. O. (ed). *Biodiversity*. National Academy Press, Washington, D.C., 1988. The importance of maintaining biological diversity is considered, along with positive solutions to the problem.

Pharmaceutical Sales Representative

ROBERT M. PINTO

Robert M. Pinto insists that persistence pays off. Still in his early twenties, he is a pharmaceutical sales representative with Miles, Inc., of New Haven, Connecticut, the manufacturer and distributor of the leading brand of antibiotic, Cipro. He works independently, calling on physicians, hospitals, and retailers in the Philadelphia area. As a college freshman Pinto entered a premedical program, but he began his sophomore year with a new goal in mind—pharmaceutical sales. The exciting combination of biology and business appealed to his sense of adventure and proved to be a successful career strategy. Although the field is extremely competitive, Pinto's determination matched the challenge. After graduating with a B.S. in biology from Trenton State College in 1991, he worked briefly for a medical supply company to get sales experience, then accepted a position with Miles, Inc., where he envisions a very bright future in pharmaceutical sales.

What changed your mind about a career in medicine?

After my freshman year, I decided to find out what else I could do with my interest in biology. My grades weren't high enough to make me a competitive candidate for medical schools, so I transferred out of premedical studies and went for straight biology at Trenton State College.

What was the biology program like at Trenton?

It was a very good program. I met with my advisor, Dr. Steven Klug, and he gave me some excellent counseling. Medicine still interested me most, so I

liked the courses that dealt with the human body. I especially liked the labs because I got a lot of hands-on experience. Microbiology lab was interesting because students were given an unknown organism to identify by doing about 20 different tests. It was a challenge to carry out all the testing and come up with the answer. We were allowed to work on our own and learn from our own mistakes, which I found very valuable.

Where did you get the idea to go into sales?

When I was a sophomore, my sister had just graduated from Bucknell Uni-

versity. One of her roommates, a biology major, had just taken a position in pharmaceuticals and was very excited about it. My sister told me about the excellent starting salary, the chance to use a biology background, and the competitive challenge. That sounded great to me, so I more or less made my career choice then and there.

How did this decision affect your college work?

I went to Dr. Klug and asked him what courses I should take to set me in the direction of pharmaceutical sales. He sent me to the business department, and I started taking business courses along with my biology. In the second semester of my sophomore year I started taking courses in micro- and macroeconomics, marketing, and accounting. When I graduated I had the equivalent of a minor in business. Also, in my senior year I was able to take pharmacology. That course is usually restricted to nursing majors, but I was so set on selling pharmaceuticals that Dr. Klug allowed me to take it.

Would you advise someone interested in pharmaceutical sales to follow a path similar to the one you created for yourself?

It's been my experience that most people going into pharmaceutical sales take one of two academic routes—a biology major with business courses on the side, or a business major along with some biology courses. I think having a biology degree is a big advantage in my field. Sales is in many ways instinctive, something you are born with or can learn on the job. But a real understanding of biology requires disciplined study in a degree program.

Did pharmaceutical firms go to your campus to recruit students?

Yes. Some of the companies I interviewed with on campus were Pfizer, Roche, and Eli Lilly. They interviewed about 30 people every day for a week, and I really felt lost in the crowd. In a 10-minute interview it is very hard to get to know a company or for the company to get to know you.

It sounds like a very competitive job market.

Pharmaceutical sales is incredibly competitive. It really helps to know someone in the industry who can get you that first interview after graduation. My father knew someone in pharmaceutical sales who helped me get an interview with Miles, Inc.

What are you selling for Miles, Inc.?

The main product we are manufacturing and selling right now is Cipro, an oral and intravenous antibiotic developed in 1987 and used for bronchitis and pneumonia as well as urinary tract infections, skin and skin structure infections, and bone and joint conditions. It is the leading brand of antibiotic on the market today.

What do you do during a typical day in the field?

I call on individual physicians in their offices, on hospitals, and on retail accounts such as drugstores. At a doctor's office I present a clinical picture of a patient who could be treated with antibiotics and try to communicate the advantages of Cipro over a competing product. I also leave samples so that doctors can start their patients on

Cipro. One advantage of my biology background is that I can understand and converse with the doctors when they talk in scientific and medical terms. They really seem to appreciate this fact, and I'm sure it helps my presentation.

Beyond the sales calls, what other responsibilities does your job entail?

When I get a question I can't answer, I ask our professional services department to send supporting documentation to the customer. I also attend seminars and meetings where the representatives of Miles, Inc., receive updated product information and discuss marketing strategies. For example, when the weather starts getting cold, we start emphasizing Cipro for the treatment of bronchitis and pneumonia.

How do you like working independently?

I enjoy working on my own. When I see overall sales figures increase in my territory, I know it is the result of my efforts. I can work my territory as if it were my own business. I love biology and working in medicine, and I love being out on my own making sales, so pharmaceutical sales is the perfect career for me.

Is there any way for new graduates to get some first-hand knowledge about this kind of work?

A very valuable experience for me was following a sales representative around for a day. Companies who interview prospective candidates want them to know what the job is really like, so they encourage this trial run.

What kind of initial training did you undergo with Miles, Inc.?

I went through two weeks of training in West Haven, Connecticut. The focus was on antibiotics and where Cipro fit into the market. My biology background really helped me in training. We were constantly tested, and I did

very well because I had just learned much of the material the year before in my biology courses. I was right on top of information concerning microbiology and different types of bacteria and antibiotics.

Where could a successful career in pharmaceutical sales lead in 5 or 10 years?

After being a general representative out in the field, you could move on to calling on hospitals exclusively, for example. A lot of companies now have specialty reps who see just urologists, or just surgeons. Another step is to become a division manager who is in charge of ten or more people. There are a lot of companies out there, and a lot of opportunities to move up.

What are some of the most widely sold pharmaceutical products on the market today, and what new products seem to have a high sales potential in the future?

There is a huge market in antihypertensive drugs for high blood pressure. Because people stay on the medication for life, there will always be a strong demand for it. Many other companies besides Miles, Inc., sell antibiotics, of course. In the future a major product is going to be nicotine patches; four or five kinds of patches are available already.

What kind of feedback do you get about patients using your product?

Many of the patients who use Cipro are elderly people who have not had any success with other antibiotics, and it is great to learn about their progress using our product. I am continually hearing success stories related to Cipro—including a recent story from a medical receptionist whose young daughter was suffering from a growth on her face. The doctor gave the child Cipro, just as a safeguard against infection, and the cyst went away. Many people consider Cipro a sort of miracle drug, and it is very exciting to sell it.

The Classification of Organisms

The system of cataloging organisms used here is described in Chapter 1 and in Part V. We have omitted many groups (especially extinct ones) in order to simplify the vast number of diverse categories of living organisms and their relationships to one another. Note that we have omitted the viruses from this survey, since they do not fit into any of the five kingdoms.

KINGDOM PROKARYOTAE: BACTERIA

Prokaryotic organisms that lack nuclear envelopes, mitochondria, and other membranous organelles. Typically unicellular, but some form colonies or filaments. The predominant mode of nutrition is heterotrophic, but some groups are photosynthetic or chemosynthetic. Reproduction is primarily asexual by fission. Bacteria are nonmotile or move by the beating of flagella. Flagella, when present, are solid (rather than the 9 + 2 type typical of eukaryotes). More than 10,000 species.

Subkingdom Archaebacteria

Anaerobic prokaryotic organisms with a number of features that set them apart from the rest of the bacteria: unusual cell wall composition, ribosomal RNA differences, lipid structure, and specific enzyme differences. Archaebacteria are found in extreme environments—hot springs, sea vents, dry and salty seashores, boiling muds, and near ash-ejecting volcanoes.

Phylum Methanocreatrices. *Methanogenic archaebacteria.* Anaerobes that produce methane from CO_2 and H_2. Found in sewage, swamps, and digestive tracts of humans and other animals.

Phylum 2. *Halophilic and thermoacidophilic bacteria.* This phylum, which has not yet been officially named, contains the halophiles, which live in extremely salty environments, and the thermoacidophiles, which normally grow in hot, acidic environments. None of these archaebacteria produce methane.

Subkingdom Eubacteria

Contains the vast majority of bacteria. This very large and very diverse group possesses three different cell wall conditions: no walls, gram-negative walls, and gram-positive walls.

On the basis of their cell walls, the eubacteria are currently divided into three divisions. (Bacterial nomenclature and taxonomic practices do not currently correspond to those of other organisms.)

Division Tenericutes. *Bacteria that lack a rigid cell wall.* Contains the mycoplasmas, which are extremely small bacteria bounded by a plasma membrane.

Division Gracilicutes. *Gram-negative bacteria.* Possess a thin cell wall. Includes nitrogen-fixing aerobic bacteria, enterobacteria, spirochetes, cyanobacteria, rickettsias, chlamydias, and myxobacteria.

Division Firmicutes. *Gram-positive bacteria.* Possess a thick cell wall of peptidoglycan. All are nonphotosynthetic, and many produce spores. Includes the lactic acid bacteria, streptococci, staphylococci, clostridia, and actinomycetes.

KINGDOM PROTISTA

Primarily unicellular or simple multicellular eukaryotic organisms that do not form tissues and that exhibit relatively little division of labor. Most modes of nutrition occur in this kingdom. Life cycles may include both sexually and asexually reproducing phases and may be extremely complex, especially in parasitic forms. Locomotion is by cilia, flagella, amoeboid movement, or by other means. Flagella and cilia have 9 + 2 structure.

Animal-like Protists

Phylum Zoomastigina. *Flagellates.* Single cells that move by means of flagella. Some free-living; many symbiotic; some pathogenic. Reproduction usually asexual by binary fission.

Phylum Rhizopoda. *Amoebas.* Shelled or naked single-celled protists whose movement is associated with pseudopods.

Phylum Ciliophora. *Ciliates.* Unicellular organisms that move by means of cilia. Reproduction is asexual by binary fission or sexual by conjugation. About 7200 species.

Phylum Apicomplexa. *Sporozoa.* Parasitic single-celled protists that reproduce by spores and have no means of locomotion. Reproduce by an unusual type of multiple fission. Some pathogenic. About 3900 species.

Plant-like Protists

Phylum Dinoflagellata. *Dinoflagellates.* Unicellular (some colonial), photosynthetic, biflagellate. Cell walls, composed of overlapping cell plates, contain cellulose. Contain chlorophylls *a* and *c* and carotenoids, including fucoxanthin. About 2100 species.

Phylum Bacillariophyta. *Diatoms.* Unicellular (some colonial), photosynthetic. Most nonmotile, but some move by gliding. Cell walls composed of silica rather than cellulose. Contain chlorophylls *a* and *c* and carotenoids, including fucoxanthin. About 5600 species.

Phylum Euglenophyta. *Euglenoids.* Unicellular, photosynthetic, two flagella (one of them very short). Flexible outer covering. Contain chlorophylls *a* and *b* and carotenoids. About 1000 species.

Phylum Chlorophyta. *Green algae.* Mainly aquatic. Unicellular, colonial, siphonous, and multicellular forms. Some motile and flagellated. Photosynthetic; contain chlorophylls *a* and *b* and carotenoids. About 7000 species.

Phylum Rhodophyta. *Red algae.* Most multicellular (some unicellular), mainly marine. Some (coralline algae) have bodies impregnated with calcium carbonate. No motile cells. Photosynthetic; contain chlorophyll *a*, carotenoids, phycocyanin, and phycoerythrin. About 4000 species.

Phylum Phaeophyta. *Brown algae.* Multicellular, often quite large (kelps). Photosynthetic; contain chlorophylls *a* and *c* and carotenoids, including fucoxanthin. Biflagellate reproductive cells. About 1500 species.

Fungal-like Protists

Phylum Myxomycota. *Plasmodial slime molds.* Spend part of life cycle as a thin, streaming, multinucleate plasmodium that creeps along on decaying leaves or wood. Flagellated or amoeboid reproductive cells; form spores in sporangia. About 500 species.

Phylum Acrasiomycota. *Cellular slime molds.* Vegetative (nonreproductive) form unicellular; move by pseudopods. Amoeba-like cells aggregate to form a multicellular pseudoplasmodium that eventually develops into a fruiting body that bears spores. About 70 species.

Phylum Oomycota. *Water molds.* Consist of branched, coenocytic mycelia. Cellulose and/or chitin in cell walls. Produce biflagellate asexual spores. Sexual stage involves production of oospores. Some parasitic. About 580 species.

KINGDOM FUNGI

All eukaryotic, mainly multicellular organisms that are heterotrophic with saprophytic or parasitic nutrition. Body form often a mycelium, and cell walls consist of chitin. No flagellated stages. Reproduce by means of spores, which may be produced sexually or asexually. Cells usually haploid or dikaryotic with brief diploid period following fertilization.

Division Zygomycota. Produce sexual resting spores called zygospores and asexual spores in a sporangium. Hyphae are coenocytic. Many are heterothallic (two mating types). About 765 species.

Division Ascomycota. *Sac fungi.* Sexual reproduction involves formation of ascospores in little sacs called asci. Asexual reproduction involves production of spores called conidia, which pinch off from conidiophores. Hyphae usually have perforated septa. About 30,000 species.

Division Basidiomycota. *Club fungi.* Sexual reproduction involves formation of basidiospores on a basidium. Asexual reproduction uncommon. Heterothallic. Hyphae usually have perforated septa. About 16,000 species.

Division Deuteromycota. *Imperfect fungi.* Sexual stage has not been observed. Most reproduce only by conidia. About 17,000 species.

KINGDOM PLANTAE

Multicellular eukaryotic organisms with differentiated tissues and organs. Cell walls contain cellulose. Cells frequently contain large vacuoles, photosynthetic pigments in plastids. Photosynthetic pigments are chlorophylls *a* and *b* and carotenoids. Nonmotile. Reproduce both asexually and sexually, with alternation of gametophyte and sporophyte generations.

Division Bryophyta. *Bryophytes (mosses, liverworts, hornworts).* Nonvascular plants that lack xylem and phloem. Marked alternation of generations with dominant gametophyte generation. Motile sperm. About 15,600 species.

Division Pterophyta. *Ferns.* Vascular plants with a dominant sporophyte generation. Generally homosporous. Gametophyte is free-living and photosynthetic. Reproduce by spores. Motile sperm. About 11,000 species.

Division Psilophyta. *Whisk ferns.* Vascular plants with a dominant sporophyte generation. Homosporous. Stem is distinctive because it branches dichotomously; plant lacks true roots and leaves. The gametophyte is subterranean and nonphotosynthetic and forms a mycorrhizal relationship with a fungus. Motile sperm. About 12 species.

Division Sphenophyta. *Horsetails.* Vascular plants with hollow, jointed stems and reduced scalelike leaves. Although modern representatives are small, some extinct species were treelike. Homosporous. Gametophyte a tiny photosynthetic plant. Motile sperm. About 15 species.

Division Lycophyta. *Club mosses.* Sporophyte plants are vascular with branching rhizomes and upright stems that bear microphylls. Although modern representatives are small, some extinct species were treelike. Some homosporous, others heterosporous. Motile sperm. About 1000 species.

Division Coniferophyta. *Conifers.* Heterosporous vascular plants with woody tissues (tress and shrubs) and needle-shaped leaves. Most are evergreen. Seeds are usually borne naked on the surface of cone scales. Nutritive tissue in the seed is haploid female gametophyte tissue. Nonmotile sperm. About 550 species.

Division Cycadophyta. *Cycads.* Heterosporous, vascular, dioecious plants that are small and shrubby or larger and palmlike. Produce naked seeds in conspicuous cones. Flagellated sperm. About 140 species.

Division Ginkgophyta. *Ginkgo.* Broad-leaved deciduous trees that bear naked seeds directly on branches. Dioecious. Contain vascular tissues. Flagellated sperm. The ginkgo tree is the only living representative. One species.

Division Gnetophyta. *Gnetophytes.* Woody shrubs, vines, or small trees that bear naked seeds in cones. Contain vascular tissues. Possess many features similar to flowering plants. About 70 species.

Division Magnoliophyta. *Flowering plants.* Largest, most successful group of plants. Heterosporous; dominant sporophytes with extremely reduced gametophytes. Contain vascular tissues. Bear flowers, fruits, and seeds (enclosed in a fruit; seeds contain endosperm as nutritive tissue). Double fertilization. About 235,000 species.

KINGDOM ANIMALIA: ANIMALS

Multicellular eukaryotic heterotrophs with differentiated cells. In most animals, cells are organized to form tissues, and tissues are organized to form organs; in complex forms, specialized body systems carry on specific functions. Most animals have a well-developed nervous system and can respond rapidly to changes in their environment. Most are capable of locomotion during some time in their life cycle. Most animals reproduce sexually with large nonmotile eggs and flagellated sperm.

Subkingdom Parazoa

Tissue differentiation very limited; no organs. Adults sessile.

Phylum Porifera. *Sponges.* Mainly marine. Body perforated with many pores to admit water from which food is filtered by collar cells (choanocytes). Solitary, or form colonies. Asexual reproduction by budding; external sexual reproduction in which sperm are released and swim to internal egg. Larva is motile. About 5000 species.

Subkingdom Eumetazoa

Tissues and organs; many at organ system level of organization.

Branch Radiata

Animals with radial symmetry. Tentacles. Digestive system with one principal opening.

Phylum Cnidaria. *Hydras, jellyfish, sea anemones, corals.* Tentacles surrounding mouth. Stinging cells (cnidocytes) that contain stinging structures called nematocysts. Polyp and medusa forms. Planula larva. Solitary or colonial. Marine, with a few freshwater forms. About 9000 species.

Phylum Ctenophora. *Comb jellies.* Biradial symmetry. Free-swimming; marine. Two tentacles and eight longitudinal rows of cilia resembling combs; animal moves by means of these bands of cilia. About 100 species.

Branch Bilateria

Animals with bilateral symmetry.

Protostomes

Spiral, determinate cleavage; mouth develops from blastopore.

Acoelomates

No body cavity; region between body wall and internal organs filled with tissue.

Phylum Platyhelminthes. *Flatworms.* Planarians are free-living; flukes and tapeworms are parasitic. Body dorsoventrally flattened; cephalization; three tissue layers. Simple nervous system with ganglia in head region. Excretory organs are protonephridia with flame cells. About 18,000 species.

Phylum Nemertinea (also called Nemertea or Rhynchocoela). *Proboscis worms.* Long, dorsoventrally flattened body with complex proboscis armed with a hook for capturing prey. Simplest animal to have definite organ systems. Complete digestive tract. Circulatory system with blood. About 900 species.

Pseudocoelomates

Body cavity not completely lined with mesoderm. Complete digestive tract extending from mouth to anus.

Phylum Nematoda. *Roundworms. Ascaris,* hookworms, pinworms. Slender, elongated, cylindrical worms; covered with cuticle. Free-living and parasitic forms. About 12,000 species.

Phylum Rotifera. *Wheel animals.* Microscopic, wormlike animals. Anterior end has ciliated crown that looks like a wheel when the cilia beat. Posterior end tapers to a foot. Constant number of cells. About 1500 species.

Schizocoelous coelomates

These animals have a true coelom that develops as a schizocoel, that is, the mesoderm splits to form the body cavity. Complete digestive tract with mouth and anus.

Phylum Mollusca. *Snails, clams, squids, octopods.* Unsegmented, soft-bodied animals usually covered by a dorsal shell. Have a ventral, muscular foot. Most organs located above foot in visceral mass. A shell-secreting mantle covers the visceral mass and forms a mantle cavity, which contains gills. Trochophore and/or veliger larva. About 60,000 species.

Phylum Annelida. *Segmented worms.* Polychaetes, earthworms, leeches. Both body wall and internal organs are segmented. Body segments separated by septa. Some have nonjointed appendages. Setae used in locomotion. Closed circulatory system; metanephridia; specialized regions of digestive tract. Trochophore larva. About 11,000 species.

Phylum Arthropoda. *Crabs, shrimp, insects, spiders, mites, ticks, centipedes, millipedes.* Segmented animals with paired, jointed appendages and a hard exoskeleton made of chitin. Open circulatory system with dorsal heart. Hemocoel occupies most of body cavity, and coelom is reduced. About 900,000 species.

Deuterostomes (enterocoelous coelomates)

Radial, indeterminate cleavage. Blastopore develops into anus, and mouth forms from a second opening. Coelom develops from outpocketings of the primitive gut.

Phylum Echinodermata. *Sea stars, sea urchins, sand dollars, sea cucumbers.* Marine animals that have pentaradial symmetry as adults but bilateral symmetry as larvae. Endoskeleton of small, calcareous plates. Water vascular system; tube feet for locomotion. About 6000 species.

Phylum Hemichordata. *Acorn worms.* Marine animals with an anterior muscular proboscis, connected by a collar region to a long wormlike body. The larval form resembles an echinoderm larva. About 85 species.

Phylum Chordata. *Tunicates, lancelets, vertebrates.* Notochord, pharyngeal gill slits, and dorsal, tubular nerve cord present at some time in life cycle. About 42,000 species.

APPENDIX B

Careers in Biology

The following organizations and professional associations will provide career information upon request.

General

*American Association for the Advancement of Science
Office of Opportunity in Sciences, 1333H, N.W.
Washington, DC 20005
202-326-6400

*American Institute of Biological Science
730 11th Street N.W.
Washington, DC 20001-4521
202-628-1500

Association for Tropical Biology
c/o W. D. Stevens, Missouri Botanical Garden
P.O. Box 299
St. Louis, MO 63166
314-577-5103

BioSciences Information Service
2100 Arch Street
Philadelphia, PA 19103-1399
215-587-4800

*Federation of American Societies for Experimental Biology
9650 Rockville Pike
Bethesda, MD 20814
301-530-7000

*These umbrella organizations represent multiple professional associations and societies and can provide information on a variety of careers.

Agronomy

American Society of Agronomy
667 South Segoe Road
Madison, WI 53711
608-273-8080

Allied Health

American Nurses Associations
24200 Pershing Road
Kansas City, MO 64108
816-474-5720

National Association for Practical Nurse Education and Service
1400 Spring Street, Suite 300
Silver Springs, MD 20910
301-588-2491

Art and Communications

American Medical Writers Association
9650 Rockville Pike
Bethesda, MD 20814
301-493-0003

Association of Medical Illustrators
1819 Peachtree Street, N.E., Suite 560
Atlanta, GA 30309
404-350-7900

Biological Photographic Association
115 Stoneridge Drive
Chapel Hill, NC 27514
919-967-8247

Medical Library Association
6 North Michigan Avenue, Suite 300
Chicago, IL 60602
312-419-9094

National Association of Science Writers
P.O. Box 294
Greenlawn, NY 11740
516-757-5664

Biochemistry

American Society for Biochemistry and Molecular Biology
9650 Rockville Pike
Bethesda, MD 20814
301-530-7145

Biomedical Engineering

Alliance for Engineering in Medicine and Biology
1101 Connecticut Avenue, N.W., Suite 700
Washington, DC 20036
202-857-1199

Biomedical Engineering Society
P.O. Box 2399
Culver City, CA 90231
213-618-9322

Biophysics

Biophysical Society
9650 Rockville Pike, Room 512
Bethesda, MD 20814
301-530-7114

Botany

American Phytopathological Society
3340 Pilot Knob Road
St. Paul, MN 55121
612-454-7250

American Society of Plant Physiologists
15501 Monona Drive
Rockville, MD 20855
301-251-0560

Botanical Society of America
c/o Christopher Haufler, Department of Botany, University
of Kansas
Lawrence, KS 66045-2106
913-864-4301

Mycological Society of America
c/o Dr. Melvin Fuller, Department of Botany, University of
Georgia
Athens, GA 30602
706-542-3030

Phycological Society of America
c/o Dr. Robert Sheath, Department of Botany, Memorial
University
St. John's, NF, Canada A1B 3X9

Cell Biology

International Society of Differentiation
Department of Genetics and Cell Biology, University of
Minnesota
750 Biological Sciences Center
St. Paul, MN 55108
612-624-2285

Dentistry

American Association of Dental Schools
1625 Massachusetts Avenue, Suite 502, N.W.
Washington, DC 20036
202-667-9433

American Dental Association
211 E. Chicago Avenue
Chicago, IL 60611
312-440-2500

Education

National Association for Research in Science Teaching
University of Cincinnati, College of Education, 401
Teachers College, ML 2
Cincinnati, OH 45221-0002
513-556-2350

National Association of Biology Teachers
11250 Roger Bacon Drive, No. 19
Reston, VA 22090
703-471-1134

Society for Public Health Education
2001 Addison Street, Suite 220
Berkley, CA 94704
415-644-9242

Entomology

Entomological Society of America
4603 Calvert Road
College Park, MD 20740
301-731-4535

Environment-Ecological

Ecological Society of America
c/o Dr. Duncan Patten, Center for Environmental Studies,
Arizona State University
Tempe, AZ 85287-3211
602-965-3000

The Nature Conservancy
1800 N. Kent Street, Suite 800
Arlington, VA 22209
703-841-5300

National Wildlife Federation
1400 16th Street, N.W.
Washington, DC 20036
202-797-6800

Western Society of Naturalists
c/o Dr. Michael Foster, Moss Landing Marine Labs, P.O.
Box 450
Moss Landing, CA 95039
408-7A-8650

Environmental Law

Environmental Defense Fund
444 Park Avenue, South, 9th Floor
New York, NY 10016
212-686-4191

Environmental Law Institute
1346 Connecticut Avenue, N.W., Suite 600
Washington, DC 20036
202-452-9600

Forensics

American Academy of Forensic Sciences
P.O. Box 669
Colorado Springs, CO 80901
719-636-1100

Genetics

Genetics Society of America
9650 Rockville Pike
Bethesda, MD 20814-3998
301-571-1825

National Society of Genetic Counselors
233 Canteburry Drive
Wallingford, PA 19086
215-872-7608

Marine Biology

Virginia Institute of Marine Science
Gloucester Point, Virginia 23062

Medicine

American Academy of Family Physicians
8880 Ward Parkway
Kansas City, MO 64114
816-333-9700

American Academy of Pediatrics
141 Northwest Point Boulevard, P.O. Box 927
Elk Grove Village, IL 60009-0927
708-228-5005

American Medical Association
515 North State Street
Chicago, IL 60610
312-464-5000

International Association of Environmental Mutagen
Societies
c/o Herbert S. Rosenkrantz, Department of Environmental
Health Science, School of Medicine, Case Western
University
Cleveland, OH 44106

National Association of Healthcare Recruitment
P.O. Box 5769
Akron, OH 44372
216-867-3088

National Environmental Health Association
720 S. Colorado Boulevard, Suite 970, S. Tower
Denver, CO 80222
303-756-9090

Research!America (Medical Research)
99 Canal Center Plaza, Suite 250
Alexandria, VA 22314
703-739-2577

Microbiology

American Society for Microbiology
1325 Massachusetts Avenue, N.W.
Washington, DC 20005
202-737-3600

Foundation for Microbiology
c/o Bruce H. Waksman, 300 E. 54th Street, Suite 5K
New York, NY 10022
212-759-8729

Society for Industrial Microbiology
1401 Wilson Boulevard
Arlington, VA 22209
703-941-5373

Microscopy

Microscopy Society of America
Box MSA
Woods Hole, MA 02543
800-538-3672

Nutrition

American Dietetic Association
216 West Jackson Boulevard
Chicago, IL 60606
312-899-0040

Institute of Food Technologists
221 N. LaSalle Street, Suite 300
Chicago, IL 60602
312-419-9094

Paramedicine

International Rescue and Emergency Care Association
8107 Ensign Curve
Bloomington, MN 55438
612-941-2926

Pharmaceuticals

American Association of Colleges of Pharmacy
1426 Prince Street
Alexandria, VA 22314
703-739-2330

American Pharmaceutical Association
2215 Constitution Avenue, N.W.
Washington, DC 20037
202-628-4410

Physical Therapy

American Physical Therapy Association
Department of Information Services
1111 N. Fairfax Street
Alexandria, VA 22314
703-684-2782

Physiology

American Physiological Society
c/o Dr. Martin Frank, 9650 Rockville Pike
Bethesda, MD 200814
301-530-7160

Psychology

American Psychiatric Association
1400 K Street, N.W.
Washington, DC 20005
202-682-6000

American Psychological Association
750 First Street, N.W.
Washington, DC 20002
202-336-5500

Taxonomy

American Society of Plant Taxonomists
c/o Dr. Fred Ganders, Department of Botany, University of
British Columbia
Vancouver, BC, Canada V6T 1W5

Zoology

American Association of Zoo Keepers
Topeka Zoological Park, S.W. Gage Boulevard
Topeka, KS 66606
913-272-5821

American Society of Mammalogists
c/o Dr. H. Duane Smith, Department of Zoology, Brigham
Young University, 501 Widtsoe Building
Provo, UT 84602
801-378-2492

American Society of Zoologists
401 N. Michigan Avenue
Chicago, IL 60611-6697
312-527-6640

APPENDIX C

Post-Test Answers

Chapter 1

1. metabolism   2. homeostasis   3. stimulus
4. locomotion   5. asexual reproduction   6. adapt
7. c   8. f   9. b   10. a   11. g   12. h   13. d
14. e   15. producers; decomposers; consumers
16. DNA   17. energy   18. genus   19. Fungi
20. Prokaryotae   21. hypothesis   22. theory

Chapter 2

1. carbon, oxygen, hydrogen, nitrogen, phosphorus,
calcium   2. C; H; O   3. trace elements
4. electrons, protons, neutrons   5. electrons   6. atomic
number   7. mass number   8. isotopes   9. orbitals
10. two   11. positive   12. noble gases
13. chemical bond   14. ions   15. cations; anions
16. f   17. g   18. e   19. b   20. d   21. c
22. a   23. specific heat   24. donor; acceptor
25. buffer

Chapter 3

1. c   2. d   3. b   4. e   5. j   6. i   7. f
8. k   9. g   10. h   11. amino acids   12. amino
acids (in its polypeptide chains)   13. glucose, fructose
14. Cellulose   15. hydrophobic   16. carboxyl, amino
17. glycogen   18. nitrogenous base (purine or
pyrimidine); 5-carbon sugar; phosphate group

Chapter 4

1. resolution   2. endoplasmic reticulum   3. DNA,
nucleoid, chromatin, chromosomes   4. lysosomes
5. peroxisomes   6. cristae, ATP   7. plastids
8. thylakoid, sunlight, carbohydrate (or glucose)
9. microtubules   10. microtubules, microfilaments,
intermediate   11. Cilia, flagella, microtubules, two, nine
12. cell wall, cellulose   13. Vacuoles   14. nucleolar,
nucleus   15. glycoproteins   16. a   17. p   18. k
19. g   20. h   21. e   22. f   23. n   24. o
25. m   26. j   27. i   28. q   29. d   30. c
31. b   32. l

Chapter 5

1. lipid bilayer   2. hydrophobic, hydrophilic
3. amphipathic, hydrophobic, hydrophilic   4. Integral,
hydrophobic, Peripheral   5. diffusion   6. water (or
solute), isotonic (or isoosmotic)   7. hypertonic (or
hyperosmotic)   8. hypotonic (or hypoosmotic)
9. facilitated diffusion   10. active transport   11. active
transport, Na^+, K^+ 12. cotransport   13. phagocytosis
14. endocytosis (receptor-mediated)   15. Desmosomes
16. Gap junctions   17. Tight junctions
18. Plasmodesmata

Chapter 6

1. energy   2. kinetic energy   3. thermodynamics
4. first law of thermodynamics   5. exothermic reaction
6. endergonic reaction   7. entropy   8. second law of
thermodynamics   9. free energy; temperature, pressure
10. negative   11. exergonic   12. coupled
13. adenine, ribose; phosphate   14. activation energy
15. catalyst   16. Enzymes   17. enzyme-substrate
complex   18. active site   19. noncompetitive

Chapter 7

1. catabolism   2. anabolism   3. reduction
4. glycolysis   5. cytosol   6. acetyl CoA   7. citrate
8. carbon dioxide   9. two   10. NAD^+, FAD (any
order)   11. oxygen   12. chemiosmotic   13. ATP
14. glycolysis   15. 2; 36–38   16. facultative anaerobes
17. fermentation   18. ethyl alcohol   19. lactate
20. oxidized

Chapter 8

1. autotrophs   2. chloroplasts   3. carbon dioxide;
water; oxygen   4. water   5. photons   6. action
spectrum   7. water   8. carotenoids   9. photosystem
10. ADP; ATP   11. noncyclic   12. water
13. protons   14. ATP; NADPH; CO_2 (any order)
15. CO_2 fixation   16. C_4 17. bundle sheath; CO_2
18. oxygen

Chapter 9

1. heredity   2. DNA, protein, RNA   3. cell cycle
4. S (or synthesis)   5. prophase, metaphase, anaphase, telophase   6. sister chromatids   7. kinetochore
8. metaphase   9. cytokinesis   10. colchicine
11. asexual   12. clone   13. homologous
14. diploid, polyploid   15. n 16. synapsis, bivalent, tetrad   17. crossing over   18. 23   19. plants

Chapter 10

1. locus   2. alleles   3. monohybrid   4. genotype
5. phenotype   6. dominant   7. recessive
8. homozygous, heterozygous   9. first filial, F_1
10. product   11. sum   12. 1, 0   13. identical
14. dihybrid   15. polygenic   16. multiple
17. linked   18. consanguineous   19. hybrid vigor

Chapter 11

1. transformation, DNA   2. deoxyribose, phosphate, nitrogenous, purines, pyrimidines   3. sugars (deoxyribose), phosphates, covalent   4. base, adenine, thymine, guanine, cytosine   5. x-ray   6. parallel, helix
7. hydrogen, thymine, cytosine   8. replication
9. semiconservative, parent, daughter (newly synthesized)
10. origin of replication   11. 5′, 3′   12. three
13. Okazaki fragments, continuous   14. DNA polymerase, DNA ligase   15. circular, linear   16. one, multiple   17. bidirectional   18. one thousandth (1/1000), 1.3 mm, 1 meter   19. nucleosomes
20. Chromatin, loops, scaffolding proteins

Chapter 12

1. transcription   2. translation   3. 3 bases, codon
4. tRNA   5. ribosome   6. RNA polymerase
7. ribose, uracil, thymine   8. promoter, 5′
9. anticodon   10. carboxyl, 3′   11. tRNA
12. protein, RNA   13. initiation, initiation, 5′
14. elongation, peptide   15. termination, termination (or stop), ribosomal   16. polyribosome (or polysome)
17. introns, exon   18. capped, guanosine
19. polyadenylated (or poly A)   20. capped, exons
21. nonsense, frameshift

Chapter 13

1. operons   2. operator   3. RNA polymerase, negative
4. active, allosteric, conformation, inactive   5. inactive, corepressor, active   6. activate   7. cyclic AMP
8. high   9. regulon   10. constitutive, continuously
11. repressor   12. grooves, hydrogen   13. feedback inhibition   14. upstream promoter, number
15. enhancers   16. mRNA   17. multiple, amplified
18. heterochromatin, inactive   19. euchromatin

Chapter 14

1. recombinant   2. palindromic   3. plasmids, bacteriophages   4. restriction enzyme, DNA ligase
5. genomic, intron   6. cDNA, reverse transcriptase
7. restriction map   8. terminate   9. probes
10. posttranslational   11. transgenic

Chapter 15

1. isogenic   2. karyotype   3. birth (or congenital)
4. aneuploidy   5. trisomic   6. monosomic
7. nondisjunction   8. translocation   9. Down
10. Klinefelter, Turner   11. metabolism
12. hemoglobin   13. cystic fibrosis   14. amniocentesis
15. Chorionic villus   16. genetic counseling

Chapter 16

1. differentiated, determination   2. morphogenesis, pattern formation   3. nuclear equivalence
4. totipotent   5. gene expression   6. polytene
7. maternal effect   8. Zygotic   9. morphogens
10. Homeotic   11. DNA   12. mosaic   13. induction
14. regulative   15. Transgenic   16. homeotic
17. genomic rearrangements   18. Gene amplification

Chapter 17

1. evolution   2. gene pool   3. populations
4. natural selection   5. survive   6. survival; reproduce
7. humans   8. neo-Darwinism   9. compression
10. index fossils   11. vestigial   12. analogous
13. range   14. great apes   15. genetic code

Chapter 18

1. microevolution   2. allele frequencies   3. genetic drift   4. demes   5. migration   6. mutation
7. natural selection   8. coadapted gene complex
9. stabilizing   10. directional   11. disruptive selection
12. polymorphism   13. heterozygote advantage
14. frequency-dependent   15. neutral   16. allozymes
17. neutralist

Chapter 19

1. gene pool   2. temporal   3. mechanical
4. postzygotic   5. allopatric   6. allopolyploid
7. punctuated equilibrium   8. macroevolution
9. preaptation   10. allometric growth   11. extinction
12. mass   13. adaptive radiation

Chapter 20

1. oxygen   2. time   3. rock (or clay)
4. coacervates   5. hydrogen sulfide   6. endosymbiont
7. Paleozoic; Mesozoic; Cenozoic   8. Cambrian
9. Paleozoic   10. Dinosaurs   11. ornithischians
12. iridium   13. Cenozoic   14. Pleistocene
15. volcanoes

Chapter 21

1. placental   2. arboreal   3. prosimians, anthropoids
4. prosimians   5. prosimians   6. prehensile
7. *Aegyptopithecus*   8. hominoids   9. brachiates
10. apes   11. *Australopithecus*   12. *A. afarensis*
13. *habilis*   14. *erectus*   15. 200,000   16. Neandertals
17. Africa   18. South American (or Central American)

Chapter 22

1. taxonomy   2. Linnaeus; genus; specific   3. family
4. Protista   5. Fungi   6. ancestor   7. homologous
8. derived   9. protein; clocks   10. phenetic
11. cladistic   12. classical evolutionary   13. Animalia
14. Chordata   15. Vertebrata   16. Mammalia
17. Eutheria   18. Primates   19. Hominidae
20. Homo   21. sapiens

Chapter 23

1. DNA, RNA (any order)   2. capsid   3. bacteria
4. nucleic acid   5. lytic   6. attachment
7. temperate   8. transduction   9. cancer   10. viroid
11. Prokaryotae   12. cell wall   13. saprobes
14. chemosynthetic autotrophs   15. conjugation
16. methanogens   17. cocci; bacilli; spirilla   18. cell
wall   19. spirochete   20. producers   21. gram-
positive   22. actinomycetes

Chapter 24

1. contractile vacuole   2. syngamy   3. microtubules
4. pseudopodia   5. tests   6. axopods
7. choanoflagellates   8. flagella   9. conjugation
10. sporozoa   11. cellulose   12. red tide
13. diatoms   14. euglenoids   15. anisogamous
16. cyanobacteria   17. brown   18. plasmodium
19. cellular   20. zoospores; oospores

Chapter 25

1. decomposers   2. plants   3. cell walls   4. spores
5. budding   6. hyphae; mycelium   7. septa;
coenocytic   8. sporocarp   9. zygospores
10. heterothallic   11. conidia; conidiophores
12. ascospores; asci   13. basidiospores   14. gills
15. asexual   16. lichen   17. crustose   18. ergot
19. haustoria   20. barberry

Chapter 26

1. vascular   2. cuticle   3. green algae   4. starch
5. stomata   6. archegonium   7. antheridium
8. fertilization; zygote   9. spores   10. alternation;
generations   11. gametophyte   12. thallus
13. hornworts   14. sori   15. megaphyll   16. roots,
leaves (any order)   17. horsetails   18. microphyll
19. heterosporous

Chapter 27

1. seeds   2. deciduous   3. monoecious   4. fruit
5. pollen   6. female gametophyte   7. pollination
8. cycads, ginkgoes (any order)   9. monocots
10. endosperm   11. carpel   12. incomplete, imperfect
(any order)   13. ovary; ovule   14. embryo sac
15. insects   16. wind   17. coevolution
18. progymnosperms   19. conifers; ginkgoes
20. gymnosperms

Chapter 28

1. invertebrates   2. sessile   3. cavity   4. ectoderm
5. mesoderm   6. mouth   7. Radial   8. one-quarter
9. sponges   10. spicules   11. spongocoel; osculum
12. polyp, medusa   13. Cnidaria; Anthozoa
14. flatworms   15. smell   16. trichina   17. a
complete digestive tract (tube-within-a-tube body plan), a
separate circulatory system   18. b   19. c   20. d
21. e   22. a   23. c   24. b   25. e   26. a
27. d

Chapter 29

1. exoskeleton   2. radula   3. open   4. trochophore
5. metamerism   6. lung (respiratory surface)   7. shell
8. locomotion   9. Hermaphroditic   10. cerebral
ganglia   11. leeches   12. arthropods
13. arthropods   14. biting and grinding food
15. excretory   16. barnacles   17. pinching claws
18. excretory   19. b   20. c   21. d   22. a   23. e
24. d   25. b

Chapter 30

1. radial   2. water vascular; tube   3. arms (rays); test
(shell)   4. notochord; nerve cord; gill slits
5. Tunicates   6. vertebral column; cranium
7. amphibians, reptiles, mammals   8. Placoid
9. cloaca   10. cartilage   11. ray-finned; tetrapods
(land vertebrates)   12. gills   13. tetrapods (land
vertebrates)   14. terrestrial; keeps the embryo moist and
acts as a shock absorber   15. birds, mammals   16. lay
eggs   17. c, d, e   18. e   19. d, e   20. f   21. c
22. d   23. g   24. b   25. c   26. a   27. d

Chapter 31

1. torpedo   2. suspensor   3. indeterminate
4. apical   5. root cap   6. leaf, bud (any order)
7. vascular cambium   8. annuals; biennials; perennials
9. parenchyma   10. collenchyma   11. tracheids
12. companion   13. epidermis; periderm
14. trichomes   15. fibrous   16. bud scales
17. stomata; lenticels   18. compound   19. opposite
20. parallel; netted

Chapter 32

1. mesophyll   2. guard cells   3. lower   4. cuticle
5. bundle sheath   6. xylem   7. phloem
8. transpiration   9. guttation   10. circadian rhythms
11. potassium   12. photoreceptor   13. dicots
14. bulliform   15. abscission   16. suberin
17. tendrils   18. storage   19. leaves   20. passive

Chapter 33

1. dicots   2. monocot   3. vascular cambium, cork
cambium (any order)   4. periderm   5. rays
6. periderm   7. secondary xylem   8. heartwood
9. late summerwood; springwood   10. hardwood;
softwood   11. knot   12. dendrochronology

13. translocation   14. water potential   15. 0
16. lowers   17. more; less   18. root pressure
19. transpiration   20. source

Chapter 34

1. adventitious   2. contractile   3. Casparian strip
4. pericycle   5. xylem   6. pith   7. active transport
8. sand; silt; clay   9. hydroponics   10. macronutrients
11. 16   12. phosphorus   13. potassium
14. calcium   15. magnesium   16. organic
17. nitrogen   18. compost   19. mulch

Chapter 35

1. sexual   2. rhizome   3. tuber   4. stolon
5. asexual   6. fruit   7. berries   8. drupe
9. dehiscent   10. indehiscent   11. two
12. aggregate; multiple   13. accessory   14. wind
15. animals   16. photoperiodism   17. darkness
18. red   19. P_{FR} 20. vernalization

Chapter 36

1. pulvinus   2. solar tracking   3. circadian rhythm
4. phototropism   5. positive   6. thigmotropism
7. growth   8. hormones   9. Darwin   10. polar
transport   11. acid growth   12. auxin
13. gibberellins   14. enzymes   15. cytokinins
16. antagonistic   17. cytokinins; ethylene
18. ethylene   19. abscisic acid   20. dormancy

Chapter 37

1. epithelial tissue   2. protection, absorption, secretion,
sensation   3. squamous, cuboidal, columnar
4. pseudostratified ciliated epithelial   5. stratified
squamous   6. glands   7. stroma   8. Reticular fibers
9. g   10. f   11. d   12. e   13. j   14. b   15. c
16. i   17. a   18. h   19. axon   20. plasma

Chapter 38

1. epidermis; dermis   2. corneum   3. keratin
4. hydrostatic   5. molt   6. endoskeletons
7. compact; spongy (cancellous)   8. lubricant; joints
9. actin (thin), myosin (thick)   10. energy
11. glycogen; ATP   12. d; c; b; a; e; f; g

Chapter 39

1. transmission   2. synapses   3. stimuli   4. neuron
5. glial   6. receive stimuli; cell body; synapse
7. regeneration of injured axons   8. cellular sheath,
myelin sheath   9. cell bodies   10. resting potential
11. Excitatory   12. depolarization   13. action potential
14. all; none   15. nodes of Ranvier   16. resting
potential; more   17. neurotransmitter
18. acetylcholine   19. norepinephrine   20. divergence

Chapter 40

1. nerve net   2. brain   3. ganglia   4. Central
nervous system (CNS) and peripheral nervous system

(PNS)   5. brain; spinal cord   6. brain stem
7. medulla; spinal canal   8. c   9. e   10. b   11. a
12. d   13. b   14. d   15. e   16. a   17. c
18. c   19. a   20. e   21. b   22. beta   23. REM
24. vagus; internal organs of chest and upper abdomen
25. energy; stress   26. dorsal   27. Increasingly larger
amounts are needed to obtain the desired effect.

Chapter 41

1. sense   2. Exteroceptors; proprioceptors   3. Photo;
mechano   4. energy; receptor potential   5. adaptation
6. gravity; statolith   7. vision; hairs; cupula
8. muscle spindles; Golgi tendon; joint   9. motion
10. pressure   11. equilibrium   12. labyrinth; saccule,
utricle; semicircular   13. otoliths; gravity
14. endolymph; ampulla   15. inner; sound   16. Corti
17. chemoreceptors   18. rhodopsins   19. c   20. d
21. b   22. e   23. a

Chapter 42

1. c, e   2. a, f   3. b, d   4. b   5. b   6. e
7. d   8. c   9. a   10. oxygen   11. serum
12. gamma globulin   13. anemia   14. K   15. fibrin
16. Arterioles   17. capillaries   18. pulmonary arteries
19. semilunar   20. systole; diastole   21. volume of
blood pumped by one ventricle in one minute   22. the
more blood the heart pumps   23. blood pressure
24. blood flow; resistance to blood flow   25. aorta
26. brain   27. kidneys; liver   28. heart attack
29. blood pressure   30. vasoconstrictors

Chapter 43

1. antigens   2. antibodies (or immunoglobulins)
3. interferons   4. redness, heat, swelling (edema), pain
5. bone marrow; thymus; lymph   6. Interleukin-1
7. memory   8. plasma (differentiated B cells)
9. antibody   10. thymus   11. antigen-antibody
12. coat pathogens and enhance phagocytosis   13. active
14. passive   15. HLA   16. immune response;
transplanted   17. privileged   18. allergen; allergic
19. histamine; inflammation

Chapter 44

1. thin; diffusion; moist; blood vessels   2. tracheal;
spiracles   3. gills; bony fish   4. lungs   5. swim
bladder   6. air sacs   7. trachea; bronchus
8. alveoli   9. diaphragm   10. water loss   11. a
12. e   13. b   14. d   15. c   16. vital capacity
17. oxygen   18. oxyhemoglobin; Bohr effect
19. bicarbonate ions   20. oxygen   21. inhaling dirty
air   22. emphysema   23. cigarette smoking

Chapter 45

1. nutrition   2. digestion   3. Elimination
4. herbivore   5. canine   6. incomplete (only one
opening)   7. two   8. amylase   9. dentin   10. b
11. d   12. a   13. c   14. b   15. e   16. rugae
17. villi   18. duodenum   19. ulcer   20. store bile

21. minerals   22. (components of) coenzymes   23. c
24. a   25. d   26. e   27. b   28. triacylglycerols
29. amino acids; glucose (monosaccharides)
30. glycogen   31. amino acids   32. BMR (basal
metabolic rate)   33. weight gain   34. protein

Chapter 46

1. excretion   2. Osmoregulation   3. uric acid
4. urea   5. protonephridia; flame   6. metanephridia
7. antennal (green) glands   8. Malpighian tubules
9. nephrons   10. a   11. c   12. e   13. d   14. b
15. a   16. capillaries; Bowman's capsule   17. afferent
arteriole; efferent arteriole   18. (glomerular) filtrate
19. excreted (in the urine)   20. salt   21. collecting
ducts; reabsorbed; decreased

Chapter 47

1. ducts; blood   2. hormones   3. AMP
4. hypothalamus   5. target   6. c   7. d   8. b
9. a   10. e   11. a   12. e   13. c   14. b (also d)
15. d   16. hypo; thyroid hormones   17. goiter
18. cortisol   19. parathyroid   20. diabetes

Chapter 48

1. fragmentation   2. metagenesis; generations
3. Parthenogenesis   4. hermaphroditic   5. gamete;
zygote   6. sterile   7. a   8. c   9. d   10. b
11. e   12. b   13. d   14. c   15. a   16. c
17. b   18. d   19. e   20. b   21. a   22. c
23. d   24. c   25. d   26. e   27. b
28. therapeutic   29. female sterilization
30. menopause

Chapter 49

1. morphogenesis; cellular differentiation   2. acrosome;
vitelline   3. fertilization cone   4. depolarization;
cortical   5. cleavage   6. holoblastic   7. meroblastic;
blastodisc   8. gastrulation   9. ectoderm; endoderm
10. streak   11. neural plate   12. brain, spinal cord
13. amniotic   14. placenta   15. inner cell mass;
embryo   16. implant; uterus (endometrium)   17. fetus
18. gestation   19. birth   20. Teratogens
21. newborn   22. aging

Chapter 50

1. Behavior   2. Ethology   3. circadian
4. crepuscular   5. releaser   6. Innate; learned
7. Imprinting   8. habituation   9. classical (Pavlovian)
10. migratory restlessness   11. environment
12. society   13. symbolic   14. Pheromones
15. dominance hierarchy   16. home range
17. conflict; population growth   18. pair bond

19. nurse; royal jelly   20. innate   21. altruistic
22. Kin   23. making more genes

Chapter 51

1. environment   2. population   3. community
4. ecosystem   5. biosphere   6. permafrost
7. Conifers   8. precipitation   9. clay
10. grasslands   11. Chaparral   12. rain forests
13. savanna   14. oxygen, light, mineral nutrients (any
two)   15. thermocline   16. littoral   17. Estuaries
18. plankton, nekton, benthos   19. neritic province
20. oceanic

Chapter 52

1. population   2. density   3. clumped dispersion (or
aggregated dispersion)   4. models   5. natality,
mortality   6. biotic potential (or intrinsic rate of
increase)   7. exponential   8. environmental resistance
9. carrying capacity   10. logistic   11. population crash
12. dependent   13. dependent   14. independent
15. r 16. K 17. zero population growth
18. infant mortality rate   19. age structure

Chapter 53

1. community   2. decomposers   3. Carnivores,
herbivores, omnivores   4. mutualism   5. parasites
6. commensalism   7. niche   8. fundamental niche
9. realized niche   10. competitive exclusion   11. edge
effect   12. less   13. succession   14. climax
15. primary   16. pioneers   17. secondary
18. facilitation   19. "superorganisms"
20. individualistic

Chapter 54

1. ecosystem   2. cyclic, linear   3. photosynthesis,
cellular respiration   4. bacteria, legumes (any order)
5. nitrifying   6. phosphorus   7. hydrologic cycle
8. trophic   9. primary consumers   10. food web
11. numbers, biomass, energy (any order)   12. biomass
13. cellular respiration   14. standing crop   15. vertical
16. Coriolis effect   17. rain shadows   18. microclimate
19. horizons   20. Gaia hypothesis

Chapter 55

1. Extinction   2. endangered   3. threatened
4. Commercial, sport, subsistence   5. habitat destruction
(or habitat modification)   6. In situ   7. deforestation
8. slash and burn   9. tropics   10. CO_2, O_3, CH_4, N_2O,
CFCs (any order)   11. CO_2, O_3, N_2O (any order)
12. infrared   13. 2, 5   14. plants   15. Ozone (or O_3)
16. CFCs   17. ultraviolet   18. decreasing

Understanding Biological Terms

Your task of mastering new terms will be greatly simplified if you learn to dissect each new word. Many terms can be divided into a prefix, the part of the word that precedes the main root, the word root itself, and often a suffix, a word ending that may add to or modify the meaning of the root. As you progress in your study of biology, you will learn to recognize the more common prefixes, word roots, and suffixes. Such recognition will help you analyze new terms so that you can more readily determine their meaning and will also help you remember them.

Prefixes

a-, ab- from, away, apart (abduct, lead away, move away from the midline of the body)

a-, an-, un- less, lack, not (asymmetrical, not symmetrical)

ad- (also **af-, ag-, an-, ap-**) to, toward (adduct, move toward the midline of the body)

allo- different (allometric growth, different rates of growth for different parts of the body during development)

ambi- both sides (ambidextrous, able to use either hand)

andro- a man (androecium, the male portion of a flower)

anis- unequal (anisogamy, sexual reproduction in which the gametes are of unequal sizes)

ante- forward, before (anteflexion, bending forward)

anti- against (antibody, proteins that have the capacity to react against foreign substances in the body)

auto- self (autotrophic, organisms that manufacture their own food)

bi- two (biennial, a plant that takes two years to complete its life cycle)

bio- life (biology, the study of life)

circum-, circ- around (circumcision, a cutting around)

co-, con- with, together (congenital, existing with or before birth)

contra- against (contraception, against conception)

cyt- cell (cytology, the study of cells)

di- two (disaccharide, a compound made of two sugar molecules chemically combined)

dis- apart (dissect, cut apart)

ecto- outside (ectoplasm, outer layer of cytoplasm)

end-, endo- within, inner (endoplasmic reticulum, a network of membranes found within the cytoplasm)

epi- on, upon (epidermis, upon the dermis)

ex-, e-, ef- out from, out of (extension, a straightening out)

extra- outside, beyond (extraembryonic membrane, a membrane that encircles and protects the embryo)

gravi- heavy (gravitropism, growth of a plant in response to gravity)

hemi- half (cerebral hemisphere, lateral half of the cerebrum)

hetero- other, different (heterozygous, unlike members of a gene pair)

homo-, hom- same (homologous, corresponding in structure; homozygous, identical members of a gene pair)

hyper- excessive, above normal (hypersecretion, excessive secretion)

hypo- under, below, deficient (hypotonic, a solution whose osmotic pressure is less than that of an isotonic solution)

in-, im- not (incomplete flower, a flower that does not have one or more of the four main parts)

inter- between, among (interstitial, situated between parts)

intra- within (intracellular, within the cell)

iso- equal, like (isotonic, equal osmotic concentration)

macro- large (macronucleus, a large, polyploid nucleus found in ciliates)

mal- bad, abnormal (malnutrition, poor nutrition)

mega- large, great (megakaryocyte, giant cell of bone marrow)

meso- middle (mesoderm, middle tissue layer of the animal embryo)

meta- after, beyond (metaphase, the stage of mitosis after prophase)

micro- small (microscope, instrument for viewing small objects)

mono- one (monocot, a group of flowering plants with one cotyledon, or seed leaf, in the seed)

oligo- small, few, scant (oligotrophic lake, a lake deficient in nutrients and organisms)

oo- egg (oocyte, developing egg cell)

paedo- a child (paedomorphosis, the preservation of a juvenile characteristic in an adult)

para- near, beside, beyond (paracentral, near the center)

peri- around (pericardial membrane, membrane that surrounds the heart)

photo- light (phototropism, growth of a plant in response to the direction of light)

poly- many, much, multiple, complex (polysaccharide, a carbohydrate composed of many simple sugars)

post- after, behind (postnatal, after birth)

pre- before (prenatal, before birth)

pseudo- false (pseudopod, a temporary protrusion of a cell, i.e., "false foot")

retro- backward (retroperitoneal, located behind the peritoneum)

semi- half (semilunar, half-moon)

sub- under (subcutaneous tissue, tissue immediately under the skin)

super-, supra- above (suprarenal, above the kidney)

sym- with, together (sympatric speciation, evolution of a new species within the same geographical region as the parent species)

syn- with, together (syndrome, a group of symptoms which occur together and characterize a disease)

trans- across, beyond (transport, carry across)

Suffixes

-able, -ible able (viable, able to live)

-ad used in anatomy to form adverbs of direction (cephalad, toward the head)

-asis, -asia, -esis condition or state of (hemostasis, stopping of bleeding)

-cide kill, destroy (biocide, substance that kills living things)

-emia condition of blood (anemia, a blood condition in which there is a lack of red blood cells)

-gen something produced or generated or something that produces or generates (pathogen, an organism that produces disease)

-gram record, write (electrocardiogram, a record of the electrical activity of the heart)

-graph record, write (electrocardiograph, an instrument for recording the electrical activity of the heart)

-ic adjective-forming suffix which means *of* or *pertaining to* (ophthalmic, of or pertaining to the eye)

-itis inflammation of (appendicitis, inflammation of the appendix)

-logy study or science of (cytology, study of cells)

-oid like, in the form of (thyroid, in the form of a shield)

-oma tumor (carcinoma, a malignant tumor)

-osis indicates disease (psychosis, a mental disease)

-pathy disease (dermopathy, disease of the skin)

-phyll leaf (mesophyll, the middle tissue of the leaf)

-scope instrument for viewing or observing (microscope, instrument for viewing small objects)

Some Common Word Roots

abscis cut off (abscission, the falling off of leaves or other plant parts)

angi, angio vessel (angiosperm, plants that produce seeds enclosed within a fruit or "vessel")

apic tip, apex (apical meristem, area of cell division located at the tips of plant stems and roots)

arthr joint (arthropods, invertebrate animals with jointed legs and segmented bodies)

aux grow, enlarge (auxin, a plant hormone involved in growth and development)

bi, bio life (biology, study of life)

blast a formative cell, germ layer (osteoblast, cell that gives rise to bone cells)

brachi arm (brachial artery, blood vessel that supplies the arm)

bry grow, swell (embryo, an organism in the early stages of development)

cardi heart (cardiac, pertaining to the heart)

carot carrot (carotene, a yellow, orange, or red pigment in plants)

cephal head (cephalad, toward the head)

cerebr brain (cerebral, pertaining to the brain)

cervic, cervix neck (cervical, pertaining to the neck)

chlor green (chlorophyll, a green pigment found in plants)

chondr cartilage (chondrocyte, a cartilage cell)

chrom color (chromosome, deeply staining body in nucleus)

cili small hair (cilium, a short, fine cytoplasmic hair projecting from the surface of a cell)

coleo a sheath (coleoptile, a protective sheath that encircles the stem in grass seeds)

conjug joined together (conjugation, a sexual phenomenon in certain protists)

cran skull (cranial, pertaining to the skull)

cyt cell (cytology, study of cells)

decid falling off (deciduous, a plant that sheds its leaves at the end of the growing season)

dehis split (dehiscent fruit, a fruit that splits open at maturity)

derm skin (dermatology, study of the skin)

ecol dwelling, house (ecology, the study of organisms in relation to their environment, i.e., "their house")

enter intestine (enterobacteria, bacteria that inhabit humans, particularly in their large intestine)

evol to unroll (evolution, descent with modification, or gradual directional change)

fil a thread (filament, the thin stalk of the stamen in flowers)

gamet a wife or husband (gametangium, the part of a plant or protist that produces reproductive cells)

gastr stomach (gastrointestinal tract, the digestive tract)

glyc, glyco sweet, sugar (glycogen, storage form of glucose)

gon seed (gonad, an organ that produces gametes)

gutt a drop (guttation, loss of water as liquid "drops" from plants)

gymn naked (gymnosperm, a plant that produces seeds that are not enclosed within a fruit, i.e., "naked")

hem blood (hemoglobin, the pigment of red blood cells)

hepat liver (hepatic, of or pertaining to the liver)

hist tissue (histology, study of tissues)

hom, homeo same, unchanging, steady (homeostasis, reaching a steady state)

hydr water (hydrolysis, a breakdown reaction involving water)

leuk white (leukocyte, white blood cell)

menin membrane (meninges, the three membranes that envelop the brain and spinal cord)

morph form (morphogenesis, development of body form)

my, myo muscle (myocardium, muscle layer of the heart)

myc a fungus (mycelium, the vegetative body of a fungus)

nephr kidney (nephron, microscopic unit of the kidney)

neur, nerv nerve (neuromuscular, involving both the nerves and muscles)

occiput back part of the head (occipital, back region of the head)

ost bone (osteology, study of bones)

path disease (pathologist, one who studies disease processes)

ped, pod foot (bipedal, walking on two feet)

pell skin (pellicle, a flexible covering over the body of certain protists)

phag eat (phagocytosis, process by which certain cells ingest particles and foreign matter)

phil love (hydrophilic, a substance that attracts, i.e. "loves," water)

phloe bark of a tree (phloem, food-conducting tissue in plants which corresponds to bark in woody plants)

phyt plant (xerophyte, a plant adapted to xeric, or dry, conditions)

plankt wandering (plankton, microscopic aquatic protists that float or drift passively)

rhiz root (rhizome, a horizontal, underground stem that superficially resembles a root)

scler hard (sclerenchyma, cells that provide strength and support in the plant body)

sipho a tube (siphonous, a type of tubular body form found in certain algae)

som body (chromosome, deeply staining body in the nucleus)

sor heap (sorus, a cluster or "heap" of sporangia in the ferns)

spor seed (spore, a reproductive cell that gives rise to individual offspring in plants and protists)

stom a mouth (stoma, a small pore, i.e. "mouth," in the epidermis of plants)

thigm a touch (thigmotropism, plant growth in response to touch)

thromb clot (thrombus, a clot within a blood vessel)

tropi turn (thigmotropism, growth of a plant in response to contact with a solid object, as when a tendril "turns" or wraps around a wire fence)

visc pertaining to an internal organ or body cavity (viscera, internal organs)

xanth yellow (xanthophyll, a yellowish pigment found in plants)

xyl wood (xylem, water-conducting tissue in plants, the "wood" of woody plants)

zoo an animal (zoology, the science of animals)

APPENDIX E

Abbreviations

The biological sciences employ a great many abbreviations, and with good reason. Many technical terms in biology and biological chemistry are both long and difficult to pronounce. Yet it can be difficult for beginners, when confronted with something like NADPH or COPD, to understand the reference. Here are some of the common abbreviations employed in biology for your ready reference.

ACTH The pituitary hormone, AdrenoCorticoTropic Hormone, that governs the secretion of adrenal cortical hormones by the adrenal cortex.

ADH The pituitary hormone, AntiDiuretic Hormone, also called vasopressin, that governs the reabsorption of water by the kidney, and thus the amount of urine that is produced. ADH is antidiuretic: The more ADH present, the less urine produced.

ADP Adenosine DiPhosphate. A form of the almost universal energy transfer substance of the cell, ATP, in its "discharged" state. Even ADP, however, contains some transferable energy which is employed in certain biochemical reactions.

AIDS Acquired Immune Deficiency Syndrome. Caused by a retrovirus, human immunodeficiency virus (HIV). AIDS is a deadly disease that is spreading through the population.

AMP Adenosine MonoPhosphate. The basic "stem" of the energy transfer substance ATP; AMP contains no readily transferable energy.

ATP Adenosine TriPhosphate. The almost universal energy transfer substance of the cell. Typically, ATP donates its terminal phosphate group to some substance, along with much of the energy formerly contained in the bond that held it to the remainder of the ATP molecule. ADP is left over, and in due course, is recycled.

ATPase An enzyme or protein that breaks down ATP, usually producing ADP. Most ATPases perform some function such as active transport or contraction which utilizes the energy that is discharged in the breakdown of ATP. One important class of ATPase, in mitochondria and chloroplasts, operates in reverse. These actually *produce* ATP, using the energy of a proton gradient to add the terminal phosphate to the ATP molecule.

AV node AtrioVentricular node. A mass of tissue located near the junction of the heart atria and ventricles that is responsible for the coordination of the contraction of the ventricles with that of the atria.

B lymphocyte or B cell The lymphocyte responsible for the production of antibody-mediated immunity. Originally named for the Bursa of Fabricius, a structure in which these cells mature in birds. (It may help to think of the B lymphocytes as producing **blood** immunity; antibodies are found in the blood.)

BMR Basal Metabolic Rate. The rate of energy production, indirectly measured by the rate of consumption. Called "basal" because it is the basic metabolic cost of living apart from any special exertion.

cAMP Cyclic Adenosine MonoPhosphate. Most commonly, a second messenger substance produced within the cell in response to a hormone. It is made from ATP.

CAP Catabolite Activator Protein. Regulatory protein that interacts with DNA to control transcription of certain genes in *E. coli*.

CNS Central Nervous System.

COPD Chronic Obstructive Pulmonary Disease.

CP Creatine Phosphate. An important energy storage substance in vertebrate muscle.

DNA DeoxyriboNucleic Acid. The fundamental substance in which hereditary information is stored.

EM Electron Microscope.

ER Endoplasmic Reticulum; Electron Micrograph.

FAD (also FADH) Flavine Adenine Dinucleotide. A hydrogen acceptor and donor involved in cellular metabolism and in photosynthesis.

FSH Follicle Stimulating Hormone. A hormone secreted by the anterior pituitary that was originally discovered in female mammals, though it also occurs in males. Stimulates the growth of the ovarian follicles and the seminiferous tubules.

GABA Gamma-AminoButyric Acid. A neurotransmitter that may play a role in pain perception.

GH Growth Hormone, otherwise known as somatotropin.

GTP Guanosine TriPhosphate. An energy-rich compound sometimes used by cells in place of ATP.

Hb Hemoglobin.

HCG Human Chorionic Gonadotropin. A peptide hormone produced by the placenta that helps to maintain pregnancy. Similar hormones occur in other mammals, but they are known simply as CG.

HDL High-Density Lipoprotein. Blood particle of relatively high density that transports fats.

HLA Human Leukocyte Antigen. A major complex of antigens found on human body cells that governs graft compatibility, which is governed by specific genes, the HLA genes.

Ig Immunoglobin, as in IgA, IgG, IgM, etc.

kb KiloBase. One thousand bases of RNA (or base pairs of DNA).

LDH Lactic DeHydrogenase enzyme.

LH Luteinizing Hormone. Although this anterior pituitary hormone also occurs and functions in males, it was discovered in females and named for its action in them, namely, to convert an ovarian follicle into a progesterone-secreting corpus luteum. In males it promotes growth and function of the cells that secrete testosterone.

MAO MonoAmine Oxidase. An enzyme that destroys epinephrine-like neurotransmitter substances.

MHC Major Histocompatibility Complex. Group of genes governing the tissue antigens, which in turn determine graft compatibility in humans.

mRNA Messenger RiboNucleic Acid. A form of RNA (see below) that carries the genetic message from DNA to the cytoplasm, where it is translated into polypeptides or proteins.

MSH Melanocyte Stimulating Hormone. An anterior pituitary hormone that darkens the skin by stepping up the activity of melanocytes.

NAD$^+$ (also **NADH + H$^+$**) Nicotine Adenine Dinucleotide. A coenzyme widely used by cells as a hydrogen acceptor or donor in a variety of metabolic reactions. NAD$^+$ is generally involved in catabolic reactions, including cellular respiration.

NADP$^+$ (also **NADPH + H$^+$**) Nicotine Adenine Dinucleotide Phosphate. A coenzyme widely used by cells as a hydrogen acceptor or donor in a variety of metabolic reactions. NADP$^+$ is generally involved in anabolic reactions, including photosynthesis.

PNS Peripheral Nervous System.

RAS Reticular Activating System. The system of the brain important in maintaining a conscious state.

RBC Red Blood Cell, erythrocyte.

RNA RiboNucleic Acid. Nucleic acid responsible for the expression of genetic information. There are three main types: mRNA, tRNA, and rRNA.

rRNA Ribosomal RiboNucleic Acid. RNA that forms part of the structure of the ribosome.

SA node SinoAtrial Node of the heart; responsible for the initiation and timing of the heartbeat; pacemaker of heart.

SEM Scanning Electron Microscope.

STD Sexually Transmitted Disease.

T lymphocyte or T cell Lymphocyte with a wide variety of functions, primarily concerned with cell-mediated immunity. Named "T" for the fact that these cells mature in the **thymus** gland.

TEM Transmission Electron Microscope.

tRNA Transfer RiboNucleic Acid. A variety of RNA responsible for carrying (transferring) amino acids to the ribosomal protein construction site.

WBC White Blood Cell, leukocyte.

GLOSSARY

abdomen (ab'doh-men)   (1) In mammals the region of the body between the diaphragm and the rim of the pelvis; (2) in arthropods, the posterior-most major division of the body.

abiogenesis (ā'-by-oh-jen'-eh-sis)   The spontaneous generation of life; the origin of living things from inanimate objects.

abiotic   Nonliving.

abortion (uh-bor'shun)   Expulsion of an embryo or fetus before it is capable of surviving.

abscisic acid (ab-sis'ik)   A plant hormone involved in dormancy and responses to stress.

abscission (ab-sizh'en)   The normal (usually seasonal) falling off of leaves or other plant parts, such as fruits or flowers.

abscission layer (abscission zone)   A special layer of thin-walled cells, loosely joined together, that extends across the base of the petiole, thus weakening the base of the leaf and finally permitting the leaf to fall.

absorption (ab-sorp'shun)   The taking up of a substance, as by the skin, mucous surfaces, or lining of the digestive tract.

absorption spectrum   A measure of the amount of light at specific wavelengths that has been absorbed as light passes through a substance. Each type of molecule has a characteristic absorption spectrum.

accessory fruit   A fruit composed primarily of tissue other than ovary tissue. Apples and pears are accessory fruits.

acclimatization (a-kly'muh-tih-zay'shun)   Gradual physiological changes in an organism in response to slow, relatively long-lasting changes in the environment.

acetyl Co A (ah-see'til)   A key intermediate compound in metabolism; consists of an acetyl group covalently bonded to coenzyme A.

acetylcholine (ah"see-til-koh'leen)   The neurotransmitter employed by cholinergic nerves.

achene (a-keen')   A simple, dry, indehiscent fruit with one seed in which the fruit wall is separate from the seed coat. Sunflower fruits are achenes.

acid   A substance that is a hydrogen ion (proton) donor. Acids have a sour taste, turn blue litmus paper red, and unite with bases to form salts.

acid-growth hypothesis   The proposed mechanism by which auxin induces cell elongation.

acoelomate organisms (a-seel'oh-mate)   Organisms that lack a body cavity (coelom).

acromegaly (ak"roh-meg'ah-lee)   A condition characterized by overgrowth of the extremities of the skeleton, nose, jaws, fingers, and toes. It may be produced by excessive secretion of growth hormone from the pituitary.

acrosome (ak'roh-sohm)   A caplike structure covering the head of a sperm cell.

actin (ak'tin)   The protein of which microfilaments are composed. Actin, together with the protein myosin, is responsible for the ability of muscles to contract.

action potential   The electrical activity developed in a muscle or nerve cell during activity; a neural impulse.

activation energy   The energy required to initiate a chemical reaction.

active site   Area of an enzyme surface that accepts one or more substrates and catalyzes a chemical reaction.

active transport   Energy-requiring transport of a molecule across a membrane from a region of low concentration to a region of high concentration.

adaptation   (1) The ability of an organism to adjust to its environment; (2) decline in the response of a receptor subjected to repeated or prolonged stimulation.

adaptive radiation   The evolution of several to many species from an unspecialized ancestor.

adenine (ad'eh-neen)   A nitrogenous base (purine) that is a component of nucleic acids.

adenosine triphosphate (a-den'oh-seen) **(ATP)**   An organic compound containing adenine, ribose, and three phosphate groups; of prime importance for energy transfers in biological systems.

adipose (ad'i-pohs)   Pertaining to fat; tissue in which fat is stored, or the fat itself.

adrenal glands (ah-dree'nul)   Paired endocrine glands, one located just superior to each kidney.

adrenaline (uh-dren'ah-lin)   See epinephrine.

adrenergic neuron (ad-ren-er'jik)   A neuron that releases norepinephrine or epinephrine as a neurotransmitter.

adsorption   The process by which a thin layer of a substance becomes held to a surface.

adventitious root (ad″ven-tish′us)   A root that arises in an unusual position on a plant.

aerobic (air-oh′bik)   Growing or metabolizing only in the presence of molecular oxygen.

aerobic metabolism   Metabolism requiring oxygen.

aerobic respiration   The process by which cells utilize oxygen to break down organic molecules into waste products (such as carbon dioxide and water), with the release of energy that can be used for biological work.

afferent (af′fur-ent)   Structure that conducts fluid or impulses toward an organ or structure, e.g., afferent neurons conduct impulses to the central nervous system.

agglutination (ah-gloo″tih-nay′shun)   The collection into clumps of cells or particles distributed in a fluid.

aggregate fruit   A fruit that develops from a single flower with many separate carpels, such as a raspberry.

agnathans (ag-na′thanz)   Jawless fishes; class of vertebrates, including lampreys, hagfishes, and many extinct forms.

albinism (al′bih-niz-em)   A hereditary inability to form melanin pigment resulting in abnormally light coloration.

albumin (al-bew′min)   A class of protein found in animal tissues; a fraction of plasma proteins.

aldosterone (al-dos′tur-ohn)   Steroid hormone produced by the vertebrate adrenal cortex and which governs the excretion or retention of sodium and potassium ions.

algae (al′gee)   Single-celled or simple multicellular photosynthetic organisms; important producers.

alkali (al′kuh-lie)   A substance that, when dissolved in water, produces a pH greater than 7; also called a solution of a base.

allantois (a-lan′toe-iss)   One of the extraembryonic membranes of reptiles, birds, and mammals; most of the allantois is detached at birth.

alleles (al-leels′)   Genes governing variations of the same characteristic that occupy corresponding positions (loci) on homologous chromosomes; alternative forms of a gene.

allergy   A hypersensitivity to some substance in the environment, manifested as hay fever, skin rash, asthma, food allergies, etc.

allometric growth   Varied rates of growth for different parts of the body during development.

allopatric speciation (al-oh-pa′trik)   Speciation that occurs when one population becomes geographically separated from the rest of the species and subsequently evolves.

allopolyploid (al″oh-pol′ee-ploid)   A polyploid formed from a hybrid combining two or more sets of chromosomes from each of two different species.

allosteric site (al-oh-steer′ik)   A site located on an enzyme molecule that enables a substance other than the normal substrate to bind to the molecule, and to change the shape of the molecule and the activity of the enzyme.

allozyme (al′loh-zime)   One of two or more slightly different versions of the same enzyme that are detectable by electrophoresis.

alternation of generations   A type of life cycle characteristic of plants in which they spend part of their life in a multicellular haploid (gametophyte) stage and part in a multicellular diploid (sporophyte) stage.

alveolus (al-vee′o-lus)   (1) An air sac of the lung through which gas exchange with the blood takes place; (2) a saclike unit of some glands; (3) a tooth socket.

ameboid motion (uh-mee′boid)   The movement of a cell by means of the slow oozing of its cellular contents through cytoskeletal rearrangements.

amino acid (uh-mee′no)   An organic compound containing an amino group ($-NH_2$) and a carboxyl group ($-COOH$). Amino acids may be linked together to form the peptide chains of protein molecules.

aminoacyl tRNA (uh-mee″no-as′seel)   Molecule consisting of an amino acid covalently linked to a tRNA.

amniocentesis (am″nee-oh-sen-tee′sis)   Sampling of the amniotic fluid surrounding a fetus in order to obtain information about its development and genetic makeup.

amnion (am′nee-on)   An extraembryonic membrane that forms a fluid-filled sac for the protection of the developing embryo.

amphipathic molecule (am″fih-pa′thik)   Molecule that contains both hydrophobic and hydrophilic regions.

amylase (am′ih-lase)   Starch-digesting enzyme, e.g., human salivary amylase or pancreatic amylase.

anabolism (an-ab′oh-lizm)   Chemical reaction in which simpler substances are combined to form more complex substances, resulting in the storage of energy, the production of new cellular materials, and growth.

anaerobic (an″air-oh′bik)   Growing or metabolizing only in the absence of molecular oxygen.

analogous   Similar in function or appearance but not in origin or development.

anaphase (an′uh-faze)   The stage of mitosis and meiosis, occurring between metaphase and telophase, in which the chromosomes move toward opposite poles of the cell.

anaphylaxis (an″uh-fih-lak′sis)   An acute allergic reaction following sensitization to a foreign protein or other substance.

androecium (an-dree′see-um)   The male portion of a flower, composed of stamens.

androgen (an′dro-jen)   Any substance that possesses masculinizing properties, such as a sex hormone.

anemia (uh-nee′mee-uh)   A deficiency of hemoglobin or red blood cells.

aneuploidy (an′-you-ploy-dee)   Any chromosomal aberration in which there are either extra or missing copies of certain chromosomes.

angiosperm (an′jee-oh-sperm″)   The traditional name for plants having flowers and seeds enclosed in fruits.

angiotensin (an-jee-o-ten′sin) A compound formed by the action of renin and found in blood; stimulates aldosterone secretion by the adrenal cortex.

anhydrase (an-high′drase) An enzyme that chemically removes water from a substance, e.g., carbonic anhydrase, which catalyzes the formation of carbon dioxide from carbonic acid.

anion (an′eye-on) A negatively charged ion such as Cl^-.

anisogamy (an″eye-sog′uh-mee) Reproductive process involving motile gametes of similar form but dissimilar size, as in certain algae.

annelids (an′eh-lids) Segmented worms with true coeloms, such as earthworms.

annual A plant that completes its entire life cycle in one growing season.

annual ring A layer of wood (secondary xylem) formed in woody plants growing in temperate areas. One layer is usually formed per year.

anther (an′thur) The part of the stamen in flowers that produces microspores and, ultimately, pollen.

antheridium (an″thur-id′ee-im) The male gametangium in certain plants. Antheridia produce sperm.

anthocyanins (an″tho-sigh′ah-ninz) A class of pigments of blue, red, and violet flowers.

anthropoid (an′thro-poid) A member of a suborder of primates that includes monkeys, apes, and humans.

antibiotic (an″ty-by-ot′ik) Substance produced by microorganisms that has the capacity, in dilute solutions, to inhibit the growth of or destroy bacteria and other microorganisms; used largely in the treatment of infectious diseases in humans, animals, and plants.

antibodies (an-tih-bod′ees) Protein compounds (immunoglobulins) produced by plasma cells in response to specific antigens and having the capacity to react against the antigens.

anticodon (an′ty-koh″don) A sequence of three nucleotides in transfer RNA that is complementary to, and combines with, the three nucleotide codon on messenger RNA, thus helping to specify the addition of a particular amino acid to the end of a growing peptide.

antidiuretic hormone (an″ty-dy-uh-ret′ik) A hormone secreted by the posterior lobe of the pituitary and that controls the rate of water reabsorption by the kidney.

antigen (an′tih-jen) Any substance capable of stimulating an immune response; usually a protein or large carbohydrate that is foreign to the body.

antitoxin (an″ty-tok′sin) An antibody produced in response to the presence of a toxin (usually protein) released by a bacterium.

anus (ay′nus) The distal end and outlet of the digestive tract.

aorta (ay-or′tah) The largest and main systemic artery of the body; arises from the left ventricle and branches to distribute blood to all parts of the body; main artery leaving the heart in vertebrates.

apical dominance (ape′ih-kl) The inhibition of lateral buds by the stem apical meristem.

apical meristem (mehr′ih-stem) An area of dividing tissue located at the tips of plant stems and roots. Apical meristems cause an increase in the length of the plant body.

apoenzyme (ap″oh-en′zime) Protein portion of an enzyme; requires the presence of a specific coenzyme to become a complete functional enzyme.

apomixis (ap″uh-mix′us) A type of reproduction in which fruits and seeds are formed asexually.

arachnids (ah-rack′nids) Eight-legged arthropods such as scorpions and spiders.

archaebacteria (ar″kuh-bak-teer′ee-uh) Biochemically unique bacteria that are different from eubacteria in many respects.

archegonium (ar″ke-go′nee-um) The female gametangium of certain plants (such as mosses).

archenteron (ar-ken′ter-on) The central cavity of the gastrula stage of embryonic development, which is lined with endoderm; primitive digestive system.

arteries Thick-walled blood vessels that carry blood away from the heart and toward the body organs.

arteriole (ar-teer′ee-ole) A very small artery.

arthritis (ar-thry′tis) Inflammation of a joint.

arthropod (ar′throh-pod) An invertebrate, such as an insect or crustacean, that has jointed legs.

artificial selection Selection by humans of traits that are desirable in other plants or animals, and breeding only those individuals that possess the desired traits.

ascospores (ass′koh-sporz) A set of sexual spores, usually eight, contained in a special spore case (an ascus) of certain fungi.

asexual reproduction Reproduction in which there is no fusion of gametes and in which the genetic makeup of parent and of offspring is usually identical.

asthma (az′muh) A disease characterized by airway constriction and often leading to difficulty in breathing.

astigmatism (ah-stig′muh-tizm) A defect of vision resulting from irregularity in the curvature of the cornea or lens.

atherosclerosis (ath″ur-oh-skle-row′sis) A progressive disease in which muscle cells and lipid deposits accumulate in the inner lining of arteries, leading eventually to impaired circulation and heart disease.

atom The smallest quantity of an element that can retain the chemical properties of that element.

atomic orbital The space surrounding the atomic nucleus in which an electron will usually be found.

atrioventricular valve (ay″tree-oh-ven-trik′you-lur) A valve between each atrium and its ventricle that prevents backflow of blood.

atrium (of the heart) (ay′tree-um) The chamber on each side of the heart that receives blood from the veins.

auricle (of the heart) (or'ih-kl) Small accessory pouch attached to the atrium of the mammalian heart.

autoimmune disease (aw"toh-ih-mune') A disease in which the body produces antibodies against its own cells or tissues.

autonomic nervous system (aw-tuh-nom'ik) The portion of the peripheral nervous system that controls the visceral functions of the body, e.g., regulates smooth muscle, cardiac muscle, and glands, thereby helping to maintain homeostasis.

autosome (aw'toh-sohm) A chromosome other than the sex (X and Y) chromosomes.

autotrophy (aw'-toh-troh"fee) Obtaining organic molecules by synthesizing them from inorganic material.

auxin (awk'sin) A plant hormone involved in various aspects of growth and development.

axon (ax'on) The long, tubular extension of the neuron that transmits nerve impulses away from the cell body.

bacillus (ba-sil'us) A rod-shaped bacterium.

background extinction The continuous, low-level extinction of species that has been evident throughout much of the history of life.

bacteria (bak-teer'ee-uh) Unicellular prokaryotic microorganisms belonging to Kingdom Prokaryotae. Most are decomposers, but some are parasites or autotrophs.

bacteriophage (bac-teer'-ee-oh-fayj) Virus that can infect a bacterium (literally, "bacteria eater").

balanced polymorphism (pol"ee-mor'fizm) The presence in a population of two or more morphs (genetic variants) that are maintained in a stable frequency over several generations.

baroreceptors (bare'oh-ree-sep"torz) Receptors within certain blood vessels that are stimulated by pressure changes.

Barr body A condensed and inactivated X-chromosome appearing as a distinctive dense spot in the nucleus of certain cells of female mammals.

basal body (bay'sl) Structure that is similar to a centriole in its arrangement of microtubules and other components, and that is involved in the organization and anchorage of a cilium or flagellum.

basal metabolic rate The amount of energy expended by the body just to keep alive, when no food is being digested and no voluntary muscular work is being done.

base A hydrogen ion (proton) acceptor; turns red litmus paper blue.

basement membrane A connective tissue sheet that underlies vertebrate epithelium.

basidium (ba-sid'ee-um) The clublike spore-producing organ of certain fungi.

batesian mimicry (bate'see-un mim'ih-kree) The resemblance of a harmless or palatable species to one that is dangerous, unpalatable, or poisonous.

behavioral isolation A prezygotic isolating mechanism in which gamete exchange between two groups is prevented because each group possesses its own characteristic courtship behavior.

benthos (ben'thos) The organisms that live on the bottom of oceans or lakes.

berry A simple, fleshy fruit in which the fruit wall is soft throughout. Tomatoes, bananas, and grapes are berries.

bicuspid (by-kus'pid) Having two points or cusps (as bicuspid teeth), or two flaps (as the mitral valve of the heart).

biennial (by-en'ee-ul) A plant that takes two years (i.e., two growing seasons) to complete its life cycle.

bile Digestive juice produced by the liver.

binary fission (by'nare-ee fish'un) Equal division of a cell or organism into two; usually a variety of asexual reproduction.

binomial nomenclature (by-nome'ee-ul) System of naming organisms by the combination of the genus name and species epithet.

biodegradable (by"oh-de-gray'dih-bl) Substance that can be eliminated from the environment by the action of decay organisms or detritus feeders; for example, paper.

biogenesis (by-oh-jen'eh-sis) The generalization that all living things come only from preexisting living things.

biogeochemical cycle Process by which matter cycles from the living world to the nonliving physical environment and back again. Examples of biogeochemical cycles include the carbon cycle, the nitrogen cycle, and the phosphorus cycle.

biogeography The study of the distribution of organisms.

biological clocks Means by which activities of plants or animals are adapted to regularly recurring changes.

biological diversity The number and variety of living organisms; includes genetic diversity, species diversity, and ecological diversity; also called biodiversity.

biomass The total weight of all the organisms in a particular habitat.

biome (by'ohm) A large ecological community arising as a result of complex interactions of climate, soil, and biotic factors.

biosphere The entire zone of air, land, and water at the surface of the Earth that is occupied by living things.

biotic potential The maximum rate of increase of a species that occurs when all environmental conditions are optimal.

bipedal Walking on two feet.

bivalent (bý-vale-ent) Association of a pair of homologous chromosomes during meiotic prophase I; also known as a tetrad.

blastocoele (blas'toh-seel) The fluid-filled cavity of the blastula.

blastocyst (blas'toh-sist) The blastula stage in the development of the mammalian embryo; a spherical mass consisting of a single layer of cells, the trophoblast, from which a small cluster, the inner cell mass, projects into a central cavity.

blastomere (blas'toh-meer) One cell of a blastula; a cell formed during early cleavage of a vertebrate embryo.

blastopore (blas'toh-pore) Primitive opening into the gut of an early embryo, which may become the mouth or anus of the adult organism.

blastula (blas'tew-lah) Usually a spherical structure produced by cleavage of a fertilized ovum; consists of a single layer of cells surrounding a fluid-filled cavity.

B lymphocyte (lim'foh-site) A type of white blood cell responsible for antibody-mediated immunity. When stimulated, B lymphocytes differentiate to become plasma cells that produce antibodies; also called B cells.

bottleneck Genetic drift that may result from the sudden decrease in a population due to environmental factors.

Bowman's capsule Double-walled, hollow sac of cells that surrounds the glomerulus at the end of each nephron.

brachiate To swing, arm to arm, from one branch to another.

brachiopods (bray'kee-oh-pods) Marine organisms possessing a pair of shells and, internally, a pair of coiled arms with ciliated tentacles.

branchial (brang'kee-ul) Pertaining to gills or the gill region.

bronchiole (bronk'ee-ole) Tiny air duct of the lung that branches from a bronchus; divides to form air sacs (alveoli).

bronchus (bronk'us) pl. **bronchi** (bronk'eye) One of the branches of the trachea and its immediate branches within the lung.

Brownian movement A random motion of microscopic particles in solution or suspension, which results from their being bumped by water molecules.

brush border The many fine hairlike processes (microvilli) extending from the free surface of certain epithelial cells, such as the cells of the proximal convoluted tubules of the mammalian kidney.

bryophytes (bry'oh-fites) Members of the plant kingdom comprising mosses, liverworts, and hornworts.

bryozoans (bry"uh-zoh'uns) Minute aquatic invertebrates that form fixed, branching, mosslike colonies or thin, lacy encrustations on rocks.

bud An undeveloped shoot that can develop into flowers, stems, or leaves. Buds are enclosed in bud scales.

bud primordium (pry-mor'dee-um) An embryonic lateral bud, evident in the stem apical meristem.

bud scale A modified leaf that covers and protects winter buds.

budding Asexual reproduction in which a small part of the parent's body bulges outward and develops into a new individual.

buffers Substances in a solution that tend to lessen the change in hydrogen ion concentration (pH) that otherwise would be produced by adding acids or bases. Buffers stabilize the pH of solutions in cells.

bulb A globose, fleshy, underground bud. A bulb is a short stem with fleshy leaves, e.g., onion.

bulliform cell (bool-ee'form) A large, thin-walled cell found in the epidermis of some monocots; aids in the folding and unfolding of leaves associated with periods of drought.

bundle sheath A ring of cells surrounding the vascular bundle in dicot and monocot leaves.

calcitonin (kal-sih-toh'nin) A hormone secreted by the thyroid gland that rapidly lowers the calcium content in the blood.

callus (kal'us) Undifferentiated tissue in plant tissue culture.

calorie (kal'oh-ree) A unit of heat. The Calorie used in the study of metabolism is the kilocalorie and is defined as the amount of heat required to raise the temperature of 1 kilogram of water 1°C.

Calvin cycle Cyclic series of reactions occurring in the light-independent phase of photosynthesis that fixes carbon dioxide and produces glucose.

calyx (kay'liks) The collective term for the sepals of a flower.

cambium (kam'bee-um) A layer of meristematic tissue that produces lateral (secondary) growth in plants.

capillaries (kap'i-lare-eez) Microscopic blood vessels occurring in the tissues that permit exchange of materials between tissues and blood.

capsule (1) The portion of the moss sporophyte that contains spores; (2) a simple, dry, dehiscent fruit that opens along many seams or pores to release seeds, such as a cotton fruit.

carbohydrate Compound containing carbon, hydrogen, and oxygen, in the approximate ratio of 1C:2H:1O, such as sugars, starches, and cellulose.

carbon cycle The worldwide circulation of carbon from the abiotic environment into living things and back into the abiotic environment.

carboxyl group (kar-bok'sil) A functional group characteristic of organic acids;

carcinogen (kar'sin-oh-jen, kar-sin'oh-gen) A substance that causes cancer or accelerates its development.

cardiac (kar'dee-ak) Pertaining to the heart.

cardiac muscle Distinctive involuntary but striated type of muscle occurring only in the vertebrate heart.

carnivore (kar'ni-vor) An animal that primarily eats flesh.

carotene (kare'oh-teen) A yellow to orange-red pigment found in carrots, sweet potatoes, leafy vegetables, etc.; can be converted in the animal body to vitamin A.

carotenoid A group of yellow to orange pigments in plants; comprises two groups: carotenes and xanthophylls.

carpel (kar'pul)   The female reproductive unit of a flower; carpels bear ovules.

carrier-mediated transport   Any form of transport across a membrane that utilizes a transport protein with a binding site for a specific substance.

carrying capacity   The maximum number of organisms that a habitat can support.

cartilage (kar'til-ij)   Flexible skeletal tissue of vertebrates.

Casparian strip (kas-pare'ee-un)   A band of waterproof material around the radial and transverse walls of endodermal root cells.

cast   Fossil formed by a mold being infiltrated by minerals that harden.

catalyst (kat'ah-list)   A substance that increases the speed at which a chemical reaction occurs without being used up during the reaction.

cation (kat'eye-un)   An ion bearing a positive charge.

cell   The basic structural and functional unit of life, which consists of living material bounded by a membrane.

cell cycle   Cyclic series of events in the life of a dividing eukaryotic cell consisting of mitosis, cytokinesis, and the stages of interphase, which are the G_1 (first gap), S (DNA synthesis), and G_2 (second gap) phases.

cell plate   Structure that forms during cytokinesis in plants, separating the two daughter cells produced by mitosis. The cell plate gives rise to the middle lamella between the daughter cells.

cellulose (sel'yoo-lohs)   A complex polysaccharide that is the main constituent of the cell walls of plants.

centriole (sen'tree-ohl)   One of a pair of small, cylindrical organelles lying at right angles to each other near the nucleus in the cytoplasm of animal cells and certain protist and plant cells; each centriole contains 9 triplets of microtubules (9 × 3 structure).

centromere (sen'tro-meer)   Specialized constricted region of a chromatid, that contains the kinetochore; sister chromatids at prophase are joined in the vicinity of their centromeres.

cercaria (sur-kar'ee-ah)   The final free-swimming larval stage of a liver fluke parasite.

cerebellum (ser-eh-bel'um)   The deeply convoluted subdivision of the brain lying beneath the cerebrum; concerned with the coordination of muscular movements.

cerebral cortex (ser-ee'brul kor'tex)   The outer layer of the cerebrum composed of gray matter and consisting of densely packed nerve cells.

cerebrum (ser-ee'brum)   Largest subdivision of the brain; functions as the center for learning, voluntary movement, and interpretation of sensation.

chaparral (shap"uh-ral')   Distinctive vegetation type characteristic of certain areas with cool moist winters and long dry summers; dominated by drought-resistant evergreen shrubs and small trees.

chelicera (kee-lis'er-ah)   Pincers; the first pair of appendages in arthropods, located immediately anterior to the mouth, and used to manipulate food into the mouth.

chemical evolution   The origin of life from nonliving matter.

chemoautotrophs (kee"moh-aw'toh-trofes)   Autotrophic organisms that obtain energy and synthesize organic compounds from inorganic compounds.

chemoreceptor (kee"moh-ree-sep'tor)   A sense organ or sensory cell that responds to chemical stimuli.

chemotropism (kee"moh-tro'pizm)   A growth response to a chemical stimulus.

chiasma (ky-az'muh) pl. **chiasmata**   A site in a tetrad where homologous (non-sister) chromatids have undergone exchange by breakage and rejoining.

chitin (ky'tin)   A polysaccharide containing nitrogen that forms the exoskeleton of arthropods and the cell walls of many fungi.

chlorophyll (klor'oh-fil)   A group of light-trapping green pigments found in most photosynthetic organisms.

chloroplast (klor'oh-plast)   A chlorophyll-bearing intracellular organelle of some plant cells; site of photosynthesis.

choanocyte (koh-an'oh-sight)   A unique cell having a flagellum surrounded by a thin cytoplasmic collar; characteristic of sponges and one group of protists.

cholinergic neuron (kohl"in-air'jik)   A nerve cell that secretes acetylcholine as a transmitter substance.

chordates (kor'dates)   A phylum of animals that possess, at some time in their lives, a cartilaginous dorsal skeletal structure called a notochord.

chorion (kor'ee-on)   An extraembryonic membrane in reptiles, birds, and mammals that forms an outer cover around the embryo, and in mammals contributes to the formation of the placenta.

chorionic villus sampling (CVS) (kor"ee-on'ik)   Study of extra-embryonic cells that are genetically identical to the cells of the embryo, making it possible to assess the genetic makeup of the embryo.

chromatid (kroh'mah-tid)   One of the two halves of a duplicated chromosome.

chromatin (kroh'mah-tin)   The complex of DNA, protein, and RNA that makes up eukaryotic chromosomes.

chromosomes (kro'moh-soms)   Structures in the nucleus, composed of chromatin and containing the genes. The chromosomes become visible with the microscope as distinct rodlike structures when the cell divides.

chrysalis (krih'suh-lis)   Pupa of a butterfly or moth; immobile stage of life cycle between larval (caterpillar) form and adult winged insect.

cilium (sil'ee-um) pl. **cilia**   One of many short, hairlike structures that project from the surface of some cells and are used for locomotion or movement of materials across the cell surface; structurally like flagella, including a cylinder of 9 doublet microtubules and 2 central single microtubules, all covered by a plasma membrane.

circadian rhythm (sir-kay′dee-un)   An internal rhythm that approximates the 24-hour day. Circadian rhythms are found in plants, animals, and many other organisms.

cisterna (sis-tur′nah)   A hollow or cavity.

citric acid cycle   Aerobic series of chemical reactions in which acetyl-CoA is completely degraded to carbon dioxide and water with the release of metabolic energy (ATP); also known as the Krebs cycle.

class   A taxon composed of related, similar orders of living organisms.

cleavage   First of several cell divisions in early embryonic development that converts the zygote into a multicellular blastula.

climax community   The more or less stable community in equilibrium with existing environmental conditions.

clitoris (klít-o-ris)   A small, erectile structure at the anterior part of the vulva in female mammals; homologous to the male penis.

cloaca (klow-a′ka)   An exit chamber in lower vertebrates that receives digestive wastes and urine; may also serve as exit for reproductive system.

clone   A population of cells descended by mitotic division from a single ancestral cell, or a population of genetically identical organisms asexually propagated from a single individual.

coacervate (koh-as′sir-vate)   A protobiont formed from a relatively complex mixture of polypeptides, nucleic acids, and polysaccharides.

coccus (kok′us) pl. **cocci**   A bacterium with a spherical shape.

cochlea (kok′lee-ah)   The structure of the inner ear of mammals that contains the auditory receptors.

codominance (koh″dom′in-ints)   Condition in which both alleles of a locus are expressed in a heterozygote.

codon (koh′don)   A triplet of mRNA bases that specifies an amino acid or a signal to terminate the polypeptide.

coelom (see′lum)   The main body cavity of most animals.

coenocyte (see′no-site)   A giant multinucleated cell.

coenzyme (koh-en′zime)   An organic substance that is required for a particular enzymatic reaction to occur; participates in the reaction by donating or accepting some reactant; loosely bound to enzyme. Most of the vitamins function as coenzymes.

coevolution   The interdependent evolution of two or more species that occurs as a result of their interactions over a long period of time. Flowering plants and their animal pollinators are an example of coevolution because each has profoundly affected the other's characteristics.

cofactor   A nonprotein substance needed by an enzyme for normal activity; some cofactors are metal ions; others are coenzymes.

coleoptile (kol-ee-op′tile)   A protective sheath that encloses the stem in certain monocots.

colinearity (koh-lin-ee-air′ih-tee)   The one-to-one serial correspondence between the linear sequence of the nucleotide codons in the mRNA, and the linear sequence of amino acids in the polypeptide coded for by that sequence.

collagen (kol′ah-jen)   Protein in connective tissue fibers; converted to gelatin by boiling.

collenchyma (kol-en′kih-mah)   Living cells with moderately but unevenly thickened cell walls. Collenchyma cells help support the primary plant body.

colloid (kol′oid)   A substance composed of very small, insoluble and nondiffusible particles larger than molecules but small enough to remain suspended in fluid without settling to the bottom.

commensal (kum-men′sul)   An organism that lives in intimate association with another organism of a different species without harming or benefiting the other.

community   An assemblage of different species of organisms that live in a defined area or habitat. The organisms constituting the community interact in various ways with one another.

companion cell   A cell in plant phloem, responsible for loading and unloading sugar into the sieve tube member for conduction.

competition   The interaction among organisms that vie for the same resources in an ecosystem (such as food, living space, or other resources).

competitive exclusion   The concept that no two species with identical living requirements can occupy the same ecological niche indefinitely. Eventually, one species will be excluded by the other as a result of interspecific (between-species) competition for a resource in limited supply.

competitive inhibition   Interference with enzyme action by an abnormal substrate that competes with the normal substrate for the site.

complete flower   A flower that possesses all four parts: sepals, petals, stamens, and carpels.

compound eye   An eye, such as that of an insect, composed of many smaller, light-sensitive units called ommatidia.

compression   A fossil in which the organism was trapped in sediments (without being completely decomposed) and subsequently flattened.

cone   (1) In botany, a reproductive structure in many gymnosperms that produces either microspores or megaspores. (2) In zoology, the conical photoreceptive cell of the retina that is particularly sensitive to bright light, and, by distinguishing light of various wave lengths, mediates color vision.

conifers (kon′ih-furs)   A group of gymnosperms that are evergreen and bear needle-like leaves and cones.

conjugation   A sexual phenomenon in certain protists that involves exchange or fusion of a cell with another similar cell. The term is also is used sometimes for DNA exchange in bacteria.

connective tissue   Vertebrate tissue consisting mostly of an intercellular matrix (composed of cell products) in which the cells are embedded, e.g., bone.

consumer   An organism that cannot synthesize its own food from inorganic materials and therefore must use the bodies of other organisms as a source of energy and body-building materials. Also called heterotroph.

continental shelf   The submerged, relatively flat ocean bottom that surrounds continents. The continental shelf extends out into the ocean to the point where the ocean floor begins a steep descent.

contractile root   A specialized type of root that contracts and pulls a bulb or shoot deeper into the soil.

contractile vacuole (vak′yoo-ohl)   A vacuole that expands, filling with water, and periodically contracts, ejecting the water from the cell.

convection   The transfer of heat within liquids and gases that results from movement of the heated particles.

convergent evolution   The independent evolution of structural or functional similarity in two or more organisms of widely different, unrelated ancestry.

copulation   Sexual union; act of physical joining of two animals during which sperm cells are transferred from one to the other.

Coriolis effect   The tendency of moving air or water to be deflected from its path to the right in the Northern Hemisphere and to the left in the Southern Hemisphere; caused by the direction of the Earth's rotation.

cork   A plant tissue produced by the cork cambium. Cork cells are dead at maturity and function for protection.

cork cambium (kam′bee-um)   A lateral meristem in plants that produces cork cells and cork parenchyma. Cork cambium and the tissues it produces make up the outer bark on a woody plant.

cork parenchyma (par-en′kih-mah)   One or more layers of parenchyma cells produced by the cork cambium.

corm   A short, thickened underground stem specialized for food storage and asexual reproduction (e.g., crocus and gladiolus).

cornea (kor′nee-ah)   Transparent anterior covering of the eye.

corolla (kor-ohl′ah)   A collective term for the petals of a flower.

corpus allatum (kor′pus al-lah′tum)   An endocrine gland located in the head of insects that secretes juvenile hormone.

corpus callosum (kah-loh′sum)   A large bundle of nerve fibers interconnecting the two cerebral hemispheres.

corpus luteum (loo-tee′um)   Pocket of endocrine tissue in the ovary that is derived from the follicle cells; secretes the hormone progesterone.

cortex (kor′tex)   The outer layer of an organ (e.g., cortex of brain); in plants, the tissue beneath the epidermis in the stems and roots of many nonwoody plants.

co-transport   The active transport of a substance from a region of low to high concentration by coupling its transport with the transport of a substance down its concentration gradient.

cotyledon (kot″i-lee′dun)   The seed leaf of the embryo of a plant, which may contain stored food for germination.

covalent bond   Chemical bond involving one or more shared pairs of electrons.

cretinism (kree′tin-izm)   A chronic condition due to congenital lack of thyroid secretion; results in retarded physical and mental development.

cristae (kris′tee)   Shelflike or finger-like inward projections of the inner membrane of a mitochondrion.

crossing over   The breaking and rejoining of homologous (non-sister) chromatids during early meiotic prophase I, resulting in an exchange of genetic material.

ctenophores (teen′oh-forz)   Marine animals ("comb jellies") whose bodies consist of two layers of cells enclosing a gelatinous mass. The outer surface is covered with comb rows of cilia, by which the animal moves.

cultural evolution   The progressive addition of knowledge to the human experience.

cuticle (kew′tih-kl)   A noncellular waxy covering over the epidermis of the above-ground portion of plants; reduces water loss.

cyanobacteria (sy-an′oh-bak-teer′ee-uh)   Prokaryotic photosynthetic microorganisms that possess chlorophyll and produce oxygen. Formerly known as blue-green algae.

cycads (sih′kads)   Members of a taxon of gymnosperms that live mainly in tropical and semitropical regions and have stout stems (to 20 meters in height) and fernlike leaves.

cyclic AMP (cAMP)   A form of adenosine monophosphate in which the phosphate is part of a ring-shaped structure; acts as a regulatory molecule and second messenger in organisms ranging from bacteria to humans.

cyclosis (sy-kloh′sis)   The streaming motion of the living material in cells.

cytochromes (sy′toh-kromz)   The iron-containing heme proteins of the electron transport system that are alternately oxidized and reduced.

cytokinesis (sy″toh-kih-nee′sis)   Stage of cell division in which the cytoplasm is divided to form two daughter cells.

cytokinin (sy′toh-kih′nin)   A plant hormone that promotes cell division and is involved in various aspects of plant growth and development.

cytoplasm (sy′toh-plazm)   General cellular contents exclusive of the nucleus.

cytosine   A nitrogenous base (a pyrimidine) found in nucleic acids.

cytoskeleton   Internal structure of fibers, including microfilaments, intermediate filaments, and microtubules.

cytosol   Fluid component of the cytoplasm in which the organelles are suspended.

cytotoxic T cells T lymphocytes that destroy cancer cells and other pathogenic cells on contact. Also known as killer T cells.

day-neutral plant A plant that does not flower in response to variations in day length which occur with changing seasons.

deamination (dee-am-ih-nay′shun) Removal of an amino group (—NH$_2$) from an amino acid or other organic compound.

deciduous tree (de-sid′yoo-us) A tree which has leaves that fall off in autumn, with new leaves produced the following spring.

decomposers Microorganisms (such as bacteria and fungi) that break down organic material.

dehiscent fruit (dih-his′sent) A simple, dry fruit that spontaneously splits open to liberate the seeds; compare with indehiscent fruit.

dehydrogenation (dee-hy″dro-jen-ay′shun) A form of oxidation in which hydrogen atoms are removed from a molecule.

deme An interbreeding local population within a species.

denature (dee-nay′ture) To alter the physical properties and three-dimensional structure of a protein, nucleic acid, or other macromolecule by treating it with excess heat, strong acids, or strong bases.

dendrite (den′drite) The projections from a nerve cell that conduct a nerve impulse toward the cell body.

denitrifying bacteria (dee-ny′tri-fy-ing) Bacteria that perform denitrification (convert ammonia to nitrogen gas).

dentition The number, arrangement, and type of teeth in the mouth.

deoxyribose Pentose sugar lacking an OH group on carbon-2′; a constituent of DNA.

depolarization (dee-pol″ar-ih-zay′shun) Change in electric charge across a plasma membrane that produces the action potential.

dermis (dur′mis) The layer of dense connective tissue beneath the epidermis in the skin of vertebrates.

desmosomes (dez′moh-somz) Button-like plaques, present on two opposing cell surfaces, that hold the cells together by means of protein filaments that span the intercellular space.

determination The progressive limitation of a cell line's potential fate during development.

detritus feeders (deh-try′tus) Organisms, other than microorganisms, that feed on dead, decaying organisms or their fragments.

deuterostome (doo′ter-oh-stome) A division of coelomate animals that includes the echinoderms and chordates; characterized by radial cleavage and development of the anus from the blastopore.

diapause (dy′uh-paws) Inactive state (arrested growth and development) of an insect during the pupal stage.

diastole (dy-as′toh-lee) Relaxation of the heart muscle, especially that of the ventricle, during which the lumen becomes filled with blood; see also systole.

dichotomous A type of branching in which the branches or veins always branch into two more or less equal parts.

dicotyledon (dy-kot-ih-lee′dun) One of the two classes of flowering plants with embryos having two seed leaves, or cotyledons; also known as a dicot; see also monocotyledon.

differentiation Development toward a more mature state; a process changing a young, relatively unspecialized cell to a more specialized cell.

diffusion The net movement of molecules from a region of high concentration to one of lower concentration of that substance.

dihybrid cross (dy-hy′brid) A genetic cross that takes into account the behavior of alleles of two loci.

dikaryotic cells (dy-kare-ee-ot′ik) Fungal cells that have two unfused nuclei per cell ($n + n$).

dimorphic (dy-mor′fik) A species that has two forms, as for example male and female (sexual dimorphism).

dinoflagellates (dy″noh-flaj′eh-lates) Single-celled, biflagellate algae that are an important component of plankton.

dioecious (dy-ee′shus) Having male and female reproductice structures on separate plants; compare with monoecious.

diploid (dip′loid) The condition of a having two sets of chromosomes per cell.

directional selection The gradual replacement of one phenotype with another (for example, an increase in size) due to environmental change.

disaccharide (dy-sak′ah-ride) A double sugar, such as sucrose, which consists of a glucose and a fructose subunit.

displacement activity In animal behavior, an innate, stereotyped response that appears to be inappropriate or irrelevant to the situation.

disruptive selection A special type of directional selection in which changes in the environment favor two or more variant phenotypes at the expense of the mean.

distal Remote; farther from the point of reference.

DNA Deoxyribonucleic acid; present in chromosomes; contains genetic information coded in specific sequences of its constituent nucleotides.

DNA replication The synthesis of DNA by using a complementary strand of DNA as a template.

dominant allele (al-leel′) The allele that is always expressed when it is present, regardless of whether it is homozygous or heterozygous.

dorsal (dor′sl) Pertaining to the back of an animal.

double fertilization A process in the flowering plant reproductive cycle in which there are two fertilizations: One results in the formation of a young plant; the second results in the formation of the endosperm.

Down syndrome An inherited defect in which individuals have abnormalities of the face, eyelids, tongue, and other parts of the body, and are retarded in both their physical and mental development; usually results from a trisomy of chromosome 21.

drupe (droop) A simple, fleshy fruit in which the inner wall of the fruit is hard and stony. Peaches and cherries are drupes.

duodenum (doo"uh-dee'num) Portion of the small intestine directly adjacent to the stomach.

ecdysone (ek'dih-sone) The hormone that induces molting (ecdysis) in insects.

echinoderms (eh-kine'oh-derms) Spiny-skinned marine animals such as sea stars, sea urchins, and sea cucumbers.

ecological isolation A prezygotic isolating mechanism in which sexual reproduction is prevented between two groups that are located in the same geographic area because of their preference for two different ecological habitats.

ecological niche The functional role of a species within a community; depends on the organism's structural adaptations, physiological responses, and behavior.

ecological pyramid A graphic representation of the relative energy value at each trophic level. See pyramid of biomass, pyramid of energy, and pyramid of numbers.

ecology (ee-kol'uh-jee) The study of the interrelations between living things and their environment, both physical and biotic.

ecosphere The interactions among and between all the Earth's living organisms and the air (atmosphere), land (lithosphere), and water (hydrosphere) that they occupy.

ecosystem (ee'koh-sis-tem) A community of organisms and its nonliving, physical environment.

ectoderm (ek'toh-derm) The outer of the three embryonic germ layers of the gastrula; gives rise to the skin and nervous systems; see also mesoderm and endoderm.

edaphic factors (ee-daf'ik) The physical, chemical, and biological properties of the soil.

effector (1) A muscle or gland that contracts or secretes in direct response to nerve impulses; (2) activator of an allosteric enzyme.

efferent (ef'fur-ent) Pertaining to a structure that leads away from another structure or organ, such as the efferent arteriole of the kidney nephron.

ejaculation (ee-jak-yoo-laý-shun) A sudden expulsion, as in the ejection of semen from the penis.

electrocardiogram (eh-lek-troh-kar'dee-oh-gram) **(ECG, EKG)** A graphic record made by an electrocardiograph machine of the electrical activity of the heart.

electrochemical potential The potential energy possessed by a system in which there is a difference in electrical charge, as well as a concentration gradient of ions across a membrane.

electroencephalogram (eh-lek-troh-en-sef'uh-loh-gram) **(EEG)** A graphic record of changes in electrical potential associated with activity of the brain.

electron A negatively charged subatomic particle located at some distance from the atomic nucleus; see also neutron and proton.

electron transport system A series of chemical reactions during which hydrogens or their electrons are passed along from one acceptor molecule to another, with the release of energy.

elimination The ejection of waste products, especially undigested food remnants, from the digestive tract (not to be confused with excretion).

embryo (em'bree-oh) A young multicullar organism before it emerges from the egg, seed, or body of its mother; the developing human organism until the end of the second month, after which it is referred to as a fetus.

embryo sac The female gametophyte generation in flowering plants.

endangered species A species whose numbers are so severely reduced that it is in imminent danger of becoming extinct. Compare threatened species.

endergonic reactions (end"er-gon'ik) Nonspontaneous reactions requiring a net input of free energy.

endocrine glands (en'doh-crin) Glands that secrete products directly into the blood or tissue fluid instead of into ducts.

endocytosis (en"doh-sy-toh'sis) The active transport of substances into a cell by the formation of invaginated regions of the plasma membrane which pinch off and become cytoplasmic vesicles.

endoderm (en'doh-derm) The inner germ layer of the gastrula lining the archenteron; becomes the digestive tract and its outgrowths—the liver, lungs, and pancreas; see also ectoderm and mesoderm.

endodermis (en"doh-der'mis) The innermost layer of the cortex in the plant root. Endodermis cells have a Casparian strip running around radial and transverse walls.

endogenous (en-doj'eh-nus) Produced from within the body, or due to internal causes.

endolymph (en'doh-limf) The fluid of the membranous labyrinth of the ear.

endometrium (en"doh-mee'tree-um) Uterine lining in female mammals.

endoplasmic reticulum (en"doh-plaz'mik reh-tik'yoo-lum) **(ER)** Interconnected network of numerous internal membranes within eukaryotic cells.

endorphins (en-dor'finz) Polypeptide transmitter substance of certain brain and visceral neurons whose action is mimicked by opiate alkaloids.

endosperm (en'doh-sperm) The triploid nutritive tissue that is found at some point in all flowering plant seeds.

endosymbiont theory (en"doh-sim'bee-ont) Certain organelles such as mitochondria and chloroplasts evolved from symbiotic prokaryotes that lived inside free-living prokaryotic cells.

endothelium (en-doh-theel′ee-um) The tissue that lines the cavities of the heart, blood, and lymph vessels.

endothermic (en″doh-ther′mik) Referring to the ability of animals to use metabolic energy to maintain a constant body temperature despite variations in environmental temperature; see also poikilothermic.

enhancers Regulatory elements that can be located long distances away from the actual coding regions of a gene.

enkephalins (en-kef′ah-linz) Polypeptide transmitter substances employed by certain brain neurons that seem to function in pain perception and whose action is, like endorphins, mimicked by opiate alkaloids.

entropy (en′trop-ee) Disorderliness; a quantitative measure of the amount of randomness or disorder of a system.

environmental resistance The sum of the physical and biological factors that prevent a species from reproducing at its maximum rate (for example, competition for food and space).

enzyme (en′zime) A protein catalyst that accelerates a specific chemical reaction by lowering the activation energy required for that reaction.

eosinophil (ee-oh-sin′oh-fil) A type of white blood cell whose cytoplasmic granules absorb acidic stains.

epicotyl (ep′ih-kot″il) The part of the stem of a young plant embryo or seedling located above the point of attachment of the cotyledon(s).

epidermis (ep-ih-dur′mis) An outer layer of cells covering the body of plants and animals; functions primarily for protection.

epididymis (ep-ih-did′ih-mis) pl. **epididymides** A coiled tube that receives sperm from the testes and conveys it to the vas deferens.

epigenesis (ep-ih-jen′eh-sis) The theory that an embryo develops from a structureless cell by the addition of new parts.

epinephrine (ep-ih-nef′rin) The chief hormone of the adrenal medulla; stimulates the sympathetic nervous system.

epiphyte (ep′ih-fite) A plant that grows attached to another plant, using it for position and support.

epistasis (ep″ih-sta′sis) Condition in which certain alleles at one locus can alter the expression of alleles at a different locus.

epithelial tissue (ep-ih-theel′ee-al) The type of tissue that covers body surfaces, lines body cavities, and forms glands; also called epithelium.

epoch A major interval of geological time; a subdivision of a period.

era In geology, one of the main divisions of geological time. Eras are divided into periods.

erythrocyte (er-eeth′roh-site) Vertebrate red blood cell.

esophagus (ee-sof′ah-gus) The muscular tube extending from the pharynx to the stomach.

estradiol (es″-trah-di′-ol) The most potent naturally occurring estrogen in humans; principal female sex hormone.

estrogens (es′troh-jens) Female sex hormones produced by the ovary; promote the development and maintenance of female reproductive structures and of secondary sexual characteristics.

estrus (es′trus) The recurrent period of heat or sexual receptivity occurring around ovulation in female mammals having estrous cycles.

estuary A coastal body of water that connects to oceans, in which freshwater from the land mixes with salt water from the oceans.

ethology (ee-thol′oh-jee) The study of animal behavior under natural conditions.

ethylene (eth′ih-leen) A plant hormone involved in various aspects of plant growth and development.

eubacteria (yoo′bak-teer″ee-ah) Bacteria other than the archaebacteria.

euchromatin (yoo-croh′-mah-tin) Loosely coiled chromatin that is generally capable of transcription.

euglenoids (yoo-glee′noids) A group of flagellated protists that usually possess chlorophyll and photosynthesize.

eukaryote (yoo″kare′ee-ote) Organism whose cells possess nuclei and other membrane-bounded organelles.

eustachian tube (yoo-stay′shee-un) The auditory tube passing between the middle ear cavity and the pharynx in vertebrates; permits the equalization of pressure on the tympanic membrane.

eutherian (yoo-theer′ee-an) Pertaining to placental mammals in which a well-formed placenta is present and the young are born at a relatively advanced stage of development; includes all living mammals except monotremes and marsupials.

evolution Any cumulative genetic change in a population of organisms from generation to generation.

excretion (ek-skree′shun) The discharge from the body of a waste product of metabolism (not to be confused with the elimination of undigested food materials).

exergonic (ex-er-gon′ik) A reaction characterized by the release of free energy.

exocrine glands (ex′oh-crin) Glands that excrete their products through ducts.

exocytosis (ex″oh-sy-toh′sis) Export of materials from the cell by fusion of cytoplasmic vesicles with the plasma membrane.

exogenous (ek-sodj′eh-nus) Due to, or produced by, an external cause; not arising within the body.

exon (1) A protein-coding region of a eukaryotic gene; (2) the RNA transcribed from such a region (see intron).

exoskeleton (ex″oh-skel′eh-ton) An external skeleton, such as the shell of mollusks or outer covering of arthropods; provides protection and sites of attachment for muscles.

extension   A straightening out; especially refers to muscular movement by which a flexed part is made straight.

extensor   A muscle that serves to extend or straighten a limb.

exteroceptor (ex'tur-oh-sep"tor)   One of the sense organs that receives sensory stimuli from the outside world, such as the eyes or touch receptors.

extinction   The disappearance of a species from a given habitat.

F₁ generation (first filial)   The first generation of filial offspring resulting from a particular cross.

F₂ generation (second filial)   The offspring of the F₁ generation.

facilitated diffusion   The transport of ions or molecules across a membrane by a specific carrier protein. As in simple diffusion, net transport is down a concentration gradient, and no additional energy has to be supplied.

facilitation   The effect of a nerve impulse on a postsynaptic neuron, which brings the postsynaptic neuron closer to firing.

family   In taxonomy, the taxon between order and genus.

fatty acid   An organic acid containing a long hydrocarbon chain. Fatty acids are components of phospholipids and triacylglycerols.

feces (fee'seez)   Solidified waste products eliminated by the digestive tract of an organism.

feedback control   System in which the accumulation of the product of a reaction leads to a decrease in its rate of production, or a deficiency of the product leads to an increase in its rate of production.

fermentation   Anaerobic respiration that utilizes organic compounds as both electron donors and acceptors.

fertilization   The fusion of male and female gametes; results in the formation of a zygote.

fetus   The unborn offspring after it has largely completed its embryonic development; from the third month of pregnancy to birth in humans.

fiber   In plants, a type of sclerenchyma. Fibers are long, tapered cells with thick walls.

fibrin   Blood protein that forms clots.

fibroblasts (fy'broh-blasts)   Connective tissue cells that secrete the intercellular material of, for example, bones and cartilage.

fibrous root system   A root system in plants that has several roots similar in length and thickness.

filament   In botany, the thin stalk of the stamen that bears the anther at its tip.

fission (fish'un)   Process of asexual reproduction in which an organism divides into two approximately equal parts; carried out by prokaryotes and certain eukaryotes.

flagellum (flah-jel'um)   Long, whiplike movable structure of cells that is used in locomotion. Eukaryote flagella are composed of two single microtubules surrounded by nine double microtubules, but prokaryote flagella are filaments ro-tated by special structures located in the plasma membrane and cell wall.

flexor (flek'sor)   A muscle that serves to bend a limb.

fluid mosaic model   The modern picture of the plasma membrane (and other cell membranes) in which protein molecules float in a phospholipid bilayer.

follicle (fol'i-kl)   (1) A simple, dry, dehiscent fruit that splits open along one seam to liberate the seeds; (2) a small sac of cells in the mammalian ovary that contains a maturing egg.

food chain   A sequence of organisms through which energy is transferred from its ultimate source in a plant; each organism eats the preceding member and is eaten by the following member of the sequence.

food web   The system of interconnected food chains in a community.

foot   In botany, the basal portion of the moss sporophyte that serves to anchor it to the gametophyte.

foramen magnum (for-ay'men)   The opening in the vertebrate skull through which the spinal cord passes.

foramen ovale (for-ay'men oh-vah'lay)   The oval window between the right and left atria in the mammalian heart, present in the fetus, by means of which blood entering the right atrium may enter the aorta without passing through the lung.

fossil   Parts or traces of an ancient organism preserved in rock.

founder effect   Genetic drift that results from a small number of individuals colonizing a new area.

frameshift mutation   Mutation that results when nucleotides are inserted into or deleted from the DNA, thereby altering the reading frame so that all of the codons downstream from the mutation will be changed.

frond   The leaf of a fern.

fruit   In flowering plants, a mature, ripened ovary. Fruits contain seeds and usually provide seed protection and dispersal.

fucoxanthin (few"koh-zan'thin)   The brown pigment found in diatoms, brown algae, and dinoflagellates.

fundamental niche   The potential ecological niche that an organism could have if there were no competition from other species. Compare realized niche.

fungus pl. **fungi**   A complex eukaryote that obtains nutrients by assimilation. Most fungi are decomposers; a few are parasitic.

G₁ phase   Gap phase in interphase of the cell cycle before DNA synthesis begins.

G₂ phase   Gap phase in interphase of the cell cycle that occurs after DNA synthesis and before mitosis.

gametangium (gam"uh-tan'gee-um)   Special multicellular or unicellular structure of plants, protists, and fungi in which gametes are formed.

gamete (gam'eet)   A sex cell; in plants and animals, an egg or sperm. In sexual reproduction, the union of gametes results in the formation of a zygote. The chromosome number of a gamete is designated *n*. Species that are not polyploid have haploid gametes and diploid zygotes.

gametic isolation (gam-ee'tik)   A prezygotic isolating mechanism in which sexual reproduction between two individuals cannot occur because of chemical differences between the gametes of the two species.

gametophyte (gam-ee'toh-fite) The haploid, gamete-producing stage in the life cycle of a plant.

ganglion (gang'glee-on)   A knotlike mass of the cell bodies of neurons located outside the central nervous system.

gap junction   Structure consisting of specialized regions of the plasma membranes of two adjacent cells containing numerous pores that allow passage of certain small molecules and ions between them.

gastrula (gas'troo-lah)   Early stage of embryonic development during which the embryo has two layers and is cup-shaped.

gemma (jem'mah)   In bryophytes, a cluster of asexual reproductive cells that develop into a new plant.

gemmae cup   Saucer-shaped structure found on certain bryophytes; it contains gemmae.

gene   A discrete unit of hereditary information that usually specifies a protein. It consists of DNA and is located in a chromosome.

gene amplification   Process by which multiple copies of a gene are produced by selective replication, thus allowing for increased synthesis of the gene product.

gene flow   The movement of alleles between local populations, or demes, due to migration and subsequent interbreeding. Gene flow can have significant evolutionary consequences.

gene pool   All the genes present in a freely interbreeding population.

genetic code   Code consisting of triplets of bases in mRNA specifying sequences of amino acids in polypeptides, or translation start and stop signals.

genetic drift   A random change in gene frequency in a small, isolated population.

genetic load   Those alleles that are advantageous in the heterozygous condition but lethal or deleterious in the homozygous condition.

genome (jee'nome)   All the DNA contained in one haploid set of chromosomes.

genotype (jeen'oh-type, jen'oh-type)   The genetic makeup of an individual.

genus (jee'nus)   A taxon immediately above the species.

germ cells   Cells within the body that give rise to gametes.

germ layer   Any of the three embryonic tissue layers—endoderm, mesoderm, or ectoderm.

germ line   In animals, the line of cells that will ultimately undergo meiosis to form gametes.

germination   The beginning of growth in seeds or spores.

gibberellin (jib"ur-el'lin)   A plant hormone involved in many aspects of plant growth and development.

gill   (1) The respiratory organ of aquatic animals. (2) The spore-bearing platelike structures under the caps of mushrooms.

gizzard   A portion of the digestive tract in some animals specialized for mechanical digestion.

gland   Body cell or organ specialized for secretion.

glial cell (glee'ul)   Supporting cell of central nervous tissue.

globulin (glob'yoo-lin)   One of a class of proteins in blood plasma, some of which (gamma-globulins) function as antibodies.

glomerulus (glom-air'yoo-lus)   The knot of capillaries at the proximal end of a nephron; the glomerulus is enclosed by the Bowman's capsule.

glucagon (gloo'kah-gahn)   A pancreatic hormone that stimulates glycogenolysis, which increases the concentration of glucose in the blood.

glycocalyx (gly"koh-kay'lix)   A coating on the outside of an animal cell, formed by polysaccharide chains attached to lipids and proteins.

glycogen (gly'koh-jen)   A polysaccharide formed from glucose and stored primarily in liver and (to a lesser extent) muscle tissue; the principal carbohydrate stored in animal cells.

glycolysis (gly-kol'ih-sis)   The first stage of cellular respiration; the metabolic conversion of glucose into pyruvate with the production of ATP.

glycoprotein (gly"koh-proh'teen)   A protein with covalently attached carbohydrates.

glyoxysome (gly-ox'ih-sohm)   Organelle containing a large array of enzymes that convert stored fat to sugar in plant seeds.

goblet cell   Mucus-secreting cell common in the mammalian intestinal lining.

Golgi complex (goal'jee)   Also **Golgi body** or **Golgi apparatus**   Organelle composed of stacks of flattened membranous sacs and mainly responsible for modifying, packaging, and sorting proteins.

gonad (goh'nad)   A gamete-producing gland; an ovary or testis.

gonadotropins (go-nad"oh-troh'pins)   Hormones produced by the anterior pituitary gland and the embryo that stimulate the function of the testes and ovaries.

gradualism   A model of evolution in which the evolutionary change of a species is due to a slow, steady transformation over time.

grain   A simple, dry, indehiscent, one-seeded fruit in which the fruit wall is fused to the seed coat, making it impossible to separate the fruit from the seed. Corn and wheat kernels are grains.

granum (gran'um) pl. **grana**   A stack of thylakoids within a chloroplast.

gravitropism (grav"ih-troh'pizm) Growth of a plant in response to gravity.

greenhouse effect The warming of the Earth resulting from the retention of atmospheric heat caused by the buildup of certain gases, especially carbon dioxide.

gross primary productivity The rate at which energy accumulates in an ecosystem (as biomass) during photosynthesis.

guanine (gwan'een) A nitrogenous base (a purine) found in nucleic acids.

guard cell A cell in the epidermis of plant stems and leaves. Two guard cells form a pore for gas exchange, collectively called a stoma.

guttation (gut-tay'shun) The emergence of liquid water droplets on leaves, forced out through special water pores by root pressure.

gymnosperms (jim'noh-sperms) Seed plants in which the seeds are not enclosed in an ovary; gymnosperms frequently bear their seeds in cones.

gynoecium (ji-nee'see-um) The female portion (all the carpels) of a flower.

habitat The natural environment or place where an organism, population, or species lives.

habituation (hab-it"yoo-ay'shun) The process by which organisms become accustomed to a stimulus and cease to respond to it.

hair follicle (fol'i-kul) An epithelial ingrowth of the epidermis into the dermis that surrounds a hair.

haploid (hap'loyd) The condition of having one set of chromosomes per cell.

Hardy-Weinberg law The principle that in a randomly mating large population, regardless of dominance or recessiveness, the relative frequencies of allelic genes do not change from generation to generation.

Haversian canals (ha-vur'zee-un) Channels extending through the matrix of bone and containing blood vessels and nerves.

heartwood The inner wood of many woody plants that contains various pigments, tannins, gums, and resins.

helper T cells T lymphocytes that facilitate the ability of B lymphocytes to form an antibody-producing clone in response to an antigen.

hemizygous (hem"ih-zy'gus) Possessing only one allele for a particular locus.

hemoglobin (hee'-moh-gloh"bin) The red, iron-containing protein pigment of erythrocytes that transports oxygen.

hemolysis (hee-mol'ih-sis) The destruction of red blood cells with the resultant release of hemoglobin.

hemophilia (hee"moh-feel'-ee-ah) "Bleeder's disease"; a rare hereditary disease in which blood does not clot properly.

hepatic (heh-pat'ih) Pertaining to the liver.

herbaceous (er-bay'shus) A nonwoody plant.

herbivore (erb'i-vore) Animals that primarily consume plants (or algae) for their nutritional requirements.

hermaphrodite (her-maf'roh-dite) An organism that possesses both male and female sex organs.

heterochromatin (het"ur-oh-kroh'mah-tin) Highly coiled and compacted chromatin in an inactive state.

heterocysts (het'ur-oh-sists") Large, thick-walled cells of certain cyanobacteria; site of nitrogen fixation.

heterogamy (het"ur-og'ah-mee) Reproduction involving two morphologically distinguishable gametes, such as the egg and sperm.

heterospory (het"ur-os'pur-ee) Production of two types of spores in plants—microspores and megaspores.

heterothallic (het-ur-oh-thal'ik) Pertaining to an organism (certain algae and fungi) having two mating types; only by combining a plus strain and a minus strain can sexual reproduction occur.

heterotrophs (het'ur-oh-trofes) Organisms that cannot synthesize their own food from inorganic materials and therefore must live either at the expense of other organisms or upon decaying matter.

heterozygote advantage A phenomenon in which the heterozygous condition confers some special advantage on an individual that either homozygous condition does not.

heterozygous (het-ur-oh-zye'gus) Possessing a pair of unlike alleles for a particular locus. Compare with homozygous.

hibernation The dormant state of decreased metabolism in which certain animals pass the winter.

histamine (his'tah-meen) Substance released from mast cells that is involved in allergic and inflammatory reactions.

histones (his'tones) Small positively charged (basic) proteins in the nucleus that bind to the negatively charged DNA.

holdfast The basal structure for attachment to solid surfaces found in multicellular algae.

homeobox (home'ee-oh box) Specific DNA sequence found in many genes that are involved in controlling the development of the body plan.

homeostasis (home"ee-oh-stay'sis) The maintenance of a constant internal environment in the body; the automatic tendency of an organism to maintain such a steady state.

homeothermic (home"ee-oh-thur'mic) See endothermic.

homeotic gene (home"ee-ot'ik) A gene that controls the formation of specific structures during development. Such genes were originally identified through insect mutants in which one body part was substituted for another.

hominid (hah'min-id) Any of a group of ancient (extinct) and living humans.

hominoids The apes and hominids.

homologous chromosomes (hom-ol'ah-gus) Chromosomes that are similar in morphology and genetic constitution. In humans there are 23 pairs of homologous chromosomes, each containing one member from the mother and one member from the father.

homology (hom-ol'oh-jee)   Similarity in basic structural plan and development, which is assumed to reflect a common evolutionary ancestry.

homospory (hoh-mos'pur-ee)   Production of one type of spore in plants. The spore gives rise to a bisexual gametophyte.

homozygous (hoh"moh-zy'gus)   Possessing a pair of identical alleles for a particular locus. Compare with heterozygous.

hormone   An organic chemical produced in one part of the body and transported to another part where it affects some aspect of metabolism.

host   The organism in a parasitic relationship that nourishes a parasite.

humoral immunity (hew'mor-ul)   Antibody-mediated immunity residing in the body fluids, based on immunoglobulin proteins produced by B lymphocytes.

humus (hew'mus)   Organic matter in various stages of decomposition in the soil; gives soil a brown or black color.

hybrid breakdown   A postzygotic isolating mechanism in which, although the interspecific hybrid is fertile and produces a second (F_2) generation, the F_2 has defects that prevent it from successfully reproducing.

hybrid inviability   A postzygotic isolating mechanism in which the embryonic development of an interspecific hybrid is aborted.

hybrid sterility   A postzygotic isolating mechanism in which the hybrid cannot reproduce successfully.

hybrid vigor   Genetic superiority of an F_1 hybrid over either parent; due to the presence of heterozygosity for a number of different loci.

hybridization   Interbreeding between members of different taxa.

hydrocarbons   Organic compounds composed solely of hydrogen and carbon.

hydrogen bond   A weak attractive force formed between a hydrogen atom with a partial positive charge and an electronegative atom (usually oxygen) with a partial negative charge.

hydrologic cycle   The water cycle, which includes evaporation, precipitation, and flow to the seas. The hydrologic cycle supplies terrestrial organisms with a continual supply of fresh water.

hydrolysis (hy-drol'ih-sis)   The splitting of a compound into parts through the addition of the equivalent of a water molecule. A hydroxyl group is incorporated into one fragment and a hydrogen atom into the other.

hydrophilic   Attracted to water.

hydrophobic   Repelled by water.

hydroponics   Growing plants in an aerated solution of dissolved inorganic minerals (that is, without soil).

hydroxide ion   A negatively charged particle consisting of oxygen and hydrogen, usually written OH^-.

hydroxyl group (hy-drok'sil)   Polar functional group, usually written —OH.

hypertonic (hyperosmotic)   Term referring to a solution having an osmotic pressure (or solute concentration) greater than that of the solution with which it is compared.

hypha (hy'fah)   One of the filaments composing the mycelium of a fungus.

hypocotyl (hy'poh-kah"tl)   The part of the axis of a plant embryo or seedling below the point of attachment of the cotyledons.

hypothalamus (hy-poh-thal'uh-mus)   Part of the brain that functions in regulating the pituitary gland, the autonomic system, emotional responses, body temperature, water balance, and appetite; located below the thalamus.

hypotonic (hypoosmotic)   Term referring to a solution having an osmotic pressure (or solute concentration) less than that of the solution with which it is compared.

immune response   The production of antibodies or T cells in response to foreign antigens.

immunoglobulins (im-yoon"oh-glob'yoo-lins)   See antibodies.

immunological tolerance (im-yoon"uh-loj'ih-kl)   The ability of an organism to accept cells transplanted from a genetically distinct organism.

imperfect flower   A flower that lacks either stamens or carpels.

implantation (im"plan-tay'shun)   The attachment of the developing embryo to the uterus of the mother.

impression   Fossil in which pressure and heat have destroyed all traces of organic material; only an imprint of the organism remains.

imprinting   A form of rapid learning by which a young bird or mammal forms a strong social attachment to an individual (usually a parent) or object within a few hours after hatching or birth.

inbreeding   Mating of genetically similar individuals. Homozygosity increases with each successive generation of inbreeding.

incomplete dominance   Condition in which neither member of a pair of contrasting alleles is completely expressed when the other is present.

incomplete flower   A flower lacking one or more of the four parts: sepals, petals, stamens, and/or carpels.

indehiscent fruit (in"dih-his'ent)   A simple, dry fruit that does not spontaneously split open to liberate the seeds; compare with dehiscent fruit.

independent assortment   The random separation of chromosomes during meiosis.

index fossil   Certain fossils that are restricted to a narrow unit of time and are found in the same sedimentary layers in different geographical areas.

induced fit Hypothesis that the active site of certain enzymes becomes conformed to the shape of the substrate molecule.

inflammation The response of body tissues to injury or infection, characterized clinically by heat, swelling, redness, and pain, and physiologically by increased dilation of blood vessels.

innate behaviors Behaviors that are inherited and typical of the species; innate behaviors are found in animals reared in isolation.

insertion In biology, the more moveable point of attachment of an organ.

insight learning The intuitive solution to a problem that has not previously been attempted.

instinct A genetically determined pattern of behavior or responses that is not based on the individual's previous experience but appears to be innate behavior.

insulin (in'suh-lin) A hormone secreted by the pancreas that lowers blood glucose content.

integral proteins Proteins that span or penetrate the lipid bilayer of cellular membranes.

integumentary system (in"teg"yoo-men'tur-ee) The body's covering, including the skin and its nails, glands, hair, and other associated structures.

interferon (in"tur-feer'on) A protein produced by animal cells when challenged by a virus. Important in immune responses, it prevents viral reproduction and enables cells of the same species to resist a variety of viruses.

intermediate filaments Cytoplasmic fibers that are part of the cytoskeletal network and intermediate in size between microtubules and microfilaments.

interneuron (in"tur-noor'on) A nerve cell that carries impulses from one nerve cell to another and is not directly associated with either an effector or a sense receptor.

internode The portion of a stem between two successive nodes.

interoceptor (in"tur-oh-sep'tor) A sense organ within the body organs that transmits information regarding chemical composition, pH, osmotic pressure, or temperature.

interphase The period in the life cycle of a cell in which there is no visible mitotic division; period between mitotic divisions.

interstitial fluid See lymph.

intertidal zone The zone of a shoreline between the high tide mark and the low tide mark.

intron A non-protein-coding region of a eukaryotic gene and also of the pre-mRNA transcribed from such a region. Introns do not appear in mature mRNA (see exon).

invagination (in-vaj"ih-nay'shun) The infolding of one part within another, specifically a process of gastrulation in which one region folds in to form a double-layered cup.

inversion, chromosomal A chromosomal mutation caused by turning a segment of a chromosome end for end and attaching it to the same chromosome.

in vitro Occurring outside a living organism (literally "in glass").

in vivo Occurring in a living organism.

ion An atom or a group of atoms bearing an electric charge, either positive (cation) or negative (anion).

iris The pigmented portion of the vertebrate eye.

islets of Langerhans (eye'lets of lahng'er-hanz) The endocrine portion of the pancreas that secretes glucagon and insulin. These hormones regulate blood-sugar level.

isogamy (eye-sog'ah-mee) Reproduction involving two morphologically similar gametes.

isomer (eye'soh-mur) One of two or more chemical compounds having the same chemical formula but a different structural formula, such as glucose and fructose.

isotonic (eye"soh-ton'ik) **(isoosmotic)** Having identical concentrations of solute and solvent molecules, and hence the same osmotic pressure as the solution with which it is compared.

isotope (eye'suh-tope) An alternate form of an element with a different number of neutrons but the same number of protons and electrons.

isozymes (eye'soh-zimes) Different molecular forms of an enzyme.

juvenile hormone An arthropod hormone that preserves juvenile morphology during a molt. Without it, metamorphosis toward the adult form takes place.

karyotype (kare'ee-oh-type) The chromosomal constitution of an individual. Representations of the karyotype are generally prepared by photographing the chromosomes and arranging the homologous pairs according to size and centromere position.

keratin (kare'ah-tin) A horny, water-insoluble protein that is a constituent of intermediate filaments in animal cells and is found in the epidermis of vertebrates: in nails, feathers, hair, horns, scales, and claws.

killer T cells See cytotoxic T cells.

kilocalorie See calorie.

kinesis (kih-nee'sis) The activity of an organism in response to a stimulus; the direction of the response is not controlled by the direction of the stimulus (in contrast to a taxis).

kinesthesis (kin"es-thee'sis) Sense that gives us our awareness of the position and movement of various parts of the body.

kinetochore (kin-eh'toh-kore) Portion of the chromosome centromere to which mitotic spindle fibers attach.

kingdom The broadest category (taxon) of classification used.

Krebs cycle See citric acid cycle.

lactation (lak-tay'shun) The production or release of milk from the breast.

lacteal (lak'tee-al) One of the many lymphatic vessels in the intestinal villi that absorb fat.

lagging strand Strand of DNA that is synthesized in short pieces, which are then covalently joined by DNA ligase. See also leading strand.

lamella (lah-mel′ah)   A thin layer or plate, as of bone.

larva   An immature free-living form in the life history of some animals in which it may be unlike the parent.

larynx (lare′inks)   The organ at the upper end of the trachea that contains the vocal cords.

latent learning   Learning in which an animal stores (without apparent reward) information about its environment that can later influence its behavior.

latent period   An interval, lasting about 0.01 second, between the application of a stimulus and the beginning of the visible shortening of a muscle.

lateral meristem   An area of cell division located on the side of the plant. There are two lateral meristems—the vascular cambium and the cork cambium.

leader sequence   Non-coding sequence of nucleotides in mRNA that is transcribed from the region that precedes (is upstream to) the coding region.

leading strand   Strand of DNA that is synthesized continuously. See also lagging strand.

leaf primordium (pry-mor′dee-um)   An embryonic leaf, evident in the stem apical meristem.

learning   A change in the behavior of an animal that results from experiences during its lifetime.

legume (leg′yoom)   A simple, dry, dehiscent fruit that splits open along two seams to release its seeds.

lenticels (len′tih-sels)   Masses of cells that rupture the epidermis and form porous swellings in stems, facilitating the exchange of gases.

leukemia (loo-kee′mee-uh)   A progessive, malignant disease of the blood-forming tissues, characterized by uncontrolled multiplication of, and abnormal development of, white blood cells and their precursors.

leukocytes (loo′koh-sites)   White blood cells; colorless cells that defend the body against disease-causing organisms; exhibit ameboid movement.

leukoplasts (loo′koh-plasts)   Colorless plastids that act as centers for the storage of materials in the cytoplasm of certain kinds of plant cells.

lichens (ly′kenz)   Compound organisms composed of symbiotic algae and fungi.

ligament (lig′uh-ment)   A connective tissue cord or band that connects bones to each other or holds other organs in place.

lignin (lig′nin)   The substance responsible for the hard, woody nature of plant stems and roots.

limbic system   An action system of the brain that plays a role in emotional responses, motivation, autonomic function, and sexual response.

limnetic zone   The open water area away from the shore of a lake or pond and that extends down as far as sunlight penetrates.

linkage   The tendency for a group of genes located on the same chromosome to be inherited together in successive generations.

lipase (lip′ase)   Fat-digesting enzyme.

lipid   Any of a group of organic compounds that are insoluble in water but soluble in fat solvents; lipids serve as a storage form of fuel and an important component of cell membranes.

liposome (lip′uh-sohm)   A protobiont made from lipids.

lithosphere (lith′oh-sfeer)   Portion of the planet that is composed of rock.

littoral (lit′or-ul)   The region of shallow water near the shore between the high and low tide marks.

locus   The place on a chromosome at which the gene for a given trait occurs.

long-day plant   A plant that flowers in response to long days (and short nights); compare with short-day plant.

loop of Henle (hen′lee)   The U-shaped loop of a mammalian kidney tubule which extends down into the medulla of the kidney.

lower epidermis   The outermost layer covering the bottom of leaf blades.

lumen (loo′men)   The cavity or channel within a tube or tubular organ, such as a blood vessel or the digestive tract; the space enclosed by a membrane, such as the lumen of the endoplasmic reticulum.

luteinizing hormone (loo′tin-iz-ing) **(LH)**   Anterior pituitary lobe hormone that stimulates ovulation and development of the corpus luteum; stimulates the production of progesterone; in males, stimulates testosterone secretion.

lymph (limf)   The colorless fluid within the lymphatic vessels that is derived from interstitial fluid; contains white cells; ultimately, returned to the blood.

lymph node   A mass of lymph tissue surrounded by a connective tissue capsule; manufactures lymphocytes and filters lymph.

lymphocyte (limf′oh-site)   White blood cell with nongranular cytoplasm that is responsible for immune responses.

lysis (ly′sis)   The process of disintegration of a cell or some other structure.

lysosomes (ly′soh-somes)   Intracellular organelles present in many animal cells; contain a variety of hydrolytic enzymes that act when the lysosome ruptures or fuses with another vesicle. Lysosomes function in development and in phagocytosis.

macroevolution (mak″roh-eh-voh-loo′shun)   Large-scale evolutionary change; evolutionary change involving higher taxa, such as genera and orders, i.e., above the level of species.

macromolecule   A very large molecule such as a protein or nucleic acid.

macronucleus   A large polyploid nucleus found, along with one or several micronuclei, in ciliates. The macronucleus regulates cell metabolism and growth.

macronutrient   An essential element that is required in fairly large amounts for normal plant growth.

macrophage (mak′roh-faje)   A large phagocytic cell capable of ingesting and digesting bacteria and cellular debris.

malpighian tubule (mal-pig′ee-an)   The excretory organ of many arthropods.

mandible (man′dih-bl)   (1) The lower jaw of vertebrates; (2) an external mouthpart of certain arthropods such as insects.

mantle   In the mollusk, a fold of tissue that covers the visceral mass and that usually produces the shell.

marsupials (mar-soo′pee-uls)   A subclass of mammals. Characterized by the possession of an abdominal pouch in which the young are carried for some time after being born in a very undeveloped condition.

mass extinction   The extinction of numerous species and higher taxa during a relatively short period of geological time.

mast cell   A type of cell found in connective tissue; contains histamine and is important in allergic reactions.

matrix (may′triks or mat′riks)   (1) Nonliving material secreted by and surrounding connective tissue cells; contains a network of microscopic fibers; (2) the interior of the compartment formed by the inner membrane of mitochondria.

mechanical isolation   A prezygotic isolating mechanism in which gamete exchange between two groups is prevented by morphological or anatomical differences between them.

mechanoreceptor (meh-kan′-oh-ree-sep″tor)   A sensory cell or organ that perceives mechanical stimuli such as those of touch, pressure, hearing, and balance.

medulla (meh-dul′uh)   (1) The inner part of an organ, such as the medulla of the kidney; (2) the most posterior part of the brain, lying next to the spinal cord.

medulla oblongata (ob-long-gah′tah)   Lowest portion of the brain; contains vital centers that control heartbeat, respiration, and blood pressure.

medusa   A jellyfish; a free-swimming, umbrella-shaped stage in the life cycle of certain cnidarians.

megaphyll (meg′uh-fil)   A large leaf that contains multiple vascular strands. Megaphylls are found in ferns, gymnosperms, and angiosperms. (Compare with microphyll.)

megasporangium (meg″ah-spor-an′jee-um)   A spore sac containing megaspores.

megaspore (meg′ah-spor)   The haploid spore in heterosporous plants that gives rise to a female gametophyte.

megaspore mother cell   A diploid cell in the megasporangium that undergoes meiosis to form megaspores.

meiosis (my-oh′sis)   Process in which a diploid cell undergoes two successive nuclear divisions to produce four haploid cells. Produces gametes in animals and spores in plants.

melanin (mel′ah-nin)   A dark brown to black pigment common in the outer covering of many animals; usually occurs within special cells called melanocytes.

meninges (meh-in′jeez) sing. **meninx**   The three membranes that envelop the brain and spinal cord: the dura mater, arachnoid, and pia mater.

menopause   The period (usually from 45 to 55 years of age) in women when the recurring menstrual cycle ceases.

menstruation (men-stroo-ay′shun)   The monthly discharge of blood and degenerated uterine lining in the human female; marks the beginning of each menstrual cycle.

meristem (mer′ih-stem)   A localized area of mitosis and growth in the plant body.

mesenchyme (mes′en-kime)   A loose, often jelly-like connective tissue containing undifferentiated cells, found in the embryos of vertebrates and the adults of some invertebrates.

mesentery (mes′en-tare″ee)   Internal membrane of vertebrates and echinoderms that holds the viscera in place.

mesoderm (mez′oh-derm)   The middle layer of the three basic tissue layers that develop in the early embryo; gives rise to connective tissue, muscle, bone, blood vessels, kidneys, and many other structures; lies between the ectoderm and the endoderm.

mesoglea (mes″oh-glee′ah)   A gelatinous matrix located between the ectoderm and endoderm of cnidarians.

mesophyll (mez′oh-fil)   Photosynthetic cells in the interior of a leaf.

mesophytes (mez′oh-fites)   Common land plants that live in a climate with an average amount of moisture.

mesosome (mez′oh-some)   Invaginated complex of membranes in some bacteria, thought to function in cell division.

mesothelium (mez-oh-theel′ee-um)   The simple squamous cell layer of epithelium (derived from mesoderm) that covers the surface of the serous membranes (peritoneum, pericardium, pleura).

messenger RNA (mRNA)   RNA that has been transcribed from DNA that specifies the amino acid sequence of a protein.

metabolism   The sum of all the physical and chemical processes by which living systems are produced and maintained; the transformations by which energy and matter are made available for use by the organism.

metamorphosis (met″ah-mor′fuh-sis)   Transition from one developmental stage to another, such as from a larva to an adult.

metaphase (met′ah-faze)   The stage of mitosis and meiosis during which the chromosomes line up on the equatorial plane of the cell.

metastasis (met-tas′tuh-sis)   The transfer of a disease such as cancer from one organ or part of the body to another not directly connected to it.

microbodies   Membrane-bounded eukaryote cellular structures containing enzymes.

microclimate   Local variations in climate produced by differences in elevation, in the steepness and direction of slopes, and in exposure to prevailing winds.

microevolution   Changes in gene frequencies that occur within a population over successive generations.

microfilaments Thin fibers composed of actin protein subunits that form part of the cytoskeleton.

micronucleus One or more smaller nuclei found, along with the macronucleus, in ciliates. The micronucleus is involved in reproduction.

micronutrient An essential element that is required in trace amounts for normal plant growth.

microphyll A small leaf that contains one vascular strand; microphylls are found in horsetails and club mosses. (Compare with megaphyll.)

microsphere A protobiont formed by adding water to proteinoids.

microsporangia (my"kroh-spor-an'jee-ah) Small "pollen" sacs that contain microspore mother cells which divide by meiosis to form microspores.

microspore The haploid spore in heterosporous plants that gives rise to a male gametophyte.

microspore mother cell A diploid cell in the microsporangium that undergoes meiosis to form microspores.

microtubules (my-kroh-too'bewls) Hollow cylindrical fibers composed of tubulin protein subunits. Microtubules are a major component of the cytoskeleton and are found in mitotic spindles, cilia, flagella, centrioles, and basal bodies.

microvilli (my-kroh-vil'ee) Minute projections of the plasma membrane that increase the surface area of the cell; found mainly in cells concerned with absorption or secretion, such as those lining the intestine or kidney tubules.

mimicry (mim'ik-ree) An adaptation for survival in which an organism resembles some other living or nonliving object.

mineralocorticoids (min"ur-al-oh-kor'tih-koidz) Hormones produced by the adrenal cortex that regulate mineral metabolism and, indirectly, fluid balance. The principal mineralocorticoid is aldosterone.

miracidium (mir"ah-sid'ee-um) The first larval stage of parasitic flukes.

mitochondria (my"toh-kon'dree-ah) Spherical or elongate intracellular organelles that are the site of oxidative phosphorylation. Sometimes referred to as the powerhouses of the cell.

mitosis (my-toh'sis) Division of the cell nucleus, resulting in two daughter nuclei with the same number of chromosomes as in the parent nucleus. Mitosis consists of four phases: prophase, metaphase, anaphase, and telophase. Cytokinesis (division of the cytoplasm to form two separate cells) usually occurs during telophase.

mitotic spindle (my-tot'ik) Structure consisting mainly of microtubules that provides the framework for chromosome movement during cell division.

mitral valve (my'trul) The bicuspid heart valve located between the left atrium and left ventricle.

mold Fossil formed by the hardening of material surrounding a buried organism and the following decay and removal of the tissues.

mole The amount of a chemical compound whose mass in grams is equivalent to its molecular weight, the sum of the atomic weights of its constituent atoms.

molecule The smallest particle of a covalently bonded element or compound that has the composition and properties of a larger part of the substance.

molting The shedding and replacement of an outer covering such as hair, feathers, and exoskeleton.

monoacylglycerol (mon'o-as"-il-glis'-er-ol) (also called **monoglyceride**) A fat consisting of a glycerol chemically combined with a single fatty acid.

monocotyledon (mon'oh-kot-ih-lee'dun) One of the two classes of angiosperms, or flowering plants. Monocots get their name (mono = one) from having one cotyledon in the seed; see also dicotyledon.

monocyte (mon'oh-site) A white blood cell; a large phagocytic, nongranular leukocyte that enters the tissues and differentiates into a macrophage.

monoecious (mon-ee'shus) Having separate male and female reproductive parts on the same plant; compare with dioecious.

monohybrid cross A genetic cross that takes into account the behavior of alleles of a single locus.

monomer (mon'oh-mer) A simple molecule of a compound of relatively low molecular weight that can be linked with others to form a polymer.

monosaccharide (mon-oh-sak'ah-ride) A simple hexose sugar; one that cannot be degraded by hydrolysis to a simpler sugar.

monosomy (mon'uh-soh"mee) Abnormal condition in which one member of a specific chromosome pair is absent.

monotremes (mon'oh-treems) Egg-laying mammals such as the duck-billed platypus of Australia.

morphogenesis (mor-foh-jen'eh-sis) The development of the form and structures of an organism and its parts.

morula (mor'yoo-lah) An early embryo consisting of a solid ball of cells.

motor unit All the skeletal muscle fibers that are stimulated by a single motor neuron.

mucosa (mew-koh'suh) A mucous membrane, especially in the lining of the digestive and respiratory tracts.

mucus (mew'cus) A sticky secretion that serves to lubricate body parts and to trap particles of dirt or other contaminants. (The adjectival form is spelled mucous.)

müllerian mimicry Mimicry of one species by another, where both species are dangerous to some predator.

multiple alleles (al'leels) Three or more alleles of a single locus (in a population), such as the alleles governing the ABO series of blood types.

multiple fruit A fruit that develops from many ovaries of many separate flowers. Pineapples are multiple fruits.

muscle An organ that produces movement by contraction.

mutagen (mew'tah-jen) Any agent that is capable of producing mutations.

mutation Any change in the DNA, including a change in the nucleotide base pairs of a gene, or a rearrangement of genes within chromosomes so that their interactions produce different effects; a change in the chromosomes themselves.

mutualism An association whereby two organisms of different species each gain from being together and are often unable to survive separately.

mycelium (my-seel'ee-um) The vegetative body of fungi and certain protists (water molds); consists of a branched network of hyphae.

mycorrhizae (my"kor-rye'zee) Mutualistic associations of fungi and plant roots that aid in the absorption of materials.

myelin (my'eh-lin) The white fatty material that forms a sheath around the axons of certain nerve cells, which are then called myelinated fibers.

myelin sheath The fatty insulating covering around axons of certain neurons.

myocardium (my-oh-kar'dee-um) The middle and thickest layer of the heart wall, composed of cardiac muscle.

myofibrils (my-oh-fy'brilz) Tiny threadlike organelles found in the cytoplasm of striated and cardiac muscle that are responsible for contractions of the cell.

myofilament (my-oh-fil'uh-ment) One of the filaments making up the myofibril; the structural unit of muscle proteins in a muscle cell.

myoglobin (my'oh-gloh"bin) A hemoglobin-like oxygen transferring protein found in muscle.

myoneural cleft (my-oh-new'rul) The space, corresponding to a synaptic cleft, between a motor neuron ending and a muscle cell.

myosin (my'oh-sin) A protein that, together with actin, is responsible for muscle contraction.

n The chromosome number of a gamete. The chromosome number of a zygote is 2*n*. If an organism is not polyploid, the *n* gametes are haploid, and the 2*n* zygote is diploid.

nares (nare'eez) The openings of the nasal cavities. External nares open to the body surface; internal nares, to the pharynx.

navigation The process in which an animal finds a goal without relying on landmarks with which it is familiar.

needle The leaf of a conifer such as pine.

nekton (nek'ton) Collective term for free-swimming aquatic animals that are essentially independent of water movements.

nematocyst (nem-at'oh-sist) A stinging structure found within cnidocytes (stinging cells) in cnidarians; used for anchorage, defense, and capturing prey.

neoteny (nee-ot'eh-nee) Sexual maturity in a larval or otherwise immature stage.

nephridium (neh-frid'ee-um) The excretory organ of the earthworm and other annelids which consists of a ciliated funnel opening into the next anterior coelomic cavity and connected by a tube to the outside of the body.

nephron (nef'ron) The functional, microscopic unit of the vertebrate kidney.

neritic province (ner-ih'tik) Open ocean from the shoreline to a depth of 200 m.

nerve A large bundle of axons (or dendrites) wrapped in connective tissue that conveys impulses between the central nervous system and some other part of the body.

net primary productivity Total carbon fixation by a plant community, minus the carbon lost by respiration.

neural crest (noor'ul) Group of cells along the neural tube that migrate and form structures of the peripheral nervous system and certain other structures.

neuroglia (noor-og'lee-ah) Connecting and supporting cells in the central nervous system.

neurohumor (noor"oh-hew'mor) A substance secreted by the tip of a neuron that is able to activate a neighboring neuron or muscle.

neuron (noor'on) A nerve cell; a conducting cell of the nervous system which typically consists of a cell body, dendrites, and an axon.

neurosecretion The production of hormones by nerve cells.

neurotransmitter Substance used by neurons to transmit impulses across a synapse. Also called transmitter substance.

neutral variation Genetic variation in a population that may confer no selective advantage to the organisms possessing it.

neutron (noo'tron) An electrically neutral particle of matter that exists along with protons in the atomic nucleus of all elements except the mass 1 isotope of hydrogen. See also proton and electron.

neutrophil (new'truh-fil) A type of granular leukocyte.

niche See ecological niche.

nitrogen cycle The worldwide circulation of nitrogen from the abiotic environment into living things and back into the abiotic environment.

nitrogen fixation The ability of certain microorganisms to bring atmospheric nitrogen into chemical combination.

node The area on a plant stem where the leaves attach.

noncompetitive inhibitor A substance that interferes with the ability of an enzyme to function but does not bind to the active site.

nondisjunction Abnormal separation of homologous chromosomes or sister chromatids caused by their failure to disjoin (move apart) properly during cell division.

nonpolar covalent bond Chemical bond in which electrons are shared equally among the participating atoms and which does not produce any electrical charge within the molecule.

nonsense mutation Mutation that results in an amino acid specifying codon being changed to a termination codon. When the abnormal mRNA is translated, the resulting protein usually is truncated and nonfunctional.

norepinephrine (nor-ep-ih-nef'rin)   A neurotransmitter substance that is also a hormone secreted by the adrenal medulla.

notochord (no'toe-kord)   The flexible, longitudinal rod in the anteroposterior axis that serves as an internal skeleton in the embryos of all chordates and in the adults of some.

nuclear envelope   The double membrane system that encloses the cell nucleus of eukaryotes.

nuclear pores   Structures in the nuclear envelope that allow passage of certain molecules between the cytoplasm and the nucleus.

nucleic acid (noo-klay'ik)   DNA or RNA. A polymer composed of nucleotides that contain the purine bases adenine and guanine and/or the pyrimidine bases cytosine, thymine, and uracil.

nucleolus (new-klee'-oh-lus)   Specialized structure in the nucleus formed from regions of several chromosomes; site of ribosome synthesis.

nucleoside (new'klee-oh-side)   Molecule consisting of a nitrogenous base and a pentose sugar.

nucleosome (new'klee-oh-sohm)   Repeating unit of chromatin structure consisting of a length of DNA wound around a complex of eight histone molecules (two of each of four different types) plus a DNA linker region associated with a fifth histone protein.

nucleotide (noo'klee-oh-tide)   A molecule composed of one or more phosphate groups, a 5-carbon sugar (ribose or deoxyribose) and a nitrogenous base (purine or pyrimidine).

nucleus (new'klee-us)   (1) That portion of an atom that contains the protons and neutrons; the core; (2) a cellular organelle containing DNA and serving as the control center of the cell; (3) a mass of nerve cell bodies in the central nervous system.

nutrients   The chemical substances in food that are used by the body as components for synthesizing needed materials and for fuel.

nymph   A juvenile insect that often resembles the adult stage and that will become an adult without an intervening pupal stage.

obligate anaerobe (ob'lih-gate an'air-obe)   An anaerobic organism that is killed by oxygen.

oceanic province   That part of the open ocean that is deeper than 200 meters and comprises most of the ocean.

ocellus (oh-sell'us)   A simple light receptor found in many different types of invertebrate animals.

olfaction (ol-fak'shun)   The act of smelling.

ommatidium (om"ah-tid'ee-um)   One of the light-detecting units of a compound eye, consisting of a cornea, lens, and rhabdome.

omnivore (om'nih-vore)   An animal that consumes both plant and animal material.

oncogene (on'koh-jeen)   Any of a number of genes that usually play an essential role in cell growth or division, and that cause the formation of a cancer cell when mutated; also known as cellular oncogenes.

oncotic pressure (on-kot'ik)   The osmotic pressure exerted by colloids in a solution; in microcirculatory fluid dynamics it operates to counterbalance capillary blood pressure.

ontogeny (on-toj'uh-nee)   The complete developmental history of the individual organism.

Onychophora (on-ih-kof'or-ah)   Rare, tropical, caterpillar-like animals, structurally intermediate between annelids and arthropods, possessing an annelidlike excretory system, an insectlike respiratory system, and claw-tipped short legs.

oocytes (oh'uh-sites)   Cells that give rise to egg cells (ova) by meiosis.

oogamy (oh-og'ah-me)   The fertilization of a large, nonmotile female gamete by a small, motile male gamete.

oogenesis (oh"oh-jen'eh-sis)   Production of female gametes (eggs).

oogonium (oh"oh-goh'nee-um)   The cell that grows to become a primary oocyte; gives rise to an egg (ovum).

operant (instrumental) conditioning   A type of learning in which an animal is rewarded or punished for performing a behavior it discovers by chance.

operator site   One of the control regions of an operon. The DNA segment to which a repressor binds, thereby inhibiting the transcription of the adjacent structural genes of the operon.

operon (op'er-on)   In prokaryotes, a group of structural genes that are coordinately controlled and transcribed as a single message, plus their adjacent regulatory elements.

optimal foraging   The theory that animals feed in a manner that maximizes benefits and/or minimizes costs.

orbital   Space in which electrons occur in an atom or molecule.

order   In taxonomic classification, a group of related, similar families.

organ   A differentiated part of the body made up of tissues and adapted to perform a specific function or group of functions, such as the heart or liver.

organelle   One of the specialized structures within the cell, such as the mitochondria, Golgi apparatus, ribosomes, or contractile vacuole.

organizer   A part of an embryo that influences some other part and directs its histological and morphological differentiation.

organogenesis   The development of organs.

osmoregulation (oz"moh-reg-yoo-lay'shun)   The active regulation of the osmotic pressure of body fluids so that they do not become excessively dilute or excessively concentrated.

osmosis (oz-moh-sis)   Diffusion of water (the principal solvent in biological systems) through a selectively permeable membrane from a region of higher concentration of water to a region of lower concentration of water.

osmotic pressure   The pressure necessary to stop the flow of water across a selectively permeable membrane; depends on the relative concentrations of the two solutions on either side of the membrane.

osteocyte (os'tee-oh-site) A mature bone cell; an osteoblast that has become embedded within the bone matrix and occupies a lacuna.

osteon (os'tee-on) Spindle-shaped unit of bone composed of concentric layers of osteocytes; Haversian system of bone.

outbreeding The mating of individuals of unrelated strains.

ovary (oh'var-ee) (1) In animals, one of the paired female gonads; responsible for producing eggs and sex hormones; (2) in flowering plants, the base of the carpel that contains ovules. Ovaries develop into fruits after fertilization.

oviduct (oh'vih-dukt) Tube that carries ova from the ovary to the uterus, cloaca, or body exterior. Also called uterine tube or fallopian tube (in humans).

oviparous (oh-vip'ur-us) Bearing young in the egg stage of development; egg-laying.

ovoviviparous (oh"voh-vih-vip'ur-us) A type of development in which the young hatch from eggs incubated inside the mother's body.

ovulation (ov-yoo-lay'shun) The release of a mature egg from the ovary.

ovule (ov'yool) The part (i.e., megasporangium) that develops into the seed after fertilization.

ovum The female gamete, or egg.

oxidation The loss of electrons, or in organic chemistry, the loss of hydrogen atoms from a compound.

oxidative phosphorylation (fos"for-ih-lay'shun) The production of ATP using energy derived from the transfer of electrons in the electron transport system of the mitochondria.

oxygen debt The oxygen necessary to metabolize the lactic acid produced during strenuous exercise.

oxytocin (ok-see-toh'sin) A hormone produced by the hypothalamus and released by the posterior lobe of the pituitary; causes the uterus to contract and stimulates the release of milk from the lactating breast.

pacemaker, of the heart See SA node.

palate (pal'ut) Horizontal partition separating the nasal and oral cavities; the roof of the mouth.

palisade mesophyll The vertically stacked photosynthetic cells near the upper epidermis in dicot leaves.

pancreas (pan'kree-us) Large digestive gland located in the vertebrate abdominal cavity. The pancreas produces pancreatic juice containing digestive enzymes; also serves as an endocrine gland, secreting the hormones insulin and glucagon.

papilla (pa-pil'ah) pl. **papillae** A small nipple-like projection or elevation, such as the papilla at the base of each hair follicle.

paramylum (par"uh-my'lum) Carbohydrate storage compound present in euglenoids; chemically distinct from both starch and glycogen.

parapodia (par"uh-poh'dee-ah) Paired, thickly bristled paddles extending laterally from each segment of polychaete worms.

parasite Any organism that obtains nourishment from the living tissue of another organism (the host).

parasitism An intimate living relationship between organisms of two different species in which one benefits and the other is harmed.

parasympathetic A division of the autonomic nervous system concerned primarily with the control of the internal organs; functions to conserve or restore energy.

parathyroids Small, pea-sized glands closely adjacent to the thyroid gland; their secretion regulates calcium and phosphate metabolism.

parenchyma (par-en'kih-mah) Plant cells that are relatively unspecialized, are thin-walled, may contain chlorophyll, and are typically rather loosely packed; they function in photosynthesis and in the storage of nutrients.

parotid glands (pah-rot'id) The largest of the three main pairs of salivary glands.

parthenogenesis (par"theh-noh-jen'eh-sis) A form of asexual reproduction in which an unfertilized egg develops into an adult organism; common among honeybees, wasps, and certain other arthropods.

passive immunity Temporary immunity derived from the immunoglobulins of another organism.

pathogen (path'oh-jen) An organism capable of producing disease.

pelagic (pel-aj'ik) Referring to an organism that inhabits open water, as in mid-ocean.

pellicle (pel'ih-kl) A flexible covering over the body of certain protists.

penis The male sexual organ of copulation in reptiles and mammals.

pepsin (pep'sin) The chief enzyme of gastric juice; hydrolyzes proteins.

peptide (pep'tide) A compound consisting of a chain of amino acid groups. A dipeptide consists of two amino acids, a polypeptide of many.

peptide bond A distinctive covalent carbon-to-nitrogen bond that links amino acids in peptides and proteins.

peptidoglycan (pep"tid-oh-gly'kan) A modified protein or peptide possessing an attached carbohydrate.

perennial (pur-en'ee-ul) A plant that grows year after year. Perennials may be woody or herbaceous.

perfect flower A flower that has both stamens and carpels.

pericardium (pare-ih-kar'dee-um) The fibrous sac that surrounds the heart and roots of the great blood vessels; also forms the outer layer of the heart wall.

pericycle (pehr'eh-sy"kl) A layer of meristematic cells in roots that gives rise to branch roots.

periderm (pehr'ih-durm) Layers of cells covering the surface of woody stems and roots (i.e., the outer bark). Anatomically, the periderm is composed of cork cells, cork cambium, and cork parenchyma, along with traces of primary tissues.

period In geology, an interval of geological time that is a subdivision of an era. Each period is divided into epochs.

peripheral nervous system (PNS) The receptors and nerves that lie outside the central nervous system.

peripheral proteins Proteins associated with the surface of biological membranes.

peripheral resistance The impedance to blood flow caused by friction between blood and the wall of the blood vessel; plays an important role in determining blood pressure.

peristalsis (pehr″ih-stal′sis) Powerful, rhythmic waves of muscular contraction and relaxation in the walls of hollow tubular organs, such as the ureter or parts of the digestive tract, that serve to move the contents through the tube.

peritoneum (pehr-ih-tuh-nee′um) The membrane lining the abdominal and pelvic cavities (the parietal peritoneum) and the membrane forming the outer layer of the stomach and intestine (the visceral peritoneum).

peroxisomes (pehr-ox′ih-somz) Lysosome-like vesicles containing enzymes that produce or degrade hydrogen peroxide.

petals The colored cluster of modified leaves that constitute the next-to-outermost whorled portion of a flower.

petiole (pet′ee-ohl) The stalk by which a leaf is attached to a stem.

petrifaction A fossil in which the soft tissues of the organism are replaced by minerals such as iron pyrites, silica, and calcium.

pH The logarithm of the reciprocal of the hydrogen ion concentration (expressed as moles per liter) of a solution. Neutral pH is 7; values less than 7 are acidic, and those greater than 7 are basic.

phagocyte (fag′oh-site) A cell such as a macrophage or neutrophil that ingests microorganisms and foreign particles.

phagocytosis (fag″oh-sy-toh′sis) Literally, ''cell eating''; a type of endocytosis by which certain cells engulf food particles, microorganisms, foreign matter, or other cells.

pharynx (far′inks) That part of the digestive tract from which the gill pouches or slits develop; in higher vertebrates it is bounded anteriorly by the mouth and nasal cavities, and posteriorly by the esophagus and larynx; the throat region in humans.

phenotype (fee′noh-type) The physical or chemical expression of an organism's genes (see also genotype).

phenylketonuria (PKU) (fee″nl-kee″toh-noor′ee-ah) An inherited disease in which there is a deficiency of the enzyme that normally converts phenylalanine to tyrosine; if untreated, results in mental retardation.

pheromone (feer′oh-mone) A substance secreted by one organism to the external environment that influences the development or behavior of other members of the same species.

phloem (floh′em) Vascular tissue that conducts food in plants.

phloem fiber cap A cap of fibers formed just outside the phloem in vascular bundles of many dicot stems.

phospholipids (fos″foh-lip′idz) Fatlike substances in which there are two fatty acids and a phosphorus-containing group attached to glycerol. Phospholipids comprise most of the plasma membrane and internal membranes of cells.

phosphorylation (fos″for-ih-lay′shun) The introduction of a phosphate group into an organic molecule.

photic zone (foh′tik) Zone of aquatic habitats lying near enough the surface so that sufficient light is present for photosynthesis to take place.

photolysis (foh-tol′uh-sis) The photochemical splitting of water in the light-dependent reactions of photosynthesis.

photon (foh′ton) A particle of electro-magnetic radiation; one quantum of radiant energy.

photoperiodism (foh″toh-peer′ee-od-izm) The physiological response of animals and plants to variations of light and darkness.

photophosphorylation (foh″toh-fos-for-ih-lay′shun) The production of ATP in photosynthesis.

photopic vision (foh-top′ik) Vision in daylight.

photoreceptor (foh′toh-ree-sep″tor) (1) A sense organ specialized to detect light. (2) A pigment that absorbs light before triggering a physiological response.

photorespiration (foh″toh-res-pur-ay′shun) The production of carbon dioxide and consumption of oxygen during photosynthesis at high light intensities by C-3 plants.

photosynthesis (foh″toh-sin′thuh-sis) The production of organic materials, especially glucose, from carbon dioxide and water using the energy of light. Photosynthesis is practiced by plants, algae, and several kinds of bacteria.

photosystem A group of chlorophyll and other molecules located in the thylakoid membrane (in photoautotrophic eukaryotes) that emits electrons in response to light.

phototropism (foh″toh-troh′pizm) The growth response of an organism to the direction of light.

phycocyanin (fy″koh-sy′ah-nin) A blue chromoprotein found in cyanobacteria and red algae.

phylogeny (fy-loj′en-ee) The complete evolutionary history of a group of organisms.

phylum (fy′lum) A taxonomic grouping of related, similar classes; a category beneath the kingdom and above the class. Phyla are used in classifying animals or protists; divisions are used for plants and fungi.

phytochrome (fy′toh-krome) A blue-green, proteinaceous pigment that is the photoreceptor for a wide variety of physiological responses, including initiation of flowering in certain plants.

phytoplankton (fy″toh-plank′tun) Microscopic floating algae, which are distributed throughout oceans or lakes; autotrophic plankton.

pia mater (pee′a may′ter)   The inner membrane covering the brain and spinal cord; the innermost of the meninges.

pili (pil′ee) sing. **pilus**   Hair or hairlike structures; especially, the external hairlike filaments of bacteria.

pinna (pin′ah)   The prominent external flap of the mammalian ear.

pinocytosis (pin″oh-sy-toh′sis)   Cell drinking; the engulfing and absorption of droplets of liquids by cells.

pioneer community   The first organisms (such as lichens or mosses) to colonize an area and begin the first stage of ecological succession.

pith   Large, thin-walled parenchyma cells found as the innermost tissue in many plants.

pith ray   Parenchyma cells that extend out from the pith to the cortex between the vascular bundles in dicot stems.

pituitary (pit-oo′ih-tehr″ee)   Small gland located at the base of the hypothalamus; secretes a variety of hormones influencing a wide range of physiological processes; also called the hypophysis.

placenta (plah-sen′tah)   The partly fetal and partly maternal organ whereby materials are exchanged between fetus and mother in the uterus of eutherian mammals.

placoderms (plak′oh-durms)   A group of extinct jawed fishes.

plankton   Free-floating, mainly microscopic aquatic organisms found in the upper layers of the water; includes phytoplankton, which are photosynthetic organisms, and zooplankton, which are heterotrophic organisms.

planula (plan′yoo-lah)   A ciliated cnidarian larval form.

plasma cells   Cells that secrete antibodies; differentiated B lymphocytes.

plasma, of blood   The fluid portion of blood consisting of a pale yellowish fluid containing proteins, salts, and other substances, and in which the blood cells and platelets are suspended.

plasma membrane   The semipermeable surface membrane that encloses the cell contents and through which all materials entering or leaving the cell must pass.

plasmids (plaz′midz)   Small circular DNA molecules that carry genes separate from the main bacterial chromosome.

plasmodesmata   Cytoplasmic channels connecting adjacent plant cells and allowing for the movement of small molecules and ions between cells.

plasmodium (plaz-moh′dee-um)   (1) Multinucleate, ameboid mass of living matter that comprises the vegetative phase of the life cycle of some slime molds; (2) a single-celled organism that reproduces by spore formation and causes malaria.

plasmolysis (plaz-mol′ih-sis)   The shrinkage of cytoplasm and the pulling away of the plasma membrane from the cell wall when a plant cell (or other walled cell) loses water, usually after being placed in a hypertonic environment.

plastids (plas′tidz)   A family of membrane-bounded organelles occurring in photosynthetic eukaryote cells; examples are chloroplasts and leukocytes.

platelets (playt′lets)   Cell fragments in the blood that function in clotting; also called thrombocytes.

pleiotropic gene (ply″oh-troh′pik)   A gene that affects a number of different characteristics in a given individual.

pleura (ploor′uh)   The membrane that lines the thoracic cavity and envelops each lung.

plexus (plek′sus)   A network of interconnected nerves, blood vessels, or lymphatics.

ploidy (ploy′dee)   Relating to the number of sets of chromosomes in a cell.

plumule (ploom′yool)   The embryonic shoot of a seed plant.

poikilothermic (poi″kil-oh-thur′mik)   Having a body temperature that fluctuates with that of the environment; "cold-blooded"; see also endothermic.

point mutation   Mutation involving a single nucleotide change in DNA.

polar body   Small cell that consists almost entirely of a nucleus that is formed during oogenesis.

polar covalent bond   A chemical bond established by electron sharing that produces some difference in the charge of the ends of the molecule.

polar nucleus   One of two haploid cells that fuse with a sperm nucleus during double fertilization in angiosperms.

polar transport   The unidirectional movement of the plant hormone, auxin, from the stem tip to the roots.

pollen   The immature male gametophytes of seed plants that produce haploid nuclei capable of fertilization.

pollination   In seed plants, the transfer of pollen from the male to the female part of the plant.

polyadenylation (pol″ee-ah-den-uh-lay′shun)   That part of eukaryotic mRNA processing in which multiple adenine bases (a poly A tail) are added to the 3′ end of the molecule.

polygenes (pol′ee-jeens″)   Two or more pairs of genes that affect the same trait in an additive fashion.

polygenic inheritance (pol″ee-jen′ik)   Inheritance in which several independently assorted or loosely linked non-allelic genes modify the intensity of a trait, or contribute to the phenotype in additive fashion.

polymer (pol′ih-mer)   A molecule built up from repeating units of the same general type, such as a protein, nucleic acid, or polysaccharide.

polymorphism (pol″ee-mor′fizm)   (1) The existence of two or more phenotypically different individuals within the same species; (2) the presence of more than one allele for a given locus in a population.

polypeptide   A chain of many amino acids linked by peptide bonds.

polyploidy (pol′ee-ploy″dee)   Possession of more than two sets of chromosomes per nucleus.

polyps (pol′ips)   Hydra-like animals; the sessile stage of the life cycle of certain cnidarians.

polyribosomes   A complex consisting of a number of ribosomes attached to an mRNA molecule during translation; also known as polysomes.

polysaccharide (pol-ee-sak′ah-ride) A carbohydrate consisting of many monosaccharide units; examples are starch, glycogen, and cellulose.

polytene A term describing a giant chromosome consisting of many (usually more than 1000) parallel DNA double helices. Polytene chromosomes are typically found in cells of the salivary glands and some other tissues of certain insects, such as the fruit fly, *Drosophila*.

polyunsaturated fat (pol″ee-un-sat′yur-ay-ted) A fat containing fatty acids that have double bonds and are not fully saturated with hydrogen.

pons (ponz) The white bulge that is the part of the brainstem between the medulla and midbrain; connects various parts of the brain.

population A group of organisms of the same species that live in the same geographical area at the same time.

portal system A circulatory pathway in which blood flows from a vein draining one region to a second capillary bed in another organ, rather than directly to the heart; an example is the hepatic portal system.

postganglionic neuron (post″gang-glee-on′ik) A neuron located distal to a ganglion.

postzygotic isolating mechanism (post″zy-got′ik) A mechanism that restricts gene flow between species and ensures reproductive failure even though fertilization took place.

potassium (K⁺) ion mechanism Mechanism by which plants open and close their stomata. The influx of potassium ions into the guard cells causes water to move in by osmosis, changing the shape of the guard cells and opening the pore.

preaptation An evolutionary change in an existing biological structure that enables it to have a different function.

predation Relationship in which a species kills and devours other animals.

prehensile (pree″hen′sil) Adapted for grasping by wrapping around an object, as in a prehensile tail.

pre-mRNA RNA precursor to mRNA in eukaryotes; contains both introns and exons.

prezygotic isolating mechanism (pree″zy-got′ik) A mechanism that restricts gene flow between species by preventing mating from taking place.

primary consumer A consumer that eats producers. Compare secondary consumer.

primary growth An increase in the length of a plant. This growth occurs at the tips of the stems and roots due to the activity of apical meristems.

primary succession An ecological succession that occurs on land that has not previously been inhabited by plants; no soil is present initially. Compare secondary succession.

primitive streak A longitudinal thickened, cellular region that develops on the embryonic disc of reptiles, birds, and mammals; it is comparable to the lips of the blastopore.

producers Organisms, such as algae and plants, that produce food materials from simple inorganic substances.

profundal zone The deepest zone of a large lake.

progesterone (pro-jes′ter-ohn) A hormone produced by the corpus luteum of the ovary and by the placenta; acts with estradiol to regulate menstrual cycles and to maintain pregnancy.

proglottid (pro-glah′tid) One of the body segments of a tapeworm.

prokaryote (pro-kar′ee-ote) Cells that lack membrane-bounded nuclei and other membrane-bounded organelles; the bacteria.

promoter Site on DNA to which RNA polymerase attaches to begin transcription.

prophage (pro′faj) A latent stage of a bacteriophage in which the viral genome is inserted into the host chromosome.

prophase The first stage of mitosis and of each of the two meiotic divisions. During prophase the chromosomes become visible, the nuclear envelope breaks down, and a spindle forms. (Meiotic prophase I is more complex.)

prop root An adventitious root that arises from the stem and provides additional support for plants.

prosimian (pro″sim′ee-un) A suborder of primates that includes the lemurs, lorises, and tarsiers.

prostaglandins (pros″tah-glan′dinz) Derivatives of unsaturated fatty acids that produce a wide variety of hormone-like effects; synthesized by most cells of the body; sometimes called local hormones.

prostate (pros′tate) The largest accessory sex gland of male mammals; it surrounds the urethra at the point where the vas deferentia join it, and it secretes a large portion of the seminal fluid.

protective coloration The coloring of an organism so that it blends into its surroundings in such a way that it is difficult to see.

protein A large, complex organic compound composed of chemically linked amino acid subunits; contains carbon, hydrogen, oxygen, nitrogen, and sulfur; proteins are the principal structural constituents of cells.

proteinoid Polypeptides obtained by heating dry amino acids; proteinoids may have formed during chemical evolution.

prothallus (pro-thal′us) The heart-shaped, haploid gametophyte plant found in ferns, whisk ferns, club mosses, and horsetails.

protist (proh′tist) One of a vast assemblage of eukaryotic organisms, primarily single-celled or simple multicellular, mostly aquatic.

protobiont (proh″toh-by′ont) Assemblages of organic polymers that spontaneously form during certain conditions. Protobionts may have been involved in chemical evolution.

proton A particle present in the nuclei of all atoms that has a positive electric charge and a mass of 1 (similar to that of a neutron); a hydrogen ion consists of a single proton. See also electron and neutron.

protonema (proh"toh-nee'mah)   A filament of haploid cells that grows from a moss spore; each protonema develops buds that grow into haploid moss plants.

protonephridium (proh"toh-nef-rid'ee-um)   The flame-cell excretory organs of lower invertebrates and of some larva of higher animals.

protoplasm   Obsolete term for cellular contents.

protoplast   Plant, fungal, or bacterial cell without its cell wall. Protoplasts are produced by enzymatically digesting the cell wall.

protostome (proh'toh-stome)   Major division of the animal kingdom in which the blastopore develops into the mouth, and the anus forms secondarily; includes the annelids, arthropods, and mollusks.

protozoa (proh"toh-zoh'ə)   Single-celled, animal-like protists, including amoebas, ciliates, flagellates, and sporozoa.

proximal   Relatively toward the body center.

proximate factors   The immediate conditions or mechanisms that cause particular behaviors.

provirus (pro"vy'rus)   A part of a virus, consisting of nucleic acid only, that has been inserted into a host genome.

pseudocoelom (soo"doh-see'lom)   A body cavity between the mesoderm and endoderm; derived from the blastocoele.

pseudoplasmodium   The aggregation of cells for reproduction in cellular slime molds.

pseudopod   A temporary extension of an ameboid cell, which the cell uses for feeding and locomotion.

pseudostratified columnar epithelium   An epithelial tissue that appears layered, but all of whose cells are attached to the same basement membrane.

pulse   The rhythmic expansion of an artery that may be felt with the finger. It is due to blood ejected with each cardiac contraction, and thus is felt in time with the heartbeat.

pulvinus (pul-vy'nus)   A special structure at the base of the petiole that functions in leaf movement by changes in turgor.

punctuated equilibrium   The concept that evolution proceeds with periods of inactivity (i.e., periods of little or no change within a species) followed by very active phases, so that major adaptations or clusters of adaptations appear suddenly in the fossil record.

pupa (pew'pah)   A stage in the development of an insect, between the larva and the imago (adult); a form that neither moves nor feeds, and may be in a cocoon.

purines (pure'eenz)   Nitrogenous bases with carbon and nitrogen atoms in two interlocking rings; components of nucleic acids ATP, NAD, and other biologically active substances. Examples are adenine and guanine.

pyramid of biomass   An ecological pyramid that illustrates the total biomass (for example, the total dry weight of all living organisms in a community) at each successive trophic level. See ecological pyramid. Compare pyramid of energy and pyramid of numbers.

pyramid of energy   An ecological pyramid that shows the energy flow through each trophic level of an ecosystem. See ecological pyramid. Compare pyramid of biomass and pyramid of numbers.

pyramid of numbers   An ecological pyramid that shows the number of organisms at each successive trophic level in a given ecosystem. See ecological pyramid. Compare pyramid of biomass and pyramid of energy.

pyrenoid (py'reh-noid)   Starch-containing granular bodies seen in the chloroplasts of certain algae.

pyrimidines (pyr-im'ih-deenz)   Nitrogenous bases composed of a single ring of carbon and nitrogen atoms; components of nucleic acids. Examples are thymine, ctyosine, and uracil.

quadrupedal   Walking on all fours.

quantum   A unit of radiant energy; the amount of energy emitted or absorbed by atoms or molecules.

radicle (rad'ih-kl)   The embryonic root of a seed plant.

radula (rad'yoo-lah)   A rasplike structure in the digestive tract of chitons, snails, squids, and certain other mollusks.

rain shadow   An area on the downwind side of a mountain range with very little precipitation. Deserts often occur in rain shadows.

range   The portion of the Earth in which a particular species occurs.

ray   A chain of parenchyma cells that functions for lateral transport of food, water, and minerals in woody plants.

reabsorption   The selective removal of certain substances from the glomerular filtrate by the cells of the tubules of the kidney and their return into the blood.

realized niche   The lifestyle that an organism actually pursues, including the resources that it actually utilizes. An organism's realized niche is narrower than its fundamental niche because of competition from other species. See ecological niche. Compare fundamental niche.

receptacle   In botany, the end of a flower stalk where the floral parts are attached.

receptor   (1) A specialized neural structure that is excited by a specific type of stimulus; (2) a site on the cell surface specialized to combine with a specific substance such as a hormone or neurotransmitter.

recessive genes   Genes not expressed in the heterozygous state.

recombinant DNA   Any DNA molecule made by combining genes from different organisms.

red tide   A population explosion, or bloom, of dinoflagellates.

redirected behaviors   Innate, stereotyped behaviors that are directed toward a substitute object.

redox reactions (ree'dox)   Chemical reactions in which one substance is oxidized and another reduced; involve the transfer of one or more electrons from one reactant to another.

reduction In chemistry, the gain of electrons by a substance, or the chemical addition of hydrogen; the opposite of oxidation.

reflex An inborn, automatic, involuntary response to a given stimulus that is determined by the anatomic relations of the involved neurons; generally functions to restore homeostasis.

refractory period The brief period of time that must elapse after the response of a neuron or muscle fiber, during which it cannot respond to another stimulus.

regulator genes Special genes that code for the synthesis of repressor or activator proteins.

regulon A group of operons that are coordinately controlled.

releaser A stimulus that triggers an unlearned behavior; a communication signal between members of a species; a natural sign stimulus.

renal (ree'nl) Pertaining to the kidney.

renal corpuscle The complex formed by a glomerulus and the surrounding Bowman's capsule; filtration, the first step in urine formation, occurs here.

renin (reh'nin) A hormone released by the kidney in response to ischemia or lowered pulse pressure, which changes angiotensinogen into angiotensin, leading to an increase in blood pressure.

repressor A regulatory protein (coded for by a regulator gene) that represses expression of a specific gene.

reproductive isolation The reproductive barriers that prevent a species from interbreeding with another species. As a result, each species' gene pool is isolated from other species.

respiration (1) Cellular respiration is the process by which cells utilize oxygen, produce carbon dioxide, and conserve the energy of food molecules in biologically useful forms, such as ATP. (2) Organismic respiration is the act or function of gas exchange.

resting potential The membrane potential (difference in electric charge) of an inactive neuron (about 70 millivolts).

reticular activating system (reh-tik'yoo-lur) **(RAS)** A diffuse network of neurons in the brainstem responsible for maintaining consciousness.

reticulum (reh-tik'-yoo-lum) A general term referring to any network (consisting of fibrils, filaments, or membranes).

retina The innermost of the three layers of the eyeball, which is continuous with the optic nerve and contains the light-sensitive rod and cone cells.

retrovirus (ret'roh-vy"rus) An RNA virus that produces a DNA intermediate in its host cell.

reverse transcriptase Enzyme produced by retroviruses to enable the transcription of DNA from the viral RNA in the host cell.

rhizoids (ry'zoids) Colorless, hairlike absorptive filaments analogous to roots in mosses, liverworts, and fern prothalli.

rhizome (ry'zome) A horizontal underground stem that gives rise to above-ground leaves.

rhodophytes (roh'doh-fites) The division of red algae, found almost entirely in the oceans.

rhodopsin (roh-dop'sin) Visual purple; a light-sensitive pigment found in the rod cells of the vertebrate eye and also employed for photosynthesis by certain bacteria.

ribonucleic acid (RNA) A family of single-stranded nucleic acids that function mainly in protein synthesis.

ribosomes (ry'boh-sohms) Organelles that are part of the protein synthesis machinery; consist of a larger and a smaller subunit each composed of ribosomal RNA (rRNA) and ribosomal proteins.

ribozyme (ry'boh-zime) A molecule of RNA that has catalytic ability.

rickettsia (rih-ket'see-uh) A type of disease organism intermediate in size and complexity between a virus and a bacterium; parasitic within cells of insects and ticks; transmitted to humans by the bite of an infected insect or tick.

ritualization The modification of a behavior pattern, through evolution, to serve a communicative function.

RNA polymerase Family of enzymes that catalyze the synthesis of RNA molecules from DNA templates.

rod The rod-shaped light-sensitive cells of the retina, which are particularly sensitive to dim light and mediate black and white vision.

root cap A covering of cells over the root tip that protects the delicate meristematic tissue directly behind it.

root hair An extension of an epidermal cell in roots. Root hairs increase the absorptive capacity of roots.

root pressure The positive pressure of the sap in the roots of plants, generated by the hypertonicity of the sap with respect to the water in the surrounding soil.

rough ER Major division of the endoplasmic reticulum that contains ribosomes and functions in protein synthesis.

rugae (roo'jee) Folds, such as those in the lining of the stomach.

SA node The sinoatrial node in the wall of the right atrium of the heart in which the impulse triggering the heartbeat originates; the pacemaker of the heart.

salt marsh A wetland dominated by grasses in which the salinity fluctuates between that of sea water and of fresh water. Salt marshes are usually located in estuaries.

saprobic nutrition (sap-roh'bik) A type of heterotrophic nutrition in which organisms absorb their required nutrients from nonliving organic material.

sapwood The outermost, youngest wood in woody plants. Sapwood conducts water and dissolved minerals; compare with heartwood.

sarcolemma (sar"koh-lem'mah) The muscle cell plasma membrane.

sarcomere (sar'koh-meer) A segment of a striated muscle cell located between adjacent Z-lines that serves as a unit of contraction.

sarcoplasm (sar'koh-plazm) The cytoplasm of a muscle cell.

sarcoplasmic reticulum System of vesicles in a skeletal or cardiac muscle cell that surrounds the myofibrils and releases calcium in muscle contraction; a modified endoplasmic reticulum.

saturated fatty acid A fatty acid with no double bonds between adjacent carbon atoms. It is completely saturated with hydrogen.

savanna A tropical or subtropical grassland containing scattered trees.

schizocoely (skiz'oh-seely) Process of a body cavity formation in which the mesoderm splits into two layers, forming a cavity between them.

scientific method The way a scientist approaches a problem (by formulating a hypothesis and then testing it by means of an experiment).

sclera, of the eye (skler'ah) The firm, fibrous outer coat of the eyeball.

sclerenchyma (skler-en'kim-uh) Cells that provide strength and support in the plant body. Sclerenchyma cells are dead at maturity and have extremely thick walls.

scrotum (skroh'tum) The external sac of skin found in most male mammals that contains the testes and their accessory organs.

sebaceous glands (seb-ay'shus) Glands in the skin that secrete sebum, an oily material that lubricates the skin surface.

secondary consumer An organism that consumes primary consumers. Compare primary consumer.

secondary growth An increase in the width of a plant due to the activity of the lateral meristems—vascular cambium and cork cambium.

secondary response A rapid production of antibodies induced by a second injection of antigen several days, weeks, or even months after the primary injection.

secondary succession An ecological succession that takes place after some disturbance destroys the existing vegetation; soil is already present. Compare primary succession.

seed A plant reproductive body that is composed of a young, multicellular plant and nutritive tissue (food).

selection coefficient A measure on a scale of 0 to 1 of the elimination of one phenotype relative to the more successful one. (0 = minimal elimination, 1 = maximal elimination)

selectively permeable membrane A membrane that allows some substances to cross it more easily than others. Biological membranes are generally permeable to water but restrict the passage of many solutes.

semen Fluid composed of sperm suspended in various glandular secretions that is ejaculated from the penis during orgasm.

semicircular canals The passages in the vertebrate inner ear which contain structures that control the sense of dynamic equilibrium.

semilunar valve (sem-eye-loo'nar) A valve with flaps shaped like half-moons; the aortic valve and the pulmonary valve.

seminal vesicles (1) In mammals, glandular sacs that secrete a component of the seminal fluid. (2) In some invertebrates, structures that store sperm.

seminiferous tubules (sem"in-if'ur-us) Tiny coiled ducts within the testis in which spermatogenesis occurs.

senescence The aging process.

sensitization An increased probability that an animal will respond to a stimulus that has been presented before.

sepals (see'puls) The outermost parts of a flower, usually leaflike in appearance, that protect the flower as a bud.

sere (seer) A sequence of communities that replace one another in succession in a given area; the transitory communities are called seral stages. The series ends with a climax community typical of the climate in that part of the world.

serotonin (seer"oh-tone'in) An amino acid–like neurotransmitter employed by certain neurons.

Sertoli cells (sur-tole'ee) Supporting cells of the tubules of the vertebrate testis.

serum Light yellow liquid left after clotting of blood has occurred.

sessile (ses'sile) Permanently attached to one location. Coral animals, for example, are sessile.

seta (seet'ah) (pl. **setae**) Bristle-like structures that aid in annelid locomotion.

sex-linked genes Genes borne on a sex chromosome. In mammals almost all sex-linked genes are borne on the X chromosome.

sexual dimorphism (dy-mor'fizm) Difference in body proportions, coloring, or other characteristics in the two sexes of a species.

sexual reproduction Form of reproduction in which two gametes (usually, but not necessarily, contributed by two different parents) fuse to form a zygote.

short-day plant A plant that flowers in response to short days and long nights; compare with long-day plant.

sieve tube member The cell that conducts food in the phloem of plants.

sign stimulus A stimulus that elicits a fixed action pattern in an animal.

simple fruit A fruit that develops from a single ovary of a single flower.

sinoatrial node See SA node.

sinus A cavity or channel such as the air cavities in the cranial bones or the dilated channels for venous blood in the cranium.

siphonous (sy'fun-us) A type of body form that is tubular and coenocytic; found in certain algae.

skeletal muscle Voluntary or striated muscle of vertebrates, so-called because it usually is directly or indirectly attached to some part of the skeleton.

smooth ER Portion of the endoplasmic reticulum that has no ribosomes and thus appears smooth; produces steroids and other lipids.

sodium-potassium pump Cellular active transport mechanism that transports sodium out of, and potassium into, cells.

soil The uppermost layer of the Earth's crust that supports terrestrial plants, animals, and microorganisms. Soil is a complex mixture of inorganic minerals (from the parent rock), organic material, water, air, and living organisms.

solute (sol′yoot) The dissolved substance in a solution.

solvent A liquid substance, such as water, in which other materials may be dissolved.

somatic cell A cell of the body not involved in sexual reproduction.

somatic nervous system That part of the nervous system that keeps the body in adjustment with the external environment; includes the sensory receptors on the body surface and within the muscles, and the nerves that link them with the central nervous system.

somites (soh′mites) Paired, blocklike masses of mesoderm, arranged in a longitudinal series alongside the neural tube of the embryo; form the vertebral column and dorsal muscles.

sorus (soh′rus) A cluster of sporangia (in the ferns).

speciation Evolution of a new species.

species A group of organisms with similar structural and functional characteristics that in nature breed only with each other and have a close common ancestry; a group of organisms with a common gene pool.

specific heat The amount of heat required to raise 1 gram of a substance 1°C.

sperm The motile, haploid male reproductive cell of animals and some plants and protists; spermatozoon.

sperm nucleus A nonflagellated male reproductive cell. Sperm nuclei are produced by flowering plants and gymnosperms.

spermatid (spur′mah-tid) An immature sperm cell.

spermatocyte (spur-mat′oh-site) A cell formed during spermatogenesis that gives rise to spermatids, and ultimately to mature sperm cells.

spermatogenesis (spur″mah-toh-jen′eh-sis) The production of sperm by meiosis.

spermatozoa (spur-mah-toh-zoh′uh) Mature sperm cells.

S-phase Phase in interphase of cell cycle during which DNA and other chromosomal components are synthesized.

sphincter (sfink′tur) A group of circularly arranged muscle fibers, the contractions of which close an opening, such as the pyloric sphincter at the exit of the stomach.

spindle The intracellular apparatus, composed mainly of microtubules, that separates chromosomes in cell division of eukaryotes.

spine A leaf that is modified for protection, such as a cactus spine; compare with thorn.

spiracle (speer′ih-kl) An opening for gas exchange, such as the opening on the body surface of a trachea in insects.

spiral cleavage Distinctive spiral pattern of blastomere production in an early protostome embryo.

spleen Abdominal organ located just below the diaphragm that removes worn-out blood cells and bacteria from the blood and plays a role in immunity.

spongy mesophyll (mes′oh-phil) The irregularly arranged, photosynthetic tissue closest to the lower epidermis in leaves.

sporangium (spor-an′jee-um) A spore case, found in plants and certain protists and fungi.

spore A reproductive cell that gives rise to individual offspring in plants, algae, fungi, and certain protozoa.

spore mother cell A diploid cell that undergoes meiosis to form haploid spores in plants.

sporophyll (spor′oh-fil) A leaf-like structure that bears spores.

sporophyte (spor′oh-fite) The multicellular 2*n* stage of a plant life cycle; produces spores by meiosis.

springwood The large, thin-walled conducting cells produced in the xylem of woody plants in the spring when water is plentiful; compare with summerwood.

squamous (skway′mus) Flat and scalelike, as in squamous epithelium.

stabilizing selection Natural selection that acts against extreme phenotypes and favors intermediate variants; associated with a population well adapted to its environment.

stamen (stay′men) The male part of flowers that produces pollen.

statocyst (stat′oh-sist) An invertebrate sense organ containing one or more granules; used in a variety of animals to sense gravity and motion.

stele (steel) Vascular cylinder of stem and root; term for the pericycle and the tissues within it: xylem, phloem, and pith.

steroids (steer′oids) Complex molecules containing carbon atoms arranged in four interlocking rings, three of which contain six carbon atoms each and the fourth of which contains five; the male and female sex hormones and the adrenal cortical hormones of vertebrates are examples, as is the insect hormone ecdysone. Steroids are chemical derivatives of cholesterol.

stigma Portion of the carpel where the pollen lands prior to fertilization.

stimulus A physical or chemical change in the internal or external environment of an organism potentially capable of provoking a response.

stipe A short stalk or stemlike structure that is a part of the body of certain algae.

stolon An above-ground, horizontal stem with long internodes. Stolons often form buds that develop into separate plants.

stomata pl. **stomata**   Small pore flanked by two guard cells located in the epidermis of plants; stomata provide for gas exchange for photosynthesis.

stoneworts   Multicellular green algae found in freshwater ponds; resemble miniature trees, with structures that superficially look like, and serve the functions of, roots, stems, leaves, and seeds, though they are not anatomically like their counterparts in plants.

stop codon   See termination codon.

stratum basale (strat'um bah-say'lee)   The deepest layer of the epidermis, consisting of cells that continuously divide.

striated muscle   See skeletal muscle.

strobilus (stroh'bil-us)   A conelike structure that bears sporangia.

stroke volume   The volume of blood pumped by one ventricle during one contraction.

stroma   The fluid region of the chloroplast, which surrounds the thylakoids.

stromatolite (stroh-mat'oh-lite)   A column-like rock that is composed of many minute layers of prokaryotic cells, usually cyanobacteria. Some stromatolites are over 3 billion years old.

style   The neck connecting the stigma to the ovary of a carpel.

suberin (soo'ber-in)   A waterproof material found in plants that occurs in the covering of leaf scars, in cork cells, and in the Casparian strip of endodermal cells.

submucosa (sub-myoo-koh'suh)   The layer of connective tissue that attaches the mucous membrane to the tissue below.

subsidiary cell   A cell associated with the guard cell in monocot leaves.

substrate   A substance on which an enzyme acts; a reactant in an enzymatically catalyzed reaction.

succession   The sequence of changes in a plant community over time. Includes the changes that occur from the initial colonization of the area to the climax community.

sucker   A shoot formed from an adventitious bud that develops on certain roots.

sulcus (sul'kus) pl. **sulci**   A groove, trench, or depression, especially one occurring on the surface of the brain separating the gyri.

summerwood   Smaller, thick-walled conducting cells formed in the secondary xylem of woody plants during the summer when water is not as plentiful as it was in spring; compare with springwood.

suppressor T cells   T lymphoctyes that suppress the immune reaction.

supraorbital ridges (soop"rah-or'bit-ul)   Prominent bony ridges above the eye sockets. Ape skulls have supraorbital ridges; human skulls do not.

suspensor   In plant embryo development, a multicellular structure that anchors the embryo and aids in nutrient absorption from the endosperm.

symbionts   The partners in a symbiotic relationship.

symbiosis (sim-bee-oh'sis)   An intimate relationship between two or more organisms of different species (see parasitism, commensal, mutualism).

sympathetic nervous system   A subdivision of the autonomic nervous system; its general effect is to mobilize energy, especially during stress situations; prepares the body for fight-or-flight response.

sympatric speciation (sim-pat'rik)   The evolution of a new species within the same geographical region as the parent species.

symplast (sim'plast)   In plants, the pathway traversed by water through the cells of the plant root rather than along the cell walls.

synapse (sin'aps)   The junction between two neurons or between a neuron and an effector.

synapsis (sin-ap'sis)   The pairing of homologous chromosomes during prophase I of meiosis.

syngamy (sin'gah-mee)   Sexual reproduction; the union of the gametes in fertilization.

systole (sis'tuh-lee)   The contraction phase of the cardiac cycle. See also diastole.

taiga (tie'gah)   Northern coniferous forest biome found primarily in Canada, northern Europe, and Siberia.

tap root   A root system in plants that has one main root with smaller roots branching off it.

taxis (tak'sis)   An orientation movement of a motile organism in response to a stimulus in its environment.

taxon   A taxonomic group of any rank.

taxonomy (tax-on'ah-mee)   The science of naming, describing, and classifying organisms.

T cell   Lymphocyte that is processed in the thymus. T cells have a wide variety of immune functions but are primarily responsible for cell-mediated immunity.

tectorial membrane (tek-tor'ee-ul)   The roof membrane of the organ of Corti in the cochlea of the ear.

telophase (teel'oh-faze or tel'oh-faze)   The last stage of mitosis and meiosis when, having reached the poles, the chromosomes become decondensed and a nuclear envelope forms around each group.

temperate forest   Distinctive forest community of the temperate zone, usually dominated by deciduous angiosperm trees.

temporal isolation   A prezygotic isolating mechanism in which genetic exchange is prevented between two groups because they reproduce at different times of the day, season, or year.

tendon   A connective tissue structure that joins a muscle to another muscle, or a muscle to a bone. Tendons transmit the force generated by a muscle.

tendril   A leaf or stem that is modified for holding or attaching onto objects.

termination codon   Any codon in mRNA that does not code for an amino acid (UAA, UAG, and UGA). This stops the translation of a peptide at that point. Also called stop codon.

territoriality   Behavior pattern in which an organism (usually a male) delineates a territory of its own and defends it against intrusion by other members of the same species and sometimes against members of other species.

tertiary structure (tur'she-air"ee)   The three-dimensional shape of a protein that forms spontaneously as a result of interactions of side chains.

testis (tes'tis)   The male gonad that produces spermatozoa; in humans and certain other mammals the testes are situated in the scrotal sac.

testosterone (tes-tos'ter-ohn)   The steroid male sex hormone of vertebrates that is secreted by the testes.

tetanus (tet'an-us)   Sustained, steady maximal contraction of a muscle, without distinct twitching, resulting from a rapid succession of nerve impulses.

tetrad   Association of a pair of homologous chromosomes during meiotic prophase I; also known as a bivalent. A tetrad contains four chromatids.

tetraploid (tet'rah-ploid")   A polyploid individual or cell having four sets of chromosomes.

tetrapods (tet'rah-podz)   Four-limbed vertebrates: the amphibians, reptiles, birds, and mammals.

thalamus (thal'uh-mus)   The part of the brain that serves as a main relay center transmitting information between the spinal cord and the cerebrum.

thallus (thal'us)   The body of a fungus or nonvascular plant without roots, stems, or leaves; for example, a liverwort thallus or a lichen thallus.

therapsids (ther-ap'sids)   A group of mammal-like reptiles of the Permian period; gave rise to the mammals.

thermodynamics (thurm"oh-dy-nam'iks)   Principles governing heat or energy transfer.

thigmotropism (thig"moh-troh'pizm)   Plant growth in response to contact with a solid object, such as plant tendrils.

thoracic (thor-as'ik)   Pertaining to the chest.

thorax   (1) The upper body of vertebrates. (2) The second major division of the arthropod body.

thorn   A stem that is modified for protection; compare with spine.

threatened species   A species in which the population is low enough for it to be at risk of becoming extinct, but not low enough that it is in imminent danger of extinction. Compare endangered species.

threshold   The value at which a stimulus just produces a sensation, is just appreciable, or comes just within the limits of perception.

thrombin (throm'bin)   The enzyme derived from prothrombin that converts fibrinogen to fibrin; participates in blood clotting.

thrombus (throm'bus)   A blood clot formed within a blood vessel or within the heart.

thylakoids (thy'lah-koidz)   Interconnected system of flattened, saclike membranous structures inside the chloroplast, where light energy is converted into ATP and NAPH that will be used in carbohydrate synthesis.

thymine (thy'meen)   A nitrogenous base (pyrimidine) found in DNA.

thymus gland (thy'mus)   An endocrine gland that functions as part of the lymphatic system; important in the development of the immune response mechanism.

thyroid gland   An endocrine gland that lies anterior to the trachea and releases hormones that regulate the rate of metabolism.

thyroxine (thy-rok'sin)   The principal hormone of the thyroid gland.

tight junctions   Specialized structures that form between some animal cells, producing a tight seal that prevents materials from passing through the spaces between the cells.

tissue   A group of closely associated, similar cells that work together to carry out specific functions.

T lymphocyte   A type of white blood cell responsible for cell-mediated immunity. Also called T cell.

tonsils   Aggregates of lymph nodules in the throat region. The tonsils are located strategically to deal with pathogens that enter through the mouth or nose.

tonus (toh'nus)   The continuous partial contraction of muscle.

totipotency (toh-ti-poh'-tun-cee)   Ability of a cell (or nucleus) to provide information for the development of an entire organism.

trachea (tray'kee-uh)   (1) Principal thoracic air duct of terrestrial vertebrates; windpipe; (2) one of the microscopic air ducts branching throughout the body of most terrestrial arthropods and some terrestrial mollusks.

tracheids (tray'kee-idz)   A type of water-conducting cell in the xylem of plants.

tracheophyte (tray'kee-oh-fite")   A vascular plant, having xylem and phloem.

transcription   The synthesis of RNA from a DNA template.

transducers   Devices receiving energy from one system in one form and emitting energy of a different form; e.g., converting radiant energy to chemical energy. Sense organs may be considered transducers.

transduction   The transfer of a genetic fragment from one cell to another, e.g., from one bacterium to another, by a virus.

transfer RNA (tRNA)   RNA molecules that bind to specific amino acids and serve as adapter molecules in protein synthesis. The tRNA anticodons bind to complementary mRNA codons.

transformation   (1) The incorporation of genetic material by a cell that causes a change in its phenotype; (2) the conversion of a normal cell to a malignant cell.

transgenic organism A plant or animal that has incorporated foreign DNA into its genome.

translation Conversion of information provided by mRNA into a specific sequence of amino acids in a polypeptide chain; the information in the mRNA is translated into a certain kind of protein.

translocation (1) The movement of materials (water, dissolved minerals, dissolved food) in the vascular tissues of a plant; (2) chromosome abnormality in which part of one chromosome has become attached to another.

transmission, neural Conduction of a neural impulse along a neuron, or from one neuron to another.

transpiration Evaporation of water from the leaves of a plant; aids in drawing water up the stem.

transport vesicles Small cytoplasmic vesicles that move substances from one membrane system to another.

transposon (tranz-poze'on) A DNA segment that is capable of moving from one chromosome to another, or to different sites within the same chromosome.

triacylglycerol (try-as"il-glis'-er-ol) Storage fat consisting of three fatty acid chains chemically linked with a glycerol. Also called triglyceride.

trichocyst (trik'oh-sist) A cellular organelle found in certain ciliated protozoa such as *Paramecium* that can discharge a filament that may aid in trapping and holding prey.

trichome (trik'ome) A hair or other appendage growing out from the epidermis of plants.

trilobite (try'loh-bite) Marine arthropods of the Paleozoic era characterized by two dorsal longitudinal furrows that separated the body into three lobes.

triplet A sequence of three nucleotides that serves as the basic unit of genetic information, usually signifying the identity and position of an amino acid unit in a protein.

triplet code The sequences of three nucleotides that compose the codons, the units of genetic information in RNA that specify the order of amino acids in a peptide chain.

triploid An individual or cell having three sets of chromosomes. Many angiosperms have a triploid endosperm in their seeds.

trisomy (try'sohm-ee) Condition in which a chromosome is present in triplicate instead of the normal pair.

trochophore (troh'koh-for) A larval form found in mollusks and many polychaetes.

troop The social unit of many primate species, consisting of several males, three or more females, and their offspring.

trophic level The distance of an organism in a food chain from the primary producers of a community.

trophoblast (troh'foh-blast) The outer layer of a late blastocyst which, in placental mammals, gives rise to the chorion and placenta.

tropic hormone A hormone that helps regulate another endocrine gland; e.g., thyroid-stimulating hormone, released by the pituitary gland, regulates the thyroid gland.

tropism (troh'pizm) A growth response in plants that is elicited by an external stimulus.

tropomyosin (troh-poh-my'oh-sin) A muscle protein involved in the control of contraction.

tubers Thickened underground stems that are adapted for food storage; found in plants such as the white potato.

tubulin (toob'yoo-lin) The protein dimers from which microtubules are constructed by cells.

tumor Mass of tissue that grows in an uncontrolled manner; a neoplasm.

tundra A treeless plain between the taiga in the south and the polar ice cap in the north; characterized by low temperatures, a short growing season, and ground that is frozen most of the year.

turgor pressure (tur'gor) Hydrostatic pressure that develops within a walled cell, such as plant cell, when the osmotic pressure of the cell's contents is greater than the osmotic pressure of the surrounding fluid.

ubiquinone (yoo-bik'kwin-ohn) Coenzyme Q, a component of the electron transport system that can take up and release electrons.

ultimate factors The long-term evolutionary causes of behavior.

ungulates (ung'yoo-lates) Four-legged mammals in which the digits may be more or less fused, and their ends protected with a horny coating, or hoof.

uniformitarianism The theory that geological changes have been caused by natural processes such as vulcanism, erosion, and glaciation that have occurred in the same way and at the same rate in the geological past as they do today.

upper epidermis The outermost, protective layer covering the top of the leaf blade.

uracil (yur'ah-sil) A nitrogenous base (pyrimidine) found in RNA.

urea (yur-ee'ah) The principal nitrogenous excretory product of mammals; one of the water-soluble end products of protein metabolism.

ureter (yoo-ree'tur) One of the paired tubular structures that conducts urine from the kidney to the bladder.

urethra (yoo-ree'thruh) The tube that conducts urine from the bladder to the outside of the body.

uric acid (yoor'ik) The principal nitrogenous excretory product of insects, birds, and reptiles; a relatively insoluble end product of protein metabolism; also occurs in mammals as an end product of purine metabolism.

uterine tubes (yoo'tur-in) Paired tubes attached to each end of the uterus that receive the ovum after it has been ovulated into the peritoneal cavity; also called fallopian tubes or oviducts.

uterus (yoo'tur-us) The womb; the hollow, muscular organ of the female reproductive tract in which the fetus undergoes development.

utricle (you'trih-kl) The larger of the two divisions of the membranous labyrinth of the inner ear; contains the receptors for static equilibrium.

vaccine (vak-seen') The commercially produced antigen of a particular disease, strong enough to stimulate the body to make antibodies, but not sufficiently strong to cause the disease's harmful effects.

vacuole (vak'yoo-ole) A fluid-filled, membrane-bounded sac found within the cytoplasm; may function in storage, digestion, or water elimination.

vagina The elastic, muscular tube, extending from the cervix to its orifice, that receives the penis during sexual intercourse and serves as the birth canal.

valence The number of electrons that an atom can donate, accept, or share in the formation of chemical bonds.

Van der Waals interactions Weak attractive forces between the atoms of nonpolar molecules in which fluctuations in charge interact.

vas deferens (vas def'er-enz) (pl. **vasa deferentia**) Paired duct of the male reproductive system that conveys sperm from the testis to the ejaculatory duct.

vascular Pertaining to, consisting of, or provided with vessels.

vascular cambium A lateral meristem in plants that produces secondary xylem (wood) and secondary phloem (inner bark).

vasoconstriction (vas-oh-kon-strik'shun) The narrowing of blood vessels; refers especially to the narrowing of arterioles.

vasodilation (vas-oh-dy-lay'shun) The widening of blood vessels, especially the arterioles.

vector (1) Agent, such as a plasmid or virus, that transfers genetic information. (2) Agent that transfers a parasite from one organism to another.

vegetal pole The yolky pole of a vertebrate or echinoderm egg.

vein A blood vessel that carries blood from the tissues toward the heart.

ventral Referring to the belly aspect of an animal's body.

ventricle A cavity in an organ, such as one of the several cavities of the brain, or one of the chambers of the heart that receives blood from the atria.

venule (ven'yool) A small vein.

vernalization Promotion of flowering in certain plants by exposing them to a cold period.

vertebrates Chordates that possess a bony vertebral column; fish, amphibians, reptiles, birds, and mammals.

vesicle (ves'ih-kl) Any small sac, especially a small spherical membrane-bounded compartment, within the cytoplasm.

vessel element A type of water-conducting cell in the xylem of plants.

vestigial (ves-tij'ee-ul) Rudimentary; an evolutionary remnant of a formerly functional structure.

villus pl. **villi** A minute elongated projection from the surface of a membrane, e.g., villi of the mucosa of the small intestine.

viroids (vy'roids) Tiny, naked viruses consisting only of nucleic acid.

virus A tiny pathogen composed of a core of nucleic acid usually encased in protein, and capable of infecting living cells. A virus is characterized by total dependence upon a living host.

viscera (vis'ur-uh) sing. **viscus** The internal body organs, especially those located in the abdominal or thoracic cavities.

visceral muscle (vis'ur-ul) Smooth or involuntary muscle.

vital capacity The total amount of air displaced when one breathes in as deeply as possible and then breathes out as completely as possible.

vitamin An organic compound necessary in small amounts for the normal metabolic functioning of a given organism; usually acts as a coenzyme.

vitreous body Mass of clear, jelly material that occupies the largest part of the eye, the posterior part of the eyeball between the lens and the retina.

viviparous (vih-vip'er-us) Bearing living young that develop within the body of the mother.

volitional behaviors Behaviors that depend on conscious choice or decision.

voltage-sensitive channel A sodium gate that opens in response to changes in voltage during cellular depolarization.

vulva The liplike external genital structures in the female.

water vascular system Unique hydraulic system of echinoderms; functions in locomotion and feeding.

wetland Land that is transitional between aquatic and terrestrial ecosystems and is covered with water for at least part of the year.

whorl An arrangement of several identical plant parts, such as petals, around a common center.

wild-type The phenotypically normal (naturally occurring) form of a gene or an organism.

woody A plant with secondary tissues—wood and bark.

xanthophyll (zan'thoh-fil) A yellow to brown pigment of plants.

X-linked gene Gene carried on an X chromosome.

X organ Organ present in crustaceans that produces hormones that regulate molting, metabolism, reproduction, the distribution of pigment in compound eyes, and the control of pigmentation of the body.

xylem (zy'lem) Vascular tissue that conducts water and dissolved minerals in plants.

yolk sac One of the extraembryonic membranes; a pouch-like outgrowth of the digestive tract of certain vertebrate embryos that grows around the yolk, digests it, and makes it available to the rest of the organism.

zona pellucida (pel-loo'sih-duh) The thick, transparent membrane surrounding the plasma membrane of the ovum.

zooplankton (zoh"oh-plank'tun) The nonphotosynthetic organisms present in plankton.

zoospore (zoh'oh-spore) A flagellated motile spore produced asexually.

zooxanthellae (zoh"oh-zan-thel'ee) Endosymbiotic dino-flagellates found in certain marine invertebrates.

zygote The 2n cell that results from the union of gametes in sexual reproduction. Species that are not polyploid have haploid gametes and diploid zygotes.

INDEX

Bold face page numbers indicate pages on which the index term is defined; "il" following the page number indicates an illustration, "t" a table, "f" a focus, and "n" a footnote.

Abdomen, **630**
Abert squirrel, 431f
ABO blood group, 351–52, 352t
Abortion, 1048t, **1049**
   spontaneous, 342, **1049**
   therapeutic, **1049**
Abscisic acid, 763t, **770**, 770il, 771t
Abscission, **707**–8
Abscission zone, **707**–8, 707il
Absolute refractory period, **822**
Absolute temperature scale, 145n
Absorption, **955**, 965–67
Absorption spectrum, **192**, 193il
Acanthodians, 654, 654il
Accessory cells, **858**
Accessory glands, 1031, 1032–33
Accessory fruit, 748t, **749**, 750il
Accessory photosynthetic pigments, 194
Accommodation, **875**
Acetabularia, 88–89f
Acetylcholine, **806**, 825–26, 825t
Acetyl coenzyme A, **166**, 167t, **170**, 170il
Achene, **747**, 748t
Acid, **39**–41
Acid-growth hypothesis, **764**, 764il
Acidity, **39**–41
Acid rain, 40il
Acne, **796**
Acoelomates, **599**
Acorn worm, 649f
Acquired immune deficiency syndrome. *See* AIDS
Acrasiomycota, 530t, 541
Acrosome, **1031**, **1056**
ACTH, 1012t, **1022**, 1024f
Actin, 104, 104il, **786**, 803, 806–9
Actin-associated proteins, 104
Actin filaments, **100**, 803
Actinomycetes, 522t, 524il, **525**
Actinopods, 530t, 531, 531il
Action potential, **806**, 820, 820il, 860–861
Action spectrum, **192**–94, 193il
Activation energy, 149il
Activator proteins, 306–7, 306t

Active immunity, **922**, 922t
Active site, **153**, 154il
Active transport, **123**–25, 123il
   carrier-mediated, **122**–25
   cotransport systems, 124
   of minerals, 733il
   sodium-potassium pump and, 123–24
Acute pancreatitis, 159
ADA, 350–51
Adaptation, **6**, 9–10, 10il, **393**, 416–20
Adaptive radiation, **440**–41, 440il
Adaptive zones, **440**
Addiction, **852**–53, 854f, 855f
Addison's disease, 1014t, **1023**
Adenine, 69, 70il, 150, 150il, 264–66, 265il
Adenoids, **902**
Adenosine deaminase. *See* ADA
Adenosine diphosphate. *See* ADP
Adenosine monophosphate. *See* AMP
Adenosine triphosphate. *See* ATP
Adenoviruses, 507, 508il, 511, 514t
Adenylate cyclase, 824, **1006**
ADH, **998**–1000, 1012t, **1014**
Adhesive forces, **37**
Adipose tissue, **783**, 784t, 972
Adolescence, **1076**, 1077t
ADP, **150**–51, 174–75, 178
Adrenal cortex, 1013t, **1021**, 1021il, **1022**–23
Adrenal glands, **1021**, 1021il
Adrenal medulla, 1013t, **1021**–22, 1021il
Adrenergic neuron, **826**
Adrenocortical hormone, 1014t
Adrenocorticotropic hormone, 1012t, **1022**, 1024f
Adsorptive endocytosis, **511**–12
Adulthood, 1077t
Adventitia, **958**
Adventitious roots, **728**
Aeration, 730il
Aerobic catabolism, **161**
Aerobic respiration, **163**, 165il, 175–76, 179–80
   in bacteria, **518**
   in cell evolution, 453
   photosynthesis and, 203f
   stages, 166–75, 166il
Afferent arteriole, **993**
Afferent neurons, **814**
Affinities, **916**, **921**
Africanized honeybee, 415f

Afterbirth, **1072**
Agar, **538**
Agassiz, Louis, 634
Age structure, **1138**
Age structure diagram, **1138**–39, 1139t
Aggregated distribution, **1128**
Aggregate fruit, 748t, **749**
Aggregations, **1093**
Aging, **1076**–79
Agnatha, **653**–54, 653il
Agonist, **809**
Agranular leukocytes, **885**
Agriculture, 482–83, 1186, 1190
Agrobacterium tumefaciens, 332, 332il
Agrostis stolonifera, 419il
A-horizon, **1174**
AIDS, 294, 345, 513, 561, 927–30, 1047
AIDS dementia complex, 929
Air, 944t, 938–39
Air pollution, 9, 948–50, 950il
Air sacs, 938, 944–45
Airway, 947f
Albatross, 1097il
Albinism, 249, 251il, 336il, 337
Alchemilla vulgaris, 707il
Alcohol abuse, 854f, 1074t
Alcohol fermentation, **179**–80, 179il
Aldosterone, **1000**, 1013t, **1022**
Algae, 185il, 198il, 496, 497t, 527il, 534–40
Algin, **540**
Alkaptonuria, **257**, 257il
Allantois, 1064il, **1065**
Allele(s), **232**–36, 233il
   dominant, 234
   frequencies, 411–17
   heterozygous, **234**
   homozygous, **234**
   multiple, **248**–49, 351
   recessive, 234
Allelopathy, **1115**, 1128il
Allergens, **926**–27, 927il
Allergic asthma, **927**
Allergies, 592f, **926**–27, 926il
Alligator, 660il, 661, 836il
Allograft, **924**
Allometric growth, **436**–37, 437il
Allopatric speciation, **429**–32, 430il, 432il
Allopolyploidy, **432**–33, 433il
All-or-none law, **822**
Allosteric binding site, **156**, 156il, **302**

SCIENTIFIC MEASUREMENT

SOME COMMON PREFIXES

Examples

kilo	1,000	a kilogram is 1,000 grams
centi	0.01	a centimeter is 0.01 meter
milli	0.001	a milliliter is 0.001 liter
micro (μ)	one millionth	a micrometer is 0.000001 (one millionth) of a meter
nano (n)	one billionth	a nanogram is 10^{-9} (one billionth) of a gram
pico (p)	one trillionth	a picogram is 10^{-12} (one trillionth) of a gram

The relationship between mass and volume of water (at 20°C)

$$1 \text{ g} = 1 \text{ cm}^3 = 1 \text{ mL}$$

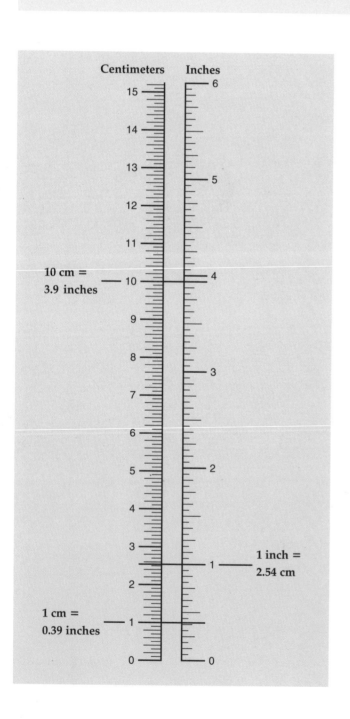

SOME COMMON UNITS OF LENGTH

Unit	Abbreviation	Equivalent
meter	m	approximately 39 in
centimeter	cm	10^{-2} m
millimeter	mm	10^{-3} m
micrometer	μm	10^{-6} m
nanometer	nm	10^{-9} m
angstrom	Å	10^{-10} m

Length Conversions

1 in = 2.5 cm	1 mm = 0.039 in
1 ft = 30 cm	1 cm = 0.39 in
1 yd = 0.9 m	1 m = 39 in
1 mi = 1.6 km	1 m = 1.094 yd
	1 km = 0.6 mi

To convert	Multiply by	To obtain
inches	2.54	centimeters
feet	30	centimeters
centimeters	0.39	inches
millimeters	0.039	inches

STANDARD METRIC UNITS

		Abbreviations
Standard unit of mass	gram	g
Standard unit of length	meter	m
Standard unit of volume	liter	L